The Courtneys of Africa

WILBUR SMITH

The Burning Shore
Power of the Sword
Rage

HEINEMANN : LONDON

William Heinemann Ltd
Michelin House, 81 Fulham Road, London SW3 6RB

LONDON MELBOURNE AUCKLAND

The Burning Shore
First published 1985

Power of the Sword
First published 1986

Rage
First published 1987

Three novels first published in one volume in 1988 as
THE COURTNEYS OF AFRICA

0 434 71421 6

Printed and bound in Great Britain by
Richard Clay Ltd, Bungay, Suffolk

The Burning Shore

This book is for Danielle Antoinette
with all my love always

So have I heard on Afric's burning shore,
A hungry lion give a grievous roar.

William Barnes Rhodes, *Bombastes Furioso*, sc. IV

Michael awoke to the mindless fury of the guns.

It was an obscene ritual celebrated in the darkness before each dawn in which the massed banks of artillery batteries on both sides of the ridges made their savage sacrifice to the gods of war.

Michael lay in the darkness under the weight of six woollen blankets and watched the gunfire flicker through the canvas of the tent like some dreadful aurora borealis. The blankets felt cold and clammy as a dead man's skin, and light rain spattered the canvas above his head. The cold struck through his bedclothes and yet he felt a glow of hope. In this weather they could not fly.

False hope withered swiftly, for when Michael listened again to the guns, this time more intently, he could judge the direction of the wind by the sound of the barrage. The wind had gone back into the south-west, muting the cacophony, and he shivered and pulled the blankets up under his chin. As if to confirm his estimate, the light breeze dropped suddenly. The patter of the rain on canvas eased and then ceased. Outside he could hear the trees of the apple orchard dripping in the silence – and then there was an abrupt gust so that the branches shook themselves like a spaniel coming out of the water and released a heavy fall of drops on to the roof of the tent.

He decided that he would not reach across to his gold half-hunter on the inverted packing-case which acted as a bedside table. It would be time all too soon. So he snuggled down in the blankets and thought about his fear. All of them suffered under the affliction of fear, and yet the rigid conventions under which they lived and flew and died forbade them to speak of it – forbade them to refer to it in even the most oblique terms.

Would it have been a comfort, Michael wondered, if last night he had been able to say to Andrew as they sat with the bottle of whisky between them, discussing this morning's mission, 'Andrew, I'm frightened gutless by what we are going to do.'?

He grinned in the darkness as he imagined Andrew's embarrassment, yet he knew that Andrew shared it with him. It was in his eyes, and in the way the little nerve twitched and jumped in his cheek so that he had constantly to touch it with a fingertip to still it. All the old hands had their little idiosyncrasies; Andrew had the nerve in his cheek and the empty cigarette-holder which he sucked like an infant's comforter. Michael ground his teeth in his sleep so loudly that he woke himself; he bit the nail of his left thumb down into the quick and every few minutes he blew on the fingers of his right hand as though he had just touched a hot coal.

The fear drove them all a little mad, and forced them to drink far too much – enough to destroy the reflexes of normal men. But they were not normal men and the alcohol did not seem to affect them, it did not dull their eyesight nor slow their feet on the rudder bars. Normal men died in the first three weeks,

they went down flaming like fir trees in a forest fire, or they smashed into the doughy, shell-ploughed earth with a force that shattered their bones and drove the splinters out through their flesh.

Andrew had survived fourteen months, and Michael eleven, many times the life-span that the gods of war had allotted to the men who flew these frail contraptions of wire and wood and canvas. So they twitched and fidgeted, and blinked their eyes, and drank whisky with everything, and laughed in a quick loud bray and then shuffled their feet with embarrassment, and lay in their cots at dawn, stiff with terror, and listened for footsteps.

Michael heard the footsteps now, it must be later than he had realized. Outside the tent Biggs muttered a curse as he splashed into a puddle, and his boots made obscene little sucking noises in the mud. His bull's-eye lantern glowed through the canvas as he fumbled with the flap and then he stooped into the tent.

'Top of the morning, sir – ' his tone was cheerful, but he kept it low, out of courtesy to the officers in the neighbouring tents who were not flying this morning ' – wind has gone sou'-sou'-west, sir, and she's clearing something lovely, she is. Stars shining out over Cambrai – ' Biggs set the tray he carried on the packing case and bustled about the tent, picking up the clothing that Michael had dropped on the duckboards the night before.

'What time is it?' Michael went through the pantomime of awaking from deep sleep, stretching and yawning so that Biggs would not know about the hour of terror, so that the legend would not be tarnished.

'Half-past five, sir.' Biggs finished folding the clothes away, then came back to hand him the thick china mug of cocoa. 'And Lord Killigerran is up and in the mess already.'

'Bloody man is made of iron,' Michael groaned, and Biggs picked the empty whisky bottle off the floor beneath the cot and placed it on the tray.

Michael drained the cocoa while Biggs worked up a lather in the shaving mug and then held the polished steel mirror and the lantern while Michael shaved with the straight razor, sitting up in his cot with the blankets over his shoulders.

'What's the book?' Michael demanded, his voice nasal as he pinched his own nostrils and lifted the tip of his nose to shave his upper lip.

'They are giving three to one that you and the major take them both with no butcher's bill.'

Michael wiped the razor while he considered the odds. The sergeant rigger who ran the betting had operated his own book at Ascot and Aintree before the war. He had decided that there was one chance in three that either Andrew or Michael, or both of them, would be dead by noon – no butcher's bill, no casualties.

'Bit steep, don't you think, Biggs?' Michael asked. 'I mean, both of them, damn it?'

'I've put half a crack on you, sir,' Biggs demurred.

'Good on you, Biggs, put on a fiver for me.' He pointed to the sovereign case that lay beside his watch, and Biggs pressed out five gold coins and pocketed them. Michael always bet on himself. It was a racing certainty: if he lost the bet, it wasn't going to hurt much, anyway.

Biggs warmed Michael's breeches over the chimney of the lamp and then held them while Michael dived out from under the blankets into them. He stuffed his nightshirt into the breeches while Biggs went on with the complicated procedure of dressing his man against the killing cold of flight in an open

cockpit. There followed a silk vest over the nightshirt, two cable-stitch woollen fisherman's jerseys, then a leather gilet, and finally an army officer's greatcoat with the skirts cut off so that they would not tangle with the controls of the aircraft.

By this time Michael was so heavily padded that he could not bend to pull on his own footwear. Biggs knelt in front of him and snugged silk undersocks over his bare feet, then two pairs of woollen hunting socks, and finally eased on the tall boots of tanned kudu skin that Michael had had made in Africa. Through their soft, pliable soles, Michael had touch and feel on the rudder bars. When he stood up, his lean muscular body was dumpy and shapeless under the burden of clothing, and his arms stuck out like the wings of a penguin. Biggs held the flap of the tent open, and then lit his way along the duckboards through the orchard towards the mess.

As they passed the other darkened tents beneath the apple trees Michael heard little coughs and stirrings from each. They were all awake, listening to his footsteps pass, fearing for him, perhaps some of them cherishing their relief that it was not they who were going out against the balloons this dawn.

Michael paused for a moment as they left the orchard and looked up at the sky. The dark clouds were rolling back into the north and the stars were pricking through, but already paling out before the threat of dawn. These stars were still strange to Michael; though he could at last recognize their constellations, they were not like his beloved southern stars – the Great Cross, Achernar, Argus and the others – so he lowered his gaze and clumped after Biggs and the bobbing lantern.

The squadron mess was a ruined labourers' *chaumière* which they had commandeered and repainted, covering the tattered thatch with tarpaulin so that it was snug and warm.

Biggs stood aside at the doorway. 'I'll 'ave your fifteen quid winnings for you when you get back, sir,' he murmured. He would never wish Michael good luck, for that was the worst of all possible luck.

There was a roaring log fire on the hearth and Major Lord Andrew Killigerran was seated before it, his booted feet crossed on the lip of the hearth, while a mess servant cleared the dirty plates.

'Porridge, my boy,' he removed the amber cigarette holder from between his even white teeth as he greeted Michael, 'with melted butter and golden syrup. Kippers poached in milk – '

Michael shuddered. 'I'll eat when we get back.' His stomach, already knotted with tension, quailed at the rich smell of kippers. With the cooperation of an uncle on the general staff who arranged priority transport, Andrew kept the squadron supplied with the finest fare that his family estates in the highlands could provide – Scotch beef, grouse and salmon and venison in season, eggs and cheeses and jams, preserved fruits – and a rare and wonderful single malt whisky with an unpronounceable name that came from the family-owned distillery.

'Coffee for Captain Courtney,' Andrew called to the mess corporal, and when it came he reached in the deep pocket of his fleece-lined flying jacket and brought out a silver flask with a big yellow cairngorm set in the stopper and poured a liberal dram into the steaming mug.

Michael held the first sip in his mouth, swirling it around, letting the fragrant spirit sting and prickle his tongue, then he swallowed and the heat hit his empty

stomach and almost instantly he felt the charge of alcohol through his bloodstream.

He smiled at Andrew across the table. 'Magic,' he whispered huskily, and blew on his fingertips.

'Water of life, my boy.'

Michael loved this dapper little man as he had never loved another man – more than his own father, more even than his Uncle Sean who had previously been the pillar of his existence.

It had not been that way from the beginning. At first meeting, Michael had been suspicious of Andrew's extravagant, almost effeminate good looks, his long, curved eyelashes, soft, full lips, his neat, small body, dainty hands and feet, and his lofty bearing.

One evening soon after his arrival on the squadron, Michael was teaching the other new chums how to play the game of Bok-Bok. Under his direction one team formed a human pyramid against a wall of the mess, while the other team attempted to collapse them by taking a full run and then hurling themselves on top of the structure. Andrew had waited for the game to end in noisy chaos and had then taken Michael aside and told him, 'We do understand that you hail from somewhere down there below the equator, and we do try to make allowances for you colonials. However – '

Their relationship had thenceforth been cool and distant, while they had watched each other shoot and fly.

As a boy, Andrew had learned to take the deflection of a red grouse, hurtling wind-driven only inches above the tops of the heather. Michael had learned the same skills on rocketing Ethiopian snipe and sandgrouse slanting on rapid wingbeat down the African sky. Both of them had been able to adapt their skills to the problem of firing a Vickers machine-gun from the unstable platform of a Sopwith Pup roaring through the three dimensions of space.

Then they watched each other fly. Flying was a gift. Those who did not have it died during the first three weeks; those who did, lasted a little longer. After a month Michael was still alive, and Andrew spoke to him again for the first time since the evening of the game of Bok-Bok in the mess.

'Courtney, you will fly on my wing today,' was all he said.

It was to have been a routine sweep down the line. They were going to 'blood' two new chums who had joined the squadron the day before, fresh from England with the grand total of fourteen flying hours as their combined experience. Andrew referred to them as 'Fokker fodder', and they were both eighteen years of age, rosy-faced and eager.

'Did you learn aerobatics?' Andrew demanded of them.

'Yes, sir.' In unison. 'We have both looped the loop.'

'How many times?'

Shamefaced they lowered their shining gaze. 'Once,' they admitted.

'God!' muttered Andrew and sucked loudly on his cigarette-holder. 'Stalls?'

They both looked bemused, and Andrew clutched his brow and groaned.

'Stalls?' Michael interposed in a kindly tone. 'You know, when you let your airspeed drop and the kite suddenly falls out of the sky.'

They shook their heads, again in unison. 'No, sir, nobody showed us that.'

'The Huns are going to love you two,' Andrew murmured, and then he went on briskly, 'Number one, forget all about aerobatics, forget about looping the loop and all that rot, or while you are hanging there upside down the Hun is going to shoot your anus out through your nostrils, understand?'

They nodded vigorously.

'Number two, follow me, do what I do, watch for my hand signals and obey them instantly, understand?' Andrew jammed his tam o' shanter down on his head and bound it in place with the green scarf that was his trademark. 'Come along, children.'

With the two novices tucked up between them they barrelled down past Arras at 10,000 feet, the Le Rhone engines of their Sopwith Pups bellowing with all their eighty horsepower, princes of the heavens, the most perfect flying fighting machines man had ever devised, the machines that had shot Max Immelmann and his vaunted Fokker Eindekkers out of the skies.

It was a glorious day, with just a little fairweather cumulus too high up there to hide a boche Jagdstaffel, and the air so clear and bright that Michael spotted the old Rumpler reconnaissance biplane from a distance of ten miles. It was circling low over the French lines, directing the fire of the German batteries on to the rear areas.

Andrew picked out the Rumpler an instant after Michael, and he flashed a laconic hand signal. He was going to let the new chums take a shot at her. Michael knew of no other squadron commander who would stand aside from an easy victory when a big score was the high road to promotion and the coveted decorations. However, he nodded agreement and they shepherded the two young pilots down, patiently pointing out the lumbering German two-seater below them, but with their untrained eyes neither of them could pick it out. They kept shooting puzzled glances across at the two senior pilots.

The Germans were so intent on the bursting high explosive beneath them that they were oblivious of the deadly formation closing swiftly from above. Suddenly the young pilot nearest Michael grinned with delight and relief and pointed ahead. He had seen the Rumpler at last.

Andrew pumped his fist over his head in the old cavalry command, 'Charge!' and the youngster put his nose down without closing the throttle. The Sopwith went into a howling dive so abrupt that Michael winced as he saw the double wings bend back under the strain and the fabric wrinkle at the wing roots. The second novice followed him just as precipitously. They reminded Michael of two half-grown lion cubs he had once watched trying to bring down a scarred old zebra stallion, falling over themselves in comical confusion as the stallion avoided them with disdain.

Both the novice pilots opened fire at a range of a thousand yards, and the German pilot looked up at this timely warning; then, judging his moment, he banked under the noses of the diving scoutplanes, forcing them into a blundering overshoot that carried them, still firing wildly, half a mile beyond their intended victim. Michael could see their heads screwing around desperately in the open cockpits as they tried to find the Rumpler again.

Andrew shook his head sadly and led Michael down. They dropped neatly under the Rumpler's tailplane, and the German pilot banked steeply to port in a climbing turn to give his rear gunner a shot at them. Together Andrew and Michael turned out in the opposite direction to frustrate him, but as soon as the German pilot realized the manoeuvre had failed and corrected his bank, they whipped the Sopwiths hard over and crossed his stern.

Andrew was leading. He fired one short burst with the Vickers at a hundred feet and the German rear gunner bucked and flung his arms open, letting the Spandau machine-gun swivel aimlessly on its mounting as the .303 bullets cut

him to pieces. The German pilot tried to dive away, and Andrew's Sopwith almost collided with his top wing as he passed over him.

Then Michael came in. He judged the deflection of the diving Rumpler, touched his port rudder bar so that his machine yawed fractionally just as though he were swinging a shotgun on a rocketing snipe, and he hooked the forefinger of his right hand under the safety bar of the Vickers and fired a short burst – a flurry of .303 ball. He saw the fabric of the Rumpler's fuselage ripped to tatters just below the rim of the pilot's cockpit, in line with where his upper body must be.

The German was twisted around staring at Michael from a distance of a mere fifty feet. Michael could see that his eyes behind the lens of his goggles were a startled blue, and that he had not shaved that morning, for his chin was covered with a short golden stubble. He opened his mouth as the shots hit, and the blood from his shattered lungs blew out between his lips and turned to pink smoke in the Rumpler's slipstream, and then Michael was past and climbing away. The Rumpler rolled sluggishly on to its back and with the dead men lolling in their straps, fell away towards the earth. It struck in the centre of an open field and collapsed in a pathetic welter of fabric and shattered struts.

As Michael settled his Sopwith back into position on Andrew's wingtip, Andrew looked across at him, nodded matter-of-factly, and then signalled him to help round up the two new chums who were still searching in frantic circles for the vanished Rumpler. This took longer than either of them anticipated, and by the time they had them safely under their protection again, the whole formation had drifted further west than either Andrew or Michael had ever flown before. On the horizon Michael could make out the fat shiny serpent of the Somme river winding across the green littoral on its way down to the sea.

They turned away from it and headed back east towards Arras, climbing steadily to reduce the chances of an attack from above by a Fokker Jagdstaffel.

As they gained height, so the vast panorama of northern France and southern Belgium opened beneath them, the fields a patchwork of a dozen shades of green interspersed with the dark brown of ploughed lands. The actual battle lines were hard to distinguish; from so high, the narrow ribbon of shell-churned earth appeared insignificant, and the misery and the mud and the death down there seemed illusory.

The two veteran pilots never ceased for an instant their search of the sky and the spaces beneath them. Their heads turned to a set rhythm in their scan, their eyes never still, never allowed to focus short or become mesmerized by the fan of the spinning propeller in front of them. In contrast, the two novices were carefree and self-congratulatory. Every time Michael glanced across in their direction they grinned and waved cheerfully. In the end he gave up trying to urge them to search the skies around them, they did not understand his signals.

They levelled out at 15,000 feet, the effective ceiling of the Sopwiths, and the sense of unease that had haunted Michael while he had been flying at low altitude over unfamiliar territory passed as he saw the town of Arras abeam of them. He knew that no Fokker could be lurking above them in that pretty bank of cumulus, they simply did not have the ability to fly that high.

He swept another searching glance along the lines. There were two German observation balloons just south of Mons, while below them a friendly flight of DH2 single-seaters was heading back towards Amiens, which meant they were from No. 24 Squadron.

In ten minutes they would be landing – Michael never finished the thought,

for suddenly and miraculously the sky all around him was filled with gaudily painted aircraft and the chatter of Spandau machine-guns.

Even in his utter bewilderment Michael reacted reflexively. As he pulled the Sopwith into a maximum-rate turn, a shark-shaped machine checkered red and black with a grinning white skull superimposed on its black Maltese cross insignia flashed across his nose. A hundredth of a second later and its Spandaus would have savaged Michael. They had come from above, Michael realized; even though he could not believe it, they had been above the Sopwiths, they had come out of the cloud bank.

One of them, painted red as blood, settled on Andrew's tail, its Spandaus already shredding and clawing away the trailing edge of the lower wing, and swinging inexorably towards where Andrew crouched in the open cockpit, his face a white blob beneath the tam o' shanter and the green scarf. Instinctively, Michael drove at him, and the German, rather than risk collision, swung away.

'Ngi dla!' Michael shouted the Zulu warcry as he came on to the killing quarter on the tail of the red machine, and then in disbelief watched it power away before he could bring the Vickers to bear. The Sopwith juddered brutally to the strike of shot and a rigging wire above his head parted with a twang like a released bow string as another one of these terrible machines attacked across his stern.

He broke away, and Andrew was below him, trying to climb away from yet another German machine which was swiftly overhauling him, coming up within an ace of the killing line. Michael went at the German head-on and the red and black wings flickered past his head – but instantly there was another German to replace him, and this time Michael could not shake him off, the bright machine was too fast, too powerful, and Michael knew he was a dead man.

Abruptly the stream of Spandau fire ceased, and Andrew plunged past Michael's wingtip, driving the German off him. Desperately Michael followed Andrew around, and they went into the defensive circle, each of them covering the other's belly and tail while the cloud of German aircraft milled around them in murderous frustration.

Only part of Michael's mind recorded the fact that both the new chums were dead. They had died in the first seconds of the assault; one was in a vertical dive under full power, the maimed Sopwith's wings buckling under the strain and at last tearing away completely, while the other was a burning torch, smearing a thick pall of black smoke down the sky as it fell.

As miraculously as they had come, the Germans were gone – untouched and invulnerable, they disappeared back towards their own lines, leaving the pair of battered, shot-torn Sopwiths to limp homewards.

Andrew landed ahead of Michael and they parked wingtip to wingtip at the edge of the orchard. Each of them clambered down and walked slowly round his own machine, inspecting the damage. Then at last they stood in front of each other, stony-faced with shock.

Andrew reached into his pocket and brought out the silver flask. He unscrewed the cairngorm and wiped the mouth of the flask with the tail of the green scarf, then handed the flask to Michael.

'Here, my boy,' he said carefully, 'have a dram. I think you earned it – I really do.'

So on the day that Allied superiority was wiped from the skies above France by the shark-nosed Albatros D type scoutplanes of the German Jagdstaffels, they had become comrades of desperate necessity, flying at each other's

wingtips, forming the defensive mutually protective circle whenever the gaily painted minions of death fell upon them. At first they were content merely to defend themselves, then between them they tested the capability of this new and deadly foe, poring together at night over the intelligence reports that belatedly came in to them – learning that the Albatros was driven by a 160 horsepower Mercedes engine, twice as powerful as the Sopwith's Le Rhône, and that it had twin Spandau 7.92 mm machine-guns with interrupter gear firing forward through the arc of the propeller, against the Sopwith's single Vickers .303. They were outgunned and outpowered. The Albatros was 700 pounds heavier than the Pup and could take tremendous weight of shot before it fell out of the sky.

'So, old boy, what we'll do is learn to fly the arses off them,' Andrew commented, and they went out against the massed formations of the Jastas and they found their weaknesses. There were only two. The Sopwiths could turn inside them, and the Albatros radiator was situated in the upper wing directly above the cockpit. A shot through the tank would send a stream of boiling coolant hissing over the pilot, scalding him to a hideous death.

Using this knowledge, they made their first kills, and found that in testing the Albatros they had tested each other and found no fault there. Comradeship became friendship, which deepened into a love and respect greater than that between brothers of the blood. So now they could sit quietly together in the dawn, drinking coffee laced with whisky, waiting to go out against the balloons, and take comfort and strength from each other.

'Spin for it?' Michael broke the silence, it was almost time to go.

Andrew flicked a sovereign into the air and slapped it on to the tabletop, covering it with his hand.

'Heads,' said Michael and Andrew lifted his hand.

'Luck of a pox-doctor!' he grunted, as they both looked down on the stern, bearded profile of George V.

'I'll take number-two slot,' said Michael, and Andrew opened his mouth to protest.

'I won, I call the shot.' Michael stood up to end the argument before it began.

Going against the balloons was like walking on to a sleeping puff-adder, that gross and sluggish serpent of the African veld; the first man woke it so that it could arch its neck into the 'S' of the strike, the second man had the long recurved fangs plunged into the flesh of his calf. With the balloons they had to attack in line astern, the first man alerted the ground defences and the second man received their full fury. Michael had deliberately chosen the number-two slot. If he had won, Andrew would have done the same.

They paused shoulder to shoulder in the door of the mess, pulling on their gauntlets, buttoning their coats and looking up at the sky, listening to the rolling fury of the guns and judging the breeze.

'The mist will hang in the valleys,' Michael murmured. 'The wind won't move it, not yet.'

'Pray for it, my boy,' Andrew answered, and, hampered by their clothing, they waddled down the duckboards, to where the Sopwiths stood at the edge of the trees.

How noble they had once appeared in Michael's eyes, but how ugly now when the huge rotary engine, limiting forward vision, was compared to the

Albatros' sleek shark-like snout, with its in-line Mercedes engine. How frail when considered against the Germans' robust airframe.

'God, when are they going to give us real aeroplanes to fly!' he grunted, and Andrew did not reply. Too often they had lamented the endless wait for the new SE5a that they had been promised – the Scout Experimental No. 5a that would perhaps allow them to meet the Jastas on equal terms at last.

Andrew's Sopwith was painted bright green, to match his scarf, and the fuselage behind the cockpit was ringed by fourteen white circles, one for each of his confirmed victories, like notches on a sniper's rifle. The aircraft's name was painted on the engine housing: 'The Flying Haggis'.

Michael had chosen bright yellow, and there was a winged tortoise with a worried frown painted below his cockpit and the appeal, 'Don't ask me – I just work here.' His fuselage was ringed by six white circles.

Assisted by their ground crews, they clambered up on to the lower wing, and then eased themselves into the narrow cockpits. Michael settled his feet on to the rudder bars and pumped them left and right, peering back over his shoulder to watch the response of the rudder as he did so. Satisfied, he held up a thumb at his mechanic who had worked most of the night to replace one of the cables shot away on the last sortie. The mechanic grinned and ran to the front of the machine.

'Switches off?' he called.

'Switches off!' Michael confirmed, leaning out of the cockpit to peer around the monstrous engine.

'Suck in!'

'Suck in!' Michael repeated, and worked at the handle of the hand fuel pump. When the mechanic swung the propeller, he heard the suck of fuel into the carburettor under the cowling as the engine primed.

'Switches on! Contact!'

'Switches on!'

At the next swing of the propeller the engine fired and blathered. Blue smoke blew out of the exhaust ports, and there was the stink of burning castor oil. The engine surged, and missed, caught again and settled down to its steady idling beat.

As Michael completed his pre-flight checks, his stomach rumbled and spasmed with colic. Castor oil lubricated the precision engines, and the fumes they breathed from the exhausts gave them all a perpetual low-grade diarrhoea. The old hands soon learned to control it; whisky had a marvellously binding effect if taken in sufficient quantity. However, the new chums were often affectionately referred to as 'treacle-bottoms' or 'slippery breeks' when they returned red-faced and odorous from a sortie.

Michael settled his goggles and glanced across at Andrew. They nodded at each other, and Andrew opened his throttle and rolled out on to the soggy turf. Michael followed him, his mechanic trotting at his starboard wingtip to help him swing and line up on the narrow muddy strip between the apple trees.

Ahead of him Andrew was airborne and Michael opened his throttle wide. Almost immediately the Sopwith threw her tail up, clearing his forward vision, and Michael felt a prick of conscience at his earlier disloyalty. She was a lovely plane and a joy to fly. Despite the sticky mud of the strip, she broke swiftly free of the earth, and at 100 feet Michael levelled out behind Andrew's green machine. The light was just good enough by now for him to make out to his right the green copper-clad spire of the church of the little village of Mort

Homme; ahead of him lay the T-shaped grove of oak and beech trees, the long leg of the T perfectly aligned with the squadron's landing strip, a most convenient navigational aid when coming in during bad weather. Beyond the trees stood the pink-roofed château set in the midst of its lawns and formal gardens, and behind the château the low knoll.

Andrew banked fractionally to the right, to pass the knoll. Michael conformed, peering ahead over the edge of his cockpit. Would she be there? It was too early – the knoll was bare. He felt the slide of disappointment and dread. Then he saw her – she was galloping up the pathway towards the crest. The big white stallion lunging powerfully under her slim girlish body.

The girl on the white horse was their good-luck talisman. If she was there waiting on the knoll to wave them away, all would be well. Today, when they were going against the balloons, they needed her – how desperately they needed her benediction.

She reached the crest of the knoll and reined the stallion down. Just a few seconds before they drew level she whipped the hat off her head and the thick dark bush of her hair burst from under it. She waved the hat, and Andrew waggled his wings as he roared past.

Michael edged in closer to the crest. The white stallion backed up and nodded nervously as the yellow machine came bellowing at him, but the girl sat him easily, waving gaily. Michael wanted to see her face. He was almost at the same height as the top of the hillock and very close to where she sat. For an instant he looked into her eyes. They were huge and dark, and he felt his heart trip. He touched his helmet in salute, and he knew now, deep down, that it would go well this day – then he put the memory of those eyes from his mind and looked ahead.

Ten miles ahead, where the low chalk ridges ran across their front, he saw with relief that he had been right, the breeze had not yet dispersed the morning mist that hung in the valleys. The chalk ridges were horribly chewed by shellfire, no vegetation remained upon them, the stumps of the shattered oak trees were nowhere as tall as a man's shoulder, and the shell craters overlapped each other, brimming with stagnant water. The ridges had been fought over, month after month, but at the moment they were in Allied hands, taken at the beginning of the preceding winter at a cost in human lives that challenged belief. The leprous and pockmarked earth seemed deserted, but it was peopled by the legions of the living and the dead rotting together in the waterlogged earth. The smell of death borne on the breeze reached even to the men in the low flying machines, an obscenity that coated the back of their throats and made them gag.

Behind the ridges the Allied troops, South Africans and New Zealanders of the Third Army, were preparing reserve positions as a contingency measure, for should the Allied offensive which was being prepared upon the Somme river further to the west fail, then all the fury of the German counter-attack would be unleashed upon them.

The preparation of the new line of defences was being seriously hampered by the massed German artillery to the north of the ridges, which deluged the area with an almost continuous barrage of high explosive. As they roared towards the front, Michael could see the yellow haze from the bursting howitzer shells hanging in a poison bank below the ridges, and he could imagine the anguish of the men toiling in the mud, harassed by the unremitting fall of explosives.

As Michael raced towards the ridges, the sound of the barrage rose above

even the thunder of the big rotary Le Rhône engine and the buffeting rush of the slipstream. The barrage was like the sound of storm surf on a rocky shore, like the beat of a demented drummer, like the fevered pulse of this sick, mad world, and Michael's fierce resentment at the men who had ordered them to go against the balloons abated as the roar of the barrage mounted. It was work that must be done – he realized it when he saw this dreadful suffering.

Yet the balloons were the most feared and hated targets that any man could fly against – that was why Andrew Killigerran would send nobody else. Michael saw them now, like fat silver slugs hanging in the dawn sky high above the ridges. One was directly ahead, the other a few miles further east. At this range the cables that tethered them to earth were invisible, and the wicker basket from which the observers obtained a grandstand view over the Allied rear areas were merely dark specks suspended beneath the shining spheres of hydrogen-filled silk.

At that moment there was a shocking disruption of air that hit the Sopwiths and rocked their wings, and immediately ahead of them a fountain of smoke and flame shot into the sky, rolling upon itself, black and bright orange, rising anvil-headed, high above the low-flying Sopwiths, forcing them to bank away steeply to avoid its fiery pillar. A German shell directed from one of the balloons had hit a forward Allied ammunition dump, and Michael felt his fear and resentment shrivel, to be replaced by a burning hatred of the gunners and of the men hanging in the sky, with eyes like vultures, calling down death with cold dispassion.

Andrew turned back toward the ridges, leaving the tall column of smoke on their right wingtips, and he dropped lower and still lower, until his undercarriage was skimming the tops of the sandbagged parapets and they could see the South African troops moving in file along the communication trenches, dun-coloured beasts of burden, not really human, toiling under the weight of their packs and equipment. Very few of them bothered to look up as the gaily painted machines thundered overhead. Those that did had grey, mud-streaked faces, the expression dulled and the eyes blank.

Ahead of them opened the mouth of one of the low passes that bisected the chalk ridges. The pass was filled with the morning mist. With the thrust of the dawn breeze agitating it, the mist bank undulated softly as though the earth was making love beneath a silver eiderdown.

There was the rattle of a Vickers machine-gun close ahead. Andrew was testfiring his weapon. Michael turned slightly out of line to clear his front and fired a short burst. The phosphorus-tipped incendiary bullets spun pretty white trails in the clear air.

Michael turned back into line behind Andrew and they hurtled into the mist, entering a new dimension of light and muted sound. The diffused light spun rainbow-coloured haloes around both aircraft and the moisture condensed on Michael's goggles. He lifted them on to his forehead and peered ahead.

The previous afternoon, Andrew and Michael had carefully reconnoitred this narrow pass between the ridges, reassuring themselves that there were no obstacles or obstructions, and memorizing the way it twisted and turned through the higher ground – and yet it was still a perilous passage, with visibility down to 600 feet or less and the chalky slopes rising steeply at each wingtip.

Michael closed up on the green tailplane and flew on that alone, trusting

Andrew to take him through, while the icy cold of the mist ate corrosively through his clothing and numbed his fingertips through the leather gauntlets.

Ahead of him Andrew banked steeply, and as Michael followed him round, he caught a glimpse of the barbed wire, brown with rust and tangled like bracken beneath his wheels.

'No man's land,' he muttered, and then the German front lines flashed beneath them, a mere glimpse of parapets beneath which crouched men in field-grey uniforms and those ugly coal-scuttle helmets.

Seconds later they burst out of the mist bank into a world lit by the first low rays of the sun, into a sky that dazzled them with its brilliance – and Michael realized that they had achieved total surprise. The mist bank had hidden them from the observers in the balloon and it had deadened the beat of their engines.

Directly ahead, the first balloon hung suspended in the sky, 1500 feet above them. Its steel anchor-cable, fine as a spider's strand of gossamer, led down to the ugly black steam winch half-buried in its employment of sandbags. It looked utterly vulnerable, until Michael's eye dropped to the peaceful-seeming fields beneath the balloon, and there were the guns.

The machine-gun nests resembled ant-lion burrows in the African soil, tiny dimples in the earth, lined with sandbags. He could not count them in the brief seconds left to him, there were so many. Instead, he picked out the anti-aircraft guns, standing tall and ungainly as giraffes on their circular baseplates, the long barrels already pointed skywards, ready to hurl their air-burst shrapnel as high as 20,000 feet into the sky.

They were waiting. They knew that sooner or later the planes would come, and they were ready. Michael realized that the mist had won them only seconds, for he could see the gunners running to man their weapons. One of the long anti-aircraft barrels began to move, depressing and swinging towards them. Then, as Michael pushed the throttle lever hard open against its stop and the Sopwith surged forward, he saw a cloud of white stream spurt from the massive winch as the ground crew began desperately to haul the balloon down into the protective fire of the banks of guns. The shimmering sphere of silk sank swiftly towards the earth, and Andrew lifted the nose of his machine and roared upwards.

With the throttle wide open and the big rotary engine howling in full power, Michael followed him up, aiming his climb at the cable halfway between the earth and the balloon, at the spot where the balloon would be when he reached it, and that was a mere 500 feet above the heads of the gunners.

Andrew was four hundred yards ahead of Michael, and still the guns had not opened up. Now he was on line with the balloon and engaging it. Michael clearly heard the clatter of his Vickers and saw the streaking phosphorous trails of the incendiary bullets, lacing through the icy dawn air, joining the balloon and the racing green aircraft for fleeting seconds. Then Andrew banked away, his wingtip brushed the billowing silk and it rocked sedately in his slipstream.

Now it was Michael's turn, and as he picked up the balloon in his gunsight, the gunners below him opened up. He heard the rip-crash of shrapnel bursts, and the Sopwith rocked dangerously in the tornado of passing shot, but the shells were all fused too long. They burst in bright silver balls of smoke three or four hundred feet above them.

The machine-gunners were more accurate, for they were at almost point-blank range. Michael felt the solid crash of shot into his plane, and tracer flew thick and white as hail about him. He hit the rudder bar and at the same time

threw on opposite stick, crossing controls to induce a gut-wrenching side-slip, throwing off the sheets of fire for a moment while he lined up for the balloon.

It seemed to rush towards him, the silk had the repulsively soft sheen of a maggot coated in silver mucus. He saw the two German observers dangling in their open wicker basket, both of them bundled in clothing against the cold. One stared at him woodenly, the other's face was contorted with terror and fury as he screamed a curse or a challenge that was lost in the blare of engines and the rattling clatter of machine-gun fire.

It was barely necessary to aim the Vickers, for the balloon filled all his vision. Michael opened the safety lock and pressed down on the firing lever; the gun hammered, shaking the entire aircraft, and the smoke of burning phosphorus from the incendiary bullets blew back into his face, choking him.

Now that he was flying straight and level, the ground gunners found him again, shooting the Sopwith to tatters – but Michael held on, pressing on alternate rudders to wing his nose slightly from side to side, directing his incendiaries into the balloon as though he was wielding a garden hose.

'Burn!' he screamed. 'Burn! Damn you, burn!'

Pure hydrogen gas is not inflammable, it has to mix with oxygen in proportions of 1:2 before it becomes violently explosive. The balloon absorbed his fire without visible effect.

'Burn!' he screamed at it. His clawed hand locked on the firing handle, the Vickers hammering, and the spent brass shells spewing from the breech. Hydrogen must be pouring from the hundreds of bullet holes that both he and Andrew had shot in the silk, the gas must be mingling with the air.

'Why won't you burn?' He heard the anguish and despair in his own wild cry. He was on the balloon – he must break away now, he must turn to avoid collision, it had all been in vain. Then, in that instant of failure, he knew that he would never give up. He knew he was going to fly into the balloon if he had to.

As he thought it, the balloon exploded in his face. It seemed to swell to a hundred times its size, to fill the sky and at the same time turn to flame. A stunning dragon's breath licked over Michael and the Sopwith, scorching the exposed skin of his cheeks, blinding him, flinging both man and machine aloft like a green leaf from a garden bonfire. Michael fought for control as the Sopwith tried to turn on her back, then tumbled down the sky. He caught her before she smashed into the earth and as he climbed away he looked back.

The hydrogen gas had burned away in that single demoniac gust, and now the empty, fiercely-burning silk shroud collapsed, spreading like a fiery umbrella over the basket and its human cargo.

One of the German observers jumped clear and fell 300 feet, his greatcoat fluttering about him, his legs kicking convulsively, disappearing abruptly, without sound or trace, into the shot green grass of the field. The second observer stayed with the basket and was enveloped by the billows of burning silk.

On the ground the crew were scrambling from the winch emplacement, like insects from a disturbed nest, but the burning silk fell too swiftly, trapping them in its fiery folds. Michael felt no pity for any of them, but was overcome instead by a savage triumph, a primeval reaction from his own terror. He opened his mouth to shout his war cry, and at that moment a shrapnel shell, fired from one of the guns near the north edge of the field, burst beneath the Sopwith.

Again it was tossed upwards, and humming, hissing shards of steel tore up through the belly of the fuselage. As Michael struggled to control this second wild urge and drop, the floor of the cockpit was ripped open so that he could see the ground below him and arctic winds howled up under his greatcoat, making the folds billow.

He held her on even keel, but she was hard-hit. Something was loose below the fuselage, it banged and whipped in the wind and she was flying one wing heavy, so he had to hold her up by brute force – but at least he was out of range of the guns at last.

Then Andrew appeared on his wingtip, craning across at him anxiously, and Michael grinned and whooped with triumph. Andrew was signalling for his attention, and stabbing his thumb in the signal, 'Return to base!'

Michael glanced around him. While he had been fighting for control, they had been roaring northwards, deeper and still deeper into German territory. They flashed over a crossroads jammed with animal-drawn and motorized transport, startled field-grey figures scattered for cover in the ditches. Michael ignored them and swivelled in the cockpit; three miles away across the flat and featureless green fields the second balloon still sailed serenely above the ridges.

Michael gave Andrew the cut-out negative and pointed at the remaining balloon. 'No – continue the attack.'

Andrew's signal was urgent. 'Return to base!' and he pointed at Michael's machine, and gave him the cut-throat signal. 'Danger!'

Michael looked down through the hole between his feet where the belly had been shot out of her. That banging was probably one of his landing wheels dangling on the bracing wires. Bullet holes had peppered the wings and body of the aircraft, and loose ribbons of torn fabric fluttered like Buddhist prayer flags as the slipstream plucked at them, but the Le Rhône engine roared angrily, still under full throttle, without check or stutter in its warlike beat.

Andrew was signalling again, urging him to turn back, but Michael gave him a curt flick of the hand – 'Follow me!' – and threw the Sopwith up on one wingtip, bringing her round in a steep turn that strained her damaged bodywork.

Michael was lost in the raptures of fighting madness, the berserker's wild passion, in which the threat of death or fearful injury was of no consequence. His vision was heightened to unnatural clarity, and he flew the damaged Sopwith as though it were an extension of his own body, as though he were part-swallow skimming the water to drink in flight, so lightly did he brush the hedgerows and touch the stubble in the fields with his single remaining landing wheel, and part-falcon, so cruel was his unblinking gaze as he bated at the ponderously descending balloon.

Of course, they had seen the fiery destruction of the first balloon, and they were winching in. They would be down before Michael reached the site. The gunners would be fully alerted, waiting with finger on the trigger. It would be a ground level attack, into the prepared positions – but even in his suicidal rage, Michael had lost none of the hunter's cunning. He was using every stick of available cover for his approach run.

A narrow country lane angled across his front, the row of slim, straight poplars that flanked it was the only feature on this dreary plain below the ridge. Michael used the line of trees, banking steeply to run parallel with them, keeping them between him and the balloon site, and he glanced up at the mirror fixed to the wing section above his head. Andrew's green Sopwith was so close

behind him that the spinning propeller almost touched his rudder. Michael grinned like a shark and gathered the Sopwith in his hands and lifted it over the palisade of poplar trees the way a hunter takes a fence at full gallop.

The balloon site was three hundred yards ahead. The balloon itself had just reached ground level. The ground crew were helping the observers out of the basket and then running in a group for the cover of the nearest trench. The machine-gunners, their aim frustrated up to that moment by the row of poplar trees, had a fair target at last, and they opened together.

Michael flew into a torrent of fire. It filled the air about him, and the shrapnel shells sucked at the air as they passed, so that his eardrums clicked and ached with the pressure drops. In the emplacements he saw the faces of the gunners turned up towards him; they were pale blobs behind the foreshortened barrels that swung to follow him and the muzzle flashes were bright and pretty as fairy lights. However, the Sopwith was roaring in at well over 100 miles an hour and he had barely 300 yards to cover. Even the solid crunch of bullets into the heavy engine block could not distract Michael as he lined up his sights with delicate touches on the rudder bars.

The group of running men escaping from the balloon was directly ahead of him, racing back towards the trench. In their midst the two observers were slow and clumsy, still stiff with the cold of the upper air, burdened by their heavy clothing. Michael hated them as he might hate a venomous snake, he dropped the Sopwith's nose fractionally and touched the firing lever. The group of men blew away, like grey smoke, and disappeared into the low stubble. Instantly Michael lifted the aim of the Vickers.

The balloon was tethered to earth, looking like a circus tent. He fired into it, bullets streaming on silvery trails of phosphorus smoke into the soft silken mass without effect.

In the berserker's rage, Michael's brain was clear, his thought so swift, that time seemed to run slower and still slower. The micro-seconds as he closed with the stranded silken monster seemed to last an eternity, so that he could follow the flight of each individual bullet from the muzzle of his Vickers.

'Why won't she burn?' he screamed the question again, and the answer came to him.

The hydrogen atom is the lightest of all in weight. The escaping gas was rising to mingle with oxygen above the balloon. It was so obvious then, that he was shooting too low. Why hadn't he realized it before?

He hauled the Sopwith up on her tail, streaming his fire upwards across the swelling side of the balloon, still up until he was shooting into empty air, over the top of the balloon – and the air turned to sudden flame. As the great exhalation of fire rolled towards him, Michael kept the Sopwith climbing into the vertical and jerked the throttle closed. Without power she hung for an instant on her nose and then stalled and dropped. Michael kicked hard at the rudder bar, spinning her into the classic stall turn, and as he opened the throttle again he was headed back, directly away from the immense funeral pyre that he had created. Beneath him he caught a green flash as Andrew banked on to his wingtip in a maximum-rate turn, breaking out left, almost colliding with Michael's undercarriage, and then hurtling away at right angles to his track.

There was no more ground fire; the sudden acrobatics of the two attackers and the roaring pillar of burning gas entirely distracted the gunners, and Michael dropped back behind the cover of the poplar trees. Now that it was all over, his rage abated almost as swiftly as it had arisen, and he swept the skies

above him, realizing that the columns of smoke would be a beacon for the Albatros Jagdstaffels. Apart from the smoke, the skies were clear, and he felt a lift of relief and looked for Andrew as he banked low over the hedgerows. There he was, a little higher than Michael, already heading back towards the ridges, but angling in to intercept him.

They came together. Stange what comfort there was in having Andrew on his wingtip, grinning at him and shaking his head in mock disapproval of the disobeyed order to return to base and the berserker fit which had seized Michael.

Side by side they roared low across the German front lines again, contemptuous of the splattering of fire they drew, and then as they began the climb to cross the ridge, Michael's engine spluttered and lost power.

He dropped towards the chalky earth, and then the engine fired again, bellowed and surged, lifting him just clear of the crest, before missing and banging unevenly once more. Andrew was still beside him, mouthing encouragement – and the engine roared again, and then missed and popped.

Michael nursed it, pumping the throttle, fiddling with the ignition setting, and whispering to the wounded Sopwith. 'Come on, my darling. Stick it out, old girl. Nearly home, there's my sweetheart.'

Then he felt something break in her body, one of the main frames shot through, and the controls went soft in his hands, and she sagged, sick unto death. 'Hold on,' Michael exhorted her – but suddenly there was the pungent stink of petrol in his nostrils, and he saw a thin transparent trickle of it ooze from under the engine cowling and turn to white vapour in the slipstream as it blew back past his head.

'Fire.' It was the airman's nightmare, but the vestiges of rage were still with Michael and he murmured stubbornly, 'We're going home, old girl. Just a little longer.'

They had crossed the ridges, there was flat terrain ahead, and he could already make out the dark T-shaped wood which marked the approach to the airstrip. 'Come on, my sweetheart.'

Beneath him there were men, out of the trenches, lining the parapets, waving and cheering as the damaged Sopwith clattered and popped close above their heads, one of its landing wheels shot away, the other dangling and slamming against its belly.

Their faces were upturned, and he saw their open mouths as they called to him. They had heard the storm of fire that heralded the attack, and seen the great balls of burning hydrogen shoot into the sky beyond the ridges, and they knew that for a little while the torment of the guns would ease, and they cheered the returning pilots, shouting themselves hoarse.

Michael left them behind, but their gratitude was uplifting and ahead lay all the familiar landmarks – the spire of the church, the pink roof of the château, the little knoll.

'We are going to make it, my sweetheart,' he called to the Sopwith, but under the engine cowling a dangling wire touched the metal of the engine block and a tiny blue spark arced across the gap. There was the whoosh of explosive combustion, and the white trail of vapour turned to flame. Heat washed over the open cockpit like the pressure flame from a blow lamp, and Michael instinctively flung the Sopwith into another side-slip so that the flames were pushed out obliquely away from his face and he could see ahead.

Now he had to get her down, anywhere, anyhow, but fast, very fast, before

he was cooked and charred in the burning carcass of the Sopwith. He dipped towards the field that opened ahead of him, and now his greatcoat was burning, the sleeve of his right arm smouldered and burst into flame.

He brought the Sopwith down, holding the nose up to bleed off speed, but she hit the ground with a force that cracked his teeth together in his jaw, and instantly she pivoted on her one remaining wheel and then cartwheeled, tearing off one wing and crashing into the hedgerow that bordered the field.

Michael's head slammed against the edge of the cockpit, stunning him, but there were flames crackling and leaping up all around him now and he clawed himself out of the cockpit, fell on to the crumpled wing and rolled on to the muddy earth. On his hands and knees he crawled desperately away from the flaming wreckage. The burning wool of the greatcoat flared and the heat spurred him to his feet with a scream. He ripped at the buttons, trying to rid himself of the agony, running and flapping his arms, wildly, fanning the flames and making them fiercer and hotter.

In the crackling roar of the burning wreckage, he did not even hear the galloping horse.

The girl put the big white stallion to the hedge and they flew over it. Horse and rider landed in balance and immediately plunged forward again after the burning, screaming figure in the centre of the field. The girl unhooked her leg from the pommel of the side-saddle, and as they came up behind Michael she pulled the stallion down to a sliding halt and at the same time launched herself from his back.

She landed with her full weight between Michael's shoulder-blades, and both arms locked around his neck, so that he was knocked sprawling flat on to his face with the girl on his back. She rolled to her feet and whipping the thick gaberdine skirt of the riding-habit from around her waist, spread it over the burning figure at her feet. Then she dropped to her knees beside him and wrapped the voluminous skirt tightly around him, beating with her bare hands at the little tendrils of flame that escaped from around it.

As soon as the flames were snuffed out, she pulled off the skirt and heaved Michael into a sitting position on the muddy ground. With quick fingers, she unbuttoned the smoking greatcoat and stripped it off his shoulders and flung it aside. She pulled away the smouldering jerseys – there was only one place where the flames had reached his flesh. They had burned through across his shoulder and down his arm. He cried out with the pain when she tried to pull the nightshirt away. 'For the love of Christ!' The cotton shirt had stuck to the burns.

The girl leaned over him, took the cloth in her teeth and worried it until it tore. Once she had started it, she ripped it open with her hands and her expression changed. 'Mon Dieu!' she said, and jumped up. She stamped on the smoking greatcoat to extinguish the last of the smouldering wool.

Michael stared at her, the agony of his burned arm receding. With her long skirt removed, her riding jacket reached only to the top of her thighs. On her feet she wore black patent-leather riding boots fastened up the sides with hooks and eyes. Her knees were bare, and the skin at the back of them was smooth and flawless as the inner lining of a nautilus shell, but her knee-caps were smudged with mud where she had knelt to help him. Above the knees she wore a pair of cami-knickers of a sheer material through which he could distinctly make out the sheen of her skin. The legs of the knickers were fastened above

the knee with pink ribbons, and they clung to her thighs and lower body as though she were naked – no, the semi-veiled lines were even more riveting than naked flesh would have been.

Michael felt his throat swell, so that he could not breathe, as she stooped to pick up his charred coat, and he was allowed a brief vision of her small, firm buttocks, round as a pair of ostrich eggs, gleaming palely in the early-morning light. He stared so hard, he felt his eyes begin to water and as she turned back to him, he saw in the fork formed by her hard young thighs a dark triangular shadow through the thin silk. She stood with that mesmeric shadow six inches from his nose while she spread the coat gently over his burned shoulder, murmuring to him in the tone a mother uses to a hurt child.

Michael caught only the words 'froid' and 'brûlé'. She was so close that he could smell her; the natural musk of a healthy young woman sweating with the exertion of hard riding was mingling with a perfume that smelled like dried rose petals. Michael tried to speak, to thank her, but he was shaking with shock and pain. His lips wobbled and he made a little slurring sound.

'Mon pauvre,' she cooed to him, and stepped back. Her voice was husky with concern and exertion, and she had the face of a pixie with huge dark Celtic eyes. He wondered if her ears were pointed, but they were hidden by the dark bush of her hair. It was windblown and kinked into dense springy curls. Her skin was tinted by her Celtic blood to the colour of old ivory and her eyebrows were thick and dark as her hair.

She began to speak again, but he could not help himself, and he glanced down again to that intriguing little shadow under the silk. She saw the movement of his eyes and her cheeks glowed with a dusky rose colour as she snatched up her muddy skirts and whipped them around her waist – and Michael ached more with embarrassment at his gaffe than he did from his burns.

The overhead roar of Andrew's Sopwith gave them both respite and they looked up gratefully as Andrew circled the field. Painfully and unsteadily Michael clambered to his feet, as the girl settled her skirts, and he waved up at Andrew. He saw Andrew lift his hand and give him a relieved salute, then the green Sopwith circled out and came in on a straight run not higher than fifty feet above their heads – and the green scarf, with something knotted in one end, fluttered down and plunked into the mud a few yards away.

The girl ran to it and brought it back to Michael. He unknotted the tail of the scarf and grinned lopsidedly as he brought out the silver flask. He unscrewed the stopper and lifted the flask to the sky. He saw the flash of Andrew's white teeth in the open cockpit and the raised gauntleted hand – and then Andrew turned away towards the airfield.

Michael lifted the flask to his lips, and swallowed twice. His eyes clouded with tears and he gasped as the heavenly liquid flowed scalding down his throat. When he lowered the flask, she was watching him, and he offered it to her.

She shook her head, and asked seriously, 'Anglais?'

'Oui – non – Sud Africain.' His voice shook.

'Ah, vous parlez francais!' She smiled for the first time, and it was a phenomenon almost as stunning as her pearly little bottom.

'*A peine* – hardly.' He denied it swiftly, staving off the flood of voluble French that he knew from experience an affirmative would have brought down on his head.

'You have blood.' Her English was appalling, only when she pointed to his head did he understand what she had said. He lifted his free hand and touched

the trickle of blood which had escaped from under his helmet. He inspected his smeared fingertips.

'Yes,' he admitted. 'Buckets of it, I'm afraid.'

The helmet had saved him from serious injury when his head had struck the side of the cockpit.

'Pardon?' She looked confused.

'J'en ai beaucoup,' he translated.

'Ah, you *do* talk French.' She clapped her hands in an endearing, childlike gesture of delight and took his arm in a proprietorial gesture.

'Come,' she ordered, and snapped her fingers for the stallion. He was cropping the grass, and pretended not to hear her.

'Viens ici tout de suite, Nuage!' She stamped her foot. 'Come here, this instant, Cloud!'

The stallion took another mouthful of grass to demonstrate his independence and then sidled across in leisurely fashion.

'Please,' she asked, and Michael made a stirrup of his cupped hands and boosted her up into the saddle. She was very light and agile.

'Come up.' She helped him, and he settled behind her on the stallion's broad rump. She took one of Michael's hands and placed it on her waist. Her flesh under his fingers was firm and he could feel the heat of it through the cloth.

'*Tenez*, hold on!' she instructed, and the stallion cantered towards the gate at the end of the field nearest the château.

Michael looked back at the smoking wreckage of his Sopwith. Only the engine block remained, the wood and canvas had burned away. He felt a shadow of deep regret at her destruction – they had come a long way together.

'How do you call yourself?' the girl asked over her shoulder, and he turned back to her.

'Michael – Michael Courtney.'

'Michael Courtney,' she repeated experimentally, and then, 'I am Mademoiselle Centaine de Thiry.'

'Enchanté, mademoiselle.' Michael paused to compose his next conversational gem in his laboured schoolboy French. 'Centaine is a strange name,' he said, and she stiffened under his hand. He had used the word 'drôle', or comical. Quickly he corrected himself, 'An exceptional name.'

Suddenly he regretted that he had not applied himself more vigorously to his French studies; shaken and shocked as he still was, he had to concentrate hard to follow her rapid explanation.

'I was born one minute after midnight on the first day of the year 1900.' So she was seventeen years and three months old, teetering on the very brink of womanhood. Then he remembered that his own mother had been barely seventeen when he was born. The thought cheered him so much that he took another quick nip from Andrew's flask.

'You are my saviour!' He meant it light-heartedly, but it sounded so crass that he expected her to burst into mocking laughter. Instead, she nodded seriously. The sentiment was in accord with Centaine's own swiftly developing emotions.

Her favourite animal, apart from Nuage the stallion, had once been a skinny mongrel puppy which she had found in the ditch, blood-smeared and shivering. She had nursed it and cherished it, and loved it until a month previously when it had died under the wheels of one of the army trucks trundling up to the front. Its death had left an aching gap in her existence. Michael was thin, almost

starved-looking under all those charred and muddy clothes; apart, then, from his physical injuries, she sensed the abuse to which he had been subjected. His eyes were a marvellous clear blue, but she read in them a terrible suffering, and he shivered and trembled just as her little mongrel had.

'Yes,' she said firmly. 'I will look after you.'

The château was larger than it had seemed from the air, and much less beautiful. Most of the windows had been broken and boarded up. The walls were pocked with shell splinters, but the shell craters on the lawns had grassed over – the fighting last autumn had come within extreme artillery range of the estate, before the final push by the Allies had driven the Germans back behind the ridges again.

The great house had a sad and neglected air, and Centaine apologized. 'Our workmen have been taken by the army, and most of the women and all the children have fled to Paris or Amiens. We are three only.' She raised herself in the saddle and called out sharply in a different language, 'Anna! Come and see what I have found.'

The woman who emerged from the vegetable gardens behind the kitchens was squat and broad with a backside like a percheron mare and huge shapeless breasts beneath the mud-stained blouse. Her thick dark hair, streaked with grey, was pulled back into a bun on top of her head, and her face was red and round as a radish, her arms, bare to the elbows, were thick and muscular as a man's and caked with mud. She held a bunch of turnips in one large, calloused hand.

'What is it, *kleinjie* – little one?'

'I have saved a gallant English airman, but he is terribly wounded – '

'He looks very well to me.'

'Anna, don't be such an old grouse! Come and help me. We must get him into the kitchen.'

The two of them were gabbling at each other, and to Michael's astonishment, he could understand every word of it.

'I will not allow a soldier in the house, you know that, *kleinjie*! I won't have a tomcat in the same basket with my little kitten – '

'He's not a soldier, Anna, he's an airman.'

'And probably as randy as any tomcat – '

She used the word 'fris', and Centaine flashed at her, 'You are a disgusting old woman – now come and help me.'

Anna looked Michael over very carefully, and then conceded reluctantly, 'He has nice eyes, but I still don't trust him – oh, all right, but if he so much as – '

'Mevrou,' Michael spoke for the first time, 'your virtue is safe with me, I give you my solemn word. Ravishing as you are, I will control myself.'

Centaine swivelled in the saddle to stare at him, and Anna reeled back with shock and then guffawed with delight.

'He speaks Flemish!'

'You speak Flemish!' Centaine echoed the accusation.

'It's not Flemish,' Michael denied. 'It's Afrikaans, South African Dutch.'

'It's Flemish,' Anna told him as she came forward. 'And anybody who speaks Flemish is welcome in this house.' She reached up to Michael.

'Be careful,' Centaine told her anxiously. 'His shoulder – ' She slipped to the ground and between the two of them they helped Michael down and led him to the door of the kitchen.

A dozen chefs could have prepared a banquet for five hundred guests in this

kitchen, but there was only a tiny wood fire burning in one of the ranges and they seated Michael on a stool in front of it.

'Get some of your famous ointment,' Centaine ordered, and Anna hurried away.

'You are Flemish?' Michael asked. He was delighted that the language barrier had evaporated.

'No, no.' Centaine was busy with an enormous pair of shears, snipping away the charred remnants of the shirt from his burns. 'Anna is from the north – she was my nurse when my mother died, and now she thinks she is my mother and not just a servant. She taught me the language in the cradle. But you, where did you learn it?'

'Where I come from, everybody speaks it.'

'I'm glad,' she said, and he was not sure what she meant, for her eyes were lowered to her task.

'I look for you every morning,' he said softly. 'We all do, when we fly.'

She said nothing, but he saw her cheeks turn that lovely dusky pink colour again.

'We call you our good luck angel, *l'ange du bonheur*,' and she laughed.

'I call you *le petit jaune*, the little yellow one,' she answered. The yellow Sopwith – Michael felt a surge of elation. She knew him as an individual, and she went on, 'All of you, I wait for you to come back, counting my chickens, but so often they do not come back, the new ones especially. Then I cry for them and pray. But you and the green one always come home, then I rejoice for you.'

'You are kind,' he started, but Anna bustled back from the pantry carrying a stone jar that smelled of turpentine and the mood was spoiled.

'Where is Papa?' Centaine demanded.

'In the basement, seeing to the animals.'

'We have to keep the livestock in the cellars,' Centaine explained as she went to the head of the stone stairs, 'otherwise the soldiers steal the chickens and geese and even the milch cows. I had to fight to keep Nuage, even.'

She yelled down the stairs, 'Papa! Where are you?'

There was a muffled response from below and Centaine called again, 'We need a bottle of cognac.' And then her tone became admonitive. 'Unopened, Papa. It is not a social need, but a medicinal one. Not for you but for a patient – here.'

Centaine tossed a bunch of keys down the stairs and minutes later there was a heavy tread and a large shaggy man with a full belly shambled into the kitchen with a cognac bottle held like an infant to his chest.

He had the same dense bush of kinky hair as Centaine, but it was woven with grey strands and hung forward on to his forehead. His moustaches were wide and beeswaxed into impressive spikes, and he peered at Michael through a single dark glittering eye. The other eye was covered by a piratical black cloth patch.

'Who is this?' he demanded.

'An English airman.'

The scowl abated. 'A fellow warrior,' he said. 'A comrade-in-arms – another destroyer of the cursed boche!'

'You have not destroyed a boche for over forty years,' Anna reminded him without looking up from Michael's burns, but he ignored her and advanced on Michael, opening his arms like a bear to envelop him.

'Papa, be careful. He is wounded.'

'Wounded!' cried Papa. 'Cognac!' as though the two words were linked, and he found two heavy glass tumblers and placed them on the kitchen table, breathed on them with a decidedly garlicky breath, wiped them on his coat-tails, and cracked the red wax from the neck of the bottle.

'Papa, *you* are not wounded,' Centaine told him severely as he filled both tumblers up to the brim.

'I would not insult a man of such obvious valour by asking him to drink alone.' He brought one tumbler to Michael.

'Comte Louis de Thiry, at your service, monsieur.'

'Captain Michael Courtney. Royal Flying Corps.'

'A votre santé, Capitaine!'

'A la vôtre, Monsieur le Comte!'

The comte drank with undisguised relish, then sighed and wiped his magnificent dark moustaches on the back of his hand and spoke to Anna.

'Proceed with the treatment, woman.'

'This will sting,' Anna warned, and for a moment Michael thought she meant the cognac, but she took a handful of the ointment from the stone jar and slapped it on to the open burns.

Michael let out an anguished whinny and tried to rise, but Anna held him down with one huge, red, work-chafed hand.

'Bind it up,' she ordered Centaine, and as the girl wound on the bandages, the agony faded and became a comforting warmth.

'It feels better,' Michael admitted.

'Of course it does,' Anna told him comfortably. 'My ointment is famous for everything from smallpox to piles.'

'So is my cognac,' murmured the comte, and recharged both tumblers.

Centaine went to the wash basket on the kitchen table and returned with one of the comte's freshly iron shirts, and despite her father's protests, she helped Michael into it. Then as she was fashioning a sling for his injured arm, there was the buzzing clatter of an engine outside the kitchen windows and Michael caught a glimpse of a familiar figure on an equally familiar motor-cycle skidding to a halt in a spray of gravel.

The engine spluttered and hiccoughed into silence and a voice called agitatedly, 'Michael, my boy, where are you?'

The door burst open and admitted Lord Andrew Killigerran in tam o' shanter, followed closely by a young officer in the uniform of the Royal Medical Corps. 'Thank God, there you are. Panic not, I've brought you a sawbones – ' Andrew pulled the doctor to Michael's stool and then, with relief and a shade of pique in his voice, 'You seem to be doing damn well without us, I'll say that for you. I raided the local field hospital. Kidnapped this medico at the point of a pistol – been eating my heart out about you, and here you are with a glass in your hand, and – '

Andrew broke off and looked at Centaine for the first time, and forgot all about Michael's condition. He swept the tam o'shanter from his head. 'It's true!' he declaimed in perfect sonorous French, rolling his Rs in true Gallic fashion. 'Angels do indeed walk the earth.'

'Go to your room immediately, child,' Anna snapped, and her face screwed up like one of those fearsome carved dragons that guard the entrance to Chinese temples.

'I am not a child,' Centaine gave her an equally ferocious glare, then

recomposed her features as she turned to Michael. 'Why does he call you his boy? You are much older than he is!'

'He's Scots,' Michael explained, already ridden by jealousy, 'and the Scots are all mad – also, he has a wife and four children.'

'That is a filthy lie,' Andrew protested. 'The children, yes, I admit to them, poor wee bairns! But no wife, definitely no wife.'

'*Ecossais*,' murmured the comte, 'great warriors and great drinkers.' Then, in reasonable English, 'May I offer you a little cognac, monsieur?' They were descending into a babble of languages, crossing from one to the other in mid-sentence.

'Will somebody kindly introduce me to this paragon among men, that I may accept his fulsome offer?'

'Le Comte de Thiry, I have the honour to present Lord Andrew Killigerran.' Michael waved them together and they shook hands.

'Tiens! A genuine English milord.'

'Scots, my dear fellow – big difference.' He saluted the comte with the tumbler. 'Enchanted, I'm sure. And this beautiful young lady is your daughter – the resemblance – beautiful – '

'Centaine,' Anna interposed, 'take your horse to the stable and groom him.'

Centaine ignored her and smiled at Andrew. The smile stopped even his banter, he stared at her, for the smile transformed her. It seemed to glow through her skin like a lamp through alabaster, and it lit her teeth and sparkled in her eyes like sunlight in a crystal jar of dark honey.

'I think I should have a look at our patient.' The young army doctor broke the spell and stepped forward to unwrap Michael's bandages. Anna understood the gesture, if not the words, and she interposed her bulk between them.

'Tell him, if he touches my work, I will break his arm.'

'Your services are not required, I'm afraid,' Michael translated for the doctor.

'Have a cognac,' Andrew consoled him. 'It's not bad stuff – not bad at all.'

'You are a landowner, milord?' the comte asked Andrew with subtlety. 'Of course?'

'Bien sûr – ' Andrew made an expansive gesture which portrayed thousands of acres and at the same time brought his glass within range of where the comte was filling the doctor's glass. The comte topped him up and Andrew repeated, 'Of course, the family estates – you understand?'

'Ah,' The comte's single eye glittered as he glanced across at his daughter. 'Your deceased wife has left you with four children?' He had not followed the earlier exchange all that clearly.

'No children, no wife – my humorous friend,' Andrew indicated Michael, 'he likes to make jokes. Very bad English jokes.'

'Ha! English jokes.' The comte roared with laughter and would have clapped Michael on his shoulder had not Centaine rushed forward to protect him from the blow.

'Papa, be careful. He is wounded.'

'You will stay for lunch – all of you,' the comte declared. 'You will see, milord, my daughter is one of the finest cooks in the province.'

'With a little help,' Anna muttered disgustedly.

'I say, I rather think I should be getting on back,' the young doctor murmured diffidently. 'I feel rather superfluous.'

'We are invited to lunch,' Andrew told him. 'Have a cognac.'

'Don't mind if I do.' The doctor succumbed without a struggle.'

The comte announced, 'It is necessary to descend to the cellars.'

'Papa – ' Centaine began ominously.

'We have guests!' The comte showed her the empty cognac bottle and she shrugged helplessly.

'Milord, you will assist me in the selection of suitable refreshments?'

'Honoured, Monsieur le Comte.'

As Centaine watched the pair, arms linked, descend the stone staircase, there was a thoughtful look in her eyes.

'He is a *drôle* one, your friend – and very loyal. See how he rushed here to your aid. See how he places a charm on my Papa.'

Michael was surprised by the strength of his dislike for Andrew at that moment. 'He smelled the cognac,' he muttered. 'That's the only reason he came.'

'But what of the four children?' Anna demanded. 'And their mother?' She was having as much difficulty as the comte in following the conversation.

'Four mothers,' Michael explained. 'Four children, four different mothers.'

'He is a polygamist!' Anna swelled with shock and affront, and her face went a shade redder.

'No, no,' Michael assured her. 'You heard him deny it. He is a man of honour, he would not do such a thing. He is married to none of them. Michael felt not a qualm, he had to have an ally somewhere in the family, but at that moment the happy pair returned from the cellars laden with black bottles.

'Aladdin's cave,' Andrew rejoiced. 'The comte has got it filled with good stuff!' He placed half a dozen bottles on the kitchen table in front of Michael. 'Look at this! Thirty years old, if it's a day!' Then he peered closely at Michael. 'You look awful, old boy. Death warmed up.'

'Thanks,' Michael grinned at him thinly. 'You are so kind.'

'Natural brotherly concern – ' Andrew struggled to draw the cork from one of the bottles, and dropped his voice to a conspiratorial whisper. 'By God, isn't she a corker!' He glanced across the kitchen to where the women were at work over the big copper pot. 'I'd rather feel her than feel sick, what?' Michael's dislike for Andrew turned to active hatred.

'I find that remark utterly revolting,' he said. 'To talk like that about a young girl, so innocent, so fine, so – so – ' Michael stuttered into silence, and Andrew held his head on one side and peered at him wonderingly.

'Michael, my boy, this is worse than just a few burns and bruises, I'm afraid. It's going to need intensive treatment.' He filled his glass. 'To start with, I prescribe a liberal dose of this excellent claret!'

At the head of the table the comte had the cork out of another of the bottles, and refilled the doctor's glass.

'A toast!' he cried. 'Confusion to the damned boche!'

'A bas les boches!' they all cried, and as soon as the toast was drunk the comte placed his hand over the black patch which covered the socket of his missing eye.

'They did this to me at Sedan in '70. They took my eye, but they paid dearly for it, the devils – *Sacré bleu*, how we fought! Tigers! We were tigers – '

'Tabby cats!' Anna called across the kitchen.

'You know nothing of battle and war – these brave young men, they know, they understand! I drink to them!' He did so copiously and then demanded, 'Now, where is the food?'

It was a savoury ragoût of ham and sausage and marrow bones. Anna brought

bowls of it steaming from the stove and Centaine piled small loaves of crisp new bread on the bare table.

'Now tell us, how goes the battle?' the comte demanded as he broke bread and dipped it into his bowl. 'When will this war end?'

'Let us not spoil good food,' Andrew waved the question away, but with crumbs and gravy on his moustache the comte insisted.

'What of a new Allied offensive?'

'It will be in the west, on the Somme river again. It is there that we have to break through the German lines.' It was Michael who answered; he spoke with quiet authority, so that almost immediately he had all their attention. Even the two women came from the stove and Centaine slipped on to the bench beside Michael, turning serious eyes up to him as she struggled to understand the English conversation.

'How do you know all this?' the comte interrupted.

'His uncle is a general,' Andrew explained.

'A general!' The comte looked at Michael with new interest 'Centaine, do you not see that our guest is in difficulty?' And while Anna gruffed and scowled, Centaine leaned over Michael's bowl and cut the meat into manageable portions so that he could eat with one hand.

'Go on! Continue!' the comte urged Michael. 'What then?'

'General Haig will pivot right. This time he will succeed in cutting across the German rear, and roll up their line.'

'Ha! So we are secure here.' The comte reached for the claret bottle, but Michael shook his head.

'I am afraid not, not entirely anyway. This section of the line is being stripped of reserves, regimental fronts of the line are being reduced to battalion strength – everything that can be spared is being moved to take part in a new push across the Somme.'

The comte looked alarmed. 'That is criminal folly – surely the Germans will counter-attack here to try and reduce pressure on their front at the Somme?'

'The line here, it will not hold?' Centaine asked anxiously and involuntarily glanced up at the kitchen windows. From where they sat, they could see the ridges on the horizon.

Michael hesitated. 'Oh, I am sure that we will be able to hold them long enough – especially if the fighting round the Somme goes as well and as quickly as we expect. Then the pressure here will swiftly be relieved as the Allied advance swings across the German rear.'

'But if the battle bogs down and is stalemated once again?' Centaine asked softly in Flemish.

For a girl, and one with little English, she had a firm grasp on the essentials. Michael treated her question with respect, answering, in Afrikaans, as though he was speaking to another man.

'Then we will be hard-pressed, especially as the Huns have aerial superiority. We may lose the ridges again.' He paused and frowned. 'They will have to rush in reserves. We may even be forced to pull back as far as Arras – '

'Arras!' Centaine gasped. 'That means – ' She did not finish, but looked around at her home as though already taking farewell of it. Arras was far to the rear.

Michael nodded. 'Once the attack begins, you will be in extreme danger here. You will be well advised to evacuate the château and go back south to Arras or even Paris.'

'Never!' cried the comte switching back into French. 'A de Thiry never retreats.'

'Except at Sedan,' Anna muttered, but the comte did not deign to hear such levity.

'I will stand here, on my own land.' He pointed at the ancient *chassepot* rifle that hung on the kitchen wall. 'That is the weapon I carried at Sedan. The boche learned to fear it there. They will relearn that lesson. Louis de Thiry will teach it to them!'

'Courage!' cried Andrew. 'I give you a toast. French valour and the triumph of French arms!'

Naturally the comte had to reply with a toast to 'General Haig and our gallant British Allies!'

'Captain Courtney is a South African,' Andrew pointed out. 'We should drink to them.'

'Ah!' the comte responded enthusiastically in English. 'To General – what is your uncle, the general, called? To General Sean Courtney and his brave South Africans.'

'This gentleman,' Andrew indicated the slightly owl-eyed doctor swaying gently on the bench beside him, 'is an officer in the Royal Medical Corps. A fine service, and worthy of our toast!'

'To the Royal Medical Corps!' the comte accepted the challenge, but as he reached for his glass again, it trembled before he touched it, and the surface of the red wine was agitated into little circular ripples which lapped against the crystal bowl. The comte froze and all their heads lifted.

The glass of the kitchen window-panes rattled in their frames and then the rumble of the guns rolled down from the north. Once again the German guns were hunting along the ridges, clamouring and barking like wild dogs, and as they listened in silence, they could imagine the misery and agony of the men in the muddy trenches only a few miles from where they sat in the warm kitchen with their bellies filled with food and fine wine.

Andrew lifted his glass and said softly, 'I give you those poor blighters out there in the mud. May they endure.' And this time even Centaine sipped from Michael's glass and her eyes swam with dark tears as she drank the toast.

'I hate to be a killjoy,' the young doctor stood up unsteadily, 'but that artillery barrage is the work-whistle for me, I'm afraid, the butchers' vans will be on their way back already.'

Michael tried to rise with him, but clutched quickly at the edge of the table for support. 'I wish to thank you, Monsieur le Comte,' he began formally, 'for your gentility – ' The word tripped on his tongue and he repeated it, but his tongue blurred and lost track of his speech. 'I salute your daughter, Mademoiselle de Thiry, *l'ange du bonheur* – ' His legs folded up under him, and he collapsed gently.

'He is wounded!' Centaine cried as she leaped forward and caught him before he hit the floor, supporting him with one slim shoulder under his armpit. 'Help me,' she pleaded. Andrew reeled forward to her assistance, and between them they half-carried, half-dragged Michael through the kitchen door.

'Careful, his poor arm,' Centaine gasped under the weight, as they lifted Michael into the side-car of the motor-cycle. 'Do not hurt him!' He lolled in the padded seat with a beatific grin on his pale features.

'Mademoiselle, rest assured he is beyond all pain, the lucky devil.' Andrew tottered around the machine to take the controls.

'Wait for me!' cried the doctor as he and the comte, giving each other mutual support, bounced off the door jamb and came crabbing down the steps in an unintended sideways charge.

'Climb aboard,' Andrew invited, and at the third attempt kick-started the Ariel in a roar of blue smoke. The doctor clambered on to the pillion behind him, and the comte thrust one of the two bottles of claret that he carried into Andrew's side pocket.

'Against the cold,' he explained.

'You are a prince among men.' Andrew let out the clutch and the Ariel screeched into a tight turn.

'Look after Michel!' cried Centaine.

'My cabbages!' screamed Anna, as Andrew took a short cut through the vegetable garden.

'A bas les boches!' howled the comte and took a last surreptitious pull at the other claret bottle, before Centaine could confiscate it from him and relieve him of the cellar keys once more.

* * *

At the end of the long drive that led down from the château Andrew braked the motor-cycle and then at a more sedate pace joined the pathetic little procession that was trickling back from the ridges along the muddy, rutted main road.

The butchers' vans, as the field ambulances were irreverently known, were heavily loaded with the fruits of the renewed German bombardment. They chugged through the muddy puddles, with the racks of canvas stretchers in the open backs swaying and lurching to each bump. The blood from the wounded men in the upper tiers soaked through the canvas and dripped on to those below.

On the verges of the lane little groups of walking wounded, straggled back, their rifles discarded, leaning on each other for support, lumpy field dressings strapped over their injuries, all their faces blank with suffering, their eyes dead of expression, their uniforms caked with mud and their movements mechanical, beyond caring.

Beginning to sober rapidly, the doctor climbed down off the pillion and selected the more seriously hurt men from the stream. They loaded two of them on to the pillion, one astride the petrol tank in front of Andrew and three more into the side-car with Michael. The doctor ran behind the overloaded Ariel, pushing it through the mud holes, and he was completely sober when a mile up the road they reached the VAD hospital in a row of cottages at the entrance to the village of Mort Homme. He helped his newly acquired patients out of the side-car and then turned back to Andrew.

'Thanks. I needed that break.' He glanced down at Michael, still passed out in the side-car. 'Look at him. We can't go on like this forever.'

'Michael is just slightly pissed, that is all.'

'But the doctor shook his head. 'Battle fatigue,' he said. 'Shell shock. We don't understand it properly yet, but it seems there is just a limit to how much these poor bastards can stand. How long has he been flying without a break – three months?'

'He will be all right,' Andrew's voice was fierce, 'he's going to get through.'

He placed a protective hand on Michael's injured shoulder, remembering that it was six months since his last leave.

'Look at him, all the signs. Thin as a starvation victim,' the doctor went on, 'twitching and trembling. Those eyes – I'll bet he is showing unbalanced illogical behaviour, sullen dark moods alternating with mad wild moods? Am I correct?'

Andew nodded reluctantly. 'One minute he calls the enemy loathsome vermin and machine-guns the survivors of crashed German aircraft, and the next they are gallant and worthy foes – he punched a newly arrived pilot last week for calling them Huns.'

'Reckless bravery?'

Andrew remembered the balloons that morning, but he did not answer the question.

'What can we do?' he asked helplessly.

The doctor sighed and shrugged, and offered his hand. 'Goodbye and good luck, major.' And as he turned away, he was already stripping off his jacket and rolling up his sleeves.

At the entrance to the orchard, just before they reached the squadron's bivouac, Michael suddenly heaved himself upright in the side-car and with all the solemnity of a judge pronouncing the death sentence, said, 'I am about to be sick.'

Andrew braked the motor cycle off the road and held his head for him.

'All that excellent claret,' he lamented. 'To say nothing of the Napoleon cognac – if there was only some way to save it!'

Having noisily unburdened himself, Michael slumped down again and said, just as solemnly, 'I want you to know that I am in love,' and his head flopped back as he pased out cold once more.

Andrew sat on the Ariel and drew the cork from the claret bottle with his teeth. 'That definitely calls for a toast. Let's drink to your true love.' He offered the bottle to the unconscious form beside him. 'Not interested?'

He drank from it himself, and when he lowered the bottle, he began unaccountably and uncontrollably to sob. He tried to choke back the tears, he had not wept since he was six years old, and then he remembered the young doctor's words, 'unbalanced and illogical behaviour', and the tears overwhelmed him. They poured down his cheeks, and he did not even attempt to wipe them away. He sat on the driver's seat on the motor-cycle, shaking with silent grief.

'Michael, my boy,' he whispered. 'What is to become of us? We are doomed, there is no hope for us, Michael, no hope at all for any of us,' and he covered his face with both hands and wept as though his heart was breaking.

* * *

Michael awoke to the clatter of the tin tray as Biggs placed it beside his field cot.

He groaned as he tried to sit up, but his injuries pulled him down again. 'What time is it, Biggs?'

''Alf past seven, sir, and a lovely spring morning.'

'Biggs – for God's sake – why didn't you wake me? I've missed the dawn patrol – '

'No, we 'aven't, sir,' Biggs murmured comfortably, 'we've been grounded.'

'Grounded?'

'Lord Killigerran's orders, grounded until further orders, sir.' Biggs ladled sugar into the cocoa mug and stirred it. ''Igh time too, if I may be allowed to say so. We've flown thirty-seven days straight.'

'Biggs, why do I feel so bloody?'

'According to Lord Killigerran – we were severely attacked by a bottle of cognac, sir.'

'Before that, I smashed up the old flying tortoise – ' Michael began to remember.

'Spread her all over France, sir, like butter on toast,' Biggs nodded.

'But we got them, Biggs!'

'Both of the blighters, sir.'

'The book paid out, I trust, Biggs? You didn't lose your money?'

'We made a nice packet, thanking you, Mr Michael,' and Biggs touched the other items on the cocoa tray. ''Ere's your loot – ' There was a neat sheaf of five one-pound notes. 'Three to one, sir, plus your original stake.'

'You are entitled to ten per cent commission, Biggs.'

'Bless you, sir.' Two notes disappeared magically into Bigg's pocket.

'Now, Biggs. What else have we here?'

'Four aspirins, compliments of Lord Killigerran.'

'He is flying, Biggs, of course?' Gratefully Michael swallowed the pills.

'Of course, sir. They took off at dawn.'

'Who is his wingman?'

'Mr Banner, sir.'

'A new chum,' Michael brooded unhappily.

'Lord Andrew will be all right, don't you worry, sir.'

'Yes, of course, he will – and what is this?' Michael roused himself.

'Keys to Lord Killigerran's motor-cycle, sir. He says as you are to give the count his salaams – whatever those may be, sir – and his tender admiration to the young lady – '

'Biggs – ' the aspirins had worked a miracle – Michael felt suddenly light and carefree and gay. His wounds no longer pulled and his head no longer ached. 'Biggs,' he repeated, 'do you think you could lay out my number ones and give the brass buckles a lick and the boots a bit of a shine?'

Biggs grinned at him fondly. 'Going calling, are we, sir?'

'That we are, Biggs, that we are.'

* * *

Centaine woke in darkness and listened to the guns. They terrified her. She knew she would never become accustomed to that bestial, insensate storm that so impersonally dealt death and unspeakable injury, and she remembered the months of late summer the previous year when, for a brief period, the German batteries had been within range of the château. That was when they had abandoned the upper levels of the great house and moved below stairs. By then the servants had long since fled – all except Anna, of course – and the tiny cell that Centaine now occupied had belonged to one of the maids.

Their whole way of life had changed dramatically since the storm-waves of

war had swept over them. Though they had never kept the same grand style as some of the other leading families of the province, there had always been dinners and house-parties and twenty servants to sustain them, but now their existence was almost as simple as had been that of their servants before the war.

Centaine threw off her forebodings with her bedclothes, and ran down the narrow stoneflagged corridor on bare feet. In the kitchen Anna was at the stove, already feeding it with split oak.

'I was on my way to you with a jug of cold water,' said she gruffly, and Centaine hugged her and kissed her until she smiled, and then went to warm herself in front of the stove.

Anna poured boiling water into the copper basin on the floor and then added cold. 'Come along, mademoiselle,' she ordered.

'Oh, Anna, do I have to?'

'Move!'

Reluctantly Centaine lifted the nightdress over her head, and shivered as the cold raised a fine rash of goose-pimples on her forearms and over her small rounded buttocks.

'Hurry.' She stepped into the basin and Anna knelt beside her and dunked a flannel. Her movements were methodical and businesslike as she soaped down Centaine's body, starting at the shoulders and working to the fingertips of each arm, but she could not conceal the love and pride that softened her ugly red face.

The child was delightfully formed, though perhaps her breasts and bottom were a little too small – Anna hoped to plump them out with a good starchy diet, once that was freely obtainable again. Her skin was a smooth, buttery colour, where the sun had not touched it, though where it had been exposed, it tended to take on a dark bronze sheen that Anna found most unsightly.

'You must wear your gloves and long sleeves this summer,' she scolded. 'Brown is so ugly.'

'Do hurry up, Anna.' Centaine hugged her soapy breasts and shivered, and Anna lifted her arms one at a time and scrubbed the dense bushes of dark curly hair under them. The suds ran in long lacy lines down her lean flanks where the rack of her ribs showed through.

'Don't be so rough,' Centaine wailed. And Anna examined her limbs critically: they were straight and long, though much too strong for a lady – all that riding and running and walking. Anna shook her head.

'Oh, what now?' Centaine demanded.

'You are as hard as a boy, your belly is too muscular for having babies.' Anna ran the flannel down her body.

'Ouch!'

'Stay still – you don't want to smell like a goat, do you?'

'Anna, don't you just love blue eyes?' Anna grunted, knowing instinctively where the discussion was headed.

'What colour eyes would a baby have, if its mother's eyes were brown and its father's a lovely shimmering blue?'

Anna slapped her bottom with the flannel. 'That is enough of that. Your father will not like that kind of talk.'

Centaine did not take the threat seriously, she went on dreamily. 'Airmen are so brave, don't you think, Anna? They must be the bravest men in the world.' She became brisk. 'Hurry, Anna, I'll be late to count my chickens.'

She sprang from the basin, scattering water drops on the flagged floor, while Anna wrapped her in a towel that she had heated in front of the stove.

'Anna, it's almost light outside.'

'You come back here immediately after,' Anna ordered. 'We have a lot of work to do today. Your father has reduced us to starvation level with his misplaced generosity.'

'We had to offer a meal to those gallant young airmen.'

Centaine pulled on her clothes and sat on the stool to hook up her riding boots.

'Don't go mooning off into the woods – '

'Oh, hush, Anna.' Centaine jumped up and went clattering down the stairs.

'You come straight back!' Anna yelled after her.

Nuage heard her coming and whickered softly. Centaine flung both arms around his neck and kissed his velvety grey muzzle.

'*Bonjour* my darling.' She had stolen two cubes of sugar from under Anna's nose and now Nuage salivated over her hand as she fed them to him. She wiped her palm on his neck and then when she turned to lift down the saddle from its rack, he bumped her in the small of the back, demanding more.

Outside it was dark and cold, and she urged the stallion into a canter, revelling in the icy flow of air across her face, her nose and ears turning bright pink and her eyes beginning to stream tears. At the crest of the hillock, she reined Nuage to a standstill and looked into the soft gunmetal sheen of dawn, watching the sky above the long horizon turn to the colour of ripe oranges. Behind her the false dawn caused by the harsh, intermittent glow of the artillery barrage flickered against the heavens, but steadfastly she turned her back to it and waited for the planes to come.

She heard the distant beat of their engines, even over the sound of the guns, and then they came snarling into the yellow dawn, as fierce and swift and beautiful as falcons, so that, as always, she felt her pulses race, and she rose high in the saddle to greet them.

The lead machine was the green one with its tiger stripes of victory, the mad Scotsman. She lifted both hands high above her head.

'Go with God – and come back safely!' she shouted her blessing, and saw the flash of white teeth under the ridiculous tartan tam o' shanter, and the green machine waggled its wings and then it was past, climbing away into the sinister sombre clouds that hung above the German lines.

She watched them go, the other aircraft closing up around the green leader into their fighting formation, and she was overwhelmed with a vast sadness, a terrible sense of inadequacy.

'Why couldn't I be a man!' she cried aloud. 'Oh, why couldn't I be going with you!' But already they were out of sight, and she turned Nuage down the hill.

'They will all die,' she thought. 'All the young and strong and beautiful young men – and we will be left only with the old and maimed and ugly.' And the sound of the distant guns counterpointed her fears. 'I wish, oh, how I wish – ' she said aloud, and the stallion flicked his ears back to listen to her, but she did not go on, for she did not know what it was she wished for. She knew only that there was a void within her that ached to be filled, a vast wanting for she did not know what, and a terrible sorrow for all the world. She turned Nuage loose to graze in the small field behind the château and carried his saddle back on her shoulder.

Her father was sitting at the kitchen table and she kissed him casually. His eyepatch gave him a rakish air despite the fact that his other eye was bloodshot; his face was as baggy and wrinkled as a bloodhound's and he smelled of garlic and stale red wine.

As usual, he and Anna were bickering in a companionable fashion, and as Centaine sat opposite him cupping the big round coffee bowl in her hands, she wondered suddenly if Anna and her father mated together, and immediately after she wondered why the notion had never occurred to her before.

As a country girl, the processes of procreation were no mystery to her. Despite Anna's original protests, she was always there to assist when mares from the surrounding district were brought to visit Nuage. She was the only one who could manage the big white stallion once he smelt the mare, and calm him sufficiently to enable him to perform his business without injuring himself or the object of his affections.

By a process of logic, she had reached the conclusion that man and woman must work on similar principles. When she had questioned Anna, she had at first threatened to report Centaine to her papa and wash her mouth out with lye soap. Patiently Centaine had persisted until at last Anna had in a hoarse whisper confirmed her suspicions, and glanced across the kitchen at the comte with a look on her face that Centaine had never seen before, and at the time could not fathom, but which now made logical sense.

Watching them argue and laugh together, it all fell into place – the occasions when after a nightmare she had gone to Anna's room for comfort and found her bed empty, the puzzling presence of one of Anna's petticoats under her father's bed when she was sweeping out his bedroom. Only last week Anna had come out of the cellar after helping the comte clean out the improvised animal stalls with straw sticking both to the back of her skirts and to the bun of greying hair on the top of her head.

The discovery seemed somehow to increase Centaine's desolation and her feeling of emptiness. She felt truly alone now, isolated and without purpose, empty and aching.

'I'm going out.' She sprang up from the kitchen table.

'Oh no.' Anna barred her way. 'We have got to get some food into this house, since your father has given away all we possess, and, m'demoiselle, you are going to help me!'

Centaine had to escape from them, to be alone, to come to terms with this terrible new desolation of her spirit. Nimbly she ducked under Anna's outstretched arm and flung open the kitchen door.

On the theshold stood the most beautiful person she had ever seen in all her life.

He was dressed in glossy boots and immaculate riding breeches of a lighter tan colour than his khaki uniform jacket. His narrow waist was belted in lustrous leather and burnished brass, his Sam Browne crossed his chest and emphasized his wide shoulders. On his left breast were the RFC wings and a row of coloured ribbons, on his epaulettes sparkled the badges of his rank, and his cap had been carefully crushed in the manner affected by veteran fighter pilots and set at a jaunty angle over his impossibly blue eyes.

Centaine fell back a pace and stared up at him, for he towered over her like a young god, and she became aware of a sensation that was entirely new to her. Her stomach seemed to turn to jelly, hot jelly, heavy as molten lead that spread downwards through her lower body until it seemed that her legs could no

longer support the weight of it. At the same time she had great difficulty breathing.

'Mademoiselle de Thiry.' This vision of martial splendour spoke and touched the peak of his cap in salute. The voice was familiar, and she recognized the eyes, those cerulean blue eyes, and the man's left arm was supported by a narrow leather strap –

'Michel – ' her voice was unsteady and she corrected herself. 'Captain Courtney,' and then she changed languages, 'Mijnheer Courtney?'

The young god smiled at her, and it did not seem possible that this was the same man, tousled, bloodied and muddied, swaddled in ill-fitting charred rags, trembling and shaking and pathetic, that she had helped load in a stupor of pain and weakness and inebriation into the side-car of the motor-cycle the previous afternoon.

When he smiled at her, Centaine felt the world lurch beneath her feet. When it steadied, she realized that it had altered its orbit and was on a new track amongst the stars. Nothing would ever be the same again.

'Entrez, monsieur.' She fell back, and as he stepped over the threshold, the comte rose from the table and hurried to meet him.

'How goes it with you, captain?' He took Michael's hand. 'Your wounds?'

'They are much better.'

'A little cognac would help them,' the comte suggested and looked at his daughter slyly. Michael's stomach quailed at the suggestion and he shook his head vehemently.

'No,' said Centaine firmly, and turned to Anna. 'We must see to the captain's dressing.'

Protesting only mildly, Michael was led to the stool in front of the stove and Anna unbuckled his belt, while Centaine stood behind him and eased his jacket off his shoulders.

Anna unwrapped the dressings and grunted with approval.

'Hot water, child,' she ordered.

Carefully they washed and dried his burns, and then smeared them with fresh ointment and rebandaged them with clean linen strips.

'They are healing beautifully,' Anna nodded, while Centaine helped him into his shirt.

She had not realized how smooth a man's skin could be, there down his flanks and across his back. His dark hair curled on to the nape of his neck, and he was so thin that each knuckle of his spine stood out as cleanly as beads on a rosary, with two ridges of lean muscle running down each side of it.

She came round to button the front of his shirt.

'You are very gentle,' he said softly, and she dared not look into his eyes, lest she betray herself in front of Anna.

His chest hair was thick and crisp and springy as she brushed it almost unintentionally with her fingertips, and the nipples on his flat hard chest were dusky-pink and tiny, yet they hardened and thrust out under her gaze, a phenomenon which both amazed and enchanted her. She had never dreamed that happened to men also.

'Come, Centaine,' Anna chided her, and she started as she realized that she had been staring at his body.

'I came to thank you,' Michael said. 'I didn't mean to make work for you.'

'It is no trouble.' Centaine still dared not look into his eyes.

'Without your help I might have burned to death.'

'No!' Centaine said with unnecessary emphasis. The idea of death and this marvellous creature was totally unacceptable to her.

Now she looked at his face again at last, and it seemed that the summer sky showed through chinks in his skull – so blue were his eyes.

'Centaine, there is much work to do.' Anna's tone was sharper still.

'Let me help you,' Michael cut in eagerly. 'I have been grounded – I am not allowed to fly.' Anna looked dubious, but the comte shrugged.

'Another pair of hands, we could use.'

'A small repayment,' Michael insisted.

'Your fine uniform.' Anna was looking for excuses, and she glanced down at his glossy boots.

'We have rubber boots and overalls,' Centaine cut in swiftly, and Anna threw up her hands in capitulation.

Centaine thought that even the blue *serge de Nim*, or denim as it was colloquially known, and black rubber boots looked elegant on Michael's tall lean body as he descended to help the comte muck out the animal stalls in the cellars.

Centaine and Anna spent the rest of the morning in the vegetable gardens, preparing the soil for the spring sowing.

Every time Centaine went down to the cellars on the flimsiest of excuses, she paused beside wherever Michael was working under the comte's direction, and the two of them made halting and self-conscious conversation until Anna came down the staircase.

'Where is that child now! Centaine! What on earth are you doing?' As if she did not know.

All four of them ate lunch in the kitchen – omelettes flavoured with onions and truffles, cheese and brown bread, and a bottle of red wine over which Centaine relented, but not enough to hand over the cellar keys to her father. She fetched it herself.

The wine softened the mood, even Anna took a glass of it and allowed Centaine to do the same, and the talk became easy and unrestrained, punctuated with bursts of laughter.

'Now, captain – ' the comte turned to Michael at last with a calculating glitter in his single eye – 'you and your family, what do you do in Africa?'

'Farmers,' Michael replied.

'Tenant farmers?' the comte probed cautiously.

'No, no – ' Michael laughed. 'We farm our own lands.'

'Landowners?' The comte's tone changed, for, as all the world knew, land was the only true form of wealth. 'What size are your family estates?'

'Well – ' Michael looked embarrassed ' – quite large. You see, it is mostly held in a family company – my father and my uncle – '

'Your uncle, the general?' the comte prompted.

'Yes, my Uncle Sean – '

'A hundred hectares?' the comte insisted.

'A little more.' Michael squirmed on the bench and fiddled with his bread roll.

'Two hundred?' The comte looked so expectant that Michael could not evade him longer.

'Altogether, if you take the plantations and the cattle ranches, and some land we own in the north, it's about forty thousand hectares.'

'Forty thousand?' The comte stared at him, and then repeated the question in English so there could be no misunderstanding. 'Forty thousand?'

Michael nodded uncomfortably. It was only recently that he had begun to feel a little self-conscious about the extent of his family's worldly possessions.

'Forty thousand hectares!' The comte breathed reverently, and then, 'and, of course, you have many brothers?'

Michael shook his head. 'No, unfortunately I am an only son.'

'Ha!' said the comte with transparent relief. 'Do not feel too badly about that!' and patted his arm in a paternal gesture.

The comte shot a glance at his daughter, and for the first time recognized the expresion on her face as she looked at the airman.

'Quite right too,' he thought comfortably. 'Forty thousand hectares, and an only son!' His daughter was a Frenchwoman, and knew the value of a sou and a franc, *sacré bleu*, she knew it better than he did himself. He smiled lovingly across the table at her. A child in many ways, but a shrewd young Frenchwoman in others. Since the comte's factor had fled to Paris, leaving the accounts and books of the estate in chaos, it had been Centaine who had taken over the purse-strings. The comte had never bothered much with money anyway, for him land would always remain the only true wealth, but his daughter was the clever one. She even counted the bottles in the cellar and the hams on the smoke-rack. He took a mouthful of red wine and mused happily to himself. There would be so few eligible young men left after this slaughter, this charnel-house . . . and forty thousand hectares!

'*Chérie*,' he said. 'If the captain were to take the shotgun and get us a few fat pigeon, and you were to fill a basket with truffles – you might still find some – what a dinner we could have this evening!' Centaine clapped her hands in delight, but Anna glared at him in red-faced indignation across the table.

'Anna will go with you as chaperone,' he said hastily. 'We don't want any unseeming scandal, now, do we?' Might as well sow a seed, he thought, if it wasn't already ripely germinating. Forty thousand hectares, *merde*!

* * *

The pig was named Kaiser Wilhelm, or Klein Willie, for short. He was a piebald boar, so gross that as he waddled into the oak forest, he reminded Michael of a bull hippopotamus. His pointed ears drooped forward over his eyes and his tail curled like a roll of barbed wire up over his back, exposing ample evidence of his gender, contained in a bright pink sac that looked as though it had been boiled in oil.

'*Vas-y, Willie! Cherche!*' cried Centaine and Anna in unison; at the same time it required both of them on the leash to restrain the enormous beast. '*Cherche!* Seek up!' And the boar snuffled eagerly at the damp, chocolate-brown earth under the oak trees, dragging the two women behind him. Michael followed them, a spade over his good shoulder, laughing delightedly at the novelty of the hunt, and trotting to keep up with it.

Deeper into the forest they came across a narrow stream, running strongly with discoloured water from the recent rains, and they followed the bank, with snorts and cries of encouragement. Suddenly the pig let out a gleeful squeal and began rooting in the soft earth with his flat wet snout.

'He's found one!' Centaine shrieked with excitement and she and Anna hauled unavailingly on the leash.

'Michel!' she panted over her shoulder. 'When we get him away, you must be very quick with the spade. Are you ready?'

'Ready!'

From the pocket of her skirt Centaine pulled a wizened nub of a truffle that was mildewed with age. She pared off a sliver with a clasp knife, and held it as close to the boar's snout as she could reach. For a few moments the pig ignored her, and then it got the fresher scent of the cut truffle and grunted gluttonously, tried to take her hand in his streaming jaws. Centaine jerked away and backed off with the boar following her.

'Quickly, Michel!' she cried, and he went at the earth with the spade. In half a dozen strokes he had exposed the buried fungus and Anna dropped on her knees and freed it from the earth with her bare hands. She lifted it out, crusty with chocolate soil, a dark knobbly lump almost the size of her fist.

'Look, what a beauty!'

At last Centaine allowed the pig to take the sliver of fungus from her fingers, and when he had gulped it, she let him return to the empty hole and snuffle around in the loose earth to satisfy himself that the truffle had disappeared, then '*Cherche!*' she shouted at him, and the hunt was on again. Within an hour the small basket was filled with the unappetizing-looking lumpy fungi, and Anna called a halt.

'More than this will merely spoil. Now for some pigeons. Let's see if our captain from Africa can shoot!'

They hurried after the boar, laughing and panting back through the open fields to the château, where Centaine locked the truffles in the pantry and Anna returned the boar to his stall in the cellars and then lifted the shotgun down from its rack on the kitchen wall. She handed the weapon to Michael and watched as he opened the breech and checked the barrels, then snapped them closed and put the gun to his shoulder and tried the balance. Despite the burns that hampered his swing a little, Anna could tell a good workman by the way he handled his tools, and her expression softened with approval.

For Michael's part he was surprised and then delighted to discover that the weapon was a venerable Holland and Holland – only the English gunsmiths could fashion a barrel that would throw a perfectly even pattern of shot no matter how fast the gun was traversed.

He nodded at Anna. 'Excellent!' And she handed him the canvas bag of cartridges.

'I will show you a good place.' Centaine took his hand to lead him and then saw Anna's expression and dropped it hurriedly. 'In the afternoon the pigeons come back to the woods,' she explained.

They skirted the edge of the forest, Centaine leading and lifting her skirts over the mud puddles so that Michael had an occasional flash of her smooth white calves, and his pulse accelerated beyond the exertion of keeping up with her. On her short, stubby legs Anna fell far behind and they ignored her calls to 'Wait, wait for me'.

At the corner of the forest, in the angle of the T that the pilots used as the landmark for the return to the airfield, there was a sunken lane with high hedges on each side.

'The pigeons come in from there,' Centaine pointed across the open fields and vineyards, all of them overgrown and neglected. 'We should wait here.'

The hedgerow afforded excellent cover, and when Anna came up they all three hid themselves and began to search the sky. Heavy low cloud had begun to roll in again from the north, threatening rain, and forming a perfect backdrop against which the tiny specks of a pigeon flock showed clearly to Michael's trained eye.

'There,' he said, 'coming straight in.'

'I don't see them,' Centaine searched agitatedly. 'Where – oh yes, now I see them.'

Although they were quick on the wing, they were flying straight and descending only gently towards the forest. For a marksman of Michael's calibre, it was simple shooting. He waited until two birds overlapped each other, and took them both with his first shot. They crumpled in mid-air and as the rest of the flock flared up and scattered, he knocked down a third pigeon in a burst of feathers with his second barrel.

The two women raced out into the open field to bring in the birds.

'Three with two shots.' Centaine came back and stood close beside him, stroking the soft warm body of the dead pigeon and looking up at Michael.

'It was a fluke,' said Anna gruffly. 'Nobody shoots two pigeons by intention – not if they are flying.'

The next flock was a larger one, and the birds were bunched. Michael took three of them with his first barrel and a fourth bird with his second, and Centaine turned triumphantly to Anna.

'Another fluke,' she gloated. 'What luck the captain is having today.'

Two more flocks came within range in the next half hour, and Centaine asked seriously, 'Do you never miss, Mijnheer?'

'Up there,' Michael looked into the sky, 'if you miss, you are dead. So far I have never missed.'

Centaine shivered. Death – that word again. Death was all around them, on the ridges over there where for the moment the sound of the guns was just a low rumble, death in the sky above them. She looked at Michael and thought, 'I don't want him to die – never! Never!'

Then she shook herself, driving away the gloom, and she smiled and said, 'Teach me to shoot.' The request was inspired. It allowed Michael to touch her, even under Anna's jealous gaze. He stood her in front of him, and coached her into the classic stance, with her left foot leading.

'This shoulder a little lower.' They were both electrically aware of each contact. 'Just turn your hips this way slightly.' He placed his hands upon them and Michael's voice sounded as though he were choking as she pushed back with her buttocks against him, an untutored but devastating pressure.

Centaine's first shot drove her back against his chest, and he clasped her protectively while the pigeons headed untouched for the horizon.

'You are looking at the muzzle of the gun, not the bird,' Michael explained, still holding her. 'Look at the bird, and the gun will follow of its own.'

At her next shot a fat pigeon tumbled out of the sky, amid shrieks of excitement from both women, but when Anna ran out to pick it up, the rain that had been holding off until that moment fell upon them in a silver curtain.

'The barn!' cried Centaine, and led them scampering down the lane. The rain slashed the tree-tops and exploded in miniature shell bursts on their skin so that they gasped at its icy sting. Centaine reached the barn first, and her blouse was sticking to her skin, so that Michael could see the exact shape of her breasts. Strands of her dark hair were plastered against her forehead, and she

shook the drops off her skirts and laughed at him, making no attempt to avoid his gaze.

The barn fronted on to the lane. It was built of squared yellow stone blocks and the thatched roof was tattered and worn as an old carpet. It was half-filled with bales of straw that rose in tiers to the roof.

'This will set in,' Anna groused darkly, staring out at the streaming rain and shaking the rain off herself like a water buffalo emerging from the swamp. 'We will be stuck here.'

'Come, Anna, let's clean the birds.'

They found comfortable perches on the straw bales, Centaine and Michael with their shoulders almost touching, and while they plucked the pigeons they chatted.

'Tell me about Africa,' Centaine demanded. 'Is it really so dark?'

'It's the sunniest land in the world – too much sun, even,' Michael told her.

'I love the sun,' Centaine shook her head. 'I hate the cold and the wet. There could never be too much sun for me.'

He told her about the deserts where it never rained. 'Not as much in a year as it does here in a single day.'

'I thought there were only black savages in Africa.'

'No,' he laughed. 'There are plenty of white savages too – and black gentlemen,' and he told her about the tiny yellow pygmies of the Ituri forests, tall as a man's waist, and the giant Watusi who considered any man under two metres tall to be a pygmy, and those noble warriors of Zulu who called themselves children of heaven.

'You talk as though you love them,' she accused.

'The Zulu?' he asked, and then nodded. 'Yes, I suppose I do. Some of them, anyway. Mbejane – '

'Mbejane?' She did not pronounce the name right.

'A Zulu – he has been with my Uncle Sean since they were lads together.' He used the Zulu word 'Umfaan' and had to translate for her.

'Tell me about the animals.' Centaine did not want him to stop talking. She could not listen to his voice and his stories for ever. 'Tell me about the lions and the tigers.'

'No tigers,' he smiled at her, 'but plenty of lions.' And even Anna's hands, busy with plucking the birds, stilled as she listened while Michael described a camp on the hunting veld where he and his Uncle Sean had been besieged by a pride of lions, and had had to stand by the horses' heads all night, protecting and soothing them, while the great pale cats prowled back and forth at the edge of the firelight, roaring and grunting, trying to drive the horses into the darkness where they would have been easy prey.

'Tell us about the elephants.' And he told her about those sagacious beasts. He described how they moved with that slow somnambulistic gait, huge ears flapping to cool their blood, picking up dirt to dash it over their heads for a dust bath.

He told them about the intricate social structures of the elephant herds, how the old bulls avoided the uproar of breeding herds. 'Just like your father,' said Anna. And how the barren old queens took upon themselves the duties of nanny and midwife: how the great grey beasts formed relationships with each other, almost like human friendships, that lasted their lifetimes; and about their strange preoccupation with death, how if they killed a hunter who had plagued

and wounded them they would often cover his body with green leaves, almost as though they were trying to make atonement. He explained how when one of the members of the herd was stricken, the others would try to succour it, holding it on its feet with their trunks, supporting it from each side with their bulks, and when it fell at last – if it was a cow, the herd bull would mount her, as though trying to frustrate death with the act of generation.

This last tale roused Anna from her listening trance and reminded her of her role of chaperone; she glanced sharply at Centaine.

'It has stopped raining,' she announced primly, and she began to gather up the naked carcasses of the pigeons.

Centaine still watched Micheal with huge shining dark eyes.

'One day I will go to Africa,' she said softly, and he returned her gaze steadily and nodded.

'Yes,' he said. 'One day.'

It was as though they had exchanged a vow. It was a thing between them, firm and understood. In that moment she became his woman and he her man.

'Come,' Anna insisted at the door of the barn. 'Come on, before it rains again,' and it took a vast effort from both of them to rise and follow her out into the wet and dripping world.

They dragged on leaden feet up the lane towards the château, side by side, not touching but so acutely aware of each other that they might as well have been locked in each other's arms.

Then the planes came out of the dusk, low and swift, the thunder of their engines rising to a crescendo as they passed overhead. In the lead was the green Sopwith. From this angle they could not see Andrew's head, but they could see daylight through the rents in the fabric of his wings, through the lines of bullet holes which the Spandaus had torn. The five aircraft that followed Andrew had all been shot up as well. There were tears and neatly punched holes in their wings and fuselages.

'It's been a hard day,' Michael murmured, with his head thrown back.

Another Sopwith trailed the others, its engine popping and missing, vapour trailing back in a stream behind it, one wing skewed out of line where the struts had been shot through. Centaine, watching them, shuddered, and crept closer to Michael.

'Some of them died out there today,' she whispered, and he did not have to reply.

'Tomorrow you will be with them again.'

'Not tomorrow.'

'Then the next day – or the next.'

Once more it was not necessary to reply.

'Michel, oh Michel!' There was physical agony in her voice. 'I must see you alone. We might never – we might never have another chance. From now on we must live each precious minute of our lives as though it is the last.'

The shock of her words was like a blow to his body. He could not speak, and her own voice dropped.

'The barn,' she whispered.

'When?' He found his voice, and it croaked in his own ears.

'Tonight, before midnight – I will come as soon as I am able to. It will be cold.' She looked directly into his face – social conventions had been burned away in the furnace of war. 'You must bring a blanket.'

She whirled then and ran to catch up with Anna, leaving Michael staring after her in a daze of disbelief and uncertain ecstasy.

* * *

Michael washed at the pump outside the kitchen and changed back into his uniform. When he entered the kitchen again, the pigeon pie was rich and redolent of fresh truffles under its crumbly brown crust, and Centaine was filling and refilling her father's glass without a protest from him. She did the same for Anna, but with a lighter more cunning hand, so that Anna did not seem to notice, though her face became redder and her laughter more raucous.

Centaine placed Michael in charge of the His Master's Voice gramophone, her most prized possession, and made it his duty to keep it fully wound up and change each of the wax discs as they ended. From the huge brass trumpet of the machine blared the recording of Toscanini conducting the La Scala orchestra in Verdi's *Aïda*, filling the kitchen with glorious sound. When Centaine brought his plate laden with pigeon pie to where he sat opposite the comte, she touched the nape of Michael's neck – those dark silky curls – and she purred in his ear as she leaned over him, 'I love *Aïda*, don't you, Captain?'

When the comte questioned him closely on the production of his family estates, Michael found it difficult to concentrate on his replies.

'We were growing a great deal of black wattle, but my father and uncle are convinced that after the war the motor car will completely supersede the horse, and therefore there will be a drastic reduction in the need for leather harness, and consequently the demand for wattle tanning – '

'What a great shame that the horse should have to give way to those noisy, stinking contraptions of the devil,' the comte sighed, 'but they are right, of course. The petrol engine is the future.'

'We are replanting with pines and Australian blue gums. Pit props for the gold mines and raw material for paper.'

'Quite right.'

'Then, of course, we have the sugar plantations and the cattle ranches. My uncle believes that soon there will be ships fitted with cold rooms that will carry our beef to the world – '

The more the comte listened, the more pleased he became.

'Drink up, my boy,' he urged Michael, as an earnest of his approval. 'You have had hardly a drop. Is it not to your taste?'

'Excellent, truly, however, *le foie* – my liver.' Michael clasped himself under the ribs and the comte made sounds of sympathy and concern. As a Frenchman he understood that most of the ills and woes of the world could be attributed to the malfunctions of that organ.

'Not serious. But please don't let my little indisposition prevent you.' Michael made a self-deprecating gesture, and obediently the comte recharged his own glass.

Having served the men, the two women brought their own plates to the table to join them. Centaine sat beside her father and spoke little. Her head turned between the two men as though in dutiful attention, until Michael felt a light pressure on his ankle and with a leap of his nerves realized that she had reached out with her foot beneath the table. He shifted guiltily under the comte's

scrutiny, not daring to look across at Centaine. Instead, he made that nervous gesture of blowing on his fingertips as though he had burned them on the stove, and he blinked his eyes rapidly.

Centaine's foot withdrew as secretly as it had advanced, and Michael waited two or three minutes before reaching out with his own. Then he found her foot and took it between both of his; from the corner of his eye he saw her start and a flush of dark blood spread up her throat to her cheeks and ears. He turned to stare at her, so enchanted that he could not pull his eyes away from her face, until the comte raised his voice.

'How many?' the comte repeated with mild asperity, and guiltily Michael jerked his feet back.

'I am sorry, I did not hear – '

'The captain is not well,' Centaine cut in quickly and a little breathlessly. 'His burns are not healed, and he has worked too hard today.'

'We should not keep him unnecessarily,' Anna agreed with alacrity, 'if he has finished his dinner.'

'Yes. Yes.' Centaine stood up. 'We must let him go home to rest.'

The comte looked truly distressed to be deprived of a drinking companion, until Centaine reassured him. 'Don't disturb yourself, Papa, you sit here and finish up your wine.'

Anna accompanied the couple out into the darkness of the kitchen yard and stood close by, eagle-eyed and arms akimbo, while they said their shy goodbyes. She had taken just enough of the claret to dull the razor-edge of her instincts, or she might have wondered why Centaine was so eager to see Michael on to his motor-cycle.

'May I call upon you again, Mademoiselle de Thiry?'

'If you wish, Captain.'

Anna's heart, softened by wine, went out to them. It took an effort to harden her resolve.

'Goodbye, Mijnheer,' she said firmly. 'This child will catch a chill. Come inside now, Centaine.

* * *

The comte had found it imperative to wash down the claret with a *fine de champagne* or two. It cut the acidity of the wine, he explained seriously to Centaine. It was, therefore, neccesary for the two women to help him to bed. He made this rather perilous ascent singing the march from *Aïda* with more gusto than talent. When he reached his bed, he went down like a felled oak, flat upon his back. Centaine took each of his legs in turn, straddled it and pulled off the boot with her knees.

'Bless you, my little one, your Papa loves you.'

Between them they sat him up and dropped his nightshirt over his head, then let him collapse back on to the bolster. His decency preserved by the nightshirt, they removed his breeches and rolled him into the bed.

'May angels guard your sleep, my pretty,' the comte mumbled, as they spread an eiderdown over him and Anna blew out the candle.

Under cover of darkness, Anna reached out and caressed the tousled wiry

bush of the comte's hair. She was rewarded by a reverberating snore and followed Centaine from the room, softly closing the door behind her.

* * *

Centaine lay and listened to the old house groan and creak around her in the night.

Wisely, she had resisted the temptation to climb fully clothed beneath her bedclothes, for Anna made one of her unannounced visits just as Centaine was about to extinguish her candle. She sat on the edge of the bed, garrulous with wine, but not so befuddled that she would not have known if Centaine had not been in her nightclothes. By yawning and sighing Centaine tried telepathically to make her feel sleepy, but when that didn't work, and she heard the distant chimes of the church clock at Mort Homme strike ten o'clock, she herself feigned sleep. It was agony to lie still and regulate her breathing, for she burned and itched with excitement.

At last Anna realized that she was talking to herself, and she moved around the tiny chamber, picking up and folding Centaine's discarded clothing, and finally stooping over her to kiss her cheek and then pinch out the wick of the lamp.

As soon as she was alone, Centaine sat up and hugged herself in a ferment of anticipation and trepidation. Although it was very clear in her mind what the final outcome of this meeting with Michael must be, the precise mechanics were at this stage still tantalizingly obscure. A process of logic had suggested to her that the broad concept could not differ too widely from what she had witnessed countless times in field and barnyard.

She had received confirmation of this one drowsy summer afternoon, when a mild commotion in one of the disused stables had attracted her attention. She had climbed into the loft and through a chink watched Elsa, the kitchenmaid, and Jacques the undergroom with amazement, until gradually it had dawned upon her that they were playing rooster and hen, stallion and mare. She had thought about it for days afterwards, and then eavesdropped with more attention upon the gossip of the female servants. Finally, she had taken her courage in both hands and gone to Anna with her questions.

All these researches had left her confused and puzzled by the contradictions. According to Anna, the procedure was extremely painful, accompanied by profuse bleeding and dire danger of pregnancy and disease. This conflicted with the unrestrained glee with which the other female servants discussed the subject, and with the giggles and muffled cries of delight that she had heard coming from Elsa as she lay beneath Jacques on the straw of the stable floor.

Centaine knew that she had a high threshold of pain, even the good doctor Le Brun had remarked upon it after he had reset her broken forearm without benefit of chloroform. 'Not a cheep out of her,' he had marvelled. No, Centaine knew she could bear pain as well as any of the peasant girls on the estate, and apart from her monthly courses she had bled before. Often, when she was certain that she was unobserved, she would take the cumbersome side-saddle from Nuage's back, tuck up her skirts and ride him astride. The previous spring, riding bare-back, she had put the stallion to the stone wall that bordered North Field, jumping him from the low side and dropping down seven feet to

the deep side of the wall. As they landed, she had come down hard on Huage's withers, and a pain like a knife blade had shot up through her body. She had bled so that Nuage's white shoulders were stained pink and she was so ashamed that despite the pain she had washed him off in the pond at the end of the field before limping home, leading Nuage behind her.

No, neither pain nor blood frightened her. Her trepidation had another source. She was deadly afraid that Michael might find her disappointing – Anna had also warned her of that.

'Afterwards men always lose interest in a woman, *les cochons*.'

'If Michael loses interest in me, I think I will die,' she thought, and for a moment she hesitated. 'I will not go – I will not take that chance.

'Oh, but how can I *not* go?' she whispered aloud, and felt her chest swelling with the strength of her love and her wanting. 'I must. I simply must.'

In an agony of impatience she listened to the sounds of Anna preparing for bed in the chamber next door. Even after there was silence, she waited on, heard the church clock strike the quarter and then the half hour before she slipped from under the eiderdown.

She found her petticoats and cami-knickers where Anna had folded them away, and then paused with one foot in the leg of the knickers.

'What for?' she asked herself and smothered a giggle with her hand as she kicked them off again.

She buttoned on the thick woollen riding skirts and jacket, then spread a dark shawl over her head and shoulders. Carrying her boots in her hand, she slipped into the passage and listened outside Anna's door.

Anna's snores were low and regular and Centaine crept down into the kitchen. Sitting on the stool bfore the fire she buckled on her boots and then lit the bull's-eye lantern with a taper from the stove. She unlocked the kitchen door and let herself out. The moon was in its last quarter, sailing sharp-prowed through wisps of flying cloud.

Centaine kept to the grassy verge, so that the gravel would not crunch under her boots, and she did not open the shutter of the lantern, but hurried down the lane by the moon's faint silvery light. In the north, up on the ridges, there was a sudden brilliance, a dawn of orange light, that subsided slowly, and then came the rumble of the explosion muted by the wind.

'A mine!' Centaine paused for a moment, wondering how many had died in that monstrous upheaval of earth and fire. The thought spurred her resolve. There was so much death and hatred, and so little love. She had to grasp at every last grain of it.

She saw the barn ahead of her at last, and started to run. There was no light showing within, no sign of the motor-cycle.

'He has not come.' The thought left her desperate with desire. She wanted to scream his name. She tripped at the threshold of the barn, and almost fell.

'Michel!' She could restrain herself no longer, she heard the panic in her own voice as she called again, 'Michel!' and opened the shutter of the lantern.

He was coming towards her, out of the gloom of the barn. Tall and broad-shouldered, his pale face beautiful in the lantern light.

'Oh, I thought you were not coming.'

He stopped in front of her. 'Nothing,' he said softly, 'nothing in this world could have kept me away.'

They stood facing each other, Centaine with her chin lifted to look up at him, staring at each other hungrily and yet neither of them knowing what to do next,

how to bridge those few inches between them that seemed like the void of all eternity.

'Nobody saw you?' he blurted.

'No, no, I don't think so.'

'Good.'

'Michel?'

'Yes, Centaine.'

'Perhaps I should not have come – perhaps I should go back?'

It was exactly the right thing to say, for the implied threat galvanized Michael and he reached out and seized her, almost roughly.

'No, never – I don't want you to go, ever.'

She laughed, a husky breathless sound, and he pulled her to him and tried to kiss her, but it was a clumsy attempt. They bumped noses and their teeth clashed together in their haste, before they found each other's lips. However, once he found them, Centaine's lips were hot and soft, and the inside of her mouth was silky and tasted like ripe apples. Then her shawl slipped forward over her head, half smothering them both and they had to break apart, breathless and laughing with excitement.

'Buttons,' she whispered, 'your buttons hurt, and I am cold.' She shivered theatrically.

'I'm sorry.' He took the lantern from her and led her to the back of the barn. He handed her up over the bales of straw, and in the lamplight she saw that he had made a nest of soft straw between the bales and lined it with grey army blankets.

'I went back to my tent to get them,' he explained, as he set the lamp down carefully, and then turned to her again, eagerly.

'*Attends!*' She used the familiar form of address to restrain him, and then unbuckled his Sam Browne belt. 'I will be covered in bruises.'

Michael tossed the belt aside and seized her again. This time they found each other's mouths and clung together. Great waves of feeling washed over Centaine, so powerful that she felt giddy and weak. Her legs sagged but Michael held her up and she tried to match the flood of kisses that he rained on her mouth and her eyes and her throat – but she wanted him to go down on to the blankets with her. Deliberately she let her legs go and pulled him off balance, so that he fell on top of her as she tumbled into the blanket-lined nest in the straw.

'I'm sorry.' He tried to disentangle himself, but she locked one arm around his neck and held his face to hers. Over his shoulder she reached out and pulled the blankets to cover them both. She heard herself making little mewing sounds like a kitten denied the teat, and she ran her hands over his face and into his hair as she kissed him. His body weight on top of her felt so good that when he tried to roll off her, she hooked her ankle into the back of his knee to prevent him.

'The light,' he croaked, and groped for the lantern to close the shutter.

'No. I want to see your face.' She caught his wrist and pulled his hand back, holding it to her bosom as she looked up into his eyes. They were so beautiful in the lamplight that she thought that her heart might break – and then she felt his hand on one of her breasts, and she held it there while her nipples ached with the need for his touch.

It all became a delirium of delight and wanting, becoming more and more powerful until at last it was unbearable, something had to happen before she fainted away with the strength of it – but it did not happen, and she felt herself

coming back off the heights and it made her impatient and almost angry with disappointment.

Her critical faculties that had been dulled by desire returned to her, and she sensed that Michael was floundering in indecision, and she became truly angry. He should have been masterful, taking her up there where she longed to go. She took his wrist again and she drew his hand downwards, at the same time she moved beneath him so that her thick woollen skirts rode up and bunched about her waist.

'Centaine,' he whispered. 'I don't want to do anything that you don't want.'

'*Tais-toi!*' she almost hissed at him. 'Be quiet!' – and she knew that she would have to lead him all the way, she would have to lead him always, for there was a diffidence in him that she had not been aware of before, but she did not resent it. Somehow it made her feel very strong and sure of herself.

They both gasped as he touched her. After a minute, she let go his wrist and searched for him and when she found him she cried out again, he was so big and hard that she felt daunted. For a moment, she wondered if she was capable of the task she had taken upon herself – then she rallied. He was so awkward above her, and she had to wriggle a little and fumble. Then abruptly, when she was not expecting it, it happened – and she gasped with the shock.

But Anna had been wrong, there was no pain, there was only a breathtaking stretching and filling sensation, and after the shock abated, a sense of great power over him.

'Yes, Michel, yes, my darling.' She encouraged him as he butted and moaned and thrashed in the enfolding crucifix of her limbs, and she rode his assault easily, knowing that in these moments he belonged to her completely, and revelling in that knowledge.

When the final convulsion gripped him, she watched his face, and saw how the colour of his eyes changed to indigo in the lamplight. Yet although she loved him then with a strength that was physically painful, still there was a tiny suspicion in the depths of her consciousness that she had missed something. She had not felt the need to scream as Elsa had screamed beneath Jacques in the straw, and immediately after that thought she was afraid.

'Michel,' she whispered urgently, 'do you still love me? Tell me you love me.'

'I love you more than my own life.' His voice was broken and gusty, she could not for an instant doubt his sincerity.

She smiled in the darkness with relief and held him close, and when she felt him going small and soft within her, she was overcome with a wave of melting compassion.

'My darling,' she whispered, 'there, my darling, there,' and she stroked his thick springing curls at the back of his head.

It was a little time before her emotions had calmed enough for her to realize that something had changed irrevocably within her during the few brief minutes of that simple act they had performed together. The man in her arms was physically stronger than she was, but he felt like a child, a sleepy child, as he cuddled against her. While she felt wiser and vital, as though her life up until that moment had been becalmed, drifting without direction, but now she had found her trade winds and like a tall ship she was at last bearing away purposefully before them.

'Wake up, Michel.' She shook him gently and he mumbled and stirred. 'You cannot sleep now – talk to me.'

'What about?'

'Anything. Tell me about Africa. Tell me how we will go to Africa together.'

'I've told you that already.'

'Tell me again. I want to hear it all again.'

And she lay against him and listened avidly, asking questions whenever he faltered.

'Tell me about your father. You haven't told me what he looks like.'

So they talked the night away cuddled in their cocoon of grey blankets.

Then, too soon for both of them, the guns began their murderous chorus along the ridges, and Centaine held him to her with desperate longing. 'Oh, Michel, I don't want to go!' then she drew away from him, sat up and began to pull on her clothes and refasten the buttons.

'That was the most wonderful thing that has ever happened to me,' Michael whispered as he watched her, and in the light of the lantern and the flickering glow of guns, her eyes were huge and soft as she turned to him again.

'We will go to Africa, won't we, Michel?'

'I promise you we will.'

'And I will have your son in the sunshine, and we will live happily ever after just like in the fairy stories, won't we, Michel?'

They went up the lane clinging together under Centaine's shawl, and at the corner of the stables they kissed with quiet intensity until Centaine broke out of his grip and fled across the paved yard.

She did not look back when she reached the kitchen door, but disappeared into the huge dark house, leaving Michael alone and unaccountably sad when he should have been joyous.

* * *

Biggs stood over the cot and looked down fondly at Michael as he slept. Biggs's eldest son who had died in the trenches at Ypres a year ago, would have been the same age. Michael looked so worn and pale and exhausted that Biggs had to force himself to touch his shoulder and wake him.

'What time is it, Biggs?' Michael sat up groggily.

'It's late, sir, and the sun's shining – but we aren't flying, we are still grounded, sir.'

Then a strange thing happened. Michael grinned at him, a sort of inane idiotic grin, that Biggs had never seen before. It alarmed him.

'God, Biggs, I feel good.'

'I'm glad, sir.' Biggs wondered with a pang if it might be fever. 'How's our arm, sir?'

'Our arm is marvellous, bloody marvellous, thank you, Biggs.'

'I would have let you sleep, but the major is asking for you, sir. There is something important that he wants to show you.'

'What is it?'

'I'm not allowed to say, Mr Michael, Lord Killigerran's strict instructions.'

'Good man, Biggs!' Michael cried without apparent reason, and bounded from his cot. 'Never do to keep Lord Killigerran waiting.'

Michael burst into the mess and was disappointed to find it empty. He wanted to share his good spirits with somebody. Andrew for preference, but

even the mess corporal had deserted his post. The breakfast dishes still cluttered the dining-table, and magazines and newspapers lay on the floor where they had obviously been dropped in haste. The adjutant's pipe, with malodorous wisps of smoke still rising from it, lay in one of the ashtrays, proof of how precipitously the mess had been abandoned.

Then Michael heard the sound of voices, distant but excited, coming through the open window that overlooked the orchard. He hurried out and into the trees.

Their full squadron strength was twenty-four pilots, but after the recent attrition they were down to sixteen, including Andrew and Michael. All of them were assembled at the edge of the orchard, and with them were the mechanics and ground staff, the crews from the anti-aircraft batteries that guarded the field, the mess servants and batmen – every living soul was on the field, and it seemed that all of them were talking at once.

They were gathered round an aircraft parked in the No. 1 position at the head of the orchard. Michael could see only the upper wings of the machine and the cowling of the motor over the heads of the crowd, but he felt a sudden thrill in his blood. He had never seen anything like it before.

The nose of the machine was long, giving the impression of great power, and the wings were beautifully raked yet with the deep dihedral which promised speed, and the control surfaces were full, which implied stability and easy handling.

Andrew pushed his way out of the excited throng around the aircraft and hurried to meet Michael with the amber cigarette-holder sticking out of the corner of his mouth at a jaunty angle.

'Hail, the sleeping beauty arises like Venus from the waves.'

'Andrew, it's the SE5a at last, isn't it?' Michael shouted above the uproar, and Andrew seized his arm and dragged him towards it.

The crowd opened before them and Michael came up short and stared at it with awe. At a glance he could see it was heavier and more robust than even the German Albatros DIIIs – and that engine! It was enormous! Gargantuan!

'Two hundred gee-gees!' Andrew patted the engine cowling lovingly.

'Two hundred horsepower,' Michael repeated. 'Bigger than the German Mercedes.' He went forward and stroked the beautifully laminated wood of the propeller as he looked up over the nose at the guns.

There was a .303 Lewis gun on a Foster mount set on the top wing, a light, reliable and effective weapon firing over the arc of the propeller, and below it mounted on the fuselage ahead of the cockpit was the heavier Vickers with interrupter gear to fire through the propeller. Two guns, at last they had two guns and an engine powerful enough to carry them into battle.

Michael let out the highland yell that Andrew had taught him, and Andrew unscrewed the cairngorm and sprinkled a few drops of whisky on the engine housing.

'Bless this kite and all who fly in her,' he intoned, and then took a swig from the flask before handing it to Michael.

'Have you flown her?' Michael demanded, his voice hoarse from the burn of whisky, and he tossed the flask to the nearest of his brother officers.

'Who the devil do you think brought her up from Arras?' Andrew demanded.

'How does she handle?'

'Just like a young lady I know in Aberdeen – quick up, quick down and soft and loving in between.'

There was a chorus of cat-calls and whistles from the assembled pilots, and somebody yelled, 'When do we get a chance to fly her, sir?'

'Order of seniority,' Andrew told them, and gave Michael a wicked grin. 'If only Captain Courtney were fit to fly!' He shook his head in mock sympathy.

'Biggs!' shouted Michael. 'Where is my flying jacket, man?'

'Thought you might want it, sir.' Biggs stepped out of the crowd behind him and opened the jacket for Michael to slide his arms into the sleeves.

The mighty Wolseley Viper engine hurled the SE5a down the narrow muddy runway, and as the tail lifted Michael had a sweeping view forward over the engine cowling. It was like sitting in a grandstand.

'I'll get Mac to strip off this piddling little windshield,' he decided, 'and I'll be able to spot any Hun within a hundred miles.'

He lifted the big machine into the air and grinned as he felt her begin to climb.

'Quick up,' Andrew had said, and he felt himself pressed down firmly into the seat, as he lifted the nose through the horizon and they went up like a vulture rising in a thermal.

'There's no Albatros been built that is going to climb away from us now,' he exalted, and at five thousand feet he levelled out and swept her into a right-hand turn, pulling the turn tighter and tighter still, hauling back hard on the stick to keep the nose up, his starboard wing pointing vertically down at the earth and the blood draining from his brain by the centrifugal force so that his vision turned grey and colourless, then he whipped her hard over the opposite way and yelled with elation in the buffet of wind and the roar of the huge engine.

'Come on, you bastards!' He twisted to look back at the German lines. 'Come and see what we have got for you now!'

When he landed, the other pilots surrounded the machine in a clamorous pack.

'What's she like, Mike?'

'How does she climb?'

'Can she turn?'

And standing on the lower wing above them, Michael bunched all his fingers together and then kissed them away towards the sky.

That afternoon Andrew led the squadron in tight formation, still in their shot-riddled, battered and patched old Sopwith Pups, down to the main airfield at Bertangles and they waited outside No. 3 hangar in an impatiently excited group as the big SE5as were trundled out by the ground crews and parked in a long line abreast on the apron.

Through his uncle at divisional headquarters, Andrew had arranged for a photographer to be in attendance. With the new fighters as a backdrop, the squadron pilots formed up around Andrew like a football team. Every one of them was differently dressed, not a single regulation RFC uniform amongst them. On their heads they wore forage caps and peaks and leather helmets, while as always Andrew sported his tam o' shanter. Their jackets were naval monkey jackets, or cavalry tunics, or cross-over leather flying coats, but every one of them wore the embroidered RFC wings on his breast.

The photographer set up his heavy wooden tripod and disappeared under the black cloth while his assistant stood by with the plates. Only one of the pilots was not included in the group. Hank Johnson was a tough little Texan, not yet twenty years old, the only American on the squadron, who had been a horse

tamer – or, as he put it, a bronco buster – before the war. He had paid his own passage over the Atlantic to join the Lafayette Squadron, and from there had found his way into Andrew's mixed bunch of Scots and Irish and colonials and other strays that made up No. 21 Squadron RFC.

Hank stood behind the tripod with a thick black Dutch cigar in his mouth giving bad advice to the harassed photographer.

'Come on, Hank,' Michael called to him. 'We need your lovely mug to give the picture some class.'

Hank rubbed his twisted nose, kicked into that shape by one of his broncos, and shook his head.

'None of you old boys ever hear that it's bad luck to have your picture took?'

They booed him, and he waved his cigar at them affably. 'Go ahead,' he invited, 'but my daddy got himself bit by a rattle snake the same day he had his picture took for the first time.'

'There aren't any rattle snakes up there in the blue,' one of them taunted.

'No,' Hank agreed. 'But what there is, is a whole lot worse than a nest of rattle snakes.' The derisive cries lost their force. They glanced at each other and one of them made as if to leave the group.

'Smile, please, gentlemen.' The photographer emerged from beneath his black cloth, freezing them, but their smiles were just a shade fixed and sickly as the shutter opened and their images were burned into silver nitrate for posterity.

Quickly Andrew acted to change the sombre mood that held them as they broke up. 'Michael, pick five,' he ordered. 'The rest of us will give you ten minutes' start, and you're to try and head us off, and make a good interception before we reach Mort Homme.'

Michael led his formation of five into the classic ambush position, up sun and screened by wisps of cloud, blocking the return route to Mort Homme. Still, Andrew almost gave them the slip; he had taken his group well south and was sneaking in right down on the ground. It would have worked with duller eyes than Michael's, but he picked up the flash of the low sun off the glass of a windshield from six miles and fired the red Very flare to signal 'Enemy in Sight' to his group. Andrew, realizing that they had been spotted, climbed up to meet them, and the two formations came together in a whirl of turning, diving, twisting machines.

Michael picked Andrew's SE5a out of the pack and went for him, and the two of them locked into an intricate aerial duet, pushing the big powerful machines harder and still harder, seeking their outer limits of speed and endurance; but evenly matched in skill and aircraft, neither was able to wrest the final advantage, until quite by chance as Andrew came up on his tail, almost into the killing line, Michael kicked on full rudder without bank and the SE5a tail skidded, turning flat, whipping him around with a force that almost dislocated his neck, and he found himself roaring back head-on to Andrew's attack.

They flashed past each other, only the lightning reflexes of veteran fighter pilots saving them from collision, and instantly Michael repeated the flat skid turn and was flung violently against the side of the cockpit, striking his partially healed shoulder on the rim so that his vision starred with the pain – but he was round in a flash and he fastened on to Andrew's tail. Andrew twisted desperately, but Michael matched every evasive twist and held him in the ring sight of the Vickers, pressing closer until the spinning boss of his propeller almost touched Andrew's rudder.

'Ngi dla!' Michael howled triumphantly. 'I have eaten!' – the ancient Zulu war cry that King Chaka's warriors had screamed as they put the long silver blade of the assegai into living flesh.

He saw Andrew's face reflected in the rear-view mirror on the cross struts of the wing above his head, and his eyes were wide with dismay and disbelief at that incredible manoeuvre.

Andrew fired a green Very flare to signal the recall to the squadron and to concede victory to Michael. The squadron was scattered across the sky, but at the recall they re-formed on Andrew and he led them back to Mort Homme.

The moment they landed, Andrew sprang from his machine and rushed to Michael, seizing him by both shoulders and shaking him impatiently.

'How did you do that – how the hell did you do that?'

Quickly Michael explained.

'It's impossible,' Andrew shook his head. 'A flat turn – if I hadn't seen it – ' He broke off. 'Come on. Let's go and try it again.'

Together the two big scout planes roared off the narrow strip, and only returned as the last light was fading. Michael and Andrew jumped down from their cockpits and fell on each other, slapping each other on the back and dancing in a circle, so padded by their flying clothes that they looked like a pair of performing bears. Their ground crews stood by with indulgent grins until they sobered a little and then Mac, the head mechanic, stepped forward and tipped his forage cap.

'Begging your pardon, sir, but that paint job is like my mother-in-law's Sunday-go-to-meeting dress, sir, dull and dirty and God-help-us.'

The SE5as were in factory drab. A colour that was intended to make them inconspicuous to the enemy.

'Green,' said Andrew. A few of the pilots on both sides, German as well as British, desired the opposite effect. With them it was a matter of pride that their paintwork should be bright enough to advertize their presence to the enemy, a direct challenge. 'Green,' Andrew repeated. 'Bright green to match my scarf, and don't forget the flying haggis on the nose.'

'Yellow, please, Mac,' Michael decided.

'Now what made me think you would choose yellow, Mr Michael?' Mac grinned.

'Oh, Mac, while you are about it, take that awful little windshield off her and tighten up the rigging wires, won't you?'

The old hands all believed that by screwing up the rigging wires and increasing the dihedral angle of the wings, they could put a few knots on their speed.

'I'll see to it,' Mac promised.

'Trim her to fly hands off,' Michael added. The aces were all fusspots, everybody knew that. If the SE5a flew straight and level with hands off the controls, the pilot could use both hands for the guns.

'Hands off it is, sir!' Mac grinned indulgently.

'Oh, and Mac, train the guns for fifty yards – '

'Anything else, sir?'

'That will do for now, Mac,' Michael answered his grin, 'but I'll work on it.'

'I'm sure you will, sir.' Mac shook his head with resignation. 'She'll be ready at dawn.'

'There's a bottle of rum for you if she is,' Michael promised.

'And now, my boy.' Andrew threw his arm around Michael's shoulders, 'how about a drink?'

'I thought you would never offer,' Michael said.

The mess was full of excited young men all eagerly and loudly discussing the new machines.

'Corporal!' Lord Killigerran called over their heads to the mess servant. 'All drinks tonight will be on my book, please,' and his pilots cheered him delightedly before turning back to the bar to make the most of the offer.

An hour later when all eyes were glittering feverishly and the laughter had reached that raucous pitch which Andrew judged to be appropriate, he hammered on the bar for their attention and announced solemnly, 'As Grand Bok-Bok Champion of Aberdeen and greater Scotland, not to mention the outer Hebrides, it behoves me to challenge all comers to a bout of that ancient and honourable sport.'

'Behoves, forsooth!' Michael cocked a mocking eye at him. 'Kindly pick your team, sir.'

Michael lost the toss and his team was required to form the rugger scrum against the far wall of the mess, while the mess servants swiftly stowed away all breakables. Then one at a time Andrew's lads took a run across the mess and landed with all possible force upon the scrum, endeavouring to collapse it for an outright win. If, however, any part of their anatomy touched the ground in the process, it would have meant an immediate disqualification of their team.

Michael's scrum withstood the weight and violence of the onslaught, and finally all eight of Andrew's men, making sure that not a toe or finger touched the ground, were perched like a troop of monkeys on top of Michael's pyramid.

From the top of the pile Andrew asked the crucial question which would decide glorious victory or ignoble defeat.

'Bok-Bok, how many fingers do I hold up?'

His voice, muffled by the weight of bodies above him, Michael guessed. 'Three.'

'Two!' Andrew claimed victory and with a dismal groan the scrum deliberately collapsed itself, and in the ensuing chaos Michael found Andrew's ear within inches of his mouth.

'I say, do you think I might borrow the motor-cycle tonight?' he asked.

Pinned as he was, Andrew could not move his head, but he rolled his eyes towards Michael.

'Going out for a breath of air, my boy, once again?' and then when Michael looked sheepish and could find no clever reply, he went on, 'All I have is yours, go with my blessing and give the lucky lady my deepest respects, won't you?'

* * *

Michael parked the motor-cycle in the woods behind the barn, and carrying the bundle of army blankets sloshed through the mud to the entrance. As he stepped in there was a flash of light as Centaine lifted the shutter of the lantern and shone it in his face.

'Bonsoir, monsieur.'

She was sitting up on top of the bales of straw with her legs tucked under her and she grinned impishly down at him. 'What a surprise to meet you here.'

He scrambled up to her and seized her.

'You are early,' he accused.

'Papa went to bed early – ' she got no further, for his mouth covered hers.

'I saw the new airplanes,' she gasped when they broke apart to breathe, 'but I didn't know which was you. They are all the same. It troubled me not to know which was you.'

'Tomorrow mine will be yellow again. Mac is re-doping it for me.'

'We must arrange signals,' she told him, as she took the blankets from him and began to build their nest in between the bales of straw.

'If I lift my hand over my head like this, this will mean that I will meet you in the barn tonight,' he suggested.

'That is the signal I will look for hardest.' She smiled up at him and then patted the blankets. 'Come here,' she ordered, and her voice had gone husky and purring.

A long time later as she lay with her ear against his naked chest and listened to his heart pumping, he stirred slightly and then whispered, 'Centaine, it's no good! You cannot travel to Africa with me.'

She sat up quickly and stared at him, her mouth hardening, and her eyes, dark as gunmetal, gleamed dangerously.

'I mean, what would people say? Think of my reputation, travelling with a woman who was not my wife.'

She went on staring at him, but her mouth softened into the beginning of a smile.

'There must be a solution, though.' He pretended to puzzle over it. 'I have it!' He snapped his fingers. 'What if I were to marry you!'

She put her cheek back against his chest. 'Only to save your reputation,' she whispered.

'You have not yet said "yes".'

'Oh, yes. Yes! A million times yes!'

And then, characteristically, her next question was pragmatic.

'When, Michel?'

'Soon, as soon as possible. I have met your family, but tomorrow I will take you to meet mine.'

'Your family?' She held him at arm's length. 'Your family is in Africa.'

'Not all of it,' he assured her. 'Most of it is here. When I say most I don't mean numbers, I mean the most important single part of it.'

'I don't understand.'

'You will, *ma chérie*, you will!' he assured her.

* * *

Michael had explained to Andrew what he had in mind.

'If you get caught I will disclaim any knowledge of the whole nefarious scheme. I will, furthermore, preside with great enjoyment at your court martial, and will personally command the firing-squad,' Andrew warned him.

Michael had paced out the firm ground at the edge of North Field on the side of the de Thiry estate furthest from the squadron base. He had to slide-slip the bright yellow SA5a down behind the line of oaks that guarded the field, and then as he skimmed over the seven-foot stone wall, he shut the throttle and let

her drop to the soft earth. He pulled up quickly, and left the engine idling as he clambered out on the wing.

Centaine was running out from the corner of the wall where she had been waiting. He saw she had followed his instructions and was warmly dressed: fur-lined boots under her yellow woollen skirt, and a yellow silk scarf at her throat. Over it all she wore a lustrous cape of silver fox fur, and the hood dangled down her back as she ran. She carried a soft leather bag on a strap over one shoulder.

Michael jumped down and swung her in his arms.

'Look!' I am wearing yellow – your favourite.'

'Clever girl.' He set her down. 'Here!' He pulled the borrowed flying helmet from the pocket of his greatcoat and showed her how to fit it over her thick dark curls and buckle the strap under the chin.

'Do I look gallant and romantic?' she asked, posing for him.

'You look marvellous.' And it was true. Her cheeks were rouged with excitement, and her eyes sparkled.

'Come on.' Michael climbed back on to the wing and then lowered himself into the tiny cockpit.

'It is so small.' Centaine hesitated on the wing.

'So are you, but I think you are also afraid, no?'

'Afraid, ha!' She flashed a look of utter scorn at him, and began to climb in on top of him.

This was a complicated business, which involved lifting her skirts above her knees and then balancing precariously over the open cockpit, like a beautiful bird settling on its clutch of eggs. Michael could not resist the temptation, and as she came down on top of him, he ran his hand up under the skirts, almost to the junction of luscious silk-clad thighs. Centaine squealed with outrage. 'You are forward, monsieur!' and she plopped down on to his lap.

Michael fastened the safety-belt over both of them and then nuzzled her neck below the edge of the helmet. 'You are in my power now. You cannot escape.'

'I am not sure that I wish to,' she giggled.

It took some further minutes for them to arrange all Centaine's skirts and furs and petticoats, and to make sure that Michael could manipulate the controls with her strapped on to his lap.

'All set,' he told her, and taxied to the end of the field, giving himself every inch of runway that he could, for the earth was soft and the strip short. He had ordered Mac to remove the ammunition from both guns and drain the coolant from the Vickers, which saved almost sixty pounds in weight, but still they were overloaded for the length of runway available to them.

'Hold on,' he said in her ear, and opened the throttle and the big scoutplane bounded forward.

'Thank God for the south wind,' he murmured as he felt her unstick from the mud and strive mightily to lift them into the air.

As they scraped over the far wall, Michael banked slightly to lift his port wing over one of the oaks, and then they were climbing away. He felt how rigid Centaine was in his lap, and he thought she was really afraid. He was disappointed.

'We are safe now,' he shouted over the engine beat, and she turned her head, and he saw in her eyes not fear but ecstasy.

'It's beautiful,' she said, and kissed him. To know that she shared his passion for flight delighted him.

'We will go over the château,' he told her, and banked away steeply, dropping down again.

For Centaine it was the second most marvellous experience of her whole life, better than riding or music, almost as good as Michael's loving. She was a bird, an eagle, she wanted to shout her joy aloud, she wanted to hold the moment for ever. She wanted to always be on high with the wild wind howling around her and the strong arm of the man she loved holding her protectively.

Below her lay a new world, familiar places that she had known since her earliest childhood, now viewed from a different and enchanting dimension. 'This is the way the angels must see the world!' she cried, and he smiled at the fancy. The château loomed ahead of them and she had not realized how big it was, or how pink and pretty was the roof of baked tiles. And there was Nuage in the field behind the stables, galloping ahead of them, racing the roaring yellow aircraft – and she laughed and shouted in the wind, 'Run, my darling!' and then they passed over him, and she saw Anna in the gardens, straightening up from her plants as she heard the engine, shading her eyes, peering up at them. She was so close that Centaine could see the frown on her red face, and she leaned far out from the cockpit. Her yellow scarf flowed behind her in the slipstream as she waved, and she saw the look of crumpled disbelief on Anna's face as they flashed by.

Centaine laughed in the wind and called to Michael, 'Go higher. Go up higher.'

He obeyed and she was never still for a moment, twisting and hopping about in his lap, leaning out of the cockpit first on one side, then on the other.

'Look! Look! There is the convent – if only the nuns could see me now. There, that is the canal – and there is the cathedral at Arras – oh, and there – ' Her excitement and enthusiasm were infectious, and Michael laughed with her, and when she turned her head back to him, he kissed her, but she broke away.

'Oh, I don't want to miss a second!'

Michael picked out the main airforce base at Bertangles; the runways formed a cross of mown green turf through the dark forest, with the clusters of hangars and buildings nestling in the arms of the cross.

'Listen to me,' he shouted in her ear. 'You must keep your head down while we land.' She nodded. 'When I give you the word, jump down and run into the trees. You will find a stone wall on your right. Follow it for three hundred metres until you reach the road. Wait there.'

Michael joined the Bertangles circuit in textbook fashion, taking advantage of his sedate down-wind leg to scrutinize the base for any activity which might indicate the presence of high-ranking officers or other potential troublemakers. There were half a dozen aircraft parked in front of the hangars, and he saw one or two figures working on them or wandering about amongst the buildings.

'Looks as though it's clear,' he muttered, and turned crosswind and then on to final approach, with Centaine scrunched down on his lap, out of sight from the ground.

Michael came in high, like a novice; he was still at fifty feet when he passed the hangars, and he touched down deep at the far end of the runway and let his roll-out carry them almost to the edge of the forest before he swung broadside and braked hard.

'Get out and run!' he told Centaine, and boosted her out of the cockpit. Hidden from the hangars and buildings by the fuselage of the SE5a, she hoisted

up her skirts, tucked her leather bag under her arm, and scampered into the trees.

Michael taxied back to the hangars and left the SE5a on the apron.

'Better sign the book, sir,' a sergeant mechanic told him as he jumped down.

'Book?'

'New procedure, sir – all flights have to log in and out.'

'Damned red tape,' Michael groused. 'Can't do a thing without a piece of paper these days.' But he went off to find the duty officer.

'Oh yes, Courtney, there is a driver for you.'

The driver was waiting behind the wheel of a black Rolls-Royce parked at the back of No. 1 hangar, but as soon as he saw Michael he sprang out and stood to attention.

'Nkosana!' he grinned with huge delight, his teeth gleaming in his dark moon-shaped face, and he threw Michael a sweeping salute that quivered at the peak of his cap. He was a tall young Zulu, taller even than Michael, and he wore the khaki uniform and puttees of the African Service Corps.

'Sangane!' Michael returned the salute, grinning as widely, then impulsively hugged him.

'To see your face is like coming home again.' Michael spoke easy fluent Zulu.

The two of them had grown up together, roaming the grassy yellow hills of Zululand with their dogs and hunting-sticks. Naked they had swum together in the cool green pools of the Tugela river, and fished them for eels as long and thick as their arms. They had cooked their game on the same smoky fire, and lain beside it in the night, studying the stars and seriously discussing the occasions of small boys, deciding on the lives they would live and the world they would build when they were grown men.

'What news from home, Sangane?' Michael demanded as the Zulu opened the door of the Rolls. 'How is your father?'

Mbejane, Sangane's father, was the old servant companion and friend of Sean Courtney, a prince of the royal house of Zulu, who had followed his master to other wars, but was now too old and infirm, and was forced to send his son in his place.

They chatted animatedly, as Sangane drove the Rolls out of the base and turned on to the main road. On the back seat Michael stripped his flying gear to reveal his dress uniform, complete with wings and decorations, that he wore beneath.

'Stop over there, Sangane, at the edge of the trees.'

Michael jumped out and called anxiously, 'Centaine!'

She stepped out from behind one of the tree trunks and Michael gaped at her. She had used the time since he had left her to good effect, and he realized now why she had brought the leather bag. Michael had never seen her wearing make-up before, but she had applied it so artfully that he could not at first fathom the transformation. It was simply that all her good points seemed enhanced, her eyes more luminous, her skin more glowing and pearly.

'You are beautiful,' he breathed. She was no longer a child-woman, she was possessed of a new poise and confidence, and he felt awed by her.

'Do you think your uncle will like me?' she asked.

'He will love you – any man would.'

The yellow suit was of a peculiar shade that seemed to gild her skin and throw golden reflections into her dark eyes. The brim of the billy cock hat was

narrow on one side and full on the other, where it was pinned up to the crown with a spike of green and yellow feathers. Beneath the jacket she wore a blouse of fine creamy crêpe-de-chine, with a high lace collar, that emphasized the line of her throat and the dainty set of her small head above it. The boots had been replaced by elegant shoes.

He took both her hands and kissed them reverently, and then handed her into the back of the limousine.

'Sangane, this woman will be my wife one day soon.'

The Zulu nodded in approval, judging her as he would a horse or a young thoroughbred heifer.

'May she bear you many sons,' he said.

When Michael translated, Centaine blushed and laughed.

'Thank him, Michel, but tell him I would like at least one daughter.' She looked about the luxurious cab of the Rolls. 'Do all the English generals have such motor-cars?'

'My uncle brought it from Africa with him.' Michael ran his hand over the fine soft leather seat. 'It was a gift from my aunt.'

'Your uncle has style to go to war in such a chariot,' she nodded, 'and your aunt has good taste. One day I hope I will be able to give you such a gift, Michel.'

'I should like to kiss you,' he said.

'Never in public,' she told him primly, 'but as much as you want when we are alone. Now tell me, how far is it?'

'Five miles or so, but with this traffic on the road, God alone knows how long it will take us.'

They had turned into the main Arras–Amiens road, and it was clogged with military transport, guns and ambulances and heavy supply lorries, horse-drawn wagons and carts, the verges of the road crowded with marching men, hunch-backed beneath their heavy packs, with the steel helmets giving them a mushroom-headed uniformity.

Michael caught resentful and envious glances as Sangane threaded the big glistening Rolls through the slower traffic. The men trudging in the mud looked into the interior and saw an elegant officer with a pretty girl on the soft leather seat beside him. However, most of those sullen stares turned to grins when Centaine waved to them.

'Tell me about your uncle,' she demanded, turning back to Michael.

'Oh, he's a very ordinary chap, not much to tell actually. He was thrown out of school for beating up his headmaster, fought in the Zulu War and killed his first man before he was eighteen, made his first million pounds before he was twenty-five and lost it in a single day. Shot a few hundred elephant while he was a professional ivory hunter – killed a leopard with his bare hands. Then, during the Boer War, he captured Leroux, the Boer general, almost unaided, made another million pounds after the war, helped negotiate the charter of Union for South Africa. He was a cabinet minister in Louis Botha's government, but he resigned to come to this war. Now he commands the regiment. He stands a few inches over six feet and can lift a 200-lb sack of maize in each hand.'

'Michel, I am afraid to meet such a man,' she murmured seriously.

'Why on earth – '

'I am afraid I might fall in love with him.'

Michael laughed delightedly. 'I also am afraid. Afraid he will fall in love with you!'

* * *

Regimental Headquarters was temporarily located in a deserted monastery on the outskirts of Amiens. The monastery grounds were unkempt and overgrown, for they had been abandoned by the monks during the fighting of the previous autumn, and the rhododrendron bushes had turned to jungle. The buildings were of red brick, moss-covered and with wistaria climbing to the grey roof. The bricks were pocked with old shell splinters.

A young second lieutenant met them at the front entrance.

'You must be Michael Courtney – I am John Pearce, the general's ADC.'

'Oh, hello.' Michael shook hands. 'What happened to Nick van der Heever?'

Nick had been at school with Michael, and he had been General Courtney's aide-de-camp ever since the regiment arrived in France.

'Oh, didn't you hear?' John Pearce looked grave, the familiar expression so often seen these days when someone asked after an acquaintance. 'Nick bought the farm, I'm afraid.'

'Oh God, no!'

'Afraid so. He was up at the front with your uncle. Sniper got him.' But the lieutenant's attention was wavering. He couldn't keep his eyes off Centaine. Obligingly, Michael introduced them and then cut short the lieutenant's pantomime of admiration.

'Where is my uncle?'

'He asked you to wait.' The young lieutenant led them through to a small enclosed garden which had probably belonged to the abbot. There were climbing roses on the stone walls and a sun-dial on a sculptured plinth in the centre of the small neat lawn.

A table had been laid for three in the corner where the sun penetrated. Uncle Sean was keeping his usual style – king's pattern silver and Stuart crystal, Michael noticed.

'The general will be with you as soon as he can, but he asked me to warn you that it will be a very short lunch. The spring offensive, you know – ' The lieutenant made a gesture towards the decanter on the small serving table. 'In the meantime, may I offer you a sherry, or something with claws?'

Centaine shook her head, but Michael nodded. 'Claws, please,' he said. Although he loved his uncle as much as he did his own father, yet he always found his imminent presence after a long absence unnerving. He needed something to soothe those nerves.

The aide-de-camp poured Michael a whisky. 'Will you forgive me, but I do have a few things – ' Michael waved him away and took Centaine's arm.

'Look, the buds are beginning to form on the roses – and the narcissus – ' She leaned against him. 'Everything is coming to life again.'

'Not everything,' Michael contradicted softly. 'For the soldier, spring is the time of death.'

'Oh, Michel,' she began, and then broke off and looked towards the glass doors behind him with an expression that made Michael turn swiftly.

A man had stepped through them, a tall man, erect and broad-shouldered.

He stopped when he saw Centaine and looked at her with penetrating appraisal. His eyes were blue and his beard was thick but neatly trimmed in the same style as the king's.

'Those are Michel's eyes!' Centaine thought, staring back at them, but so much fiercer, she realized.

'Uncle Sean!' Michael cried and released her arm. He stepped forward to shake hands, and those fierce eyes swivelled to him and softened.

'My boy.'

'He loves him – ' Centaine understood. 'They love each other very deeply,' and she studied the general's face. His skin was sun-darkened and tanned like leather, with deep creases at the corners of his mouth and around those incredible eyes. His nose was large, like Michael's, and hooked, his forehead broad and deep, and above it was a dense dark cap of hair, shot through with silver threads, that glistened in the spring sunlight.

They were talking earnestly, still gripping each other's hands, exchanging the vital assurances, and as Centaine watched them, the full extent of their resemblance came through to her.

'They are the same,' she realized, 'differing only in age and in force. More like father and son, than – '

The fierce blue eyes came back to her. 'So this is the young lady.'

'May I present Mademoiselle Centaine de Thiry. Centaine, this is my uncle, General Sean Courtney.'

'Michel has told me much – a great deal – ' Centaine stumbled over the English.

'Speak Flemish!' Michael cut in quickly.

'Michel has told me all about you,' she obeyed, and the general grinned delightedly.

'You speak Afrikaans!' he answered in that language. When he smiled, his whole person changed. That savage, almost cruel streak that she had sensed seemed illusory.

'It isn't Afrikaans,' she denied, and they fell into an animated discussion and argument, and within the first few minutes Cntaine found that she liked him – liked him for his resemblances to Michael, and for the vast differences that she detected between them.

'Let's eat!' Sean Courtney exclaimed, and took her arm. 'We have so little time – ' He seated her at the table.

'Michael over here – and we'll let him carve the chicken. I'll take care of the wine.'

Sean gave them the toast. 'To the next time the three of us meet again,' and they all drank it fervently, all too aware of what lay behind it, though here they were out of earshot of the guns.

They chatted easily, the general quickly and effortlessly smoothing over any uneasy silences, so that Centaine realized that for all his bluff exterior he was intuitively gracious, but always she was aware of the scrutiny of those eyes, the valuations and appraisals that were in progress behind them.

'Very well, *mon Général,*' she thought defiantly, 'look all you want, but I am me and Michel is mine.' And she lifted her chin and held his gaze, and answered him directly and without simperings or hesitations, until she saw him smile – and nod almost imperceptibly.

'So this is the one Michael has chosen,' Sean mused. 'I would have hoped for a girl of his own people, who spoke his own language and observed the same

faith. I would have wanted to know a damned sight more about her before I gave my blessing. I would have made them take their time to consider each other and the consequences, but there is no time. Tomorrow or the next day, God knows what will happen. How can I spoil what might be their only moment of happiness ever?' For a moment longer he looked at her, searching for signs of spite or meanness, for weakness or vanity, and saw only the small determined jaw, the mouth that could smile easily but just as easily harden, and the dark intelligent eyes. 'She's tough and she's proud,' he decided, 'but I think she will be loyal, with stength to stay the full distance.' So he smiled and nodded and saw her relax, and he saw also true affection and liking dawn in her eyes before he turned to Michael.

'All right, my boy, you didn't come all this way to chew on this stringy little bird. Tell me why you came, and see if you can surprise me.'

'Uncle Sean, I have asked Centaine to be my wife.'

Sean wiped his moustaches carefully and then laid down his napkin.

'Do not spoil it for them,' he warned himself. 'Don't put the smallest cloud on their joy.'

He looked up at them and he began to smile.

'You don't surprise me, you stun me! I had given up expecting you to do something sensible.' He turned to Centaine. 'Of course, young lady, you had too much good sense to accept, didn't you?'

'General, I hang my head when I admit that I did not. I have accepted him.'

Sean looked fondly at Michael. 'Lucky blighter! She is too darned good for you, but don't let her get away.'

'Don't worry, sir.' Michael laughed with relief. He hadn't expected such instant acceptance. The old boy could still surprise him. He reached across the table to take Centaine's hand, and Centaine looked at Sean Courtney with puzzlement. 'Thank you, General, but you know nothing about me – or my family.' She remembered the catechism to which her own father had subjected Michael.

'I doubt that Michael is intending to marry your family,' Sean said drily. 'And about you, my dear. Well, I am one of the best judges of horseflesh in Africa, and that's not false modesty. I can judge a likely filly when I see one.'

'You are calling me a horse, General?' she bridled playfully.

'I'm calling you a thoroughbred, and I'll be surprised if you aren't a country girl and a horsewoman, and if you haven't got some pretty fancy bloodlines – tell me that I'm wrong,' he challenged.

'Her papa is a count, she rides like a centaur, and they have an estate that was mostly vineyards before the Huns shelled it.'

'Ha!' Sean looked triumphant, and Centaine made a gesture of resignation.

'He knows everything, your uncle.'

'Not everything – ' Sean turned back to Michael. 'When do you plan to do it?'

'I would have liked my father – ' Michael did not have to finish the thought, ' – but we have so little time.'

Sean, who knew truly how little time there was, nodded. 'Garry, your father, will understand.'

'We want to marry before the spring offensive begins,' Michael went on.

'Yes. I know.' Sean frowned and sighed. Some of his peers could send the young men out there with dispassion, but he was not a professional as they were. He knew he would never grow hardened to the pain and the guilt of it,

sending men to die. He began to speak and stopped himself, sighed again and then went on.

'Michael, this is for you alone. Though you'll learn of it soon enough, anyway. A field order has been issued to all fighter squadrons. That order is to prevent all enemy aerial observations over our lines. We will be throwing in all our squadrons to keep the German spotters from following our preparations over the next weeks.'

Michael sat quietly, considering what his uncle had told him. It meant that as far ahead as he could anticipate, the future would be an incessant and ruthless battle with the German Jagdstaffels. He was being warned that few of the fighter pilots could expect to survive that battle.

'Thank you, sir,' he said softly. 'Centaine and I will marry soon – as soon as we can. May I hope that you will be there?'

'I can only promise you that I will do my level best to be there.' Sean looked up as John Pearce came back into the garden. 'What is it, John?'

'I'm sorry, sir. Urgent despatch from General Rawlinson.'

'I'm coming. Give me two minutes.' He turned to his young guests.

'Bloody awful lunch, I'm sorry.'

'The wine was excellent, and the company was even better,' Centaine demurred.

'Michael, go and find Sangane and the Rolls. I want a word with this young lady in private.'

He offered Centaine his arm, and they followed Michael out of the small garden and down the cloisters towards the stone portals of the monastery. Only when she stood at his side did Centaine realize how big he was, and that he had a slight limp, so that his footfalls on the stone paving were uneven. He spoke quietly but with force, leaning over her slightly to make each word tell.

'Michael is fine young man – he is kind, he is thoughtful, he is sensitive. But he does not have the ruthlessness that a man needs in this world to get to the top of the mountain.' Sean paused, and she looked up at him attentively.

'I think you have that strength. You are still very young, but I believe that you will grow stronger. I want you to be strong for Michael.'

Centaine nodded, finding no words to reply.

'Be strong for my son,' Sean said softly, and she started.

'Your son?' and she saw the consternation in his eyes, which was swiftly masked, and he corrected himself.

'I'm sorry, his father is my twin – sometimes I think of him that way.'

'I understand,' she said, but somehow she sensed that it had not been a mistake. 'One day I will follow that until I find the truth,' she thought, and Sean repeated, 'Look after him well, Centaine, and I will be your friend to the gates of hell.'

'I promise you that I will.' She squeezed his arm, and they had reached the entrance where Sangane waited with the Rolls.

'Au revoir, Général,' Centaine said.

'Yes,' Sean nodded. 'Until we meet again,' and helped her into the back seat of the Rolls.

'I will let you know as soon as we decide the day, sir.' Michael shook his uncle's hand.

'Even if I can't be there, be happy, my boy,' said Sean Courtney, and watched the Rolls purr sedately down the driveway, then with an impatient

shrug, he turned and marched back down the cloisters with that long uneven stride.

* * *

With her hat and jewellery and shoes packed back into the soft leather bag, and with the fur-lined boots on her feet and the flying helmet on her head, Centaine crouched at the edge of the forest.

When Michael taxied the SE5a down to where she waited and swung it broadside to the distant airport buildings, she sprinted out from cover, tossed the bag up to him, and scrambled on to the wing. This time there was no hesitation and she clambered up into the cockpit like an old hand.

'Head down,' Michael ordered and swung the aircraft on to line for the take-off.

'All clear,' he told her once they were airborne and she popped her head up again, just as eager and excited as she had been on the first flight. They climbed higher and still higher.

'See how the clouds look like fields of snow – and the sunshine fills them with rainbows.'

She wriggled around in his lap, to look back over the tailplane, and then a quizzical look came into her eyes and she seemed to lose interest in the rainbows.

'Michel?' She moved again in his lap, but with deliberation.

'Michel!' No longer a query, and her tight round buttocks performed a cunning little oscillation that made him squirm.

'Forgive me!' He tried desperately to move out of contact, but her posterior hunted after him, and she twisted her upper body around so that she could place both arms around his neck and she whispered to him.

'Not in broad daylight – not at five thousand feet!' He was shocked by her suggestion.

'Why not, *mon chéri?*' She kissed him lingeringly. 'Nobody will ever know,' and Michael realized that the SE5a had dropped a wing and was starting a shallow spiral dive. Hastily he corrected the machine, and she hugged him and began to move in a slow voluptuous rhythm in his lap.

'Don't you want to?' she asked.

'But, but – nobody has ever done it before, not in an SE5a. I don't know if it's possible.' His voice was becoming weaker, his flying more erratic.

'We will find out,' she said firmly. 'You fly the aeroplane and do not fret yourself,' and she hoisted herself slightly and began drawing up the back of her fur coat and the yellow skirt with it.

'Centaine,' he said uncertaintly, and then a little later, 'Centaine!' more definitely, and a little later still, 'Oh my God, Centaine!'

'It *is* possible!' she cried triumphantly, and almost immediately she was aware of sensations which she had never suspected were harboured within her. She felt herslf borne upwards and outwards as though she was departing her own body, and as though she were drawing Michael's soul out with her. At first she was terrified by the strength and strangeness of it, and then all other emotions were swept away.

She felt herself tumbling and swirling, upwards and upwards, with the wild

wind roaring about her, and the rainbow-girded clouds undulating on every side – and then she heard herself screaming, and she thrust her fingers into her mouth to still her own cries, but it was too strong to be contained, and she threw her head back and screamed and sobbed and laughed with the wonder of it, as she went over the peak and fell down the other side into the gulf, spinning downwards, settling softly as a snowflake into her own body again, and feeling his arms around her, hearing him groaning and gasping in her ear, and she twisted and held him fiercely and cried, 'I love you, Michel, I will always love you!'

* * *

Mac hurried to meet Michael as soon as he cut the engine and climbed out of the cockpit.

'You're just in time, sir. There is a pilots' briefing in the mess. The major has been asking for you – best hurry, sir,' and then, as Michael started along the duckboards towards the mess, he called after him, 'How is she flying, sir?'

'Like a bird, Mac. Just reload the guns for me.'

First time ever that he hadn't fussed about his machine, Mac thought wonderingly, as he watched Michael walk away.

The mess was full of pilots, all the armchairs were taken and one or two new chums were standing against the wall at the back. Andrew sat on the bar counter swinging his legs and sucking on the amber cigarette-holder. He broke off as Michael appeared in the doorway.

'Gentlemen, we are being honoured. Captain Michael Courtney has graciously consented to join us. Despite other pressing and important business, he has been kind enough to devote an hour or two to help us settle our little difference with Kaiser Wilhelm II. I think we should show our appreciation.'

There were howls and catcalls, and somebody blew a loud raspberry.

'Barbarians,' Michael told them haughtily, and dropped into the armchair hastily vacated by a new chum.

'Are you comfortable?' Andrew asked him solicitously. 'Do you mind if I carry on? Good! Well, as I was saying, the squadron has received an urgent despatch, delivered by motor-cyclist less than half an hour ago, direct from divisional headquarters.'

He held it up and waved it at arm's length, pinching his nostrils with the other hand so that his voice was nasal as he went on.

'You will be able to smell the quality of the literary style and the contents from where you are sitting – '

There were a few polite guffaws, but the eyes that watched him were screwed up nervously, and here and there were little nervous movements, the snuffling of feet, one of the old hands cracking his knuckles, another nibbling on his thumbnail, Michael unconsciously blowing on his fingertips – for all of them knew that the scrap of coarse yellow paper that Andrew was waving at them might be their death warrant.

Andrew held it at arm's length and read from it.

From Divisional Headquarters, Arras.
To the Officer Commanding No. 21 Squadron RFC. Near Mort Homme.

As of 2400 hrs 4th April 1917, you will at all costs prevent any enemy aerial observation over your designated sector until further orders to the contrary.

'That's all, gentlemen. Four lines, a mere bagatelle, but let me point out to you the succinct phrase "at all costs" without dwelling upon it.'

He paused and looked over the mess slowly, watching it register on each strained and gaunt face.

'My God, look how old they have grown,' he thought, irrelevantly. 'Hank looks fifty years old, and Michael – ' he glanced up at the mirror over the mantelpiece, and when he saw his reflection, he brushed nervously at his own forehead where in the last few weeks the sandy hair had receded in two deep bays, leaving pink skin like a beach at low tide. Then he dropped his hand selfconsciously and went on.

'Beginning at 0500 hours tomorrow morning, all pilots will fly four daily sorties until further notice,' he announced. 'There will be the usual dawn and dusk sweeps, but from now on they will be at full squadron strength.' He looked around for questions, there were none. 'Then each flight of aircraft will make an additional two sorties – one hour on, and two hours off – or as our friends in the Royal Navy are wont to say, "Standing watch and watch". That way we will maintain a perpetual presence over the squadron's designated area.'

They all stirred again and then heads turned towards Michael, for he was the eldest and their natural spokesman. Michael blew on his fingers and then studied them minutely.

'Do I have any questions?'

Hank cleared his throat.

'Yes?' Andrew turned to him expectantly, but Hank subsided back into his armchair.

'Just to get this straight,' Michael spoke at last. 'We will all fly the two hours' dawn and dusk patrols, that's four hours – and then an additional four hours during the day? Is my arthithmetic correct, or does that make eight hours of combat a day?'

'Give Captain Courtney a coconut,' Andrew nodded.

'My trade union isn't going to like it,' and they laughed, a nervous braying chorus quickly cut off. Eight hours was too much, far too much, no man could exercise the vigilance and nervous response necessary to sustain that length of combat flight for a single day. They were being asked to do it day after day without promise of respite.

'Any other questions?'

'Service and maintenance of the aircraft?'

'Mac has promised me that he can do it,' Andrew replied to Hank. 'Anything else? No? All right, gentlemen, my book is open.'

But the pilgrimage to the bar to take advantage of Andrew's offer was subdued, and nobody discussed the new orders. They drank quietly but determinedly, avoiding each other's eyes. What was there to discuss?

* * *

The Comte de Thiry, with a vista of forty thousand hectares of lush farming land before his eyes, gave his rapturous approval to the wedding, and shook hands with Michael as though he were wringing an ostrich's neck.

Anna hugged Centaine to her bosom. 'My baby!' she wheezed, slow fat tears seeping out of the creases around her eyes and coursing down her face. 'You are going to leave Anna.'

'Don't be a goose, Anna, I will need you still. You can come with me to Africa,' and Anna sobbed aloud.

'Africa!' and then even more dolorously, 'What kind of wedding will it be? There are no guests to invite, Raoul the chef is in the trenches fighting the boche – oh, my baby, it will be a scandalous wedding!'

'The priest will come over, and the general, Michel's uncle, has promised – and the pilots from the squadron. It will be a wonderful wedding,' Centaine contradicted her.

'No choir,' sobbed Anna. 'No wedding feast, no wedding dress, no honeymoon.'

'Papa will sing, he has a wonderful voice, and you and I will bake the cake and kill one of the sucking pigs. We can alter Mama's dress, and Michel and I will have our honeymoon here, just the way Papa and Mama did.'

'Oh, my baby!' Once Anna's tears had started, they would not that readily be dried.

'When will it be?' The comte had not yet relinquished Michael's hand. 'Name the day.'

'Saturday – at eight in the evening.'

'So soon!' wailed Anna. 'Why so soon?'

The comte struck his thigh as inspiration came to him.

'We will open a bottle of the very best champagne – and perhaps even a bottle of the Napoleon cognac! Centaine, my little one, where are the keys?' And this time she could not refuse him.

* * *

In their nest of blankets and straw they lay in each other's embrace, and in halting sentences Michael tried to explain the new squadron orders to her. She could not fully comprehend their dreadful significance. She understood only that he was going into dire peril and she held him with all her strength.

'But you will be there on our wedding day? Whatever happens, you will come to me on our wedding day?'

'Yes, Centaine, I will be there.'

'Swear it to me, Michel.'

'I swear it.'

'No! No! Swear the most dreadful oath you can think of.'

'I swear it on my life and on my love for you.'

'Ah, Michel,' she sighed and pressed against him, satisfied at last. 'I will watch for you as you fly by each dawn and each dusk – and I will meet you here each night.'

They made love in a frenzy, a madness of the blood, as though they were trying to consume each other, and the fury of it left them exhausted so that they

slept in each other's arms until Centaine woke, and it was late. The birds were calling in the forest and the first light filtered into the barn.

'Michel! Michel! It is almost half past four.' By the light of the lantern she checked the gold watch pinned to her jacket.

'Oh, my God,' Michael began pulling on his clothes, still groggy with sleep, 'I'll miss the dawn patrol – '

'No. Not if you go directly.'

'I can't leave you.'

'Don't argue! Go, Michel! Go quickly.'

Centaine ran all the way, slipping and sliding in the mud of the lane, but determined to be on the hill for the squadron take-off, to wave them away.

At the stables she stopped, panting and clutching her chest to try and control her breathing. The château was in darkness, lying like a sleeping beast in the dawn, and she felt a rush of relief.

She crossed the yard slowly, giving herself time to catch her breath, and at the door she listened carefully before letting herself into the kitchen. She slipped off her muddy boots and placed them in the airing cupboard behind the stove, then she climbed the stairs, keeping close to the wall so that the tread would not squeak under her bare feet.

With another lift of relief she opened the door to her cell, crept in and then closed it behind her. She turned to face the bed, and then froze with surprise as a match flared and was touched to a lantern wick, and the room bloomed with yellow light.

Anna, who had just lit the lantern, was sitting on her bed, with a shawl around her shoulders and a lace night-cap on her head. Her red face was stony and forbidding.

'Anna!' Centaine whispered. 'I can explain – you haven't told Papa?'

Then the chair by the window creaked and she turned to find her father sitting in it and staring at her with his single malevolent eye.

She had never seen such an expression upon his face.

Anna spoke first. 'My little baby creeping out at night to go whoring after soldiers.'

'He is not a soldier,' Centaine protested. 'He is an airman.'

'Harlotry,' said the comte. 'A daughter of the house of de Thiry behaving like a common harlot.'

'Papa, I am to be Michel's wife. We are as good as married to each other.'

'Not until Saturday night, you are not.' The comte rose to his feet. There was a dark smudge of sleeplessness under his one eye and his thick mane of hair stood on end.

'Until Saturday,' his voice rose to an angry bellow, 'you are confined to this room, child. You will remain here until one hour before the ceremony begins.'

'But Papa, I have to go to the hill – '

'Anna, take the key. I place you in charge of her. She is not to leave the house.'

Centaine stood in the centre of the room looking around her, as though for escape, but Anna rose and took her wrist in a powerful calloused hand and Centaine's shoulders slumped as she was led to the bed.

* * *

The pilots of the squadron were scattered in dark groups of threes and fours amongst the trees at the edge of the orchard, talking softly and smoking the last cigarettes before take-off, when Michael came clumping down the duckboards, still buttoning his greatcoat and pulling on his flying gauntlets. He had missed the pre-flight briefing.

Andrew nodded a gretting as he joined them, making no mention of Michael's late arrival or of the example to the new pilots, and Michael did not apologize. They were both acutely aware of the dereliction of his duty, and Andrew unscrewed his silver flask and drank without offering it to Michael; the rebuke was deliberate.

'Take-off in five minutes,' Andrew studied the sky, 'and it looks like a good day to die.' It was his term for good flying weather, but today it jarred on Michael.

'I'm getting married on Saturday,' he said, as though the ideas were linked, and Andrew stopped with the flask halfway back to his lips and stared at him.

'The little French girl up at the château?' he asked, and Michael nodded.

'Centaine – Centaine de Thiry.'

'You crafty old dog!' Andrew began to grin, his disapproval forgotten. 'So that is what you've been up to. Well, you have my blessing, my boy.'

He made a benedictory gesture with the flask. 'I drink to your long life and joy together.'

He passed the flask to Michael, but Michael paused before drinking.

'I'd be honoured if you would agree to act as my best man.'

'Don't worry, my boy, I will be flying at your wingtip as you go into action, I give you my oath on it.' He punched Michael's arm and they grinned happily at each other and then marched side by side to the green and yellow machines standing at the head of the squadron line-up.

One after another the Wolseley Viper engines crackled and snarled and blue exhaust smoke misted the trees of the orchard. Thn the SE5as bumped and rocked over the uneven ground for the massed take-off.

Today, because it was a full squadron sweep, Michael would not be flying as Andrew's wingman, but as leader of 'B' flight. He had five other machines in his flight, and two of his pilots were new chums and would need protecting and shepherding. Hank Johnson was leading 'C' flight and he waved across as Michael taxied past him, and then gunned his machine into his slot behind him.

As soon as they were airborne, Michael signalled to his flight to close the formation into a tight V and he followed Andrew, conforming to his slight left-hand turn that would carry them past the hillock beyond the château.

He lifted the goggles on to his forehead and slipped his scarf down off his nose and mouth so that Centaine would be able to see his face, and flying one-handed he prepared to make their private rendezvous signal to her as he passed. There was the knoll – he started smiling in anticipation, then the smile faded.

He could not see Nuage, the white stallion. He leaned far out of the cockpit, and ahead of him Andrew was doing the same, screwing his head around as he searched for the girl and the white horse.

They roared past and she was not there. The hillock was deserted. Michael peered back over his shoulder as it receded, making doubly sure. He felt the dull weight in his belly, the cold and heavy stone of foreboding. She wasn't there, their talisman had forsaken them.

He lifted the scarf over his mouth and covered his eyes with the goggles, as the three flights of aircraft bore upwards, climbing for the vital advantage of

height, aiming to cross the ridges at 12,000 feet before levelling out into the patrol pattern.

His mind kept going back to Centaine. Why wasn't she there? Was something wrong?

He found it hard to concentrate on the sky around him. 'She has taken our luck. She knows what it means to us and she has let us down.'

He shook his head. 'I mustn't think about it – watch the sky! Don't think about anything but the sky and the enemy.'

The light was strengthening, and the air was clear and icy cold. The land beneath them was patched with the geometrical patterns of fields and studded with the villages and towns of northern France, but directly ahead was that dung-brown strip of torn and savaged earth that marked the lines, and above it the scattered blobs of morning cloud, dull as bruises on one side and brilliant gold on the side struck by the rising sun.

To the west lay the wide basin of the Somme river where the beast of war crouched ready to spring, and in the east the sun hurled great burning lances of fire through the sky, so that when Michael looked away, his vision was starred with the memory of its brilliance.

'Never look at the sun,' he reminded himself testily. Because of his distraction, he was making the mistakes of novices.

They crossed the ridges, looking down on the patterns of opposing trenches, like worm castings on a putting green.

'Don't fix!' Michael warned himself again. 'Never stare at any object.' He resumed the veteran fight pilot's scan, the quick flitting search that covered the sky above him, sweeping back and forth, and down and over.

Despite all his efforts to prevent it, the thought of Centaine and her absence from the knoll crept insidiously back into his mind again, so that suddenly he realized that he had been staring at one whale-shaped cloud for five or six seconds. He was fixing again.

'God, man, pull yourself together!' he snarled aloud.

Andrew, in the leading flight, was signalling, and Michael swivelled to pick out his sighting.

It was a flight of three aircraft, four miles south-west of their position, and 2,000 feet below them.

'Friendlies.' He recognized them as De Havilland two-seaters. Why hadn't he seen them first? He had the best eyes in the squadron.

'Concentrate.' He scanned the line of woods south of Douai, the German-held town just east of Lens, and he picked out the freshly dug gun emplacements at the edge of the trees.

'About six new batteries,' he estimated, and made a note for his flight log without interrupting the pattern of his scan again.

They reached the western limit of their designated patrol area, and each flight turned in succession. They stared back down the line, but with the sun directly into their eyes now, and that line of dirty grey-blue cloud on their left hand.

'Cold front building,' Michael thought, and then suddenly he was thinking of Centaine again, as though she had slipped in through the back door of his mind.

'Why wasn't she there?' She could be sick. Out at night in the rain and cold – pneumonia is a killer.' The idea shocked him. He imagined her wasting away, drowning in her own fluids.

A red Very pistol flare arched across the nose of his machine, and he started guiltily. Andrew had fired the 'Enemy in Sight' signal while he was dreaming.

Michael searched frantically. 'Ah!' with relief. 'There it is!' Below and to the left.

It was a German two-seater, a solitary artillery spotter, just east of the ridges, bustling down in the direction of Arras, a slow and outdated type, easy prey for the swift and deadly SE5as. Andrew was signalling again, looking back at Michael, the green scarf aflutter, and that devil-may-care grin on his lips.

'I am attacking! Give me top cover.'

Both Michael and Hank acknowledged the hand signals and stayed on high as Andrew banked away into a shallow diving interception, with the other five aircraft of his flight streaming down behind in attacking line astern.

'What a grand sight!' Michael watched them go. Thrilling to the chase, that wild charge down the sky, cavalry of the heavens in full flight, swiftly overhauling their slow and cumbersome prey.

Michael led the rest of the squadron into a series of slow shallow S-turns, holding them in position to cover the attack, and he was leaning from the cockpit waiting for the kill when abruptly he felt a slide of unease, that cold weight of premonition in his guts again, the instinct of impending disaster, and he swept the sky above and around him.

It was clear and peacefully empty, then his gaze switched towards the blinding glare of the sun and he held up his hand to cover it, and with one eye only looked past his fingers – and there they were.

They were boiling out of the cloud line like a swarm of gaudy glittering poisonous insects. It was the classic ambush. The decoy sent in low and slow to draw the enemy, and then the swift and deadly onslaught from out of the sun and the clouds.

'Oh, sweet Mother of God,' Michael breathed, as he snatched the Very pistol out of its holster beside his seat.

How many? It was impossible to count that vicious host. Sixty, perhaps more – three full Jagdstaffels of Albatros DIIIs in their rainbow colours dropping falcon-swift upon Andrew's puny flight of SE5as.

Michael fired the red Very flare to warn his pilots and then winged over into a dive, aiming to intercept the enemy squadron before it could reach Andrew. Swiftly he estimated the triangle of speeds and distances and realized that they were too late, four or five seconds too late to save Andrew's flight.

Those four or five seconds which he had squandered in dreaming and fruitlessly watching the attack on the German decoy plane, those crucial seconds in which he had neglected his duty, weighed on him like leaden bars as he pushed the throttle of the SE5a to its stop. The engine whined, that peculiar wailing protest of overdriven machinery as the tip of the spinning propeller accelerated through the speed of sound, and he could feel the wings flexing and bending under the strain as the speed and pressure built up in that suicidal dive.

'Andrew!' he shouted. 'Look behind you, man!' and his voice was lost in the howl of wind and the scream of the overdriven engine.

All Andrew's attention was fixed on his quarry, for the German decoy pilot had seen them and was also diving away towards the earth, drawing the SE5as after him and transforming the hunters into unwitting prey.

The massed German Jagdstaffel held their diving attack, though they must have been fully aware of Michael's desperate attempt to head them off. They

would know as well as Michael did that his attempt was futile, that he had left it too late. The Albatroses would be able to make an attacking run over Andrew's flight, and with complete surprise aiding them must destroy most of the SE5as in that single stroke before turning back to face Michael's avenging counter-stroke.

Michael felt the adrenalin surge burning in his blood like the clean bright flame of a spirit lamp. Time seemed to slow down into those eternal micro-seconds of combat, so that he floated sedately downwards, and the horde of enemy aircraft appeared to hang suspended on their multicoloured wings, as through they were set like gems in the heavens.

The colours and patterns of the Albatroses were fantastic, with scarlet and black the dominant colours, but some were chequered like harlequins, and others had the silhouettes of bat wings or birds outlined on their wings and fuselage.

At last he could see the faces of the German airmen, turning towards him and then back towards their primary quarry.

'Andrew! Andrew!' Michael lamented in agony as each second made it clearer just how late he would be to prevent the ambush succeeding.

His fingers numb with cold and dread, Michael reloaded the Very pistol and fired another flare forward over his own nose, trying to attract Andrew's attention, but the red ball of flame fell away towards the earth, fizzling and spinning a pathetic thread of smoke, while half a mile further on Andrew lined up on the hapless German spotter plane, and Michael heard the tut-tut-tuttering of his Vickers as he attacked from astern.

In that same instant the wave of Albatroses broke over Andrew's flight, from above.

Michael saw two of the SE5as mortally struck in the first seconds, and spin away with smoke and pieces of fuselage flying from them; the rest of them scattered widely, each with two or three Albatroses racing after them, almost jostling each other for a chance to take the killing line.

Only Andrew survived. His response to the first crackle of the Spandau machine-guns was instantaneous. He kicked the big green machine into that flat skidding turn that he and Michael had practised so often. He went tearing back straight into the heart of the pack, forcing the Albatroses to swerve wildly away from his head-on-charge, firing furiously into their faces, emerging from behind them seemingly unscathed.

'Good on you!' Michael rejoiced aloud, and then he saw the rest of Andrew's flight shot out of the sky, burning and twisting downwards, and his guilt turned to anger.

The German machines, having wrought quick destruction, were wheeling now to face the charge of Michael's and Hank's flights. They came together and the entire pattern of aircraft disintegated into a milling cloud, turning like dust and debris in a whirlwind.

Michael came out on the quarter of a solid black Albatros with scarlet wings on which the black Maltese crosses stood out like gravestones. As he crossed, he laid off his aim for the deflection of their combined tracks and speeds, and fired for the radiator in the junction of the scarlet wings above the German pilot's head, attempting to cook him alive in boiling coolant liquid.

He saw his bullets hitting exactly where he had aimed, and at the same time noticed the small modification in the Albatros's wing structure. The Germans had altered the Albatros. They had been forcibly shown the lethal design fault,

and they had relocated the radiator. The German ducked from Michael's field of fire, and Michael pulled up the nose of his machine.

An Albatros had picked on one of Michael's new chums, sticking on his tail like a vampire, within an ace of the killing line. Michael came out under the Albatros's belly and reached up to swivel the Lewis gun on its Foster mounting, aiming upwards, so close that the muzzle of the Lewis gun almost touched the bright pink belly of the Albatros.

He fired the full drum of ammunition into the German's guts, waggling his wings slightly to spray his fire from side to side, and the Albatros reared up on its tail like a harpooned shark, and then fell over its wing and dropped away in its death plunge.

The new chum waved his thanks to Michael – they were almost touching wingtips, and Michael signalled imperiously, 'Return to base!' and then gave him the clenched fist. 'Imperative!'

'Get out of here, you bloody fool!' he shouted uselessly, but his contorted face emphasized the hand signal, and the novice broke off and fled.

Another Albatros came at Michael and he turned out hard, climbing and twisting, firing at fleeting targets, turning – turning for very life. They were outnumbered six or seven to one, and the enemy were all veterans, it showed in the way they flew, quick and agile, and unafraid. To stay and fight was folly. Michael managed to reload the Very pistol, and he fired the green flare of the recall. In these circumstances it was the order to the squadron to break off and run for home with all possible speed.

He came round hard, fired at a pink and blue Albatros, and saw his bullets cut through the cowling of the engine a few inches too low to hit the German's fuel tank.

'Damn! Damn it to hell!' he swore, and he and the Albatros turned out in opposite directions and Mihcael had a clear run for home. He saw his remaining pilots already tearing away, and he put the yellow machine's nose down and went after them, heading for the ridges and Mort Homme.

He swivelled his head just once more, to make sure that his tail was clear – and at that moment he saw Andrew.

Andrew was a thousand metres out on Michael's starboard side. He had been separated from the main dogfight, engaged with three of the attacking Albatroses, fighting them single-handed, but he had given them the slip and now he too was running for home like the rest of the British squadron.

Then Michael looked above Andrew and he realized that not all the German Albatroses had come down in that first attacking wave. Six of them had remained up there under the clouds, led by the only Albatros that was painted pure scarlet from tail to nose, and from wingtip to wingtip. They had waited for the dogfight to develop and for stragglers to emerge. They were the second set of jaws to the trap – and Michael knew who piloted the all-red Albatros. The man was a living legend on both sides of the lines, for he had already killed over thirty Allied aircraft. It was the man they called the Red Baron of Germany.

The Allies were countering the legend, trying to smear the invincible image that Baron Manfred Von Richthofen was building, by calling him a coward and a hyena who had built up his scores of kills by avoiding combat on equal terms and by singling out novices and stragglers and damaged aircraft before attacking.

Perhaps there was truth to that claim, for there he was, hovering above the

battlefield like a scarlet vulture, and there was Andrew, isolated and vulnerable below him, his nearest ally, Michael, 1,000 metres away – and Andrew seemed unware of this new menace. The scarlet machine dropped from above, the shark-like nose aimed directly at Andrew. The five other hand-picked veteran German fighter pilots followed him down.

Without thought, Michael began the turn that would carry him to Andrew's assistance, and then his hands and feet, acting without conscious volition, countered the turn and kept the yellow SE5a roaring on its shallow dive for the safety of the British lines.

Michael stared over his shoulder and superimposed on the pattern of swirling aircraft was Centaine's beloved face, the great dark eyes dark with tears, and her words whispered in his head louder than guns and screaming engines, 'Swear to me you will be there, Michel!'

With Centaine's words still ringing in his ears, Michael saw the German attack sweep over Andrew's solitary aircraft, and once again miraculously Andrew survived that first deadly wave and whirled to face and fight them.

Michael tried to force himself to turn the yellow SE5a, but his hands would not obey, and his feet were paralysed upon the rudder bars. He watched while the German pilots worked the solitary green aircraft the way a pack of sheepdogs might round up a stray ewe, driving Andrew relentlessly into each other's crossfire.

He saw Andrew fighting them off with a magnificent display of courage and flying skill, turning into each new attack, and facing it head-on, forcing each antagonist to break away, but always there were others crossing his flanks and quarters, raking him with Spandau fire.

Then Michael saw that Andrew's guns were silenced. The drum of his Lewis gun was empty, and he knew that it was a lengthy process to reload it. Clearly the Vickers machine-gun on the cowling had overheated and jammed. Andrew was standing in the cockpit, hammering at the breech of the weapon with both fists, trying to clear it, and Von Richthofen's red Albatros dropped into the killing line behind Andrew.

'Oh God, no!' Michael heard himself whimpering, still running for safety, stricken as much by his own cowardice as by Andrew's peril.

Then another miracle happened, for without opening fire the red Albatros turned away slightly, and for an instant flew level with the green SE5a.

Von Richthofen must have seen that Andrew was unarmed, and he had declined to kill a helpless man. As he passed only feet from the cockpit in which Andrew was struggling with the blocked Vickers, he lifted one hand in a laconic salute – homage to a courageous enemy – and then turned away in pursuit of the rest of the fleeing British SE5as.

'Thank you, God,' Michael croaked.

Von Richthofen's flight followed him into the turn. No, not all of them followed him. There was a single Albatros that had not broken off the engagement with Andrew. It was a sky-blue machine with its top wing chequered black and white, like a chessboard. It fell into the killing line behind Andrew that Von Richthofen had vacated, and Michael heard the stuttering rush of its Spandau.

Flame burst into full bloom around the silhouette of Andrew's head and shoulders as his fuel tank exploded. Fire, the airman's ultimate dread, enveloped him and Michael saw Andrew lift himself out of the flames like a blackened

and scorched insect and throw himself over the side of the cockpit, choosing the swift death of the fall to that of the flames.

The green scarf around Andrew's throat was on fire, so that he wore a garland of flame until his body accelerated and the flames were snuffed out by the wind. His body turned with his arms and legs spread out in the form of a crucifix, and dwindled swiftly away. Michael lost sight of him before he struck the earth 10,000 feet below.

* * *

'In the name of all that is holy, couldn't anyone have let us know that Von Richthofen had moved back into the sector?' Michael shouted at the squadron adjutant. 'Isn't there any bloody inelligence in this army? Those desk wallahs at Division are responsible for the murder of Andrew and the six other men we lost today!'

'That is really unfair, old man,' the adjutant murmured, as he puffed on his pipe. 'You know how this fellow Von Richthofen works. Will-o'-the-wisp, and all that stuff.'

Von Richthofen had devised the strategy of loading his aircraft on to open good trucks and shuttling the entire Jagdstaffel up and down the line. Appearing abruptly, with his sixty crack pilots, wherever he was least expected, wreacking dreadful execution amongst the unprepared Allied airmen for a few days or a week, and then moving on again.

'I telephoned Division as soon as the first of our planes landed, and they had only just received the intelligence themselves. They think Von Richthofen and his circus have taken up temporary residence at the old airstrip just south of Douai – '

'A lot of good that does us now, with Andrew dead.' As he said it, the enormity of it at last hit Mihcael, and his hands began to shake. He felt a nerve jumping in his cheek. He had to turn away to the small window of the cottage that the adjutant used as the squadron office. Behind him the adjutant remained silent, giving Michael time to collect himself.

'The old airstrip at Douai – ' Michael thrust his hands into his pockets to keep them still, and he drove his mind from the memory of Andrew to consider instead the technical aspects ' – those new gun emplacements, they must have moved up to guard Von Richthofen's Jagdstaffel.'

'Michael, you are commanding the squadron – at least temporarily, until Division confirms or appoints another commander.'

Michael turned back, hands still in his pockets, and nodded, not yet trusting his voice.

'You will have to draw up a new duty roster,' the adjutant prompted him gently, and Michael shook his head slightly as though to clear it.

'We can't send out less than full squadron strength,' he said, 'not with the circus out there. Which means that we can't maintain full-time daylight cover over the designated squadron sector.'

The adjutant nodded in agreement. It was obvious that to send out single flights was suicidal.

'What is our operational strength?' Michael demanded.

'At the moment, eight – four machines were badly shot up. If it goes on like this, it's going to be a bloody April, I am afraid.'

'All right,' Michael nodded. 'We will scrub the old roster. We can only fly two more sorties today. All eight aircraft. Noon and dusk. Keep the new chums out of it as much as possible.'

The adjutant was making notes, and as Michael concentrated on his new duties, his hands stopped shaking and that corpse-grey pallor of his face improved. 'Telephone Division and warn them that we will not be able to cover the sector adequately. Ask them when we can expect to be reinforced. Tell them that an estimated six new batteries have been moved up to – ' Michael read the map references off his note-pad ' – and tell them also that I noticed a design modification on the Albatroses of the circus.' He explained the relocation of the engine radiator. 'Tell them I estimate the boche have sixty of these new Albatroses in Von Richthofen's Jagdstaffel. When you have done all that call me, and we will work out a new roster, but warn the lads there will be a squadron sweep at noon. Now I need a shave and a bath.'

Mercifully, there was no time during the rest of that day for Michael to dwell on Andrew's death. He flew both sorties with the depleted squadron and although the knowledge that the German circus was in the sector worked on all their nerves, the patrols were completely uneventful. They saw not a single enemy machine.

When they landed for the last time in the dusk, Michael took a bottle of rum down to where Mac and his team of mechanics were working by lantern light on the damaged SE5as and spent an hour with them, giving them encouragement, for they were all anxious and depressed by the day's losses – particularly the death of Andrew, whom they had all adored and hero-worshipped.

'He was a good 'un.' Mac, with black grease to the elbows, looked up from the engine he was working on, and accepted the tin mug of rum that Michael handed him. 'He was a real good 'un, the major was.' He said it for all of them. 'Don't often find one like him, you don't.'

Michael trudged back through the orchard; looking up at the sky through the trees, he could see the stars. It would be flying weather again tomorrow – and he was deadly afraid.

'I've lost it,' he whispered. 'My nerve has gone. I am a coward, and my cowardice killed Andrew.' That knowledge had been at the back of his mind all that day, but he had suppressed it. Now, when he faced it squarely, it was like a hunter following a wounded leopard into cover. He knew it was there, but the actual sight of it as they came face to face turned a man's belly to water.

'A coward,' he said aloud, lashing himself with the word, and he remembered Andrew's smile and the tam o'shanter set jauntily on his head.

'What cheer, my boy?' He could almost hear Andrew's voice, and then he saw him falling down the sky with the burning green scarf around his throat, and Michael's hands began to shake again.

'A coward,' he repeated, and the pain was too much to bear alone and he hurried to the mess, blinded by his guilt so that he missed his footing and stumbled more than once.

The adjutant and the other pilots, some of them still in flying rig, were waiting for Michael. It was the senior officers' duty to begin the wake, that was squadron ritual. On a table in the centre of the mess were seven bottles of Black Label Johnny Walker whisky, one for each of the missing airmen.

When Michael entered the room, everybody stood – not for him, but as a last respect to the missing men.

'All right, gentlemen,' Michael said. 'Let us send them on their way.'

The most junior officer, already briefed by the others in his duties, opened a bottle of whisky. The black labels gave the correct funereal touch. He came to Michael and filled his glass, then moved on to the others, in order of seniority. They held the brimming glasses and waited while the adjutant, his briar still clamped in his teeth, seated himself at the ancient piano in the corner of the mess and began to bang out the opening chord of Chopin's Funeral March. The officers of No. 21 Squadron stood to attention and tapped their glasses on table-tops and the bar counter, keeping time with the piano, and one or two of them hummed quietly.

On the bar counter were laid out the personal possessions of the missing pilots. After dinner these would be auctioned off, and the squadron pilots would pay extravagant prices so that a few guineas could be sent to a new widow or a bereaved mother. There were Andrew's golf clubs, which Michael had never seen him use, and the Hardy trout rod, and his grief came back fresh and strong so that he thumped his glass on the counter with such force that whisky slopped over the rim, and the fumes prickled his eyes. Michael wiped them on his sleeve.

The adjutant crashed through the last bar and then stood up and took his glass. Nobody said a word, but they all lifted their own glasses, thought their own thoughts for a second, and then drained them. Immediately the junior officer refilled each tumbler. All seven bottles must be finished, that was part of the tradition. Michael ate no supper, but stood by the bar and helped consume the seven bottles. He was still sober, the liquor seemed to have no effect on him.

'I must be an alcoholic at last,' he thought. 'Andrew always said I had great potential.' And the liquor did not even deaden the pain that Andrew's name inflicted.

He bid five guineas each for Andrew's golf clubs and the Hardy split-cane rod. By that time the seven bottles were all empty. He ordered another bottle for himself and went alone to his tent. He sat on the cot with the rod on his lap. Andrew had boasted that he had landed a fifty-pound salmon with that stick, and Michael had called him a liar.

'Oh ye of little faith,' Andrew had chided him sorrowfully.

'I believed you all along.' Michael caressed the old rod and drank straight from the bottle.'

A little later, Biggs looked in. 'Congratulations on your victory, sir.' Three other pilots had confirmed Michael's shooting down of the pink Albatros.

'Biggs – will you do me a favour?'

'Of course, sir.'

'Bugger off – there's a good fellow.'

* * *

There was three-quarters of the bottle of whisky left when Michael, still in his flying clothes, stumbled out to where Andrew's motor-cycle was parked. The ride in the cold night air cleared his head, but left him feeling brittle and fragile

as old glass. He parked the motor-cycle behind the barn, and went to wait among the bales of straw.

The hours, marked by the church clock, passed slowly, and with each of them his need for Centaine grew until it was almost too intense to bear. Every half hour he would go to the door of the barn and peer up the dark lane, before returning to the bottle and the nest of blankets.

He sipped the whisky, and in his head those few seconds of battle in which Andrew had died played over and over, like a gramophone record that had been scratched. He tried to shut out the images, but he could not. He was forced to relive, time and again, Andrew's last agony.

'Where are you, Centaine? I need you so much now.' He longed for her, but she did not come, and again he saw the sky-blue Albatros with the black and white chequered wings bank steeply on to the killing line behind Andrew's green aircraft, and yet again he glimpsed Andrew's pale face as he looked back over his shoulder and saw the Spandaus open fire. Michael covered his eyes and pressed his fingers into the sockets until the pain drove out the images.

'Centaine,' he whispered. 'Please come to me.'

The chuch clock struck three o'clock and the whisky bottle was empty.

'She isn't coming.' He faced it at last, and as he staggered to the door of the barn and looked up at the night sky, he knew what he had to do to expiate his guilt and grief and shame.

* * *

The depleted squadron took off for the dawn patrol in the grey half-light. Hank Johnson was now second-in-command, and he flew on the other wing.

Michael turned out slightly, as soon as they were above the trees, and headed for the knoll beyond the château. Somehow he knew that she would not be there this morning, yet he pushed up his goggles and searched for her.

The hill top was deserted, and he did not even look back.

'It's my wedding day,' he thought, searching the sky above the ridges, 'and my best man is dead, and my bride – ' He did not finish the thought.

The cloud had built up again during the night. There was a solid ceiling at 12,000 feet, dark and forbidding, stretching unbroken to every reach of the horizon. Below that it was clear to 5,000 feet where straggly grey cloud formed a layer that varied in thickness between 500 and 1,000 feet.

Michael led the squadron up through one of the holes in this intermittent layer, and then levelled out just below the top bank of cloud. The sky below them was empty of aircraft. To a novice it would seem impossible that two large formations of fighter planes could patrol the same area, each searching for the other, and still fail to make contact. However, the sky was so deep and wide that the chances were much against a meeting, unless the one knew precisely where the other would be at a given time.

While his eyes raked back and forth, Michael reached with his free hand into the pocket of his greatcoat and assured himself that the package he had prepared just before take-off was still there.

'God, I could use a drink,' he thought. His mouth was parched and there was a dull ache deep in his skull. His eyes burned, but his vision was still clear. He licked his dry lips.

'Andrew always used to say that only a confirmed drunkard can drink on top of a hangover. I just wish I'd had the courage and commonsense to bring a bottle.'

Through the holes in the cloud beneath him he kept a running check on the squadron's position. He knew every inch of the squadron's designated area the way a farmer knows his lands.

They reached the outward limit and Michael made the turn, with the squadron coming round behind him, and he checked his watch. Eleven minutes later he picked out the bend in the river, and a peculiarly shaped copse of beech trees that gave him an exact positional fix.

He eased the throttle a fraction and his yellow machine drifted back a few yards until he was flying on Hank Johnson's wingtip. He glanced across at the Texan and nodded. He had discussed his intentions with Hank before take-off and Hank had tried to dissuade him. Across the gap Hank screwed up his mouth as though he had sucked a green persimmon, to show his disapproval, then raised a war-weary eyebrow and waved Michael away.

Michael backed the throttle a little further and dropped below the squadron. Hank kept leading them eastwards, but Michael made an easy turn into the north and began to descend.

Within a few minutes the squadron had disappeared into the limitless sky, and Michael was alone. He went down until he reached the lower layer of broken cloud and then used it as cover. Dodging in and out of the cold damp banks and the intervening open patches, he crossed the front lines a few miles south of Douai, and then picked out the new German gun emplacements at the edge of the woods.

The old airstrip was marked on his field map. He was able to pick it out from a distance of four miles or more, for the wheels of the German Albatroses on landing and take-off had traced muddy ruts in the turf. Two miles out, he could see the German machines parked along the edge of the forest, and in the trees beyond he made out the rows of tents and portable sheds which housed the German crews.

Suddenly there was a woof and crack of bursting explosive, and an anti-aircraft shell burst above and slighly ahead of him. It looked like a ripe cotton pod, popping open and spilling fluffy white smoke, deceptively pretty in the muted light below the clouds.

'Good morning, Archie,' Michael greeted it grimly.

It was a ranging burst from one of the guns, and was followed immediately by the thud and crack of a full salvo. The air all around him was studded with shrapnel bursts.

Michael pushed his nose down and let the speed build up, and the needle of the rev counter in front of him began to wind upwards into the red sector. He fumbled in his pocket, pulled out the cloth package and placed it on his lap.

The earth and forest came up swiftly towards him, and he dragged a long smear of bursting shrapnel behind him. Two hundred feet above the tree-tops he levelled out, and the airfield was directly ahead of him. He could see the multicoloured biplanes standing in a long row, their shark-like snouts pointed up towards him. He looked for the sky-blue machine with the chequered wings, but could not pick it out.

There was agitated movement all along the edge of the field. German ground crews, anticipating a torrent of Vickers machine-gun fire, were running into the forest, while off-duty pilots, trying to struggle into their flying jackets, were

racing towards the parked aircraft. They must know it was useless to take off and try to intercept the British machine, but they were making the attempt nonetheless.

Michael reached for the firing-handle. The aircraft were parked in a neat line, the pilots crowding towards them – and he smiled without humour and depressed his nose, picking them up in the ring sight of the Vickers.

At 100 feet he levelled again, dropped his right hand from the firing handle and picked up the cloth package from his lap. As he passed over the centre of the German line, he leaned from the cockpit and tossed the package overboard. The ribbon he had attached to it unrolled in the slipstream of the SE5a and fluttered down to the edge of the field.

As Michael opened the throttle and climbed away again towards the cloud layer, he glanced up into the mirror above his head and saw one of the German pilots stoop over the package – and then the SE5a bounced and rocked as the German anti-aircraft guns opened up on him again, and a shell burst just below him. Within seconds he was into the haven of the cloud bank with his guns cold and unfired, and a few shrapnel tears in the belly and the underwings.

He turned on to a heading for Mort Homme. While he flew he thought about the package he had just dropped.

During the night he had torn a long ribbon from one of his old shirts to use as a marker and weighted the end of it with a handful of .303 cartridges. Then he had stitched his handwritten message into the other end of the ribbon.

He had at first considered attempting the message in German, and then admitted to himself that his German was hopelessly inadequate. Almost certainly there would be an officer on Von Richthofen's Jagdstaffel who could read English well enough to translate what he had written:

To the German pilot of the blue albatros with black and white chequered wings.

Sir,

The unarmed and helpless British airman whom you murdered yesterday was my friend.

Between 1600 hrs and 1630 hrs today I will be patrolling over the villages of Cantin and Aubigny-au-Bac, at a height of 8,000 feet.

I will be flying an SE5a scoutplane painted yellow.

I hope to meet you.

The rest of the squadron had already landed when Michael returned to the base.

'Mac, I seemed to have picked up some shrapnel.'

'I noticed, sir. Don't worry, fix it in a jiffy.'

'I haven't fired the guns, but check the sights again, will you.'

'Fifty yards?' Mac asked for the range at which he wanted fire from both Lewis and Vickers gun to converge.

'Make it thirty, Mac.'

'Working close, sir,' Mac whistled through his teeth.

'I hope so, Mac, and by the way, she is a touch tail-heavy. Trim her hands-off.'

'See to it myself, sir,' Mac promised.

'Thank you, Mac.'

'Give the bastards one for Mr Andrew, sir.'

The adjutant was waiting for him. 'We have all aircraft operational again, Michael. Twelve on the duty roster.'

'All right. Hank will take the noon patrol, and I will fly at 15.39 hrs alone.'

'Alone?' The adjutant took his pipe out of his mouth in surprise.

'Alone,' Michael confirmed. 'Then a full squadron sweep at dusk, as usual.'

The adjutant made a note. 'By the way, message from General Courtney. He will do his best to attend the ceremony this evening. He thinks he will almost certainly be there.'

Michael smiled for the first time that day. He had wanted very badly for Sean Courtney to be at his wedding.

'Hope you can make it also, Bob.'

'You can bet on it. Whole squadron will be there. Looking forward to it no end.'

Michael wanted a drink badly. He started towards the mess.

'God, it's eight o'clock in the morning,' he thought, and stopped. He felt brittle and dried-out, whisky would put warmth and juice into his body again, and he felt his hands begin to tremble with his deep need for it. It took all his resolve to turn away from the mess and go to his tent. He remembered then that he hadn't slept the previous night.

Biggs was sitting on a packing case outside the tent, polishing Michael's boots, but he jumped to attention, his face expressionless.

'Enough of that!' Michael smiled at him. 'Sorry about last night, Biggs. Bloody rude of me. I didn't mean it.'

'I know, sir.' Biggs relaxed. 'I felt the same way about the major.'

'Biggs, wake me at three. I've got some sleep to catch up on.'

It was not Biggs who woke him but the shouts of the ground crews, the sound of running men, the deep belling tone of the anti-aircraft guns along the edge of the orchard, and the roaring overhead of a Mercedes aircraft engine.

Michael staggered out of his tent with tousled hair and bloodshot eyes, still half-asleep.

'What the hell is happening, Biggs?'

'A Hun, sir – cheeky blighter beating up the base.'

'He's pushed off again.' Other pilots and groundcrew were shouting amongst the trees as they ran to the edge of the field.

'Didn't even fire a shot.'

'Did you see him?'

'An Albatros – blue with black and white wings. The devil almost took the roof off the mess.'

'He dropped something – Bob's picked it up.'

Michael ducked back into the tent and pulled on his jacket and a pair of tennis shoes. He heard two or three of the aircraft starting up as he ran out of the tent again. Some of his own pilots were setting off in pursuit of the German interloper.

'Stop those men from taking off!' Michael yelled, and before he reached the adjutant's office he heard the engines switched off again in response to his order.

There was a small crowd of curious pilots at the door, and Michael pushed through them just as the adjutant untied the drawstring that closed the mouth of the canvas bag that the German machine had dropped. The chorus of question and comment and speculation was silenced immediately as they all realized what the bag contained. The adjutant gently ran the strip of green silk through his fingers. There were black-rimmed holes burned through it and it was stained with dried black blood.

'Andrew's scarf,' he said unnecessarily, 'and his silver flask.' The silver was

badly dented, but the cairngorm stopper gleamed yellow and gold as he turned it in his hands, and the contents gurgled softly. He set it aside and one by one drew the other items from the bag: Andrew's medal ribbons, the amber cigarette-holder, a spring-loaded sovereign case that still contained three coins, his pigskin wallet. The photograph of Andrew's parents standing in the grounds of the castle fell from the wallet as he turned it over.

'What's this?' The adjutant picked out a buff-coloured envelope of thick glossy paper sealed with a wax wafer. 'It's addressed – ' he read the face of the envelope ' – to the pilot of the yellow SA5a.' The adjutant looked up at Michael, startled.

'That's you, Michael – how the hell?'

Michael took the envelope from him and split the seal with his thumbnail.

There was a single sheet of the same first-quality paper. The letter was handwritten, and though the writing was obviously continental, for the capitals were formed in Gothic script, the text was in perfect English:

Sir,

Your friend, Lord Andrew Killigerran, was buried this morning in the cemetery of the Protestant church at Douai. This Jagdstaffel accorded him full military honours.

I have the honour to inform you, and at the same time also to warn you, that no death in war is murder. The object of warfare is the destruction of the enemy by all means possible.

I look forward to meeting you.

OTTO VON GREIM.

Jasta II Near Douai.

They were all looking expectantly at Michael as he folded the letter and thrust it into his pocket.

'They recovered Andrew's body,' he said quietly, 'and he was buried with full military honours at Douai this morning.'

'Bloody decent of them,' one of the pilots murmured.

'Yes, for Huns, that is,' said Michael, and turned towards the door.

'Michael,' the adjutant stopped him. 'I think Andrew would have wanted you to have this.'

He handed the silver hip flask to Michael. Michael turned it slowly in his hands. The dent in the metal had probably been caused by the impact, he thought, and he shivered.

'Yes,' he nodded. 'I'll look after it for him.' He turned back to the door and pushed his way through the group of silent officers.

* * *

Biggs helped him dress with even more than his usual attention to detail.

'I gave them a good rub of dubbin, sir,' he pointed out as he helped Michael into the soft kudu-skin boots.

Michael appeared not to have heard the remark. Although he had lain down again after the disturbance of the German aircraft's fly-over, he had not managed to sleep. Yet he felt calm, even placid. 'What's that, Biggs?' he asked vaguely.

'I said, I'll have your number ones laid out for you when you come back – and I've arranged with the cook for a good five gallons of hot water for your bath.'

'Thank you, Biggs.'

'Not every day it happens, Mr Michael.'

'That's true, Biggs, once in a lifetime is enough.'

'I'm sure you and the young lady are going to be very happy. Me and my missus been married twenty-two years come June, sir.'

'A long time, Biggs.'

'I hope you break my record, Mr Michael.'

'I'll try.'

'One other thing, sir.' Biggs was embarrassed, he did not look up from the lacings of the boots. 'We shouldn't ought to be flying alone, sir. Not safe at all, sir, we should take Mr Johnson with us at least, beg your pardon, sir – I know it's not my place to say so.'

Michael laid his hand on Bigg's shoulder for a moment. He had never done that before.

'Have that bath ready for me when I get home,' he said as he stood up.

Biggs watched him stoop out through the flap of the tent, without saying goodbye or wishing him luck, though it took an effort to restrain himself from doing so, then he picked up Michael's discarded jacket and folded it with exaggerated care.

* * *

When the Wolseley engine fired and caught, Michael advanced the ignition until she settled to a fine deep rumble. Then he listened to it critically for thirty seconds before he looked up at Mac who was standing on the wing beside the cockpit, his hair and overalls fluttering in the wash of the propeller.

'Lovely, Mac!' he shouted above the engine beat, and Mac grinned.

'Give them hell, sir,' and jumped down to pull the chocks from in front of the landing-wheels.

Instinctively Michael drew a deep breath, as though he were about to dive into one of those cool green pools of the Tugela river, and then eased the throttle open and the big machine rolled forward.

The knoll behind the château was deserted once again, but he had not expected anything else. He lifted the nose into the climb attitude and then changed his mind, let it drop again and brought her round in a tight turn, his wingtip almost brushing the tops of the oaks.

He came out of the turn with the château directly ahead, and he flew past it at the height of the pink-tiled roof. He saw no sign of life and as soon as he was past, he banked the SE5a into a figure-of-eight turn and came around again, still at roof level.

This time he saw movement. One of the windows at ground level, near the kitchens, was thrown open. Someone was waving a yellow cloth from it, but he could not make out who it was.

He came around again and this time dropped down until his landing-wheels almost touched the stone wall that enclosed Anna's vegetable garden. He saw Centaine in the window. He could not mistake that dark bush of hair and the huge eyes. She was leaning far out over the sill, shouting something and waving the yellow scarf that she had worn the day they flew together to meet Sean Courtney.

As Michael lifted the nose and opened the throttle to climb away, he felt rejuvenated. The placid and passive mood that had held him evaporated and he felt charged and vital again. He had seen her, and now it would be all right.

'It was Michel,' Centaine cried happily as she turned back from the window to where Anna sat on the bed. 'I saw him, Anna, it was surely him. Oh, he is so handsome – he came to find me, despite Papa!'

Anna's face crumpled and reddened with disapproval. 'It is bad luck for a groom to see his bride on the wedding day.'

'Oh nonsense, Anna, sometimes you talk such rubbish. Oh, Anna, he is so beautiful!'

'And you will not be if we do not finish before this evening.'

Centaine fluffed out her skirts and settled on to the bed beside Anna. She took the antique ivory-coloured lace of the wedding dress into her lap, and then held the needle up to the light and squinted as she threaded it.

'I have decided,' she told Anna as she recommenced work on the hem of the dress, 'I will have only sons, at least six sons, but no daughters. Being a girl is such a bore, I don't wish to inflict it on any of my children.'

She completed a dozen stitches and then stopped. 'I'm so happy, Anna, and so excited. Do you think the general will come? When do you think this silly war will end, so that Michel and I can go to Africa?'

Listening to her chatter Anna turned her head slightly to hide her doting smile.

* * *

The yellow SE5a bored up powerfully into the soft grey belly of the sky. Michael chose one of the gaps in the lower layer of cloud, roared swiftly through it and burst out into the open corridor. High above there was still the same high roof of solid cloud, but below it the air was limpid as crystal. When his altimeter registered 8,000 feet, Michael levelled out. He was in the clear, equidistant from the layers of cloud above and below him, but through the gaps he could pick up his landmarks.

The villages of Cantin and Aubigny-au-Bac were deserted, shell-shattered skeletons. Only a few stone chimney-pieces had survived the waves of war which had washed back and forth over them. These stuck up like funeral monuments from the muddy torn earth.

The two villages were four miles apart, the road that once joined them had been obliterated, and the front lines twisted like a pair of maimed adders through the brown fields between them. The shell holes, filled with stagnant water, blinked up at him like the eyes of the blind.

Michael glanced at his watch. It was four minutes to four o'clock, and his eyes immediately returned to their endless search of the empty sky. One at a time he lifted his hands from the controls and flexed his fingers, at the same time wriggling his toes in the kudu-skin boots – loosening up like a runner before the pistol. He reached up to the firing-handle with both hands, to test the trim of the machine, and she flew on straight and level. He fired both his guns, a short burst from each of them, and he nodded and blew on the gloved fingers of his right hand.

'I need a drink,' he told himself, and took Andrew's silver flask from his

pocket. He took a mouthful and gargled it softly, and then swallowed. The fire of it bloomed in his bloodstream, but he resisted the temptation to drink again. He stoppered the flask and dropped it back into his pocket. He touched the left rudder to begin his turn into the square-patrol pattern and at that moment he picked up the flea-black speck on the grey mattress of the clouds far ahead and he met the turn, holding her steady while he blinked his eyes rapidly and checked his sighting.

The other machine was at 8,000 feet, exactly his own height, and it was closing swiftly, coming in from the north, from the direction of Douai, and he felt the spurt of adrenalin mingle with the alcohol in his blood. His cheeks burned and his guts spasmed. He eased the throttle open and flew on to meet it.

The combined speeds of the two aircraft hurled them together, so that the other machine swelled miraculously in front of Michael's eyes. He saw the bright blue of the nose and propeller-boss hazed by the spinning blades, and the wide black hawk's wings outstretched. He saw the helmeted top of the pilot's head between the two black Spandau machine-guns mounted on the engine cowling, and the flash of his goggles as he leaned forward to peer into his sights.

Michael pushed the thottle fully open and the engine bellowed. His left hand held the joystick like an artist holding his brush with the lightest pressure of his fingertips, as he positioned the German exactly in the centre of the concentric rings of his own gun-sight, and his right hand reached up for the firing-handle.

His hatred and his anger grew as swiftly as the image of his enemy, and he held his fire. The battle clock in his head started to run so that the passage of time slowed. He saw the muzzles of the Spandau machine-guns begin to wink at him, bright sparks of fire, flickering red as the planet Mars on a moonless night. He aimed for the head of the other pilot, and he pressed down on the trigger and felt the aircraft pulse about him as his guns shook and rattled.

No thought of breaking out of that head-on charge even occurred to Michael. He was completely absorbed by his aim, trying to stream his bullets into the German's face, to rip out his eyes, and blow his brains out of the casket of his skull. He felt the Spandau bullets plucking and tugging at the fabric and frame of his machine, heard them passing his head with sharp flitting sounds like wild locusts, and he ignored them.

He saw his own bullets kicking white splinters off the German's spinning propeller, and in anger knew that they were being deflected from his true aim. The two aircraft were almost in collision, and Michael braced himself for the impact without lifting his hand from the firing-handle, without attempting to turn.

Then the Albatros winged up violently, at the very last instant avoiding the collision, flicking out to starboard as the German hurled her over. There was a jarring bang that shook the SE5a. The two wings had just brushed each other as they passed. Michael saw the torn strip of fabric trailing from his own wingtip. He kicked on full rudder, into that flat skidding turn that only the SE5a was capable of, and felt the wings flex at the strain, and then he was around. The Albatros was ahead of him, but still out of effective range.

Michael thrust with all his strength on the throttle handle, but it was already wide open, the engine straining at full power and still the Albatros was holding him off.

The German turned and went up left, and Michael followed him. They

climbed more steeply, going up almost into the vertical, and the speed of both machines began to bleed off, but the SE5a more rapidly so that the German was pulling ahead.

'It's not the same Albatros.' Michael realized with a shock that the relocation of the radiator was not the only modification. He was fighting a new type of aircraft, an advanced type, faster and more powerful than even his own SE5a.

He saw the wide sweep of those black and white chequered wings, and the head of the German pilot craning to watch him in his mirror, and he tried to bring his guns to bear, swinging his ring sight in a short arc as he wrenched his nose across.

The German flipped his Albatros into a stall-turn and came straight back at Michael, head-on again with the Spandaus flicking their little red eyes at him, and this time Michael was forced to break, for the German had height and speed.

For a crucial moment, Michael was hanging in his turn, his speed had dwindled and the German rounded on him, and dropped on to his tail. The German was good, Michael's guts tightened as he realized it. He pushed his nose down for speed, and at the same time flung the SE5a into a vertical turn. The Albatros followed him round, turning with him, so that they were revolving around each other like two planets caught in immutable orbits.

He looked across at the other pilot, lifting his chin to do so, for each of them was standing on one wingtip. The German stared back at him, the goggles making him appear monstrous and inhuman, and then for an instant Michael looked beyond the bright blue fuselage, up towards the high cloud ceiling, his hunter's eyes drawn by a tiny insect speckle of movement.

For an instant his heart ceased to pump and his blood seemed to thicken and slow in his veins – then with a leap like a startled animal, his heart raced away and his breathing hissed in his throat.

'I have the honour to inform you, and at the same time also to warn you,' the German had written, 'the object of warfare is the destruction of the enemy by all means possible.'

Michael had read the warning, but only now did he understand. They had turned his woolly-headed romantic notion of a single duel into a death-trap. Like a child, he had placed himself in their power. He had given them time and place, even the altitude. They had used the blue machine merely as a decoy. His own naivety amazed him now, as he saw them come swarming down out of the high cloud.

'How many of them?' There was no time to count them, but it looked like a full Jasta of the new-type Albatroses, twenty of them at least, in that swift and silent flock, their brilliant colours sparkling jewel-like against the sombre backdrop of cloud.

'I'm not going to be able to keep my promise to Centaine,' he thought, and looked down. The low cloud was 2,000 feet below him, it was a remote haven, but there was no other. He could not hope to fight twenty of Germany's most skilled aces, he would not last for more than a few seconds when they reached him, and they were coming fast, while the blue machine pinned and held him for the killing stroke.

Suddenly, faced with the death which he had deliberately sought, Michael wanted to live. He had been dragging back on the joystick with all his weight, holding the SE5a into its turn. He flicked the stick forward and she was flung outwards, like a stone from a slingshot.

Michael was hurled up against his shoulder straps as the forces of gravity were inverted, but he collected the big machine and used its own impetus to push it into a steep dive, going down with a gut-swooping rush towards the low cloud bank. The manoeuvre caught his opponent off-balance, but he recovered instantly and the Albatros was after him in a blue flash of speed, while the swarming multicoloured pack was overhauling them both from above.

Michael watched them in the mirror above his head, realizing how much quicker this new type of Albatros was in the dive. He glanced ahead to the clouds. Their grey folds which had seemed so clammy and uninviting a few seconds before were his only hope of life and salvation, and now that he had started to flee his terror came back and settled upon him like a dark and terrible succubus, draining him of his courage and manhood.

He wasn't going to make it, they would catch him before he reached cover, and he clung to the joystick, frozen with his new and crippling terror.

The clatter of twin Spandaus roused him. In the mirror he saw the dancing red muzzle flashes, so close behind him, and something hit him a numbing blow low down in his back. The force of it drove the air from his lungs, and he knew he must turn out of the killing line of the blue Albatros's guns.

He hit the rudder bar with all his force, attempting the flat skidding turn that would bring him face to face with his tormentors, but his speed was too great, the angle of dive too steep – the SE5a would not respond. She lurched and yawed into a turn that brought him broadside on to the pursuing pack, and although the blue Albatros overshot, the others fell upon him one after the other, each successive attack a split second after the last. The sky was filled with flashing wings and bright-coloured fuselages. The crash of shot into his aircraft was continuous and unbearable, the SE5a dropped a wing and went into a spin.

Sky and cloud and patches of earth, interspersed with bright-coloured Albatroses with flickering, chattering guns, spun through Michael's field of vision in dizzying array. He felt another blow, this time in his leg, just below the fork of his crotch. He looked down and saw that a burst had come up through the floor, and a bullet, misshapen and deformed, had ripped through his thigh. Blood pumped from it in bright arterial jets. He had seen a Zulu gunbearer, savaged by a wounded buffalo, bleed this way from a ruptured femoral artery; he had died in three minutes.

Streams of machine-gun fire were still coming in at him from every angle, and he could not defend himself for his aircraft was out of control, flicking through the turns of the spin, throwing her nose up viciously, and then dropping it again in that savage rhythm.

Michael fought her, thrusting on opposite rudder to try to break the pattern of her rotation, and at the exertion the blood pumped more strongly from his torn thigh and he felt the first giddy weakness in his head. He dropped one hand from the joystick and thrust his thumb into his own groin, seeking the pressure point, and the great pulsing red spurts shrivelled as he found it.

Again he coaxed the maimed aircraft, stick foward to stop that high-nose altitude, and a burst of throttle to power her out of the spin. She responded reluctantly, and he tried not to think about the machine-gun fire that tore at him from every side.

The clouds and earth stopped revolving about him, as her tight turns slowed and she dropped straight. Then with one hand only he pulled her nose up and felt the overstressing of her wings and the suck of gravity in his belly, but at last the world tilted before his eyes as she came back on to an even keel.

He glanced in the mirror and saw that the blue Albatros had found him again and was pressing in close on his tailplane for the *coup de grâce*.

Before that dreadful rattling chatter of the Spandau could begin again, Michael felt the cold damp rush across his face as grey streamers of cloud blew over the open cockpit, and then the light was blotted out and he was into a dim, blind world, a quiet, muted world where the Spandaus could no longer desecrate the silences of the sky. They could not find him in the clouds.

Automatically his eyes fastened on the tiny glycerine-filled glass tubs set on the dashboard in front of him, and with small controlled adjustments he aligned the bubbles in the tubes within their markers so that the SE5a was flying straight and level through the cloud. Then he turned her gently on to a compass heading for Mort Homme.

He wanted to be sick – that was his first reaction from terror and the stress of combat. He swallowed and panted to control it, and then he felt the weakness come at him again. It was as though a bat was trapped in his skull. The dark soft wings beat behind his eyes and his vision faded in patches.

He blinked away the darkness and looked down. His thumb was still thrust into his own groin, but he had never seen so much blood. His hand was coated, his fingers sticky with it. The sleeve of his jacket was soaked to the elbow. Blood had turned his breeches into a sodden mass and it had run down into his boots. There were pools of blood on the floor of the cockpit, already congealing into lumps like blackcurrant jam, and snakes of it slithering back and forth with each movement of the machine.

He let go of the stick for a moment, leaned forward against his shoulder straps and groped behind his back. He found the other bullet wound, three inches to the side of his spine and just above the girdle of his pelvis. There was no exit wound. It was still in there and he was bleeding internally, he was certain of it. There was a swollen, stretched feeling in his belly as his stomach cavity filled with blood.

The machine dropped a wing, and he snatched for the joystick to level her, but it took him many seconds to make the simple adjustment. His fingers prickled with pins and needles, and he felt very cold. His reactions were slowing down, so that each movement, no matter how small, was becoming an effort.

However, there was no pain, just a numbness that spread down from the small of his back to his knees. He removed his thumb to test the wound in his thigh, and immediately there was a full spray of bright blood from it like a flamingo's feather, and hastily he stopped it again and concentrated on his flying instruments.

How long to reach Mort Homme? He tried to work it out, but his brain was slow and muzzy. Nine minutes from Cantin, he reckoned, how long had he been flying? He did not know, and he rolled his wrist so that he could see his watch. He found he had to count the divisions on the dial like a child.

'Don't want to come out of the cloud too soon, they'll be waiting for me,' he thought heavily, and the dial of his wristwatch multiplied before his eyes.

'Double vision,' he realized.

Quickly he looked ahead, and the silver clouds billowed around him, and he had the sensation of falling. He almost lurched at the stick to counteract it, but his training restrained him and he checked the bubbles in his artificial horizon – they were still aligned. His senses were tricking him.

'Centaine,' he said suddenly, 'what time is it? I'm going to be late for the

wedding.' He felt panic surface through the swamp of his weakness, and the wings of darkness beat more frantically behind his eyes.

'I promised her. I swore an oath!' He checked his watch.

'Six minutes past four – that's impossible,' he thought wildly. 'Bloody watch is wrong.' He was losing track of reality.

The SE5a burst out of the cloud into one of the holes in the layer.

Michael flung up his hand to protect his eyes from the brilliance of the light, and then looked around him.

He was on the correct heading for the airfield, he recognized the road and railway line and the star-shaped field between them. 'Another six minutes flying,' he calculated. The sight of earth had orientated him again. He took a grip on the real world and looked upwards. He saw them there, circling like vultures above the lion kill, waiting for him to emerge from the cloud. They had spotted him, he saw them turn towards him on their rainbow-coloured wings – but he plunged into the cloud on the far side of the opening, and the cold wet billows enfolded him, hid him from their cruel eyes.

'I've got to keep my promise,' he mumbled. The loss of contact with the earth confused him. He felt the waves of vertigo wash over him again. He let the SE5a sink slowly down through the layer of cloud, and once again came out into the light. There was all the familiar countryside below him, the ridges and the battle lines far behind him, the woods and the village and the church spire ahead, so peaceful and idyllic.

'Centaine, I'm coming home,' he thought, and a terrible weariness fell over him, its great weight seemed to smother him and crush him down in the cockpit.

He rolled his head and he saw the châtau. Its pink roof was a beacon, drawing him irresistibly, the nose of his aircraft turned towards it seemingly without his bidding.

'Centaine,' he whispered. 'I'm coming – wait for me, I'm coming.' And the darkness drew in upon him, so that it seemed that he was receding into a long tunnel.

There was a roaring in his ears, like the sound of surf heard in a seashell, and he concentrated with all his remaining strength, staring down the ever-narrowing tunnel through the darkness, looking for her face, and listening over the sea sounds in his ears for her voice.

'Centaine, where are you? Oh God, where are you, my love?'

* * *

Centaine stood before the heavy mirror in its walnut and gilt frame, and she looked at her reflection with dark and serious eyes.

'Tomorrow I will be Madame Michel Courtney,' she said solemnly, 'never again Centaine de Thiry. Isn't that a formidable thought, Anna?' She touched her own temples. 'Do you think I will feel different? Surely such a momentous event must alter me – I can never be the same person after that!'

'Wake up, child,' Anna prodded her. 'There is still so much to do. This is no time for dreaming.' She lifted the bulky skirt and dropped it over Centaine's head, then, standing behind her, she fastened the waistband.

'I wonder if Mama is watching, Anna. I wonder if she knows I am wearing her dress, and if she is happy for me?'

Anna grunted as she went down on her knees to check the hem. Centaine smoothed the delicate old lace over her hips and listened to the muffled sound of men's laughter from the *grand salon* on the floor below.

'I am so happy that the general could come. Isn't he a handsome man, Anna, just like Michel? Those eyes – did you notice them?'

Again Anna grunted, but with more emphasis, for a moment her hands faltered as she thought about the general.

'Now that is a real man,' she told herself, as she watched Sean Courtney step down from the Rolls and come up the front staircase of the château.

'He looks so grand in his uniform and medals,' Centaine went on. 'When Michel is older, I will insist that he grows a beard like that. So much presence – '

There was another burst of laughter from below. 'He and Papa like each other, don't you think, Anna? Listen to them!'

'I hope they leave some cognac for the other guests,' Anna grumped, and hoisted herself to her feet, then paused with one hand on the small of her back as a thought struck her.

'We should have laid out the blue Dresden service rather than the Sèvres. It would have looked better with the pink roses.'

'You should have thought of that yesterday,' Centaine cut in quickly. 'I'm not going to go over all that again.'

The two of them had worked all the previous day and most of the night to reopen the *grand salon* which had been closed ever since the servants left. The draperies had been floury with dust, and the high ceilings so laced with cobwebs that the scenes from mythology that decorated them were almost obscured.

They had finished the cleaning red-eyed and sneezing before beginning on the silver, which had been all tarnished and spotted. Then each piece of the red and gold Sèvres dinner service had to be washed and hand-dried. The comte, protesting volubly – 'A veteran of Sedan and the army of the Third Empire forced to labour like a common varlet' – had been dragooned in to assist.

Finally it had all been done. The *salon* once again splendid, the floor of intricately fitted and patterned wooden blocks glossy with wax, the nymphs and goddesses and fauns dancing and cavorting and chasing each other across the domed ceiling, the silver aglitter and the first of Anna's cherished roses from the greenhouse glowing like great gems in the candlelight.

'We should have made a few more pies,' Anna worried, 'those soldiers have appetites like horses.'

'They are not soldiers, they are airmen,' Centaine corrected her, 'and we have enough to feed the entire Allied army, not merely a single squadron – ' Centaine broke off. 'Listen, Anna!'

Anna waddled to the window and looked out. 'It is them!' she declared. 'So early!' The drab brown truck came puttering up the long gravel drive, looking prim and old-maidish on its high narrow wheels, the back crowded with all the off-duty officers from the squadron, the adjutant at the wheel with his pipe clamped in his jaws and a fixed and terrified expression on his face as he steered the vehicle on an uneven course from one verge of the wide driveway to the other, loudly encouraged by his passengers.

'Have you locked the pantry?' Anna demanded anxiously. 'If that tribe find the food before we are ready to serve – '

Anna had enlisted her cronies from the village, those who had not fled the

war, and the pantry was an Aladdin's cave of cold pies and pâtés and the wonderful local terrines, of hams and apple tarts, of pigs' trotters with truffles in aspic, and a dozen other delights.

'It's not the food they have come for so early in the day.' Centaine joined her at the window. 'Papa has the keys to the cellar. They will be well taken care of.'

Her father was already halfway down the marble staircase to greet them, and the adjutant braked with such abruptness that two of his pilots landed in the front seat with him in a tangle of legs and arms.

'I say,' he cried in obvious relief at being once again at a standstill, 'you must be the jolly old count, what? We are the advance guard, how do you say it in French, *le d'avant garde*, don't you know?'

'Ah, to be sure!' The comte seized his hand. 'Our brave allies. You are welcome! Welcome! May I offer you a small glass of something?'

'You see, Anna,' Centaine smiled as she turned back from the window, 'there is no need to worry. They understand each other. Your food will be safe from them, for a while at least.'

She picked up the wedding veil from the bed and arranged it loosely over her head, and studied herself in the mirror.

'This must be the happiest day of my life,' she whispered. 'Nothing must happen to spoil it.'

'Nothing will, my child,' Anna came up behind her and arranged the filmy lace of the veil upon her shoulders.

'You will be the loveliest bride, what a pity that none of the gentry will be here to see you.'

'Enough, Anna,' Centaine told her gently. 'No regrets. Everything is perfect. I would not have it any other way.'

She cocked her head slightly. 'Anna!' Her expression became animated.

'What is it?'

'Do you hear?' Centaine spun away from the mirror. 'It's him. It's Michel. He is coming back to me.'

She ran to the window, and unable to contain herself, she hopped up and down, dancing like a little girl at the window of a toy shop.

'Listen! He is coming this way!' She could recognize the distinctive beat of the engine that she had so often listened for.

'I don't see him.' Anna was behind her, screwing up her eyes, looking upwards in the ragged clouds.

'He must be very low,' Centaine began. 'Yes! There he is, just above the forest.'

'I see him. Is he going to the airfield in the orchard?'

'No, not with this wind. I think he is coming this way.'

'Is it him? Are you sure?'

'Of course I'm sure – can't you see the colour? *Mon petit jaune!*'

Others had heard it also. There were voices below the window, and a dozen of the wedding guests trooped out through the french doors of the *salon* on to the terrace. They were led by Sean Courtney in the full dress uniform of a British general, and the comte even more resplendent in the blue and gold of a colonel of the infantry of Napoleon III. They all carried their glasses and their voices were raised in mounting spirits and cheerful camaraderie.

'That's Michael all right,' someone called. 'I'll bet he's going to give us a low-level beat-up. Take the roof off the château, you'll see!'

'It should be a victory roll, considering what he's got in store.'

Centaine found herself laughing with them, and she clapped her hands as she watched the yellow machine approaching – then her hands froze an instant before they came together.

'Anna,' she said, 'there is something wrong.'

The aircraft was close enough now for them to see how irregularly it was flying – one wing dropped and the machine yawed and dipped towards the tree-tops, then pulled up sharply, and its wings wobbled, and then it dropped on the opposite side.

'What's he up to?' The timbre of the voices from the terrace changed.

'By God, he's in trouble – I think – '

The SE5a began a meandering, purposeless turn to starboard, and they could see the side of the damaged fuselage and the torn wing surfaces as it banked. It looked like the carcass of a fish that had been attacked by a pack of sharks.

'He's been badly shot up!' one of the pilots yelled.

'Yes, he's hard hit.'

The SE5a turned back too steeply, the nose dropped and almost hit the trees.

'He's going to try for a forced landing!' Some of the pilots jumped over the wall of the terrace and ran out on to the lawns, frantically signalling to the crippled aircraft.

'This way, Michael!'

'Keep the nose up, man!'

'Too slow!' screamed another. 'You'll stall in! Open the throttle. Give her the gun!'

They shouted their futile advice, and the aircraft settled heavily towards the open lawns.

'Michel,' Centaine breathed, twisting the lace between her fingers and not even feeling it tear, 'come to me, Michel.'

There was one last row of trees, ancient copper beech, with the new leaf buds on their gnarled branches just beginning to pop open. They guarded the bottom of the lawns furthest from the château.

The yellow SE5a dropped behind them, the beat of her engine faltering.

'Get her up, Michael!'

'Pull her up! Damn it!'

They were shouting to him, and Centaine added her own entreaty.

'Please, Michel, fly over the trees. Come to me, my darling.'

The Viper engine roared again at full power, and they saw the machine rocket up like a great yellow pheasant rising from cover.

'He's going to make it.'

The nose was too high, they all saw it, she seemed to hover above the stark, leafless branches, and they reached up like the claws of a monster – then the yellow nose dropped.

'He's over!' one of the pilots exulted, but one of the landing-wheels caught on a heavy curved branch, and the SE5a somersaulted in mid-air, then fell out of the sky.

It hit the soft earth at the edge of the lawn, landing on its nose, the spinning propeller exploding in a blur of white splinters, and then with the wooden frames of the fuselage crackling, the entire machine collapsed, crushed like a butterfly, its bright yellow wings folding around the crumpled body – and Centaine saw Michel.

He was daubed with his own blood, it had streaked his face, his head was

thrown back, and he was hanging halfway out of the open cockpit, dangling in his straps like a man on the gallows.

Michael's brother officers were streaming down the lawn. She saw the general throw his glass aside and hurl himself over the terrace wall. He ran with a desperate, uneven gait, the limp throwing him off balance, but he was gaining on the younger men.

The first of them had almost reached the wrecked aircraft when the flames engulfed it with miraculous suddenness. They shot upwards with a drumming, roaring sound, very pale-coloured but plumed with black smoke at their crests – and the running men stopped and hesitated and then drew back, holding up their hands to protect their faces from the heat.

Sean Courtney charged through them, going straight into the flames, oblivious of the searing, dancing waves of heat, but four of the young officers leaped forward and seized his arms and his shoulders, and pulled him back.

Sean was struggling in their grip, so wildly that three others had to run up and help to restrain him. Sean was roaring a deep, throaty, incoherent sound, like a bull buffalo in a trap, trying to reach out through the flames to the man trapped in the crumpled body of the yellow aircraft.

Then quite suddenly the sound ceased and he sagged. If the men had not been holding him, he would have fallen to his knees. His hands dropped to his sides, but he went on staring into the wall of flame.

Years before, on a visit to England, Centaine had watched with horrid fascination as the children of her host had burnt the effigy of an English assassin called Guy Fawkes on a pyre that they had built themselves in the garden. The effigy had been cleverly fashioned, and as the flames rose up over it, it had blackened and begun to twist and writhe in a most lifelike fashion. Centaine had woken up in the sweat of nightmare for weeks afterwards. Now, as she watched from the upper window of the château, she heard somebody near her begin to scream. She thought it might be Anna. They were cries of the utmost anguish, and she found herself shaking to them the way a sapling shakes to the high wind.

It was the same nightmare as before. She could not look away as the effigy turned black and began to shrivel, its limbs spasming and jack-knifing slowly in the heat, and the screams filled her head and deafened her. Only then did she realize that it was not Anna, but that the screams were her own. As these gusts of agonized sound came up from the depths of her chest, they seemed to be of some abrasive substance, like particles of crushed glass, that ripped at the lining of her throat.

She felt Anna's strong arms around her lifting her off her feet, carrying her away from the window. She fought with all her strength, but Anna was too powerful for her. She laid Centaine on the bed and held her face to her vast soft bosom, stifling those wild screams. When at last she was quiet, she stroked her hair and began to rock her gently, humming to her as she used to do when Centaine was an infant.

* * *

They buried Michael Courtney in the churchyard of Mort Homme, in the section reserved for the de Thiry family.

They buried him that night by lantern light. His brother officers dug his grave, and the padre who should have married them said the office for the burial of the dead over him.

'I am the resurrection and the life, said the Lord – '

Centaine was on the arm of her father, with black lace covering her face. Anna took her other arm, holding her protectively.

Centaine did not weep. After those screams had silenced, there had been no tears. It was as though her soul had been scorched by the flames into a Saharan dryness.

'O remember not the sins and offences of my youth – '

The words were remote, as though spoken from the far side of a barrier.

'Michael had no sin,' she thought. 'He was without offence, but, yes, he was too young – oh Lord, too young. Why did he have to die?'

Sean Courtney stood opposite her across the hastily prepared grave, and a pace behind him was his Zulu driver and servant, Sangane. Centaine had never seen a black man weep before. His tears shone on his velvety skin like drops of dew running down the petals of a dark flower.

'Man that is born of a woman hath but a short time to live, and is full of misery – '

Centaine looked down into the deep muddy trench, at the pathetic box of raw deal, so swiftly knocked together in the squadron workshop, and she thought, 'That is not Michel. This is not real. It is still some awful nightmare. Soon I will wake and Michel will come flying back – and I will be waiting with Nuage on the hilltop to welcome him.'

A harsh, unpleasant sound roused her. The general had stepped forward, and one of the junior officers had handed him a spade. The clods rattled and thumped on the lid of the coffin and Centaine loked upwards, not wanting to watch.

'Not down there, Michel,' she whispered behind the dark veil. 'You don't belong down there. For me, you will always be a creature of the sky. For me, you will be always up there in the blue – ' And then, '*Au revoir*, Michel, till we meet again, my darling. Each time I look to the sky I will think of you.'

* * *

Centaine sat by the window. When she placed the lace wedding veil over her shoulders Anna started to object, and then stopped herself.

Anna sat on the bed near her, and neither of them spoke.

They could hear the men in the *salon* below. Someone had been playing the piano a short while before, playing it very badly, but Centaine had been able to recognize Chopin's Funeral March, and the others had been humming along and beating time to it.

Centaine had instinctively understood what was happening, that it was their special farewell to one of their own, but she had remained untouched by it. Then later she had heard their voices take on that rough raw quality. They were becoming very drunk, and she knew that this too was part of the ritual. Then there was laughter – drunken laughter but with a sorrowful underlying timbre to it – and then more singing, raucous and untuneful, and she had felt nothing.

She had sat dry-eyed in the candlelight and watched the shell-fire flickering on the horizon and listened to the singing and the sounds of war.

'You must go to bed, child,' Anna had said once, gentle as a mother, but Centaine had shaken her head and Anna had not insisted. Instead, she had trimmed the wick, spread a quilt over Centaine's knees and gone down to fetch a plate of ham and cold pie and a glass of wine from the *salon*. The food and wine lay untouched on the table at Centaine's elbow now.

'You must eat, child,' Anna whispered, reluctant to intrude – and Centaine turned her head slowly to her.

'No, Anna,' she said. 'I am not a child any longer. That part of me died today – with Michel. You should never call me that again.'

'I promise you I will not,' and Centaine turned slowly back to the window.

The village clock struck two and a little later they heard the officers of the squadron leaving. Some of them were so drunk that they had to be carried by their companions and thrown into the back of the truck like sacks of corn, and then the truck pattered away into the night.

There was a soft tap on the door, and Anna rose from the bed and went to open it.

'Is she awake?'

'Yes,' Anna whispered back.

'May I speak to her?'

'Enter.'

Sean Courtney came in and stood near Centaine's chair. She could smell the whisky, but he was steady as a granite boulder on his feet and his voice was low and controlled: despite that, she sensed there was a wall within him, holding back his grief.

'I have to leave now, my dear,' he said in Afrikaans, and she rose from the chair, letting the quilt slip off her knees, and with the wedding veil over her shoulders went to stand before him, looking up into his eyes.

'You were his father,' she said, and his control shattered. He reeled and put his hand on the table for support, staring at her.

'How did you know that?' he whispered, and now she saw his grief come to the surface, and at last she allowed her own to rise and mingle with his. The tears started, and her shoulders shook silently. He opened his arms to her, and she went into them and he held her to his chest. Neither of them spoke again for a long time, until her sobs muted and at last ceased. Then Sean said, 'I will always think of you as Michael's wife, as my own daughter. If you need me, no matter where or when, you have only to send for me.'

She nodded rapidly, blinking her eyes, and then stepped back as he opened his embrace.

'You are brave and strong,' he said. 'I recognized that when first we met. You will endure.'

He turned and limped from the room, and minutes later she heard the crunch of wheels on the gravel of the drive as the Rolls with the big Zulu at the wheel pulled away.

* * *

At sunrise Centaine was on the knoll behind the château, mounted on Nuage, and as the squadron took off on dawn patrol, she rose high in the saddle and waved them away.

The little American whom Michel had called Hank was flying in the lead, and he waggled his wings and waved to her, and she laughed and waved back, and the tears ran down her cheeks while she laughed and they felt like icicles on her skin in the cold morning wind.

She and Anna worked all morning to close the *salon* again, cover the furniture with dust sheets, and pack away the service and the silver. The three of them ate lunch in the kitchen, terrines and ham left over from the previous evening. Though Centaine was pale and her eyes were underscored with blue as dark as bruises, and though she barely tasted the food or sipped her wine, she spoke normally, discussing the chores and tasks that must be done that afternoon. The comte and Anna watched her anxiously but surreptitiously, uncertain how to take her unnatural calm, and at the end of the meal the comte could contain himself no longer.

'Are you all right, my little one?'

'The general said that I would endure,' she answered. 'I want to prove him to be right.' She stood up from the table. 'I will be back within the hour to help you, Anna.'

She took the armful of roses that they had salvaged from the *salon*, and went out to the stables. She rode Nuage down to the end of the lane, and the long columns of khaki-clad men, bowed under their weapons and packs, called to her as she passed, and she smiled and waved at them, and they looked back after her wistfully.

She hitched Nuage to the churchyard gate, and with her arms full of flowers, went around the side of the moss-covered stone church. A dark green yew tree spread its branches over the de Thiry plot, but the newly turned earth was trampled and muddy and the grave looked like one of Anna's vegetable beds, only not as neatly dressed and squared.

Centaine fetched a spade from the shed at the far end of the churchyard and set to work. When she had finished, she arranged the roses and stood back. Her skirts were muddy and there was dirt under her fingernails.

'There,' she said with satisfaction. 'That's much better. As soon as I can find a mason I will arrange the headstone, Michel, and I'll come again tomorrow with fresh flowers.'

That afternoon she worked with Anna, hardly looking up from her tasks or pausing for a moment, breaking off just before dusk to ride up to the knoll and watch the planes come back from the north. That evening, there were two more of them missing from the squadron, and the burden of mourning that she carried as she rode home was for them as well as for Michel.

After dinner she went to her bedchamber as soon as she and Anna had washed the dishes. She knew that she was exhausted and she longed for sleep, but instead the grief that she had held at bay all that day came at her out of the darkness and she pulled the bolster over her face to smother it.

Still Anna heard it, for she had been listening for it. She came through in her frilled bed-cap and nightdress, carrying a candle. She blew out the candle and slipped under the bedclothes and took Centaine in her arms, crooning to her and holding her until at last she slept.

At dawn Centaine was on the knoll again, and the days and weeks repeated themselves, so that she felt trapped and hopeless in the routine of despair.

There were only small variations from this routine: a dozen new SE5as in the squadron flights, still painted in factory drab, and flown by pilots whose every manoeuvre proclaimed even to Centaine that they were new chums, while the numbers of the brightly painted machines that she knew dwindled at each return. The columns of men and equipment and guns moving up the main road below the château became denser each day, and there was a building current of anxiety and tension that infected even the three of them in the château.

'Any day now,' the comte kept repeating, 'it's going to begin. You see if I'm wrong.'

Then one morning the little American circled back over where Centaine waited on the hillock and he leaned far out of the open cockpit and let something drop. It was a small package, with a long bright ribbon attached to it as a marker. It fell beyond the crest of the hillock and Centaine urged Nuage down the slope and found the ribbon dangling in the hedgerow at the bottom. She reached up and disentangled it from the thorns, and when Hank circled back again, she held it up to show him that she had retrieved it, and he saluted her and climbed away towards the ridges.

In the privacy of her room Centaine opened the package. It contained a pair of embroidered RFC wings and a medal in its red leather case. She stroked the lustrous silk from which the silver cross was suspended, and then turned it over to find the date and Michael's name and rank engraved upon it. The third item, in a buff envelope, was a photograph. It showed the squadron aircraft drawn up in a wide semi-circle, wingtip to wingtip, in front of the hangars at Bertangles, and in the foreground the pilots stood in a group and grinned self-consciously at the photographer. The mad Scotsman, Andrew, stood beside Michael, barely reaching to his shoulder, while Michael had his cap on the back of his head and his hands in his pockets. He looked so debonair and carefree that Centaine's heart squeezed until she felt she was suffocating.

She placed the photograph in the same silver frame as that of her mother, and kept it beside her bed. The medal and the RFC wings she placed in her jewelbox with her other treasures.

Then every afternoon Centaine spent an hour in the churchyard. She paved the raw grave with red bricks that she had found behind the toolshed.

'Only until we can find a mason, Michel,' she explained to him as she worked on her hands and knees, and she scoured the fields and the forest for wild flowers to bring to him.

In the evenings she played the *Aïda* recording and pored over that page of her atlas that depicted the horse-head-shaped continent of Africa, and the vast red expanses of empire that were its predominant coloration, or she read aloud from the English books, Kipling and Bernard Shaw, that she had retrieved from her mother's upstairs bedroom, while the comte listened attentively and corrected her pronounciation. None of them mentioned Michael, but they were all aware of him every minute; he seemed to be part of the atlas and the English books and the jubilant strains of *Aïda*.

When at last Centaine was certain she was utterly exhausted, she would kiss her father and go to her room. However, as soon as she blew out the candle, her grief would overwhelm her once again, and within minutes the door would open softly and Anna would come to take her in her arms, and the whole cycle would begin again.

The comte broke it. He hammered on Centaine's bedroom door, awakening

them in those dark and early hours of the morning when all human energy is at its lowest ebb.

'What is it?' Anna called sleepily.

'Come!' the comte shouted back. 'Come and see.'

With gowns hastily thrown over their shoulders, they followed him through the kitchens and out into the paved yard. There they stopped and stared up at the eastern sky in wonder, for although there was no moon, it glowed with a strange wavering orange light as though somewhere below the horizon Vulcan had thrown open the door to the furnace of the gods.

'Listen!' commanded the comte, and they heard the sussuration upon the light breeze, and it seemed that the earth beneath their feet trembled to the force of that distant conflagration.

'It has begun,' he said, and only then did they realize that this was the opening barrage of the great new Allied offensive upon the Western Front.

* * *

They sat up the rest of that night in the kitchen, drinking pots of black coffee, and every little while trooping out again into the yard to watch the fiery display as though it were some astronomical phenomenon.

The comte was exultant as he described to them what was taking place. 'This is the saturation barrage which will flatten the barbed wire and destroy the enemy trenches. The boche will be annihilated,' he pointed to the fiery sky, 'who could withstand that!'

The thousands of artillery batteries were each firing on a front of a hundred yards, and over the next seven days and nights they never ceased. The sheer weight of metal which they hurled on to the German lines obliterated the trench works and parapets, and ploughed and reploughed the earth.

The comte was aflame with warlike and patriotic ardour. 'You are living in history. You are witness to one of the great battles of the ages – ' But for Centaine and Anna, seven days and seven nights was too long a time; the first amazement soon turned to apathy and disinterest. They went about the daily life of the château, no longer heeding the distant bombardment, and at night slept through the pyrotechnics and the comte's summonses to 'Come and watch!'

Then on the seventh morning, while they were at breakfast, even they were aware of the change in the sound and intensity of the guns.

The comte sprang up from the table and ran into the yard again, his mouth still full of bread and cheese, and the coffee bowl in his hand.

'Listen! Do you hear it? The rolling barrage has begun!'

The artillery batteries were rolling their fire forward, creating a moving barrier of high explosive through which no living thing could advance or retreat.

'The brave Allies will be ready for the final assault now – '

In the forward British trenches they waited below the parapets. With each man in full battle-dress, his equipment burden was almost sixty pounds in weight.

The thunder of the bursting high-explosives rolled away from them, leaving them with dulled senses and singing eardrums. The whistles of the section leaders shrilled along the trenches, and they roused themselves and crowded to

the feet of the assault ladders. Then, like an army of khaki lemmings, they swarmed out of their burrows into the open, and peered around them dazedly.

They were in a transformed and devastated land, so ravaged by the guns that no blade of grass nor twig of tree remained. Only the shattered tree stumps stuck up from the soft fecal-coloured porridge of mud before them. This dreadful landscape was shrouded in the yellowish fog of burned explosives.

'Forward!' the cry passed down the line, and again the whistles trilled and goaded them on.

The long Lee Enfield rifles held out before them, the fixed bayonets aglitter, sinking ankle and knee deep into the soft earth, slipping into the overlapping shell holes and dragging themselves out again, their line bulging and lagging, their horizon limited to a mere hundred paces by swirling nitrous fog, they trudged forward.

Of the enemy trenches they saw no sign, the parapets had been obliterated and flattened. Overhead passed the continuous roar of the barrage, while every few seconds a short shell from their own guns fell into their densely packed lines.

'Close up in the centre!' The gaps torn in their ranks by the guns were filled by other amorphous khaki bodies.

'Keep the line! Keep the line!' The orders were almost drowned by the tumult of the guns.

Then in the wilderness ahead of them they saw the glint of metal through the smoke. It was a low wall of metal, interlocking scales of grey steel like those on the back of a crocodile.

The German machine-gunners had had the benefit of seven days' forewarning, and as the British barrage rolled away behind them, they carried their weapons up the shafts from their dugouts to the surface and set them up on their tripods on the churned muddy lip of the ruined trenches. The Maxim machine-guns were each fitted with a steel shield to protect the crews from rifle-fire, and the guns were so closely aligned that the edges of the shields overlapped each other.

The British infantry was out in the open, walking down on a wall of machine-guns. The front ranks yelled when they saw the guns and started forward at a run, trying to reach them with the bayonet. Then they ran into the wire.

They had been assured that the barbed wire would be cut to pieces by the barrage. It was not. The high-explosive had made no impression upon it, except to tangle and twist it into an even more formidable barrier. While they floundered and struggled in the grip of the wire, the German Maxim machine-guns opened up on them.

The Maxim machine-gun has a cyclic rate of fire of 500 rounds per minute. It has the reputation of being the most reliable and rugged machine-gun ever built, and that day it added to that reputation the distinction of becoming the most lethal weapon that man had ever devised. As the plodding ranks of British infantry emerged from the fog of nitro-smoke, still attempting to maintain their rigid formation, shoulder to shoulder and four ranks deep, they made a perfect target for the Maxims. The solid sheets of fire swung back and forth, the scythe-blades of the harvesters, and the carnage surpassed anything seen before upon the battlefields of history.

The losses would certainly have been greater had not the troops, under the extreme duress of the Maxims, used their common sense and broken ranks. Instead of that ponderous, wooden-headed advance, they had tried to creep and

crawl forward in small groups, but even these had finally been beaten back by the wall of machine-guns.

Then with another grand offensive on the Western Front decimated almost as it began, the German force holding the ridges opposite Mort Homme counter-attacked jubilantly.

* * *

Centaine became gradually aware of the cessation of that distant holocaust, and the strange stillness which followed it.

'What has happened, Papa?'

'The British troops have overrun the German artillery positions,' the comte explained excitedly. 'I have a mind to ride across and view the battlefield. I want to bear witness to this turning-point in history – '

'You will do no such idiotic thing,' Anna told him brusquely.

'You don't understand, woman, even as we stand here talking, our Allies are rolling forward, eating up the German lines – '

'What I understand is that the milch cow has to be fed, and the cellars have to be mucked out.'

'While history passes me by,' the comte capitulated ungraciously, and went muttering down to the cellar.

Then the guns began again, much closer, and the windows rattled in their frames. The comte shot up the stairs and into the yard.

'What is happening now, Papa?'

'It is the death-throes of the German army,' the comte explained, 'the last thrashings of a dying giant. But do not worry, my little one, the British will soon invest their positions. We have nothing to fear.'

The thunder of the guns rose to a crescendo and was heightened by the din of the British counter-barrages as they sought to destroy the German counter-attack that was massing in the front-line trenches facing the ridges.

'It sounds just like last summer,' Centaine stared with foreboding at the stark outline of the chalk ridges upon the horizon. They were blurring slightly before her eyes, shrouding in the haze of shell-bursts.

'We must do what we can for them,' she told Anna.

'We have to think of ourselves,' Anna protested. 'We still have to go on living, and we cannot – '

'Come, Anna, we are wasting time.'

Under Centaine's insistence they cooked up four of the huge copper kettles of soup, turnip and dried peas and potato, flavoured with ham bones. They used up their reserves of flour at a prodigious rate to bake ovenful after ovenful of bread loaves, and then they loaded the small hand-cart and trundled it down the lane to the main road.

Centaine remembered clearly the fighting of the previous summer, but what she witnessed now shocked her afresh.

The highway was choked, filled from hedgerow to hedgerow with the tides of war, flowing in both directions, piling up and intermingling and then separating again.

Down from the ridges came the human detritus of the battle, torn and bloody, multilated and bleeding, crowded into the slowly moving ambulances,

into horse-drawn carts and drays, or limping on improvized crutches, borne on the shoulders of their stronger fellows, or clinging to the sides of the over-crowded ambulances for support as they stumbled through the deep muddy ruts.

In the opposite direction marched the reserves and reinforcements moving up to help hold the ridges against the German assault. They were in long files, already worn down under the weight of equipment they carried, not even glancing at the torn remnants of the battle which they might soon be joining. They trudged forward, watching their feet, and stopped when the way ahead was blocked, standing with bovine patience, only moving forward again when the man ahead of them started.

After the initial shock, Centaine helped Anna push the hand-cart up on to the verge, and then while Anna ladled out the thick soup, she handed the mugs, each with a thick slice of newly baked bread, to the exhausted and injured soldiers as they stumbled past.

There was not nearly enough, she could feed only one man in a hundred. Those whom she picked out as being in greatest need gulped down the soup and wolfed the bread.

'Bless yer, missus,' they mumbled, and then staggered on.

'Look at their eyes, Anna,' Centaine whispered as she held up the mugs to be refilled. 'They have already seen beyond the grave.'

'Enough of that fanciful nonsense,' Anna scolded her, 'you will give yourself nightmares again.'

'No nightmare can be worse than this,' Centaine answered quietly. 'Look at that one!'

His eyes had been torn out of his head by shrapnel and the empty sockets bound up with bloody rags. He followed another soldier, both of whose shattered arms were strapped across his chest. The blind man held on to his belt, and almost dragged him down when he tripped on the rough and slippery roadway.

Centaine drew them out of the stream, and she held the mug to the lips of the armless soldier.

'You are a good girl,' he whispered. 'Do you have a cigarette?'

'I'm sorry.' She shook her head and turned to rearrange the bandages over the other man's eyes. She had a glimpse of what lay beneath them, and she gagged and her hands faltered.

'You sound so young and pretty – ' The blinded man was about the same age as Michael, he also had thick dark hair, but it was clotted with dried blood.

'Yes, Fred, she's a pretty girl.' His companion helped him to his feet again. 'We'd best be getting on again, miss.'

'What is happening up there?' Centaine asked them.

'All hell is what is happening.'

'Will the line hold?'

'Nobody knows that, miss,' and the two of them were washed away on the slowly moving river of misery.

The soup and bread were soon finished, and they wheeled the cart back to the château to prepare more. Remembering the wounded soldiers' pleas, Centaine raided the cupboard in the gunroom where the comte kept his hoard of tobacco, and when she and Anna returned to their post at the end of the lane, she was able for a short time to give that extra comfort to some of them.

'There is so little we can do,' she lamented.

'We are doing all we can,' Anna pointed out. 'No sense in grieving for the impossible.'

They laboured on after dark, by the feeble yellow light of the storm lantern, and the stream of suffering never dried up, rather it seemed to grow even denser, so that the pale ravaged faces in the lantern light blurred before Centaine's exhausted eyes and became indistinguishable one from the other, and the feeble words of cheer which she gave each of them were repetitive and meaningless in her own ears.

At last, well after midnight, Anna led her back to the château, and they slept in each other's arms, still in their muddy, bloodstained clothes, and woke in the dawn to boil up fresh kettles of soup and bake more bread.

Standing over the stove, Centaine cocked her head as she heard the distant roar of engines.

'The airplanes!' she cried. 'I forgot them! They will fly without me today – that is bad luck!'

'Today there will be many suffering from bad luck,' Anna grunted as she wrapped a blanket around one of the soup kettles to prevent it cooling too quickly, and then lugged it to the kitchen door.

Halfway down the lane Centaine straightened up from the handle of the cart.

'Look, Anna, over there on the edge of North Field!'

The fields were swarming with men. They had discarded their heavy back-packs and helmets and weapons, and they were labouring in the early summer sun, stripped to the waist or in grubby vests.

'What are they doing, Anna?'

There were thousands of them, working under the direction of their officers. They were armed with pointed shovels, tearing at the yellow earth, piling it up in long lines, sinking into it so swiftly that as they watched, many of them were already knee-deep, then waist-deep behind the rising earth parapets.

'Trenches.' Centaine found the answer to her own question. 'Trenches, Anna, they are digging new trenches.'

'Why, why are they doing that?'

'Because,' Centaine hesitated. She did not want to say it aloud, 'Because they are not going to be able to hold the ridges,' she said softly, and both of them looked up to the high ground where the shell-fire sullied the bright morning with its sulphurous yellow mists.

When they reached the end of the lane, they found that the roadway was clogged with traffic, the opposing streams of vehicles and men hopelessly interlocked, defying the efforts of the military police to disentangle them and get them moving again. One of the ambulances had slid off the road into the muddy ditch, adding to the confusion, and a doctor and the ambulance driver were struggling to unload the stretchers from the back of the stranded vehicle.

'Anna, we must help them.'

Anna was as strong as a man, and Centaine was as determined. Between them they seized the handles of one of the stretchers and dragged it up out of the ditch.

The doctor scrambled out of the mud.

'Well done,' he panted. He was bare-headed, but his tunic sported the serpent and staff insignia of the medical corps at the collar, and the white armbands with the scarlet crosses.

'Ah, Mademoiselle de Thiry!' He recognized Centaine, over the wounded man on the stretcher between them. 'I should have known it was you.'

'Doctor, of course – ' It was the same officer who had arrived on the motor-cycle with Lord Andrew, and who had helped the comte with the consumption of Napoleon cognac on the day that Michael crashed in North Field.

They set the stretcher down under the hedgerow and the young doctor knelt beside it, working over the still figure under the grey blanket.

'He might make it – if we can get help for him soon.' He jumped up. 'But there are others still in there. We must get them out.'

Between them they unloaded the other stretchers from the back of the ambulance and laid them in a row.

'This one is finished.' With his thumb and forefinger the doctor closed the lids of the staring eyes, and then covered the dead man's face with the flap of the blanket.

'The road is blocked – it's hopeless trying to get through, and we are going to lose these others,' he indicated the row of stretchers, 'unless we can get them under cover, where we can work on them.'

He was looking directly at Centaine, and for a moment she did not understand his enquiring gaze.

'The cottages at Mort Homme are overfilled, and the road is blocked,' he repeated.

'Of course,' Centaine cut in quickly. 'You must bring them up to the château.'

* * *

The comte met them on the staircase on the château and when Centaine hastily explained their needs, he joined enthusiastically in transforming the *grand salon* into a hospital ward.

They pushed the furniture against the walls to clear the centre of the floor and then stripped the mattresses from the upstairs bedrooms and bundled them down the stairs. Assisted by the ambulance driver and three medical orderlies the young doctor had recruited, they laid the mattresses out on the fine woollen Aubusson carpet.

In the meantime the military police, under instructions from the doctor, were signalling the ambulances out of the stalled traffic on the main road and directing them up the lane to the château. The doctor rode on the running-board of the leading vehicle, and when he saw Centaine, he jumped down and seized her arm urgently.

'Mademoiselle! Is there another way to reach the field hospital at Mort Homme? I need supplies – chloroform, disinfectant, bandages – and another doctor to help me.'

His French was passable, but Centaine answered him in English.

'I can ride across the fields.'

'You're a champion. I'll give you a note.' He pulled the pad from his top pocket and scribbled a short message. 'Ask for Major Sinclair,' he tore out the sheet of paper and folded it, 'the advance hospital is in the cottages.'

'Yes, I know it. Who are you? Who must I tell them sent me?' With recent practice, the English words came more readily to Centine's lips.

'Forgive me, Mademoiselle, I haven't had a chance to introduce myself before. My name is Clarke, Captain Robert Clarke, but they call me Bobby.'

Nuage seemed to sense from her the urgency of their mission, and he flew furiously at the jumps and threw clods of mud from his hooves as he raced across the fields and down the rows of vineyards. The streets of the village were jammed with men and vehicles, and the advance hospital in the row of cottages was chaotic.

The officer she had been sent to find was a big man with arms like a bear, and thick greying curls that flopped forward on his forehead as he leaned over the soldier on whom he was operating.

'Where the hell is Bobby?' he demanded, without looking up at Centaine, concentrating on the neat stitches he was putting into the deep gash across the soldier's back. As he pulled the thread tight and knotted it, the flesh rose in a peak and Centaine's gorge rose with it, but she explained quickly.

'All right, tell Bobby I'll send what I can, but we are running short of dressings ourselves.'

They lifted his patient off the table, and in his place laid a boy with his entrails hanging out of him in an untidy bunch.

'I can't spare anybody to help him either. Off you go, and tell him.'

The young soldier writhed and shrieked as the doctor began to stuff his stomach back into him.

'If you give me the supplies, I will carry them back with me.' Centaine stood her ground, and he glanced up at her and gave her the ghost of a smile.

'You don't give up easily,' he grudged. 'All right, speak to him.' He pointed across the crowded room of the cottage with the scalpel in his right hand. Tell him I sent you, and good luck, young lady.'

'To you also, doctor.'

'God knows, we all need it,' he agreed, and stooped once more to his work.

Centaine pressed Nuage as hard as before on the ride back and left him in his stall. As she entered the courtyard, she saw that there were three more ambulances parked in the yard, the drivers unloading their cargoes of wounded and dying men. She hurried past them into the house, carrying a heavy kitbag over her shoulder, and paused at the door of the *salon* in amazement.

All the mattresses were full, and other wounded men were lying on the bare floor, or propped against the panelled walls. Bobby Clarke had lit every branch of the silver candelabra in the centre of the massive ormolu dinner table and was operating by candlelight.

He looked up and saw Centaine. 'Did you bring the chloroform?' he called across to her.

For a moment she could not reply and she hesitated at the tall double doors, for the *salon* already stank. The cloying odour of blood mingled with the reek of bodies and clothing of men who had come from the mud of the trenches, mud in which the dead had been buried and had decomposed to the same soupy consistency, men with the acrid sweat of fear and pain still upon them.

'Did you get it?' he repeated impatiently, and she forced herself to go forward.

'They do not have anyone to help you.'

'You'll have to do it. Here, stand on this side of me,' he ordered. 'Now hold this.'

* * *

For Centaine it all became a blur of horrors and blood and labour that exhausted her both physically and nervously. There was no time to rest, barely time to snatch a hasty mug of coffee and one of the sandwiches which Anna turned out in the kitchen. Just when she believed that she had seen and experienced so much that nothing else could shock her, then there would be something even more harrowing.

She stood beside Bobby Clarke as he cut down through the muscles of a man's thigh, tying off each blood vessel as he came to it. When he exposed the white bone of the femur and took up the gleaming silver bone-saw, she thought she would faint with the sound it made, like a carpenter sawing a hard-wood plank.

'Take it away!' Bobby ordered, and she had to force herself to touch the disembodied limb. She exclaimed and jerked back when it twitched under her fingers.

'Don't waste time,' Bobby snapped, and she took it in her hands; it was still warm and surprisingly weighty.

'Now there is nothing that I will not dare to do,' she realized as she carried it away.

At last she reached the stage of exhaustion when even Bobby realized that she could not stay on her feet.

'Go and lie down somewhere,' he ordered, but instead she went to sit beside a young private on one of the mattresses. She held his hand, and he called her 'mother' and spoke disjointedly of a day at the seaside long ago. At the end she sat helplessly and listened to his breathing change, panting to stay alive, and his grip tightened as he felt the darkness coming on. The skin of his hand turned clammy with sweat and his eyes opened very wide and he called out, 'Oh Mother, save me!' and then relaxed, and she wanted to cry for him, but she did not have the tears. So she closed those staring eyes as she had seen Bobby Clarke do and stood up and went to the next man.

He was a sergeant, a heavily built fellow almost her father's age, with a broad, pleasant face covered with grey stubble, and a hole in his chest through which each breath puffed in a froth of pink bubbles. She had to put her ear almost to his lips to hear the request, and then she looked round quickly and saw the silver Louis XV soup tureen on the sideboard. She brought it to him and unfastened his breeches and held the tureen for him, and he kept whispering, 'I'm sorry – please forgive me, a young lady like you. It isn't proper.'

So they worked on through the night, and when Centaine went down to find fresh candles to replace those that were guttering in the holders of the candelabra, she had just reached the kitchen floor when she was seized by sudden compelling nausea, and she stumbled to the servants' toilet and knelt over the noisome bucket. She finished, pale and trembling, and went to wash her face at the kitchen tap. Anna was waiting for her.

'You cannot go on like this,' she scolded. 'Just look at you, you are killing yourself – ' she almost added 'child', but caught herself. 'You must rest. Have a bowl of soup and sit by me for a while.'

'It never ends, Anna – there are always more of them.'

By now the wounded had overflowed the *salon* and were lying on the landing of the staircase and down the passageways, so that the orderlies bringing out the dead on the canvas stretchers had to step over their recumbent bodies. They laid the dead on the cobbles at the side of the stables, each wrapped in a grey blanket, and the row grew longer every hour.

'Centaine!' Bobby Clarke shouted from the head of the stairs.

'He is familiar, he should call you Mademoiselle,' Anna huffed indignantly, but Centaine leapt up and ran up the stairs, dodging the bodies that sprawled upon them.

'Can you get through to the village again?' We need more chloroform and iodine.' Bobby was haggard and unshaven, his eyes red-rimmed and bloodshot, and his bare arms caked with drying blood.

'It's almost light outside,' Centaine nodded.

'Go past the crossroads,' he said. 'Find out if the road is clearing, we have to begin moving some of these.'

Centaine had to turn Nuage back twice from the crowded roads and find a short cut across the fields, so by the time she reached the hospital at Mort Homme, it was almost full daylight.

She saw at once that they were evacuating the hospital. Equipment and patients were being loaded into a mongrel convoy of ambulances and animal-drawn vehicles, and those wounded who could walk were being assembled into groups and led out into the road to begin the trek southwards.

Major Sinclair was bellowing instructions to the ambulance-drivers. 'By God, man, be careful, that chap has a bullet though his lung – ' but he looked up at Centaine as she rode up on the big stallion.

'You again! Damn it all, I'd forgotten all about you. Where is Bobby Clarke?'

'Still at the château, he sent me to ask – '

'How many wounded has he got there?' the major interrupted.

'I do not know.'

'Dash it all, girl, is it fifty or a hundred, or more?'

'Perhaps fifty or a few more.'

'We have to get them out – the Germans have broken through at Haut Pommier.' He paused and examined her critically, noting the purple weals under her eyes and the almost translucent sheen of her skin. 'At the end of her tether,' he decided, and then saw that she still held her head up and that there was light in her eyes, and he changed his estimate. 'She's made of good stuff,' he thought. 'She can still go on.'

'When will the Germans get here?' Centaine asked.

He shook his head. 'I don't know, soon I think. We are digging in just beyond the village, but we may not even be able to hold them there. We have to get them out – you, too, young lady. Tell Bobby Clarke I'll send him as many vehicles as I can. He must get back to Arras. You can ride with the ambulances.'

'Good.' She turned Nuage's head. 'I will wait for them at the crossroads and guide them to the château.'

'Good girl,' he called after her as she galloped out of the yard and swung the stallion into the vineyard on the eastern side of the village.

Beyond the wall of the vineyard she reached the path that led up to her knoll above the forest. Then she gave Nuage his head and they went flying up the slope and came out on the crest. It was her favourite lookout, and she had a fine view northward to the ridges and over the fields and woods surrounding the village. The early sun was shining, the air bright and clean.

Instinctively she looked first to the orchard at the base of the T-shaped forest, picking out the open strip of turf that served as the airstrip for Michael's squadron.

The tents were gone, the edge of the orchard where the brightly painted

SE5as were usually drawn up was now deserted, there was no sign of life, the squadron had moved out during the night, gone like gypsies and Centaine's spirits lurched and sank. While they had been there it was as though something of Michael also remained, but now they had gone and they had left an empty hole in her existence.

She turned away, and looked to the ridges. At first glance the countryside seemed so peaceful and undisturbed. The early summer weather painted it a lovely green in the early sunlight, and near her in the brambles a lark was calling.

Then she stared harder and saw the tiny specks of many men in the fields, scurrying back from the ridges like insects. They were so distant and insignificant that she had almost overlooked them, but now she realized how many there were, and she tried to work out what they were doing.

Abruptly she saw a tiny greyish-yellow puff of smoke spurt up in the midst of one of the groups of running men, and as it drifted aside, she saw four or five of the antlike figures lying in an untidy tangle, while the others ran on.

Then there were more of those smoke puffs, scattered haphazardly on the green carpet of the fields, and she heard the sound of it on the wind.

'Shellfire!' she whispered, and understood what was going on out there. These were troops that had been driven out of their trenches and earthworks by the German attack, and in the open ground they were being harassed by the artillery batteries which the Germans must have brought up behind their advancing infantry.

Now, when she looked down at the base of the hillock on which she stood, she could make out the line of hastily dug trenches that she and Anna had seen them preparing the previous morning. The trenches ran like a brown serpent along the edge of the oak forest, then under the lee of the stone wall on the top side of North Field, turning slightly to follow the bank of the stream and then losing themselves amongst the vineyards that belonged to the Concourt family.

She could see the helmets of the troops in the trenches, and make out the stubby swollen barrels of the machine-guns protruding over the earthen parapets as they were lifted into position. Some of the running figures began to reach the trench line, and fell out of sight into it.

She started at a crashing explosion close behind her, and when she looked around, she saw the thin grey feathers of smoke drifting from a British artillery battery at the foot of the hill. The guns were so cleverly concealed beneath their camouflage nets that she had not noticed them until they fired.

Then she saw other guns, concealed in forest and orchard, begin firing at the unseen enemy, and the answering German salvoes burst in random fury along the line of freshly dug fortifications. A raised voice roused her from her fearful fascination, and she looked around to see a platoon of infantry men doubling up the path to the crest of the hill. They were led by a subaltern who waved his arms wildly at her.

'Get out of here, you damned fool! Can't you see that you are in the middle of a battle!'

She swung Nuage's head around to the path and urged him into a gallop. She swept past the file of soldiers and when she looked back, they were already frantically digging into the stony earth at the crest of the hill.

Centaine checked her mount as they reached the crossroads. All the vehicles had passed, except those stuck in the ditches and abandoned. However, the roadway was crowded with a rabble of retreating infantry who staggered under

their load, carrying on their backs the dismembered machine-guns and boxes of ammunition, and the other equipment that they had managed to salvage. Amid the squeal of whistle and shouted orders their officers were rallying them and sending them off the roadway to the freshly dug trenches.

Suddenly over Centaine's head passed a mighty rushing sound, like a hurricane wind, and she ducked fearfully. A shell burst a hundred paces from where she sat, and Nuage reared on his hind legs. She caught her balance and gentled him with voice and touch.

Then she saw a lorry come towards the crosroads from the village, and when she stood in her stirrups she could make out the red cross in its white circle painted on the side. She galloped down to meet it, and seven more ambulances followed the first through the bend. She reined in beside the cab of the leading ambulance.

'Have you been sent to the château?'

'What's that, luv?'

The driver could not understand her heavily accented English, and she bounced on the saddle with frustration.

'Captain Clarke?' she tried again, and he understood. 'You seek Captain Clarke?'

'Yes, that's it. Captain Clarke! Where is he?'

'Come!' Centaine raised her voice as another shell burst beyond the stone wall beside them and there was the electric sound of shrapnel passing overhead. 'Come!' she gestured, and swung Nuage into the lane.

With the line of ambulances following her, she galloped up the driveway towards the château, and saw a shell burst just beyond the stables and another hit the greenhouse at the bottom of the vegetable gardens. The glass panels splintered into a diamond spray in the sunlight.

'The château is a natural target,' she realized, and galloped Nuage into the yard.

Already they were bringing out the wounded, and as the first ambulance pulled up at the bottom of the stairs, the driver and his orderly sprang out to help load the stretchers into the back of the truck.

Centaine turned Nuage into the paddock beside the stables and ran back to the kitchen door. Behind her a howitzer shell hit the tiled roof of the long stable building, blowing a hole through it and knocking out part of the stone wall. However, the stables were empty, so Centaine darted into the kitchen.

'Where have you been?' Anna demanded. 'I have been so worried – '

Centaine pushed past her and ran through to her own room. She pulled the carpet bag from the top of her wardrobe and began to throw clothing into it.

There was a deafening crash from somewhere above, and the plaster ceiling cracked and chunks of it fell around her. Centaine swept the silver frame of photographs off the bedside table into the bag, then opened the drawer and found her jewelbox and her travelling toilet set. The air was full of white plaster dust.

Another shell burst on the terrace outside her room, and the window over her bed exploded. Flying glass rattled against the walls and a shard grazed her forearm and left a bloody line on her skin. She licked the blood away and dropped on her knees, creeping half under the bed, and prised up the loose floorboard.

The leather purse with their hoard of cash lay in the recess beneath it. She

weighed the purse in one hand – almost two hundred francs in gold *louis d'or* – then dropped it into the bag.

Lugging the carpet bag, she ran down the stairs into the kitchen.

'Where is Papa?' she shouted at Anna.

'He went up to the top floor.' Anna was stuffing strings of onions, hams and bread loaves into a grain sack. She pointed with her chin at the empty hooks on the wall. 'He has taken his gun and plenty of cognac.'

'I will fetch him,' Containe panted. 'Take care of my bag.'

She hitched up her skirts and raced back up the stairs.

The upper levels of the châtau were in confusion. The ambulance orderlies were trying to clear the *salon* and the main staircase.

'Centaine!' Bobby Clarke called across the stairwell at her. 'Are you ready to leave?'

He was manhandling one end of a stretcher, and he had to raise his voice above the shouts of the orderlies and the groans of the wounded.

Centaine fought her way up against the press of humanity descending the stairs, and Bobby caught her sleeve as she came level with him.

'Where are you going? We have to get out!'

'My father – I must find my father.' She shook off his hand and went on.

The topmost levels of the house were deserted and Centaine ran through them, shouting shrilly, 'Papa! Papa! Where are you?'

She ran down the long gallery, and from the walls the portraits of her ancestors gazed down haughtily upon her. At the end of the gallery she threw her weight on to the double doors which led through into the suite of bedrooms that had been her mother's and which the comte had kept unchanged all these years.

He was in the dressing-room, slumped in the high-backed tapestry-covered chair in front of the portrait of Centaine's mother, and he looked up as Centaine burst into the room.

'Papa, we must leave immediately.'

He did not seem to recognize her. There were three unopened cognac bottles on the floor between his feet, and he held another by the neck. It was half-empty, and he lifted it and took a mouthful of the raw spirit, still gazing at the portrait.

'Please, Papa, we must go!'

His single eye did not even blink as another shell crashed into the château, somewhere in the east wing.

She seized his arm and tried to pull him to his feet, but he was a big man and heavy. Some of the brandy spilled down his shirt front.

'The Germans have broken through, Papa! Please come with me.'

'The Germans!' he roared suddenly, and pushed her away from him. 'I will fight them once again.'

He threw up he long-barrelled *chassepot* rifle that had lain across his lap and fired a shot into the painted ceiling. Plaster dust filtered down on his hair and moustache, ageing him dramatically.

'Let them come!' he roared. 'I, Louis de Thiry, say, let them all come! I am ready for them!'

He was mad with liquor and despair, but she tried to pull him to his feet.

'We must leave.'

'Never!' he bellowed, and threw her aside, more roughly than before. 'I will never leave. This is my land, my home – the home of my dear wife – ' his eye

glittered insanely ' – my dear wife.' He reached towards the portrait. 'I will stay here with her, I will fight them here on my own soil.'

Centaine caught the outstretched wrist and tugged at it, but with a heave he threw her back against the wall, and began to reload the ancient rifle on his lap.

Centaine whispered, 'I must fetch Anna to help me.'

She ran to the door and another shell ploughed into the north side of the château. The crash of bursting brickwork and splintering glass was followed immediately by the blast wave. It threw her to her knees, and some of the heavy portraits were torn from the gallery walls.

She pulled herself up and raced down the gallery. The nitro-acid stink of explosive was mingled with the biting odour of smoke and burning. The staircase was almost empty. The very last of the wounded were being carried out. As Centaine ran into the yard two of the ambulances, both of them overloaded, pulled out through the gateway and turned down the driveway.

'Anna!' Centaine screamed. She was strapping the carpet bag and bulging sack on to the roof of one of the ambulances, but she jumped down and ran to Centaine.

'You must help me,' Centaine gasped. 'It's Papa.'

Three shells hit the château in quick succession, and more burst in the stable field and in the gardens. The German observers must have noted the activity around the building. Their batteries were finding the range.

'Where is he?' Anna ignored the shellfire.

'Upstairs. Mama's dressing-room. He is mad, Anna. Mad drunk. I cannot move him.'

The moment they entered the house they smelt the smoke, and as they climbed the stairs the stench became stronger and dense wreaths of it eddied about them. By the time they reached the second level, they were both coughing and wheezing for breath.

The gallery was thick with smoke, so they could not see more than a dozen paces ahead, and through the smoke shone a wavering orange glow – the fire had taken hold in the front rooms and was burning through the doors.

'Go back,' Anna gasped, 'I will find him.'

Centaine shook her head stubbornly and stared down the gallery. Another salvo of howitzer fire crashed into the château, and part of the gallery wall collapsed, partially blocking it, and swirling brick dust mingled with the dense smoke, blinding them so that they crouched at the head of the staircase.

It cleared slightly and again they ran forward, but the opening that had been torn in the wall acted as a flue for the flames. They roared up furiously and the heat came at them like a solid thing, barring their way.

'Papa!' screamed Centaine, as they cringed away from it. 'Papa! Where are you?'

The floor jumped under them as more shellfire hit the ancient building, and they were deafened by the thunder of collapsing walls and falling ceilings, and by the rising roar of the flames.

'Papa!' Centaine's voice was almost drowned, but Anna bellowed over her.

'Louis, *viens, chéri* – come to me, darling.'

Even in her distress, Centaine realized that she had never heard Anna use an endearment to her father. It seemed to summon him.

Through the smoke and the dust the comte loomed. Flames roared all around him, rising around his feet as the floorboards burned, licking at him from the

panelled walls, and smoke covered him in a dark mantle, so that he seemed like a creature from hell itself.

His mouth was open and he was making a wild, anguished noise.

'He is singing,' whispered Anna. 'The *Marseillaise*.'

'To arms, Citizens! Form the ship of State.'

Only then did Centaine recognize the garbled chorus.

'Let an impure blood swirl in the gutters – '

The words became indistinguishable and the comte's voice weakened as the heat enveloped him. The rifle he was carrying slipped from his hand, and he fell and dragged himself up and began to crawl towards them. Centaine tried to go to him again, but the heat stopped her dead and Anna pulled her back.

Dark brown blotches began to appear on her father's shirt, as the white linen scorched, but still that terrible sound came from his open mouth, and still he crawled along the burning floor of the gallery.

Suddenly the thick dark bush of his hair burst into flames, so that it seemed that he wore a golden crown. Centaine could not look away, could not speak again, but she clung helplessly to Anna and felt the sobs wracking the older woman's body, and the arm around Centaine's shoulder tightened so that the grip was crushingly painful.

Then the floor of the gallery gave way beneath her father's weight, and the burning floorboards opened like a dark mouth with fangs of fire and sucked him in.

'No!' Centaine shrieked, and Anna lifted her off her feet and ran with her to the head of the stairs. Anna was still sobbing and tears streamed down her fat red cheeks, but her strength was unimpaired.

Behind them part of the burning ceiling fell, taking the rest of the gallery floor with it, and Anna set Centaine on her feet and dragged her down the staircase. The smoke cleared as they went down, and at last they burst out into the yard again, and sucked in the sweet air.

The château was in flames from end to end, and shellfire still crashed into it or burst in tall columns of smoke and singing shrapnel upon the lawns and in the surrounding fields.

Bobby Clarke was supervising the loading of the last ambulances, but his face lit with relief as he saw Centaine, and he ran to her. The flames had frizzled the ends of her hair and scorched her eyelashes, soot streaked her cheeks.

'We have to get out of here – where is your father?' Bobby took her arm.

She could not answer him. She was shaking and the smoke had burned her throat and her eyes were red and streaming tears.

'Is he coming?'

She shook her head and saw the quick sympathy in his expression. He glanced up at the flaming building.

He took her other arm and led her towards the nearest ambulance.

'Nuage,' Centaine croaked. 'My horse.' Her voice was roughened by smoke and shock.

'No – ' Bobby Clake said sharply and tried to hold her, but she pulled out of his grip and ran towards the stable paddock.

'Nuage!' She tried to whistle, but no sound came through her parchd lips, and Bobby Clarke caught up with her at the paddock gate.

'Don't go in there!' His voice was desperate, and he held her.

Confused and bewildered, she craned to look over the gate.

'No, Centaine!' He pulled her back, and she saw the horse and screamed.

'Nuage!' The rushing roar and thunder of another salvo drowned out her heart cry, but she fought in his grip.

'Nuage!' she screamed again, and the stallion lifted his head. He lay upon his side; one of the shell bursts had shattered both his back legs and ripped open his belly.

'Nuage!' he heard her voice and he tried to lift himself on to his forefeet, but the effort was too much and he fell back. His head thudded on the earth and he blew a soft fluttering sound through his wide nostrils.

Anna ran to help Bobby and between them they dragged Centaine to the waiting ambulance.

'You can't leave him like that!' she pleaded, trying with all her might to resist them. 'Please, please, don't let him suffer.'

Another salvo of shells straddled the yard, driving in their eardrums and filling the air around them with hissing chips of stone and steel fragments. 'No time,' Bobby grunted, 'we must go.'

They forced Centaine into the rear of the vehicle, between the tiers of stretchers, and crowded in after her. Immediately the driver clashed the gears and pulled away, the ambulance swung in a tight circle, bouncing over the cobbles, and then accelerated through the gateway and out into the driveway.

Centaine dragged herself to the tailboard of the speeding vehicle and looked back at the château. The flames were rushing up through the shell holes in the pink tiles, and dark black smoke towered above it, rising straight up into the sunlit sky.

'Everything,' Centaine whispered. 'You've taken everything that I love. Why? Oh Lord, why have you done this to me?'

Ahead of them the other vehicles had pulled off the road at the edge of the forest, and parked under the trees to avoid the shellfire. Bobby Clarke jumped down and ran to each in turn, giving orders to the drivers and regrouping them into a convoy. Then, with his own vehicle in the lead, they sped down to the crossroads and turned into the main road. Again shell-fire fell close about them, for the German observers already had the crossroads well covered. Like a conga line the convoy wove from one side of the road to the other to avoid the shell holes and the litter of destroyed carts, dead draught-animals and abandoned equipment.

As soon as they were clear, they closed up and followed the curve of the road down towards the village. As they passed the churchyard, Centaine saw that there was already a shell hole through the green copper-clad spire. Although she glimpsed the upper branches of the yew tree that marked the family plot, Michael's grave was out of sight from the road.

'I wonder if we will ever come back, Anna?' Centaine whispered. 'I promised Michel – ' her voice trailed off.

'Of course we will. Where else would we ever go?' Anna's voice was rough with her own grief and the jolting of the ambulance.

Both of them stared back at the shot-holed church spire and the ugly black column of smoke that poured up into the sky above the forest marking the pyre of their home.

* * *

The ambulance convoy caught up with the tail of the main British retreat on the outskirts of the village. Here the military police had set up a temporary roadblock. They were sending all able-bodied troops off the road to regroup and to set up a secondary line of defence, and they were searching all vehicles for deserters from the battlefield.

'Is the new line holding, sergeant?' Bobby Clarke asked the policeman who checked his papers. 'Can we halt in the village? Some of my patients – '

He was interrupted by a shellburst that hit one of the cottages beside the road. They were still within extreme range of the German guns.

'There is no telling, sir,' the sergeant handed Bobby back his papers. 'If I were you I would pull back as far as the main base hospital at Arras. It's going to be a bit hairy around here.'

So the long, slow retreat began. They were a part of the solid stream of traffic that blocked the road for as far ahead as they could see, and reduced to the same excruciating pace.

The ambulances would start with a jolt, roll forward a few yards with noses to tails, and then pull up again for another interminable wait. As the day wore on so the heat built up, and the roads so recently running with winter mud turned to talcum dust. The flies came from the surrounding farmyards to the bloody bandages and crawled on the faces of the wounded men in the tiers of stretchers, and they moaned and cried out for water.

Anna and Centaine went to ask for water at one of the farm houses alongside the road, and found it already deserted. They helped themselves to milk pails and filled them from the pump.

They moved down the convoy, giving out mugs of water, bathing the faces of those in fever from their wounds, helping the ambulance orderlies clean those who had not been able to contain their bodily functions, and all the time trying to appear cheerful and confident, giving what comfort they could, despite their own grief and bereavement.

By nightfall the convoy had covered less than five miles, and they could still hear the din of the battle raging behind them. Once more the convoy was stalled, waiting to move on.

'It looks like we have managed to hold them at Mort Homme,' Bobby Clarke paused beside Centaine. 'It should be safe to stop for the night.' He looked more closely at the face of the soldier who Centaine was tending. 'God knows, these poor devils cannot take much more of this. They need food and rest. There is a farmyard with a large barn around the next bend. It hasn't been taken over by anyone else yet – we'll bag it.'

Anna produced a bunch of onions from her sack and used them to flavour the stew of canned bully beef that they boiled up over an open fire. They served the stew with dry army biscuit and mugs of black tea, all of it begged from the commissary trucks parked in the stalled column of traffic.

Centaine fed the men who were too weak to help themselves, and then worked with the orderlies changing the dressings. The heat and dust had done their worst, and many of the wounds were inflamed and swollen and beginning to ooze yellow pus.

After midnight Centaine slipped out of the barn and went to the water pump in the yard. She felt soiled and sweaty and longed to bathe her entire body and change into clean, freshly ironed clothes. There was no privacy for that, and the few clothes she had packed in the carpet bag she knew she must hoard. Instead she slipped off her petticoat and knickers from under her skirt and

washed them out under the tap, then wrung them and hung them over the gate while she bathed her face and arms with cold water.

She let the night breeze dry her skin and slipped her underclothes on again, still damp. Then she combed out her hair and she felt a little better, although her eyes still felt raw and swollen from the smoke and there was the heavy weight of her grief like a stone in her chest, and an enormous physical fatigue dragged at her legs and arms. The images of her father in the smoke and the white stallion lying on the green grass assailed her once again, but she shut her mind to them.

'Enough,' she said aloud as she leaned against the gate to the yard. 'Enough for today, I'll cry again tomorrow.'

'Tomorrow never comes.' A voice replied in broken French from the darkness, and she was startled.

'Bobby?'

She saw the glow of his cigarette then, and he came out of the shadows and leaned over the gate beside her.

'You are an amazing girl,' he went on in English, 'I have six sisters, but I've never known a girl like you. Matter of fact, I've known damned few chaps that could match you, either.'

She was silent, but when he drew on his cigarette, she studied his face in the glow. He was about Michael's age, and handsome. His mouth was full and sensitive-looking, and there was a gentleness about him that she had never had an opportunity to notice before.

'I say – ' he was suddenly embarrassed by her silence ' – you don't mind me talking to you, do you? I'll leave you alone if you prefer.'

She shook her head. 'I don't mind.' And for a while they were silent, Bobby puffing on his cigarette and both of them listening to the distant sound of the battle and to the occasional soft groan from one of the wounded in the barn.

Then Centaine stirred and asked, 'Do you remember the young airman, the first day you came up to the château?'

'Yes. The one with the burned arm. What was his name again – Andrew?'

'No, that was his friend.'

'The wild Scot – yes, of course.'

'His name was Michel.'

'I remember both of them. What became of them?'

'Michel and I were to be married, but he is dead – ' and her pent-up emotions came pouring out.

He was a stranger and gentle, and she found it so easy to talk to him in the darkness. She told him in her quaint English about Michel and how they had planned to live in Africa, then she told him about her father and how he had changed since her mother had died, and how she had tried to look after him and stop him drinking so much. Then she described what had taken place that morning in the burning château.

'I think that was what he wanted. In his own way he was tired of living. I think he wanted to die and be with Mama again. But now both he and Michel are gone. I have nothing.'

When at last she finished she felt drained and tired, but quietly resigned.

'You have really been through the grinder.' Bobby reached out and squeezed her arm. 'I wish I could help you.'

'You have helped me. Thank you.'

'I could give you something – a little laudanum, it would help you sleep.'

Centaine felt a surge in her blood, a longing for the quick oblivion he offered her, it was so strong that it frightened her. 'No,' she refused with unnecessary emphasis. 'I will be all right.' She shivered. 'I'm cold and it's late now. Thank you again for listening to me.'

Anna had hung a blanket as a screen at one end of the barn and made a mattress of straw for them. Centaine dropped almost immediately into a deathlike sleep, and woke in the dawn in a sickly sweat with the urgent nausea on her again.

Still groggy with sleep, she stumbled out and managed to get behind the stone wall of the yard before heaving up a little bitter yellow bile. When she straightened up and wiped her mouth, clinging to the wall for support, she found that Bobby Clarke was beside her, his expression troubled as he took her wrist and checked her pulse rate.

'I think I had better have a look at you,' he said.

'No.' She felt vulnerable. This new sickness worried her for she had always been so healthy and strong. She was afraid he might discover some dreadful disease.

'I am all right, truly.' But he led her firmly by the hand to the parked ambulance and drew down the canvas side screens to give them privacy.

'Lie there, please.' He ignored her protests and unfastened her blouse to sound her chest.

His manner was so clinical and professional, that she no longer argued, and submitted meekly to his examination, sitting up and coughing and breathing at his instruction.

'Now I will examine you,' he said. 'Do you wish your maid to be present as a chaperone?'

She shook her head mutely and he said, 'Please remove your skirt and petticoat.'

When he had finished, he made a show of packing his instruments back in the roll and tying up the retaining ribbons, while she rearranged her clothing.

Then he looked up at her with such a peculiar expression that she was alarmed. 'Is it something serious?'

He shook his head. 'Centaine, your fiancé is dead. You told me that last night.'

She nodded.

'It is still very early to be certain, very early – but I believe that you will need a father for the child that you are carrying.'

Her hands flew to her stomach, an involuntary protective gesture. 'I have really known you only a few days, but that is long enough for me to realize that I have fallen in love with you. I would be honoured – ' his voice trailed off, for she was not listening to him.

'Michel,' she whispered. 'Michel's baby. I have not lost everything. I still have a part of him.

* * *

Centaine ate the sandwich of ham and cheese that Anna brought her with such relish that Anna examined her suspiciously.

'I feel so much better now,' Centaine forestalled her inquiry.

They helped feed the wounded and ready them for the day's trek. Two of their critical cases had died during the night, and the orderlies buried them hastily in shallow graves at the edge of the field and then the ambulances started up and pulled out into the main stream of traffic.

The congestion of the previous day's route had abated as the army shook itself out of mindless confusion into a semblance of order. The traffic still rolled slowly, but with fewer halts and false starts, and alongside the road they passed the rudimentary supply dumps and advanced headquarters echelons that had been set up during the night.

During one of their halts on the outskirts of a tiny village, half-concealed by trees and vineyards, Centaine made out the shapes of aircraft parked at the edge of the vineyard.

She climbed up on the running-board of the ambulance for a better view, and a flight of aircraft took off from the field and flew low over the road.

Her disappointment was intense as she realized that they were ungraceful two-seater De Havilland scouts, not the lovely SE5as of Michael's squadron. She waved to them, and not one of the pilots looked down at her and waved back.

It cheered her somehow and as she returned to her self-imposed duties, she felt strong and lighthearted, and she joked with the wounded men in her accented English, and they reacted with delight. One of them called her 'Sunshine' and the name passed quickly down the line of ambulances.

Bobby Clarke stopped her as she passed. 'Great stuff – but remember, don't overdo it.'

'I will be all right. Don't worry about me.'

'I can't help it.' He dropped his voice. 'Have you thought about my offer? When will you give me an answer?'

'Not now, Bobby.' She pronounced his name with equal emphasis on each syllable, 'Bob-bee', and every time she said it he lost his breath. 'We will talk later – but you are very *gentil*, very kind.'

Now the roadway was almost impassable once more, for the reserves were being hastened up to help hold the new line at Mort Homme. Endless columns of marching men slogged past them, and interspersed between the ranks of bobbing steel helmets were batteries of guns and lines of supply trucks loaded with all the accoutrements of war.

Their forward progress faltered, and for hours at a time the ambulances were signalled off the roadway into a field or a side lane while the fresh hordes streamed past.

'I'll have to send the ambulances back soon,' Bobby told Centaine during one of their halts. 'They are needed back there. As soon as we can find a field hospital, I'll hand over these patients.'

Centaine nodded and made as if to go to the next vehicle where one of the men was calling weakly, 'Over here, Sunshine, can you give me a hand.'

Bobby caught her wrist. 'Centaine, when we reach the hospital, there is bound to be a chaplain there. It would only take a few minutes – '

She gave him her new smile, and reached up to touch his unshaven cheek with her fingertips. 'You are a kind man, Bobby – but Michel is the father of my son. I have thought about it, and I do not need another father.'

'Centaine, you don't understand! What will people think? A child without a father, a young mother without a husband – what will they say?'

'As long as I have my baby, Bobby, I don't give a – how do you say in

English – I don't give them a fig! They can say what they like. I am the widow of Michel Courtney.'

* * *

In the late afternoon they found the field hospital they were searching for. It was a field outside Arras.

There were two cottage tents, emblazoned with the red crosses. These were serving as operating theatres. Rough shelters had also been hastily thrown up around them to accommodate the hundreds of wounded waiting their turns on the tables. They were built of tarpaulins over timber frames, or of corrugated iron scavenged from the surrounding farms.

Anna and Centaine helped unload their own wounded and carry them into one of the crowded shelters, then they retrieved their baggage from the roof of the leading ambulance. One of their patients noticed their preparations to leave.

'You aren't going, Sunshine, are you?' And hearing him, others pulled themselves up on an elbow to protest.

'What are we going to do without you, luv?'

She went to them for the last time, passing from one to the next with a smile and a joke, stooping to kiss their filthy, pain-contorted faces, and then at last unable to bear it any more, hurrying back to where Anna waited for her.

They picked up the carpet bag and Anna's sack, and started along the convoy of ambulances which were being refuelled, ready to return to the battlefield.

Bobby Clarke had waited for them, and now he ran after Centaine.

'We are going back, orders from Major Sinclair.'

'*Au revoir*, Bobby.'

'I'll always remember you, Centaine.'

She went up on tiptoe to kiss his cheek.

'I hope it will be a boy,' he whispered.

'It will be,' she told him seriously. 'A boy, I am certain of it.'

The convoy of ambulances trundled away, back into the north, and Bobby Clarke waved and shouted something that she did not catch, as they were carried away on the river of marching men and lumbering equipment.

'What do we do now?' Anna asked.

'We go on,' Centaine told her. Somehow, subtly she had taken charge, and Anna, increasingly indecisive with each mile between her and Mort Homme, plodded after her. They left the sprawling hospital area and turned southwards once again into the crowded roadway.

Ahead of them over the trees Centaine could make out the roofs and spires of the town of Arras against the fading evening sky.

'Look, Anna!' she pointed. 'There is the evening star – we are allowed a wish. What is yours?'

Anna looked at her curiously. What had come over the child? She had seen her father burned to death and her favourite animal mutilated barely two days before, and yet there was a ferocious gaiety about her. It was unnatural.

'I wish for a bath and a hot meal.'

'Oh, Anna, you always ask for the impossible,' Centaine smiled at her over her shoulder, transferring the heavy carpet bag from one hand to the other.

'What is your wish then?' Anna challenged.

'I wish that the star leads us to the general, like it led the three wise men – '

'Don't blaspheme, girl.' But Anna was too tired and uncertain for the rebuke to have real force behind it.

* * *

Centaine knew the town well, for it contained the convent where she had spent her schooldays. It was dark by the time they made their way through the town centre. The fighting of the early years of the war had left terrible scars on the lovely seventeenth-century Flemish architecture. The picturesque old town hall was pocked with shrapnel splinters and part of the roof destroyed. Many of the gabled brick houses surrounding the Grande Place were also roofless and deserted, although the windows of others were candlelit. The more stubborn of the population had moved back again immediately the tides of war had rolled by.

Centaine had not made a special note of the way to the monastery that General Courtney was using as his headquarters when she had last visited it with Michael, so she could not hope to find it in the dark. She and Anna camped in a deserted cottage, eating the last scraps of stale bread and dried-out cheese from Anna's sack, using the carpet bag for a pillow and each other for warmth as they lay on the bare floor.

The next morning Centaine dreaded finding the monastery deserted when she finally rediscovered the lane leading to it, but there was a guard on the main gate.

'Sorry, miss, Army property. Nobody goes in.'

She was still pleading with him when the black Rolls came racing down the lane behind her and braked as it reached the gates. It was coated with dried mud and dust, and there was a long ugly scratch down both the doors on the nearest side.

The guard recognized the pennant on the bonnet and waved the Zulu driver on, and the Rolls accelerated through the tall gates, but Centaine ran foward and shouted desperately after the car. In the back seat was the young officer she had met on her last visit.

'Lieutenant Pearce!' She remembered his name, and he glanced back, then looked startled as he recognized her. Quickly he leaned across to speak to the driver, and the Rolls pulled up sharply and then reversed.

'Mademoiselle de Thiry!' John Pearce jumped out and hurried to her. 'The last person I expected – what on earth are you doing here?'

'I must see Michael's uncle, General Courtney. It's important.'

'He is not here at the moment,' the young officer told her, 'but you can come with me. He should be back fairly soon, and in the meantime we'll find you a place to rest, and something to eat. It seems to me that you could use both.'

He took Centaine's carpet bag from her. 'Come along – is this woman with you?'

'Anna, my servant.'

'She can sit in front with Sangane.' He helped Centaine into the Rolls. 'The Germans have made it a pretty busy few days,' he settled beside her on the soft leather, 'and it looks as though you have been through it as well.'

Centaine looked down at herself: her clothes were dusty and bedraggled, her

hands were dirty and her fingernails had black half-moons under them. She could guess what her hair looked like.

'I have just come back from the front. General Courtney went up to take a look for himself.' John Pearce politely looked away as she tried to put her hair into place again. 'He likes to be right up there – still thinks he's fighting the Boer War, the old devil. We got as far as Mort Homme – '

'That is my village.'

'Not any more,' he told her grimly. 'It's German now, or almost so. The new front line runs just north of it, and the village is under fire. Most of it shot away already – you wouldn't recognize it, I'm sure.'

Centaine nodded again. 'My home was shelled and burned down.'

'I'm sorry.' John Pearce went on quickly, 'Anyway, it looks as though we have stopped them. General Courtney is sure we can hold them at Mort Homme – '

'Where is the general?'

'Staff meeting at Divisional HQ. He should be back later this evening. Ah, here we are.'

John Pearce found a monk's cell for them, and had a servant bring them a meal and two buckets of hot water. Once they had eaten, Anna stripped off Centaine's clothes, and then stood her over one of the buckets and sponged her down with hot water.

'Oh, that feels marvellous.'

'For once there are no squeals,' Anna muttered. She used her petticoat to dry Centaine, then slipped a clean shift from the carpet bag over her head and brushed out her hair. The thick dark curls were tangled.

'*Oh là*, Anna, that hurts!'

'It was too good to last,' Anna sighed.

When she had finished, she insisted that Centaine lie on the cot to rest, while she bathed herself and washed out their soiled clothes. However, Centaine could not lie still and she sat up and hugged her knees.

'Oh darling Anna, I have the most wonderful surprise for you – '

Anna twisted the thick grey horse-tail of her damp hair on to her head and looked at Centaine quizzically.

'Darling Anna, is it? It must be good news indeed.'

'Oh it is, it is! I'm going to have Michel's baby.'

Anna froze. The blood drained from her ruddy features, leaving them grey with shock, and she stared at Centaine, unable to speak.

'It's going to be a boy, I'm sure of it. I can just feel it. He will be just like Michel!'

'How can you be sure?' Anna blurted.

'Oh, I am sure.' Centaine knelt quickly and pulled up the shift. 'Look at my tummy – can't you just see, Anna?'

Her pale smooth stomach was flat as ever, with the neat dimple of the navel its only blemish. Centaine pushed it out strenuously.

'Can't you see, Anna? It might even be twins, Michel's father and the general were twins. It may run in the family – think of it, Anna, two like Michel.'

'No,' Anna shook her head, aghast. 'This is one of your fairy stories. I won't believe that you and that soldier – '

'Michel isn't a soldier, he's a – ' Centaine began, but Anna went on, 'I won't believe that a daughter of the house of de Thiry allowed a common soldier to use her like a kitchen maid.'

'Allowed, Anna!' Centaine pulled down her shift angrily. 'I didn't allow it, I

helped him do it. He didn't seem to know what to do, at first, so I helped him, and we worked it out beautifully.'

Anna clapped both hands over her ears. 'I don't believe it, I'm not going to listen. Not after I taught you to be a lady – I just won't listen.'

'Then what do you think we were doing at night when I went out to meet him – you know I went out, you and Papa caught me at it, didn't you?'

'My baby!' wailed Anna. 'He took advantage – '

'Nonsense, Anna, I loved it. I loved every little thing he did to me.'

'Oh no! I won't believe it. Besides, you couldn't possibly know, not so soon. You are teasing old Anna. You are being wicked and cruel.'

'You know how I've been sick in the morning.'

'That doesn't prove – '

'The doctor, Bobby Clarke, the army doctor. He examined me. He told me.'

Anna was struck dumb at last, there were no more protests. It was inescapable: the child *had* been out at night, she *had* been sick in the morning and Anna believed implicitly in the infallibility of doctors. Then there was Centaine's strange and unnatural elation in the face of all her adversity, it was inescapable.

'It's true, then,' she capitulated. 'Oh, what are we going to do? Oh, the good Lord save us from scandal and disgrace – what are we going to do?'

'Do, Anna?' Centaine laughed at her theatrical lamentations. 'We are going to have the most beautiful baby boy, or if we are lucky, two of them, and I'm going to need you to help me care for them. You will help me, won't you, Anna? I know nothing about babies, and you know everything.'

Anna's first shock passed swiftly, and she began to consider not the disgrace and scandal, but the existence of a real live infant; it was over seventeen years since she had experienced that joy. Now, miraculously, she was being promised another infant. Centaine saw the change in her, the first stirrings of maternal passion.

'You are going to help me with our baby. You won't leave us, we need you, the baby and I! Anna, promise me, please promise me,' and Anna flew to the cot and swept Centaine into her arms and held her with all her strength, and Centaine laughed with joy in her crushing embrace.

* * *

It was after dark when John Pearce knocked again at the door of the monk's cell.

'The general has returned, Mademoiselle de Thiry. I have told him you are here, and he wishes to speak to you as soon as possible.'

Centaine followed the aide-de-camp down the cloisters and into the large refectory which had been converted into the regimental operations room. Half a dozen officers were poring over the large scale map that had been spread over one of the refectory tables. The map was porcupined with coloured pins, and the atmosphere in the room was tense and charged.

As Centaine entered, the officers glanced up at her, but even a young and pretty girl could not hold their attention for more than a few seconds and they returned to their tasks.

On the far side of the room, General Sean Courtney was standing with his

back to her. His jacket, resplendent with red tabs and insignia and ribbons, hung over the chair on which he was resting one booted foot. He leaned his elbow on his knee and scowled furiously at the earpiece of a field telephone from which a faint distorted voice quacked at him.

Sean wore a woollen singlet with sweat-stained armpits and marvellously flamboyant embroidered braces, decorated with stags and running hounds, over his shoulders. He was chewing on an unlit Havana cigar, and suddenly he bellowed into the field telephone without removing the cigar from his mouth.

'That is utter horse-shit! I was there myself two hours ago. I know! I need at least four more batteries of 25-pounders in that gap, and I need them before dawn – don't give me excuses, just do it, and tell me when it's done!' He slammed down the hand-set, and saw Centaine.

'My dear,' his voice altered and he came to her quickly and took her hand. 'I was worried. The château has been completely destroyed. The new front line runs not a mile beyond it – ' He paused, and studied her for a moment. What he saw reassured him and he asked, 'Your father?'

She shook her head. 'He was killed in the shelling.'

'I'm sorry.' Sean said simply, and turned to John Pearce. 'Take Miss de Thiry through to my quarters.' Then to her, 'I will follow you in five minutes.'

The general's room opened directly into the main refectory, so that with the door open Sean Courtney could lie on his cot and watch everything that went on in his operations room. It was sparsely furnished, just the cot and a desk with two chairs, and his locker at the foot of the cot.

'Won't you sit here, Mademoiselle?' John Pearce offered her one of the chairs, and while she waited, Centaine glanced round the small room.

The only item of interest was the desk. On it stood a hinged photograph frame, one leaf of which contained the picture of a magnificent mature woman, with dark Jewish beauty. It was inscribed across the bottom corner, 'Come home safely to your loving wife, Ruth.'

The second leaf of the frame held the picture of a girl of about Centaine's age. The resemblance to the older woman was apparent – they could only be mother and daughter – but the girl's beauty was marred by a petulant, spoiled expression; the pretty mouth had a hard, acquisitive quirk to it, and Centaine decided that she did not like her very much at all.

'My wife and daughter,' Sean Courtney said from the doorway. He had put on his jacket and was buttoning it as he came in.

'You have eaten?' he asked as he sank into the chair opposite Centaine.

'Yes, thank you.' Centaine stood up and picked up the silver box of Vestas from the desk, struck one and held it for him to light the Havana. He looked surprised, then leaned forward and sucked the flame into the tip of the cigar. When it was well lit, he leaned back in the chair and said, 'My daughter, Storm, does that for me.'

Centaine blew out the match, sat down again and waited quietly for him to enjoy the first few puffs of fragrant smoke. He had aged since their last meeting – or perhaps it was only that he was very tired, she thought.

'When did you last sleep?' she asked, and he grinned. Suddenly he looked thirty years younger.

'You sound like my wife.'

'She is very beautiful.'

'Yes,' Sean nodded and glanced at the photograph, then back to Centaine. 'You have lost everything,' he said.

'The château, my home – and my father.' She tried to be calm, not let the terrible hurt show.

'You have other family, of course.'

'Of course,' she agreed. 'My uncle lives in Lyon, and I have two aunts in Paris.

'I will arrange for you to travel to Lyon.'

'No.'

'Why not?' He looked piqued at her abrupt refusal.

'I don't want to go to Lyon, or Paris. I am going to Africa.'

'Africa? Now he was taken aback. 'Africa? Good Lord, why Africa?'

'Because I promised Michel – we promised each other we would go to Africa.'

'But my dear – ' He dropped his eyes, and studied the ash of his cigar. She saw the pain that the mention of Michael's name inflicted, she shared it with him for a moment, and then said, 'You were going to say, "But Michel is dead."'

He nodded. 'Yes.' His voice was almost a whisper.

'I promised Michel something else, General. I told him that his son would be born in the sunshine of Africa.'

Slowly Sean lifted his head and stared at her.

'Michael's son?'

'His son.'

'You are bearing Michael's child?'

'Yes.'

All the stupid mundane questions rushed to his lips.

'Are you sure?'

'How can you be certain?'

'How do I know it's Michael's child?'

And he bit them back. He had to have time to think – to adjust to this incredible twist of fate.

'Excuse me.' He stood up and limped back into the operations room.

'Are we in contact with the third battalion yet?' he demanded of the group of officers.

'We had them for a minute, then lost them again. They are ready to counter-attack, sir, but they need artillery support.'

'Get on to those damned shell wallahs again, and keep trying to get through to Caithness.' He turned to another of his staff. 'Roger, what is happening to the First?'

'No change, sir. They have broken two enemy attacks, but they are taking a beating from the German guns. Colonel Stevens thinks they can hold.'

'Good man!' Sean grunted. It was like trying to close the leaks in a dyke holding back the ocean with handfuls of clay, but somehow they were doing it, and every hour they held on was blunting the cutting edge of the German attack.

'The guns are the key, if we can get them up soon enough. How is the traffic on the main road?'

'Clearing and moving faster, it seems, sir.'

If they could move the 25-pounders into the gap before morning, then they could make the enemy pay dearly for their gains. They would have them in a salient, they could hit them from three sides, pound them with artillery.

Sean felt his spirits droop again. This was a war of guns, it all came back in the end to the bloody attrition of the guns. At the front of his mind Sean made

the calculations, assessed the risks and the costs and gave the orders, but behind that he was making other calculations. He was thinking of the girl and her claims upon him.

First he had to control his natural reaction to what she had told him, for Sean was a son of Victoria, and he expected all people, but especially his own family, to live by the code that had been set in the previous century. Of course, young men were expected to sow their wild oats – by God, Sean himself had sown them by the barrow-load – and he grinned shamefacedly at the memory. But decent young men left decent young girls alone, until after they were married.

'I'm shocked,' he realized, and smiled again. The officers at the operations table saw the smile and looked puzzled and uneasy. 'What is the old devil up to now?' They exchanged nervous glances.

'Have you got hold of Colonel Caithness yet?' Sean covered the smile with a ferocious scowl, and they applied themselves diligently to their tasks once more.

'I'm shocked,' Sean told himself again, still amused at himself but this time keeping his face impassive, 'And yet Michael himself was your own love-baby, the fruit of one of your escapades. Your first-born – ' The pain of Michael's death assailed him again, but he drove it back.

'Now, the girl.' He began to think it out. 'Is she really pregnant, or is this some elaborate form of blackmail?' It did not take him more than a few seconds to decide.

'I can't be that wrong in my estimate of her. She truly believes she is pregnant.' There were areas of the female anatomy and the feminine mind that were completely alien terrain to Sean. He had learned, however, that when a girl believed she was pregnant, she sure as all hell was. How she knew escaped him, but he was prepared to accept it. 'All right, she's pregnant, but is it Michael's child, and not some other young – '

Again his rejection of the idea was swift. 'She's a child of a decent family, carefully guarded by her father and that dragon of hers. How she and Michael managed it beats me – ' He almost grinned again as he recalled how often and adroitly he had managed it in his youth, against equally fearsome odds. 'The ingenuity of young love.' He shook his head. 'All right, I accept it. It's Michael's child. Michael's son!'

And only then did he allow the joy to rise in him. 'Michael's son! Something of Michael still lives on.' Then he cautioned himself quickly. 'Steady on now, don't lets go overboard. She wants to come out to Africa, but what the hell are we going to do with her? I can't take her in at Emoyeni.' For a moment the image appeared in his mind of the beautiful home on the hill, 'The place of the wind' in Zulu, which he had built for his wife. The longing to be back there with her came powerfully upon him. He had to fight it off and apply himself to the immediate problems again.

'Three of them – three pretty girls, all of them proud and strong-willed, living in the same house.' Instinctively he knew that this little French girl and his own beloved but lovingly indulged daughter would fight like two wild cats in a sack. He shook his head. 'By God, that would be the perfect recipe for disaster, and I wouldn't be there to turn them over my knee. I've got to come up with something better than that. What in the name of all that is holy do we do with this pregnant little filly?'

'Sir! Sir!' one of the officers called, and offered Sean the head-set of the field telephone. 'I've got through to Colonel Caithness at last.'

Sean snatched the set from him. 'Douglas!' He barked into it. The line was

bad, the background hissed and rushed like the sea, so Douglas Caithness's voice seemed to come from across an ocean.

'Hello, sir, the guns have just come up – '

'Thank God,' Sean growled.

'I have deployed them – ' Caithness gave the map reference. 'They are hammering away already and the Huns seem to have run out of steam. I am going to raid them at dawn.'

'Douglas, be careful, there are no reserves behind you, I won't be able to support you before noon.'

'All right, I understand, but we can't let them regroup unopposed.'

'Of course not,' Sean agreed. 'Keep me informed. In the meantime I'm moving up four more batteries, and elements of the Second Battalion, but they won't reach you before noon.'

'Thank you, sir, we can use them.'

'Go to it, man.' Sean handed the instrument back, and while he watched the coloured pins rearranged on the map, the solution to his personal problem came to him.

'Garry – ' He thought of his twin brother, and felt the familiar twinge of guilt and compassion. Garrick Courtney, the brother who Sean had crippled.

It had happened so many years ago and yet every instant of that dreadful day was still so clear in Sean's mind that it might have taken place that very morning. The two of them, teenage scamps, arguing over the shotgun that they had stolen out of their father's gunroom and loaded with buckshot, as they trotted through the golden grass of the Zululand hills.

'I saw the inkonka first,' Garry protested. They were going out to hunt an old bushbuck ram whose lair they had discovered the previous day.

'I thought of the shotgun,' Sean told him, tightening his grip on the weapon, 'so I do the shooting.' And, of course, Sean prevailed. It was always that way.

It was Garry who took Tinker, their mongrel hunting dog, and circled out along the edge of thick bush to drive the antelope back to where Sean waited with the shotgun.

Sean heard again Garry's faint shouts at the bottom of the hill, and Tinker's frantic barks as he picked up the scent of the wary bushbuck. Then the rush in the grass, and the long yellow stems bursting open as the inkonka came out, heading straight up to where Sean lay on the crest of the hill.

He looked immense in the sunlight, for in alarm his shaggy mane was erected and his dark head with the heavy spiral horns was raised high on the thick powerful neck. He stood three foot high at the shoulder and weighed almost two hundred pounds, and his chest and flanks were barred and spotted with delicate patterns, pale as chalk on the dark rufous ground. He was a magnificent creature, quick and formidable, those horns were sharp as pikes and could rip the belly out of a man or slice through his femoral artery – and he came straight at Sean.

Sean fired the choke barrel, and he was so close that the charge of buckshot struck in a solid blast, and tore through the animal's barrel chest into lung and heart. The bushbuck screamed and went down, kicking and bleating, its sharp black hooves clashing on the rocky ground as it slid back down the hill.

'I got him!' howled Sean, leaping from his hiding place. 'I got him first shot. Garry! I got him!'

From below Garry and the dog came pelting through the coarse golden grass. It was a race as to which of them could get to the dying animal first. Sean

carried the shotgun, the second barrel still loaded, and the hammer at full cock, and as he ran a loose stone rolled under his foot and he fell. The gun flew from his grip. He hit the ground with his shoulder and the second barrel fired with a stunning thump of sound.

When Sean scrambled up again, Garry was sitting beside the dead bushbuck, whimpering. His leg had taken the full charge of buckshot at almost point blank range. It had hit him below the knee, and the flesh was wet red ribbons, the bone white chips and slivers and the blood a bright fountain in the sunlight.

'Poor Garry,' Sean thought, 'now a lonely one-legged old cripple.' The woman whom Sean had put with child, and whom Garry had married before she gave birth to Michael, had finally been driven insane by her own hatred and bitterness and died in the flames she herself had set. Now Michael, too, was gone, and Garry had nothing – nothing except his books and his scribblings.

'I'll send him this bright pert girl and her unborn infant.' The solution came to Sean with a flood of relief. 'At last I can make some retribution for all I have done to him. I will send him my own grandchild, the grandchild I should so dearly love to claim as my own; I'll send to him in part payment.'

He turned from the map and limped quickly back to where the girl waited.

She rose to meet him and stood quietly, her hands clasped demurely in front of her, and Sean saw the worry and fear of rejection in her dark eyes, and the way her lower lip trembled as she waited for his judgment.

He closed the door behind him, and he went to her and took her small neat hands in his great hairy paws and he stooped over her and kissed her gently. His beard scratched her soft cheek, but she sobbed with relief and flung both arms around him.

'I'm sorry, my dear,' he said. 'You took me by surprise. I just had to get used to the idea.' Sean hugged her – but very gently, for the mystery of pregnancy was one of the very few things that daunted and awed Sean Courtney. Then he settled her back in the chair.

'Can I go to Africa?' She was smiling, though the tears still trembled in the corners of her eyes.

'Yes, of course, that's your home now, for as far as I am concerned, you are Michael's wife. Africa is where you belong.'

'I'm so happy,' she told him softly, but it was more than mere happiness. It was a vast sense of security and protection, this man's aura of power and strength was now held over her like a shield.

'You are Michael's wife,' he had said. He had acknowledged that which she herself believed, somehow his endorsement made it a fact.

'This is what I am going to do. The German U-boats have been playing such havoc. A sailing for you on one of the Red Cross hospital ships that leave directly from the French Channel ports will be the safest way of getting you home.'

'Anna – ' Centaine cut in quickly.

'Yes, of course, she must go with you. I'll fix that also. You will both volunteer for nursing duties, and I'm afraid you'll be expected to work your passage.'

Centaine nodded eagerly.

'Michael's father, my brother, Garrick Courtney – ' Sean started.

'Yes, yes! Michel told me all about him. He is a great hero – he won the cross of the English Queen Victoria for his courage in a battle against the Zulus,' Centaine cut in excitedly, 'and he is a scholar who writes books of history.'

Sean blinked at the description of poor Garry, but of course it was factually correct and he nodded.

'He is also a kind and gentle person, a widower who has just lost his only son – ' An almost telepathic understanding passed between them; although Centaine knew the truth, from now on Michael would always be referred to as Garrick Courtney's son. 'Michael was his whole life, and you and I know how he must feel at the loss, for we share it.'

Centaine's eyes sparkled with unshed tears and she bit down on her lower lip as she nodded vehemently.

'I will cable him. He will be at Cape Town to meet you when the ship docks. I will also give you a letter to take to him. You can be certain of his welcome and his protection, for both you and Michael's child.'

'Michael's son,' said Centaine firmly, and then hesitantly, 'but I will see you also, General, sometimes?'

'Often,' Sean assured her, leaning forward to pat her hand gently. 'Probably more often than you wish.'

* * *

After that it all happened very quickly; she would learn that with Sean Courtney, this was always the way.

She remained only five more days at the monastery, but in that time the German breakthrough at Mort Homme was contained by dour bloody fighting, and once the line was stabilized and reinforced, Sean Courtney had a few hours each day to spare for her.

They dined together every evening, and he answered her endless questions about Africa and its people and animals, about the Courtney family and its members, with good-natured patience. Mostly they spoke English, but when at a loss for a word, Centaine lapsed into Flemish again. Then at the end of the meal she would prepare his cigar and light it for him, pour his cognac and then perch beside him, talking still, until Anna came to fetch her or Sean was summoned to the operations room; then she would come to him and hold up her face for his kiss with such a childlike innocence, that Sean found himelf dreading the approaching hour of her departure.

John Pearce brought their nursing uniforms to Centaine and Anna. The white veils and the white cross-straps of the apron were worn over a blue-grey dress and Centaine and Anna made the finer adjustments themselves, their needles giving a touch of French flair to the baggy shapeless outfits.

Then it was time to leave, and Sangane loaded their meagre baggage into the Rolls, and Sean Courtney came down the cloisters, gruff and stern with the pain of leave-taking.

'Look after her,' he ordered Anna, and Anna glowered at him in righteous indignation at this gratuitous advice.

'I will be at the docks to meet you when you come home,' Centaine promised him, and Sean scowled with embarrassment and pleasure when she went up on tiptoe to kiss him in front of his staff. He watched the Rolls pull away with the girl waving at him through the back window, then roused himself and rounded on his staff.

'Well, gentlemen, what are we all gawking at – we're fighting a war here, not conducting a bloody Sunday-school picnic.'

And he stomped back down the cloisters, angry at himself for already feeling the girl's absence so painfully.

* * *

The *Protea Castle* had been a mailship of the Union Castle Line. She was a fast three-funnel passenger liner which had operated on the Cape to Southampton run before being converted to a hospital ship and repainted pristine white with scarlet crosses on her sides and funnels.

She lay at the dock of the inner harbour of Calais, taking on her passengers for the southward voyage, and they were a far cry from the elegant affluent travellers who had filled her pre-war lists. Five railway coaches had been shunted on to the rail spur of the wharf, and from these the pathetic stream of humanity crossed to the liner and went up her fore and aft gangways.

These were the veritable sweepings of the battlefield. They had been rejected by the medical board as so incapacitated that they could not even be patched up sufficiently to feed the man-hungry Baal of the British Expeditionary Force.

There would be twelve hundred on board for the southbound voyage, and on the return northbound leg the *Protea Castle* would be repainted in the camouflage of an ordinary troopship and bring another load of young eager and healthy young men for a sojourn in the hell of the trenches of northern France.

Centaine stood beside the Rolls at the wharfside and stared with dismay at this ruined legion as they went aboard. There were the amputees, missing an arm or a leg, the lucky ones with the severance below knee or elbow. They swung across the wharf on their crutches, or with an empty sleeve of their tunic pinned up neatly.

Then there were the blind, led by their companions, and the spinal cases carted aboard on their stretchers, and the gas victims with the mucous membranes of their noses and throats burned away by the chlorine gas; and the shell-shocked who twitched and jerked and rolled their eyes uncontrollably, and the burn victims with monstrous pink shiny scar tissue that had contracted to trap their limbs into the bent position, or drawn down their ravaged heads on to their chests, so that they were as twisted and contorted as hunchbacks.

'You can give us a hand here, luv.' One of the orderlies had spotted her uniform, and Centaine roused herself. She turned quickly to the Zulu driver.

'I will find your father – Mbejane? – '

'Mbejane!' Sangane grinned happily that she had the name right.

'And I will give him your message.'

'Go in peace, little lady.' Centaine clasped his hand, then snatched her carpet bag from him and, followed by Anna, hurried to her new duties.

The loading went on through the night, and only when it was completed a little before dawn were they free to try and find the quarters that they had been allocated.

The senior medical officer was a grim-faced major, and it was apparent that word had been whispered to him from on high.

'Where have you been?' he demanded when Centaine reported to his cabin. 'I have been expecting you since noon yesterday. We sail in two hours.'

'I have been here since noon down on "C" Deck, helping Doctor Solomon.'

'You should have reported to me,' he told her coldly. 'You can't just wander around the ship, suiting yourself. I am responsible to General – ' he cut himself off, and went off on a new tack. 'Besides, "C" Deck is other ranks.'

'*Pardon?*' Through practice, Centaine's English had improved immeasurably, but many terms still eluded her.

'Other ranks, not officers. From now on you will be working with officers only. The lower decks are out of bounds to you – out of bounds,' he repeated slowly, as though speaking to a backward child. 'Am I making myself clear to you?'

Centaine was tired, and not used to this type of treatment. 'Those men down there hurt just as much as the officers do,' she told him furiously. 'They bleed and die just like officers do.'

The major blinked and sat back in his chair. He had a daughter the same age as this French chippy, but she would never have dared answer him like that.

'I can see, young lady, that you are going to be a handful,' he said ominously. 'I did not like the idea of having you ladies on board – I knew it would lead to trouble. Now you listen to me. You are going to be quartered in the cabin across from mine,' he pointed through the open door. 'You will report to Doctor Stewart and work to his orders. You will eat in the officers' mess, and the lower decks are out of bounds to you. I expect you to conduct yourself with the utmost propriety at all times, and you can be certain that I will be keeping a very sharp eye on you.'

After such a bleak introduction, the quarters that she and Anna had been allocated came as a delightful surprise, and again she suspected that the hand of General Sean Courtney had moved. They had a suite that would have cost 200 guineas before the war, twin beds rather than bunks, a small drawing-room with sofa and armchairs and writing-desk, and their own shower and toilet, all tastefully furnished in autumn shades.

Centaine bounced on the bed and then fell back on the pillows and sighed blissfully.

'Anna, I am too tired to undress.'

'Into your nightdress,' Anna ordered. 'And don't forget to clean your teeth.'

They were wakened by the alarm gongs ringing, the blast of whistles in the companionway and a hammering on the cabin door. The ship was under way, vibrating to her engines and working to the scend of the sea.

After the first moments of panic, they learned from their cabin steward that it was a boat drill. Dressing and strapping themselves hastily into their bulky life-jackets, they trooped on to the upper deck and found their life-boat station.

The ship had just cleared the harbour breakwater and was standing out into the Channel. It was a grey misty morning and the wind whipped about their ears so that there was a general murmur of relief when the 'stand-down' was sounded and breakfast was served in the first-class dining-room, which had been converted into the officers' mess for the walking wounded.

Centaine's entrance caused a genteel pandemonium. Very few of the officers had realized that there was a pretty girl on board, and they found it difficult to conceal their delight. There was a great deal of jockeying for position, but very quickly the first officer, taking advantage of the fact that the captain was still on the bridge, exercized his rank, and Centaine found herself installed at his right hand surrounded by a dozen attentive and solicitous gentlemen, with Anna seated opposite, glowering like a guardian bull-dog.

The ship's officers were all British, but the patients were colonials, for the *Protea Castle* was going on eastwards after rounding the Cape of Good Hope. Seated around Centaine there were a captain of Australian Light Horse who had lost a hand, a pair of New Zealanders, one with a piratical black patch over his missing eye, and the other with an equally piratical Long John Silver wooden stump, a young Rhodesian named Jonathan Ballantyne who had won an MC at the Somme but paid for it with a burst of machine-gun fire through the belly, and other eager young men who had all lost parts of their anatomy.

They plied her with food from the buffet. 'No, no, I cannot eat your great English breakfasts, you will make me fat and ugly like a pig.' And she glowed at their concerted denials. The war had been in progress since Centaine was a mere fourteen years old, and with all the young men gone, she had never known the pleasure of being surrounded by a horde of admirers.

She saw the senior medical officer scowling at her from the captain's table, and as much to spite him as for her own amusement, she set herself out to be pleasant to the young men surrounding her. Although she felt a stirring of guilt that she might be less than faithful to Michael's memory, she consoled herself.

'It is my duty, they are my patients. A nurse must be good to her patients.' And she smiled and laughed with them, and they were pathetically eager to catch her attention, render small services for her and answer all her questions.

'Why are we not sailing in convoy?' she asked. 'Is it not dangerous to go down Channel *en plein soleil* – in broad daylight? I have heard about the *Rewa*.'

The *Rewa* was the British hospital ship, with 300 wounded on board, that had been torpedoed by a German U-boat in the British Channel on January 4th that year. Fortunately, the ship had been abandoned with the loss of only three lives, but it had fuelled the anti-German propaganda. Displayed in most public places were the posters headed: 'What a *Red Rag* is to a bull, the *Red Cross* is to the Hun,' with a graphic account of the atrocity beneath.

Centaine's question precipitated a lively argument at the breakfast table.

'The *Rewa* was torpedoed at night,' Jonathan Ballantyne pointed out reasonably. 'The U-boat commander probably didn't see the red crosses.'

'Oh, come now! Those U-boat chaps are absolute butchers – '

'I don't agree. They are just ordinary fellows like you and me. The captain of this ship obviously believes that too – that's why we are covering the most dangerous down-channel leg in daylight, to let the U-boats get a good look at our Red Cross markings. I think they'll leave us alone, once they know what we are.'

'Nonsense, damned Huns would torpedo their own mother-in-law – '

'So would I, mind you!'

'This ship is steaming at twenty-two knots,' the first officer reassured Centaine. 'The U-boat is capable of only seven knots when submerged. It would have to be lying directly in our track to have any chance of a shot at us. Odds of a million to one, miss, you don't have to worry at all. Just enjoy the voyage.'

A tall, round-shouldered young doctor with a mild scholarly air and steel-rimmed spectacles stood before Centaine as she rose from the breakfast table.

'I am Dr Archibald Stewart, Nurse de Thiry, and Major Wright has put you in my charge.'

Centaine liked the new form of address. 'Nurse de Thiry' had a nice professional ring to it. She was not so certain that she enjoyed being in anyone's charge, however.

'Do you have any medical or nursing training?' Dr Stewart went on, and

Centaine's initial liking for him cooled. He had exposed her in the first few seconds, and in front of her new-found admirers. She shook her head, trying not to make the confession public, but he went on remorselessly.

'I thought not.' He eyed her dubiously, and then seemed to become aware of her embarrassment. 'Never mind, a nurse's most important duty is to cheer up her patients. From what little I've seen, you are very good at that. I think we'll make you chief cheerer-upper, but only on "A" Deck. Strict orders from Major Wright. "A" Deck only.'

Dr Archibald Stewart's appointment turned out to be inspired. From an early age, Centaine's organizational skills had been honed in the running of the château of Mort Homme, where she had been her father's hostess and assistant housekeeper. Effortlessly she manipulated the band of young men that had gathered about her into an entertainments team.

The *Protea Castle* had a library of many thousands of volumes, and she quickly instituted a distribution and collection scheme for the bedridden cases, and a roster of readers for the blind and illiterate amongst the men on the lower decks. She arranged smoking concerts and deck games and card tournaments – the comte had been a wicked bridge player and taught her his skills.

Her team of one-eyed, one-legged, maimed assistant alleviators of the boredom of the long voyage vied with each other to win her approval and render their services; and the patients in the tiers of bunks thought up a dozen tricks to delay her beside them when she made her unofficial rounds each morning.

Amongst the patients was a captain of the Natal Mounted Rifles who had been in the convoy of ambulances during the retreat from Mort Homme, and he greeted her ecstatically the first time she entered his ward with her armful of books.

'Sunshine! It's Sunshine herself!' and the nickname followed her about the ship.

'Nurse Sunshine.' When the usually surly chief medical officer, Major Wright, used the nickname for the first time, Centaine's adoption by the ship's company was unanimous.

In the circumstances there was little time for mourning, but every night just before composing herself for sleep, Centaine lay in the darkness and conjured up Michael's image in her mind's eye, and then clasped both hands over her lower stomach.

'Our son, Michel, our son!'

The brooding skies and brutal black seas of the Bay of Biscay were left behind on the long white wake, and ahead of the bows the flying fish spun like silver coins across the blue velve surface of the ocean.

At latitude 30 degrees north, the debonair young Captain Jonathan Ballantyne, who was the reputed heir to the 100,000-acre cattle ranches of his father Sir Ralph Ballantyne, Prime Minister of Rhodesia, proposed marriage to Centaine.

'I can hear poor papa,' Centaine mimicked the comte so accurately that it cast a shadow in Anna's eyes. '"100,000 acres, you crazy wicked child. *Tiens alors!* How can you refuse 100,000 acres?"'

After that the marriage proposals became an epidemic – even Dr Archibald Stewart, her immediate superior, blinking through his steel-rimmed spectacles and sweating nervously, stammered through a carefully rehearsed speech, and looked more gratified than abashed when Centaine kissed both his cheeks in polite refusal.

At the equator Centaine prevailed on Major Wright to don the regalia of King Neptune, and the crossing ceremony was conducted amidst wild hilarity and widespread inebriation. Centaine herself turned out to be the main attraction, clad in a mermaid costume of her own design. Anna had protested strenuously at the *décolleté*, all the while she helped to sew it, but the ship's company adored it. They whistled and clapped and stamped, and there was another rash of proposals immediately after the crossing.

Anna huffed and gruffed, but secretly was well content with the change she saw coming over her charge. Before her eyes Centaine was making that wonderful transformation from girl to young womanhood. Physically she was beginning to bloom with early pregnancy. Her fine skin took on a lustre like mother-of-pearl, she lost the last vestiges of adolescent gawkiness as her body filled without losing any of its grace.

However, more powerful were the other changes – the growing confidence and poise, the awareness of her own powers and gifts that she was only now beginning to exercise fully. Anna had known that Centaine was a natural mimic, could switch from the *midi* accent of Jacques, the groom, to the Walloon of the chambermaids and then to the Parisian intellectual of her music teacher, but now she realized that the child had a talent for languages which had never been tested. Centaine was already speaking such fluent English that she could differentiate between the Australian and South African and pure Oxford English accents, and take them off with startling accuracy. When she greeted her Aussies with a dinky 'Gid die!', they hooted with delight.

Anna had known also that Centaine had a way with figures and money. She had taken over the family accounts when the estate factor had fled to Paris in the first months of the war, and Anna had marvelled at her ability to cast a long column of figures simply by running her pen down it, without the laborious carrying over of digits, and without moving her lips, all of which Anna considered miraculous.

Now Centaine demonstrated the same acumen. She partnered Major Wright at the bridge table and they made a formidable pair, and her share of the winnings flabbergasted Anna who did not really approve of gambling. Centaine reinvested these. She organized a syndicate with Jonathan Ballantyne and Dr Stevens and they were big punters on the daily auction and sweepstake on the ship's run. By the time they crossed the equator, Centaine had added nearly two hundred sovereigns to the hoard of *louis d'or* they had salvaged from the château.

Anna had always known that Centaine read too much. 'It will damage your eyes,' she had warned her often enough, but she had never realized the depth of the knowledge that Centaine had gathered from her books, not until she heard it demonstrated in conversation and discussion. She held her own even against such formidable debaters as Dr Archibald Stewart, and yet Anna noticed that she was cunning enough not to antagonize her audience by ostentatiously flaunting her learning, and would usually end an argument on a conciliatory note that allowed her male victim to retreat with only slightly ruffled dignity.

'Yes,' Anna nodded comfortably to herself, as she watched the girl blooming and opening like some lovely flower in the tropical sunshine, 'she's a clever one, just like her Mama.'

It seemed that Centaine really had a physical need for warmth and sunlight. She would turn her face up to the sun every time she went on deck. 'Oh, Anna, I did so hate the cold and the rain. Doesn't this feel wonderful?'

'You are turning ugly brown,' Anna warned her. 'It's so unladylike.'

And Centaine considered her own limbs thoughtfully. 'Not brown, Anna, gold!'

Centaine had read so much and queried so many people, that she seemed already to know the southern hemisphere into which their ship now thrust its bows. Centaine would wake Anna and take her on to the upper deck to act as chaperone while the officer of the watch showed her the southern stars. And despite the late hour, Anna was dazzled by the splendours of this sky that each evening revealed more of itself before their upturned eyes.

'Look, Anna, there is Achernar at last! It was Michel's own special star. We should all have a special star, he said, and he chose mine for me.'

'Which is it?' Anna asked. 'Which is your star?'

'Acrux. There! The brightest star in the Great Cross. There is nothing between it and Michael's star, except the pivot of the whole world, the celestial South Pole. He said between us we would hold the axis of the earth. Wasn't that romantic, Anna?'

'Romantic twaddle,' Anna sniffed, and secretly regretted that she had never had a man to say such things to her.

Then Anna came to recognize in her charge a talent that seemed to make all the others pale. It was the ability of making men listen to her. It was quite extraordinary to see men like Major Wright and the *Protea Castle*'s captain actually keep silent and attend, without that infuriatingly indulgent masculine smirk, when Centaine spoke seriously.

'She's only a child,' Anna marvelled, 'yet they treat her like a woman – no, no, more than that even, they are beginning to treat her like an equal.'

That was truly astonishing. Here were these men according to a young girl the respect that thousands of other women, Emmeline Pankhurst and Annie Kenney at their head, had been burning property, throwing themselves under racehorses, hunger-striking and enduring prison sentences to obtain – so far unsuccessfully.

Centaine made the men listen to her, and very often she made them do what she wanted, although she was not above using the sly sexual tricks to which women of the ages have been forced to resort; Centaine achieved her ends by adding logic, cogent argument and force of character. These, combined with an appealing smile and level look from dark, fathomless eyes, seemed irresistible. For instance, it took her a mere five days to get Major Wright to rescind his order confining her to 'A' Deck.

Although Centaine's days were filled to the last minute, she never for a moment lost sight of the ultimate destination. Each day her longing for first sight of the land where Michael had been born, and where his son would be born, became stronger.

However busy she was, she never missed the noonshot, and a few minutes before the hour she would race up the companion-way to the bridge and arrive in a swirl of her uniform skirts, gabbling breathlessly, 'Permission to enter the bridge, sir?' And the officer of the watch, who had been waiting for her, would salute.

'Permission granted. You are only just in time, Sunshine.'

Then she would watch fascinated as the navigating officers stood on the wing of the bridge with their sextants raised and made the noonday shot of the sun, and then worked out the day's run and the ship's position and marked it on the chart.

'There you are, Sunshine, 17°23′ south. One hundred and sixty nautical miles north-west of the mouth of the Cunene river. Cape Town in four days' time, God and the weather permitting.'

Centaine studied the map eagerly. 'So we are already off the South African coast?'

'No, no! That is German West Africa; it was one of the Kaiser's colonies, until the South Africans captured it two years ago.'

'What is it like – jungles? Savannahs?'

'No such luck, Sunshine, it's one of the most God-forsaken deserts in the entire world.'

And Centaine left the chartroom and went out on to the wing of the bridge again and stared into the east, towards the great continent that still lay far below her watery horizon.

'Oh, I can barely wait to see it at last!'

* * *

This horse was an animal of the desert, its distant ancestors had carried kings and Bedouin chieftains over the burning wastes of Arabia. Its blood-lines had been taken north by the crusaders to the colder climes of Europe, and then hundreds of years later they had been brought out to Africa again by the colonial expedition of Germany and landed at the port of Lüderitzbucht with the cavalry squadrons of Bismarck. In Africa these horses had been crossed and recrossed with the shaggy hardy mounts of the Boers and the desert-forged animals of the Hottentots until this animal emerged, a creature well suited to this rugged environment and to the tasks to which it was committed.

It had the wide nostrils and fine head of its Arabian type, broad spatulate hooves to cover the soft desert earth, great lungs in its barrel chest, pale chestnut coloration to repel the worst of the sun's rays, a shaggy coat to insulate it from both the burning noon heat and the crackling cold of the desert nights, and the legs and heart to carry its rider to far milky horizons and beyond.

The man upon his back was also of mixed blood-lines and, like his mount, a creature of the desert and the boundless land.

His mother had come out from Berlin when her father had been appointed second-in-command of the military forces in German West Africa. She had met and, despite her family's opposition, married a young Boer from a family rich only in land and spirit. Lothar was the only child of that union, and at his mother's insistence had been sent back to Germany to complete his schooling. He had proved a good scholar, but the outbreak of the Boer War had interrupted his studies. The first his mother had known of his decision to join the Boer forces was when he arrived back in Windhoek unannounced. Hers was a warrior family, so her pride was fierce when Lothar had ridden away with a Hottentot servant and three spare horses to seek his father who was already in the field against the English.

Lothar had found his father at Magersfontein with his uncle Koos De La Rey, the legendary Boer commander, and had undergone his initiation to battle two days later when the British tried to force the passage through the Magersfontein hills and relieve the siege of Kimberley.

Lothar De La Rey was five days past his fourteenth birthday on the dawn of

the battle, and he killed his first Englishman before six that morning. It had been a less difficult target than a hundred springbok and running kudu had offered him before.

Lothar, one of the five hundred picked marksmen, had stood to the parapet of the trench that he had helped dig along the foot of the Magersfontein hills. The idea of digging a trench and using it as cover had at first repelled the Boers, who were essentially horsemen and loved to range fast and wide. Yet General De La Rey had persuaded them to try this new tactic, and the lines of advancing English infantry had walked unsuspectingly on to the trenches in the deceptive early light.

Leading the advance towards where Lothar lay was a powerful, thickset man with flaming red muttonchop whiskers. He strode a dozen paces ahead of the line, his kilts swinging jauntily, a tropical pith helmet set at a rakish angle over one eye and a bared sword in his right hand.

At that moment the sun rose over the Magersfontein hills, and its ripe orange light flooded the open, featureless veld. It lit the ranks of advancing highlanders like a stage effect – perfect shooting light – and the Boers had paced out the ranges in front of their trenches and marked them with cairns of stones.

Lothar took his aim on the centre of the Englishman's forehead, but like the men beside him was held by a strange reluctance, for this seemed not much short of murder. Then, almost at its own volition, the Mauser jumped against his shoulder and the crack of the shot seemed to come from very far away. The British officer's helmet sprang from his head and spun end over end. He was driven back a pace and his arms flew open. The sound of the bullet striking the man's skull came back to Lothar, like a ripe watermelon dropped on to a stone floor. The sword flashed in the sunlight as it fell from the soldier's hand, then with a slow, almost elegant pirouette, he sank into the low coarse scrub.

Hundreds of highlanders had lain pinned in front of the trenches all that day. Not a man of them dared lift his head, for the waiting rifles in the trenches a hundred paces from where they lay were wielded by some of the finest marksmen in the world.

The African sun burned the backs of their knees below the kilts until they swelled, and the skin burst open like over-ripe fruit. The wounded highlanders cried for water and some of the Boers in the trenches threw their water-bottles towards them, but they fell short.

Though Lothar had killed fifty men since then, that was the day he would remember all his life. He always marked it as the day he had become a man.

Lothar was not among those who had thrown his water-bottle. Instead, he had shot dead two of the Englishmen as they wriggled forward on their bellies to try and reach the water-bottles. His hatred of the English, learned at the knees of both his mother and his father, had truly begun to flower that day and had come into full fruiting in the years that followed.

The English had hunted him and his father like wild animals across the veld. His beloved aunt and three female cousins had died of diphtheria, the white sore throat, in the English concentration camps, but Lothar had made himself believe the story that the English had put fish-hooks in the bread that they fed the Boer women to rip out their throats. It was an English thing, this war on the women and the young girls and the children.

He and his father and his uncles had fought on long after all hope of victory was gone, the Bitter Enders, they called themselves with pride. When the others, starved to walking skeletons, sick with dysentery and covered with the

running ulcerations which they called veld sores, caused by exposure and malnutrition, dressed in their rags and sacking, with only three rounds a piece remaining in their bandoliers, had gone in to surrender to the English at Vereeniging, Petrus De La Rey and his son Lothar had not gone in with them.

'Witness my oath, oh Lord of my people,' Petrus had stood bareheaded in the veld, with his seventeen-year-old son Lothar beside him. 'The war against the English will never end. This I swear in your sight, oh Lord God of Israel.'

Then he had placed the black leather-covered Bible in Lothar's hands and made him swear the same oath.

'The war against the English will never end – ' Lothar had stood beside his father as he cursed the traitors, the cowards who would no longer fight on, Louis Botha and Jannie Smuts, even his own brother Koos De La Rey. 'You, who would sell your people to the Philistine, may you live all your lives under the English yoke and all burn in hell for ten thousand years.'

Then the father and the boy had turned their backs and ridden away, towards the vast arid land that was the domain of Imperial Germany, and left the others to make peace with England.

Because both father and son were strong, hard workers, both of them endowed with natural shrewdness and courage, because Lothar's mother was a German of good family with excellent connections and some wealth, they had prospered in German South-West Africa.

Petrus De La Rey, Lothar's father, was a self-taught engineer of considerable skill and ingenuity. What he did not know he could improvize: the saying was, *'N Boer maak altyd 'n plan'* – a Boer will always make a plan. Through his wife's connections he obtained the contract to reconstruct the breakwater of Lüderitzbucht harbour, and when that was successfully completed, the contract to build the railway line nothwards from the Orange river to Windhoek, the capital of German South-West. He taught Lothar his engineering skills. The boy learned swiftly, and by the age of twenty-one was a full partner in the construction and road-building company of De La Rey and Son.

His mother, Christina De La Rey, selected a pretty blonde German girl of good family and moved her diplomatically into her son's orbit, and they were married before Lothar's twenty-third birthday. She bore Lothar a beautiful blond son on whom he doted.

Then the English intruded upon their lives once more, threatening to plunge the entire world into war by opposing the legitimate ambitions of the German empire. Lothar and his father had gone to Governor Seitz with an offer to build up, at their own expense, supply dumps in the remote areas of the territory to be used by the German forces to resist the English invasion, which would surely come from the Union of South Africa, now governed by those traitors and turncoats Smuts and Louis Botha.

There had been a German naval captain in Windhoek at the time; he had quickly recognized the value of the De La Rey offer and prevailed on the governor to accept it. He had sailed with the father and son along that dreadful littoral that so well deserved the name Skeleton Coast, to select a site for a base from which German naval vessels could refuel and revictual, even after the ports of Lüderitzbucht and Walvis Bay were captured by the Union forces.

They discovered a remote and protected bay three hundred miles north of the tenuous settlements at Walvis Bay and Swakopmund, a site almost impossible to reach overland, for it was guarded by the fiery deserts. They loaded a small coastal steamer with the naval stores sent out to them secretly

from Bremerhaven in a German cruise ship. There were 500 tons of fuel oil in 44-gallon drums, engine spares and canned foods, small arms and ammunition, nine-inch naval shells, and fourteen of the long Mark VII acoustic torpedoes, to re-arm the German U-boats if they should ever operate in these southern oceans. These supplies were ferried ashore and buried amongst the towering dunes. The lighters were painted with protective tar and buried with the stores.

This secret supply base was finally established only weeks before the Archduke Franz Ferdinand was assassinated at Sarejevo and the Kaiser was forced to move against the Serbian revolutionaries to protect the interests of the German empire. Immediately France and Britain had seized upon this as a pretext for precipitating the war after which they had been lusting.

Lothar and his father saddled their horses and called out their Hottentot servants, kissed their women and Lothar's son farewell, and rode out on commando against the English and their unionist minions once again. They were six hundred strong, riding under the Boer General Maritz, when they reached the Orange river and built their laager and waited for the moment to strike.

Each day armed men rode in to join them, tough, bearded men, proud, hard fighters with the Mausers slung on their shoulders and the bandoliers of ammunition criss-crossing their wide chests. After each joyous greeting, they gave their news, and it was all good.

The old comrades were flocking to the cry of 'Commando!' Everywhere Boers were repudiating the treacherous peace which Smuts and Botha had negotiated with the English. All the old Boer generals were taking to the field. De Wet was camped at Mushroom Valley, Kemp was at Treurfontein with eight hundred, Beyers and Fourie were all out and had declared for Germany against England.

Smuts and Botha seemed reluctant to precipitate a conflict between Boer and Boer, for the Union forces consisted of seventy per cent Dutch-born soldiers. They were begging, wheedling and pleading with the rebels, sending envoys to their camps, prostrating themselves in the attempt to avoid bloodshed, but each day the rebel forces grew stronger and more confident.

Then a message reached them, carried by a horseman riding in great haste across the desert from Windhoek. It was a message from the Kaiser himself, relayed to them by Governor Seitz.

Admiral Graf Von Spee with his squadron of battle-cruisers had won a devastating naval battle at Coronel on the Chilean coast. The Kaiser had ordered Von Spee to round the Horn and cross the southern Atlantic to blockade and bombard the South African ports in support of their rebellion against the English and the Unionists.

They stood under the fierce desert sun and cheered and sang, united and sure of their cause, and certain of their victory. They were waiting only for the last of the Boer generals to come in to join them before they marched on Pretoria.

Koos De La Rey, Lothar's uncle, grown old and feeble and indecisive, had still not come in. Lothar's father sent messages to him, urging him to do his duty, but he vacillated, swayed by the treacherous oratory of Jannie Smuts and his misguided love and loyalty for Louis Botha.

Koen Brits was the other Boer leader they were waiting for, that giant of granite, standing six foot six inches tall, who could drink a bottle of fiery Cape Smoke the way a lesser man might quaff a mug of ginger beer, who could lift a trek ox off its feet, spit a stream of tobacco juice a measured twenty paces and with his Mauser hit a running springbok at two hundred paces. They needed

him, for a thousand fighting men would follow him when he decided which way to ride.

However, Jannie Smuts sent this remarkable man a message: 'Call out your commando, Oom Koen, and ride with me.' The reply was immediate. '*Ja*, my old friend, we are mounted and ready to ride – but who do we fight, Germany or England?' So they lost Brits to the Unionists.

Then Koos De La Rey, travelling to a final meeting with Jannie Smuts at which he would make his decision, ran into a police roadblock outside Pretoria and instructed his chauffeur to drive through it. The police marksmen shot him in the head. So they lost De La Rey.

Of course, Jannie Smuts, that cold, crafty devil, had an excuse. He said that the roadblock had been ordered to prevent the escape of the notorious band of bank robbers, the Foster gang, from the area, and that the police had opened fire on a mistaken identity. However, the rebels knew better. Lothar's father had wept openly when they received the news of his brother's murder, and they had known that there was no turning back, no further chance for parley, they would have to carry the land at rifle-point.

The plan was for all the rebel commandos to join up with Maritz on the Orange river, but they had underestimated the new mobility of the forces against them, afforded by the petrol-driven motor car. They had forgotten also that Botha and Smuts had long ago proved themselves the most able of all the Boer generals. When at last they moved, these two moved with the deadly speed of angry mambas.

They caught De Wet at Mushroom Valley and smashed his commando with artillery and machine-guns. There were terrible casualties, and De Wet fled into the Kalahari, pursued by Koen Brits and a motorized column that captured him at Waterburg in the desert.

Then the Unionists swung back and engaged Beyers and his commando near Rustenberg. Once the battle was lost Beyers tried to escape by swimming the flooded Vaal river. His boot-laces became entangled and they found his body three days later on the bank downstream.

On the Orange river, Lothar and his father waited for the inevitable onslaught, but bad news reached them before the Unionists did.

The English Admiral, Sir Doveton Sturdee, had intercepted Von Spee at the Falkland Islands, and sunk his great cruisers *Scharnhorst* and *Gneisenau* and the rest of his squadron with only ten British seamen killed. The rebels' hope of succour had gone down with the German fleet.

Still they fought doggedly when the Unionists came, but it was in vain. Lothar's father took a bullet through the gut, and Lothar carried him off the field and tried to get him back across the desert to Windhoek where Christina could nurse him. It was five hundred miles of terrible going through the waterless wastes. The old man's pain was so fierce that Lothar wept for him, and the wound was contaminated by the contents of his perforated intestines and mortified so that the stench brought the hyenas howling around the camp at night.

But he was a tough old man and it took him many days to die.

'Promise me, my son,' he demanded with his last breath that stank of death, 'promise me that the war with the English will never end.'

'I promise you, Father.' Lothar leaned over him to kiss his cheek, and the old man smiled and closed his eyes.

Lothar buried him under a camelthorn tree in the wilderness; he buried him

deeply so that the hyena would not smell him and dig him up. Then he rode on home to Windhoek.

Colonel Franke, the German commander, recognized Lothar's value, and asked him to raise a levy of scouts. Lothar assembled a small band of hardy Boers, German settlers, Bondelswart Hottentots and black tribesmen, and took them out into the desert to await the invasion of Unionist troops.

Smuts and Botha came with 45,000 men and landed at Swakopmund and Lüderitzbucht. From there they drove into the interior, employing their usual tactics, lightning forced marches, often without water for great distances, double-pronged attacks and encircling movements, using the new-fangled petrol-driven motor cars the same way they had used horses during the Boer War. Against this multitude Franke had 8,000 German troops to defend a territory of over 300,000 square miles with a 1,000-mile coastline.

Lothar and his scouts fought the Unionists with their own tactics, poisoning the water-holes ahead of the Union troops, dynamiting the railway lines, hooking around them to attack their supply lines, setting ambushes and landmines, raiding at night and at dawn, driving off the horses, pushing his scouts to even their far borders of endurance.

It was all unavailing. Botha and Smuts caught the tiny German army between them, and with a casualty list of only 530 dead and wounded exacted an unconditional surrender from Colonel Franke, but not from Lothar De La Rey. To honour the promise he had made to his father, he took what remained of his band of scouts northwards into the dreaded kakao veld to continue the struggle.

Lothar's mother, Christina, and his wife and child went into the internment camp for German nationals that was set up by the Unionists at Windhoek, and there all three of them died.

They died in a typhoid epidemic, but Lothar De La Rey knew who was ultimately to blame for their deaths, and in the desert he cherished and nourished his hatred, for it was all he had left. His family were slain by the English and his estates seized and confiscated. Hatred was the fuel that drove him forward.

He was thinking of his murdered family now as he stood at his horse's head on the crest of one of the high dunes that overlooked the green Atlantic Ocean where the Benguela current steamed in the early sunlight.

His mother's face seemed to rise out of the twisting fog banks before him. She had been a beautiful woman. Tall and statuesque, with thick blonde hair that hung to her knees when she brushed it out, but which she wore twisted into thick plaited golden ropes on top of her head to enhance her height. Her eyes had been golden also, with the direct cold gaze of a leopardess.

She could sing like one of the Valkyries from Wagner, and she had passed on to Lothar her love of music and learning and art. She had passed on to him also her fine looks, classical Teutonic features, and the dense curls that now hung to his shoulders from under the wide terai hat with the waving bunch of ostrich feathers stuck jauntily in the puggaree. Like Christina's, his hair was the colour of newly minted bronze, but his eyebrows were thick and dark over the golden leopard eyes that were now probing the silver mists of the Benguela.

The beauty of the scene moved Lothar the way that music could; like the violins playing Mozart – it induced in him the same feeling of mystic melancholy at the centre of his soul. The sea was green and still, not a ripple spoiled its velvety sheen. The low and gentle sound of the ocean swelled and subsided like the breathing of all creation. Yet along the shoreline the dense growth of dark

sea-kelp absorbed the sea's motion and there was no break of white water. The kelp beds danced a slow, graceful minuet, bowing and undulating to the rhythm of the ocean.

The horns of the bay were armed with rock, split into geometric shapes and streaked white with the droppings of the seabirds and seals that basked upon them. The coats of the seals glowed in the mist-filtered sunlight, and their weird honking cries carried on the windless air to where Lothar stood on the crest of the dune high above them.

In the throat of the bay the rock gave way to tawny, lion-coloured beach, and behind the first dune was trapped a wide lagoon hemmed in by nodding reedbeds, the only green in this landscape. In its shallow waters there waded troops of long-legged flamingo. The marvellous pink of their massed formations burned like unearthly fire, drawing Lothar's gaze away from his search of the sea.

The flamingo were not the only birds upon the lagoon. There were troops of pelican and white egrets, solitary blue herons and a legion of smaller long-legged waders foraging the food-rich waters.

The dunes upon which Lothar waited rose like the crested back of a monstrous serpent, writhing and twisting along the shoreline, rising five hundred feet and more against the misty sea, their restless, ever-changing bulk sculptured by the sea wind into soft plastic coils and knife-sharp peaks.

Suddenly, far out on the sea there was a dark boil of movement, and the silky green surface changed to the colour of gunmetal. Lothar felt the jump of his nerves and the race of anicipation through his veins as his gaze darted to it. Was this what he had waited and kept vigil for all these weary weeks? He lifted the binoculars that hung upon his chest, and felt the slide of disappointment.

What he had seen was merely a shoal of fish, but what a shoal! The tip-top of the living mass dimpled the surface, but as he watched, the rest of the vast shoal rose to feed on the rich green plankton and the commotion spread out until as far as he could see, to the edge of the fog banks three miles out; the ocean seethed and boiled with life. It was a shoal of pilchards five miles across, each individual only as long as a man's open hand, but in their countless millions generating the power to move the ocean.

Over this mighty multitude, the yellow-headed gannets and hysterical gulls shrieked and wheeled and plunged, their bodies kicking up white puffs of spray as they hit the water. Squadrons of seals charged back and forth, like the cavalry of the sea, breaking the water white as they gorged on the silver masses, and through this gluttonous chaos, the triangular fins of the great sharks passed with the stately motion of tall sailing ships.

For an hour Lothar watched in wonder, and then abruptly, as though at a signal, the entire living mass sounded, and within minutes the stillness descended over the ocean again. The only movement was the gentle swell of waters and the soft advance and retreat of the silver fog banks under the watery sun.

Lothar hobbled his horse, took a book from his saddle-bag and settled on the warm sand. Every few minutes he raised his eyes from the page, but the hours wore away and at last he stood and stretched and went to his horse, his fruitless vigil ended for another day. With one foot in the stirrup, he paused and made a last careful survey of a seascape smudged to bloody carnelian and dull brass by the sunset.

Then, even as he watched, the sea opened before his eyes, and out of it rose

an enormous dark shape, in the image of Leviathan, but greater than any living denizen of the oceans. Shining with wetness, gleaming water streaming from its decks and steel sides, it wallowed upon the surface.

'At last!' Lothar shouted with excitement and relief. 'I thought they would never come.'

He stared avidly through his binoculars at the long sinister black vessel. He saw the encrustations of barnacle and weed that fouled the hull. She had been long at sea, and battered by the elements. On the tall conning tower her registration numerals were almost obliterated. 'U–32.' Lothar read them with difficulty, and then his attention was diverted by acivity on the submarine's foredeck.

From one of the hatches a gun team swarmed out and ran forward to man the quick-firing cannon near the bows. They were taking no chances. Lothar saw the weapon traverse towards him, ready to reply to any hostile gesture from the shore. On the conning tower human heads appeared, and he saw binoculars trained towards him.

Hastily Lothar found the signal rocket in his saddle-bag. Its glowing red fireball arced out over the sea, and was answered immediately by a rocket from the submarine hurling skyward on a tail of smoke.

Lothar flung himself on to the back of his mount and pushed him over the edge of the dune. They went sliding down, the horse squatting on its haunches and bringing down a slipping, hissing cascade of sand around them.

At the bottom of the dune Lothar gathered his mount and they went flying across the hard damp beach, with Lothar waving his hat, standing in the stirrups and shouting with laughter. He rode into the camp at the edge of the lagoon and sprang from the saddle. He ran from one of the crude shelters of driftwood and canvas to the next, dragging out his men and kicking them from their blankets.

'They have come, you sleeping lizards. They have come, you pups of desert jackals. Come on! Get off your buttocks before they rot!'

They were an unlikely gang of cut-throats that Lothar had assembled: tall, muscled Hereros, yellow, mongol-faced Hottentots with slanted eyes, fierce Koranas and sly, handsome Ovambos, dressed in tribal finery and the lootings of the battlefields, in cloaks of softly tanned hide of kudu and zebra, in the feathers of ostrich and the tattered tunics and helmets of the Union soldiers they had killed. Armed with Mannlicher and Mauser and Martini Henry and Lee-Enfield 303s, with knife and spear, they were as bloodthirsty as hunting dogs, as wild and savage and unpredictable as the desert that had spawned them. They called only one man their master; if any other had lifted a hand to them or spurned them with his foot, they would have slit his throat or put a ball through the back of his skull, but Lothar De La Rey kicked them to their feet and drove the laggards before him with his fists.

'Move, you devourers of hyena dung, the English will be upon you before you have finished scratching your lice.'

The two lighters were hidden in the reeds. They had come up on the transport with the rest of the stores in those heady days just before the outbreak of war. In the weeks that they had waited for the U-boat, his men had recaulked the seams with oakum and tar, and fashioned rollers from the driftwood that littered the beaches.

Now at Lothar's urging they dragged the sturdy wooden boats from the reeds, twenty men straining at each, for the boats were heavy. They had been

built to carry forty tons of guano each and still stank of sea-bird droppings. They had wide beam and deep draught, and the wooden rollers laid across the beach sank into the tawny sand as the weight of the hulls passed over them.

They left the two boats at the edge of the water and then hurried back to where the drums of fuel oil were buried at the foot of the dune. They heaved them from the damp sand and rolled them down the beach. Already Lothar had rigged a tripod and tackle and the 44-gallon drums were hoisted and lowered into the lighters. As they worked, the light faded away into the desert night, and the submarine merged with the darkness of the ocean.

'Everybody to help launch!' Lothar bellowed, and his men swarmed out of the darkness and began the rhythmic work chant, each concerted heave moving the heavily laden lighter a few inches forward, until the water lifted her and she slid forward and floated free.

Lothar stood in the bows with a storm lantern held high, and his oarsmen drove the lighter, almost gunwale deep, through the cold black waters. In the blackness ahead, a signal lamp flashed to guide them, and then abruptly the high dark bulk of the U-boat loomed out of the night and the lighter bumped against its side. German seamen were ready with mooring lines and one of them gave Lothar an arm as he leaped the gap and scrambled up the steep steel side.

The U-boat captain was waiting for him on the bridge.

'Unterseeboot Kapitän Kurt Kohler.' He clicked his heels and saluted, then stepped forward to shake Lothar's hand.

'I am very happy to see you, Herr De La Rey, we have only enough fuel oil left for two days' steaming.' In the glow of the bright light the submariner was gaunt-faced. His skin had the waxy pallor of a creature that had lived away from the light for a long time. His eyes had sunk into dark cavities, and his mouth was like the scar from a sabre cut. Lothar could recognize that here was a man who had come intimately to understand death and fear down there in the dark and secret depths.

'You have had a successful cruise, Kapitän?'

'One hundred and twenty-six days at sea and twenty-six thousand tons of enemy shipping,' the submariner nodded.

'With God's help, another twenty-six thousand tons,' Lothar suggested.

'With God's help, and your fuel oil,' the captain agreed, and glanced down at the deck where the first drums were being swayed aboard. Then he looked back at Lothar. 'You have torpedoes?' he asked anxiously.

'Content yourself,' Lothar reassured him. 'The torpedoes are ready, but I thought it prudent to refuel before rearming.'

'Of course.' Neither of them had to mention the consequence of the U-boat, with her tanks empty, being caught against a hostile shore by an English warship.

'I still have a little schnapps,' the captain changed the subject, 'my officers and I would be honoured.'

As Lothar descended the steel ladder into the submarine's interior, he felt his gorge rise. The stench was a solid thing, so that he wondered that any man could endure it more than a few minutes. It was the smell of sixty men living in a confined space for months on end, living without sunlight or fresh air, without the means of washing their bodies or their clothing. It was the smell of pervading damp and of the fungus that turned their uniforms green and rotted the cloth off their bodies, the stench of hot fuel oil and bilges, of greasy food and the sickly sweat of fear, the clinging odour of bedding that had been slept

in for 126 days and nights, of socks and boots that were never changed and the reek of the sewage buckets which could only be emptied once every twenty-four hours.

Lothar hid his revulsion and clicked his heels and bowed when the captain introduced his junior officers. The overhead deck was so low that Lothar had to hunch his head down on his shoulders, and the space between the bulkheads was so narrow that two men were forced to turn sideways to pass each other. He tried to imagine living in these conditions and found his face beading with cold sweat.

'Do you have any intelligence of enemy shipping, Herr De La Rey?' The captain poured a tiny measure of schnapps into each of the crystal glasses and sighed when the last drop fell from the bottle.

'I regret that my intelligence is seven days old.' Lothar saluted the naval officers with a raised glass, and when they had all drunk went on, 'The troopship *Auckland* docked at Durban eight days ago for bunkers. She is carrying 2,000 New Zealand infantry, and was expected to sail again on the 15th – '

There were many sympathizers in the civil service of the Union of South Africa, men and women whose fathers and family had fought in the Boer War, and had ridden with Maritz and De Wet against the Union troops. Some of them had relatives who had been imprisoned and even executed for treason once Smuts and Botha had crushed the rebellion. Many of these were employed by the South African Railway and Harbours Authority, others had key positions in the Department of Post and Telegraphs. Thus vital information was gathered and swiftly encoded and disseminated to German agents and rebel activists over the Union government's own communication network.

Lothar reeled off the list of arrivals and sailings from South African ports, and again apologized. 'My information is received at the telegraph station at Okahandja, but it takes five to seven days for it to be carried across the desert by one of my men.'

'I understand,' the German captain nodded. 'Nevertheless, the information you have given me will be invaluable in helping me plan the next stage of my operations.' He looked up from the chart on which he had been marking the enemy dispositions which Lothar had given him, and for the first time noticed his guest's discomfort. He kept his expression attentive and courteous, but inwardly he gloated, 'You great hero, handsome as an opera star, so brave out there with the wind in your face and the sun shining over your head, I wish I could take you with me and teach you the true meaning of courage and sacrifice! How would you like to hear the English destroyers go drumming overhead as they hunt you, how would you like to hear the click of the primer as the death-charge sinks down towards you? Oh, I would enjoy watching your face when the blast beats against the pressure hull and water squirts in though the cracks and the lights go out. How would you like to smell yourself shit with fear in the dark and feel it running hot and liquid down your legs?' Instead he smiled and murmured, 'I wish I was able to offer you a little more schnapps – '

'No, no!' Lothar waved the offer aside. This corpse-faced creature and his stinking vessel disgusted and sickened him. 'You have been most gracious. I must go ashore and supervize the loading. These Schwarzes, you cannot trust them. Lazy dogs and born thieves, all of them. They understand only the whip and the goad.'

Lothar escaped thankfully up the ladder and in the conning tower sucked the

sweet cool night air greedily into his lungs. The submarine captain followed him up.

'Herr De La Rey, it is essential that we complete bunkering and stores before dawn – you realize how vulnerable we are here, how helpless we would be, trapped against the shore, with our hatches open and our tanks empty?'

'If you could send some of your seamen ashore to assist with the loading – '

The captain hesitated. Placing his valuable crew on land would make him more vulnerable still. He weighed the odds swiftly. War was all a gambler's throw, risk against reward, for the stakes of death and glory.

'I will send twenty men to the beach with you.' He made the decision in seconds, and Lothar, who had understood his quandary, nodded with reluctant admiration.

They had to have light. Lothar built a bonfire of driftwood on the beach, but built a screen between it and the sea, trusting on this and the hovering fog banks to shield them from any searching English warships. By the diffused glow they loaded and reloaded the lighters and rowed them out to the submarine. As each drum of fuel oil was funnelled into the vessel's tanks, the empty canister was holed and thrown overboard to sink into the kelp beds, and gradually the long slim vessel sank lower in the water.

It was four in the morning before the fuel tanks were brimming, and the U-boat captain fretted and fumed on his bridge, glancing every few seconds towards the land where the false dawn was giving a hard knife-edge to the dark crests of the dunes – and then down again to the approaching lighter with the long glistening shape of a torpedo balanced delicately across the thwarts.

'Hurry.' He leaned over the gunwale of the conning tower to urge on his men, as they fitted the slings around the monstrous weapon, gingerly took the weight on the straining tackle and swung it on board. The second lighter was already alongside with its murderous burden, and the first lighter was thrashing back towards the beach, as the torpedo was eased gently into the forward hatch and slid into the empty tube below deck.

Swiftly the light strengthened and the efforts of the crew and the black guerrillas became frantic as they fought off their fatigue and struggled to complete the loading before full daylight exposed them to their enemies.

Lothar rode out with the last torpedo, sitting casually astride its shining back as though upon his Arab, and the captain watching him in the dawn found himself resenting him more fiercely, hating him for being tall and sungilded and handsome, hating him for his casual arrogance, and for the ostrich feathers in his hat and the golden curls that hung to his shoulders, but hating him most of all because he would ride away into the desert and leave the U-boat commander to go down again into the cold and deadly waters.

'Captain,' Lothar scrambled out of the lighter and climbed the ladder to the bridge of the conning tower. The captain realized that his handsome face was glowing with excitement.

'Captain, one of my men has just ridden into camp. He has been five days reaching me from Okahandja, and he has news. Splendid news.'

The captain tried not to let the excitement infect him, but his hands began to tremble as Lothar went on.

'The assistant harbour master at Cape Town is one of our men. They are expecting the English heavy battle cruiser *Inflexible* to reach Cape Town within eight days. She left Gibraltar on the 5th and is sailing direct.'

The captain dived back into the hatch, and Lothar suppressed his repugnance

and followed him down the steel ladder. The captain was already bending eagerly over the chart-table with the dividers in his hands firing questions at his navigating officer.

'Give me the cruising speed of the enemy "I" class battle cruisers!'

The navigator thumbed swiftly through intelligence files. 'Estimated 22 knots at 260 revolutions, captain.'

'Ha!' The captain was chalking in the approximate course from Gibraltar down the western coastline of the African continent, around the great bulge and then on to the Cape of Good Hope.

'Ha!' Again, this time with delight and anticipation. 'We can be in patrol position by 1800 hours today, if we sail within the hour, and she cannot possibly have passed by then.'

He raised his head from the chart and looked at his officers crowded around him.

'An English battle cruiser, gentlemen, but not an ordinary one. The *Inflexible*, the same ship that sank the *Scharnhorst* at the Falkland Islands. A prize! What a prize for us to take to the Kaiser and *Das Vaterland*.'

* * *

Except for the two lookouts in the wings, Captain Kurt Kohler stood alone in the conning tower of U-32 and shivered in the cold sea mist despite the thick white rollneck sweater he wore under his blue peajacket. 'Start main engine secure to diving stations!' He bent to the voice tube, and immediately his lieutenant's confirmation echoed back to him.

'Start main engine. Secure to diving stations.'

The deck trembled under Kohler's feet and the diesel exhaust blurted above his head. The oily reek of burned oil made his nostrils flare.

'Ship ready to dive!' the lieutenant's voice confirmed, and Kohler felt as though a crushing burden had been lifted from his back. How he had fretted through those helpless and vulnerable hours of refuelling and rearming. However, that was past – once again the ship was alive beneath his feet, ready to his hand, and relief buoyed him up above his fatigue.

'Revolutions for seven knots,' he ordered. 'New course 270°.' As his order was repeated, he tipped his cap with its gold-braided peak on to the back of his head, and turned his binoculars towards land.

Already the heavy wooden lighters had been dragged away and hidden amongst the dunes; there remained only the drag marks of their keels in the sand. The beach was empty, except for a single mounted figure.

As Kohler watched him, Lothar De La Rey lifted the wide-brimmed hat from his brazen curls and the ostrich feathers fluttered as he waved. Kohler lifted his own right hand in salute and the horseman swung away, still brandishing his hat, and galloped into the screed of reeds that choked the valley between two soaring dunes. A cloud of water fowl, alarmed by the horseman, rose from the surface of the lagoon and milled in a gaudily coloured cloud above the forbidden dunes, and the horse and rider disappeared.

Kohler turned his back upon the land, and the long pointed bows of the U-boat sliced into the standing curtains of silver fog. The hull was shaped like a sword, a broadsword 170 feet long, to be driven at the throat of the enemy by

her great 600-horsepower diesel engine, and Kohler did not try to suppress the choking sense of pride that he always felt at the beginning of a cruise.

He was under no illusion but that the outcome of this global conflict rested upon him and his brother officers in the submarine service. It was in their power alone to break the terrible stalemate of the trenches where two vast armies faced each other like exhausted heavyweight boxers, neither having enough strength left to lift their arms to throw a decisive punch, slowly rotting in the mud and decay of their own monstrous strivings.

It was these slim and secret and deadly craft that could still wrest victory out of despair and desperation before the breaking-point was reached. If only the Kaiser had decided to use his submarines to their full potential from the very beginning, Kurt Kohler brooded, how different the outcome might have been.

In September 1914, the very first year of the war, a single submarine, the U–9, had sunk three British cruisers in quick succession, but even with this conclusive demonstration, the German high command had hesitated to use the weapon that had been placed in their hands, fearful of the outrage and condemnation of the entire world, of the simplistic cry of 'the beastly underwater butchers'.

Of course, the American threats after the sinking of the *Lusitania* and *Arabic* with the loss of American lives had served also to constrain the use of the undersea weapon. The Kaiser had feared to arouse the sleeping American giant, and to have its mighty weight hurled against the German Empire.

Now, when it was almost too late, the German high command had at last let slip the U–boats, and the results were staggering, surpassing even their own expectations.

The last three months of 1916 saw more than 300,000 tons of Allied shipping go down before the torpedoes. That was only a beginning; in the first ten days of April 1917, alone, another incredible 250,000 tons was destroyed, 875,000 tons for the full month – the Allies were reeling under this fearful infliction.

Now that two million fresh and eager young American troops were ready to cross the Atlantic to join the conflict, it was the duty of every officer and seaman of the German submarine service to make whatever sacrifice was demanded of him. If the gods of war chose to place a British heavy battle cruiser of such illustrious lineage as the *Inflexible* on a converging course with his battered little vessel, Kurt Kohler would gladly give up his own life and the lives of his crew for an opportunity to empty his torpedo tubes at her.

'Revolutions for 12 knots,' Kurt spoke into the voice tube. That was the U–32's top surface speed, he had to get into patrol position as swiftly as possible. His calculations indicated that the *Inflexible* must pass between 110 and 140 nautical miles offshore, but Kurt refused to calculate his chances of making a good interception, even if he reached the patrol area before the cruiser passed by.

The horizon from the U–32's lookout wings was a mere seven miles, the range of her torpedoes 2,500 yards, the quarry capable of a sustained speed of 22 knots or more. He had to manoeuvre his vessel within 2,500 yards of the speeding cruiser, but the chances were many thousands of times against him even sighting her. Even if he obtained a sighting, it would probably be only to watch the distinctive tripod-shaped superstructure of the cruiser pass hull down on his limited horizon.

He thrust his forebodings aside. 'Lieutenant Horsthauzen to the bridge.'

When his first officer clambered up to the bridge, Kurt gave him orders to

drive out to the patrol area with all possible speed, with the ship secured to diving stations ready for instant action.

'Call me at 1830 hours if there is no change.'

Kurt's exhausion was aggravated by the dull headache from the diesel fumes. He took one last look around the horizon before going below. The fog banks were being stripped away by the rising wind, the sea was darkening, its anger rising at the whip of the elements. The U–32 thrust her bows into the next swell, and white water broke over her foredeck. Spray splattered icily into Kurt's face.

'The glass is dropping swiftly, sir,' Horsthauzen told him quietly. 'I think we are in for a sharp blow.'

'Stay on the surface, maintain speed.' Kurt ignored the opinion. He didn't want to hear anything that might complicate the hunt. He slid down the ladder and went immediately to the ship's logbook on the chart-table.

He made his entry in his meticulous formal script. 'Course 270 degrees. Speed 12 knots. Wind north-west, 15 knots and freshening.' Then he signed it with his full signature and pressed his fingers into his temples to still the ache within his skull.

'My God, I am tired,' he thought, and then saw the navigation officer watching his reflection surreptitiously, in the polished brass of the main control panel. He dropped his hands to his sides, brushed aside the temptation to go to his bunk immediately and instead told his coxswain, 'I will inspect the ship.'

He made a point of stopping in the engine compartment to compliment the engineers on the swift and efficient refuelling procedure, and in the torpedo compartment in the bows he ordered the men to remain in their bunks when he stooped in through the narrow entrance.

The three torpedo tubes were loaded and under compression, and the spare torpedoes were stacked in the narrow space; their long shiny bulk almost filled the entire cabin and made any movement difficult. The torpedo men would be forced to spend much of their time crouched in their tiny bunks, like animals in a tier of cages.

Kurt patted one of the torpedoes. 'We'll make more room for you soon,' he promised them, 'just as soon as we mail these little parcels off to Tommy.'

It was an antique joke, but they responded dutifully and, noting the timbre of their laughter, Kurt realized how those few hours on the surface in the sweet desert air had refreshed and enlivened them all.

Back in the tiny curtained cubicle which was his cabin, he could let himself relax at last, and instantly his exhaustion overcame him. He had not slept for forty hours, every minute of that time he had been exposed to constant nervous strain. Still, before he crawled laboriously into his narrow, confined bunk, he took down the framed photograph from its niche above his desk and studied the image of the placid young woman and the small boy at her knee, dressed in Lederhosen.

'Goodnight, my darlings,' he whispered. 'Goodnight to you, also, my other son, whom I have never seen.'

* * *

The diving klaxon woke him, bellowing like a wounded beast, echoing painfully in the confines of the steel hull, so that he was torn from deep black sleep and cracked his head on the jamb of the bunk as he tried to struggle out of it.

He was aware instantly of the pitch and roll of the hull. The weather had deteriorated, and then he felt the deck cant under his feet as the bows dropped and the submarine plunged below the surface. He ripped open the curtains and burst fully dressed into the control centre, just as the two lookouts came tumbling down the ladder from the bridge. The dive had been so swift that seawater cascaded down on to their heads and shoulders before Horsthauzen could secure the main hatch in the tower.

Kurt glanced at the clock at the top of the brass control panel as he took control. '18.23 hours.' He made the calculation and estimated that they must be 100 nautical miles offshore on the edge of their patrol area. Horsthauzen would probably have called him in another few minutes, if he had not been forced to make this emergency dive.

'Periscope depth,' he snapped at the senior helmsman seated before the control panel, and used the few moments of respite to rally his senses and orientate himself fully by studying the navigational plot.

'Depth nine metres, sir,' said the helmsman, spinning the wheel to check her wild plunge.

'Up periscope,' Kurt ordered, as Horsthauzen dropped down the tower, jumped off the ladder and took up his action station at the attack table.

'The sighting is a large vessel showing green and red navigation lights, bearing 060 degrees,' he reported quietly to Kurt. 'I could make out no details.'

As the periscope rose up through the deck, the hydraulic rams hissing loudly, Kurt ducked down, unfolded the side handles and pressed his face into the rubber pads, peering into the Zeiss lens of the eyepiece and straightening his body to follow the telescope up, already swinging it on to the bearing marks 060 degrees.

The lens was obscured by water, and he waited for it to clear.

'Late twilight – ' he judged the light up there on the surface, and then to Horsthauzen, 'range estimate?'

'Sighting is hull down.' That meant she was probably eight or nine miles, but red and green navigation lights indicated that she was headed almost directly towards the U-32. That she should be showing lights at all indicated the vessel's supreme confidence that she was alone on the ocean.

The lens cleared of water and Kurt traversed slowly.

There she was. He felt his pulse leap and his breathing check. It never failed – no matter how often he saw the enemy, the shock and the thrill was as intense as the very first time.

'Bearing mark!' he snapped at Horsthauzen, and the lieutenant entered the bearing on the attack table.

Kurt stared at the quarry, feeling the hunger in his guts, the almost sexual ache in his loin as though he were watching a beautiful naked and available woman; at the same time he was gently manipulating the knob of the rangefinder with his right hand.

In the lens of the periscope the double images of the target ship were brought together by the viewfinder.

'Range mark!' Kurt said clearly as the images coalesced into a single sharp silhouette.

'Bearing 075 degrees,' said Horsthauzen. 'Range 7,650 metres!' and entered the numerals into the attack table.

'Down periscope! New heading 340 degrees!' ordered Kurt, and the thick telescoping steel sections of the periscope hissed down into their well in the deck between his feet. Even at this range and in the bad light Kurt was taking no chances that a wary lookout might pick out the plume of spray thrown up by the tip of the periscope as it cut the surface, turning on to an interception course into the north.

Kurt was watching the second hand of the clock on the control panel. He must give Horsthauzen at least two minutes before he made his next sighting. He glanced across at his first officer and found him totally absorbed in his calculations, stopwatch in his right hand, left hand manipulating the tumblers of the attack table like a Chinaman with an abacus.

Kurt switched his attention to his own calculations concerning the light and the surface condition of the sea. The fading light favoured him. As always, the hunter needed stealth and secrecy, but the rising sea would hamper his approach; breaking over the lens of the periscope, it might even affect the running of his torpedoes.

'Up periscope!' he ordered. The two minutes had expired. He found the image almost instantly.

'Bearing mark! Range mark!'

Now Horsthauzen had his references, elapsed time between sights and the relative ranges and bearings of the submarine and its target, together with the U–32's own speed and course.

'Target is on a heading of 175 degrees. Speed 22 knots,' he read off the attack table.

Kurt did not look away from the eyepiece of the periscope, but felt the thrill of the chase in his blood like the flush of strong spirits. The other ship was coming straight down on them, and its speed was almost exactly that to be expected of a British battle cruiser making a long passage. He stared at the distant image, but the light was going even as he studied the shadowy superstructure just visible between the pinpricks of the navigational lights – and yet, and yet – he was not absolutely certain, perhaps he was seeing what he wished to see – but there was a vague triangular shape against the darkening sky, the sure tripod mark of the new 'I'-class battle cruiser.

'Down periscope.' He made his decision. 'New heading 355 degrees,' the head-on course to intercept the target, 'designate the target as the "chase".' That was the intimation to his officers that he was attacking, and he saw their expression turn wolfish in the subdued light and they exchanged eager gloating glances. 'The chase is an enemy cruiser. We will attack with our bow tubes. Report battle stations.'

In quick succession the reports came in assuring him of the instant readiness of the entire ship. Kurt nodded with satisfaction, standing facing the brass control panel, studying the dials over the heads of his seated helmsmen, his hands thrust deeply into the pockets of his peajacket so that their trembling did not betray his agitated excitement, but a nerve jumped in his lower eyelid, making him wink sardonically, and his thin pale lips trembled uncontrollably. Each second seemed an eternity, until he could ask, 'Estimated bearing?'

The seaman with the hydrophones over his ears looked up. He had been closely monitoring the distant sound of the chase's propellers.

'Bearing steady,' he replied, and Kurt glanced at Horsthauzen.

'Estimated range?' Horsthauzen kept all his attention on his attack table.

'Estimated range 4,000 metres.'

'Up periscope.'

She was still there, exactly where he had expected her – she had not turned away. Kurt felt almost nauseated with relief. At any time that she suspected his presence the chase could simply turn and run away from him, without even bothering to increase speed, and he would be helpless to stop her. But she was coming on unsuspectingly.

It was fully dark in the world above the surface, and the sea was breaking and tumbling with white caps. Kurt had to make the decision which he had postponed to the last possible moment. He made one last sweep of the entire horizon, swinging the handles of the periscope the full 360 degrees, shuffling around behind the eyepiece, satisfying himself that there was no other enemy creeping up behind his stern, no destroyers escorting the cruiser, and then he said, 'I will shoot from the bridge.'

Even Horsthauzen glanced up momentarily, and he heard the sharp intake of breath from his junior officers when they realized they were going to surface almost under the bows of an enemy battle cruiser.

'Down periscope!' Kurt ordered his senior helmsman. 'Reduce speed to five knots and come to tower depth.'

He saw the needles on the control dials tremble and then begin to move, the speed dropping back, the depth decreasing gently, and he moved across to the ladder.

'I am transferring to the bridge,' he told Horsthauzen, and stepped on to the ladder. He climbed nimbly and at the top spun the locking wheel of the main hatch.

As the submarine broke through the surface, the internal air pressure blew the hatch open and Kurt sprang through it.

The wind lashed him immediately, tugging at his clothing and blowing spray into his face. All about him the sea was breaking and boiling, and the ship rolled and wallowed. Kurt had relied on the turmoil of waters to disguise the disturbance that the U–32 would make as she surfaced. With one glance, he satisfied himself that the enemy was almost dead ahead and coming on swiftly and unswervingly. He bowed to the aiming table at the forward end of the bridge, unstoppered the voice pipe and spoke into it.

'Prepare to attack! Stand by bow tubes.'

'Bow tubes closed up,' Horsthauzen answered him from below, and Kurt began to feed him the details of range and bearing, while on the deck below, the lieutenant read off from the attack table the firing heading and passed it to the helmsman. The submarine's bows swung gradually as the helmsman kept her on the exact aiming mark.

'Range 2,500 metres,' Kurt intoned. She was at extreme range now, but closing swiftly.

There were lights burning on her upper decks but apart from that she was merely a huge dark shape. There was no longer any definite silhouette against the night sky, although Kurt could make out the shapeless loom of her triple funnels.

The lights troubled Kurt. No Royal Naval captain should be so negligent of the most elementary precautions. He felt a small chill wind of doubt cool his excitement and battle ardour. He stared at the enormous vessel through the

spray and darkness and for the first time in a hundred such dangerous nerve-racking situations, he felt himself hesitant and uncertain.

The vessel before him was in the exact position and on the exact course where he had expected to find the *Inflexible*. It was the right size, it had three funnels and a tripod superstructure, it was steaming at 22 knots – and yet it was showing lights.

'Repeat range mark!' Horsthauzen spoke through the voice tube, gently prodding him, and Kurt started. He had been staring at the chase, neglecting the rangefinder. Quickly he gave the decreasing range and then realized that within thirty seconds he would have to make his final decision.

'I will shoot at 1,000 metres,' he said into the voice tube.

It was pointblank range; even in this confused sea there was no question of missing with one of the long sharklike missiles.

Kurt stared into the lens of the rangefinder, watching the numerals decreasing steadily as hunter and hunted came together. He drew a deep breath like a diver about to plunge into the cold black waters and then he raised his voice for the first time.

'Number one tube – *los*!'

Almost immediately Horsthauzen's voice came back to him, with that slight catchy stutter that always afflicted him when he was overexcited.

'Number one fired and running.'

There was no sound, nor recoil. No movement of the submarine's hull to signal the release of the first torpedo.

In the darkness and the breaking white waters, Kurt could not even distinguish the wake of the speeding torpedo.

'Number two tube – *los*!'

Kurt was firing a spread of torpedoes, each on a minutely diverging course – the first aimed forward, the second amidships, the third aft.

'Number three tube – *los*!'

'All three fired and running!'

Kurt raised his eyes from the aiming table and slitted them against the flying spray and the wind as he gazed down the track of his torpedoes. It was standard service procedure to crash dive immediately all torpedoes were fired and to await the explosions of the hits down in the safety of the depths, but this time Kurt felt compelled to remain on top and watch it happen.

'Running time?' he demanded of Horsthauzen, watching the tall bulk of his victim festooned with lights like a cruise ship, so that she paled out the fields of stars that sprinkled the black curtain of the sky behind her.

'Two minutes fifteen seconds to run,' Horsthauzen told him, and Kurt clicked down the button of his stopwatch.

Always in this time of waiting after his weapons were sped upon their way, the remorse assailed Kurt. Before the firing there was only the heat of the chase and the tingling excitement of the stalk, but now he thought of the brave men, brothers of the sea, whom he had consigned to the cold dark and merciless waters.

The seconds dragged, so that he had to check the luminous dial of his stopwatch to assure himself that his torpedoes had not sounded or swerved nor run past.

Then there was that vast blurt of sound which even when expected made him flinch, and he saw the pearly fountain of spray rise against the bulk of the battle

cruiser, shining in the starlight and in the decklights with a beautiful iridescent radiance.

'Number one – hit.' Horsthauzen's shout of triumph came from the voice pipe, followed immediately by another thunderous roar as though a mountain had fallen into the sea.

'Number two – hit.'

And yet again, while the first two tall shining columns of spray still hovered, the third leapt high in the dark air beside them.

'Number three – hit.'

As Kurt still watched, the columns of spray mingled, subsided and blew away on the wind, and the great ship ran on, seemingly unscathed.

'Chase is losing speed,' Horsthauzen exalted. 'Altering course to starboard.'

The doomed ship began a wide aimless turn into the wind. It would not be necessary to fire their stern tubes.

'Lieutenant Horsthauzen to the bridge,' Kurt said into the voice tube. It was a reward for a task perfectly performed. He knew how avidly the young lieutenant would relate every detail of the sinking to his brother officers later. The memory of this victory would sustain them all through the long days and nights of privation and hardship that lay ahead. Horsthauzen burst from the hatch and stood shoulder to shoulder with his captain, peering at their monstrous victim.

'She has stopped!' he cried. The British ship lay like a rock in the sea.

'We will move closer,' Kurt decided, and relayed the order to the helmsman.

The U–32 crept forward, butting into the creaming waves, only her conning tower above the surface, closing the range gradually and gingerly. The cruiser's guns might still be manned and only a single lucky shot was needed to hole the submarine's thin plating.

'Listen!' Kurt ordered abruptly, turning his head to catch the sounds that came to them faintly above the clamour of the wind.

'I hear nothing.'

'Stop engines!' Kurt ordered, and the vibration and hum of the diesels ceased. Now they could hear it more clearly.

'Voices!' Horsthauzen whispered. It was a pathetic chorus, borne to them on the wind. The shouts and cries of men in dire distress, rising and falling on the vagaries of the wind, punctuated by a wild scream as somebody fell or leapt from the high deck.

'She is listing heavily.' They were close enough to see her against the stars.

'She's sinking by the bows.'

The great stern was rearing out of the black.

'She's going quickly – very quickly.'

They could hear the crackle and rumble of her hull as the waters raced through her, and twisted and distorted her plating.

'Man the searchlight,' Kurt ordered, and Horsthauzen turned to stare at him.

'Did you hear my order?' Horsthauzen roused himself. It went against all a submariner's instincts to betray himself so blatantly to the eyes of the enemy, but he crossed to the searchlight in the wing of the deck.

'Switch on!' Kurt urged him when he hesitated still, and the long white beam leapt out across half a mile of tempestuous sea and darkness. It struck the hull of the ship and was reflected in a dazzle of purest white.

Kurt threw himself across the bridge and shouldered his lieutenant from the searchlight. He gripped the handles and swung the solid beam across and down,

slitting his eyes against the dazzling reflection from the ship's paintwork; he searched frantically and then froze, with his fingers hooked like claws over the searchlight handles.

In the perfect round circle of the searchlight beam, the scarlet arms of the huge painted cross were outflung, like the limbs of a condemned man upon the crucifix.

'Mother of the Almighty God,' Kurt whispered, 'what have I done?'

With horrid fascination he moved the beam slowly from side to side. The decks of the white ship were canted steeply towards him, so he could see the clusters of human figures that scurried about them, trying to reach the lifeboats dangling from their davits. Some of them were dragging stretchers or leading stumbling figures dressed in long blue hospital robes, and their cries and supplications sounded like a colony of nesting birds at sunset.

As Kurt watched, the ship suddenly tipped towards him with a rush, and the men on the decks were sent sliding across them, piling up against the railings. Then singly and in clusters they began to fall overboard.

One of the lifeboats let go and dropped out of control to hit the water alongside the hull and immediately capsized. Still men were dropping from the high decks, and he could hear their faint shrieks above the wind, see the small spouts of white spray as they struck the water.

'What can we do?' Horsthauzen whispered beside Kurt, staring with him down the searchlight beam, his expression pale and appalled.

Kurt switched off the searchlight. After the intense light, the darkness was crushing.

'Nothing,' said Kurt in the darkness. 'There is nothing we can do.' And he turned and stumbled to the hatchway.

By the time he reached the bottom of the ladder, he had control of himself again, and his voice was flat and his expression stony as he gave his orders.

'Lookouts to the bridge. Revolutions for 12 knots, new course 150 degrees.'

He stood at ease as they turned away from the sinking ship, fighting the urge to lift their hands to cover their ears. He knew he could not shut out the cries and shrieks that still echoed in his skull. He knew he would never be able to shut them out, and that he would hear them again at the hour of his own death.

'Secure from action stations,' he said with dead eyes, his waxen features wet with spray and sweat.

'Resume patrol routine.'

* * *

Centaine was perched on the foot of the lowest bunk in her favourite ward on 'C' deck. She had the book open on her lap.

It was one of the larger cabins, with eight bunks, and all the young men in the bunks were spinals. Not one of them would ever walk again, and almost in defiance of this fact they were the noisiest, gayest and most opinionated bunch on board the *Protea Castle*.

Every evening, during the hour before lights-out, Centaine read to them – or that was the intention. It usually only required a few minutes of the author's opinions to trigger a spirited debate which ran unchecked until the dinner gong finally intervened.

Centaine enjoyed these sessions as much as any of them, and she invariably chose a book on a subject about which she wanted to know more, always an African theme.

This evening she had selected volume II of Levaillant's *Voyage dans l' intérieur de l' Afrique* in the original French. She translated directly from the page of Levaillant's description of a hippopotamus hunt which her audience followed avidly, until she reached the description: 'The female beast was flayed and cut up on the spot. I ordered a bowl to be brought me, which I filled with her milk. It appears to be much less disagreeable than that of the elephant and the next day had changed almost wholly to cream. It had an amphibious taste, and a filthy smell which gave disgust, but in coffee it was even pleasant.'

There were cries of revulsion from the bunks. 'My God!' somebody exclaimed. 'Those Frenchies! Anybody who will drink hippo milk and eat frogs – '

Instantly they all turned upon him. 'Sunshine is a Frenchy, you dog! Apologize immediately!' and a barrage of pillows was hurled across the cabin at the offender.

Laughing, Certaine jumped up to restore order, and as she did so the deck bucked under her feet and she was hurled backwards on to the bunk again, and the blast of a massive explosion ripped through the ship.

Centaine struggled up and was knocked down again by another explosion more violent than the first.

'What is happening?' she screamed, and a third explosion plunged them into darkness and threw her from the bunk on to the deck. In the utter darkness somebody tumbled on top of her, pinning her in a welter of bedclothes.

She felt herself suffocating and she screamed again. The ship rang to other cries and shouts.

'Get off me!' Centaine fought to free herself, crawled to the doorway and pulled herself upright. The pandemonium all around her, the rush of bodies in the dark, the shouts and senseless bawling of orders, the sudden terrifying tilt of the deck under Centaine's feet panicked her. She lashed out to protect herself as an unseen body crashed into her. Amd then groped her way down the long narrow corridor.

The alarm bells began to ring through the darkness, a shrill, nerve-ripping sound that added to the confusion, and a voice roared, 'The ship is sinking – they are abandoning ship. We'll be trapped down here.'

There was an immediate rush to the companionway, and Centaine found herself borne along helplessly, fighting to keep her balance, for she knew if she fell she would be trampled. Instinctively she tried to protect her belly, but she was sent reeling into the bulkhead with a force that clashed her teeth and she bit her own tongue. As she fell, her mouth filled with the slick metallic taste of blood; she flung out both hands and they closed on the guide rail of the companionway and she hung on with all her strength. She dragged herself up the staircase, sobbing with the effort to keep her feet in the crush of panic-stricken bodies.

'My baby!' She heard herself saying it aloud. 'You can't kill my baby.'

The ship lurched, and there was the crackle and shriek of metal on metal, the crash of breaking glass, and the renewed rush and trample of feet all around her.

'It's going down!' shrieked a voice beside her. 'We've got to get out! Let me out – '

The lights went on again, and she saw the companionway to the upper deck choked with struggling, cursing men. She felt bruised and crushed and helpless.

'My baby!' she sobbed, as she was pinned against the bulkhead. The lights seemed to sober the men around her, shaming them out of their blind terror.

'Here's Sunshine!' a voice bellowed. It was a big Afrikaner, one of her most fervent admirers, and he swung his crutch to forge an opening for her.

'Let her through – stand back, you bastards, let Sunshine through.'

Hands seized her, and she was lifted off her feet.

'Let Sunshine through!'

They passed her overhead, like a doll. She lost her veil and one of her shoes.

'Here's Sunshine, pass her up!' She found herself sobbing as she was jostled and hard fingers seized her and bit painfully into her flesh, but she was borne swiftly upwards.

At the top of the companionway, other hands grabbed her and hustled her out on to the open deck. It was dark out here and the wind snatched at her hair and wrapped her skirts constrictingly about her legs. The deck was listing heavily, but as she stepped upon it, it canted even more viciously and she was hurled against a stanchion with a force that made her cry out.

Suddenly she thought about the helplessly maimed young men that she had left down there on 'C' deck.

'I should have tried to help them,' she told herself, and then she thought of Anna. Hesitating and confused she looked back. Men still swarmed up and out of the companionways. It would be impossible to move against that throng, and she knew that she did not have the strength needed to assist a man who could not walk himself.

All around her the officers were trying to restore order, but most of these men who had stoically borne the hell of the trenches were terrified witless by the thought of being trapped in a sinking ship, and their faces were contorted and their eyes wild with unreasoning terror. However, there were others who were dragging out the cripples and the blind and leading them to the lifeboats along the rail.

Clinging to the stanchion, Centaine was torn with indecision and fear and horror for the hundreds of men below who she knew would never reach the deck. Then beneath her the ship rumbled and belched in its death throes, air rushed from the holes beneath her waterline with the roarings of a sea monster and the sound decided Centaine.

'My baby,' she thought. 'I have to save him, the others don't matter – only my baby!'

'Sunshine!' One of the officers had seen her and he slid down the steep deck to her and put an arm around her protectively.

'You've got to get to a lifeboat – the ship will go at any moment.'

With his free hand he ripped open the tapes that secured his bulky canvas lifejacket, and he pulled it off his shoulders and lifted it over Centaine's head.

'What happened?' Centaine gasped as he knotted the tapes of the lifejacket under her chin and down her chest.

'We've been torpedoed. Come on.'

He dragged her along with him, reaching for handholds, for it was impossible to stand unaided on the steep angle of the deck.

'That lifeboat! We've got to get you into it.'

Just ahead of them a crowded lifeboat was swinging wildly on its davits, an officer was bellowing orders as they tried to clear the jammed tackle.

Looking down the ship's side, Centaine saw the black sea boiling and foaming, and the wind blew her hair into her face and half-blinded her.

Then, from far out on the black waters, a solid white shaft of light burst over them, and they flung up their hands to protect their eyes from the cruel glare.

'Submarine!' shouted the officer who held Centaine in the crook of his arm. 'The swine has come to gloat on his butchery.'

'The beam of light left them and swivelled away down the side of the hull.

'Come on, Sunshine.' He dragged her towards the ship's rail, but at that moment the tackle of the lifeboat gave way at the bows, and spilled its frantic cargo screaming into the pounding waves far below.

With yet another vast exhalation of air from her underwater wounds the ship swung further outwards to an impossible angle, and Centaine and the officer slid irresistibly across the deck and hit the rail together.

The merciless beam of white light moved from one end of the ship to the other and when it passed over them, it left them blinded and it seemed the night was even blacker and more menacing than before.

'The swines! The bloody swines!' The officer's voice was rough and hoarse with rage.

'We must jump!' Centaine shouted back at him. 'We have to get off!'

* * *

When the first torpedo struck, Anna was seated at the dressing-table in the cabin. She also had spent the afternoon working with the men on 'C' deck and had left them only to help Centaine prepare for dinner. She had expected Centaine to be in the cabin waiting for her and was mildly irritated when she was not.

'That child has no idea of time,' she muttered, but laid out clean underwear for her charge before beginning her own toilet.

The first explosion threw Anna off the stool and she struck the back of her head on the corner of the bed. She lay there stunned while the successive blasts tore into the ship, and then darkness blinded her. She dragged herself on to her knees with the alarm bells deafening her, and forced herself to begin the drill that they had practised almost daily since leaving Calais.

'Lifejacket!' She groped under the bed and pulled the clumsy apparatus over her head and began to crawl towards the door. Suddenly the lights went on again and she dragged herself to her feet and leaned against the bulkhead and massaged the lump on the back of her head.

Her senses cleared and immediately she thought of Centaine.

'My baby!' She started towards the door and the ship lurched under her. She was thrown back against the dressing-table and at the same moment Centaine's jewelbox slid across the table-top and would have fallen, but instinctively Anna caught it and held it to her chest.

'Abandon ship!' a voice shrieked outside the cabin. 'The ship is sinking! Abandon ship!'

Anna had learned enough English to understand. Her practical phlegmatic sense reasserted itself.

The jewelbox contained all their money and documents. She dropped the locker over her head and pulled out the carpet bag and dropped the box into it.

Then she looked around her swiftly. She swept the silver frame with the photographs of Centaine, her mother and Michael's squadron into the bag, then she jerked open the drawer and stuffed warm clothing for Centaine and herself on top of the jewelbox and the picture frame. She fastened the bag as she glanced quickly about the cabin. That was all of value that they possessed, and she heaved open the door and stepped into the passageway beyond.

Immediately she was picked up in the relentless stream of men, most of them still struggling with their lifejackets. She tried to turn back – 'I must find Centaine, I must find my baby!' – but she was borne out on to the dark deck and hustled towards one of the lifeboats.

Two seamen grabbed her. 'Come on then, luv. Ups-a-daisy!' and though she aimed a blow at the head of one of them with the carpet bag, they boosted her over the side of the lifeboat and she landed in a tangle of skirts and limbs between the thwarts. She dragged herself up, still clutching the carpet bag, and tried to climb out of the boat again.

'Catch hold of that silly bitch, somebody!' a seaman shouted with exasperation, and rough hands seized her and pulled her down.

In minutes the lifeboat was so crowded that Anna was packed helplessly between bodies and could only rave and implore in Flemish and French and broken English.

'You must let me out. I have to find my little girl – '

Nobody took any notice of her, and her voice was drowned out by the shouting and scurrying, by the moaning of the wind and the crash of waves against the steel hull, and by the ship's own groans and squeals and dying roars.

'We can't take any more!' a commanding voice shouted. 'Swing her out and let go!'

There was a gut-swooping drop down through the darkness and the lifeboat struck the surface with such force that water was sprayed over them and Anna was once more thrown to the half-flooded deck with a huddle of bodies on top of her. She dragged herself up again, with the lifeboat tossing and leaping and thudding against the ship's side.

'Get those oars out!' The voice again, harsh with authority. 'Fend her off there, you men. That's right! All right, give way starboard. Pull, damn you, pull!'

They dragged themselves away from the ship's side and got their bows into the seas before they were swamped. Anna crouched in the bottom of the boat, clutching her bag to her chest, and looked up at the tall hull that rose above them like a cliff.

At that instant a great white shaft of light sprang out of the darkness behind them and struck the ship. It played slowly across the glistening white hull, like the spotlight of a theatre, picking out brief tragic vignettes before passing on – groups of men trapped at the rail, a twisting figure in an unattended stretcher sliding across the deck, a seaman caught in the tackle of a lifeboat and swinging like a figure on the gallows tree – and finally the beam rested for a few moments on the huge red crosses painted on the white hull.

'Yes, take a good look, you bloody swine!' one of the men near Anna in the lifeboat yelled, and immediately the cry was taken up.

'You murdering Hun – '

'You filthy butchers – '

All around Anna they were howling their anger and outrage.

Implacably the beam of searchlight travelled on, swinging down to the

waterline of the hull. The surface of the sea was dotted with the heads of hundreds of swimmers. There were clusters of them, and individuals whose pale faces shone like mirrors in the intense white light, and still others were dropping and splashing into the water amongst them, while the sea surged and sucked them back and forth and threw them against the steel cliff of the hull.

The searchlight lifted up to the high decks again, and they were canted at an improbable angle while the ship's bows were already thrusting below the surface and the stern was rising swiftly against the star-riddled sky.

For an instant the searchlight settled on a tiny group of figures pinned against the ship's rail and Anna shrieked, 'Centaine!'

The girl was in the middle of the group, her face turned towards the sea, looking down at the dark drop beneath her, the wild bush of her dark hair whipping in the wind.

'Centaine!' Anna screamed again, and with a lithe movement the girl had leaped to the top of the brass rail. She had lifted the heavy woollen skirts to her waist and for an instant she balanced like an acrobat. Her bare legs were pale and slim and shapely, but she looked frail as a bird as she leaped away from the rail and with her skirts ballooning wildly about her, fell out of the beam of light into the darkness beneath.

'Centaine!' Anna screamed one last time with despair in her voice and ice in her heart. She tried to rise, the better to watch the fall of that small body but somebody pulled her down again, and then the searchlight beam was extinguished and Anna crouched in the lifeboat and listened to the cries of the drowning men.

'Pull, you men! We must get clear, or she will suck us down with her when she goes.'

They had oars out on both sides of the lifeboat and were striking out raggedly, inching away from the stricken liner.

'There she goes!' somebody yelled. 'Oh God, will you look at that!'

The stern of the huge ship swung up, higher and still higher into the night sky, and the rowers rested on their oars and stared up at her.

When she reached the vertical she hung for long seconds. They could see the silhouette of her propeller against the stars, and her lights were still burning in the rows of portholes.

Slowly she began to slide downwards, bows first, her lights still shining beneath the water like drowning moons. Faster and still faster she slid downwards, and her plates began to buckle and crackle with pressure, air burst out of her in a seething frothy turmoil, and then she was gone. Vast spoutings and eruptions of air and white foam still fountained up out of the black waters, but slowly these subsided and once again they could hear the lonely cries of the swimmers.

'Pull back! We must pick up as many as we can!'

All the rest of that night they worked under the direction of the ship's first officer who stood at the tiller in the stern of the lifeboat. They dragged the sodden shivering wretches from the sea, packing them in until the lifeboat wallowed dangerously and took water over her gunwales at every swell, and they had to bale continuously.

'No more!' the officers shouted. 'You men will have to tie yourselves on to the lifelines.'

The swimmers clustered around the overloaded vessel like drowning rats, and Anna was close enough to the stern to hear the first officer murmur, 'The

poor devils won't last until morning – the cold will get them, even if the sharks don't.'

They could hear other lifeboats around them in the night, the splash of oars and voices on the wind.

'The current is running up into the north-north-east at four knots,' Anna overheard the first officer again, 'we will be scattered to the horizon by dawn. We must try and keep together.' He rose in the stern and hailed, 'Ahoy there! This is lifeboat sixteen.'

'Lifeboat five,' a faint voice hailed back.

'We will come to you!'

They rowed through the darkness, guided by cries from the other boat, and when they found each other they lashed the two hulls together. During the night they called two other lifeboats to them.

In the watery grey dawn they found another lifeboat half a mile away; the sea between them was strewn with wreckage and dotted with the heads of swimmers, but all of them were insignificant specks in the immense reaches of ocean and sky.

In the boats they huddled together like cattle in the abattoir truck, already slumping into bovine lethargy and indifference, while those in the water bobbed and nodded as they hung in their lifejackets, a macabre dance of death, for already the icy green water that tumbled over their heads had sucked the body warmth from many of them and they lolled pale and lifeless.

'Sit down, woman!' Anna's neighbours roused themselves as she tried to stand on the thwart.

'You'll have us all in the water, for God's sake!' But Anna ignored their protests.

'Centaine!' she called. 'Is Centaine anywhere?' And when they stared at her uncomprehendingly, she searched for the nickname and remembered it at last.

'Sunshine!' she cried. '*Het iemand Sunshine gesien*? Has anybody seen Sunshine?' and there was a stir of interest and concern.

'Sunshine?' Is she with you?' The query was passed swiftly about the cluster of tossing lifeboats.

'I saw her on the deck just before the ship went down.'

'She had a lifejacket.'

'She isn't here?'

'No, she isn't here.'

'I saw her jump, but I lost her after that.'

'She isn't here – not in any of the boats.'

Anna sagged down again. Her baby was gone. She felt despair ovewhelm and begin to suffocate her. She looked over the side of the lifeboat at the dead men hanging in their lifejackets, and imagined Centaine killed by the green waters, dead of the cold and the infant in her womb dead also, and she groaned aloud.

'No,' she whispered, 'God cannot be that cruel. I don't believe it. I'll never believe it.' The denial gave her strength and the will to endure. 'There were other lifeboats, Centaine is alive somewhere out there,' she looked to the wind-smeared horizon, 'she's alive, and I will find her. If it takes my whole life, I will find her again.'

The small incident of the search for the missing girl had broken the torpor of cold and shock that had gripped them all during the night, and now the leaders emerged to rally them, to adjust the loading and the trim of the lifeboats, to count and take charge of the fresh-water containers and the emergency rations, to see to the injured, to cut loose the dead men and let them float away and to

allocate duties to the rowers – and finally to set a course for the mainland a hundred miles and more out there in the east.

With teams of rowers alternating at the long oars, they began to inch across the wild sea, nearly every small gain wasted by the following wave that dashed into their bows and drove them back.

'That's it, lads,' the first officer exhorted from stern. 'Keep it up – ' any activity would stave off despondency, their ultimate enemy ' – let's sing, shall we? Who'll give us a tune? What about *Tipperary?* Come along, then.

'"It's a long way to Tipperary, It's a long way to go – "' But the wind and the sea grew stronger, and flung them about so that the oars would not bite, and one after the other the rowers gave up and slumped glumly, and the song died away and they sat and waited. After a while the sense of waiting for something to happen passed, and they merely sat. Long after midday, the sun broke through the low scudding cloud for a few minutes and they lifted their faces to it, but then the cloud obscured it again and their heads drooped like wild Namaqua daisies at sunset.

Then from the lifeboat alongside where Anna sat a voice spoke in a dull, almost disinterested tone.

'Look, isn't that a ship?'

For a while there was silence, as though it took time to understand such an unlikely proposition, and then another voice, sharper and more alive.

'It is – it's a ship!'

'Where? Where is it?'

A babble of excited voices now.

'There, just below that dark patch of cloud.'

'Low down, just the top – '

'It's a ship!'

'A ship!'

Men were trying to stand, some of them had stripped off their jackets and were waving frantically and shouting as though their lungs might burst.

Anna blinked her eyes and stared in the direction they were all pointing in. After a moment she saw a tiny triangular shape, darker grey against the dreary grey of the horizon.

The first officer was busy in the stern, and abruptly there was a fierce whooshing sound and a trail of smoke shot up into the sky and burst in a cluster of bright red stars as he fired one of the signal rockets from the stern locker.

'She has seen us!'

'Look! Look, she's altering course!'

'It's a warship – three funnels.'

'Look at the tripod director tower – she's one of the "I" class cruisers – '

'By God, it's the *Inflexible!* I saw her at Scapa Flow last year – '

'God bless her, whoever she is. She's seen us! Oh, thank God, she's seen us!'

Anna found herself laughing and sobbing, and clutching the carpet bag that was her only link with Centaine.

'It will be all right now, my baby,' she promised. 'Anna will find you now. You don't have to worry any more, Anna is coming to get you.'

And the deadly grey shape of the warship raced down upon them, shouldering and breaking the waters aside with her tall, axe-sharp bows.

* * *

Anna stood at the rail of HMS *Inflexible* in a group of the survivors from the lifeboats and watched that immense flat-topped mountain rise out of the southern ocean.

From this distance the proportions of the mountain were so perfect, the tableland at its summit so precisely cut and the steep slopes so artfully fashioned that it might have been sculptured by a divine Michelangelo. The men around her were excited and voluble, hanging on the rail and pointing out the familiar features of the land as their swift approach made each apparent. This was a homecoming of which most of them had many times despaired, and their relief and joy were pathetically childlike.

Anna shared none of it with them. The sight of land induced in her only a corrosive impatience that she knew she could not long abide. The drive of the great ship under her was too puny, too snail-like for her anticipation – every minute spent out here upon the ocean was wasted, for it delayed the moment when she could set out on the quest which had in a few short days become the central driving force of her existence.

She fretted while the drama of sea and elements unfolded before her, while the wind which had crossed the wide sweep of the Atlantic free and unfettered, met the sudden constraint of the great mountain, and like a wild horse feeling the bit for the first time, reared and struggled in monstrous pique.

Before Anna's eyes a dense white cloud blossomed upon the broad flat summit of the mountain and began to boil over the sheer lip in a slow, gelatinous tide down the stark cliffs, and when the men around her exclaimed with wonder, she had only an insufferable desire to feel the land beneath her feet, and to turn those feet back into the north to begin the search.

Now the angry wind racing down the cliffs came again to the sea and ripped the placid sweet blue first to sombre gunmetal and then to foam-flecked fury. As the *Inflexible* came out of the lee of the mountain into the narrow roadway between Table Harbour and Roben Island, the south-easter struck her like a mallet, and even she was forced to make obeisance and heel to the power of the wind.

In the days of sail, many great ships had come this close to the mountain only to be blown out again with rigging in disarray, not to sight land again for days or even weeks, but *Inflexible*, once she had acknowledged its force, drove in through the concrete breakwater, and surrendered only to the attentions of the fussy little steam tugs which bustled out to meet her. Like a lover she kissed the wharf, and the crowd that lined it waved up at the decks, the women struggling with rebellious skirts and the men cluching their hats to their heads, the strains of the Marine band on the cruiser's foredeck rising and falling as the wind squalls gave 'Rule Britannia' an unusual cadence.

As soon as the gangways were lowered, a group of figures hurried up them, harbour officials and naval officers in tropical whites and gold braid, together with a few obviously important civilians.

Now, despite herself, Anna felt a slight prickle of interest as she studied the white buildings of the town that were scattered along the foot of the high grey cliffs.

'Africa,' she murmured. 'So what was all the fuss about? I wonder what Centaine – '

At the thought of the girl, all else was banished from her mind; although she still stared towards the shore, she saw nothing and heard nothing, until a light touch on her shoulder pulled her back to the present.

One of the ship's midshipmen, callow as a schoolboy even in his smart tropical whites, saluted her diffidently.

'There is a visitor for you in the wardroom, ma'am.'

When it was obvious that Anna did not understand, he beckoned her to follow him.

At the door of the wardroom, the midshipman stood aside and ushered her through. Anna stood in the entrance and glowered around her suspiciously, holding the carpet bag protectively in front of her hips. Visitors and officers were already doing full justice to the ship's store of gin and tonic, but the cruiser's flag lieutenant saw Anna.

'Ah, here we are. This is the woman,' and he drew one of the civilians from the group of men and led him to meet Anna.

Anna looked him over carefully. He was a slim, boyish figure dressed in a dove-grey three-piece suit of expensive material and superior cut.

'Mevrou Stok?' he asked, almost diffidently, and with surprise Anna realized that, far from being a boy, he was probably twenty years or so her senior.

'Anna Stok?' he repeated. His hair had receded in deep bays on each side of the smooth scholarly forehead, but had been allowed to grow feathery wisps down his neck and on to his shoulders.

'We should take the scissors to you,' she thought, and said '*Ja*, I am Anna Stok,' and he replied in Afrikaans that she understood readily.

'A pleasant meeting – *aangename kennis* – I am Colonel Garrick Courtney, but I am saddened, as you must be, by the terrible loss we have experienced.'

For a few moments Anna did not understand what he was talking about. Instead she studied him more closely, and now she saw that his unbarbered hair had sprinkled the shoulder of his expensive suit with flakes of white dandruff. There was a button missing from his waistcoat and the thread dangled loosely. There was a grease spot on his silk cravat and the toe of one of his boots was scuffed.

'A bachelor,' Anna decided. Despite his intelligent eyes and the sensitive gentle mouth, there was something childlike and vulnerable about him, and Anna felt her maternal instincts stir.

He stepped closer to her, and the clumsy movement reminded Anna of what General Courtney had told Centaine and her, that Garrick Courtney had lost one of his legs in a hunting accident when he was a boy.

'Coming on top of the death in action of my only son,' Garrick lowered his voice and the look in his eyes was enough to soften Anna's reserves, 'this new loss is almost too much to bear. I have not only lost my son, but my daughter and my grandson before even I had a chance to know them.'

Now at last Anna understood what he was talking about, and her face flushed with such fury that Garry recoiled instinctively.

'Never say that again!' She followed him as he retreated, thrusting her face so close to his that their noses almost touched. 'Don't you dare ever to say that again!'

'Madam,' Garry faltered, 'I am sorry, I don't understand – have I given you offence?'

'Centaine is not dead and don't you ever dare again to speak as though she is! Do you understand?'

'You mean Michael's wife is alive?'

'Yes, Centaine is alive. Of course she is alive.'

'Where is she?' Slow delight dawned in Garry's faded blue eyes.

'That is what we have got to find out,' Anna told him firmly. 'We have got to find her again – you and I.'

* * *

Garry Courtney had a suite at the Mount Nelson Hotel above the centre of Cape Town.

There was, of course, no real alternative lodging for a gentleman traveller visiting the Cape of Good Hope. Its guest book read like a roll of honour: statesmen and explorers, diamond magnates and big game hunters, gallant soldiers and illustrious peers of the realm, princes and admirals had all made it their temporary home.

The Courtney brothers, Garry and Sean, always had the same suite on the corner of the top floor with a view on one side over the gardens laid out by the governors of the Dutch East India Company, across the waters of Table Bay to the smoky blue mountains on the far side; on the other side the grey rock ramparts of the mountain were so close that they blotted out half the sky.

These legendary views did not distract Anna for a moment. She glanced quickly around the sitting-room, then placed the carpet bag on the centre table and rummaged in it. She brought out the silver picture frame and showed it to Garry, who was hovering behind her indecisively.

'Good Lord – that's Michael – ' He took the frame from her and stared hungrily at the photograph of No. 21 Squadron, taken only a few months previously. 'It's so hard to believe – ' Garry broke off and gulped before going on. 'Could I please have a copy of this made for myself?'

Anna nodded, and Garry transferred his attention to the two photographs in the second leaf. 'This is Centaine?' He pronounced it in the English way.

'Her mother.' Anna touched the others 'This is Centaine.' She corrected his pronunciation.

'They are so much alike,' Garry turned the photographs to catch the light. 'Yet the mother is prettier, but the daughter – Centaine – has more force of character.'

Anna nodded again. 'Now you know why she cannot be dead, she does not give up easily.' Her manner became brusque, 'But we are wasting time. We need a map.'

The hotel porter knocked on the door within minutes of Garry's call, and they spread the chart he brought between them.

'I do not understand these things,' Anna told him. 'Show me where the ship was torpedoed.'

Garry had the position from the *Inflexible*'s navigating officer, and he marked it for her.

'Do you see?' Anna was triumphant. 'It is only a few centimetres from the land.' She stroked the outline of Africa with her finger. 'So close, so very close – '

'It's a hundred miles – even further perhaps.'

'Are you always so miserable?' Anna snapped. 'They told me that the tide runs towards the land, and the wind also was blowing so strongly towards the land – anyway, I know my little girl.'

'The current runs at four knots and the wind,' Garry made a quick calculation. 'It's possible. But it would have taken days.'

Already Garry was enjoying himself. He liked this woman's absolute assurance. All his life he had been a victim of his own doubts and indecision, he could not remember even once being as certain of a single thing as she seemed certain of everything.

'So, with the wind and water pushing her, where has she come ashore?' Anna demanded. 'Show me.'

Garry pencilled in his estimates. 'I would say – about here!'

'Ah!' Anna placed a thick powerful finger on the map and smiled. When she smiled, she looked less like Chaka, Garry's huge fierce mastiff, and Garry grinned at her. 'Ah, so! Do you know this place?'

'Well, I know a bit about it. I went with Botha and Smuts in 1914, as a special correspondent for *The Times*. We landed here, at Walvis Bay, the Bay of Whales.'

'Good! Good!' Anna cut him short. 'So there is no problem. We will go there and find Centaine, yes? When can we leave, tomorrow?'

'It isn't quite that easy.' Garry was taken aback. 'You see, that is one of the fiercest deserts in the world.'

Anna's smile disappeared. 'Always you find problems,' she told him ominously. 'Always you want to talk instead of doing things, and while you talk, what is happening to Centaine, hey? We must go quickly!'

Garry stared at her in awe. Already she seemed to know him intimately. She had recognized that he was a dreamer and a romantic, content to live in his imagination, to live through the characters of his writings rather than in the real harsh world which frightened him so.

'Now there is no more time for your talking. There are things to be done. First, we will make a list of these things – and then we will do them. Now begin. What is the first thing?'

Nobody had ever spoken to Garry like this, not at least since his childhood. With his military rank and his Victoria Cross, with his inherited wealth, his scholarly works of history and his reputation as a philosopher, the world treated him with the respect accorded to a sage. He knew he did not truly merit any of these considerations, so they terrified and confused Garry, and his defence was to withdraw further into his imaginary world.

'While you make the list, take off your waistcoat.'

'Madam?' Garry looked shocked.

'I am not madam, I am Anna. Now give me your waistcoat – there is a button missing.'

He obeyed quietly.

'The first thing,' Garry, in his shirtsleeves, wrote on a sheet of hotel notepaper, 'is to cable the military governor in Windhoek. We will need permits, this is all a closed military area. We will need his cooperation, he will be able to arrange provisions and water points.'

Now that Garry had been prodded into taking action, he was working quickly. Anna sat opposite him, stitching on the button with those strong, capable fingers.

'What provisions? You will need a second list for those.'

'Of course – ' Garry pulled another sheet towards him.

'There!' Anna bit off the thread and handed him back his waistcoat. 'You can put it on now.'

'Yes, Mevrou,' said Garry meekly, but he could not remember when last he had felt so good.

It was after midnight when Garry went out on to the small balcony of his bedroom in his dressing-gown to take a last breath of night air, and while he reviewed the events of the day, the buoyant feeling of well-being remained with him.

Between them, he and Anna had performed prodigies of labour. They already had a reply from the military governor in Windhoek. As always, the Courtney name had opened the door to wholehearted cooperation. Their reservations had been made on the passenger train that would leave tomorrow afternoon, and take them over the Orange river and across the wastes of Namaqualand and Bushmanland, four days' travel to Windhoek.

They had even completed the major part of outfitting the expedition. Garry had spoken on the telephone, an instrument which he usually viewed with grave misgivings, to the owner of Stuttafords General Dealer Stores. The stores he required would be packed in wooden cases, the contents of each clearly labelled on it, and delivered to the railway station the following afternoon. Mr Stuttaford had given Garry his personal assurance that it would all be ready in time, and had sent one of his green motor vans up to the Mount Nelson Hotel with a selection of safari clothing for both Garry and Anna.

Anna had rejected most of Mr Stuttaford's offerings as being either too expensive or too frivolous – 'I am not a *poule*' – and she chose long thick calico skirts and heavy lace-up boots with hob-nailed soles, flannel underwear and only at Garry's insistence – 'the African sun is a killer' – a cork solar toppee with a green neck-flap.

Garry had also arranged a transfer of £3,000 to the Standard Bank in Windhoek to cover the expedition's final outfitting. It had all been done swiftly, decisively and efficiently.

Garry took a long draw on his cigar and flicked the butt over the edge of the balcony, then turned back into his bedroom. He dropped his dressing-gown over the chair and climbed in between white sheets as crisp as lettuce leaves, and switched out the bedside light. Instantly all his old misgivings and self-doubts came crowding out of the darkness.

'It's madness,' he whispered, and in his mind's eye saw again those terrible deserts, shimmering endlessly in the blinding heat. A thousand miles of coastline, swept by a cruel current so cold that even a strong man could survive in those waters for only a few hours before hypothermia sucked the life out of him.

They were setting out to look for a young girl of delicate breeding, a pregnant girl, who had last been seen plunging from the high deck of a stricken liner into the icy dark sea a hundred miles from this savage coast. What were their chances of finding her? He flinched from even trying to estimate them.

'Madness,' he repeated miserably, and suddenly he wished that Anna was there to bolster him. He was still trying to find an excuse to summon her from her single bedroom at the end of the corridor when he fell asleep.

* * *

Centaine knew that she was drowning. She had been sucked so deeply beneath the surface that her lungs were crushing under the weight of the dark waters.

Her head was full of the monstrous roaring of the sinking ship, and of the crackle and squeal of the pressure in her own eardrums.

She knew she was doomed, but she fought with all her strength and determination, kicking and clawing for life against the cold leaden drag of waters, fighting against the burning agony of her lungs and the need to breathe, but the turbulence swirled her into vertigo so that she lost any sense of upward and downward movement, but still she fought on and she knew that she would die fighting for her baby's life.

Then suddenly she felt the cracking weight of water on her ribs releasing, felt her lungs swelling in her chest, and an updraught of air and bubbles from the ruptured hull picked her up like a spark from a campfire and hurled her towards the surface with the pressure pain burning in her eardrums, and the drag of the lifejacket cutting into her armpits.

She broke through the surface and was thrown high on the seething fountain of escaping air. She tried to breathe but took water into her straining lungs and coughed and wheezed in agonized paroxysms until she cleared her air passages, and then it was almost as though the sweet sea air was too strong and rich for her, it burned like fire and she gasped and laboured like an asthmatic.

Slowly she managed to control her breathing, but the waves came at her unexpectedly out of the darkness, breaking over her head, smothering her again so she had to train herself to regulate each breath to the rhythm of the ocean. Between the breaking swells, she tried to assess her own condition and found herself undamaged. No bones seemed broken or cracked, despite that terrible gut-swooping drop from the ship's rail and the stunning impact on water as hard as a cobbled street. She still had full control of her limbs and her senses, but then she felt the first stealthy invasion of the cold through her clothing, into her body and her blood.

'I have to get out of the water,' she realized. 'One of the lifeboats.'

Now for the first time she listened for sounds and at first there was only the wind and the rushing break of white caps. Then she heard faintly, very faintly, a gabble of human voices, a magpie chorus of croaks and cries, and she opened her mouth and called for help, but a wave broke in her face and she took more water and gasped and choked.

It took her minutes to recover, but as soon as her lungs were clear, she struck out grimly towards where she thought the voices were, no longer wasting strength on vainly beseeching the aid of others. The heavy lifejacket dragged and the crests broke over her, she was lifted on the swells and dropped into the troughs, but she kept swimming.

'I have to get out of the water,' she kept telling herself. 'The cold is the killer – I have to reach one of the boats.'

She reached out for the next stroke and hit something solid with a force that broke the skin of her knuckles, but instantly she grasped for it. It was something large that floated higher than her head, but she could find no secure handholds upon it and in panic realized that already she was too far gone to drag herself up by main strength. She began to grope her way around the piece of floating wreckage, searching for a handhold.

'Not big – ' In the darkness she judged it to be not more than twelve feet long, and half as broad, made of timber but coated with smooth oil paint, one edge of it torn and splintered so that she scratched her hand on it. She felt the sting of the tearing skin, but the cold numbed the pain.

One end of the wreckage floated high, the other end dipped below the surface, and she pulled herself on to it, belly down.

Immediately she felt how precariously balanced the structure was. Although she had only dragged her upper body on to it, and her legs from the waist down were still hanging in the water, the wreckage tipped dangerously towards her, and there was a hoarse cry of protest.

'Be careful, you bloody fool – you'll have us over.'

Somebody else had found the raft before her.

'I'm sorry,' she gasped. 'I didn't realize – '

'All right, lad. Just be careful.' The man on the raft had mistaken her voice for that of one of the ship's boys. 'Here, give me a hand.'

Centaine groped frantically and touched outstretched fingers. She seized the offered hand.

'Easy does it.' She kicked as the man pulled her up the sloping angle of slippery painted wreckage, and then with her free hand she found a hold. She lay belly down on the tossing, unstable deck, and felt suddenly too weak and trembling to lift her head.

She was out of the deadly water.

'Are you all right, son?' Her rescuer was lying beside her, his head close to hers.

'I'm all right.' She felt the touch of his hand on her back.

'You've got a lifejacket, good boy. Use the tapes to tie yourself to this strut – here, let me show you.'

He lashed Centaine to the strut in front of her.

'I've tied a slippery knot. If we capsize, just pull this end, savvy?'

'Yes – thank you. Thank you very much.'

'Save it for later, lad.' The man beside her lowered his head on to his arms and they lay shivering and sodden and rode the headlong rush of waves out of the night on their frail, unstable vessel.

Without speaking again, without even being able to see more than each other's vague shapes in the darkness, they quickly learned to balnce the raft between them with coordinated, subtle movements of their bodies. The wind increased in viciousness, but although the sea rose with it, they managed to keep the higher side of the raft headed into it, and only an occasional burst of spray splattered over them.

After a while, Centaine lapsed into an exhausted sleep, so deep that it was almost comatose. She awoke in daylight, a muted grey and dreary light in a world of wild grey waters and low sagging grey clouds. Her companion on the raft was squatting on the canted insecure deck beside her, and he was watching her steadfastly.

'Miss Sunshine,' he said, as soon as she stirred and opened her eyes. 'Never guessed it was you when you came aboard last night.'

She sat up quickly and the tiny raft dipped and rocked dangerously under them.

'Steady on, luv, that's the ticket.' He put out a gnarled hand to restrain her. There was a tattoo of a mermaid on his forearm.

'My name's Ernie, miss. Leading Seaman Ernie Simpson. Of course, I knew you right away. Everybody on board knows Miss Sunshine.' He was skinny and old, thin grey hair plastered with salt to his forehead, and his face wrinkled as a prune, but though his teeth were yellow and crooked, his smile was kindly.

'What has happened to the others, Ernie?' Frantically, Centaine looked around her, the true horror of their situation coming over her again.

'Gone to Davy Jones – most of them.'

'Davy Jones, who is he?'

'Drowned, I mean. Rot the bloody Hun who did it.'

The night had hidden the true extremity of their situation from Centaine. The reality that was revealed now was infinitely more frightening than her imaginings. As they dropped into the swells, they were dwarfed by the cold opaque canyons of the sea, and as they rode up and over the crests, the vista of loneliness was such as to force Centaine to cringe down on the tiny deck. There was nothing but the water and the sky, no lifeboat nor swimmer, not even a seabird.

'We are alone,' she whispered. '*Tous seuls*'.

'Cheer up, luv. We are still kicking, that's what counts.'

Ernie had been busy while she still slept. She saw that he had managed to glean a few fragments of debris and floating wreckage from the sea around them. There was a sheet of heavy-gauge canvas dragging behind the raft, around its edge short lengths of hemp rope had been spliced into eye holes. It floated like some monstrous octopus with limp tentacles.

'Lifeboat cover,' Ernie saw her interest. 'And those are ship's spars and some other odds and sods – begging your pardon, miss – never know what will come in useful.'

He had lashed this collection of wreckage together with the lengths of rope from the lifeboat cover, and even while he explained to Centaine, he was working with scarred but nimble fingers splicing short pieces of rope into a single length.

'I'm thirsty,' Centaine whispered. The salt had scalded her mouth and her lips felt hot and bloated.

'Think about something else,' Ernie advised. 'Here, give us a hand with this. Can you splice?'

Centaine shook her head. Ernie dropped all his aitches and as a French woman, she sympathized with him, and found it easy to like him.

'It's easy, come on, luv. I'll learn you how. Watch!'

Ernie had a clasp knife attached by a lanyard to his belt, and he used the spike on the back of it to open the weave of the hemp.

'One over one, like a snake into its hole! See!'

Quickly Centaine got the hang of it. The work helped to take her mind off their awful predicament.

'Do you know where we are, Ernie?'

'I'm no navigator, Miss Sunshine, but we are west of the coast of Africa – how far off, I haven't a clue, but somewhere out there is Africa.'

'Yesterday at noonsight, we were 110 miles offshore.'

'I'm sure you're right,' Ernie nodded. 'All I know is we've got the current helping us, and the wind also – ' He turned his face up to the sky. 'If only we can use the wind.'

'Have you got a plan, Ernie?'

'Always got a plan, miss – not always a good one, I admit.' He grinned at her. 'Just get this rope finished first.'

As soon as they had a single length of rope, twenty feet long, Ernie handed her the clasp knife.

'Tie it around your middle, luv. That's the ticket. We don't want to drop it now, do we?'

He slid over the side of the raft and paddled like a dog to the dragging wreckage. With Centaine heaving and shoving under his direction, they worked two of the salvaged spars into position and lashed them securely with the hemp rope.

'Outriggers,' Ernie spluttered with seawater. 'A trick I learned from the darkies in Hawaii.'

The raft was dramatically stabilized, and Ernie crawled back on board. 'Now we can think about putting up some kind of sail.'

It took four abortive attempts before the two of them were able to rig a jury mast, and hoist a sail hacked from the canvas of the boat cover.

'We aren't going to win the America's Cup, luv, but we are moving. Look at the wake, Miss Sunshine.'

They were spreading a sluggish oily wake behind their cumbersome craft, and Ernie trimmed their tiny sail carefully.

'Two knots at least,' he estimated. 'Well done, Miss Sunshine, you're a game one, and no mistake. Couldn't have done that alone.' He was perched on the stern of the raft, steering with a salvaged length of timber as a tiller. 'Now you settle down and take a rest, luv, you and I will have to stand watches, back to back.'

All the rest of that day the wind came at them in gusts and squalls, and twice the clumsy mast was thrown overboard. Each time Ernie had to go into the water to retrieve it, and the effort required to lift the heavy spar and the wet canvas, then to restep and lash it back in place, left Centaine trembling and exhausted.

At nightfall the wind moderated and held steady and gently out of the south-west. The clouds broke up so they had glimpses of the stars.

'I'm tuckered out. You'll have to take a turn at the tiller, Miss Sunshine.' Ernie showed her how to steer, and the raft rsponded sullenly to the push of the tiller. 'That red star there, that's Antares, with the small white star on each side of him, just like a sailor on shore leave with a girlfriend on each arm, begging your pardon, Miss Sunshine, but you just keep heading towards Antares and we'll be all right.'

The old seaman curled up at her feet like a friendly dog, and Centaine crouched on the stern of the raft and held the crude tiller under one arm. The swells dropped with the wind and it seemed to her that their passage through the water was faster. Looking back, she could see the green phosphorescence of their wake spreading out behind them. She watched the red giant Antares with his two consorts climb up the black velvet curtain of the sky. Because she was lonely and still afraid, she thought of Anna.

'My darling Anna, where are you? Are you still alive? Did you reach one of the lifeboats, or are you, too, clinging to some scrap of wreckage, waiting for the judgement of the sea?'

Her longing for the solid bulky assurance of her old nurse was so intense that it threatened to turn her into a child once more, and she felt the childlike tears scalding her eyelids, and Antares' glaring red light blurred and multiplied before her. She wanted to crawl into Anna's lap and bury her face in the warm, soapy smell of her vast bosom, and she felt all the resolve and purpose of the day's struggle melt in her, and she thought how easy it would be to lie down beside Ernie and not have to try any more.

She sobbed aloud.

The sound of her own sob startled her, and suddenly she was angry with herself and her own weakness. She wiped the tears away with her thumbs and felt the gritty crunch of dried salt crystals on her eyelashes. Her anger grew stronger, and deliberately she turned it away from herself to the fates which so afflicted her.

'Why?' she demanded of the great red star. 'What have I ever done that you single me out? Are you punishing me? Michel, and my father. Nuage and Anna – everything I have ever loved. Why do you do this to me?' She broke off the thought, appalled at how close she had come to blasphemy. She hunched over, placed her free hand on her own belly and shivered with the cold. She tried to feel some sign of the life in her body, some swelling, some lump, some movement, but she was disappointed and her anger returned full strength, and with it a kind of wild defiance.

'I make a vow. As mercilessly as I have been afflicted, so hard will I fight to survive. You, whether you are God or Devil, have thrust this upon me. So I give you my oath. I will endure, and my son will endure through me.'

She was raving. She realized it but did not care, she had risen to her knees and was shaking her fist at the red star in defiance and anger.

'Come!' she challenged. 'Do your worst, and let's have done!'

If she had expected a blast of thunder and a lightning bolt, there was none – only the sound of the wind in the rude mast and the scrap of sail, and the bubble of the wake under the stern of the raft. Centaine sagged back on to her haunches and gripped the tiller and grimly pointed the raft up into the east.

In the first light of the day, a bird came and hovered above Centaine's head. It was a small seabird, the dark blue-grey of a rifle barrel with soft white chalky marks over its beady black eyes, and its wings were beautifully shaped and delicate, and its cry was lonely and soft.

'Wake up, Ernie,' Centaine cried, and her swollen lips split at the effort and a bubble of blood ran down her chin. The inside of her mouth was furry and dry as an old rabbit skin, and her thirst was a bright, burning thing.

Ernie struggled up and looked about him dazedly. He seemed to have shrunk and withered during the night, and his lips were flaky and white and encrusted with salt crystals.

'Look, Ernie, a bird!' Centaine mumbled through her bleeding lips.

'A bird,' Ernie echoed, staring up at it. 'Land close.'

The bird turned and darted away, low over the water, and was lost to sight, steel-grey against the dark grey sea.

In the middle of the morning Centaine pointed ahead, her mouth and her lips so dessicated that she could not speak. There was a dark tangled object floating on the surface just ahead of the raft. It wallowed and waved its tentacles like a monster from the depths.

'Sea kelp!' Ernie whispered, and when they were close enough, he gaffed it with the tiller arm and drew the heavy mat of vegetation alongside the raft.

The stalk of the kelp was thick as a man's arm and five metres long, with a bushy head of leaves at the end. It had obviously been torn from the rocks by the storm.

Moaning softly with thirst, Ernie cut a length of the thick stalk. Under the rubbery skin there was a pulpy section of stem, and a hollow air chamber within. Ernie shaved the pulp with the clasp knife and thrust a handful of the shavings into Centaine's mouth. It was running with sap. The taste was strong

and unpleasant, iodine and peppery, but Centaine let the liquid trickle down her throat and whispered with delight. They gorged themselves on the juice of the kelp and spat out the pith. Then they rested a while and felt the strength flowing back into their bodies.

Ernie took the tiller again and headed the raft down the path of the wind. The storm clouds had blown away, and the sun warmed them and dried their clothing. At first they held their faces up to its caress, but soon it became oppressive, and they tried to huddle away from it in the tiny patch of shade from the sail.

When the sun reached its zenith, they were exposed to the scourge of its full strength and it sucked the moisture from their bodies. They squeezed a little more of the kelp juice, but now the unpleasant chemical taste nauseated Centaine and she realized that if she vomited, she would lose so much of her precious fluids. They could drink the kelp juice only sparingly.

With her back against the jury mast, Centaine stared out at the horizon, the great ring of threatening water that surrounded them unbroken except in the east where a line of sombre cloud lay low on the sea. It took her almost an hour to realize that despite the wind, the cloud had not changed shape. If anything, it had firmed and grown a hairline taller along the horizon. She could make out tiny irregularities, low peaks and valleys that did no alter shape as ordinary clouds would.

'Ernie,' she whispered. 'Ernie, look at those clouds.'

The old man blinked his eyes and then rose slowly into a crouch. He started to make a soft moaning sound in his throat, and Centaine realized it was a sound of joy.

She rose beside him, and for the first time looked upon the continent of Africa.

* * *

Africa rose from the sea with tantalizing deliberation, and then almost shyly swathed herself in the velvet robes of night and retreated once more from their gaze.

The raft trundled on gently through the hours of darkness, and neither of them slept. Then the eastern sky began to soften and glow with the dawn, the stars paled out and there close before them rose the great purple dunes of the Namibian Desert.

'How beautiful it is!' Centaine breathed.

'It's a hard fierce land, miss,' Ernie cautioned her.

'But so beautiful.'

The dunes were sculptured in mauve and violet, and when the first rays of the sun touched the crests, they burned red gold and bronze.

'Beauty is as beauty does,' mumbled Ernie. 'Give me the green fields of old blighty and bugger the rest, begging your pardon, Miss Sunshine.'

The yellow-throated gannets came out in long formations from the land, flying high enough to be gilded by the sunlight, and the surf upon the beaches sighed and rumbled like the breathing of the sleeping continent. The wind that had stood steadily behind them for so long now felt the land and eddied and

twisted. It caught their tiny sail aback, and the mast collapsed and fell overboard in a tangle of canvas and ropes.

They stared at each other in dismay. The land was so very close, it seemed that they might reach out and touch it – and yet they were forced to go through the whole weary business of restepping the mast. Neither of them had the energy for this new endeavour.

Eric roused himself at last, wordlessly untied the lanyard of the clasp knife and handed it to Centaine. She fastened it around her own waist as the old man slid over the side of the raft once again and paddled to the peak of the stubby mast. On her knees, Centaine began to untangle the sheets and lines. The knots had all swollen with moisture and she had to use the spike of the clasp knife to break them open.

She coiled the ropes, and looked up as Ernie called, 'Are you ready, luv?'

'Ready.' She stood and balanced uncertainly on the tossing raft with the guide rope from the top of the mast in her hands taking up the slack, ready to assist Ernie to raise it back into position.

Then something moved beyond the old man's bobbing head, and she froze and lifted her head to shade her eyes. She puzzled over the strangely shaped object. It rode high on the green current, as high as a man's waist, and the early morning sun glinted upon it like metal. No, not metal, but like a lustrous dark velvet. It was shaped like the sail of a child's yacht – and with a nostalgic pang she remembered the little boys around the village pond on a Sunday afternoon, dressed in their sailor suits, sailing their boats.

'What is it, luv?' Ernie had seen her expectant pose and her puzzled expression.

'I don't know,' she pointed. 'Something strange, coming towards us – fast, very fast!'

Ernie swivelled his head.

'Where?' I don't see – ' At that moment a swell lifted the raft high.

'God help us!' screamed Ernie, and flailed the water with his arms, tearing at it in an ungainly frenzy as he tried to reach the raft.

'What is it?'

'Help me out!' Ernie gulped, smothering in his own wild spray. 'It's a bloody great shark.'

The word paralysed Centaine. She stared in stony horror at the beast, as another swell lifted it high, and the angle of the sunlight changed to pierce the surface and spotlight it.

The shark was a lovely slaty-blue colour, dappled by the rippling surface shadows, and it was immense, much longer than their tiny raft, wider acoss the back than one of the hogsheads of cognac from the estate at Mort Homme. The double-bladed tail slashed as it drove forward, irresistibly attracted by the wild struggles of the man in the water, and it surged down the face of the swell.

Centaine screamed and recoiled.

The shark's eyes were a catlike golden colour with black, spade-shaped pupils. She saw the nostril slits in its massive, pointed snout.

'Help me!' screamed Ernie. He had reached the edge of the raft and was trying to drag himself on board. He was kicking up a froth of water and the raft rocked wildly and listed towards him.

Centaine dropped to her knees and grabbed his wrist. She leaned back and pulled with all the strength of her terror, and Ernie slid halfway up on to the raft, but his legs still dangled over the side.

The shark seemed to hump out of the water, its back rose glistening blue, streaming with sea water, and the tall fin stood up like an executioner's blade. Centaine had read somewhere that a shark rolled on its back to attack, so she was unprepared for what happened now.

The great shark reared back and the grinning slit of its mouth seemed to bulge open. The lines of porcelain-white fangs, rank upon rank of them, came erect like the quills of a porcupine as the jaws projected outwards, and then they closed over Ernie's kicking legs. She clearly heard the grating rasp of the serrated edges of its fangs on bone, then the shark slid back, and Ernie was jerked backwards with it.

Centaine kept her grip on his wrist, although she was pulled down on to her knees and started to slide across the wet deck. The raft listed over steeply under their combined weight and the heavy drag of the shark on Ernie's legs.

Centaine could see its head under the surface for an instant. Its eye stared back at her with a fathomless savagery, and then the inner nictitating membrane slid across it in a sardonic wink, and quite slowly the shark rolled in the water with the irresistible weight of a teak log, exerting a shearing strain on to the jaws still clamped over Ernie's legs.

Centaine heard the bones part with a sound like breaking green sticks. The drag on the old man's body was released so suddenly that the raft bobbed up and swung like a crazy pendulum in the opposite direction.

Centaine, still with her grip on Ernie's arm, fell backwards, dragging him up on to the raft after her. He was still kicking, but both his legs were grotesquely foreshortened, taken off a few inches below the knee, the stumps protruding from the torn cuffs of his duck trousers. The cuts were not clean, dangling ribbons of torn meat and skin flapped from the stumps as Ernie kicked, and the blood was a bright fountain in the sunlight.

He rolled over and sat up on the pitching raft, and stared at his stumps. 'Oh merciful mother, help me!' he moaned. 'I'm a dead man.'

Blood spurted from the open arteries, dribbled and ran in ribulets across the white deck, cascaded to the surface of the sea and stained it cloudy brown. The blood looked like smoke in the water.

'My legs!' Ernie clutched at his wounds, and the blood fountained up between his fingers. 'My legs are gone. The devil has taken my legs.'

There was a huge swirl almost under the raft, and the dark triangular fin came up and knifed the surface, cutting through the discoloured water.

'He smells the blood,' Ernie cried. 'He won't give up, the devil. We are all dead men.'

The shark turned, rolling on his side, so they saw his snowy belly and the wide grinning jaws, and he came back, sliding through the bright clear water with majestic sweeps of his tail. He thrust his head into the blood clouds, and the wide jaws opened as he gulped at the taste. The scent and the taste infuriated him and he turned again; the waters roiled and churned at the massive movement below the surface, and this time he drove straight under the raft.

There was a crash as the shark struck the underside of the raft with his back, and Centaine was thrown flat with the force of the impact. She clung to the raft with clawed fingers.

'He is trying to capsize us,' shouted Ernie. Centaine had never seen so much blood. She could not believe that the thin ancient body held so much, and still it spurted from Ernie's severed stumps.

The shark turned and came back. Again the heavy crash of rubbery flesh into

the timbers of the raft and they were lifted high. The raft hovered on the edge of capsizing and then fell back on to an even keel and bobbed like a cork.

'He won't give up,' Ernie was sobbing weakly. 'Here he comes again.'

The shark's great blue head rose out of the water, the jaws opened and then closed on the side of the raft. Long white fangs locked into the timber, and it crunched and splintered as the shark hung on.

It seemed to be staring directly at Centaine as she lay on her belly clinging to the struts of the raft with both hands. It looked like a monstrous blue hog, snuffling and rooting at the frail timbers of the little raft. Once again it blinked its eyes – the pale translucent membrane slipping over inscrutable black pupils was the most obscene and terrifying thing Centaine had ever seen – and then it began to shake its head, still gripping the side of the raft in its jaws. They were thrown about roughly, as the raft was lifted out of the water and swung from side to side.

'Good Christ, he'll have us yet!' Ernie dragged himself away from the grinning head. 'He'll never stop till he gets us!'

Centaine leapt to her feet, balancing like an acrobat, and she seized the thick wooden tiller and swung it high overhead. With all her strength she brought it down on the tip of the shark's hoglike snout. The blow jarred her arms to the shoulders, and she swung again and then again. The tiller landed with a rubbery thump, then bounced off the great head without even marking the sandpapery blue hide, and the shark seemed not to feel it.

He went on worrying the side of the raft, rocking it wildly, and Centaine lost her balance and fell half overboard, but instantly she dragged herself back and on her knees kept beating the huge invulnerable head, sobbing with the effort of each stroke. A section of the woodwork tore away in the shark's jaws, and the blue head slipped below the surface again, giving Centaine a moment's respite.

'He's coming back!' Ernie cried weakly. 'He will keep coming back – he won't give up!' And as he said it, Centaine knew what she had to do. She couldn't allow herself to think about it. She had to do it for the baby's sake. That was all that counted, Michel's son.

Ernie was sitting flat on the edge of the raft, those fearfully mutilated limbs thrust out in front of him, turned half away from Centaine, leaning forward to peer down into the green waters below the raft.

'Here he comes again!' he shrieked. His sparse grey hairs were slicked down over his pate by seawater and diluted blood. His scalp gleamed palely through this thin covering. Beneath them the waters roiled, as the shark turned to attack one more, and Centaine saw the dark bulk of him coming up from the depths, driving back at the raft.

Centaine came to her feet again. Her expression was stricken, her eyes filled with horror, and she tightened her grip on the heavy wooden tiller. The shark crashed into the bottom of the raft, and Centaine reeled, almost fell, then caught her balance.

'He said himself he was a dead man.' She steeled herself.

She lifted the tiller high and fixed her gaze on the naked pink patch at the back of Ernie's head and then with all her strength she swung the tiller down in an axe-stroke.

She saw Ernie's skull collapse under the blow.

'Forgive me, Ernie,' she sobbed, as the old man fell forward and rolled to the

edge of the raft. 'You were dead already, and there was no other way to save my baby.'

The back of his skull was crushed in but he rolled his head and looked at her. His eyes were afire with some turbulent emotion and he tried to speak. His mouth opened, then the fire in his eyes died and his limbs stretched and relaxed.

Centaine was weeping as she knelt beside him.

'God forgive me,' she whispered, 'but my baby must live.'

The shark turned and came back, its dorsal fin standing higher than the deck of the raft, and gently, almost tenderly, Centaine rolled Ernie's body over the side.

The shark whirled. It picked up the body in its jaws and began to worry it like a mastiff with a bone, and as it did so the raft drifted away. The shark and its victim sank gradually out of sight into the green waters and Centaine found she still had the tiller in her hands.

She began to paddle with it, pushing the raft towards the beach. She sobbed with each stroke, and her vision was blurred. Through her tears she saw the kelp beds swaying and dancing at the edge of the ocean and beyond them the surf humping up and then hissing over a beach of brassy yellow sands. She paddled in a dedicated frenzy, and an eddy of the current caught the raft, assisting her efforts, and bore it in towards the beach. Now she could see the bottom, the corrugated pattern of sea-washed sands through the limpid green water.

'Thank you, God – oh thank you, thank you!' she sobbed in time to her strokes, and then again there came that shattering impact of a huge body into the underside of the raft.

Centaine clung desperately to the strut again, her spirits plunging with despair. 'It's come back again.'

She saw the massive dappled shape pass beneath the raft, starkly outlined against the gleaming sandy bottom.

'It never gives up.' She had won only temporary respite. The shark had devoured the sacrifice she had offered it within minutes, then drawn by the odour of the blood that was still splattered over the raft, it had followed her into water barely as deep as a man's shoulder.

It came around in a wide circle and then raced in from the sea side to attack the raft again, and this time the impact was so shattering that the raft began to break up. The planks had been worked loose by the heavy flogging of the storm, and they opened now under Centaine, so her legs dropped through and she touched the horrid beast beneath the raft. She felt the rasping of its coarse hide across the soft skin of her calf, and screamed as she jack-knifed her lower body up away from it.

Inexorably the shark circled and came back, but the slope of the beach forced it to come from the sea-side and its next attack, murderous as it was, drove the raft in closer to the beach, and for a moment or two the colossal beast was stranded on the shelving sand. Then, with a swirl and a high splash, it pulled free and circled out into deeper water, but with its fin and broad blue back exposed.

A wave hit the raft, completing the demolition that the shark had begun, and the raft shattered into a welter of planks and canvas and dangling ropes. Centaine was tumbled into the surging waters, and spluttering and coughing came to her feet.

She was breast-deep in the cold green surf, and through eyes streaming with salt water, she saw the shark come boring full at her. She screamed and tried to back up the shelving beach, brandishing the tiller she still had in her hands.

'Get away!' she screamed. 'Get away! Leave me!'

The shark hit her with his snout and threw her high in the air. She fell back on top of the huge blue back, and it reared under her like a wild horse. The feel of it was cold and rough and unspeakably loathsome. She was thrown clear of it and then was struck a heavy blow by the flailing tail. She knew it had been a glancing blow – a full sweep of that tail would have crushed in her ribcage.

The shark's own wild thrashing had churned up the sandy bottom, blinding it so that it could not see its prey, but it sought her with its mouth in the turbid water. The jaws champed like an iron gate slamming in a hurricane, and Centaine was beaten and hammered by the swinging tail and the massive contortions of the blue body.

Slowly she fought her way up the sloping beach. Every time she was knocked down, she struggled up, gasping and blinded and striking out with the tiller. The gnashing fangs closed on the thick folds of her skirt and ripped them away, and immediately her legs were freed. As she stumbled back a last few paces, the level of the water fell below her waist.

At the same moment, the surf drew back, sucking away from the beach, and the shark was stranded, suddenly powerless as it was deprived of its natural element. It wriggled and writhed on the sand, helpless as a bull elephant in a pitfall, and Centaine backed away from it, knee-deep in the dragging surf, too exhausted to turn and run – until miraculously she realized that she was standing on hard-packed sand above the waterline.

She threw the tiller aside and staggered up the beach towards the high dunes. She did not have the strength to go that far. She collapsed just above the high-water line and lay face down in the sand. The sand coated her face and body like sugar, and she lay in the sunlight and wept with the fierce gales of fear and sorrow and remorse and relief that racked her entire body.

She had no idea how long she lay in the sand, but after a while she became aware of the sting of the harsh sunlight on the backs of her bare legs, and she sat up slowly. Fearfully she looked back to the edge of the surf, expecting still to see the great blue beast stranded there, but the flooding tide must have lifted it and it had escaped out into deep water. There was no sign of it at all. She let out her breath in an involuntary gasp of relief and stood up uncertainly.

Her body felt battered and crushed and very weak, and looking down at it she saw how contact with the rough abrasive hide of the shark had grazed her skin raw, and that already there were dark blue bruises spreading across her thighs. Her skirts had been torn off her by the shark, and she had discarded her shoes before she jumped from the deck of the hospital ship, so except for her sodden uniform blouse and a pair of silk cami-knickers, she was naked. She felt a rush of shame, and looked around her quickly. She had never been further from other human presence in her life.

'No one to peek at me here.' She had instinctively covered her pudenda with her hands, and she let them fall to her sides again, and she touched something hanging from her waist. It was Ernie's clasp knife, dangling on its lanyard.

She took it in her hand and stared out over the ocean. All her guilt and remorse returned to her with a rush.

'I owe you my life,' she whispered, 'and the life of my son. Oh, Ernie, how I wish you were still with us.'

The loneliness came upon her with such an overpowering rush that she sagged down on to the sand again and covered her face with her hands. The sun roused her once again. She felt her skin beginning to prickle and burn again under its baleful rays, and immediately her thirst returned to nag at her.

'Must protect myself from the sun.' She dragged herself upright and looked around her with more attention.

She was on a wide yellow beach backed by mountainous dunes. The beach was totally deserted. It stretched away in sweeping curves on each side of her to the very limit of her vision, twenty or thirty kilometres, she estimated, before it shaded into the sea fret. It seemed to Centaine to be the picture of desolation, there was no rock or leaf of vegetation, no bird or animal, and no cover from the sun.

Then she looked at the edge of the beach where she had struggled ashore, and she saw the remnants of her raft swirling and tumbling in the surf. Fighting down her terror of the shark, she waded in knee-deep and dragged the tangled sail and sheets of the raft high above the tideline.

For a skirt, she cut a strip of canvas and belted it around her waist with a length of hemp rope. Then she cut another piece of canvas to cover her head and shoulders from the sun.

'Oh! I'm so thirsty!' She stood at the edge of the beach and longingly peered out to where the kelp beds danced in the current. Her thirst was more powerful than her distaste for the kelp juice, but her terror of the shark was greater than both, and she turned away.

Though her body ached and the bruises were purple and black across her arms and legs, she knew that her best chance was to start walking, and there was only one direction to take. Cape Town lay to the south. However, nearer than that were the German towns with strange names – she recalled them with an effort, Swakopmund and Lüderitzbucht. The nearest of these was probably five hundred kilometres away.

Five hundred kilometres – the enormity of that distance came over her, and her legs turned to water under her and she sat down heavily on the sand.

'I won't think about how far it is,' she roused herself at last. 'I will think only one step ahead at a time.'

She pushed herself to her feet and her whole body ached with bruises. She began to limp along the edge of the sea, where the sand was wet and firm, and after a while her muscles warmed and the stiffness eased so she could extend her stride.

'Just one step at a time!' she told herself. The loneliness was a burden that would weigh her down if she let it. She lifted her chin and looked ahead.

The beach was endless, and there was a frightening sameness to the vista that stretched before her. The hours that she trudged on seemed to have no effect upon it and she began to believe that she was on a treadmill with always the unbroken sands ahead of her, the changeless sea on her right hand, the tall wall of the dunes on her left, and over it all the vast milky blue bowl of the sky.

'I am walking from nothingness on to nothing,' she whispered, and she longed with all her soul for the glimpse of another human form.

The soles of her bare feet began to hurt and when she sat down to examine them, she found that seawater had softened her skin and the coarse yellow sand had abraded it almost down to the flesh. She bound up her feet with strips of canvas and went on. The sun and the exertion dampened her blouse with sweat, and thirst became her constant spectral companion.

The sun was halfway down the western sky when in the distance ahead of her a rocky headland appeared, and merely because it altered the dreary vista, she quickened her pace. But her step soon faltered again and she realized how the single day's trek had already weakened her.

'I haven't eaten for three days, and I haven't drunk since yesterday – '

The rocky headland seemed to come no nearer, and at last she had to sit down to rest, and almost immediately her thirst began to rage.

'If I don't drink very soon, I won't be able to go on,' she whispered, and she peered ahead at the low rampart of black rock and straightened up incredulously; her eyes were tricking her. She blinked them rapidly and stared again.

'People!' she whispered and pulled herself to her feet. 'People!' She began to stagger forward.

They were sitting on the rocks, she could see the movement of their heads silhouetted against the pale sky, and she laughed aloud and waved to them.

'There are so many – am I going mad?' She tried to shout, but it came out as a reedy little whine.

Disappointment, when it struck, was so intense that she reeled as though from a physical blow.

'Seals,' she whispered, and their mournful honking cries carried to her on the soft sea breeze.

For a while she did not think that she had the strength to go on. And then she forced one foot in front of the other, and plodded on towards the headland.

Several hundred seals were draped over the rocks, and there were many more bobbing about in the waves that broke over the rocky point, and the stench of them came to Centaine on the wind. As she approached, they began to retreat towards the sea, clopping over the rocks in their ludicrously clownish way, and she saw that there were dozens of calves amongst them.

'If I could only catch one of those.' She gripped the clasp knife in her right hand and opened the blade. 'I have to eat soon – ' But already alarmed by her approach, the leaders were sliding from the rocks into the surging green water, their ungainly lumberings transformed instantly into miraculous grace.

She started to run, and the movement precipitated a rush of dark bodies over the rocks; she was still a hundred yards from the nearest of them. She gave up and stood panting weakly, watching the colony escape into the sea.

Then suddenly there was a wild commotion amongst them, a chorus of squeals and terrified cries, and she saw two dark agile wolf-like shapes dart from amongst the rocks and drive into the densely packed troop of seals. She realized that her approach had distracted the colony, and given these other predators a chance to launch their own attack. She did not recognize them as brown hyena for she had only seen illustrations of the bigger and more ferocious spotted hyena which almost every book on African exploration contained.

These animals were the 'beach wolf' of the Dutch settlers, the size of a mastiff, but with sharp pointed ears and a shaggy mane of long ashy yellow fur that was now erect in excitation as they dashed into the colony of seals; unerringly they picked out the smallest and most defenceless of the infants, seizing them from the flanks of their cumbersome dams, and dragged them away, easily avoiding the grotesque efforts that the mothers made to defend their young.

Centaine began running again, and at her approach the female seals gave up and flopped down the black rocks into the surf. She snatched up a club of

driftwood from the pile of rubbish on the high-tide mark and raced across the end of the headland to cut off the nearest of the brown hyena.

The hyena was hampered by the squealing baby seal that it was dragging, and Centaine managed to get ahead of it. The animal stopped and lowered its head in a threatening stance, and watched Centaine approaching. The young seal was bleeding copiously from where the hyena's fangs were locked into its glossy pelt, and it was crying like a human infant.

The hyena growled fiercely and Centaine stopped, facing the beast, and swung the club and shrieked at it.

'Drop it! Get away, you brute! Leave it!'

She sensed that the hyena was perplexed by her aggressive attitude, and though it growled again, it backed up a few steps and crouched protectively over its wriggling prey.

Centaine tried to stare it down, holding the gaze of the formidable yellow eyes as she shouted and brandished the club. Abruptly the hyena dropped the badly injured seal cub and rushed directly at Centaine, baring long yellow fangs and making a roaring bellow in its throat. Instinctively Centaine knew that this was the crucial moment. If she ran the hyena would follow her and savage her.

She rushed forward to meet the animal's charge, redoubling her yells and swinging the club with all her strength. Evidently the hyena had not expected this reaction. Its courage failed. It turned and ran back to its floundering prey, and burying its fangs in the silky skin of its neck, began to drag it away again.

At Centaine's feet was a crevice in the rocks and it was filled with waterworn round stones. She grabbed one of these, the size of a ripe orange, and hurled it at the hyena. She aimed for the head, but the heavy stone fell short and it hit the creature's paw, crushing it against the rocky ground. The hyena squealed, dropped the seal cub and limped swiftly away on three legs.

Centaine ran forward and opened the clasp knife. She was a country girl and had helped Anna and her father slaughter and dress animals before. With a single, swift, merciful stroke, she cut the seal's throat and let it bleed. The hyena circled back, growling and whining, limping heavily, undecided and confused by the attack.

Centaine snatched up stones from the crevice in both hands and threw them. One of them struck the hyena on the side of its bushy-maned head and it yelped and fled fifty paces before stopping and staring back at her over its shoulder with hatred.

She worked swiftly. As she had watched Anna do so often with a sheep's carcass, she slit open the belly cavity, angling the point of the blade so as not to nick the stomach sac or the entrails, sawing through the cartilage that closed the front of the ribcage.

With bloodied hand she hurled another stone at the circling hyena, and then carefully lifted out the infant seal's stomach. The need for moisture was a raging fever within her; already she sensed that lack of it was threatening the existence of the embryo in her own womb, and yet her gorge rose at the thought of what she must do.

'When I was a girl,' Anna had told her, 'the shepherds used to do it whenever a suckling lamb died.'

Centaine held the seal cub's little stomach bag in her cupped and bloodied hands. The stomach lining was yellowish and translucent so that she fancied that she could see the contents through the walls. The cub must obviously have

been lying with its mother up to the moment of the hyena attack, and it must have been suckling greedily. The small stomach was drum-tight with milk.

Centaine gulped with revulsion and then told herself, 'If you don't drink, you'll be dead by morning – you and Michel's son, both.'

She made a tiny incision in the stomach wall, and immediately the thick white curds of milk oozed from it. Centaine closed her eyes and placed her mouth over the slit. She forced herself to suck the hot curdled milk. Her empty stomach heaved and she choked with an involuntary retching reflex, but she fought and at last controlled it.

The curds had a slightly fishy taste but were not altogether repulsive. After she had forced down the first mouthful, she thought it tasted a little of the goat's-milk cheese that Anna made, strong with rennet.

She rested after a while, and wiped the blood and mucus from her mouth with the back of her hand. She could almost feel the fluid soaking back to replace that lost by her body tissues, and new strength seemed to radiate through her exhausted body.

She hurled another rock at the hyena, and then drank the rest of the thick curdled milk. Carefully she slit open the tiny empty stomach sac, and licked up the last drops. Then she threw the empty membrane to the hyena.

'I will share it with you,' she told the snarling beast.

She skinned the carcass, cutting off the head and the rudimentary limbs, and threw those to the hyena also. The big doglike carnivore seemed to have resigned itself. It sat on its haunches twenty paces from Centaine, with its pointed ears pricked up and a comically expectant expression, waiting for the scraps she threw it.

Centaine cut as many long narrow strips of the bright red seal meat as she could get off the skeleton, and wrapped them in the canvas of her headdress. Then she retreated and the hyena rushed forward to lick up the spilled blood from the rocks and to crush the small skeleton in its ugly, over-developed jaws.

At the top of the headland the wind and wave action had cut a shallow overhang from the compacted sandstone, and it had provided a shelter for others before Centaine. She found the scattered ashes of a long-dead cooking fire on the sandy floor of the cave, and when she scratched in the dirt, she turned up a small triangular flint scraper or cutting tool, similar to those for which she and Anna had hunted on the hillock behind the château at Mort Homme. It gave her a peculiarly nostalgic pang to hold the scrap of flint in the grubby palm of her hand, and when she felt self-pity overcoming her, she placed the sliver of stone in the pocket of her blouse, and forced herself to face harsh reality rather than mope over bygone days in a far-off land.

'Fire,' she said, as she examined the dead sticks of charcoal, and she laid out the precious scraps of seal meat on a rock at the mouth of the cave to dry in the wind and went back to gather an armful of driftwood.

She piled this beside the ancient hearth and tried to remember everything she had ever read about making fire.

'Two sticks – rub them together,' she muttered.

'It was a human need so basic, so taken for granted in her life until then, that now the lack of fire with its warmth and comfort was an appalling deprivation.

The driftwood was impregnated with salt and damp. She selected two pieces, not having the vaguest notion of the qualities of the wood she required, and she set about experimenting. She worked until her fingers were raw and hurting,

but she could not induce a single spark or even a wisp of smoke from her scraps of wood shavings.

Depressed and despondent, she lay back against the rear wall of the rock shelter and watched the sun set into the darkening sea. She shivered with the chill of the evening breeze and wrapped the canvas shawl more securely around her shoulders; she felt the small lump of flint press into her breast.

She noticed how tender her nipples had become recently, and how her breasts had begun to swell and harden, and she massaged them now. Somehow the thought of her pregnancy gave her renewed strength, and when she looked southwards, she saw Michel's special star hanging low on the horizon where a sombre ocean was blending into the night sky.

'Achernar,' she whispered. 'Michel – ' and as she said his name her fingers touched the flint in her pocket again. It was almost as though it was Michel's gift to her, and her hands shook with excitement as she struck the flint against the steel blade of the clasp knife, and the white sparks flared in the darkness of the rocky shelter.

She worried the threads of canvas into a loose ball, mixed with fine wood shavings, and struck flint and steel over it. Although each attempt produced a shower of bright white sparks, it took all her care and persistence before at last a wisp of smoke rose from the ball of kindling and she blew it into a tiny yellow flame.

She grilled the strips of seal meat over the coals. They tasted like both veal and rabbit. She savoured each bite and after she had eaten, she anointed the painful red blisters that the sun had raised on her skin with seal fat.

She set aside the remaining strips of cooked meat for the days ahead, built up the fire, wrapped the canvas around her shoulders and settled herself against the near wall of the shelter with the club beside her.

'I should pray – ' and as she began, Anna seemed very close, watching over her as she had so often before when Centaine, the child, knelt beside her bed with hands clasped before her.

'Thank you, Almighty God, for saving me from the sea and thank you for the food and drink you have provided, but – ' The prayer petered out, and Centaine felt recriminations rather than gratitude pressing to her lips.

'Blasphemy.' She almost heard Anna's voice and she ended the prayer hastily.

'And, oh Lord, please give me the strength to face whatever further trials you have in store for me in the days ahead, and if it please you, give me also the wisdom to see your design and purpose in heaping these tribulations upon me.' That was as much of a protest as she would risk, and while she was still trying to decide on a suitable ending for the prayer, she fell asleep.

When she awoke, the fire had died down to embers, and she did not at first know where she was or what had woken her. Then her circumstances came back to her with a sickening rush, and she heard some large animal out in the darkness just beyond the opening of the shelter. It sounded as though it was feeding.

Quickly she piled driftwood on the fire and blew up a flame. At the edge of the firelight she saw the lurking shape of the hyena and she realized that the package of cooked seal meat that she had so carefully wrapped in a strip of canvas the previous evening was gone from the rock beside the fire.

Sobbing with rage and frustration, she picked up a flaming brand and hurled it at the hyena.

'You horrible thieving brute!' she screamed, and it yelped and galloped away into the darkness.

* * *

The seal colony lay basking on the rocks below her shelter in the early morning sunlight, and already Centaine felt the first stirrings of the hunger and the thirst that the day would bring.

She armed herself with two stones, each the size of her fist, and the driftwood club, and with elaborate stealth crawled down one of the gulleys in the rocks, attempting to get within range of the nearest members of the colony. However, the seals fled honking before she had covered half the distance and they would not emerge from the surf again while she was in sight.

Frustrated and hungry, she went back to the shelter. There were spots of congealed white seal fat on the rock beside the hearth. She crushed a knob of charcoal from the dead fire to powder and mixed it with the fat in the palm of her hand, then she carefully blacked the tip of her nose and her cheeks, the exposed areas which had been burned by the sun the previous day.

Then she looked around the shelter. She had the knife and the scrap of flint, the club and canvas hood, all her worldly possessions, and yet she felt a dragging reluctance to leave the shelter. For a few hours it had been her home. She had to force herself to turn and go down to the beach, and to set out southwards into that ominously monotonous seascape once again.

That night there was no cave shelter and no pile of driftwood trapped against a rocky headland. There was no food and nothing to drink and she rolled herself in the strip of canvas and lay on the hard sand under the dunes. All night a chill little wind blew the fine sands over her so that at dawn she was coated with sparkling sugary particles. Sand had encrusted her eyelashes, and salt and sand were thick in her hair. She was so stiff with cold and bruises and over-taxed muscles that at first she hobbled like an old woman, using the club as a staff. As her muscles warmed, the stiffness abated, but she knew she was getting weaker and as the sun rose higher, so her thirst became a silent scream in the depths of her body. Her lips swelled and cracked, her tongue bloated and furred over with thickening gluey saliva that she could not swallow.

She knelt in the edge of the surf and bathed her face, soaked the canvas shawl and her skimpy clothing, and resisted somehow the temptation to swallow a mouthful of the cool, clear sea water.

The relief was only temporary. When the sea water dried on her skin, the salt crystals stung the sun-tender spots and burned her cracked, dry lips, her skin seemed to stretch to the point of tearing like parchment, and her thirst was an obsession.

In the middle of the afternoon far ahead of her on the smooth wet sand, she saw a cluster of black moving shapes, and she shaded her eyes hopefully. However, the specks resolved into four large seagulls, with pure white chests and black backs, squabbling and threatening each other with open yellow bills as the competed for a piece of flotsam washed ashore by the tide.

They rose on outstretched wings as Centaine staggered towards them, leaving their disputed prize, too heavy for them to carry, lying on the sand. It was a large dead fish, already badly mutilated by the gulls, and with new strength

Centaine ran the last few paces and dropped on her knees. She lifted the fish with both hands and then gagged and dropped it again, wiping her hands on her canvas skirt. The fish was stinking rotten, her fingers had sunk into the soft putrefying flesh as though into cold suet.

She crawled away and sat with her arms wrapped around her knees, hugging them to her breast, staring at the lump of stinking carrion and trying to subdue her thirst.

It took all her courage, but at last she crawled back to it, and with her face turned away from the stench, hacked off a fillet of the maggot-white flesh. She cut a small square of it and placed it cautiously in her mouth. Her stomach heaved at the taste of sickly sweet corruption, but she chewed it carefully, sucked out the reeking juices, spat out the pulpy flesh and then cut another lump from the fillet.

Sickened as much by her own degradation as by the rotten flesh, she kept sucking out the juices and when she reckoned that she had forced a large cupful down her throat, she rested a while.

Gradually the fluids fortified her. She felt much stronger, strong emough to go on again. She waded into the sea and tried to wash the stench of rotten fish from her hands and lips. The taste lingered in her mouth as she started once more plodding along the edge of the beach.

Just before sunset a new, crippling wave of weakness came over her and she sank down on to the sand. Suddenly an icy sweat broke across her forehead and cramp, like a sword thrust through her belly, doubled her over. She belched, and the taste of rotten fish filled her mouth and nostrils.

She heaved, and hot reeking vomit shot up her throat. She felt despair as she saw so much of her vital fluids splash on to the sand, but she heaved again, and at the contraction she felt a spluttery explosive release of diarrhoea.

'I'm poisoned.' She fell and writhed on the sand as spasm after spasm gripped her and her body involuntarily purged itself of the toxic juices. It was dark by the time the attack passed, and she dragged off her soiled camiknickers and threw them aside. She crawled painfully into the sea and washed her body, splashed her face and rinsed the taste of rotten fish and vomit from her mouth, prepared to pay for the momentary relief of a clean mouth with later thirst.

Then still on her hands and knees, she crawled up above the high-water mark, and in the darkness, shaking with cold, she lay down to die.

* * *

At first Garry Courtney was so involved in the excitement of planning the rescue expedition into the Namib desert, across that dreaded littoral that was named the Skeleton Coast for very good reason, that he did not have the leisure to weigh the chances of success.

It was enough for Garry to be playing the man of action. Like all romantics, he had daydreamed of himself in this role on so many occasions, and now that the opportunity was thrust upon him, he seized it with a frenzy of dedicated effort.

In the long months after the war department cable had arrived – that coarse buff envelope with its laconic message, 'His Majesty regrets to inform you that your son Captain Michael Courtney has been reported killed in action' – Garry's

existence had been a dark void, without purpose or direction. Then had come the miracle of the second cable from his twin brother: 'Michael's widow expecting your grandson has been rendered homeless and destitute by tides of war stop I am arranging priority passage on first sailing for Cape Town stop will you meet and take into your care stop reply urgent stop letter follows Sean.'

A new sun had risen in his life. When that in its turn had been cruelly extinguished, plunged into the cruel green waters of the Benguela Current, Garry had realized instinctively that he could not afford to let reason and reality beat him down once again into the dark night of despair. He had to believe, he had to push aside any calculation of the probabilities and cling mindlessly to the remote possibility that Michael's wife and her unborn child had somehow survived sea and desert, and were waiting only for him to find and rescue them. The only way to do this was to replace reasoned thought with feverish activity, however meaningless and futile, and when that failed, to draw upon the limitless reserve of Anna Stok's rock-solid and unwavering faith. The two of them arrived at Windhoek, the old capital of German South West Africa which had been captured two years before, and were met at the railway station by Colonel John Wickenham, who was acting military governor of the territory.

'How do you do, sir.'

Wickenham's salute was diffident. He had received a string of cables in the last few days, amongst them one from General Jannie Smuts and another from the ailing prime minister, General Louis Botha – all of them instructing him to extend to his visitor full assistance and co-operation.

This alone did not account for the measure of his respect towards his guest. Colonel Garrick Courtney was the holder of the highest award for gallantry, and his book on the Anglo-Boer War, *The Elusive Enemy*, was required reading at the Staff College that Wickenham had attended, while the political and financial influence of the brothers Courtney was legend. 'I should like to offer you my condolences on your loss, Colonel Courtney,' Wickenham told him as they shook hands.

'That is very decent of you.' Garry felt like an imposter when addressed by his rank. He always felt the need to explain that it had been a temporary appointment with an irregular regiment in a war almost twenty years past; to cover his uneasiness he turned to Anna, standing foursquare beside him in her solar topee and long calico skirts.

'I would like to introduce Mevrou Stok,' Garry switched to Afrikaans for her benefit, and Wickenham followed him quickly.

'*Aangename kennis* – a pleasant meeting, Mevrou.'

'Mevrou Stok was a passenger on the *Protea Castle*, and one of the survivors picked up by the *Inflexible*.'

Wickenham gave a little whistle of sympathy. 'A most unpleasant experience.' He turned back to Garry. 'Let me assure you, Colonel Courtney, that it will be my pleasure to offer you any possible assistance.'

Anna replied for him. 'We will need motor-cars, many motor-cars, and men to help us. We will need them quick, very quickly!'

For the command car they had a new 'T' model Ford, repainted from factory black to a pale sand colour. Despite its frail appearance it was to prove a formidable vehicle in the desert conditions. The light vanadium steel body and slow-revving engine carried it over soft sand that would have sucked down heavier machines. Its only weakness was a tendency to over-heat and send a jet

of precious water streaming high in the air to scald driver and passengers in the open body.

As supply vehicles, Wickenham provided them with four Austin lorries, each capable of carrying half a ton of cargo, and a fifth vehicle which had been modified in the railway workshops by army engineers and fitted with a cylindrical steel tank with a capacity of five hundred gallons of water. Each of the vehicles was assigned a corporal driver and an assistant.

With Anna firmly crushing any tendency of Garry's to procrastinate, and riding roughly over the practical objections of engineers and mechanics and military experts, the convoy was ready to leave from the capital thirty-six hours after her arrival. It was fourteen days since the German torpedoes had struck the *Protea Castle*.

They clattered out of the sleeping town at four in the morning, the trucks piled high with equipment and fuel and stores and the passengers bundled against the cold highland night airs. They took the wagon road that ran beside the narrow-gauge railway line down to the coastal town at Swakopmund, over two hundred miles away.

Steel-shod wagon wheels had cut ruts so deep that the rubber tyres of the vehicles were trapped in them and could not be steered out except at the rocky sections where the double ruts became boulder-strewn gulleys more like the bed of a dry mountain stream than a road. Laboriously they climbed down those rugged passes, crashing and jolting over the heavy going, forced to stop unexpectedly to repair a punctured tyre or replace a broken spring leaf, descending four thousand feet in fourteen hours of bone-cracking, neck-wrenching travel.

They came out on the flat, scrub-covered coastal plains at last, and raced across them at an exhilarating twenty-five miles per hour, dragging behind them a long rolling pall of dun-coloured dust like the smoke from a runaway bush fire.

The town of Swakopmund was a startling touch of Bavaria transported to the southern African desert, complete with quaint Black Forest architecture and a long pier stretching out into the green sea.

It was Sunday noon when their dusty cavalcade trundled down the paved main street. There was a German oom-pa-pa band playing in the gardens of the residency, the band members dressed in green Lederhosen and alpine hats. They lost the beat and trailed into silence as Garry's convoy pulled up outside the hotel across the road. Their trepidation was understandable, for the walls of the buildings were still pitted with shrapnel from the last British invasion.

After the dust and heat of the desert crossing, the local Pilsner, product of a master brewer from Munich, tasted like resurrection in Valhalla.

'Set them up again, barman,' Garry ordered, revelling in the masculine camaraderie, in the after-glow of the achievement of having brought his command safely down from the mountains. His men bellied up to the long teak bar with a will, and when they raised their tankards and grinned at him, their masks of packed dust cracked and powdered into their beer.

'Mijnheer!' Anna had performed her perfunctory ablutions and appeared in the doorway of the saloon. She stood with her thickly muscled arms akimbo, and her face, already inflamed by sun and wind, was slowly becoming truly fiery with outrage.

'Mijnheer, you are wasting time!'

Garry rounded on his men swiftly. 'Come on, you fellows, there is work to do. Let's got on with it.

By this time none of them had any doubts as to who was in ultimate command of the expedition, and they gulped their beers and trooped out into the sunlight, shamefacedly wiping the froth from their lips and unable to meet Anna's eye as they sidled past her.

While his men refuelled, filled the water tanks, repacked the loads that had come loose on the journey, and carried out maintenance and running repairs on the vehicles, Garry went off to make inquiries at the police station.

The police sergeant had been warned of Garry's arrival. 'I'm very sorry, Colonel, we weren't expecting you for three or four days. If only I had known – ' He was eager to be of assistance. 'Nobody knows much about that country up there,' as he glanced from the window of the charge office towards the north, the sergeant shivered involuntarily, 'but I have a man who can act as a guide for you.' He took down his key-ring from the hook on the wall behind the desk and led Garry through to the cells.

'Hey, you *swart donder* – you black thunder!' he growled as he unlocked one of the cells, and Garry blinked as his chosen guide shuffled out sullenly and glowered about him.

He was a villainous-looking Bondelswart Hottentot with a single malevolent eye; the other was covered by a leather eye-patch, and he smelled like a wild goat.

'He knows that land out there, he should do,' the sergeant grinned. 'That's where he poached the rhinoceros horn and ivory that is going to send him to the clanger for five years, isn't that right, Kali Piet?'

Kali Piet opened his leather jerkin and searched his chest hair reflectively.

'If he works well for you, and you are pleased with him, he might get off with only two or three years' breaking stones,' the sergeant explained, and Kali Piet found something amongst his body hair and cracked it between his fingernails.

'And if I am not pleased with him?' Garry asked uncertainly. *Kali* was the Swahili word for 'bad' or 'wicked', and it inspired no great confidence.

'Oh,' the sergeant said airily, 'then don't bother to bring him back. Just bury him where nobody will find him.' Kali Piet's attitude changed miraculously.

'Good master,' he whined in Afrikaans, 'I know every tree, every rock, every grain of sand. I will be your dog.'

Anna was waiting for Garry, already seated in the rear seat of the 'T' model.

'What took you so long?' she demanded. 'My baby has been out there in the wilderness alone for sixteen days now!'

'Corporal,' Garry handed Kali Piet into the care and keeping of the senior NCO. 'If he tries to escape,' Garry tried unconvincingly to look leeringly sadistic, 'shoot him!'

As the last whitewashed red-tiled buildings fell away behind them, Garry's driver belched softly and retasted the beer with a dreamy smile.

'Enjoy it,' Garry warned him, 'it will be a long trek to the next tankard.'

The track ran along the edge of the beach, while at their left hand the green surf tipped with ostrich feathers of spume pounded the smooth yellow sands, and before them stretched that dismal featureless littoral, shrouded in a haze of sea fret.

The track was used by kelp gatherers who collected the cast-up seaweed for fertilizer, but as they followed it northwards, so it became progressively less defined until it petered out altogether.

'What is ahead?' Garry demanded of Kali Piet, who had been led forward from the rear vehicle.

'Nothing,' said Kali Piet, and never had Garry sensed in a commonplace word such menace.

'We will make our own road from here on,' Garry told them with a confidence he did not feel, and the next forty miles took four days to cover.

There were ancient water courses, dry for a hundred years perhaps, but with steep sides and their bottoms strewn with boulders like cannon balls. There were treacherous flats on which the vehicles sank unexpectedly to their axles in soft sand and had to be manhandled through. There was broken ground where one of the lorries toppled over on its side and another broke a rear axle and had to be abandoned, together with a pile of luggage which they had discovered was superfluous, tents and camp chairs, tables and an enamel bath, boxes of trade goods to bribe savage chieftains, cases of tea and tinned butter and all the other equipment which had seemed essential when they were shopping in Windhoek.

The abbreviated and lightened convoy struggled northwards.

In the noonday heat the water boiled in the radiators, and they drove with plumes of white steam spurting from the saftey valves, and they were forced to halt every half hour to allow the engines to cool. In other places there were fields of black stone, sharp as obsidian knives, which slashed through the thin casing of their tyres. In one day Garry counted fifteen halts to change wheels, and at night the stink of rubber solution hung over their bivouac as exhausted men sat up until midnight repairing the ruined inner tubes by the light of hurricane lanterns.

On the fifth day they camped with the seared bare peak of the Brandberg, the Burned Mountain, rising out of the purple evening mist ahead of them, and in the morning Kali Piet was gone.

He had taken a rifle and fifty rounds of ammunition, a blanket and five water-bottles, and as a final touch, the gold hunter watch and the coin case with twenty gold sovereigns in it that Garry had placed carefully beside his blanket roll the previous evening.

Furiously, threatening to shoot him on sight, Garry led a punitive expedition after him in the 'T' model. However, Kali Piet had chosen his moment, and less than a mile beyond the camp he had entered an area of broken hills and sheer valleys where no vehicle could follow him.

'Let him go,' Anna ordered. 'We are safer without him, and it's twenty days since my darling – ' she broke off. 'We must go forward, Mijnheer, nothing must stand in our way. Nothing.'

Each day now the going became more difficult, and their progress slower, more frustrating.

At last, facing another barrier of rock that rose out of the sea like the crest on the back of a dinosaur and ran inland, jagged and glittering in the sunlight, Garry felt suddenly physically exhausted.

'This is madness,' he muttered to himself as he stood on the cab of one of the trucks, shading his eyes against the flat blinding glare and trying to spy out a way through this high impenetrable wall. 'The men have had enough.' They were standing in dispirited little groups beside the dusty, battered trucks. 'It's almost a month – nobody could have survived out here that long, even if they had been able to get ashore.' The stump of Garry's missing leg ached and every muscle in his back was bruised, every vertebra in his spine felt crushed by the vicious jolting over rough ground. 'We'll have to turn back!'

He clambered down off the cab, moving stiffly as an old man, and limped forward to where Anna stood beside the Ford at the head of the column.

'Mevrou,' he began, and she turned to him and laid a big red hand on his arm.

'Mijnheer – ' Her voice was low, and when she smiled at him Garry's protests stilled, and he thought not for the first time that except for the redness of her face and the forbidding frown lines, she was a handsome woman. The line of her jaw was powerful and determined, her teeth were white and even, and there was a gentleness in her eyes that he had never noticed before.

'Mijnheer, I have been standing here thinking that there are few men who would have brought us this far. Without you we would have failed.' She squeezed his arm. 'Of course I knew that you were wise, that you had written many books, but now I know also that you are strong and determined, and that you are a man who allows nothing to stand in your way.' She squeezed his arm again. Her hand was warm and strong. Garry found that he was enjoying her touch. He straightened his shoulders, and tipped his slouch hat forward at a debonair angle. His back was not quite so painful. Anna smiled again.

'I will take a party over the rocks on foot – we must search the sea front, every foot of it, while you lead the convoy inland and find another way around.'

They had to slog four miles inland before they found a narrow precarious route over the rocks and could turn back towards the ocean.

When Garry saw Anna's distant figure striding manfully through the heavy beach sands far ahead, with her party straggling along behind her, he felt an unexpected relief, and realized how painfully he had missed her for even those few brief hours.

That evening as the two of them sat side by side, with their backs against the side of the 'T' model Ford, eating bully beef and hard biscuit and washing it down with strong coffee heavily sweetened with condensed milk, Garry told her shyly:

'My wife's name was Anna also. She died a long time ago.'

'Yes,' Anna agreed, chewing steadily. 'I know.'

'How do you know?' Garry was startled.

'Michel told Centaine.' The variation of Michael's name still disconcerted Garry.

'I always forget that you know so much about Michael.' He took a spoonful of bully, and stared out into the darkness. As usual, the men had bivouaced a short distance away to give them privacy, and their fire of driftwood cast a yellow nimbus and their voices were a murmur in the night.

'On the other hand, I don't know anything about Centaine. Tell me more about her, please, Mevrou.'

This was a subject that never palled for either of them. 'She's a good girl,' Anna always began with this statement, 'but spirited and headstrong. Did I ever tell you about the time – ?'

Garry sat close to her with his head cocked towards her attentively, but this evening he wasn't really listening.

The light of the camp fire played on Anna's homely lined face, and he watched it with a feeling of comfort and familiarity. Women usually made Garry feel inadequate and afraid, and the more beautiful or sophisticated they were, the greater his fear of them. He had long ago come to terms with the fact that he was impotent, he had found that out on his honeymoon, and the mocking

laughter of his bride still rang in his ears over thirty years later. He had never given another woman the opportunity to laugh at him again – his son had not truly been his son, his twin brother had done that work for him – and at well over fifty years of age Garry was still a virgin. Occasionally, as now, when he thought about it, that fact made him feel mildly guilty.

With an effort he put the thought aside and tried to recapture the feeling of content and calm, but now he was aware of the smell of the body of the woman beside him. There had been no water to spare for bathing since they had left Swakopmund, and her odour was strong. She smelled of earth and sweat and other secret feminine musks, and Garry leaned a little closer to her to savour it. The few other women he had known smelled of cologne and rosewater, insipid and artificial, but this one smelled like an animal, a strong warm, healthy animal.

He watched her with fascination, and still talking in her low thick voice she lifted her hand and pushed back a few strands of grey hair from her temple. There was a a thick dark bush of curls in her armpit, still damp with the day's heat, and staring at it Garry's arousal was sudden and savage as a heavy blow in his groin. It grew out of him like the branch of a tree, rigid and aching with sensations that he had never dreamed of, thick with yearning and loneliness, tense with a wanting that came from the very depths of his soul.

He stared at her, unable to move or speak, and when he did not reply to one of her questions, Anna glanced up from the fire and saw his face. Gently, almost tenderly, she reached out and touched his cheek.

'I think, Mijnheer, it is time for my bed. I wish you good sleep and pleasant dreams.' She stood up and moved heavily behind the tarpaulin that screened her sleeping place.

Garry lay on his own blankets, his hands clenched at his sides, and listened to the rustle of her clothing from behind the tarpaulin screen, and his body hurt like a fresh bruise. From behind the screen came a long-drawn-out rumble that startled him; for a moment he could not place it. Then he realized that Anna was snoring. It was the most reassuring sound he had ever heard, for it was impossible to be afraid of a woman who snored; he wanted to shout his joy into the desert night.

'I'm in love,' he exulted. 'For the first time in over thirty years, I'm in love.'

However, in the dawn all the transient courage he had gathered in the night had evaporated, only his love was still intact. Anna's eyes were swollen and red with sleep, her grey-streaked hair was powdered with crystals of sand that the night wind had blown over her, but Garry watched her with adoration until she ordered him brusquely, 'Eat quickly – we must go forward at first light. I have a feeling that today will be good. Eat up, Mijnheer!'

'What a woman!' Garry told himself admiringly. 'If only I could inspire a little of such devotion, such loyalty!'

Anna's premonition seemed at first to be well-founded, for there were no more rocky barriers in their path, instead an open undulating plain ran right down to where the beach began, and the surface was firm gravel studded with knee-high salt bush. They could motor over it as though it were an open highway, forced only to swerve and weave in column to avoid the lumpy scrub, keeping just above the coppery beach so that they could spot any wreckage, or the signs left by a castaway on the soft sand.

Garry sat beside Anna on the back seat of the Ford and when they bumped over uneven ground, they were thrown together. Garry murmured an apology

but left his good leg pressed against her thigh, and she made no effort to withdraw from his touch.

Suddenly, in the middle of an afternoon that trembled with heat, the watery curtain of mirage opened ahead of them for a few moments and they saw the beginning of the dunelands rise sheer out of the plain. The little convoy stopped before them, and everybody climbed out and stared up at them with awe and disbelief.

'Mountains,' Garry said softly, 'a mountain range of sand. Nobody ever warned us of this.'

'There must be a way through!'

Garry shook his head dubiously. 'They must be five hundred feet high.'

'Come,' Anna said firmly. 'We will go to the top.'

'Good Lord!' Garry exclaimed. 'The sand is so soft – it's so high, it might be dangerous – '

'Let's go! The others will wait here.'

They toiled upwards with Anna leading, following the sloping razorback spine of one of the sand ridges. Far below them the cluster of vehicles was toylike, the waiting men tiny as ants. Beneath their feet the orange-coloured sand squeaked as their feet sank in to the ankles. When they stepped too close to the edge of the razorback, the lip collapsed and an avalanche of sand went hissing down the slip-face.

'This is dangerous!' Garry murmured. 'If you went over the edge, you'd be smothered.'

Anna hoisted her thick calico skirts and tucked them into her bloomers, then she plodded on upwards, and Garry stared after her, his mouth dry and his heart banging against his ribs, driven with exertion and shock at the sight of her bared legs. They were massive and as solid as tree trunks, but the skin at the backs of her knees was creamy and velvety, dimpled like that of a little girl, the most exciting thing he had ever seen.

Incredibly, Garry felt his body react again, as though a giant's hand had seized his crotch, and his fatigue fell away. Sliding and stumbling in the soft footing, he scrambled upwards after her, and Anna's haunches, wide as those of a brood mare under the thick skirts, swayed and rolled at the level of his starting eyes.

He came out on the crest of the dune before he realized it, and Anna put out a hand to steady him.

'My God,' he whispered, 'it's a world of sand, an entire universe of sand.'

They stood upon the foothills of the great dunes and even Anna's faith wilted.

'Nobody – nothing could get through them.'

Anna was still holding his arm, and now she shook him.

'She is out there. I can almost hear her voice calling to me. We cannot fail her, we must get through to her. She can't last much longer.'

'To attempt to go in on foot would be certain death. A man wouldn't last a day in there.'

'We *must* find a way round.' Ann shook herself like a huge St Bernard dog, throwing off her doubts and momentary weakness. 'Come.' She led him back from the crest. 'We must find the way round.'

The convoy with the Ford leading turned inland, skirting the edge of the high dunes while the day wasted away and the sun fell down the sky and bled to death upon their soaring crests. That night as they camped below them, the

dunes were black and remote, implacable and hostile against the moonlit silver of the sky.

'There is no way round.' Garry stared into the fire, unable to meet Anna's eyes. 'They go on for ever.'

'In the morning we will go back towards the coast,' she told him placidly, and rose to go to her sleeping place, leaving him aching with his want of her.

The next day they retraced their tracks, riding in their own tyreprints, and it was evening again before they had returned to the point where the dunes met the ocean.

'There is no way,' Garry repeated hopelessly, for the surf ran right up under the sand mountains and even Anna sagged miserably, staring silently into the flames of their camp fire.

'If we wait here,' she whispered huskily, 'perhaps Centaine is making her way down towards us. Surely she knows that her only hope is to head southwards. If we cannot go to her, we must wait for her to come to us.'

'We are running out of water,' Garry told her, quietly. 'We can't – '

'How long can we last?'

'Three days, no more.'

'Four days,' Anna implored, and there was such a desolation in her voice and her expression that Garry acted without thought. He reached for her with both arms. He felt a kind of delicious terror as she came to meet him, and they clung to each other, she in despair and he in a fearful frenzy of lust. For a few moments Garry worried that the men at the other fire would see them – then he no longer cared.

'Come.' She raised him to his feet and led him behind the canvas screen. His hands were shaking so that he could not unfasten the buttons of his shirt. Anna chuckled fondly.

'Here,' she undressed him, 'my silly baby.'

The desert wind was cool on his back and flanks, but he was burning internally with fires of long-suppressed passion. He was no longer ashamed of his hairy belly that bulged out in a little pot, nor of his thighs that were thin as those of a stork and too long for the rest of his body. He scrambled on top of her with frantic haste, desperate to bury himself in her, to lose himself in that great white softness, to hide there from the world that had been so cruel to him for so long.

Then suddenly it happened again, he felt the heat and strength drain from his groin, he felt himself wilt and shrivel just as he had on that other dreadful night over thirty years before. And he lay on the white mattress of her belly, cradled between her thick, powerful thighs, and he wished to die of shame and futility. He waited for her taunting laughter and her scorn. He knew it would destroy him utterly this time. He could not escape, for her powerful arms were wrapped around him and her thighs held his hips in a fleshy vice.

'Mevrou,' he blurted, 'I am sorry, I'm no good – I've never been any good.'

She chuckled again, and it was a fond and compassionate sound.

'There's my baby,' she whispered huskily in his ear. 'Let me help you a little.' And he felt her hand go down, pressing between their naked bellies.

'Where's my puppy?' she said, and he felt her fingers fold about him and he panicked. He began to struggle to be free, but she held him easily and he could not escape her fingers. They were rough as sandpaper from hard manual work, but cunning and insistent, tugging and plucking at him, and her voice was purring and happy.

'There's a big boy, then. What a big boy.'

He couldn't struggle any more, but every nerve and muscle in his body was tensed to the point of pain, and her fingers kneaded and coaxed and her voice became deeper, almost drowsy, without urgency, calming him so he felt his body unclenching.

'Ah!' she gloated. 'What's happening to our big puppy, then?'

Suddenly there was a stiffening resistance to her touch, and she chuckled again, and he felt the great thighs that held him fall slowly apart. 'Gently, gently,' she cautioned him, for he was beginning to struggle again, bucking against her. 'Like that! Yes, there, that's it.' She was guiding him, trying to control him, but he was desperate with haste.

Suddenly there was a hot gust of her body smell in his nostrils, rich and strong, the marvellous aroma of her own arousal, and he felt the new surge of strength into the core of his being. He was a hero, an eagle, the very hammer of the gods. He was strong as a bull, long as a sword, hard as granite.

'Oh yes!' she gasped. 'There, like that!' and resistance to him was not to be brooked, he drove forward and broke through and went sliding into the depths of her and the exquisite heat which was far beyond any place he had been in his entire existence. With increasing urgency and violence, she rose and fell beneath him as though he were a ship in an ocean gale and she made little crooning sounds, and urged him on in a ragged throaty voice, until the sky crashed down upon him and he was crushed between it and the earth.

He came back slowly from far away, and she was holding him and caressing him and talking to him like a child again.

'There, my baby. It's all right. It's all right now.'

And he knew that it was so. It was all right now. He had never felt so safe and secure. He had never known such deep pervading peace. He pressed his face between her breasts, and smothered himself in her abundant motherly flesh and wanted to rest there forever.

She stroked the sparse silky hairs back from off his ears, looking down on him fondly, and the bald pink patch at the crown of his scalp gleamed in the firelight and made her breasts ache with the need to comfort him. All her pent-up love and concern for the missing girl found new direction, for she was born to give succour and loyalty and duty to others. She began to rock him, cradling him and crooning to him.

Then, in the dawn, Garry found that there had been another miracle. For when he crept out of the camp and went down to the head of the beach, he found the way was open for them. Under the influence of a waxing moon, the ocean was building up to full spring tides, and the waters had drawn back, leaving a wide strip of hard smooth wet sand below the dunes.

Garry rushed back to the bivouac and hauled his senior NCO out of his blankets.

'Get your men looking alive, Corporal!' he shouted. 'I want the Ford refuelled, loaded with rations including water-cans for four people for three days, and I want it ready to leave in fifteen minutes, is that clear? Well then, get on with it, man, don't stand there gaping at me!'

He turned and ran back to meet Anna as she emerged from behind the tarpaulin.

'Mevrou, the tide! We can get through.'

'I knew you would find a way, Mijnheer!'

'We'll go in with the Ford, you and I and two men. We will drive hard until

the tide turns, then push the Ford up above the high-water mark, and when it's out again we'll press on. Can you be ready to leave in ten minutes? We have to take full advantage of the tide.' He wheeled away from her. 'Come on, Corporal, get these men moving!'

And as he turned away, the Corporal rolled his eyes and grumbled just loudly enough for the others to hear him. 'What's come over our old sparrow – damned if all of a sudden he isn't acting like a turkey cock!'

They had two hours of hard driving, pushing the Ford to her top speed of forty miles an hour when the sand was firm and hard. When it turned soft, the three pasengers, including Anna, leaped over the side and kept her rolling, throwing their full combined weight behind her, and then, as the sand firmed again, they scrambled on board, and hooting with excitement, sped northwards again.

At last the tide came surging back at them, and Garry picked out a gap in the dunes into which they backed the Ford, manhandling her through the dry, floury sand until she was well above the high-water mark.

They built a fire of driftwood, brewed coffee, and ate a picnic meal, and then settled down to wait for the next low tide to open the beach for them. The three men stretched out in the shade of the vehicle, but Anna left them and began picking her way along the high-water mark, pausing every once in a while to shade her eyes against the glare of sea and sand and peer restlessly into the north again.

Propped on one elbow, Garry watched her with such overwhelming affection and gratitude, that he found difficulty in breathing.

'In the autumn of my life she has given me the youth that I never knew. She has brought me the love that passed me by,' he thought, and when she reached the corner of the next sandy bay and disappeared behind the guardian dune, he could not bear to let her out of his sight.

He sprang up and hurried after her. As he reached the corner, he saw her a quarter of a mile ahead. She was stooped over something at the head of the beach, but now she straightened and saw him, and waved both hands over her head, shouting at him. The boom of the surf drowned out her voice, but her excitement and agitation was so obvious that the began to run.

'Mijnheer,' she ran to meet him, 'I have found – ' She could not finish, but seized his arm and dragged him after her.

'Look!' She fell on her knees next to the object. It was almost completely buried in the beach sand, and already the incoming tide was washing and swirling around it.

'It's part of a boat!' Garry dropped beside her, and together they attacked the sand with their bare hands, frantic to expose the fragment of white-painted woodwork.

'Clinker-built,' Garry grunted. Looks like part of an Admiralty-type lifeboat.'

The next wave rushed up the beach and wetted them to the waist, but as it drew back it washed away the sand they they had loosened and exposed the name that was painted in black letters on the shattered hull.

'*Protea C* – ' The rest of it was missing, the timbers were raw and splintered where they had broken up in the hammering surf.

'The *Protea Castle*,' whispered Anna, and wiped the sand away from the lettering with her sodden skirts.

'Proof!' she turned her face to Garry, and tears were running freely down her

red cheeks. 'Proof, Mijnheer, it's proof that my darling has reached the shore and is safe.'

Even Garry, who was as eager as a bridegroom to please her, who wanted desperately to believe that he would have a grandson to replace Michael, even he gawked at her.

'It's proof that she is alive – you do believe that now, don't you, Mijnheer?'

'Mevrou,' Garry fluttered his hands in an agony of embarrassment, 'there is an excellent chance, I do agree.'

'She is alive. I know it. How can you doubt it? Unless you believe – ' Her red face folded into a ferocious scowl, and Garry capitulated nervously.

'I do – oh yes! I certainly believe it! No question she's alive, absolutely no question.'

Having carried the field, Anna faced the incoming tide, and turned the full force of her displeasure upon the ocean.

'How long must we wait here, Mijnheer?'

'Well, Mevrou, the tide flows for six hours and then ebbs for six,' he explained apologetically. 'It will be another three hours before we can go on.'

'Every minute we waste now could make all the difference,' she told him fiercely.

'Well, I'm frightfully sorry, Mevrou.' Humbly Garry took full responsibililty for the rhythm of the universe upon himself, and Anna's expression softened. She glanced around her to make certain they were unobserved and then slipped her hand into the crook of his elbow.

'Well, at least we know she is still alive. We will go forward again the very minute we are able. In the meantime, Mijnheer, we have three hours.' She looked at him speculatively, and Garry's knees began to shake so that they could barely support him.

Neither of them spoke again while she led him back off the beach into a secluded gulley between two tall dunes.

* * *

As the tide turned and began its ebb, they drove the Ford down on to the sand. The rear wheels threw fish-tails of glistening seawater and wet sand high into the air behind them as they sped northwards.

Twice within five miles they found flotsam cast up on the beach, a canvas lifejacket and a broken oar. They had obviously been exposed to the elements for a considerable time, and although neither of these were marked with identifying numbers or lettering, they confirmed Anna's faith. She sat in the back seat of the Ford with a scarf knotted under her chin, holding her solar topee on her head, and every few minutes Garry darted a loving glance at her like an amorous fox terrier paying court to a bulldog.

It was the slack of low tide, and the Ford was travelling at thirty miles per hour when they hit the quicksand. There was little warning. The beach appeared as hard and smooth as it had been for the last mile. There was only a slight change in its contour. It was dished and the surface trembled like jelly as seawater welled up beneath the sand, but they had been moving too fast to notice the warning signs, and they went in at speed.

The front wheels dropped into the soft porridge, and stopped dead. It was

like running into the side of a mountain. The driver was hurled against the steering column. With a harsh crackle the spokes of the steering wheel collapsed, but the steel shaft tore through his sternum, pinning him like a mullet on a fish spear, and the jagged point ripped out of his back below his shoulder-blade.

Anna was thrown high out of the back seat, and landed in the soft mire of quicksand. Garry's forehead thudded into the dashboard, a flap of skin was torn from the bone and dangled over his eyebrow, while blood poured down his face. The corporal was caught in a tangle of loose equipment, and his arm broke with a crack like a dry stick.

Anna was the first to recover and she waded knee-deep through the soft sand, and with an arm around Garry's shoulder, helped him out of the front seat and dragged him to where the beach sand hardened.

Garry fell on his knees. 'I'm blind,' he whispered.

'Just a little blood!' Anna wiped his face with her skirt. She ripped a strip of calico from the hem of her skirt and hastily bound the flap of skin back in place, then left him and waded back to the Ford.

It was sinking slowly, tipping forward as it went down. Already the engine bonnet was covered by soft yellow mush, and it was pouring gluttonously over the doors and filling the interior. She seized the driver by the shoulders and tried to drag him clear, but he was firmly impaled on the steering shaft, and bone grated on steel as she tugged at him. His head rolled lifelessly from side to side, and she left him and turned to the corporal.

He was mumbling and twitching spasmodically as he regained consciousness. Anna pulled him free and dragged him back to the hard sand, grunting and red-faced with the effort. He screamed weakly with pain and his left arm dangled and twisted as she lowered him to the sand.

'Mijnheer,' Anna shook Garry roughly, 'we must save the water before it sinks also.'

Garry staggered to his feet. His face was painted with his own blood, and his shirt was streaked and splattered, but the flow had quenched. He followed her back to the doomed Ford and between them they dragged the water-cans to the beach.

'There is nothing we can do for the driver,' Anna grunted, as they watched the Ford and the dead man gradually settle below the treacherous surface. Within minutes there was no trace of them. She turned her attention to the corporal.

'The bone is broken.' His forearm was swelling alarmingly, and he was pale and haggard with agony. 'Help me!' While Garry held him, Anna straightened the damaged limb and using a piece of diftwood as a splint, strapped it. Then she fashioned a sling from another strip of her skirt, and while she settled the arm into it, Garry said hoarseley, 'I calculate it's forty miles back – ' but he could not finish, for Anna glared at him.

'You are talking of turning back!'

'Mevrou,' he made a little fluttery, conciliatory gesture, 'we have to turn back. Two gallons of water, and an injured man – we will be extremely fortunate to save ourselves.'

She continued to glare at him for a few seconds longer, then gradually her shoulders slumped.

'We are so close to finding her, so near to Centaine. I can sense it – she may be around the next headland. How can we give her up?' Anna whispered. It

was the first time that he had ever seen her defeated, and he thought his heart might burst with love and pity.

'We will never give her up!' he declared. We will never give up the search, this is only a setback. We will go on until we find her.'

'Promise me that, Mijnheer.' Anna looked up at him with pathetic eagerness. 'Swear to me that you will never give up, that you will never doubt that Centaine and her baby are alive. Swear to me here and now in the sight of God that you will never give up the search for your grandson. Give me your hand and swear it!'

Kneeling together on the beach, with the incoming tide swirling around their knees, facing each other and holding hands, he made the oath.

'Now we can go back.' Anna climbed heavily to her feet. 'But we will return, and go on until we find her.'

'Yes,' Garry agreed. 'We will return.'

* * *

Centaine must indeed have died a small death, because when she regained consciousness, she was aware of the morning light through her closed lids. The prospect of another day of torment and suffering made her clench her eyelids tightly and try to retreat again into black oblivion.

Then she became aware of a small sound like the morning breeze in a pile a dry twigs, or the noise of an insect moving with clicking armoured limbs over a rocky surface. The sound troubled her, until she made the enormous effort required to roll her head towards it and open her eyes.

A small humanoid gnome squatted ten feet from where she lay, and she knew that she must be hallucinating. She blinked her eyes rapidly and the congealed mucus that gummed her lids smeared across her eyeballs and blurred her vision, but she could just make out a second small figure squatting behind the first. She rubbed her eyes and tried to sit up, and her movements provoked a fresh outburst of the strange soft crepitating and clicking sounds, but still it took her a few seconds to realize that the two little gomes were talking to each other in suppressed excitement, and that they were real, not merely the figments of her weakness and illness.

The one nearest to Centaine was a woman, for a pair of floppy dugs hung from her chest to well below her belly-button. They looked like empty pig-skin tobacco pouches. She was an old woman – no, Centaine realized that old was not the word to describe her antiquity. She was as wrinkled as a sun-dried raisin. There was not an inch of her skin that did not hang in loose folds and tucks, that was not crinkled and riven. The wrinkles were not aligned in one direction only, but crossed each other in deep patterns like stars or puckered rosettes. Her dangling breasts were wrinkled, as was her fat little belly, and baggy wrinkled skin hung from her knees and elbows. In a dreamlike way, Centaine was utterly enchanted. She had never seen another human being that vaguely resembled this one, not even in the travelling circus that had visited Mort Homme every summer before the war. She struggled up on one elbow and stared at her.

The little old woman was an extraordinary colour, she seemed to glow like amber in the sunlight, and Centaine thought of the polished bowl of her father's

meerschaum pipe which he had cured with such care. But this colour was even brighter than that, bright as a ripe apricot on the tree, and despite her weakness, a little smile flickered over Centaine's lips.

Instantly the old woman who had been studying Centaine with equal attention, smiled back. The network of wrinkles constricted about her eyes, reducing them to slanted Chinese slits. Yet there was such a merry sparkle in those black shiny pupils that Centaine wanted to reach out and embrace her, as she would have embraced Anna. The old woman's teeth were worn down almost to the gums and were stained tobacco brown, but there were no gaps in them, and they appeared even and strong.

'Who are you?' Centaine whispered through her dark swollen dry lips, and the woman clicked and hissed softly back at her.

Under the loose wrinkled skin she had a small, finely shaped skull, and her face was sweetly heart-shaped. Her scalp was dotted with faded grey woolly hair that was twisted into small tight kernels, each the size of a green pea, and there was bare scalp between them. She had small pointed ears lying close to the skull like the pixies in Centaine's nursery books, but there were no lobes to the ears, and the effect of sparkling eyes and pricked ears was to give her an alert, quizzical expression.

'Do you have water?' Centaine whispered. 'Water. Please.'

The old woman turned her head and spoke in that sibilant clicking tongue to the figure behind her. He was almost her twin, the same impossibly wrinkled, apricot, glowing skin, the same tight wisps of hair dotting the scalp, bright eyes and pointed lobeless ears, but he was male. This was more than evident, for the leather loincloth had pulled aside as he squatted and a penis out of all proportion to his size hung free, the uncircumcised tip brushing the sand. It had the peculiar arrogance and half-erect tension of the member of a man in full prime. Centaine found herself staring at it, and swiftly averted her eyes.

'Water,' she repeated, and this time Centaine made the motion of drinking. Immediately a spirited discussion flickered back and forth between the two little old people.

'O'wa, this child is dying from lack of water,' the old Bushwoman told her husband of thirty years. She pronounced the first syllable of his name with the popping sound of a kiss. 'Kiss-wa.'

'She is already dead,' the Bushman replied quickly. 'It is too late, H'ani.' His wife's name began with a sharp, explosive aspirate and ended with a soft click made with the tongue against the back of the top teeth, the sound that in Western speech usually signifies mild annoyance.

'Water belongs to all, the living and the dying, that is the first law of the desert. You know it well, old grandfather.' H'ani was being particularly persuasive, so she used the enormously respectful term 'old grandfather'.

'Water belongs to all the people,' he agreed, nodding and blinking. 'But this one is not San, she is not a person. She belongs to the others.' With that sort of pronouncement O'wa had succinctly stated the Bushman's view of himself in relation to the world about him.

The Bushman was the first man. His tribal memories went back beyond the veils of the ages to the time when his ancestors had been alone in the land. From the far northern lakes to the dragon mountains in the south, their hunting grounds had encompassed the entire continent. They were the aboriginals. They were the men, the San.

The others were creatures apart. The first of these others had come down the

corridors of migration from the north, huge black men driving their herds before them. Much later, the others with skins the colour of a fish's belly that redden in the sun, and pale, blind-looking eyes had come out of the sea from the south. This female was one of those. They had grazed sheep and cattle on the ancient hunting grounds, and slaughtered the game which were the Bushman's kine.

With his own means of sustenance wiped out, the Bushman had looked upon the domesticated herds that had replaced wild game on the veld. He had no sense of property, no tradition of ownership nor of private possession. He had taken of the herds of the others as he would have taken of wild game, and in so doing had given the owners deadly offence. Black and white, they had made war upon the Bushmen with pitiless ferocity, ferocity heightened by their dread of his tiny childlike arrows that were tipped with a venom that inflicted certain, excruciating death.

In impis armed with double-edged stabbing assegais, and in mounted commandos carrying firearms, they had hunted down the Bushmen as though they were noxious animals. They had shot them and stabbed them and sealed them in their caves and burned them alive, they had poisoned and tortured them, sparing only the youngest children from the massacre. These they chained in bunches, for those that did not pine and die of broken hearts could be 'tamed'. They made gentle, loyal and rather lovable little slaves.

The Bushmen bands that survived this deliberate genocide retreated into the bad and waterless lands where they alone, with their marvellous knowledge and understanding of the land and its creatures could survive.

'She is one of the others,' O'wa repeated, 'and she is already dead. The water is only sufficient for our journey.'

H'ani had not taken her eyes off Centaine's face, but she reproached herself silently. 'Old woman, it was not necessary to discuss the water. If you had given it without question, then you would not have been forced to endure this male foolishness.' Now she turned and smiled at her husband.

'Wise old grandfather, look at the child's eyes,' she wheedled. 'There is life there yet, and courage also. This one will not die until she empties her body of its last breath.' Deliberately, H'ani unslung the rawhide carrying bag from her shoulder, and ignored the little hissing sound of disapproval that her husband made. 'In the desert the water belongs to everybody, the San and the others, there is no distinction, such as you have argued.'

From the bag she took out an ostrich egg, an almost perfect orb the colour of polished ivory. The shell had been lovingly engraved with a decorative circlet of bird and animal silhouettes and the end was stoppered with a wooden plug. The contents sloshed as H'ani weighed the egg in her cupped hands and Centaine whimpered like a puppy denied the teat.

'You are a wilful old woman,' said O'wa disgustedly. It was the strongest protest that Bushman tradition allowed him. He could not command her, he could not forbid her. A Bushman could only advise another, he had no rights over his fellows; amongst them there were no chiefs nor captains, and all were equal, man and woman, old and young.

Carefully H'ani unplugged the egg and shuffled closer to Centaine. She put her arm round the back of Centaine's neck to steady her and lifted the egg to her lips. Centaine gulped greedily and choked, and water dribbled down her chin. This time H'ani and O'wa hissed with dismay, each drop was as precious

as life blood. H'ani withdrew the egg, and Centaine sobbed and tried to reach for it.

'You are impolite,' H'ani admonished her. She lifted the egg to her own lips and filled her mouth until her cheeks bulged. Then she placed her hand under Centaine's chin, bent forward and covered Centaine's mouth with her own lips. Carefully she injected a few drops into Centaine's mouth and waited while she swallowed before giving her more. When she had passed the last drop into Centaine's mouth, she sat back and watched her until she deemed that she was ready for more. Then she gave her a second mouthful, and later a third.

'This female drinks like a cow elephant at a water-hole,' O'wa said sourly. 'Already she has taken enough water to flood the dry riverbed of the Kuiseb.'

He was right, of course, H'ani conceded reluctantly. The girl had already used up a full day's adult ration. She replugged the ostrich egg, and though Centaine pleaded and stretched out both hands appealingly, she replaced it firmly in the leather carrying satchel.

'Just a little more, please,' Centaine whispered, but the old woman ignored her and turned to her companion. They argued, using their hands, graceful birdlike gestures, fluttering and flicking their fingers.

The old woman wore a headband of flat white beads round her forehead, and a dozen strings of the same white beads round her neck and upper arms. Around her waist was a short leather skirt and over one shoulder a cape of spotted fur. Both garments were made from a single skin, unshaped and unstitched. The skirt was held in place by a rawhide girdle from which were suspended a collection of tiny gourds and antelope-horn containers, and she carried a long stave, the sharp end of which was weighted by a pierced stone.

Centaine lay and watched her avidly. She recognized intuitively that her life was under discussion, and that the old woman was her advocate.

'All that you say, revered old grandfather, is undoubtedly true. We are on a journey, and those who cannot keep up and endanger the rest, must be left. That is the tradition. Yet, if we would wait that long,' H'ani pointed to a segment of the sun's transit across the sky which was approximately an hour, 'then this child might find enough strength, and such a short wait would put us in no danger.'

O'wa kept making a deep glottal sound and flicking both hands from the wrist. It was an expressive gesture that alarmed Centaine.

'Our journey is an arduous one, and we still have great distances to travel. The next water is many days; to loiter here is folly.'

O'wa wore a crown on his head, and despite her plight Centaine found herself intrigued by it, until suddenly she realized what it was. In a beaded rawhide headband the old man had placed fourteen tiny arrows. The arrows were made of river reeds, the flights were eagles' feathers, and the heads, which were pointed skywards, were carved from white bone. Each barb was discoloured by a dried paste, like freshly made toffee, and this it was that recalled to Centaine the description from Levaillant's book of African travels.

'Poison!' Centaine whispered. 'Poisoned arrows.' She shuddered, and then remembered the hand-drawn illustration from the book. 'They are Bushmen. These are real live Bushmen!'

She managed to push herself upright, and both the little people looked back at her.

'Already she is stronger,' H'ani pointed out, but O'wa began to rise.

'We are on a journey, the most important journey, and the days are wasting.'

Suddenly H'ani's expression altered. She was staring at Centaine's body. When Centaine sat up, the cotton blouse, already ragged, had caught and exposed one of her breasts. Seeing the old woman's interest, Centaine realized her nudity and hastily covered herself, but now the old woman hopped close to her and leaned over her. Impatiently she pushed Centaine's hands aside and with the surprisingly powerful fingers of her narrow, delicate-looking hands, she pressed and squeezed Centaine's breasts.

Centaine winced and protested and tried to pull away, but the old woman was as determined and authoritative as Anna had been. She opened the torn blouse and took one of Centaine's nipples between forefinger and thumb and milked it gently. A clear droplet appeared on the tip and H'ani hummed to herself and pushed Centaine backwards on to the sand. She put her hand up under the canvas skirt, and her little finger prodded and probed skilfully into Centaine's lower belly.

At last H'ani sat back on her heels and grinned at her mate triumphantly.

'Now you cannot leave her,' she gloated. 'It is the strongest tradition of the people that you cannot desert a woman, any woman San or other, who carries new life within her.'

And O'wa made a weary gesture of capitulation and sank down on to his haunches again. He affected an aloof air, sitting a little detached as his wife trotted down to the edge of the sea with the weighted digging stick in her hands. She inspected the wet sand carefully as the wavelets swirled around her ankles and then she thrust the point of the stick into the sand and walked backwards, ploughing a shallow furrow. The point of the stick struck a solid object beneath the sand and H'ani darted forward, and digging with her fingers, picked out something and dropped it into her carrying bag. Then she repeated the process.

Within a short time she returned to where Centaine lay and emptied a pile of shellfish from her bag on to the sand. They were double-shelled sand clams, Centaine saw at once, and she was bitterly angry at her own stupidity. For days she had starved and thirsted as she had hobbled over a beach alive with these luscious shellfish.

The old woman used a bone cutting tool to open one of the clams, holding it carefully so as not to spill the juices from the mother-of-pearl-lined shell, and she passed it to Centaine. Ecstatically, Centaine slurped the juices from the half-shell and then dug out the meat with her grubby fingers and popped it into her mouth.

'Bon!' she told H'ani, her whole face screwed up with exquisite pleasure as she chewed, *'Très bon!'*

H'ani grinned and bobbed her head, working on the next clam with the bone knife. It was an inefficient tool that made the opening of each shell a laborious business and broke chips of shell on to the body of the clam that gritted under Centaine's teeth. After three more clams, Centaine groped for her clasp knife and opened the blade.

O'wa had been demonstrating his disapproval by squatting a little apart and staring out to sea, but at the click of the knife blade his eyes swivelled to Centaine and then widened with intense interest.

The San were men of the Stone Age, but although the quarrying and smelting and working of iron were beyond their culture, O'wa had seen iron implements before. He had seen those picked up by his people from the battlefields of the black giants, others that had been taken secretly from camps and bivouacs of

strangers and travellers, and once he had known a man of the San who had possessed an implement such as this girl now held in her hand.

The man's name had been Xja, the clicking sound at the back of his teeth that a horsemen makes to urge on his steed, and Xja had taken O'wa's eldest sister to wife thirty-five years before. As a young man, Xja had found the skeleton of a white man at a dry water-hole at the edge of the Kalahari. The body of the old elephant hunter had lain beside the skeleton of his horse, with his long four-to-the-pound elephant gun at his side.

Xja had not touched the gun, because he knew from legend and bitter experience that thunder lived in this strange magical stick, but gingerly he had examined the contents of the rotting leather saddle-bags and discovered such treasures as Bushmen before him had only dreamed of.

Firstly there was a leather pouch of tobacco, a month's supply of it, and Xja had tucked a pinch of it under his upper lip and happily examined the rest of the hoard. Quickly he discarded a book and a roll of cardboard, which contained small balls of heavy grey metal – they were ugly and of no possible use. Then he discovered a beautiful flask of yellow metal on a leather strap. The flask was filled with useless grey powder which he spilled into the sand, but the flask itself was so marvellously shiny that he knew no woman would be able to resist it. Xja, who was not a mighty hunter nor a great dancer or singer, had long pined after the sister of O'wa who had a laugh that sounded like running water. He had despaired of ever catching her attention, had not even dared to shoot a miniature feather-tipped arrow from his ceremonial love bow in her direction, but with his shiny flask in his hand he knew that at last she would be his woman.

Then Xja found the knife, and he knew that with it he would win the respect of the men of his tribe for which he longed almost as much as he longed for the lovely sister of O'wa. It was almost thirty years since O'wa had last seen Xja and his sister. They had disappeared into the lonely wastes of the dry land to the east, driven from the clan by the strange emotions of envy and hatred that the knife had evoked in the other men of the tribe.

Now O'wa stared at a similar knife in this female's hands as she split open the clam shells and wolfed raw the sweet yellow meat, and drank the running juices.

To this moment he had been merely repelled by the female's huge ungainly body, bigger than any man of the San, and her enormous hands and feet, by her thick wild bush of hair and her skin which the sun had parboiled, but when he looked at the knife, all the confusing feelings of long ago flooded back and he knew he would lie awake at night thinking about the knife.

O'wa stood up. 'Enough,' he said to H'ani. 'It is time to go on.'

'A little longer.'

'Whether carrying a child or not, no one can endanger the lives of all. We must go on,' and again H'ani knew he was right. They had already waited much longer than was wise. She stood up with him and adjusted the carrying bag on her shoulder.

She saw panic flare in Centaine's eyes as she realized their intention. 'Wait for me! *Attendez!*' Centaine scrambled to her feet, terrified at the thought of being deserted.

Now O'wa shifted the small bow into his left hand, tucked his dangling penis back into the leather loincloth and tightened the waistband. Then, without glancing back at the women, he started off along the edge of the beach.

H'ani fell in behind him. The two of them moved with a swaying jog trot and for the first time Centaine noticed their pronounced buttocks, enormous protuberances that jutted out so sharply behind that Centaine was sure that she could sit astride H'ani's backside and ride on it as though on a pony's back, and the idea made her want to giggle. H'ani glanced back at her and flashed an encouraging smile, and then looked ahead. Her backside bobbed and joggled and her ancient breasts flapped against her belly.

Centaine took a step after them and then came up short, stricken by dismay.

'Wrong way!' she cried. 'You're going the wrong way!'

The two little pygmies were heading back into the north, away from Cape Town and Walvis Bay and Lüderitzbucht and all of civilization.

'You can't go that way. Come back, you can't leave me alone here. You can't – ' Centaine was frantic, the loneliness of the desert lay in wait for her and like a ravening beast it would consume her if she were left alone again. But if she followed the two little people she was turning her back on her kind and the succour that they might hold out for her.

She took a few uncertain paces after H'ani. 'Please don't go!'

The old woman understood the appeal, but she knew there was only one way to get the child moving. She did not look back.

'Please! Please!'

That rhythmic jog trot carried the two little people away disturbingly quickly.

For a few moments longer Centaine hesitated, turning to look away southwards, torn and desperate. H'ani was almost quarter of a mile down the beach and showing no sign of slackening.

'Wait for me!' Centaine cried and snatched up her driftwood club. She tried to run but after a hundred paces settled down to a short, hampered but determined walk.

By noon the two figures she followed had dwindled to specks and finally disappeared into the sea fret far ahead up the beach. However, their footprints were left upon the brassy sands, tiny childlike footprints, and Centaine fastened her whole attention upon them and never really knew how or where she found the strength to stay on her feet and live out that day.

Then in the evening when her resolve was almost gone, she lifted her eyes from the footprints and far ahead she saw a drift of pale blue smoke wafting out to sea. It emanated from an outcrop of yellow sandstone boulders above the high-water mark and it took the last of her strength to carry her to the encampment of the San.

She sank down, utterly exhausted, beside the fire of driftwood, and H'ani came to her, chittering and clucking, and like a bird with its chick fed her water from mouth to mouth. The water was warm and slimy with the old woman's saliva, but Centaine had never tasted anything so delicious. As before, there was not enough of it and the old woman stoppered the ostrich-egg shell before Centaine's thirst was nearly slaked.

Centaine tore her gaze away from the leather carrying bag full of eggs and looked for the old man.

She saw him at last. Only his head was visible as he ferreted amongst the kelp beds out in the green waters. He had stripped naked, except for the beads around his neck and waist, and had armed himself with H'ani's pointed digging stick. Centaine watched him stiffen to point like a gundog and then launch a cunning thrust with the stick, and the water exploded as O'wa wrestled with some large and active prey. H'ani clapped her hands and ululated encourage-

ment, and finally the old man dragged a kicking struggling creature on to the beach.

Despite her weariness and weakness, Centaine rose up on her knees and exclaimed with amazement. She knew what the quarry was, indeed lobster was one of her favourite dishes, but still she thought that her senses must have at last deserted her for this creature was too big for O'wa to lift. Its great armoured tail dragged in the sand, clattering as it flapped, and its long thick whiskers reached above O'wa's head as he gripped one in each of his little fists. H'ani rushed down to the water's edge armed with a rock the size of her own head and between them they beat the huge crustacean to death.

Before it was dark O'wa killed two more, each almost as large as the first, and then he and H'ani scraped a shallow hole in the sand and lined it with kelp leaves.

While they prepared the cooking hole, Centaine examined the three huge crustaceans. She saw immediately that they were not armed with claws like a lobster, and so must be the same species as the Mediterranean *langouste* that she had eaten at her uncle's table in the château at Lyon. But these were a mammoth variety. Their whiskers were as long as Centaine's arm and at the root were as thick as her thumb. They were so old that barnacles and seaweed adhered to their spiny carapaces as if they were rocks.

O'wa and H'ani buried them in a kelp-lined pit under a thin layer of sand and then heaped a bonfire of driftwood over them. The flames lit their glowing apricot-coloured bodies as they chatted exuberantly. When their work was finished O'wa sprang up and began a shuffling little dance, singing in a cracked falsetto voice as he circled the fire. H'ani clapped a rhythm for him and hummed in her throat, swaying where she sat, and O'wa danced on and on while Centaine lay exhausted and marvelled at the little man's energy, and wondered vaguely at the purpose of the dance and the meaning of the words of the song.

'I greet you, Spirit of red spider from the sea, And I dedicate this dance to you,' sang O'wa, jerking his legs so that his naked buttocks that protruded from under the leather loincloth bounced like jellies.

'I offer you my dance and my respect, for you have died that we may live – '

And H'ani punctuated the song with shrill piping cries.

O'wa, the skilled and cunning hunter, had never killed without giving thanks to the game that had fallen to his arrows or his snares, and no creature was too small and mean not to be so honoured. For being himself a small creature, he recognized the excellence of many small things, and he knew that the scaly anteater, and pangolin, was to be honoured even more than the lion, and the praying mantis, an insect, was more worthy then the elephant or the gemsbok, for in each of them reposed a special part of the godhead of nature which he worshipped.

He saw himself as no more worthy than any other of these creatures, with no rights over them other than those dictated by the survival of himself and his clan, and so he thanked the spirits of his quarry for giving him life, and when the dance ended he had beaten a pathway in the sand around the fire.

He and H'ani scraped away the ashes and sand and exposed the carcasses of the giant crayfish now turned deep vermillion in colour and steaming on the bed of kelp. They burned their fingers and squealed with laughter as they broke open the scaly red tails and dug out the rich white meat.

H'ani beckoned to Centaine and she squatted beside them. The legs of the crayfish contained sticks of flesh the size of her finger, the thorax was filled with

the yellow livers which had been broken down in the cooking to a custard. The San used this as sauce for the flesh.

Centaine could not remember ever having so much enjoyed eating. She used the knife to slice bite-sized chunks off the tail of the crayfish. H'ani smiled at her in the firelight, her cheeks bulging with food, and she said, 'Nam!' and then again, 'Nam!'

Centaine listened carefully, then repeated it, with the same inflexion as the old woman had used.

'Nam!'

And H'ani squealed gleefully. 'Did you hear, O'wa, the child said "Good!"'

O'wa grunted and watched the knife in the female's hand. He found he could not take his eyes off it. The blade sliced through the meat so cleanly that it left a sheen on it. How sharp it must be, thought O'wa, and the sharpness of the blade spoiled his appetite.

With her stomach so full that it was almost painful, Centaine lay down beside the fire, and H'ani came to her and scraped out a hollow for her hip in the sand beneath her. It was was immediately more comfortable and she settled down again, but H'ani was trying to show her something else.

'You must not lay your head on the ground, Nam Child,' she explained. 'You must keep it up, like this.' H'ani propped herself on one elbow and then laid her head on her own shoulder. It looked awkward and uncomfortable, and Centaine smiled her thanks but lay flat.

'Leave her,' grunted O'wa. 'When a scorpion crawls into her ear during the night, she will understand.'

'She has learned enough for one day,' H'ani agreed. 'Did you hear her say "Nam"? That is her first word and this is the name I will give her, "Nam",' she repeated it, 'Nam Child.'

O'wa grunted and went off into the darkness to relieve himself. He understood his wife's unnatural interest in the stranger and the child she carried in her womb, but there was a fearful journey ahead and the woman would be a dangerous nuisance. Then, of course, there was the knife – thinking about the knife made him angry.

* * *

Centaine awoke screaming. It had been a terrible dream, confused but deeply distressing – she had seen Michael again, not in the flaming body of the aeroplane, but riding Nuage. Michael's body was still blackened by the flames and his hair was burning like a torch, and beneath him Nuage was torn and mutilated by the shells and his blood was bright on the snowy hide and his entrails dangled from the torn belly as he ran.

'There is my star, Centaine,' Michael pointed ahead with a hand like a black claw. 'Why don't you follow it?'

'I cannot, Michel,' Centaine cried, 'oh, I cannot.'

And Michael galloped away across the dunes into the south without looking back and Centaine screamed after him, 'Wait, Michel, wait for me!'

She was still screaming when gentle hands shook her awake.

'Peace, Nam Child,' H'ani whispered to her. 'Your head is full of the sleep demons – but see, they have gone now.'

Centaine was still sobbing and shivering and the old woman lay down beside her and spread her fur cape over them both and held her and stroked her hair. After a while Centaine quietened down. The old woman's body smelled of woodsmoke and animal fat and wild herbs, but it was not offensive and her warmth comforted Centaine, and after a while she slept again, this time without the nightmares.

H'ani did not sleep. Old people do not need the sleep that the young do. But she felt at peace. The bodily contact with another human being was something she had missed all these long months. She had known from childhood how important it was. The infant San was strapped close to its mother's body, and lived the rest of its life in intimate physical contact with the rest of the clan. There was a saying of the clan, 'The zebra on his own falls easy prey to the hunting lion,' and the clan was a close-knit entity.

Thinking thus, the old woman became sad again, and the loss of her people became a great stone in her chest too heavy to carry. There had been nineteen of them in the clan of O'wa and H'ani – their three sons and their wives and the eleven children of their sons. The youngest of H'ani's grandchildren was still unweaned and the eldest, a girl whom she loved most dearly, had just menstruated for the first time when the sickness came on the clan.

It had been a plague beyond anything in the annals of the clan and of the San; something so swift and savage that H'ani still could not comprehend it or come to terms with it. It had started first as a sore throat which changed to raging fever, a skin so hot that it was almost searing to the touch and a thirst beyond anything the Kalahari itself, which the can called 'the Great Dry', could generate.

At this stage the little ones had died, just a day or two after the first symptoms, and the elders had been so debilitated by the sickness that they did not have the strength to bury them and their tiny bodies decomposed swiftly in the heat.

Then the fever passed and they believed that they had been spared. They buried the babies, but they were too weak even to dance for the spirits of the infants or to sing them away on their journey into the other world.

They had not been spared, however, for the sickness had only changed its form, and now there came a new fever, but at the same time their lungs filled with water and they rattled and choked as they died.

They died, all of them except O'wa and H'ani – but even they were so close to death that it was many days and many nights before they were strong enough to appreciate the full extent of the disaster that had overtaken them. When the two old people were sufficiently recovered, they danced for their doomed clan, and H'ani cried for her babies that she would never again carry on her hip nor enchant with her fairy-tales.

Then they had discussed the cause and the meaning of the tragedy, they discussed it endlessly around their campfire in the night, grieving still to the depths of their beings, until one night O'wa had said, 'When we are strong enough for the journey – and you know, H'ani, what a fearsome journey it is – then we must go back to the Place of All Life, for only there will we find the meaning of this thing, and learn how we can make recompense to the angry spirits who have smitten us so.'

H'ani became once more aware of the young and fruitful body in her arms and her sadness lifted a little and she felt the resurgence of the mother instinct

in her milkless and withered bosom, which had been snuffed out by the great sickness.

'It may be,' she thought, 'that already the spirits are mollified because we have begun the pilgrimage, and that they will grant this old woman the boon of hearing once more the birth cry of a new infant before she dies.'

In the dawn H'ani unstoppered one of the little buckhorns that hung from her girdle and with an aromatic paste dressed the sun blisters on Centaine's cheeks and nose and lips, and the grazes and bruises on her legs and arms, chattering away to her as she worked. Then she allowed Centaine a carefully measured ration of water. Centaine was still savouring it, holding it in her mouth as though it were a rare Bordeaux, when without further ceremony the two San stood up, turned their faces northwards and set off along the beach in that rhythmic jogtrot.

Centaine sprang up in consternation and without wasting breath on entreaties, she snatched up her club, adjusted the canvas hood over her head and started after them.

Within the first mile she realized how the food and rest had strengthened her. She was at first able to hold the pair of tiny figures in sight. She saw H'ani prod the sand with her digging stick, scoop up a sand clam almost without breaking stride and hand it to O'wa, then pluck another for herself and eat it on the run.

Centaine shapened one end of her club to a point and imitated her, at first unsuccessfully, until she realized that the clams were in pockets in the beach – and H'ani had some means of locating them. It was useless to scrape at random. From then on she dug only where H'ani had marked the sand and drank the juice from the shells thankfully as she trotted along.

Despite her best efforts, Centaine's pace soon flagged and gradually the two San drew away from her and once again disappeared from her view. By midday Centaine was down to a dragging walk and knew that she had to rest. As she accepted it, she lifted her eyes and recognized far ahead of her the headland of the seal colony. It was almost as though H'ani had divined the exact limit of her endurance, for she and O'wa were waiting for her in the rock shelter, and she smiled and chittered with pleasure as Centaine dragged herself up the slope into the cave and fell exhausted on to the floor beside the fire.

H'ani gave her a ration of water, and while she did so, there was another lively argument between the old people which Centaine watched with interest, noticing that every time H'ani pointed at her she used the word '*nam*'. The gestures that the old people made were so expressive that Centaine was sure she understood the old woman wanted to stay for her sake, while O'wa wanted to go on.

Every time H'ani pointed at her mate, she made that kissing pop of her lips. Suddenly Centaine interrupted the discussion by also pointing at the little Bushman and saying, 'O'wa!'

They both stared at her in stupefied amazement, and then with delighted squeals of glee acknowledged her accomplishment.

'O'wa!' H'ani prodded her husband in the ribs, and hooted.

'O'wa!' The old man slapped his own chest, and bobbed up and down with gratification.

For the moment the argument was forgotten, as Centaine had intended, and as soon as the first excitement had passed, she pointed at the old woman, who was quick to understand her query.

'H'ani?' she enunciated clearly.

On the third attempt, Centaine sounded the final click to H'ani's satisfaction and high delight.

'Centaine.' She touched her own chest, but this precipitated shrill denials and a fluttering of hands.

'Nam Child!' H'ani slapped her gently on the shoulder, and Centaine resigned herself to another christening. 'Nam Child!' she agreed.

'So, revered old grandfather,' H'ani rounded on her husband, 'Nam Child may be ugly, but she learns fast and she is with child. We will rest here and go on tomorrow. The matter is at an end!' And grumbling under his breath O'wa shuffled out of the shelter, but when he came back at dusk, he carried the fresh carcass of a half-grown seal over one shoulder, and Centaine felt so rested that she joined in the ceremony of thanksgiving, clapping with H'ani and imitating her piping cries while O'wa danced around them and the seal meat grilled over the embers.

The ointment which H'ani had used on her injuries brought rapid results. The raw burns and blisters on her face dried up, and her skin with its Celtic pigmentation darkened to the colour of teak as it became conditioned to the sun, though she used her fingers to brush out her thick dark hair to shade as much of her face as possible.

Each day she grew stronger as her body responded to hard work and the protein-rich diet of seafood. Soon she could really reach out with her long legs and match the pace that O'wa set, and there was no more lagging behind, or argument about early halts. For Centaine it became a matter of pride to keep up with the old couple from dawn until dusk.

'I'll show you, you old devil,' she muttered to herself, fully aware of the strange antagonism which O'wa felt towards her but believing that it was her weakness and helplessness and her drag on the party that was the cause.

One day as they were about to begin, and despite the old woman's protests, she took half the water-filled ostrich eggs from H'ani's load and slung them in her canvas shawl. Once H'ani realized her intention, she acquiesced willingly and ribbed the old man mercilessly as they set out on the day's trek.

'Nam Child carries her share, just like a woman of the San,' she said, and when she had exhausted her gibes she turned all her attention to Centaine and began her instruction in earnest, pointing with her digging stick and not satisfied until Centaine had the word right or showed that she understood the lesson.

At first Centaine was merely humouring the old woman, but soon she was delighting in each fresh discovery and the day's journey seemed lighter and swifter as her body strengthened and her understanding grew.

What she had at first believed was a barren wasteland was instead a world teeming with strange and wonderfully adapted life. The kelp beds and underwater reefs were treasure houses of crustaceans and shellfish and seaworms, and occasionally the low tide left a shoal of fish trapped in a shallow rock pool. They were deep, full-bodied fish with gunmetal gleaming scales and a slightly greenish tinge to the flesh, but when split and grilled on the coals, were better than turbot.

Once they came across a nesting colony of jackass penguins. The penguins were on a rocky island, connected to the mainland by a reef across which they waded at low tide, although Centaine had shark horrors all the way over. The thousands of black and white jackass penguins nested on the bare ground, and hissed and brayed with outrage as the Bushmen harvested the big green eggs

and filled the canvas carrying bag with them. Roasted in the sand under the fire they were delicious, with transparent, jelly-like whites and bright yellow yolks, but so rich that they could only be eaten one at a time and the supply lasted many days.

Even the shifting dunes with precipitous slip-faces of loosely running sand were the homes of sand-burrowing lizards and the venomous side-winding adders that preyed upon them. They clubbed both lizards and adders and cooked them in their scaly skins, and after Centaine had mastered her initial aversion, she found that they tasted like chicken.

As they trekked northwards, the dunes became intermittent, no longer presenting an unbroken rampart, and between them were valleys whose bottoms were of firm earth, albeit as bare and as blasted as the dunes or the beaches. H'ani led Centaine over the rocky ground and showed her succulent plants which exactly resembled stones. They dug beneath the tiny inconspicuous leaves and found a bloated root the size of a football.

Centaine watched while H'ani grated the pulp of the root with her stone scraper, then took a handful of the shavings, held them high with her thumb pointed downwards like a teat on a cow's udder and squeezed. Milky liquid ran down her thumb and dribbled into her open mouth, and when she had squeezed out the last drop, she used the remaining damp pulp to scrub her face and arms, grinning all the while with pleasure.

Quickly Centaine followed her example. The juice was quinine-bitter, but after the first shock of the taste, Centaine found that it slaked her thirst more effectively than water alone, and when she had scrubbed her body with the pulp, the dryness caused by wind and sun and salt was alleviated and her skin felt and looked cleaner and smoother. The effect was to make her aware of herself for the first time since the shipwreck.

That evening as they sat around the fire waiting for the kebabs of limpets threaded on a piece of driftwood to broil, Centaine whittled a stick and with the point cleansed between her teeth, and then used her forefinger dipped in evaporated crystals of seasalt that she had scraped from the rocks to scrub them again. H'ani watched her knowingly, and after they had eaten, she came and squatted behind Centaine and crooned softly to her as she used a twig to pick the knots and tangles out of her hair, and then dressed it into tight new braids.

* * *

Centaine woke when it was still dark to the realization that a change had taken place while she slept. Although the fire had been built up, the light was weirdly diffused, and the excited voices of H'ani and O'wa were muted as though they came from a distance. The air was cold and heavy with moisture and it took Centaine a while to realize that they were enveloped in dense fog that had rolled in from the sea during the night.

H'ani was hopping with excitement and impatience.

'Come, Nam Child, hurry.' Centaine's vocabulary already contained a hundred or so of the most important words of San, and she scrambled up.

'Carry. Bring.' H'ani pointed at the canvas container of ostrich eggs and then picking up her own leather bag scampered away into the fog. Centaine ran after

her to keep her in sight, for the world had been obliterated by the pearly fog banks.

In the valley between the dunes H'ani dropped to her knees.

'Look, Nam child.' She seized Centaine's wrist and drew her down beside her, and pointed to the desert plant that was spread out flat against the ground. The thick smooth skin that covered the stone-like leaves chameleoned to the exact colour of the surrounding earth.

'Water, H'ani!' Centaine exclaimed delightedly.

'Water, Nam Child.' H'ani cackled with laughter.

The fog had condensed on the smooth leaves and had run down the slanted surface to gather in the trough-like depressions of the point where the foreshortened stems disappeared into the earth. The plant was a marvellously designed gatherer of moisture, and Centaine understood now how that bloated subterranean root was replenished at each coming of the fog.

'Quick!' H'ani ordered. 'Sun come soon.' She stood one of the empty ostrich shells upright in the soft earth and unplugged it. With a ball of animal fur she mopped up the glistening pool of dew and then squeezed it carefully into the egg-bottle. With that demonstration, she handed Centaine a wad of fur.

'Work!' she ordered.

Centaine worked as quickly as the old woman, listening to her chattering happily and understanding only an occasional word as they hurried from plant to plant.

'This is a blessing indeed, the spirits are kind to send the water-smoke from the sea. Now the crossing to the Place of All Life will be less arduous. Without the water-smoke we might have perished. They have made the road smooth for us, Nam child – perhaps your baby will be born at the Place of All Life. What a prodigious benevolence that would be. For then your child would have the special mark of the spirits upon him for all his life, he would be the greatest of hunters, the sweetest of singers, the nimblest of dancers and the most fortunate of all his clan.'

Centaine did not understand, but she laughed at the old woman, feeling lighthearted and happy, and the sound of her own laughter startled her, it had been so long – and she replied to the old woman's chatter in French.

'I had begun truly to hate this harsh land of yours, H'ani. After all the anticipation I had to see it, after all the wonderful things that Michel told me and all the things I had read about it, how different it all was, how cruel and how malicious.'

Hearing the tone of her voice, H'ani paused with the wet wad of fur poised over the egg-bottle and looked at her quizzically.

'Just now was the first time I have laughed since I have been in Africa.' Centaine laughed again, and H'ani giggled with relief and returned her attention to the bottle. 'This day Africa has shown me its first kindness.' Centaine lifted the sodden fur to her lips and sucked the cold sweet dew from it. 'This is a special day, H'ani, this is a special day for me and my baby.'

When all the egg-bottles were brimming full and carefully replugged, they indulged themselves, drinking the dew until they were satiated, and only then did Centaine look around her and begin to appreciate what the fog meant to the plants and creatures of the desert.

Bright red ants had come up from their deep nests to take advantage of it. The worker-ants scurried from plant to plant, sucking up the droplets so that their abdomens swelled and became translucent, on the point of bursting before

they disappeared back into the burrows. At the entrance to each burrow a cluster of other ants were assembled, the wedding party to see off the breeding queens and their consorts as they lifted into the foggy air on paper-white wings, fluttering off, most of them to die in the desert, but a very few of them to survive and found new colonies.

The sand lizards had come down from the dunes to feast on the flights of ants, and there were small rodents, gingery-red in colour, that hopped down the valley floor on overdeveloped hindlegs like miniature kangaroos.

'Look, H'ani, what is this?' Centaine had discovered a strange insect the size of a locust which was standing on its head in an exposed position. The dew consensed in silver droplets on its shiny iridescent armour plating, then trickled slowly down the grooves in the carapace and were channelled into the creature's hooked beak.

'Good eat,' H'ani told her and popped the insect into her mouth, crunched it up and swallowed it down with relish.

Centaine laughed at her, 'You dear, funny old thing.' Then she looked around at the small secret life of the desert. 'What an enchanted land Africa is! At last I can understand a little of what Michel tried to explain to me.'

With an African abruptness that no longer surprised Centaine, the mood changed. The curtains of fog peeled away, the sun struck through and within minutes the gem-like droplets of dew had vanished from the stone plants. The ants disappeared into their burrows, sealing the entrances behind them, and the sand lizards scurried back into the slippery dunes, leaving the dismembered paper wings of the flying ants they had devoured to blow idly on the small offshore wind.

At first the lizards, still chilled by the fog, basked on the sunny front of the dunes, but within minutes the heat was oppressive and they ran across the ridges of the slip-face to shelter on the shady side. Later, when the noon sun dispelled all the shadows, they would dive below the surface and swim down through it to the cooler sands beneath.

H'ani and Centaine shouldered their carrying bags and, bowed under the weight of the egg-bottles, went down to the beach. O'wa was already at the camp and he had a dozen fat lizards impaled on a stick of driftwood, and a goodly bag of the gingery desert rats laid out on the flat stone beside the fire.

'Oh, husband, what an intrepid provider you are.' H'ani laid down her carrying bag the better to praise the old man's efforts. 'Surely there has never been a hunter of all the San to match your skills!'

O'wa preened quite unashamedly at the old woman's blatant flattery, and H'ani averted her face for a moment and her eyes flashed a message to Centaine in the secret language of womankind.

'They are little boys,' her smile said clearly. 'From eight to eighty, they remain children.' And Centaine laughed again and clapped her hands and joined in H'ani's little pantomime of approbation.

'O'wa good! O'wa clever!' And the old man bobbed his head and looked solemn and important.

* * *

The moon was only four or five days from full, so that after they had eaten, it was bright enough to throw purple dark shadows below the dunes. They were all still too excited by the fog visitation to sleep, and Centaine was trying to follow and even join in the chatter of the two old San.

Centaine had by now learned the four click sounds of the San language, as well as the glottal choke which sounded as though the speaker was being strangulated. However, she was still struggling to understand the tonal variations. The different tones were almost undetectable to the Western ear, and it was only in the last few days that Centaine had even become aware of their existence. She had puzzled over the way H'ani seemed to repeat the same word and showed exasperation when Centaine had obviously not been able to detect any difference in the pronunciations. Then, quite suddenly, as though wax plugs had been removed from her ears, Centaine had heard the five distinct inflexions, high, middle, low, rising and falling, that changed not only the sense of a word but the relationship of the word to the rest of the sentence.

It was difficult and challenging and she was sitting close to H'ani so she could watch her lips, when suddenly she let out a surprised gasp and clutched her stomach with both hands.

'It moved!' Centaine's voice was filled with wonder. 'He moved – the baby moved!'

H'ani understood immediately and she reached out swiftly and lifted Centaine's brief tattered canvas skirt and clasped her stomach. Deep in her body there was another spasm of life.

'Ai! Ai!' shrilled H'ani. 'Feel him! Feel him kick like a zebra stallion!' Fat litle tears of joy squeezed out of her slanted Chinese eyes and as they ran down the deep corrugated wrinkles on her cheeks, they sparkled in the light of the fire and the moon. 'So strong – so brave and strong! Feel him, old grandfather.'

O'wa could not refuse such an invitation, and Centaine, kneeling in the firelight with her skirts lifted high over her naked lower body, felt no embarrassment at the old man's touch.

'This,' announced O'wa solemnly, 'is a most propitious thing. It is fitting that I should dance to celebrate it.' And O'wa stood up and danced in the moonlight for Centaine's unborn infant.

* * *

The moon dipped into the dark, slumbrous sea, but already the sky over the land was turning to the colour of ripe orange at the approach of day and Centaine lay for only a few seconds after she woke. She was surprised that the two old people still lay beside the dead ash of last night's fire, but she left the camp hurriedly, knowing that the day's trek would begin before sunrise.

At a discreet distance from the camp she squatted to relieve herself, then stripped off her rags and ran into the sea, gasping at the cold invigorating water as she scrubbed her body with handfuls of sand. She pulled her clothing over her wet body and ran back to the camp. The old people were still wrapped in their leather cloaks and lying so still that Centaine felt a moment of panic, but then H'ani coughed throatily and stirred.

'They are still alive, anyway,' Centaine smiled and assembled her few

possessions, feeling virtuous for usually H'ani had to chivvy her, but now the old woman stirred again and mumbled sleepily.

Centaine understood only the words, 'Wait, rest, sleep.' Then H'ani subsided and pulled her cloak over her head again.

Centaine was puzzled. She fed a few sticks to the fire and blew up a flame, then sat to wait.

Venus, the morning star, lay on the backs of the dunes, but paled and faded at the approach of the sun, and still the two San slept on, and Centaine began to feel irritated by the inactivity. She was so strong and healthy already that she had actually been looking forward to the day's journey.

Only when the sun cleared the tops of the dunes did H'ani sit up and yawn and belch and scratch herself.

'Go?' Centaine used the rising tone that changed the word into a question.

'No, no,' H'ani made the negative waving sign. 'Wait – night – moon – go there.' And she pointed with a quick stabbing thumb at the dunes.

'Go land?' Centaine asked, not sure that she understood.

'Go land,' H'ani agreed, and Centaine felt a quick thrill. They were going to leave the seashore at last.

'Go now?' Centaine demanded impatiently.

Twice during the last few days when they had stopped to make camp, Centaine had climbed to the top of the nearest dune and stared inland. Once she had imagined the distant outline of blue mountains against the evening sky, and she had felt her spirit summoned away from this monotonous seascape towards that mysterious interior.

'Go now?' she repeated eagerly, and O'wa laughed derisively as he came to squat at the fire.

'The monkey is eager to meet the leopard,' he said, 'but listen to it squeal when it does!'

H'ani clucked at him in disapproval and then turned to Centaine. 'Today we will rest. Tonight we will begin the hardest part of our journey. Tonight, Nam Child, do you understand that? Tonight, with the moon to light us. Tonight, while the sun sleeps, for no man nor woman can walk hand in hand with the sun through the land of the singing sands. Tonight. Rest now.'

'Tonight,' Centaine repeated. 'Rest now.' But she left the camp and once again climbed up through the sliding slippery sands to the top of the first line of dunes.

On the beach four hundred feet below her, the two tiny figures sitting at the campfire were insignificant specks. Then she turned to look inland and she saw that the dune on which she stood was a mere foothill to the great mountains of sand that rose before her.

The colours of the dunes shaded from pale daffodil yellow, through gold and orange, to purplish-brown and dark *sang de boeuf*, but beyond them she imagined she saw ghost mountains with rocky crenellated peaks. Even as she stared, however, the horizon turned milky-blue and began to waver and dissolve, and she felt the heat come out of the desert, a whiff of it only, but she recoiled from its scalding breath, and before her eyes the land was veiled by the glassy shimmering veils of heat mirage.

She turned and went down to the camp again. Neither O'wa nor H'ani was ever completely idle. Now the old man was shaping arrow-heads of white bone, while his wife was putting together another necklace, fashioning the beads from pieces of broken ostrich shell, chipping them into coins between two small

stones and then drilling a hole through each with a bone sliver, and finally stringing the finished beads on a length of gut.

Watching her work Centaine was reminded vividly of Anna. She stood up quickly and left the camp again, and H'ani looked up from the string of beads.

'Nam Child is unhappy,' she said.

'There is water in the egg-bottles and food in her belly,' O'wa grunted as he sharpened his arrowhead. 'She has no reason to be unhappy.'

'She pines for her own clan,' H'ani whispered, and the old man did not reply. Both of them understood vividly and were silent as they remembered those they had left in shallow graves in the wilderness.

'I am strong enough now,' Centaine spoke aloud, 'and I have learned how to keep alive. I don't have to follow them any more. I could turn back to the south again – alone.' She stood uncertainly, imagining what it would be like, and it was that single word that decided her. 'Alone,' she repeated. 'If only Anna were still alive, if only there was somewhere out there for me to go to, then I might attempt it.' And she slumped down on the beach and hugged her knees despondently. 'There is no way back. I just have to go on. Living each day like an animal, living like a savage, living with savages.' And she looked down at the rags which barely covered her body. 'I just have to go on, and I don't even know where,' and her despair threatened to overwhelm her completely. She had to fight it off as though it were a living adversary. 'I won't give in,' she muttered, 'I just won't give in, and when this is over I will never want again. I'll never thirst and starve nor wear rags and stinking skins again.' She looked down at her hands. The nails were ragged and black with dirt and broken off down to the quick. She made a fist to cover them. 'Never again. My son and I will never want again, I swear it.'

It was late afternoon when she wandered back into the primitive camp site under the dunes. H'ani looked up at her and grinned like a wizened little ape, and Centaine felt a sudden rush of affection for her.

'Dear H'ani,' she whispered. 'You're all I have got left.' And the old woman scrambled to her feet and came towards her, carrying the finished necklace of ostrich shell in both hands.

She stood on tiptoe and placed the necklace carefully over Centaine's head and arranged it fussily down her bosom, cooing with self-satisfaction at her handiwork.

'It's beautiful, H'ani,' Centaine's voice husked. 'Thank you, thank you so very much,' and suddenly she burst into tears. 'And I called you a savage. Oh, forgive me. With Anna you are the sweetest, dearest person I've ever known.' She knelt so that their faces were level and she hugged the old woman with a desperate strength, pressing her temple against H'ani's withered wrinkled cheek.

'Why is she weeping?' O'wa demanded from beside the fire.

'Because she is happy.'

'That,' O'wa opined, 'is a most stupid reason. I think this female is a little moon-touched.'

He stood up, and still shaking his head, began the final preparations for the night's journey.

* * *

The little old people were unusually solemn, Centaine noticed, as they adjusted their cloaks and carrying satchels, and H'ani came to her and checked the sling of her bag, then knelt to adjust the canvas booties bound around Centaine's feet.

'What is it?' Their serious mien made Centaine uneasy.

H'ani understood the question, but did not try to explain. Instead she called Centaine and the two of them fell in behind O'wa.

O'wa raised his voice. 'Spirit of Moon, make a light for us in this night to show us the path.' He used the cracked falsetto tone which all the spirits particularly enjoyed, and he performed a few shuffling dance steps in the sand. 'Spirit of Great Sun, sleep well, and when you rise tomorrow be not angry, that your anger burn us up in the singing sands. Then when we have passed safely through and have reached the sip-wells, we will dance for you and sing our thanks.'

He finished the short dance with a leap and a stamp of his small childlike feet. That was enough for now, a small down payment, with the balance promised when the spirits had honoured their part of the contract.

'Come, old grandmother,' he said. 'Make sure that Nam Child stays close and does not fall behind. You know that we cannot turn back to search for her if she does.' And in that quick, swaying jog, he started up the slope of the beach into the mouth of the valley, just as the moon broke clear of the darkening horizon and started its journey across the starry heavens.

It was strange to travel in the night, for the desert seemed to take on new and mysterious dimensions, the dunes seemed taller and closer, decked in silver moonlight and dark purple shadows, and the valleys between them were canyons of silence, while above it all the vast panoply of the stars and the milky way and the moon were closer and brighter than Centaine had ever believed possible. She had the illusion that by simply reaching up she could pluck them down like ripe fruit from the bough.

The memory of the ocean stayed with them long after it was out of sight, the soft hiss of the footsteps in the sand seemed to echo its gentle kissing surf on the yellow beaches, and the air was still cooled by its vast green waters.

They had been following the valley for almost a half of the moon's rise to its zenith when suddenly Centaine trotted into an eddy of heat. After the ocean-cooled airs it was like running into a solid barrier. Centaine gasped with surprise and H'ani murmured without breaking the rhythm of her gait, 'Now it begins.' But they passed swiftly through it, and beyond the air was so cold by contrast that Centaine shivered and drew her cloak closer about her shoulders.

The valley twisted and as they came around the corner of a towering dune on which the moon shadows lay like bruises, the desert breathed upon them again.

'Stay close, Nam child.' But the heat had a viscosity and weight so that Centaine felt that she was wading into a lava flow. At midnight it was hotter than in the boiler room at Mort Homme with the furnace stoked with oak logs, and as she breathed it into her lungs, she felt the heat entering her body like an invader, and with each breath expelled, she could feel it taking her moisture like a thief.

They paused once, only briefly, and drank from an egg-bottle. Both H'ani and O'wa watched carefully as Centaine lifted it to her lips, but neither of them had to caution her now.

When the sky began to lighten, O'wa slackened his pace a little, and once or twice paused to survey the valley with a critical eye. It was obvious that he was

choosing a place to wait out the day, and when at last they halted, it was close under the lee of a steep dune wall.

There was no material for a fire, and H'ani offered Centaine a piece of sun-dried fish wrapped in seaweed, but she was too tired and hot to eat and afraid also that food would increase her thirst during the day ahead. She drank her ration of water from the egg-bottle, and then wearily stood up and moved a short distance from the others. But as soon as she squatted, H'ani let out a shrill reprimand and hurried to her.

'No!' she repeated, and Centaine was embarrassed and confused, until the old woman fished in her satchel and brought out the dried wild gourd that she used as a bowl and ladle.

'Here, this one – ' She proffered it to Centaine, who still did not understand. Exasperated, the old woman snatched back the gourd and holding it between her own legs urinated into it.

'Here – do.' She offered the bowl to Centaine again.

'I can't, H'ani, not in front of everybody,' Centaine protested modestly.

'O'wa, come here,' H'ani called. 'Show the child.' The old man came across and noisily reinforced H'ani's demonstration.

Despite her embarrassment, Centaine could not help feeling a touch of envy. 'How much more convenient!'

'Now, do!' H'ani offered her the gourd once again, and Centaine capitulated. She turned away modestly and with both the old people encouraging her loudly, she added her own tinkling stream to the communal gourd. H'ani bore it away triumphantly.

'Hurry, Nam Child,' she beckoned. 'The sun will come soon.' And she showed Centaine how to scoop a shallow trench in the sand in which to lie.

The sun struck the face of the dune on the opposite side of the valley, and it flung reflected heat at them like a mirror of polished bronze. They lay in the strip of shade and cringed into their trenches.

The sun rose higher and the dune shadow shrank. The heat rose and filled the valley with silvery mirage so that the dunes began to dance, and then the sands started to sing. It was a low but pervading vibration as though the desert was the sounding box of a gigantic string instrument. It rose and fell and died away and then started again.

'The sands are singing,' H'ani told her quietly, and Centaine understood. She lay with her ear to the ground and listened to the strange and wonderful music of the desert.

Still the heat increased, and following the example of the San, Centaine covered her head with the canvas shawl and lay quietly. It was too hot to sleep, but she fell into a sort of stupefied coma, and rode the long swelling waves of heat as though they were the sound of the sea.

Still it became hotter, and the shade shrivelled away as the sun nooned, and there was no relief or asylum from its merciless lash. Centaine lay and panted like a maimed animal, and each quick and shallow breath seemed to abrade her throat and burn the strength from her body.

'It can't get worse,' she told herself. 'This is the end of it, soon it will begin to cool.'

She was wrong. The heat grew stronger yet and the desert hissed and vibrated like a tortured beast, and Centaine was almost afraid to open her eyes lest it sear her eyeballs.

Then she heard the old woman moving and she lifted the corner of her head

cover and watched her carefully mixing sand into the gourdful of urine. She brought the bowl to where Centaine lay and plastered the wet sand over her baking skin.

Centaine gasped with relief at the cool touch of it, and before it could dry in the fierce heat, H'ani filled in the shallow trench with loose sand, burying Centaine under a thin layer and then arranging the shawl over her head.

'Thank you, H'ani,' Centaine whispered, and the old woman went to cover her husband.

With the damp sand next to her skin and the protective layer over that, Centaine lasted out those hottest hours of the desert day, and then with that African suddenness she felt the temperature on her cheeks change, and the sunlight was no longer stark dazzling white, but shaded with a mellow, buttery tone.

At nightfull they rose out of their beds and shook themselves, throwing off the sand. They drank in a transport that was almost religious, but again Centaine could not force herself to eat, and then O'wa led them off.

Now there was no novelty or fascination for Centaine in the night's trek, and the heavenly bodies were no longer marvels to gaze upon with awe but merely instruments to mark the long tortuous passage of the hours.

The earth beneath her changed its character from loose sand that gave under each step and dragged at her feet, to hard, compacted mica flats where the flowerlike crystals called 'desert roses' had edges to them like knives; they cut through her canvas sandals, and she had to pause to rebind them. Then they left the flats and crossed the low spine of a sub-dune, and from its crest saw another vast valley yawn before them.

O'wa never wavered or showed the least hesitation. Although Centaine realized that these mountains of sand would walk before the prevailing winds, endlessly changing shape, trackless and unknowable, yet the little man moved through them the way a master mariner rides upon the shifting currents of the ocean.

The silence of the desert seemed to enter Centaine's head like molten wax, deadening her sense of hearing, filling her eardrums with the sussurations of nothingness as though she held a seashell to her ear.

'Will the sand never end?' she asked herself. 'Is this a continent of dunes?'

In the dawn they halted and prepared their defences to resist the siege of the sun, and in the hottest hour of the day as Centaine lay in her shallow grave-like bed, coated with urine-damp sand, she felt her baby move within her more strongly this time, as though he too were fighting the heat and the thirst.

'Patience, my darling' she whispered to him. 'Save your strength. We must learn the lessons and the ways of this land, so that we will never have to suffer like this again. Never again.'

That evening, when she rose from the sand, she ate a little of the dried fish for the baby's sake, but as she had feared, the food made her thirst almost insupportable. However, the strength it gave her bore her up through the night's journey.

She did not waste strength by speaking aloud. All three of them were conserving energy and moisture, no unnecessary words or actions, but Centaine looked up at the sky as it made its grand and ponderous revolution, and she could still see Michael's star standing across the black void of the South Pole from her own.

'Please let it end,' she prayed silently to his star. 'Let it end soon, for I don't know how much longer I can go on.'

But it did not end, and it seemed that the nights grew longer, and sand deeper and more cloying around her feet, while each day seemed fiercer than the last and the heat beat down upon them like a blacksmith's hammer-strokes on the iron of the anvil.

Centaine found that she had lost track of the days and the nights, they had blended in her mind into a single endless torment of heat and thirst.

'Five days, or six or even seven?' she wondered vaguely, and then she counted the empty egg-bottles. 'It must be six,' she decided. 'Only two full bottles left.'

Centaine and H'ani each placed one of the full bottles in their pack, sharing the load exactly, then they ate the last shreds of dried fish and stood up to face the night's journey, but this time it did not begin immediately.

O'wa stared for a while into the east, turning his head slightly from side to side as though he were listening, and for the first time Centaine detected a fine shade of uncertainty in the way he held his small head with its crownlike nimbus of arrow shafts. Then O'wa began to sing softly in what Centaine had come to recognize as his ghost-voice.

'Spirit of great Lion Star,' he looked up to Sirius shining in the constellation of Canis Major, 'you are the only one who can see us here, for all the other spirits avoid the land of singing sand. We are alone, and the journey is harder than I remember it when I passed here as a young man. The path has become obscure, great Lion Star, but you have the bright eye of a vulture and can see it all. Lead us, I beg you. Make the path clear for us.'

Then he took the egg-bottle from H'ani's satchel and drew the stopper and spilled a little of the water on to the sand. It formed small round balls, and Centaine made a little moaning sound in her throat and sank on to her knees.

'See, spirit of great Lion Star, we share water with you,' O'wa sang and replugged the bottle, but Centaine stared at the little wet balls of sand and moaned again.

'Peace, Nam Child,' H'ani whispered to her. 'To receive a special boon, it is sometimes necessary to give up what is precious.'

She took Centaine's wrist and pulled her gently to her feet, and then turned to follow O'wa over the endless dunes.

With the silences deafening her, and weariness a crushing burden to carry, and thirst a raging torment, Centaine struggled on, once again losing all sense of time or distance or direction, seeing nothing but the two dancing figures ahead of her, transformed by the rays of the waning moon into tiny hobgoblins.

They stopped so suddenly that Centaine ran into H'ani and would have fallen had not the old woman steadied her, and then quietly drawn her down until they lay side by side.

'What – ' Centaine began, but H'ani placed a hand over her mouth to quieten her.

O'wa lay beside them, and when Centaine was quiet he pointed over the lip of the dune on which they were lying.

Two hundred feet below at the dune's foot began a level plain, awash with soft silver moonlight. It reached to the very limit of Centaine's night vision, flat, without end, and it gave her hope that at last the dunes were behind them. Upon this plain stood a scattered forest of long-dead trees. Leprous-grey in the moonlight, they lifted the blighted and twisted limbs of arthritic beggars to an

uncaring sky. The weird scene invoked in Centaine a superstitious chill, and when something large but shapeless moved amongst the ancient trees like a monster from mythology, she shivered and wriggled closer to H'ani.

Both the San were trembling with eagerness like hunting dogs on the leash, and H'ani took Centaine's hand and pointed silently. As Centaine's eyes adjusted, she saw that there were more living shapes than the one she had first spotted, but they were as still as great grey boulders. She counted five of them altogether.

Lying on his side, O'wa was restringing his little hunting bow, and when he had tested the tension of its string, he selected a pair of arrows from the leather band around his forehead, made a sign to H'ani and then slithered back from the crest of the dune. Once he was off the skyline, he leaped to his feet and slipped away into the shadows and folds of windblown sands.

The two women lay behind the ridge, still and silent as the shadows. Centaine was learning the animal patience that this ancient wilderness demanded of all its creatures. The sky began to bloom with the first promise of day, and now she could see more clearly the creatures on the plain below them.

They were huge antelopes. Four of them lying quietly, while one of them, larger and more thickset in shoulders and neck, stood a little apart. Centaine judged that he was the herd bull, for at his shoulder he stood as tall as Nuage, her beloved stallion, but he carried a magnificent pair of horns, long and straight and vicious, and Centaine was reminded vividly of the tapestry *La Dame à la Licorne* at the Musée de Cluny, which her father had taken her to see on her twelfth birthday.

The light strengthened and the bull gleamed a lovely soft mulberry-fawn colour. His face was marked with darker lines in a diamond pattern, that looked as though he were wearing a head halter, but there was that wild dignity about him that immediately dispelled any suggesion of captivity.

He swung his noble head towards where Centaine lay, extended his trumpet-like ears and swished his dark bushy horse-like tail uneasily. H'ani laid her hand on Centaine's arm and they shrank down. The bull stared in their direction for many minutes, rigid and still as a marble carving, but neither of the women moved, and at last the bull lowered his head and began to dig in the loose earth of the plain with his sharp black forehooves.

'Ah, yes! Dig for the sweet root of the bi plant, great and splendid bull,' O'wa exhorted him silently. 'Do not lift your head, you marvellous chieftain of all gemsbok, feed well, and I will dance you such a dance that all the spirits of the gemsbok will envy you for ever!'

O'wa lay one hundred and fifty feet from where the gemsbok bull was standing, still far beyond the range of his puny bow. He had left the shadow of the dune valley almost an hour before, and in that time had covered less then five hundred paces.

There was a slight depression in the surface of the plain, a mere indentation less than a hand's span deep, but even in the vague light of the moon O'wa had picked it out unerringly with his hunter's eye and he had slid into it like a small amber-coloured serpent, and like a serpent moved on his belly with slow, sinuous undulations and silent prayers to the spirits of Lion Star who had guided him to this quarry. Suddenly the gemsbok flung his head and stared about him suspiciously, ears flared wide.

'Don't be alarmed, sweet bull,' O'wa urged him. 'Smell the bi tuber and let peace enter your heart again.'

The minutes stretched out, and then the bull blew a small fluttery sound through his nostrils, and lowered his head. His harem of fawn-coloured cows who had been watching him warily relaxed, and their jaws began working again as they chewed on the cud.

O'wa slithered forward, moving under the flattened lip of the depression, his cheek touching the earth so as not to show a head silhouette, pushing himself over the soft earth with his hips and his knees and his toes.

The gemsbok had rooted out the tuber and was chewing on it with noisy gusto, holding it down with a forehoof to break off a mouthful, and O'wa closed the gap between them with elaborate, patient stealth.

'Feast well, sweet bull, without you three persons and an unborn child will be dead by tomorrow's sun. Do not go, great gemsbok, stay a while, just a little longer.'

He was as close as he dared approach now, but it was still too far. The gemsbok's hide was tough and his fur thick. The arrow was a light reed, and the point was bone that could not take the same keen edge as iron.

'Spirit of Lion Star, do not turn your face away now,' O'wa beseeched, and raised his left hand so that the tiny pale-coloured palm was turned towards the bull.

For almost a minute nothing happened, and then the bull noticed the disembodied hand that seemed to rise out of the earth, and he lifted his head and stared at it. It seemed too small to be dangerous.

After a minute of utter stillness, O'wa wriggled his fingers seductively and the bull blew through his nostrils and stretched out his muzzle, sucking in air, trying to get the scent, but O'wa was working into the small, fitful morning breeze, with the deceptive dawn light behind him.

He held his hand still again and then slowly lowered it to his side. The bull took a few paces towards him and then froze – another few paces, craning inquisitively, ears pricked forward, he peered at the shallow indentation where O'wa lay pressed to the earth without breathing. Then the bull's curiosity took him forward again into range of O'wa's bow.

In a flash of movement, like the strike of the adder, O'wa rolled on to his side, drew the eagle feather flights to his cheek and let the arrow fly. It darted like a bee across the space between them and alighted with a slapping sound on the patterned cheek of the bull, fixing its barbs in the soft skin below his trumpet-like ear.

The bull reared back at the sting of it, and whirled away. Instantly his harem cows sprang from their sandy couches into full gallop and the whole herd went away after the running bull, switching their long dark tails and dragging a pale train of dust behind them.

The bull was shaking his head, trying to rid himself of the arrow that dangled from his cheek, and he swerved in his run and deliberately brushed his head against the trunk of one of the ancient dead trees.

'Stick deep!' O'wa was on his feet, capering and yelling. 'Hold fast, arrow, carry the poison of O'wa to his heart. Carry it swiftly, little arrow.'

The women came running down from the dune to join him.

'Oh, what a cunning hunter,' H'ani lauded her husband, and Centaine was breathless but disappointed for the herd was already out of sight across the dark plain, lost in the grey of pre-dawn.

'Gone?' she asked H'ani.

'Wait,' the old woman answered. 'Follow soon. Watch now. O'wa make magic.'

The old man had laid aside his weapons, except for two arrows which he arranged in his headband to prick up at the same angle as the horns of a gemsbok. Then he cupped his hands on each side of his head into trumpet-shaped ears, and subtly altered his entire stance and the way he carried his head. He snorted through his nostrils and pawed at the ground, and before Centaine's eyes was transformed into a gemsbok. The mimicry was so faithful that Centaine clapped her hands delightedly.

O'wa went through the pantomime of seeing the beckoning hand, approaching it warily, and then being struck by the arrow. Centaine had a sense of *déjà vu*, so accurately was the incident portrayed.

O'wa galloped away with the same stride and carriage as the gemsbok, but then he began to weaken and stagger. He was panting, his head drooping, and Centaine felt a pang of sympathy for the stricken beast. She thought of Nuage and tears sprang into her eyes, but H'ani was clapping and uttering little shrieks of encouragement.

'Die, oh bull that we revere, die that we may live!'

O'wa blundered in a wide circle, his horned head too heavy to carry, and he sagged to the earth and went into the final convulsions as the poison coursed through his blood.

It was all so convincing that Centaine was no longer seeing the little San, but rather the bull that he was portraying. She did not for a moment doubt the efficacy of the sympathetic spell that O'wa was weaving over his quarry.

'Ah!' H'ani cried. 'He is down. The great bull is finished,' and Centaine believed without question.

They drank from the egg-bottles, and then O'wa broke a straight branch from one of the dead trees and shaped one end to fit the spearhead made from the thighbone of a buffalo which he carried in his pouch. He bound the spearhead in place and weighed the heavy weapon in his hand.

'It is time to go after the bull,' he announced, and led off across the plain.

Centaine's first impression was correct. They had passed beyond the dune country, but the plain that lay ahead of them was every bit as forbidding, and the strange shapes of the dead forest gave it a surreal and other-worldly feeling. Centaine wondered how long ago the forest had died, and shivered as she realized that these trees might have stood like this for a thousand years, preserved by the desiccated air as the mummies of the pharaohs had been.

O'wa was following the tracks of the gemsbok herd, and even over the hard pebbled expanses of the plain where Centaine could see no sign of their passing, the little San led them at a confident unwavering trot. He paused only once to pick up the shaft of his arrow, lying at the base of the dead tree upon which the bull had brushed itself. He held it up and showed it to the women.

'See. The barb has struck.'

The head of the arrow was missing. O'wa had deliberately designed it in two pieces with a weak section just at the back of the poisoned barb so that it would break away.

The light improved swiftly, and H'ani, trotting ahead of Centaine, pointed with her digging stick. At first Centaine could not see what she was indicating, then she noticed a small dried vine with a few parched brown leaves lying close to the earth, the first sign of living plant life since they had left the coast.

Because she now knew where and how to look, Centaine noticed other plants,

brown and blasted and insignificant, but she had learned enough of this desert to guess what lay beneath the surface. It gave her spirits a small lift when she noticed the first scattered clumps of fine silver dry desert grass. The dunes were behind them, and the land about them was coming alive again.

The morning breeze that had aided O'wa in his stalk persisted after the sun had cleared the horizon, so the heat was not as oppressive as it had been in the dune country. The whole temper of the San was lighter and more carefree, and even without H'ani's assurances – 'Good now, eat, drink soon' – Centaine was sure that they had passed through the worst stage of the journey. She had to screw up her eyes and shade them, for already the low sun sparkled in dazzling points of white light from the mica chips and bright pebbles and the sky was aglow with a hot soapy radiance that dissolved the horizon and washed out all colour and altered shape and substance.

Far ahead of them Centaine saw the humped shape lying, and beyond it the four gemsbok cows lingering loyally but fearfully by their fallen liege bull. They abandoned him at last only when the little file of human shapes was within a mile, and they galloped away into the shimmering heat haze.

The bull lay as O'wa had mimed him, panting and so weakened by the poison of the arrowhead that his head rolled and his long straight annulated horns waggled from side to side. His eyes glistened with tears and his eyelashes were as long and curved as those of a beautiful woman, yet he tried to rise to defend himself as O'wa faced him, and hooked with those rapier horns that could impale a full-grown lion, swinging them in a vicious flashing arc, before sagging back.

O'wa circled him cautiously, seeming so frail against the animal's bulk, waiting for his opening, the clumsy spear poised, but the bull dragged its semi-paralysed body around to face him. The arrowhead still dangled from the wound beneath his ear, and the lovely black and white pattern of his face mask was smeared with dark coagulated blood from the poisoned wound.

Centaine thought of Nuage again, and she wanted the suffering to end quickly. She laid down her satchel, loosened her skirt and held it like a matador's cape and sidled up to the stricken bull on the far side from O'wa.

'Be ready, O'wa, be ready!' The bull turned to her voice. She caped the bull and he lunged at her, his horns hissed in the air like a swinging cutlass, and he dragged himself towards her, kicking up dust with his giant hooves, and Centaine leaped nimbly aside.

As he was distracted, O'wa rushed forward and lanced the bull in the throat, driving the bone spearhead deep, twisting and worrying it, seeking the carotid artery. Bright arterial blood sprayed like a flamingo feather in the sunlight, and O'wa leapt back and watched him die.

'Thank you, great bull. Thank you for letting us live.'

* * *

Between them they rolled the carcass on to its back, but when O'wa prepared to make the first cut with his flint knife, Centaine opened the blade of her clasp knife and handed it to him.

O'wa hesitated. He had never touched that beautiful weapon. He believed

that if he did it might cleave to his fingers and he would never be able to give it up again.

'Take, O'wa,' Centaine urged him, and when he still hesitated, staring at the knife with a timid reverence, Centaine with a sudden intuitive flash realized the true reason for O'wa's antagonism towards her.

'He wants the knife, he is lusting after it.'

She almost laughed but controlled it. 'Take, O'wa,' and the little man reached out slowly and took it from her hand.

He turned it lovingly between his fingers. He stroked the steel, caressing the blade, and then tested the edge with his thumb.

'Ai! Ai!' he exclaimed as the steel sliced through his skin and raised a beaded chain of blood drops across the ball of his thumb. 'What a weapon. Look, H'ani!' He displayed his injured thumb proudly. 'See how sharp it is!'

'My stupid husband, it is usual to cut the game and not the hunter!'

O'wa cackled happily at the joke, and bent to the task. He took the bull's scrotum in his left hand and drew it out, then with a single stroke lopped it free.

'Ai! How sharp!' He laid the scrotum aside – the testicles grilled on the coals were a delicacy and the sac of soft skin would make a fine pouch for arrowheads and other small valuables.

Starting from the wound between the bull's hindlegs, he made a shallow cut through the skin, angling the blade forward so as not to pierce the belly cavity. He led the cut with his forefinger hooked under the skin, up between the bull's forelegs under its throat to the point of the chin. He made ring cuts around the bull's neck, and around the hocks of all four limbs, then sliced down the inside of the legs until he intercepted the first long lateral incision. With the women pulling on the flaps of free skin, and O'wa pushing his balled fist down between the white underside of the skin and the blue marbled muscles sheathed in their transparent capsules, they flayed the hide off the carcass in a single sheet. It made a soft, tearing crackling sound as it came away; they spread it out, fur-side down on the ground.

Then O'wa opened the stomach cavity with the precision of a surgeon, lifted out the heavy wet viscera and laid them on the sheet of skin.

H'ani scurried away and collected a bunch of the fine pale desert grass. She had to range widely, for the clumps of grass were scattered and sparse. She hurried back and arranged the grass over the gourd bowl, while O'wa slit open the slippery white bag of the bull's rumen and lifted out a double handful of the contents. Water dribbled from the undigested vegitation even before O'wa began to squeeze it out.

Using the bunch of grass as a sieve, O'wa filled the gourd with fluid and then lffted it with both hands to his lips. He drank deeply, closing his eyes with ecstasy, and when he lowered the bowl, he belched thunderously and grinned hugely as he passed the gourd to H'ani. She drank noisily and finished with a belch and a hoot of appreciation, wiping her mouth on the back of her hand as she passed the gourd to Centaine.

Centaine examined the pale greenish-brown liquid. 'It's only vegetable juice,' she consoled herself. 'It hasn't even been chewed or mixed with gastric juices yet – ' and she lifted the gourd.

It was much easier than she had anticipated, and it tasted like a broth of herbs and grass, with the bitter aftertaste of the bi tuber. She handed the empty gourd back to O'wa, and while he squeezed and strained the rest of the contents

of the rumen, she imagined the long table at Mort Homme set with silver and crystal and Sèvres porcelain, and the way Anna fussed over the flowers, the freshness of the turbot, the temperature of the wine and the exact shade of pink of the slices of freshly carved *filet*, and she laughed aloud. She had come a long, long way from Mort Homme.

The two little San laughed with her in complete misunderstanding, and they all drank again and then again.

'Look at the child,' H'ani invited her husband. 'In the land of the singing sand I feared for her, but already she blooms like the desert flowers after the rain. She is a strong one, with the liver of a lion – did you see how she helped at the moment of the kill, by drawing the eye of the bull to herself?' H'ani nodded and cackled and belched. 'She will breed a fine son – you hear the word of old H'ani – a fine son indeed.'

O'wa, his belly ballooning with good water, grinned and was about to concede, when his eye dropped to the knife that lay between his feet, and the grin faded.

'Silly old woman, you chatter like the brainless spotted guinea fowl, while the meat spoils.' He snatched up the knife. Envy was an emotion so alien to his nature that O'wa was deeply unhappy and not really certain of the reason why, but the thought of handing the knife back to the girl filled him with a corrosive anger that he had never known before. He frowned and muttered as he dressed out the viscera of the bull, cutting thin slices of the rubbery white tripes and chewing them raw as he worked.

It was mid-morning before they had festooned the branches of one of the dead trees with long ribbons of bright scarlet gemsbok meat, and the heat built up so swiftly that the meat darkened and dried out almost immediately.

It was too hot to eat. Between them H'ani and Centaine spread the wet gemsbok skin over a framework of dead branches and they huddled under this tent-like structure, taking refuge from the sun, cooling their bodies with the evaporating fluids of the gemsbok's secondary stomach.

At sundown O'wa took out his fire sticks and began the laborious process of coaxing a spark from them, but impatiently Centaine took the ball of dry kindling from him. Up to that time she had always been too intimidated by the little San and her own feeling of total inadequacy to make any show of initiative. Now, somehow, the crossing of the dunes and her part in the gemsbok hunt emboldened her, and she laid out the kindling and the knife and flint with the San looking on curiously.

She struck a shower of sparks into the kindling and stooped quickly to blow it into flame. The San shrieked in amazement and consternation, and backed away in superstitious awe. Only once the fire was burning steadily could Centaine reassure them, and they crept back and marvelled over the steel and the flint. Under Centaine's tutelage, O'wa at last succeeded in striking sparks, and his joy was spontaneous and childlike.

As soon as the night brought relief from the heat of the sun, they prepared a feast of broiled liver and tripes and kidneys wrapped in the lacework of white fat that had enclosed the intestines. While the women worked at the fire, O'wa danced for the spirit of the gemsbok, and as he had promised, he leaped as high as he had done when he was a young man, and he sang until his voice cracked and failed. Then he squatted down at the fire and began to eat.

The two San ate with the fat greasing their chins and running down on to their chests; they ate until their stomachs were distended and bulged out like

balloons, hanging down on their laps; they went on eating long after Centaine was gorged and satiated.

Every once in a while Centaine was sure they were faltering, as their jaws slowed and they blinked at each other like sleepy owls in the firelight. Then O'wa would place both hands on his bulging stomach and roll onto one buttock, his wrinkled face contorted, and he would grunt and strain until he was able to clap off a resounding fart. Across the fire, H'ani would answer him with a squealing blast every bit as earsplitting, and they both hooted with laughter and crammed more meat into their mouths.

As Centaine drifted off into sleep with her own stomach stuffed with meat, she realized that this orgy was a natural reaction of a people accustomed to privation faced suddenly with a mountain of food and no means of preserving it. When she woke at dawn they were still feasting.

With the sun the two San lay under the tent of gemsbok hide, their bellies distended, and snored through the heat, but at sunset they blew up the fire and began feasting again. By this time what remained of the gemsbok was smelling high and strong, but this seemed if anything to stimulate their appetite.

When O'wa rose to stagger out of the firelight on private business, Centaine saw that his buttocks which had been slack and sagging and wrinkled when they came down from the dunes, were now tight and round and polished.

'Just like a camel's hump,' Centaine giggled, and H'ani giggled with her and offered her a slice of the belly fat, cooked brown and crisp.

Once again they slept through the day like a nest of pythons digesting the gargantuan banquet, but at sunset with the carrying bags packed with the hard black strips of dried gemsbok meat, O'wa led them eastwards across the moonlit plain. He carried the folded gemsbok skin balanced on his head.

* * *

Gradually the plain over which they travelled altered in character. Amongst the fine desert grasses there appeared scraggy little scrubs, not as high as Centaine's knee, and once O'wa stopped and pointed ahead at a tall ghostly shape that crossed with a high-stepping trot ahead of them in the night, a dark body fringed with fluffy white, and only as it disappeared into the shadows did Centaine realize that it was a wild ostrich.

At dawn O'wa spread the gemsbok hide as a sunshelter and they waited out the day. At sunset they drank the last drops of water from the egg-bottles, and the San were quiet and serious as they set out again. Without water, death was only hours away.

At dawn, instead of going into camp immediately, O'wa stood for a long time examining the sky, and then he ranged in a half-circle ahead of their track, like a gundog quartering for the bird, lifting his head, turning it slowly from side to side, his nostrils sucking at the air.

'What is O'wa doing?' Centaine asked.

'Smell.' H'ani snuffled to show her. 'Smell water.'

Centaine was incredulous. 'No smell water, H'ani.'

'Yes! Yes! Wait, you see.'

O'wa reached a decision. 'Come!' he beckoned, and the women snatched up their satchels and hurried after him. Within an hour Centaine realized that if

O'wa was mistaken, then she was dead. The egg-bottles were empty, the heat and the sun were sucking the moisture out of her, and she would be finished before the real burning heat of noon fell upon them.

O'wa broke into a full run, the gait that the San called 'the horns', the run of the hunter when he sees the horns of his quarry on the skyline ahead, and the women under their burdens could not try to match him.

An hour later they made out his tiny form far ahead, and when they at last came up with him, he smiled a broad welcome and with a sweep of his arm announced grandly, 'O'wa has led you unerringly to the sip-wells of the elephant with one tusk.' The origins of the name were lost far back in the oral history of the San. O'wa swaggered shamelessly as he led them down the gentle slope of the river bed.

It was a wide water-course, but Centaine saw immediately that it was completely dry, filled with sand as loose and friable as that of the dune country, and she felt her spirits drop sharply as she looked about her.

The winding serpentine water course was about a hundred paces wide, cutting through the gravel beds of the plain, and although there was no water, both banks were dark with much denser plant growth than the arid flats beyond. The scrub was almost waist-high, with an occasional dull green bush rising above the rest. The San were chattering brightly, and H'ani followed closely behind her husband as he strutted about importantly in the sand of the river bed.

Centaine sank down, picked up a handful of the bright orange-coloured sand and let it trickle through her fingers disconsolately. Then for the first time she noticed that the river bed was widely trampled by the hooves of gemsbok, and that in places and sand had been heaped as though children had been digging sandcastles. O'wa was now examining one of these piles critically, and Centaine dragged herself up and went to see what he had found. The gemsbok must have been digging in the river bed, but sand had trickled back into the hole, almost filling it. O'wa nodded sagely, and he turned to H'ani.

'This is a good place. Here we will make our sip-well. Take the child and show her how to build a shelter.'

Centaine was so thirsty and heat-lashed that she felt dizzy and sick, but she slipped off the strap of her bag and wearily climbed the river bank after H'ani to help her cut whippy saplings and thorny branches from the scrub.

In the river bed they quickly erected two rudimentary shelters, sticking the saplings into the sand in a circle, bending them over to meet on top and roofing one of them with branches and other with the stiff, stinking gemsbok skin. They were the most primitive of shelters, without sides and floored with river sand, but Centaine flopped gratefully into the shade and watched O'wa.

Firstly he removed the poisoned heads from his arrows, handling them with elaborate care, for a single scratch would be fatal. He wrapped each arrowhead in a scrap of raw hide and packed them into one of the pouches on his belt.

Then he began to fit the reed arrows together, sealing the joints with a ball of acacia gum, until he had a single length of hollow reeds longer then he was tall.

'Help me, little flower of my life,' he sweetened H'ani blatantly, and with their hands they began to dig together in the sand. To prevent the sand running back into the hole, they made it funnel-shaped – wide at the top and gradually narrowing until O'wa's head and shoulders disappeared into it, and at last he started throwing up handfuls of darker, damp sand. Deeper still he dug, until H'ani had to hold him by the ankles while his entire body was jammed in the

hole. At last, in response to muffled cries from the depths, she passed the long hollow reed down to him.

Upside down in the well, O'wa placed the open end of the reed carefully and then fitted a filter of twigs and leaves around the open end of it to prevent it becoming clogged. With both the women hauling on his ankles, they drew him out of the narrow well, and he emerged coated with orange sand. H'ani had to clean out his ears and brush it from the corms of his grey hair, and from his eyelashes.

Carefully, a handful at a time, O'wa refilled the well, leaving the filter and the reed undisturbed, and when he was finished, he patted the sand down firmly, leaving a short length of the end of the reed pipe sticking out above the surface.

While O'wa put the finishing touches to his well, H'ani chose a green twig, stripped of the thorns and peeled it. Then she helped Centaine unplug the egg-bottles and set them out in a neat row beside the well.

O'wa stretched himself out, belly down on the sand, and placed his lips over the end of the reed tube. H'ani squatted beside him attentively, the row of egg-bottles within reach and the peeled green twig in her hand.

'I am ready, hunter of my heart!' she told him, and O'wa began to suck.

From under her shelter Centaine watched as O'wa turned himself into a human bellows; his chest swelled and subsided, seeming to double in size with each hissing intake of air, and then Centain could sense the impediment of a heavy load in the tube. O'wa's eyes closed tightly, disappearing behind a network of baggy wrinkles, and his face darkened with effort to the colour of toffee. His body pumped and pulsated, he swelled like a bull frog and shrank and swelled again, straining to draw a heavy weight up the long thin reed tube.

Suddenly he made a mewing sound in his throat without breaking the rhythm of his powerful suctions, and H'ani leaned forward and gently fitted the peeled twig into the corner of his mouth. A diamond-bright drop of water bubbled out between O'wa's lips and slid down the twig; it quivered on the tip for an instant and then dropped into the egg-bottle that H'ani held below it.

'Good water, singer of my soul,' H'ani encouraged him. 'Good sweet water!' And the flow from the old man's mouth became a steady silver dribble, as he sucked it in and let it run on the exhale.

The effort required was enormous, for O'wa was lifting the water over six feet, and Centaine watched in awe as he filled one egg-bottle, then another, and still a third without a pause.

H'ani squatted over him, tending him, encouraging him, adjusting the twig and the bottles, cooing to him softly, and suddenly Centaine was struck with a strange feeling of empathy for this pair of little old people. She realized how they had been forged by joy and tragedy and unremitting hardship into a union so fast and strong that they were almost a single entity. She saw how the hard years had gifted them with humour and sensitivity and simple wisdom and fortitude, but most of all with love, and she envied them without rancour.

'If only,' she thought, 'if only I could be bound to another human being as these two are bound to each other!' And in that moment she realized that she had come to love them.

At last O'wa rolled away from the tube and lay gasping and panting and shaking in the sand like a marathon runner when the race is run, and H'ani brought one of the egg-bottles to Centaine.

'Drink, Nam Child,' she offered it to Centaine.

Almost reluctantly, achingly aware of the effort that had gone into reaping each priceless drop, Centaine drank.

She drank sparingly, piously, and then handed the bottle back.

'Good water, H'ani,' she said. Though it was brackish and mingled with the old man's saliva, Centaine now understood completely that the San definition of 'good water' was any fluid which would sustain life in the desert.

She rose and went to where O'wa lay in the sand.

'Good water, O'wa.' She knelt beside him, and she saw how the effort had drained him, but he grinned up at her and bobbed his head, still too tired to rise.

'Good water, Nam Child,' he agreed.

Centaine unfastened the lanyard from around her waist and held the knife in both hands. It had saved her life already. It might do so again in the hard days ahead, if she kept it.

'Take, O'wa,' she offered it to him. 'Knife for O'wa.'

He stared at the knife, and the dark, blood-suffused tones of his wrinkled face paled, and a great devastation seemed to empty all expression from his eyes.

'Take, O'wa,' Centaine urged him.

'It is too much,' he whispered, staring at the knife with stricken eyes. It was a gift without price.

Centaine reached out, took his wrist and turned his hand upwards. She placed the knife in his hand and folded his fingers over it. Sitting in the harsh sunlight with the knife in his hand, O'wa's chest heaved as powerfully as it had as he drew water from the sip-well, and a tear welled out of the corner of one eye and ran down the deep groove alongside his nose.

'Why are you weeping, you silly old man?' H'ani demanded.

'I weep for joy at this gift.' O'wa tried to maintain dignity, but his voice choked.

'That is a stupid reason to weep,' H'ani told him, and twinkled mischievously as she covered her laughter with one slim, graceful little hand.

* * *

They followed the dry river bed into the east, but now the urgency that had accompanied their night marches through the dune country was left behind them, for there was good water under the sand.

They travelled from before sunrise until the heat drove them into shelter, and then from late afternoon until after dark; the pace was leisurely for they foraged and hunted on the march.

H'ani cut a special digging stick for Centaine, peeled it and hardened the point in the fire, and showed her how to use it. Within a few short days Centaine was recognizing the surface indications of many of the edible and useful tubers and plants. It soon became evident that though O'wa was so adept in the bushcraft and lore of the desert and that although his hunting and tracking skills were almost supernatural, it was the foraging and gathering of the women that provided their little clan with the staples of life. In the days and weeks when game was scarce or simply non-existent, they lived on the plants which the two of them brought into camp.

Although Centaine learned swiftly and her young eyes were hawk-sharp, she knew that she would never be able to match the innate knowledge and gifts of perception of the old woman. H'ani could find the plants and insects that gave no sign on the surface of their hiding-place deep down in the earth, and when she dug the hard dirt flew in all directions.

'How do you do it?' Centaine could at last demand, for her command of the San language increased every day she spent listening and responding to the old woman's chatter.

'Like O'wa found the sip-wells from afar,' H'ani explained. 'I smell it, Nam Child. Smell! Use your nose!'

'You tease me, revered old grandmother!' Centaine protested, but she watched H'ani carefully after that, and she saw that she indeed gave every indication of smelling out the deep nests of termites to raid them of the crumbling white ant 'bread' which she made into a foul-tasting but nutritious porridge.

'Just like Kaiser Wilhelm,' Centaine marvelled, and she called to H'ani *'Cherche!'* the way that she and Anna had called to the gross boar when they had hunted truffles in the forest at Mort Homme.

'*Cherche*, H'ani!' and the old woman laughed and hugged herself with glee at the joke she did not understand, and then quite casually produced a miracle.

She and Centaine had fallen behind O'wa on the evening stage of the journey, for the old man had gone ahead to search for an ostrich nesting ground that he remembered from his last visit so many years before.

The two of them were arguing amiably.

'No, no! Nam Child, you must not dig two roots from the same place. You must always walk past one before you dig again – I have told you that before!' H'ani scolded.

'Why?' Centaine straightened up and pushed the thick bushy curls off her forehead, leaving a sweaty smear of mud on her face.

'You must leave one for the children.'

'Silly old woman, there are no children.'

'There will be – ' H'ani pointed at Centaine's belly significantly. 'There will be. And if we leave nothing for them, what will they say of us when they are starving?'

'But there are so many plants!' Centaine was exasperated.

'When O'wa finds the nest of the ostrich, he will leave some of the eggs. When you find two tubers, you will leave one of them, and your son will grow strong and smile when he repeats your name to his children.

H'ani broke off from her lecture and scurried forward to a bare, stony patch on the bank of the dry river bed, her nose twitching as she stooped to examine the earth.

'*Cherche*, H'ani!' Centaine laughed at her, and H'ani laughed back as she started to dig, and then she dropped to her knees and lifted something from the shallow excavation.

'This is the first one you have seen, Nam Child. Smell it. It tastes very good.'

She handed the lumpy, dirt-crusted, potato-like tuber to Centaine, and Centaine sniffed it gingerly, and her eyes flew wide open at the well-remembered aroma. Quickly she wiped the clinging dirt from the lumpy surface and bit into it.

'H'ani, you old darling,' she cried. 'It's a truffle! A real truffle. It's not the

same shape or colour, but it smells and tastes just like the truffles from my own land!'

O'wa had found his ostrich nests and Centaine whipped one of the eggs in its own half-shell and mixed in the chopped truffles and cooked an enormous *omelette aux truffes* on a flat stone heated in the camp fire.

Despite the dirt from Centaine's fingers, which gave it a faintly greyish colour, and the grains of sand and eggshell chips that crunched under their teeth, they ate it with relish.

It was only afterwards as she lay under the primitive roof of twigs and leaves, that Centaine gave in to the homesickness which the taste of truffles had invoked, and she buried her face in the crook of her arm to muffle her sobs.

'Oh, Anna – I would give anything, anything at all just to see your lovely ugly old face again.'

* * *

As they followed the dry river bed, and the weeks turned into months, so Centaine's unborn child grew strongly.

With her sparse but healthy diet and the daily exercise of walking and digging and carrying and reaching, the child never grew big and she carried it high, but her breasts filled out and sometimes when she was alone, scrubbing her body with the juicy pith of the bi tuber, she looked down at them proudly and admired the jaunty upward tilt of the rosy tips.

'I wish you could see them now, Anna,' she murmured. 'You couldn't tell me I still look like a boy. But as always you'd complain about my legs, too long and thin and with hard muscles – oh, Anna, I wonder where you are.'

* * *

One morning at sunrise when they had already been travelling for many hours, Centaine stopped on the top of a low rise and looked around her slowly.

The air was still cool from the night and so clear that she could see to the horizon. Later, with the heat, it would thicken to an opaline translucence and the sun would drain all colour from the landscape. The heat mirage would close in around her, and shapes would be weirdly deformed, the most mundane group of rocks or clump of vegetation transformed into quivering monsters.

Now they were sharp-edged and rich with their true colours. The undulating plains were hazed with pale silver grasses, and there were trees, real, living trees, not those heat-struck ancient mummies that had stood upon the plains below the dunes.

These stately camel-thorn acacias grew well separated. Their massive trunks, clad in rough crocodile-skin bark, were at odds with the wide umbrella-shaped crown of airy and delicate silvery-green foliage. In the nearest of them a colony of sociable weavers had built a communal nest the size of a haystack, each generation of these insignificant, dun-coloured little birds adding to it, until one day the weight would be too much and would split the great tree. Centaine had seen others lying on the earth beneath the shattered acacia, still attached to the

supporting branch and stinking with the carcasses of hundreds of fledglings and broken eggs.

Beyond this open forest there were steep hills rising abruptly out of the plain, the kopjes of Africa, riven by wind and split by the sun's heat into geometrical shapes as hard-edged as dragon's teeth. The soft light of the early sun struck hues of sepia and red and bronze from their rocky walls, and the antediluvian kokerboom trees with their fleshy trunks and palm-like heads crowned their summits.

Centaine paused and leaned on her digging stick, awed by the harsh grandeur of the scene. Upon the dust-coloured plains grazed herds of dainty antelope. They were pale as smoke and as insubstantial, graceful little animals with lyre-shaped horns, the lovely bright cinnamon-brown of their backs divided from their snowy white lower parts by a lateral band of chocolate red.

As Centaine watched, the nearest antelopes took fright at the human presence, and began stotting, the characteristic alarm behaviour that gave them their name of springbok. They lowered their heads until their muzzles almost touched their four bunched hooves and shot stiff-legged straight into the air, at the same time opening the long folded pouch of skin that ran down their backs and flashing the feathery mane of white hair that it concealed.

'Oh, look at them, H'ani!' Centaine cried. 'They are so beautiful.'

The alarm stotting was wildly infectious, and across the plain hundreds of springbok bounced on high, with white manes flashing.

O'wa dropped his burden, lowered his head and imitated them perfectly, prancing stiff-legged, flicking his fingers over his back, so that he seemed transformed into one of the fleet little antelope, and the two women were so overcome with laughter that they had to sit down and hug each other. The joy of it lasted long after the mountains had receded into the heat mists, and it alleviated the crushing misery of the noonday sun.

* * *

During those long halts in the middle of the day, O'wa took to separating himself from the women, and Centaine became accustomed to seeing his tiny figure sitting crosslegged in the shade of an adjacent camel-thorn tree, scraping with the clasp knife at the gemsbok skin that was spread across his lap. He carried the skin carefully folded and rolled into a bundle on his head during the day's march, and once when Centaine had begun to examine it casually, O'wa had become so agitated that she quickly placated him.

'I meant no harm, old grandfather.'

But her curiosity had been piqued. The old man was a craftsman, and usually he was delighted to show off his handiwork. He had not protested when Centaine watched as he split the pliable yellow bark off the trunk of a kokerboom tree, rolled it into a quiver to hold his spare arrows and decorated it with designs of birds and animals burned into the bark with a coal from the camp fire.

He showed her how to shape arrowheads from hard white bone by patiently grinding them against a flat stone, and Centaine was surprised at the keenness of the cutting edges and the points. He even took Centaine with him when he went out to hunt for the grubs from which he made the arrow poisons which

had brought down the great gemsbok bull, and which could kill a man within hours. She helped him dig beneath a particular type of scrub and pick out of the dirt the brown pellet-like capsules which were the chrysalis in which the fat white grubs of the embryo *diamphidia* beetle were enclosed.

Handling the insects with elaborate caution, for the minutest quantity of their body juice entering through a scratch would mean lingering but certain death, O'wa pounded them to paste which he thickened with the juice of the wild sansevieria plant before dressing his arrowheads with the sticky mixture. From the sansevieria he separated the fibres from which he braided the twine to bind the arrowhead to the shaft.

He even allowed Centaine to watch while he whittled a primitive pen-like flute on which he accompanied himself with piercing blasts when he danced, or while he carved the decorations into the heavy throwing stick which he used to knock the rocketing coqui francolin out of the air in a puff of pretty feathers or the blue-headed lizards from the uppermost branches of the camel-thorn trees – but when he worked on the gemsbok skin he went off to a discreet distance and he worked alone.

* * *

The river of sand which they had followed for so long finally contorted into a series of tight bends, like the convulsions of a dying adder, and then abruptly ended in a dry pan, so wide that the trees on the far side were merely a dark wavering line on the horizon. The surface of the pan was white with crystals of evaporated salts. The reflection of the noon sun from this surface was painful to look at directly, and it turned the sky above it to pale silver. The Bushmen's name for it was 'the big white place'.

On the steep bank of the pan they built shelters sturdier and better thatched than any of the others had been, giving an air of permanence to the camp, and the two little San settled down to an undemanding routine, albeit with an underlying air of expectancy which Centaine detected and queried.

'Why do we stop here, H'ani?' Each uneventful day made her more impatient and restless.

'We wait to make the crossing,' was all that the old woman would tell her.

'Crossing to where? Where are we going?' Centaine insisted, but H'ani became vague and pointed in a wide arc into the east, and answered with a name that Centaine could only translate as 'a place where nothing must die'.

* * *

Centaine's child grew strongly within her pouting belly. Sometimes it was difficult to breathe, and almost impossible to be comfortable on the bare ground. She made herself a nest of soft desert grass in her little sun shelter, which amused the two old people. For them the bare earth was bed enough, and they used their own shoulders as pillows.

Centaine lay in her nest and tried to count the days and months since she and Michael had been together, but time was blurred and telescoped so that all she

could be sure of was that her time would be upon her soon. H'ani confirmed her estimate, probing her belly with gentle, knowing fingers.

'The baby rides high and fights to be free. It will be a boy, Nam Child,' she promised, and took Centaine off into the desert to gather the special herbs that they would need for the birthing.

Unlike many Stone Age peoples, the San were fully aware of the processes of procreation and saw sexual intercourse not as an isolated and random act, but as the first step in the long voyage to birth.

'Where is the father of your growing infant, Nam Child?' H'ani asked, and when she saw the tears in Centaine's eyes she answered herself softly, 'He is dead in the north lands at the ends of the earth. Is that not so?'

'How did you know that I came from the north?' Centaine asked, glad to turn away from the pain of Michael's memory.

'You are big – bigger than any of the San of the desert,' H'ani explained. 'Therefore you must come from a rich land where living is easy, a land of good rains and plentiful food.' To the old woman water was all of life. 'The rain winds come from the north, so you also must come from the north.'

Intrigued by her logic, Centaine smiled. 'And how did you know I was from far away?'

'Your skin is pale, not darkened like the skin of the San. Here in the centre of the world the sun stands overhead, but it never goes north or south, and in the east and west it is low and wasting, so you must come from far away where the sun lacks the warmth and strength to darken your skin.'

'Do you know of other people like me, H'ani, big people with pale skins? Have you ever before seen people like me?' Centaine asked eagerly, and when she saw the shift in the old woman's gaze, she seized her arm. 'Tell me, wise old grandmother, where have you seen my people? In what direction, and how far away? Would I be able to reach them? Please tell me.'

H'ani's eyes clouded with a film of incomprehension and she picked a grain of dried mucus from her nostril and examined it with minute attention.

'Tell me, H'ani.' Centaine shook her arm gently.

'I have heard the old people talk of such things,' H'ani grudgingly admitted, 'but I have never seen these people, and I do not know where they could be found.' And Centaine knew she was lying. Then, in a sudden vehement gabble, H'ani went on, 'They are fierce as lions and poisonous as the scorpion, the San hide from them – ' She jumped up in agitation, seized her satchel and digging stick and hurried from the camp and did not return until sunset.

That night after Centaine had curled in her grass bed, H'ani whispered to O'wa, 'The child yearns for her own people.'

'I have seen her look southwards with sadness in her eyes,' O'wa admitted.

'How many days' travel to reach the land of the pale giants?' H'ani asked reluctantly. 'How far to travel to her own clan?'

'Less than a moon,' O'wa grunted, and they were both silent for a long time, staring into the hot bluish flames of the camel-thorn log fire.

'I want to hear a baby cry once more before I die,' H'ani said at last and O'wa nodded. And both their little heart-shaped faces turned towards the east. They stared out into the darkness, towards the Place of All Life.

* * *

Once when H'ani found Centaine kneeling alone and praying in the wilderness, she asked, 'Who are you speaking to, Nam child?' and Centaine was at a loss, for though the San language was rich and complex in its descriptive powers of the material aspects of the desert world, it was extremely difficult to use it to convey abstract ideas.

However, after long discussion spread over many days while they foraged in the desert or worked over the cooking fire, Centaine managed to describe her concept of the Godhead, and H'ani nodded dubiously and mumbled and frowned as she considered it.

'You are talking to the spirits?' she asked. 'But most of the spirits live in the stars, and if you speak so softly, how will they hear you? It is necessary to dance and sing and whistle loudly to attract their attention.' She lowered her voice. 'And it is even then not certain they will listen to you, for I have found the star spirits to be fickle and forgetful.' H'ani glanced around her like a conspirator. 'It is my experience, Nam Child, the Mantis and Eland are much more reliable.'

'Mantis and Eland?' Centaine tried not to show her amusement.

'Mantis is an insect with huge eyes that see all and with arms like a little man. Eland is an animal – oh, yes, much larger than the gemsbok, with a dewlap so full of rich fat that it sweeps the earth.' The San's love of fat was almost equal to their love of wild honey. 'And twisted horns that sweep the sky. If we are fortunate we will find both Mantis and Eland at the place to which we are going. In the meantime, talk to the stars, Nam Child, for they are beautiful, but put your trust in Mantis and Eland.

Thus simply H'ani explained the religion of the San, and that night she and Centaine sat under a brilliant sky and she pointed out Orion's glittering train.

'That is the herd of celestial zebras, Nam Child – and there is the inept huntsman,' she picked out the star Aldebaran, 'sent by his seven wives,' she stabbed a gnarled finger at the Pleiades, 'to find meat. See how he has shot his arrow, and it has flown high and wide to fall at the feet of Lion Star.' Sirius, the brightest of all the fixed stars, seemed truly lionlike. 'And now the huntsman is afraid to retrieve his arrow and afraid to return to his seven wives, and he sits there forever twinkling with fear, which is just like a man, Nam Child.' H'ani hooted with laughter, and dug her bony thumb into her husband's scrawny ribs.

Because the San were also star-lovers, Centaine's bond of affection for them was so strengthened that she pointed out Michael's star and her own in the far south.

'But, Nam Child,' O'wa protested, 'how can that star belong to you? It belongs to no one and to everybody, like the shade of the camelthorn, and the water in the desert pool, or the land on which we tread – to nobody and yet to everybody. Nobody owns the eland, but we may take of his fat if we have need. Nobody owns the bi plants but we may gather them on condition that we leave some for the children. How can you say that a star belongs to you alone?' It was an expression of the philosophy which was the tragedy of his people, a denial of the existence of property which had doomed them to merciless persecution, to massacre and slavery or to exile in the far reaches of the desert where no other people could exist.

* * *

So the monotonous days of waiting were passed in discussion and the leisurely routine of hunting and foraging, and then one evening both the San were galvanized by excitement and they faced into the north with their little amber faces turned up to a sky that was the flawless blue of a heron's egg.

It took Centaine a few minutes to discover what had excited them, and then she saw the cloud. It groped up over the rim of the northern horizon like the finger of a gargantuan hand, and it grew as she watched it, the top of it flattened into an anvil shape, and the distant thunder growled like a hunting lion. Soon the cloud stood tall and heaven-high, burning with the colours of the sunset and lit with its own wondrous internal lightnings.

That night O'wa danced and whistled and sang the praises of the cloud spirits until at last he collapsed with exhaustion, but in the morning the thunderhead had dispersed.

However, the sky had changed from unsullied blue, and there were streaks of high mare's tail cirrus smeared across it. The air itself seemed also to have changed. It was charged with static that made Centaine's skin prickle, and the heat was heavy and languorous, even harder to bear than the dry harsh noons had been, and the thunderheads climbed above the northern horizon and tossed their monstrous billowing heads to the sky.

Each day they grew taller and more numerous, and they massed in the north like a legion of giants and marched southward, while an enervating blanket of humid air lay upon the earth and smothered it and everything upon it.

'Please let it rain,' Centaine whispered each day, while the sweat snaked down her cheeks and the child weighted her womb like an ironstone boulder.

In the night O'wa danced and sang.

'Spirit of Cloud, see how the earth waits for you the way that a great cow eland in heat trembles for the bull. Come down from on high, Spirit of Cloud whom we venerate, and spill your generative fluids upon your earth wife. Mount your lover and from your seed she will bring forth new life in abundance.' And when H'ani trilled and piped the chorus, Centaine cried out just as fervently.

One morning there was no sun, the clouds stretched in a solid grey mass from horizon to horizon. Low to begin with, they sank lower still, and a stupendous bolt of lightning tore from their great grey sowlike belly and clanged upon the earth so that it seemed to jump beneath their feet. A single raindrop struck Centaine in the centre of her forehead, and it was as heavy as a stone, so that she reeled back at the shock of it and cried out in astonishment.

Then the hanging clouds burst open and the rain fell from them thick as locusts. Each drop as it struck the surface of the pan rolled into a globule of mud, or made the wiry scrub branches around the edge jump and quiver as though flocks of invisible birds had alighted upon them.

The rain stung Centaine's skin, and one drop struck her in the eye and blinded her for a second. She blinked it clear and laughed to see O'wa and H'ani capering across the pan. They had thrown aside their meagre clothing and they danced naked in the rain. Each drop burst in a silver puff upon their wrinkled amber skin and they howled delightedly at the pricks of it.

Centaine ripped off her own canvas skirt, threw aside her shawl, and mother-naked stood with her arms thrown open and her face turned to the clouds. The rain thrashed her, and melted her long dark hair down across face and shoulders. She pushed it aside with both hands and opened her mouth wide.

It was as though she stood under a waterfall. The rain poured into her mouth

as fast as she could swallow. The far edge of the pan disappeared behind the blue veils of falling rain, and the surface turned to yellow mud.

The rain was so cold that a rash of goose bumps ran down Centaine's forearms and her nipples darkened and hardened, but she laughed with joy and ran out on to the pan to dance with the San, and the thunder sounded as though massive boulders were rolling across the roof of the sky.

The earth seemed to dissolve under the solid sheets of silver water. The pan was ankle-deep and the silky mud squelched up between Centaine's toes. The rain gave them new life and strength and they danced and sang until O'wa stopped abruptly and cocked his head to listen.

Centaine could hear nothing above the thunder and the lash of the rain, but O'wa shouted a warning. They floundered to the steep bank of the pan, slipping in the glutinous mud and the yellow waters which by now reached to their knees. From the bank Centaine heard the sound which had alarmed O'wa, a low rushing like a high wind in tall trees.

'The river,' O'wa pointed through the thick palisade of silver rain, 'the river is alive again.'

It came like a living thing, a monstrous frothing yellow python down the sandy river bed, and it hissed from bank to bank, carrying the bodies of drowned animals and the branches of trees in its flood. It burst into the flooded pan and raced in serried waves across the surface, breaking on the bank beneath their feet, swirling on to catch them around the legs and threatening to drag them under.

They snatched up their few possessions and waded to higher ground, clinging to each other for support. The rain clouds brought on premature night, and it was cold. There was no chance of a fire and they huddled together for warmth and shivered miserably.

The rain fell without slackening all that night.

In the dull leaden dawn they looked across a drowned landscape, a vast shimmering lake with islands of higher ground from which the water streamed, and stranded acacia trees like the backs of whales.

'Will it never stop?' Centaine whispered. Her teeth chattered uncontrollably, and the chill seemed to have to reached into her womb, for the infant writhed and kicked in protest.

'Please let it stop now.' The San suffered the cold with the fortitude they showed for all hardship. Rather than slackening, the rain seemed to increase in tempo, and hid the sorry drowned land from them behind a glassy curtain.

Then the rain stopped. There was no warning, no faltering or tapering off; one second it was falling in a solid cascade and the next it was over. The ceiling of low bruised cloud split open and peeled away like the skin from a ripe fruit, revealing the clean washed blue of the sky, and the sun burst upon them with blinding brilliance, once more stunning Centaine with the sudden contrasts of this wild continent.

Before noon, the thirsty earth had drunk down the waters that had fallen upon it. The floods sank away without trace. Only in the pan itself surface water still lay glittering suphurous-yellow from bank to far bank. However, the land was cleansed and vivid with colour. The dust that had coated each bush and tree was washed away and Centaine saw greens that she had never dreamed this tan, lion-coloured land could contain. The earth, still damp, was rich with ochres and oranges and reds and the songs of the little desert larks were joyous.

They laid out their scant possessions in the sun and they steamed as they dried. O'wa could not contain himself and he danced ecstatically.

'The cloud spirits have opened the road for us. They have replenished the water-holes to the east. Make ready, H'ani, my little flower of the desert: before the dawn tomorrow we will march.'

* * *

Within the first day's march they entered a new country, so different that Centaine could scarcely believe it was on the same continent. Here the ancient dunes had compacted and consolidated into gentle undulations, and they now supported abundant plant life.

Stands of mopani and tall kiaat, alternating with almost impenetrable thickets of paper-bark, stood tall along the ridges of high ground where the dunes' crests had weathered and flattened. Occasionally a giant silver terminalia or a monumental baobab soared seventy feet above the rest of the forest.

In the valleys, fields of sweet golden grasses and scattered giraffe acacias with flat tops gave the scene a park-like and cultivated aspect. Here also, in the lowest depressions, the recent rains had been trapped in the shallow water-holes, and the land seemed to hum and seethe with life.

Through the yellow grasses fresh tender shoots of delicate green appeared. Gardens of wild flowers, daisies and arum lilies and gladioli and fifty other varieties which Centaine did not recognize, sprang up as though at a magician's flourish, delighting her with their colours and delicate beauty, and causing her to wonder anew at Africa's prolificness. She picked the blooms and plaited them into necklaces for herself and H'ani, and the old woman preened like a bride.

'Oh, I wish I had a mirror to show you how adorable you look.' Centaine embraced her.

Even from the sky Africa gave of her abundance. There were flocks of quelea thick as hiving bees as they wheeled overhead, shrikes in the undergrowth with chests of purest flowing ruby, sandgrouse and francolin fat as domestic chickens, and water fowl on the brimming water-holes, wild duck and long-legged stilts and gaunt blue heron.

'It's all so beautiful,' Centaine exulted. Each day's journey was light and carefree after the hardships of the arid western plains, and when they camped, there was the untold luxury of unlimited water and a feast of wild fruits and nuts and game from O'wa's snares and arrows.

One evening O'wa climbed high into the swollen fleshy branches of a monstrous baobab and smoked the hive that had inhabited its hollow trunk since his great-grandfather's time and beyond. He came down with a gourd full of thick waxen combs running with dark honey redolent of the perfume of the yellow acacia blossoms.

Each day they met new species of wild animals: sable antelope, black as night with long scimitar horns that swept back almost to their hind quarters, and Cape buffalo with mournful drooping heads of massively bossed horn stinking like herds of domestic cattle.

'They have come down from the big river and the swamps,' O'wa explained. 'They follow the water, and when it dries again they will go back into the north.'

In the night Centaine woke to a new sound infinitely more fearsome than the yelping of the black-backed jackal or the maniacal screams and sobs of the hyena packs. It was a storm of sound that filled the darkness, rising to an impossible crescendo and then dying away in a series of deep grunts. Centaine scrambled out of her little hut and ran to H'ani.

'What was that, old grandmother? It is a sound to turn the belly to water!' Centaine found she was trembling and the old woman hugged her.

'Even the bravest of men trembles the first time he hears the roar of the lion,' she placated her. 'But do not fear, Nam Child, O'wa has made a charm to protect us. The lion will find other game tonight.'

But they crowded close to the fire all the rest of the night, feeding it with fresh logs, and it was obvious that H'ani had as little faith in her husband's magical charms as Centaine did.

The lion pride circled their camp site, keeping at the very limit of the firelight so that Centaine caught only an occasional pale flicker of movement amongst the dark, encroaching bushes, but with the dawn their dreadful chorus receded as they moved away into the east, and when O'wa showed her the huge catlike pugmurks in the soft earth, he was garrulous with relief.

Then on the ninth morning after they had left the pan of 'the big white place', they were approaching another water-hole through the open mopani forests when ahead of them there was a crack like a shot of cannon and they all froze.

'What is it, H'ani?' But she waved Centaine to silence, and now she heard the crackle of breaking undergrowth and then suddenly a ringing blast of sound clear as a trumpet call.

Quickly O'wa tested the wind as Centaine had seen him do at the beginning of every hunt, and then he led them in a wide stealthy circuit through the forest until he stopped again beneath the spreading glossy green foliage of a tall mopani tree when he laid aside his weapons and his pack.

'Come!' he signalled to Centaine and, swiftly as a monkey, shinned up the trunk. Hardly hampered at all by her fruitful belly, Centaine followed him into the tree and from a fork in the top branches looked down into the valley of grassland beyond and the water-hole that it contained in its shallow bottom.

'Elephant!' She recognized the huge grey beasts instantly. They were streaming down the far slope of the valley towards the water, striding out with their ponderous rolling gait, heads swinging so that their enormous ears flapped, and their trunks rolling and reaching reflexively as they anticipated the sweet taste of water.

There were rangy old queens with tattered ear-lobes and the knuckles of their spines sticking out of their gaunt backs, young bulls with yellow ivories, tuskless youngsters, boisterous unweaned calves running to keep up with their dams and, at their head, the herd bull strode majestically.

He stood over ten feet tall at the shoulder and he was scarred and grey, thick baggy skin hanging from his knees and bunched between his back legs. His ears were spread like the mainsail of a tall ship, and his tusks were twice as long and thick as any of his lesser bulls.

He seemed aged and yet ageless, huge and rugged, possessed of a grandeur and mystery which seemed to Centaine to contain the very essence of this land.

* * *

Lothar De La Rey cut the spoor of the elephant herd three days after they had left the Cunene river, and he and his Ovambo trackers studied it carefully, spreading out and circling over the trodden earth like gundogs. When they assembled again, Lothar nodded at his headman.

'Speak, Hendrick.' The Ovambo was as tall as Lothar, but heavier in the shoulders. His skin was dark and smooth as molten chocolate.

'A good herd,' Hendrick gave his opinion, 'forty cows, many with calf, eight young bulls.' The dark turban of the warrior was wound around his proud head, and garlands of necklaces strung with trade beads hung down on to his muscular chest, but he wore riding breeches and a bandolier of ammunition over one shoulder.

'And the herd bull is so old that his pads are smooth, so old that he can no longer chew his food and his dung is coarse with bark and twigs. He walks heavily on his forelegs, his ivory weighs him down, he is a bull to follow,' Hendrick said, and shifted the Mauser rifle into his right hand and hefted it in anticipation.

'The spoor is windblown,' Lothar pointed out quietly, 'and scrtatched over by insect and quail. Three days old.'

'They are feeding,' Hendrick opened his arms, 'spread out, moving slowly, the calves slow them down.'

'We will have to send the horses back,' Lothar persisted. 'We cannot risk them in the tsetse fly. Can we catch them on foot?'

Lothar unknotted his scarf and wiped his face thoughtfully. He needed that ivory. He had ridden north to the Cunene as soon as his scouts had sent him word that good rains had fallen. He knew that the new growth and surface water would lure the herds across the river out of Portuguese territory.

'On foot we can make them in two days,' Hendrick promised, but he was a notorious optimist and Lothar teased him.

'And at each night's camp we will find ten pretty Herero girls each carrying a beerpot on her head waiting for us.'

Hendrick threw back his head and laughed his deep growling laugh. 'Three days then,' he conceded with a chuckle, 'and perhaps only one Herero girl, but very beautiful and obliging.'

Lothar pondered the chances a moment longer. It was a good bull, and the younger bulls would all carry mature ivory, even the cows would yield twenty pounds each, and ivory was commanding 22s 6d a pound.

He had twelve of his best men with him, though two would have to be sent back with the horses, but there were still enough riflemen to do the job. If they could come up with the herd they had a good chance of killing every animal that showed ivory.

Lothar De La Rey was flat broke. He had lost his family fortune, he had been declared a traitor and an outlaw for continuing the fight after the surrender of Colonel Franke, and there was a price on his head. Perhaps this would be his very last chance to repair his fortune. He knew the British well enough to realize that when the war was over, they would turn their attention to administering the new territories that they had won. Soon there would be district commissioners and officers in even the remotest areas, enforcing every detail of the law and paying special attention to the illegal hunting of ivory. The old free-booting days were probably numbered. This could be his last hunt.

'Send back the horses!' he orderd. 'Take the spoor!'

Lothar wore light hunting velskoen. His men were all tempered and hardened

by long years of war, and they ran on the spoor, taking it in turns to come to the front and take the point, then dropping back to rest as another man hit the front.

They entered the fly-belt in the late afternoon, and the vicious little tsetse swarmed out of the shade of the forest to plague them, settling light-footed on their backs to drive their blood-sucking probosces deep into the flesh. The men cut switches of green leaves and brushed the tsetse off each other's backs as they ran. By nightfall they had gained two days on the herd, and the spoor was so fresh that the ant-lions had not yet built their tiny funnel-shaped traps in the crisply trodden pad marks.

Darkness stopped them. They lay on the hard earth and slept like a pack of hounds, but when the moon climbed over the tops of the mopani trees, Lothar kicked them to their feet. The slant of moonlight was in their favour, outlining the spoor with a rim of shadow, and the raw trunks of the mopani trees, from which the feeding elephant had stripped the bark, shone like morrors to guide them through the night, and when the sun rose they lengthened their stride.

An hour after sunrise they suddenly ran out of the tsetse fly-belt. The territory of these little winged killers was sharply demarcated, the border could be crossed in a hundred paces, from swarming multitudes to complete relief. The swollen itching lumps on the back of their necks were the only souvenirs of their onslaught.

Two hours before noon, they reached a good water-hole in one of the valleys of the mopani forest. They were only hours behind the herd.

'Drink quickly,' Lothar ordered, and waded knee-deep into the filthy water which the bathing elephant had churned to the colour of *café au lait*. He filled his hat and poured the water over his own head. His thick, red-gold locks streamed down over his face, and he snorted with pleasure. The water was acrid and bitter with the salt of the elephant urine – the great beasts always emptied their bladders at the shock of cold water – but the hunters drank and refilled the water-bottles.

'Quickly,' Lothar chivvied them, keeping his voice low, for sound carries in the bush and the herd was very close.

'Baas!' Hendrick signalled him urgently, and Lothar waded to the edge of the pool, and skirted it quickly.

'What is it?'

Wordlessly the big Ovambo pointed at the ground. The spoor was perfectly imprinted in the stiff yellow clay, and it was so fresh that it overlaid that of the elephant herd; water was still seeping into the indentations.

'Men!' Lothar exclaimed. 'Men have been here since the herd left.'

Hendrick corrected him harshly. 'San, not men. The little yellow cattle-killers.' The Ovambo were herdsmen, their cattle were their treasure and their deep love. 'The desert dogs who cut the teats off the udders of our finest cows,' the traditional revenge of the San for the atrocities committed upon them, 'they are only minutes ahead of us. We could catch them within the hour.'

'The sound of gunfire would carry to the herd.' Lothar shared his headman's hatred of the Bushmen. They were dangerous vermin, cattle-thieves and killers. His own great-uncle had been killed during one of the great Bushmen hunts of fifty years before, a tiny bone-tipped arrow had found the chink in his rawhide armour, and family history had recorded his death in every excruciating detail.

Even the English with their sickly sentimentality towards the black races had realized that there was no place in this twentieth-century world for the San. The

standing orders of Cecil Rhodes' famous British South Africa Police contained instructions that all San and wild dogs encountered on patrol were to be shot out of hand. The two species were considered as one.

Lothar was tempted, torn between the pleasure of performing the public service of following and destroying the pack of San, and of mending his own fortune by following the elephant.

'The ivory,' he decided. 'No, the ivory is more important than culling a few yellow baboons.'

'Baas – here!' Hendrick had moved around the edge of the pool and stopped abruptly. His tone and the alert set of his head made Lothar hurry to him, and then sit quickly on his heels, the better to examine this new set of prints.

'Not San!' Hendrick whispered. 'Too big.'

'But a woman,' Lothar replied. The narrow foot and small shapely toe marks were unmistakable. 'A young woman.' The toe marks were deeper than the heel, a springy step, a young step.

'It is not possible!' Hendrick sank down beside him and without touching the print traced the arched portion between ball and heel. Lothar sat back and shook his wet dangling locks again.

The black people of Africa who go barefooted from their very first step leave a distinctive flat imprint.

'A wearer of shoes,' Hendrick said softly.

'A white woman? No, it's impossible!' Lothar repeated. 'Not here, not travelling in the company of wild San! For the love of God, we are hundreds of miles from civilization!'

'It is so, a young white girl, a captive of the San,' Hendrick confirmed and Lothar frowned.

The tradition of chivalry towards women of his own race was an integral part of Lothar's upbringing, one of the pillars of his Protestant religion. Because he was a soldier and hunter, because it was part of the art of his trade, Lothar could read the sign left upon the earth as though he were actually seeing the beast or the man, or woman, who had made it. Now as he squatted over these dainty prints, an image formed in his mind. He saw a girl, fine-boned, long-legged, gracefully proportioned, but strong and proud, with a raking stride that drove her forward on the balls of her feet. She would be brave also, and determined. There was no place in this wilderness for weaklings, and clearly this girl was flourishing. As the image formed, Lothar became aware of an emptiness deep in his soul.

'We must go after this woman,' he said softly, 'to rescue her from the San.'

Hendrick rolled his eyes towards the sky and reached for his snuff gourd, and poured a little of the red powder into his pink palm.

'The wind is against us,' he waved on hand along the run of the spoor, 'they are travelling downwind. We will never come up with them.'

'There are always one hundred good reasons why we should not do what you don't want to do.' Lothar raked his wet hair back with is fingers and retied it with the leather thong at the nape of his neck. We will be following San, not animals. The wind is of no consequence.'

'The San are animals.' Hendrick blocked one of his wide flat nostrils with his thumb and sucked red snuff up the other before going on. 'With this wind they will smell you from two miles and hear you long before you sight them.' He dusted his hands and flicked the residual grains from his upper lip.

'A beautiful story!' Lothar scoffed. 'Even for you, the greatest liar in all of Ovamboland.' And then, brusquely, 'Enough chatter, we are going after the white girl. Take the spoor.'

* * *

From the high fork of the mopani tree, Centaine watched the elephant herd at the water-hole with mounting delight. Once she had got over the trepidation caused by their size and monumental ugliness, she swiftly became aware of the endearing bond that seemed to unite all the members of the herd. They began to seem almost human to her.

The patriarch bull was crotchety and his arthritic joints obviously ached. They all treated him with respect, and left one side of the pool for him alone. He drank noisily, squirting the water down his throat. Then he lowered himself, groaning with pleasure, into the mud, and scooped it up in his trunk to slap it on to his dusty grey head. It ran down his cheeks, and he closed his eyes ecstatically.

On the opposite side of the pool the young bulls and cows drank and bathed, blowing mud and water out of their trunks like fire hoses, squirting themselves between the forelegs and down the flanks, lifting their heads and thrusting their trunks deep down their throats to send gallons of water hissing into their bellies. Satiated, they stood happily, trunks entwined in a loving embrace, and seemed to beam indulgently at the calves cavorting around their legs and under their bellies.

One of the smallest calves, not much bigger than a pig and just as fat, tried to wriggle under the trunk of a dead tree that had fallen into the pool and stuck fast in the mud. In comical panic it let out a squeal of alarm and terror. Every elephant in the herd reacted instantly, changing from contented indolence into raging behemoths of vengeance. They rushed back into the pool, beating the water and kicking it in a froth with their great hooves.

'They think a crocodile has caught the calf,' O'wa whispered.

'Poor crocodile!' Centaine whispered back.

The mother yanked the calf out from under the dead tree, hindfeet first, and it shot between her front legs and fastened on to one of her teats where it suckled with almost hysterical relief. The enraged herd quietened down, but with every evidence of disappointment that they had been denied the pleasure of tearing the hated crocodile into small pieces.

When the old bull finally heaved himself upright and, glistening with mud, strode away into the forest, the cows hastily rounded up their offspring, chasing them from their muddy pleasures with swinging trunks, and obediently they all trooped after the patriarch. Long after they had disappeared into the forest, Centaine could hear the crack of breaking branches and the rumble of their water-filled bellies as they fled away southwards.

She and O'wa climbed down from the mopani grinning with pleasure.

'The little ones were so naughty,' Centaine told H'ani, 'just like human babies.'

'We call them the big people,' H'ani agreed, 'for they are wise and loving as the San.'

They went down to the edge of the water-hole and Centaine marvelled at the

mountainous piles of yellow dung that the elephants had dropped. Already the clucking francolin were scratching in the steaming mounds for undigested nuts and seeds.

'Anna would love that for the vegetable garden – ' she caught herself. 'I mustn't think so much of the past.'

She stooped to bathe her face, for even the muddy water offered relief from the rising heat, but suddenly O'wa stiffened and cocked his head, turning it towards the north, in the direction from which the elephant herd had come.

'What is it, old grandfather?' H'ani was instantly sensitive to his mood.

O'wa did not answer for a second, but his eyes were troubled and his lips twitched nervously.

'There is something, something on the wind – a sound, a scent, I am not sure,' he whispered. Then, with sudden decision, 'There is danger – close. We must go.'

H'ani jumped up instantly and snatched up the satchel of egg bottles. She would never argue with her husband's intuition, it had saved them often during their lifetime together.

'Nam Child,' she said softly but urgently, 'hurry.'

'H'ani – ' Centaine turned to her with dismay. She was already knee-deep in the muddy pool. 'It is so hot, I want to – '

'There is danger, great danger.' The two San whirled together like startled birds and flew back towards the forest refuge. Centaine knew that in seconds she would be left alone, and loneliness was still her greatest terror. She ran from the pool, kicking spray before her, grabbed her carrying bag and stick and dressed as she ran.

O'wa circled quickly through the mopani forest, moving across the wind until it blew upon the back of his neck. The San, like the buffalo and the elephant, always fled downwind when alarmed, so that the scent of the pursuer would be carried down to them.

O'wa paused for Centaine to catch up with them.

'What is it, O'wa?' she gasped.

'Danger. Deadly danger.' The agitation of both the old people was obvious, and infectious. Centaine had learned not to ask questions in a situation such as this.

'What must I do?'

'Cover sign, the way I showed you,' O'wa ordered her, and she remembered the patient instruction that he had given her in the art of anti-tracking, of confusing and hiding the spoor so that a pursuer would find it difficult if not impossible to follow them. It was one of the skills on which San survival depended.

'H'ani first, then you.' O'wa was in completed command now. 'Follow her. Do as she does. I will come at the back and cover your mistakes.'

The old woman was as quick and agile as a little brown francolin. She flitted through the forest, avoiding the game paths and open ground on which their tracks would stand out clearly, picking the difficult line, ducking under thorn thickets where a pursuer would not expect them to pass, stepping on grass clumps or running along the trunks of fallen trees, changing her length of stride, hopping sideways over harder ground, employing every ruse she had learned in a long hard lifetime.

Centaine followed her, not as nimble, leaving an occasional blurred footprint, knocking a green leaf from a bush as she passed, disturbing the grass slightly.

O'wa came close behind her, a broom of grass stalks in his hand to brush over the sign that Centaine left, stooping to pick up the tell-tale green leaf, delicately rearranging the bent grass stems that signposted the direction of their flight.

He guided H'ani with small chirping bird calls and whistles, and she responded instantly, turning left or right, speeding up or freezing for a few seconds so that O'wa could listen and sniff the breeze for the scent of the pursuit, then plunging forward again at his signal.

Suddenly another open glade spread before them, half a mile wide, studded with a few tall flat-topped giraffe acacia; beyond it rose the low ridge, heavily forested with paper-bark trees and dense wild ebony thickets for which O'wa was heading.

He knew that the ridge was composed of rock-hard calcrete, lumpy and broken, and he knew also that no human being could follow him over that ground. Once they reached it, they were safe, but the glade lay before them, and if they were caught there in the open, they would be easy prey, especially if their pursuers were armed with the smoke that kills from far off.

He wasted a few precious seconds to sniff at the air. It was hard to judge the distance of that faint offensive taint upon the light breeze, the stink of carbolic soap and snuff, of unwashed woollen clothing and socks, of the rancid cattle fat with which the Ovambo anointed their bodies, but he knew that he had to risk the open ground.

His most skilful anti-tracking could not cover all the signs that Nam Child had left over the soft sandy earth. His efforts to do so would merely impede the pursuit, but he knew that the bushcraft of the Ovambo was almost equal to his own. Only on the hard calcrete ridge could he be certain of losing them. He whistled, the call of a crimson-breasted shrike, and obediently H'ani started out into the open glade, scuttling through the short yellow grass.

'Run, little bird,' O'wa called softly. 'If they catch us in the open, we are dead.'

* * *

'They have smelled us,' Hendrick looked back at Lothar. 'See how they are covering sign.'

At the forest edge it seemed as though their quarry had turned into birds and taken to the air. All trace of them seemed to disappear. Brusquely Hendrick signalled to the other Ovambo hunters, and they spread out swiftly. Throwing a wide net, they moved forward in line. A man on the right flank whistled softly and then waved underhanded, indicating a new direction.

'They have turned down the wind,' Hendrick murmured to Lothar, who was ten paces out on his flank, 'I should have guessed it.'

The net of trackers wheeled on to the line, and moved forward. A man whistled on the left, and confirmed the line with that graceful underhand wave; they speeded up, breaking into a trot.

Just ahead Lothar noticed a faint colour difference on the seemingly undisturbed earth, a tiny patch of lighter sand no bigger then a man's foot, and he stooped to examine it. A footprint had been carefully brushed over and obliterated. Lothar whistled softly, and waved them forward on the line.

'Now do you believe the San can smell like an elephant?' Hendrick asked him as they jogged on.

'I believe only what I see,' Lothar grinned. 'When I see a Bushman sniffing the ground, then I will believe.'

Hendrick chuckled, but his eyes were cold and humourless.

'They will have arrows,' he said.

'Do not let them get close,' Lothar replied. 'Shoot them down the moment you see them, but be careful of the white woman. I will kill the man who harms her. Pass it on to the others.'

Lothar's order was called softly down the line. 'Shoot the San, but take great care of the white woman.'

Twice they lost the spoor. They had to back up to the last marked sign, cast around it, and then move off again on the new line. The San were winning time and distance with every check, and Lothar fretted.

'They are getting away from us,' he called to Hendrick. 'I am going to run ahead on this line – you follow on the spoor, in case they jink again.'

'Be careful!' Hendrick shouted after him. 'They may lie in ambush. Watch out for the arrows.'

Lothar ignored the warning and raced through the forest, no longer tracking the sign, but taking the chance that it was straight ahead, hoping to startle the Bushmen and force them to show themselves, or to push them so hard that they would abandon their captive. He took no notice of the hooked thorns that ripped at his clothing. He ducked under the low mopani branches and hurdled fallen logs, running at the very peak of his speed.

Suddenly he burst from the forest into an open glade and he pulled up, his chest heaving for breath, sweat running into his eyes and soaking the back of his shirt between the shoulder-blades.

On the far side of the glade below the low forested ridge he saw movement, small black specks above the tops of the swaying yellow grass, and he turned back to the nearest tree and scrambled into the first fork for a better view.

Gasping wildly for breath, he fumbled the small brass telescope out of his hunting bag and pulled it to full extension. His hands were shaking, so it was difficult to focus the telescope, but he swept the far edge of the open glade.

Three human shapes appeared in the round field of the lens. They were in Indian file, heading directly away from him, almost at the palisade formed by the trunks of the paper-bark trees. Only their heads and shoulders showed above the grass, bobbing up and down as they ran. One was taller then the other two.

He watched them for seconds only before they reached the tree line, and two of them disappeared instantly, but the tallest figure paused, stepped up on to a fallen log and looked back across the glade towards Lothar.

It was a girl. Her long dark hair was divided into two thick braids that hung on to her shoulders. Through the telescope Lothar could see her expression, fearful, yet defiant. The lines of her chin and brow were aristocratic, and her mouth was full and firm, dark eyes proud and bright, her skin stained to deep honey-gold, so for an instant he thought she might be a mulatto. As he watched she shifted the bag she carried from one shoulder to the other, and the coarse material that clothed her upper body fell open for an instant.

Lothar saw a flash of pale smooth skin, untouched by the sun, the form of a full young breast, rosy tipped and delicately shaped, and he felt a weakness in

his legs that was not from hard running. His breath stopped for an instant, and then roared in his own ears as he panted to fill his lungs.

The girl turned her head away from him, offering him a profile, and in that instant, Lothar knew that he had never seen a woman more appealing. Everything in him yearned towards her. She turned her back to him and sprang lithely out of the field lens, and disappeared. The branches of the edge of the forest trembled for a few seconds after she was gone.

Lothar felt like a man blind from birth, who for a fleeting instant had been shown the miracle of sight, only to be plunged back into darkness again. He stared after the girl, his feeling of deprivation so appalling that he could not move for many seconds, and then he leapt from the tree, rolling to his knees, breaking his fall, and sprang to his feet again.

He whistled sharply and heard his call answered by Hendrick far behind him in the mopani, but he did not wait for his men to come up. He crossed the glade at a full run, but his feet seemed weighted with lead. He reached the spot where the girl had stopped to look back towards him, and found the tree stump on to which she had climbed. The marks of her bare feet that she had left in the soft earth as she jumped down from the stump were deep and clear, but a few paces farther she had reached the calcrete of the ridge. It was hard as marble, rough and broken, and Lothar knew that it would hold no sign. He did not waste a moment searching for it, but forced his way up through the thick bush to the crest of the ridge, hoping for another sighting from there.

The forest hemmed him in, and even when he climbed into the top branches of a solitary baobab, he looked down on the unbroken roof of the forest that spread away, grey and forbidding, to the horizon.

He climbed down and wearily retraced his steps to the edge of the glade. His Ovambos were waiting for him there.

'We have lost them on the hard ground,' Hendrick greeted him.

'Cast ahead, we must find them,' Lothar ordered.

'I have tried already, the spoor is closed.'

'We cannot give up. We will work at it – I will not let them go.'

'You saw them,' Hendrick said softly, watching his master's face.

'Yes.'

'It was a white girl,' Hendrick insisted. 'You saw the girl, did you not?'

'We cannot leave her here in the desert.' Lothar looked away. He did not want Hendrick to see into the empty place in his soul. 'We must find her.'

'We will try again,' Hendrick agreed, and then with a sly telling grin, 'She was beautiful, this girl?'

'Yes,' Lothar whispered softly, still not looking at him. 'She was beautiful.' He shook himself, as though waking from a dream, and the line of his jaw hardened.

'Get your men on to the ridge,' he ordered.

They worked over it like a pack of hunting dogs, quartering every inch of the adamant yellow rock, stooping over it and moving in a slow painstaking line, but they found only one further mark of the passage of the San and the girl.

In one of the overhanging branches of a paper-bark tree, near the crest of the ridge, just at the level of Lothar's shoulder, a lock of human hair was caught, torn from the girl's scalp as she ducked beneath the branch. It was curly and springy, as long as his forearm, and it glistened in the sunlight like black silk. Lothar wound it carefully around his finger, and then when none of his men was watching, he opened the locket that hung around his neck on a golden

chain. In the recess was a miniature of his mother. He placed the curl of hair over it and snapped the lid of the locket closed.

Lothar kept them hunting for sign until it was dark, and in the morning he started them again as soon as they could see the ground at their feet. He split them into two teams. Hendrick took one team along the eastern side of the ridge, and Lothar worked the western extremity where the calcrete merged into the Kalahari sands, trying to discover the spot at which their quarry had left the ridge again.

Four days later they had still not intersected the spoor, and two of the Ovambo had deserted. They slipped away during the night, taking their rifles with them.

'We will lose the rest of them,' Hendrick warned him quietly. 'They are saying that this is a madness. They cannot understand it. Already we have lost the elephant herd, and there is no profit in this business any longer. The spoor is dead. The San and the woman have slipped away. You will not find them now.'

Hendrick was right – it had become an obsession. A single glimpse of a woman's face had driven him mad. Lothar sighed, and slowly turned away from the ridge on which the pursuit had foundered.

'Very well.' He raised his voice so that the rest of his men, who had been trailing disconsolately, could hear him. 'Drop the spoor. It is dead. We are going back.' The effect upon them was miraculous. Their step quickened and their expressions sparkled to life again.

Lothar remained on the ridge as the gang started back down the slope. He stared out over the forest towards the east, towards the mysterious interior where few white men had ventured, and he fingered the locket at his throat.

'Where did you go? Was it that way, deeper into the Kalahari? Why didn't you wait for me – why did you run?' There were no answers, and he dropped the locket back into the front of his shirt. 'If I ever cut your spoor again, you won't lose me so easily, my pretty. Next time I'll follow you to the ends of the earth,' he whispered, and turned back down the slope.

* * *

O'wa jinked back and followed the ridge towards the south, keeping just below the crest, driving the women as hard as they could run heavily laden over the rough footing. He would not allow them to rest, although Centaine was beginning to tire badly, and pleaded with him over her shoulder.

In the middle of the afternoon he allowed them to drop their satchels and sprawl on the rocky slope while he scurried on down to reconnoitre the contact line of the sands and the calcrete intrusion for a point at which to make the crossover. Halfway down he paused and sniffed; picking up the faint stench of carrion, he turned aside and found the carcass of an old zebra stallion. Reading the sign, O'wa saw that hunting lions had caught him as he crossed the ridge and dragged him down. The kill was weeks old, the tatters of skin and flesh had dried hard and the bones were scattered amongst the rocks.

O'wa searched quickly and found all four of the zebra's feet intact. The hyena had not yet crunched them to splinters. With the clasp knife he prised the horny sheath of the actual hooves from the bony mass of the metatarsals, and

hurried back to fetch the women. He led them down to the edge of the soft ground, and knelt in front of Centaine.

'I will take Nam Child off, and then come back for you,' he told H'ani as he bound the hoof sheaths to Centaine's feet with sansevieria twine.

'We must hurry, old grandfather, they could be close behind us.' H'ani sniffed the light breeze anxiously, and cocked her head towards each small forest sound.

'Who are they?' Centaine had recovered not only her breath, but her curiosity and reason. 'Who is chasing us? I haven't seen or heard a thing. Are they people like me, O'wa, are they my people?'

Swiftly H'ani cut in before O'wa could reply. 'They are black men. Big black men from the north, not your people.' Although she and O'wa had both seen the white man at the edge of the glade when they looked back from the ridge, they had reached agreement in a few words that they would keep Nam Child with them.

'Are you sure, H'ani?' Centaine teetered on the zebra hooves, like a little girl in her first high-heeled shoes. 'They were not pale-skinned like me?' The dreadful possibility that she was fleeing from her rescuers had suddenly occurred to her.

'No! No!' H'ani fluttered her hands in extreme agitation. The child was so close to birth – to witness that moment was the last thing in her life that she still cared about. 'Not pale-skinned like you.' She thought of the most horrific being in San mythology. 'They are big black giants who eat human flesh.'

'Cannibals!' Centaine was shocked.

'Yes! Yes! That is why they pursue us. They will cut the child from your womb and – '

'Let's go, O'wa!' Centaine gasped. 'Hurry! Hurry!'

O'wa, with the other pair of hooves strapped to his own feet, guided Centaine away from the ridge, walking behind her and creating the illusion of a zebra having left the rocky ground and wandered away into the forest.

A mile from the ridge he hid Centaine in a clump of thorny scrub, removed the hooves from her feet, reversed the pair upon his own feet and set off back to fetch H'ani. The two San, each of them wearing hoof sandals, tracked back along the same trail and then they reached Centaine's hiding-place, discarded the hooves and all three of them fled into the east.

O'wa kept them going all that night, and in the dawn while the women slept exhausted, he circled back on their trail and guarded it against the possibility that the pursuers had not been deceived by his ruse with the zebra hooves. Although he could discover no evidence of pursuit, for three more days and nights he force-marched, allowing no cooking fires, and used every natural feature to anti-track and hide their trail.

On the third night, he was confident enought to tell the women, 'We can make fire.' And by its ruddy wavering light he danced with dedicated frenzy and sang the praise of the spirits in turn, including Mantis and Eland, for, as he explained seriously to Centaine, it was uncertain who had aided their escape, who had directed the wind to carry the warning scent to them in the first place, and who had subsequently placed the zebra carcass so conveniently to hand. 'It is necessary, therefore, to thank them all.' He danced until moonset, and the next morning slept until sunrise. Then they resumed the familiar leisurely pattern of march, and even halted early that first day when O'wa discovered a colony of spring-hare.

'This is the last time we can hunt, the spirits are most insistent. No man of the San may kill any living thing within five day's march of "the Place of All Life",' he explained to Centaine, as he selected long whippy saplings of the grewia bush, peeled them and lashed them together until he had a strong flexible rod almost thirty feet long. On the final section, he left a side branch that grew back at an acute angle to the main stem, like a crude fish-hook, and he sharpened the point of this hook and hardened it in the fire. Then he spent a long time carefully examining the burrows of the spring-hare colony, before selecting one which suited his design.

While the women knelt beside him, he introduced the hooked end of the rod into the opening of the burrow, and like a chimney-sweep worked it gently down the shaft, deftly guiding it around the subterranean curves and bends until almost the entire length was down in the earth.

Suddenly the rod pulsed strongly in his hands, and immediately O'wa struck, jerking back like a handline fisherman who feels the pull of the fish.

'He is kicking at the rod now, trying to hit it with his back legs,' O'wa grunted, pushing the rod deeper into the hole, tempting the trapped spring-hare to kick out at it again.

This time, as he struck, the rod came alive in his hands, kicking and twitching and jerking.

'I have hooked him!' He threw his weight back on the rod, driving the sharpened wooden point deeper into the animal's flesh. 'Dig, H'ani. Dig, Nam Child!'

The two women flew at the soft friable earth with their staves, digging down swiftly. The muffled shrieks of the hooked spring-hare grew louder as they came nearer to end of the long gaff, until finally O'wa heaved the furry creature clear of its earth. It was the size of a large yellow cat, and it leaped about wildly on the end of the pliant rod on its powerful kangaroo back legs, until H'ani despatched it with a swinging blow of her stave.

By nightfall they had killed two more spring-hare, and after they had thanked them, they feasted on the sweet tender roasted flesh, the last they would eat for a long time.

In the morning when they set out again on the final leg of the journey, a sharp hot wind blew into their faces.

* * *

Although it was taboo for O'wa to hunt, the Kalahari bloomed in a rich and rare abundance both below and above the ground. There were flowers and green leafy plants to be eaten as salads, roots and tubers, fruits and protein-rich nuts, and the water-holes, all of them brimming, were easy marches apart. Only the wind hampered them, standing steadily into their faces, hot and abrasive with blown sand, forcing them to cover their faces with their leather shawls and lean into it.

The mixed herds of fat handsome zebra and ungainly blue wildebeest with their scraggy manes and skinny legs standing out in the wide pans or on the grassy glades turned their rumps into the sultry blast. The wind ripped the talcum-fine dust off the surface of the pans and whirled it into the sky, turning

the air misty, so the sun itself was a hazy orange globe and the horizons shrank in upon them.

The dust floated on the surface of the water-holes in a thin scum, and it turned to mud in their nostrils and grated between their teeth. It formed little wet beads in the corners of their eyes and dried and cracked their skins so the H'ani and Centaine had to roast and crush seeds of the sour plum tree to extract the oil to dress their skins and the soles of their feet.

However, with each day's march the old people became stronger, more active and excited. They seemed less and less affected by the scouring wind. There was a new jauntiness in their step and they chattered animatedly to each other on the march, while Centaine faltered and dropped far behind, almost as she had done at the beginning.

On the fifth evening after crossing the ridge, Centaine staggered into the camp that the San had already set up on the edge of yet another open pan. Centaine lay on the bare earth, too hot and exhausted to gather grass for her bed.

When H'ani came to her with food, she pushed it away petulantly. 'I don't want it. I don't want anything. I hate this land – I hate the heat and the dust.'

'Soon,' H'ani soothed her, 'very soon we will reach the Place of All Life, and your baby will be born.'

But Centaine rolled away from her. 'Leave me – just leave me alone.'

She woke to the cries of the old people, and she dragged herself up, feeling fat and dirty and unrested, even though she had slept so late that the sun was already tipping the tops of the trees on the far side of the pan. Immediately she saw that the wind had dropped during the night and most of the dust had settled out of the air. The residue transformed the dawn to a kaleidoscope of flamboyant colour.

'Nam Child, do you see it!' H'ani called to her, and then trilled like a Christmas beetle, inarticulate with excitement. Centaine straightened up slowly and stared at the scene that the dust clouds had obscured the previous evening.

Across the pan a great whale-backed mountain rose abruptly out of the desert, steep-sided and with a symmetrically rounded summit. Aglow with all the rich reds and golds of the dawn, it looked like a headless monster. Parts of the mountain were bald and bare, glowing red rock and smooth cliffs, while in other places it was heavily forested; trees much taller and more robust than those of the plain crowned the summit or grew up the steep sides. The strange reddish light suffused with dust and the silences of the African dawn cloaked the entire mountain in majestic serenity.

Centaine felt all her miseries and her woes fall away as she stared at it.

'"The Place of All Life"!' As H'ani said the name, her agitation passed and her voice sank to a whisper. 'This is the sight we have travelled so far and so hard to look upon for the last time.'

O'wa had fallen silent as well, but now he bobbed his head in agreement. 'This is where we will make our peace at last with all the spirits of our people.'

Centaine felt the same sense of deep religious awe that had overcome her when first she had entered the cathedral of Arras, holding her father's hand, and looked up at the gemlike stained glass in the high gloomy recesses of the towering nave. She knew that she stood on the threshold of a holy place, and

she sank slowly to her knees and clasped her hands over the swell of her stomach.

* * *

The mountain was further off than it had seemed in the red light of the dawn. As they marched towards it, it seemed to recede rather than draw closer. As the light changed, so the mountain changed its mood. It became remote and austere, and the stone cliffs glittered in the sunlight like a crocodile's scales.

O'wa sang as he trotted at the head of the file:

> See, spirits of the San
> We come to your secret place
> With clean hands, unstained by blood.
> See, spirit of Eland and Mantis,
> We come to visit you with
> Joyous hearts, and songs for your amusement –

The mountain changed again, began to quiver and tremble in the rising heat. It was no longer massive stone, but rippled like water and wavered like smoke.

It broke free of the earth and floated in the air on a shimmering silver mirage.

> O, bird mountain
> That flies in the sky
> We bring you praises.
> O, Elephant Mountain, greater than
> Any beast of earth or sky, we hail you,

O'wa sang, and as the sun swung through its zenith and the air cooled, so the Mountain of All Life settled to earth again and loomed high above them.

They reached the scree slopes, loose stone and debris that lay piled against the cliffs, and paused to look up at the high summit. The rocks were painted with lichen growth, sulphur-yellow and acid-green, and the little hyrax rock rabbits had stained the cliffs with seepage from their middens, like tears from an elephant's eyes.

On a ledge three hundred feet above them stood a tiny antelope. It took fright and with a bleat like a child's penny whistle, shot straight up the cliff, leaping from ledge to unseen ledge with all the nimbleness of a chamois, until it disappeared over the crest.

They scrambled up the steep scree slope until they touched the base of the cliff. The rock was smooth and cool and overhung them, leaning out at a gentle angle like a vast cathedral roof.

'Be not angry, ye spirits, that we come into your secret place,' H'ani whispered, and tears were coursing down her ancient yellow cheeks. 'We come in humble peace, kind spirits, we come to learn what our offence has been, and how we can make amends.'

O'wa reached out and took his wife's hand and they stood like two tiny naked children before the smooth rock.

'We come to sing for you and to dance,' O'wa whispered. 'We come to make peace, and then with your favour to be reunited with the children of our clan who died of the great fever in a far place.'

There was such vulnerability in this intimate moment that Centaine felt embarrassed to watch them. She drew away from the two old people, and wandered alone along the narrow gallery before the cliff. Suddenly she stopped, and stared up in wonder at the high rock wall that hung out over her head.

'Animals,' she whispered.

She felt the goose-flesh of superstitious fear rise along her forearms, for the walls were decorated with paintings, frescoes of weirdly wrought animals, the childlike simplicity of form giving them a beauty that was dreamlike, and yet a touching resemblance to the beasts that they depicted. She recognized the darkly massive outlines of tusked elephants and horned rhinoceros, the wildebeest and sassaby with horns like crescent moons marching in closely packed phalanxes across the rock walls.

'And people,' Centaine whispered, as she picked out the sticklike human shapes that ran in pursuit of the herds of wild game. Fairy beings, the San's view of himself, armed with bows and crowned with wreaths of arrows, the men adorned with proudly erect penises, disproportionately large, and the women with prominent breasts and buttocks, the badges of feminine beauty.

The paintings climbed so high up the sheer walls that the artists must have built platforms, in the fashion of Michelangelo, to work from. The perspectives were naive, one human figure larger than the rhinoceros he was hunting, but this seemed to deepen the enchantment, and Centaine lost herself in wonder, sinking down at last to examine and admire a lovely flowing waterfall of overlapping eland, ochre and red, with dewlaps and humped shoulders, so lovingly depicted that their special place in San mythology could not be overlooked.

H'ani found her there, and squatted beside her.

'Who painted these things?' Centaine asked her.

'The spirits of the San, long, long ago.'

'Were they not painted by men?'

'No! No! Men do not have the art, these are spirit drawings.'

So the artists' skills were lost. Centaine was disappointed. She had hoped that the old woman was one of the artists and that she would have an opportunity to watch her work.

'Long ago,' H'ani repeated, 'before the memory of my father or my grandfather.'

Centaine swallowed her disappointment and gave herself up to enjoyment of the marvellous display.

There was little left of the daylight, but while it lasted, they picked their way slowly around the base of the cliff, walking with heads thrown back to marvel at the gallery of ancient art. At places the rock had broken away, or the storms and winds of the ages had destroyed the frescoes, but in the protected gulleys and beneath the sheltering overhangs the paint seemed so fresh, and the colours so vivid, that they might have been painted that very day.

In the last minutes of daylight they reached a shelter where others had camped before them, for the hearth was thick with wood ash and the cliff was blackened with soot, and there was a pile of dead wood left beside it, ready for use.

'Tomorrow we will learn if the spirits are hostile still, or if we will be allowed to proceed,' H'ani warned Centaine. 'We will start very early, for we must reach the hidden place before the sun rises, while it is still cool. The guardians become restless and dangerous in the heat.'

'What is this place?' Centaine insisted, but once again the old woman became vague and deliberately absent-minded. She repeated the San word which had the various meanings 'hidden place' or 'safe shelter' or 'vagina', and would say no more.

As H'ani had warned, they started out long before sunrise the next morning and the old people were quiet and anxious and, Centaine suspected, fearful.

The sky was barely lighting with the dawn when abruptly the path turned a sharp corner in the cliff and entered a narrow wedge-shaped valley, the floor was thickly covered with such luxuriant growth that Centaine realized there must be good water below the surface. The path was ill-defined, overgrown and clearly had not been trodden for many months or years. They had to duck under the interlocking branches and step over fallen boughs and new growth. In the cliffs high above them Centaine made out the huge shaggy nests of vultures, and the grossly ugly birds with their bare pink heads crouched on the rim of their nests.

'The Place of All Life,' H'ani saw her interest in the nesting birds. 'Any creature born here is special, blessed by the spirits. Even the birds seem to know this.'

The high cliffs closed in upon them as the valley narrowed, and at last the path ended against the rock in the angled corner where the valley finally pinched out, and the sky was hidden from them.

O'wa stood before the wall and sang in his hoarse ghost-chant, 'We wish to enter your most secret place, Spirits of all Creatures, Spirits of our clan. Open the way for us.' He spread his arms in entreaty. 'May the guardians of this passage let us pass through.'

O'wa lowered his arms, and stepped into the black rock of the cliff and disappeared from Centaine's sight. She gasped with alarm, and started forward, but H'ani touched her arm to restrain her.

'There is great danger now, Nam Child. If the guardians reject us, we will die. Do not run, do not wave your arms. Walk slowly, but with purpose, and ask the blessing of the spirits as you pass through.' H'ani released her arm, and stepped into the rock following her husband.

Centaine hesitated. For a moment she almost turned back, but at last curiosity and fear of loneliness spurred her and she went slowly to the wall where H'ani had disappeared. Now she saw the opening in the rock, a narrow vertical crack, just wide enough for her to pass through if she turned her shoulders.

She drew a deep breath and slipped through.

Beyond the narrow portals she paused to allow her eyes to become accustomed to the gloom, and she found herself in a long dark tunnel. It was a natural opening, she saw at once, for the walls had not been worked by tools, and there were side branches and openings high overhead. She heard the rustle of the old people's bare feet on the rocky floor ahead of her, and then another sound. A low, murmurous hum, like the sea surf heard from afar.

'Follow, Nam Child. Stay close,' H'ani's voice floated back to her and Centaine went forward slowly, staring into the shadows, trying to find the source of that deep vibrating murmur.

In the gloom above her she saw strange shapes, plate-like projections from the walls, like the leaves of fungus growing on the trunk of a dead tree, or the multiple wings of roosting butterflies. They drooped so low that she had to duck beneath them – and with a sudden chill she realized where she was.

The cavern was an enormous beehive. These deep wing-like structures were

the honeycombs, so massive that each would contain hundreds of gallons of honey. Now she could see the insects swarming over the combs, glittering dully in the poor light, and she remembered the stories that Michael had told her of the African bees.

'Bigger and blacker than your bees,' he had boasted, 'and so vicious that I have seen them sting a bull buffalo to death.'

Barely allowing herself to breathe, her skin crawling in anticipation of the first burning dart, forcing herself not to run, she followed the diminutive figures ahead of her. The swarming masses of venomous insects were only inches above her, and the humming chorus seemed to rise angrily until it threatened to deafen her.

'This way, Nam Child. Do not fear, for the little winged people will smell your fear,' H'ani called softly, and a bee alighted on Centaine's cheek.

She raised her hand instinctively to strike it off her, and then with an effort checked the movement. The bee tickled across her face on to her upper lip – then another settled on her upraised forearm.

She peered at it in horror. It was enormous, black as coal, with dark golden rings around its abdomen. The filmy wings were closed like scissor-blades and its multiple eyes twinkled in the poor light.

'Please, little bee, please – ' Centaine whispered, and the insect arched its back, and from its banded abdomen the point of its sting protruded, a dark red needle-point.

'Please, let me and my baby pass!'

The bee curved its body and the sting touched the soft tanned skin of her inner elbow. Centaine tensed herself; she knew that the stabbing pain would be followed by the sickly sweet odour of the venom that would madden and infuriate the vast swarm above her. She imagined herself smothered under a living carpet of bees, writhing on the floor of the cavern, dying the most hideous of deaths.

'Please,' she whispered. 'Let my baby be born in your secret place, and we will honour you all the days of our lives.'

The bee retracted the throbbing sting and performed an intricate weaving dance upon her arm, turning and curtseying and reversing, and then with a quicksilver flicker of its wings darted away.

Centaine walked on slowly, and ahead of her she saw a golden nimbus of reflected light. The insect on her face crawled down over her lips, so she could not speak again, but she prayed silently.

'"Though I walk through the valley of the shadow of death" please, little bee, let me go for my baby's sake.'

A sharp buzz and the bee flashed before her eyes, a golden mote as it left her, and though her skin tingled and itched from the memory of its horny feet, she kept her hands at her sides and walked on with a measured step. It seemed for ever, then she reached the tunnel's end and stooped through it into the early dawn light, and her legs began to fold in reaction to her terror. She might have fallen if O'wa had not steadied her.

'You are safe now. The guardians have allowed us to enter the sacred place.'

The words roused her, and though she still trembled and her breathing was rough, Centaine looked around her.

They had passed through into a hidden basin in the heart of the mountain, a perfectly round amphitheatre in the rock. The walls were sheer, hundreds of

feet high and with a dark satanic sheen to them, as though scorched in the flames of a blast furnace, but above that it was open to the sky.

The deep bowl of rock was perhaps a mile across at its widest point. At this time of day the sunlight had not penetrated down to the floor, and the groves of graceful trees that covered it were cool and dewy. They reminded Centaine of olives, with fine pale leaves and bunches of reddish-yellow fruit on the wide-spread boughs. The floor of the valley was gently dished, and as Centaine followed H'ani down through the trees, the ground beneath them was carpeted with fallen fruit.

H'ani picked up one of them and offered it to Centaine.

'Mongongo – very good.'

Centaine bit into it and exclaimed as her tooth struck painfully on the large kernel in its centre. There was only a thin layer of flesh around it, but it was tart and tasty as a palm date, though not as sweet.

From the branches above them a flight of plump green pigeons exploded into noisy flight, and Centaine realized that the valley was alive with birds and small animals come in the dawn to feast on the fruits of the mongongo groves.

'The Place of All Life,' she whispered, entranced by the weird beauty, by the stark contrast of bare blasted rock cliffs against this gently wooded bottom land.

O'wa hurried along the rough path that led down into the centre of the bowl, and as Centaine followed she glimpsed a small hillock of black volcanic rock through the trees ahead. Centaine saw that the hill was symmetrical and cone-shaped, and set in the exact centre of the amphitheatre like the boss in the centre of a shield.

Like the valley floor, the hill itself was heavily forested. Tall elephant grass and mongongo trees grew profusely among the black volcanic boulders. A troop of black-faced vervet monkeys chattered at them from the trees and ducked their heads threateningly, grimacing with alarm, as they approached the hillock.

When Centaine and H'ani caught up with O'wa, he was standing facing a dark opening in the side of the hill. It looked like the mouth of a mine-shaft, but as she peered into it Centaine realized that the floor of the shaft sloped down at a gentle angle. She pushed past O'wa the better to examine it, but the old man seized her arm.

'Be not hasty, Nam Child, we must make preparation in the correct manner.' And he drew her back and led her gently away.

A little further on, there was an acient San camp-site amongst the sheltering rocks. The thatched roofs of the shelters had collapsed with age. O'wa burned them to the ground, for disused huts habour snakes and vermin, and the two women rebuilt them with saplings and freshly cut grass.

'I am hungry.' Centaine realized that she had not eaten since the previous evening.

'Come.' H'ani led her into the grove, and they filled their satchels with the fallen fruit of the mongongo trees. Back in the camp, H'ani showed Centaine how to strip off the outer layer of flesh and then to crack the hard central nut between two flat stones. The kernal looked like a dried almond. They ate a few of these, to take the edge off their hunger. They tasted like walnuts.

'We will eat them in many ways,' H'ani promised. 'And each way they taste different, roasted, pounded with leaves, boiled like maize bread – they will be our only food in this place where all killing is forbidden.'

While they prepared the meal, O'wa returned to camp with a bundle of

freshly dug roots, and went aside to prepare them in private, scraping and chopping with his beloved clasp knife.

They ate before dark, and Centaine found the meal of nuts unexpectedly satisfying. As soon as her stomach was filled, the effect of the day's excitements and exertions caught up with her, and she could barely drag herself to her shelter.

She awoke refreshed and with a sense of unexplained excitement. The San were already busy around the camp fire and as soon as she joined them and squatted in the circle, O'wa, puffed up with nervous anticipation and self-importance, told them, 'We must now prepare to go down into the most secret of places. Do you agree to the purification, old grandmother?' It was obviously a formal question.

'I agree, old grandfather.' H'ani clapped softly in acquiescence.

'Do you agree to the purification, Nam Child?'

'I agree, old grandfather.' Centaine clapped in imitation and O'wa bobbed his head and from the pouch on his belt brought out a buckhorn. The tip had been pierced, and O'wa had stuffed the horn with the chopped roots and herbs that he had gathered the previous afternoon.

Now he picked a live coal out of the fire with his fingers, and juggling it to prevent it burning his skin, he dropped it into the trumpet-shaped opening of the buckhorn. He blew upon it and a tendril of blue smoke rose in the still air as the herbs smouldered.

Once the pipe was burning evenly, O'wa rose and stood behind the two squatting women. He placed his mouth over the pierced tip of the horn and sucked on it strongly, then blew the smoke over them. It was acrid and sharply unpleasant, and left a bitter taste in Centaine's throat. She murmured a protest and began to rise, but H'ani pulled her down again. O'wa kept puffing and exhaling, and after a while Centaine found the smoke less offensive. She relaxed and leaned against H'ani. The old woman placed an arm around her shoulders. Slowly Centaine became aware of a marvellous sense of well-being. Her body felt as light as that of a bird, she felt she could float up with the spirals of blue smoke.

'Oh, H'ani, I feel so good,' she whispered.

The air around her seemed sparkling clear, her vision sharp and magnified so she could see every crack and crevice in the surrounding cliffs, and the groves of trees seemed to be made of green crystals. They reflected the sunlight with an ethereal radiance.

She became aware that O'wa was kneeling in front of her, and she smiled at him dreamily. He was offering something, holding it out towards her with both hands.

'It is for the child,' he told her, and his voice seemed to come from far away and echo strangely in her ears. 'It is the birthing mat. His father should have made it for him, but that could not be. Here, Nam Child, take it and bear a brave son upon it.'

O'wa leaned forward and placed the gift upon her lap. It look long seconds before she realized that it was the gemsbok skin over which O'wa had worked so long and so intently. She unfolded it with exaggerated care. The skin had been scraped and tanned to the pliability and softness of fine cloth. She stroked it and the fur felt like satin.

'Thank you, old grandfather,' her voice came from far away, and reverberated strangely in her own ears.

'It is for the child,' he repeated, and sucked on the buckhorn pipe.

'For the child, yes,' Centaine nodded and her head seemed to float free of her body. O'wa gently exhaled a stream of blue smoke into her face and she made no effort to avoid it, rather she leaned forward to stare into his eyes. O'wa's pupils had shrunk to glittering black pin-pricks, the irises were the colour of dark amber with a fanlike pattern of black lines surrounding the pupils. They mesmerized her.

'For the child's sake, let the peace of this place enter your soul.' O'wa spoke through the smoke, and Centaine felt it happen.

'Peace,' she murmured, and at the centre of her being was a wondrous stillness, a monumental calm.

Time and space and white sunlight mingled and became one. She sat at the centre of the universe and smiled serenely. She heard O'wa singing far away, and she swayed gently to the rhythm and felt each beat of her heart and the slow pump of her blood through her veins. She felt the child lying deep within her, curled in an attitude of prayer, then unbelievably, she felt the tiny heart beating like that of a trapped bird, and the wonder of it engulfed her whole being.

'We have come to be cleansed,' O'wa said. 'We have come to wash away all offence, we have come to make atonement – '

Centaine felt H'ani's hand creep into hers like a fragile-boned animal, and she turned her head slowly and smiled into the beloved old face.

'It is time, Nam Child.'

Centaine drew the gemsbok skin over her shoulders. It required no effort to rise. She floated above the earth, with H'ani's little hand clutched in hers.

They came to the opening in the hillside, and though it was dark and steep, Centaine went forward smiling and she did not feel the coarse volcanic rock beneath her feet. The passageway descended for a short distance, and then levelled out and opened into a natural cavern. They followed O'wa down.

Light filtered from the stairway behind them and from a number of small openings in the domed roof. The air was warm and moist and steamy. The clouds of steam rose gently from the surface of a circular pool that filled the cavern from side to side. The surface of the pool seethed and bubbled softly, and the steam smelled strongly of sulphur. The waters were cloudy green.

O'wa let his loincloth fall to the rocky floor and stepped into the pool. It reached to his knees but as he waded forward it deepened, until only his head was above the surface. H'ani followed him naked into the pool, and Centaine laid the gemsbok skin aside, and let her skirt fall.

The water was hot, almost scalding, a thermal spring welling up out of the matrix, but Centaine felt no discomfort. She moved deeper and then sank down slowly on to her knees until the water came to her chin. The floor of the pool was coarse pebble and gravel. The fierce heat of the waters soaked into her body. It swirled and eddied about her, kneading her flesh, as it bubbled up out of the depths of the earth.

She heard O'wa singing softly, but the steam clouds closed in around her and blinded her.

'We wish to make atonement,' O'wa sang. 'We wish to be forgiven our offences to the Spirits – '

Centaine saw a shape forming in the steam clouds, a dark, insubstantial phantom.

'Who are you?' she murmured, and the shape firmed, and she recognized the

eyes – the other features were obscure – as those of the old seaman she had sacrificed to the shark.

'Please,' she whispered, 'forgive me. It was for my baby. Please forgive my offence.' It seemed that for a moment there was understanding in those sad old eyes, and then the image faded and vanished in the steam banks, to be replaced by others, a host of memories and dream creatures, and she spoke to them.

'Oh, Papa, if I had only been strong enough, if only I could have filled Mama's place – '

She heard the voices of the San in the steam, crying out in greeting to their own ghosts and memories. O'wa hunted again with his sons, and H'ani saw her babies and her grandchildren and crooned her love and mourning.

'Oh, Michel,' his eyes were a marvellous blue, 'I will love you forever. Yes, oh yes, I will name your son for you. I promise you that, my love, he will carry your name.'

How long she remained in the pool she did not know, but gradually the fantasies and the phantoms faded, and then she felt H'ani's hands leading her to the rocky lip. The scalding waters seemed to have drained all the strength from her. Her body glowed a bright brick colour, and the ingrained dirt of the desert was scoured from the pores of her skin. Her knees were weak and rubbery.

H'ani draped the gemsbok skin over her wet body and helped her up the rocky passage to the surface. Night had fallen already, and the moon shone bright enough to cast shadows at their feet. H'ani led her to the rude shelter and wrapped her in the gemsbok skin.

'The spirits have forgiven,' she whispered. 'They are pleased that we have made the journey. They sent my babies to greet me and tell me so. You can sleep well, Nam child, there is no more offence. We are welcome in this place.'

* * *

Centaine woke in confusion, not sure what was happening to her, not even certain where she was, imagining for the first few seconds that she was back in her chamber at Mort Homme and that Anna was standing beside her bed. Then she became aware of the coarse grass and hard earth beneath her and the smell of the rawhide that covered her, and immediately following that the pain came again. It was as though a claw had closed on her lower body, a cruel taloned claw, cramping and crushing her, and she cried out involuntarily and doubled over, clutching her stomach.

With the pain, reality rushed back upon her. Her mind was clear and sharp after the hallucinations of the previous day. She knew what was happening, she knew instinctively that the immersion in the heated waters of the pool and the drugged smoke she had breathed must have precipitated it.

'H'ani!' she called, and the old woman materialized out of the grey half light. 'It has begun!'

H'ani helped her to her feet, then gathered up the gemsbok skin.

'Come,' she whispered. 'We must go where we can be alone.'

H'ani must have already chosen the place, for she led Centaine directly to a hollow a short way beyond the camp, but screened from it by the mongongo grove. She spread the gemsbok skin at the base of a large mongongo tree and

settled Centaine upon it. She knelt over her and removed her ragged canvas skirt, then with quick, strong fingers, she made a brief but thorough examination and then rocked back on her heels.

'Soon, Nam Child – very soon now,' she smiled happily, but Centaine's reply choked off as another spasm caught her.

'Ah, the child is impatient!' H'ani nodded.

The spasm passed and Centaine lay and panted, but she had barely caught her breath before she stiffened again.

'Oh, H'ani, hold my hand – please! Please!'

Something burst deep within Centaine's body and hot liquid poured from her, and sprayed down her legs.

'Close – very close now,' H'ani assured her, and Centaine gave a little hunted cry.

'Now – ' H'ani pulled her into a sitting position, but she slumped back.

'It's coming, H'ani.'

'Get up!' H'ani snapped at her. 'You must help it now. Get up. You cannot help the baby if you lie on your back!' She forced Centaine into a squatting position, with her feet and knees splayed apart, the natural position for voiding.

'Hold the tree to steady yourself,' she instructed her urgently. 'There!' She guided Centaine's hands on to the rough bark and Centaine moaned and pressed her forehead hard against the trunk.

'Now!' H'ani knelt behind her, and encircled Centaine's body with her thin wiry arms.

'Oh, H'ani – 'Centaine's cry rose sharply.

'Yes! I will help you push him out.' And she tightened her grip as Centaine bore down instinctively. 'Push, Nam Child – hard! Hard! Push!' H'ani entreated her as she felt the girl's stomach muscles bunch up and harden into bands of iron.

There was a great blockade within her and Centaine clung to the tree and strained and moaned – and then she felt the obstruction move a little, then jam hard again.

'H'ani!' she cried, and the thin arms locked around her and the old woman moaned with her as they strained together. H'ani's naked body was pressed to Centaine's arched back, and she felt strength flowing out of the old wizened flesh like an electrical current.

'Again, Nam child,' H'ani grunted in her ear. 'He is close – so close. Now! Nam Child, push hard.'

Centaine bore down with all her strength and will. Her jaws were clenched so that she thought her teeth would crack, and her eyes swelled in their sockets. Then she felt something tear, a stinging burning pain, but despite the pain she found strength for another rigorous convulsion. It moved again, then there was a rush, a release and something enormous and impossibly heavy slid out of her and at the same moment H'ani's hand reached under her buttocks to guide and welcome and protect.

Like a benediction, the pain wilted away, and left her shaking as though in high fever and running with her own sweat – but empty, blessedly empty, as though her viscera had been drawn out of her.

H'ani released her grip, and Centaine clutched at the treetrunk for support, and drew long ragged breaths.

Then she felt something hot and wet and slippery squirming between her feet, and she pushed herself wearily away from the treetrunk and looked down.

A tangle of fleshy glistening tubes still dangled out of her, and joined to them, enmeshed in their coils, the infant lay in a pool of blood-speckled fluid on the gemsbok-skin mat.

It was small, she was surprised at how small, but its limbs were stretching in spasmodic clutching and kicking gestures. The face was turned away from her but the small neat head was covered with a dense cap of sodden black curls, plastered to the skull.

H'ani's hands reached down between her legs from behind and lifted the baby out of her sight. Instantly Centaine felt a devastating sense of deprivation – but she was too weak to protest. She felt a gentle twitching and tugging on the umbilical cord as H'ani handled the child, and then suddenly there was a furious squalling howl. It struck Centaine to the heart.

Then H'ani's laughter joined in chorus with the angry bawls. Centaine had never hear a sound of such unequivocal joy.

'Oh, listen to him, Nam Child. He roars like a lion cub!'

Centaine waddled around awkwardly, hampered by the fleshy ropes dangling from her own body and still linking her to the infant. He was struggling in H'ani's hands, all wet and defiant, his face red with anger and his bee-stung eyes tight closed, but his toothless pink mouth wide as he howled his outrage.

'A boy, H'ani?' Centaine panted wildly.

'Oh yes,' H'ani laughed, 'by all means, a boy,' and with the tip of her forefinger she tickled his tiny penis. It stuck out stiffly as though to endorse his anger, and at H'ani's touch released a powerful arcing jet of urine.

'Look! Look!' H'ani choked with laughter. 'He pisses on the world. Bear witness, all the Spirits of this place, a veritable lion cub has been birthed this day.'

She offered the squirming red-faced infant to Centaine.

'Clean his eyes and nose,' she ordered, and, like a mother cat, Centaine did not need further instruction. She licked the mucus from the tiny swollen eyelids, from his nostrils and mouth.

Then H'ani took the child, handling him with familiar expertise, and she tied off the umbilical cord with the soft white inner bark threads of the mongongo tree, before severing it with a quick slash of her bone knife. Then she rolled the end of the tube in the medicinal leaves of the wild quince and bound it in place with a rawhide strip around his middle.

Sitting on the soiled gemsbok skin, in a puddle of her own blood and amniotic fluids, Centaine watched her work with shining eyes.

'Now!' H'ani nodded with vast self-satisfaction. 'He is ready for the breast.' And she placed him in Centaine's lap.

He and Centaine needed only the barest introduction. H'ani squeezed Centaine's nipple and touched the milk-wet tip to the infant's lips, and he fastened on it like a leech, with a noisy rhythmic suction. For a few moments Centaine was startled by the sudden sharp sympathetic contractions of her womb as the child suckled, but this was lost and forgotten in the wonder and mystery of examining her incredible accomplishment.

Gently she unfolded his fist and marvelled at the perfection of each tiny pink finger, at the pearly nails, each no bigger than a grain of rice, and when he suddenly seized her finger in the surprisingly powerful grip, he squeezed her heart as well. She stroked his damp dark hair, and as it dried it sprang up into ringlets. It awed her to see the pulsing movement under the thin membrane that covered the opening of his skull.

He stopped suckling and lay quiescent in her arms, so she could take him from her breast and examine his face. He was smiling. Apart from the puffy eyelids, his features were well-formed, not squashed and rubbery like those of the other newborn infants she had seen. His brow was broad and deep and his nose was large. She thought of Michael – no it was more arrogant then Michael's nose – and then she remembered General Sean Courtney.

'That's it!' she chuckled aloud. 'The true Courtney nose.'

The infant stiffened and broke wind simultaneously both fore and aft, a trickle of her milk dribbled from the corner of his mouth, and instantly he began to hunt for the nipple again, mouthing demandingly, rolling his head from side to side. Centaine changed him to her other arm, and guided her nipple into his open mouth.

Kneeling in front of her, H'ani was working between Centaine's knees. Centaine winced and bit her lip as the afterbirth came free, and H'ani wrapped it in the leaves of the elephant-ear plant, tied it with bark and scampered away into the grove with the bundle.

When she returned, the child was asleep in Centaine's lap, with his legs splayed and his belly tight as a balloon.

'If you permit, I will fetch O'wa,' H'ani suggested. 'He will have heard the birth cries.'

'Oh, yes, fetch him quickly!' Centaine had forgotten the old man, and now was delighted at the opportunity to exhibit her marvellous acquisition.

O'wa came shyly and squatted a little way off, showing the usual masculine lack of temerity when faced with the feminine mystery of birth.

'Approach, old grandfather,' Centaine encouraged him, and he shuffled closer on his haunches and peered solemnly at the sleeping child.

'What do you think?' Centaine asked. 'Will he be a hunter? As skilful and brave a hunter as O'wa?'

O'wa made a little clicking sound reserved for those rare occasions when he was at a loss for words, and his face was a web of convoluted wrinkles like that of a worried Pekinese lap dog. Suddenly the child kicked out strongly and yelped in his sleep, and the old man dissolved into uncontrolled giggles.

'I never thought I would see it again,' he wheezed, and gingerly reached out and took a tiny pink foot in his hand.

The child kicked again and it was too much for O'wa. He sprang up and began to dance. Shuffling and stamping, circling the mother and child on the gemsbok skin, around and around he went, and H'ani controlled herself for three circuits, then she too leaped to her feet and danced with her husband. She followed him, with her hands on his hips, leaping when he leaped, twitching her protruding backside, performing the intricate stamp and double shuffle, and singing the chorus to O'wa's praise song:

> His arrows will fly to the stars
> and when men speak his name
> it will be heard as far –

and H'ani came in with the chorus.

> – And he will find good water,
> wherever he travels, he will find good water.

O'wa squeaked and jerked his legs and made his shoulders shake.

His bright eye will pick out the game
when other men are blind.
Effortlessly he will follow the spoor over rocky ground –
– And he will find good water,
at every camp site he will find good water –
– prettiest maidens will smile and
tiptoe to his camp fire in the night –

And H'ani reiterated in her reedy singsong:

– And he will find good water,
wherever he goes, he will find good water.

They were blessing the child, wishing upon him all the treasures of the San people, and Centaine felt that her heart would break with love for them and for the small pink bundle in her lap.

When at last the old people could dance and sing no more, they knelt in front of Centaine.

'As the great-grandparents of the child, we would like to give him a name,' H'ani explained shyly. 'Is it permitted?'

'Speak, old grandmother. Speak, old grandfather.'

H'ani looked at her husband and he nodded encouragement.

'We would name the child Shasa.'

Tears prickled Centaine's eyelids as she realized the great honour. They were naming him after the most precious, life-sustaining element in the San universe.

'Shasa – Good Water.'

Centaine blinked back the tears and smiled at them.

'I name this child Michel Shasa de Thiry Courtney,' she said softly, and each of the old people reached out in turn and touched his eyes and mouth in blessing.

* * *

The sulphurous, mineralized waters of the subterranean pool were possessed of extraordinary qualities. Every noon and evening Centaine soaked in their heat, and the manner in which her birth injuries healed was almost miraculous. Of course, she was in superb physical health, without an ounce of superfluous fat or flesh upon her, and Shasa's neat lean body and the ease of his delivery was a consequence of this. Furthermore the San looked upon parturition as such a routine process that H'ani neither pampered her, nor encouraged her to treat herself as an invalid.

Young muscles, elastic and well exercised, swiftly regained their resilience and strength. Her skin, not over-stretched, was free of stria, and her belly swiftly shrank back into its greyhound profile. Only her breasts were swollen hard with copious milk, and Shasa gorged and grew like one of the desert plants after rain.

Then again there was the pool and its waters.

'It is strange,' H'ani told her, 'the nursing mothers who drink this water always grow children with bones as hard as rock and teeth that shine like polished ivory. It is one of the blessings of the spirits that guard this place.'

At noon the sun struck through one of the apertures in the domed roof of the cavern, a solid white shaft of light through the steam-laden air, and Centaine loved to bask in it, moving across the pool as the beam swung, to keep in its charmed circle of light.

She lay chin-deep in the seething green water, and listened to Shasa snuffling and mewing in his sleep. She had wrapped him in the gemsbok skin and laid him on the ledge beside the pool where she could see him merely by turning her head.

The bottom of the pool was lined with gravel and pebbles. She scooped up handfuls of them and held them up in the sunlight, and they gave her a special kind of pleasure for they were strange and beautiful. They were veined agates, waterworn and smooth as swallows' eggs, stones of soft blue with lines of red through them, or pink or yellow, and jaspers and carnelians in a hundred shades of burgundy, shiny black onyx and tiger's eyes of gold barred with iridescent waves of shifting colour.

'I will make a necklace, for H'ani. A gift to thank her, from Shasa!'

She began to collect the prettiest stones with the most interesting and unusual shapes.

'I need a centrepiece for the necklace,' she decided, and she dredged handfuls of gravel and washed them in the hot green waters, then examined them in the sunlight until at last she found exactly what she was searching for.

It was a colourless stone, clear as water, but when it caught the sunlight it contained a captive rainbow, an internal fire that burned with all the colours of the spectrum. Centaine spent a long lazy hour in the pool, turning this stone slowly in the beam of sunlight to make it flash and sparkle, staring into its depths with delight, watching it explode into wondrous cascades of light. The stone was not large – only the size of one of the ripe mongongo fruit – but it was a symmetrical many-sided crystal, perfect for the centrepiece of the necklace.

She designed H'ani's necklace with infinite care, spending many hours while Shasa nursed at her breast, arranging and rearranging her collection of pebbles until at last she had them in the order which most pleased her. Yet still she was not entirely satisfied, for the colourless central stone, so sparkling and regular in shape, made all the other coloured stones seem somehow drab and uninteresting.

Nevertheless, she began to experiment in stringing the pebbles in a necklace and here she immediately encountered problems. One or two of the pebbles were so soft that by dint of persistent effort and many worn-out bone augers she was finally able to drill a stringing hole through them. Others were brittle and shattered, and others again were too hard. In particular the sparkling crystal resisted her best efforts, and remained absolutely unblemished after she had broken a dozen bone tools upon it.

She appealed to O'wa for assistance, and once he understood what she was working on, he was boyishly enthusiastic. They experimented and met with failure a dozen times before they finally worked out a means of cementing the harder stones on to the plaited sansevieria twine with acacia gum. Centaine began to assemble the necklace, and almost drove O'wa to distraction in the process, for she discarded fifty lengths of twine.

'This is too thick,' she would say, or 'This is not strong enough.' And O'wa, who, when working on his own weapons and tools, was also a perfectionist, took the problem very seriously.

Finally Centaine unravelled the hem of her canvas skirt and by plaiting the threads with the sansevieria fibres, they had a string for the necklace that was fine and strong enough to satisfy both of them.

When the necklace was at last finished, O'wa's self-satisfaction could not have been more overbearing had he conceived, planned and executed the project entirely on his own. It was a more of a pectoral than a necklace, with a single string around the back of the neck and the stones woven together in a plate-like decoration which hung on the breast with the big crystal in the centre, and a mosaic of coloured agates and jaspers and beryls surrounding it.

Even Centaine was delighted with her handiwork.

'It's turning out better than I had hoped,' she told O'wa, speaking in French and holding it up and turning it to catch the sunlight. 'Not as good as Monsieur Cartier,' she remembered her father's wedding gift to her mother which he had allowed her to wear on her birthdays ' – but not too bad for a wild girl's first effort in a wild place!'

They made a little ceremony of the presentation, and H'ani sat beaming like a little amber-coloured hobgoblin while Centaine thanked her for being such a paragon of a grandmother and the best midwife of the San, but when she placed the gift around the old woman's neck it seemed too big and weighty for the frail wrinkled body.

'Ha, old man, you are so proud of that knife of yours, but it is as nothing to this,' H'ani told O'wa as she stroked the necklace lovingly. 'This is a true gift. Look you! Now I wear the moon and the stars around my throat!'

She refused to remove it. It thumped against her breastbone as she wielded her digging stick or stooped to gather the mongongo nuts. When she crouched over the cooking fires, it dangled between the empty pouches of her swinging dugs. Even in the night as she slept with her head cradled on her own bare shoulder, Centaine looked across from her own shelter and saw the necklace shining on her chest, and it seemed to weigh the little old body down to the earth.

* * *

Once Centaine's preoccupation with the necklace was over, and her strength and vitality fully recovered after childbirth, she began to find the days too long and the rock cliffs of the valley as restrictive as the high walls of a prison.

The daily routine of life was undemanding, and Shasa slept on her hip or strapped to her back while she gathered the fallen nuts in the grove or helped H'ani bring in the firewood. Her menses resumed their course, and she itched with unexpended energy.

She had sudden moods of black depression, when even H'ani's innocent chatter irritated her, and she went off alone with the baby. Though he slept soundly through it all, she held him on her lap and spoke to him in French or English. She told him about his father and the château, about Nuage and Anna and General Courtney, and the names and the memories instilled in her a deep and undirected melancholy. Sometimes in the night, when she could not sleep, she lay and listened to the music in her head, the strains of *Aïda* or the songs the peasants sang in the fields at Mort Homme during the *vendange*.

So the months passed and the seasons of the desert rotated. The mongongo

tree flowered and fruited again, and one day Shasa lifted himself on to hands and knees and to the delight of all set off on his first explorations of the valley. Yet Centaine's mood swung more violently then the seasons, her joy in Shasa and her contentment in the old people's company alternating with blacker moods when she felt like a life prisoner in the valley.

'They have come here to die,' she realized as she saw how the old San had settled into an established routine, 'but I don't want to die – I want to live, to live!'

H'ani watched her shrewdly until she realized it was time, and then told O'wa, 'Tomorrow Nam Child and I are going out of the valley.'

'Why, old woman?' O'wa looked startled. He was entirely contented and had not yet thought about leaving.

'We need medicines, and a change of food.'

'That is no reason to risk passing the guardians of the tunnel.'

'We will go out in the cool of the dawn, when the bees are sleepy, and return in the late evening – besides, the guardians have accepted us.'

O'wa started to protest further, but she cut him short. 'It is necessary, old grandfather, there are things that a man does not understand.'

As H'ani had intended, Centaine was excited and happy with the promised outing, and she shook H'ani awake long before the agreed hour. They slipped quietly through the tunnel of the bees, and with Shasa bound tightly to her back and her carrying satchel slung over one shoulder, Centaine ran down the narrow valley and out into the endless spaces of the desert like a schoolchild released from the classroom. Her mood lasted through the morning and she and H'ani chattered happily as they moved through the forest, searching and digging for the roots that H'ani said she needed.

In the heat of the noonday they found shelter under an acacia, and while Centaine nursed the baby, H'ani curled up in the shade and slept like an old yellow cat. Once Shasa had drunk his fill, Centaine leaned back again the trunk of the acacia and dozed off as well.

The stamp of hooves and horsy snorts disturbed her, and she opened her eyes, but remained absolutely still. With the breeze behind them, a herd of zebra had grazed down upon the sleeping group, not noticing them in the waist-high grass.

There were at least a hundred animals in the herd – newly born foals with legs too long for their fluffy bodies and with smudged chocolate-coloured stripes not yet set into definite patterns, staying close to their dams and staring around at the world with huge dark apprehensive eyes, older foals quick and surefooted as they chased each other in circles through the trees, the breeding mares, sleek and glossy, with stiff upstanding manes and pricked ears, some of them huge with foal, milk already swelling in their black udders. Then there were the stallions with powerful bulging quarters, necks arched proudly as they challenged each other or snuffled one of the mares, reminding Centaine vividly of Nuage in his prime. Barely daring to breathe, she lay against the acacia trunk and watched them with deep pleasure. They moved down still closer, she could have reached out and touched one of the foals as it gambolled past her. They passed so close that she could see that each animal was different from the others, the intricate patterns of their hides as distinct as finger-prints, and the dark stripes were shadowed by a paler orangey-cream duplicate, so that every animal was a separate work of art.

As she watched, one of the stallions, a magnificent animal standing twelve

hands and with a bushy tail sweeping below his hocks, cut a young mare out of the main pack of the herd, nipping at her flanks and her neck with square yellow teeth, heading her off when she tried to circle back, pushing her well away from the other mares, but closer to the acacia tree, before he started to gentle her by nuzzling her neck.

The mare bridled flirtatiously, well aware of her highly desirable condition, and she rolled her eyes and bit him viciously on his muscled glossy shoulder so that he snorted and reared away, but then circled back and tried to push his nose up under her tail where she was swollen tensely with her season. She squealed with a modest outrage and lashed out with both back legs, her shiny black hooves flying past his head, and she spun around to face him, baring her teeth.

Centaine found herself unaccountably moved. She shared the mare's mounting excitation, empathized with her charade of reluctance that was spurring the circling stallion to greater ardour. At last the mare submitted and stood stock-still, her tail lifted as the stallion nosed her gently. Centaine felt her own body stiffen in anticipation – then when the stallion reared over her and buried his long pulsing black root deeply in her, Centaine gasped and pressed her own knees together sharply.

That night in her rude thatched shelter beside the steaming thermal pool, she dreamed of Michael and the old barn near North Field, and woke to a deep corroding loneliness and an undirected discontent that did not subside even when she held Shasa to her breast and felt him tugging demandingly at her.

Her dark mood persisted, and the high rocky walls of the valley closed in around her so she felt she could not breathe. However, four more days passed before she could wheedle H'ani into another expedition out into the open forests.

Centaine looked for the zebra herd again as they meandered amongst the mopani trees, but this time the forests seemed strangely deserted and what wild game they did see was mistrusting and skittish, taking instant alarm at the first distant sight of the upright human figures.

'There is something,' H'ani muttered as they rested in the noon heat, 'I do not know what it is, but the wild things sense it also. It makes me uneasy, we should return to the valley that I might talk with O'wa. He understands these things better than I do.'

'Oh H'ani, not yet,' Centaine pleaded. 'Let us stay here a little longer. I feel so free.'

'I do not like whatever is happening out here,' H'ani insisted.

'The bees – ' Centaine found inspiration ' – we cannot pass through the tunnel until nightfall,' and though H'ani grumped and frowned, she at last agreed.

'But listen to this old woman, there is something unusual, something bad – ' and she sniffed at the air and neither of them could sleep when they rested at noon.

H'ani took Shasa from her as soon as he had fed.

'He grows so,' she whispered, and there was a shadow of regret in her bright black eyes. 'I wish I could see him in his full growth, straight and tall as the mopani tree.'

'You will, old grandmother,' Centaine smiled, 'you will live to see him as a man.'

H'ani did not look up at her. 'You will go, both of you, one day soon. I sense

it, you will go back to your own people.' Her voice was hoarse with regret. 'You will go, and when you do there will be nothing left in life for this old woman.'

'No, old grandmother,' Centaine reached out and took her hand. 'Perhaps we will have to go one day. But we will come back to you. I give you my word on that.'

Gently H'ani disentangled her grip, and still without looking at Centaine, stood up. 'The heat is past.'

They worked back towards the mountain, moving widely separated through the forest, keeping each other just in sight, except when denser bush intervened. As was her habit, Centaine chatted to the sleeping infant on her hip, speaking French to train his ear to the sound of the language, and to keep her own tongue exercised.

They had almost reached the scree slope below the cliffs when Centaine saw the fresh tracks of a pair of zebra stallions imprinted deeply in the soft earth ahead of her. Under H'ani's instruction, she had developed acute powers of observation, and O'wa had taught her to read the signs of the wild with fluent ease. There was something about these tracks that puzzled her. They ran side by side, as though the animals that made them had been harnessed to each other. She hefted Shasa on to her other hip and turned aside to examine them more closely.

She stopped with a jerk that alarmed the child, and he squawked in protest. Centaine stood paralysed with shock, staring at the hoof prints, not yet able to comprehend what she was seeing. Then suddenly a rush of emotions and understanding made her reel back. She understood the agitated behaviour of the wild creatures, and H'ani's undirected premonition of evil. She began to tremble, at the same moment filled with fear and joy, with confusion and shaking excitement.

'Shasa,' she whispered, 'they are not zebra prints.' The hooves that had made these chains of tracks were shod with crescents of steel. 'Horsemen, Shasa, civilized men riding horses shod with steel!' It seemed impossible. Not here, not in this desert fastness.

Instinctively her hands flew to the opening of the canvas shawl she wore about her shoulders, and from which her breasts thrust out unashamedly. She covered them and glanced around her fearfully. With the San she had come to accept nudity as completely natural. Now she was aware that her skirts rode high on her long slim thighs, and she was ashamed.

She backed away from the prints as though from an accuser's finger.

'Man – a civilized man,' she repeated, and immediately the image of Michael formed in her mind, and her longing overcame her shame. She crept forward again and knelt beside the spoor, staring at it avidly, not able to bring herself to touch it in case it proved to be hallucination.

It was fresh, so very fresh that even as she watched the crisply outlined edge of one hoofprint, it collapsed and slid in upon itself in a trickle of loose sand.

'An hour ago, Shasa, they passed only an hour ago, not longer.'

The riders had been walking their horses, moving at less than five miles an hours.

'There is a civilized man within five miles of us at this very moment, Shasa.'

She jumped up and ran along the line, fifty paces, before she stopped again and dropped to her knees. She would not have seen it before – without O'wa's instruction she had been blind – but now she picked out the alien texture of

metal, even though it was only the size of a thumbnail and had fallen into a clump of dry grass.

She picked it out and laid it in her palm. It was a tarnished brass button, a military button with an embossed crest, and the broken thread still knotted in the tang.

She stared at it as though it were a priceless jewel. The design upon it depicted a unicorn and an antelope guarding a shield and below there was a motto in a ribbon.

'Ex Unitate Vires,' she read aloud. She had seen the same buttons on General Sean Courtney's tunic, but his were brightly polished. 'From Unity Strength.' The coat of arms of the Union of South Africa.

'A soldier, Shasa! One of General Courtney's men!'

At that moment there was a distant whistle, H'ani's summons, and Centaine sprang to her feet and hovered undecidedly. All her instinct was to race desperately after the horsemen, and to plead to be allowed to travel with them back to civilization, but then H'ani whistled again and she turned to look back.

She knew how terrified the San were of all foreigners, for the old people had told her all the stories of brutal persecution. 'H'ani must not see these tracks.'

She shaded her eyes and stared longingly in the direction in which the spoor pointed, but nothing moved amongst the mopani trees. 'She will try to stop us following them, Shasa, she and O'wa will do anything to stop us. How can we leave the old people, and yet they can't come with us, they will be in great danger – ' she was torn and undecided ' – but we can't let this chance go. It might be our only – '

H'ani whistled again, this time much closer, and Centaine saw her small figure amongst the trees coming towards her. Centaine's hand closed guiltily on the brass button and she thrust it into the bottom of her satchel.

'H'ani mustn't see the tracks,' she repeated, and glanced quickly up at the cliffs, orientating herself so that she could return and find them herself, and then she whirled and ran to meet the old woman and led her away, back towards the hidden valley.

That evening, as they performed the routine camp chores, Centaine had difficulty in disguising the nervous excitement that gripped her, and she replied distractedly to H'ani's questions. As soon as they had eaten and the short African dusk ended, she went to her shelter and settled down as though to sleep, pulling the gemsbok skin over both the infant and herself. Although she lay quietly, and regulated her breathing, she was fretting and worrying, as she tried to reach her decision.

She had no means of guessing who the horsemen were, and she was determined not to lead the San into mortal danger, yet she was equally determined to take her own chances and to follow up those tantalizing tracks for the promise they held of salvation and return to her own world – of escape from this harsh existence which would at last turn her and her infant into savages.

'We must give ourselves a start, so that we can catch up with the horsemen befor H'ani and O'wa even realize we have gone. That way they will not follow us, will not be exposed to danger. We will go as soon as the moon rises, my baby.'

She lay tense and still, feigning sleep, until the gibbous moon showed over the rim of the valley. Then she rose quietly and Shasa murmured and grunted

sleepily as she gathered up her satchel and stave and crept quietly out on to the path.

She paused at the corner of the hill and looked back. The fire had died to embers, but the moonlight played into the old people's shelter. O'wa was in the shadows, just a small dark shape, but the moonlight washed H'ani.

Her amber skin seemed to glow in the soft light, and her head, propped on her own shoulder, was turned towards Centaine. Her expression seemed forlorn and hopeless, a harbinger of the terrible sorrow and loss that Centaine knew she would suffer when she woke, and the necklace of pebbles gleamed dully on her bony old chest.

'Goodbye, old grandmother,' Centaine whispered. 'Thank you for your great humanity and kindness to us. I will always love you. Forgive us, little H'ani, but we have to go.'

Centaine had to steel herself before she could turn the rocky corner that cut her off from the camp. As she hurried up the rough pathway to the tunnel of the bees, her own tears blurred the moonlight and tasted of seawater as they ran into the corners of her mouth.

She groped her way through the utter darkness and the warm honey smell of the tunnel and out into the moonlight in the narrow valley beyond. She paused to listen for the sound of bare feet on the rocks behind her, but the only sound was the yelp of the jackal packs out on the plains below, and she started forward again.

As she reached the plain Shasa mewed and wriggled on her hip, and without stopping she adjusted his sling so that he could reach her breast. He fastened on it greedily, and she whispered to him as she hurried through the forest, 'Don't be afraid, baby, even though this is the first time we have been alone at night. The horsemen will be camped just a short way ahead. We will catch up with them before sunrise, before H'ani and O'wa are even awake. Don't look at the shadows, don't imagine things, Shasa – ' She kept talking softly, trying to shore up her own courage, for the night was full of mystery and menace, and she had never realized until that moment how she had come to rely on the two old people.

'We should have found the spoor by now, Shasa.' Centaine stopped uncertainly and peered about her. Everything looked different in the moonlight. 'We must have missed it.'

She turned back, breaking into an anxious trot. 'I'm sure it was at the head of this glade.' And then, with a rush of relief, 'There it is, the moon was against us before.' Now the hoof-prints were rimmed clearly with shadow and the steel shoes had bitten deeply into the sandy earth. How much O'wa had taught her! She saw the tracks so clearly that she could break into a trot.

The horsemen had made no effort to hide their spoor, and there was no wind to wipe it out. They had ridden the easy line, keeping out in the open, following well-beaten game paths, not pushing their mounts above an easy ambling walk, and once Centaine found where one of them had dismounted and led his horse for a short distance.

She was elated when she saw that this man wore boots. Riding-boots with medium high heels, and well-worn soles. Even in the uncertain moonlight, Centaine could tell by the length of his stride and the slight toe-out gait that he was a tall man with long narrow feet and an easy, yet confident stride. It seemed to confirm all her hopes.

'Wait for us,' she whispered. 'Please, sir, wait for Shasa and me to catch up.'

She was gaining rapidly. 'We must look for their camp fire, Shasa, they will be camped not far from – ' she broke off. 'There! What's that, Shasa? Did you see it?'

She stared into the forest.

'I'm sure I saw something.' She stared about her. 'But it's gone now.' She changed Shasa to her other hip.

'What a big lump you are becoming! But never mind, we'll be there soon.' She started forward again, and the trees thinned out and Centaine found herself at the head of another long open glade. The moonlight laid a pale metallic sheen on the short grass.

Eagerly she surveyed the open ground, focusing her attention on each dark irregularity, hoping to see hobbled horses near a smouldering fire and human shapes rolled into their blankets, but the shapes were only tree stumps or anthills, and at the far side of the glade a small herd of wildebeest grazing heads down.

'Don't worry, Shasa,' she spoke louder to cover her own intense disappointment, 'I'm sure they'll be camped in the trees.'

The wildebeest threw up their heads and erupted into a rumbling snorting stampede, streaming away into the trees, fine dust hanging behind them like mist.

'What frightened them, Shasa? The wind is with us, they could not have taken our scent.' The sound of the running herd dwindled. 'Something chased them!'

She looked around her carefully. 'I'm imagining things. I'm seeing things that aren't there. We mustn't start panicking at shadows.' Centaine started forward firmly, but within a short distance she stopped again fearfully.

'Did you hear that, Shasa? There is something following us. I heard the footfalls, but it's stopped now. It's watching us, I can feel it.'

At that moment a small cloud passed over the moon and the world turned dark.

'The moon will come out again soon.' Centaine hugged the infant so hard that Shasa gave a little bleat of protest. 'I'm sorry, baby.' She relaxed her grip and then stumbled as she started forward.

'I wish we hadn't come – no, that's not true. We had to come. We must be brave, Shasa. We can't follow the spoor without the moon.'

She sank down to rest, looking up into the sky. The moon was a pale nimbus through the thin gunmetal cloud, and then it broke out into a hole in the cloud layer and for a moment flooded the glade with soft platinum light.

'Shasa!' Centaine's voice rose into a high thin scream.

There was something out there, a huge pale shape, as big as a horse, but with a sinister, stealthy, unhorselike carriage. At her cry, it sank out of sight below the tops of the grass.

Centaine leapt to her feet and raced towards the trees, but before she reached them the moon was snuffed out again, and in the darkness Centaine fell full length. Shasa wailed fretfully against her chest.

'Please be quiet, baby.' Centaine hugged him, but the child sensed her terror and screamed. 'Don't, Shasa. You'll bring it after us.'

Centaine was trembling wildly. That big pale thing out there in the darkness was possessed of an unearthly menace, a palpable aura of evil, and she knew what it was. She had seen it before.

She pressed herself flat to the earth, trying to cover Shasa with her own body.

Then there was a sound, a hurricane of sound that filled the night, filled her head – seemed to fill her very soul. She had heard that sound before, but never so close, never so soul-shattering.

'Oh, sweet mother of God,' she whispered. It was the full-blooded roar of a lion. The most terrifying sound of the African wilds.

At that moment, the moon broke out of the cloud again, and she saw the lion clearly. It stood facing her, fifty paces away, and it was immense, with its mane fully extended, a peacock's tail of ruddy hair around the massive flat head. Its tail swung from side to side, flicking the black tuft like a metronome, and then it extended its neck and humped its shoulders, lowering and opening its jaws so that the long ivory fangs gleamed in the moonlight like daggers – and it roared again.

All the ferocity and cruelty of Africa seemed to be distilled into that dreadful blast. Though she had read the descriptions of the travellers and hunters, they could not prepare her for the actuality. The blast seemed to crush in her chest, so that her heart checked and her lungs seized. It loosened her bowels and her bladder so she had to clench fiercely to keep control of herself. In her arms Shasa screeched and wriggled, and that was enough to jar Centaine out of her paroxysm of terror.

The lion was an old red tom, an outcast from the pride. His teeth and claws were worn, his skin scarred and almost bald across the shoulders. In the succession battle with the young prime male who had driven him from the pride, he had lost one eye, a hooked claw had ripped it from the socket.

He was sick and starving, his ribs racked out under his scraggy hide, and in his hunger he had attacked a porcupine three days before. A dozen long poisonous barbed quills had driven deeply into his neck and cheeks and were already suppurating and festering. He was old and weak and uncertain, his confidence shattered, and he was wary of man and the man odour. His ancestral memories, his own long experince had warned him to stay clear of these strange frail upright creatures. His roarings were symptoms of his nervousness and uncertainty. There was a a time when, as hungry as he was now, he would have gone in swiftly and silently. Even now his jaws had the strength to crunch through a skull or thighbone and a single blow of one massive forepaw could shatter a man's spine. However, he hung back, circling the prey. Perhaps, if there had been no moon, he would have been bolder, or if he had ever eaten human flesh before, or if the agony of the buried quills had been less crippling, but now he roared indecisively. Centaine leaped to her feet. It was instinctive. She had watched the old black stable tom cat at Mort Homme with a mouse, and his reflex action to his victim's attempted flight. Somehow she knew that to run would be to bring the great cat down on her immediately.

She screamed, and holding the pointed stave high, she rushed straight at the lion. He whirled and galloped off through the grass, fifty paces, and then stopped and looked back at her, lashing his tail from side to side, and he growled with frustration.

Still facing him, clutching Shasa under one arm and the stave in the other hand, Centaine backed away. She glanced over her shoulder – the nearest mopani tree stood isolated from the rest of the forest. It was straight and sturdy with a fork high above the ground, but it seemed to be at the other end of the earth from where she stood.

'We mustn't run, Shasa,' she whispered, and her voice shook. 'Slowly.

Slowly, now.' Her sweat was running into her eyes though she shivered wildly with cold and terror.

The lion circled around towards the forest, swinging its head low, ears pricked, and she saw the gleam of his single eye like the flash of a knife-blade.

'We must get to the tree, Shasa,' and the infant whined and kicked on her hip. The lion stopped and she could hear it sniffing.

'Oh God, it's so big.' Her foot caught and she almost fell. The lion rushed forward, grunting terrible exhalations of sound, like the pistons of a locomotive, and she screamed and waved the stave.

The lion stopped, but this time stood its ground, facing her, lowering its great shaggy head threateningly and lashing the long, black-tipped tail, and when Centaine began to back away, it moved forward, slinking low to the earth.

'The tree, Shasa, we must reach the tree!'

The lion started to circle again, and Centaine glanced up at the moon. There was another dark blot of cloud trundling down from the north.

'Please don't cover the moon!' she whispered brokenly. She realized how their lives depended on that soft uncertain light, she instinctively knew how bold the great cat would become in darkness. Even now its circles were becoming narrower, it was working in, still cautious and wary, but watching her and perhaps beginning to realize how utterly helpless she truly was. The final killing charge was only seconds away.

Something hit her from behind and she shrieked and almost fell, before she realized that she had walked backwards into the base of the mopani tree. She clung to it for support, for her legs could not hold her, so intense was her relief.

Shaking so much that she almost dropped it, she unslung the leather satchel from her shoulder and tipped the ostrich-egg bottles out of it. Then she pushed Shasa feet first into the bag, so only his head protruded, and slung him over her back. Shasa was redfaced and yelling angrily.

'Be quiet, please be quiet – ' She snatched up her stave again, and stuck it into her rope belt like a sword. She jumped to catch the first branch above her head and she got a hold and scrambled with her bare feet for a grip on the rough bark. She would never have believed it possible, but in desperation she found untapped reserves and she hauled herself and her load upwards by the main strength of arms and legs, and crawled on to the branch.

Still, she was only five feet above the ground, and the lion grunted fearsomely and made a short rush forward. She teetered on the branch and reached up for another hold, and then another. The bark was rough and abrasive as crocodile skin and her fingers and shins were bleeding by the time she scrambled into the fork of the mopani thirty feet above the ground.

The lion smelled the blood from her grazed skin and it drove him frantic with hunger. He roared and prowled around the base of the mopani stopping to sniff at the ostrich eggs that Centaine had dropped, and then roaring again.

'We are safe, Shasa,' Centaine was sobbing with relief, crouched in the high fork, holding the child on her lap and peering down through the leaves and branches on to the broad muscled back of the old lion. She realized that she could see more clearly, the light of dawn was flushing the eastern sky. She could clearly make out that the great cat was a gingery reddish colour, and unlike the drawings she had seen, his mane was not black but the same ruddy colour.

'O'wa called them red devils,' she remembered, hugging Shasa and trying to still his outraged yells. 'How long until it's light?' She looked anxiously to the

east and saw the dawn coming in a splendour of molten copper and furnace reds.

'It will be day soon, Shasa,' she told him. 'Then the beast will go away – '

Below her the lion reared up on its hindlegs and stood against the trunk, looking up at her.

'One eye – he's only got one eye.' The black scarred socket somehow made the other glowing yellow eye more murderous, and Centaine shuddered wildly.

The lion ripped at the trunk of the tree with the claws of both front feet, erupting into those terrible crackling roars once more. It ripped slabs and long shreds of bark from the trunk, leaving wet wounds weeping with sap.

'Go away!' Centaine screamed at it, and the lion gathered itself on its hindquarters and launched itself upwards, hooking with all four feet.

'No! Go away!'

Michael had told her and she had read in Levaillant that lions did not climb trees, but this great red cat came swarming up the trunk and then pulled itself on the main branch ten feet above the ground and balanced there staring up at her.

'Shasa!' She realized then that the lion was going to get her, her climb had merely delayed the moment. 'We've got to save you, Shasa.'

She dragged herself upward, standing in the fork, and clutching the side branch.

'There!' Above her head there was a broken branch that stuck out like a hatpeg, and using all that remained of her strength, she lifted the rawhide bag with Shasa in it and hooked the strap over the peg.

'Goodbye, my darling,' she panted. 'Perhaps H'ani will find you.'

Shasa was struggling and kicking, the bag swung and twisted, and Centaine sank back on to the fork and drew the sharpened stave from her belt.

'Be still, baby, please be still.' She did not look up at him. She was watching the lion below her. 'If you are quiet it might not see you, it might be satisfied.'

The lion stretched up with its forelegs, balancing on the branch, and roared again. She smelt it now, the stink of its festering wounds and the dead carrion reek of its breath, and then the beast hurled itself upwards.

With its claws ripping the bark, clinging with all four paws, it came up in a series of convulsive leaps. Its head was thrown back, its single yellow eye fastened on Centaine, and with those monstrous explosions of sound bursting up out of its gaping pink jaws, it came straight at her.

Centaine screamed and drove the point of her stave down into the jaws with all her strength. She felt the sharpened end bite into the soft pink mucus membrane in the back of its throat, saw the spurt of scarlet blood, and then the lion locked its jaws on the stave and with a toss of its flying mane ripped it out of her hands and sent it windmilling out and down to hit the earth below.

Then with bright blood streaming from its jaws, blowing a pink cloud every time it roared, the lion reached up with one huge paw.

Centaine jack-knifed her legs upwards, trying to avoid it, but she was not quick enough; one of the curved yellow claws, as long and thick as a man's forefinger, sank into her flesh above her bare ankle, and she was jerked savagely downwards.

As she was pulled out of the fork, she flung both her arms around the side of the branch and with all her remaining strength she held on. She felt her whole body racked, drawn out, the unbearable weight of the lion stretching her leg

until she felt her knee and hip joint crack, and pain shot up her spine and filled her skull like a bursting sky rocket.

She felt the lion's claws curling in her flash, and her arms started to give way. Inch by inch she was drawn out of the tree.

'Look after my baby,' she screamed. 'Please God, protect my baby.'

* * *

It was another wild-goose chase, Garry was absolutely convinced of it, though of course he would never be foolhardy enough to say so. Even the thought made him feel guilty, and he glanced sideways at the woman he loved.

Anna had learned English and lost a little weight in the eighteen short sweet months since he had met her, and the latter was the only circumstance in his life he would have altered if it had been in his power, indeed he was always urging food upon her. There was a German pâtisserie and confectioner's opposite the Kaiserhof Hotel in Windhoek where Garry had taken a permanent suite. He never passed the shop without going in to buy a box of the marvellous black chocolates or a creamy cake – Black Forest Cherry Cake was a favourite – which he took back to Anna. When he carved, he always reserved the fattest, juiciest cuts for her, and replenished the plate without allowing her time to protest. However, she had still lost weight.

They didn't spend enough time in the hotel suite, he brooded. They spent too much of their time chasing about the bush, as they were doing now. No sooner had he put a few pounds on her than they were off again, banging and jolting over remote tracks in the open Fiat tourer that had replaced the 'T' model Ford, or when the tracks faded, resorting to horses and mules to carry them over rugged ranges of mountains or through the yawning canyons and rock deserts of the interior, chasing the will-o-the-wisp of rumour and chance and often of deliberately misleading information.

'The crazy old people', *'Die twee ou onbeskofters'* – that was the title which they had gained themselves from one end of the territory to the other, and Garry took a perverse and defiant pleasure in the fact that he had earned it the hard way. When he had totted up the actual cost in hard cash of the continuing search, he had been utterly appalled, until suddenly he had thought, 'What else have I got to spend it on anyway, except Anna?' And then, after a little further reflection, 'What else is there except Anna?' And with that discovery he had thrown himself headlong into the madness.

Of course, sometimes when he woke in the night and thought about it clearly and sensibly, he knew that his grandson did not exist, he knew that the daughter-in-law that he had never seen had drowned eighteen months ago, out there in the cold green waters of the Atlantic, taking with her the last contact he could ever have with Michael. Then that terrible sorrow came upon him once again, threatening to crush him, until he groped for Anna in the bed beside him and crept to her, and even in her sleep she seemed to sense his need and she would roll towards him and take him to her.

Then in the morning he awoke refreshed and revitalized, logic banished and blind faith restored, ready to set out on the next fantastic adventure that awaited them.

Garry had arranged for five thousand posters to be printed in Cape Town,

and distributed to every police station, magistrate's court, post office and railway station in South West Africa. Wherever he and Anna travelled, there was always a bundle of posters on the back seat of the Fiat or in one of the saddle-bags, and they stuck them on every blank wall of every general dealer's or bar-room they passed, they nailed them to tree trunks at desolate crossroads in the deep bush, and with a bribe of a handful of sweets dished them out to black and white and brown urchins they met on the roadside, with instructions to take them to their homestead or kraal or camp and hand them to their elders.

£5000 REWARD £5000
For information leading to the rescue of CENTAINE DE THIRY COURTNEY a survivor of the HOSPITAL SHIP PROTEA CASTLE most barbarously torpedoed by a GERMAN SUBMARINE on the 28th Aug. 1917 off the coast north of SWAKOPMUND.
MRS COURTNEY would have been cast ashore and may be in the care of wild TRIBESMEN or alone in the WILDERNESS.
Any information concerning her whereabouts should be conveyed to the undersigned at the KAISERHOF HOTEL WINDHOEK.
LT. COL. G. C. COURTNEY

Five thousand pounds was a fortune, twenty years' salary for the average working man, enough to buy a ranch and stock it with cattle and sheep, enough to provide a man with a secure living for his entire life, and there were dozens eager to try for the reward, or for any lesser amount that they could wheedle out of Garry by vague promises and fanciful stories and outright lies.

In the Kaiserhof suite he and Anna interviewed hopefuls who had never ventured beyond the line of rail but were willing to lead expeditions into the desert, others who knew exactly where the lost girl could be found, still others who had actually seen Centaine and only needed a grubstake of £1,000 to go and fetch her in. There were spiritualists and clairvoyants who were in constant contact with her, on a higher plane, and even one gentleman who offered to sell his own daughter, at a bargain rate, to replace the missing girl.

Garry met them all cheerfully. He listened to their stories and chased their theories and instructions, or sat around an ouija board with the spiritualists, even followed one of them who was using one of Centaine's rings suspended on a piece of string as a lodestone, on a five-hundred-mile pilgrimage through the desert. He was presented with a number of young ladies, varying in texture and colour from blond to *café au lait*, all claiming to be Centaine de Thiry Courtney, or willing to do for him anything that she could do. Some of them became loudly abusive when they were refused and had to be evicted from the suite by Anna in person.

'No wonder she is losing weight,' Garry told himself, and leaned over to pat Anna's thigh as she sat beside him in the open Fiat tourer. The words of the blasphemous old grace came into his mind:

'We thank the Lord for what we have,
But for a little more we would be glad.'

He grinned at her fondly, and aloud he told her, 'We should be there soon.' She nodded and replied, 'This time I know we will find her. I have a sure feeling!'

'Yes,' Garry agreed dutifully. 'This time will be different.'

He was quite safe in that assertion. No other of their many expeditions had begun in such a mysterious manner.

One of their own reward posters had arrived folded upon itself and sealed

with wax, bearing a postmark dated four days previously at Usakos, a way station on the narrow-gauge railway line halfway between Windhoek and the coast. The package was unstamped – Garry had been obliged to pay the postage – and it was addressed in a bold but educated hand, the script unmistakably German. When Garry split the wax seal and unfolded it he found a laconic invitation to a rendezvous written on the foot of the sheet, and hand-drawn map to guide him. The sheet was unsigned.

Garry immediately telegraphed the postmaster Usakos, confident that the volume of business at such a remote station would be so low that the postmaster would remember every package handed in for postage. The postmaster did indeed recall the package and the circumstances of its delivery. It had been left on the threshold of the post office during the night and nobody had even glimpsed the correspondent.

As the writer probably intended, all this intrigued both Garry and Anna, and they were eager to keep the rendezvous. It was set for a site in the barren Kamas Hochtland a hundred and fifty miles from Windhoek.

It had taken them all of three days to negotiate the atrocious roads, but after losing themselves at least a dozen times, changing approximately the same number of punctured tyres, and sleeping rough on the hard ground beside the Fiat, they had now almost reached the appointed meeting place.

The sun blazed down from a cloudless sky and the breeze from behind blew eddies of red dust over them as they rattled and rumbled over the stony ruts. Anna seemed impervious to all the heat and dust and hardship of the desert and Garry, gazing at her in unstinted admiration, almost missed the next tight bend in the track. His offwheels skidded over the verge, and the Fiat teetered and rocked over the yawning void that opened abruptly before them. He hauled the steering over, and as they bumped back into the wheel ruts he pulled on the handbrake.

They were on the rim of a deep canyon that cut the plateau like an axe stroke. The track descended into the depths in a series of hairpin twists like the contortions of a maimed serpent, and hundreds of feet below them the river was a narrow ribbon that threw dazzling reflections of the noon sun up the orange-coloured cliffs.

'This is the place,' Garry told her, 'and I don't like it. Down there we will be at the mercy of any bandit or murderer.'

'Mijnheer, we are already late for the meeting – '

'I don't know if we'll ever get out of there again, and God knows, nobody is likely to find us here. Probably just our bare bones.'

'Come, Mijnheer, we can talk later.'

Garry drew a deep breath. Sometimes there were distinct drawbacks to being paired with a strong-willed woman. He let off the handbrake and the Fiat rolled over the rim of the canyon, and once they were committed, there was no turning back.

It was a nightmare descent, the gradient so steep that the brake shoes smoked, and the hairpin bends so tight that he had to back and fill to coax the Fiat through them.

'Now I know why our friend chose this place. He has us at his mercy down here.'

Forty minutes later they came out in the gut of the canyon. The walls above them were so sheer that they blotted out the sun. They were in shadow, but it

was stiflingly hot. No breeze reached down here, and the air had a flinty bite on the back of the throat.

There was a narrow strip of level land on each bank of the river, covered with coarse thorn growth, and Garry backed the Fiat off the track and they climbed down stiffly and beat the red dust from their clothing. The stream bubbled sullenly over a low causeway of rock, and the water was opaque and a poisonous yellow colour like the effluent from a chemical factory.

'Well,' Garry surveyed both banks and the cliffs above them, 'we seem to have the place to ourselves. Our friend is nowhere to be seen.'

'We will wait.' Anna forestalled the suggestion she knew was coming.

'Of course, Mevrou.' Garry lifted his hat and mopped his face with the cotton bandanna from around his neck. 'May I suggest a cup of tea?'

Anna took the kettle and went down the bank. She tasted the river water suspiciously, and then filled it. When she climbed back, Garry had a fire of thornwood crackling between two hearthstones. While the kettle boiled, Garry fetched a blanket from the back of the Fiat, and the bottle of schnapps from the cubbyhole. He poured a liberal dram into each of the mugs, added a heaped spoon of sugar, then topped them up with strong tea. He had found that schnapps, like chocolate, had a most tempering effect on Anna, and he was never without a bottle. Perhaps the journey would not be entirely wasted, he thought, as he added another judicious splash of spirits to Anna's mug and carried it to where she sat in the middle of the rug.

Before he reached her, Garry let out a startled cry and dropped the mug, splashing his boots with hot tea. He stood staring into the bush behind her, and raised both hands high above his head. Anna glanced round and then bounded to her feet and seized a brand of firewood which she brandished before her. Garry edged swiftly to her side and stood close to her protective bulk.

'Keep away!' Anna bellowed. 'I warn you, I'll break the first skull – '

They were surrounded. The gang had crept up on them through the dense scrub.

'Oh Lord, I knew it was a trap!' Garry muttered. They were almost certainly the most dangerous-looking band of cut-throats he had ever seen.

'We have no money, nothing worth stealing – ' How many of them? he wondered desperately. Three – no, there was another behind that tree – four murderous ruffians. The obvious leader was a purple-black giant with bandoliers of ammunition criss-crossing his chest, and a Mauser rifle in the crook of his arm. A ruff of thick woolly beard framed his broad African features like the mane of a man-eating lion.

The others were all armed, a mixed band of Khoisan Hottentots and Ovambo tribesmen, wearing odd items of military uniform and civilian clothing, all of it heavily worn and faded, patched and tattered, some of them barefooted and others with scuffed boots, shapeless and battered from hard marches. Only their weapons were well cared for, glistening with oil and borne lovingly, almost the way a father might carry his firstborn son.

Garry thought fleetingly of the service revolver he kept holstered under the dashboard of the Fiat, and then swiftly abandoned such a reckless notion.

'Don't harm us,' he pleaded, crowding up behind Anna, and then with a feeling of utter disbelief, Garry found himself abandoned as Anna launched her attack.

Swinging the burning log like a Viking's axe, she charged straight at the huge black leader.

'Back, you swine!' she roared in Flemish. 'Get out of here, you bitch-born son of Hades!'

Taken by surprise, the gang scattered in pandemonium, trying to duck the smoking log as it hissed about their heads.

'How dare you, you stinking bastard spawn of diseased whores – '

Still shaking with shock, Garry stared after her, torn between terror and admiration for this new revelation of his lover's accomplishments. He had heard some great cursers in his life – there had been the legendary sergeant-major whom he had known during the Zulu rebellion; men travelled miles to listen to him addressing a parade ground. The man was a Sunday School preacher in comparison. Garry could have charged admission fees to Anna's performance. Her eloquence was matched only by her dexterity with the log.

She caught one of the Hottentots a crashing blow between the shoulders and he was hurled into a thorn bush, his jacket smoking with live coals, shrieking like a wounded warthog. Two others, reluctant to face Anna's wrath, leaped over the river bank and disappeared with high splashes beneath the yellow waters. That left only the big black Ovambo to bear the full brunt of Anna's onslaught. He was quick and agile for such a big man, and he avoided the wild swings of the log and danced behind the nearest camel-thorn tree. With nimble footwork he kept the trunk between Anna and himself, until at last she stopped, gasping and redfaced, and panted at him, 'Come out, you yellow-bellied black-faced apology for a blue-testicled baboon!' Garry noticed with awe how she managed to cram the metaphor with colour. 'Come out where I can kill you!'

Warily the Ovambo declined, backing off out of reach. 'No! No! We did not come to fight you, we came to fetch you – ' he answered in Afrikaans. She lowered the log slowly.

'Did you write the letter?' and the Ovambo shook his head. 'I have come to take you to the man who did.'

The Ovambo ordered two of his men to remain and guard the Fiat. Then he led them away along the floor of the canyon. Although there were stretches of open easy-going on the river bank, there were also narrow gorges through which the river roared and swirled, and the path was steep and so narrow that only one man could pass at a time.

These gaps were guarded by other guerrillas. Garry saw only the tops of their heads and the glint of their rifle barrels amongst the rocks, and he noticed how cunningly the site or the rendezvous had been chosen. Nobody could follow them undetected. An army would not be able to rescue them. They were totally vulnerable, completely at the mercy of these rough hard men. Garry shivered in the sweltering gut of the canyon.

'We'll be damned lucky to get out of this,' he muttered to himself, and then aloud, 'My leg is hurting. Can't we rest?' But no one even looked back at him, and he stumbled forward to keep as close to Anna as he was able.

Quite unexpectedly, long after Garry had relapsed into resigned misery, the Ovambo guide stepped around the corner of a yellow sandstone monolith and into a temporary camp site under an overhanging cliff on the river bank. Even in his exhaustion and unhappiness, Garry saw that there was a steep pathway up the canyon wall behind the camp, an escape route against surprise attack.

'They have thought of everything.' He touched Anna'a arm and pointed out the path, but all her attention was on the man who sauntered out from the deep shadow of the cavern.

He was a young man, half Garry's age, but in the first seconds of their

meeting he made Garry feel inadequate and foolish. He didn't have to say a word. He merely stood in the sunlight and stared at Garry with a catlike stillness about his tall elegant frame, and Garry was reminded of all the things he was not.

His hair was golden, hanging to his bare shoulders, streaked white by the sun, yet as lustrous as raw silk, offering a startling contrast to his deeply tanned features. These might once have been as beautiful as those of a comely girl, but all softness had been burned by the flames of life's furnace, and like forged iron, the marks of the anvil had been left upon them.

He was tall but not gawky or round-shouldered, and he was lean, with hard, flat muscle. He wore only riding-breeches and boots, and the hair on his chest sparkled like fine copper wire. Around his neck on a gold chain he had hung a small gold locket, something that no English gentleman would ever do. Garry tried to feel superior, but under that flat level gaze it was difficult.

'Colonel Courtney,' he said, and again Garry was taken off balance. Though accented, it was the voice of an educated and cultivated man, and his mouth altered shape, losing its hard stern line as he smiled.

'Please do not be alarmed. You *are* Colonel Courtney, are you not?'

'Yes.' It took an effort to Garry to speak. 'I am Colonel Courtney – did you write this letter?'

He took the poster from his breast pocket, and tried to unfold it, but his hands were shaking so that it fluttered and tore in his fingers. The man's smile gently mocked him as he nodded, 'Yes, I sent for you.'

'You know where the lost girl can be found?' Anna demanded, stepping closer to him in her eagerness.

'Perhaps,' he shrugged.

'You have seen her?' Anna insisted.

'First things come first.'

'You want money – ' Garry's voice was unnecessarily loud. 'Well, I have not brought a single sovereign with me. You can be sure of that. If your intention is to rob us, I have nothing of value on me.'

'Ah, Colonel,' the golden man smiled at him, and it was so charming, so unexpectedly exuberant and boyish that he could feel Anna's stiff and antagonistic stance melt beneath that smile, 'my nose tells me that is not true.' He sniffed theatrically. 'You have something of immense value – Havana!' he said and sniffed again. 'No doubt about it, Havana! Colonel, I must warn you that I would kill for a Havana cigar.'

Garry took a hurried step backwards involuntarily before he realized it was a jest. Then he grinned weakly and reached for the cigar case in his hip pocket.

The golden man inspected the long black cigar. 'Romeo y Julieta!' he murmured reverently and then sniffed it lovingly. 'A whiff of Paradise.' He bit off the tip and struck a match off the sole of his boot. He sucked the flame into the cigar and closed his eyes with ecstasy. When he opened them again, he bowed slightly to Anna.

'I beg your pardon, madam, but it has been a long time, over two years, since I tasted a good cigar.'

'All right,' Garry was bolder now. 'You know my name and you are smoking my cigar – the least you can do is introduce yourself.'

'Forgive me.' He drew himself up and snapped his heels together in the teutonic manner. 'I am Lothar De La Rey, at your service.'

'Oh my God,' all Garry's new-found courage deserted him. 'I know all about

you. There is a price on your head – they'll hang you when they catch you. You are a wanted criminal and a notorious outlaw, sir.'

'My dear Colonel, I prefer to think of myself as a soldier and patriot.'

'Soldiers do not go on fighting and destroying property after a formal surrender. Colonel Franke capitulated nealy four years ago – '

'I did not recognize Colonel Franke's right to surrender,' Lothar interjected contemptuously. 'I was a soldier of the Kaiser and Imperial Germany.'

'Even Germany surrendered three months ago.'

'Yes,' Lothar agreed. 'And I have not perpetrated an act of war since then.'

'But you are still in the field,' Garry pointed out indignantly. 'You are still under arms, and – '

'I have not gone in to give myself up yet for the very good reason that you have so succinctly stated: if I do, your people will hang me.'

As if under Garry's scrutiny he had suddenly become aware that he was bare to the waist, Lothar reached for his tunic. Freshly laundered, it hung from a thorn bush beside the entrance to the cave. As he shrugged into it, the brass buttons sparkled and Garry's eyes narrowed.

'Damn you, sir, your insolence is insupportable. That's a British military tunic – you are wearing one of our uniforms. That in itself is cause enough to shoot you out of hand!'

'Would you prefer I went naked, Colonel? It must be obvious even to you that we are in reduced circumstances. It gives me no pleasure to wear a British jacket. Unfortunately there is no choice.'

'You insult the uniform in which my son died.'

'I take no pleasure in your son's death, just as I take no pleasure in these rags.'

'By God, man, you have the effrontery – ' Garry puffed himself up to deliver a devastating broadside, but Anna cut across him impatiently.

'Mijnheer De La Rey, have you seen my little girl?' And Garry subsided as Lothar turned back to her, his features taking on a strangely compassionate cast.

'I saw a girl – yes, I saw a young girl in the wilderness, but I do not know if she was the one you seek.'

'Could you lead us to her?' Garry demanded, and Lothar glanced at him, his expression hardening again.

'I would try to find her again on certain conditions.'

'Money,' said Garry flatly.

'Why are rich men always obsessed with their money?' Lothar drew on the cigar, and let the fragrant smoke trickle over his tongue. 'Yes, Colonel, I would need some money,' he nodded. 'But not £5,000. I would need £1,000 to equip an expedition to go into the desert fastness where I first saw her. We would need good horses – ours are almost worn out – and wagons to carry water, and I would need to pay my men. £1,000 would cover those expenses.'

'What else?' Garry demanded. 'There must be some other price.'

'Yes' Lothar nodded. 'There is. I am tired of living in the shadow of the gallows.'

'You want a pardon for your crimes!' Garry stared incredulously. 'What makes you think that is in my power!'

'You are a powerful man, Colonel. A personal friend of both Smuts and Botha, your brother is a general, a cabinet minster in the Botha Government – '

'I would not thwart the course of justice.'

'I fought an honourable war, Colonel. I fought it to the bitter end, like your friends Smuts and Botha once fought their war. I am no criminal, I am no murderer. I lost a father, a mother, a wife and and son – I paid the price of defeat in a heavy coin. Now, I want the right to live the life of an ordinary man – and you want this girl.'

'I couldn't agree to that. You are an enemy,' Garry blustered.

'You find the girl,' said Anna softly, 'and you will be a free man. Colonel Courtney will arrange it. I give you my word on it.'

Lothar glanced at her and then back at Garry, and he smiled again as he divined the true chain of authority here.

'Well, Colonel, do we have an agreement?'

'How do I know who this girl is? How do I know she is my daughter-in-law?' Garry hedged uncomfortably. 'Will you agree to a test?'

Lothar shrugged. 'As you wish.' And Garry turned to Anna.

'Show him,' he said. 'Let him choose.'

Between them, Garry and Anna had designed this test to thwart the rogues and chancers that the reward posters had attracted. Anna snapped open the clasp of the voluminous carpet bag she carried on a strap over one shoulder and took out a thick buff envelope. It contained a pack of postcard-sized photographs, and she handed these to Lothar.

He studied the top photograph. It was a studio portrait of a young girl, a pretty girl in a velvet dress and feathered hat; dark ringlets hung to her shoulders. Lothar shook his head and placed the photograph at the bottom of the pack. Swiftly he flicked through the rest of them, all of young women, and then haded them back to Anna.

'No,' he said. 'I'm sorry to have brought you so far for nothing. The girl I saw is not amongst those,' he looked over his shoulder at the big Ovambo. 'Very well, Hendrick, take them back to the drift.'

'Wait, Mijnheer.' Anna dropped the pile of photographs into the bag and took out another smaller stack. 'There are more.'

'You are careful,' Lothar smiled in acknowledgement.

'We have had many try to cheat us – £5,000 is a great deal of money,' Garry told him, but Lothar did not even look up from the photographs.

He turned over two of the paste boards, then stopped at the third.

'That's her.'

Centaine de Thiry, in her white confirmation dress, smiled self-consciously up at him.

'She is older now, and her hair – ' Lothar made a gesture describing a thick wild bush. 'But those eyes. Yes, that's her.'

Neither Garry nor Anna could speak. For a year and a half they had worked for this moment, and now that it had come they could not truly believe it.

'I have to sit down!' Anna said faintly, and Garry helped her to the log beside the entrance to the cave. While he tended her, Lothar pulled the gold locket from his shirt front, and snapped open the lid. He took out a lock of dark hair and offered it to Anna. She accepted it from him almost fearfully, and then with a fiercely protective gesture she pressed the lock to her lips. She closed her eyes, but from the corners of her clenched lids two fat oily tears squeezed out and began to trickle slowly down her red cheeks.

'It's just a hank of hair. It could be anyone's hair. How do you know?' Garry asked uncomfortably.

'Oh, you silly man,' Anna whispered hoarsely. 'On a thousand nights I brushed her hair. Do you think I would not know it again – anywhere?'

* * *

'How long will you need?' Garry asked again, and Lothar frowned with irritation.

'In the name of all that's merciful, how many times must I tell you I don't know?'

The three of them were seated around the fire at the entrance to the overhanging cave. They had been talking for hours, already the stars showed along the narrow strip of sky that the canyon walls framed.

'I have explained where I saw the girl, and the circumstances. Didn't you understand, must I go over it all again?'

Anna lifted a hand to placate him. 'We are very anxious. We ask stupid questions. Forgive us.'

'Very well.' Lothar relit the butt of the cigar with a burning twig from the fire. 'The girl was the captive of wild San. They are cunning and cruel as animals. They knew I was following them and they threw me off the spoor with ease. They could do it again, if I ever find their spoor. The area I will have to search is enormous, almost the size of Belgium. It's over a year since I last saw the girl, she could be dead of disease or wild animals or those murderous little yellow apes.'

'Do not even say it, Mijnheer,' Anna pleaded, and Lothar threw up both hands.

'I do not know,' he said. 'Months, a year? How can I tell how long I will need?'

'We should come with you,' Garry muttered. 'We should be allowed to take part in the search, at least be told in what area of the territory you first saw her.'

'Colonel, you did not trust me. Very good. Now I don't trust you. As soon as the girl is in your hands, my usefulness to you is at an end.' Lothar took the cigar butt from his mouth and inspected it ruefully. There was not another puff left in it; sadly he dropped it into the fire.

'No, Colonel, when I find the girl we will make a formal exchange – amnesty for me, and your daughter for you.'

'We accept, Mijnheer.' Anna touched Garry's elbow. 'We will deliver the sum of £1,000 to you as soon as possible. When you have Centaine safely with you, you will send us the name of her white stallion. Only she can tell you that, so that way we will know you are not cheating us. We will have your pardon signed and ready.'

Lothar held out his hand across the fire.

'Colonel, is it agreed?'

Garry hesitated a moment, but Anna prodded him so heavily in the ribs that he grunted and reached to take the proffered hand.

'It's agreed.'

'One last favour, Mijnheer De La Rey. I will prepare a package for Centaine. She will need good clothes, women's things. I will deliver it to you with the money. Will you give it to her when you find her?' Anna asked.

'If I find her,' Lothar nodded.

'When you find her,' Anna told him firmly.

* * *

It took almost five weeks for Lothar to make his preparations and then trek back to that remote water-hole below the Cunene river where he had cut the spoor of his quarry.

There was still water in the pan – it was amazing how long those shallow unshaded basins retained water even in the sweltering desert conditions, and Lothar wondered, as he had before, if there wasn't some subterranean seepage from the rivers in the north that found its way into them. In any event, the fact that there was still surface water boded well for their chances of being able to penetrate deeper eastwards, the direction which the long-dead spoor had taken.

While his men were refilling the water barrels from the water-hole, Lothar strolled around the periphery of the circular pan and there, incredibly, was the girl's footprint still preserved in the clay, just as he had last seen it.

He knelt beside it, and with his finger traced out the shape of the small, graceful foot. The cast was baked by the sun as hard as a brick. Though all around it the mud had been trampled by buffalo and rhinoceros and elephant, this single print remained.

'It's an omen,' he told himself, and then chuckled cynically. 'I've never believed in omens – why should I begin now?' Yet his mood was buoyant and optimistic when he assembled his men around the camp fire that evening.

Apart from the camp servants and the wagoners, he had four mounted riflemen to help him conduct the actual search. All four of them had been with him since the days of the rebellion. They had fought and bled together, shared a looted bottle of Cape smoke, or a woollen blanket on a frosty desert night, or the last shreds of tobacco in the pouch, and he loved them a little, though he trusted them not at all.

There was 'Swart Hendrick' or 'Black Henry', the tall, purplish-black Ovambo and 'Klein Boy' or 'Little Boy', his bastard son by a Herero woman. There was 'Vark Jan' or 'Pig John', the wrinkled yellow Khoisan. Mixed blood of Nama and Bergdama and even of the true San ran in his veins, for his grandmother had been a Bushman slave, captured as a child on one of the great commando raids of the last century that the Boers had ridden against the San people. Lastly there was 'Vuil Lippe', the Bondleswart Hottentot with lips like fresh-cut liver and a vocabulary that gave him his name 'Dirty Lips'.

'My hunting pack,' Lothar smiled, half-affectionately and half in revulsion as he looked them over. Truly the term 'outlaw' had meaning when applied to them, they were beyond the rules of tribe or tradition. He studied their faces in the firelight. 'Like half-tamed wolves, they would turn and savage me at the first sign of weakness,' he thought.

'All right, you sons of the great hyena, listen to me. We are looking for San, the little yellow killers.' Their eyes sparkled. 'We are looking for the white girl they had as their captive, and there are a hundred gold sovereigns for the man who cuts her spoor. This is how we will conduct the hunt – ' Lothar smoothed the sand between his feet and then traced out the plan for them with a twig.

'The wagons will follow the line of the water-holes, here and here, and we will fan out, like this and like this. Between us we can sweep fifty miles of country.'

So they rode into the east, as he had planned it, and within the first ten days they cut the spoor of a small party of wild San. Lothar called in his outriders and they followed up the trail of tiny childlike footprints.

They moved with extreme caution, carefully spying out the terrain ahead through Lothar's telescope, and skirting each stand where an ambush could be laid. The idea of a poisoned bone arrowhead burying itself in his flesh made Lothar shudder every time he let himself think about it. Bullets and bayonets were the tools of his trade, but the filthy poisons that these little pygmies brewed unmanned him, and he hated them more each hot tortuous nerve-wracking mile that they followed the spoor.

Reading the sign, Lothar learned that there were eight San in the party they were following: two adult males and two women, probably their wives. There were also four small children, two still at the breast and two just old enough to walk on their own.

'The children will slow them down,' Vark Jan gloated, 'they will not be able to stand the pace.'

'I want one of them alive,' Lothar warned them. 'I want to know about the girl.'

Vark Jan's slave grandmother had taught him enough of the San language to interrogate a captive and he grinned. 'Catch one of them and I will make him talk, be sure of that.'

The San were hunting and foraging and Lothar's band gained on them rapidly. They were only an hour behind when the San, with their animal perceptions, sensed their presence.

Lothar found the spot where they had become aware, the spot where the trail seemed to vanish.

'They are anti-tracking,' he growled. 'Get down and search,' he ordered.

'They are carrying the children,' Vark Jan squatted to examine the earth, 'the babies are too young to cover their own spoor. The women are carrying them, but they will tire quickly under the load.'

Though the trail seemed to end and the ground beyond seemed unmarked even to Lothar's experienced eye, yet even the San had left sign that Vark Jan and Swart Hendrick could follow. The pace was slower, for they had to dismount to be closer to the earth, but still they followed, and within four hours Swart Hendrick nodded and grinned.

'The women are tiring quickly. They are leaving better sign and moving slower. We are gaining on them now.'

Far ahead the San women, toiling under the weight of the children, looked back and wailed softly. The following horses showed across the plain, magnified by the mirage until they loomed like monsters, but even the sight of their pursuers could not drive the women on at a better speed.

'So I must play the plover,' said the oldest of the San hunters. He was referring to the way the plover feigns injury to lead a predator away from its nest. 'If I can make them follow me, I may be able to burn up their horses with thirst,' he told his clan. 'Then when you reach the next water-hole and after you have drunk and filled the water-eggs – ' He proffered a sealed buckhorn container to his wife and he did not have to say the fateful words. Poisoning a water-hole was such a desperate deed that none of them wanted to talk of it. 'If

you can kill the horses, you will be safe,' the hunter told them. 'I will try to give you time to do it.'

The old San hunter went quickly to each of the children and touched their eyelids and lips in blessing and farewell, and they stared at him solemnly. When he went to his woman who had borne him two sons, she gave a short keening wail. He admonished her with a glance which told her clearly, 'Show no fear in front of the little ones.'

Then as he shed his clothing and his leather satchel, the old San whispered to the younger man, his companion in a thousand hunts, 'Be a father to my sons.' He handed his satchel to him, and stepped back. 'Now, go!'

While he watched his clan trot away, the old man restrung his little bow and then carefully unwound the strips of leather that protected the heads of his arrows. His family disappeared across the plain, and he turned his back upon them and went to meet his pursuers.

Lothar was fretting at the pace. Though he knew that the quarry was only an hour ahead, they had lost the spoor again and were held up while his flanks cast forward to pick it up. They were in open country, a flat plain that stretched away to an indeterminate meeting with the sky. The plain was dotted with dark clumps of low scrub, and the mirage made them dance and squirm in the field of the telescope. It would be impossible to pick out a human figure amongst them at more than a mile distance.

The horses were almost knocked up, they had to have water soon. Within the next hour he would have to call off the pursuit and turn back to the water wagon. He lifted the telescope again, but a wild shout made him start and glance around. Swart Hendrick was pointing out to the left. The man on the extreme left flank, 'Vuil Lippe', the Bondelswart, was trying to control his mount. It was rearing and walking on its hindlegs, dragging him with it in a sheet of flying dust.

Lothar had heard that a horse would react to the hot scent of a wild Bushman as though to that of a lion, but he had doubted it. Vuil Lippe was helpless, both hands on the reins, his rifle in the boot on the saddle, and as Lothar watched he was dragged over one of the salt bushes and sprawled in the dirt.

Then quite miraculously another human shape seemed to appear out of the very earth. The tiny naked pixie-like shape stood up only twenty paces beyond the dragging rider. Unlikely as it seemed, he must have been completely concealed behind a clump of scrub that should not have hidden a hare.

As Lothar watched with helpless horror, the little mannikin drew his bow and let fly. Lothar saw the flight of the arrow, like a dust mote in the sunlight, and then the naked Bushman whirled and trotted directly away from the line of horsemen.

Lothar's men were all shouting and struggling to remount, but terror seemed to have infected the horses, and they pranced and circled. Lothar was the first up. He did not touch the stirrups, but with his hand on his horse's withers, sprang into the saddle, turned its head and galloped down the line.

Already the running Bushman was disappearing amongst the low mirage-shrouded scrub, in a swinging trot that carried him away at an incredible rate. The man he had fired at had let his horse run free and had pulled himself to his feet. He stood with his legs braced apart, swaying slightly from side to side.

'Are you all right?' Lothar shouted as he rode up, and then he saw the arrow.

It dangled down Vuil Lippe's chest, but the arrow-head was buried in his

cheek, and he stared up at Lothar with a bewildered expression. Lothar jumped down and caught him by the shoulders.

'I'm a dead man,' Lippe said softly, his hands hanging by his sides, and Lothar seized the dangling arrow and tried to pull it free. The flesh of Lippe's cheek was drawn out in a peak and he screamed and staggered. Gritting his teeth, Lothar heaved again, but this time the frail reed shaft snapped, leaving the bone arrowhead embedded in the man's flesh, and he began to struggle.

Lothar seized a handful of his greasy black hair and twisted his head over to examine the wound. 'Keep still, damn you.' A short length of bone protruded from the wound. It was caked with a black rubbery coating.

'Euphorbia latex.' Lothar had examined San weapons before, his father had once possessed an important collection of tribal artefacts. Now Lothar recognized the poison, the distilled latex from the roots of one of the rare desert euphorbia plants. Even as he studied it, he could see the poison spreading beneath the skin, discolouring it a deep lavender-purple, blooming like crystals of permanganate of potash dropped into water, following the course of the shallow blood vessels as it was absorbed.

'How long?' Lippe's tortured eyes held Lothar's, beseeching comfort.

The latex looked freshly distilled, none of its virulence dissipated, but Vuil Lippe was big and strong and healthy, his body would fight the toxin. It would take time, a few dreadful hours that would seem like eternity.

'Can't you cut it out?' Lippe pleaded.

'It's gone deep, you'd bleed to death.'

'Burn it out!'

'The pain would kill you.'

Lothar helped him down into a sitting position, just as Hendrick rode up with the bunch.

'Two men stay to look after him,' Lothar ordered. 'Hendrick, you and I will go after the little yellow swine.'

They pushed the tired horses, and within twenty minutes they saw the Bushman ahead of them. He seemed to dissolve and dance in the heat mirage, and Lothar felt a dark rage seize him, the kind of hatred a man can only feel towards something he fears in the deep places of his soul.

'Go right!' Lothar waved Hendrick over. 'Head him off if he turns.' And they spurred forward, riding down swiftly on the fleeing figure.

'I'll give you a death to wipe out the other,' Lothar promised grimly, as he loosened his blanket roll from the pommel in front of him.

The sheepskin that he used as a mattress would shield him from the frail bone-tipped arrows. He wrapped it around his torso, and tucked the end over his mouth and nose. He pulled his wide-brimmed hat low, leaving only a slit for his eyes.

The running Bushman was two hundred yards ahead. He was naked, except for the bow in one hand and the halo of tiny arrows in the leather thong around his head. His body shone with a coating of sweat, and it was the colour of bright amber, almost translucent in the sunlight. He ran lightly as a gazelle, his small neat feet seemed to skim the earth.

There was the crack of a Mauser and a bullet kicked a fountain of pale dust just beyond the running Bushman like the spout of a sperm whale, and the Bushman jerked and then, unbelievably, increased the speed of his flight, drawing away from the two galloping horsemen. Lothar glanced across at

Hendrick; he was riding with a loose rein, using both hands to reload the Mauser.

'Don't shoot!' Lothar yelled angrily. 'I want him alive!' and Hendrick lowered the Mauser.

For another mile the Bushman kept up that last wild spring, then gradually he faltered. Once again they began to overhaul him.

Lothar saw his legs begin to wobble under him, his feet flopping from the ankles with exhaustion, but Lothar's mount was almost blown. It was lathering heavily, and froth splattered his boots as he drove it forward.

Fifty yards ahead the exhausted Bushman spun round to face him, standing at bay, his chest pumping like a bellows, and sweat dripping from his small spade-shaped beard. His eyes were wild and fierce and defiant as he fitted an arrow to the bow.

'Come on, you little monster!' Lothar yelled, to draw the Bushman's aim from the horse to himself, and the ruse succeeded.

The Bushman threw up the bow, and drew and loosed in a single movement, and the arrow flew like a beam of light. It struck Lothar at the level of the throat, but the thick wool of the sheepskin smothered it, and it fell away, tapping against his riding boot and falling to the dry earth.

The Bushman was trying desperately to notch another arrow as Lothar leaned out of the saddle like a polo player reaching for a forehand drive, and swung the Mauser. The rifle barrel crunched into the side of the Bushman's skull above the ear and he collapsed.

Lothar reined down his horse and sprang from the saddle, but Hendrick was there before him, swinging wildly with his Mauser butt at the Bushman's head as he lay against the earth. Lothar grabbed his shoulder and pushed him away with such force that he staggered and almost fell.

'Alive, I told you!' Lothar snarled, and went down on his knees beside the sprawling body.

There was a sluggish trickle of blood out of the Bushman's earhole, and Lothar felt a prickle of concern as he felt for the pulse of the carotid artery in the throat, and then grunted with relief. He picked up the tiny bow and snapped it in his hands and threw the pices aside, then with his hunting knife he cut the leather thong around the Bushman's forehead and one at a time broke the poisoned arrow heads from their shafts, and handling them with extreme care threw them as far from him as he could.

As he rolled the Bushman on to his belly, he shouted at Hendrick to bring the leather thongs from his saddle-bag. He trussed the captive securely, surprised at his perfect muscular development and at the graceful little feet and hands. He knotted the leather thongs at wrist and elbow, and at knee and ankle, and pulled the knots so tight that they bit deeply into the bright amber skin.

Then he picked up the Bushman in one hand, as though he were a doll, and slung him over the saddle. The movement revived the Bushman and he lifted his head and opened his eyes. They were the colour of new honey, and the whites were smoky yellow. It was like looking into the eyes of a trapped leopard – so ferocious that Lothar stepped back involuntarily.

'They are animals,' he said, and Hendrick nodded.

'Worse than animals, for they have the cunning of a man without being human.'

Lothar took the reins and led his exhausted steed back to where they had left the wounded Vuil Lippe.

The others had rolled him in a grey woollen blanket and laid him on a sheepskin. Clearly they were waiting on Lothar to attend to him, but Lothar was reluctant to involve himself. He knew that Vuil Lippe was beyond any help he could give, and he put off the moment by dragging the bound Bushman out of the saddle and dropping him on the sandy earth. The little body curled up defensively, and Lothar hobbled his horse and went slowly to join the circle around the blanket-wrapped form.

He could see immediately that the poison was acting swiftly. One side of Lippe's face was grotesquely swollen and laced with furious purple lines. One eye was closed by the swelling, and the lid looked like an over-ripe grape, shining and black. The other eye was wide open but the pupil was shrunken to a pinprick. He made no sign of recognition as Lothar stooped over him and had probably already lost his sight. He was breathing with extreme difficulty, fighting wildly for each breath as the poison paralysed his lungs.

Lothar touched his forehead and the skin was cold and clammy as that of a reptile. Lothar knew that Hendrick and the others were watching him. On many occasions they had seen him dress a bullet wound, set a broken leg, draw a rotten aching tooth, and perform all manner of minor surgery. They were waiting for him to do something for the dying man, and their expectations and his own helplessness infuriated Lothar.

Suddenly Lippe uttered a strangled cry and began to shake like an epileptic, his single open eye rolled back into his skull, showing the yellow blood-shot white, and his body arched under the blanket.

'Convulsions,' said Lothar, 'like a mamba bite. It won't be long now.'

The dying man bit down, grinding his teeth together, and his swollen protruding tongue was caught between them. He chewed on his tongue, mincing it to ribbons while Lothar tried desperately and futilely to prise his jaws open, and the blood poured down the Hottentot's own throat into his semi-paralysed lungs and he choked and moaned through his locked jaws.

His body arched in another rigid convulsion, and there was a spluttering explosion beneath the blanket as his wracked body voided itself. The sweet fecal stench was nauseating in the heat. It was a long-drawn-out and messy death, and when it was over at last, it left even those hardened men shaken and morose.

They scraped a shallow grave and rolled Vuil Lippe's corpse, still in the soiled grey blanket, into it. Then they hastily covered it, as though to be rid of their own loathing and horror.

One of them built a small fire of brush twigs, and brewed a canteen of coffee. Lothar fetched the half-bottle of Cape brandy from his saddle-bag. As they passed it from hand to hand, they avoided looking at where the Bushman lay curled naked in the sand.

They drank the coffee in silence, squatting in a circle, and then Vark Jan, the Khoisan Hottentot who spoke the San language, flicked his coffee grounds on to the fire and stood up.

He crossed to where the San lay and picked him up by his bound wrists, forcing his arms high behind him as they bore his full weight. He carried him back to the fire and picked out a burning twig. Still holding the San dangling from one hand he touched the naked glans of his penis with the glowing tip of the twig. The San gasped and wriggled wildly and a blister formed miraculously on the skin of his gentials. It looked like a soft silver slug.

The man around the fire laughed, and in their laughter was the sound of their

loathing and their terror of the death by poison, and their sorrow for their companion, of their craving for vengeance and the sadistic need to inflict pain and humiliation, the worst that they could devise.

Lothar felt himself shaken by the quality of that laughter, felt the insecure foundations of his humanity totter, and the same animal passions arise in him. With a supreme effort he forced them back. He rose to his feet. He knew he could not prevent what was about to happen, just as you cannot drive hungry lions from their fresh kill. They would turn on him if he tried.

He averted his eyes from the Bushman's face, from those wild hunted eyes. It was clear that he knew that death awaited him, but even he could not guess at the manner of it. Instead Lothar looked at the faces of his own men, and he felt sickened and soiled by what he saw. Their features seemed distorted as though seen through a poorly glazed window, thickened and smeared with lust.

He thought that after the Bushman had been mounted by each of them in turn, ravished as though he were a woman, he would probably welcome what awaited him at the very end.

'So.' Lothar tried to keep his expression neutral, but his voice was hoarse with disgust. 'I am returning to the wagons now. The San is yours, but I must know if he has seen or has heard of the white girl. He must answer that one question. That is all.'

Lothar went to his horse and mounted. He rode away towards the wagons without looking back. Just once, far behind, he heard a cry of such outrage and agony that it made his skin prickle, but then it was muted and lost on the moan of the desert wind.

Much later when his men rode up to the wagons, Lothar was lying under the side awning of his living wagon, reading his faithful old copy of Goethe by the light of a hurricane lantern – stained and battered, it had sustained him a hundred times before when the substance of his being had been drawn thin.

The laughter of his men as they dismounted and unsaddled had a fat, satisfied sound, like that of men who had well feasted and drunk, and were replete. Swart Hendrick came to where he lay, swaggering as though he had taken wine, and the front of his breeches was speckled with black drops of dried blood.

'The San had not seen a white woman, but there was something strange and unexplained that he had heard whispered at the fire when they met other San in the desert; a tale of a woman and a child from a strange land where the sun never shines, who lived with two old people of the San.'

Lothar came up on his elbow. He remembered the two little Bushmen he had seen with the girl.

'Where? Did he say where?' he damanded eagerly.

'There is a place, deep in the Kalahari, that is sacred to all the San. He gave us the direction – '

'Where, Hendrick, damn you. Where?'

'A long journey, fifteen days of their travel.'

'What is this place? How will we know it?'

'That,' Hendrick admitted sadly, 'he did not say. His will to stay alive was not as great as we thought it might be. He died before he could tell us.'

'Tomorrow we will turn in that direction,' Lothar ordered.

'There are the other San that we lost today. With fresh horses we might catch them before sundown tomorrow. They have women with them – '

'No!' Lothar snarled at him. 'We go on towards this sacred place in the wilderness.'

* * *

When the great bald mountain rose abruptly out of the plain, Lothar believed at first that it must be some trick of the desert light.

He knew of no description in the folklore or verbal history of the desert tribes to warn that the existence of such a place was possible. The only white men who had travelled this country – Livingstone and Oswell on their route to the discovery of Lake Ngami, and Anderson and Galton on their hunting forays – had made no mention of such a mountain in their writing.

Thus Lothar doubted what he was seeing in the uncertain evening light, and the sunset was so laden with dust, so garish and theatrical as to heighten the effect of a stage illusion.

However, in the first light of the next day when he looked for it eagerly, the silhouette was still there, dark and clearly incised against a sky that was turned to mother-of-pearl by the coming of the dawn. As he rode towards it, so it rose higher and still higher from the plain, and finally detached itself from the earth and floated in the sky on its own shimmering mirage.

When at last Lothar stood beneath the tall cliffs, he did not doubt that this was the sacred place of which the San had spoken as he died, and his conviction was made complete when he scrambled up the scree slopes and discovered the wondrous paintings upon the sheltered cliff face.

'This is the place, but it's so extensive,' Lothar realized. 'If the girl is here, we might never find her. So many caves and valleys and hidden places – we could search for ever.'

He divided his men again and sent them on foot to explore and search the nearest slopes of the mountain. Then he left the wagons in a shaded grove in the charge of Swart Hendrick, whom he mistrusted least, and taking only a spare horse set out to circumnavigate the mountain's bulk.

After two days of travel, during which he kept notes and sketched a rough map with the aid of his pocket compass, he could estimate with some certainty that the mountain was probably about thirty miles long and four or five miles wide, a long extended ride of gneiss and intruding sandstone strata.

He rounded the eastern extremity of the mountain and deduced from his compass headings that he was heading back along the opposite side from where he had left the wagons. Whenever some feature of the cliffs caught his attention, a fissure or a complex of caves, for instance, he hobbled the horses and climbed up to explore.

Once he discovered a small spring of clear sweet water welling up from the base of the cliff and trickling into a natural rock basin. He filled his water canteens, then he stripped and washed his clothes. At last he bathed, gasping with delight at the cold, and went on refreshed.

At other places he found more of the San paintings covering the rock face, and he marvelled at the accuracy of the artist's eye and hand that depicted the shape of eland and buffalo so that even his hunter's eye could find no fault. However, these were all ancient signs and he found nothing of recent human presence.

The forest and plain below the cliffs teemed with game, and he had no difficulty in shooting a plump young gazelle or antelope each day and keeping himself in fresh meat. On the third evening, he killed an impala ewe and made a kebab of the tripes and kidneys and liver, impaling them on a green twig and grilling them over the coals.

However, the scent of fresh meat attracted unwelcome attention to his camp, and he had to spend the rest of the night standing by the horses with his rifle in his hand while a hungry lion grunted and moaned in the darkness just outside the circle of firelight. He examined the beast's track's in the morning and found that it was an adult male, past its prime and with a damaged limb that forced it to limp heavily.

'A dangerous brute,' he muttered, and hoped that it had moved away. But this was a vain hope, he discovered that evening when the horses began to fidget and whicker as the sun set. The lion must have followed him at a distance during the day, and emboldened by the gathering dark, it again closed in and began to prowl around his camp fire.

'Another sleepless night.' He resigned himself and heaped wood on the fire. Preparing to stand guard, he pulled on his overcoat, and suffered another minor irritation. One of the brass buttons was missing, which would let in the cold of the desert night.

It was a long, unpleasant night, but a little after midnight the lion seemed at last to tire of its fruitless vigil and it moved away. He heard it utter one last string of moaning grunts at the head of the grassy vlei half a mile away, then there was silence.

Wearily Lothar checked the head halters on the horses and then went to the fire and rolled himself in his blankets, still fully dressed and keeping his boots on. Within minutes he had fallen into a deep dreamless sleep.

He came awake with bewildering suddenness and found himself sitting up with the rifle in his hands, and the din of an angry lion's thunderous roars echoing in his ears.

* * *

The fire had died down to white ash but the tree-tops were black against the paling morning sky. Lothar threw off his blankets and scrambled to his feet. The horses were stiff with alarm, their ears pricked forward, staring towards the open glade whose silver grasses just showed through the screen of mopani forest.

The lion roared again, and he judged it was a half-mile distant, in the direction in which the horses were staring. So clearly does the roar of a lion carry in the night, that an inexperienced ear would have reckoned it much closer and been unable to pinpoint the direction, for it played ventriloquist tricks upon the ear.

Once more the awful cacophony filled the forest. Lothar had never heard one of these beasts behaving like this, such sustained anger and frustration in those great blasts of sound, and then his head jerked with shock. In the lull between this roar and the next, he heard another unmistakable sound, a human scream of utmost terror.

Lothar reacted without thought. He seized the head halter of his favourite

hunting horse and leaped to its bare back. He socked his heels into its ribs, urging it into a gallop, and guided it with his knees, turning it towards the head of the glade. He lay forward on the horse's neck as the low branches lashed past his head, but as he broke into the open glade, he straightened and looked about him frantically.

In the few minutes since he had woken, the light had strengthened, and the eastern sky was a throbbing orange glow. There was a single tall mopani tree standing detached from the rest of the forest, surrounded by the low dry grass of the glade. High in its branches was a huge dark mass, and indistinct but violent movement made the branches of the mopani wave the thrash against the sky.

Lothar turned his horse towards it, and the thunderous growls of a lion were punctuated by yet another high-pitched shriek. Only then could Lothar distinguish what was happening in the top of the mopani, and he found it hard to believe.

'Great God!' he swore with surprise, for he had never heard of a lion climbing a tree. There was the great tawny cat high in the waving branches, clinging with its hindlegs to the trunk and reaching up with vicious swipes of its forepaws towards the human shape just beyond its reach.

'Ya! Ya!' Lothar worked his horse with elbows and heels, urging it to its top speed, and as he reached the mopani he flung himself from its back, and rode the shock of landing with his legs and back. Then he danced out to one side, head thrown back, rifle at high port across his chest, trying for a clear shot at the animal high above him.

The lion and its victim made an indistinguishably confused silhouette against the sky, a shot from below could hit one as easily as the other, and there were thick intervening branches of the mopani to deflect his bullet.

Lothar dodged sideways until he found a hole in the branches, and he flung the rifle up to his shoulder, braced himself over backwards, aiming straight up, but still reluctant to chance the shot. Then the lion snatched the human shape half off its precarious perch, dragging it down – and the screams were so piteous, so agonized, that Lothar could not wait longer.

He aimed for the lion's spine, at the root of the tail, a point as far as possible from the twisting body of its victim who was still clinging with desperate strength to one of the mopani branches. He fired and heavy Mauser bullet smashed into the base of the lion's spine, between its bunched and straining haunches, and tore upwards, following the line of the vertebrae for the span of a hand, shattering and crushing the bony knuckles, destroying the great nerves of the legs at their roots, before ripping out again from the centre of the lion's back.

The lion's hindlegs spasmed, the long yellow claws retracted involuntarily into their sheaths in the leathery pads, loosening their grip on the mopani bark, and the paralysed legs could hold no longer. The great tawny cat came sliding and twisting and roaring down out of the tree, crashing against the lower branches as it fell, arching back on itself, snapping at the pain in its shattered spine with gaping pink jaws.

It brought its human victim down with it, its foreclaws still hooked deeply into tender flesh, shaking and throwing the frail body about with its convulsions. They hit the earth in a tangle, with an impact that jarred up through the soles of Lothar's boots. He had jumped clear as they came down through the branches, but now he ran forward.

The lion's back legs were splayed behind it like those of a toad, and it lay half over the human body. Now it reared up on its forelags, pinned by its paralysed hindquarters, and as it dragged itself towards Lothar, it opened its jaws and bellowed. The stench of its breath was carrion and corruption, and hot stinking froth splattered his face and bare arms.

Lothar thrust the muzzle of the Mauser almost into that dreadful mouth and without aiming, he fired. The bullet entered the soft palate at the back of the lion's throat, tore through the back of its skull, and erupted in a fountain of pink blood and brains. For a second longer, it stood braced on its stiff forelegs, then with a gusty sigh its lungs emptied and it rolled slowly over on to its side.

Lothar dropped the Mauser and fell on his knees beside the huge twitching yellow carcass, and tried to reach the body beneath it, but only the bottom half protruded, a pair of slim brown naked legs, the narrow, boyish loins bound up in a tattered canvas kilt.

Lothar sprang up and seized the lion's tail; he flung all his weight upon it, and sluggishly the furry carcass rolled over on to its back, freeing the body beneath it. A woman, he saw at once, and he stooped and lifted her. Her head with its thick mop of dark curling hair flopped lifelessly, and he cupped his hand at the back of her neck, as though her were holding a newborn infant, and he looked into her face.

It was the face of the photograph, the face he had glimpsed so long ago in the field of his telescope, the face that had haunted and driven him, but there was no life in it.

The long dark eyelashes were closed and meshed together, the smooth, darkly tanned features were without expression, and the strong wide mouth was slack; the soft lips drooped open to reveal the small white even teeth and a little string of saliva dribble from one corner of her mouth.

'No!' Lothar shook his head vehemently. 'You can't be dead – no, it's not possible, after all this. I won't – ' He broke off. Out of the thick dark mane of her hair a serpent crawled down across the broad forehead towards her eye, a slow dark red serpent of new blood.

Lothar snatched the cotton bandanna from around his neck and wiped away the blood, but it flooded down her face as fast as he could clear it. He parted her crown of curls and found the wound in her shiny white scalp, a short but deep cut where she had hit one of the mopani branches. He could see the gleam of bone in the bottom of the wound. He pressed the lips of the cut together and wadded his kerchief over it, then bound it in place with the bandanna.

He cradled the injured head against his shoulder and lifted the limp body into a sitting position. One of her breasts flopped out of her skimpy fur cloak, and he felt an almost blasphemous shock, it was so pale and tender and vulnerable. He covered it swiftly and guiltily, then turned his attention to her injured leg.

The wounds were frightening; parallel slashes that had ripped deep into the flesh of her calf, cutting down to the heel of her left foot. He laid her back gently and knelt at her feet, lifting the leg and dreading the sudden spurting rush of arterial blood. It did not come, there was only the dark seepage of venous blood, and he sighed.

'Thank you, God.' He dragged off his heavy military greatcoat, and placed the wounded leg upon it to keep it out of the dirt, then he pulled his shirt over his head. It had not been washed since the rock spring two days before and it stank of his stale sweat.

'Nothing else for it.' He ripped the shirt into strips and bound up the leg.

He knew that this was the real danger, the infections that a carrion eater, such as a lion, carried on its fangs and its claws were almost as deadly as the poisons of a Bushman's arrowhead. The claws of a lion particularly were sheathed in deep scabbards in the pads. Old blood and putrefied meat lodged in the cavities, an almost certain source of virulent mortification and gas-gangrene.

'We have to get you to the camp, Centaine.' He used her name for the first time, and it gave him a tiny flicker of pleasure, quickly smothered by fear as he touched her skin again and felt the cold, the mortuary chill upon it.

Quickly he checked her pulse and was shocked at its weak, irregular flutter. He lifted her shoulders and wrapped her in the thick greatcoat, then looked about him for his horse. It was down at the far end of the glade, grazing head down. Bare to the waist and shivering in the cold, he ran after it and led it back to the mopani.

As he stooped to lift the girl's unconscious body, he froze with shock.

From above his head came a sound that ripped along his nerves and triggered his deepest instincts. It was the loud cry of an infant in distress, and he straightened swiftly and stared up the tall trunk. There was a bundle hanging in the top branches, and it twitched and swung agitatedly from side to side.

'A woman and a child.' The words of the dying Bushman came back to Lothar.

He pillowed the unconscious girl's head against the warm carcass of the lion, then jumped to catch the lowest mopani branch. He drew himself bodily upwards and swung one leg over the branch. He climbed swiftly up to the suspended bundle, and found it was a rawhide satchel. He unhooked the straps and lowered it until he could peer into the opening.

A small, indignant face scowled up at him, and as it saw him, it flushed and yelled with fright.

The memory of Lothar's own son assailed him so suddenly and bitterly that he winced and swayed on the high branch, and then drew the kicking, yelling child more securely against his own body and smiled, a painful, lopsided smile.

'That is a big voice for a small man,' he whispered huskily. It never occurred to him that it might be a girl – that arrogant anger could only be male.

* * *

It was easier to shift his camp to the mopani tree under which Centaine lay, than move her to the camp. He had to carry the child with him, but he managed it in less than twenty minutes. He was fearful every minute that he left the helpless mother alone, and vastly relieved when he led the pack horse back to where she lay. Centaine was still unconscious, and the child he carried had soiled itself and was ravenous with hunger.

He wiped off the boy's small pink bottom with a handful of dry grass, remembering how he had performed the same service for his own son, and then placed him under the greatcoat where he could reach his unconscious mother's breast.

Then he set a canteen of water on a small fire and dropped the curved sacking needle and a hank of white cotton thread from his canvas housewife into the

boiling water to sterilize. He washed his own hands in a mug of hot water and carbolic soap, emptied the mug, refilled it and began to scrub out the deep tears in the girl's calf. The water was painfully hot, and he lathered carbolic soap and forced his finger to the bottom of each wound, poured hot water into it, and then washed it out again and again.

Centaine moaned and thrashed about weakly, but he held her down and scrubbed grimly at the fearful lacerations. At last, not truly satisfied, but certain that if he persisted in his rough cleansing he would do irreparable damage to delicate tissue, he went to his saddle-bag and fetched a whisky bottle which he had carried with him for four years. It had been given to him by the German Lutheran missionary doctor who had nursed him through the wounds he had received during the campaign against Smuts' and Botha's invasion. 'It may save your life one day,' the doctor had told him. The handwritten label was illegible now, 'Acriflavin' – with an effort he remembered the name, and the dark yellow-brown liquid had evaporated to half its volume.

He poured it into the open wounds and worked it in with his forefinger, making certain that it reached the bottom of each deep cut. He used the last drops from the bottle on the rent in Centaine's scalp.

He fished the needle and cotton from the boiling canteen. With the girl's leg in his lap, he took a deep breath. 'Thank the Lord she's unconscious,' and he held the lips of raw flesh together and worked the point of the needle through them.

It took him nearly two hours to sew the meat of her tattered calf together again, and his stitches were crude but effective, the work of a sailmaker rather than a surgeon. He used strips from one of his clean shirts to bind up the leg, but as he worked he knew that despite his best efforts, infection was almost certain. He transferred his attention to her scalp. Three stitches were sufficient to close that wound, and afterwards the nervous strain of the last hours swamped him, and he felt shaken and exhausted.

It took an effort of will to begin work on the litter. He skinned out the carcass of the lion, and strung the wet hide between two long limber mopani saplings with the fur side uppermost. The horses shied and fidgeted at the rank smell of lion, but he gentled them and fitted the straight poles of the drag litter on to the pack horse, then tenderly lifted Centaine's limp body, wrapped in the greatcoat, into the litter and strapped her securely with strips of mopani bark.

Carrying the now sleeping child in the satchel and leading the pack horse with the litter sliding along behind it he set off at a walk towards the wagons. He calculated that it was a full day's march, and it was now long past noon, but he could not force the pace without risk of injuring the girl in the litter.

A little before sundown, Shasa woke and howled like a hungry wolf. Lothar hobbled the horses and took him to his mother. Within minutes Shasa was howling with frustration and kicking under the flap of the greatcoat, presenting Lothar with a difficult decision.

'It's for the child, and she will never know,' he decided.

He lifted the flap of the greatcoat, and hesitated again before touching her so intimately.

'Forgive me, please,' he apologized to the unconscious girl, and took her bared breast in his hand. The weight and the heat and velvet feel of it was a shock in his loins, but he tried to ignore it. He pressed and kneaded, with Shasa blustering and mouthing furiously at his hand, and then rocked back on his heels and covered Centaine with the coat.

'Now, what the hell do we do, boy? Your mother's lost her milk.' He picked Shasa up. 'No, don't try me, my friend, this is another dry house, I'm afraid. We'll have to camp here while I go shopping.'

He cut thorn branches and dragged them into a circular laager to keep out hyena or other predators and built a large fire in the centre.

'You'll have to come with me,' he said to the querulous infant, and strapping the canvas bag across his shoulder, he rode out on his hunting horse.

He found a herd of zebra around the next bluff of the mountain. Using his horse as a screen, he worked to within easy rifle-shot of the herd and picked out a mare with a young foal at her side. He hit her cleanly in the head and she dropped instantly. When he walked up to the dead zebra, the foal ran only a few yards, and then circled back.

'Sorry, old fellow,' Lothar said to it. The orphan would have no chance of survival and the bullet he gave it in the head was swift mercy.

Lothar knelt beside the dead mare and pulled back her top leg to expose the swollen black udders. He was able to draw half a canteen of warm milk from her. It was rich and topped with thick yellow cream. He diluted it with an equal quantity of warm water and soaked a folded square of cotton torn from his shirt into the mixture.

Shasa spluttered and kicked and turned his head away, but Lothar persisted. 'This is the only item on the menu.'

Suddenly Shasa learned the trick of it. Milk dribbled down his chin, but some of it went down his throat, and he yelled impatiently evey time Lothar pulled the wad of shirt out of his mouth to resoak it.

Lothar slept that night with Shasa against his chest, and woke before dawn when the child demanded his breakfast. There was zebra milk remaining from the previous evening. By the time he had fed the boy, and then washed him in a mug of water warmed on the fire, it was after sunrise. When Lothar set him down, Shasa set off at a gallop on his hands and knees towards the horses, giving breathless cries of excitement.

Lothar felt that swollen feeling in his chest that he had not known since the death of his own son, and lifted him on to the horse's back. Shasa kicked and gurgled with laughter, and the hunting pony reached back and snuffled at him with ears pricked.

'We'll make a horseman of you before you walk,' Lothar laughed.

However, when he went to Centaine's litter and tried gently to rouse her, his concern was intense. She was still unconscious, though she moaned and rolled her head from side to side when he touched the leg. It was swollen and bruised, and clotted blood had dried on the stitches.

'My God, what a mess,' he whispered, but when he searched for the livid lines of gangrene up her thigh, he found none.

There was another unpleasant discovery, however. Centaine needed the same attention as her son.

He undressed her quickly. The canvas skirt and mantel were her only clothing, and he tried to remain unmoved and clinical when he looked at her.

He could not do so. Up to this time Lothar had based his concept of feminine beauty on the placid round blonde Rubensesque charms of his mother, and after her, his wife Amelia. Now he found his standards abruptly overturned. This woman was lean as a greyhound, with a tucked-in belly in which he could see the separate muscles clearly defined beneath the skin. That skin, even where it was untouched by the sun, was cream rather then pure milk. Her body hair,

instead of being pale and wispy, was thick and dark and curly. Her limbs were long and willowy, not round and dimpled at elbow and knee. She was firm to the touch, his fingers did not sink into her flesh as they had into other flesh he had known, and where the sun had reached her legs and arms and face, she was the colour of lightly oiled teak.

He tried not to dwell upon these things, as he rolled her deftly but gently on to her face, but when he saw that her buttocks were round and hard and white as a perfect pair of ostrich eggs, something flopped in his stomach, and his hands shook uncontrollably as he finished cleaning her.

He experienced no revulsion at the task, it was as natural as his attentions to the child had been, and afterwards he wrapped her in the greatcoat again and squatted on his heels beside her to examine her face minutely.

Again he found her features differed from his previous conception of feminine beauty. That halo of thick, kinky dark hair was almost African, those black eyebrows were too stark, her chin too thrusting and stubborn, the whole cast and set of her features was far too assertive to bear comparison with the gentle compliance of those other women. Even though she was totally relaxed, Lothar could still read on her face the marks of great suffering and hardship, perhaps as great as his own, and as he touched the smooth brown cheek, he felt almost fatalistically drawn to her, as though it had been ordained from that first glimpse of her so many months before. Abruptly he shook his head with annoyance and a quick sense of his own ridiculous sentimentality.

'I know nothing of you, or you of me.' He looked up quickly, and with a guilty start realized that the child had crawled away under the horses' hooves. With chuckles of glee, he was snatching at their inquisitive puffing nostrils, as they stretched down to him, sniffing at him.

Leading the pack horse and carrying the child, Lothar reached his wagons late that same afternoon.

* * *

Swart Hendrick and the camp servants ran out to meet him, agog with curiosity, and Lothar gave his orders.

'I want a separate shelter for the woman, alongside mine. Thatch the roof to keep it cool, and hang canvas sides we can raise to let in the breeze – and I want it ready by nightfall.'

He carried Centaine to his own cot and bathed her again before dressing her in one of the long nightgowns that Anna Stok had provided.

She was still not conscious, though once she opened her eyes. They were unfocused and dreamy, and she muttered in French so he could not understand.

He told her, 'You are safe. You are with friends.'

The pupils of her eyes reacted to light, which he knew was an encouraging sign, but the lids fluttered closed and she relapsed into unconsciousness, or sleep from which he was careful not to rouse her.

With access to his medicine chest again, Lothar was able to redress her wounds, spreading them liberally with an ointment which was his favourite cure-all inherited from his mother. He bound them up in fresh bandages.

By this time the child was once again hungry and letting it be widely known. Lothar had a milch-goat amongst his stock, and he held Shasa on his lap while

he fed him the diluted goat's milk. Afterwards he tried to make Centaine drink a little warm soup, but she struggled weakly and almost choked. So he carried her to the shelter which his servants had completed, and laid her on a cot of laced rawhide thongs with a sheepskin mattress and fresh blankets. He placed the child beside her and during the night he woke more than once from a light sleep to go to them.

Just before dawn he at last fell into deep sleep, only to be shaken awake almost immediately.

'What is it?' He reached instinctively for the rifle at his head.

'Come quickly!' Swart Hendrick's hoarse whisper at his ear. 'The cattle were restless. I thought it might be a lion.'

'What is it, man?' Lothar demanded irritably. 'Get on with it, spit it out.'

'It was not a lion – much worse! There are wild San out there. They have been creeping around the camp all night. I think they are after the cattle.'

Lothar swung his legs over the cot and groped for his boots.

'Have Vark Jan and Kein Boy returned yet?' It would be easier with a large party.

'Not yet,' Hendrick shook his head.

'Very well, we'll hunt alone. Saddle the horses. We must not let the little yellow devils get too much of a start on us.

As he stood up, he checked the load of the Mauser, then pulled the sheepskin off his cot and stooped out of the shelter. He hurried to where Swart Hendrick was holding the horses.

* * *

O'wa had not been able to force himself to approach closer than two hundred paces to the camp of strangers. Even at that distance the strange sounds and odours that carried to him confused him. The ring of axe on wood, the clatter of a bucket, the bleat of a goat made him start; the smell of paraffin and soap, of coffee and woollen clothing troubled him, while the sounds of men speaking in unfamiliar cadence and harsh sibilance were as terrifying to him as the hissing of serpents.

He lay against the earth, his heart hammering painfully, and whispered to H'ani, 'Nam Child is with her own kind at last. She is lost to us, old grandmother. This is a sickness of the head, this crazy following after her. We both know well that the *others* will murder us if they discover that we are here.'

'Nam Child is hurt. You read the sign beneath the mopani tree where the naked carcass of the lion lay,' H'ani whispered back. 'You saw her blood on the earth.'

'She is with her own kind,' O'wa repeated stubbornly. 'They will care for her. She does not need us any more. She went in the night and left us without a word of farewell.'

'Old grandfather, I know that what you say is true, but how will I ever smile again if I never know how badly she has been hurt? How will I ever sleep again if I never see little Shasa safe at her breast?'

'You risk both our lives for a glimpse of someone who has departed. They are dead to us now, leave them be.'

'I risk my own life, my husband, for to me it has no further value if I do not

know that Nam Child, the daughter of my heart if not of my own womb, is alive and will stay alive. I risk my own life for the touch of Shasa once more. I do not ask you to come with me.'

H'ani rose, and before he could protest, scuttled away into the shadows, heading towards the faint glow where the watch-fire showed through the trees. O'wa came up on his knees, but his courage failed him again, and he lay and covered his head with an arm.

'Oh, stupid woman,' he lamented. 'Do you not know that without you my heart is a desert? When they kill you, I will die a hundred deaths to your one.'

H'ani crept towards the camp, circling downwind, watching the drift of smoke from the fire, for she knew that if the cattle or the horses scented her, they would stamp and mill and alert the camp. Every few paces she sank to the ground and listened with all her soul, staring into the shadows around the wagons and the crude huts of the encampment, watching for those tall, very black men, dressed in outlandish apparel and hung with glittering metal weapons.

They were all asleep, she could make out the shapes around the fire and the stink of their bodies in her nostrils made her shake with fear. She forced herself to rise and go forward, keeping one of the wagons between her and the sleeping men, until she could crouch beside the tall rear wheel of the wagon.

She was certain that Nam Child was in one of the thatched shelters, but to choose the wrong one would bring disaster upon her. She decided on the nearest of the shelters and crawled on her hands and knees to the entrance. Her eyes were good in the gloom, almost like those of a cat, but all she could see was a dark indefinite bundle on a raised structure at the far end of the shelter, a human shape, perhaps, but there was no way of being certain.

The shape stirred, and then coughed and grunted.

'A man!' Her heart thudded so loudly, she was certain it would wake him. She drew back, and crawled to the second shelter.

Here there was another sleeping form. H'ani crept towards it timidly, and when she was within arm's length, her nostrils flared. She recognized the milky smell of Shasa, and the odour of Nam Child's skin which to the old woman was as sweet as the wild melon.

She knelt beside the cot, and Shasa sensed her presence and whimpered. H'ani touched his forehead, and then slipped the tip of her little finger into his mouth. She had taught him well, all Bushmen children learned to be still under this special restraint, for the safety of the clan could depend on their silence. Shasa relaxed under the familiar touch and smell of the old woman.

H'ani felt for Nam Child's face. The heat of her cheeks told her that Nam Child was in light fever, and she leaned forward and smelled her breath. It was soured with pain and sickness, but lacked the rank feral stench of virulent infection. H'ani longed for the opportunity to examine and dress her wounds, but knew it was vain.

Instead she placed her lips against the girl's ear and whispered, 'My heart, my little bird, I call all the spirits of the clan to protect you. Your old grandfather and I will dance for you, to strengthen and cure you.'

The old woman's voice reached something deep in the unconscious girl's being. Images formed in her mind.

'Old grandmother,' she muttered, and smiled at the dream images. 'Old grandmother – '

'I am with you,' H'ani replied. 'I will be with you always and always – ' That

was all she could say, for she could not risk the sob that crouched in her throat ready to burst through her lips. She touched them each once more, the child and the mother, on their lips and their closed eyes, then she rose and scuttled from the shelter. Her tears blinded her, her grief swamped her senses, she passed close to the thorn laager where the horses stood.

One of the horses snorted and stamped and tossed its head at the sharp unfamiliar scent. As H'ani disappeared into the night, one of the men lying beside the fire sat up and threw aside his blanket to go to the restless horses. Halfway there, he paused and then stooped over the tiny footprint in the dust.

* * *

It was strange how weary H'ani felt now, as she and O'wa made their way back around the base of the mountain towards the secret valley.

While they had followed the trail of Nam Child and Shasa, she had felt as though she could run for ever, as though she were a young woman again, imbued with boundless energy and strength in her concern for the safety of the two she loved as dearly as she loved her ancient husband. Now, however, when she had turned her back upon them for ever, she felt the full weight of her age, and it pressed her down so that her usual alert swinging trot was reduced to a heavy plod, and the weariness ached in her legs and up her spine.

In front of her O'wa moved as slowly, and she sensed the effort that each pace cost him. In the time that it had taken the sun to rise a hand-span above the horizon, both of them had been deprived of the force and purpose that made survival in their harsh world possible. Once more they had suffered terrible bereavement, but this time they did not have the will to rise above it.

Ahead of her O'wa halted and sank down on his haunches. She had never in all the long years seen him so beaten, and when she squatted beside him, he turned his head slowly to her. 'Old grandmother, I am tired,' he whispered. 'I would like to sleep for a long time. The sun hurts my eyes.' He held up his hand to shield them.

'It has been a long hard road, old grandfather, but we are at peace with the spirits of our clan, and Nam Child is safe with her own kind. We can rest awhile now.' Suddenly she felt the grief come up her throat and she choked upon it, but there were no tears. It seemed that all the moisture had dried from her wizened old frame. There were no tears, but the need to weep was like an arrow in her chest, and she rocked on her heels and made a little humming sound in her throat to try to alleviate the pain, so she did not hear the horses coming.

It was O'wa who dropped his hand from his eyes and cocked his head to the tremor on the still morning air, and when H'ani saw the fright in his eyes, she listened and heard it also.

'We are discovered,' said O'wa, and for a moment H'ani felt drained of even the will to run and to hide.

'They are close already.' The same resignation was in his eyes, and it spurred the old woman.

She pulled him to his feet. 'On the open ground they will run us down with the ease of a cheetah taking a lame gazelle.' She turned and looked to the mountain.

They were at the foot of the scree slope, with scattered brush and loose rock ramping gently up to the mountain's bulk.

'If,' H'ani whispered, 'if we could reach the top, no horse could follow us.'

'It is too high, too steep,' O'wa protested.

'There is a way.' With a bony finger, H'ani pointed out the faint track that zigzagged up the vast bare rocky flank of the mountain.

'Look, old grandfather, see, the spirits of the mountain are showing us the way.'

'Those are klipspringer,' O'wa muttered. The two tiny chamois-like antelope, alarmed by the approach of horsemen in the forest below, went prancing lightly up the barely discernible track. 'They are not mountain spirits,' O'wa repeated, watching the nimble brown animals fly almost straight up the tall rock-face.

'I say they *are* spirits in the guise of antelope.' H'ani dragged him towards the scree slope. 'I say they *are* showing us the way to escape our enemies. Hurry, you stupid and argumentative old man, there is no other way open to us.'

She took his hand in hers, and together they hopped and skipped from boulder to boulder, climbing with the awkward agility of a pair of ancient baboons up the tumbled rock of the scree slope.

However, before they reached the base of the cliff, O'wa was dragging back on her hand, and gasping with pain, reeling weakly as she urged him on.

'My chest,' he cried and staggered. 'In my chest an animal is eating my flesh, I can feel its teeth – ' and he fell heavily between two boulders.

'We cannot stop,' H'ani pleaded as she stood over him. 'We must go on.' She tried to drag him up.

'There is such pain,' he wheezed. 'I can feel its teeth ripping out my heart.'

With all her strength she heaved him into a sitting position, and at that moment there was a faint shout from the foot of the scree slope below them.

'They have seen us,' H'ani said, looking down at the two horsemen as they rode out of the forest. 'They are coming up after us.'

She watched them jump down from their horses, tether them and then come at the slope. One was a black man and the other had a head that shone like sunlight off a sheet of still water, and as they came on to the slope they shouted again, a fierce and jubilant sound, like the clamour of hunting hounds when they first take the scent.

That sound roused O'wa and with H'ani's help he came unsteadily to his feet, clutching at his chest. His lips had blanched and his eyes were like those of a mortally wounded gazelle; they terrified her as much as the shouts of the men below.

'We must go on.' Half-carrying, half-dragging him, she led him to the base of the cliff.

'I cannot do it.' His voice was so faint she had to put her ear to his lips. 'I cannot go up there.'

'You can,' she told him stoutly. 'I will lead you, place your feet where I place mine.' And she went on to the rock, on to the steep pathway that the klipspringer had marked with their sharp pointed hooves, and behind her the old man came on unsteadily.

One hundred feet up they found a ledge, and it shielded them from the men below. They toiled upwards, clinging to the harsh abrasive surface with their fingertips, and the open drop below them seemed to steady O'wa. He climbed more determinedly. Once when he hesitated and swayed outwards from the

wall, she reached back and caught his arm and held him until the fit of vertigo passed.

'Follow me,' she told him. 'Do not look down, old grandfather. Watch my feet and follow me.'

They went upwards, higher and still higher, and although the plain opened below them, yet the hunters were hidden beneath the sheer of the cliff.

'Only a little further,' she told him. 'See, there is the crest, just a little further and we will be safe. Here, give me your hand.' And she reached out to help him over a bad place where the drop opened below them and they had to step across the void.

H'ani looked down between her feet and she saw them again, dwarfed by distance and foreshortened and misshapened by the overhead perspective. The two hunters were still at the base of the cliff, directly below her, looking up at her. The white man's face shone like a cloud, so strangely pale and yet so malignant, she thought. He lifted his arms and pointed at her with the long staff he carried. H'ani had never seen a rifle before, and made no effort to hide herself as she stared down at him. She knew she was far out of range of an arrow from even the most powerful bow, and, unafraid, she leaned out from the narrow ledge for a better view of her enemy. She saw the white man's extended arms jerk, and a little feather of white smoke flew from the tip of his staff.

She never heard the rifle shot, for the bullet arrived before the sound. It was a soft lead-nosed Mauser bullet and it entered low down in the front of her stomach and passed obliquely upwards, traversing her body, tearing through her bowels and her stomach, up through one lung and out through her back a few inches to one side of the spinal column. The force of the impact flung her backwards against the rock wall, and then her lifeless body bounced loosely forward and spun out over the edge.

O'wa cried out and reached for her as she went over. He touched her with his fingertips, before she fell away from him and he teetered on the brink of the precipice.

'My life!' he called after her. 'My little heart!' And the pain and the grief were too intense to be borne. He let his body sway outwards, and as it passed its centre of gravity, he cried softly, 'I am coming with you, old grandmother, to the very end of the journey.' And he let himself plunge unresisting into the void, and the wind ripped at him as he fell, but he made not another sound, not ever.

* * *

Lothar De La Rey had to climb twenty feet to where the body of one Bushman had wedged in a crack in the cliff face.

He saw it was the corpse of an old man, wrinkled and skeletal-thin, crushed by the fall and with skin and flesh ripped away to expose the bone of his skull. There was very little blood, almost as though the sun and wind had desiccated the tiny body while it was still alive.

About the narrow, childlike waist there was a brief loin-cover of tanned rawhide and then, remarkably, a lanyard from which dangled a clasp knife. It was an Admiralty-type knife with a horn handle such as British sailors carried,

and Lothar had not expected to find a tool like this one on a Bushman's corpse in the wastes of the Kalahari. He unlooped the lanyard and dropped the knife into his pocket. There was nothing else of value or interest on the body, and he certainly would not bother to bury it. He left the old man jammed into the rocky crevice and climbed back down to where Swart Hendrick waited for him.

'What did you find?' Hendrick demanded.

'Just an old man, but he had this.' Lothar showed him the knife, and Swart Hendrick nodded without particular interest.

'*Ja*. They are terrible thieves, like monkeys. That's why they were creeping around our camp.'

'Where did the other one fall?'

'Into the kloof there, amongst that thorn bush. It will be dangerous to climb down. I would leave it.'

'Stay here, then,' Lothar told him and went to the edge of the deep ravine and looked down. The bottom was choked with dense thorn growth, and the climb would indeed be dangerous, but Lothar felt a perverse whim to go against Swart Hendrick's advice.

It took him twenty minutes to reach the bottom of the ravine, and as long again to find the corpse of the Bushman he had shot. It was like trying to find a dead pheasant in thick scrub without a good gundog to sniff it out, and in the end it was only the buzz of big metallic-blue flies that led him to the hand protruding from a clump of scrub, with the pink palm uppermost. He dragged the body out of the thorn scrub by the wrist and realized that it was a female, an ancient hag with impossibly wrinkled skin and dangling breasts like a pair of empty tobacco pouches.

He grunted with satisfaction when he saw the bullet hole exactly where he had aimed. It had been an extremely difficult shot, at that range and deflection. He transferred his attention immediately from the bullet wound to the extraordinary decoration that the old woman wore around her neck.

Lothar had never seen anything like it in southern Africa, although in his father's collection there had been a Masai necklace from east Africa, which was vaguely similar. However, the Masai jewellery had been made with trade beads, while for this collar the old woman had collected coloured pebbles and had graded and arranged them with remarkable aesthetic appreciation. Then she had most cunningly fastened them into a breast plate that was at once strong and decorative.

Lothar realized that it would have considerable value for its rarity, and he rolled the old woman on to her face to unknot the string that held it at the back of her neck. Blood from the massive exit wound had soaked the string, run down it and clotted on some of the coloured stones, but he wiped it off carefully.

Many of the stones were in their original crystalline form, and others were water-worn and polished. The old woman had probably picked them out of the gravel banks in the dry river beds. He turned them to catch the light and smiled with pleasure at the lovely sparkle of reflected sunlight. He wrapped the necklace in his bandanna and placed it carefully in his breast pocket.

One last glance at the dead Bushwoman convinced him that there was nothing else of interest about her, and Lothar left her lying on her face and turned to the difficult climb up the ravine wall to where Swart Hendrick waited above him.

* * *

Centaine became aware of the feeling of woven cloth upon her body, and it was so unfamiliar that it brought her to the very threshold of consciousness. She thought that she lay upon something soft, but she knew that was impossible, as was the filtered light through green canvas. She was too tired to ponder these things, and when she tried to keep her eyelids open, they drooped against her best efforts and she became aware of her weakness. Her insides had been scooped out of her as though she were a soft-boiled egg, and only her brittle outer shell remained. The thought made her want to smile, but even that effort was too great and she drifted away into that lulling darkness again.

When next she became aware, it was to the sound of someone singing softly. She lay with her eyes closed and realized that she could understand the words. It was a love song, a lament for a girl that the singer had known before the war began.

It was a man's voice, and she thought it was one of the most thrilling voices she had ever heard. She did not want the song to end, but suddenly it broke off, and the man laughed.

'So, you like that do you?' he said in Afrikaans, and a child said, 'Da! Da!' so loudly and so clearly that Centaine's eyelids flew open. It was Shasa's voice and every memory of that night with the lion in the mopani came rushing back at her, and she wanted to scream again.

'My baby, save my baby!' and she rolled her head from side to side, and found she was alone in a hut with thatched roof and canvas sides. She lay on a camp cot, and she was dressed in a long cool cotton nightgown.

'Shasa!' she called out, and tried to sit up. She managed only a spasmodic jerk, and her voice was a dull, hoarse whisper.

'Shasa!' This time she summoned all her strength. 'Shasa!' and it came out as a croak.

There was a startled exclamation, and she heard a stool clatter as it was overturned. The hut darkened as someone stepped into the doorway, and she rolled her head towards the opening.

A man stood there. He was holding Shasa on his hip.

He was tall, with wide shoulders, but the light was behind him so she could not see his face.

'So, the sleeping princess awakes – ' that deep, thrilling voice ' – at last, at long last.'

Still carrying her son, he stepped to the side of her cot and bent over her.

'We have been worried,' he said gently, and she looked up into the face of the most beautiful man she had ever seen, a golden man, with golden hair and yellow leopard's eyes in his tanned golden face.

On his hip Shasa bounced up the down and reached towards her.

'Mama!'

'My baby!' She lifted one hand, and the stranger swung Shasa off his hip and placed him beside her on the cot.

Then he lifted Centaine's shoulders and propped her into a sitting position with a bolster behind her. His hands were brown and strong, yet the fingers were as elegant as those of a pianist.

'Who are you?' Her voice was a husky whisper, and there were dark smears below her eyes, the colour of fresh bruises.

'My name is Lothar De La Rey,' he answered, and Shasa clenched his fists and pounded his mother's shoulder in a gesture of overwhelming affection.

'Gently!' Lothar caught his wrist to restrain him. 'Your mama is not up to so

much love, not yet.' She saw how Lothar's expression softened as he looked at the child.

'What happened to me?' Centaine asked. 'Where am I?'

'You were attacked and mauled by a lion. When I shot the beast, you fell out of the tree.'

She nodded. 'Yes, I remember that, but afterwards – '

'You suffered concussion and then the wounds from the lion claws mortified.'

'How long?' she breathed.

'Six days, but the worst is past. Your leg is still very swollen and inflamed, Mevrou Courtney.'

She started. 'You use that name. Where did you learn that name?'

'I know that your name is Mevrou Centaine Courtney and that you were a survivor from the hospital ship *Protea Castle*.'

'How? How do you know these things?'

'I was sent by your father-in-law to search for you.'

'My father-in-law?'

'Colonel Courtney, and that woman, Anna Stok.'

'Anna? Anna is alive?' Centaine reached out and seized his wrist.

'There is no doubt about that at all!' Lothar laughed. 'She is very much alive.'

'That is the most wonderful news! I thought she was drowned – ' Centaine broke off as she realized that she was still holding his wrist. She let her hand fall to her side and sank back against the bolster.

'Tell me,' she whispered, 'tell me everything. How is she? How did you know where to find me? Where is Anna now? When will I see her?'

Lothar laughed again. His teeth were very white. 'So many questions!' He drew the stool to her cot. 'Where shall I begin?'

'Begin with Anna, tell me all about her.'

He talked and she listened avidly, watching his face, asking another question as soon as one was answered, fighting off the weakness of her body to revel in the sound of his voice, in the intense pleasure of hearing glad tidings of the real world from which she had been so long excluded, of communicating with one of her own kind and looking on a white and civilized face again.

The day was almost gone, the evening gloom filling her little shelter when Shasa let out a demanding shout and Lothar broke off.

'He is hungry.'

'I will feed him if you will leave us a while, Mijnheer.'

'No,' Lothar shook his head. 'You have lost your milk.'

Centaine's head jerked as though the words were a blow in her face and she stared at him while thoughts tumbled and crowded in her mind. Up to that moment she had been so wrapped up in listening and questioning that she had not considered that there was no other woman in the camp, that for six days she had been entirely helpless, and that somebody had tended her, washed her and changed her, fed her and dressed her wounds. But his words, such an intimate subject spoken of in direct fashion, brought all this home to her, and as she stared at him, she felt herself begin to blush with shame. Her cheeks flamed – those long brown fingers of his must have touched her where only one other man had touched her before. She felt her eyes smart, as she realized what those yellow eyes of his must have looked upon.

She felt herself burning up with embarrassment, and then incredibly with a hot and shameful excitement, so that she had difficulty breathing, and she

lowered her eyes and turned her head away so that he could not see her scarlet cheeks.

Lothar seemed to be entirely unaware of her predicament. 'Come on, soldier, let's show mama our new trick.' He lifted Shasa and fed him with a spoon, and Shasa bounced on his hip and said, 'Hum! Hum!' as he saw each spoonful coming, and then launched himself at it with mouth wide open.

'He likes you,' Centaine said.

'We are friends,' Lothar admitted, as he removed the heavy coating of gruel from Shasa's forehead and chin and ears with a damp coth.

'You are good with children,' Centaine whispered and saw the sudden biting pain reflected in the darkening gold of his eyes.

'Once I had a son,' he said, and placed Shasa at her side, then picked up the spoon and empty bowl and went to the doorway.

'Where is your son?' she called softly after him, and he paused in the opening, then turned slowly back to her.

'My son is dead,' he said softly.

* * *

She was ripe and over-ripe for love. Her loneliness was a hunger so intense that it seemed it could not be assuaged, not even by those long languid conversations under the awning of the wagon tent when, with Shasa between them, they talked away the hottest hours of those lazy African days.

Mostly they discussed the things she held dearest, music and books. Although he preferred Goethe to Victor Hugo and Wagner to Verdi, these differences gave them grounds for amusing and satisfying dispute. In those arguments she discovered that his learning and scholarship far exceeded her own, but she strangely did not resent it. It merely made her more attentive to his voice. It was a marvellous voice; after the clicking and grunting of the San language, she could listen to it for the lilt and cadence as though it were music in itself.

'Sing for me!' she ordered, when they had for the moment exhausted a particular topic. 'Both Shasa and I command it.'

'Your servant, of course!' he smiled, and gave them a mocking little bow, then he sang without any self-consciousness.

'Take the chick and the hen will follow you.' Centaine had often heard Anna repeat the old proverb, and when she watched Shasa riding around the camp on Lothar's shoulders, she realized the wisdom behind if, for her eyes and her heart followed both of them.

At first she felt quick resentment whenever Shasa greeted Lothar with cries of 'Da! Da!'. That name should have been reserved for Michael alone. Then with a painful stab she remembered that Michael was lying in the cemetery at Mort Homme.

After that it was easy to smile when Shasa's first attempts at walking unaided on his own two legs ended with a precipitous and headlong return to earth and he bawled for Lothar and crawled to him, seeking comfort. It was Lothar's tenderness and gentleness with her son that nudged her affections and her need for him forward, for she recognized that beneath that handsome exterior he was a hard man and fierce. She saw the awe and respect in which his own men held him, and they were tough men themselves.

Just once she witnessed him in a cold, killing rage that terrified her as much as it did the man against whom it was directed. Vark Jan, the wrinkled yellow Khoisan, in indolence and ignorance had ridden Lothar's hunting horse with an ill-fitting saddle and galled the creature's back almost to the bone. Lothar had knocked Vark Jan down with a fist to the head, and then cut the jacket and shirt off his back with razor strokes from his sjambok, a five-foot whip of cured hippo-hide, and left him unconscious in a puddle of his own blood.

The violence had appalled and frightened Centaine, for she had witnessed every brutal detail from where she lay on her cot beneath the awning. Later, however, when she was alone in her shelter, her revulsion faded and in its place was a trembly feeling of exhilaration and a heat in the pit of her stomach.

'He's so dangerous,' she thought, 'so dangerous and cruel,' and she shivered again and could not sleep. She lay and listened to his breathing in the shelter beside hers, and thought about how he must have undressed her and touched her while she was unconscious, and her flesh tingled at the memory and she blushed in the darkness.

In startling contrast the next day he was gentle and tender, holding her injured leg in his lap while he snipped the threads of cotton and plucked them from her swollen, inflamed flesh. They left dark punctures in her skin, and he bent over her leg and sniffed the wound.

'It's clean now. That redness is only your body attempting to rid itself of the stitches. It will heal swiftly now they are gone.'

Lothar was right. Within two days she was able, with the help of the crutch he had whittled for her, to make her first foray out of the canvas shelter.

'My legs feel wobbly,' she protested, 'And I am as weak as Shasa.'

'You'll soon be strong again.' He placed his arm around her shoulders to steady her, and she trembled at his touch and hoped he would not notice and withdraw his arm.

They paused by the horse lines and Centaine petted the animals, stroking their silky muzzles and revelling in that nostalgic horse odour.

'I want to ride again,' she told him.

'Anna Stok told me you were a skilled horsewoman – she told me you had a stallion, a white stallion.'

'Nuage,' Tears pricked her eyes as she remembered, and she pressed her face against the neck of Lothar's hunting horse to hide them. 'My white cloud, he was so beautiful, so strong and swift.'

'Nuage.' Lothar took her arm, 'a lovely name.' Then he went on, 'Yes, you will ride again soon. We have a long journey ahead of us, back to where your father-in-law and Anna Stok will be waiting for you.'

It was the first time she had considered an end to this magical interlude, and she pulled away from the horse and stared at him over its back. She didn't want it to end, she didn't want him to leave her, as she knew he soon would.

'I'm tired,' she said. 'I don't think I am ready to start riding just yet.'

That evening as she sat under the awning with a book in her lap, pretending to read, while watching him from under her lowered lids, he looked up suddenly and smiled with such a knowing glint in his eye that she blushed and looked away in confusion.

'I'm writing to Colonel Courtney,' he told her, sitting at the collapsible travelling bureau with the pen in his hand smiling across at her, 'I will send a rider back to Windhoek tomorrow, but it will take him two weeks or more to

get there and back. I am letting Colonel Courtney know when and where we can meet, and I have suggested a rendezvous for the 19th day of next month.'

She wanted to say, 'So soon?' but instead, she nodded silently.

'I am sure you are most anxious to be reunited with your family, but I don't think we will be able to reach the rendezvous before that date.'

'I understand.'

'However, I would be delighted to send any letter that you might care to write, with the messenger.'

'Oh, that would be wonderful – Anna, dear Anna, she will be fussing like an old hen.'

Lothar stood up from the bureau. 'Please seat yourself here and use the pen and what paper you need, Mrs Courtney. While you are busy, Master Shasa and I will see to his dinner.'

Surprisingly, once she penned the opening salutation, 'My dearest dear Anna,' she could think of nothing to follow it, mere words seemed so paltry.

'I give thanks to God that you survived that terrible night, and I have thought of you every day since then – ' The dam holding back the words burst, and they flooded out on to the paper.

'We will need a pack horse to carry that epistle.' Lothar stood behind her shoulder, and she started as she realized that she had covered a dozen sheets with close script.

'There is so much still to tell her, but the rest will have to wait.' Centaine folded the sheets and sealed them with a wax wafer from the silver box fitted into the top of the bureau, while Lothar held the candle for her.

'It was strange,' she whispered. 'I had almost forgotten how to hold a pen. It has been so long.'

'You have never told me what happened to you, how you escaped from the sinking ship, how you survived so long, how you came to be so many hundreds of miles from the coast where you must have come ashore – '

'I don't want to talk about it.' She cut him off quickly. She saw for a moment in her mind's eye, the little heart-shaped, wrinkled, amber-coloured faces, and suppressed her nagging guilt at having deserted them so cruelly.

'I don't even want to think about that. Kindly never address the subject again, sir.' Her tone was stingingly severe.

'Of course, Mrs Courtney.' He picked up the two sealed letters. 'If you will excuse me, I will give these to Vark Jan now. He can leave before dawn tomorrow.' He was stiff-faced and resentful of the rebuff.

She watched him cross to the servants' fire and heard the murmur of voices as he gave Vark Jan his orders.

When he returned to the shelter, she made a pretence of being engrossed with her book, hoping that he would interrupt her, but he seated himself at the bureau and opened his journal. It was his nightly ritual, his entry in the leather-bound journal. She listened to his pen scratching on the paper, and she resented his attention being focused anywhere but on herself.

'There is so little time left to us,' she thought, 'and he squanders it so.' She closed her book loudly but he did not look up.

'What are you writing?' she demanded.

'You know what I am writing, since we have discussed it before, Mrs Courtney.'

'Do you write everything in your journal?'

'Almost everything.'

'Do you write about me?'

He laid down the pen and stared at her, and she was flustered by the direct gaze of those serene yellow eyes, but could not bring herself to apologize.

'You were prying into things that did not concern you,' she told him.

'Yes,' he agreed with her, and to cover her discomfort, she demanded, 'What have you written about me in your famous journal?'

'And now, madam, it is you who are inquisitive,' he told her as he closed his diary, placed it in the drawer of the bureau and stood up. 'If you will excuse me, I must make my rounds of the camp.'

* * *

So she learned that she could not treat him the way she had treated her father, or even the way she had treated Michael Courtney. Lothar was a proud man and would not allow her to trespass on his dignity, a man who had fought his whole life for the right to be his own master. He would not permit her to take advantage of his strong sense of chivalry to her and to little Shasa. She learned that she could not bully him.

The next morning she found herself dismayed by his formal aloof bearing, but as the day wore on she became angry. 'Such a small tiff, and he sulks like a spoiled child,' she told herself. 'Well, we'll see who sulks the longest and hardest.'

By the second day her anger had given way to loneliness and unhappiness. She found herself longing for his smile, for the pleasure of one of their long convoluted discussions, for the sound of his laughter and his voice when he sang to her.

She watched Shasa tottering around the camp, hanging on to one of Lothar's hands and engaging him in loquacious conversation that only the two of them could understand, and was appalled to find that she was jealous of her own child.

'I will give Shasa his food,' she told him coldly. 'It is time I resumed my duties. You need no longer discommode yourself, sir.'

'Of course, Mrs Courtney.'

And she wanted to cry, 'Please, I am truly sorry.' But their pride was a mountain range between them.

She listened all that afternoon for the sound of his horse returning. She heard only the sound of distant rifle fire, but it was after dark when Lothar rode in, and she and Shasa were already in their cots. She lay in the darkness and listened to the voices and the sounds as the carcasses of the springbok that Lothar had shot were offloaded from his hunting horse and hung upon the butchering rack. Lothar sat late at the fire with his men, and bursts of their laughter carried to her as she tried to compose herself to sleep.

At last she heard him come to the shelter beside hers, and she listened to the splash of water as he washed in the bucket at the entrance, the rustle of his clothing and finally the creak of the lacings of his cot as he settled upon it.

Shasa's cries awoke her, and she knew instantly that he was in pain, and she swung her legs off the cot and still half-asleep groped for him. A match flared and lantern light bloomed in Lothar's shelter.

'Shh! Quiet, my little one.' She cradled Shasa against her chest, and his hot little body alarmed her.

'May I enter?' Lothar asked from the entrance.

'Oh, yes.'

He stooped into the tent and set down the lantern.

'Shasa, he's sick.'

Lothar took the child from her. He wore only a pair of breeches, his chest and feet were bare. His hair was tangled from the pillow.

He touched Shasa's flushed cheek and then slipped a finger into his squalling mouth. Shasa choked off his next howl and bit down on the finger like a shark.

'Another tooth,' Lothar smiled, 'I felt it this morning.' He handed Shasa back to her and he let out a howl of rejection.

'I'll be back, soldier,' and she heard him rummaging in the medicine chest he kept bolted to the floor of his wagon.

He had a small bottle in his hand when he returned, and she wrinkled her nose at the pungent odour of oil of cloves as he pulled the cork.

'We'll fix that bad old tooth, won't we just.' Lothar massaged the child's gums as Shasa sucked on his finger. 'That's a brave soldier.'

He laid Shasa back in his cot and within minutes he had fallen asleep again.

Lothar picked up the lantern. 'Good night, Mrs Courtney,' he said quietly, and went to the entrance.

'Lothar!' His name on her lips startled her as much as it did him.

'Please,' she whispered, 'I've been alone for so long. Please, don't be cruel to me any more.'

She held out both arms towards him and he crossed to her and sank down on the edge of the cot beside her.

'Oh, Lothar – ' Her voice was choked and gusty, and she wrapped her arms around his neck. 'Love me,' she pleaded, 'oh, please love me,' and his mouth was hot as fever on hers, his arms about her so fierce that she gasped as the breath was driven from her lungs.

'Yes, I was cruel to you,' he told her softly, his voice trembling in his throat, 'but only because I wanted so desperately to hold you, because I ached and burned with my love for you – '

'Oh, Lothar, hold me and love me – and never ever let me go.'

* * *

The days that followed were full recompense for all the hardships and loneliness of the months and years. It was as though the fates had conspired to heap upon Centaine all the delights that she had been denied for so long.

She woke each dawn in the narrow cot and before her eyes were open, she was groping for him with a tantalizing terror that he might no longer be there – but he always was. Sometimes he was feigning sleep and she had to try and open one of his eyelids with her fingertips, and when she succeeded, he rolled his eyeball upwards until only white showed, and she giggled and thrust her tongue deeply into his ear, having discovered that that was the one torture he could not endure, and the gooseflesh sprang up on his bare arms and he came awake like a lion and seized her and turned her giggles to gasps and then to moans.

In the cool of the morning they rode out together with Shasa on the saddle in front of Lothar. For the first few days they kept the horses to a walk and stayed close by the camp. However, as Centaine's strength returned, they ventured further and on the return they covered the last mile at a mad flying gallop, racing each other, and Shasa, secure in Lothar's arms, shrieked with excitement as they tore into the camp, all of them flushed and ravenous for their breakfasts.

The long sultry desert noondays they spent under the thatched shelter, sitting apart, touching only fleetingly when he handed her a book or when passing Shasa between them, but caressing each other with their eyes and their voices until the suspense was a kind of exquisite torment.

As the heat passed and the sun mellowed, Lothar again called for the horses and they rode to the foot of the scree slope below the mountain. They hobbled the horses and with Shasa riding on Lothar's shoulder climbed up into one of the narrow sheer-sided valleys. Here, below a fresco of ancient Bushman paintings, screened by dense foliage, Lothar had discovered another of the thermal springs. It spurted from out of the cliff face and drained into a small circular rock pool.

On their first visit, it was Lothar who had to be coaxed out of his clothes, while Centaine, happy to be rid of long skirts and petticoats which still irked her, delighting in the freedom of nakedness to which the desert had accustomed her, splashed him with water and teased and challenged him until at last, almost defiantly, he dropped his breeches and plunged hurriedly into the pool.

'You are shameless,' he told her, only half-jokingly.

Shasa's presence placed a restraint upon them, and they touched lightly and furtively under the concealment of the green waters, driving each other to trembling distraction, until Lothar could bear it no longer, and reached for her with that determined set to his jaw that she had come to know so well. Then she would evade his clutches with a maidenly squeal, and leap from the pool, slipping on her skirts over her long wet gleaming legs and her bottom that glowed pink from the heat of the water.

'Last one home misses his dinner!'

It was only after she had laid Shasa in his cot, and blown out the lantern, that she crept breathlessly through to Lothar's shelter. He was waiting for her, strung out by all the touching and teasing and artful withdrawals of the day. Then they went at each other in a desperate frenzy, almost as though they were anatagonists locked in mortal combat.

Much later, lying in the darkness in each other's arms, talking very softly so as not to distrub Shasa, they made their plans and their promises for a future that stretched before them as though they stood on the threshold of paradise itself.

* * *

It seemed he had been gone only a few days, when in the middle of a baking afternoon, on a lathered horse, Vark Jan rode back into camp.

He carried a package of letters, sewed up in canvas wrapping and sealed with tar. One letter was for Lothar, a single sheet, and he read it at a glance.

I have the honour to inform you that I have in my possession a document of amnesty in your favour, signed by both the Attorney-General of the Cape of Good Hope and the Minister of Justice of the Union of South Africa.

I congratulate you on the success of your endeavours and I look forward to our meeting at the time and place nominated when I shall take pleasure in handing the document to you.

Yours truly,
Garrick Courtney (Col.)

The other letters were both for Centaine. One was also from Garry Courtney, welcoming her and Shasa to the family and assuring them both of all the love and consideration and privilege that that entailed.

From the most miserable creature, immersed in unbearable grief, you have transformed me at a stroke into the happiest and most joyful of all fathers and grandfathers.

I long to embrace you both.

Speed that day,

Your affectionate and dutiful father-in-law,
Garrick Courtney

The third letter, many times thicker than the other two combined, was in Anna Stok's clumsy, semi-literate scrawl. Her face flushed with excitement, alternately laughing aloud with joy or her eyes sparkling with tears, Centaine read snatches aloud for Lothar's benefit, and when she had reached the end, she folded both letters carefully.

'I long to see them, and yet I am reluctant to let the world intrude upon our happiness together. I want to go, and yet I want to stay here for ever with you. Is that silly?'

'Yes,' he laughed. 'It certainly is. We leave at sunset.'

* * *

They travelled at night to avoid the heat of the desert day.

With Shasa sound asleep in the wagon cot, lulled by the motion of rolling wheels, Centaine rode stirrup to stirrup with Lothar. His hair shone in the moonlight, and the shadows softened the marks of hardship and suffering on his features, so she found it difficult to take her eyes from his face.

Each morning before dawn, they went into laager. If they were between water-holes, they watered the cattle and the horses from the bucket before they sought the shade of the wagon awnings to wait out the heat of the day.

In the late afternoon while the servants packed up the camp and inspanned for the night's trek, Lothar would ride out to hunt. At first Centaine rode with him, for she could not bear to be parted from him for even an hour. Then one evening in failing light Lothar made a poor shot and the Mauser bullet ripped through the belly of a beautiful little springbok.

It ran before the horses with amazing stamina, a tangle of entrails swinging from the gaping wound. Even when at last it went down, it lifted its head to watch Lothar as he dismounted and unsheathed his hunting knife. After that Centaine stayed in camp when Lothar went out for fresh meat.

So Centaine was alone this evening when the wind came suddenly out of the north, niggling and chill. Centaine climbed up into the living wagon to fetch a warm jacket for Shasa.

The interior of the wagon was crammed with gear, packed and ready for the night's trek. The carpet bag which contained all the clothing that Anna had

provided, was stowed at the rear and she had to scramble over a yellow wood chest to reach it. Her long skirts hampered her, and she teetered on the top of the chest and put out her hand to steady herself.

Her nearest handhold was the brass handle of the front of Lothar's travelling bureau which was lashed to the wagon bed. As she put her weight on it the handle gave slightly, and the drawer slid open an inch.

'He has forgotten to lock it,' she thought, 'I must warn him.' She pushed the drawer closed and crawled over the chest, reached the stowed carpet bag, pulled out Shasa's jacket, and was crawling back when her eye fell again on the drawer of the bureau – and she checked herself sharply and stared at it.

Temptation was like the prickle of a burr. Lothar's journal was in that drawer.

'What an awful thing to do,' she told herself primly, and yet her hand went out and touched the brass handle again.

'What has he written about me?' She pulled the drawer open slowly and stared at the thick, leather-covered volume. 'Do I really want to know?' She began to close the drawer again, and then capitulated to that overwhelming temptation. 'I'll only read about me,' she promised herself.

She crawled quickly to the wagon flap and peered out guiltily. Swart Hendrick was bringing up the draught oxen preparatory to inspanning.

'Has the master returned yet?' she called to him.

'No, missus, and we have heard no shots. He will be late tonight.'

'Call me if you see him coming,' she ordered, and crept back to the bureau.

She squatted beside it with the heavy journal in her lap, and she was relieved to find it was written almost entirely in Afrikaans with only occasional passages in German. She rifled through the pages until she found the date on which he had rescued her. The entry was four pages long, the longest single entry in the entire journal.

Lothar had given a full account of the lion attack and the rescue, of their return to the wagons while she was unconscious, and a description of Shasa. She smiled as she read:

'A sturdy lad, of the same age as Manfred when last I saw him, and I find myself much affected.'

Still smiling, she scanned the page for a description of herself, and her eyes stopped at the paragraph:

'I have no doubt that this is indeed the woman, though she in changed from the photograph and from my brief memory of her. Her hair is thick and fuzzy as that of a Nama girl, her face thin and brown as a monkey – ' Centaine gasped with affront ' – yet when she opened her eyes for a moment, I thought my heart might crack, they were so big and soft.'

She was slightly mollified and skimmed forward, turning the pages quickly, listening life a thief for the sound of Lothar's horse. A word caught her eye in the neat blocks of teutonic script; '*Boesmanne.*' Her attention flicked to it. 'Bushmen' – and her heart tripped, her interest entirely captivated.

'Bushmen harassing the camp during the night. Hendrick discovered their spoor near the horse lines and the cattle. We followed at first light. A difficult hunt – '

The word '*jag*' stopped Centaine's eye. 'Hunt?' she puzzled. This was a word only applied to the chase, to the killing of animals, and she raced on.

'We came up with the two Bushmen, but they almost gave us the slip by climbing the cliff with the agility of baboons. We could not follow and would have lost them, but their curiosity was too strong – again, just like baboons. One of them paused at the top of the cliff and looked down at us. It was a difficult shot, at extreme upward deflection and long range – '

The blood drained from Centaine's face. She could not believe what she was reading, each word reverberated in her skull as though it were an empty place, cavernous and echoing.

'However, I held true and brought the Bushman down. Then I witnessed a remarkable incident. I had no need of a second shot, for the remaining Bushman fell from the cliff top. From below it seemed almost as though he threw himself over the edge. However, I do not believe that this was the case, an animal is not capable of suicide. It is more likely that in terror and panic, he lost his footing. Both bodies fell in difficult positions. However, I was determined to examine them. The climb was awkward and dangerous, but I was in fact, well rewarded fo my endeavours. The first body, that of a very old man, the one that had slipped from the cliff, was unremarkable except that he carried a clasp knife made by "Joseph Rodgers" of Sheffield on a lanyard about his waist.'

Centaine began to shake her head from side to side.

'No!' she whispered, 'No!'

'This, I believe, must have been stolen from some other traveller. The old rogue probably entered our camp in the hope of similar booty.'

Centaine saw again little O'wa squatting naked in the sunlight with the knife in his hands and the tears of pleasure running down his withered cheeks.

'Oh, in the name of mercy, no!' she whimpered, but her eye was drawn remorselessly on by the orderly ranks of brutal words.

'The second body, however, yielded the greater trophy. It was that of a woman. If anything she was more aged than the man, but around her neck she wore a most unusual decoration – '

The book slid from Centaine's lap and she covered her face with both hands.

'H'ani!' she cried out in the San tongue. 'My old grandmother, my old and revered grandmother, you came to us. And he shot you down!'

She was rocking from side to side, humming in her throat, the San attitude of grief.

Suddenly she hurled herself at the bureau. She pulled the drawer from its runners, scattering loose pages of writing-paper and pens and sticks of wax on the floor of the wagon.

'The necklace,' she sobbed. 'The necklace. I have to be certain!'

She seized the handle of one of the small lower compartments and tugged at it. It was locked. She snatched the handle of the wagon jack from its slot in the frame, and with the steel point shattered the lock and jerked the compartment open. It contained a silver framed photograph of a plump blond woman with a child in her lap and a wad of letters tied up with a silk ribbon.

She spilled them on to the floor and smashed open the next compartment. There was a Luger pistol in a wooden holster, and a packet of ammunition. She threw them on top of the letters, and at the bottom of the compartment she found a cigar box.

She lifted the lid. It contained a bundle wrapped in a patterned bandanna and as she picked it out with shaking hands, H'ani's necklace tumbled from the

roll of cloth. She stared at it as though it was a deadly mamba, holding her hands behind her back and blubbering softly, 'H'ani – oh, my grandmother.'

She brought her hands to her mouth, and pressed her lips to stop them quivering. Then she reached out slowly for the necklace and held it up, but at the full stretch of her arms.

'He murdered you,' she whispered, and then gagged as she saw the black stains of blood still upon the gaudy stones. 'He shot you down like an animal.'

She hugged the necklace to her breast, and began to hum and rock herself again, her eyes tightly closed to dam back her tears. She was still sitting like that when she heard the drum of hooves and the shouts of the servants welcoming Lothar back to the wagons.

She stood up and swayed on her feet as an attack of giddiness seized her. Her grief was like an affliction, but then when she heard his voice, 'Here, Hendrick, take my horse! Where is the missus?' her grief changed shape, and though her hands still shook, her chin lifted and her eyes burned not with tears but with a consuming rage.

She snatched up the Luger pistol and drew it from its curved wooden holster. She snapped back the slide and watched a shiny brass cartridge feed up into the chamber. Then she dropped it into the pocket of her skirt and turned to the wagon flap.

As she jumped down, Lothar was coming towards her, and his face brightened with pleasure at the sight of her.

'Centaine – ' he paused as he saw her expression. 'Centaine, something is wrong!'

She held out the necklace towards him, and it glittered and twinkled between her shaking fingers. She could not speak.

His face darkened and his eyes were hard and furious.

'You have opened my bureau!'

'You killed her!'

'Who?' He was truly puzzled, and then, 'Oh, the Bushwoman – '

'H'ani!'

'I don't understand.'

'My little old grandmother.'

He was alarmed now. 'Something is very wrong, let me – '

He stepped towards her, but she backed away and screamed, 'Keep away – don't touch me! Don't ever touch me again!' She reached for the pistol in her skirt.

'Centaine, calm yourself.' And then he stopped as he saw the Luger in her hands.

'Are you mad?' He gazed at her in amazement. 'Here, give that to me.' Again he stepped forward.

'You murderer, you cold-blooded monster – you killed her.' And she held the pistol double-handed, the necklace entangled with the weapon, the barrel waving in erratic circles. 'You killed my little H'ani. I hate you for it!'

'Centaine!' He put out his hand to take the pistol from her.

There was a flash of gunsmoke and the Luger kicked upwards, flinging Centaine's hands above her head. The shot cracked like a trek whip, numbing her eardrums.

Lothar's body jerked backwards and he spun on his heels. His long golden locks flickered like ripe wheat in a high wind as he collapsed on to his knees, and then toppled forward on to his face.

Centaine dropped the Luger and fell back against the side of the wagon, as Hendrick rushed forward and snatched the Luger out of her hand.

'I hate you,' she panted at Lothar. 'Die, damn you. Die and go to hell!'

* * *

Centaine rode with a slack rein, letting her mount choose its own pace and path. She had Shasa on her hip with a sling under him to support his weight. She held his head in the crook of her arm, and he slept quietly against her.

The wind had scourged the desert for five days now without cease, and the driven sands hissed and slithered across the earth's surface like sea spume across a beach, and the round seed pods of tumbleweed trundled across the plain like footballs. The small herds of springbok turned their backs to its chilling blast and tucked their tails up between their legs.

Centaine had wound a scarf around her head like a turban, and thrown a blanket over her shoulders to cover Shasa and herself. She hunched down in the saddle and the cold wind tugged at the corners of the blanket and tangled her horse's long mane. She slitted her eyes against the gritty wind, and saw the Finger of God.

It was still far ahead, indistinct through the dun dust-laden air, but it spiked the low sky, even in this haze visible from five miles off. This was the reason that Lothar De La Rey had chosen it. It was unique, there could be no confusion with any other natural feature.

Centaine pulled up the pony's head and urged him into a trot. Shasa whimpered a protest in his sleep at the change of gait, but Centaine staightened in the saddle, trying to throw off the sorrow and rage that lay upon her with a weight that threatened to crush her soul.

Slowly the silhouette of the Finger of God hardened against the dusty yellow sky, a slim pillar of rock, thrusting towards the heavens and then thickening into a flaring cobra's head, two hundred feet above the plain. Staring at it, Centaine was aware of the same superstitious awe that must have gripped the old Hottentots who named it 'Mukurob'.

Then from the base of the great stone monument a dart of light, reflected off metal, pricked her eyes and she shaded them with the blanket and peered intently.

'Shasa,' she whispered. 'They are there! They are waiting for us.'

She urged the weary pony into a canter, and rose in the stirrups.

In the shadow of the stone pillar was parked a motor vehicle, and beside it a small green cottage tent had been erected. There was a camp fire burning in front of the tent, and a plume of smoke, blue as a heron's feather, smeared by the wind across the plain.

Centaine whipped the turban from her head and waved it like a banner.

'Here!' she screamed. 'Hullo! Here I am!'

The two indistinct human figures rose from beside the fire, staring towards her.

She waved and hulloed, still at full gallop, and one of the figures broke into a run. It was a woman, a big woman in long skirts. She held them up over her knees, ploughing with desperate haste through the soft footing. Her face was bright scarlet with effort and emotion.

'Anna!' Centaine screamed. 'Oh, Anna!'

There were tears streaming down that broad red face, and Anna dropped her skirts and stood with her arms spread wide.

'My baby!' she cried, and Centaine flung herself from the saddle and clutching Shasa to her breast ran into her embrace.

They were both weeping, holding hard to each other, trying to talk at once, but incoherently, laughing between sobs, when Shasa, crushed between them, let out a protesting howl.

Anna snatched him from her and hugged him.

'A boy – he's a boy.'

'Michel.' Centaine sobbed happily. 'I named him Michel Shasa.' And Shasa let out a hoot and grabbed with both hands at that marvellous face, so big and red as a fruit ripe for eating.

'Michel!' Anna wept as she kissed him. Shasa, who knew all about kissing, opened his mouth wide and smeared warm saliva down her chin.

Still carrying Shasa, Anna dragged Centaine by one arm towards the tent and the camp fire.

A tall, round-shouldered figure came towards them diffidently. His thinning sandy-grey hair was swept back from a high scholarly forehead, and his mild, vaguely myopic eyes were a muddier shade of the Courtney blue than Michael's had been; his nose, while every bit as large as General Sean Courtney's, seemed somehow to be ashamed of the fact.

'I am Michael's father,' he said shyly, and it was like looking at a faded and smudged photograph of her Michael. Centaine felt a rush of guilt, for she had been false to her vows and to Michael's memory. It was as though Michael confronted her now. For an instant she remembered his twisted body in the cockpit of the burning aircraft, and in grief and guilt she ran to Garry and threw her arms around his neck.

'Papa!' she said, and at that word Garry's reserve collapsed and he choked and clung to her.

'I had given up hope – ' Garry could not go on, and the sight of his tears set Anna off again, which was too much for Shasa. He let out a doleful wail, and all four of them stood together beneath the Finger of God and wept.

* * *

The wagons seemed to swim towards them through the streaming dust, rolling and pitching over the uneven ground, and as they waited for them to come up, Anna murmured, 'We must be eternally grateful to this man – ' She sat in the back seat of the Fiat tourer with Shasa on her lap and Centaine beside her.

'He will be well paid.' Garry stood with one booted foot on the running-board of the Fiat. In his hand he held a rolled document, secured with a red ribbon. He tapped the roll against his artificial leg.

'Whatever you pay him will not be enough,' Anna affirmed, and hugged Shasa.

'He is an outlaw and a renegade,' Garry scowled. 'It goes very much against the grain – '

'Please give him what we owe him, Papa,' Centaine said softly, 'then let him go. I don't want ever to see him again.'

The small, half-naked Nama boy leading the ox-team whistled them to a halt, and Lothar De La Rey climbed down slowly from the wagon seat, wincing at the effort.

When he reached the ground, he paused for a moment, steadying himself with his free hand against the wagon body. His other arm was in a sling across his chest. His face was a yellowish putty colour beneath the smoothly tanned skin. His eyes were darkly underscored, the lines of suffering at the corners of his mouth accentuated, and a dense stubble of pale beard covered his jaws and sparkled even in the poor light.

'He has been hurt,' Anna murmured. 'What happened to him?' And beside her Centaine silently turned her head away.

Lothar braced himself and went to meet Garry. Halfway between the Fiat and the wagon they shook hands briefly, Lothar awkwardly offering his uninjured left hand.

They spoke in low tones that did not reach to where Centaine sat. Garry offered him the roll of parchment, and Lothar loosened the ribbon with his teeth and spread the sheet against his thigh, holding it with his one good hand as he stooped to read it.

After a minute he straightened and let the parchment spring back into a roll. He nodded at Garry and said something. His face was expressionless, and Garry shuffled selfconsciously and made an uncertain gesture, half-offering another handshake and then thinking better of it, for Lothar was not looking at him.

He was staring at Centaine, and now he pushed past Garry and started slowly towards her. Immediately Centaine snatched Shasa off Anna's lap and crouched in the furthest corner of the seat, glaring at him, holding Shasa away from him protectively. Lothar stopped, lifted his good hand towards her in a small gesture of appeal, but let it drop to his side when her expression did not change.

Puzzled, Garry glanced from one to the other of them.

'Can we go, Papa?' Centaine spoke in a clear sharp voice.

'Of course, my dear.' Garry hurried to the front of the Fiat and stooped to the crank handle. As the engine fired, he ran round to the driver's seat and adjusted the ignition lever.

'Is there nothing you wish to say to the man?' he asked, and when she shook her head, he clambered up behind the wheel and the Fiat jerked forward.

Centaine looked back only once, after they had bumped over a mile of the sandy track. Lothar De La Rey still stood below the towering monument of rock, a tiny lonely figure in the desert, and he stared after them.

* * *

The green hills of Zululand were so utterly different from the desolation of the Kalahari or the monstrous dunes of the Namib, that Centaine had difficulty believing that she was on the same continent. But then, she remembered, they were on the opposite side of Africa, a thousand miles and more from the Finger of God.

Garry Courtney stopped the Fiat on the crest of the steep escarpment high above the Baboonstroom river and switched off the engine and helped both women down.

He took Shasa from Centaine and led them to the edge.

'There,' he pointed. 'That's Theuniskraal where both Sean and I – and then Michael – were all born.'

It stood at the foot of the slope, surrounded by rambling gardens. Even from this distance Centaine could see that the gardens were unkempt and overgrown as tropical jungle. Tall palms and flowering spathodea trees were hung with untrammelled mantles of purple bougainvillaea creepers, and the ornamental fish ponds were poisonous green with algae growth.

'Of course the house was rebuilt after the fire,' Garry hesitated, and a shadow passed behind his muddy blue eyes, for in that fire Michael's mother had died, then he hurried on, 'I've added to it over the years.'

Centaine smiled, for the house reminded her of a haphazard old woman who had thrown on garments of a dozen different fashions, none of which suited her. Grecian columns and Georgian red brick flared sullenly at the white painted curlicue gables in the Cape Dutch style. The twisted barley sugar chimney-pots huddled in uneasy alliance with crenallated buttresses and towers of stonework. Beyond it, stretching to the horizon, were waving fields of green sugar cane that moved in the light wind like the surface of a summer sea.

'And over there is Lion Kop.' Garry turned to point to the west where the escarpment made a stately sweep, forming a heavily forested amphitheatre around the town of Ladyburg. 'That's Sean's land – all of it from my boundary. There! Right as far as you can see. Between us, we own the whole escarpment. That's the homestead of Lion Kop, you can just make out the roof through the trees.'

'It's so beautiful,' Centaine breathed. 'Oh look, there are mountains beyond, with snow on the peaks!'

'The Drakensberg Mountains, a hundred miles away.'

'And that?' Centaine pointed over the roofs of the town, over the complex of sugar refinery and lumber mills, to an elegant white mansion on the slope of the valley. 'Is that Courtney land also?'

'Yes.' Garry's expression changed. 'Dirk Courtney, Sean's son.'

'I didn't know that General Courtney had a son.'

'Sometimes he wishes he did not,' Garry murmured, and then briskly, before she could pursue it, 'Come along everybody, it's almost lunchtime, and if we are in luck and the postman has delivered my cable, the servants will be expecting us.'

'How many gardeners do you keep, Mijnheer?' Anna asked, as the Fiat puttered up Theuniskraal's long twisting driveway, and Anna surveyed the confusion of vegetation with a disapproving frown.

'Four, I think – or maybe five.'

'Well, Mijnheer, you are not getting your money's worth,' Anna told him severely, and Centaine smiled at the certainty that from now on the unsuspecting bevy of gardeners would be earning every sou of their wages. Then her attention was diverted.

'Oh, look!' She stood up impulsively and gripped the front seat, holding on to her hat with the other hand. On the far side of the white-painted fence that ran beside the driveway, a troop of yearlings took mock alarm at the clattering Fiat and fled across the lush green kikuyu grass paddock, manes streaming, hooves flying and glossy hides slashing in the sunlight.

'One of your duties, my dear, will be to see that the horses are kept in exercise.' Garry twisted round in the driver's seat to smile at her. 'And we will have to pick out a pony for young Michel here.'

'He is not yet two years old,' Anna intervened.

'Never too young, Mevrou.' Garry transferred the smile to her, and it changed to a lascivious leer. 'Or too old!'

Although her frown stayed firmly in place, Anna could not prevent the softening of her eyes before she turned her face away from him.

'Ah, good! The servants are expecting us after all!' Garry exclaimed, and braked the Fiat to a halt before the double teak front doors. The servants stepped forward in order of seniority to be introduced, beginning with the Zulu chef in his tall white hat and ending with the grooms and the gardeners and stable boys, all of them clapping their hands respectfully and beaming with white teeth so that Shasa leaped in Centaine's arms and let out an excited shout.

'Ah, Bayete,' the chef laughed, as he gave Shasa the royal salute, 'all hail, little chieftain, and may you grow as strong and straight as your father!'

They went into Theuniskraal, and Garry led them proudly through the cavernous rooms in their genteel disarray. Though Anna ran her finger over every object that came in range and scowled at the dust that came off on it, yet from the long baronial dining-room with hunting trophies decorating the walls to the library with more expensive but dusty volumes stacked on the desk and the floor than on the shelves, the homestead of Theuniskraal possessed a benign and friendly atmosphere.

Centaine felt at home almost immediately.

'Oh, it will be so good to have young people here again, and pretty girls, and a small boy.' Garry put it into words, 'The old place so needs livening up.'

'And a little cleaning up won't hurt it either,' growled Anna, but Garry was dashing up the central staircase, sprightly as a lad with excitement.

'Come along, let me show you your rooms.'

The room Garry had selected for Anna was beside his own suite, and although the significance of this was lost on Centaine, Anna lowered her eyes and looked like a demure bulldog as she noticed that a discreet door connected with Garry's dressing-room.

'This will be your room, my dear.' Garry led Centaine along the upper gallery and ushered her into a huge sunny room with french doors opening on to a wide terrace that overlooked the gardens.

'It's lovely.' Centaine clapped her hands with delight and ran out on to the terrace.

'Of course it needs redecorating, but you must choose your own colours and carpets and curtains – now, come along, let's look at young Michel's room.'

As Garry opened the door across the gallery facing Centaine's room, his mood changed dramatically, and as she stepped into the room, Centaine realized the reason.

Michael's presence was everywhere. From the framed photographs on the walls he smiled down at her; Michael in rugby football togs standing arms folded across his chest with fourteen other grinning young men, Michael in white cricket flannels with bat in hand, Michael with a shotgun and a brace of pheasant, and the shock drained the blood from Centaine's face.

'I thought it would be appropriate for Michel to have his father's room, Garry murmured apologetically. 'Of course, my dear, if you don't agree, there are fifteen other rooms to choose from.'

Slowly Centaine looked around her at the shotguns in their racks, and the fishing-rods and cricket-bats standing in the corner, at the books on the shelves

above the writing-desk, at the oilskins and tweed jackets hanging from their pegs.

'Yes,' she nodded. 'This will be Shasa's room, and we'll keep it just as it is.'

'Oh, good!' Garry nodded happily. 'I'm so glad you agree.' And he bustled out into the gallery, shouting orders at the servants in Zulu.

Centaine moved slowly around the room, touching the bed on which Michael had slept, stopping to press a fold of the rough tweed jacket against her cheek and imagining she could smell that special clean odour of his body upon the cloth, moving on to his desk and tracing with her fingertips his initials 'MC' carved in the oaken top, lifting down a copy of *Jock of the Bushveld* from the shelf and opening it at the fly leaf: 'This book was stolen from Michael Courtney.' She closed the book and turned back to the door.

There was a mild commotion in the passageway, and Garry bustled back, directing two of the Zulu servants who were staggering under the weight of a child's cot. Its high sliding sides and massive mahogany construction would have caged a full-grown lion.

'This was Michael's – I think it should hold his son, what do you think, my dear?' Before Centaine could answer, the telephone rang demandingly in the hall downstairs.

'Show them where to put it, my dear,' Garry called as he dashed out again. He was gone for almost half an hour, and Centaine heard the telephone jangling at irregular intervals. When Garry came rushing in again, he was bubbling over.

'Damned telephone just won't stop. Everybody wants to meet you, my dear. You are a very famous lady. Another ruddy journalist wants to interview you – '

'I hope you told them "no", Papa.' It seemed that in the last two months every journalist in the Union had requested an interview. The story of the lost girl rescued from the African wilds with her infant had, for the moment, captivated the fickle interest of every newspaper editor from Johannesburg and Sydney to London and New York.

'I sent him packing,' Garry assured her. 'But there is someone else very eager to see you again.'

'Who is it?'

'My brother, General Courtney – he and his wife have come up from their home in Durban to their other home in Lion Kop. They want us to go across to have luncheon and spend the day with them tomorrow. I accepted on your behalf. I hope I did the right thing?'

'Oh, yes – oh, indeed yes!'

* * *

Anna refused to accompany them to the luncheon at Lion Kop.

'There is too much that needs doing here!' she declared. The servants of Theuniskraal had already given her the name '*Checha*' – 'Hurry Up!' the first word of the Zulu language Anna had learned, and all of them had conceived for her a wary and growing respect.

So Garry and Centaine drove up the escarpment with Shasa on the seat between them and as they pulled up before the sprawling homestead of Lion

Kop with its lovely thatched roof, the familiar burly, bearded figure came limping swiftly down the front stairs to take both of Centaine's hands in his.

'It's like having you back from the dead,' Sean Courtney said softly. 'Words cannot express what I feel.' Then he turned to take Shasa from Garry's arms. 'So this is Michael's son!' Shasa crowed with delight, grabbed a double handful of the general's beard and attempted to pull it out by the roots.

Ruth Courtney, Sean's wife, in that period of her life beyond forty years of age and below fifty when a magnificent woman reaches the zenith of her beauty and elegance, kissed Centaine's cheek and told her gently, 'Michael was a very special person to us, and you will take his place in our hearts.'

Waiting behind her was a young woman, and Centaine recognized her immediately from the framed photograph that the general had kept with him in France. Storm Courtney was even more beautiful than her photograph, with a skin like a rose petal and her mother's glowing Jewish eyes, but there was a pout to her lovely mouth and the petulant expression of a child indulged to the highest degree of discontent. She greeted Centaine in French.

'Comment vas-tu, chérie?' Her accent was atrocious. They looked into each other's eyes and their dislike was strong, mutual and clearly acknowledged by both of them.

Beside Storm was a tall, slim young man with a serious mien and gentle eyes. Mark Anders was the general's private secretary, and Centaine liked him as instinctively as she had disliked the girl.

General Sean Courtney took Centaine on one arm and his wife on the other and led them into the homestead of Lion Kop.

Though the two houses were separated by only a few miles, they could have been worlds apart. The yellow wood floor of Lion Kop gleamed with wax, the paintings were in light cheerful colours – Centaine recognized a whimsical Tahitian scene by Paul Gauguin, and everywhere there were great bowls of fresh flowers.

'If you'll excuse Garry and myself for a few minutes, ladies, we'll leave young Mark here to entertain you.' Sean led his brother away to his study while his secretary poured each of the ladies a cordial.

'I was in France with the general,' Mark told Centaine, as he brought her glass to her, 'and I know your village of Mort Homme quite well. We were billeted there while waiting to go up the line.'

'Oh, how wonderful to have a memory of my home!' Centaine cried, and impulsively touched his arm, and from across the drawing-room Storm Courtney, who was curled with an elaborately languid air on the silk-covered sofa, shot Centaine a look of such undiluted venom as to make her exult silently.

'*Alors, chérie!* So that is the way it is!' And she turned back to Mark Anders and looked up into his eyes and exaggerated her throaty French accent.

'Do you perhaps recall the château, beyond the church to the north of the village?' she asked, making the question sound like an invitation to forbidden delights, but Ruth Courtney intuitively caught the whiff of gunpowder in the air and intervened smoothly.

'Now, Centaine, come and sit by me,' she ordered. 'I want to hear all about your incredible adventures.'

So Centaine repeated, for the fiftieth time since her rescue, her carefully edited version of the torpedoing and her subsequent wanderings in the desert.

'Extraordinary!' Mark Anders interjected at one stage. 'I have often admired the Bushman paintings in the caves of the Drakensberg Mountains, some of

them are really quite beautiful, but I did not realize that there were still wild Bushmen in existence. They were hunted out of the mountains sixty years ago – dangerous and treacherous little blighters by all accounts – and I understood that they had all been exterminated.'

On the silk sofa Storm Courtney shuddered theatrically. 'I just can't think how you could bear to let one of those little yellow monsters touch you, *chérie*. I know I would have simply expired!'

'*Bien sûr, chérie*, and you would not have enjoyed eating live lizards and locusts either?' Centaine asked sweetly, and Storm paled.

Sean Courtney stumped back into the drawing room and interrupted them. 'Well,now, it's good to see how already you are one of the family, Centaine. I know that you and Storm are going to be great chums, what?'

'Indubitably, Pater,' Storm murmured and Centaine laughed.

'She is so sweet, your Storm, I love her already.' Centaine chose unerringly the one adjective 'sweet' that brought forth a blooming of furious roses in Storm's perfect cheeks.

'Good! Good! Is the lunch ready, my love?' and Ruth rose to take Sean's arm and lead them all out on to the patio where the table was set under a canopy of jacaranda. The very air seemed coloured purple and green by the sunlight through the blossom-laden boughs, and they might have been in an underwater grotto.

The Zulu servants, who had been hovering expectantly, at a nod from Sean bore Shasa away like a prince to the kitchens. His pleasure in their smiling black faces was as obvious as their delight in him.

'They'll spoil him, if you let them,' Ruth warned Centaine. 'Only one thing a Zulu loves better than his cattle, and that's a boy child. Now, will you sit next to the general, my dear?'

During the luncheon Sean made Centaine the complete centre of attention, while Storm tried to look aloof and bored at the end of the table.

'Now, my dear, I want to hear all about it.'

'Oh God, Pater, we've just been over it all.' Storm rolled her eyes.

'Language, girl,' Sean warned her, and then to Centaine, 'Begin on the last day I saw you, and don't leave anything out, do you hear? Not a single thing!'

Throughout the meal Garry was withdrawn and silent, in contrast to his ebullient mood of the last weeks, and after the coffee he stood up quickly when Sean said, 'Well, everybody, you must excuse us for a few minutes. Garry and I are taking Centaine off for a little chat.'

The general's study was panelled in mahogany, the books on the shelves were bound in maroon calf, while the chairs were upholstered in buttoned brown leather.

There were oriental carpets on the floor and an exquisite little bronze by Anton Van Wouw on the corner of his desk, ironically a sculpture of a Bushman hunter with his bow in his hand, peering out across the desert plains from under his other hand. It reminded Centaine so vividly of O'wa that she drew breath sharply.

With his cigar Sean waved her into the wingback chair facing his desk, and it seemed to dwarf her. Garry took another chair to the side.

'I've spoken to Garry,' Sean opened, without preliminaries. 'I've told him the circumstances of Michael's death, before the wedding.'

He sat down behind his desk and turned his own gold wedding ring on his finger thoughtfully.

'We all of us here know that in every sense but the legal one, Michael was your husband, and the natural father of Michel. However, technically Michel is,' he hesitated, 'Michel is illegitimate. In the eyes of the law, he is a bastard.'

The words shocked Centaine. She stared at Sean through the rising wreaths of cigar smoke while the silence drew out.

'We can't have that,' Garry broke it. 'He's my grandson. We can't have that.'

'No,' Sean agreed. 'We can't have that.'

'With your consent, my dear,' Garry's voice was almost a whisper, 'I should like to adopt the lad.' Centaine turned her head towards him slowly, and he hurried on, 'It would only be a formality, a legal device to ensure his status in the world. It could be done most discreetly, and it would in no way affect the relationship between you. You would still be his mother and have custody of him, while I would be honoured to become his guardian and do for him all the things that his father cannot.' Centaine winced, and Garry blurted, 'Forgive me, my dear, but we have to talk about it. As Sean has said, we all accept that you are Michael's widow, we would want you to use the family name and we would all treat you as though the ceremony had taken place that day,' he broke off, and coughed throatily. 'Nobody would ever know, except the three of us in this room, and Anna. Would you give your consent, for the child's sake?'

Centaine stood up and crossed to where Garry sat. She sank on to her knees before him and placed her head in his lap.

'Thank you,' she whispered. 'You are the kindest man I know. You have truly taken the place of my own father now.'

* * *

The months that followed were the most contented that Centaine had ever known, secure and sunny and rewarding, filled with the sound of Shasa's laughter, and with the benign if diffident presence of Garry Courtney always in the background and the more substantial figure of Anna in the foreground.

Centaine rode every morning before breakfast and again in the cool of the evening, and often Garry accompanied her, regaling her with tales of Michael's childhood or relating the family history as they climbed the forested tracks along the escarpment or paused to water the horses at the pool below the falls of the river where the spray and white water fell a hundred feet over wet black rock.

The rest of the day was spent in choosing curtaining and wallpaper and supervising the artisans who were redecorating the house, consulting with Anna on the restructuring of Theuniskraal's domestic arrangements, romping with Shasa and trying to prevent the Zulu servants from spoiling him utterly, taking instruction from Garry Courtney in the subtle art of steering and driving the big Fiat tourer, in pondering the printed invitations that arrived with every day's mail, and generally taking over the management and running of Theuniskraal as she had that of the château at Mort Homme.

Every afternoon she and Shasa took tea with Garry in the library where he had been ensconced for most of the day, and with his gold-rimmed spectacles on the end of his nose he would read aloud to her his day's writings.

'Oh, it must be wonderful to have such a gift!' she exclaimed, and he lowered the sheaf of manuscript.

'You admire those of us that write?' he asked.

'You are a breed apart.

'Nonsense, my dear, we are very ordinary people except that we are vain enough to believe that other people might want to read what we have to say.'

'I wish I could write.'

'You can, your penmanship is excellent.'

'I mean really *write*.'

'You can. Help yourself to paper and get on with it. If that's what you want.'

'But,' she stared at him aghast, 'what could I write about?'

'Write about what happened to you out there in the desert. That would do very well for a beginning, I should say.'

It took three days for her to accustom herself to the idea, and brace herself to the effort. Then she had the servants move a table into the gazebo at the end of the lawns and sat down at it with a pencil in her hand, a pile of Garry's blank paper in front of her and terror in her heart. She experienced that same terror each day thereafter when she drew the first blank sheet of paper towards her, but it passed swiftly as the ranks of words began to march down across the emptiness.

She moved pleasant and familiar things into the gazebo to alleviate the loneliness of creative endeavour, a pretty rug for the tiled floor, a Delft vase on the table-top which Anna filled with fresh flowers each day, and in front of her she placed O'wa's clasp knife. She used it to resharpen her pencils.

At her right hand she placed a velvet-lined jewelbox and in it she laid H'ani's necklace. Whenever she lacked inspiration, she threw down her pencil and took up the necklace. She rubbed the bright stones between her fingers like Greek worry beads and their cool smooth touch seemed to calm her and recharge her determination.

Every afternoon from the end of lunch until it was time to take tea with Garry in the library, she wrote at the table in the gazebo, and Shasa slept in the cot beside her or climbed over her feet.

It did not take many days for Centaine to realize that she could never show what she was putting on to the paper to another living soul. She found that she could hold nothing back, that she was writing with a brutal candour that admitted no reserve or equivocation. Whether it was the details of her lovemaking with Michael, or the description of the taste of rotten fish in her mouth as she lay dying beside the Atlantic, she knew that nobody could read them without being shocked and horrified.

'It's for myself alone,' she decided. At the end of each session when she laid the handwritten sheets on the jewelbox on top of H'ani's necklace, she was suffused with a sense of satisfaction and worthwhile achievement.

There were, however, a few jarring notes in this symphony of contentment.

Sometimes in the night she would rise to the surface of consciousness and reach instinctively for the lithe golden body that should have been beside hers, longing for the feel of hard smooth muscle and the touch of long silky hair that smelled like the sweet grasses of the desert. Then she would come fully awake and lie in the darkness hating herself for her treacherous longings and burning with shame that she had so debased the memory of Michael and O'wa and little H'ani.

On another morning Garry Courtney sent for her and, when she was seated, handed her a package.

'This came with a covering note to me. It's from a lawyer in Paris.'

'What does it say, Papa?'

'My French is awful, I'm afraid, but the gist of the matter is that your father's estates at Mort Homme have been sold to defray his debts.'

'Oh, poor papa.'

'They had presumed that you were dead, my dear, and the sale was ordered by a French court.'

'I understand.'

'The lawyer read of your rescue in a Parisian paper, and has written to me explaining the situation. Unfortunately the Comte de Thiry's debts were considerable, and as you are too well aware, the château and its contents were destroyed in the fire. The lawyer has set out an accounting, and after all the debts were paid and the legal expenses, including this fellow's not inconsiderable fees, were deducted, there is very little that remains to you.'

Centaine's healthy acquisitive instincts were aroused. 'How much, Papa?' she asked sharply.

'A little less than £2,000 sterling, I'm afraid. He will send a bank draft when we return the acknowledgement to him duly signed and attested. Fortunately I am a commissioner of oaths, so we can do the business privately.'

When the draft finally arrived, Centaine deposited the most part with the Ladyburg Bank at 3½ per cent interest, indulging only her new passion for speed. She used £120 to buy herself a 'T' model Ford, resplendent in brass and glistening black paintwork, and when for the first time she tore up the driveway of Theuniskraal at thirty miles per hour, the entire household turned out to admire the machine. Even Garry Courtney hurried from the library, his gold-rimmed spectacles pushed up on top of his head, and it was the first time he ever chided her.

'You must consult me, my dear, before you do these things – I will not have you squandering your own savings. I am your provider, and besides which – ' he looked lugubrious ' – I was looking forward to buying you a motor-car for your next birthday. You have gone and spoiled my plans.'

'Oh, Papa, do forgive me. You have given us so much already, and we love you for it.'

It was true. She had come to love this gentle person in many ways, as she had loved her own father, but in some ways even more strongly, for her feelings towards him were bolstered by growing respect for and awareness of his unvaunted talents and his hidden qualities, his deep humanity and his fortitude in the face of a fate that had deprived him of a limb, a wife and a son, and had withheld from him until this late hour a loving family.

He treated her like the mistress of his household, and this evening he was discussing the guest list for the dinner-party they were planning.

'I must warn you about this fellow Robinson. I gave myself pause before inviting him, I'll tell you!'

Her mind had been on these other things, however, not on the invitation list, and she started.

'I am so sorry, Papa,' she apologized, 'I did not hear what you were saying. I am afraid I was dreaming.'

'Dear me,' Garry smiled at her. 'I thought I was the only dreamer in the family. I was warning you about our guest of honour.'

Garry liked to entertain twice a month, not more often, and there were always ten dinner guests, never more.

'I like to hear what everybody has to say,' he explained. 'Hate to miss a good story at the end of the table.'

He had a discerning palate and had accumulated one of the finest cellars in the country. He had stolen his Zulu chef from the Country Club in Durban, so his invitations were sought after even though acceptance usually involved a train journey and an overnight stay at Theuniskraal.

'This fellow Joseph Robinson may have a baronetcy, which in many cases is the mark of an unprincipled scoundrel too cunning to have been caught out, he may have more money than even old Cecil John ever accumulated – the Robinson Deep and Robinson Goldmine belong to him, as does the Robinson Bank – but he is as mean as any man I've ever met. He'll spend £10,000 on a painting and grudge a starving man a penny. He is also a bully and the greediest most heartless man I've ever met. When the prime minister first tried to get a peerage for him, there was such an outcry that he had to drop the idea.'

'If he is so awful, why do we invite him, papa?'

Garry sighed theatrically. 'A price I have to pay for my art, my dear. I am going to try to prise from the fellow a few facts that I need for my new book. He is the only living person who can give them to me.'

'Do you want me to charm him for you?'

'Oh no, no! We don't have to go that far, but you could wear a pretty dress, I suppose.'

Centaine chose the yellow taffeta with the embroidered seed-pearl bodice that exposed her shoulders, still lightly tanned by the desert sun. As always, Anna was there to prepare her hair and help her dress for the dinner.

Centaine came through from her private bathroom, which was one of the great luxuries of her new life, with a bathrobe wrapped around her still damp body and a hand towel around her head. She left wet footprints on the yellow wood floor as she crossed to her dressing-table.

Anna, who was seated on the bed restitching the hook and eye on the back of the yellow dress, bit off the thread, spat it out and mumbled, 'I have let it out three full centimetres. Too many of these fancy dinner-parties, young lady.' She laid out the dress with care and came to stand behind Centaine.

'I do wish you would sit down to dinner with us,' Centaine grumbled. 'You aren't a servant here.' Centaine would have had to be blind not to have realized the relationship that was flourishing between Garry and Anna. So far, however, she had not found an opportunity of discussing it, though she longed to share Anna's joy, if only vicariously.

Anna seized the silver-backed brush and attacked Centaine's hair with long powerful strokes which jerked her head backwards.

'You want me to waste my time listening to a lot of fancy folk hissing away like a gaggle of geese?' She imitated the sibilance of the English tongue so cleverly that Centaine giggled delightedly. 'No, thank you, I can't understand a word of that clever chatter and old Anna is a lot happier and more useful in the kitchen keeping an eye on those grinning black rogues.'

'Papa Garry so wants you to join the company, he's spoken to me ever so often. I think he is becoming so fond of you.'

Anna pursed her lips and sniffed. 'That's enough of that nonsense, young lady,' she said firmly, as she set down the brush and arranged the fine yellow net over Centaine's hair, capturing its springing curls in the spangled mesh set

with yellow sequins. '*Pas mal!*' She stood back and nodded critical approval 'Now for the dress.'

She went to fetch it from the bed, while Centaine stood up and slipped the bathrobe from her shoulders. She let it fall to the floor and stood naked before the mirror.

'The scar on your leg is healing well, but you are still so brown,' Anna lamented, and then broke off and stood with the yellow dress half-extended, frowning thoughtfully, staring at Centaine.

'Centaine!' Her voice was sharp. 'When did you last see your moon?' she demanded, and Centaine stooped and snatched up the fallen robe, covering herself with it defensively.

'I was sick, Anna. The blow on my head – and the infection.'

'How long since your last moon?' Anna was remorseless.

'You don't understand, I was sick. Don't you remember when I had pneumonia I also missed – '

'Not since the desert!' Anna answered her own question. 'Not since you came out of the desert with that German, that cross-breed German Afrikaner.' She threw the dress on to the bed and pulled the covering robe away from Centaine's body.

'No, Anna, I was sick.' Centaine was trembling. Up to that minute she had truly closed her mind against the awful possibility that Anna now presented.

Anna placed her big callused hand on Centaine's belly, and she cringed from the touch.

'I never trusted him, with his cat's eyes and yellow hair and that great bulge in his breeches,' Anna muttered furiously. 'Now I understand why you would not speak to him when we left, why you treated him like an enemy, not a saviour.'

'Anna, I have missed before. It could be – '

'He raped you, my poor child! He violated you! You could not help it. That is how it happened?'

Centaine recognized the escape that Anna was offering her, and she yearned to take it.

'He forced you, my baby, didn't he? Tell Anna.'

'No, Anna. He did not force me.'

'You allowed him – you let him?' Anna's expression was formidable.

'I was so lonely.' Centaine sank down on to the stool and covered her face with her hands. 'I had not seen another white person for almost two years, and he was so kind and beautiful, and I owed him my life. Don't you understand, Anna? Please say you understand!'

Anna enfolded her in those thick powerful arms, and Centaine pressed her face into her soft warm bosom. Both of them were silent, shaken and afraid.

'You cannot have it,' Anna said at last. 'We will have to get rid of it.'

The shock of her words racked Centaine, so she trembled afresh and tried to hide from the dreadful thought.

'We cannot bring another bastard to Theuniskraal, they would not stand for it. The shame would be too much. They have taken one, but Mijnheer and the general could not take another. For the sake of all of us, Michael's family and Shasa, for yourself, for all those whom I love, there is no choice in the matter. You must get rid of it.'

'Anna, I can't do that.'

'Do you love this man who put it in your belly?'

'Not now. Not any more. I hate him,' she whispered. 'Oh God, how I hate him!'

'Then get rid of his brat before it destroys you and Shasa and all of us.'

* * *

The dinner was a nightmare. Centaine sat at the bottom of the long table and smiled brightly, though her eyes burned with shame and the bastard in her belly felt like an adder, coiled and ready to strike.

The tall elderly man beside her droned on in a particularly rasping and irritating tone, directing his monologue almost exclusively at Centaine. His bald head had been turned by the sun to the colour of a plover's egg, but his eyes were strangely lifeless, like those of a marble statue. Centaine could not concentrate on what he was saying, and it became unintelligible as though he were speaking an unknown language. Her mind wandered off to pluck and worry at this new threat that had loomed up suddenly, a threat to her entire existence and that of her son.

She knew that Anna was right. Neither the general nor Garry Courtney could allow another bastard into Theuniskraal. Even if they were able to condone what she had done, and it was beyond reason or hope that they could, even then they could not allow her to bring disgrace and scandal not only upon Michael's memory, but upon the entire family. It was not possible – Anna's way was the only escape open to her.

She jumped in her seat and almost screamed aloud. Below the level of the dinner-table, the man beside her had placed his hand upon her thigh.

'Excuse me, Papa.' She pushed back her chair hurriedly, and Garry looked down the length of the table with concern. 'I must go through for a moment,' and she fled into the kitchen.

Anna saw her distress and ran to meet her, then led her into the pantry. She locked the door behind them.

'Hold me, please Anna, I am so confused and afraid – and that awful man – ' she shuddered.

Anna's arms quieted her, and after a while she whispered, 'You are right, Anna. We must get rid of it.'

'We will talk about it tomorrow,' Anna told her gently. 'Now bathe your eyes with cold water and go back to the dining-room before you make a scene.'

Centaine's rebuff had served its purpose, and the tall, bald-headed mining magnate did not even glance at her when she came back to her seat beside him. He was addressing the woman on his other hand, but the rest of the company was listening to him with the attention due to one of the richest men in the world.

'Those were the days,' he was saying. 'The country was wide open, a fortune under every stone, by gad. Barnato started with a box of cigars to trade, bloody awful cigars too, and when Rhodes bought him out he gave him a cheque of £3,000,000, the largest cheque ever issued up to that time, though I can tell you I myself have written a few bigger since then – '

'And how did you start, Sir Joseph?'

'Five pounds in my pocket and a nose to sniff out a real diamond from a *schlenter* – that's how I got my start.'

'And how do you do that, Sir Joseph? How do you tell a real diamond?'

'The quickest way is to dip it into a glass of water, my dear. If it comes out wet, it's a *schlenter*. If it comes out dry, it's a diamond.'

The words passed Centaine without seeming to leave any impression, for she was so preoccupied, and Garry was signalling her from the head of the table that it was time to take the ladies through.

However, Robinson's words must have made a mark deep in her subconscious, for the next afternoon as she sat in the gazebo staring unseeingly out across the sun-drenched lawns, fiddling miserably with H'ani's necklace, rubbing the stones between her fingers, almost without conscious thought she suddenly leaned over the table and from the crystal carafe poured a tumbler full of spring water.

Then she lifted the necklace over the tumbler and slowly lowered it into the water. After a few seconds she lifted it out and studied it distractedly. The coloured stones glistened with water, and then suddenly her heart began to race. The white stone, the huge crystal in the centre of the necklace, was dry.

She dropped the necklace back into the water and pulled it out again. Her hand began to shake. Like the breast of a swan, shining white, the stone had shed even the tiniest droplets, although it glistened more luminously than the wet stones that surrounded it.

Guiltily she looked around her, but Shasa slept on his back with a thumb deep in his mouth and the lawns were deserted in the noonday heat. For the third time she lowered the necklace into the glass and when the white stone came out dry once again, she whispered softly, 'H'ani, my beloved old grandmother, will you save us again? It is possible that you are still watching over me?'

* * *

Centaine could not consult the Courtney family doctor in Ladyburg, so she and Anna planned a journey to the capital town of the province of Natal, the sea port of Durban. The pretext for the journey was the perennial feminine favourite, shopping to be done.

They had hoped to get away from Theuniskraal on their own, but Garry would not hear of it.

'Leave me behind, forsooth! You've been on at me, both of you, about a new suit. Well, it's a fine excuse for me to visit my tailor, and while I'm about it I might even pick up a pair of bonnets or some other little gewgaws for two ladies of my acquaintance.'

So it was a full-scale family expedition, with Shasa and his two Zulu nannies, with both the Fiat and the Ford needed to convey them all down the winding dusty hundred and fifty miles of road to the coast. They descended on the Majestic Hotel on the beach front of the Indian Ocean, and Garry took the two front suites.

It needed all the ingenuity of both Anna and Centaine to evade him for a few hours, but they managed it. Anna had made discreet enquiries and had the name of a doctor with consulting-rooms in Point Road. They visited him under assumed names, and he confirmed what they had both known to be true.

'My niece has been a widow for two years,' Anna explained delicately. 'She cannot afford scandal.'

'I'm sorry, madam. There is nothing I can do to help you,' the doctor replied primly, but when Centaine paid him his guinea, he murmured, 'I will give you a receipt.' And he scribbled on the slip of paper a name and an address.

In the street Anna took her arm. 'We have an hour before Mijnheer expects us back at the hotel We will go – to make the arrangements.'

'No, Anna,' Centaine stopped. 'I have to think about this. I want to be alone for a while.'

'There is nothing to think about,' said Anna gruffly.

'Leave me, Anna, I will be back long before dinner. We will go tomorrow.' Anna knew that tone and that expression. She threw up her hands and climbed into the waiting rickshaw.

As the Zulu runner bore her off in the high two-wheeled carriage, she called, 'Think all you like, child, but tomorrow we do it my way.'

Centaine waved and smiled until the rickshaw turned into West Street, then she spun round and hurried back towards the harbour.

She had noticed the shop when they passed it earlier: M. NAIDOO. JEWELLER.

The interior was small, but clean and neat, with inexpensive jewellery set out in glass-topped display cabinets. The moment she entered, a plump, dark-skinned Hindu in a tropical suit came through the bead screen from the rear of the building.

'Good afternoon, honoured madam, I am Mr Moonsamy Naidoo at madam's service.' He had a bland face and thick wavy hair dressed with coconut oil until it glowed like coal fresh from the face.

'I would like to look at your wares.' Centaine leaned over the glass-topped counter and studied the display of silver filigree bracelets.

'A gift for a loved one, of course, good madam, these are truly 100 per cent pure silver hand-manufactured by learned craftsmen of the highest calibre.'

Centaine did not reply. She knew the risks that she was about to take, and she was trying to form some estimate of the man. He was doing the same to her. He looked at her gloves and shoes, infallible gauges of a lady's quality.

'Of course, these trinkets are a mere bagatelle. If esteemed madam would care to see something more princely, or more princessly?'

'Do you deal in – diamonds?'

'Diamonds, most reverend madam?' his bland plump face creased into a smile. 'I can show you a diamond fit for a king – or a queen.'

'And I will do the same for you,' Centaine said quietly, and placed the huge white crystal on the glass counter top between them.

The Hindu jeweller choked with shock, and flapped his hands like a penguin. 'Sweet madam!' he gasped. 'Cover it, I beseech you. Hide it from my gaze!'

Centaine dropped the crystal back into her purse and turned towards the door, but the jeweller was there before her.

'An instant more of your time, devout madam.'

He drew down the blinds over the windows and the glass door, then turned the key in the lock, before he came back to her.

'There are extreme penalties,' his voice was unsteady, 'ten years of durance of the vilest sort – and I am not a well man. The gaolers are most ugly and unkind, good madam, the risks are infinite – '

'I will trouble you no further. Unlock the door.'

'Please, dear madam, if you will follow me.' He backed towards the bead screen, bowing from the waist and making wide flourishing gestures of invitation.

His office was tiny, and the glass-topped desk filled it so there was barely

room for both of them. There was one small high window. The air was stifling and redolent with the aroma of curry powder.

'May I see the object again, good madam?'

Centaine placed it on the centre of the desk, and the Hindu screwed a jeweller's loupe into his eye before he picked up the stone and held it towards the light from the window.

'Is it permitted to ask where this was obtained, kind madam?'

'No.'

He turned it slowly under the magnifying lens, and then placed it on the small brass tray of the jeweller's balance that stood on the side of the desk. As he weighed it he murmured, 'IDB, madam, Illicit Diamond Buying – oh, the police are most strict and severe.'

Satisfied with the weight, he opened the drawer of the desk and brought out a cheap glass-cutter, shaped like a pen, but with a sharp chip of boart, the black industrial-grade diamond, set in the tip.

'What are you going to do?' Centaine asked suspiciously.

'The only real test, madam,' the jeweller explained. 'A diamond will scratch any other substance on earth except another diamond.' To illustrate the point he drew the stylus of boart across the glass top of the desk. It screeched so that Centaine's skin prickled and her teeth were set on edge, but the point left a deep white scratch across the glass surface. He looked up at her for permission and when Centaine nodded, he braced the white stone firmly against the desk-top, and drew the point of the stylus across it.

It slipped smoothly over one plane of the crystal as though it had been lubricated, and it left no mark upon the surface.

A droplet of sweat fell from the Hindu's chin and splashed loudly on the glass. He ignored it and made another stroke across the stone, putting more strength behind the stylus. There was no sound, no mark.

His hand began to tremble, and this time he leaned with the full weight of his arm and shoulder as he attempted to make the cut. The wooden shaft of the stylus snapped in half, but the white crystal was unmarked. They both stared at it, until Centaine asked softly, 'How much?'

'The risks are terrible, good madam, and I am an excessively honest man.'

'How much?'

'One thousand pounds,' he whispered.

'Five,' said Centaine.

'Madam, deart sweet madam, I am a man of impeccably high reputation. If I were apprehended in the act of IDB – '

'Five,' she repeated.

'Two,' he croaked, and Centaine reached for the stone.

'Three,' he said hurriedly, and Centaine held back.

'Four,' she said firmly.

'Three and a half, dear madam, my very last and most earnest offer. Three and a half thousand pounds.'

'Done,' she said. 'Where is the money?'

'I do not keep such vast sums of lucre on my person, good madam.'

'I will return tomorrow at the same time, with the diamond. Have the money ready.'

* * *

'I don't understand,' Garry Courtney wrung his hands miserably. 'Surely all of us could accompany you?'

'No, Papa. It is something I have to do alone.'

'One of us, then, Anna or myself. I can't just let you go off again.'

'Anna must stay to look after Shasa.'

'I will come with you, then. You need a man – '

'No, papa. I beg your indulgence and understanding. I have to do this alone. Entirely on my own.'

'Centaine, you know how much I have come to love you. Surely I have some rights – the right to know where it is you are going, what you intend doing?'

'I am desolated, for much as I love you in return, I cannot tell you. To do so would destroy the whole point of my going. Think of it as a pilgrimage which I am obliged to make. That is all I can tell you.'

Garry rose from his desk, crossed to the tall library windows and stood looking out into the sunlight with his hands clasped behind his back.

'How long will you be gone?'

'I am not sure,' she told him quietly. 'I don't know how long it will take – some months at least, perhaps much longer,' and he lowered his head and sighed.

When he returned to the desk he was sad but resigned.

'What can I do to help you?' he asked.

'Nothing, papa, except to look after Shasa while I am gone and forgive me for not being able to confide in you fully.'

'Money?'

'You know I have money, my inheritance.'

'Letters of introduction? You will at least let me do that for you?'

'They will be invaluable, thank you.'

With Anna it was not so easy. She suspected part of what Centaine planned and she was angry and stubborn.

'I cannot let you go. You will bring disaster on yourself and on all of us. Enough of this madness. Get rid of it the way I have arranged, it will be swift and final.'

'No, Anna, I cannot murder my own baby, you can't make me do that – '

'I forbid you to leave.'

'No.' Centaine went to her and kissed her. 'You know you can't do that either. Just hold me a while – and look after Shasa once I am gone.'

'At least tell Anna where you are going.'

'No more questions, dearest Anna. Just promise me that you will not try to follow me, and that you will prevent Papa Garry from doing so, for you know what he will find if he does.'

'Oh, you wicked stubborn girl!' Anna seized her in a bear-hug. 'If you don't come back, you will break old Anna's heart.'

'Don't even talk like that, you silly old woman.'

* * *

The smell of the desert was like the smell of flint struck off steel, a burnt dry odour that Centaine could detect underlying the harsher odour of coal smoke

from the locomotive. The bogey clattered to the rhythm of the cross-ties and the carriage kept the beat, lurching and swaying in time.

Centaine sat in the corner of the small coupé compartment upon the green leather seat and stared through the window. A flat yellow plain stretched to the long far horizon, while in the sky above it was traced the faint promise of blue mountains. There were clusters of springbok grazing on the plain, and when the steam whistle of the locomotive shrilled abruptly, they dissolved into pale cinnamon-coloured smoke and blew away towards the horizon. The animals closest to her carriage pranced high in the air, and painfully Centaine remembered little O'wa miming that arched-back and head-down stotting gait. Then the pain passed and only the joy of his memory remained to her, and she smiled as she stared out into the desert.

The great spaces, seared by the sun, seemed to draw out her soul, like iron to the magnet, and slowly she became aware of a sense of building anticipation, that peculiar excitement that a traveller feels on the last homeward mile of a long journey.

When later the evening shadows turned the plains soft mauve, they gave definition to the land so that the undulations and low hillocks emerged from the glare of midday and the glassy curtains of heat mirage, and she looked upon this austere and majestic landscape and felt a deep sense of joy.

At sunset she put a coat around her shoulders and went out on to the open balcony at the rear of the coach. In fuming dusty reds and orange the sun went under, and the stars pricked out through the purple night. She looked up and there were the two particular stars, Michael's star and hers with only the ghostly Magellanic clouds shining between them.

'I haven't looked up at the sky, not since I left this wild land,' she thought, and suddenly the green fields of her native France and the lush rolling hills of Zululand were only an effete and insipid memory. 'This is where I belong – the desert is my home now.'

* * *

Garry Courtney's lawyer met her at the Windhoek railway station. She had telegraphed him before the train left from Cape Town. His name was Abraham Abrahams, and he was a dapper little man with large pricked-up ears and sharp alert eyes, very much like one of the tiny bat-eared desert foxes. He waved away the letter of introduction from Garry that Centaine offered him.

'My dear Mrs Courtney, everybody in the territory knows who you are. The story of your incredible adventure has captured all our imaginations. I can truthfully say that you are a living legend, and that I am honoured to be in a position to render you assistance.'

He drove her to the Kaiserhof Hotel and after he had made sure she was settled and well cared for, he left her for a few hours to bath and rest.

'The coal dust gets into everything, even the pores of the skin,' he sympathized.

When he returned and they were seated in the lounge with a tray of tea between them, he asked, 'Now, Mrs Courtney, what can I do for you?'

'I have a list, a long list.' She handed it to him. 'And as you see, the first thing I want you to do is to find a man for me.'

'That won't be too difficult.' He studied the list. 'The man is well known, almost as well known as you are.'

* * *

The road was rough, the surface freshly blasted rock, sharp as knife-blades. Long ranks of black labourers, stripped to the waist and glistening with sweat, were pounding the rock with sledgehammers, breaking up the lumps and levelling the roadway. They stood aside, resting on their hammers, as Centaine drove up the pass in Abraham Abrahams' dusty Ford, bumping slowly over the jagged stone, and when she shouted a question, they grinned and pointed on upwards.

The road became steeper as it wound into the mountains and the gradients became so severe that at one place Centaine had to turn the Ford and reverse up the slope. At last she could go no further. A Hottentot foreman ran down the rough track to meet her, waving a red flag over his head.

'*Pasop*, missus! Look out, madam! They are going to fire the charges.'

Centaine parked on the verge of the half-built road under a signboard that read:

De La Ray Construction Company
Road-building and Civil-Engineering.

And she climbed down, and stretched her long legs. She was wearing breeches and boots and a man's shirt. The Hottentot foreman stared at her legs until she told him sharply, 'That will be all. Go about your duties, man, or your boss will know of it.'

She unwound the scarf from around her head and fluffed out her hair. Then she dampened a cloth from the canvas water-cooler that hung on the side of the Ford and wiped the dust from her face. It was fifty miles from Windhoek, and she had been driving since before dawn. She lifted the wicker basket off the back seat and set it beside her as she settled on the running-board of the Ford. The hotel chef had provided ham and egg sandwiches and a bottle of cold sweetened tea, and she was suddenly hungry.

As she ate she gazed out across the open plains far below her. She had forgotten how the grass shone in the sunlight like woven silver cloth – then suddenly she thought of long blond hair that shone the same way, and against her will she felt a rising heat in the pit of her belly and her nipples tightened and started out.

Instantly she was ashamed of the momentary weakness, and she told herself fiercely, 'I hate him – and I hate this thing he has placed inside me.'

Almost as though the thought might have triggered it, it squirmed within her, a deep and secret movement, and her hatred wavered like a candle flame in a draght.

'I must be strong,' she told herself. 'I must be constant, for Shasa's sake.'

From behind her, up the head of the pass, there came the distant shrilling of a warning whistle, followed by a brittle waiting silence. Centaine stood up and shaded her eyes, involuntarily tensing in expectation.

Then the earth leaped beneath her and the shock wave of the explosion beat

upon her eardrums. A dust column shot high into the blue desert air, and the mountain was cleaved as though by a gargantuan axe-stroke. Sheets of grey-blue shale peeled away from the slope and slid in a liquid avalanche down into the valley below. The echoes of the explosion leapt from kloof to kloof, dwindling gradually, and the dust column blew softly away.

Centaine remained standing, staring up the slope, and after a while the figure of a horseman was outlined on the high crest. Slowly he rode down the raw track, the horse picking its way gingerly over the broken treacherous footing, and he was tall in the saddle, graceful and limber as a sapling in the wind.

'If only he were not so beautiful,' she whispered.

He lifted the wide-brimmed hat with its ostrich feathers from his head and slapped the dust from his breeches. His golden hair burned like a beacon fire, and she swayed slightly on her feet. At the foot of the slope, a hundred paces from Centaine, he threw his leg over the horse's neck, slipped to the ground, and threw the reins to the Hottentot foreman.

The foreman spoke urgently and pointed to where Centaine waited. Lothar nodded and came striding down towards her. Halfway, he stopped abruptly and stared at her. Even at that distance she saw his eyes turn bright as yellow sapphires and he launched into a run.

Centaine did not move. She stood stiffly, staring up at him, and ten paces from her he saw her expression and halted again.

'Centaine. I never thought to see you again, my darling.' He started forward.

'Don't touch me,' she said coldly, fighting down the panic rising within her. 'I warned you once – don't ever touch me again.'

'Why do you come here then?' he asked harshly. 'Isn't it enough that your memory has plagued me these long lonely months since I last saw you? Must you come in the flesh to torment me?'

'I have come to make a bargain with you.' Her voice was icy, for she had control over herself now. 'I come to offer you a trade.'

'What is your bargain? If you are a part of it, then I accept before you state your terms.'

'No,' she shook her head. 'I would kill myself first.'

His chin came up angrily, though his eyes were wretched and hurting. 'You are without mercy.'

'That I must have learned from you!'

'State your terms.'

'You will take me back to the place in the desert where you found me. You will provide transport and servants and all that is necessary for me to reach the mountain, and to exist there for a year.'

'Why do you want to go there?'

'That does not concern you.'

'That is not true, it does concern me. Why do you need me?'

'I could search for years, and die without finding it.'

He nodded. 'You are right, of course, but what you are asking will cost a great deal. Everything I have is in this company, I don't have a shilling in my pocket.'

'I want your services only,' she told him. 'I will pay for the vehicles, the equipment and the wages of the servants.'

'Then it is possible – but what is my side of the bargain?'

'In exchange,' she placed her right hand over her stomach, 'I will give you the bastard you left in me.'

He gaped at her. 'Centaine – ' Slow, deep joy spread over his face. 'A child! You are to have our child!' Instinctively, he came towards her again.

'Stay back,' she warned him, 'not our child. It's yours alone. I want nothing to do with it after it is born. I don't even want to see it. You will take it from the childbed, and do whatever you want with it. I don't want it. I hate it – and I hate the man who put it in me.'

* * *

With Lothar's wagons the journey from the Place of All Life to their rendezvous with Garry Courtney at the Finger of God had taken weeks. Their return to the mountain range took only eight days, and would have been quicker, except that they had to build the road for the motor vehicles through several rocky valleys and numerous dry river beds. Twice Lothar had to resort to dynamite to break a way through obdurate rock.

The convoy consisted of the Ford and two lorries, which Centaine had purchased in Windhoek. Lothar had chosen six camp servants, two black drivers for the lorries, and as a bodyguard for Centaine and camp overseer, he selected Swart Hendrick, his Ovambo henchman.

'I cannot trust him,' Centaine had protested. 'He's like a man-eating lion.'

'You can trust him,' Lothar assured her, 'because he knows that if he fails you in even the smallest degree, I will kill him very, very slowly.' He said it in front of Swart Hendrick, who grinned cheerfully.

'It is true, missus, he has done it to others.'

Lothar travelled in the lead truck with Swart Hendrick and the construction gang. In forest country the black gang ran ahead of the slow-moving convoy, hacking out the road, and when the forest opened, they swarmed on to the back of the truck and the convoy bowled forward at a good speed. The second lorry, heavily laden with stores and equipment, followed the first, and Centaine brought up the rear at the wheel of the Ford.

Each night she ordered her tent set up well separated from the rest of the camp. She ate her meals there and slept with a loaded shotgun beside the bed. Lothar seemed to have accepted her terms of contract; his bearing was proud, but he became increasingly silent and he spoke to her only when the conduct of the expedition demanded it.

Once in the middle of the morning when they halted unexpectedly, Centaine climbed down from the Ford and impatiently hurried up to the head of the convoy. The lead truck had hit a spring-hare burrow and broken a half-shaft. Lothar and the driver were working on it, and Lothar had stripped off his shirt. He had his back to her and did not hear her come up.

She stopped abruptly when she saw the pale muscles of his back bulging as he pumped on the jack-handle, and she stared fascinated at the ugly purple scar where the Luger bullet had torn out of his back.

'How close it must have come to his lung!'

She felt quick sharp remorse and turned away, the angry words that had been on her lips unspoken, and she went softly back to her place at the end of the column.

* * *

When at last on the eighth day the mountain appeared ahead of them, floating on its glistening lake of mirage like some great ark of orange stone, Centaine stopped and climbed up on to the bonnet of the Ford, and as she stared at it, she relived a hundred memories and found herself swayed by many conflicting emotions, borne up on the joy of homecoming and at the same time crushed down by the leaden burden of grief and doubt.

Lothar roused her from her reverie; he had come back from the head of the column without her even seeing him.

'You have not told me exactly where you wish me to take you.'

'To the lion tree,' she told him. 'To the place where you found me.'

The marks of the beast's great claws were still slashed into the trunk of the mopani, and its bones were scattered in the grass beneath it, white as stars and shining in the sun.

Lothar worked with his construction gang for two days to establish a permanent camp for her. He built a private stockade of mopani poles around the solitary tree and piled thorn branches against the exterior wall of the stockade to reinforce it and make it proof against predators. He dug a screened latrine pit connected to the stockade by a tunnel of poles and woven thorn branches, and then he set up Centaine's tent in the centre of the stockade, shaded by the mopani, and built an open hearth for her camp fire in front of it. At the entrance to her stockade he constructed a heavy timber gate and a guard house.

'Swart Hendrick will sleep here, always within call,' he told Centaine.

At the edge of the forest, two hundred paces from her camp, he built another larger stockade for the servants and the labourers, and when it was all finished, he came to Centaine again.

'I have done all that is necessary.'

She nodded. 'Yes, you have completed your side of the bargain,' she agreed. 'Come back in three months' time, and I will complete my side.'

He left her within the hour in the second truck, taking only the black driver with him and sufficient water and gasoline for the return journey to Windhoek.

As they watched the truck disappear into the mopani, Centaine said to Swart Hendrick, 'I will wake you at three o'clock tomorrow morning. I want four of the contruction men to come with us. They must bring their blankets and cooking pots, and rations for ten days.'

* * *

The moon lit their way as Centaine led them up the narrow valley to the cavern of the bees. At the dark entrance, she explained where she was going to take them, and Swart Hendrick translated for those who could not understand Afrikaans.

'There is no danger if you remain calm and do not run.' But when they heard the deep hum resound through the cavern, the labourers backed out hurriedly, threw down their loads and gathered into a mutinous, sullen bunch.

'Swart Hendrick, tell them they have a choice,' Centaine ordered. 'They can either follow me through or you will shoot them, one at a time.'

Hendrick repeated this with such relish, and unslung his Mauser in such workmanlike fashion, that they hurriedly gathered up their loads again and

crowded up behind Centaine. As always, the transit of the cavern was nerve-racking but swift, and as they filed out into the secret valley, the moon was silvering the mongongo grove and polishing the high surrounding cliffs.

'There is much work to do, and we will live here, in this valley, until it is finished. That way you will only have to pass through the place of the bees one more time. That is when we leave.'

Abraham Abrahams had instructed Centaine in every aspect of pegging a mining claim. He had written out a sample notice for her and showed her how to set it up. With a steel measuring tape he had demonstrated the trick of squaring a claim across the diagonals, and how to overlap each claim slightly so that there were no holes to give a claim-jumper a toehold.

Still it was hot, exhausting and monotonous work. Even with the four labourers and Swart Hendrick to help her, Centaine had to make every measurement herself and write out each claim notice and attach it to the claim posts of Mongongo timber that they set up ahead of her.

At dusk every evening, Centaine dragged herself wearily down to the thermal pool in the subterranean grotto and soaked away her sweat and the aches of her body in the steaming waters. She was already starting to feel the drag of her advancing pregnancy. She was bigger this time and it seemed harder and more wearying than Shasa's pregnancy had been, almost as though the foetus sensed her feeling towards it, and was responding vindictively. Her back ached particularly viciously, and by the end of the ninth day she knew that she could not contine much longer without a rest.

However, the bottom land of the valley was criss-crossed with neat lines of claim pegs, each standing on its little cairn of stones. The gang had by now become accustomed to the work and it was going more quickly.

'One more day,' she promised herself, 'and then you can rest.'

On the evening of the tenth day it was done. She had pegged out every square foot on the valley bottom.

'Pack up,' she told Swart Hendrick. 'We are going out tonight.' And as he turned away, 'Well done, Hendrick, you are a lion and you can be sure I will remember that on pay day.'

Hard work shared had made them companions.

He grinned at her. 'If I had ten wives as strong as you, and who worked like you, missus, I could sit in the shade and drink beer all day long.'

'That is the nicest compliment anyone ever paid me,' she replied in French, and found just enough strength left for a short, breathless laugh.

* * *

Back in Lion Tree Camp Centaine rested for a day and then the next morning settled down at her camp table in the mopani shade to fill in the claim forms. This was also monotonous and demanding work, for there were 416 claims to process, and every number had to be transposed from her notebook and then fitted into her sketch-map of the valley. Abraham Abrahams had explained to her just how important this was, for each claim would be scrutinized by the government mining inspector and his surveyor and a careless error could invalidate the entire property.

It was another five days before she placed the last completed form on the pile and then bundled them into a brown paper package and sealed them with wax.

'Dear Mr Abrahams,' she wrote, 'please file the accompanying claims with the mining office in my name and deposit the claim deeds with the Standard Bank in Windhoek to the account over which you hold my power of attorney.

'I would be grateful if you could then make enquiry for the most eminent independent mining consultant available. Make a contract with him to survey and evaluate the property which is the subject of these claims and send him to me here by return of the vehicle which brings you this letter.

'When the vehicle returns to me, please see that it is loaded with the stores I have listed below and pay for these from my account.

'One final favour. I would be most grateful if, without disclosing my whereabouts, you would be good enough to telegraph Colonel Garrick Courtney at Theuniskraal to make enquiry of my son, Michel, and my companion, Anna Stok. Convey to all three of them my affection and duty, assure them of my good health and my longing to see them again.

'To you my sincere thanks and good wishes.

'Centaine de Thiry Courtney'

She gave the package and letter to the driver of the lorry and set him on the track back to Windhoek. Because the track was by now well blazed and all the difficult places had been made good, the truck was back within eight days. There was a tall elderly gentleman sitting up beside the driver in the cab.

'May I introduce myself, Mrs Courtney? My name is Rupert Twentyman-Jones.'

He looked more like an undertaker than a mining engineer. He even affected a black alpaca jacket with high collar and black string tie. His hair was dead black and sleeked down, but his sideburns were fluffy and white as cotton wool. His nose and the tops of his ears were eroded by rodent ulcers from the tropical sun so that they looked as though mice had been nibbling at them. There were bags under his eyes like those of a basset, and he wore the same lugubrious expression.

'How do you do, Mr Jones.'

'Doctor Twentyman-Jones,' he corrected her mournfully. 'Double barrel, as in shotgun. I have a letter for you from Mr Abrahams.' He handed it over like an eviction notice.

'Thank you, Dr Twentyman-Jones. Won't you take a cup of tea while I read it?'

'Please do not be misled by the man's sad mien,' Abraham Abrahams assured her in the letter. 'He was assistant to Doctor Merensky who discovered the elevated diamond terraces of the Spieregebied, and is now regularly consulted by the directors of De Beers Consolidated Mines. If further evidence of his standing is required, consider the fact that his fee for this contract is 1,200 guineas.

'I am assured by Colonel Courtney that both Mevrou Anna Stok and your son Michel are in astonishingly good health and all of them send their loving wishes and hopes for your swift return.

'I am sending the stores you require, and after paying for these and settling Dr Twentyman-Jones' fee in advance, the balance standing to the credit of your account at the Standard Bank is £6. 11s. 6d. The deeds to your claims are safely deposited in the bank's strong room.'

Centaine folded the letter carefully. Of her inheritance and the proceeds of the sale of H'ani's diamond, there was a little over £6 remaining – she did not even have the price of a fare back to Theuniskraal, unless she sold the vehicles.

However, Twentyman-Jones had been paid and she could survive for three months longer on the stores she had in camp.

She looked up at him, sitting on her camp chair sipping hot tea.

'Twelve hundred guineas, sir – you must be good!'

'No, madam,' he shook his head mournfully. 'I am quite simply the best.'

* * *

She led Twentyman-Jones through the cavern of the bees in the night, and when they emerged into the secret valley, he sat down on a rock and mopped his face with a handkerchief.

'This really isn't good enough, madam. Something must be done about those revolting insects. We will have to get rid of them, I'm afraid.'

'No.' Centaine's reply was swift and decisive. 'I want as little damage done to this place and its creatures as possible, until – '

'Until, madam?'

'Until we discover if it is necessary.'

'I do not like bees. I swell most horribly from their stings. I will return the balance of the fees to you, and you can find another consultant.' He began to stand up.

'Wait!' Centaine restrained him. 'I have explored the cliffs over there. There is a way to get into this valley over the crest. It will, unfortunately, mean rigging a bucket and pulley system from the top of the cliffs.'

'That will greatly complicate my endeavours.'

'Please, Dr Twentyman-Jones, without your help – ' and he made grumpy little noncommittal noises and stumped off into the darkness, holding his lantern high.

As the dawn light strengthened, he began his preliminary survey. All that day as Centaine sat in the shade of the mongongo, she caught glimpses of his lanky figure striding here and there, chin against his chest, pausing every few minutes to pick up a chip of rock or a handful of soil, and then disappearing again amongst the trees and the rocks.

It was late afternoon before he returned to where she waited.

'Well?' she asked.

'If you are asking for an opinion, madam, then you are a little premature. It will take me some months before – '

'Months?' Centaine cried out in alarm.

'Certainly – ' and then he saw her face, and his voice dropped. 'You didn't pay me all that money for a guess. I have to open it up and see what's down there. That will take time and hard work. I will need all the labourers you have available, as well as those I have with me.'

'I hadn't thought of that.'

'Tell me, Mrs Courtney,' he asked gently, 'just what is it you are hoping to find here?'

She drew a deep breath and behind her back she made the sign of the horns, which Anna had taught her averted the evil eye.

'Diamonds,' she said, and was immediately terrified that saying it out aloud would bring the worst possible luck upon her.

'Diamonds!' Twentyman-Jones repeated, as though it was news of his father's death. 'We'll see.' His expression was lugubrious. 'We'll see!'

'When do we start?'

'We, Mrs Courtney? You will remain out of this place. I do not allow anyone else around me when I am working.'

'But,' she protested, 'am I not allowed even to watch?'

'That, Mrs Courtney, is a rule I never vary – you will have to contain yourself, I'm afraid.'

* * *

So Centaine was banished from her valley, and the days in Lion Tree Camp passed slowly. From her stockade she could see Twentyman-Jones's labour gangs toiling up the cliff path under their loads of equipment to the summit and then disappearing over the crest.

After almost a month of waiting she made the ascent herself. It was an onerous and taxing climb, and she was aware of the load in her womb every step of the way. However, from the top she had an exhilarating eagle's view of the plains that seemed to stretch to the ends of the earth, and when she looked down into the secret valley, it was as though she were looking into the very core of the earth.

The pulley and rope system from the lip of the cliff looked as insubstantial as a spider's thread, and she shuddered at the thought of stepping into the canvas bucket and being lowered down into the depths of the amphitheatre. Far below she could make out the antlike specks of the prospect teams and the mounds of earth that they had thrown up from their potholes. She could even distinguish Twentyman-Jones's lanky storklike gait as he passed from one to another of the prospects.

She sent down a note to him in the bucket. 'Sir, have you found anything?'

And the reply came back an hour later. 'Patience, madam, is one of the great virtues.'

That was the last time she went up the cliff, for the child seemed to be growing like a malignant tumour. She had borne Shasa with joy, but this pregnancy brought pain and discomfort and unhappiness. She found no surcease even in the books she had brought with her, for she found it difficult to concentrate to the end of a page. Always her eyes would go up from the printed word to the cliff path, as though for sight of that lanky figure coming down to her.

The heat became every day more oppressive as the summer advanced into the suicide days of late November, and she could not sleep. She lay in her cot and sweated away the nights, then dragged herself out again in the dawn, feeling drained and depressed and lonely. She was eating too much, her only opiate against the boredom of those long sultry days. She had developed a craving for devilled kidneys, and Swart Hendrick hunted every day to being them fresh to her.

Her belly swelled and the child grew huge, so that it forced her knees apart when she sat, and it buffeted her mercilessly, thumping and kicking and rolling inside her like a great fish struggling on the end of a line until she moaned, 'Be still, you little monster – oh God, how I long to be rid of you.'

Then one afternoon, when she had almost despaired, Twentyman-Jones came down the mountain. Swart Hendrick saw him on the cliff path and came

hurrying to her tent to warn her, so that she had time to rise from her cot, bathe her face and change her sweat-damp clothes.

When he strode into the stockade, she was seated at her camp table, concealing her great belly behind it, and she did not rise to greet him.

'Well, madam, there is your report.' He laid a thick folder on the table before her.

She untied the tapes and opened it. There, in his neat pedantic handwriting, was page after page of figures and numbers, and words she had never seen before. She turned the pages slowly while Twentyman-Jones watched her sadly. Once he shook his head and looked as though he were about to speak, instead he pulled the handkerchief from his top pocket and noisily blew his nose.

Finally, she looked up at him.

'I'm sorry,' she whispered, 'I don't understand any of this. Explain it to me.'

'I'll be brief, madam. I sank forty-six prospect holes, each to a depth of fifty feet and sampled at six-foot intervals.'

'Yes,' she nodded. 'But what did you find?'

'I found that there is a layer of yellow ground overlaying the entire property to an average depth of thirty-five feet.'

Centaine felt suddenly dizzy and sick. 'Yellow ground' sounded so ominous. Twentyman-Jones broke off and blew his nose again. It was quite obvious to Centaine that he did not want to say the fatal words that would kill for ever her hopes and dreams.

'Please, go on,' she whispered.

'Below this stratum we ran into – ' his voice fell and he looked as though his heart was aching for her ' – we ran into blue ground.'

Centaine lifted her hand to her mouth, and she thought she might faint.

'Blue ground.' It sounded even worse than yellow ground, and the child heaved and struggled in her, and despair came down upon her like a flow of poisonous lava.

'All for nothing,' she thought, and she was no longer listening as he went on.

'It's the classic pipe formation, of course, the decomposing breccia composite above with the harder impermeable slaty-blue formation below.'

'So there were no diamonds after all,' she said softly, and he stared at her.

'Diamonds? Well, madam, I've worked out an average value of twenty-six carats to a hundred loads.'

'I still don't understand,' she shook her head stupidly. 'What does that mean, sir? What is a hundred loads?'

'A hundred loads is approximately eighty tons of earth.'

'And what does twenty-six carats mean?'

'Madam, the Jagersfontein assays at eleven carats to a hundred loads, even the Wesselton goes only sixteen carats to a hundred loads – and they are the two richest diamond mines in the world. This property is almost twice as rich.'

'So there are diamonds, after all?' She stared at him, and from the side pocket of his alpaca jacket he took a bundle of small buff-coloured envelopes, tied together with string, and placed these on top of the report folder.

'Please do not mix them up, Mrs Courtney, the stones from each prospect hold are in separate envolopes, all carefully notated.'

With fingers that felt numb and swollen, she untied the string and fumbled open the top envelope. She poured the contents into her hand. Some of the stones were chips not much bigger then sugar grains, one was the size of a large ripe pea.

'Diamonds?' she asked again, wanting his assurance.

'Yes, madam, and of peculiarly good quality on the average.'

She stared dumbly at the little pile of stones in her hand, they looked murky and small and mundane.

'You will excuse the liberty, madam, but may I ask you a question? You might of course, choose not to answer.'

She nodded.

'Are you a member of a syndicate – do you have partners in this venture?'

She shook her head.

'You mean, you are the sole holder and owner of this property? That you discovered this pipe and pegged the claims entirely on your own account?'

She nodded again.

'Then,' he shook his head mournfully, 'at this moment, Mrs Courtney, you are probably one of the wealthiest women in the world.'

* * *

Twentyman-Jones remained at Lion Tree Camp for three days longer.

He went over every line of his report with her, explaining any item of which her understanding was unclear. He opened each of the packages of sample stones, and picked out unusual or typical diamonds with a pair of jeweller's forceps, laid them on the palm of her hand and pointed out their special features to her.

'Some of these are so small – do they have any worth at all?' She rolled the sugar-grain chips under her forefinger.

'Those industrials, madam, will be your bread and butter. They will pay your costs. And the big jewellery-grade stones, like this one, will be the jam on top of it all. Strawberry jam, madam, of the very best quality – Crosse and Blackwell, if you like!' It was as close as she ever heard him come to a witticism, and even then his expression was morose.

The last section of his report was twenty-one pages of recommendations for the exploitation of the property.

'You are extremely fortunate, madam, to be able to open this pipe systematically. All the other great diamond pipes, from Kimberely to Wesselton, were pegged by hundreds of individual miners, and each started working independently of his neighbour's efforts. The result was utter chaos.' He shook his head and tugged at his fluffy white sideburns mournfully. 'Hundreds of plots each thirty feet square all going down at different speeds, with roadways in between and a tangle of wires and pulleys and buckets connecting each to the lip. Chaos, madam, pandemonium! Costs inflated, men killed in cave-ins, thousands of extra labourers required – madness!' He looked up at her. 'While you, madam, have here the opportunity of constructing a model working, and this report,' he laid his hand upon it, 'explains exactly how you should do it. I have even surveyed the ground and put in numbered pegs to guide you. I have calculated your volumes of earth at each stage. I have laid out your first incline shaft for you, and explained how you should plan each level of excavation.'

Centaine broke in on his dissertation. 'Dr Twentyman-Jones, you keep saying "*you*". You don't expect me personally to perform all these complicated tasks, do you?'

'Good Lord, no! You will have to have an engineer, a good man, with experience of earth-moving. Ultimately I envisage that you will be employing several engineers and many hundreds, possibly thousands, of men here at the – ' he hesitated ' – do you have a name for the property? The Courtney Mine, perhaps?'

She shook her head. 'The H'ani Mine,' she told him.

'Unusual. What does it mean?'

'It is the name of the San woman who guided me here.'

'Very appropriate, then. Now, as I was saying, you will require a good engineer to put in hand the initial developments that I have outlined.'

'Do you have a man in mind, sir?'

'Difficult,' he mused. 'Most of the best men are employed permanently by De Beers, and of the others the one that comes to mind first was recently crippled in a blasting accident.' He thought for a moment. 'Now then, I have heard good reports of a young Afrikaner chappie. Never worked with him myself – damn me, what was his name again. Oh, yes, that's it. De La Rey!'

'No!' Centaine exclaimed violently.

'I'm sorry, madam. Do you know him?'

'Yes. I don't want him.'

'As you wish – I'll try and think of someone else.'

In her cot that night Centaine tossed from side to side, trying to get comfortable, trying to adjust the suffocating weight of the child so that she could sleep, and she thought of Twentyman-Jones's suggestion and sat up slowly.

'Why not?' she said aloud in the darkness. 'He must return here, anyway. A stranger coming here at this time might see more than I would wish him to.' And she cupped both hands under her belly. 'It need only be for the initial development stages. I'll write to Abraham Abrahams right now and tell him to send Lothar!' And she lit the lantern and waddled across the tent to her camp table.

* * *

In the morning Twentyman-Jones was ready to leave. All his gear was packed into the back of the lorry and his black labourers were sitting on top of it.

Centaine handed him back the report.

'Would you be so good as to give your report to my lawyer in Windhoek, sir, together with this letter?'

'Of course, madam.'

'He will want to go over the report with you, and then, as I have instructed Mr Abrahams to solicit a loan from my bank, the bank-manager will probably want to speak to you as well, to have your views on the value of the property.'

'I expected that,' he nodded. 'You can rest assured that I will inform him of the enormous value of your discovery.'

'Thank you. In this letter I have instructed Mr Abrahams to pay you from the loan an amount equal again to your original fee.'

'That is unnecessary, madam, but very generous.'

'You see, Dr Twentyman-Jones, at some future date I might wish to retain

your services as a permanent consultant to the H'ani Mine – I wish you to have a good opinion of me.'

'It does not require a fee for that, Mrs Courtney, I find you an extraordinarily plucky, intelligent and comely young lady. I would consider it an honour to work with you again.'

'Then I will ask one final service of you.'

'Anything, madam.'

'Please do not repeat anything of my personal circumstances that you may have observed here.'

His eyes dropped for just a fleeting instant to the front of her dress.

'Discretion, madam, is not the least prerequisite of my profession. Besides which I would never do anything to injure a friend.'

'A good friend, Dr Twentyman-Jones,' she assured him, as she held out her right hand.

'A very good friend, Mrs Courtney,' he agreed, as he took her hand, and for one incredible moment she thought he was going to smile. But he controlled himself and turned from her to the waiting lorry.

* * *

Once again the journey and the return from Lion Tree Camp to Windhoek took her truck-driver eight days, and Centaine wondered more than once during that time if she had not left it too late. The child in her was big and urgent. Impatiently it demanded release, so that when she at last heard the distant beat of the motors of the returning vehicles, her relief was intense.

From the canvas flap she watched the arrival. In the lead truck rode Lothar De La Rey, and though she tried to ignore it, she felt her pulse quicken when she watched him climb down from the cab, tall and elegant and graceful, despite the dust and heat of the long journey.

The next traveller whom Lothar handed down from the truck took Centaine by surprise. A nun in habit and hood of the Benedictine order.

'I told him a nurse, I didn't expect a sister,' she muttered angrily. In the back of the truck were two young Nama girls. Golden-brown skins and pretty little cheerful pug faces, each of them with an infant on her hip, their breasts heavy with milk beneath the cotton print trade dresses they wore, so much alike that they must be sisters.

'The wet nurses,' she realized, and now that they were here, these brown strangers of another race that would give suck to her child, Centaine felt the first truly bitter pang of regret at what she must do.

Lothar came to her tent, his bearing still aloof and reserved, and handed her a packet of letters before introducing the nun to her.

'This is Sister Ameliana of the hospital of St Anne,' he told her. 'She is of my mother's family, a cousin. She is a trained midwife, but she speaks only German. We can rely upon her completely.'

A gaunt, white-faced woman, Sister Ameliana had the smell of dried rose petals about her, and her eyes were frosty and disapproving as she looked at Centaine and said something to Lothar.

'She wishes to examine you,' Lothar translated. 'I will return later to discuss the work you have for my company.'

'She does not like me.' Centaine returned Sister Ameliana's flat hostile stare, and Lothar hesitated before he explained.

'She does not approve of our bargain. Her whole life is devoted to the birth and care of babies. She does not understand how you can give up your own infant – as is apparent, neither do I.'

'Tell her that I do not like her either, but she is to perform the task she came for and not place herself in judgment over me.'

'Centaine – ' he protested.

'Tell her,' Centaine insisted, and they spoke rapidly in German before he turned back to Centaine.

'She says that you understand each other. That is good. She has come only for the child. As to judgment, she leaves that to our Heavenly Father.'

'Tell her to get on with the examination then.'

After Sister Ameliana had finished and left, Centaine read her letters. There was one from Garry Courtney, full of all of Theuniskraal's news, and at the end he had affixed Shasa's inky thumbprint below his own signature with the notation: 'Michel Courtney, his mark.'

Anna's voluminous wad of notepaper, covered with her large ill-formed scrawl though difficult to decipher, left Centaine with a warm after-glow of pleasure.

Then she broke the seal on Abraham Abrahams's letter, the last in the package.

My dear Mrs Courtney,

Your letter and Dr Twentyman-Jones's intelligence have thrown me into a fever of incredulous amazement. I cannot find the words to express my admiration for your achievement nor the pleasure I feel for your great good fortune. However, I will not weary you with my felicitations and will come directly to business.

Dr Twentyman-Jones and I have conducted extensive negotiations with the directors and managers of the Standard Bank, who have studied and evaluated the samples and report. The bank has agreed to make available to you a loan at 5½ per cent interest per annum in the sum of £100,000. You may draw upon this as you require it, and it is further agreed that this is merely a preliminary figure, and that additional amounts will be forthcoming to you in future. The loan is secured by the claim deeds of the H'ani Mine.

Dr Twentyman-Jones has also met with Mr Lothar De La Rey, and set out for him in detail the requirements of "phase one" of the development of the property.

Mr De la Rey has tendered a contract price of £5,000 for the commission of this work. By virtue of your authority, I have accepted this tender and delivered to him the initial payment of £1,000, for which I hold his receipt – '

Centaine skimmed through the rest of the letter, smiling at Abrahams's comment:

I have sent you the stores you required. However, I am much intrigued by the two dozen mosquito nets you have asked for. Perhaps one day you will explain what you intend to do with these, and thereby allay my burning curiosity.'

Then she set the letter aside for later rereading and sent for Lothar.

He came immediately. 'Sister Ameliana assures me that all is well, that the pregnancy proceeds naturally without any complication, and that it is very nearly over.'

Centaine nodded and indicated the camp chair facing her.

'I have not yet congratulated you on your discovery,' he said as he sat down.

'Doctor Twentyman-Jones puts a conservative value on your mining property of £3,000,000 sterling. It almost surpasses belief, Centaine.'

She inclined her head slightly and told him in a straight and level voice, 'As you are working for me and because of the circumstances of our personal relationship, I believe the correct address in future will be Mrs Courtney. The use of my given name suggests a familiarity that no longer exists between us.'

His smile shrivelled and died. He remained silent.

'Now for the work you have undertaken. Let us discuss it.'

'You wish me to begin at once, not after the birth?'

'At once, sir,' she said sharply, 'and I will personally oversee the clearing of the tunnel that leads into the valley, which is the first step. We will begin tomorrow night.'

* * *

By dusk they were ready. The pathway leading up the valley to the entrance of the cavern of the bees had been cleared and widened, and Lothar's labour gangs had carried up the cords of mopani wood and stacked them at hand.

It was as though the bees of the great hive were aware of the threat, for as the sun set, its rays were shot through with the darting golden motes of the swift little insects, and the heated air trapped between the cliffs vibrated with the hum of their wings as they swirled about the heads of the sweating labourers. If it had not been for the protective mosquito nets, it was certain that all of them would have been stung repeatedly.

As the darkness fell, however, the flights of disturbed insects vanished back into the depths of the cavern. Centaine allowed an hour to pass, for the hive to quieten and settle for the night. Then she told Lothar quietly, 'You can light the smoke-pots.'

Four men, Lothar's most reliable, bent over their pots. These were five-pound bully-beef cans, the sides perforated, the insides packed with charcoal and the herbs which Centaine had pointed out to them for gathering. The secret of the herbs was a legacy to her from O'wa, and she thought of the old Bushman now as they lit the smoke-pots and the acrid odour of burning herbs prickled her nostrils. Lothar's men were swinging the smoke-pots on short lengths of wire, to fan the charcoal. They reminded Centaine of the incense bearers in the Easter procession to the cathedral of Arras on Good Friday.

When all four smoke-pots were burning evenly, Lothar gave a quiet order to his men and they moved towards the entrance of the cavern. In the lantern light, they looked like wraiths. Their lower bodies were protected by heavy calf boots and leather breeches, while over their heads and torsos were draped the ghostly white mosquito nets. One by one they stooped into the entrance of the cavern, thick blue smoke boiling up from the swinging smoke-pots.

Centaine let another hour pass before she and Lothar followed them into the cavern.

The acrid smoke had fogged the interior so that she could only see a few paces ahead, and the eddying blue clouds made her giddy and nauseated. However, the dynamo hum of the great hive had been lulled by the smoke. The multitudes of flittering insects hung in drugged clusters from the ceiling and the honeycombs. There was only a sleepy whisper of sound.

Centaine hurried out of the cavern and lifted the net from her sweating face, drinking down draughts of the cool sweet night air to still her nausea, and when she could speak again, she told Lothar, 'They can begin stacking the cordwood now, but warn them not to disturb the combs. They hang low from the roof.'

She did not enter the dark cavern again, but sat aside while Lothar's men carried in the cords of mopani.

It was after midnight when he came out to report to her.

'It is ready.'

'I want you to take your men and go down to the bottom of the valley. Stay there for two hours, and then return.'

'I don't understand.'

'I want to be alone here for a while.'

She sat alone and listened to their voices recede down into the dark gut of the valley. When it was silent, she looked up and there was O'wa's star above the valley.

'Spirit of great Lion Star,' she whispered, 'will you forgive this thing?'

She stood up, and moved heavily to the cliff face.

Standing below it she raised the lantern high over her head and stared up at the gallery of Bushman paintings that glowed in the yellow light. The shadows wavered so that the giant paintings of Eland and Mantis seemed to pulse with life.

'Spirit of Eland and of Mantis, forgive me. All your guardians of the "Place where nothing must die" forgive me for this slaughter. I do it not for myself but to provide good water for the child who was born in your secret place.'

She went back to the entrance of the cavern, moving heavily with child and remorse and guilt.

'Spirits of O'wa and of H'ani, are you watching? Will you withdraw your protection once this is done? Will you still love and protect us, Nam Child and Shasa, after this terrible betrayal?'

She sank down on her knees and prayed in silence to all the spirits of all the San gods, and she did not realize that two hours had passed until she heard the voices of the men coming back up the valley.

Lothar De La Rey held a can of gasoline in each hand as he stood before her at the entrance of the cavern.

'Do it!' she said, and he went into the cavern of the bees.

She heard the clank of a knife-blade piercing the thin metal of the cans, and then the gurgle of running liquid. The pungent stench of raw gasoline flooded from the dark narrow entrance in the rock, and in her ears was the sound of a million bees roused from their smoke-drugged stupor by the reek.

Lothar came out of the cavern, running backwards, spilling the last of the gasoline on to the rocky floor, leaving a wet trail behind him, then dropped the empty can and ran back past her.

'Quickly!' he panted. 'Before the bees come out!'

Already bees were darting about in the lantern light, settling on the netting that screened her face, and more and still more boiled from the apertures in the cliff face above her.

Centaine backed away, and then swung the lantern over her head and hurled it into the entrance of the cavern. The lantern bounced off the rock, the glass shattered and it rolled over the uneven floor. The little yellow flame flickered and was almost snuffed from the wick and then suddenly the spilled gasoline caught. In a whooshing implosion that seemed to rock the earth beneath

Centaine's feet and which hurled her backwards, a great breath of flame shot down the mountain's throat and its gaping mouth filled with fire. The cavern was shaped like a blast furnace, a gale of wind was sucked into it and red flames shot from the openings high up in the cliff-face, burning like fifty torches, illuminating the valley with noon light. The rushing wind swiftly drowned out the agonized din of a million burning bees, and within seconds there remained only the steady roar of the flames.

As the stacked mopani timbers caught and burned, she could feel the heat leap out at her like a savage thing, and Centaine backed away from it and gazed with a horrid fascination at the destruction. From the fiery cavern she heard a new sound that puzzled her, the sound of soft heavy weights thudding to the stone floor, almost as though many living bodies were dropping from the roof of the cavern. She did not understand what it was until she saw a snake of dark liquid, slow and viscous as oil, creep out of the cavern's entrance.

'Honey!' she whispered. 'The honeycombs are melting!'

Those huge combs, the product of a century of labour by a myriad bees, were softening in the heat and falling, a hundredweight at a time, from the high roof into the flames below. The trickle of molten honey and wax turned into a running rivulet, then into a flood of boiling steaming liquid that seethed in the ruddy furnace glow. The hot sweet stench of boiling honey seemed to thicken the air, and the flood of molten gold drove Centaine back before it.

'Oh God,' she whispered, 'oh God, forgive me for what I have done.'

Centaine stood by as the flames burned through the rest of that night, and in the dawn light the cliffs were blackened with soot, the cavern was a ruined black maw and the floor of the valley was coated thickly with a caramelized layer of black sticky sugar.

When Centaine staggered wearily into the stockade of Lion Tree Camp, Sister Ameliana was waiting to help her to her cot, and to bathe the sugar-reeking soot from her face and body.

An hour after noon, Centaine went into labour.

* * *

It was more like mortal combat than giving birth.

Centaine and the child fought each other through the rest of that burning afternoon and on into the night.

'I will not cry out,' Centaine muttered through clenched teeth, 'you will not make me cry, damn you.'

And the pain came in waves that made her think of the high surf of the Atlantic breaking on the barren beaches of the Skeleton Coast. She rode them, from their crests into the depths of each sickening trough.

Each time, at the pinnacle of the pain, she tried to struggle up into the squatting birthing stance that H'ani had taught her, but Sister Ameliana pushed her down on to her back, and the child was locked within her.

'I hate you,' she snarled at the nun, and the sweat burned her eyes and blinded her. 'I hate you – and I hate this thing inside me.' And the child felt her hatred and ripped her, twisting its limbs to block her.

'Out!' she hissed. 'Get out of me!' and she longed to feel H'ani's thin strong arms around her, sharing the strain as she bore down.

Once Lothar asked at the tent, 'How does it go, Sister?'

The nun replied, 'It is a terrible thing – she fights like a warrior, not a mother.'

Two hours before dawn in one last spasm that seemed to cleave through her spine and separate the great joints of her thighs from her pelvis, Centaine forced out the child's head, big and round as a cannon-ball, and a minute later the birth cry rang out into the night.

'You cried,' she whispered triumphantly, 'not me!'

As she subsided on to the cot all the strength and resolve and hatred flowed out of her, so she was left an empty, aching husk.

* * *

When Centaine woke, Lothar was standing at the foot of her cot. The dawn was lighting the canvas of the tent behind him, so he was in dark silhouette only.

'It's a boy,' he told her. 'You have a son.'

'No,' she croaked. 'Not mine. He's yours.'

A son, she thought, a boy – part of me, part of my body, blood of my blood.

'His hair will be gold,' Lothar said.

'I didn't want to know – that was our bargain.'

So his hair will burn in the sunlight, she thought, and will he be as beautiful as his father?

'His name is Manfred, after my firstborn.'

'Call him what you will,' she whispered, 'and take him far away from me.'

Manfred, my son, and she felt her heart breaking, tearing like silk in her chest.

'He is at the nurse's breast now – she can bring him to you if you wish to see him.'

'Never. I never want to see him. That was our bargain. Take him away.' And her swollen untapped breasts ached to give suck to her golden-headed son.

'Very well.' He waited for a minute for her to speak again, but she turned her face away from him. 'Sister Ameliana will take him with her. They are ready to leave for Windhoek immediately.'

'Tell her to go, and let her take your bastard with her.'

The light was behind him, so she could not see his face. He turned and left the tent and minutes later she heard the motor of the truck, as it started and then dwindled away across the plain.

She lay in the quiet tent watching the sunrise through the green canvas of the wall. She breathed the flinty desert air that she loved, but it was tainted by the sweet odour of blood, the birth blood of her son, or was it the blood of a little old San woman clotting and congealing in the hot Kalahari sun? The image of H'ani's blood on the rocks changed in her mind's eye, and became dark seething puddles of boiling honey running like water from the sacred places of the San, and the choking sugary smoke blotted out the smell of blood.

Through the smoke she thought she saw H'ani's little heart-shaped face peering sadly out at her.

'For the child,' she whispered, 'for Shasa.' And the face faded and she saw her firstborn son in its place.

'Shasa, my baby, may you always find good water.' But his image smudged

also and his dark hair turned to gold. 'You, too, my little one, I wish you good water also.'

But it was Lothar's face now, or was it Michael's face – she was no longer certain.

'I'm so alone!' she cried into the silent spaces of her soul. 'And I don't want to be alone.'

Then she remembered the word: 'At this moment, Mrs Courtney, you are probably one of the wealthiest women in the world.'

She thought, 'I would give it all, every single diamond in the H'ani Mine, for the right to love a man, and have him love me – for the chance to have both my babies, both my sons, for ever at my side.'

She crushed down the thought angrily. 'Those are the woolly sentimental notions of a weak and cowardly woman. You are sick and weary. You will sleep now,' she told herself harshly. 'And tomorrow – ' she closed her eyes ' – you will be brave again, tomorrow.'

Author's Note

For the sake of the story, I hope that the reader will forgive the small liberties that I have taken with historical chronology.

In particular I have delayed the introduction of the Albatros scoutplane into the German air force by some months, and I have anticipated the outbreak of the 1918 'flu epidemic by almost a year.

Power of the Sword

For Danielle
with all my love

'If I would have given way to an
arbitrary way, for to have all
Laws chang'd according to the Power of the
Sword, I needed not to have come here.'

King Charles I of England.
Speech on the scaffold, 30 January 1649.

The fog smothered the ocean, muting all colour and sound. It undulated and seethed as the first eddy of the morning breeze washed in towards the land. The trawler lay in the fog three miles offshore on the edge of the current line, where the vast upwellings from the oceanic depths, rich in life-bringing plankton, met the gentle inshore waters in a line of darker green.

Lothar De La Rey stood in the wheelhouse and leaned on the spoked wooden wheel as he peered out into the fog. He loved these quiet charged minutes of waiting in the dawn. He could feel the electric tingle starting in his blood, the lust of the huntsman that had sustained him countless times before, an addiction as powerful as opium or strong spirits.

Casting back in his mind he remembered that soft pink dawn creeping stealthily over the Magersfontein Hills as he lay against the parapets of the trenches and waited for the lines of Highland infantry to come in out of the darkness, to march with kilts swinging and bonnet ribbons flutting onto their waiting Mausers, and his skin prickled with gooseflesh at the memory.

There had been a hundred other dawns since then, waiting like this to go out against great game – shaggy-maned Kalahari lion, scabby old buffalo with heads of armoured horn, sagacious grey elephant with wrinkled hides and precious teeth of long ivory, but now the game was smaller than any other and yet in its multitudes as vast as the ocean from which it came.

His train of thought was interrupted as the boy came down the open deck from the galley. He was barefoot and his legs were long and brown and strong. He was almost as tall as a grown man, so he was forced to stoop through the wheelhouse door balancing a steaming tin mug of coffee in each hand.

'Sugar?' Lothar asked.

'Four spoons, Pa.' The boy grinned back at him.

The fog had condensed in dew droplets on his long eyelashes, and he blinked them away like a sleepy cat. Though his curling blond head was bleached to streaks of platinum by the sun, his eyebrows and lashes were dense and black; they framed and emphasized his amber-coloured eyes.

'Wild fish today.' Lothar crossed the fingers of his right hand in his trouser pocket to ward off the ill luck of having said it aloud. 'We need it,' he thought. 'To survive we need good wild fish.'

Five years previously he had succumbed once more to the call of the hunter's horn, to the lure of the chase and the wilds. He had sold out the prosperous road and railway construction company which he had painstakingly built up, taken everything he could borrow and gambled it all.

He had known the limitless treasures that the cold green waters of the Benguela Current hid. He had glimpsed them first during those chaotic final days of the Great War when he was making his last stand against the hated

English and their traitorous puppet Jan Smuts at the head of his army of the Union of South Africa.

From a secret supply base among the tall desert dunes that flanked the South Atlantic, Lothar had refuelled and armed the German U-boats that were scourging the British mercantile fleets, and while he waited out those dreary days at the edge of the ocean for the submarines to come, he had seen the very ocean moved by its own limitless bounty. It was there merely for the taking, and in the years that followed that ignoble peace at Versailles he made his plans while he laboured in the dust and the heat, blasting and cleaving the mountain passes or driving his roads straight across the shimmering plains. He had saved and planned and schemed for this taking.

The boats he had found in Portugal, sardine trawlers, neglected and rotten. There he had found Da Silva also, old and wise in the ways of the sea. Between them they had repaired and re-equipped the four ancient trawlers and then with skeleton crews had sailed them southwards down the length of the African continent.

The canning factory he had found in California, sited there to exploit the tuna shoals by a company which had overestimated their abundance and underestimated the costs of catching these elusive unpredictable 'chicken of the sea'. Lothar had purchased the factory for a small fraction of its original cost and shipped it out to Africa in its entirety. He had re-erected it on the compacted desert sands alongside the ruined and abandoned whaling station which had given the desolate bay its name of Walvis Bay.

For the first three seasons he and old Da Silva had found wild fish, and they had reaped the endless shoals until Lothar had paid off the loans that had fettered him. He had immediately ordered new boats to replace the decrepit Portuguese trawlers which had reached the end of their useful lives, and in so doing had plunged himself more deeply into debt than he had been at the outset of the venture.

Then the fish had gone. For no reason that they could divine, the huge shoals of the pilchards had disappeared, only tiny scattered pockets remaining. While they searched futilely, running out to sea a hundred miles and more, scouring the long desert coastline far beyond economic range from the canning factory, the months marched past remorselessly, each one bringing a note for accrued interest that Lothar could not meet, and the running costs of factory and boats piled up so that he had to plead and beg for further loans.

Two years with no fish. Then dramatically, just when Lothar knew himself beaten, there had been some subtle shift in the ocean current or a change in the prevailing wind and the fish had returned, good wild fish, rising thick as new grass in each dawn.

'Let it last,' Lothar prayed silently, as he stared out into the fog. 'Please God, let it last.' Another three months, that was all he needed, just another three short months and he would pay it off and be free again.

'She's lifting,' the boy said, and Lothar blinked and shook his head slightly, returning from his memories.

The fog was opening like a theatre curtain, and the scene it revealed was melodramatic and stagey, seemingly too riotously coloured to be natural as the dawn fumed and glowed like a display of fireworks, orange and gold and green where it sparkled on the ocean, turning the twisting columns of fog the colour of blood and roses so that the very waters seemed to burn with unearthly fires. The silence enhanced the magical show, a silence heavy and lucid as crystal so

that it seemed they had been struck deaf, as though all their other senses had been taken from them and concentrated in their vision as they stared in wonder.

Then the sun struck through, a brilliant beam of solid golden light through the roof of the fogbank. It played across the surface, so that the current line was starkly lit. The inshore water was smudged with cloudy blue, as calm and smooth as oil. The line where it met the upwelling of the true oceanic current was straight and sharp as the edge of a knifeblade, and beyond it the surface was dark and ruffled as green velvet stroked against the pile.

'*Daar spring hy*!' Da Silva yelled from the foredeck, pointed out to the line of dark water 'There he jumps!'

As the low sun struck the water a single fish jumped. It was just a little longer than a man's hand, a tiny sliver of burnished silver.

'Start up!' Lothar's voice was husky with excitement, and the boy flung his mug onto the chart-table, the last few drops of coffee splashing, and dived down the ladderway to the engine-room below.

Lothar flipped on the switches and set the throttle as below him the boy stooped to the crankhandle.

'Swing it!' Lothar shouted down and the boy braced himself and heaved against the compression of all four cylinders. He was not quite thirteen years old but already he was almost as strong as a man, and there was bulging muscle in his back as he worked.

'Now!' Lothar closed the valves, and the engine, still warm from the run out from the harbour, fired and caught and roared. There was a belch of oily black smoke from the exhaust port in the side of the hull and then she settled to a regular beat.

The boy scrambled up the ladder and shot out onto the deck, racing up into the bows beside Da Silva.

Lothar swung the bows over and they ran down on the current line. The fog blew away, and they saw the other boats. They, too, had been lying quietly in the fogbank, waiting for the first rays of the sun, but now they were running down eagerly on the current line, their wakes cutting long rippling Vs across the placid surface and the bow waves creaming and flashing in the new sunlight. Along each rail the crews craned out to peer ahead, and the jabber of their excited voices carried above the beat of the engines.

From the glassed wheelhouse Lothar had an all-round view over the working areas of the fifty-foot trawler and he made one final check of the preparations. The long net was laid out down the starboard rail, the corkline coiled into meticulous spirals. The dry weight of the net was seven and a half tons, wet it would weigh many times heavier. It was five hundred feet long and in the water hung down from the cork floats like a gauzy curtain seventy feet deep. It had cost Lothar over five thousand pounds, more money than an ordinary fisherman would earn in twenty years of unremitting toil, and each of his other three boats was so equipped. From the stern, secured by a heavy painter, each trawler towed its 'bucky', an eighteen-foot-long clinker-built dinghy.

With one long hard glance, Lothar satisfied himself that all was ready for the throw, and then looked ahead just as another fish jumped. This time it was so close that he could see the dark lateral lines along its gleaming flank, and the colour difference – ethereal green above the line and hard gleaming silver below. Then it plopped back, leaving a dark dimple on the surface.

As though it was a signal, instantly the ocean came alive. The waters turned dark as though suddenly shaded by heavy cloud, but this cloud was from below,

rising up from the depths, and the waters roiled as though a monster moved beneath them.

'Wild fish!' screamed Da Silva, turning his weathered and creased brown face back over his shoulder towards Lothar, and at the same time spreading his arms to take in the sweep of ocean which moved with fish.

A mile wide and so deep that its far edge was hidden in the lingering fogbanks, a single dark shoal lay before them. In all the years as a hunter, Lothar had never seen such an accumulation of life, such a multitude of a single species. Besides this the locusts that could curtain and block off the African noon sun and the flocks of tiny quelea birds whose combined weight broke the boughs from the great trees on which they roosted, were insignificant. Even the crews of the racing trawlers fell silent and stared in awe as the shoal broke the surface and the waters turned white and sparkled like a snow bank; countless millions of tiny scaly bodies caught the sunlight as they were lifted clear of the water by the press of an infinity of their own kind beneath them.

Da Silva was the first to rouse himself. He turned and ran back down the deck, quick and agile as a youth, pausing only at the door of the wheelhouse. 'Maria, Mother of God, grant we still have a net when this day ends.'

It was a poignant warning and then the old man ran to the stern and scrambled over the gunwale into the trailing dinghy while at his example the rest of the crew roused themselves and hurried to their stations.

'Manfred!' Lothar called his son, and the boy who had stood mesmerized in the bows bobbed his head obediently and ran back to his father.

'Take the wheel.' It was an enormous responsibility for one so young, but Manfred had proved himself so many times before that Lothar felt no misgiving as he ducked out of the wheelhouse. In the bows he signalled without looking over his shoulder and he felt the deck cant beneath his feet as Manfred spun the wheel, following his father's signal to begin a wide circle around the shoal.

'So much fish,' Lothar whispered. As his estimated distance and wind and current, old Da Silva's warning was in the forefront of his calculations: the trawler and its net could handle 150 tons of these nimble silver pilchards, with skill and luck perhaps 200 tons.

Before him lay a shoal of millions of tons of fish. An injudicious throw could fill the net with ten or twenty thousand tons whose weight and momentum could rip the mesh to tatters, might even tear the entire net loose, snapping the main cork line or pulling the bollards from the deck and dragging it down into the depths. Worse still, if the lines and bollards held, the trawler might be pulled over by the weight and capsize. Lothar might lose not only a valuable net but the boat and the lives of his crew and his son as well.

Involuntarily he glanced over his shoulder and Manfred grinned at him through the window of the wheelhouse, his face alight with excitement. With his dark amber eyes glowing and white teeth flashing, he was an image of his mother and Lothar felt a bitter pang before he turned back to work.

Those few moments of inattention had nearly undone Lothar. The trawler was rushing down on the shoal, within moments it would drive over the mass of fish and they would sound; the entire shoal, moving in that mysterious unison as though it were a single organism, would vanish back into the ocean depths. Sharply he signalled the turn away, and the boy responded instantly. The trawler spun on its heel and they bore down the edge of the shoal, keeping fifty feet off, waiting for the opportunity.

Another quick glance around showed Lothar that his other skippers were

warily backing off also, daunted by the sheer mass of pilchards they were circling. Swart Hendrick glared across at him, a huge black bull of a man with his bald head shining like a cannonball in the early sunlight. Companion of war and a hundred desperate endeavours, like Lothar he had readily made the transition from land to sea and now was as skilled a fisherman as once he had been a hunter of ivory and of men. Lothar flashed him the underhand cut-out signal for 'caution' and 'danger' and Swart Hendrick laughed soundlessly and waved an acknowledgement.

Gracefully as dancers, the four boats weaved and pirouetted around the massive shoal as the last shreds of the fog dissolved and blew away on the light breeze. The sun cleared the horizon and the distant dunes of the desert glowed like bronze fresh from the forge, a dramatic backdrop to the developing hunt.

Still the massed fish held its compact formation, and Lothar was becoming desperate. They had been on the surface for over an hour now and that was longer than usual. At any moment they might sound and vanish, and not one of his boats had thrown a net. They were thwarted by abundance, beggars in the presence of limitless treasure, and Lothar felt a recklessness rising in him. He had waited too long already.

'Throw, and be damned!' he thought, and signalled Manfred in closer, narrowing his eyes against the glare as they turned into the sun.

Before he could commit himself to folly, he heard Da Silva whistle, and when he looked back the Portuguese was standing on the thwart of the dinghy and gesticulating wildly. Behind them the shoal was beginning to bulge. The solid circular mass was altering shape. Out of it grew a tentacle, a pimple, no it was more the shape of a head on a thin neck as part of the shoal detached itself from the main body. This was what they had been waiting for.

'Manfred!' Lothar yelled and windmilled his right arm. The boy spun the wheel, and she came around and they went tearing back, aiming the bows at the neck of the shoal like the blade of an executioner's axe.

'Slow down!' Lothar flapped his hand and the trawler checked. Gently she nosed up to the narrow neck of the shoal. The water was so clear that Lothar could see the individual fish, each encapsuled in its rainbow of prismed sunlight, and beneath the dark green bulk of the rest of the shoal as dense as an iceberg.

Delicately Lothar and Manfred eased the trawler's bows into the living mass, the propeller barely turning so as not to alarm it and force it to sound. The narrow neck split before the bows, and the small pocket of fish that was the bulge detached itself. Like a sheepdog with its flock, Lothar worked them clear, backing and turning and easing ahead as Manfred followed his hand signals.

'Still too much!' Lothar muttered to himself. They had separated a minute portion of the shoal from the main body, but Lothar estimated it was still well over a thousand tons – even more depending on the depth of fish beneath that he could only guess at.

It was a risk, a high risk. From the corner of his eye he could see Da Silva agitatedly signalling caution, and now he whistled, squeaking with agitation. The old man was afraid of this much fish and Lothar grinned; his yellow eyes narrowed and glittered like polished topaz as he signalled Manfred up to throwing speed and deliberately turned his back on the old man.

At five knots he checked Manfred and brought him around in a tight turn, forcing the pocket of fish to bunch up in the centre of the circle, and then as they came around the second time and the trawler passed downwind of the shoal, Lothar spun to face the stern and cupped both hands to his mouth.

'*Los!*' he bellowed. 'Throw her loose!'

The black Herero crewman standing on the stern flipped the slippery knot that held the painter of the dinghy and threw it overboard. The little wooden dinghy, with Da Silva clinging to the gunwale and still howling protests, fell away behind them, bobbing in their wake, and it pulled the end of the heavy brown net over the side with it.

As the trawler steamed in its circle about the shoal, the coarse brown mesh rasped and hissed out over the wooden rail, the cork line uncoiled like a python and streamed overside, an umbilical cord between the trawler and the dinghy. coming around across the wind, the line of corks, evenly spaced as beads on a string, formed a circle around the dense dark shoal and now the dinghy with Da Silva slumped in resignation was dead ahead.

Manfred balanced the wheel against the drag of the great net, making minute adjustments as he laid the trawler alongside the rocking dinghy and shut the throttle as they touched lightly. Now the nest was closed, hemming in the shoal, and Da Silva scrambled up the side of the trawler with the ends of the heavy three-inch manila lines over his shoulder.

'You'll lose your net,' he howled at Lothar. 'Only a crazy man would close the purse on this shoal – they'll run away with your net. St Anthony and the blessed St Mark are my witnesses – ' But under Lothar's terse direction the Herero crewmen were already into the routine of net recovery. Two of them lifted the main cork line off Da Silva's shoulders and made it fast, while another was helping Lothar lead the purse line to the main winch.

'It's my net, and my fish,' Lothar grunted at him as he started the winch with a clattering roar. 'Get the bucky hooked on!'

The net was hanging seventy feet deep into the clear green water, but the bottom was open. The first and urgent task was to close it before the shoal discovered this escape. Crouched over the winch, the muscles in his bare arms knotting and bunching beneath the tanned brown skin, Lothar was swinging his shoulders rhythmically as he brought the purse line in hand over hand around the revolving drum of the winch. The purse line running through the steel rings around the bottom of the net was closing the mouth like the drawstring of a monstrous tobacco pouch.

In the wheelhouse Manfred was using delicate touches of forward and reverse to manoeuvre the stern of the trawler away from the net and prevent it fouling the propeller, while old Da Silva had worked the dinghy out to the far side of the cork line and hooked onto it to provide extra buoyancy for the critical moment when the oversized shoal realized that it was trapped and began to panic. Working swiftly, Lothar hauled in the heavy purse line until at last the bunch of steel rings came in glistening and streaming over the side. The net was closed, the shoal was in the bag.

With sweat running down his cheeks and soaking his shirt, Lothar leaned against the gunwale so winded that he could not speak. His long silver-white hair, heavy with sweat, streamed down over his forehead and into his eyes as he gesticulated to Da Silva.

The cork line was laid out in a neat circle on the gentle undulating swells of the cold green Benguela Current, with the bucky hooked onto the side farthest from the trawler. But as Lothar watched it, gasping and heaving for breath, the circle of bobbing corks changed shape, elongating swiftly as the shoal felt the net for the first time and in a concerted rush pushed against it. Then the thrust

was reversed as the shoal turned and rushed back, dragging the net and the dinghy with it as though it were a scrap of floating seaweed.

The power of the shoal was as irresistible as Leviathan.

'By God, we've got even more than I reckoned,' Lothar panted. Then, rousing himself, he flicked the wet blond hair from his eyes and ran to the wheelhouse.

The shoal was surging back and forth in the net, tossing the dinghy about lightly on the churning waters, and Lothar felt the deck of the trawler list sharply under him as the mass of fish dragged abruptly on the heavy lines.

'Da Silva was right. They are going crazy,' he whispered, and reached for the handle of the foghorn. He blew three sharp ringing blasts, the request for assistance, and as he ran back onto the deck he saw the other three trawlers turn and race towards him. None of them had as yet plucked up the courage to throw their own nets at the huge shoal.

'Hurry! Damn you, hurry!' Lothar snarled ineffectually at them, and then at his crew, 'All hands to dry up!'

His crew hesitated, hanging back, reluctant to handle that net.

'Move, you black bastards!' Lothar bellowed at them, setting the example by leaping to the gunwale. They had to compress the shoal, pack the tiny fish so closely as to rob them of their strength.

The net was coarse and sharp as barbed wire, but they bent to it in a row, using the roll of the hull in the low swell to work the net in by hand, recovering a few feet with each concerted heave.

Then the shoal surged again, and all the net they had won was ripped from their hands. One of the Herero crew was too slow to let it go and the fingers of his right hand were caught in the coarse mesh. The flesh was stripped of his fingers like a glove, leaving bare white bone and raw flesh. He screamed and clutched the maimed hand to his chest, trying to staunch the spurt of bright blood. It sprayed into his own face and ran down the sweat-polished black skin of his chest and belly and soaked into his breeches.

'Manfred!' Lothar yelled. 'See to him!' and he switched all his attention back to the net. The shoal was sounding, dragging one end of the cork line below the surface, and a small part of the shoal escaped over the top, spreading like dark green smoke across the bright waters.

'Good riddance,' Lothar muttered, but the vast bulk of the shoal was still trapped and the cork line bobbed to the surface. Again the shoal surged downwards, and this time the heavy fifty-foot trawler lister over dangerously so that the crew clutched for handholds, their faces turning ashy grey beneath their dark skin.

Across the circle of the cork line the dinghy was dragged over sharply, and it did not have the buoyancy to resist. Green water poured in over the gunwale, swamping it.

'Jump!' Lothar yelled at the old man. 'Get clear of the net!' They both understood the danger.

The previous season one of their crew had fallen into the net. The fish had immediately pushed against him in unison, driving him below the surface, fighting against the resistance of his body in their efforts to escape.

When, hours later, they had at last recovered the corpse from the bottom of the net, they had found that the fish had been forced by their own efforts and the enormous pressure in the depths of the trapped shoal into all the man's body openings. They had thrust down his open mouth into his belly; they had

been driven like silver daggers into the eye-sockets, displacing the eyeballs and entering the brain. They had even burst through the threadbare stuff of his breeches and penetrated his anus so that his belly and bowels were stuffed with dead fish and he was bloated like a grotesque balloon. It was a sight none of them would ever forget.

'Get clear of the net!' Lothar screamed again and Da Silva threw himself over the far side of the sinking dinghy just as it was dragged beneath the surface. He splashed frantically as his heavy seaboots began to drag him under.

However, Swart Hendrick was there to rescue him. He laid his trawler neatly alongside the bulging cork line, and two of his crew hauled Da Silva up the side while the others crowded the rail and under Swart Hendrick's direction hooked onto the far side of the net.

'If only the net holds,' Lothar grunted, for the two other trawlers had come up now and fastened onto the cork line. The four big boats formed a circle around the captive shoal and, working in a frenzy, the crewmen stooped over the net and started to 'dry up'.

Foot by foot they hauled up the net, twelve men on each trawler, even Manfred taking his place at his father's shoulder. They grunted and heaved and sweated, fresh blood on their torn hands when the shoal surged and burning agony in their backs and bellies, but slowly, an inch at a time, they subdued the hug shoal, until at last it was 'dried up', and the upper fish were flapping helplessly high and dry on the compacted mass of their fellows, who were drowning and dying in the crush.

'Dip them out!' Lothar shouted, and on each of the trawlers the three dip-men pulled the long-handed dip-nets from the racks over the top of the wheelhouses and dragged them down the deck.

The dip-nets were the same shape as a butterfly-net, or those little hand nets with which children catch shrimps and crabs in rock pools at the seaside. The handles of these nets, however, were thirty feet long and the net purse could scoop up a ton of living fish at a time. At three points around the steel ring that formed the mouth of the net were attached manila lines; these were spliced to the heavier winch line by which the dip-net was lifted and lowered. The foot of the net could be opened or closed by a purse line through a set of smaller rings, exactly the same arrangement as the closure of the great main net.

While the dip-net was manhandled into position, Lothar and Manfred were knocking the covers off the hatch of the hold. Then they hurried to their positions, Lothar on the winch and Manfred holding the end of the purse line of the dip-net. With a squeal and clatter Lothar winched the dip-net onto the derrick above their heads while the three men on the long handle swung the net outboard over the trapped and struggling shoal. Manfred jerked hard on the purse line, closing the bottom of the dip-net.

Lothar slammed the winch gear into reverse and with another squeal of the pulley block the heavy head of the net dropped into the silver mass of fish. The three dip-men leaned all their weight on the handle, forcing the net deeply into the living porridge of pilchards.

'Coming up!' Lothar yelled and changed the winch into forward gear. The net was dragged upwards through the shoal and burst out filled with a ton of quivering, flapping pilchards. With Manfred grimly hanging onto the purse line, the full net was swung inboard over the gaping hatch of the hold.

'Let go!' Lothar shouted at his son, and Manfred released the purse line. The bottom of the net opened and a ton of pilchards showered down into the open

hold. The tiny scales had been rubbed from the bodies of the fish by this rough treatment and now they swirled down over the men on the deck like snowflakes, sparkling in the sunlight with pretty shades of pink and rose and gold.

As the net emptied, Manfred jerked the purse line closed and the dip-men swung the handle outboards, the winch squealed into reverse and the net dropped into the shoal for the whole sequence to be repeated. On each of the other three trawlers the dip-men and winch driver also were hard at work, and every few seconds another ton load of fish, seawater and clouds of translucent scales streaming from it, was swung over the waiting hatches and poured into them.

It was heartbreaking, back-straining work, monotonous and repetitive, and each time the net swung overhead the crew were drenched with icy seawater and covered with scales. As the dip-men faltered with exhaustion, the skippers changed them without breaking the rhythm of swing and lift and drop, spelling the men working on the main net with those on the handle of the dip-net, although Lothar remained at the winch, tall and alert and indefatigable, his white-blond hair, thick with glittering fish scales, shining in the sunlight like a beacon fire.

'Silver threepennies.' He grinned to himself, as the fish showered into the holds on all four of his trawlers. 'Shiny threepenny bits, not fish. We will take in a deckload of tickeys today.' 'Tickey' was the slang for a threepenny coin.

'Deckload!' he bellowed across the diminishing circle of the main net to where Swart Hendrick worked at his own winch, stripped to the waist and glistening like polished ebony.

'Deckload!' he bellowed back at Lothar, revelling in the physical effort which allowed him to flaunt his superior strength in the faces of his crew. Already the holds of the trawlers were brimming full, each of them had over a hundred and fifty tons aboard, and now they were going to deckload.

Again it was a risk. Once loaded, the boats could not be lightened again until they reached harbour and were pumped out into the factory. Deckloading would burden each hull with another hundred tons of dead weight, far over the safe limit. If the weather turned, if the wind switched into the north-west, then the giant sea that would build up rapidly would hammer the overloaded trawlers into the cold green depths.

'The weather will hold,' Lothar assured himself as he toiled at the winch. He was on the crest of a wave; nothing could stop him now. He had taken one fearsome risk and it had paid him with nearly a thousand tons of fish, four deckloads of fish, worth fifty pounds a ton in profits. Fifty thousand pounds in a single throw. The greatest stoke of fortune of his life. He could have lost his net or his boat or his life – instead he had paid off his debts with one throw of the net.

'By God,' he whispered, as he slaved at the winch, 'nothing can go wrong now, nothing can touch me now. I'm free and clear.'

So with the holds full they began to deckload the trawlers, filling them to the tops of the gunwales with a silver swamp of fish into which the crew sank waist-deep as they dried the net and swung the long handle of the dip.

Over the four trawlers hovered a dense white cloud of seabirds, adding their voracious squawking and screeching to the cacophony of the winches, diving into the purse of the net to gorge themselves until they could eat no more, could not even fly but drifted away on the current, bloated and uncomfortable, feathers started and throats straining to keep down the contents of their swollen

crops. At the bows and stern of each trawler stood a man with a sharpened boathook, with which he stabbed and hacked at the big sharks that thrashed at the surface in their efforts to reach the mass of trapped fish. Their razor-sharp triangular fangs could cut through even the tough mesh of the net.

While the birds and sharks gorged, the hulls of the trawlers sank lower and still lower into the water, until at last a little after the sun had nooned even Lothar had to call enough. There was no reason for another load; each time they swung one aboard it merely slithered over the side to feed the circling sharks.

Lothar switched off the winch. There was probably another hundred tons of fish still floating in the main net, most of them drowned and crushed. 'Empty the net,' he ordered. 'Let them go! Get the net on board.'

The four trawlers, each of them so low in the water that seawater washed in through the scuppers at each roll, and their speed reduced to an ungainly waddling motion like a string of heavily pregnant ducks, turned towards the land in line astern with Lothar leading them.

Behind them they left an area of almost half a square mile of the ocean carpeted with dead fish, floating silver belly up, as thick as autumn leaves on the forest floor. On top of them drifted thousands of satiated seagulls and beneath them the big sharks swirled and feasted still.

The exhausted crews dragged themselves through the quicksands of still quivering kicking fish that glutted the deck to the forecastle companionway. Below deck they threw themselves still soaked with fish-slime and seawater onto their cramped bunks.

In the wheelhouse Lothar drank two mugs of hot coffee then checked the chronometer above his head.

'Four hours' run back to the factory,' he said. 'Just time for our lessons.'

'Oh Pa!' the boy pleaded. 'Not today, today is special. Do we have to learn today?'

There was no school at Walvis Bay. The nearest was the German School at Swakopmund, thirty kilometres away. Lothar had been both father and mother to the boy from the very day of his birth. He had taken him wet and bloody from the childbed. His mother had never even laid eyes upon him. That had been part of their unnatural bargain. He had reared the boy alone, unaided except for the milk that the brown Nama wetnurses had provided. They had grown so close that Lothar could not bear to be parted from him for a single day. He had even taken over his education rather than send him away.

'No day is that special,' he told Manfred. 'Every day we learn. Muscles don't make a man strong.' He tapped his head. 'This is what makes a man strong. Get the books!'

Manfred rolled his eyes at Da Silva for sympathy but he knew better than to argue further.

'Take the wheel.' Lothar handed over to the old boatman and went to sit beside his son at the small chart-table. 'Not arithmetic.' He shook his head. 'It's English today.'

'I hate English!' Manfred declared vehemently. 'I hate English and I hate the English.'

Lothar nodded. 'Yes.' he agreed. 'The English are our enemies. They have always been and always will be our enemies. That is why we have to arm ourselves with their weapons. That is why we learn the language – so when the time comes we will be able to use it in the battle against them.'

He spoke in English for the first time that day. Manfred started to reply in Afrikaans, the South African Dutch patois that had only obtained recognition as a separate language and been adopted as an official language of the Union of South Africa in 1918, over a year before Manfred was born. Lothar held up his hand to stop him.

'English,' he admonished. 'Speak English only.'

For an hour they worked together, reading aloud from the King James version of the Bible and from a two-month-old copy of the *Cape Times*, and then Lothar set him a page of dictation. The labour in this unfamiliar language made Manfred fidget and frown and nibble his pencil, until at last he could contain himself no longer.

'Tell me about Grandpa, and the oath!' he wheedled his father.

Lothar grinned. 'You're a cunning little monkey, aren't you. Anything to get out of work.'

'Please Pa – '

'I've told you a hundred times.'

'Tell me again. It's a special day.'

Lothar glanced out of the wheelhouse window at the precious silver cargo. The boy was right, it was a very special day. Today he was free and clear of debt, after five long hard years.

'All right.' He nodded. 'I'll tell you again, but in English.' And Manfred shut his exercise book with an enthusiastic snap and leaned across the table, his amber eyes glowing with anticipation.

The story of the great rebellion had been repeated so often that Manfred had it by heart and he corrected any discrepancy or departure from the original, or called his father back if he left out any of the details.

'Well then,' Lothar started, 'when the treacherous English King George V declared war on Kaiser Wilhelm of Germany in 1914, your grandpa and I knew our duty. We kissed your grandmother goodbye – '

'What colour was my grandmother's hair?' Manfred demanded.

'Your grandmother was a beautiful German noblewoman, and her hair was the colour of ripe wheat in the sunlight.'

'Just like mine,' Manfred prompted him.

'Just like yours,' Lothar smiled. 'And Grandpa and I rode out on our warhorses to join old General Maritz and his six hundred heroes on the banks of the Orange river where he was about to go out against old *Slim* Jannie Smuts.' *Slim* was the Afrikaans word for tricky or treacherous, and Manfred nodded avidly.

'Go on, Pa, go on!'

When Lothar reached the description of the first battle in which Jannie Smuts' troops had smashed the rebellion with machine-guns and artillery, the boy's eyes clouded with sorrow.

'But you fought like demons, didn't you, Pa?'

'We fought like madmen, but there were too many of them and they were armed with great cannons and machine-guns. Then your grandpa was hit in the stomach and I put him up on my horse and carried him off the battlefield.' Fat tears glistened in the boy's eyes now as Lothar ended.

'When at last he was dying your grandfather took the old black Bible from the saddle bag on which his head was pillowed, and he made me swear on oath upon the book.'

'I know the oath.' Manfred cut in. 'Let me tell it!'

'What was the oath?' Lothar nodded agreement.

'Grandpa said: "Promise me, my son, with your hand upon the book, promise me that the war with the English will never end."'

'Yes,' Lothar nodded again. 'That was the oath, the solemn oath I made to my father as he lay dying.' He reached out and took the boy's hand and squeezed it hard.

Old Da Silva broke the mood; he coughed and hawked and spat through the wheelhouse window.

'You should be ashamed – filling the child's head with hatred and death,' he said, and Lothar stood up abruptly.

'Guard your mouth, old man,' he warned. 'This is no business of yours.'

'Thank the Holy Virgin,' Da Silva grumbled, 'for that is devil's business indeed.'

Lothar scowled and turned away from him. 'Manfred, that's enough for today. Put the books away.'

He swung out of the wheelhouse and scrambled up onto the roof. As he settled comfortably against the coaming, he took a long black cheroot from his top pocket and bit off the tip. He spat the stub overside and patted his pockets for the matches. The boy stuck his head over the edge of the coaming, hesitated shyly and when his father did not send him away – sometimes he was moody and withdrawn and wanted to be alone – Manfred crept up and sat beside him.

Lothar cupped his hands around the flare of the match and sucked the cheroot smoke down deeply into his lungs and then he held up the match and let the wind extinguish it. He flicked it overboard, and let his arm fall casually over his son's shoulders.

The boy shivered with delight, physical display of affection from his father was so rare, and he prressed closer to him and sat still as he could, barely breathing so as not to disturb or spoil the moment.

The little fleet ran in towards the land, and turned the sharp northern horn of the bay. The seabirds were returning with them, squadrons of yellow-throated gannets in long regular lines skimming low over the cloudy green waters, and the lowering sun gilded them and burned upon the tall bronze dunes that rose like a mountain range behind the tiny insignificant cluster of buildings that stood at the edge of the bay.

'I hope Willem has had enough sense to fire up the boilers,' Lothar murmured. 'We have enough work here to keep the factory busy all night and all tomorrow.

'We'll never to be able to can all this fish,' the boy whispered.

'No, we will have to turn most of it to fish oil and fish meal – ' Lothar broke off and stared across the bay. Manfred felt his body stiffen and then, to the boy's dismay, he lifted his arm off his son's shoulders and shaded his eyes.

'The bloody fool,' he growled. With his hunter's vision he had picked out the distant stack of the factory boilerhouse. It was smokeless. 'What the hell is he playing at?' Lothar leapt to his feet and balanced easily against the trawler's motion. 'He has let the boilers go cold. It will take five or six hours to refire them and our fish will begin to spoil. Damn him, damn him to hell!' Raging still, Lothar dropped down to the wheelhouse. As he yanked the foghorn to alert the factory, he snapped, 'With the money from the fish I'm going to buy one of Marconi's new-fangled shortwave radio machines so we can talk to the factory while we are at sea; then this sort of thing won't happen.'

He broke off again and stared. 'What the hell is going on!' He snatched the

binoculars from the bin next to the control panel and focused them. They were close enough now to see the small crowd at the main doors of the factory. The cutters and packers in their rubber aprons and boots. They should have been at their places in the factory.

'There is Willem.' The factory manager was standing on the end of the long wooden unloading jetty that thrust out into the still waters of the bay on its heavy teak pilings. 'What the hell is he playing at – the boilers cold and everybody hanging about outside?' There were two strangers with Willem, standing one on each side of him. They were dressed in dark civilian suits and they had that self-important, puffed-up look of petty officialdom that Lothar knew and dreaded.

'Tax collectors or other civil servants,' Lothar whispered, and his anger cooled and was replaced with unease. No minion of the government had ever brought him good news.

'Trouble,' he guessed. 'Just now when I have a thousand tons of fish to cook and can – '

Then he noticed the motor cars. They had been screened by the factory building until Da Silva made the turn into the main channel that would bring the trawler up to the off-loading jetty. There were two cars. One was a battered old 'T' model Ford, but the other, even though covered with a pale coating of fine desert dust, was a much grander machine – and Lothar felt his heart trip and his breathing alter.

There could not be two similar vehicles in the whole of Africa. It was an elephantine Daimler, painted daffodil yellow. The last time he had seen it, it had been parked outside the offices of the Courtney Mining and Finance Company in the Main Street of Windhoek.

Lothar had been on his way to discuss an extension of his loans from the company. He had stood on the opposite side of the wide dusty unpaved street and watched as she came down the broad marble steps, flanked by two of her obsequious employees in dark suits and high celluloid collars; one of them had opened the door of the magnificent yellow machine for her and bowed her into the driver's seat while the other had run to take the crank handle. Scorning a chauffeur, she had driven off herself, not even glancing in Lothar's direction, and left him pale and trembling with the conflicting emotions that the mere sight of her had evoked. That had been almost a year before.

Now he roused himself as Da Silva laid the heavily burdened trawler alongside the jetty. They were so low in the water that Manfred had to toss the bow mooring-line up to one of the men on the jetty above him.

'Lothar, these men – they want to speak to you.' Willem called down. He was sweating nervously as he jerked a thumb at the man who flanked him.

'Are you Mr Lothar De La Rey?' the smaller of the two strangers demanded, pushing his dusty fedora hat onto the back of his head and mopping the pale line of skin that was exposed beneath the brim.

'That's right.' Lothar glared up at at him with his clenched fists upon his hips. 'And who the hell are you?'

'Are you the owner of the South West African Canning and Fishing Company?'

'*Ja*!' Lothar answered him in Afrikaans. 'I am the owner – and what of it?'

'I am the sheriff of the court in Windhoek, and I have here a writ of attachment over all the assets of the company.' The sheriff brandished the document he held.

'They've closed the factory,' Willem called down to Lothar miserably, his moustaches quivering. 'They made me draw the fires on my boilers.'

'You can't do that!' Lothar snarled, and his eyes slitted yellow and fierce as those of an angry leopard. 'I've got a thousand tons of fish to process.'

'Are these the four trawlers registered in the company's name?' the sheriff went on, unperturbed by the outburst, but he unbuttoned his dark jacket and pulled it back as he placed both hands on his hips. A heavy Webley service revolver hung on a leather holster from his belt. He turned his head to watch the other trawlers mooring at their berths on each side of the jetty, then without waiting for Lothar to answer he went on placidly, 'My assistant will place the court seals on them and their cargoes. I must warn you that it will be a criminal offence to remove either the boats or their cargoes.'

'You can't do this to me!' Lothar swarmed up the ladder onto the jetty. His tone was no longer belligerent. 'I have to get my fish processed. Don't you understand? They'll be stinking to the heavens by tomorrow morning – '

'They are not your fish.' The sheriff shook his head. 'They belong to the Courtney Mining and Finance Company.' He gestured to his assistant impatiently. 'Get on with it, man.' And he began to turn away.

'She's here,' Lothar called after him, and the sheriff turned back to face him again.

'She's here,' Lothar repeated. 'That's her car. She has come herself, hasn't she?'

The sheriff dropped his eyes and shrugged, but Willem gobbled a reply.

'Yes, she's here – she's waiting in my office.

Lothar turned away from the group and strode down the jetty, his heavy oilskin breeches rustling and his fists still bunched as though he were going into a fight.

The agitated crowd of factory hands was waiting for him at the head of the jetty.

'What is happening, *Baas*?' they pleaded. 'They won't let us work. What must we do, *Ou Baas*?'

'Wait!' Lothar ordered them brusquely. 'I will fix this.'

'Will we get our pay, *Baas*? We've got children – '

'You'll be paid,' Lothar snapped, 'I promise you that.' It was a promise he could not keep, not until he had sold his fish, and he pushed his way through them and strode around the corner of the factory towards the manager's office.

The Daimler was parked outside the door, and a boy leaned against the front mudguard of the big yellow machine. It was obvious that he was disgruntled and bored. He was perhaps a year older then Manfred but an inch or so shorter and his body was slimmer and neater. He wore a white shirt that had wilted a little in the heat, and his fashionable Oxford bags of grey flannel were dusty and too modish for a boy of his age, but there was an unstudied grace about him, and he was beautiful as a girl, with flawless skin and dark indigo eyes.

Lothar came up short at the sight of him, and before he could stop himself, he said, 'Shasa!'

The boy straightened up quickly and flicked the lock of dark hair off his forehead.

'How do you know my name?' he asked, and despite his tone the dark blue eyes sparkled with interest as he studied Lothar with a level, almost adult self-assurance.

There were a hundred answers Lothar could have given, and they crowded

to his lips: 'Once, many years ago, I saved you and your mother from death in the desert. . . . I helped wean you, and carried you on the pommel of my saddle when you were a baby. . . . I loved you, almost as much as once I loved your mother. . . . You are Manfred's brother – you are half brother to my own son. I'd recognize you anywhere, even after all this time.'

But instead he said, 'Shasa is the Bushman word for "Good Water", the most precious substance in the Bushman world.'

'That's right,' Shasa Courtney nodded. The man interested him. There was a restrained violence and cruelty in him, an impression of untapped strength, and his eyes were strangely light coloured, almost yellow like those of a cat. 'You're right. It's a Bushman name, but my Christian name is Michel. That's French. My mother is French.'

'Where is she?' Lothar demanded, and Shasa glanced at the office door.

'She doesn't want to be disturbed,' he warned, but Lothar Da La Rey stepped past him, so closely that Shasa could smell the fish slime on his oilskins and see the small white fish scales stuck to his tanned skin.

'You'd best knock – ' Shasa dropped his voice, but Lothar ignored him and flung the door of the office open so that it crashed back on its hinges. He stood in the open door and Shasa could see past him. His mother rose from the straight-backed chair by the window and faced the door.

She was slim as a girl, and the yellow crêpe-de-chine of her dress was draped over her small fashionably flattened breasts and was gathered in a narrow girdle low around her hips. Her narrow-brimmed cloche hat was pulled down, covering the dense dark bush of her hair, and her eyes were huge and almost black.

She looked very young, not much older than her son, until she raised her chin and showed the hard, determined line of her jaw and the corners of her eyes lifted also and those honey-coloured lights burned in their dark depths. Then she was formidable as any man Lothar had ever met.

They stared at each other, assessing the changes that the years had wrought since their last meeting.

'How old is she?' Lothar wondered, and then immediately remembered. 'She was born an hour after midnight on the first day of the century. She is as old as the twentieth century – that's why she was named Centaine. So she's thirty-one years old, and she still looks nineteen, as young as the day I found her, bleeding and dying in the desert with the wounds of lion claws deep in her sweet young flesh.'

'He has aged,' Centaine thought. 'Those silver streaks in the blond, those lines around the mouth and eyes. He'll be over forty now, and he has suffered – but not enough. I am glad I didn't kill him, I'm glad my bullet missed his heart. It would have been too quick. Now he is in my power and he'll begin to learn the true – '

Suddenly, against her will and inclination, she remembered the feel of his golden body over hers, naked and smooth and hard, and her loins clenched and then dissolved so she could feel their hot soft flooding, as hot as the blood that mounted to her cheeks and as hot as her anger against herself and her inability to master that animal corner of her emotions. In all other things she had trained herself like an athlete, but always that unruly streak of sensuality was just beyond her control.

She looked beyond the man in the doorway, and she saw Shasa standing out in the sunlight, her beautiful child, watching her curiously, and she was

ashamed and angry to have been caught in that naked and unguarded moment when she was certain that her basest feelings had been on open display.

'Close the door,' she ordered, and her voice was husky and level. 'Come in and close the door.' She turned away and stared out of the window, bringing herself under complete control once more before turning back to face the man she had set herself to destroy.

* * *

The door closed and Shasa suffered an acute pang of disappointment. He sensed that something vitally important was taking place. That blond stranger with the cat-yellow eyes who knew his name and its derivation stirred something in him, something dangerous and exciting. Then his mother's reaction, that sudden high colour coming up her throat into her cheeks and something in her eyes that he had never seen before – not guilt, surely? Then uncertainty, which was totally uncharacteristic. She had never been uncertain of anything in the world that Shasa knew of. He wanted desperately to know what was taking place behind that closed door. The walls of the building were of corrugated galvanized iron sheeting.

'If you want to know something, go and find out.' It was one of his mother's adages, and his only compunction was that she might catch him at it as he crossed to the side wall of the office, stepping lightly so that the gravel would not crunch under his feet, and laid his ear against the sun-heated corrugated metal.

Though he strained, he could only hear the murmur of voices. Even when the blond stranger spoke sharply, he could not catch the words, while his mother's voice was low and husky and inaudible.

'The window,' he thought, and moved quickly to the corner. As he stepped around it, intent on eavesdropping at the open window, he was suddenly the subject of attention of fifty pairs of eyes. The factory manager and his idle workers were still clustered at the main doors, and they fell silent and turned their full attention upon him as he appeared round the corner.

Shasa tossed his head and veered away from the window. They were all still watching him and he thrust his hands into the pockets of his Oxford bags and, with an elaborate show of nonchalance, sauntered down towards the long wooden jetty as though this had been his intention all along. Whatever was going on in the office now was beyond him, unless he could wheedle it out of his mother later, and he didn't think there was much hope of that. Then suddenly he noticed the four squat wooden trawlers moored alongside the jetty, each lying low in the water under the glittering silver cargo they carried, and his disappointment was a little mollified. Here was something to break the monotony of his hot dreary desert afternoon and his step quickened as he went onto the timbers of the jetty. Boats always fascinated him.

This was new and exciting. He had never seen so many fish, there must be tons of them. He came level with the first boat. It was grubby and ugly, with streaks of human excrement down the sides where the crew had squatted on the gunwale, and it stank of bilges and fuel oil and unwashed humanity living in confined quarters. It had not even been graced with a name: there were only the registration and licence numbers painted on the wave-battered bows.

'A boat should have a name,' Shasa thought. 'It's insulting and unlucky not to give it a name.' His own twenty-five-foot yacht that his mother had given him for his thirteenth birthday was named *The Midas Touch*, a name that his mother had suggested.

Shasa wrinkled his nose at the smell of the trawler, disgusted and saddened by her disgracefully neglected condition.

'If this is what Mater drove all the way from Windhoek for – ' He did not finish the thought for a boy stepped around the far side of the tall angular wheelhouse.

He wore patched shorts of canvas duck, his legs were brown and muscled and he balanced easily on the hatch coaming on bare feet.

As they became aware of each other both boys bridled and stiffened, like dogs meeting unexpectedly; silently they scrutinized each other.

'A dandy, a fancy boy,' Manfred thought. He had seen one or two like him on infrequent visits to the resort town of Swakopmund up the coast. Rich men's children dressed in ridiculous stiff clothing, walking dutifully behind their parents with that infuriating supercilious expression upon their faces. 'Look at his hair, all shiny with brilliantine, and he stinks like a bunch of flowers.'

'One of the poor white Afrikaners,' Shasa recognized his type. 'A *bywoner*, a squatter's kid.' His mother had forbidden him to play with them, but he had found that some of them were jolly good fun. Their attraction was of course enhanced by his mother's prohibition. One of the sons of the machine-shop foreman at the mine imitated bird calls in such an amazingly lifelike manner that he could actually call the birds down from the trees, and he had shown Shasa how to adjust the carburettor and ignition on the old Ford which his mother allowed him to use, even though he was too young to have a driver's licence. While the same boy's elder sister, a year older than Shasa, had shown him something even more remarkable when they had shared a few forbidden moments together behind the pumphouse at the mine. She had even allowed him to touch it and it had been warm and soft and furry as a newborn kitten cuddling up there under her short cotton skirt, a most remarkable experience which he intended to repeat at the very next opportunity.

This boy looked interesting also, and perhaps he could show Shasa over the trawler's engine-room. Shasa glanced at the factory. His mother was not watching and he was prepared to be magnanimous.

'Hello.' He made a lordly gesture and smiled carefully. His grandfather, Sir Garrick Courtney, the most important male person in his existence, was always admonishing him. 'By birth you have a specially exalted position in society. This gives you not only benefit and privilege, but a duty also. A true gentleman treats those beneath his station, black or white, old or young, man or woman, with consideration and courtesy.'

'My name is Courtney,' Shasa told him. 'Shasa Courtney. My uncle is Sir Garrick Courtney and my mother is Mrs Centaine de Thiry Courtney.' He waited for the deference that those names usually commanded, and when it was not evident, he went on rather lamely. 'What's your name?'

'My name is Manfred,' the other boy replied in Afrikaans and arched those dense black eyebrows over the amber eyes. They were so much darker than his streaked blond hair that they looked as though they had been painted on. 'Manfred De La Rey, and my grandfather and my great-uncle and my father

were De La Rey also and they shot the shit out of the English every time they met them.'

Shasa blushed at his unexpected attack and was on the point of turning away when he saw that there was an old man leaning in the window of the wheelhouse, watching them, and two coloured crewmen had come up from the trawler's forecastle. He could not retreat.

'We English won the war and in 1914 we beat the hell out of the rebels,' he snapped.

'We!' Manfred repeated, and turned to his audience. 'This little gentleman with perfume on his hair won the war.' The crewmen chuckled encouragement. 'Smell him, his name should be Lily – Lily the perfumed soldier.' Manfred turned back to him, and for the first time Shasa realized that he was taller by a good inch and his arms were alarmingly thick and brown. 'So you are English, are you, Lily? Then you must live in London, is that right, sweet Lily?'

Shasa had not expected a poor white boy to be so articulate, nor his wit to be so acerbic. Usually he was in control of any discussion.

'Of course I'm English,' he affirmed furiously, and was seeking a final retort to end the exchange and allow him to retire in good order from a situation over which he was swiftly losing control.

'Then you must live in London,' Manfred persisted.

'I live in Cape Town.'

'Hah!' Manfred turned to his growing audience. Swart Hendrick had come across the jetty from his own trawler, and all the crew were up from the forecastle. 'That's why they are called *Soutpiel*,' Manfred announced.

There was an outburst of delighted guffaws at the coarse expression. Manfred would never have used it if his father had been present. The translation was 'Salt Prick' and Shasa flushed and instinctively bunched his fists at the insult.

'A *Soutpiel* has one foot in London and the other in Cape Town,' Manfred explained with relish, 'and his willy-wagger dangling in the middle of the salty old Atlantic Ocean.'

'You'll take that back!' Anger had robbed Shasa of a more telling rejoinder. He had never been spoken to in this fashion by one of his inferiors.

'Take it back – you mean like you pull back your salty foreskin? When you play with it? Is that what you mean?' Manfred asked. The applause had made him reckless, and he had moved closer, directly under the boy on the jetty.

Shasa launched himself without warning, and Manfred had not anticipated that so soon. He had expected to trade a few more insults before they were both sufficiently worked up to attack each other.

Shasa dropped six feet and hit him with the full weight of his body and his outrage. The wind was driven out of Manfred's lungs in a whoosh as, locked together, they went flying backwards into the morass of dead fish.

They rolled over and with a shock Shasa felt the other boy's strength. His arms were hard as timber balks and his fingers felt like iron butcher's hooks as he clawed for Shasa's face. Only surprise and Manfred's winded lungs saved him from immediate humiliation and almost too late he remembered the admonitions of Jock Murphy, his boxing instructor.

'Don't let a bigger man force you to fight close. Fight him off. Keep him at arm's length.'

Manfred was clawing at his face, trying to get an arm around him in a half

Nelson, and they were floundering into the cold slippery mass of fish. Shasa brought up his right knee and, as Manfred reared up over him, he drove it into his chest. Manfred gasped and reeled back, but then as Shasa tried to roll away, he lunged forward again for the head lock. Shasa ducked his head and with his right hand forced Manfred's elbow up to break the grip, then as Jock had taught him, he twisted out against the opening he had created. He was helped by the fish slime that coated his neck and Manfred's arm like oil, and the instant he was free he threw a punch with his left hand.

Jock had drilled him endlessly on the short straight left. 'The most important punch you'll ever use.'

It wasn't one of Shasa's best, but it caught the other boy in the eye with sufficient force to snap his head back and distract him just long enough to let Shasa get onto his feet and back away.

By now the jetty above them was crowded with coloured trawlermen in rubber boots and blue rollneck jerseys. They were roaring with delight and excitement, egging on the two boys as though they were game cocks.

Blinking the tears out of his swelling eye, Manfred went after Shasa, but the fish clinging to his legs hampered him, and that left shot out again. There was no warning; it came straight and hard and unexpectedly, stinging his injured eye so that he shouted with anger and groped wildly for the lighter boy.

Shasa ducked under his arm and fired the left again, just the way Jock had taught him.

'Never telegraph it by moving the shoulders or the head,' he could almost hear Jock's voice, 'just shoot it – with the arm alone.'

He caught Manfred in the mouth, and immediately there was blood as Manfred's lip was crushed onto his own teeth. The sight of his adversary's blood elated Shasa and the concerted bellow of the crowd evoked a primeval response deep within him. He used the left again, cracking it into the pink swollen eye.

'When you mark him, then keep hitting the same spot.' Jock's voice in his head, and Manfred shouted again, but this time he could hear the pain as well as the rage in the sound.

'It's working,' Shasa exulted. But at that moment he ran backwards into the wheelhouse and Manfred, realizing his opponent was cornered, rushed at him through the slimy fish, spreading both arms wide, grinning triumphantly, his mouth full of blood from his cut lip and his teeth dyed bright pink.

In panic Sasha dropped his shoulders, braced himself for an instant against the wheelhouse timbers and then shot forward, butting the top of his head into Manfred's stomach.

Once again Manfred wheezed as the air was forced up his throat, and for a few confused seconds they writhed together in the mess of pilchards, with Manfred gurgling for breath and unable to get a hold on his opponent's slippery limbs. Then Sasha wriggled away and half crawled, half swam to the foot of the wooden ladder of the jetty and dragged himself onto it.

The crowd was laughing and booing derisively as he fled, and Manfred clawed angrily after him, spitting blood and fish slime out of his injured mouth, his chest heaving violently to refill his lungs.

Sasha was halfway up the ladder when Manfred reached up and grabbed his ankle, pulling both his feet off the rungs. Sasha was stretched out by the heavier boy's weight like a victim on the rack, clinging with desperate strength to the top of the ladder, and the faces of the coloured fishermen were only

inches from his as they leaned over the jetty and howled for his blood, favouring their own.

With his free leg Shasa kicked backwards, and his heel caught Manfred in his swollen eye. He yelled and let go, and Shasa scrambled up onto the jetty and looked around him wildly. His fighting ardour had cooled and he was trembling.

His escape down the jetty was open and he longed to take it. But the men around him were laughing and jeering and pride shackled him. He glanced around and, with a surge of dismay that was so strong that it almost physically nauseated him, he saw that Manfred had reached the top of the ladder.

Shasa was not quite sure how he had got himself into this fight, or what was the point at issue, and miserably he wished he could extricate himself. That was impossible, his entire breeding and training precluded it. He tried to stop himself trembling as he turned back to face Manfred again.

The bigger boy was trembling also, but not with fear. His face was swollen and dark red with killing rage, and he was making an unconscious hissing sound through his bloody lips. His damaged eye was turning purplish mauve and puffing into a narrow slit.

'Kill him, *kleinbasie*,' screamed the coloured trawlermen. 'Murder him, little boss.' And their taunts rallied Shasa. He took a deep steadying breath and lifted his fists in the classic boxer's stance, left foot leading and his hands held high in front of his face.

'Keep moving,' he heard Jock's advice again, and he went up on his toes and danced.

'Look at him!' the crowd hooted. 'He thinks he is Jack Dempsey! He wants to dance with you, Manie. Show him the Walvis Bay Waltz!'

However, Manfred was daunted by the desperate determination in those dark blue eyes and by the clenched white knuckles of Shasa's left hand. He began to circle him, hissing threats.

'I'm going to rip your arm off and stick it down your throat. I'm going to make your teeth march out of your backside like soldiers.'

Shasa blinked but kept his guard up, turning slowly to face Manfred as he circled. Though both of them were soaked and glistening with fish slime and their hair was thick with the gelatinous stuff and speckled with loose scales, there was nothing ludicrous nor childlike about them. It was a good fight and promised to become even better, and the audience gradually fell silent. Their eyes glittered like those of a wolf pack and they craned forward expectantly to watch the ill-matched pair.

Manfred feinted left and then charged and rushed from the side. He was very fast, despite his size and the heaviness of his legs and shoulders. He carried his shining blond head low and the black curved eyebrows emphasized the ferocity of his scowl.

In front of him Shasa seemed almost girlishly fragile. His arms were slim and pale, and his legs under the sodden grey flannel seemed too long and thin, but he moved well on them. He dodged Manfred's charge and as he pulled away, his left arm shot out again, and Manfred's teeth clicked audibly at the punch and his head was flicked back as he was brought up on his heels.

The crowd growled, '*Vat hom*, Manie, get him!' and Manfred rushed in again, throwing a powerful round-house punch at Shasa's pale petal-smooth face.

Shasa ducked under it and, in the instant that Manfred was screwed off

balance by his own momentum, stabbed his left fist unexpectedly and painfully into the purple, puffed-up eye. Manfred clasped his hand over the eye and snarled at him. 'Fight properly, you cheating *Soutie*.'

'*Ja*!' a voice called from the crowd. 'Stop running away. Stand and fight like a man.'

At the same time Manfred changed his tactics. Instead of feinting and weaving, he came straight at Shasa, and kept on coming, swinging with both hands in a terrifying mechanical sequence of blows. Shasa fell back frantically, ducking and swaying and dodging, at first stabbing out with his left hand as Manfred followed him relentlessly, cutting the swollen skin that had begun to bag under his eye, hitting him in the mouth again and then again until his lips were distorted and lumpy. But it was as though Manfred was inured to the sting of these blows now and he did not alter the rhythm of punches nor slacken his attack.

His brown fists, hardened by work at the winch and net, flipped Shasa's hair as he ducked or hissed past his face as he ran backwards. Then one caught him a glancing blow on the temple and Shasa stopped aiming his own counter-punches and struggled merely to stay clear of those swinging fists, for his legs started to turn numb and heavy under him.

Manfred was tireless, pressing him relentlessly, and despair combined with exhaustion to slow Shasa's legs. A fist crashed into his ribs, and he grunted and staggered and saw the other fist coming at his face. He could not avoid it, his feet seemed planted in buckets of treacle and he grabbed at Manfred's arm and hung on grimly. That was exactly what Manfred had been trying to force him to do, and he whipped his other arm around Shasa's neck.

'Now, I've got you,' he mumbled through swollen bloody lips, as he forced Shasa to double over, his head pinned under Manfred's left arm. Manfred lifted his right hand high and swung it in a brutal upper-cut.

Shasa sensed rather than saw the fist coming, and twisted so violently that he felt as though his neck had snapped. But he managed to take the blow on the top of his forehead rather than in his unprotected face. The shock of it was driven like an iron spike from the top of his skull down his spine. He knew he could not take another blow like that.

Through his starring vision he realized that he had tottered to the edge of the jetty, and he used the last vestiges of his strength to drive them both towards the very edge. Manfred had not been expecting him to push in that direction and was braced the wrong way. He could not resist as they went flying over and fell back onto the trawler's fish-laden deck six feet below.

Shasa was pinned beneath Manfred's body, still caught in the headlock, and instantly he sank into the quicksand of silver pilchards. Manfred tried to swing another punch at his face, but it slogged into the soft layer of fish that was spreading over Shasa's head. He abandoned the effort and merely leaned his full weight on Shasa's neck, forcing his head deeper and still deeper below the surface.

Shasa started to drown. He tried to scream but a dead pilchard slid into his open mouth and its head jammed in his throat. He kicked and lashed out with both hands and writhed with all his remaining strength, but remorselessly his head was thrust downward. The fish lodged in his throat choked him. The darkness filled his head with a sound like the wind, blotting out the murderous chorus from the jetty above, and his struggles became less urgent until he was flopping and flapping his limbs loosely.

'I'm going to die,' he thought with a kind of detached wonder. 'I'm drowning – ' and the thought faded with his consciousness.

* * *

'You have come here to destroy me,' Lothar De Lay Rey accused her with his back against the closed door. 'You have come all this way to watch it happen, and to gloat on it.'

'You flatter yourself.' Centaine answered him disdainfully. 'I have not that much interest in you personally. I have come to protect my considerable investment. I have come for fifty thousand pounds plus accrued interest.'

'If that was true you wouldn't stop me running my catch through the plant. I've got a thousand tons out there – by sunset tomorrow evening I could turn it into fifty thousand pounds.'

Impatiently Centaine lifted her hand to stop him. The skin of the hand was tanned a creamy coffee colour in contrast to the silver white diamond as long as the top joint of the tapered forefinger that she pointed at him.

'You are living in a dream world,' she told him. 'Your fish is worth nothing. Nobody wants it – not at any price, certainly not fifty thousand.'

'It's worth all of that – fish meal and canned goods – '

Again she gestured him to silence. 'The warehouses of the world are filled with unwanted goods. Don't you understand that? Don't you read a newspaper? Don't you listen to the wireless out here in the desert? It's worthless – not even worth the cost of processing it.'

'That's not possible.' He was angry and stubborn. 'Of course I've heard about the stock market, but people have still got to eat.'

'I've thought many things about you,' she had not raised her voice, she was speaking as though to a child, 'but I have never thought you stupid. Try to understand that something has happened out there in the world that has never happened before. The commerce of the world has died; the factories of the world are closing; the streets of all the major cities are filled with the legions of the unemployed.'

'You are using this as an excuse for what you are doing. You are conducting a vendetta against me.' He came towards her. His lips were icy pale against the dark mahogany tan. 'You are hounding me for some fancied offence committed long ago. You are punishing me.'

'The offence was real.' She stepped back from his advance, but she held his gaze and her voice though low-pitched was bleak and hard. 'It was monstrous and cruel and unforgivable, but there is no punishment I could deal out to you which would fit that crime. If there is a God, he will demand retribution.'

'The child,' he started. 'The child you bore me in the wilderness – ' For the first time he penetrated the armour of her composure.

'You'll not mention your bastard to me.' She clasped one hand with the other to prevent them trembling. 'That was our bargain.'

'He's our son. You cannot avoid that fact. Are you content to destroy him also?'

'He's your son,' she denied. 'I have no part of him. He does not affect me or my decision. Your factory is insolvent, hopelessly, irredeemably insolvent. I cannot expect to recover my investment, I can only hope to retrieve a part.'

Through the open window there came the sound of men's voices, even at a distance they sounded excited and lustful, baying like hounds as they take the scent. Neither of them glanced in that direction; all their attention was concentrated on each other.

'Give me a chance, Centaine.' He heard the pleading timbre in his own voice and it disgusted him. He had never begged before, not with anybody, not once in his life, but now he could not bear the prospect of having to begin all over again. It would not be the first time. Twice before he had been rendered destitute, stripped of everything but pride and courage and determination by war and the fortunes of war. Always it had been the same enemy, the British and their aspirations of empire. Each time he had started again from the beginning and laboriously rebuilt his fortune.

This time the prospect appalled him. To be struck down by the mother of his child, the woman he had loved – and, God forgive him, the woman he loved still against all probabilities. He felt the exhaustion of his spirit and his body. He was forty-six years old; he no longer had a young man's store of energy on which to draw, and he thought he glimpsed a softening in her eyes as though she was moved by his plea, wavering at the point of relenting.

'Give me a week – just one week, Centaine, that's all I ask,' he abased himself, and immediately realized that he had misread her.

She did not alter her expression, but in her eyes he could see that what he had mistaken for compassion was instead the shine of deep satisfaction. He was where she had wanted him all these years.

'I have told you never to use my Christian name,' she said. 'I told you that when I first learned that you had murdered two people I loved as dearly as I have ever loved anyone. I tell you that again.'

'A week. Just one week.'

'I have already given you two years.'

Now she turned her head towards the window, no longer able to ignore the sound of harsh voices, like the blood roar of a bullfight heard at a distance.

'Another week will only get you deeper into my debt and force heavier loss on me.' She shook her head, but he was staring out the window and now her voice sharpened. 'What is happening down there on the jetty?' She leaned her hands on the sill and peered down the beach.

He stepped up beside her. There was a dense knot of humanity halfway down the jetty, and from the factory all the idle packers were running down to join it.

'Shasa!' Centaine cried with an intuitive surge of maternal concern. 'Where's Shasa?' Lothar vaulted lightly over the sill and raced for the jetty, overhauling the stragglers and then shouldering his way through the circle of yelling, howling trawlermen just as the two boys teetered on the edge of the jetty.

'Manfred!' he roared. 'Stop that! Let him go!'

His son had the lighter boy in a vicious headlock, and he was swinging overhand punches at the trapped head. Lothar heard one crack against the bone of Shasa's skull.

'You fool!' Lothar started towards them. They had not heard his voice above the din of the crowd, and Lothar felt a slide of dread, a real concern for the child and a realization of what Centaine's reaction would be if he were injured.

'Leave him!' Before he could reach the wildly struggling pair, they reeled backwards and tumbled over the edge of the jetty. 'Oh my God!' He heard them hit the deck of the trawler below, and by the time he reached the side and looked down they were half buried in the deckload of glittering pilchards.

Lothar tried to reach the ladder head, impeded by the press of coloured trawlermen who crowded forward to the edge so as not to miss a moment of the contest. He struck out with both fists, clearing his way, shoving his men aside, and then clambered down to the deck of the trawler.

Manfred was lying on top of the other boy, forcing his head and shoulders beneath the mass of pilchards. His own face was contorted with rage, and lumped and discoloured with bruises. He was mouthing incoherent threats through blood-smeared and puffed lips, and Shasa was no longer struggling. His head and shoulders had disappeared but his trunk and his legs twitched and shuddered in the spontaneous nerveless movements of a man shot through the head.

Lothar seized his son by the shoulders and tried to drag him off. It was like trying to separate a pair of mastiffs and he had to use all his strength. He lifted Manfred bodily and threw him against the wheelhouse with a force that knocked the belligerence out of him and then grabbed Shasa's legs and pulled him out of the engulfing quicksilver of dead pilchards. He came slithering free, wet and slippery. His eyes were open and rolled back into his skull exposing the whites.

'You've killed him,' Lothar snarled at his son, and the furious tide of blood receded from Manfred's face leaving him white and shivering with shock.

'I didn't mean it, Pa. I didn't – '

There was a dead fish jammed into Shasa's slack mouth, choking him, and fish slime bubbled out of his nostrils.

'You fool, you little fool!' Lothar thrust his finger into the corner of the child's slack mouth and prised the pilchard out.

'I'm sorry, Pa. I didn't mean it,' Manfred whispered.

'If you've killed him, you've committed a terrible offence in the sight of God.' Lothar lifted Shasa's limp body in his arms. 'You'll have killed your own – ' He did not say the fateful word, but bit down hard on it and turned to the ladder.

'I haven't killed him,' Manfred pleaded for assurance. 'He's not dead. It will be all right, won't it, Pa?'

'No.' Lothar shook his head grimly. 'It won't be all right – not ever.' Carrying the unconscious boy, he climbed up onto the jetty.

The crowd opened silently for Lothar. Like Manfred, they were appalled and guilty, unable to meet his eyes as he shouldered past them.

'Swart Hendrick,' Lothar called over their heads to the tall black man. 'You should have known better. You should have stopped them.'

Lothar strode away up the jetty, and none of them followed him.

Halfway up the breach path to the factory Centaine Courtney waited for him. Lothar stopped in front of her with the boy hanging limply in his arms.

'He's dead,' Centaine whispered hopelessly.

'No.' Lothar denied with passion. It was too horrible to think about, and as though in response Shasa moaned and vomited from the corner of his mouth.

'Quickly.' Centaine stepped forward. 'Turn him over your shoulder before he chokes on his own vomit.'

With Shasa hanging limply over his shoulder like a haversack, Lothar ran the last few yards to the office and Centaine swept the desktop clear.

'Lay him here,' she ordered, but Shasa was struggling weakly and trying to sit up. Centaine supported his shoulders and wiped his mouth and nostrils with the fine cloth of her sleeve.

'It was your bastard.' She glared across the desk at Lothar. 'He did this to

my son, didn't he?' And she saw the confirmation in his face before he looked away.

Shasa coughed and brought up another trickle of fish slime and yellow vomitus, and immediately he was stronger. His eyes focused and his breathing eased.

'Get out of here.' Centaine leaned protectively over Shasa's body. 'I'll see you both in hell – you and your bastard. Now get out of my sight.'

* * *

The track from Walvis Bay ran through the convoluted valleys of the great orange dunes, thirty kilometres to the railhead at Swakopmund. The dunes towered three and four hundred feet on either side. Mountains of sand with knife-edge crests and smooth slip faces, they trapped the desert heat in the canyons between them.

The track was merely a set of deep ruts in the sand, marked on each side by the sparkling glass of broken beer bottles. No traveller took this thirsty road without adequate supplies for the journey. At intervals the tracks had been obliterated by the efforts of other drivers, unskilled in the art of desert travel, to extract their vehicles from the clinging sands, leaving gaping traps for those who followed.

Centaine drove hard and fast, never allowing her engine revolutions to drop, keeping her momentum even through the churned-up areas and holes where the other vehicles had bogged down, directing the big yellow car with deft little touches of the wheel so that the tyres ran straight and the sand did not pile and block them.

She held the wheel in a racing driver's grip, leaning back against the leather seat with straight arms ready for the kick of the wheel, watching the tracks far ahead and anticipating each contingency long before she reached it, sometimes snapping down through the gears and swinging out of the ruts to cut her own way around a bad stretch. She scorned even the elementary precaution of travelling with a pair of black servants in the back seat to push the Daimler out of a sand trap. Shasa had never know his mother to bog down, not even on the worst sections of the track out to the mine.

He sat up beside her on the front seat. He wore a suit of old but freshly laundered canvas overalls from the stores of the canning factory. His soiled clothing stinking of fish and speckled with vomit was in the boot of the Daimler.

His mother hadn't spoken since they had driven away from the factory. Shasa glanced surreptitiously at her, dreading her pent-up wrath, not wanting to draw attention to himself, yet despite himself unable to keep his eyes from her face.

She had removed the cloche hat and her thick dark cap of hair, cut fashionably into a short Eton crop, rippled in the wind and shone like washed anthracite.

'Who started it?' she asked, without taking her eyes from the road.

Shasa thought about it. 'I'm not sure. I hit him first, but – ' he paused. His throat was still painful.

'Yes?' she demanded.

'It was as though it was arranged. We looked at each other and we knew we were going to fight.' She said nothing and he finished lamely. 'He called me a name.'

'What name?'

'I can't tell you. It's rude.'

'I asked what name?' Her voice was level and low, but he recognized that husky warning quality.

'He called me a *Soutpiel*,' he replied hastily. He dropped his voice and looked away in shame at the dreadful insult, so he did not see Centaine struggle to stifle the smile and turn her head slightly to hide the sparkle of amusement in her eyes.

'I told you it was rude,' he recognized.

'So you hit him – and he's younger than you.'

He had not known that he was the elder, but he was not surprised that she knew it. She knew everything.

'He may be younger, but he's a big Afrikaner ox, at least two inches taller than I am,' he defended himself quickly.

She wanted to ask Shasa what her other son looked like. Was he blond and handsome as his father had been? What colour were his eyes? Instead she said, 'And so he thrashed you.'

'I nearly won.' Shasa protested stoutly. 'I closed his eyes and I bloodied him nicely. I nearly won.'

'Nearly isn't good enough,' she said. 'In our family we don't nearly win – we simply win.'

He fidgeted uncomfortably and coughed to relieve the pain in his injured throat.

'You can't win, not when someone is bigger and stronger than you,' he whispered miserably.

'Then you don't fight him with your fists,' she told him. 'You only fight when you are sure you can win.'

He considered that carefully, examining it from every angle. 'That's what you did to his father, didn't you?' he asked softly, and she was startled by his perception so that she stared at him and the Daimler bumped out of the ruts.

Quickly she caught and controlled the machine, and then she nodded. 'Yes. That's what I did. You see, we are Courtneys. We don't have to fight with our fists. We fight with power and money and influence. Nobody can beat us on our own ground.'

He was silent again, digesting it carefully, and at last he smiled. He was so beautiful when he smiled, even more beautiful than his father had been, that she felt her heart squeezed by her love.

'I'll remember that,' he said. 'Next time I meet him, I'll remember what you said.'

Neither of them doubted for a moment that the two boys would meet again – and that when they did, they would continue the conflict that had begun that day.

* * *

The breeze was onshore and the stink of rotting fish was so strong that it coated the back of Lothar De La Rey's throat and sickened him to the gut.

The four trawlers still lay at their berths but their cargoes were no longer glittering silver. The fish had packed down and the top layer of pilchards had

dried out in the sun and turned a dark, dirty grey, crawling with metallic green flies as big as wasps. The fish in the holds had squashed under their own weight, and the bilge pumps were pouring out steady streams of stinking brown blood and fish oil that discoloured the waters of the bay in a spreading cloud.

All day Lothar had sat at the window of the factory office while his coloured trawlermen and packers lined up to be paid. Lothar had sold his old Packard truck and the few sticks of furniture from the corrugated shack in which he and Manfred lived. These were the only assets that did not belong to the company and had not been attached. The second-hand dealer had come across from Swakopmund within hours, smelling disaster the way the vultures do, and he had paid Lothar a fraction of their real value.

'There is a depression going on, Mr De La Rey, everybody is selling, nobody is buying. I'll lose money, believe me.'

With the cash that Lothar had buried under the sandy floor of the shack there was enough to pay his people two shillings on each pound that he owed them for back wages. He did not have to pay them, of course, it was the company's responsibility – but that did not occur to him, they were his people.

'I'm sorry,' he repeated to each one of them as they came to the pay window. 'That's all there is.' And he avoided their eyes.

When it was all gone, and the last of his coloured people had wandered away in disconsolate little groups, Lothar locked the office door and handed the key to the deputy sheriff.

Then he and the boy had gone down to the jetty for the last time and sat together with their legs dangling over the end. The stink of dead fish was as heavy as their mood.

'I don't understand, Pa.' Manfred spoke through his distorted mouth with the crusty red scab on the upper lip. 'We caught good fish. We should be rich. What happened, Pa?'

'We were cheated,' Lothar said quietly. Until that moment there had been anger, no bitterness – just a feeling of numbness. Twice before he had been struck by a bullet. The ·303 Lee Enfield bullet on the road to Omaruru when they were opposing Smuts' invasion of German South West Africa, and then much later the Luger bullet fired by the boy's mother. He touched his chest at the memory, and felt the rubbery puckered pit of the scar through the thin cotton of his khaki shirt.

It was the same thing, first the shock and the numbness and then only much later the pain and the anger. Now the anger came at him in black waves, and he did not try to resist. Rather he revelled in it; it helped to assuage the memory of abasing himself, pleading for time from the woman with the taunting smile in her dark eyes.

'Can't we stop them, Pa?' the boy asked, and neither of them had to define that 'them'. They knew their enemy. They had grown to know them in three wars; in 1881 the first Boer War, then again in the Great Boer War of 1899 when Victoria called her khaki multitudes from across the oceans to crush them, and then in 1914 when the British puppet Jannie Smuts had carried out the orders of his imperial masters.

Lothar shook his head, unable to answer, choked by the strength of his anger.

'There must be a way,' the boy insisted. 'We are strong.' He recalled the feeling of Shasa's body slowly weakening in his grip and he flexed his hands involuntarily. 'It's ours, Pa. This is our land. God gave it to us – it says so in

the Bible.' Like so many before him, the Afrikaner had interpreted that book in his own way. He saw his people as the children of Israel, and Southern Africa as the promised land flowing with milk and honey.

Lothar was silent and Manfred took his sleeve. 'God did give it to us, didn't he, Pa?'

'Yes.' Lothar nodded heavily.

'Then they've stolen it from us: the land, the diamonds, and the gold and everything – and now they have taken our boats and our fish. There must be a way to stop them, to win back what belongs to us.

'It's not as easy as that.' Lothar hesitated how to explain it to the child. Did he truly understand it himself, how it had happened? They were squatters in the land that their fathers had wrested from the savages and the wilderness at the point of their long muzzle-loading guns.

'When you grow up you'll understand, Manie,' he said.

'When I grow up I'll find a way to beat them.' Manfred said it so forcefully that the scab on his lip cracked open and a droplet like a tiny ruby glowed upon it. 'I'll find a way to get it back from them. You'll see if I don't, Pa.'

'Well, my son, perhaps you will.' Lothar placed his arm around the boy's shoulders.

'Remember Grandpa's oath, Pa? I'll always remember. The war against the English will never end.'

They sat together until the sun touched the waters of the bay and turned them to molten copper, and then in the darkness they went up the jetty, out of the stench of decaying fish and along the edge of the dunes.

As they approached the shack there was smoke rising from the chimney and when they entered the lean-to kitchen, there was a fire on the open hearth. Swart Hendrick looked up from it.

'The Jew has taken the table and the chairs,' he said. 'But I hid the pots and the mugs.'

They sat on the floor and ate straight from the pot, a porridge of maize meal flavoured with salty wind-dried fish. Nobody spoke until they had finished.

'You didn't have to stay.' Lothar broke the silence and Hendrick shrugged.

'I bought coffee and tobacco at the store. The money you paid me was just enough.'

'There is no more,' Lothar said. 'It is all gone.'

'It's all been gone before.' Hendrick lit his pipe with a twig from the fire. 'We have been broke many times before.'

'This time it is different,' Lothar said. 'This time there is no ivory to hunt or – ' He broke off as his anger choked him again, and Hendrick poured more coffee into the tin mugs.

'It is strange,' Hendrick said. 'When we found her, she was dressed in skins. Now she comes in her big yellow car,' he shook his head and chuckled, 'and we are the ones in rags.'

'It was you and I that saved her,' Lothar agreed. 'More than that, we found her diamonds for her, and dug them from the ground.'

'Now she is rich,' Hendrick said, 'and she comes to take what we have also. She shouldn't have done that.' He shook his great black head. 'No, she shouldn't have done that.'

Lothar straightened up slowly. Hendrick saw his expression and leaned forward eagerly, and the boy stirred and smiled for the first time.

'Yes.' Hendrick began to grin. 'What is it? Ivory is finished – it's all been hunted out long ago.'

'No, not ivory. This time it will be diamonds,' Lothar replied.

'Diamonds?' Hendrick rocked back on his heels. 'What diamonds?'

'What diamonds?' Lothar smiled at him, and his yellow eyes glowed. 'Why, the diamonds we found for her, of course.'

'Her diamonds?' Hendrick stared at him. 'The diamonds from the H'ani Mine?'

'How much money have you got?' Lothar demanded and Hendrick's eyes shifted. 'I know you well,' Lothar went on impatiently and seized his shoulder. 'You've always got a little bit salted away. How much?'

'Not much.' Hendrick tried to rise but Lothar held him down.

'You have earned well this last season. I know exactly how much I have paid you.'

'Fifty pounds,' grunted Hendrick.

'No.' Lothar shook his head. 'You've got more than that.'

'Perhaps a little more.' Hendrick resigned himself.

'You have got a hundred pounds,' Lothar said definitely. 'That's how much we will need. Give it to me. You know you will get it back many times over. You always have, and you always will.'

* * *

The track was steep and rocky and the party straggled up it in the early sunlight. They had left the yellow Daimler at the bottom of the mountain on the banks of the Liesbeek stream and begun the climb in the ghostly grey light of pre-dawn.

In the lead were two old men in disreputable clothing, scuffed velskoen on their feet and sweatstained shapeless straw hats on their heads. They were both so lean as to appear half starved, skinny but sprightly, their skin darkened and creased by long exposure to the elements, so that a casual observer might have thought them a couple of old hoboes – and there were enough of that type on the roads and byroads in these days of the great Depression.

The casual observer would have been in error. The taller of the two old men limped slightly on an artifical leg and was a Knight Commander of the Order of the British Empire, a holder of the highest award for valour that the Empire could offer, the Victoria Cross, and he was also one of the most eminent military historians of the age, a man so rich and careless of worldly wealth that he seldom bothered to count his fortune.

'Old Garry,' his companion addressed him, rather than as Sir Garrick Courtney. 'That is the biggest problem we have to deal with, old Garry.' He was explaining in his high, almost girlish voice, rolling his Rs in that extraordinary fashion that was known as the 'Malmesbury bray'. 'Our people are deserting the land and flocking to the cities. The farms are dying, and there is no work for them in the cities.' His voice was unwinded although they had climbed 2,000 feet up the sheer turreted side of Table Mountain without a pause, maintaining the pace that had outdistanced all the younger members of the party.

'It's a recipe for disaster,' Sir Garrick agreed. 'They are poor on the farms,

but when they leave them they starve in the cities. Starving men are dangerous men, *Ou Baas*. History teaches us that.'

The man he called 'old master' was smaller in stature, though he carried himself straighter. He had merry blue eyes under the drooping brim of his Panama hat and a grey goatee beard that waggled as he spoke. Unlike Garry, he was not rich; he owned only a small farm on the high frost-browned veld of the Transvaal, and he was as careless of his debts as Garry was of his fortune, but the world was his paddock and had heaped honours upon him. He had been awarded honorary doctorates by fifteen of the world's leading universities, Oxford and Cambridge and Columbia amongst them. He was the freeman of ten cities, London and Edinburgh and the rest. He had been a general in the Boer forces and now he was general in the army of the British Empire, a Privy Councillor, a Companion of Honour, a King's Counsel, a bencher of the Middle Temple and a Fellow of the Royal Society. His chest was not wide enough for all the stars and ribbons he was entitled to wear. He was without question the cleverest, wisest, most charismatic and influential man that South Africa had ever produced. It was almost as though his spirit was too big to be contained by terrestrial borders, as though he were a true citizen of the wide world. This was the one chink in his armour, and his enemies had sent their poison-tipped arrows through it. 'His heart is across the sea, not with you,' and it had brought down his government of the South African Party of which he had been prime minister, minister of defence and of native affairs. Now he was leader of the opposition. However, he was a man who thought of himself as a botanist by preference and a soldier and politician by necessity.

'We should wait for the others to catch up.' General Jan Smuts paused on a lichen-covered rocky platform and leaned on his staff. The two of them peered back down the slope.

A hundred paces below them a woman plodded grimly up the path; the outline of her thighs through her heavy calico skirts were thick and powerful as the haunches of a brood mare, and her bare arms were as muscled as those of a wrestler.

'My little dove,' Sir Garry murmured fondly as he watched his bride. After fourteen long years of courtship she had only acceded to his suit six months before.

'Do hurry, Anna,' the boy behind her on the narrow path entreated. 'It will be noon before we reach the top and I'm dying for breakfast.' Shasa was as tall as she was, though half her bulk.

'Go ahead if you are in such a big hurry,' she growled at him. The thick solar topee was pulled low over her red, round face. Her features were as folded as those of a friendly bulldog. 'Though why anybody should want to reach the top of this cursed mountain – '

'I'll give you a shove,' Shasa offered, and placed both hands on Lady Courtney's massive round buttocks. 'Heave ho! And up she rises!'

'Stop that, you wicked boy,' Anna gasped as she scrambled to adjust to her sudden rapid ascent, 'or I'll break this stick over your backside. Oh! Stop now. That's enough.'

Until she had become Lady Courtney, she had been plain Anna, Shasa's nurse and his mother's beloved maid. Her meteoric rise up the social ladder had in no way altered their relationship.

They arrived gasping and protesting and laughing on the ledge. 'Here she is, Grandpater! Special delivery!' Shasa grinned at Garry Courtney, who separated

them firmly and fondly. The beautiful boy and the homely red-faced woman were the most precious of all his treasures, his wife and his only grandson.

'Anna, my sweeting, you mustn't tax the boy's strength so,' he warned her with a straight face, and she struck him on the arm half playfully and half in exasperation.

'I should be seeing to the lunch rather than gallivanting around on this mountain.' Her accent was still thick Flemish, and she relapsed thankfully into Afrikaans as she turned to General Smuts. 'How much further is it, *Ou Baas*?'

'Not far, Lady Courtney, not far at all. Ah! Here are the others. I was beginning to worry about them.

Centaine and her companions emerged from the edge of the forest further down the slope. She wore a loose white skirt that left her legs bare from the knees and a white straw hat decorated with artificial cherries. When they caught up with the leaders, Centaine smiled at General Smuts. 'I'm winded, *Ou Baas*. May I lean on you for the last lap?' And though she was barely glowing with exertion he gallantly offered her his arm and they were first to reach the crest.

These annual picnics on Table Mountain were the traditional family way of celebrating Sir Garrick Courtney's birthday, and his old friend General Smuts made a point of never missing the occasion.

On the crest they all spread out to sit in the grass and catch their breath. Centaine and the old general were a little apart from the others. Below them lay the whole sweep of the Constantia Valley, patchworked with vineyards in full green summer livery. Scattered amongst them the Dutch gables of the great châteaux glowed like pearls in the low rays of the sun and the smoky mountains of the Muizenberg and Kabonkelberg formed a solid amphitheatre of grey rock, hemming in the valley to the south while in the north the far mountains of the Hottentots Holland were a rampart that cut off the Cape of Good Hope from the continental shield of the African Continent. Directly ahead, wedged between the mountains, the waters of False Bay were ruffling and flecking at the rising importunity of the south-easter. It was so beautiful that they were silenced for many minutes.

General Smuts spoke first. 'So, Centaine, my dear, what did you want to talk about?'

'You are a mind-reader, *Ou Baas*.' She laughed ruefully. 'How do you know these things?'

'These days, when a pretty girl takes me aside, I can be sure it's business and not pleasure.' He twinkled at her.

'You are one of the most attractive men I've ever met – '

'Ah ha! Such a compliment! It must be serious.'

Her change of expression confirmed it. 'It's Shasa,' she said simply.

'No problem there – or I miss my guess.'

She took a single-paged document from her skirt pocket and handed it to him. It was a school report. The embossed crest was a bishop's mitre, the emblem of the country's most exclusive public school.

The general glanced at it. She knew how swiftly he could read even a complicated legal document, so when he handed it back to her almost immediately she was not put out. He would have it all, even down to the headmaster's summation on the last line: 'Michel Shasa is a credit to himself and to Bishops.'

General Smuts smiled at her. 'You must be very proud of him.'

'He is my entire life.'

'I know,' he said, 'and that is not always wise. A child soon becomes a man, and when he leaves he will take your life with him. However, in what way can I help you, my dear?'

'He is bright and personable and he has a way with people, even those much older than himself,' she replied. 'I would like to have a seat for him in Parliament, to begin with.'

The general removed the Panama hat from his head and smoothed back his sparkling silver hair with the palm of his hand. 'I do think he should finish his schooling before he enters Parliament, don't you, my dear!' he chuckled.

'That's it. That is exactly what I want to know from you, *Ou Baas*. Should Shasa go home to Oxford or Cambridge, or will that count against him later when he goes to the electorate? Should he rather attend one of the local universities – and if so, should it be Stellenbosch or the University of Cape Town?'

'I will think about it, Centaine, and I will give you my advice when it is time to make the final decision. But in the meantime may I be bold enough to warn you of something else, a state of mind which could prejudice your plans for the young man.'

'Please, *Ou Baas*,' she begged. 'A word of yours is worth – ' she did not have to find a comparison, for the general went on softly.

'That word "home" – it is a fatal one. Shasa must decide where his true home is, and if it is across the sea, then he must not count on my assistance.

'How foolish of me.' He saw that she was truly angry with herself. Her cheeks darkened and her lips hardened. *Soutpiel*. She remembered that jeer. One foot in London, the other in Cape Town. It was no longer amusing.

'It won't happen again,' she said, and she laid her hand on his arm to impress him with her sincerity. 'So you will help him?'

'Can we have breakfast now, Mater?' Shasa called across.

'All right, put the basket on the bank of the stream over there.' She turned back to the old man. 'Can I count on you?'

'I am in opposition, Centaine – '

'You won't be for long. The country must come to its senses at the next election.'

'You must realize I cannot promise you anything now.' He was choosing his words carefully. 'He is still a child. However, I will be watching him. If he fulfils this early promise, if he meets my standards, then he will have all my support. God knows how we need good men.

She sighed with pleasure and relief, and he went on more easily. 'Sean Courtney was an able minister in my government.'

Centaine started at the name. It brought back so many memories, so much intense pleasure, and deep sorrow, so many dark and secret things. But the old man appeared not to have noticed her consternation as he went on. 'He was also a dear and trusted friend. I would like to have another Courtney in my government, someone to trust, a good friend, perhaps one day another Courtney in my cabinet.'

He stood and helped her to her feet. 'I'm as hungry as Shasa, and the smell of food is too good to resist.'

Yet when the food was offered, the general ate most frugally, while the rest of them, led by Shasa, attacked the food with ravenous appetites sharpened by the climb. Sir Garry carved from the cold cuts of lamb and pork and the turkey,

and Anna dished out slices of the pies, Melton Mowbray, ham and egg, minced fruit and cubes of pigs' trotter embedded in delicious clear gelatine.

'One thing is certain,' Cyril Slaine, one of Centaine's general managers, declared with relief. 'The basket will be a sight lighter on the way down.'

'And now,' the general roused them from where they sprawled, satiated, on the bank of the tiny burbling stream, 'and now for the main business of the day.'

'Come on everybody.' Centaine was the first on her feet in a swirl of skirts, gay as a girl. 'Cyril, leave the basket here. We'll pick it up on the way back.'

They skirted the very edge of the grey cliff, with the world spread below them, until the general suddenly darted off to the left and scrambled over rock and through flowering heather and protea bush, disturbing the sugar birds that were sipping from the blooms. They rose in the air, flirting their long tail feathers and flashing their bright yellow belly patches with indignation at the intrusion.

Only Shasa could keep up with the general, and when the rest of the party caught the pair of them again, they were standing on the lip of a narrow rocky glen with bright green swamp grass carpeting the bottom.

'Here we are, and the first one to find a disa wins a sixpence,' General Smuts offered.

Shasa dashed away down the steep side of the glen, and before they were halfway down he was yelling excitedly.

'I've found one! The sixpence is mine!'

They straggled down from the rough rim and at the edge of the swampy ground formed a hushed and attentive circle around the graceful lily-stemmed orchid.

The general went down on one knee before it like a worshipper. 'It is indeed a blue disa, one of the rarest flowers on our earth.' The blossoms that adorned the stem were a marvellous cerulean blue, shaped like dragon's heads, their gaping throats lined with imperial purple and butter yellow. 'They only grow here on Table Mountain, nowhere else in the world.'

He looked up at Shasa. 'Would you like to do the honours for your grandfather this year, young man?'

Shasa stepped forward importantly to pick the wild orchid and hand it to Sir Garry. This little ceremony of the blue disa was part of the traditional birthday ceremony and they all laughed and applauded the presentation.

Watching her son proudly, Centaine's mind went back to the day of his birth, to the day the old Bushman had named him Shasa, 'Good Water', and had danced for him in the sacred valley deep in the Kalahari. She remembered the birth song that the old man had composed and sung, the Bushman language clicking and rustling in her head again, so well remembered, so well loved:

> His arrows will fly to the stars
> And when men speak his name
> It will be heard as far –

The old Bushman had sung,

> And he will find good water,
> Wherever he travels, he will find good water.

She saw again in her mind, the old long-dead Bushman's face, impossibly wrinkled and yet glowing that marvellous apricot colour, like amber or mellowed meerschaum, and she whispered deep in her throat, using the Bushman tongue.

'Let it be so, old grandfather. Let it be so.'

* * *

On the return journey the Daimler was only just large enough to accommodate all of them, with Anna sitting on Sir Garry's lap and submerging him beneath her abundance.

As Centaine drove down the twisting road through the forest of tall blue gum trees, Shasa leaned over the seat from behind her and encouraged her to greater speed. 'Come on, Mater, you've still got the hand brake on!'

Sitting beside Centaine, the general clutched his hat and stared fixedly at the speedometer. 'That can't be right. It feels more like one hundred miles an hour.'

Centaine swung the Daimler between the elaborately gabled white main gates of the estate. The pediment above, depicting a party of dancing nymphs bearing bunches of grapes, had been designed by the famous sculptor Anton Anreith. The name of the estate was blazoned in raised letters above the sculpture:

WELTEVREDEN 1790

'Well Satisfied' was the translation from the Dutch and Centaine had purchased it from the illustrious Cloete family exactly one year after she had pegged the claims to the H'ani Mine. Since then she had lavished money and care and love upon it.

She slowed the Daimler almost to walking pace. 'I don't want dust blowing over the grapes,' she explained to General Smuts, and her face reflected such deep content as she looked out on the neatly pruned rows of trellised vines that he thought how the estate had been aptly named.

The coloured labourers straightened up from the vines and waved as they passed. Shasa leaned from the window and shouted the names of his favourites and they grinned with huge gratification at being singled out.

The road, lined with mature oaks, led up through two hundred acres of vines to the château. The lawns around the great house were bright green Kikuyu grass. General Smuts had brought shoots of the grass back from his East African campaign in 1917 and it had flourished all over the country. In the centre of the lawn stood the tall tower of the slave bell, still used to toll the beginning and end of the day's labours. Beyond it rose the glacial white walls and massive Anreith gables of Weltevreden under its thatched roof.

Already the house servants were hurrying out to fuss around them as they spilled out of the big yellow machine.

'Lunch will be at one-thirty,' Centaine told them briskly. '*Ou Baas*, I know Sir Garry wants to read his latest chapter to you. Cyril and I have a full morning's work ahead,' she broke off. 'Shasa, where do you think you are off to?'

The boy had sidled to the end of the stoep and was within an ace of escaping.

Now he turned back with a sigh. 'Jock and I were going to work out the new pony.' The new polo pony had been Cyril's Christmas present to Shasa.

'Madame Claire will be waiting for you,' Centaine pointed out. 'We agreed that your mathematics needed attention, didn't we?'

'Oh Mater, it's holiday time – '

'Every day you spend idly, there is someone out there working. And when he meets you he is going to whip you hollow.'

'Yes, Mater.' Shasa had heard that prediction many times before, and he looked to his grandfather for support.

'Oh, I'm sure your mother will allow you a few hours to yourself after your maths tuition,' he came in dutifully. 'As you pointed out, it is officially holiday time.' He looked hopefully at Centaine.

'Might I also enter a plea on my young client's behalf?' General Smuts backed him, and Centaine capitulated with a laugh.

'You have such distinguished champions, but you will work with Madame Claire until elevenses.'

Shasa thrust his hands into his pockets and with slumped shoulders went to find his tutor. Anna disappeared into the house to chivy the servants and Garry led General Smuts away to discuss his new manuscript.

'All right.' Centaine jerked her head at Cyril. 'Let's get to work.' He followed her through the double teak front doors down the long *voorkamer*, her heels clicking on the black and white marble floors, to her study at the far end.

Her male secretaries were waiting for her. Centaine could not abide the continual presence of other females. Her secretaries were both handsome young men. The study was filled with flowers. Every day the vases were refilled from the gardens of Weltevreden. Today it was blue hydrangeas and yellow roses.

She seated herself at the long Louis XIV table she used as a desk. The legs were in richly ornate ormolu and the top was expansive enough to hold the memorabilia she had assembled.

There were a dozen photographs of Shasa's father in separate silver frames covering his life from schoolboy to dashing young airman in the RFC. The last photograph depicted him with the other pilots of his squadron standing in front of their single-seater scout planes. Hands thrust into his pockets, cap on the back of his head, Michael Courtney grinned at her, seemingly as certain of his immortality as he had been on the day that he died in the pyre of his burning aircraft. As she settled into her leather wingbacked chair, she touched the photograph, rearranging it slightly. The maid could never get it exactly right.

'I've read through the contract,' she told Cyril as he took the chair facing her. 'There are just two clauses I am not happy with. The first is clause twenty-six.' He turned to it obediently, and with her secretaries standing attentively on each side of her chair she began the day's work.

Always it was the mine which occupied Centaine first. The H'ani Mine was the source, the spring from which it all flowed, and as she worked she felt her soul yearning towards the vastness of the Kalahari, towards those mystic blue hills and the secret valley which had concealed the treasures of the H'ani for countless aeons before she had stumbled upon them, dressed in skins and a last tattered remnant of cloth, great with the child in her womb and living like an animal of the desert herself.

The desert had captured part of her soul, and she felt joyous anticipation rising in her. 'Tomorrow,' she thought, 'tomorrow Shasa and I will be going back.' The lush vineyards of the Constantia Valley and the château of

Weltevreden filled with beautiful things were part of her also, but when they cloyed she had to go back to the desert and have her soul burned clean and bright once more by the white Kalahari sun. As she signed the last of the documents and handed them to her senior secretary for witnessing and sealing, she stood and crossed to the open french doors.

Down in the paddock beyond the old slave quarters Shasa, released from his mathematics, was schooling his pony under Jock Murphy's critical eye.

It was a big horse; the limitation on size had recently been dropped by the International Polo Association, but he moved well. Shasa turned him neatly at the end of the paddock and brought him back at a full gallop. Jock tossed a ball to his nearside and Shasa leaned out to take it on his backhand. He had a firm seat and a strong arm for one so young. He swung in a good full arc and the crisp click of the bamboo-root ball carried to where Centaine stood and she saw the white flash of its trajectory in the sunlight.

Shasa reined the pony down and swung him back. As he passed again Jock Murphy tossed another ball to his offside forehand. Shasa topped the shot and it bounced away sloppily.

'Shame on you, Master Shasa,' Jock called. 'You are chopping again. Let the head of your stick take your shot through.'

Jock Murphy was one of Centaine's finds. He was a stocky, muscular man with a short neck and perfectly bald head. He had done everything: Royal Marines, professional boxer, opium runner, master at arms to an Indian maharajah, racehorse trainer, bouncer in a Mayfair gambling club and now he was Shasa's physical instructor. He was a champion shot with rifle, shotgun and pistol, a ten-goal polo player, deadly on the snooker table. He had killed a man in the ring, ridden in the Grand National, and he treated Shasa like his own son.

Once in every three months or so he went on the whisky and turned into a devil incarnate. Then Centaine would send someone down to the police station to pay the damages and bail Jock out. He would stand in front of her desk, his Derby hat held in front of his chest, shaky and hungover, his bald head shiny with shame, and apologize humbly.

'It won't happen again, missus. I don't know what came over me. Give me another chance, missus, I won't let you down.'

It was useful to know a man's weakness: a leash to hold him and a lever to move him.

* * *

There was no work for them in Windhoek. When they arrived, having walked and begged lifts on trucks and wagons all the way from the coast, they moved into the hobo encampment near the railway tracks on the outskirts of the town.

By tacit agreement the hundred or so down-and-outers and drifters and out-of-workers were allowed to camp here with their families, but the local police kept a wary eye on them. The huts were of tarpaper and old corrugated iron sheets and rough thatch and in front of each squatted dejected clusters of men and women. Only the children, dusty and skinny and sun-browned, were noisy and almost defiantly rambunctious. The encampment smelled of wood smoke and the shallow pit latrines.

Somebody had erected a crudely lettered sign facing the railway tracks: 'Vaal Hartz? Hell No!' Anyone who applied for unemployment benefits was immediately sent by the government labour department to work on the huge Vaal Hartz river irrigation project for two shillings a day. Rumours of the conditions in the labour camps there had filtered back, and in the Transvaal there had been riots when the police had attempted forcibly to transport men to the scheme.

All the better spots in the encampment were already occupied, so they camped under a small camelthorn bush and hung scraps of tarpaper in the branches for shade. Swart Hendrick was squatting beside the fire, slowly trickling handfuls of white maize meal into a soot-blackened billy of boiling water. He looked up as Lothar came back from another unsuccessful job hunt in the town. When Lothar shook his head, Hendrick returned to his cookery.

'Where is Manfred?'

Hendrick pointed with his chin at another shack near by. A dozen or so ragged men were sitting in a fascinated knot listening to a tall bearded man in their midst. He had the intense expression and fanatically dark eyes of a zealot.

'Mal Willem,' Henrick muttered. 'Crazy William,' and Lothar grunted as he searched for Manfred and then recognized his son's shining blond head amongst the others.

Satisfied that the boy was safe, Lothar took his pipe from his top pocket, blew through it and then filled it with Magaliesberg shag. The pipe stank, and the black tobacco was rank and harsh, but cheap. He longed for a cheroot as he lit the pipe with a twig from the fire. It tasted disgusting, but he felt the soothing effect almost immediately and he tossed the tobacco pouch to Hendrick and leaned back against the trunk of the thorn tree.

'What did *you* find out?'

Hendrick had spent most of the night and morning in the coloured shanty town across the other side of Windhoek. If you want to know a man's intimate secrets, ask the servants who wait at his table and make his bed.

'I found out that you can't get a drink on credit – and the Windhoek maids don't do it for love alone.' He grinned.

Lothar spat tobacco juice and glanced across at his son. It worried him a little that the boy avoided the camp urchins of his own age and sat with the men. Yet the men seemed to accept him.

'What else?' he asked Hendrick.

'The man is called Fourie. He has been working at the mine for ten years. He comes in with four or five trucks every week and goes back loaded with stores.' For a minute Hendrick concentrated on mixing the maize porridge, applying exactly the right heat from the fire.

'Go on.'

'Then, on the first Monday of every month, he comes in one small truck, the four other drivers with him riding in the back, all of them armed with shotguns and pistols. They go directly to the Standard Bank in Main Street. The manager and his staff come to the side door. Fourie and one of his drivers carry a small iron box from the truck into the bank. Afterwards Fourie and his men go down to the corner bar and drink until closing time. In the morning they go back to the mine.'

'Once a month,' Lothar whispered. 'They bring in a whole month's production at one time.' Then he looked up at Hendrick. 'You said the corner bar?' And when the big black man nodded, 'I'll need at least ten shillings.'

'What for?' Hendrick was immediately suspicious.

'One of us has to buy the barman a drink and they don't serve blacks at the corner bar.' Lothar smiled maliciously, then raised his voice. 'Manfred!'

The boy had been so mesmerized by the speaker that he had not noticed his father's return. He scrambled to his feet guiltily.

Hendrick dumped a lump of fluffy white maize porridge into the lid of the billy and poured *maas*, thick soured milk, over it before he handed it to Manfred where he squatted crosslegged beside his father.

'Did you know that it's all a plot by the Jewish owners of the gold mines in Johannesburg, Papa?' Manfred asked, his eyes shining like a religious convert's.

'What is?' Lothar grunted.

'The Depression.' Manfred used the word importantly, for he had just learned it. 'It's been arranged by the Jews and the English so that they will have all the men they want to work for them for nothing on their mines and in their factories.'

'Is that so?' Lothar smiled as he spooned up the *maas* and maize meal. 'And did the Jews and the English arrange the drought as well?' His hatred of the English did not extend beyond the borders of reason, though it could not have been more intense had the English indeed engineered the drought that had turned so many of his people's farms into sandy wastelands, the topsoil blown away on the wind, and the livestock into desiccated mummies embalmed in their own plank-hard skins.

'It's so, Papa!' Manfred cried. '*Oom* Willem explained it to us.' He pulled a rolled sheet of newsprint from his back pocket and spread it across his knee. 'Just look at this!'

The newspaper was *Die Vaderland*, an Afrikaans-language publication, 'The Fatherland', and the cartoon that Manfred was pointing out with a forefinger that trembled with indignation was in its typical style: 'Look what the Jews are doing to us!'

The main character in the cartoon was 'Hoggenheimer', one of *Die Vaderland's* creations, depicted as a gross creature in frock coat and spats, a huge diamond sparkling in his cravat, diamond rings on the fingers of both his hands, a top hat over his dark Semitic curls, a thick drooping lower lip and a great hooked beak of a nose the tip of which almost touched his chin. His pockets were stuffed with five-pound notes and he brandished a long whip as he drove a loaded wagon towards distant steel headgear towers labelled 'gold mines'. In the traces of the wagon were human beings instead of trek-oxen. Lines of men and women, skeletal and starving, with huge tortured eyes as they toiled onwards under Hoggenheimer's whip. The women wore the traditional *voortrekker* bonnets, and the men slouch hats, and so that there could be no mistake, the artist had labelled them *Die Afrikaner Volk*, 'the Afrikaans people', and the caption to the cartoon was 'The New Great Trek'.

Lothar chuckled and handed the news-sheet back to his son. He knew very few Jews, and none who looked like Hoggenheimer. Most of them were as hardworking and ordinary as anyone else, and now were as poor and starving.

'If life were as simple as that . . .' He shook his head.

'It is, Papa! All we have to do is get rid of the Jews, *Oom* Willem explained it.'

Lothar was about to reply when he realized that the smell of their food had attracted three of the camp's children, who were standing at a polite distance

watching each spoonful he raised to his mouth. The cartoon was no longer important.

There was one older girl, about twelve years of age. She was blonde, her long braids bleached as silver and fine as the Kalahari grass in winter. She was so thin that her face seemed all bone and eyes, prominent cheekbones and a high straight forehead. Her eyes were the light blue of the desert sky. Her dress was of old flour sacks sewn together, and her feet were bare.

Clinging to her skirts were two smaller children. A boy with a shaven head and large ears. His skinny brown legs stuck out of his patched khaki shorts. The small girl had a runny nose, and she sucked her thumb as she clung to her elder sister's skirts with the other hand.

Lothar looked away but suddenly the food lost its flavour and he chewed with difficulty. He saw that Hendrick was not looking at the children either. Manfred had not noticed them and was still poring over the news-sheet.

'If we feed them, we'll have every kid in the camp on our backs,' Lothar murmured, and he made a resolution never to eat in public again.

'We've got just enough left for tonight,' Hendrick agreed. 'We cannot share it.'

Lothar raised the spoon to his mouth, and then lowered it. He stared at the food on his tin plate for a moment and then beckoned the eldest girl.

She came forward shyly.

'Take it,' Lothar ordered gruffly.

'Thank you, Uncle,' she whispered. '*Dankie, Oom.*'

She whipped the plate under her skirt, hiding it from other eyes, and then dragged the two little ones away. They disappeared amongst the huts.

The girl returned an hour later. The plate and spoon had been polished until they shone. 'Does *Oom* have a shirt or anything that I can wash for him,' she asked.

Lothar opened his pack and handed over his and Manfred's soiled clothing. She brought the laundry back at sunset, smelling faintly of carbolic soap and neatly folded.

'Sorry, *Oom*, I didn't have a smoothing iron.'

'What is your name?' Manfred asked her suddenly. She glanced around at him, blushed scarlet and looked at the ground.

'Sarah,' she whispered.

* * *

Lothar buttoned the clean shirt. 'Give me the ten shillings,' he ordered.

'We'd have our throats cut if anybody knew that I have that much money,' Hendrick grumbled.

'You are wasting my time.'

'Time is the only thing we have plenty of.'

Including the barman, there were only three men in the corner bar when Lothar pushed through the swing doors.

'Quiet tonight,' Lothar remarked as he ordered a beer, and the barman grunted. He was a nondescript little man with wispy grey hair and steel-framed spectacles.

'Take a drink for yourself,' Lothar offered, and the man's expression changed.

'I'll take a gin, thank you.' He poured from a special bottle that he produced from under the counter. They both knew that the colourless liquid was water and the silver shilling would go directly into the barman's pocket.

'Your health.' He leaned over the counter, prepared to be affable for a shilling and the possibility of another.

They chatted idly, agreeing that times were hard and would get harder, that they needed rain and that the Government was to blame for it all.

'How long have you been in town? I haven't seen you around.'

'One day – one day too long,' Lothar smiled.

'I didn't catch your name.' And when Lothar told him, he showed genuine interest for the first time.

'Hey,' he called down the bar to his other customers. 'Do you know who this is? It's Lothar De La Rey! Don't you remember the reward posters during the war? He is the one that broke the hearts of the *rooinekke*.' 'Red neck' was the derogatory term for the newly arrived Englishman whose neck was inflamed by the sun. 'Man, he blew up the train at Gemsbokfontein.'

So great was their approbation that one of them even bought him another beer, but prudently limited his largesse to Lothar alone.

'I'm looking for a job,' Lothar told them when they had all become firm friends, and they all laughed.

'I heard there was work out at the H'ani Mine,' Lothar persisted.

'I'd know if there was,' the barman assured him. 'The drivers from the mine come in here every week.'

'Would you give them a good word about me?' Lothar asked.

'I'll do better. You come in Monday and I'll set you up with Gerhard Fourie, the chief driver. He is a good pal of mine. He'll know what's happening out there.'

By the time Lothar left, he was established as a good fellow and a member of the inner clique of the corner bar, and when he returned four nights later he was hailed by the barman.

'Fourie is here,' he told Lothar. 'Down at the end of the bar. I'll introduce you after I've served these others.'

The bar-room was half full this evening, and Lothar was able to study the driver. He was a powerful-looking man of middle age, with a big slack gut from sitting hours each day behind the driving-wheel. He was balding but had grown the hair above his right ear and then plastered it across his pate with brilliantine. His manner was bluff and loud; he and his mates had the well-satisfied air of men who had just performed a difficult task. He didn't look like a man that you could threaten or frighten, but Lothar had not yet finally decided on what approach to make.

The barman beckoned to him. 'Like you to meet a good friend.' They shook hands. The driver turned it into a contest but Lothar had half-expected that and shortened his grip, taking his fingers rather than his palm so that Fourie could not exert full force. They held each other's eyes until the driver winced and tried to pull his hand away. Lothar let him go.

'Buy you a drink.' Lothar felt easier now – the man was not as tough as he put out, and when the barman told them who Lothar was and related an exaggerated version of some of his exploits during the war, Fourie's manner became almost fawning and obsequious.

'Look here, man.' He drew Lothar aside and lowered his voice. 'Erik tells me you're looking for a job out at the H'ani Mine. Well, you can forget it, and that's straight. They haven't taken on any new men in a year or longer.'

'Yes.' Lothar nodded glumly. 'Since I asked Erik about the job, I've learned the truth about the H'ani Mine. It will be terrible for you all when it happens.'

The driver looked uneasy. 'What are you talking about, man? What truth is this?'

'Why, I thought you'd know.' Lothar seemed amazed by his ignorance. 'They are going to close the mine in August. Shut it down. Pay everybody off.'

'Good Christ, no!' There was fear in Fourie's eyes. 'That's not true – it can't be true.' The man was a coward, gullible, easily impressed and even more easily influenced. Lothar was grimly satisfied.

'I'm sorry, but it's best to know the truth isn't it?'

'Who told you this?' Fourie was terrified. He drove past the hobo camp down by the railway every week. He had seen the legion of the unemployed.

'I am walking out with one of the women who works for Abraham Abrahams.' He was the attorney who conducted all the business of the H'ani Mine in Windhoek. 'She saw the letters from Mrs Courtney in Cape Town. There is no doubt. The mine is shutting down. They can't sell the diamonds. Nobody is buying diamonds, not even in London and New York.

'Oh my God! My God!' whispered Fourie. 'What are we going to do? My wife isn't well and we've got the six children. Sweet Jesus, my kids will starve.

'It's all right for somebody like you. I'll bet you've got a couple of hundred quid saved up. You'll be all right.'

But Fourie shook his head.

'Well, if you haven't got anything saved, you'd best put a few pounds aside before they lay you off in August.'

'How does a man do that? How do I save – with a wife and six kids?' Fourie demanded hopelessly.

'I tell you what.' Lothar took his arm in a friendly concerned grip. 'Let's get out of here. I'll buy a bottle of brandy. Let's go some place where we can talk.'

The sun was up by the time Lothar got back to the camp the following morning. They had emptied the brandy bottle while they talked the night away. The driver was intrigued and tempted by Lothar's proposition but unsure and afraid.

Lothar had to explain and convince him of every single point particularly of his own safety. 'Nobody will ever be able to point a finger at you. I give you my sacred word on it. You'll be protected even if something goes wrong – and nothing will go wrong.'

Lothar had used all his powers of persuasion, and he was tired now as he trudged through the encampment and squatted down beside Hendrick.

'Coffee?' he asked and belched the taste of old brandy into his mouth.

'Finished.' Hendrick shook his head.

'Where is Manfred?'

Hendrick pointed with his chin. Manfred was sitting under a thorn bush at the far end of the camp. The girl Sarah was beside him, their blond heads almost touching as they pored over a sheet of newsprint. Manfred was writing on the margin of the page with a charcoal stick from the camp fire.

'Manie is teaching her to read and write,' Hendrick explained.

Lothar grunted and rubbed his bloodshot eyes. His head ached from the brandy.

'Well,' he said. 'We've got our man.'

'Ah!' Hendrick grinned. 'Then we will need the horses.'

* * *

The private railway coach had once belonged to Cecil Rhodes and the De Beers Diamond Company. Centaine Courtney had purchased it for a fraction of the price that a new carriage would have cost her, a fact that gave her satisfaction. She was still a Frenchwoman and knew the value of a sou and a franc. She had brought out a young designer from Paris to redecorate the carriage in the Art Deco style, which was all the rage, and he had been worth every penny of his fee.

She looked around the saloon, at the uncluttered lines of the furnishings, at the whimsical nude nymphs which supported the bronze light-fittings and the Aubrey Beardsley designs inlaid with exquisite workmanship into the lightwood panelling and she remembered that the designer had stuck her at first as being a homosexual, with his long flowing locks, his darkly decadent eyes and the features of a beautiful, bored and cynical faun. Her first estimate had been far wide of the truth, as she had discovered to her delight on the circular bed which he had installed in the coach's main bedroom suite. She smiled at the memory and then checked the smile as she saw that Shasa was watching her.

'You know, Mater, I sometimes think I can see what you are thinking, just by looking into your eyes.' He said these disconcerting things sometimes, and she was sure that he had grown another inch in the last week.

'I certainly hope that you cannot.' She shivered. 'It's cold in here.' The designer had incorporated, at enormous expense, a refrigeration machine which cooled the air in the saloon. 'Do turn that thing off, *chéri*.'

She stood up from her desk and went out through the frosted glass doors onto the balcony of the coach and the hot desert air rushed at her and flattened her skirts across her narrow boyish hips. She lifted her face to the sun and let the wind ruffle her short curly hair.

'What time is it?' she asked with her eyes closed and face uplifted, and Shasa who had followed her out leaned against the balcony rail and consulted his wristwatch.

'We should be crossing the Orange river in the next ten minutes, if the engine driver has kept us on schedule.'

'I never feel as though we are home until I cross the Orange.' Centaine went to lean beside him and slipped her arm through his.

The Orange river drained the western watershed of the southern African continent, rising high in the snowy mountains of Basutoland and running down fourteen hundred miles through grassy veld and wild gorges, at some season a clear slow trickle and at other times a thunderous brown flood bringing down the rich chocolate silts so that some called it the Nile of the south. It was the boundary between the Cape of Good Hope and the former German colony of South West Africa.

The locomotive whistled and the coupling jolted as the brakes squealed.

'We are slowing for the bridge.' Shasa leaned out over the balcony, and Centaine bit back the caution that came automatically to her lips.

'Beg your pardon, you can't baby him forever, Missus,' Jock Murphy had advised her. 'He's a man now, and a man's got to take his own chances.'

The tracks curved down towards the river, and they could see the Daimler riding on the flat bed behind the locomotive. It was a new vehicle; Centaine changed them every year. However, it also was yellow, as they all were, but with a black bonnet and black piping around the doors. The train journey to Windhoek saved them the onerous drive across the desert, but there was no line out to the mine.

'There it is!' Shasa called. 'There is the bridge!'

The steelwork seemed feathery and insubstantial as it crossed the half mile of riverbed, leapfrogging across its concrete buttresses. The regular beat of the bogey wheels over the cross ties altered as they ran out onto the span, and the steel girders beneath them rang like an orchestra.

'The river of diamonds,' Centaine murmured as she leaned shoulder to shoulder with Shasa and peered down into the coffee-brown waters that swirled around the piers of the bridge beneath them.

'Where do the diamonds come from?' Shasa asked. He knew the answer, of course, but he liked to hear her tell it to him.

'The river gathers them up, from every little pocket and crevice and pipe along its course. It picks up those that were flung into the air during the volcanic eruptions at the beginning of the continent's existence. For hundreds of millions of years it has been concentrating the diamonds and carrying them down towards the coast.' She glanced sideways at him. 'And why aren't they worn away, like all the other pebbles?'

'Because they are the hardest substance in nature. Nothing wears or scratches a diamond,' he answered promptly.

'Nothing is harder or more beautiful,' she agreed, and held up her right hand before his face so that the huge marquis cut diamond on her forefinger dazzled him. 'You will grow to love them. Everybody who works with them comes to love them.'

'The river,' he reminded her. He loved her voice. The husky trace of her accent intrigued him. 'Tell me about the river,' he demanded, and listened avidly as she went on.

'Where the river runs into the sea, it has thrown its diamonds up on the beaches. Those beaches are so rich in diamonds that they are the forbidden area, the Spieregebied.'

'Could you fill your pockets with diamonds, just pick them up like fallen fruit in the orchard?'

'It's not as easy as that,' she laughed. 'You could search for twenty years and not find a single stone, but if you knew where to look and had even the most primitive equipment and a great deal of luck – '

'Why can't we go in there, Mater?'

'Because, *mon chéri*, it is all taken. It belongs to a man named Oppenheimer – Sir Ernest Oppenheimer – and his company called De Beers.'

'One company owns it all. That's not fair!' he protested, and Centaine was delighted to notice the acquisitive sparkle in his eyes for the first time. Without a healthy measure of avarice, he would not be capable of carrying through the plans she was so carefully laying for him. She had to teach him to be greedy – for wealth and for power.

'He owns the Orange river concessions,' she nodded, 'and he owns the Kimberley and Wesselton and Bultfontein and all the other great producing

mines, but more, much more than that, he controls the sale of every single stone, even those produced by us, the few little independents – '

'He controls us – he controls the H'ani?' Shasa demanded indignantly, his smooth cheeks flushing.

Centaine nodded. 'We have to offer every diamond we mine to his Central Selling Organization, and he will set a price upon it.'

'And we have to accept his price?'

'No, we don't! But we would be very unwise not to do so.'

'What could he do to us if we refused?'

'Shasa, I have told you often before. Don't fight with somebody stronger than yourself. There aren't many people stronger than us – not in Africa anyway – but Sir Ernest Oppenheimer is one of them.'

'What could he do?' Shasa persisted.

'He could eat us up, my darling, and nothing would give him greater pleasure. Each year we become richer and more attractive to him. He is the one man in the world that we have to be afraid of, especially if we were rash enough to come near this river of his.' She swept a gesture across the wide river.

Although it had been named Orange by its Dutch discoverers for the Stadtholders of the House of Orange, the name could have as readily applied to its startling orange-coloured sandbanks. The bright plumage of the waterfowl clustered upon them were like precious stones set in red gold.

'He owns the river?' Shasa was surprised and perplexed.

'Not legally, but you approach it at your own peril for he protects it and the diamonds it contains with his jealous wrath.'

'So there are diamonds here?'

Eagerly Shasa scanned the banks as though he expected to see them sparkling seductively in the sunlight.

'Dr Twentyman-Jones and I both believe it – and we have isolated some very interesting areas. Two hundred miles upstream is a waterfall that the Bushmen called the Place of the Great Noise, Aughrabies. There the Orange thunders through a narrow rocky chute and falls into the deep, inaccessible gorge below. The gorge should be a treasurehouse of captured diamonds. Then there are other ancient alluvial beds where the river has changed its course.'

They left the river and its narrow strip of greenery and the loco accelerated again as they ran on northwards into the desert. Centaine watched Shasa's face carefully as she went on explaining and lecturing. She would never go on until she reached the point of boredom – at the first sign of inattention, she would stop. She did not have to press. There was all the time necessary for his education, but the one single most important consideration was never to tire him, never to outrun his immature strength or his undeveloped powers of concentration. She must retain his enthusiasm intact and never jade him. This time his interest persisted beyond its usual span, and she recognized it was time for another advance.

'It will have warmed up in the saloon. Let's go in.' She led him to her desk. 'There are some things I want to show you.' She opened the confidential summary of the annual financial reports of the Courtney Mining and Finance Company.

This wold be the difficult part, even for her the paperwork was deadly dull, and she saw him immediately daunted by the columns of figures. Mathematics was his only weak subject.

'You enjoy chess, don't you?'

'Yes,' he agreed cautiously.

'This is a game also,' she assured him. 'But a thousand times more fascinating and rewarding, once you understand the rules.' He cheered up visibly – games and rewards Shasa understood.

'Teach me the rules,' he invited.

'Not all at one time. Bit by bit, until you know enough to start playing.'

It was evening before she saw the fatigue in the lines at the corners of his mouth and the white rims to his nostrils, but he was still frowning with concentration.

'That's enough for today.' She closed the thick folder. 'What are the golden rules?'

'You must always sell something for more than it cost you.'

She nodded encouragement.

'And you must buy when everybody else is selling, and you must sell when everybody else is buying.'

'Good.' She stood up. 'Now a breath of fresh air before we change for dinner.'

On the balcony of the coach she placed her arm around his shoulders, and she had to reach up to do so. 'When we get to the mine, I want you to work with Dr Twentyman-Jones in the mornings. You may have the afternoons free, but you'll work in the mornings. I want you to get to know the mine and all its workings. Of course, I will pay you.'

'That isn't necessary, Mater.'

'Another golden rule, my darling, never refuse a fair offer.'

Through the night and all the following day they ran on northwards across great spaces bleached by the sun, with blue mountains traced in darker blue against the desert horizons.

'We should get into Windhoek a little after sunset,' Centaine explained. 'But I have arranged for the coach to be shunted on to a quiet spur and we will spend the night aboard and leave for the mine in the morning. Dr Twentyman-Jones and Abraham Abrahams will be dining with us, so we will dress.'

In his shirtsleeves Shasa was standing in front of the long mirror in his compartment, struggling with his black bow tie – he had not yet entirely mastered the art of shaping the butterfly – when he felt the coach slowing and heard the loco blow a long eeerie blast.

He felt a prickle of excitement and turned to the open window. They were crossing the shoulder of hills above the town of Windhoek, and the street lights came on even as he watched. The town was the size of one of Cape Town's suburbs and only the few central streets were lit.

The train slowed to a walking pace as they reached the outskirts of the town, and Shasa smelled wood-smoke. Then he noticed that there was some sort of encampment amongst the thorn trees beside the tracks. He leaned out of the window to see more clearly and stared at the clusters of untidy shanties, wreathed in the blue smoke of campfires and shaded by the deepening dusk. There was a crudely lettered sign facing the tracks and Shasa read it with difficulty: 'Vaal Hartz? Hell No!' It made no sense and he frowned as he noticed two figures standing near the sign, watching the passing train.

The shorter of the two was a girl, barefoot and with a thin shapeless dress over her frail body. She did not interest him and he transferred his attention to the taller, more robust figure beside her. Immediately he straightened in shock and rising indignation. Even in the poor light, he recognized that silver-blond

shock of hair and the black eyebrows. They stared at each other expressionlessly, the boy in the white dress shirt and black tie in the lighted window and the boy in dusty khaki. Then the train slid past and hid them from each other.

'Darling – ' Shasa turned from the window to face his mother. She was wearing sapphires tonight and a blue dress as filmy and light as woodsmoke. 'You aren't ready yet. We'll be in the station in a minute – and what a mess you have made of your tie. Come here and let me do it for you.'

As she stood in front of him and shaped the bow with dextrous fingers, Shasa shrugged to contain and suppress the anger and sense of inadequacy that a mere glimpse of the other boy had aroused in him.

* * *

The driver of the locomotive shunted them off the main track on to a private spur beyond the sheds of the railway workshop and uncoupled them beside the concrete ramp where Abraham Abrahams' Ford was already parked, and Abe scampered up on to the balcony the moment the coach came to a stop.

'Centaine, you are more beautiful than ever.' He kissed her hand and then each of her cheeks. He was a little man, just Centaine's height, with a lively expression and quick, alert eyes. His ears were pricked up as though he were listening to a sound that nobody else could hear.

His studs were diamonds and onyx, which was flashy, and his dinner jacket was a little too extravagantly cut, but he was one of Centaine's favourite people. He had stood by her when her total wealth had amounted to something less than ten pounds. He had filed the claims for the H'ani Mine and since then conducted most of her legal business and many of her private affairs as well. He was an old and dear friend but, more important, he did not make mistakes in his work. He wouldn't have been here if he did.

'Dear Abe.' She took both his hands and squeezed them. 'How is Rachel?'

'Outstanding,' he assured her. It was his favourite adjective. 'She sends her apologies, but the new baby – '

'Of course.' Centaine nodded, understanding. Abraham knew her preferences for masculine company and seldom brought his wife with him, even when invited to do so.

Centaine turned from her lawyer to the other tall stoop-shouldered figure that was hovering at the gate of the balcony.

'Dr Twentyman-Jones.' She held out her hands.

'Mrs Courtney,' he murmured like an undertaker.

Centaine put on her most radiant smile. It was her own little game, to see if she could inveigle him into the smallest display of pleasure. She lost again. His apparent gloom deepened until he looked like a bloodhound in mourning.

Their relationship went back almost as far as Centaine's with Abraham. He had been a consulting mining engineer with the De Beers Diamond Company, but he had evaluated and opened the H'ani workings for her back in 1919. It had taken almost five years of her most winning persuasion before he had agreed to come to work for the H'ani Mine as Resident Engineer. He was probably the best diamond man in South Africa, which meant the best in the world.

Centaine led the two of them into the saloon and waved the white-jacketed barman aside.

'Abraham, a glass of champagne?' She poured the wine with her own hands. 'And Dr Twentyman-Jones, a little Madeira?'

'You never forget, Mrs Courtney,' he admitted miserably as she carried the glass to him. Between them it was always full titles and surnames, although their friendship had stood all the tests.

'I give you good health, gentlemen.' Centaine saluted them, and when they had drunk she glanced across at the far door.

On cue Shasa came through and Centaine watched critically as he shook hands with each of the men. He conducted himself with just the correct amount of deference for their age, showed no discomfort when Abraham over-effusively embraced him and then returned Twentyman-Jones's greeting with equal solemnity. She gave a small nod of approval and took her seat behind her desk. It was her sign that the niceties had been observed and they could get on to business. The two men quickly perched on the elegant but uncomfortable Art Deco chairs and leaned towards her attentively.

'It has come at last,' Centaine told them. 'They have cut our quota.' They rocked back in their seats and exchanged a brief glance before turning back to Centaine.

'We have been expecting it for almost a year,' Abraham pointed out.

'Which does not make the actuality any more pleasant,' Centaine told him tartly.

'How much?' Twentyman-Jones asked.

'Forty per cent,' Centaine answered, and he looked as though he might burst into tears while he considered it.

Each of the independent diamonds producers was allocated a quota by the Central Selling Organization. The arrangement was informal and probably illegal, but nonetheless rigorously enforced, and none of the independents had ever been foolhardy enough to test the legality of the system or the share of the market they were given.

'Forty per cent!' Abraham burst out. 'That's iniquitous!'

'An accurate observation, dear Abe, but not particularly useful at this stage.' Centaine looked to Twentyman-Jones.

'No change in the categories?' he asked. The quotas were broken down by carat weight into the different types of stones, from dark industrial boart to the finest gem quality, and by size from the tiny crystals of ten points and smaller to the big valuable stones.

'Same percentages,' Centaine agreed, and he slumped in his chair, pulled a notebook from his inside pocket and began a series of quick calculations. Centaine glanced behind her to where Shasa leaned against the panelled bulkhead.

'Do you understand what we are talking about?'

'The quota? Yes, I think so, Mater.'

'If you don't understand, then ask,' she ordered brusquely and turned back to Twentyman-Jones.

'Could you appeal for a ten per cent increase at the top end?' he asked, but she shook her head.

'I have already done so and they turned me down. De Beers in their infinite compassion point out that the biggest drop in demand has been at the top end, at the gem and jewellery level.'

He returned to his notebook, and they listened to his pencil scratching on the paper until he looked up.

'Can we break even?' Centaine asked quietly, and Twentyman-Jones looked as though he might shoot himself rather than reply.

'It will be close,' he whispered, 'and we'll have to fire and cut and hone, but we should be able to pay costs, and perhaps even turn a small profit still, depending upon the floor price that De Beers sets. But the cream will be skimmed off the top, I'm afraid, Mrs Courtney.'

Centaine felt weak and trembly with relief. She took her hands off the desk and placed them in her lap so the others might not notice. She did not speak for a few moments, and then she cleared her throat to make certain her voice did not quaver.

'The effective date for the quota cut is the first of March,' she said. 'That means we can deliver one more full package. You know what to do, Dr Twentyman-Jones.'

'We will fill the package with sweeteners, Mrs Courtney.'

'What is a sweetener, Dr Twentyman-Jones?' Shasa spoke for the first time, and the engineer turned to him seriously.

'When we turn up a number of truly excellent diamonds in one period of production, we reserve some of the best of them, set them aside to include in a future package which might be of inferior quality. We have a reserve of these high quality stones which we will now deliver to the CSO while we still have the opportunity.'

'I understand,' Shasa nodded. 'Thank you, Dr Twentyman-Jones.'

'Pleased to be of service, Master Shasa.'

Centaine stood up. 'We can go in to dinner now,' and the white-jacketed servant opened the sliding doors through into the dining-room where the long table gleamed with silver and crystal and the yellow roses stood tall in their antique celadon vases.

* * *

A mile down the railway track from where Centaine's coach stood, two men sat huddled over a smoky campfire watching the maize porridge bubbling in the billy-can and discussing the horses. The entire plan hinged on the horses. They needed at least fifteen, and they had to be strong, desert-hardened animals.

'The man I am thinking of is a good friend,' Lothar said.

'Even the best friend in the world won't lend you fifteen good horses. We can't do it with less than fifteen, and you won't buy them for a hundred pounds.'

Lothar sucked on the stinking clay pipe and it gurgled obscenely. He spat the yellow juice into the fire. 'I'd pay a hundred pounds for a decent cheroot,' he murmured.

'Not my hundred, you won't,' Hendrick contradicted him.

'Leave the horses for now,' Lothar suggested. 'Let's go over the men we need for the relays.'

'The men are easier than the horses.' Hendrick grinned. 'These days you can buy a good man for the price of a meal, and have his wife for the pudding. I have already sent messages to them to meet us at Wild Horse Pan.'

They both glanced up as Manfred came out of the darkness, and when Lothar saw his son's expression he stuffed the notebook into his pocket and stood up quickly.

'Papa, you must come quickly,' Manfred pleaded.

'What is it, Manie?'

'Sarah's mother and the little ones. They are all sick. I told them you would come, Papa.'

Lothar had the reputation of being able to heal humans and animals of all their ills, from gunshot wounds and measles to staggers and distemper.

Sarah's family was living under a tattered sheet of tarpaulin near the centre of the encampment. The woman lay beneath a greasy blanket with the two small children beside her. Though she was probably not older than thirty years, care and punishing labour and poor food had greyed and shrunken her into an old woman. She had lost most of her upper teeth so that her face seemed to have collapsed.

Sarah knelt beside her with a damp rag with which she was trying to wipe her flushed face. The woman rolled her head from side to side and mumbled in delirium.

Lothar knelt on the woman's other side, facing the girl. 'Where is your pa, Sarah? He should be here.'

'He went away to find work on the mines,' she whispered.

'When?'

'Long ago.' And then she went on loyally, 'But he is going to send for us, and we are going to live in a nice house – '

'How long has your ma been sick?'

'Since last night.' Sarah tried again to place the rag on the woman's forehead but she struck it away weakly.

'And the babies?' Lothar studied their swollen faces.

'Since the morning.'

Lothar drew back the blanket and the stench of liquid faeces was thick and choaking.

'I tried to clean them,' Sarah whispered defensively, 'but they just dirty themselves again. I don't know what to do.'

Lothar lifted the little girl's soiled dress. Her small pot belly was swollen with malnutrition and her skin was chalky white. An angry crimson rash was blazoned across it.

Involuntarily Lothar jerked his hand away. 'Manfred,' he demanded sharply. 'Have you touched them – any of them?'

'Yes, Pa. I tried to help Sarah clean them.'

'Go to Hendrick,' Lothar ordered. 'Tell him we are leaving immediately. We have to get out of here.'

'What is it, Pa?' Manfred lingered.

'Do as I tell you,' Lothar told him angrily, and when Manfred backed away into the darkness, he returned to the girl.

'Have you been boiling your drinking water?' he asked, and she shook her head.

It was always the same, Lothar thought. Simple country people who had lived far from other human habitation all their lives, drinking at sweet clean springs and defecating careflessly in the open veld. They did not understand the hazards when forced to live in close proximity to others.

'What is it, *Oom*?' Sarah asked softly. 'What is wrong with them?'

'Enteric fever.' Lothar saw that it meant nothing to her. 'Typhoid fever,' he tried again.

'Is it bad?' she asked helplessly, and he could not meet her eyes. He looked again at the two small children. The fever had burned them out, and the diarrhoea had dehydrated them. Already it was too late. With the mother there was perhaps still a chance, but she had been weakened also.

'Yes,' Lothar said. 'It is bad.' The typhoid would be spreading through the encampment like fire in the winter-dry veld. There was already a good chance that Manfred might have been infected, and at the thought he stood up quicky and stepped away from the foulsmelling mattress.

'What must I do?' Sarah pleaded.

'Give them plenty to drink, but make sure the water is boiled.' Lothar backed away. He had seen typhoid in the concentration camps of the English during the war. The death-toll had been more horrible than that of the battlefield. He had to get Manfred away from here.

'Do you have medicine for it, *Oom*?' Sarah followed him. 'I don't want my ma to die – I don't want my baby sister – if you can give me some medicine – ' She was struggling with her tears, bewildered and afraid, turning to him in pathetic trust.

Lothar's only duty was to his own, yet he was torn by the child's little display of courage. He wanted to tell her, 'There is no medicine for them. There is nothing that can be done for them. They are in God's hands now.'

Sarah came after him and took Lothar's hand, tugging desperately at it as she tried to lead him back to the shelter where the woman and the two children lay dying.

'Help me, *Oom*. Help me to make them better.'

Lothar's skin crawled at the girl's touch. He could imagine the loathsome infection being transferred from her warm soft skin. He had to get away.

'Stay here,' he told her, trying to disguise his revulsion. 'Give them water to drink. I will go to fetch medicine.'

'When will you come back?' She looked up trustingly into his face, and it took all his strength to tell the lie.

'I will come back as soon as I can,' he promised, and gently broke her grip.

'Give them water,' he repeated, and turned away.

'Thank you,' she called after him softly. 'God bless you, you are a kind man, *Oom*.'

Lothar could not reply. He could not even look back. Instead he hurried through the darkened camp. This time, because he was listening for them, he picked up the other little sounds from the huts he passed: the fretful feverish cry of a child, the gasp and moan of a woman in the terrible abdominal cramps of enteric fever, the concerned murmurs of those who tended them.

From one of the tarpaper huts a gaunt dark creature emerged and clutched at his arm. He was not sure whether it was man or woman until she spoke in a cracked almost demented falsetto.

'Are you a doctor? I have to find a doctor.'

Lothr shrugged off the clawed hand and broke into a run.

Swart Hendrick was waiting for him. He had the pack on his shoulder already and was kicking sand over the embers of the campfire. Manfred squatted on one side, beneath the thorn tree.

'Enteric.' Lothar said the dread word. 'It's through the camp already.'

Hendrick froze. Lothar had seen him stand down the charge of a wounded

bull elephant, but he was afraid now. Lothar could see it in the way he held his great black head and smell it on him, a strange odour like that of one of the copper-hooded desert cobras when aroused.

'Come on, Manfred. We are getting out.'

'Where are we going, Pa?' Manfred remained squatting.

'Away from here – away from the town and this plague.'

'What about Sarah?' Manfred ducked his head on to his shoulders, a stubborn gesture which Lothar recognized.

'She is nothing to us. There is nothing we can do.'

'She's going to die – like her ma, and the little kids.' Manfred looked up at his father. 'She's going to die, isn't she?'

'Get up on your feet,' Lothar snarled at him. His guilt made him fierce. 'We are going.' He made an authoritative gesture and Hendrick reached down and hauled Manfred to his feet.

'Come, Manie, listen to your Pa.' He followed Lothar, dragging the boy by his arm.

They crossed the railway embankment and Manfred stopped pulling back. Hendrick released him, and he followed obediently. Within the hour they reached the main road, a dusty silver river in the moonlight running down the pass through the hills, and Lothar halted.

'Are we going for the horses now?' Hendrick asked.

'Yes.' Lothar nodded. 'That's the next step.' But his head turned back in the direction they had come and they were all silent, looking back with him.

'I couldn't take the chance,' Lothar explained. 'I couldn't let Manfred stay near them.' Neither of them answered. 'We have to get on with our preparations – the horses, we have to get the horses – ' His voice trailed off.

Suddenly Lothar snatched the pack from Hendrick's shoulder and threw it to the ground. He ripped it open angrily and snatched out the small canvas roll in which he kept his surgical instruments and store of medicines.

'Take Manie,' he ordered Hendrick. 'Wait for me in the gorge of the Gamas river, at the same place we camped on the march from Usakos. You remember it?'

Hendrick nodded. 'How long will it be before you come?'

'As long as it takes them to die,' said Lothar. He stood up and looked at Manfred.

'Do what Hendrick tells you,' he ordered.

'Can't I come with you, Pa?'

Lothar did not bother to reply. He turned and strode back amongst the moonlit thorn trees and they watched him until he disappeared. Then Hendrick dropped to his knees and began re-rolling the pack.

* * *

Sarah squatted beside the fire, her skirts pulled up around her skinny brown thighs, slitting her eyes against the smoke as she waited for the soot-blackened billy to boil.

She looked up and saw Lothar standing at the edge of the firelight. She stared at him, and then slowly her pale delicate features seemed to crumple and the tears streamed down her cheeks, glistening in the light of the flames.

'I thought you weren't coming back,' she whispered. 'I thought you had gone.'

Lothar shook his head abruptly, still so angry with his own weakness that he could not trust himself to speak. Instead he squatted across the fire from her and spread the canvas roll. Its contents were pitifully inadequate. He could draw a rotten tooth, lance a boil or a snakebite, or set a broken limb, but to treat runaway enteric there was almost nothing. He measure a spoonful of a black patent medicine, Chamberlain's Famous Diarrhoea Remedy, into the tin mug and filled it with hot water from the billy.

'Help me,' he ordered Sarah and between them they lifted the youngest child into a sitting position. She was without weight and he could feel every bone in her tiny body, like that of the fledgling taken from the nest. It was hopeless.

'She'll be dead by morning,' he thought, and held the mug to her lips. She did not last that long; she slipped away a few hours before dawn. The moment of death was ill-defined, and Lothar was not certain it was over until he felt for the child's pulse at the carotid and felt the chill of eternity in her wasted flesh.

The little boy lasted until noon and died with as little fuss as his sister. Lothar wrapped them in the same grey, soiled blanket and carried them in his arms to the communal grave that had been already dug at the edge of the camp. They made a small lonely little package on the sandy floor of the square excavation, at the end of the row of larger bodies.

Sarah's mother fought for her life.

'God knows why she should want to go on living,' Lothar thought, 'there isn't much in it for her.' But she moaned and rolled her head and cried out in the delirium of fever. Lothar began to hate her for the stubborn struggle to survive that kept him beside her foul mattress, forced to share in her degradation, to touch her hot fever-wracked skin and dribble liquid into her toothless mouth.

At dusk he thought she had won. Her skin cooled and she was quieter. She reached out feebly for Sarah's hand and tried to speak, staring up at her face as though she recognized her, the words catching and cawing in the back of her throat and thick yellow mucus bubbling in the corners of her lips.

The effort was too much. She closed her eyes and seemed to sleep. Sarah wiped her lips and held on to the thin bony hand with the blue veins swelling under the thin skin.

An hour later the woman sat up suddenly, and said clearly: 'Sarah, where are you, child?' then fell back and fought for a long strangling breath. The breath ended in the middle and her bony chest subsided gradually, and the flesh seemed to droop from her face like warm candlewax.

This time Sarah walked beside him as Lothar carried the woman to the grave site. He laid her at the end of the row of corpses. Then they walked back to the hut.

Sarah stood and watched Lothar roll the canvas pack, and her small white face was desolate. He went half a dozen paces and then turned back. She was quivering like a rejected puppy, but she had not moved.

'All right,' he sighed with resignation. 'Come on, then.' And she scampered to his side.

'I won't be any trouble,' she gabbled, almost hysterical with relief. 'I'll help you. I can cook and sew and wash. I won't be any trouble.'

* * *

'What are you going to do with her?' Hendrick asked. 'She can't stay with us. We could never do what we have to do with a child of her age.'

'I could not leave her there,' Lothar defended himself, 'in that death camp.'

'It would have been better for us.' Hendrick shrugged. 'But what do we do now?'

They had left the camp in the bottom of the gorge and climbed to the top of the rocky wall. The children were far below on the sandbank at the edge of the only stagnant green pool in the gorge that still held water.

They squatted side by side, Manfred with his right hand extended as he held the handline. They saw him lean back and strike, then heave the line in hand over hand. Sarah jumped up and her excited shrieks carried up to where they sat. They watched Manfred swing the kicking slippery black catfish out of the green water. It squirmed on the sand, glistening with wetness.

'I will decide what to do with her,' Lothar assured him, but Hendrick interrupted.

'It better be soon. Every day we waste the waterholes in the north are drying out, and we still don't even have the horses.'

Lothar stuffed his clay pipe with fresh shag and thought about it. Hendrick was right; the girl complicated everything. He had to get rid of her somehow. Suddenly he looked up from the pipe and smiled.

'My cousin,' he said, and Hendrick was puzzled.

'I did not know you had a cousin.'

'Most of them perished in the camps, but Trudi survived.'

'Where is she, this beloved cousin of yours?'

'She lives on our road to the north. We'll waste no time in dumping the brat with her.

* * *

'I don't want to go,' Sarah whispered miserably. 'I don't know your aunt. I want to stay here with you.'

'Hush,' Manfred cautioned her. 'You'll wake Pa and Henny.' He pressed closer to her and touched her lips to quieten her. The fire had died down and the moon had set. Only the desert stars lit them, big as candles against the black velvet curtain of the sky.

Sarah's voice was so small now that he could barely make out the words, though her lips were inches from his ear. 'You are the only friend I have ever had,' she said, 'and who will teach me to read and write?'

Manfred felt an enormous weight of responsibility conferred upon him by her words. His feelings for her to this moment had been ambivalent. Like her he had never had friends of his own age, never attended a school, never lived in a town. His only teacher had been his father. He had lived all his life with grown men; his father and Hendrick and the rough hard men of the road camps and trawler fleet. There had been no woman to caress or gentle him.

She had been his first female companion, though her weakness and silliness irritated him. He had to wait for her to catch up when they climbed the hills and she wept when he beat a squirming catfish to death or wrung the neck of a fat feathered brown francolin taken in one of his noose snares. However, she could make him laugh and he enjoyed her voice when she sang, thin but sweet

and melodious. Then again although her adulation was sometimes cloying and excessive, he experienced an unaccountable sense of wellbeing when she was with him. She was quick to learn and in the few days they had been together she already had the alphabet by heart and the multiplication tables from two to ten.

It would have been much better if she had been a boy, but then there was something else. The smell of her skin and the softness of her intrigued him. Her hair was so fine and silky. Sometimes he would touch it as though by accident and she would freeze and keep very still under his fingers, so that he was embarrassed and dropped his hand self-consciously.

Occasionally she would brush against him like an affectionate cat and the strange pleasure this gave him was out of all proportion to the brief contact; and when they slept under the same blanket, he would awake in the night and listen to her breathing and her hair tickled his face.

The road to Okahandja was long and hard and dusty. They had been on it for five days now. They travelled only in the early morning and late evening. In the noonday the men would rest up in the shade, and the two children could sneak away to talk and set snares or go over Sarah's lessons. They did not play games of make-believe as other children of their age might have done. Their lives were too close to harsh reality. And now a new threat had been thrust upon them: the threat of separation which grew more menacing with each mile of road that fell behind them. Manfred could not find the words of comfort for her. His own sense of coming loss was aggravated by her declaration of friendship. She snuggled against him under the single blanket and the heat that emanated from her thin frail body was startling. Awkwardly he slipped an arm around her thin shoulders and her hair was soft against his cheek.

'I'll come back for you.' He had not meant to say that. He had not even thought it before that moment.

'Promise me.' She twisted so that her lips were by his ear. 'Promise me you will come back to fetch me.'

'I promise I will come back to you,' he repeated solemnly, appalled at what he was doing. He had no control over his future, could never be certain of honouring a promise like that.

'When?' She fastened on it eagerly.

'We have something to do.' Manfred did not know the details of what his father and Henny were planning. He only understood that it was arduous and somehow dangerous. 'Something important. No, I can't tell you about it. But, when it is over, we will come back for you.'

It seemed to satisfy her. She sighed, and he felt the tension go out of her limbs. Her whole body softened with sleepiness, and her voice drifted into a low murmur.

'You are my friend, aren't you, Manie?'

'Yes. I'm your friend.'

'My best friend?'

'Yes, your best friend.'

She sighed again and fell asleep. He stroked her hair, so soft and fluffy under his hand, and he was assailed by the melancholy of impending loss. He felt that he would weep, but that was a girlish thing and he would not let it happen.

The following evening they trudged ankle-deep in the floury white dust up another fold in the vast undulating plain, and when the children caught up with Lothar at the crest, he pointed wordlessly ahead.

The cluster of iron roofs of the little frontier town of Okahandja shone in the lowering sunlight like mirrors, and in their midst was the single spire of a church. Also clad in corrugated iron, it barely topped the trees which grew around it.

'We'll be there after dark.' Lothar eased his pack to his other shoulder and looked down at the girl. Her fine hair was plastered with dust and sweat to her forehead and cheeks, and her untidy sunstreaked blonde pigtails stuck out behind her ears like horns. The sun had burned her so dark that were it not for the fair hair she might have been a Nama child. She was dressed as simply and her bare feet were white with floury dust.

Lothar had considered and then rejected the idea of buying her a new dress and shoes at one of the little general-dealer's stores along the road. The expense might have been worthwhile, for if the child were rejected by his cousin – He did not follow the thought further. He would clean her up a little at the borehole that supplied the town's water.

'The lady you will be staying with is *Mevrou* Trudi Bierman. She is a very kind religious lady.'

Lothar had little in common with his cousin. They had not met in thirteen years. 'She is married to the dominie of the Dutch Reformed Church here at Okahandja. He is also a fine God-fearing man. They have children your age. You will be very happy with them.'

'Will he teach me to read like Manie does?'

'Of course he will.' Lothar was prepared to give any assurance to rid himself of the child. 'He teaches his own children and you will be like one of them.'

'Why can't Manie stay with me?'

'Manie has to come with me.'

'Please, can't I come with you too?'

'No, you cannot. You'll stay here – and I don't want to go over that again.'

At the reservoir of the borehole pump Sarah bathed the dust from her legs and arms and dampened her hair before re-plaiting her pigtails.'

'I'm ready,' she told Lothar at last, and her lips trembled while he looked her over critically. She was a grubby little urchin, a burden upon them, but somehow a fondness for her had crept in upon him. He could not help but admire her spirit and her courage. Suddenly he found himself wondering if there was no other way than abandoning the child and it took an effort to thrust the idea aside and steel himself to what must be done.

'Come on then.' He took her hand and turned to Manfred. 'You wait here with Henny.'

'Please let me come with you, Pa,' Manfred begged. 'Just as far as the gate. Just to say goodbye to Sarah.'

Lothar wavered and then agreed gruffly. 'All right, but keep your mouth shut and remember your manners.'

He led them down the narrow sanitary lane at the rear of the row of cottages until they came to the back gate of the large house beside the church and obviously attached to it. There was no mistaking that it was the pastory. There was a light burning in the back room, the fierce white light of a Petromax lamp, and the bugs and moths were drumming against the wire screening that covered the back door.

The sound of voices raised in a dolorous religious chant carried to them as they opened the gate and went up the kitchen path. When they reached the

screen door they could see in the lighted kitchen beyond a family seated at a long deal table, singing together.

Lothar knocked on the door and the hymn trailed away. From the head of the table a man rose and came towards the door. He was dressed in a black suit that bagged at the knees and elbows but was stretched tightly across his broad shoulders. His hair was thick and long, hanging in a greying mane to his shoulders and sprinkling the dark cloth with a flurry of dandruff.

'Who is it?' he demanded, in a voice trained to boom out from the pulpit. He flung open the screen door and peered out into the dark. He had a broad intelligent forehead with the arrowhead of a sharp widow's peak emphasizing its depth, and his eyes were deep-set and fierce as those of a prophet from the Old Testament.

'You!' He recognized Lothar, but made no attempt to greet him further. Instead he looked back over his shoulder. '*Mevrou*, it is your godless cousin come in from the wilderness like Cain!'

The fair-headed woman rose from the foot of the table, hushing the children and signalling them to remain in their seats. She was almost as tall as her husband, in her forties and well fleshed, with a rosy complexion and braids piled on top of her head in the Germanic fashion. She folded her thick creamy-skinned arms across her bulky shapeless bosom.

'What do you want with us, Lothar De La Rey?' she demanded. 'This is the God-fearing home of Christian folk; we want nothing of your wanton ways and wild behaviour.' She broke off as she noticed the children and stared at them with interest.

'Hello, Trudi.' Lothar drew Sarah forward into the light. 'It has been many years. You look well and happy.'

'I am happy in God's love,' his cousin agreed. 'But you know I have seldom been well.' She assumed an expression of suffering and Lothar went on quickly.

'I am giving you another chance of Christian service.' He pushed Sarah forward. 'This poor little orphan – she is alone. She needs a home. You could take her in, Trudi, and God will love you for it.'

'Is it another of your – ' His cousin glanced back into the kitchen at the interested faces of her own two daughters, and then lowered her voice and hissed at him, 'Another of your bastards?'

'Her family died in the typhoid epidemic.'

It was a mistake. He saw her recoil from the girl. 'That was weeks ago. She is free of the disease.

Trudi relaxed a little and Lothar went on quickly. 'I can't care for her. We are travelling, and she needs a woman.'

'We have too many mouths already – ' she began, but her husband interrupted her.

'Come here, child,' he boomed and Lothar shoved Sarah towards him. 'What is your name?'

'Sarah Bester, *Oom*.'

'So you are of the *Volk*?' the tall dominie demanded. 'One of the true Afrikaner blood?'

Sarah nodded uncertainly.

'And your dead mother and father were wed in the Reformed Church?' She nodded again. 'And you believe in the Lord God of Israel?'

'Yes, *Oom*. My mother taught me,' Sarah whispered.

'Then we cannot turn the child away,' he told his wife. 'Bring her in, woman. God will provide. God always provides for his chosen people.'

Trudi Bierman sighed theatrically and reached for Sarah's arm. 'So thin, and filthy as a Nama piccaninny.'

'And you, Lothar De La Rey,' the dominie pointed a finger at him. 'Has not the merciful Lord yet shown you the error of your ways, and placed your feet on the path of righteousness?'

'Not yet, dear cousin.' Lothar backed away from the door, his relief undisguised.

The dominie's attention flicked to the boy standing in the shadows behind Lothar. 'Who is this?'

'My son, Manfred.' Lothar placed a protective arm over the boy's shoulder, and the dominie came closer and stooped to study his face closely. His great dark beard bristled and his eyes were wild and fanatical, but Manfred stared directly into them, and saw them change. They warmed and lightened with the sparkle of good humour and compassion.

'Do I frighten you, *Jong*?' His voice mellowed, and Manfred shook his head.

'No, *Oomie* – or not too much anyway.'

The dominie chuckled. 'Who teaches you your Bible, *Jong*?' He used the expression meaning 'young' or 'young man'.

'My father, *Oom*.'

'Then God have mercy on your soul.' He stood up and thrust his beard out at Lothar.

'I would you had left the boy, rather than the girl,' he told him, and Lothar tightened his grip on Manfred's shoulder. 'He is a likely looking lad, and we need good men in the service of God and the *Volk*.'

'He is well taken care of.' Lothar could not conceal his agitation, but the dominie dropped his compelling gaze back to Manfred.

'I think, *Jong*, that you and I are destined by Almighty God to meet again. When your father drowns or is eaten by a lion or hanged by the English, or in some other fashion punished by the Lord God of Israel, then come back here. Do you hear me, *Jong*? I need you, the *Volk* need you, and God needs you! My name is Tromp Bierman, the Trumpet of the Lord. Come back to this house!'

Manfred nodded. 'I will come back to see Sarah. I promised her.'

As he said it the girl's courage broke and she sobbed and tried to pull free from Trudi's grip.

'Stop that, child.' Trudi Bierman shook her irritably. 'Stop blubbering.' Sarah gulped and swallowed the next sob.

Lothar turned Manfred away from the door. 'The child is hardworking and willing, cousin. You will not regret this charity,' he called over his shoulder.

'That we shall see,' his cousin muttered dubiously, and Lothar started back down the path.

'Remember the Lord's word, Lothar De La Rey,' the Trumpet of the Lord bugled after them. '"I am the Way and the Light. Whosoever believeth in me – "'

Manfred twisted in his father's grip and looked back. The tall gaunt figure of the dominie almost filled the kitchen doorway, but at the level of his waist Sarah's small face peered around him – in the light of the Petromax it was white as bone china and glistened with her tears.

* * *

Four men were waiting for them at the rendezvous. During the desperate years when they had fought together in guerilla commando, it had been necessary for every man to know the reassembly points. When cut up and separated in the running battles against the Union troops, they had scattered away into the veld and days later come together at one of the safe places.

There was always water at these assembly points, a seep in the rocky crevice of a hillside, a Bushman well or a dry riverbed where they could dig for the precious stuff. The assembly points were always sited with an all-round view so that a following enemy could never take them by surprise. In addition, there was always grazing nearby for the horses and shelter for the men, and they had laid down caches of supplies at these places.

The rendezvous that Lothar had chosen for this meeting had an additional advantage. It was in the hills only a few miles north of the homestead of a prosperous German cattle-rancher, a good friend of Lothar's family, a sympathizer who could be relied upon to tolerate their presence on his lands.

Lothar entered the hills along the dried watercourse that twisted through them like a maimed puffadder. He walked in the open so that the waiting men could see him from afar, and they were still two miles from the rendezvous when a tiny figure appeared on the rocky crest ahead of them, windmilling his arms in welcome. He was quickly joined by the other three and then they came running down the rough hillside to meet Lothar's party in the riverbed.

Leading them was 'Vark Jan', or 'Pig John', the old Khoisan warrior with his yellow wrinkled features that bespoke his mixed lineage of Nama and Bergdama and, so he boasted, of even the true Bushman. Allegedly, his grandmother had been a Bushman slave captured by the Boers in one of the last great slave raids of the previous century. But then he was a famous liar and opinion was divided as to the truth of this claim. He was followed closely by Klein Boy, Swart Hendrick's bastard son by a Herero mother.

He came directly to his father and greeted him with the traditional deferential clapping of hands. He was as tall and as powerfully built as Hendrick himself, but with the finer features and slanted eyes of his mother, and his skin was not as dark. Like wild honey it changed colour as the sunlight played upon it. These two had worked on the trawlers at Walvis Bay, and Hendrick had sent them ahead to find the other men they needed and bring them to the rendezvous.

Lothar turned to these men now. It was twelve years since last he had seen them. He remembered them as wild fighting men – his hunting dogs, he had called them with affection and total lack of trust. For like wild dogs they would have turned and savaged him at the first sign of weakness.

Now he greeted them by their old *noms de guerre*: 'Legs', the Ovambo with legs like a stork and 'Buffalo', who carried his head hunched on his thick neck like that animal. They clasped hands, then wrists and then hands again in the ritual greeting of the band reserved for special occasions, as after long separation or a successful foray, and Lothar studied them and saw how twelve years and easy living had altered them. They were fat and soft and middle-aged but, he consoled himself, the tasks he had for them were not demanding.

'So!' He grinned at them. 'We have pulled you off the fat bellies of your wives, and away from your beer-pots.' And they roared with laughter.

'We came the same minute that Klein Boy and Pig John spoke your name to us,' they assured him.

'Of course, you came only because of the love and loyalty you bear me – '

Lothar's sarcasm was biting, 'the way the vulture and the jackal come for love of the dead, not of the feast.'

They roared again. How they had missed the whip of his tongue.

'Pig John did mention gold,' the Buffalo admitted, between sobs of laughter. 'And Klein Boy whispered that there might be fighting again.'

'It is sad, but a man of my age can pleasure his wives only once or twice a day, but he can fight and enjoy old companions and plunder day and night without end – and the loyalty we bear you is wide as the Kalahari,' Stork Legs said, and they hooted with laughter and beat each other upon the back.

Still rumbling with occasional laughter, the group left the riverbed and climbed up to the old rendezvous point. It was a low overhanging shelf of rock, the roof blackened with the soot of countless campfires and the rear wall decorated with the ochre-coloured designs and drawings of the little yellow Bushmen who, before them, had used this shelter down the ages. From the entrance of the shelter there was a sweeping view out across the shimmering plains. It would be almost impossible to approach the hilltop undetected.

The four firstcomers had already opened the cache. It had been hidden in a cleft of rock further down the side of the hill, and the entrance closed with boulders and plastered over with clay from the riverbank. The contents had survived the years better than Lothar had expected. Of course, the canned food and the ammunition cases had all been sealed, while the Mauser rifles were packed in thick yellow grease and wrapped in greasepaper. They were in perfect condition. Even most of the spare saddlery and clothing had been preserved by the desert's dry air.

They feasted on fried bully beef and toasted ship's biscuit, food they had once hated for its monotony but now was delicious and evocative of countless other meals, back in those desperate days rendered attractive by the passage of the years. After they had eaten they picked over the saddlery and boots and clothing, rejecting those items damaged by insects and rodents or dried out like parchment, cannibalizing and re-stitching and polishing with dubbin until they had equipment and arms for all of them.

While they worked Lothar considered that there were dozens of these caches, scattered through the wilderness, while in the north at the secret coastal base from which he had refuelled and re-equipped the German U-boats there must still be thousands of pounds' worth of store. Until now it had never occurred to him to raid them for his own account – somehow they had always been in patriotic trust.

He felt the prickle of temptation: 'Perhaps if I chartered a boat at Walvis and sailed up the coast – ' But then with a sudden chill he remembered that he would never see Walvis Bay or this land again. There would be no return after they had done what they were setting out to do.

He jumped to his feet and strode to the entrance of the rock shelter. As he stared out across the dun and heatshot plain with its dotted camel-thorn trees, he felt a premonition of terrible suffering and unhappiness.

'Could I ever be happy elsewhere?' he wondered. 'Away from this harsh and beautiful land?' His resolve wavered. He turned and saw Manfred watching him with a trouble frown. 'Can I make this decision for my son?' He stared back at the boy. 'Can I condemn him to the life of an exile?'

He thrust the doubts aside with an effort, shaking them off with a shudder like a horse driving the stinging flies from its hide, and called Manfred to him.

He led him away from the shelter, and when they were out of earshot of the others told him what lay ahead of them, speaking to him as an equal.

'All we have worked for has been stolen from us, Manie, not in the sight of the law but in the sight of God and natural justice. The Bible gives us redress against those who have deceived or cheated us – an eye for an eye, a tooth for a tooth. We will take back what has been stolen from us. But, Manie, the English law will look upon us as criminals. We will have to fly, to run and hide, and they will hunt us like wild animals. We will survive only by our courage and our wits.'

Manfred stirred eagerly, watching his father's face with bright eager eyes. It all sounded romantic and exciting and he was proud of his father's trust in discussing such adult matters with him.

'We will go north. There is good farming land in Tanganyika and Nyasaland and Kenya. Many of our own *Volk* have already gone there. Of course, we will have to change our name, and we can never return here, but we will make a fine new life in a new land.'

'Never come back?' Manfred's expression changed. 'But what about Sarah?'

Lothar ignored the question. 'Perhaps we will buy a beautiful coffee shamba in Nyasaland or on the lower slopes of Kilimanjaro. There are still great herds of wild game upon the plains of Serengeti, and we will hunt and farm.'

Manfred listened dutifully but his expression had dulled. How could he say it? How could he tell his father: 'Pa, I don't want to go to a strange land. I want to stay here.'?

He lay awake long after the others were snoring and the camp-fire had burned down to a red smear of embers, and he thought about Sarah, remembering the pale pixie face smeared with tears and the hot thin little body under the blanket beside him: 'She is the only friend I've ever had.'

He was jerked back to reality by a strange and disturbing sound. It came from the plain below them but it seemed that distance could not take the fierce edge from the din.

His father coughed softly and sat up, letting his blanket fall to his waist. The awful sound came again, rising to an impossible crescendo and then dying away in a series of deep grunts, the death rattle of a strangling monster.

'What is it, Pa?' The hair at the back of Manfred's neck had risen and prickled as though to the touch of a nettle.

'They say even the bravest of men is afraid the first time he hears that sound,' his father told him softly. 'That is the hunting roar of a hungry Kalahari lion, my son.'

* * *

In the dawn when they climbed down the hillside and reached the plain, Lothar, who was leading, stopped abruptly and beckoned Manfred to his side.

'You have heard his voice – now here is the track of his feet.' He stooped and touched one of the pad marks, the size of a dinner plate, that was pressed deeply into the soft yellow earth.

'An old *maanhar*, a solitary, old, maned male.' Lothar traced the outline of the spoor. Manfred would see him do that often in the months ahead, always touching the sign as though to draw out its secrets through his fingertips. 'See

how his pads are worn smooth, and how he walks with his weight back towards his ankles. He favours his righ fore, a cripple. He will find a meal hard to take, perhaps that is why he keeps close to the ranch. Cattle are easier to kill than wild game.'

Lothar reached out and plucked something from the lowest branch of thorns. 'Here, Manie,' he placed a small tuft of coarse red-gold hair in Manfred's palm. 'There is a tress of his mane he left for you.' Then he stood up and stepped over the spoor. He led them on down into the broad saucer of land, watered by a string of natural artesian springs, where the grass grew thick and green and high as their knees, and they passed the first herds of cattle, humpbacked and with dewlaps that almost brushed the earth, their coasts shiny in the early sunlight.

The homestead of the ranch stood on the high ground beyond the wells, in a plantation of exotic date palms imported from Egypt. It was an old colonial German fort, a legacy from the Herero war of 1904 when the whole territory had erupted in rebellion against the excesses of German colonization. Even the Bondelswarts and Namas had joined the Herero tribe and it had taken 20,000 white troops and an expenditure of £60 million to quell the rebellion. Added to the cost, in the final accounting, were the 2,500 German officers and men killed and the 70,000 men, women and children of the Herero people shot, burned and starved to death. This casualty list constituted almost precisely seventy per cent of the entire tribe.

The homestead had orginally been a frontier fort, built to hold off the Herero regiments. Its thick whitewashed outer walls were crenellated and even the central tower was furnished with battlements and a flagstaff upon which the German imperial eagle still defiantly flew.

The count saw them from afar, coming down the dusty road past the springs, and sent out a trap to bring them in. He was of Lothar's mother's generation, but still tall and lean and straight. A white duelling scar puckered the corner of his mouth and his manners were old-fashioned and formal. He sent Swart Hendrick to quarters in the servants' wing and then led Lothar and Manfred through to the cool dark central hall where the countess had black bottles of good German beer and jugs of homemade ginger beer already set out for them.

Their clothes were whisked away by the servants while they bathed, and were returned within the hour, laundered and ironed, their boots polished until they gleamed. For dinner there was a baron of tender beef from the estate, running with its own fragrant juices, and marvellous Rhine wines to wash it down. To Manfred's unqualified delight, this was followed by a dozen various tarts and puddings and trifles, while for Lothar the greater treat was the civilized discourse of his host and hostess. It was a deep pleasure to discuss books and music, and to listen to the precise and beautifully enunciated German of his hosts.

When Manfred could eat not another spoonful, and had to use both hands to cover his yawns, one of the Herero serving-maids led him away to his room, and the count poured schnapps for Lothar and brought a box of Havanas for his approval while his wife fussed over the silver coffee pot.

When his cigar was drawing evenly the count told Lothar: 'I received the letter you sent me from Windhoek, and I was most distressed to hear of your misfortune. Times are very difficult for all of us.' He polished his monocle upon his sleeve before screwing it back into his eye and focusing it upon Lothar again. 'Your sainted mother was a fine lady. There is nothing that I would not

do for her son.' He paused and drew upon the Havana, smiled thinly at the flavour and then said. 'However – '

Lothar's spirits dropped at that word, always the harbinger of denial and disappointment.

'However, not two weeks before I received your letter the purchasing officer for the army remount department came out to the ranch and I sold him all our excess animals. I have retained only sufficient for our own needs.'

Though Lothar had seen at least forty fine horses in the herd grazing on the young pasture that grew around the ranch, he merely nodded in understanding.

'Of course, I have a pair of excellent mules – big, strong beasts, that I could let you have at a nominal price – say fifty pounds.'

'The pair?' Lothar asked deferentially.

'Each,' said the count firmly. 'As to the other suggestion in your letter, I make it a firm rule never to lend money to a friend. That way one avoids losing both friend and money.'

Lothar let that slide by, and instead returned to the count's earlier remarks. 'The army remount officer – he has been buying horses from all the estates in the district?'

'I understand he has purchased almost a hundred.' The count showed relief at Lothar's gentlemanly acceptance of his refusal. 'All excellent animals. He was interested only in the best – desert-hardened and salted against the horse-sickness.'

'And he has shipped them south on the railway, I expect?'

'Not yet,' the count shook his head. 'Or he had not done so when last I heard. He is holding them on the pool of the Swakop river on the far side of the town, resting them and letting them build up their strength for the rail journey. I heard that he plans to send them down the line when he has a hundred and fifty altogether.'

They left the fort the following morning after a gargantuan breakfast of sausage and prepared meats and eggs, all three of them riding up on the broad back of the grey mule for which Lothar had finally paid twenty pounds with the head halter thrown in to sweeten the bargain.

'How were the servants' quarters at the fort?' Lothar asked.

'Slave quarters, not servants' quarters,' Hendrick corrected him. 'In them a man could starve to death or, from what I heard, be flogged to death by the count.' Hendrick sighed. 'If it had not been for the generosity and good nature of the youngest of the Herero maids – '

Lothar nudged him sharply in the ribs and shot a warning glanced towards Manfred, and Hendrick went on smoothly.

'So do we all escape on one sway-backed ancient mule,' he observed. 'They will never catch us on this gazelle-swift creature.' He slapped the fat rump and the mule maintained its easy swaying gait, its hooves plopping in the dust.

'We are going to use him for hunting,' Lothar told him, and grinned at Hendrick's perplexed frown.

Back at the rock shelter, Lothar worked quickly, making up twelve pack-saddles of ammunition, food and equipment. When they were lashed and loaded, he laid them out at the entrance of the shelter.

'Well,' Hendrick grinned. 'We've got the saddles. All we need are the horses.'

'We should leave a guard here.' Lothar ignored him, 'But we'll need every man with us.'

He gave the money to Pig John, the least untrustworthy of the gang.

'Five pounds is enough to buy a bathtub full of Cape Smoke,' he pointed out, 'and a glassful of it will kill a bull buffalo. But remember this, Pig John, if you are too drunk to stay in the saddle when we ride, I'll not leave you for the police to question. I'll leave you with a bullet in the head. I give you my oath on it.'

Pig John tucked the banknote into the sweatband of his slouch hat. 'Not a drop of it will touch my lips,' he whined ingratiatingly. 'The *baas* knows he can trust me with liquor and women and money.'

It was almost twenty miles back to the town of Okahandja and Pig John set out immediately to be there well in advance of Lothar's arrival. The rest of the party, with Manfred leading the mule, climbed down the hillside.

There had been no wind since the previous day, so the lion's tracks were still clearly etched and uneroded, even in that loose soil. The hunters, all armed with the new Mausers, and with bandoliers of ammunition belted over their shoulders, spread out in a fan across the lion spoor and went away at a trot.

Manfred had been warned by his father to keep well back, and with the memories of the beast's wild roarings still in his ears, was pleased to amble along at the mule's slow plod. The hunters were out of sight ahead, but they had marked their trail for him with broken branches and blazes on the trunks of the camel-thorn trees so he had no difficulty following.

Within an hour they found the spot at which the old red tom had killed one of the count's heifers. He had stayed on the carcass until he had consumed everything but the head and hooves and larger bones. But even from these he had licked the flesh as proof of his hunger and restricted hunting prowess.

Quickly Lothar and Hendrick cast forward in a circle around the trampled area of the kill and almost immediately cut the outgoing spoor.

'He left not more than a few hours ago,' Lothar estimated, and then as one of the grass stalks trodden down by the big cat's paws, slowly rose and straightened of its own accord, he amended his guess.

'No.' Hendrick touched the spoor with the long peeled twig he carried. 'He has gone on at a walk. He isn't worried, he hasn't heard us. He is full of meat and will go now to the nearest water.'

'He's going south.' Lothar squinted against the sun to check the run of the spoor. 'Probably heading for the river and that will take him closer to the town, which suits us very well.'

He reslung the Mauser on his shoulder and signalled his men to stay in extended order. They went on up the low rise of a consolidated dune and before they reached the top the lion broke, flushing from the cover of a low clump of scrub directly ahead of them, and went away from them across the open ground at an extended catlike run. But his belly, gorged with meat, swung weightily at each stride as though he were heavily pregnant.

It was long range, but the Mausers whip-cracked all along the line as they opened up on the running beast. Dust spurted wide and beyond him. All Lothar's men except Hendrick were appalling marksmen. He could never convince them that the speed of the bullet was not directly proportional to the force with which one pulled the trigger, or break them of the habit of tightly closing their eyes as they ejected the bullet from the barrel with all their strength.

Lothar saw his own first shot kick dust from beneath the lion's belly. He had misjudged the range, always a problem over open desert terrain. He worked the bolt of the Mauser without taking the butt from his shoulder and lifted his aim

until the pip of the foresight rode just above the beast's shaggy flowing red mane.

The lion checked to the next shot, breaking his stride, swinging his great head around to snap at his flank where it had stung him, and the sound of the jacketed bullet slapping into his flesh carried clearly to the line of hunters. Then the lion flattened once more into his gallop, ears back, growling with pain and outrage as he vanished over the rise.

'He won't go far!' Hendrick waved the line of hunters forward.

The lion is a sprinter. He can only maintain that blazing gallop over a very short distance before he is forced back into a trot. If you press him further, he will usually turn and come back at you.

Lothar, Hendrick and Klein Boy, the strongest and fittest of them, pulled ahead of the line.

'Blood!' Hendrick shouted as they reached the spot where the lion had taken Lothar's bullet. 'Lung blood!' The splashes of crimson were frothy with the wind of the ruptured lungs. They raced along the bloody spoor.

'*Pasop*!' Lothar called as they reached the rise over which the beast had disappeared. 'Look out! He'll be lying in wait for us – ' And at the warning the lion charged back at them.

He had been lying in a patch of sansevieria just beyond the crest, flattened against the earth with his ears laid back upon his skull. But the moment Lothar led them over the crest, he launched himself at him from a distance of only fifty feet.

The lion kept low to the ground, with his ears still back so that his forehead was flat and broad as that of an adder and his eyes were a bright implacable yellow. His gingery red mane was fully erect, increasing his bulk until he appeared monstrous, and such a blast of sound came out of those gaping fang-lined jaws that Lothar flinched and was an instant slow on the shot. As the butt of the Mauser touched his shoulder, the lion rose from the ground in front of him, filling all his vision and the blood from his torn lungs blew in a pink cloud and spattered into Lothar's face.

His instinct was to fire as swiftly as possible into the enormous shaggy bulk of the lion as it towered over him on its hindlegs, but he forced himself to shift his aim. A shot in the chest or neck would not stop the beast from killing him, the Mauser bullet was light, designed for men not great game, and that first bullet would have desensitized the lion's nervous system and flooded his system with adrenalin. The brain shot was the only one which would stop him at such close quarters.

Lothar shot him on the point of his muzzle, between the flared pink pits of his nostrils, and the bullet tore up between the cat's eyes, through the butter-yellow brain in its bony casket and out through the back of his skull – but still the lion was driven on by the momentum of its charge. The huge muscular body slammed into Lothar's chest, and the rifle cartwheeled from his hands as he was hurled backwards to hit the earth with his shoulder and the side of his head.

Hendrick dragged him into a sitting position and wiped the sand from his mouth and nostrils with his bare hands, and then the alarm faded from his eyes and he grinned as Lothar struck his hands away weakly.

'You are getting old and slow, *Baas*,' Hendrick laughed.

'Get me up before Manie sees me,' Lothar ordered him, and Hendrick put a shoulder under him and hoisted him.

He swayed on his feet, leaning heavily on Hendrick, holding the side of his head where it had struck but already he was giving orders.

'Klein Boy! Legs! go back and hold the mule before it smells the lion and bolts with Manie!'

He pulled away from Hendrick and crossed unsteadily to the lion's carcass. It lay on its side and already the flies were gathering on the shattered head. 'We'll need every man and a bit of luck to get him loaded.'

Even though the cat was old and lean and out of condition, scarred by years of hunting in thorn veld and his coat dull and shaggy, yet his belly was crammed with beef and he would weigh four hundred pounds or more. Lothar picked his rifle out of the sand and wiped it down carefully, then he propped it against the carcass and hurried back over the ridge, still limping from the fall and massaging his neck and temple.

The mule with Manfred perched on his back was coming towards him, and Lothar broke into a run.

'Did you get him, Pa?' Manfred yelled excitedly. He had heard the firing.

'Yes.' Lothar yanked him down from the mule's back. 'He's lying just beyond the rise.

Lothar checked the mule's head halter. It was new and strong, but he clipped an extra length of rope on to the iron chin ring and put two men on each rope. Then carefully he blindfolded the mule with a strip of canvas.

'All right. Let's see how he takes it.' The men on the head halter dragged on it with their concerted weight, but the mule dug in his hooves, mutinying against the blindfold, and would not budge.

Lothar went round behind him, taking care to keep out of the way of his back hooves, and twisted the mule's tail. Still the animal stood like a rock. Lothar leaned over and bit him at the root of the tail, sinking his teeth into the soft tender skin, and the mule let fly with both back hooves in a head-high kick.

Lothar bit him again, and he capitulated and trotted forward towards the ridge, but as he reached it the light breeze shifted and the mule filled both nostrils with the fresh hot smell of lion.

The scent of lion has a remarkable effect on all other animals, domestic or wild, even on exotics from an environment where it is impossible that either they or even their remote ancestors could possibly ever have had contact with a lion.

Lothar's father had always selected his hunting dogs by offering the litter of puppies a green wet lion skin to sniff. Most of the pups would howl with terror and stumble away with their tails tucked up between their hind legs. A very few pups, not more than one in twenty, nearly always bitches, would stand, albeit with every hair on their bodies erect and small growls shaking them from tail to tip of quivering nostrils. These were the dogs he kept.

Now the mule smelt the lion and went berserk. The men on the head ropes were hauled off their feet as it reared and whinnied, and Lothar ducked out from under its lashing hooves. Then it burst into a ponderous gallop and dragged the four handlers, stumbling and falling and shouting, half a mile over thorn scrub and through deep waterworn dongas, before at last it stopped in a cloud of its own dust, sweating and trembling, its flanks heaving with terror.

They dragged him back again, the blindfold firmly in place, but the moment he smelled the carcass again the entire performance was repeated, though this time he only managed a gallop of a few hundred yards before exhaustion and the weight of four men brought him up short.

Twice more they led him back to the dead lion and twice more he bolted, each time for a shorter distance, but finally he stood, trembling in all four legs, and sweating with terror and fatigue as they lifted the carcass onto his back and tried to lash the lion's paws under his chest. That was too much. Another copious flood of nervous sweat drenched the mule's body, and he reared and bucked and kicked until the carcass slid off his back in a heap.

They wore him down, and after an hour of struggling, the mule stood at last, shaking piteously and blowing like a blacksmith's bellows, but with the dead lion securely lashed upon his back.

When Lothar took the lead rope and tugged upon it, the mule stumbled along meekly behind him, following him down towards the bend in the river.

* * *

From the top of one of the low wooded kopjes Lothar looked down across the Swakop river to the roofs and the church spire of the village beyond. The Swakop made a wide bend, and in the elbow directly below there were three small green pools hemmed in with yellow sandbanks. The river flowed only in the brief periods after rain.

They were watering the horses at the pools, bringing them down from the stockades of thorn branches to drink before closing them in for the night. The count had been right, the army buyers has chosen the best. Lothar watched them avariciously through his binoculars. Desert bred, they were powerful animals, full of vigour as they frolicked and milled at the edge of the pool or rolled in the sand with their legs kicking in the air.

Lothar switched his attention to the drovers, and counted five of them, all coloured troopers in casual khaki uniform, and he looked for white officers in vain.

'They could be in camp,' he muttered and focused the glasses on the cluster of brown army tents beyond the horse stockades.

There was a low whistle from behind him, and when he looked over his shoulder, Hendrick was signalling from the foot of the kopje. Lothar slid off the skyline and then scrambled down the slope. The mule, his blood-soaked burden still on his back, was tethered in the shade. He had become almost resigned to it, though every now and again he gave a spontaneous shudder and shifted his weight nervously. The men were lying under the sparse branches of the thorn trees, eating bully out of the cans and Pig John stood up as Lothar reached him.

'You are late,' Lothar accused him, and seizing the front of his leather vest he pulled him close and sniffed his breath.

'Not a drop, Master,' Pig John whined. 'I swear on my sister's virginity.'

'That is a mythical beast.' Lothar released him, and glanced down at the sack at Pig John's feet.

'Twelve bottles. Just like you said.'

Lothar opened the sack and took out a bottle of the notorious Cape Smoke. The neck was sealed with wax and the brandy was a dark poisonous brown when he held it to the light.

'What did you find out in the village?' He returned the bottle to the sack.

'There are seven horse handlers at the camp – '

'I counted five.'

'Seven.' Pig John was definite and Lothar grunted.

'What about the white officers?'

'They rode out towards Otjiwaronga yesterday, to buy more horses.'

'It will be dark in an hour.' Lothar glanced at the sun. 'Take the sack and go to the camp.'

'What shall I tell them?'

'Tell them you are selling – cheap, and then give them a free taste. You are a famous liar, tell them anything.'

'What if they don't drink?'

Lothar laughed at the improbability but didn't bother to answer. 'I will move after moonrise, when it clears the treetops. That will give you and your brandy four hours to soften them up.'

The sack clinked as Pig John slung it over his shoulder.

'Remember, Pig John, I want you sober or I'll have you dead – and I mean it.'

'Does Master think I am some kind of animal, that I can't take a drink like a gentleman?' Pig John demanded and drawing himself up marched out of the camp with affronted dignity.

From his look-out Lothar watched Pig John cross the dry sandbanks of the Swakop and trudge up the far side under his sack. At the stockade the guard challenged him and Lothar watched through the glasses as they talked, until at last the coloured trooper set his carbine aside and peered into the neck of the sack that Pig John held open for him.

Even at that distance and in the deepening dusk, Lothar saw the flash of the guard's white teeth as he grinned with delight and turned to call his companions from the tented encampment. Two of them came out in their underclothes, and a long heated discussion ensued with a great deal of gesticulation and shoulder slapping and head shaking, until Pig John cracked the wax seal on one of the bottles and handed it to them. The bottle passed quickly from one to the other, and each of them pointed the base briefly at the sky like a bugler sounding the charge and then gasped and grinned through watering eyes. Finally, Pig John was led like an honoured guest into the encampment, lugging his sack, and disappeared from Lothar's view.

The sun set and night fell and Lothar remained on the ridge. Like a yachtsman he was intensely aware of the strength and direction of the night breeze as it switched erratically. An hour after dark it settled down into a steady warm stream on the back of Lothar's neck.

'Let it hold,' Lothar murmured, and then whistled softly, the cry of a scops owlet. Hendrick came almost at once and Lothar indicated the wind.

'Cross the river well upstream and circle out beyond the camp. Not too close. Then turn back and keep the wind in your face.'

At that moment there was a faint shout from across the river and they both looked up. The camp-fire in front of the tents had been built up until the flames roared high enough to lick the under branches of the camel-thorn trees and silhouetted against them were the dark figures of the coloured troopers.

'What the hell do you think they are doing?' Lothar wondered. 'Dancing or fighting?'

'By now they don't know themselves,' Hendrick chuckled. They were reeling around the fire, colliding and clinging together, then separating, collapsing in the dust and crawling on their knees, or with enormous effort heaving

themselves to their feet only to stand swaying with legs braced apart and then collapse again. One of them was stripped naked, his thin yellow body gleaming with sweat as he pirouetted wildly and then fell into the fire, to be dragged out by the heels by a pair of his companions, all three of them screeching with laughter.

'Time for you to go.' Lothar slapped Hendrick's shoulder. 'Take Manie with you and let him be your horse holder.'

Hendrick started back down the slope but paused as Lothar called softly after him, 'Manie is in your charge. You'll answer for him with your own life.'

Hendrick did not reply but disappeared into the night. Half an hour later Lothar glimpsed them crossing the pale sandbanks of the river, a dark shapeless movement in the starlight, and then they were gone into the scrub beyond.

The horizon lightened and the stars in the east paled before the rising moon, but in the camp across the river the drunken gyrations of the troopers had now descended into swinish inertia. Through the glasses Lothar could make out bodies, scattered haphazard like casualties on the battlefield, and one of them looked very much like Pig John, although Lothar couldn't be certain for he lay face down in the shadow on the far side of the fire.

'If it's him, he's a dead man,' Lothar promised and stood up. It was time to move at last, for the moon was clear of the horizon, horned and glowing like a horseshoe from the blacksmith's forge.

Lothar picked his way down the slope, and the mule snorted and blew through his nostrils, still standing miserably under his dreadful burden.

'Almost over now.' Lothar stroked his forehead. 'You've done well, old fellow.' He loosed the head halter, adjusted the Mauser slung over his shoulder and led the mule around the side of the kopje and down the bank to the river.

There was no question of a stealthy approach, not with that great pale animal and his swaying load. Lothar unslung the rifle and rammed a cartridge into the breech as they plodded through the sand of the riverbed and he watched the line of trees on the bank ahead, even though he expected no challenge.

The camp-fire had died down, and there was complete silence until they climbed the bank and Lothar heard the stamp of a hoof and the soft fluttering breath of one of the animals in the stockade ahead. The breeze was behind Lothar, steady still, and suddenly there was a shrill unhappy whinny.

'That's it – get a good whiff of it.' Lothar led the mule towards the stockade.

Now there was the trample of hooves and the sound of restless animals as they began to mill and jostle one another. Alarm transmitted by the rank smell of the bleeding lion carcass was spreading infectiously through the herd. A horse whinnied in terror, and immediately others reared in panic. Lothar could see their heads above the thornbush wall of the stockade, manes flying in the moonlight, front hooves lashing out wildly.

Against the windward wall of the stockade Lothar held the mule, and then cut the rope that held the lion to its back. The carcass slid over and hit the ground, the wind from its lungs was driven up the dead throat with a low belching roar and the animals on the far side of the brush wall surged and screamed and began to swirl around the stockade in a living whirlpool of horseflesh.

Lothar stooped and split the lion's belly from the crotch of the back legs to the sternum of the ribs, driving his blade deeply so that it slashed through the bladder and guts, and instantly the stench was thick and rank.

The horse herd was in chaos. He could hear them crashing into the far wall

of the stockade as they attempted to escape from the awful scent. Lothar lifted the rifle to his shoulder, aiming only feet over the maddened horses, and emptied the magazine. The shots crashed out in quick succession, the muzzle-flashes lighting the stockade, and the herd in terrified concert burst through the wall of the stockade, pouring through it in a dark river, their manes tossing like foam as they galloped away into the night, heading downwind to where Hendrick waited with his men.

Hurriedly Lothar tethered the mule, and reloading the rifle as he ran, headed for the dying camp-fire. One of the troopers, aroused by the escaping horses even from his drunken stupor, was on his feet, staggering determinedly towards the stockade.

'The horses,' he was screaming. 'Come on you drunken thunders! We have to stop the horses!' he saw Lothar. 'Help me! The horses – '

Lothar lifted the butt of the Mauser under his chin. The trooper's teeth clicked together and he sat down in the sand and then slowly toppled over backwards again. Lothar stepped over him and ran forward.

'Pig John!' he called urgently. 'Where are you?' There was no reply and he went past the fire to the inert figure he had seen from the lookout. He rolled it over his foot, and Pig John looked up at the moon with sightless eyes and a tranquil smile on his wrinkled yellow face.

'Up!' Lothar kicked him with a full swing of the boot. Pig John's smile did not waver. He was far past any pain. 'All right, I warned you!'

Lothar worked the Mauser's bolt and flicked over the safety-catch with his thumb. He put the muzzle of the rifle to Pig John's head. If he was handed over to the police alive it would take only a few strokes of the hippo-hide sjambok whip to get Pig John talking. Though he did not know the full details of the plan, he knew enough to ruin their chances and to put Lothar on the wanted list for horse-theft and the destruction of army property. He took up the slack in the trigger of the Mauser.

'It's too good for him,' he thought grimly. 'He should be flogged to death.' But his finger relaxed, and he swore at himself for his own foolishness as he flipped the safety-catch and ran back to fetch the mule.

Even though Pig John was a skinny little man, it took all of Lothar's strength to swing his relaxed rubbery body over the mule's back. He hung there like a piece of laundry on the drying line, arms and legs dangling on opposite sides. Lothar leapt up behind him, whipped the mule into his top gait, a laboured lumbering trot, and steered him directly down the wind.

After a mile Lothar thought he must have missed them, and slowed the mule just as Hendrick stepped out of the moon shadows ahead of him.

'How goes it? How many did you get?' Lothar called anxiously, and Hendrick laughed.

'So many we ran out of halters.'

Once each of his men had captured one of the escaped horses, he had gone up on its bare back and cut off the bunches of fleeing animals, turning them and holding them while Manfred ran in and slipped the halters over their heads.

'Twenty-six!' Lothar exulted as he counted the strings of roped horses. 'We'll be able to pick and choose.' He tempered his own jubilation. 'All right, we'll move out right away. The army will be after us as soon as they can get troops up here.'

He slipped the halter of the mule's head and slapped his rump. 'Thank you, old fellow,' he said. 'You can get on back home.' The mule accepted the offer

with alacrity and actually managed to gallop the first hundred yards of his homeward journey.

Each of them picked a horse and mounted bareback with a string of three or four loose horses behind him, and Lothar led them back towards the rock shelter in the hills.

At dawn they paused briefly while Lothar checked over each of the stolen horses. Two had been injured in the mêlée in the stockade and he turned them loose. The others were of such fine quality and condition that he could not choose between them though they had many more than they required.

While they were sorting the horses Pig John regained consciousness and sat up weakly. He muttered prayers to his ancestors and Hottentot gods for a release from his suffering and then vomited a painful gush of vile brandy.

'You and I still have business to settle,' Lothar promised him unsmilingly, then turned to Hendrick. 'We'll take all these horses. We are certain to lose some in the desert.' Then he raised his right arm in the cavalry command: 'Move out!'

They reached the rock shelter a little before noon, but they paused only to load the waiting pack-saddles onto the spare horse and then each of them chose a mount and saddled up. They led the horses down the hill and watered them, allowing them to drink their fill.

'How much of a start do we have?' Hendrick asked.

'The coloured troopers can do nothing without their white officers and it might take them two or three days to get back. They will have to telegraph Windhoek for orders, and then they will have to make up a patrol. I'd say three days at least, more likely four or five.'

'We can go a long way in three days,' Hendrick said with satisfaction.

'Nobody can go further,' Lothar agreed. It was a fact not a boast. The desert was his dominion. Few white men knew it as well as he, and none better.

'Shall we mount up?' Hendrick asked.

'One more chore.' Lothar took the spare leather reins out of his saddle-bag and looped them over his right wrist with the brass buckles hanging to his ankles as he crossed to where Pig John sat miserably in the shade of the riverbank with his face buried in his hands. In his extremity he did not hear Lothar's tread in the soft sand until he stood over him.

'I promised you,' Lothar told him flatly, and shook out the heavy leather throngs.

'Master, I could not help it,' shrieked Pig John and he tried to scramble to his feet.

Lothar swung the thongs and the brass buckles blurred in a bright arc in the sunlight. The blow caught Pig John around the back and the buckles snapped around his rib and gouged out a groove in his flesh below the armpit.

Pig John howled. 'They forced me. They made me drink – '

The next blow knocked him off his feet. He kept screaming, although now the words were no longer coherent, and the leathers cracked on his yellow skin, the weals rising in thick shiny ridges and turning purple-red as ripe grapeskins. The sharp buckles shredded his shirt as though it had been torn off him by lion's claws, and the sand clotted his blood into wet balls as it dribbled into the riverbed.

He stopped screaming at last and Lothar stood back panting and wiped the wet red leather thongs on a saddle cloth and looked at the faces of his men. The

beating had been for them as much as for the man curled at his feet. They were wild dogs and they understood only strength, respected only cruelty.

Hendrick spoke for them all. 'He was paid a fair price. Shall I finish him?'

'No! Leave a horse for him.' Lothar turned away. 'When he comes round he can follow us, or he can go to hell where he belongs.' He swung up into the saddle of his own mount and avoided his son's stricken eyes as he raised his voice. 'All right – we are moving out.'

He rode with long stirrups in the Boer fashion, slouched down comfortably in the saddle, and Hendrick pushed his mount up on one side of him and Manfred on the other.

Lothar felt elated; the adrenalin of violence was like a drug in his blood still and the open desert lay ahead of him. With the taking of the horses he had crossed the frontier of law – he was an outlaw once again, free of society's restraint, and he felt his spirit towering on high like a hunting falcon.

'By God. I'd almost forgotten what it was like to have a rifle in my hand and a good horse between my legs.'

'We are men once again,' Hendrick agreed, and leaned across to embrace Manfred. 'You too. Your father was your age when he and I first rode out to war. We are going to war again. You are a man as he was.' And Manfred forgot the spectacle he had just witnessed and swelled with pride at being counted in this company. He sat up straight in the saddle and lifted his chin.

Lothar turned his face into the north-east, towards the hinterland where the vast Kalahari brooded, and led them away.

That night while they camped in a deep gorge which shielded the light of their small fire, the sentinel roused them with a low whistle. They rolled out of their blankets, snatched up their rifles and slipped away into the darkness.

The horses stirred and whickered, and then Pig John rode in out of the darkness and dismounted. He stood wretchedly by the fire, his face swollen and discoloured with bruises like a cur dog expecting to be driven away. The others came out of the shadows and without looking at him or otherwise acknowledging his existence climbed back into their blankets.

'Sleep on the other side of the fire from me,' Lothar told him harshly. 'You stink of brandy.' And Pig John wriggled with relief and gratification that he had been accepted back into the band.

In the dawn they mounted again and rode on into the wide hot emptiness of the desert.

* * *

The road out to H'ani Mine was probably one of the most rugged in South West Africa and every time she negotiated it Centaine promised herself: We must really do something about having it repaired. Then Dr Twentyman-Jones would give her an estimate of the cost of resurfacing hundreds of miles of desert track and of erecting bridges over the river courses and consolidating the passes through the hills, and Centaine's good frugal sense would reassert itself.

'After all it only takes three days, and I seldom have to drive it more than three times a year, and it is really quite an adventure.'

The telegraph line that connected the mine to Windhoek had been expensive enough. After an estimate of fifty pounds it had finally cost her a hundred

pounds for every single mile and she still felt resentment every time she looked at that endless line of poles strung together with gleaming copper wire that ran beside the track. Apart from the cost, it spoiled the view, detracting from the feeling of wildness and isolation which she so treasured when she was out in the Kalahari.

She remembered with a twinge of nostalgia how they had slept on the ground and carried their water in the first years. Now there were regular stages at each night's stop, thatched rondavels and windmills to raise water from the deep bores, servants living permanently at each station to service the rest houses, providing meals and hot baths and a log fire in the hearth on those crisp frosty nights of the Kalahari winter – even paraffin refrigerators manufacturing heavenly ice for the sundowner whisky in the fierce summer heat. The traffic on the road was heavy, the regular convoy under Gerhard Fourie carrying out fuel and stores had cut deep ruts in the soft earth and churned up the crossings in the dried riverbeds, and worst of all the gauge of the tyres of the big Ford trucks was wider than that of the yellow Daimler so that she had to drive with one wheel in the rut and the other bouncing and jolting over the uneven middle ridge.

Added to all this it was high summer and the heat was crushing. The metal of the Daimler's coachwork could raise blisters on the skin, and they were forced to halt regularly when the water in the radiator boiled and blew a singing plume of steam high in the air. The very heavens seemed to quiver with blue fire, and the far desert horizons were washed away by the shimmering glassy whirlpools of heat mirage.

If only they could make a machine small enough to cool the air in the Daimler, she thought, like the one in the railway coach – and then she burst out laughing. *Tiens* : I must be getting soft! She remembered how, with the two old Bushmen who had rescued her, she had travelled on foot through the terrible dune country of the Namib and they had been forced to cover their bodies with a plaster of sand and their own urine to survive the monstrous heat of the desert noons.

'Why are you laughing, Mater?' Shasa demanded.

'Oh, just something that happened long ago, before you were born.'

'Tell me, oh please tell me.' He seemed unaffected by the heat and the dust and the merciless jolting of the chassis. But then why should he be? She smiled at him. This is where he was born. He too is a creature of the desert.

Shasa took her smile for acquiescence. 'Come on, Mater. Tell me the story.'

'*Pourquoi pas*? Why not?' And she told him and watched the shock in his expression.

'Your own pee-pee?' He was aghast.

'That surprises you?' She mocked him. 'Then let me tell you what we did when the water in our ostrich-egg bottles was finished. Old O'wa, the Bushman hunter, killed a gemsbok bull with his poisoned arrow and we took out the first stomach, the rumen, and we squeezed out the liquid from the undigested contents and we drank that. It kept us going just long enough to reach the sip-wells.'

'Mater!'

'That's right, chéri, I drink champagne when I can, but I'll drink whatever keeps me alive when I have to.'

She was silent while he considered that, and she glanced at his face and saw the revulsion turn to respect.

'What would you have done, chéri, drunk it or died?' she asked, to make sure the lesson was learned.

'I would have drunk,' he answered without hesitation, and then with affectionate pride, 'You know, Mater, you really are a crackerjack.' It was his ultimate accolade.

'Look!' She pointed ahead to where the lion-coloured plain, its far limits lost in the curtains of mirage, seemed to be covered with a gauzy cinnamon-coloured veil of thin smoke.

Centaine pulled the Daimler off the track and they climbed out onto the running-board for a better view.

'Springbok. The first we have seen on this trip.' The beautiful gazelle were moving steadily across the flats, all in the same direction.

'There must be tens of thousands.'

The springbok were elegant little animals with long delicate legs and lyre-shaped horns.

'They are migrating into the north,' Centaine told him. 'There must have been good rains up there, and they are moving to the water.'

Suddenly the nearest gazelles took fright at their presence and began the peculiar alarm display that the Boers called 'pronking'. They arched their backs and bowed their long necks until their muzzles touched their fore hooves, and they bounced on stiff legs, flying high and lightly into the shimmering hot air while from the fold of skin along their backs they flashed a flowing white crest of hair.

This alarm behaviour was infectious and soon thousands of gazelle were bounding across the plain like a flock of birds. Centaine jumped down from the running-board and mimicked them, forking the fingers of one hand over her head as horns and with the fingers of the other showing the crest hair down her back. She did it so skilfully that Shasa hooted with laugher and clapped his hands.

'Bully for you, Mater!' He jumped down and joined her, and they pranced in a circle, until they were weak with laughter and exertion. Then they leaned against the Daimler and clung to each other for support.

'Old O'wa taught me that,' Centaine gasped. 'He could imitate every animal of the veld.'

When they drove on she let Shasa take the wheel, for the crossing of the plain was one of the easier stretches of the journey and he drove well. She lay back in the corner of her seat and after a while Shasa broke the silence.

'When we are alone you are so different.' He searched for the words. 'You are such jolly good fun. I wish we could just be like this forever.'

'Anything you do too long becomes a bore,' she told him gently. 'The trick is to do it all, not just one thing. This is good fun but tomorrow we will be at the mine and there will be another type of excitement for us to experience and after that there will be something else. We'll do it all, and we will wring from each moment the last drop it has to offer.'

Twentyman-Jones had gone ahead to the mine while Centaine stayed on for three days in Windhoek to go over the paperwork with Abraham Abrahams. So he had alerted the servants at the rest houses as he passed through.

When they reached the last stage that evening, the bath water was so hot that even Centaine who enjoyed her bath at the correct temperature for boiling lobster was forced to add cold before she could bear it. The champagne was that marvellous 1928 Krug, pale and chilled to the temperature she preferred,

just low enough to frost the bottle, and though there was ice, she would not allow the barbaric habit of standing the bottle in a bucket of it.

'Cold feet, hot head – bad combination for both men and wine,' her father had taught her. As always she drank only a single glass from the bottle and afterwards there was the cold collation that Twentyman-Jones had provided for her and stored in the paraffin refrigerator, fare suitable for this heat and which he knew she enjoyed – rock lobster from the green Benguela current with rich white flesh curled in their spiny red tails and salad vegetables grown in the cooler highlands of Windhoek, lettuce crackling crisp, tomatoes crimson ripe and pungent onions purple-tinted – then, as the final treat, wild truffles gleaned from the surrounding desert by the tame Bushmen who tended the milk herd. She ate them raw and the salty fungus taste was the taste of Kalahari.

They left again in the pitch darkness before dawn, and at sunrise they stopped and brewed coffee on a fire of camel-thorn branches; the grainy red wood burned with an intense blue flame and gave to the coffee a peculiar and delicious aroma. They ate the picnic breakfast that the rest-house cook had provided and washed it down with the smoky coffee and watched the sunrise smearing the sky and desert with bronze and gilding it with gold leaf. As they went on, so the sun rose higher and drained the land of colour, washing it with its silver-white bleach.

'Stop here!' Centaine ordered suddenly, and when they climbed up onto the roof of the Daimler and stared ahead, Shasa was puzzled.

'What is it, Mater?'

'Don't you see it, *chéri*?' She pointed, 'There! Above the horizon.'

It floated in the sky, indistinct and ethereal.

'It's standing in the sky,' Shasa exclaimed, discerning it as last.

'The mountain that floats in the sky,' Centaine murmured. Each time she saw it like this the wonder of it was still as fresh and enchanting as the first time. 'The place of All Life.' She gave the hills their Bushman name.

As they drove on so the shape of the hills hardened, becoming a sheer rock palisade below which were spread the open mopani forests. In places the cliffs were split and riven with gulleys and gorges. In others they were solid and tall and daubed with bright lichens, sulphur yellow and green and orange.

The H'ani Mine was nestled beneath one of these sheer expanses of rock, and the buildings seemed insignificant and incongruous in this place.

Centaine's brief to Twentyman-Jones had been to make them as unobtrusive as possible, without, of course, affecting the productivity of the workings, but there was a limit to just how far he had been able to follow her instructions. The fenced compounds of the black workers and the weathering grounds for the blue diamondiferous earth were extensive, while the steel tower and elevator of the washing gear stuck up high as the derrick of an oil rig.

However, the worst depredation had been caused by the appetite of the steam boiler, hungry as some infernal Baal for cordwood. The forest along the foot of the hills had been cut down to satisfy it, and the second growth had formed a scraggly unsightly thicket in place of the tall grey-barked timber.

Twentyman-Jones was waiting for them as they climbed out of the dusty Daimler in front of the thatched administration building.

'Good trip, Mrs Courtney?' he asked, lugubrious with pleasure. 'You'll want a rest and clean up, I expect.'

'You know better than that, Dr Twentyman-Jones. Let's get down to work.'

Centaine led the way down the wide verandah to her own office. 'Sit beside me,' she ordered Shasa as she took her seat at the stinkwood desk.

They began with the recovery reports, then went on to the cost schedules; and as Shasa struggled to keep up with the quick calling and discussion of figures, he wondered how his mother could change so swiftly from the girl companion who had hopped around in imitation of a springbok only the previous day.

'Shasa, what did we establish was the cost per carat if we average twenty-three carats per load?' She fired the question at Shasa suddenly, and when he muffed it she frowned. 'This isn't the time for dreams.' And she turned her shoulder to him to emphasize the rebuke. 'Very well, Dr Twentyman-Jones, we have avoided the unpleasant long enough. Let us consider what economies we have to institute to meet the quota cut and still keep the H'ani Mine working and turning a profit.'

It was dusk before Centaine broke off and stood up. 'We'll pick it up from here tomorrrow.' She stretched like a cat and then led them out onto the wide verandah.

'Shasa will be working for you as we agreed. I think he should begin on the haulage.'

'I was about to suggest it, Ma'am.'

'What time do you want me?' Shasa asked.

'The shift come on at five am but I expect Master Shasa will want to come on later?' Twentyman-Jones glanced at Centaine. It was, of course, a challenge and a test, and she remained silent, waiting for Shasa to make the decision on his own account. She saw him struggling with himself. He was at that stage of growth when sleep is a drug and rising in the morning a brutal penance.

'I'll be at the main haulage at four-thirty, sir,' he said, and Centaine relaxed and took his arm.

'Then it had best be an early night.'

She turned the Daimler into the avenue of small iron-roofed cottages which housed the white shift bosses and artisans and their families. The orders of society were strictly observed on the H'ani Mine. It was a microcosm of the young nation. The black labourers lived in the fenced and guarded compounds where whitewashed buildings resembled rows of stables. There were separate, more elaborate quarters for the black boss-boys, who were allowed to have their families living with them. The white artisans and shift bosses were housed in the avenues laid out at the foot of the hills, while the management lived up the slopes, each building larger and the lawns around it more extensive the higher it was sited.

As they turned at the end of the avenues there was a girl sitting on the stoep of the last cottage and she stuck her tongue out at Shasa as the Daimler passed. It was almost a year since Shasa had last seen her and nature had wrought wondrous changes in her during that time. Her feet were still bare and dirty to the ankles, and her curls were still wind-tousled and sun-streaked, but the faded cotton of her blouse was not so tight that it constricted her blossoming breasts. They were forced upwards and bulged out over the top in a deep cleavage and Shasa wriggled in the seat as he realized that the twin red-brown coin-shaped marks on the blouse, though they looked like stains, were in fact showing through the thin cloth from beneath.

Her legs had grown longer, her knees were no longer knobbly, and they shaded from coffee brown at the ankles to smooth cream on the inside of her

thighs. She sat on the edge of the verandah with her knees apart and her skirts pulled high and rucked up between her legs. As Shasa's gaze dropped, she let her knees fall a little further open. Her nose was snubbed and sprinkled with freckles, and she wrinkled it as she grinned. It was a sly cheeky grin, and her tongue was bright pink between white teeth.

Guiltily Shasa jerked his eyes away and stared ahead through the windshield. But he remembered vividly every last detail of those forbidden minutes behind the pumphouse and the heat rose in his cheeks. He could not help glancing at his mother. She was looking ahead at the road and had not noticed. He felt relief until she murmured. 'She is a common little hussy, ogling everything in pants. Her father is one of the men we are retrenching. We'll be rid of her before she causes real trouble for us and herself.'

He should have known she had not missed that brief exchange. She saw everything, he thought, and then he felt the impact of her words. The girl was being sent away, and he was surprised by his feeling of deprivation. It was a physical ache in the floor of his stomach.

'What will happen to them, Mater?' he asked softly. 'I mean the people we are firing.' While he had listened to his mother and Twentyman-Jones discussing the retrenchments, he had thought of them merely as numbers; but with that glimpse of the girl, they had become flesh and blood. He remembered his adversary the blond boy, and the little girl that he had seen from the window of the railway coach, standing beside the tracks in the hobo camp, and he imagined Annalisa Botha in the place of that strange girl.

'I don't know what will become of them.' His mother's mouth tightened. 'I don't think it is anything that should concern us. This world is a place of harsh reality, and each of us has to face it in his own way. I think we should rather consider what would be the consequences if we did not let them go.'

'We would lose money.'

'That is right, and if we lose money, we have to close down the mine, which would mean that all the others would lose their jobs, not just the few that we have to fire. Then we all suffer. If we did that with everything we own, in the end we would lose everything. We would be like the rest of them. Would you prefer that?'

Suddenly Shasa had a new mental image. Instead of the blond boy standing in the hobo camp, it was himself, barefoot in dusty, tattered khakis, and he could almost feel the night chill through the thin shirt and the rumble of hunger in his guts.

'No!' he said explosively, and then dropped his voice. 'I wouldn't like that.' He shivered at the persistent images her words had invoked. 'Is that going to happen, Mater? Could it happen? Might we also be poor?'

'We could be, *chéri*. It could happen quickly and cruelly if we are not on guard every minute. A fortune is extremely difficult to build but easy to destroy.'

'Is it going to happen?' he insisted, and he thought about the *Midas Touch*, his yacht, and the polo ponies, and his friends at Bishops, and the vineyards of Weltevreden and he was afraid.

'Nothing is certain.' She reached across and took his hand. 'That's the fun of this game of life, if it was then it wouldn't be worth playing.'

'I wouldn't like to be poor.'

'No!' She said it as vehemently as he had. 'It will not happen, not if we are cunning and bold.'

'What you said about the trade of the world coming to a halt. People no longer able to buy our diamonds. . . .' Before those had been merely words, now they were a dreadful possibility.

'We must believe that the wheels will one day begin to turn again, one day soon, and we must play the golden rules. Do you remember them?' She swung the Daimler through the climbing turns up the slope and around the spur of the hills so that the mine buildings disappeared behind the rock wall of the cliff.

'What was the first golden rule, Shasa?' she prompted him.

'Sell when everybody else is buying and buy when everybody else is selling,' he repeated.

'Good. And what is happening now?'

'Everybody is trying to sell.' It dawned upon him and his grin was triumphant.

'He's so beautiful, and he has the sense and the instinct,' she thought as she waited for him to follow the coils of the serpent until he reached its head and disovered the fangs. His expression changed as it happened. He looked at her crestfallen.

'But, Mater, how can we buy if we haven't got the money?'

She pulled to the side of the track and cut the engine. Then turned to him seriously and took both his hands.

'I am going to treat you as a man,' she said. 'What I tell you is our secret, our private business that we share with nobody. Not Grandpater or Anna, or Abraham Abrahams or Twentyman-Jones. It's our thing, yours and mine alone.' He nodded and she drew a deep breath. 'I have a premonition that this catastrophe that has engulfed the world is our pivot, an opportunity that very few are ever offered. For the last few years I have been preparing to exploit it. How did I do that, *chéri*?'

He shook his head, staring at her fascinated.

'I have turned everything, with the exception of the mine and Weltevreden, into cash, and even on those I have borrowed heavily, very heavily.'

'That's why you called all the loans. That's why we went to Walvis for that fish factory and the trawlers – you wanted the money.'

'Yes, *chéri*, yes,' she encouraged him, unconsciously shaking hands, willing him to see it. And his face lit again.

'You are going to buy!' he exclaimed.

'I have already begun,' she told him. 'I have bought land and mining concessions, fishing concessions and guano concessions, buildings. I have even bought the Alhambra Theatre in Cape Town and the Coliseum in Johannesburg. But most of all I have bought land, and the option to buy more land, tens and hundreds of thousands of acres, *chéri*, at two shillings an acre. Land is the only true store of wealth.'

He could not already grasp it, but he sensed the enormity of what she told him and she saw it in his eyes.

'Now you know our secret,' she laughed. 'If I have guessed right, we will double and redouble our fortunes.'

'And if it doesn't change. If the,' he searched for the word, 'if the Depression goes on and on for ever, what then, Mater?'

She pouted and dropped his hands. 'Then, *chéri*, nothing will matter very much, one way or the other.'

She started the Daimler and drove up the last pitch of the road to the bungalow standing alone in its wide lawns, with lights burning in the windows

and the servants lined up respectfully on the front verandah in their immaculate white livery to welcome her.

She parked at the bottom of the steps, turned off the engine and turned to him again.

'No, Shasa *chéri*, we are not going to be poor. We are going to be richer, much richer than we ever were before. And then later, through you, my darling, we will have power to go with our wealth. Great fortune, enormous power. Oh, I have it all planned, so carefully planned!'

* * *

Her words filled Shasa's head with turbulent thoughts. He could not sleep.

'Great fortune, enormous power.' The words excited and disturbed him. He tried to visualize what they meant and saw himself like a strongman at the circus, in leopardskins and leather wristbands, standing with arms akimbo, huge biceps flexed, upon a pyramid of golden sovereigns, while a congregation in white robes knelt and made obeisance before him.

He ran the images through his head over and over, each time altering some detail, all of them pleasurable but lacking the final touch until he bestowed upon one of his white-robed worshippers a crown of unruly wind-tousled sun-streaked curls. He placed her in the front rank, and she lifted her forehead from the ground and stuck her tongue out at him.

His erection was so quick and hard that it made him gasp, and before he could prevent himself he had slipped his hand under the sheet and prised it out of the fly of his pyjamas.

Jock Murphy had warned him about it. 'It will spoil your eye, Master Shasa. I have seen many a good man with a bat or a polo stick ruined by Mrs Palm and her fiver daughters.'

But in his fantasy Annalisa was sitting up, her long legs apart, and she was slowly drawing up the skirt of her white robe. The skin of her legs was smooth as butter, and he moaned softly. She was staring at the front of his leopardskin costume, her tongue whisking lightly over her parted lips, and the white skirt rose higher and higher, and his fist began to jerk rhythmically. He could not prevent it.

Up and up rode the white skirt, never quite reaching the fork of her crotch. Her legs seemed to stretch forever, like the railway tracks across the desert, running on and on and never meeting. He choked and jerked into a sitting position on the feather mattress, doubled over his flying fist, and when it came it was sharp and painful as a bayonet driven up into his intestines, and he cried out and fell back against the pillows.

Annalisa's sly grinning freckled face receded, and the wet front of his pyjamas began to turn icy cold, but he did not have the will to strip them off.

When the servant woke him with a tray of coffee and a dish of hard sweet rusks, he felt dazed and exhausted. It was still dark outside, and he rolled over and pulled the pillows over his head.

'Madam your mother, she says I wait here until you get up,' said the Ovambo servant darkly, and Shasa dragged himself to the bathroom trying to conceal the dry stain on the front of his pyjamas.

One of the grooms had his pony saddled and waiting at the front steps of the

bungalow. Shasa took a moment to joke and laugh with the groom and then greet and caress his pony, rubbing foreheads with him and blowing softly into his nostrils.

'You are getting fat, Prester John,' he chided the pony. 'We'll have to work that off you with the polo sticks.'

He swung up into the saddle and took the short cut, following the pipe track around the shoulder of the hill. The pipeline carried the water from the spring around the hills to the mine and the washing gear. He passed the pumphouse and felt a guilty pang at its associations with last night's depravity, but then the dawn lit the plains below the cliffs and he forgot that in the pleasure of watching the veld come alive and greet the sun.

On this side of the hills Centaine had ordered that the forest be left untouched and the mopani was tall and stately. A covey of francolin were dawn-crying in the thicket down the slope, and a grey duiker, returning from the spring, bounded across the track under the pony's nose. Shasa laughed as he shied theatrically.

'Stop that, you old show-off!'

He turned the corner of the cliff and the contrast was depressing. The desecrated forest, the deforming scar of the workings on the hillside, the graceless square iron buildings and the stark skeletal girders of the washing gear, how ugly there were.

He gave the pony a touch with his heels and they galloped the last mile and reached the main haulage just as Twentyman-Jones' old Ford came up the track from the village with headlights still burning. He checked his watch as he stepped out and looked sad as he saw that Shasa was three minutes ahead of time.

'Have you ever been down the haulage, Master Shasa?'

'No, sir.' He was going to add, 'My Mater has never allowed it,' but somehow that seemed superfluous, and for the first time he felt a twinge of resentment at his mother's all-pervading presence.

Twentyman-Jones led him to the head of the haulage and introduced him to the shift boss.

'Master Shasa will be working with you,' he explained. 'Treat him normally – just like you would treat any other young man who will one day be your managing director,' he instructed. It was impossible to tell by Twentyman-Jones' expression when he was joking, so nobody laughed.

'Get a tin helmet for him,' Twentyman-Jones ordered, and while Shasa adjusted the straps of the helmet he led him to the foot of the sheer cliff.

The incline tunnel had been cut into the base of the cliff, a round aperture into which the steel rail tracks angled downwards at forty-five degrees before disappearing into the dark depths. A string of cocopans stood at the head of the tracks, and Twentyman-Jones led him to the first truck and they climbed into the steel bin. The shift swarmed into the trucks behind them, a dozen white foremen and one hundred and fifty black workers in ragged dusty overalls and helmets of bright unpainted metal, laughing and ragging each other in boisterous horseplay.

The steam winch of the winding gear clattered and hissed and the string of trucks jerked forward and then, rocking and swaying, ran down the steeply inclined ramp on the narrow-gauge railway tracks. The steel wheels rumbling and clacking over the joints of the track, they dropped down into the dark maw of the tunnel.

Shasa stirred uneasily, stabbed with unreasoning fear at the sudden absolute blackness that engulfed them. However, in the trucks behind him the Ovambo miners were singing, their deep melodious voices echoing in the dark confines of the tunnel, a marvellous chorus raised in an African work chant, and Shasa relaxed and leaned closer to Twentyman-Jones to follow his explanation.

'The incline is forty-five degrees and the capacity of the winding gear is one hundred tons, in mining parlance that is sixty loads of ore. Our target is six hundred loads a shift raised to the surface.'

Shasa was trying to concentrate on the figures; he knew his mother would question him this evening, but the darkness and singing and the rumble of the swaying trucks distracted him. Ahead of him there was a tiny coin of brilliant white light that grew swiftly in size until abruptly they burst out of the far end of the tunnel and involuntarily Shasa gasped with astonishment.

He had studied the diagrams of the pipe and, of course, there were photographs on his mother's desk at Weltevreden but they had not adequately prepared him for its immensity.

It was an almost perfectly round hole in the centre of the hills. It was open to the sky, and the sides of the excavation were vertical and sheer, a circular wall of grey rock like a cockpit. They had entered it through the tunnel that connected the workings to the far side of the hills and the narrow ramp on which they were riding continued down at the same angle of forty-five degrees until it reached the floor of the excavation two hundred feet below them. The drop on either hand was breathtaking. The great rock-lined hole was a mile across, and its sheer walls four hundred feet from the tip of the floor.

Twentyman-Jones was still lecturing him. 'This is a volcanic pipe, a blow hole from the earth's depths up which the molten magma was forced to the surface in the beginning of time. In those temperatures, as hot as the sun, and enormous pressures diamonds were forged, and they were brought up in the fiery lava.' Shasa stared around him, screwing his head to take in the proportions of the huge excavation as Twentyman-Jones went on, 'Then the pipe was pinched off at depth, and the magma in it cooled and solidified. The upper layer, exposed to air and sun, was oxidized into the classical "yellow ground" of the diamondiferous formation. We worked down through that for eleven years, and only recently we reached the "blue ground".' He made an expansive gesture that took in the slaty blue rock that formed the floor of the huge pit. 'That is the deeper deposit of the solidified magma, hard as iron and as full of diamonds as currants in a hot cross bun.'

They reached the floor of the workings and climbed down from the truck.

'The operation is fairly straightforward,' Twentyman-Jones went on. 'The new shift comes in at first light and begins work on the previous evening's blast. The broken ground is lashed and loaded into the cocopans and sent up the haulage to the surface. After that they mark out and drill the shot-holes for the next blast and then they set the charges. At dusk we pull out the shift, and the shift boss lights the fuses. After the blast we leave the workings overnight to settle and for the fumes to disperse, then the next morning we begin the whole process over again. 'There,' he pointed to an area of shattered blue grey rock, 'that's last night's blast. That's where we will begin today.'

Shasa had not expected to be so absorbed by the fascination of this mighty excavation, but his interest grew more intense as the day went on. Not even the heat and the dust daunted him. The heat was trapped between the sheer walls when at noon the sun beat down directly onto the uneven broken floor. The

dust was floury, rising from the shattered ore body as the hammer-men swung their ten-pound sledges to crack the larger lumps into manageable pieces. The dust hung in a fog over the lashing teams as they loaded the cocopans, and it coated their faces and their bodies and turned them into ghostly grey albinos.

'We get a bit of miners' phthisis,' Twentyman-Jones admitted. 'The dust gets into their lungs and turns to stone. Ideally we shold hose the ore down and keep it wet to lay the dust, but we are short of water. We haven't enough for the washing gear. We certainly can't afford to splash it around. So men die and are crippled, but it takes ten years to build up in the lungs, and we give them, or their widows, a good pension, and the miners' inspector is sympathetic, though his sympathy costs a penny.'

At noon Twentyman-Jones called Shasa across. 'Your mother said you need only work half the shift. I'm going up now. Are you coming?'

'I'd rather not, sir,' Shasa answered diffidently. 'I'd like to watch them charge the holes for the blast.'

Twentyman-Jones shook his head sorrowfully. 'Chip off the old block!' and went away still muttering.

The shift boss allowed Shasa to light the fuses, under his careful supervision. It gave Shasa a sense of importance and power to touch the flaring chesa stick, the igniter, to the bunched tips of the fuses, passing quickly down the line and watching the fire run down the twisted white fuses, turning them sizzling black in the swirl of blue smoke.

He and the shift boss rode up on the haulage to the cry of 'Fire in the hole!' and Shasa lingered at the head of the main haulage until the shots fired and he felt the earth tremble beneath his feet.

Then he saddled Prester John and, dusty, streaked with sweat, bone-tired and happy as he had seldom been in his life, he rode back along the pipe track.

He was not even thinking about her when he reached the pumphouse, but there she was, perched up on top of the silver-painted waterpipe. The shock was such that when Prester John shied under him he almost lost his seat and had to snatch at the pommel.

She had plaited a wreath of wild flowers into her hair and unbuttoned the top of her blouse. In one of the books in the library at Weltevreden there was an illustration of satyrs and nymphs dancing in the forest. The book was kept in the forbidden section to which his mother guarded the key, but Shasa had invested some of his pocket money in a duplicate and lightly clad nymphs were among his favourites of all that treasure house of erotica.

Annalisa was one of these, a wood nymph, only part human, and she slanted her eyes at him slyly and her eye teeth were pointed and very white.

'Hello, Annalisa.' His voice cracked treacherously, and his heart was beating so wildly that he thought it might spring into his throat and choke him.

She smiled but did not reply, instead she caressed her own arm, a slow lingering stroke from her wrist to her bare shoulder. He watched her fingers raising the fine coppery hair on her forearm and his loins swelled.

She leaned forward and placed her forefinger on her lower lip, still grinning slyly, and her bosom changed shape and the opening of her blouse gaped and he saw that the skin in the vee was so white and translucent that the tiny blue veins showed through it.

He kicked out of the stirrups and swung a leg over Prester John's withers in the showy polo player's forward dismount, but the girl whirled to her feet,

hoisted her skirts high and, with a flash of creamy thighs, sprang lightly over the pipeline and disappeared into the thick scrub on the hillside beyond.

Shasa raced after her, and found himself struggling through dense undergrowth. It clawed at his face and seized his legs. He heard her giggle once, not far ahead of him, but a rock twisted under his boot and he fell heavily, winding himself. When he pulled himself up and limped after her, she was gone.

A while longer he floundered around in the scrub, his ardour swiftly cooling, and by the time he battled his way back to the pipe track to find that Prester John had taken full advantage of the diversion and decamped, he was bubbling over with anger at himself and the girl.

It was a long tramp back to the bungalow and he hadn't realized how tired he was. It was dark by the time he got home. The pony with empty saddle had raised the alarm and Centaine's concern changed instantly to relieved fury when she saw him.

* * *

A week in the heat and dust of the workings and the monotony of the work began to pall, so Twentyman-Jones sent Shasa to work in the winch room of the main haulage. The winch driver was a taciturn, morose man and jealous of his job. He would not allow Shasa to touch the controls of the winch.

'My union doesn't allow it.' He stood his ground stubbornly and after two days Twentyman-Jones moved Shasa to the weathering ground.

Here the ore was tipped out and spread in the open by gangs of Ovambo labourers, all stripped to the waist and chanting in chorus as they went through the laborious repetitive process of tip and spread under the urgings of their white supervisor and his gang of black boss-boys.

On this weathering ground lay the stockpile of the H'ani Mine, thousands of tons of ore spread out on an area the size of four polo fields. When the blue ground was blasted out of the pipe it was hard as concrete; only gelignite and the ten-pound sledge hammers would break it. But after it had been lying in the sun of the weathering ground for six months it began to break down and crumble until it was chalky and friable and could be reloaded in the cocopans and taken to the mill and the washing gear.

Shasa was placed in charge of a gang of forty labourers, and soon struck up a friendship with the Ovambo boss-boy. Like all the black tribesmen he had two names, his tribal name which he did not divulge to his white employers, and his work name. The Ovambo's work name was Moses. He was fifteen years or so younger than the other boss-boys, and had been selected for his intelligence and initiative. He spoke both English and Afrikaans well, and the respect that the black labourers usually reserved for the grey hair of age he earned from them with his billy club and boot and acid wit.

'If I was a white man,' he told Shasa, 'one day I would have Doctela's job.' 'Doctela' was the Ovambo name for Twentyman-Jones, and Moses went on, 'I might still have it, one day – or if not me, then my son.' Shasa was shocked and then intrigued by such an outrageous notion. He had never before met a black who did not know his place in society. There was a disturbing presence about the tall Ovambo, who looked like one of the drawings of an Egyptian pharaoh

from the forbidden section of the Weltevreden library, but that hint of danger made him more intriguing to Shasa.

They usually spent the lunch-hour break together, Shasa helping Moses to perfect his reading and writing in the grubby ruled notebook which was his most prized possession. In return the Ovambo taught Shasa the rudiments of his language, especially the oaths and insults, and the meaning of some of the work chants, most of which were ribald.

'Is baby-making work or pleasure?' was the rhetorical opening question of Shasa's favourite chant, and he joined in the response to the delight of the gang he was supervising: 'It cannot be work or the white man would make us do it for him!'

Shasa was just over fourteen years old. Some of the men he supervised were three times his age, and none of them thought it strange. Instead they responded to his teasing and his sunny smile and his sorry attempts to speak their language. His men were soon spreading five loads to four of the other teams, and they ended the second week as top gang on the grounds.

Shasa was too involved with the work and his new friend to notice the dark looks of the white supervisor, and even when he made a pointed remark about *kafferboeties*, or 'nigger-lovers', Shasa did not take the reference personally.

On the third Saturday, after the men had been paid at noon, he rode down to the boss-boys' cottage at Moses' invitation and spent an hour sitting in the sun on the front doorstep of the cottage drinking sour milk from the calabash that Moses' shy and pretty young wife offered, and helping him read aloud from the copy of Macaulay's *History of England* he had smuggled out of the bungalow and brought down in his saddlebag.

The book was one of his set works at school so Shasa considered himself something of an authority on it, and he was enjoying the unusual role of teacher and instructor until at last Moses closed the book.

'This is very heavy work, Good Water,' he had translated Shasa's name directly into the Ovambo, 'worse than spreading ore in the summer. I will work on it later,' and he went into the single-roomed cottage, placed the book in his locker and came back with a roll of newspaper.

'Let us try this.' He offered the paper to Shasa, who spread it on his lap. It was poor quality yellow newsprint and the ink smudged onto his fingers. The name on the top of the page was *Umlomo Wa Bantu*, and Shasa translated it without difficulty: 'The Mouth of the Black Nations', and he glanced down the columns of print. The articles were mostly in English, though there were a few in the vernacular.

Moses pointed out the editorial, and they started working through it.

'What is the African National Congress?' Shasa was puzzled. 'And who is Jabavu?'

Eagerly the Ovambo began to explain, and Shasa's interest turned to unease as he listened.

'Jabavu is the father of the Bantu, of all the tribes, of all the black people. The African National Congress is the herder who guards our cattle.'

'I don't understand.' Shasa shook his head. He did not like the direction that the discussion was taking, and he began to squirm as Moses quoted:

> Your cattle are gone, my people
> Go rescue them! Go rescue them!
> Leave your breechloader
> And turn instead to the pen.

Take paper and ink,
For that will be your shield.
Your rights are going
So take up your pen
Load it with ink.
And do battle with the pen.

'That is politics,' Shasa interrupted him. 'Blacks don't take part in politics. That's white men's business.' This was the cornerstone of the South African way of life.

The glow went out of Moses' expression and he lifted the newspaper off Shasa's lap and stood up.

'I will return your book to you when I have read it.' He avoided Shasa's eyes and went back into the cottage.

* * *

On the Monday Twentyman-Jones stopped Shasa at the main gate of the weathering grounds. 'I think you have learned all there is to know about weathering, Master Shasa. It's about time we moved you along to the mill house and washing gear.'

And as they followed the railway tracks up to the main plant, walking beside one of the cocopans which was full of the crumbling weathered ore, Twentyman-Jones remarked: 'It is just as well not to become too familiar with the black labourers, Master Shasa, you will find they tend to take advantage if you do.'

Shasa was puzzled for a moment, then he laughed. 'Oh, you mean Moses. He isn't a labourer, he is a boss-boy, and he is jolly bright, sir.'

'A bit too bright for his own good,' Twentyman-Jones agreed bitterly. 'The bright ones are always the malcontents and trouble-stirrers. Give me an honest dumb nigger every time. Your friend Moses is trying to organize a black mineworkers' union.'

Shasa knew from his grandfather and his mother that Bolsheviks and trade unionists were the most dreaded monsters, intent on tearing down the framework of civilized society. He was appalled to learn that Moses was one of these, but Twentyman-Jones was going on:

'We also suspect that he is at the centre of a nice little IDB operation.'

IDB was the other monster of civilized existence – Illicit Diamond Buying – the trade in stolen diamonds, and Shasa was revolted by the idea that his friend could be both a trade unionist and an illicit dealer.

Yet Twentyman-Jones' next words depressed him. 'I am afraid Mister Moses will head the list of those we will be laying off at the end of the month. He is a dangerous man. We will simply have to get shot of him.'

'They are getting rid of him simply because the two of us are friends.' Shasa saw through it. 'It's because of me.' He was swamped with a sense of guilt, and guilt was followed almost immediately by anger. Quick words leapt to his tongue. He wanted to cry, 'It's not fair!' But before he spoke he looked at Twentyman-Jones and knew intuitively that any defence he attempted of Moses would only seal the boss-boy's fate.

He shrugged. 'You know what is best, sir,' he agreed, and he saw the slight relaxation in the set of the old man's shoulders.

'Mater,' he thought, 'I will talk to Mater,' and then, with intense frustration, 'If only I could do it myself, if only I could say what must be done.' And then it dawned upon him that this was what his mother had meant when she spoke of power. The ability to charge and direct the orders of existence that surrounded him.

'Power,' he whispered to himself. 'One day I will have power. Enormous power.'

* * *

The work in the mill house was more exacting and interesting. The friable weathered ore was loaded into the bins and then fed through the hoppers into the rollers which crushed it to the correct consistency for the washing gear. The machinery was massive and powerful, the din almost deafening as the ore tumbled out of the hoppers into the feed chute and was sucked into the spinning steel rollers with a continuous roar. One hundred and fifty tons an hour; it went in one end as chalky lumps the size of ripe watermelons and poured out the far end as gravel and dust.

Annalisa's brother, Stoffel, who had on Shasa's last visit to the H'ani adjusted the timing on his old Ford and who was also the skilled mimic of bird calls, was now an apprentice in the mill house. He was delegated to show Shasa around, and undertook the assignment with gusto and relish.

'You have to be goddamned careful with the mucking settings on the rollers or you crush the bloody diamonds to powder.' Stoffel emphasized his newly acquired manliness and authority with oaths and obscenity.

'Come on, Shasa, I'll show you the grease points. All points have to be grease-gunned at the beginning of every shift.' He crawled under the bank of thundering rollers, shouting into Shasa's ear to make himself heard. 'Last month one of the other apprentices got his mucking arm in the bearing. It pulled it off like a chicken's wing, man. You should have seen the blood.' Ghoulishly he pointed out the dried stains on the concrete floor and galvanized walls. 'Man, I tell you, he squirted blood like a garden hose.'

Stoffel climbed the steel catwalk like a monkey and they looked down on the roller mill tables. 'One of the Ovambo kaffirs fell off here, right smack into the ore bin, there wasn't even a scrap of bone bigger than your finger left of him when he came out the other end of the rollers. *Ja*, man, it's a bloody dangerous job,' he told Shasa proudly. 'You've got to keep on your mucking toes all the time.'

When the mine hooter blew the lunch hour he led Shasa around to the shady side of the mill house and they perched comfortably on the ventilator housing. Under the sanction of the work place they could associate quite openly, and Shasa felt grown-up and important in his blue workman's overalls as he opened the lunch box that the chef at the bungalow had sent down for him.

'Chicken and tongue sandwiches and jam roly-poly,' he checked the contents. 'Do you want some, Stoffel?'

'No, man. Here comes my sister with my lunch.' And Shasa lost all interest in his own lunch box.

Annalisa was pedalling down the avenue on a black-framed Rudge with the nest of canteens dangling from the handlebars. It was the first time that he had

seen her since the meeting at the pumphouse, though he had looked for her each day since then. She had tucked her skirts into her bloomers to keep them clear of the chain. She stood up on the pedals and her legs pumped rhythmically as she came through the gates of the mill house and the wind flattened the thin stuff of her dress against the front of her body. Her breasts were disproportionately large for her slim brown limbs.

Shasa watched her with total fascination. She became aware of him, sitting beside her brother, and her entire bearing changed. She dropped back onto the saddle and squared her shoulders, lifting one hand from the handlebars to try and smooth the windblown tangle of her hair. She braked the Rudge, stepped down off the pedals and propped the machine against the bottom of the ventilator housing.

'What's for lunch, Lisa?' Stoffel Botha demanded.

'Sausage and mash.' She handed the canteens up to him. 'Same as always.'

The sleeves of her dress were cut back and when she lifted her arms Shasa saw the bush of coarse blonde hair in her armpits tangled and wet with perspiration and he crossed his legs quickly.

'Sis, man!' Stoffel registered his disgust. 'It's always sausage and mash!'

'Next time I'll ask Ma to cook fillet steak and mushrooms.' She lowered her arms and Shasa realized he was staring but could not stop himself. She pulled the opening at the neck of her blouse closed and he saw a faint flush under the suntanned skin at her throat, but she had not yet looked directly at him.

'Thanks for nothing,' Stoffel dismissed her, but she lingered.

'You can have some of mine,' Shasa offered.

'I'll swop you,' Stoffel offered generously, and Shasa glanced into the canteen and saw the lumpy potato mash swimming in thin greasy gravy.

'I'm not hungry.' He spoke to the girl for the first time. 'Would you like a sandwich, Annalisa?'

She smoothed the skirt over her hips and looked directly at him at last. Her eyes slanted like a wild cat's, and she grinned slyly.

'When I want something from you, Shasa Courtney, I will whistle for it – like this.' She pouted her lips into a rosy cupid's bow and whistled like a snake charmer, at the same time slowly raising her forefinger in an unmistakably obscene gesture.

Stoffel let out a delighted guffaw and punched Shasa's arm. 'Man, she's got the hots for you!'

While Shasa blushed scarlet, and sat speechless with shock, Annalisa turned away deliberately and picked up the bicycle. She went out through the gates standing on the pedals and swinging the Rudge from side to side under her so that her tight round buttocks oscillated with each stroke.

That evening as he turned Prester John onto the pipe track Shasa's pulse started to gallop with anticipation, and as he approached the pumphouse he slowed the pony to a walk, afraid of disappointment, reluctant to turn the corner of the building.

Yet he was still not prepared for the shock when he saw her. She was draped languidly against one of the stanchions of the pipeline, and Shasa was speechless as she came slowly upright and sauntered to the head of his pony without looking up at the rider.

She held the cheek strap of his halter and crooned to the pony. 'What a pretty boy.' The pony blew through his nostrils, and shifted his weight. 'What a lovely soft nose.' She stroked his muzzle with a lingering touch.

'Would you like a little kiss then, my pretty boy.' She pursed her lips, pink and soft and moist, and glanced up at Shasa before she leaned forward and deliberately kissed the pony's muzzle, slipping her arms around his neck. She held the kiss for long seconds and then laid her cheek against the pony's cheek. Beginning to sway, humming softly in her throat and rocking her hips gently, she at last looked up at Shasa with those sly slanting eyes.

He was struggling to find something to say, confused by the rush of his emotions, and she moved slowly to the pony's shoulder and stroke his flank.

'So strong.' Her hand brushed Shasa's thigh slightly, almost unintentionally, and then came back more deliberately and she was no longer looking at his face. He could not cover himself, could not hide his violent reaction to her touch, and suddenly she let out a shocking screech of laughter and stood back with both hands on her hips.

'Are you going to camp out, Shasa Courtney?' she demanded, and he was puzzled and embarrassed. He shook his head dumbly.

'Then what are you putting up a tent for?' She hooted, gazing shamelessly at the front of his breeches and he doubled up awkwardly in the saddle. With a disconcerting change of mood, she seemed to take pity on him and she went back to the pony's head and led him along the track, giving Shasa a chance to recover his composure.

'What did my brother tell you about me?' she asked, without looking round.

'Nothing,' he assured her.

'Don't believe what he says.' She was unconvinced. 'He always tries to make out bad things about me. Did he tell you about Fourie, the driver?' Everybody at the mine knew how Gerhard Fourie's wife had caught the two of them in the cab of his truck after the Christmas party. Fourie's wife was older than Annalisa's mother, but she had blackened both the girl's eyes and torn her only good dress to tatters.

'He didn't tell me anything,' Shasa reiterated stoutly, and then with interest, 'What happened?'

'Nothing,' she said quickly. 'It was all lies.' And then, with another change of direction, 'Would you like me to show you something?'

'Yes, please.' Shasa answered with alacrity. He had an inkling of what it might be.

'Give me an arm.' She came to his stirrup and he leaned down and they locked elbows. He swung her up and she was light and strong. She sat behind him astride the pony's rump and slid both arms around Shasa's waist.

'Take the path to the left.' She directed him and they rode in silence for ten minutes.

'How old are you?' she asked at last.

'Almost fifteen.' He stretched the truth a little and she said, 'I'll be sixteen in two months.' If there had been any doubts as to who was in charge, this declaration effectively settled it. Shasa deferred to her and she felt it in his carriage. She pressed her breasts to his back as though to emphasize her control and they were big and rubbery hard and burned him through his thin cotton shirt.

'Where are we going?' he asked after another long silence. They had by-passed the bungalow.

'Hush up! I'll show you when we get there.'

The track had narrowed and become rougher. Shasa doubted anybody had passed this way in months, other than the small wild beasts that still lived this

close to the mine. Finally it petered out altogether against the base of the cliff, and Annalisa slid down from the pony's back.

'Leave your horse here.'

He tethered the pony and looked around him with interest. He had never been so far along the base of the cliffs. They must be three miles from the bungalow at least.

Below them the scree slope plunged downwards at a steep angle, and the ground was riven with gorges and ravines, all of them choked with rank thorny undergrowth.

'Come on,' Annalisa ordered. 'We haven't got much time. It will be dark soon.' She ducked under a branch and started down the slope.

'Hey!' Shasa cautioned her. 'You can't go down there. You'll hurt yourself.'

'You're scared,' she mocked.

'I am not.' The taunt goaded him onto the rock-strewn slope and they climbed downwards. Once Annalisa paused to pluck a spray of yellow flowers from a thorn bush, then they went on, helping each other over the bad places, crouching under the thorn branches, teetering on the boulders and hopping across the gaps like a pair of rock rabbits until they reached the bottom of the ravine and paused to catch their breath.

Shasa bent backwards from the waist and stared up at the cliff that towered above them, sheer as a fortress wall, but Annalisa tugged his arm to gain his attention.

'It's a secret. You have to swear on oath not to tell anybody, especially not my brother.'

'All right, I swear.'

'You have to do it properly. Lift your right hand and put the other on your heart.' Solemnly she led him through the oath, and then took his hand and drew him to a lichen-covered pile of boulders. 'Kneel down!'

He obeyed, and she carefully pulled aside a leafy branch that screened a niche amongst the boulders. Shasa gasped and pulled back, coming half to his feet. The niche was shape like a shrine. There was a collection of empty glass jars arranged on the floor but the wild flowers in them had withered and turned brown. Beyond the floral offering a pile of white bones had been carefully arranged in a small pyramid and surmounting this was a human skull, with gaping eye sockets and yellow teeth.

'Who is it?' Shasa whispered, his eyes wide with superstitious awe.

'The witch of the mountain.' Annalisa took his hand. 'I found her bones lying here, and I made this magic place.'

'How do you know she's a witch?' Shasa had a bad attack of the creeps by now, and his whisper shook and cracked.

'She told me so.'

That raised such frightful images that he did not question her further; skulls and bones were creepy enough, voices from beyond were a hundred times worse, and the hairs at the back of his neck and along his arms itched and stood erect. He watched while she changed the withered flowers for the fresh yellow acacia blossom and then sat back on her ankles and took his hand again.

'The witch will grant you one wish,' she whispered, and he thought about it.

'What do you want?' she tugged his hand.

'Can I wish for anything?'

'Yes, anything,' she nodded, watching his face eagerly.

Staring at the bleached skull his awe faded; he was suddenly aware of a new

sensation. Something seemed to reach out to him, a sensation of warmth and familiar comfort that he had known before only as an infant when his mother held him to her bosom.

There were still small pieces of dried scalp attached to the dome of the skull, like brown parchment, and tiny peppercorns of black hair, soft furry little balls like those on the head of the tame Bushman who herded the milk cows at the way station on the road from Windhoek.

'Anything?' he repeated. 'I can wish for anything?'

'Yes, anything you want.' Annalisa leaned against his side, and she was soft and warm and her body smelled of fresh sweet young sweat.

Shasa leaned forward and touched the skull of its white bony forehead, and the sense of warmth and comfort was stronger. He was aware of a benign feeling – of love – that was not too strong a word, yes, of love, as though he were being overlooked by someone or something that cared for him very deeply.

'I wish,' he said softly, almost dreamily, 'I wish for enormous power.'

He imagined a prickling sensation in the fingertips that touched the skull, like the discharge of static electricity, and he jerked his hand away sharply.

Annalisa exclaimed in exasperation and pulled her body away from him at the same time. 'That's a silly wish.' She was clearly piqued, and he could not understand why. 'You are a stupid boy, and the witch won't grant a stupid wish like that.'

She flounced to her feet and drew the screening branch over the niche. 'It's late. We must go back.'

Shasa did not want to leave this place, and he lingered.

Annalisa called from up the slope. 'Come on, it will be dark in an hour.'

When he reached the path again she was sitting propped against the rock wall of the cliff facing him.

'I've hurt myself.' She said it like an accusation. They were both flushed and panting from the climb.

'I'm sorry,' he gasped. 'How did you hurt yourself?'

She pulled the hem of her skirt halfway up her thigh. One of the red-tipped wait-a-bit thorns had rowelled her, raising a long red scratch across the smooth buttery skin of her inner thigh. It had barely broken the skin, but a line of blood droplets had welled up, like a necklace of tiny bright rubies. He stared at it as though mesmerized and she sank back against the rock, lifted her knees and spread her thighs, holding the bunch of her skirts into her crotch.

'Put some spit on it,' she ordered.

Obediently he knelt between her feet and wet his forefinger.

'Your finger is dirty,' she admonished him.

'What shall I do then?' He was at a loss.

'With your tongue – put spit on it with your tongue.'

He leaned forward and touched the wound with the tip of his tongue. Her blood had a strange salty metallic taste as he licked it.

She placed one hand on the nape of his neck and stroked the dense dark curl of his hair.

'Yes, like that, clean it,' she murmured. Her fingers twisted into his hair and she held his head, pressing his face to her skin, and then deliberately directed him higher, raising her skirt slowly with her free hand as his mouth travelled upwards.

Then peering between the spread of her thighs, he saw that she was sitting on a piece of her clothing, a scrap of white cloth printed with pink roses, and

with a tingle of shock he realized that in the few minutes that she had been alone she must have removed her panties and spread them as a cushion on the soft moss-covered earth. She was naked under the skirt.

* * *

Shasa woke with a start and he could not think where he was. The ground was hard under his back and a pebble was digging into his shoulder, there was a weight across his chest making it difficult for him to breathe. He was cold, and it was dark. Prester John stamped and snorted and he saw the pony's head silhouetted against the stars.

Suddenly he remembered. Annalisa's leg was thrown over his and her face was against his throat; she sprawled half across his chest. He pushed her off so violently that she woke with a cry.

'It's dark!' he said stupidly. 'They'll be out looking for us by now!'

He tried to stand but his breeches were around his knees. He remembered vividly the practised way that she had unbuttoned them and worked them over his hips. He yanked them up and fumbled with his fly.

'We've got to get back. My mother – '

Annalisa was on her feet beside him, hopping on one leg as she tried to find the opening of her panties with her bare foot. Shasa looked at the stars. Orion was on the horizon. 'It's after nine o'clock,' he said gloomily.

'You should have stayed awake,' she whined, and put a hand on his shoulder to steady herself. 'My Pa will lather me. He said next time he'd kill me.'

Shasa shrugged off her hand. He wanted to get away from her yet he knew he could not.

'It was your fault.' She stooped and grabbed her panties at the ankles, hoisted them to her waist and then settled her skirts over them. 'I'm going to tell Pa that it was your fault. He'll take the sjambok to me this time. Oh! he'll whop the skin off me.'

Shasa unhitched the pony and his hands were shaking. He could not think clearly, he was still half asleep and groggy. 'I won't let him.' His gallantry was half-hearted and unconvincing. 'I won't let him hurt you.'

It seemed only to infuriate her. 'What can you do? You're only a baby.' The word triggered something else in her mind. 'What will happen if you've given me a baby, hey? It will be a bastard; did you think of that while you were sticking that thing of yours into me?' she demanded waspishly.

Shasa was stung by the unfairness of her accusation. 'You showed me how. I wouldn't have done it if you hadn't.'

'A fat lot of good that's going to do us.' She was weeping now. 'I wish we could just run away.'

The notion held a definite appeal for Shasa, and he discarded it only reluctantly. 'Come on,' he said, and boosted her up onto Prester John's back and then swung up behind her.

They saw the torches of the search parties down on the plain below them as they turned the shoulder of the mountain. There were headlights on the road also, moving slowly, obviously searching the verges, and faintly they heard the shouts of the searchers, calling for them as they moved about in the forest below.

'My Pa's going to kill me this time. He'll know what we've been doing,' she snuffled and sobbed and her self-pity irritated him. He had long ago given up trying to comfort her.

'How will he know?' he snapped. 'He wasn't there.'

'You don't think you were the first one I've done it with,' she demanded, seeking to injure him. 'I've done it with plenty of others, and Pa has caught me twice. Oh, he'll know all right.'

At the thought of her performing those strangely marvellous tricks of hers with others, Shasa felt a hot rush of jealousy which was gradually cooled by reason.

'Well,' he pointed out. 'If he knows about all the others, it isn't going to do you much good to try to put the blame on me.'

She had trapped herself and she let out another broken-hearted sob, and was still weeping theatrically when they met the search party coming on foot along the pipe track.

* * *

Shasa and Annalisa sat on opposite sides of the bungalow's drawing-room, instinctively keeping as far from each other as possible. As they heard the Daimler pull up outside in a flare of headlights and crunch of gravel, Annalisa began to weep again, snuffling and rubbing her eyes to work up a few more tears.

They heard Centaine's quick light tread across the verandah, followed by Twentyman-Jones' more deliberate storklike steps.

Shasa stood up and held his hands in front of him in the attitude of the penitent as Centaine stopped in the doorway. She was dressed in jodhpurs and riding-boots and a tweed hacking jacket, with a yellow scarf knotted at her throat. She was flushed, and relieved and furious as an avenging angel.

Annalisa saw her face and let out a howl of anguish, only half acting.

'Shut your mouth, girl,' Centaine told her quietly. 'Or I'll see you get good reason to blubber.' She turned to Shasa. 'Are either of you hurt?'

'No, Mater.' He hung his head.

'Prester John?'

'Oh, he's in good fettle.'

'So, that's it then.' She did not have to elaborate. 'Dr Twentyman-Jones, will you take this young lady down to her father? I have no doubt that he will know how to deal with her.' Centaine had spoken briefly to the father only an hour before, big and bald and paunchy with tattoos on his muscled arms, belligerent and red-eyed, reeking of cheap brandy and opening and closing his hairy paws as he mouthed his intentions towards his only daughter.

Twentyman-Jones took the girl by her wrist, pulled her to her feet, and led her snivelling towards the door. As he passed Centaine, her expression softened and she touched his arm. 'What ever would I do without you, Dr Twentyman-Jones?' she asked quietly.

'I suspect that you would get along very well on your own, Mrs Courtney, but I'm glad I could help.' He dragged Annalisa from the room and they heard the whirr of the Daimler's engine.

Centaine's expression hardened again and she turned back to Shasa. He fidgeted under her scrutiny.

'You've been disobedient,' she told him. 'I warned you away from the little *poule*.'

'Yes, Mater.'

'She's been with half the men on the mine. We'll have to take you to a doctor when we get back to Windhoek.'

He shuddered and glanced down at himself involuntarily at the thought of a host of disgusting microbes crawling over his most intimate flesh.

'Disobedience is bad enough, but what have you done that is truly unforgivable?' she demanded.

Shasa could think of at least a dozen trespasses without really extending himself.

'You've been stupid,' Centaine said. 'You've been stupid enough to get caught out. That is the worst sin. You've made a laughing stock of yourself with everybody on the mine. How will you ever be able to lead and command when you cheapen yourself like this?'

'I didn't think of that, Mater. I didn't think of anything much. It just all sort of happened.'

'Well, think of it now,' she told him. 'While you are taking a long hot bath with half a bottle Lysol in it, think hard about it. Goodnight.'

'Goodnight, Mater.' He came to her and after a moment she offered her cheek. 'I'm sorry, Mater.' He kissed her cheek. 'I'm sorry I made you ashamed of me.'

She wanted to throw her arms around him and pull his beautiful beloved head to her and hold him hard and tell him that she would never be ashamed of him.

'Goodnight, Shasa,' she said, standing cool and erect until he left the room and she heard his footsteps drag disconsolately down the passage. Then her shoulders slumped.

'Oh, my darling – oh my baby,' she whispered. Suddenly, for the first time in many years, she felt the need for an opiate. She crossed quickly to the massive stinkwood cabinet and poured cognac from one of the heavy decanters and took a mouthful. The spirit was peppery on her tongue and the fumes brought tears to her eyes. She swallowed it down and set the glass aside.

'That isn't going to help much,' she decided, and crossed to her desk. She sat down in the wingbacked buttoned leather chair and she felt small and frail and vulnerable. For Centaine, it was an alien emotion and it frightened her.

'It's happened,' she whispered. 'He is becoming a man.' Suddenly she hated the girl. 'The dirty little harlot. He isn't ready for that yet. Too early she has let the demon out, the demon of his de Thiry blood.' She was intimate with that same demon, for it had plagued her all her life. That wild passionate de Thiry blood.

'Oh my darling.' She was going to lose some part of him now – had already lost it, she realized. Loneliness came to her like a ravening beast that had lain in ambush for her all these years.

There had only been two men who might have assuaged that loneliness. Shasa's father had died in his frail machine of canvas and wood while she had stood by helplessly and watched him blacken and burn. The other man had placed himself beyond her reach for ever with one brutal senseless act. Michael Courtney and Lothar De La Rey – both dead to her now.

Since then there had been lovers, many lovers, brief transient affairs experienced only at the level of the flesh, a mere antidote for the boil of her blood. None of them had been allowed to pass into that deep place of her soul. But now the beast of loneliness burst through those guarded portals and laid waste her secret places.

'If only there was someone,' she lamented as she had done only once before in her life, when she lay upon the childbed on which she had given birth to Lothar De La Rey's gold-headed bastard. 'If only there was somebody I could love and who would love me in return.'

She leaned forward in the big leather chair and picked up the silver-framed photograph, the photograph that she carried with her wherever she travelled, and studied the face of the young man in the centre of the group of fliers. For the first time she realized that over the years the picture had faded and yellowed and the features of Michael Courtney, Shasa's father, had blurred. She stared at the handsome young face and tried desperately to make the picture clearer and crisper in her own memory, but it seemed to smear and recede even further from her.

'Oh Michel,' she whispered. 'It was all so long ago. Forgive me. Please forgive me. I have tried to be strong and brave. I've tried for your sake and the sake of your son, but – '

She set the frame back upon the desk and crossed to the window. She stared out into the darkness. 'I'm going to lose my baby,' she thought. 'And then one day I will be alone and old and ugly – and I'm afraid.' She found she was shivering, hugging her own arms, but then her reaction was swift and unequivocal.

'There is no time for weakness and self-pity on the journey that you have chosen.' She steeled herself, standing small and erect and alone in the silent darkened house. 'You have to go on. There is no turning back, no faltering, you have to go on to the end.'

* * *

'Where is Stoffel Botha?' Shasa demanded of the mill house supervisor when the mine hooter blew to signal the beginning of the lunch hour. 'Why isn't he here?'

'Who knows?' The supervisor shrugged. 'I had a note from the main office saying he wasn't coming. They didn't tell me why. Perhaps he has been fired. I don't know. I don't care – he was a cocky little bastard, anyway.' And for the rest of the shift Shasa tried to suppress his feeling of guilt by concentrating on the run of ore through the thundering rollers.

When the final hooter blew, and the cry of *Shahile!* 'It has struck!' was shouted from one gang of black labourers to the next, Shasa mounted Prester John and turned his head towards the avenue of cottages in which Annalisa's family lived. He knew he was risking his mother's wrath, but a defiant sense of chivalry urged him on. He had to find out how much damage and unhappiness he had caused.

However, at the gates of the mill house he was distracted.

Moses, the boss-boy from the weathering grounds, stepped in front of Prester John and took his head.

'I see you, Good Water,' he greeted Shasa in his soft deep voice.

'Oh Moses.' Shasa smiled with pleasure, his other troubles forgotten for the moment. 'I was going to visit you.'

'I have brought your book.' The Ovambo handed the thick copy of *History of England* up to him.

'You couldn't possibly have read it,' Shasa protested. 'Not so soon. It took even me months.'

'I will never read it, Good Water. I am leaving the H'ani Mine. I go with the trucks to Windhoek tomorrow morning.'

'Oh no!' Shasa swung down out of the saddle and gripped his arm. 'Why do you want to go, Moses?' Shasa feigned ignorance out of a sense of his guilt and complicity.

'It is not for me to want or not to want.' The tall boss-boy shrugged. 'Many men are leaving on the trucks tomorrow. Doctela has chosen them, and the lady your mother has explained the reason and given us a month's wages. A man like me does not ask questions, Good Water.' He smiled, a sad bitter grimace. 'Here is your book.'

'Keep it.' Shasa pushed it back. 'It is my gift to you.'

'Very well, Good Water. I will keep it to remind me of you. Stay in peace.' He turned away.

'Moses – ' Shasa called him back and then could find nothing to say. He thrust out his hand impulsively and the Ovambo stepped back from it. A white man and a black man did not shake hands.

'Go in peace,' Shasa insisted, and Moses glanced around almost furtively before he accepted the grip. His skin was strangely cool. Shasa wondered if all black skin was like that.

'We are friends,' Shasa said, prolonging the contact. 'We are, aren't we?'

'I do not know.'

'What do you mean?'

'I do not know if it is possible for us to be friends.' Gently he freed his hand and turned away. He did not look back at Shasa as he skirted the security fence and went down to the compound.

* * *

The convoy of heavy trucks ground across the plains, keeping open intervals to avoid the dust thrown up by the preceding vehicle. The dust rose in a feathery spray, high in the still heated air like the yellow smoke from a bush fire burning on a wide front.

Gerhard Fourie, in the lead truck, slumped at the wheel with his belly hanging into his lap; it had forced open the buttons of his shirt, exposing the hairy pit of his navel. Every few seconds he glanced up from the road to the rearview mirror above his head.

The back of the truck was piled with the baggage and furniture of the families, both black and white, that had been laid off from the mine. On top of this load were perched the unfortunate owners. The women had knotted scarves over their hair for the dust; they clutched their young children as the trucks bounced and swayed over the uneven tracks. The elder children had made nests for themselves amongst the baggage.

Fourie reached up and readjusted the mirror slightly, centring the image of the girl behind him. She was wedged between an old tea chest and a shabby suitcase of imitation leather. She had propped a blanket roll behind her back and she was dozing, her streaky blonde head nodding and lolling to the truck's motion. One knee was slightly raised, her short skirt rucked up and as she fell asleep so her knee dropped to one side and Fourie caught a glimpse of her underpants, patterned with pink roses, wedged between those smooth young thighs. Then the girl jerked awake and closed her legs and rolled on her side.

Fourie was sweating, not merely from the heat; drops of it glinted in the dark unshaven stubble that covered his jowls. He took the stub of cigarette from between his lips with shaky fingers and inspected it. Saliva had soaked through the ricepaper and stained it with yellow tobacco juice. He flicked it out of the side window and lit another, driving with one hand and watching the mirror, waiting for the girl to move again. He had sampled that young flesh, he knew how sweet and warm and available it was, and he wanted it again with a sickness of desire. He was prepared to take any risk for just another taste of it.

Ahead of him the clump of grey camel-thorn trees swam out of the heat mirage. He had travelled this road so often that the journey had its landmarks and rituals. He checked his pocket watch and grunted. They were twenty minutes late on this stage. But then the trucks were all overloaded with this throng of newly unemployed and their pathetic possessions.

He pulled the truck off the track beside the trees and climbed stiffly out onto the running-board and shouted: 'All right, everybody. Pinkle pause. Women on the left, men on the right. Anybody who isn't back in ten minutes gets left behind.'

He was the first back to the truck, and he busied himself at the left-hand rear wheel, making a show of checking the valve but watching for the girl.

She came out from amongst the trees, smoothing her skirts. She looked petulant and hot and grubby with floury dust. But when she saw Fourie watching her, she tossed her head and swung her tight little buttocks and ostentatiously ignored him.

'Annalisa,' he whispered, as she raised one bare foot to climb over the tailboard of the truck beside him.

'Your mother's, Gerhard Fourie!' she hissed back at him. 'You just leave me alone, or I'll tell my Pa!'

At any other time she might have responded more amiably, but her thighs and buttocks and the small of her back were still criss-crossed with purple weals from where her father had lambasted her. Temporarily she had lost interest in the male sex.

'I want to talk to you,' Fourie insisted.

'Talk, ha! I know what you want.'

'Meet me outside the camp tonight,' he pleaded.

'Your bollocks in a barrel.' She jumped up into the truck and his stomach turned over as he saw the full length of those slim brown legs.

'Annalisa. I'll give you money.' He was desperate; the sickness was burning him up.

Annalisa paused and looked down at him thoughtfully. His offer was a revelation that opened a chink into a new world of fascinating possibilities. Up to that moment it had never occurred to her that a man might give her money to do something which she enjoyed more than eating or sleeping.

'How much?' she asked with interest.

'A pound,' he offered.

It was a great deal of money, more than she had ever had in her hand at any one time, but her mercenary instinct was aroused, she wanted to see how far this could be taken. So she tossed her head and flounced, watching him out of the corner of her eye.

'Two pounds,' Fourie whispered urgently, and Annalisa's spirits soared. Two whole pounds! She felt bold and pretty and borne along by good fortune. The stripes across her back and legs were fading. She slanted her eyes in that sly knowing expression that maddened him and she saw the sweat start on his chin and his lower lip trembled.

It emboldened her even further, and she drew breath and held it, and then whispered daringly: 'Five pounds!' She ran the tip of her tongue around her lips, shocked by her own courage in naming such an enormous sum. It was almost as much as her father earned in a week.

Fourie blanched and wavered. 'Three,' he blurted, but she sensed how close he was to agreement and she drew back affronted.

'You are a smelly old man.' She filled her voice with scorn and turned away.

'All right! All right!' he capitulated. 'Five pounds.' She grinned at him victoriously. She had discovered and entered a new world of endless riches and pleasure.

She put the tip of her finger in her mouth. 'And if you want that too, it will cost you another pound.' There were no limits to her daring now.

* * *

The moon was only days from full and it washed the desert with molten platinum, while the shadows along the ravine walls were leaden blue smudges. The camp sounds carried faintly along the ravine, somebody was chopping firewood, a bucket clanged and the women's voices at the cooking fires were like bird sounds heard from afar. Closer at hand a pair of prowling jackal cried, the odours from the cooking pots exciting them into their wild, wailing, almost agonized chorus.

Fourie squatted against the wall of the ravine and lit a cigarette, watching the ravine along which the girl must come. The flare of the match illuminated his fleshy unshaven features and he was so intent that he was totally unaware of the predatory eyes that watched him out of the blue moon shadows close by. His whole existence centred on the arrival of the girl and already he was breathing with eager little grunts of anticipation.

She was like a wraith in the moonlight, silvery and ethereal, and he heaved himself to his feet and crushed out the cigarette.

'Annalisa!' he called, his voice low and quivering with the need of her.

She stopped just out of reach before him, and when he lunged for her she danced away lightly and laughed with a mocking tinkle.

'Five pounds, *Meneer*,' she reminded him, and drew nearer as he fumbled the crumpled bank notes out of his back pocket. She took them and held them up to the moon. Then, satisfied, tucked them away in her clothing and stepped boldly up to him.

He seized her around the waist and covered her mouth with his wet lips. She

broke away at last, laughing breathlessly, and held his wrist as he reached under her skirt.

'Do you want the other pound's worth?'

'It's too much,' he panted. 'I haven't got that much.'

'Ten shillings, then,' she offered, and touched the front of his body with a small cunning hand.

'Half a crown,' he gasped. 'That's all I have got.' And she stared at him, still touching him, and saw she could get no more out of him.

'All right, give it to me,' she agreed, and hid the coin before she went down on her knees in front of him as though for his blessing. He placed both hands on her curly sun-streaked head and drew her towards him, bowing his head over her and then closing his eyes.

Something hard was thrust into his ribs from behind with such force that the wind was driven from his lungs and a voice grated in his ear.

'Tell the little bitch to disappear.' The voice was low and dangerous and dreadfully familiar.

The girl leaped to her feet, wiping her mouth on the back of her hand. She stared for an instant over Fourie's shoulder with wide terrified eyes, then whirled and raced up the ravine towards the camp on long flying legs.

Fourie fumbled clumsily with his clothing and turned to face the man who stood behind him with the Mauser rifle pointed at his belly.

'De La Rey!' he blurted.

'Were you expecting somebody else?'

'No! No!' Fourie shook his head wildly. 'It's just – so soon.' Since last they had met Fourie had had time to repent of their bargain. Cowardice had won the long battle over avarice, and because he wanted it so he had convinced himself that Lothar De La Rey's scheme was like so many others that he had dreamed about, merely one of those fantasies with which those for ever doomed to poverty and futile labour consoled themselves.

He had expected, and hoped, never to hear of Lothar De La Rey again. But now he stood before him, tall and deadly with his head shining like a beacon in the moonlight and topaz lights glinting in those leopard eyes.

'Soon!' Lothar asked. 'So soon? It's been weeks, my old and dear friend. It all took longer to arrange then I expected.' Then Lothar's voice hardened as he asked, 'Have you taken the diamond shipment into Windhoek yet?'

'No, not yet – ' Fourie broke off, and silently reviled himself. That would have been his escape. He should have said 'Yes! I took it in myself last week.' But it was done, and miserably he hung his head and concentrated on fastening the last buttons of his breeches. Those few words spoken too hastily might yet cost him a lifetime in prison and he was afraid.

'When will the shipment go in?' Lothar placed the muzzle of the Mauser under Fourie's chin and lifted his face to the moon. He wanted to watch the man's eyes. He did not trust him.

'They have delayed it. I don't know how long. I heard some rumour that they have to send in a big package of stones.'

'Why?' Lothar asked softly, and Fourie shrugged.

'I just heard it will be a big package.'

'As I warned you, it's because they are going to close the mine.' Lothar watched his face carefully. He sensed that the man was wavering. He had to steel him. 'It will be the last shipment, and then you will be out of work. Just like those poor bastards you have on your trucks.'

Fourie nodded glumly. 'Yes, they have fired them.'

'It wil be you next, old friend. And you told me what a good family man you are, how much you love your family.'

'*Ja.*'

'Then no more money to feed your children, no money to clothe them, not even a few pounds to pay the little girls for their clever tricks.'

'Man, you mustn't talk like that.'

'You do what we agreed and there will be all the little girls you want, any way you want them.'

'Don't talk like that. It's dirty, man.'

'You know the arrangements. You know what to do just as soon as they tell you when the shipment is going in.'

Fourie nodded but Lothar insisted. 'Tell me about it. Repeat it to me.' And he listened while Fourie reluctantly recited his instructions, correcting him once on a detail, and at last smiled with satisfaction.

'Don't let us down, old friend. I do not like to be disappointed.' He leaned close to Fourie and stared into his eyes, then quite suddenly turned and slipped away into the moon shadows.

Fourie shuddered and stumbled away up the ravine towards the camp like a drunkard. He was almost there before he remembered that the girl had his money but had not completed her part of the bargain. He wondered if he could talk her into doing so at the next camp, and then morosely decided that his chances were not very good. Yet somehow it didn't seem so urgent now. The ice that Lothar De La Rey had injected into his blood seemed to have settled in his loins.

* * *

They rode through the open forest below the cliffs, and their mood was carefree and gay with anticipation of the days that lay ahead.

Shasa rode Prester John, with the 7mm Mannlicher sporting rifle in the leather scabbard under his left knee. It was a beautiful weapon, the butt and foregrip in choice selected walnut, and the blue steel engraved and inlaid with silver and pure gold: hunting scenes exquisitely rendered and Shasa's name scripted in precious metal. The rifle had been a fourteenth birthday present from his grandfather.

Centaine rode her grey stallion, a magnificent animal. His hide was marbled with black in a lacy pattern across his shoulders and croup, while his mane and muzzle and eye patches were also shiny jet black, in startling contrast to the snowy hide beneath. She called him Nuage, Cloud, after a stallion that her father had given her when she was a girl.

Centaine wore an Australian cattleman's wide-brimmed hat and a kudu-skin gilet over her shirt. There was a yellow silk scarf knotted loosely at her throat, and a sparkle in her eyes.

'Oh, Shasa, I feel like a schoolgirl playing hookey! We've got two whole days to ourselves.'

'Race you to the spring!' he challenged her, but Prester John was no match for Nuage and when they reached the spring Centaine had already dismounted and was holding the stallion's head to prevent him bloating himself with water.

They remounted and rode on deeper into the wilderness of the Kalahari. The further they went from the mine the less had been the intrusion of human presence, and the wild life more abundant and confident.

Centaine had been trained in the ways of the wild by the finest of all instructors, the wild Bushmen of the San, and she had lost none of her skills. It was not only the larger game that engaged her. She pointed out a pair of quaint little bat-eared foxes that Shasa would have missed. They were hunting grasshoppers in the sparse silver grass, pricking their enormous ears as they crept forward in a pantomime of stealth before the heroic leap onto their formidable prey. They laid their tell-tale ears against their fluffy necks and flattened against the earth as the horses passed.

They startled a yellow sand-cat from an ant-bear burrow, and so intent was the big cat on its escape that it ran headlong into the sticky yellow web of a crab spider. The animal's comical efforts to wipe the web from its face with both front paws while at the same time continuing its flight had them both reeling in the saddle.

Once in the middle of the afternoon they spotted a herd of stately gemsbok trotting in single file across the horizon. They held their heads high, the long straight slender horns transformed by distance and the angle of view into the single straight horn of the unicorn. The mirage turned them into strange long-legged monsters and then swallowed them up completely.

As the lowering sun painted the desert with shadow and fresh colour, Centaine picked out another small herd of springbok and pointed out a plump young ram to Shasa. 'We are only half a mile from camp and we need our dinner.'

Eagerly Shasa drew the Mannlicher from its scabbard.

'Cleanly!' she cautioned him. It troubled her a little to see how he enjoyed the chase.

She stayed back and watched him dismount. Using Prester John as a stalking horse, Shasa angled in towards the herd. Prester John understood his role and kept himself between Shasa and the game, even pausing to graze when the springbok became restless, only moving closer when they had settled down again.

At two hundred paces Shasa squatted and braced his elbows on his knees, and Centaine felt a rush of relief as the springbok ram dropped instantly to the shot. She had once seen Lothar De La Rey gut shoot one of the lovely gazelle. The memory still haunted her.

When she rode up she saw that Shasa had hit the animal cleanly behind the shoulder, and the bullet had passed through the heart. She watched critically as Shasa dressed out the game the way Sir Garry had taught him.

'Keep all the offal,' she told him. 'The servants love the tripes.' So he wrapped it in the wet skin and bundled the carcass up onto Prestor John's back and tied it behind the saddle.

The camp was at the foot of the hills, below a seep well in the cliff which provided water. The previous day Centaine had sent three servants ahead with the pack horses and the camp was comfortable and secure.

They dined on grilled kebabs of liver, kidneys and heart, larded with laces of fat from the springbok's belly cavity. Then they sat late at the fire, drinking coffee that tasted of wood smoke, talking quietly and watching the moon rise.

In the dawn they rode out, bundled in sheepskin jackets against the chill.

They had not gone a mile before Centaine pulled up Nuage's head and leaned far out of the saddle to examine the earth.

'What is it, Mater?' Shasa was always sensitive to every nuance of her moods, and he saw how excited she was.

'Come quickly, *chéri*.' She pointed out the tracks in the soft earth. 'What do you make of these?'

Shasa swung down from the saddle and stooped over the sign.

'Human beings?' He was puzzled. 'But so small. Children?' He looked up at her, and her shining expression gave him the clue.

'Bushmen!' he exclaimed. 'Wild Bushmen.'

'Oh yes,' she laughed. 'A pair of hunters. They are after a giraffe. Look! Their tracks are overlaying those of the quarry.'

'Can we follow them, Mater? Can we?' Now Shasa was as excited as she was.

Centaine agreed. 'Their spoor is only a day old. We can catch them if we hurry.'

Centaine rode on the spoor with Shasa trailing behind her, careful not to spoil the sign. He had never seen her work like this, taking it at a canter over the bad places where even his sharp young eyes could see nothing.

'Look, a Bushman toothbrush.' She pointed to a fresh twig, the end chewed to a brush, that lay discarded beside the spoor and they rode on.

'This is where they first spotted the giraffe.'

'How do you know that?'

'They have strung their bows. There are the marks of the butts.' The little men had pressed the tips of their bows against the earth to arch them.

'Look, Shasa, now they have begun stalking.'

He could see no change in the spoor and said so.

'Shorter and stealthier paces – weight forward on the toes,' she explained, and then, a few hundred paces farther, 'Here they went down on their bellies, snake-crawling in for the kill. Here they went up on their knees to loose their arrows, and here they leapt to their feet to watch them strike.' Twenty paces farther on she exclaimed, 'See how close they were to the quarry. This is where the giraffe felt the sting of the barbs and started to gallop – look how the hunters followed at a run, waiting for the poison of the arrows to take effect.'

They galloped along the line of the chase until Centaine rose in the stirrups and pointed ahead.

'Vultures!'

Four or five miles ahead the blue of the heavens was dusted with a fine cloud of black specks. The cloud turned in slow vortex, high above the earth.

'Slowly now, *chéri*,' Centaine cautioned him. 'It could be dangerous if we frighten and panic them.'

They brought the horses down to a walk and rode up slowly to the site of the kill.

The giraffe's huge carcass, partly flayed and dismembered, lay on its side. Against the surrounding thorn bushes crude sunshelters of thatch had been erected, and the bushes were festooned with strips of meat and ribbons of entrails set out to dry in the sun, the branches bowed under their weight.

The area was widely trodden by small feet.

'They have brought the women and children to help cut up and carry,' Centaine said.

'Phew! It pongs terribly!' Shasa screwed up his nose. 'Where are they, anyway?'

'Hiding.' Centaine said. 'They saw us coming, probably from five miles away.' She stood up in the stirrups and swept the broad-brimmed hat from her head to show her face more clearly, and she called out in a strange guttural clicking tongue, turning slowly and repeating the message to every quarter of the silent brooding desert that encompassed them.

'It's creepy.' Shasa shivered involuntarily in the bright sunlight. 'Are you sure they are still here?'

'They're watching us. They aren't in a hurry.'

Then a man rose out of the earth so close to them that the stallion shied and nodded his head nervously. The man wore only a loincloth of animal skin. He was a small man, yet perfectly formed, with elegant and graceful limbs built for running. Hard muscle lay flat down his chest and sculpted his naked belly into the same ripples that the ebb tide leaves on a sandy beach.

He held his head proudly, and though he was cleanshaven, it was evident he was in the full flowering of his manhood. His eyes had a Mongolian slant to the corners and his skin glowed with a marvellous amber colour seeming almost translucent in the sunlight.

He lifted his right hand in a greeting and a sign of peace and he called, birdlike and high, 'I see you, Nam Child,' using Centaine's Bushman name, and she cried aloud for joy.

'I see you also, Kwi!'

'Who is with you?' the bushman demanded.

'This is my son, Good Water. As I told you when first we met, he was born in the holy place of your people and O'wa was his adopted grandfather and H'ani was his grandmother.'

Kwi, the Bushman, turned and called out into the empty desert. 'This is the truth, oh people of the San. This woman is Nam Child, our friend, and the boy is he of the legend. Greet them!'

Out of the seemingly barren earth against which they had hidden rose the little golden people of the San. With Kwi there were twelve of them; two men, Kwi and his brother Fat Kwi, their wives and the naked children. They had hidden with all the art of wild creatures, but now they crowded forward chirruping and clicking and laughing and Centaine swung down from the saddle to meet and embrace them, greeting each of them by name and finally picking up two of the toddlers and holding one on each hip.

'How do you know them so well, Mater?' Shasa wanted to know.

'Kwi and his brother are related to O'wa, your adopted Bushman grandfather. I first met them when you were very small and we were developing the H'ani Mine. These are their hunting grounds.'

They passed the rest of that day with the clan, and when it was time to leave Centaine gave each of the women a handful of brass 7mm cartidges and they shrieked with joy and danced their thanks. The cartridges would be strung with ostrich shell beads into necklaces that would make them the envy of every other San woman they met in their wandering. Shasa gave Kwi his ivory-handled hunting knife and the little man tried the edge with his thumb and grunted with wonder as the skin parted, and he displayed the bloody thumb proudly to each of the women.

'What a weapon I have now.'

Fat Kwi got Centaine's belt, and they left him studying the reflection of his own face in the polished brass buckle.

'If you wish to visit us again,' Kwi called after him, 'we will be at the mongongo tree grove near O'chee Pan until the rains break.'

'They are so happy with so little,' Shasa said, looking back at the tiny dancing figures.

'They are the happiest people in this earth,' Centaine agreed. 'But I wonder for how much longer.'

'Did you truly live like that, Mater?' Shasa asked. 'Like a Bushman? Did you really wear skins and eat roots?'

'So did you, Shasa. Or rather you wore nothing at all just like one of those grubby little scamps.'

He frowned with the effort of memory. 'Sometimes I dream about a dark place, like a cave with water that smoked.'

'That was the thermal spring in which we bathed, and in which I found the first diamond of the H'ani Mine.'

'I would like to visit it again, Mater.'

'That isn't possible.' He saw her mood change. 'The spring was in the centre of the H'ani pipe, in what is now the main excavation of the mine. We dug it out and destroyed the spring.' They rode on in silence for a while. 'It was the holy place of the San – and yet, strangely, they did not seem to resent it when we,' she hesitated over the word and then said it firmly, 'when we desecrated it.'

'I wonder why. I mean if some strange race turned Westminster Abbey into a diamond mine!'

'A long time ago I discussed it with Kwi. He said that the secret place belonged not to them but the spirits and if the spirits had not wanted it so they would not have let it happen. He said the spirits had lived there so long that perhaps they were bored and wished to move on to another home, just like the San do.'

'I still cannot imagine you living like one of the San women, Mater. Not you. I mean it just goes beyond imagination.'

'It was hard,' she said softly. 'It was hard beyond the telling of it, beyond imagination – and yet without that tempering and toughening I would not be what I am now. You see, Shasa, out here in the desert when I had almost reached the breaking point I swore on oath. I swore that I, and my son, would never again be so deprived. I swore that we would never again have to suffer those terrible extremes.'

'But I was not with you then.'

'Oh yes,' she nodded. 'Oh yes, you were. I carried you within me on the Skeleton Coast and through the heat of the dune lands and you were part of that oath when I made it. We are creatures of the desert, my darling, and we will survive and prosper when others fail and fall. Remember that. Remember it well, Shasa, my darling.'

* * *

Early the next morning they left the servants to break camp, load the pack horses and follow them as they turned their horses regretfully in the direction of the H'ani Mine. At noon they rested under a camel-thorn tree, lying against their saddles and lazily watching the drab little weavers abover thier heads

busily adding to their communal nest that was already the size of an untidy haystack. When the heat went out of the sun, they caught the hobbled horses, upsaddled and rode along the base of the hills.

Shasa straightened in the saddle suddenly and shaded his eyes with one hand as he looked up at the hills.

'What is it, *chéri*?'

He had recognized the rocky gorge to which Annalisa had led him.

'Something is worrying you,' Centaine insisted, and Shasa felt a sudden urge to lead his mother up the gorge to the shrine of the witch of the mountain. He was about to speak when he remembered his oath and he stopped, teetering uneasily on the brink of betrayal.

'Don't you want to tell me?' She was watching the struggle on his face.

'Mater doesn't count. She's like me. It's not as though I were telling a stranger,' he justified himself and burst out before his conscience could overtake him. 'There is the skeleton of a Bushman in the gorge up there, Mater. Would you like me to show you?'

Centaine paled under her suntan and stared at him. 'A Bushman?' she whispered. 'How do you know it's a Bushman?'

'The hair is still on the skull – little Bushman peppercorn curls, just like Kwi and his clan.'

'How did you find it?'

'Anna – ' he broke off and flushed with guilt.

'The girl showed you?' Centaine helped him.

'Yes.' He nodded and hung his head.

'Can you find it again?' Centaine's colour had returned, and she seemed eager and excited as she leaned across and tugged his sleeve.

'Yes, I think so, I marked the place.' He pointed up the cliffs. 'That notch in the rocks and that cleft shaped like an eye.'

'Show me, Shasa,' she ordered.

'We will have to leave the horses and go up on foot.'

The climb was onerous, the heat in the gorge fierce and the hooked thorns snatched at them as they toiled upwards.

'It must be about here.' Shasa climbed up on one of the tumbled boulders and orientated himself. 'Perhaps just a little more to the left. Look for a pile of rock with a mimosa growing below it. There is a branch covering a small niche. Let's spread out and search.

They picked their way slowly up the gorge, moving a little apart to cover more ground and keeping in touch with whistles and calls when scrub and rocks separated them.

Centaine did not respond to Shasa's whistle, and he stopped and repeated it, cocking his head for her reply and feeling a prickle of concern in the silence.

'Mater, where are you!'

'Here!' Her voice was faint, wracked with pain or some deep emotion and he scrambled over the rock to reach her.

She stood small and forlorn in the sunlight, holding her hat against the front of her hips. Moisture sparkled on her cheeks. He thought it was sweat, until he saw the soft slow slide of tears down her face.

'Mater?' He moved up behind her and realized that she had found the shrine.

She had drawn the screening branch aside. The small circle of glass jars was still in place, the floral offering brown and withered.

'Annalisa said the skeleton was a witch,' Shasa breathed with superstitious

awe as he stared over Centaine's shoulder at the pathetic pile of bones and the small neat white skull that surmounted it.

Centaine shook her head, unable to speak.

'She said the witch guarded the mountain and that she would grant a wish.'

'H'ani.' Centained choked on the name. 'My beloved old mother.'

'Mater!' Shasa seized her shoulders and steadied her as she swayed on her feet. 'How do you know?'

Centaine leaned against his chest for support but did not reply.

'There could be hundreds of Bushman skeletons in the caves and gorges,' he went on lamely, and she shook her head vehemently.

'How can you be certain?'

'It's her.' Centaine's voice was blurred with grief. 'It's H'ani, the chipped canine tooth, the design of ostrich shell beads on her loincloth.' Shasa had not noticed the scrap of dry leather decorated with beads that lay beneath the pile of bones, half buried in dust. 'I don't even need that proof. I know it's her. I just know it.'

'Sit down, Mater.' He lowered her to sit on one of the lichen-covered boulders.

'I'm all right now. It was just such a shock. I've searched for her so often over the years. I knew where she must be.' She looked around her vaguely. 'O'wa's body must be somewhere close at hand.' She looked up at the cliff that seemed to hang over them like a cathedral roof. 'They were up there trying to escape when he gunned them down. They must have fallen close together.'

'Who shot them, Mater?'

She drew a deep breath, but even then her voice shook as she said his name. 'Lothar. Lothar De La Rey!'

* * *

For an hour longer they searched the bottom and sides of the gorge, looking for the second skeleton.

'It's no good.' Centaine gave up at last. 'We will never find him. Let him lie undisturbed, Shasa, as he has all these years.'

They climbed down to the little rock shrine, and as they returned they plucked the wild flowers along the way.

'My first instinct was to gather her remains and give them a decent burial,' Centaine whispered as she knelt in front of the shrine, 'but H'ani wasn't a Christian. These hills were her holy place. She will be at peace here.'

She arranged the flowers with care and then sat back on her heels.

'I'll see that you are never disturbed, my beloved old grandmother, and I will come to visit you again.' She stood up and took Shasa's hand. 'She was the finest, gentlest person I have ever known,' she said softly. 'And I loved her so.' Still hand in hand they went down to where they had tethered the horses.

They did not speak again on the ride home, and the sun had set and the servants were anxious by the time they reached the bungalow.

* * *

At breakfast the next morning Centaine was brisk and brittly cheerful, though there were dark bruised smudges beneath her eyes and the lids were puffed from weeping.

'This is our last week before we must return to Cape Town.'

'I wish we could stay here for ever.'

'For ever is a long time. You have school waiting for you, and I have my duties. We will come back here, you know that.' He nodded and she went on. 'I have arranged for you to spend this last week working in the washing plant and sorting rooms. You'll enjoy that. I guarantee it.'

She was right, as usual. The washing plant was a pleasant place. The flow of water over the wiffle boards cooled the air, and after the unremitting thunder of the mill plant it was blessedly quiet. The atmosphere in the long brick room was like the cathedral calm of a holy place, for here the worship of Mammon and Adamant reached its climax.

Shasa watched with fascination as the crushings from the mill plant were carried in on the slowly moving conveyor belt. The oversize rubble had been screened off and returned for another crushing under the spinning rollers. These were the fines. They dropped from the end of the moving belt into the puddling tank, and from there were pushed by the agitating arms of the revolving sweep down the sloping boards of the wiffle table.

The lighter materials floated away and were run off to the waste dump. The heavier gravels, containing the diamonds, were carried on through a series of similiar ingenious separating devices until there remained only the concentrates, one thousandth part of the original gravels.

These were washed over the grease drums. The drums revolved slowly, each of them coated with a thick layer of heavy yellow grease. The wet gravel flowed easily over the surface, but the diamonds were dry. One of the diamond's peculiar qualities is its unwettability. Soak it, boil it as long as you wish, but it remains dry. Once the dry surface of the precious stones touched the grease they stuck to it like insects to fly paper.

The grease drums were locked behind heavy bars and a white supervisor sat overlooking each of them, watching them constantly. Shasa peered through the bars for the first time and saw the small miracle occur only a few inches from his nose: a wild diamond captured and tamed like some marvellous creature of the desert. He actually witnessed the moment when it flowed out of the upper bin in a wet porridge of gravel, and he saw it touch the grease and adhere precariously to the slick yellow surface, causing a tiny V-shaped disturbance to the flow like a rock in the ebb of the tide. It moved, seeming to lose its grip in the grease for an instant, and Shasa wanted to thrust out his hand and seize it before it was for ever lost, but the gaps between the steel bars were too narrow. Then the diamond stuck fast and breasted the gentle flood of gravel, sitting up proudly, dry and transparent like a blister on the yellow skin of a gigantic reptile. It left him with a feeling of awe, the same feelings as he had experienced when he witnessed his mare Celeste give birth to her first foal.

He spent his entire morning passing from one to the other of the huge yellow drums and then back again down the line, watching the diamonds sticking on the grease more and more thickly with each hour that passed.

At noon the washroom manager came down the line with his four white assistants, more than were necessary, other than to watch each other and forestall any opportunity for theft. With a broad-bladed spatula they scraped

the grease from the drums and collected it in the boiling pot, then meticulously spread each drum with a fresh coating of yellow grease.

In the locked de-greasing room at the far end of the building the manager placed the steel pot on the spirit stove and boiled off the grease until finally he was left with a pot half full of diamonds, and Dr Twentyman-Jones was there to weigh each stone separately and record it in the leatherbound recovery book.

'Of course you will notice, Master Shasa, that none of these stones is smaller than half a carat.'

'Yes, sir.' Shasa had not thought of that. 'What happened to the smaller ones.'

'The grease table is not infallible – indeed the stones must have a certain minimum weight to get them to adhere. The others, even a few large valuable stones, pass across the table.'

He led Shasa back to the washroom and showed him the trough of wet gravel that had survived the journey over the drums. 'We drain all the water and reuse it. Out here water is precious stuff, as you know. Then all the gravel has to be hand picked.' As he spoke two men emerged from the door at the end of the room and each scooped a bucket of gravel from the trough.

Shasa and Twentyman-Jones followed them back through the doorway into a long narrow room well lit with glass skylights and high windows. A single long table ran the length of the room, its top clad in a polished metal sheet.

On each side of the table sat rows of women. They looked up as the two men entered and Shasa recognized the wives and daughters of many of the white workers as well as those of the black boss-boys. The white women sat altogether nearest the door and, with a decent and proper distance between them, and the black women sat separated at the far end of the room.

The bucket boys dumped the damp gravel onto the metal table top and the women transferred their attention back to it. Each had a pair of forceps in one hand and a flat wooden scoop in the other. They drew a little of the gravel towards them, spread it with the scoop and then picked over it swiftly.

'It's a job at which the women excel,' Twentyman-Jones explained as they passed down the line, watching over the stooped shoulders of the women. 'They have the patience and the sharp eyes and the dexterity that men lack.'

Shasa saw that they were picking out tiny opaque stones, some as small as sugar grains, others the size of small green peas, from the duller mass of gravel.

'Those are our bread and butter stones,' Twentyman-Jones remarked. 'They are used in industry. The jewellery grade stones that you saw in the grease room are the strawberry jam and the cream.'

When the mine hooter signalled the end of the day shift, Shasa rode down with Twentyman-Jones in the front seat of his Ford from the washing gear to the office block. On his lap he carried the small locked steel box in which was the day's recovery.

Centaine met them on the verandah of the administration building and led them into her office. 'Well, did you find it interesting?' she asked, and smiled at Shasa's hearty response.

'It was fascinating, Mater, and we got one real beauty. Thirty-six carats – it's a jolly great monster of a diamond!' He set the box on her desk and when Twentyman-Jones unlocked it he showed her the diamond as proudly as if he had mined it with his own hands.

'It's big,' Centaine agreed, 'but the colour isn't particularly good. There, hold it to the light. See, it's as brown as whisky and soda, and even with the

naked eye you can see the inclusions and flaws, those little black specks inside the stone and that tear through the middle.'

Shasa looked crestfallen that his stone was so denigrated and she laughed and turned to Twentyman-Jones. 'Let's show him some really good diamonds. Will you open the vault please, Dr Twentyman-Jones?'

Twentyman-Jones pulled out the bunch of keys from the fob pocket of his waistcoat and led Shasa down the passage to the steel grille door at the end. He opened it with his key and relocked it behind them before they went down the stairs to the underground vault. Even from Shasa he screened the lock with his body as he tumbled the combination and then used a second key before the thick green Chubb steel door swung ponderously aside and they went into the strongroom.

'The industrial-grade stones are kept in these canisters.' He touched them as he passed. 'But we keep the high-grade stuff separately.'

He unlocked the smaller steel door set in the rear wall of the vault and selected five numbered brown paper packages from the crowded shelf.

'These are our best stones.' He handed them to Shasa as a mark of his trust, and then they went back again, opening and re-locking each door as they passed through.

Centaine was waiting for them in her office, and when Shasa placed the packages in front of her she opened the first and gently spread the contents on her blotter.

'Golly gee!' Shasa goggled at the array of large stones glittering with a soapy sheen. 'They are gi-normous!'

'Let's ask Dr Twentyman-Jones to give us a dissertation,' Centaine suggested, and hiding his gratification behind a sombre countenance, he picked up one of the gem stones.

'Well, Master Shasa, here is a diamond in its natural crystalline formation, the octahedron of eight faces – count them. Here is another in a more complicated crystalline form, the dodecahedron of twelve faces, while these others are massive and uncrystallized. See how rounded and amorphous they are. Diamonds come in many guises.'

He laid each in Shasa's open palm, and not even his prim monotonous recital could dull the fascination of this shining treasure. 'The diamond has a perfect cleavage, or as we all it "grain", and can be split in all four directions, parallel to the octahedral crystal planes.'

'That's how the cutters cleave a stone before polishing,' Centaine cut in. 'During your next holidays I will take you to Amsterdam so you can see it done.'

'This rather greasy sheen will disappear when the stones are cut and polished.' Twentyman-Jones took over again, resenting her intrusion. 'Then all their fire will be revealed as their very high refractive power captures the light within and dispersive powers separate it into the spectral colours.'

'How much does this one weigh?'

'Forty-eight carats.' Centaine consulted the recovery book. 'But remember it may lose more than half its weight when it is cut and polished.'

'Then how much will it be worth?'

Centaine glanced at Twentyman-Jones.

'A great deal of money, Master Shasa.' Like the true lover of any beautiful object, gem or painting, horse or statue, he disliked placing a monetary value

upon it, so he hedged and returned to his lecture. 'Now I want you to compare the colours of these stones – '

Darkness fell outside the windows, but Centaine switched on the lights and they huddled over the small pile of stones for another hour, meeting question with answer and talking quietly and intently until at last Twentyman-Jones swept the stones back into their packages and stood up.

'"Thou hast been in Eden, the Garden of god;"' he quoted unexpectedly, '"every precious stone was thy covering, the sardius, topaz and diamond. . . . Thou wast upon the holy mountain of God; thou hast walked up and down in the midst of the stones of fire."' He stopped and looked self-conscious. 'Forgive me. I don't know what got into me.'

'Ezekiel?' Centaine asked, smiling fondly at him.

'Chapter 28, verses thirteen and fourteen.' He nodded, trying not to show how impressed he was by her knowledge. 'I'll put these away now.'

'Dr Twentyman-Jones,' Shasa stopped him. 'You didn't answer my question. How much are these stones worth?'

'Are you referring to the entire package?' He looked uncomfortable. 'Including the industrials and boart still in the strong room?'

'Yes, sir, how much sir?'

'Well, if De Beers accepts them at the same prices as our last package they will fetch considerably in excess of a million pounds sterling,' he replied sadly.

'A million pounds,' Shasa repeated, but Centaine saw in his expression that such a figure was incomprehensible to him, like the astronomical distances between stars that must be expressed in light years. He will learn, she thought, I will teach him.

'Remember, Shasa, that is not all profit. From that sum we will have to pay all the expenses of the mine over the past months before we can figure a profit. And even from that we have to give the tax collectors their pound of bleeding flesh.'

She stood up behind the desk and then held out her hand to prevent Twentyman-Jones leaving the room as an idea struck her.

'As you know Shasa and I are going in to Windhoek this coming Friday. Shasa has to return to school at the end of next week. I will take the diamonds into the bank with me in the Daimler – '

'Mrs Courtney!' Twentyman-Jones was horrified. 'I couldn't allow that. A million pounds' worth, good Lord alive. It would be criminally irresponsible of me to agree.' He broke off as he saw her expression alter; her mouth settled into that familiar stubborn shape and the lights of battle glinted in her eyes. He knew her so well, like his own daughter, and loved her as much, he realized that he had made the grievous error of challenging and forbidding her. He knew what her reaction must be and he sought desperately to head her off.

'I was thinking only of you, Mrs Courtney. A million pounds of diamonds would attract every scavenger and predator, every robber and footpad for a thousand miles around.'

'It was not my intention to bruit it abroad. I will not broadcast it a thousand miles around,' she said coldly.

'The insurance,' inspiration came to him at last, 'the insurance will not cover losses if the package is not sent in by armed convoy. Can you truly afford to take that chance – a loss of a million pounds of revenue against a few days saved?'

He had hit upon the one argument that might stop her. He saw her thinking

about it carefully, a chance of losing a million pounds against a minimal loss of face, and he sighed silently with relief when she shrugged.

'Oh, very well then, Dr Twentyman-Jones, have it your own way.'

* * *

Lothar had carved the road to H'ani Mine through the desert with his own hands and sprinkled every mile of it with the sweat of his brow. But that had been twelve years before, and now his memory of it had grown hazy. Still he remembered half a dozen points along the road which might serve his purpose.

From the stage camp where he had intercepted Gerhard Fourie's convoy they followed the rutted tracks south and west in the direction of Windhoek, travelling at night to save them from discovery by unexpected traffic on the road.

On the second morning, just as the sun was rising, Lothar reached one of the points he remembered and found it ideal. Here the road ran parallel to the deep rocky bed of a dry river before looping down through the deep cutting that Lothar had excavated to cross the riverbed and climb out the far side through another cutting.

He dismounted and walked out along the edge of the high bank to study it carefully. They could trap the diamond truck in the gut of the cutting, and block it with rocks rolled down from the top of the bank. There was certain to be water under the sand in the riverbed for the horses while they waited for the truck to show up; they would need to keep in condition for the long hard journey ahead. The riverbed would hide them.

Then again this was the remotest stretch of the road, it would take days for the police officers to be alerted and then to reach the ambush spot. He could certainly expect to establish an early and convincing lead, even if they chose the risky alternative of following him into the hard unrelenting wilderness across which he would retreat.

'This is where we will do it,' he told Swart Hendrick.

They set up their primitive camp in the sheer bank of the riverbed at the point where the telegraph line took the short cut across the loop in the road. The copper wires were strung over the riverbed from a pole on the near bank that was out of sight of the road.

Lothar climbed the pole and clipped on his taps to the main telegraph line, then led his wires down the pole, tacking them to the timber to avoid casual discovery, and then to his listening post in the dug-out that Swart Hendrick had burrowed into the bank of the river.

The waiting was monotonous, and Lothar chafed at being tied to the earphones of the telegraph tap but he could not afford to miss the vital message when it was flashed from the H'ani Mine, the message which would give him the exact departure time of the diamond truck. So during the dreary hot hours of daylight he had to listen to all the mundane traffic of the mine's daily business, and the distant operator's skills on the keyboard were such that they taxed his ability to follow and translate the rapid fire of dots and dashes that echoed in his earphones. He scribbled them into his notebook and afterwards translated the groups and jotted in the words between the lines. This was a

private telegraph line and therefore no effort had been made to encode the transmission, the traffic was in the clear.

During the day he was alone in the dugout. Swart Hendrick took Manfred and the horses out into the desert, ostensibly to hunt, but really to school and harden both the boy and the animals for the journey that lay ahead and to keep them out of sight of any traffic on the road.

For Lothar the long monotonous days were full of doubts and foreboding. There was so much that could go wrong, so many details that had to mesh perfectly to ensure success. There were weak links, and Gerhard Fourie was the weakest of these. The whole plain hinged on the man, and he was a coward, a man wasily distracted and discouraged.

'Waiting is always the worst time,' Lothar thought, and he remembered the fears that had assailed him on the eve of other battles and desperate endeavours. 'If you could just do it and have done with it, instead of having to sit out these dragging days.'

Suddenly the buzz of the call sign echoed in his earphones and he reached quickly for his notebook. The operator at the H'ani Mine began to transmit and Lothar's pencil danced across the pages as he kept up with him. There was a curt double tap of acknowledgement from the Windhoek station as the message ended, and Lothar let the earphones drop around his neck as he translated the groups:

For Pettifogger Prepare Juno's private coach for inclusion in the Sunday night express mailtrain to Cape Town Stop Juno arriving your end noon Sunday Ends Vingt

Pettifogger was Abraham Abrahams. Centaine must have selected the code name when she was annoyed with him, while *Vingt* was a pun on Twentyman-Jones' name; the French connotation suggested Centaine's influence again, but Lothar wondered who had selected Juno as Centaine Courtney's code name and grimaced at how appropriate it was.

So Centaine was leaving for Cape Town in her private coach. Somehow he felt guilty relief that she would not be close at hand when it happened, as though distance might lessen the shock for her. To reach Windhoek comfortably by noon on Sunday, Centaine must leave the H'ani Mine early on Friday, he calculated quickly; that would bring her to the cutting here on the riverbank on Saturday afternoon. Then he deducted a few hours from his estimate; she drove that Daimler like a demon.

He sat in the hot, stuffy little dugout and suddenly he felt an overwhelming desire to see her again, to have just a glimpse of her as she passed. 'We can use it as a rehearsal for the diamond truck,' he justified himself.

The Daimler came out of the shimmering distances like one of the whirling dust devils of the hot desert noons. Lothar saw the dust column from ten miles or more and signalled Manfred and Swart Hendrick into their positions at the top of the cutting.

They had dug shallow trenches at the key points, scattering the disturbed earth and letting the dry breeze smooth and blend it with the surroundings. Then they had screened the positions with branches of thorn scrub until Lothar was satisfied that they were undetectable from further than a few paces.

The rocks with which they would block both ends of the cutting had been gathered laboriously from the riverbed and poised on the edge of the bank. Lothar had taken great care to make them seem natural, and yet a single slash

with a knife across the rope that held the prop under the rock pile would send them tumbling down onto the narrow track at the bottom of the cutting.

This was a rehearsal, so none of them were wearing masks.

Lothar made one last hard scrutiny of the arrangements and then turned back to watch the swiftly approaching column of dust. It was already close enough for him to make out the tiny shape of the vehicle beneath it and hear the faint beat of its engine.

'She shouldn't drive like that,' he thought angrily. 'She'll kill herself.' He broke off and shook his head ruefully. 'I'm acting like a doting husband,' he realized. 'Let her break her damned neck, if that is what she wants.' Yet the idea of her death gave him a painful pang, and he crossed his fingers to turn the chance away. Then he crouched down in his trench and watched her through the screen of thorn branches.

The stately vehicle rocked and bounced over the tracks as it swung onto the loop of the road. The engine beat strengthened as Centaine changed down and then accelerated out of the turn, using power to pull out of the incipient skid as the floury dust clutched at the front wheels. It was done with élan, he thought grudgingly, as she hit the gears again and bore down on the head of the cutting at speed.

'Merciful God, is she going to take it at full bore?' he wondered. But at the last moment she cut the throttle and used the gearbox and the drag of the clinging dust to pull up at the top end of the cutting.

As she opened the door and stepped out onto the running-board with dust billowing around her, she was only twenty paces from where he lay, and he felt his heart banging against the earth. 'Can she still do this to me?' he wondered at himself. 'I should hate her. She has cheated and humiliated me and she has spurned my son and denied him a mother's love, and yet, and yet – ' He would not let the words form, and he tried deliberately to harden himself against her.

'She's not beautiful,' he told himself, as he studied her face; but she was much more. She was vital and vibrant, and there was an aura about her. 'Juno,' he recalled the code name, 'the goddess. Powerful and dangerous, mercurial and unpredictable, but endlessly fascinating and infinitely desirable.'

She looked directly towards him for a moment and he felt the strength and resolve flow out of him at the touch of those dark eyes, but she had not seen him and she turned away.

'We will walk down, *chéri*,' she called to the young man who stepped out of the opposite side of the Daimler, 'to see if the crossing is safe.'

Shasa seemed to have grown inches in the short time since Lothar had last seen him. They left the vehicle and went side by side down the track below where Lothar lay.

Manfred was in his trench at the bottom end of the cutting. He also watched the pair come down the track. The woman meant nothing to him. She was his mother but he did not know that and there was no instinctive response within him. She had never given him suck or even held him in her arms. She was a stranger, and he glanced at her without any emotion, then turned all his attention to the youth at her side.

Shasa's good looks offended him. 'He's pretty as a girl,' he thought, trying to scorn him, but he saw the new breadth to his rival's shoulders and fine muscle in his brown arms where he had rolled his sleeves high.

'I would like another bout with you, my friend.' The almost forgotten sting and humiliation of Shasa's left fist hurt again like a fresh wound, and he touched

his own face with his fingertips, scowling at the memory. 'Next time I won't let you do your little dance.' And he thought about how hard it had been to touch that pretty face, the way it had swayed and dipped just beyond his reach and he felt the frustration anew.

The couple reached the foot of the cutting below where Manfred lay and stood talking quietly for a while, then Shasa trudged out into the wide riverbed. The roadway through the sand had been corduroyed with branches of acacia, but the wheels of heavy trucks had broken them up. Shasa rearranged them, stamping the jagged ends into the sand.

While he worked Centaine turned back to the Daimler. There was a canvas water bag hanging on the bracket of the spare wheel and she unhooked it, raised it to her lips and took a mouthful. She gargled softly and then spat it into the dust. Then she slipped off the long white dustjacket that protected her clothing and unbuttoned her blouse. She soaked the yellow scarf and wiped the damp cloth down her throat and over her bosom, gasping with pleasure at the coolness on her skin.

Lothar wanted to turn his head away, but he could not; instead he stared at her. She wore nothing under the pale blue cotton blouse. The skin of her bosom was untouched by the sun, pale smooth and pearly as fine bone china. Her breasts were small, without any puckering and sagging, the tips pointed and still clear rose-coloured as those of a girl, not of a woman who had borne two sons. They bounced elastically as she drew the wet scarf over them and she looked down at them as she bathed the gleam of perspiration from them. Lothar moaned softly in his throat at the need of her that rose freshly and strongly from deep within him.

'All set, Mater,' Shasa called as he started back up the track, and quickly Centaine rebuttoned the front of her blouse.

'We've wasted enough time,' she agreed and slipped back behind the wheel of the Daimler. As Shasa slammed the door she gunned the big motor down the track, kicking up sand and splinters of acacia in a spray from the back wheels as she crossed the riverbed and flew up the far bank. The rumble of the engine dwindled into the desert silence and Lothar found he was trembling.

None of them moved for many minutes. It was Swart Hendrick who rose to his feet first. He opened his mouth to speak and then saw the expression on Lothar's face and remained silent. He scrambled down the bank and set off back towards the camp.

Lothar climbed down to the spot where the Daimler had stopped. He stood looking down at the damp earth where she had spat that mouthful of water. Her footprints were narrow and neat in the dust, and he felt a strong urge to stoop and touch them but suddenly Manfred spoke close behind him.

'He is a boxer,' he said, and it took Lothar a moment to realize that he was talking about Shasa. 'He looks a real sissy, but he can fight. You can't hit him.' He put up his fists and shadow-boxed, shuffling and dancing in the dust, imitating Shasa.

'Let's get back to the camp, out of sight,' Lothar said, and Manfred dropped his guard and thrust his hands into his pockets. Neither of them spoke again until they reached the dugout.

'Can you box, Pa?' Manfred asked. 'Can you teach me to box?'

Lothar smiled and shook his head. 'I always found it easier to kick a man between his legs,' he said. 'And then hit him with a bottle or a gun butt.'

'I would like to learn to box,' Manfred said. 'Someday I *will* learn.'

Perhaps the idea had been germinating there all along but suddenly it was a firm declaration. His father smiled indulgently and clapped him on the shoulder.

'Get out the flour bag,' he said. 'And I will teach you to bake soda bread instead.'

* * *

'Oh, Abe, you know how much I detest these soirées,' Centaine exclaimed irritably. 'Crowded rooms filled with tobacco smoke, exchanging inanities with strangers.'

'This man could be very valuable to know, Centaine. I will go further than that, he could be the most valuable friend you'll ever make in this territory.'

Centaine pulled a face. Abe was right, of course. The administrator was in fact the governor of the territory with wide executive powers. He was appointed by the Government of the Union of South Africa under the powers of mandate conferred on it by the Treaty of Versailles.

'I expect he is another pompous old bore, just like his predecessor was.'

'I haven't met him,' Abe admitted. 'He only arrived in Windhoek to take up his appointment within the last few days and will not be sworn in until the first of next month, but our new concessions in the Tsumeb area are in his desk at this moment, awaiting his signature.'

He saw her eyes shift and he pressed the advantage. 'Two thousand square miles of exclusive prospecting rights – worth a few hours of boredom?'

But she wouldn't give in that easily, and she counterattacked. 'We are due to hook onto the express that leaves this evening. Shasa must be back at Bishops on Wednesday morning.' Centaine stood up and paced the saloon of her coach, stopping to rearrange the roses in the vase above her desk so she did not have to look at him as he deflected her thrust.

'The next express leaves Tuesday evening. I have made arrangements for your coach to hook on. Master Shasa can leave on this evening's express, I have booked a coupé for him. Sir Garry and his wife are still at Weltevreden, they would meet him at Cape Town station. It needs only a telegraph to arrange it.' Abraham smiled across the saloon at Shasa. 'I'm sure, young man, you can make the journey without anyone to hold your hand?'

Abe was a cunning little devil, Centaine conceded, as Shasa rushed indignantly to take up the challenge.

'Of course I can, Mater. You stay here. It's important to meet the new administrator. I can get home on my own. Anna will help me pack for school.'

Centaine threw up her hands. 'If I die of boredom, Abe, let it be on your conscience for as long as you live!'

She had at first planned to wear her full suite of diamonds, but decided against it at the last moment. 'After all, it's only a little provincial reception, with fat farmers' wives and petty civil servants. Besides, I don't want to blind the poor old dear.'

So she settled for a yellow silk evening dress by Coco Chanel. She had worn it before, but in Cape Town, so it was unlikely anybody here had seen it.

'It was expensive enough to bear two airings,' she consoled herself. 'Too good for them, anyway.'

She settled on a pair of solitaire diamond ear studs, not too large to be ostentatious, but around her neck she wore the huge yellow diamond the colour of champagne on a platinum chain. It drew attention to her small pointed breasts; she liked the effect.

Her hair was a worry, as always. It was fully of electricity from the dry desert air. She wished Anna was here, for she was the only one who could manage that lustrous unruly bush. In despair she tried to make a virtue of its disorder, deliberately fluffing it out into a halo and holding it up with a velvet band around her forehead.

'That's enough fuss.' She didn't feel like a party at all. Shasa had left on the mail train as Abe had planned and already she was missing him keenly. On top of that she was anxious to get back to Weltevreden herself and resented having to stay over.

Abe called for her an hour after the time stipulated on the invitation card that was embossed with the administrator's coat of arm. During the drive Rachel, Abe's wife, regaled them with an account of her recent domestic triumphs and tragedies, including a detailed report of her youngest offspring's bowel movements.

The administrative building, the Ink Palace, had been designed by the German colonial administration in heavy Gothic imperial style; when Centaine swept a glance around the ballroom, she saw that the company was no better than she had expected. It comprised mainly senior civil servants, heads and deputy heads of departments with their wives, the officers of the local garrison and police force, together with all the town's prominent businessmen and the big landowners who lived close enough to Windhoek to respond to the invitation.

Amongst them were a number of Centaine's own people, all the managers and under-managers of the Courtney Finance and Mining Company. Abe had provided her with an up-to-date bulletin so that as each came forward diffidently to present their spouses, Centaine was able to make some gracious personal comment which had them glowing and grinning with gratification. Abe stood by to make sure that none of them imposed upon her, and after the appropriate interval gave her the excuse to escape.

'I think we should pay our respects to the new administrator, Mrs Courtney.' He took her arm and led her towards the reception line.

'I have been able to get a few facts about him. He is a Lieutenant-Colonel Blaine Malcomess and commanded a battalion of the Natal Mounted Rifles. He had a good war and ended with a bar to his Military Cross. In private life he is a lawyer, and – '

The police band was belting out a Strauss waltz with zeal and gusto and the dance floor was already crowded. As they came up to the tail of the reception line, Centaine saw with satisfaction that they would be the last to be presented.

Centaine was paying little attention to their host at the head of the line as she moved along on Abe's arm, leaning across him to listen to Rachel on his other arm who was giving her a family recipe for chicken soup but at the same time Centaine was trying to decide just how early she could make her escape.

Abruptly she realized that they had reached the head of the line, the very last to do so, and that the administrator's A.D.C. was announcing them to their host.

'Mr and Mrs Abraham Abrahams and Mrs Centaine de Thiry Courtney.' She looked up at the man who stood before her and involuntarily she dug her

fingernails into the soft inside of Abraham Abrahams' elbow with such force that he winced. She did not notice it, for she was staring at Colonel Blaine Malcomess.

He was tall and lean, and he stood well over six feet. His bearing was relaxed without any military stiffness and yet he seemed to be balanced on the balls of his feet as though he could explode into movement at any moment.

'Mrs Courtney,' he offered her his hand, 'I am delighted you were able to come. You were the one person I particularly wanted to meet.' His voice was a clear tenor, with a faint lilt to it that might have been Welsh. An educated and cultivated voice, with modulations which lifted a little electric rash of pleasure on her forearms and at the nape of her neck.

She took his hand. The skin was dry and warm, and she could feel the restrained strength of his fingers as they pressed hers gently. 'He could crush my hand like an eggshell,' she thought, and the idea gave her a delicious little chill of apprehension. She studied his face.

His features were large, the bones of his jaw and cheek and forehead seemed weighty and massive as stone. His nose was big with a Roman bridge to it, his brow was beetling and his mouth was big and mobile. He reminded her strongly of a younger more handsome Abraham Lincoln. He isn't yet forty, she estimated, so young for the rank and the job.

Then he realized with a start that she was still holding his hand, and that she had not replied to his greeting. He was leaning over her, studying her as openly and intently as she was him, and Abe and Rachel were looking from one to the other of them with interest and amusement. Centaine had to shake her hand lightly to free it from his grip, and to her horror she felt the hot rush of blood up her throat into her cheeks.

'I'm blushing!' It was something she had not done in years.

'I have been fortunate enough to be associated with your family before this,' Blaine Malcomess told her. His teeth also were large and square and very white. His mouth was wide, even wider when he smiled. A little shakily she smiled back.

'Have you?' She realized that it wasn't the most sparkling conversational gambit, but her wits seemed to have deserted her. She was standing there like a school girl, blushing and gawking at him. His eyes were a most startling shade of green. They distracted her.

'I served under General Sean Courtney in France,' he told her, still smiling. Somebody had cut his hair too short at the temples, it made his large ears stick out. That irritated her – and yet the sticking-out ears made him endearing and appealing.

'He was a fine gentleman,' Blaine Malcomess went on.

'Yes, he was,' she replied and upbraided herself, 'Say something witty, something intelligent – he'll think you a clod.'

He was wearing dress uniform, dark blue and gold with a double row of medal ribbons. Since girlhood uniforms had always affected her.

'I heard that you were at General Courtney's headquarters in Arras for a few weeks in 1917. I was still in the line then; I didn't go on his staff until the end of that year.'

She took a deep breath to steady herself and at last managed to get control again. 'What turbulent days those were, with the universe crashing in ruins about us,' she said, her voice low and husky, her French accent emphasized a little, and she thought, 'What is this? What's happening to you, Centaine? This

is not the way it is supposed to be. Remember Michael and Shasa. Give this man a friendly nod and pass on.'

'It seems that I have performed my duties for the moment,' Blaine Malcomess glanced at his A.D.C. for confirmation and then turned back to Centaine. 'May I have the honour of this waltz, Mrs Courtney?' He offered his arm, and without a moment's hesitation she laid her fingers lightly in the crook of his elbow.

The other dancers veered away, leaving them an open space as they walked out side by side onto the floor. She turned to face Blaine and stepped into the circle of his arm.

He didn't have to move, merely the way he held her told her that he would be a marvellous dancer. Immediately she felt light and dainty and fleet of foot, and she arched her back and leaned out against the circle of his arm while his lower body seemed to meld with hers.

He took her on one spinning whirling circuit of the floor, and when she matched his every move feather light and swift, he began a complicated series of dips and counter-turns, and she followed him without conscious effort, seeming to skim the ground, yet totally under his control, responding to his every whim.

When at last the music ended with a crashing chord and the musicians fell back in their seats sweating and panting, Centaine felt unreasonable resentment towards them. They had not played long enough. Blaine Malcomess was still holding her in the middle of the floor and they were laughing delightedly at each other while the other dancers formed a ring around them and applauded.

'Unfortunately that seems to be it for the moment,' he said, still making no effort to release her, and his words roused her. There was no longer any excuse for physical contact and she stepped back from him reluctantly and acknowledged the applause with a small curtsey.

'I do think we have earned a glass of champagne.' Blaine signalled one of the white-jacketed waiters and they stood at the edge of the dance floor and sipped the wine and watched each other's eyes avidly as they talked. The exertion had raised a light sheen of sweat on his broad forehead and she could smell it on his body.

They were alone in the centre of the crowded room. With a subtle inclination of her shoulders and head Centaine dissuaded the one or two bolder souls who approached as if to join them, and after that the others stayed back.

The band, refreshed and eager, took their seats on the bandstand once more and this time launched into a foxtrot. Blaine Malcomess did not have to ask. Centaine set her almost untouched champagne on the silver tray that the waiter proffered and lifted her arms as Blaine faced her.

The more sedate rhythm of the foxtrot enabled them to continue talking, and there was so much to talk about. He had known Sean Courtney well, and held him in affection and admiration. Centaine had loved him almost as much as she had loved her own father. They discussed the dreadful circumstances in which Sean Courtney and his wife had been murdered, and their mutual horror and outrage at the deed seemed to draw them still closer together.

Blaine knew the beloved northern provinces around Arras in her native France, and his battalion had held a section of the line near Mort Homme, her home village. He remembered the burnt-out ruins of her family's château.

'We used it as an artillery observation post,' he told her. 'I spent many hours

perched up in the north wing.' His description induced a pleasant nostalgia, a fine sadness to heighten her emotions.

He loved horses as she did, and was a twelve-goal polo player.

'Twelve goals!' she exclaimed. 'My son will be most impressed. He has just been rated a four-goal man.'

'How old is your son?'

'Fourteen.'

'Very good for a youngster of that age. I'd like to see him in action.'

'That would be fun,' she agreed, and suddenly she wanted to tell him all about Shasa, but again the music ended and cut her short, and this time he frowned also.

'They are playing very short pieces, aren't they?'

Then she felt him start and he released her waist. Though she kept her hand on his arm, the strange elated mood which had gripped them both shattered, and something dark and intrusive passed like a shadow between them. She was not sure what it was.

'Ah,' he said sombrely. 'I see she has returned. She really wasn't at all well this evening but she always was a plucky one.'

'To whom are you referring?' Centaine asked. His tone had filled her with foreboding and she should have been warned by it, but still the shock of it made her flinch when he said softly:

'My wife.'

Centaine felt quite giddy for a moment, and she only kept her balance with an effort when she let her hand fall from his arm.

'I would like you to meet my wife,' he said. 'May I introduce you to her?'

She nodded, unwilling to trust her voice, and when he offered his arm again she hesitated before she took it, and this time laid her fingertips only lightly upon it.

He led her across the floor towards the group at the foot of the main staircase, and as they approached Centaine searched the faces of the women, trying to guess which one it would be. Only two of them were young and none was beautiful, none could compete with her in looks or strength or poise or talent or wealth. She felt a surge of confidence and anticipation replace the momentary confusion and despondency that had thrown her off balance. Without thinking about it she knew she was going into a desperate contest, and she was buoyed up with battle lust and the enormity of the prize at stake. She was eager to identify and assess her adversary and she lifted her chin and set her shoulders as they stopped before the group.

The ranks of men and women opened respectfully, and there she was, looking up at Centaine with lovely tragic eyes. She was younger than Centaine and possessed of a rare and exquisite beauty. She wore her gentle nature and goodness like a shining cloak for all to see, but her sadness was in the smile she gave Centaine as Blaine Malcomess introduced them.

'Mrs Courtney, may I present my wife Isabella?'

'You dance exquisitely, Mrs Courtney. I have been watching you and Blaine with great pleasure,' she said. 'He does so love dancing.'

'Thank you, Mrs Malcomess,' Centaine whispered huskily, while inside she raged. 'Oh, you little bitch. It's not fair. You aren't fighting fair. How can I ever win now? Oh God, how I hate you.'

Isabella Malcomess sat in a wheelchair with her nurse behind her. The ankles of her thin paralysed legs showed under the hem of her evening dress. They

were pale and skeletal and her feet seemed fragile and vulnerable in their sequined dancing pumps.

'He'll never leave you.' Centaine felt herself choke on her grief. 'He's that kind of man – he'll never desert a crippled wife!'

* * *

Centaine woke an hour before dawn and lay for a moment wondering at the strange sense of wellbeing that possessed her. Then she remembered and threw back the sheets, eager for the day to begin. With both bare feet upon the floor she paused, and her eyes instinctively went to the framed photograph of Michael Courtney on the bedside table.

'Michel, I'm sorry,' she whispered. 'I love you. I still love you, I always will, but I can't help this other thing. I didn't want it. I didn't look for it. Please forgive me, my darling. It's been so long and so lonely. I want him, Michel. I want to marry him and have him for myself.' She took up the frame and for a moment held it to her bosom. Then she opened the drawer, laid the photograph face down upon her folded lace underwear, and closed the drawer again.

She jumped to her feet and reached for the yellow Chinese silk dressing-gown with the bird of paradise embroidered down the back. Belting it she hurried through to the saloon of the coach and seated herself at her desk to compose the telegraph to Sir Garry in their private code, for the message would be transmitted over the public lines.

Please urgently forward all intelligence on Lieutenant-Colonel Blaines Malcomess, newly appointed administrator of South West Africa. Reply in code. Love Juno.

She rang for her secretary and chafed while she waited for him. He came through in a flannel dressing-gown, owl-eyed and unshaven

'Get that off right away.' She handed him the flimsy. 'Then get me Abraham Abrahams on the telephone.'

'Centaine, it's six o'clock in the morning,' Abe protested, 'and we didn't get to bed until three o'clock.'

'Three hours is enough sleep for any good lawyer. Abe, I want you to invite Colonel Malcomess and his wife to dine with me in my coach this evening.'

There was a long weighty silence, and the static hissed on the line.

'You and Rachel are invited, of course.' She filled the silence.

'It's much too short notice,' he said carefully, obviously choosing his words with precision. 'The administrator is a busy man. He won't come.'

'Get the invitation to him personally.' Centaine ignored the protest. 'Send your messenger round to his office and see he gets it. Under no circumstances let his wife receive the invitation first.'

'He won't come,' Abe repeated stubbornly. 'At least I hope to God he won't come.'

'What do you mean by that?' she snapped.

'You are playing with fire, Centaine. Not just a little candle flame, but a great raging bush fire.'

She pursed her lips. 'Mind your own business, and I'll mind mine – ' she started, and he broke in on her.

' – Kiss your own sweetheart, and I'll kiss mine,' he finished the childhood law for her, and she giggled. He had never heard Centaine Courtney giggle before; it took him by surprise.

'How appropriate, dear Abe.'

She giggled again, and his voice was truly agitated when he told her, 'You pay me an enormous retainer to mind your business for you. Centaine, you set a hundred tongues wagging last night – the whole town will be agog this morning. You are a marked woman, everybody watches you. You just cannot afford to carry on like this.'

'Abe, you and I both know that I can afford to do any damned thing I choose. Send that invitation – please!'

She rested that afternoon. It had been a late night and she was determined to look her best for the evening. Abe had received a reply to the invitation. The administrator and his lady would be pleased to dine with her that evening. She smiled triumphantly, then turned to decode the telegram from Sir Garry which had also arrived while she was asleep.

'For Juno stop. Subject's full names Blaine Marsden Malcomess born Johannesburg 28 July 1893.'

'So he is nearly thirty-nine years old,' she exclaimed, 'and he is a Leo. My big growly lion!' She returned eagerly to the cable:

Second son of James Marsden Malcomess lawyer and mining entrepreneur, chairman Consolidated Goldfields and director numerous associated companies, deceased 1922. Subject was educated St John's College Johannesburg and Oriel College Oxford. Academic honours include Rhodes scholarship and Oriel scholarship. Sporting honours include full blue cricket and half blues athletics and polo. Graduated MA (Hons) Oxon 1912. Called to the Bar 1913. Commissioned 2nd-Lieutenant Natal Mounted Rifles 1914. Service in South West Africa Campaign. Mentioned in despatches twice. Promoted Captain 1915. France with BEF 1915. Military Cross August 1915. Promoted Major and Bar to MC 1916. Promoted Lieutenant-Colonel O.C. 3rd Battalion 1917. Staff of General Officer Commanding 6th Division 1918. Versailles Armistice negotiations on staff of General Smuts. Partner in law firm Stirling & Malcomess from 1919. Member Parliament for Gardens 1924. Deputy Minister Justice 1926–9. Appointed Administrator South West Africa 11 May 1932. Married Isabella Tara née Harrison 1918. Two daughters Tara Isabella and Mathilda Janine.

That came as a further shock to Centaine. She had not thought about children.

'At least she hasn't given him a son.' The thought was so cruel that she assuaged the prickle of guilt by calculating the age of his daughters. 'I expect that they look like their mother. Horrible little angels that he dotes on,' she decided bitterly, and read the few comments with which Sir Garry had ended the long cable.

'Enquiries addressed to *Ou Baas* indicate that subject is considered a rising force in law and politics. Cabinet rank a strong probability when SA Party returns to power.' Centaine smiled fondly at the mention of General Jan Christian Smuts and then read on:

Wife thrown from horse 1927. Extensive spinal damage. Prognosis unfavourable. Stop. Father James Marsden left estate probated £655,000 in equal shares to two sons. Stop. Subject's present financial circumstances not ascertained, but estimated as substantial. Stop. Presently rated 12 goals polo. Captained SA team versus Argentine 1929. Stop. Hope and expect your query businesslike. If not implore you exercise restraint and caution as consequences highly prejudicial all parties. Stop. Shasa safely ensconced Bishops. Stop. Anna joins me in sending all love. Ends. Ovid.

She had selected Sir Garry's codename out of affection and respect for his craft, but now she threw the telegraph flimsy down on her desk angrily.

'Why does everybody know what's best for me – except me?' she asked aloud. 'And why isn't Anna here to help me with my hair? I look an absolute fright.' She looked in the mirror over the mantel for confirmation that it was not true. Then she dragged her hair back from her face with both hands while she studied her skin for blemish or wrinkles. She found only the faintest hairlines at the corners of her eyes yet they made her discontent extreme.

'Why is it that all the most attractive men are already married? And why, oh why couldn't that silly little namby-pamby have stuck in the saddle instead of falling on her pretty little backside.'

* * *

Centaine had contrived to make a great deal of fuss over Isabella Malcomess' reception and the transfer of her wheelchair from the platform to the balcony of the coach. She had four of the coach attendants and her secretaries standing by to assist.

Blaine Malcomess waved them away irritably, then he stooped over his wife. She slipped both her arms around his neck and he lifted her as though she were as light as a little girl. With their faces almost touching he smiled at her tenderly and then went up the steps onto the balcony as though he were unburdened. Isabella's legs dangled pathetically from under her skirts. They were wasted and lifeless and Centaine experienced an unexpected and unwelcome rush of sympathy for her.

'I don't want to pity her,' she thought fiercely as she followed them into the saloon.

Blaine set her down, without asking Centaine's permission, in the chair that subtly dominated the saloon and was naturally the focus of all attention, the chair that was always and exclusively reserved for Centaine herself. Blaine went down on one knee before his wife and gently arranged her feet, setting them neatly side by side on the silk carpet. Then he smoothed her skirt over her knees. It was obvious that he had done all this countless times before.

Isabella touched his cheek lightly with her fingertips, and smiled down on his head with such trust and adoration that Centaine felt entirely superfluous. Despair overwhelmed her. She could not intervene between these two. Sir Garry and Abe were both right. She had to relinquish him without a struggle, and she felt an almost saintly sense of righteousness.

Then Isabella looked up at Centaine over the head of her kneeling husband. Against the fashion she wore her hair long and straight. It was so fine and silky that it formed a thick sheet, lustrous as watered satin, that flowed down over her bare shoulders. Her hair was the colour of roasted chestnuts, but it flickered with glowing red stars and highlights each time she moved her head. Her face was round as a medieval madonna's, and lit with serenity. Her eyes were brown and starred with rods of gold that fanned out from the luminous black pupils.

Isabella looked at Centaine across the full length of the saloon, then she smiled – a slow complacent possessive smile – and the light in her brown and gold eyes changed. She stared into Centaine's dark wild honey eyes and she challenged her. It was as clear to Centaine as if she had stripped off one of her

elbow-length gloves with its embroidered seed pearls and struck Centaine in the mouth with it.

'You silly little thing – you shouldn't have done that!' All Centaine's noble resolutions crumbled before that gaze. 'I was ready to let you keep him, I truly was. But if you want to fight for him – well then, so do I.' And she stared back at Isabella and silently took up her challenge.

The dinner was a resounding success. Centaine had carefully vetted the menu but had not trusted her chef with either the dressing for the rock lobster or the sauce for the roast sirloin and had prepared both of these with her own hands. They drank champagne with the lobster and a marvellous velvety Richebourg with the sirloin.

Abe and Blaine were relieved and delighted that Isabella and Centaine were being so utterly charming and considerate to each other. It was obvious that they would become close friends. Centaine included the crippled girl in almost every remark she made, and was solicitous of Isabella's comfort, herself arranging cushions at her back or feet.

Centaine's stories were self-mocking and entertaining as she made light of how she had survived the dreadful crossing of the dune lands, widowed and pregnant, with only wild Bushmen as companions.

'How brave of you.' Isabella Malcomess got the point of the story. 'I am sure there are very few women who would have had your resourcefulness and strength.'

'Colonel Malcomess, can I prevail on you to carve the roast. Sometimes being a woman alone does have its drawbacks. There are things that only a man does well, wouldn't you agree, Mrs Malcomess?'

Rachel Abraham sat quietly and apprehensively. She was the only one apart from the two principals who understood what was happening, and her sympathy was all with Isabella Malcomess, for she could imagine her own little nest and nestlings being threatened by a circling predator.

'You have two daughters, Mrs Malcomess?' Centaine asked sweetly. 'Tara and Mathilda Janine, such pretty names.' She let her rival know that she had done her researches thoroughly. 'But you must find it difficult to cope, girls being always much more of a handful than boys?'

Rachel Abrahams, at the end of the table, winced. With a single light flick of the blade Centaine had pointed up Isabella's disability and her failure to provide a son and heir for her husband.

'Oh, I have plenty of time to devote to my domestic duties,' Isabella assured her, 'not being in trade, as it were. And the girls are such darlings, they are devoted to their father, of course.'

Isabella was a skilled duellist. 'Trade' was a word that made Centaine's aristocratic blood seethe behind her concerned smile, and it was a master stroke to link the girls so securely to Blaine. Centaine had seen his doting expression at mention of them. She turned to him and changed the subject to politics.

'Recently General Smuts was a guest at Weltevreden, my Cape home. He is deeply concerned by the growth of secret militant societies amongst the lower classes of Afrikanerdom. In particular the so-called *Ossewa-Brandwag* and the *Afrikaner Broederbond*, the best translation of which would be the "Nightguard of the Wagon Train" and the "Afrikaner Brotherhood". I also feel they are highly dangerous and prejudicial to the nation's best interests. Do you share this concern, Colonel Malcomess?'

'Indeed, Mrs Courtney, I have made a special study of these phenomena. But

I do not think that you are correct in saying these secret societies include the lower classes of Afrikanerdom, quite the opposite. The membership is restricted to pure-blooded Afrikaners in positions of potential or actual influence in politics, government, religion and education. However, I agree with your conclusions. They are dangerous, more dangerous than most people realize, for their ultimate aim is to gain control of every facet of our lives, from the minds of the young to the machinery of justice and government, and to prefer their members above all consideration of merit or worth. In many ways this movement is the counterpart of the rising wave of National Socialism in Germany under Herr Hitler.'

Centaine leaned across the table to enjoy every nuance and inflection of his voice, encouraging him with question or shrewd sharp comment. With that voice, she thought, he could sway me and a million voters. Then she realized that the two of them were behaving as if they were the only ones at the table and she returned quickly to Isabella.

'Would you agree with your husband on that, Mrs Malcomess?' and Blaine laughed indulgently and answered for her.

'I'm afraid my wife finds politics a total bore, don't you, my dear? And I'm not sure that she isn't very perceptive in that belief.' He drew a gold watch from the fob pocket of his dinner jacket.

'It is after midnight. I have enjoyed myself so hugely that we have overstayed our welcome, I'm sure.'

'You are right, darling.' Isabella was relieved and eager to end it. 'Tara has been sickly. She complained of a stomach ache before we left.

'Tara, the little vixen, always complains of a stomach ache when she knows we are going out,' he chuckled, but they all rose.

'I won't let you go without the solace of a brandy and a cigar,' Centaine demurred. 'Although I refuse to accept the barbaric custom of leaving the men to those pleasures alone while we poor females gather to giggle and talk babies so we will all go through to the saloon together.'

However, as she led them through, her secretary was hovering nervously.

'Yes, what is it?' She was annoyed until she saw that he was holding a telegraph flimsy like a warrant for his own execution.

'From Dr Twentyman-Jones, ma'am, and it's urgent.

She accepted the flimsy but did not unfold it until she had made sure that her guest had coffee and liqueurs and that both Blaine and Abe were each armed with a Havana. The she excused herself and slipped through to her bedroom.

For Juno. Strike committee headed by Gerhard Fourie has called out all white employees. Stop. Plant and pit under picket lines and shipment of goods embargoed. Stop. Strikers demanding reinstatement of all retrenched white employees and guaranteed job security for all. Stop. Request your instructions. Ends. Vingt.

Centaine sat down on her bed. The paper in her hand fluttered. She had never been more angry in her life. It was treachery, a gross and unforgivable betrayal. It was her mine, they were her diamonds. She paid their wages, and hers was the absolute right to hire and fire. "The shipment of goods" that Twentyman-Jones referred to was the parcel of diamonds on which her fortune hinged. Their demands, if pandered to, would render the H'ani Mine unprofitable. Who was this Gerhard Fourie, she wondered, and then remembered he was the chief transport driver.

She went to the door and opened it. Her secretary was waiting in the corridor.

'Ask Mr Abrahams to come to me.'

When Abe stepped through the door she handed him the telegraph flimsy.

'They don't have the right to do this to me,' she said fiercely, and waited impatiently while he read it through.

'Unfortunately, Centaine, they do have the right. Under the Industrial Conciliation Act of 1924 – '

'Don't spout acts at me now, Abe,' she cut him off. 'They are a bunch of bolsheviks biting the hand that feeds them.'

'Centaine, don't do anything hasty. If we were to – '

'Abe, get the Daimler offloaded from the truck immediately and send Dr Twentyman-Jones a telegraph. Tell him I'm coming and he is to do nothing, make no concessions nor promises until I arrive.'

'You'll leave in the morning, of course?'

'I will not,' she snapped. 'I will leave in half an hour from now, just as soon as my guests have gone and you have the Daimler detrained.'

'It's one in the morning – ' He saw her face and abandoned that line of protest. 'I'll telegraph the staff at the first staging station to expect you.'

'Just tell them to be ready to refuel. I won't be staying over. I'm driving straight through to the mine.' And she went to the door, paused to compose herself and then, smiling easily, went back into the saloon.

'Is something wrong, Mrs Courtney?' The smile had not deceived Blaine Malcomess, and he rose to his feet. 'Is there anything I can do to help you?'

'Oh, just a small nuisance. Trouble out at the mine. I have to go back there right away.'

'Not tonight, surely?'

'Yes, tonight – '

'On your own?' He was troubled, and his concern pleased her. 'It's a long hard journey.'

'I prefer to travel alone.' Then she added with a meaningful intensity, 'Or to chose my travelling companion with great care.' She paused, then went on, 'Some of my employees have called a strike. It's unreasonable and they have no case to justify their action. I'm certain that I can smooth it over. However, sometimes these things get out of hand. There might be violence, or vandalism.'

Quickly Blaine reassured her. 'I can guarantee you full government co-operation. A police detachment could be sent to maintain the peace, if you so wish.'

'Thank you. I would appreciate that. Knowing that I can call upon you is a great relief and comfort.'

'I will arrange it first thing tomorrow,' he said. 'But of course it will take a few days.' Again they were behaving as though they were alone; their voices were low and filled with significance beyond what the words suggested.

'Darling, we should leave Mrs Courtney to prepare for her journey.' Isabella spoke from her chair and he started as though he had forgotten she were there.

'Yes, of course. We will leave at once.'

Centaine went with them down the railway platform to where Blaine's Chevrolet tourer was parked beneath the single streetlight. She walked beside Isabella's wheelchair.

'I did so enjoy meeting you, Mrs Malcomess, and I'd love to meet your girls. Won't you bring them out to Weltevreden when next you are in Cape Town?'

'I don't know when that will be,' Isabella refused politely. 'My husband will be immersed in his new appointment.'

They reached the waiting vehicle and while the chauffeur held the rear door open, Blaine lifted Isabella from the chair and seated her on the leather seat. He closed the door carefully and turned to Centaine. His back was to his wife, and the chauffeur was loading the wheelchair into the boot. They were alone for the time being.

'She is a courageous and wonderful woman,' he said softly as he took Centaine's hand. 'I love her and can never leave her, but I wish – ' he broke off and his grip on her fingers was painful.

'Yes,' Centaine answered as softly. 'I also wish – ' and she revelled in the pain of his grip. He ended it too soon for her and went around to the opposite side of the Chevrolet, while Centaine stooped to the crippled girl at the open window.

'Please do remember my invitation,' she began, but Isabella thrust her face closer and the serene and beautiful mask cracked so that the terror and the hatred showed through.

'He's mine,' she said. 'And I won't let you have him.' Then she leaned back in her seat and Blaine slid in beside her and took her hand.

The Chevrolet pulled away, the official pennant on the bonnet fluttering, and Centaine stood under the streetlight and stared after it until the headlights faded.

* * *

Lothar De La Rey slept with the earphones of the telegraph tap on the sheepskin roll beside his head, so that the first bleep of the transmission woke him and he snatched up the headset and called to Swart Hendrick. 'Light the candle, Hennie, they are transmitting. At this time of night it must be important.'

Yet he was still unprepared for the import of the message when he scribbled it out in his notebook: 'Strike Committee headed by Gerhard Fourie has called out all white employees – '

Lothar was stunned by Twentyman-Jones' message.

'Gerhard Fourie. What on earth is that miserable bastard playing at,' he asked himself aloud, and then leapt up and went out of the dugout to pace agitatedly in the loose sand of the riverbed while he attempted to work it out.

'A strike – why would he call a strike now? *Shipment of goods embargoed*. That has to mean the diamonds. The strikers are refusing to let the diamonds leave the mine.' He stopped suddenly and punched his fist into his own palm. 'That's it. That's what it's all about. He has called the strike to worm himself out of our bargain. His nerve has given in, but he knows I will kill him for it. This is his way out. He isn't going to co-operate. The whole thing has fallen through.'

He stood out in the riverbed and a dark impotent rage overwhelmed him.

'All the risks I have taken, all the time and work and hardship. The theft of the horses, all for nothing, all wasted because of one yellow-bellied – '

If Fourie had been there he would have shot him down without compunction.

'*Baas*!' Hendrick yelled urgently. 'Come quickly! The telegraph!'

Lothar sprinted back to the dugout and snatched up the headset. The

operator at the Courtney Mining and Finance Company in Windhoek was transmitting.

'For Vingt. I am returning with all speed. Stop. Make no concessions nor promises. Stop. See that all loyal employees are armed and protected from intimidation. Stop. Assure them of my gratitude and material appreciation. Stop. Close the company store immediately, no food or supplies to be sold to strikers or their families. Stop. Cut off water reticulation and electricity supply to strikers' cottages. Stop. Inform Strike Committee that police detachment en route. Ends. Juno.'

Despite himself and his rage at Fourie, Lothar threw back his head and laughed with delight and admiration.

'Fourie and his strikers don't realize what they are taking on,' he roared. 'By God, I'd prefer to tickle an angry black mamba with a short stick than get in Centaine Courtney's way right now.' He sobered and thought about it for a while, then he told Hendrcik and Manfred quietly.

'I have a feeling that those diamonds will be coming through to Windhoek, strike or no strike. But I don't think Fourie will be driving the truck, in fact I don't give Fourie much chance of driving anything again. So we won't have a nice polite co-operative escort to hand the package over to us as we had planned. But the diamonds will be coming through, and we are going to be here when they do.'

The yellow Daimler passed their position at eleven o'clock the following night. Lothar watched the glow of the headlights gradually harden into solid white beams of light that swept across the plain towards him and then dipped and disappeared into the riverbed only to blaze up into the moonless sky as the Daimler pointed its nose up the cutting and climbed out of the riverbed again. The engine bellowed in low gear on the steep incline and then settled to a high whine as it shot over the top and sped away into the north-east towards the H'ani Mine.

Lothar struck a match and checked his watch. 'Say she left Windhoek an hour after her telegraph last night – that means she has reached here in twenty-two hours' straight driving, over these roads in the dark.' He whistled softly. 'If she keeps going like that, she'll be at the H'ani Mine before noon tomorrow. It doesn't seem possible.'

* * *

The blue hills rose out of the heat mirage ahead of Centaine, but this time their magic was unable to captivate her. She had been at the wheel for thirty-two hours with only brief intervals of rest while she refuelled at the staging posts, and once when she had pulled to the side of the road and slept for two hours.

She was tired. The weariness ached in the marrow of her bones, burned her eyes like acid and lay upon her shoulders and crushed her down in the leather seat of the Daimler as though she wore a suit of heavy chain mail. Yet her anger fuelled her, and when she saw the galvanized iron roofs of the mine buildings shining in the sun her weariness dropped away.

She stopped the Daimler and stepped down in the road to stretch and swing her arms, forcing fresh blood into her stiff limbs. Then she twisted the rearview mirror and examined her face in it. Her eyes were bloodshot and red-rimmed

with little wet balls of mud and mucus in the corners. Her face was deathly white, powdered with pale dust and drained of blood by her fatigue.

She wet a cloth with cool water from the canvas water bag and cleaned the dust from her skin. Then from her toilet bag she took the bottle of eyewash and little blue eyebath. She bathed her eyes. They were clear and bright again when she checked in the mirror, and she patted her pale cheeks until the blood rouged them. She readjusted the scarf around her head, stripped off the full-length white dust-jacket that protected her clothes and she looked clean and rested and ready for trouble.

There were little groups of women and children gathered at the corners of the avenues. They watched her sullenly and a little apprehensively as she drove past them on the way to the administration building. She sat straightbacked behind the wheel and looked directly ahead.

As she neared the office, she saw the pickets who had been lolling under the thorn tree outside the gates hastily reorganizing themselves. There were twenty at least, most of the able-bodied white artisans on the mine. They formed a line across the road and linked arms facing her. Their faces were ugly and threatening.

'Nothing goes in! Nothing goes out!' they began to chant as she slowed. She saw that most of them had armed themselves with clubs and pick handles.

Centaine thrust the palm of her hand down on the button and the Daimler's horn squealed like a wounded bull elephant and she drove hard at the centre of the picket line with the accelerator pedal pressed to the floorboards. The men in the centre saw her face behind the windshield and realized that she would run them down. At the last minute they scattered.

One of them yelled, 'We want our jobs!' and swung his pick handle against the rear window. The glass starred and collapsed over the leather seat, but Centaine was through.

She pulled up in front of the verandah just as Twentyman-Jones hurried out of his office struggling with his jacket and necktie.

'We weren't expecting you until tomorrow at the very earliest.'

'Your friends were.' She pointed at the shattered window, and his voice went shrill with indignation.

'They attacked you? That's unforgivable.'

'I agree,' she said. 'And I'm not going to be the one who does the forgiving.'

Twentyman-Jones wore a huge service pistol holstered on his skinny hip. Behind him was little Mr Brantingham, the mine bookkeeper, his head bald as an ostrich egg and much too large for his narrow rounded shoulders. Behind his gold-rimmed pince-nez he was close to tears, but he carried a double-barrelled shotgun in his pudgy white hands.

'You are a brave man,' Centaine told him. 'I won't forget your loyalty.'

She led Twentyman-Jones into her office and sat down thankfully at her desk. 'How many other men are with us?'

'Only the office staff, eight of them. The artisans and mine staff are all out, though I suspect there has been pressure on some of them.'

'Even Rodgers and Maclear?' They were her senior overseers. 'Are they out also?'

'I'm afraid so. Both of them are on the strike committee.'

'With Fourie?'

'The three of them are the ringleaders.'

'I'll see that they never work again,' she said bitterly, and he dropped his eyes and mumbled:

'I think we have to bear in mind that they haven't broken the law. They have the legal right to withhold their labour, and to bargain collectively – '

'Not when I am struggling to keep the mine running. Not when I am trying to ensure that there will be jobs for at least some of them. Not after all I've done for them.'

'I'm afraid they do have that right,' he insisted.

'Whose side are you on, Dr Twentyman-Jones?'

He looked stricken. 'You should never have to ask that question,' he said. 'From the first day we met I've been your man. You know that. I was merely pointing out your legal position.'

Immediately contrite, Centaine stood up and reached for his arm to console him.

'Forgive me. I'm tired and jumpy.' She had stood up too quickly and the blood drained from her head. She turned deathly pale and swayed giddily on her feet. He seized her and steadied her.

'When did you last sleep? You have driven from Windhoek without rest.' He led her to the leather sofa and forced her gently down upon it.

'You are going to sleep now, for at least eight hours. I'll have fresh clothes brought down from your bungalow.'

'I must speak to the ringleaders.'

'No.' He shook his head as he drew the curtains. 'Not until you are refreshed and strong again. Otherwise you could make mistakes of judgement.'

She sagged back and pressed her fingers into her closed eyelids. 'You are right – as always.'

'I'll wake you at six this evening, and I'll inform the strike committee that you will interview them at eight. That will give us two hours to plan our strategy.'

* * *

The three members of the strike committee filed into Centaine's office, and she stared at them for fully three minutes without speaking. She had deliberately had all the chairs removed, except those in which she and Twentyman-Jones sat. The strikers were forced to stand before her like schoolboys.

'There are over a hundred thousand men out of work in this country at the present time,' she said in a dispassionate voice. 'Any one of whom would go down on his knees for your jobs.'

'That won't bloody work,' said Maclear. He was a nondescript-looking man, of medium height and uncertain age, but Centaine knew he was quick-witted, tenacious and resourceful. She wished he was with her rather than against.

'If you are going to use foul language in front of me, Mr Maclear,' she said, 'you can leave immediately.'

'That won't work either, Mrs Courtney.' He smiled sadly in acknowledgement of her spirit. 'You know our rights, and we know our rights.'

Centaine looked at Rodgers. 'How is your wife, Mr Rodgers?' A year previously she had paid for the woman to travel to Johannesburg for urgent

treatment by one of the leading abdominal surgeons in the Union. Rodgers had gone with her on full pay, and all expenses paid.

'She's well, Mrs Courtney,' he said sheepishly.

'What does she think of this nonsense of yours?' He looked down at his feet. 'She's a sensible lady,' Centaine went on. 'I would think she is worrying about her three little ones.'

'We are all together,' Fourie cut in. 'We are all solid, and the women are behind us. You can forget all that – '

'Mr Fourie, please do not interrupt me when I am speaking.'

'Playing the high and mighty lady muck-a-muck around here is going to get you nowhere,' he blustered. 'We've got you and your bloody mine and your bloody diamonds over a barrel. You are the one who has got to do the listening when we speak, and that's the plain fact of the matter.' He grinned cockily and looked to his mates for approbation. The grin concealed his trepidation. On one side he had Lothar De La Rey and his threat. If he could not come up with a good enough excuse for not performing his obligations he knew he was a dead man. He had to aggravate the strike until someone else transported the diamonds and gave him an escape. 'You aren't going to get one single bloody diamond off this property until we say so, lady. We're keeping them here as hostages. We know you've got a really whopping packet sitting there in the strongroom, and that's where it will stay, until you listen to what we have to say.' He was a good enough judge of character to guess what Centaine Courtney's reaction to that threat would be.

Centaine studied his face intently. There was something that did not ring true, something devious and convoluted in his manner. He was being too deliberately aggressive and provocative.

'All right,' she agreed quietly. 'I'll listen. Tell me what you want.'

She sat quietly while Fourie read the list of demands. Her face was impassive, the only signs of her anger that Twentyman-Jones knew so well were the soft flush of blood that stained her throat and the steady rhythmic tap of her foot on the wooden floor.

Fourie reached the end of the reading and there was another long silence. Then he proffered the document.

'This is your copy.'

'Put it on my desk,' she ordered, disdaining to touch it. 'The people that were retrenched from this mine last month were given three months' pay in lieu of notice,' she said, 'Three times more than they were entitled to, you know that. They were all given good letters of reference, you know that also.'

'They are our mates,' Fourie said stubbornly. 'Some of them our family.'

'All right.' She nodded. 'You have made your position clear. You may leave now.' She rose and they looked at one another in consternation.

'Aren't you going to give us an answer?' Maclear asked.

'Eventually,' she nodded.

'When will that be?'

'When I am ready and not before.'

They filed towards the door, but before he reached it, Maclear turned back and faced her defiantly.

'They've closed the company store and cut off the water and electricity to our cottages,' he challenged her.

'On my orders,' she agreed.

'You can't do that.'

'I don't see why not. I own the store, the generator, the pumphouse and the cottages.'

'We've got wives and children to feed.'

'You should have thought about them before you started your strike.'

'We can take what we want, you know. Even your diamonds. You can't stop us.'

'Make me a very happy woman,' she invited. 'Do it. Break into the store and steal the goods from the shelves. Dynamite the strongroom and take my diamonds. Assault my loyal people. Nothing would please me more than to see the three of you in gaol for life – or dancing on the gallows tree.'

As soon as they were alone again, she turned to Twentyman-Jones.

'He is right. The first and only consideration is the diamonds. I have to get them safely into the bank vaults in Windhoek.'

'We can send them in under police escort,' he agreed, but she shook her head.

'It might take five more days for the police to reach here. There is all sorts of red tape before they can move. No, I want those diamonds away from here before dawn. You know the insurance doesn't cover riot and civil disturbance. If something happens to them I will be ruined, Dr Twentyman-Jones. They are my lifeblood. I cannot risk them falling into the hands of these ignorant arrogant brutes.'

'Tell me what you intend.'

'I want you to take the Daimler round to its garage in the rear. Have it refuelled and checked. We will load the diamonds through the back door.' She pointed across her office to the concealed door she used sometimes when she wished to avoid being seen entering or leaving. 'At midnight when the pickets are asleep you will cut the barbed-wire fence directly opposite the garage door.'

'Good.' He was following her intentions. 'That will let us out into the sanitary lane. The pickets are at the main gates on the opposite side of the compound. They haven't posted anyone on the rear side. Once we are clear of the lane it's a straight run out onto the main road to Windhoek, we'll be clear in a matter of seconds.'

'Not we, Dr Twentyman-Jones,' she said, and he stared at her.

'You don't intend going alone?' he asked.

'I have just made the journey alone, swiftly and with not the least sign of trouble. I anticipate no problem with the return. I need you here. You know I cannot leave the mine to Brantingham or one of the clerks. You have to be here to deal with these strikers. Wihout you they may wreck the plant or sabotage the workings. It would only take a stick or two of dynamite.'

He wiped his face with his open hand, from forehead to chin, in an agony of indecision, torn between two duties: the mine which he had built up from nothing and which was his pride, and the woman who he loved as dearly as a daughter or a wife he had never had. At last he sighed. She was right, it had to be that way.

'Then take one of the men with you,' he pleaded.

'Brantingham, bless him?' she asked, raising her eyebrows, and he threw up both hands as he saw how ridiculous that idea was.

'I'll take the Daimler around to the back,' he said. 'Then I'll get a telegraph through to Abe in Windhoek. He can send out an escort immediately to meet you on the road, that is if the strikers haven't cut the wires yet.'

'Don't send that until I am clear,' Centaine instructed. 'The strikers may just

have had enough sense to have put a tap on the line, in fact that is probaby why they have not cut it yet.'

Twentyman-Jones nodded. 'Very well. What time do you intend breaking out?'

'Three o'clock tomorrow morning,' she said, without hesitation. It was the hour when human vitality was at its lowest ebb. That was when the strike picket would be least prepared for swift reaction.

'Very well, Mrs Courtney. I will have my cook prepare you a light dinner – and then I suggest you get some rest. I will have everything ready and wake you at two-thirty.'

* * *

She woke the instant he touched her shoulder and sat up.

'Half past two o'clock,' Twentyman-Jones said. 'The Daimler is refuelled and the diamonds loaded. The barbed wire is cut. I have drawn you a bath and there is a selection of fresh clothes from the bungalow.'

'I will be ready in fifteen minutes,' she said.

They stood beside the Daimler in the darkened garage and spoke in whispers. The double doors were open, and there was a crescent moon lighting the yard.

'I have marked the gap in the wire.' Twentyman-Jones pointed and she saw the small white flags drooping from the barbed wire strands fifty yards away.

'The canisters of industrial diamonds are in the boot, but I have put the package of top stones on the passenger seat beside you.' He leaned through the open window and patted the black despatch box. It was the size and shape of a small suitcase, but of japanned steel with a brass lock.

'Good.' Centaine buttoned her dust-jacket and pulled on her soft dogskin driving gauntlets.

'The shotgun is loaded with Number Ten birdshot, so you fire at anybody who tries to stop you without risk of committing murder. It'll just give them a good sting. But if you mean business, there is a box of buckshot in the glove compartment.'

Centaine slid in behind the wheel and pulled the door closed gently so as not to alert a listener out in the silent night. She placed the double-barrelled shotgun on top of the diamond chest and cocked both hammers.

'There is a basket in the boot, sandwiches and a Thermos of coffee.'

She looked at him out of the side window and said seriously, 'You are my tower.'

'Don't let anything happen to you,' he said. 'A pox on the diamonds, we can dig more of them. You are unique, there's only one of you.' Impulsively he unbuckled the service revolver from around his waist and leaned into the Daimler to push it into the pocket at the back of the driver's seat. 'It's the only insurance I can offer you. Remember there is a cartridge under the hammer,' he said. 'Pray you never need it.' He stepped back and gave her a laconic salute. 'God speed.'

She started the Daimler and the great seven-litre engine rumbled softly. She flipped off the handbrake, switched on the headlights and gunned the Daimler out through the open doors and across the yard, going up through the gears in a deft series of racing changes.

She aimed the mascot on the bonnet between the white markers, roared through the gap in the fence at forty miles an hour, and felt a loose strand of barbed wire scrape down the side of the coachwork. Then she tramped down on the brake and spun the wheel, steering the front wheels onto the dusty lane, meeting the skid and then going flat on the accelerator pedal again. She shot down the lane with the Daimler roaring at full power.

Above the engine she heard faint shouts and saw the dark indistinct figures of a mob of strikers racing down the fence from the main gate to try and intercept her at the corner of the lane. She picked up the shotgun and thrust the double muzzles through the window beside her. In the headlights the faces of the running men were ugly with rage, their mouths dark pits as they shouted at her.

Two of them were swifter than their mates, and they reached the corner of the lane as the Daimler came level. One of the strikers flung his pick handle and it cartwheeled through the beam of the headlights and clanged off the bonnet.

Centaine depressed the shotgun, aiming for their legs, and fired both barrels with long spurts of orange flame and blurts of sound. Birdshot lashed their legs and the strikers howled with shock and pain and leapt off the road as Centaine roared past them and turned onto the main road down the slope and out into the desert.

* * *

For Pettifogger. Urgent and Imperative. Juno unaccompanied departed this end 3 am instant carrying goods. Stop. Immediately despatch armed escort to intercept her en route. Ends. Vingt.

Lothar De La Rey stared at the message he had copied onto his pad by the guttering flame of the candle.

'Unaccompanied,' he whispered. 'Juno unaccompanied. Carrying goods. By Christ Almighty, she's coming through alone – with the diamonds.' He calculated swiftly. 'She left the mine at three am. She'll be here an hour or so after noon.'

He left the dugout and climbed the bank. He found a place to sit and lit one of his precious cheroots. He looked at the sky, watching the crescent moon sink into the desert. When the dawn turned the eastern horizon into a peacock's tail of colour, he went down to the camp and blew flame from last night's ashes.

Swart Hendrick came out of the dugout and went to urinate noisily in the sand. He came back to the fire buttoning his breeches, yawning widely and sniffing the coffee in the billy.

'We are changing the plan,' Lothar told him, and Hendrick blinked and became warily attentive.

'Why?'

'The woman is bring the diamonds through alone. She won't give in easily. I don't want her hurt in any way.'

'I wouldn't – '

'The hell you wouldn't. When you get excited, you shoot,' Lothar cut him off brusquely. 'But that's not the only reason.' He ticked off the others on his

fingers. 'First: one woman alone requires only one man. I have time enough to re-rig the ropes to bring down the boulders into the cutting from my position. Two: the woman knows you, it doubles the risk of having us recognized. Three,' he paused, the true reason was that he wanted to be alone with Centaine again. It would be the last time. He would never be coming back this way again. 'Lastly, we will do it this way because I say we will. You will stay here with Manfred and the horses, ready to ride as soon as I have done the job.'

Hendrick shrugged. 'I will help you rig the ropes,' he grunted.

* * *

Centaine stopped the Daimler at the head of the cutting and left the engine running as she jumped out onto the running-board and surveyed the crossing.

Her own outward tracks were still clear and sharp and untouched in the soft lemon-coloured dust. There had been no other traffic through the drift since she had passed the night before last. She unhooked the water bag and drank three mouthfuls, and then corked it again and hung it on the spare wheel bracket, climbed back into the cab, slammed the door and let off the handbrake.

She let the Daimler trundle down the incline, swiftly gathering speed, when suddenly there was a rush of earth and rock, a swirling cloud of dust obscured the cutting directly ahead of her and she hit the brake hard.

The bank had collapsed on one side, and had almost filled the cutting with rock and loose earth.

'*Merde*!' she swore. It would mean a delay while she cleared the rubble or found another place to cross. She snapped the Daimler into reverse and twisted in her seat looking back through the missing rear window that the striker had knocked out, preparing to back up the incline – and she felt the first flutter of alarm against her ribs.

The bank had collapsed behind the Daimler also, sliding down in a soft churned ramp. She was trapped in the cutting, and she leaned out of the open window and looked about her anxiously, coughing in the dust that still billowed around her vehicle.

As it cleared she saw that the road ahead was only partially blocked. On the opposite side to the landslide there was still a narrow gap, not sufficient for the wide track of the Daimler to get through, but there was a spade strapped to the roof-rack. A few hours' work in the burning sun should clear the way enough for her to work the Daimler through, but the setback galled her. She reached for the door handle, then a premonition of danger stopped her hand and she looked up the bank beside her.

There was a man standing at the top of the rise, looking down at her. His boots at the level of her eyes were scuffed and white with dust. There were dark sweat patches on his blue shirt. He was a tall man, but he had the lean hard look of a soldier or a hunter. However, it was the rifle that he carried across his hip, pointing down into her face and the mask he wore that terrified her.

The mask was a white flour bag. She could read the red and blue lettering on it: 'Premier Milling Co Ltd', an innocuous kitchen article endowed with infinite menace by the two eye-holes that had been cut into the cloth. The mask and the rifle told her exactly what to expect.

A whole series of thoughts flashed through her mind as she sat frozen at the wheel staring up at him.

The *diamonds are not insured*. That was the thought at the forefront of her mind. The *next staging post is forty miles ahead*, was the next thought, and then: and then: I *forgot to reload the shotgun – spent shells in both barrels*.

The man above her spoke, his voice muffled by the mask and obviously disguised.

'Switch off the engine!' He gestured with the rifle to enforce the order. 'Get out!'

She got out and looked around her desperately, her terror gone now, burned away by the need to think and act. Her eyes fastened directly ahead on the narrow gap left between the soft ramp of raw earth where the landslide had poured down in front of her and the steep firm bank on the other side.

'I can get through,' she thought, 'or at least I can try.' And she ducked back into the cab.

'Stop!' The man above her yelled, but she slammed the Daimler into low gear.

The rear wheels spun in the fine yellow dust, throwing it back in twin fountains. The Daimler lurched forward, the tail swaying and skidding, but it gathered speed sharply and Centaine aimed the bonnet at the narrow gap between the bank and the slide of earth and rock.

She heard the man above her shout again, and then a warning rifle shot cracked over the top of the cab but she ignored it and concentrated on taking the Daimler out of the trap.

She rode her offside wheels high up the incline of the bank, and the Daimler reared over on its side almost to the point of capsizing, but its speed was still building up. Centaine was heavily shaken and tossed about so that she had only her grip on the steering wheel to keep her in her seat as the big car canted even further over.

Still the gap was too narrow; her nearside wheels smashed into the piled earth and rock. The Daimler bucked wildly, throwing its nose high, flying up and forward like a hunter at a fence. Centaine was hurled towards the windshield, but she flung up a hand to brace herself and clung to the wheel with the other.

The Daimler came down again with a rending crash, jerking Centaine back against the padded leather seat. She felt unyielding rock slam up into the Daimler's belly like a boxer taking a heavy body blow, and the back wheels crabbed over the pile of broken earth, the rubber tyres screeching as they sought purchase on the tumbled boulders. Then they caught and flung the Daimler forward again.

It dropped down the far side of the obstacle, and hit hard. Centaine heard something break, the clanging rupture of one of the steering rods and the wheel spun without resistance in her hands. The Daimler had fought its way over the barrier, but it was mortally wounded and out of control. The steering gone and the throttle linkage jammed wide open.

Centaine screamed and clung to the walnut dashboard as it roared down the cutting towards the riverbed, slamming into one bank and then hurling across and crashing into the other, the coachwork banging and ripping and buckling at each impact.

She tried desperately to reach the ignition switch, but the speedometer needle was flicking at the 30 mph notch and she was thrown across the passenger seat.

The steel corner of the diamond case gouged her ribs, then she was thrown back the other way.

The door beside her burst open just as the Daimler roared out of the cutting into the riverbed and Centaine was hurled out through it. Instinctively she doubled herself into a ball, as though she were taking a fall from a galloping horse, and she rolled in the soft white sand, head over heels, coming up at last on her knees.

The Daimler was slewing wildly across the riverbed, the engine still roaring, and one of the front wheels, damaged by the rocks of the barrier, flew off, bounding and leaping like a wild creature until it struck the far bank.

The front end of the Daimler dropped and the nose dug into the sand. The engine was still roaring and the huge vehicle somersaulted end over end and came down on its back. The three remaining wheels pointed at the sky, spinning in a blur, the glass in the windows crackling and splintering into diamond chips, the cab buckling and sagging, hot oil pouring out of the slats in the bonnet and soaking into the sand.

Centaine pushed herself up and was running as she regained her feet. The sand clung to her ankles. It was like running in a bath of treacle, and terror had heightened her senses so that time seemed to stand still. It was like one of those terrible dreams in which all her movements were reduced to slow motion.

She dared not look behind her. That menacing masked figure must surely be close. She tensed for the grip of the hand that would seize her at any instant or the slam of a bullet into her back, but she reached the Daimler and dropped on her knees in the sand beside it.

The driver's door had been torn off and she crawled halfway into the aperture. The shotgun was wedged against the steering control but she dragged it clear and ripped open the small door of the glove compartment. The cardboard box of shotgun shells was scarlet with black lettering:

ELEY KYNOCH
12 GAUGE
25 X SSG

It broke open under her frantic fingers and the red brass-tipped shells spilled into the sand around her knees.

She pushed across the breech lock of the shotgun with her thumb and broke open the gun. The two empty birdshot cartridges flew out with a crisp click-click of the ejectors – and the gun was snatched out of her hands.

The masked man stood over her. He must have moved like a hunting leopard to come down the bank and across the riverbed so quickly. He flung the empty shotgun out across the sand. It landed fifty feet away, but the impetus of the throw had swung him off balance. Centaine launched herself at him, coming off her knees and driving her whole weight into his chest, just below the raised left arm that he had used to throw the shotgun.

It was unexpected, and he was balanced on one foot. They went over together in the sand. For an instant Centaine was on top of him, and then she wriggled away, came to her feet and floundered back towards the Daimler. The engine was still racing, blue smoke pouring from the engine as the oil drained away from the sump and it overheated.

The pistol! Centaine seized the handle of the rear door and threw her weight against it. Through the window she could see the leather holster and the

chequered butt of Twentyman-Jones' service revolver protruding from the seat pocket, but the door was jammed.

She ducked back to the gaping front door and tried to reach it over the back of the driver's seat, but bone-hard fingers dug into her shoulder and she was dragged bodily out of the doorway. Instantly she spun in his grip, and his face was very close to hers. The thin white cotton bag covered his entire head, like the head of a Ku-Klux Klansman. The eye-holes were dark as the hollow sockets in a skull, but there was a glint of human eyes deep in the shadow and she went for them with her fingernails.

He jerked his head away but her forefinger hooked in the thin cloth and ripped it down to his chin. He seized her wrists and instead of pulling away she hurled herself against him and drove her right knee up into his groin. He twisted violently and caught her knee on the side of his upper thigh. She felt the shock of the blow drive into the rubbery muscle of his leg, but his grip on her wrists tightened as though she had been caught in the jaws of a steel gin trap.

She ducked her head and fastened her teeth into his wrist like a ferret, at the same time kicking and kneeing him in the lower body and shins, raining blows at him, most of them slogging into his hard flesh or bouncing off bone.

He was grunting and trying to control her. Obviously he hadn't expected this type of wild resistance, and the pain in his wrist must have been excruciating. Already the hinges of her jaws were cramping with the force of her bite. She could feel tissue and flesh splitting and tearing between her teeth and his blood welled into her mouth, hot and coppery and salt-tasting.

With his free hand the masked man seized a handful of her thick curly hair and tried to pull her head back. She was breathing through her nose, snuffling like a bulldog and gritting her teeth in with all her strength, and she reached the bone. It grated under her teeth, and the man was tugging and jerking at her head, giving small agonized cries and grunts.

She closed her eyes, expecting him at any moment to slam his fist into the side of her head and break the grip of her teeth, but he was strangely gentle and considerate in his reaction, not attempting to inflict injury or pain, merely trying to pull her off.

She felt something burst in her mouth. She had bitten through an artery in his wrist. Blood pumped against the roof of her palate with hot spurts that threatened to choke and drown her. She let it pour from the corners of her mouth without relaxing her bite. It sprayed from her lips and splattered them both as he jerked her head from side to side. He was moaning with agony now, and at last he used punitive force.

He dug thumb and forefinger into the hinges of her jaw. His fingers were like iron spikes. Pain shot down into her locked jaws and up behind her eyes, and she opened her mouth and flung herself backwards, again taking him by surprise, breaking out of his grip and darting away back towards the Daimler.

This time she thrust her arm over the back of the driver's seat and reached up to the butt of the revolver. It slipped from the greased holster, and while she fumbled with a shaking hand to get a hold on it, the masked man seize her hair from behind and jerked her backwards. The heavy pistol fell through her fingers and clattered against the steel of the inverted cab.

She rounded on him again, snapping at his face with teeth that were still stained pink with his blood. The torn mask flapped over his face, blinding him for an instant and he stumbled and fell holding her in his arms. She was kicking

and scratching and slashing at him as he rolled on top of her and pinned her with his full weight, holding her arms spread like a crucifix – and suddenly she stopped struggling and stared up at him.

The flap of his mask hung open and she could see his eyes. Those strange pale topaz-coloured eyes with the long dark lashes, and she gasped.

'Lothar!'

He stiffened with the shock of his name, and they lay, locked like lovers, legs entangled, their lower bodies pressed together, both panting wildly and smeared with his blood, staring at each other wordlessly.

Abruptly he released her and stood up. He pulled the mask off his head and his tousled golden locks fell about his ears and tumbled down his forehead into his eyes as he wrapped the mask tightly around his mutilated wrist. He realized that it was seriously injured, the tendons and bone were exposed and the flesh was mangled and tattered where she had chewed it. Bright scarlet arterial blood soaked through the white cloth immediately and dripped into the sand.

Centaine pulled herself into a sitting position and watched him. The engine of the Daimler had stalled, and there was silence except for their breathing.

'Why are you doing this?' she whispered.

'You know why.' He knotted the cloth with his teeth, and suddenly she flung herself sideways and reached desperately into the cab, her fingers scrabbling again for the pistol. She touched it, but could not get her fingers around the butt before he pulled her away and pushed her over backwards in the sand.

He picked up the pistol and unclipped the lanyard. He wound the lanyard around his forearm as a tourniquet and grunted with satisfaction as the seep of blood shrivelled.

'Where are they?' He looked down at her where she lay.

'What are you talking about?'

He stooped and looked into the cab of the Daimler, then pulled out the black japanned despatch box.

'Keys?' he asked.

She stared back at him defiantly and he squatted and placed the box firmly in the sand, then stepped back a pace. He cocked the pistol and fired a single shot. The report was stunning in the desert silence, and Centaine's ear drums buzzed with the memory. The bullet had torn the lock of the despatch box away and a circle of the black paint flaked from the lid leaving the metal beneath shiny and bright.

Lothar pocketed the pistol, and knelt and lifted the lid. The case was filled with small packages, each neatly wrapped in brown paper and sealed with red wax. He picked out one package, favouring his injured hand, and read aloud the inscription in Twentyman-Jones' ornate old-fashioned penmanship:

156 PIECES TOTAL 382 CARATS

He tore open the heavy cartridge paper with his teeth and shook out a sprinkle of gems into the palm of his injured hand. In the white sunlight they had that peculiar soapy sheen of uncut diamonds.

'Very pretty,' he murmured and dropped the loose stones into his pocket. He packed the torn parcel back into the despatch case and closed the lid.

'I knew you were a murderer,' she said. 'I never thought you a common thief.'

'You stole my boats and my company. Don't talk to me about thieves.' He

tucked the despatch case under his arm and stood up. He went round to the boot of the Daimler and managed to open it a crack, even though the vehicle was inverted, and he checked the contents.

'Good,' he said. 'You've had the sense to bring spare water. Twenty gallons will last you a week, but they'll find you before then. Abrahams is sending out an escort to meet you. I intercepted the instruction from Twentyman-Jones.'

'You swine,' she whispered.

'I will cut the telegraph wires before I leave. As soon as that happens they will realize at both ends that something is wrong. You'll be all right.'

'Oh God, I hate you.'

'Stay with the vehicle. That's the first law of desert survival. Don't go wandering off. They will rescue you in about two days – and I will have two days' start.

'I thought I hated you before, but now I know the real meaning of the word.'

'I could have taught it to you,' he said quietly, as he picked the abandoned shotgun out of the sand. 'I came to know it well – over the years that I was rearing your son. Then again when you came back into my life only to tear down everything I ever dreamed about and worked for.' He swung the shotgun like an axe against one of the boulders. The butt shattered but he went on until it was bent and battered and useless. He dropped it.

Then he slung the Mauser over his shoulder and transferred the despatch case to his other hand. He held the injured hand in its blood-wet wrapping against his chest. Clearly the pain was fierce; he had paled under his deep bronze tan and there was a catch in his voice as he went on.

'I tried not to hurt you – if you hadn't struggled – ' he broke off. 'We will not meet again, ever. Goodbye, Centaine.'

'We will meet again,' she contradicted him. 'You know me well enough, you must realize that I will not rest until I have full retribution for this day's work.'

He nodded. 'I know you will try.' He turned away.

'Lothar!' she called sharply, and then softened her voice when he turned back. 'I'll make you a bargain – your company and your boats free of all debt for my diamonds.'

'A bad bargain.' He smiled sadly. 'By now the plant and boats are worth nothing, while your diamonds – '

'Plus fifty thousand pounds and my promise not to report this affair to the police.' She tried to keep the edge of desperation out of her voice.

'Last time it was I who was begging – do you recall? No, Centaine, even if I wanted, I could not go back now. I have burned my bridges.' He thought about the horses, but could not tell her. 'No bargain, Centaine. Now I must go.'

'Half the diamonds – leave half, Lothar.'

'Why?'

'For the love we once shared.'

He laughed bitterly. 'You will have to give me a better reason than that.'

'All right. If you take them you will destroy me, Lothar. I cannot survive their loss. Already I am finely drawn. I will be utterly ruined.'

'As I was when you took my boats.' He turned and trudged through the sand to the bank, and she stood up.

'Lothar De La Rey!' she shouted after him. 'You refused my offer – then take my oath instead. I swear, and I call on God and all his saints to witness, I swear that I will never rest again until you swing by the neck from the gallows.'

He did not look back, but she saw him flinch his head at the threat. Then

cradling his injured wrist and burdened by the rifle and the despatch case, he climbed the high bank and was gone.

She sank down on the sand and a wave of reaction swept over her. She found she was shaking wildly and uncontrollably. Despondency and humiliation and despair came at her in waves like a storm surf battering an unresisting beach, sweeping over it then sucking back and gathering and rushing forwards again. She found she was weeping, thick, slow tears dissolving the clots of his drying blood from her lips and chin, and her tears disgusted her as much as the taste of blood at the back of her throat.

Disgust gave her the strength and resolution to pull herself to her feet and cross to the Daimler. Miraculously the water bag was still on it bracket. She washed away the blood and the tears. She gargled the taste of his blood from her mouth and spat it pink into the sand and she thought of following him.

He had taken the revolver and the shotgun was a battered and twisted piece of steel.

'Not yet – ' she whispered, 'but very soon. I have given you my oath on it, Lothar De La Rey.'

Instead she went to the boot of the inverted Daimler. She had to scoop away the sand with her hands before she could get if fully open. She took out the two ten-gallon cans of water and the canisters of industrial diamonds, carried them to the shade of the bank and buried them in the sand to hide them and to keep the water as cool as possible.

Then she returned to the Daimler and impatiently unpacked the other survival equipment that she always carried, suddenly deadly afraid that the telegraph tap had been offloaded or forgotten – but it was there in the tool box with the wheel jack and spanners.

She lugged the reel of wire and the haversack containing the tap as she followed Lothar's tracks up the bank and found where he had tethered his horse.

'He said he was going to cut the telegraph – ' She shaded her eyes and peered along the river course. 'He should have guessed I would have carried a tap with me. He isn't going to get his two day's start.'

She picked out the line of telegraph poles cutting across the road loop and the bend of the river. The tracks of Lothar's horse followed the bank, and she broke into a run and trotted along them.

She saw the break in the wires from two hundred yards off. The severed copper wires dangled to earth in two lazy inverted parabolas and she quickened her pace. When she reached the spot where the telegraph line crossed the river and looked down the bank she immediately recognized the remnants of Lothar's camp. Sand had been hastily kicked over the fire, but the embers still smouldered.

She dropped the coil of wire and the haversack and scrambled down the bank. She found the dugout and realized that more than one man had been living here for some considerable time. There were three mattresses of cut grass.

'Three.' She puzzled over it for a few moments, and then worked it out. 'He has his bastard with him.' She still couldn't bring herself to think of Manfred as her son. 'And the other one will be Swart Hendrick. He and Lothar are inseparable.'

She ducked from the dugout and stood for a moment undecided. It would take time to rig the tap to the severed wires, and it was vitally important to find

out which way Lothar had ridden if she was to set the pursuit on him before he got clear.

She made her decision. 'I'll rig the telegraph after I know which way to send them.'

It was unlikely he would head east into the Kalahari. There was nothing out there.

'He'll head back towards Windhoek,' she guessed, and she made her first cast in that direction. The area around the camp was thickly trodden with spoor of horse and men. They had been here for at least two weeks, she judged. Only her Bushman training enable her to make sense of the tangled tracks.

'They didn't go out that way,' she decided at last. 'Then they must have headed south for Gobabis and the Orange river.'

She made her next cast in that direction, circling the southern perimeter of the camp, and when she found no spoor fresher than the previous day, she looked to the north.

'Surely not.' She was confused. 'There is nothing out there before the Okavango river and Portuguese territory – the horses will never make it across the wastes of Bushmanland.'

Nevertheless she made her next cast across that northern segment and almost immediately cut the outgoing spoor, fresh and cleanly printed in the soft earth.

'Three riders each leading a spare horse, not an hour ago. Lothar must be taking the northern route after all. He is crazy – or he has worked out something.' She followed the fresh spoor for a mile, to make certain that he had not doubled or backtracked. The spoor ran straight and unwavering into the shimmering heat mists of the northern wastes, and she shivered as she remembered what it was like out there.

'He must be crazy,' she whispered. 'But I know he isn't. He's going for the Angola border. That's his old base from the ivory-poaching days. If he reaches the river we'll never see him again. He has friends over there, the Portuguese traders who bought his ivory. This time Lothar will have a million pounds of diamonds in his pocket and the wide world to choose from. I have to catch him before he gets across.'

Her spirits quailed at the enormity of the idea and she felt despondency come at her again. 'He has prepared this carefully – everything is in his favour. We'll never catch him.' She fought off the beast of despair. 'Yes, we will. We have to. I have to outwit and beat him. I simply have to, just to survive.'

She whirled and ran back to the abandoned camp.

The severed telegraph wires drooped to earth and she gathered the ends and clipped the bridging wires from the coil to them, drawing them just taut enough to keep them clear of the earth.

She put her tap into the circuit and screwed the terminals to the pack of dry-cell batteries. The batteries had been renewed before she left Windhoek. They should still be full of life. For a dreadful moment her mind went blank and she could not remember a single letter of the Morse code, then it returned with a rush and she hammered quickly on brass key.

'Juno for Vingt. Acknowledge.'

For long seconds there was only echoing silence in her headphones, then the startling beep of the reply:

'Vingt for Juno. Go ahead.'

She tried to pick the short word and terse abridged phrase as she told Twentyman-Jones of the robbery and gave her position, then went on:

'Negotiate stand-off with strikers as recovery of goods mutually essential. Stop. Take truck to northern tip of O'chee Pan and locate Bushman encampment in mongongo forest. Stop. Bushleader named Kwi. Stop. Tell Kwi "Nam Child *kaleya*". Repeat "Nam Child *kaleya*"' – and she gave thanks that the word *kaleya* bore phonetic rendition into the Roman alphabet and required neither the complicated tonals nor the clicks of the Bushman language. *Kaleya* was the distress call, the cry for help that no clan member could ignore. 'Bring Kwi with you,' she went on and continued with her further instructions; and when she signed off Twentyman-Jones acknowledged and then sent:

'Are you safe and unharmed. Query. Vingt.'

'Affirmative. Ends. Juno.'

She mopped the sweat off her face with the yellow silk scarf. She was sitting in the direct rays of the sun. Then she flexed her fingers and bent once more to the keyboard and tapped out the call sign of her operator in the offices of Courtney Mining and Finance Company in Windhoek.

The acknowledgement was prompt. Obviously the operator had been following her transmission to Twentyman-Jones, but she asked:

'Have you copied previous?'

'Affirmative,' he tapped back.

'Relay previous to Administrator Colonel Blaine Malcomess plus following for Malcomess. Quote: Request co-operation in capture of culprits and recovery of stolen goods. Stop. Do you have report on large number stolen horses or purchase of horses by one Lothar De La Rey within last three months. Respond soonest. Ends. Juno.'

The distant operator acknowledged and then continued:

'Pettifogger for Juno.' Abe must have been summoned to the telegraph office the minute they received their first transmision. 'Greatly concerned for your safety. Stop. Remain your present position. Stop.'

And Centaine exclaimed irritably, 'I sucked that egg long ago, Abe.' But she copied the rest of it.

'Armed escort left Windhoek 5 am instant. Stop. Should reach you early tomorrow. Stop. Stand by for Malcomess. Ends. Pettifogger.'

The wires were long enough to allow her to move the keyboard into the strip of shade below the bank and while she waited she gave all her concentration to the task ahead.

Certain facts were apparent and the first of these was that they were never going to catch Lothar De La Rey in a stern chase. He had too long a lead, and he was going into country over which he had travelled and hunted for half his life. He knew it better than any living white man, better than even she did, but not better than little Kwi.

'We have to work out his route and cut him off, and we will have to use horses. Trucks will be useless over that terrain. Lothar knows that, he is banking on that. He will choose a route that trucks can never follow.'

She closed her eyes and visualized a map of the northern territory, the vast forbidding sweep of desert called Bushmanland.

She only knew of surface water at two points, one the place she always thought of as Elephant Pan, and the other a deep seep below a hillock of shale. They were secret Bushman places, both of which old O'wa, her adopted grandfather, had shown her fifteen years before. She wondered if she could find either water-hole again, but she was certain that Lothar knew them and could ride directly to them. He probably knew of other water-holes that she did not.

The beep of the telegraph disturbed her and she reached for it eagerly.

'Malcomess for Juno. Police report theft of 26 horses from military remount depot Okahandja 3rd of last monh. Stop. Only two animals recovered. Stop. State your further requirements.'

'I was right! Lothar has set up staging posts across the desert,' she exclaimed, and she closed her eyes and tried to visualize a map of the northern territory, estimating distances and times. At last she opened her eyes again, and bent to the telegraph key.

'Convinced fugitives attempting to reach Okavango river direct. Stop. Assemble small mobile force of desert-trained men with spare horses. Stop. Rendezvous Kalkrand Mission Station soonest. Stop. I will join you with Bushman trackers.'

* * *

Twentyman-Jones reached her before the escort from Windhoek. O'chee Pan was on his direct route, only a few miles from the road. The company truck came rumbling over the plain and Centaine ran down the tracks to meet it, waving both hands above her head and laughing wildly with relief. She had changed into breeches and riding-boots from her luggage in the Daimler.

Twentyman-Jones jumped down from the cab and came to her in a long-legged lolloping run. He caught her and held her to his chest.

'Thank God,' he muttered fervently. 'Thank God you are safe.'

It was the first time ever that he had embraced her and he was immediately embarrassed. He released her and stepped back scowling to cover it.

'Did you get Kwi?' she demanded.

'In the truck.'

Centaine ran to the truck. Kwi and Fat Kwi were crouched in the back, clearly both of them terrified by the experience. They looked like wild animals in a cage, their dark eyes huge and swimming.

'Nam Child!' shrieked Kwi, and both of them rushed to her for comfort, twittering and clicking with relief and joy. She hugged them like frightened children, murmuring assurance and endearments.

'I will be with you now. There is nothing to fear. These are good men and I will not leave you. Think what stories you will be able to tell the clan when you return. You will be famous amongst all the San, your names will be spoken through all the Kalahari.' And they giggled merrily at the notion, childlike, their fears all forgotten.

'I will be even more famous than Fat Kwi,' Kwi boasted, 'for I am older and fleeter and cleverer than he is,' and fat Kwi bridled.

'You will both be famous.' Hastily Centaine averted the brewing dispute. 'For we are going to track evil men who have done me great harm. You will follow them and lead me to them, and afterwards I will give you such gifts as you have seen only in your dreams and all men will say that there were never before two hunters and trackers such as Kwi and his brother Fat Kwi. But now we must hurry before the evil ones escape us.'

She ran back to Twentyman-Jones and the little San stayed close at her heels like faithful dogs.

'De La Rey left the industrials. I've buried them in the riverbed.' She

stopped with surprise when she recognized the two other men with Twentyman-Jones. The driver was Gerhard Fourie and his companion was Maclear, one of the other members of the strike committee. Both of them looked sheepish as Maclear spoke for them.

'Right pleased we all are to see you safe and well, Mrs Courtney. Wasn't a man at the mine who wasn't worried sick about you.'

'Thank you, Mr Maclear.'

'Anything we can do, we'll do. We are in this together, Mrs Courtney.'

'That's right, Mr Maclear. No diamonds, no wages. Will you please help me recover the industrials that the thieves left and then we will head for Kalkrand. Have you got enough fuel to get us there, Mr Fourie?'

'I'll have you there by morning, Mrs Courtney,' the driver promised. Kalkrand was the end of the line. The track went no further.

The road that Fourie took to bring them to Kalkrand was a wide circle, avoiding the bad land of central Bushmanland. It headed north and west and then back to the east, so they would be 150 miles north of the point where Lothar had intercepted Centaine but 70 miles farther west when they reached Kalkrand. Their net gain on Lothar would be barely 80 miles, even less if he had taken a more easterly route towards the Okavango river. Of course it was also possible that Centaine's guess was wrong and that he had escaped in some other direction. She wouldn't let herself even think about that possibility.

'There has been other traffic on this road within the last few hours,' she told Twentyman-Jones as she peered ahead through the windscreen. 'It looks like two other trucks. Do you think it could be police detachment that Colonel Malcomess is sending?'

'If it is, then the man is a marvel to have got them away so quickly.'

'Of course they would have followed the main road north to Okahandja before turning off in this direction.' Centaine wanted so badly for it to be so, but Twentyman-Jones shook his head dubiously.

'More likely a supply convoy for the mission station. My bet is that we will have to hang around the mission station waiting for the police and the horses to arrive.'

The galvanized roofs of the mission station appeared out of the morning haze ahead of them. It was a desolate spot below a low ridge of red shale probably chosen for the subterranean water supply. A pair of gaunt windmills stood like crowned sentinels over the boreholes that supplied the station.

'German Dominican fathers,' Twentyman-Jones told Centaine as they bumped over the last mile. 'They serve the nomadic Ovahimba tribes of this area.'

'Look!' Centaine interrupted him eagerly. 'There are the trucks parked next to the church, and horses watering at the windmill. And there, look! A uniformed trooper. 'It's them! They are waiting for us. Colonel Malcomess was as good as his promise.'

Fourie pulled up alongside the two sand-coloured police trucks and Centaine jumped down and shouted at the police trooper as he ran to meet them from the water troughs below the windmill.

'Hello, Constable, who is in charge here – ' and then she broke off and stared as a tall figure appeared on the verandah of the stone-walled building beside the little church.

He wore khaki gaberdine riding breeches and polished brown boots, and he

was shrugging on a field officer's tunic over his shirt and suspenders, as he ran lightly down the steps and came towards her.

'Colonel Malcomess. I never expected you to be here in person.'

'You asked for full co-operation, Mrs Courtney.' He offered his hand and static electricity flashed a blue spark between their fingertips. Centaine laughed and jerked her hand away. Then, when he still held his hand towards her, she took it again. His grip was firm and dry and reassuring.

'You aren't going into the desert with us, are you? You have your duties as administrator.'

'If I don't go, then you don't either.' He smiled. 'I have received strict instructions from both the prime minister, General Hertzog, and from the leader of the opposition, General Smuts, that I am not to let you out of my personal charge. Apparently, madam, you have a reputation for headstrong action. The two old gentlemen are very perturbed.'

'I have to go,' she broke in. 'Nobody else can handle the Bushman trackers. Without them the robbers will get clean away.'

He inclined his head in agreement. 'I am sure the intention of the two worthy generals is that neither of us go, but I chose to interpret their orders rather as instruction that both of us should.' And suddenly he grinned like a naughty schoolboy about to play truant. 'You are stuck with me, I'm afraid.'

She thought of being with him out in the desert, far from his wife. For a moment she forgot Lothar De Lay Rey and the diamonds, and suddenly she realized that they were still holding hands and that everybody was watching them. She dropped his hand and asked briskly:

'When can we leave?'

In reply he turned and bellowed, 'Upsaddle! Upsaddle! We ride immediately!'

While the troopers ran to the horses, he turned back to her, businesslike and competent.

'And now, Mrs Courtney, will you be good enough to let me know your intentions – and where the hell we are going?'

She laughed. 'Do you have a map?'

'This way.' He led her into the mission office and quickly introduced her to the two German Dominican fathers who ran the station. Then he leant over his large-scale map spread on the desk.

'Show me what you have in mind,' he invited, and she stood beside him, not quite touching him.

'The robbery took place here.' She touched the spot with her forefinger. 'I followed the tracks in this direction. He is heading for Portuguese territory. I am absolutely sure of that. But he has to go three hundred miles to reach it.'

'So what you have done is circled out ahead of him,' he nodded 'and now you want to ride eastwards into the desert and cut him off. But it's a big piece of country. Needle in a haystack, don't you think?'

'Water,' she said. 'He has left his spare horses at water. I'm sure of that.'

'The horses stolen from the army? Yes, I understand, but there is no water out there.'

'There is,' she told him. 'It's not marked on the map but he knows where it is. My bushmen know where it is. We will intercept him at one of the water-holes, or we will cut his spoor there if he has beaten us to it.

He straightened up and rolled the map. 'Do you think that possible?'

'That he has got ahead of us?' Centaine asked. 'You have to remember he is

a hard man, and this desert is his home paddock. Never underestimate him, Colonel. That would be a serious mistake.'

'I have examined the man's record.' He stuffed his map into the leather case and then placed on his head a khaki solar helmet of thick cork with a sweeping rim that protected his neck. It covered his ears and increased his already impressive height. 'He is a dangerous man. He once had a price of ten thousand pounds on his head. I don't expect this to be easy.'

A police sergeant appeared in the doorway behind him. 'All ready, Colonel.'

'Do you have Mrs Courtney's mount saddled?'

'Yes, sir!' The sergeant was lean and brown and muscular, with thick drooping moustaches, and Centaine approved the choice. Blaine Malcomess saw her scrutiny.

'This is Sergeant Hansmeyer. He and I are old companions from Smuts' campaign.'

'How do you do, Mrs Courtney. Heard all about you, ma'am,' the sergeant saluted her.

'Glad to have you with us, Sergeant.'

Quickly they shook hands with the Dominican fathers and went out into the sunlight. Centaine went to the big strong bay gelding Blaine had allocated to her and adjusted her stirrup leathers.

'Mount up!' Blaine Malcomess ordered, and while the sergeant and his four troopers swung up into the saddle, Centaine turned quickly to Twentyman-Jones.

'I wish I was coming with you, Mrs Courtney,' he said. 'Twenty years ago nothing would have stopped me.'

She smiled. 'Hold thumbs for us. If we don't get those diamonds back you'll probably be working for De Beers again and I'll be doing needlework in the poorhouse.'

'Rot the swine who did this to you,' he said. 'Bring him back in chains.'

Centaine went up onto the gelding's back and he felt good and steady under her. She kneed him up beside Blaine's horse.

'You can slip your hunting dogs, Mrs Courtney.' He smiled at her.

'Take us to the water, Kwi,' she called, and the two little Bushmen, their bows and quivers of poisoned arrows on their naked backs turned to face the east. Their small heads covered with peppercorns of dark wool bobbing, their tight round buttocks bulging out from their brief loincloths and neat childlike feet flying, they went away. They were born to run, and the horses extended into a trot to hold them in sight.

Centaine and Blaine rode side by side at the head of the column. The sergeant and his four troopers followed in single file, each of them trailing two spare horses on lead reins. The spare horses carried water, twenty gallons in big felt-covered round bottles, three days' supply if they used it with care, for men and animals were desert-hardened.

Centaine and Blaine rode in silence, though every once in a while she glanced at him out of the corner of her eye. Impressive on his feet, Blaine was imperial in the saddle. Mounted he had become a centaur, part of the horse beneath him, and she saw now how he had earned his international reputation as a polo player.

Watching him she found herself correcting little flaws in her own carriage and seat on the horse, bad habits which she had drifted into over the years,

until she looked as good as he did in the saddle. She felt she could ride for ever across this desert she loved with this man at her side.

They crossed the ridge of weathered shale and Blaine spoke for the first time. 'You were right. We would never have got the trucks across there. It had to be on horseback.'

'We haven't hit the calcrete yet, and then there is the sand. We'd be forever digging out the wheels,' she agreed.

The miles drifted back behind them. The Bushmen bobbed ahead of them, never wavering but running straight and certain towards their distant goal. Every hour Blaine halted the column and let the horses blow while he dismounted and went back to talk quietly to his men, getting to know them, checking the panniers on the spare horses, making certain that they were not galling, taking precautions to avert fatigue and injury before they arose. Then when the five minutes was up he ordered them forward again at the trot.

They rode until it was fully dark before he halted them; then he supervised the issue of water and made sure the horses were rubbed down and knee-haltered before he came to the small fire at which Centaine sat. She had completed her own chores, seeing the Bushmen fed and settled for the night, and now she was preparing the meal for Blaine and herself. She handed him the mess tin as he squatted opposite her.

'I regret, sir, that the pheasant and caviar is off the menu. However, I can heartily recommend the bully beef stew.'

'Strange how good it tastes when you eat it like this.' He ate with honest appetite, then scrubbed the empty plate with dry sand and handed it back to her. He lit a cheroot with a twig from the fire. 'And how good a cheroot tastes with a trace of woodsmoke.'

She tidied and packed for a quick start in the morning and then came back to the fire and hesitated as she reached her seat opposite him. He moved over on the saddle cloth on which he was sitting, leaving half of it free, and without a word she crossed to it and sat with her legs curled up under her. Only inches separated them.

'It's so beautiful,' she murmured, looking up at the night sky. 'The stars are so close. I feel I could reach up and pluck them, and wear them around my neck like a garland of wild flowers.'

'Poor stars,' he said softly. 'They would pale into insignificance.'

She turned her head and smiled at him, letting the compliment lie between them, savouring it for a moment before she lifted her face to the sky again. 'That is my personal star.' She pointed out Acrux in the Great Cross. Michael had chosen it for her. Michael – she felt a sting of guilt at his memory, but it was not so sharp now.

'Which is your star?' she asked.

'Should I have one?'

'Oh, yes,' she nodded. 'It's absolutely essential.' She paused, then went on almost shyly, 'Would you let me choose one for you?'

'I would be honoured.' He wasn't mocking her, he was serious as she was.

'There.' She swivelled towards the north, where the path of the Zodiac was blazed across the sky. 'That star there, Regulus, in the constellation of the Lion, your birth sign. I choose that and I give it to you, Blaine.' She used his given name at last.

'And I accept it most gratefully. Every time I see if from now on, I will think of you, Centaine.'

It was a love token, given and accepted, both of them understood that and they were silenced by the significance of the moment.

'How did you know that my birth sign was Leo?' he asked at last.

'I found out,' she answered guilelessly. 'I thought it was necessary to know. You were born on 28 July 1893.'

'And you,' he replied, 'were born on the first day of the new century. You were named for that. I found out. I also thought it necessary to know.'

* * *

They were riding long before it was light the next morning, eastwards again with the Bushmen their harbingers.

The sun rose and its heat crushed down upon them, drying the sweat upon the horses' flanks into white salt crystals. The troopers rode hunched down as though under a heavy burden. The sun swung through its zenith and slid down into the west. Their shadows stretched out on the earth ahead of them and colour returned to the desert shades of ochre and peach rose and burnt amber.

Ahead of them Kwi stopped suddenly and snuffled the dry flinty air with his flattened nostrils. Fat Kwi imitated him, like a pair of gundogs scenting the pheasant.

'What are they doing?' Blaine asked, as they reined up behind. Before she could answer, Kwi let out a piping cry and then went away at a full run, Fat Kwi streaking after him.

'Water.' Centaine stood in the stirrups. 'They have smelled the water.'

'Are you serious?' he stared at her.

'I couldn't believe it the first time,' she laughed. 'O'wa could smell it from five miles. Come on, I'll prove it to you.' She urged the gelding into a canter.

Ahead of them a low irregularity in the terrain appeared out of the dusty haze, a hillock of purple shale, bare of all vegetation except for a strange antediluvian tree on its summit, a kokerboom with bark like a reptile's skin. Centaine felt a pang of memory and nostalgia. She recognized the place. She had last been here with the two little yellow people she had loved, and Shasa heavy in her womb.

Before they reached the hillock, Kwi and Fat Kwi broke their run and stopped, side by side, to examine the earth at their feet. They were chattering excitedly when Centaine rode up, and she translated for Blaine, her tongue tripping with her own excitement.

'We have cut the spoor. It's De La Rey, no doubt about it. Three riders coming up from the south heading for the fountain. They have abandoned their used-up horses, and they're riding hard, pushing their mounts to the limit. The horses are floundering already. De La Rey has judged it finely.'

Centaine could barely contain her relief. She had guessed right. Lothar was heading for the Portuguese border after all. He and the diamonds were not far ahead of them.

'How long, Kwi?' she demanded anxiously, springing down to examine the spoor for herself.'

'This morning, Nam Child,' the little Bushman told her, pointing to the sky, showing where the sun had stood when Lothar passed.

'Just after dawn. We are eight hours or so behind them,' she told Blaine.

'That's a lot to make up.' He looked serious. 'Every minute we can save will count from now on. Troop forward!'

When they were half a mile from the hillock with its kokerboom crest, Centaine told Blaine, 'There have been other horses grazing around here. A large troop of them over many weeks. Their sign is everywhere. It was just as we guessed, De La Rey has had one of his men herding them here. We should find further evidence of that at the water-hole.' She broke off and peered ahead. There were three dark amorphous heaps lying at the base of the hill.

'What are they?' Blaine was as puzzled as she was. Only when they rode up did they realize what they were.

'Dead horses!' Centaine exclaimed. 'De La Rey must have shot his used-up horses.'

'No.' Blaine had dismounted to examine the carcasses. 'No bullet holes.'

Centaine looked around. She saw the primitive stockade in which the fresh horses had been kept awaiting Lothar's arrival and the small thatched hut where the man left to tend them had lived.

'Kwi,' she called to the Bushman. 'Find the spoor going away from here. Fat Kwi, search the camp. Look for anything which will tell us more about these evil men that we are chasing.' Then she urged her gelding towards the fountain head.

It lay beneath the hillock. Subterranean water had been trapped between strata of the impervious purple shale and brought to the surface here. The hooves of wild game and the bare feet of San people who had drunk here over the millennia had worn down the shale banks. The water lay fifteen feet down in the bottom of a steep conical depression.

On the side nearest the hillock a layer of shale overhung the pool like the roof of a verandah, shading the water from direct rays of the sun, cooling it and protecting it from rapid evaporation. It was a tiny clear pool, not much larger than a bath tub, fed constantly by the upwelling from the earth. From experience, Centaine knew that it was brackish with dissolved minerals and salts, and strongly tainted with the droppings and urine of the birds and animals that drank from the spring.

The pool itself held her attention for only a second, and then she stiffened in the saddle and her hand flew to her mouth, an instinctive expression of her horror as she stared at the crude manmade structure that had been erected on the bank at the edge of the pool.

A thick branch of camel-thorn had been peeled of its bark and planted in the hard earth as a signpost. At its base rocks had been piled in a pyramid to support it, and on its summit an empty half-gallon can had been placed like a helmet. Below the can a plank was nailed to the post, and on it were burned black charred words, probably written with the tip of a ramrod heated in the fire:

THIS WELL IS POISONED

The empty can was bright red with a black skull and crossbones device and below that the dreaded title:

ARSENIC

Blaine had come up beside her and they were both so silent that Centaine imagined she could hear the shale beneath them ticking softly like a cooling oven, then Blaine spoke:

'The dead horses,' he said, 'that accounts for it. The dirty bastard.' His voice crackled with outrage. He pulled his horse around and galloped across to join the troop. Centaine heard him calling,' 'Sergeant. Check the water that is left. The well is poisoned,' and Sergeant Hansmeyer whistled softly.

'Well, that's the end of the chase. We will be lucky to get back to Kalkrand again.'

Centaine found she was trembling with anger and frustration. 'He is going to get clean away,' she told herself. 'He was won on the first trick.'

The gelding smelled the water and tried to get down the bank. She forced him away with her knees, slapping him across the beck with the loose end of the reins. She tethered him at the end of the horse line and measured a ration of oats and mash into his nose bag.

Blaine came to her. 'I'm sorry, Centaine,' he said quietly. 'We'll have to turn back. To go on without water is suicide.'

'I know.'

'It's a pretty filthy trick.' He shook his head. 'Poisoning a waterhole that supports so much desert life. The destruction will be horrible. I have only seen it done once before. When we were on the march up from Walvis in 1915 – ' he broke off as little Kwi came trotting up to them chattering excitedly. 'What does he say?' Blaine asked.

'One of the men we are following is sick,' Centaine answered quickly. 'Kwi has found these bandages.'

Kwi had a double handful of stained and soiled cloth which he offered to Centaine.

'Put them down, Kwi,' she ordered sharply. She could smell the pus and corruption on the bundle. Obediently Kwi set it down at her feet, and Blaine drew the bayonet from its scabbard on his belt to spread the strips of cloth on the sand.

'The mask!' Centaine exclaimed, as she recognized the flour sack that Lothar had worn over his head. It was stiff with dried blood and yellow pus, as were the strips torn from a khaki shirt.

'The sick man lay down while the other changed the saddles to the new horses, and then they had to lift him to his feet and help him to mount.' Kwi had read all this from the spoor.

'I bit him,' Centaine said softly. 'While we were struggling I sank my teeth into his wrist. I felt the bone. It was a very deep wound I gave him.'

'A human bite is almost as dangerous as a snake bite,' Blaine nodded. 'Untreated it will nearly always turn to blood-poisoning. De La Rey is a sick man, and his arm must be a mess, judging by these.' He touched the reeking bandages with the toe of his riding-boot. 'We would have had him. In his condition, we would almost certainly have caught him before he reached the Okavango river. If only we had enough water to go on.' He turned away, unwilling to watch her unhappiness, and he spoke sharply to Sergeant Hansmeyer. 'Half water rations from now on, Sergeant. We will start back to the mission at nightfall. Travel in the cool of the night.'

Centaine could not stand still. She whirled and strode back towards the water-hole, and stood at the top of the bank staring at the notice board with its fatal message.

'How could you do it, Lothar?' she whispered. 'You are a hard and desperate man, but this a dreadful thing – '

She went slowly down the steep bank and squatted at the edge of the water. She reached out and touched the water with her fingertip. It was cold, cold as death, she thought, and wiped the finger carefully on the leg of her breeches as she stared into the pool.

She thought about Blaine's remark, 'I have only seen it done once before. When we were on the march up from Walvis in 1915,' and suddenly a forgotten conversation sprang up from deep in her mind where it had lain buried all these years. She remembered Lothar De La Rey's face in the firelight, his eyes haunted as he confessed to her.

'We had to do it, or at least at the time I thought we did. The Union forces were pressing us so hard. If I had guessed at the consequences – ' He had broken off and stared into the fire. She had loved him so dearly then. She had been his woman. Though she did not yet know it, she already had his child in her womb, and she had reached out and taken his hand to comfort him.

'It doesn't matter,' she had whispered, but he had turned a tragic face to her.

'It does matter, Centaine,' he had told her. 'It was the foulest thing I have ever done. I returned to the water-hole a month later like a murderer. I could smell it from a mile or more. The dead were everywhere, zebra and gemsbok, jackals and little desert foxes, birds, even the vultures that had feasted on the rotting carcasses. So much death. It was something that I will remember on the day I die, the one thing in my life of which I am truly ashamed, something I will have to answer for.'

Centaine straightened up slowly. She felt her rage and disappointment slowly snuffed out by a rising tide of excitement. She touched the water again and watched the circle of ripples spread out across the limpid surface.

'He meant it,' she spoke aloud. 'He was truly ashamed. He could never have done the same thing again.' She shivered with dread as she decided what she was going to do, and to bolster her courage she went on in a voice that shook slightly, 'It's a bluff. The notice is a bluff. It must be – ' then she broke off as she remembered the three dead horses. 'He put them down. They were finished, and he used poison on them as part of the bluff. Probably gave it to them in a bucket, but not the water-hole. He wouldn't have done that twice.'

Slowly she took the hat from her head and used the wide brim to skim the floating layer of dust and rubbish from the surface of the pool. Then she scooped a hatful of the clear cool water, holding it in both hands, steeling herself to do it. She took a deep breath and touched the water with her lips.

'Centaine!' Blaine roared in shock and rage as he bounded down the bank and snatched the hat out of her hands. The water splashed over her legs soaking her breeches. He seized her by the arms and jerked her to her feet. His face was swollen and dark, his eyes blazing with anger as he shouted in her face. 'Have you gone stark staring mad, woman?'

He was shaking her brutually, his fingers digging into the flesh of her upper arms.

'Blaine, you are hurting me.'

'Hurting you? I could willingly thrash you, you crazy – '

'Blaine, it's a bluff, I'm sure of it.' She was frightened of him. His rage was a terrible thing to watch. 'Blaine. Please! Please listen to me.'

She saw the change in his eyes as he regained control. 'Oh God,' he said, 'I thought – '

'You are hurting me,' she repeated stupidly, and he released her.

'I'm sorry.' He was panting as though he had run a marathon. 'Don't do that to me again, woman – next time I don't know what I will do.'

'Blaine! Listen to me. It's a bluff. He didn't poison the water. I would stake my life on it.'

'You almost did,' he growled at her, but he was listening now. 'How did you reach that conclusion?' He leaned closer to her, interested and ready to be convinced.

'I knew him once. Knew him well. I heard him make an oath. It was he who poisoned the water-hole you talked about, back in 1915. He admitted it, but he swore that he would never be able to do it again. He described the carnage at the water-hole, and he swore an oath.'

'The dead horses lying out there,' Blaine demanded, 'how do you explain them?'

'All right. He poisoned them. He would have to have destroyed them anyway. They were broken; he couldn't leave them for the lions.'

He strode to the edge of the water and stared down into it.

'You were going to take that chance – ' he broke off and shuddered, then turned from the water and called sharply.

'Sergeant Hansmeyer!'

'Sir.' The sergeant hurried across from the horse lines.

'Sergeant, bring the lame mare to me,' and Hansmeyer went to the lines and led the animal back. She was favouring her right fore and they would have to leave her anyway.

'Let her drink!' Blaine ordered.

'Sir?' Hansmeyer looked puzzled, and then when he realized Blaine's intention, he became alarmed. 'From the spring? It's poisoned, sir.'

'That's what we are going to find out,' Blaine told him grimly. 'Let her drink!'

Eagerly the black mare scrambled down the bank and bent her long neck to the pool.

She sucked up the water in great gulps. It sloshed and gurgled into her belly, and she seemed to swell before their eyes.

'I didn't think to use one of the horses,' Centaine whispered. 'Oh it will be terrible if I have guessed wrongly.'

Hansmeyer let the mare drink until she was satiated, and then Blaine ordered, 'Take her back to the lines.'

He checked his wristwatch. 'We'll give her an hour,' he decided, and took Centaine's hand. He led her to the shade thrown by the overhang of the bank and they sat together.

'You say you knew him?' he asked at last. 'How well did you know him?'

'He worked for me – years ago. He did the first development work at the mine. He is an engineer, you know.'

'Yes. I know he is an engineer. It's in his file.' He was silent. 'You must have got to know him very well for him to admit something like that to you? It's a very intimate thing, a man's guilt.'

She did not reply. 'What can I tell him?' she thought. 'That I was Lothar De La Rey's mistress? That I loved him and bore him a son?'

Suddenly Blaine chuckled. 'Jealousy is really one of the most unlovely emotions isn't it? I withdraw the questions. It was impertinent. Forgive me.'

She laid her hand on his arm and smiled at him gratefully.

'That doesn't mean I have forgiven you for the fright you gave me,' he told her with mock severity. 'I could still quite happily turn you over my knee.'

The thought of it gave her a funny little perverse twinge of excitement. His rage had frightened her and that excited her also. He had not shaved since they had left the mission. His new beard was thick and dark as the pelt of an otter, except there was a single silver hair in it. It grew at the corner of his mouth, shining like a star in the night.

'What are you staring at?' he asked.

'I was wondering if your beard would scratch – if you decided to kiss me instead of spanking me.'

She saw him struggling like a drowning man in a rip tide of temptation. She imagined the fears and the doubts and the anguish of wanting that boiled behind those green eyes, and she waited, her face turned up to him, neither pulling back nor thrusting forward, waiting for him to accept the inevitability of it.

When he took her mouth it was fiercely, almost roughly, as though he was angry with his own inability to resist, and angry with her for leading him into his dangerous wilderness of infidelity. He sucked all the strength out of her body so that she went limp in his arms, only the grip of her own arms around his neck matched his and her mouth was deep and wet and soft and open for him to probe.

He broke away from her at last and sprang to his feet. He stood over her, looking down at her. 'May God have pity on us,' he whispered, and strode away up the bank, leaving her alone with her joy and disquiet and guilt and with the raging flame he had kindled in her belly.

Sergeant Hansmeyer summoned her at last. He came to the pool and stood at the top of the bank.

'Colonel Malcomess is asking for you, Missus.'

She followed him back to the horse lines, and she felt strangely detached from reality. Her feet seemed not to touch the earth and everything was dreamlike and far away.

Blaine stood with the lame mare, holding her head and stroking her neck. She made little fluttering sounds in her nostrils and nibbled at the front of his tunic. Blaine looked over her head as Centaine came up on the mare's other side. They stared at each other.

'No turning back,' he said softly, and she accepted the ambiguity of his words. 'We go forward – together.'

'Yes, Blaine,' she agreed meekly.

'And to hell with the consequences,' he said harshly.

A second longer they held each other's eyes, and then Blaine lifted her voice. 'Sergeant, water all the horses and fill the bottle. We have nine hours to make up on the chase.'

* * *

They kept going through the night. The little Bushmen stayed on the spoor with only the stars and a sliver of moon to light it for them, and when the sun rose the tracks were still strung out ahead of them, each filled with purple shadow by the acutely slanted rays.

Now there were four riders in the fleeing band, for the horse herder from the fountain had joined them and they were leading a spare horse each.

An hour after dawn, they found where the fugitives had camped the previous night. Lothar had abandoned two of his horses here; they had broken down from the brutal treatment, hard riding in these severe conditions. They stood beside the remains of the camp fire which Lothar had smothered with sand. Kwi brushed away the sand and knelt to blow on the ashes, a tiny flame sprang up under his breath and he grinned like a pixie.

'We have made up five or six hours on them while they slept,' Blaine murmured, and looked at Centaine. She straightened up immediately from her weary slump but she was pale and light-headed with fatigue.

'He's using up his horses like a prodigal,' she said, and they both looked at the two animals that Lothar had abandoned. They stood with heads hanging, muzzles almost touching the ground, a pair of chestnut mares, one with a white blazed forehead and the other with white socks. Both of them moved only with pain and difficulty, and their tongues were black and swollen, protruding from the sides of their mouths.

'He did not waste water on them,' Blaine agreed. 'Poor devils.'

'You will have to put them down,' Centaine said.

'That's why he left them, Centaine,' he said gently.

'I don't understand.'

'The shots,' he explained. 'He'll be listening for gunfire – '

'Oh Blaine! What are we going to do? We can't leave them.'

'Make coffee and breakfast. We are all played out – horses and men. We must rest for a few hours before we go on.' He swung down from the saddle and untied his blanket roll. 'In the meantime I will take care of the cripples.'

He shook out his sheepskin underblanket as he walked across to the first mare. He stopped in front of her and unbuckled the flap of his holster. He drew his service pistol and wrapped the sheepskin over his right hand that held the pistol.

The mare dropped instantly to the muted thud of the pistol, and kicked spasmodically before relaxing into stillness. Centaine looked away, busying herself with measuring coffee into the billy as Blaine walked heavily across to the blazed chestnut mare.

* * *

There was a tiny movement of air, not truly a sound, light as the flirt of a sunbird's wing, but both Swart Hendrick and Lothar De La Rey lifted their heads and pulled up their mounts. Lothar raised his hand for silence and they waited, holding their breath.

It came again, another spit of distant muted gunfire, and Lothar and Hendrick glanced at each other.

'The arsenic trick did not work,' grunted the big black Ovambo. 'You should have really poisoned the water, not pretended,' and Lothar shook his head wearily.

'She must be riding like a she-devil. They are only four hours behind us, less if they push their horses. I never believed she could come on so quickly.'

'You cannot be sure that it is her,' Hendrick told him.

'It's her.' Lothar showed no trace of doubt. 'She promised me she would come.' His voice was hoarse, his lips cracked and flaky with dry skin. His eyes were bloodshot, gummed with yellow mucus thick as clotted cream and deeply underscored with bruised purple smudges. His beard was parti-coloured, gold and ginger and white.

His arm was wrapped in bandage to the elbow, the yellow discharge had seeped through the cloth. He had looped a cartridge belt around his neck as a sling, and the arm was supported partly by the belt and partly by the black japanned despatch case strapped to the pommel of his saddle.

He turned to look back across the plain with its sparse covering of scrub and camel-thorn, but the movement brought on another wave of giddiness and he swayed and snatched at the despatch case to prevent himself falling.

'Pa!' Manfred grabbed his good arm, his face contorted with concern. 'Pa! Are you all right?'

Lothar closed his eyes before he could answer. 'All right,' he croaked. He could feel the infection swelling and distorting the flesh of his hand and forearm. The skin felt thin and stretched to the point of bursting like an overripe plum, and the heat of the poison flowed with his blood. He could feel it throbbing painfully in the glands below his armpit and from there spreading out through his whole body, squeezing the sweat out through his skin, burning his eyes and pounding in his temples, shimmering a desert mirage in his brain.

'Go on,' he whispered. 'Got to go on,' and Hendrick picked up the lead rein with which he was guiding Lothar's horse.

'Wait!' blurted Lothar, rocking in the saddle. 'How far to the next water?'

'We'll be there before noon tomorrow.'

Lothar was trying to concentrate but the fever filled his head with steam and heat.

'Those horse irons. It's time for the horse irons.'

Hendrick nodded. They had carried the horse irons from the cache in the hills. They weighed seventy pounds, a heavy burden for one of the lead horses. It was time to be rid of some of that weight now.

'We'll give her a bait to lead her onto them,' Lothar croaked.

* * *

The short rest, the hasty meal and even the strong, hot, over-sweetened coffee seemed only to have increased Centaine's fatigue.

'I will not let him see it,' she told herself firmly. 'I'll not give in until they do.' But her skin felt so dry that it might tear like paper and the glare ached in her eyes, filling her skull with pain.

She glanced sideways at Blaine. He sat straight and tall in the saddle, invincible and indefatigable, but he turned his head and his eyes softened as he looked at her.

'We'll break for a drink in ten minutes,' he told her softly.

'I'm all right,' she protested.

'We are all tired,' he said. 'There is no shame in admitting it.' He broke off and shaded his eyes, peering ahead.

'What is it?' she demanded.

'I'm not sure.' He lifted the binoculars that hung on his chest and focused

them on the dark blob far ahead that had caught his attention. 'I still can't recognize what it is.' He passed the glasses to her and Centaine stared through them.

'Blaine!' she exclaimed. 'The diamonds!' It's the diamond case! They have dropped the diamonds.'

Her fatigue fell away from her like a discarded cape and before he could stop her she put her heels into her gelding's flanks and urged him into a gallop, overtaking the Bushmen. The two spare horse were forced to follow her, straining on their lead reins, the water bottles bouncing wildly on their backs.

'Centaine!' Blaine shouted, and spurred his mount after her, trying to catch her.

Sergeant Hansmeyer had been drooping in the saddle, but he roused himself instantly as the two leaders galloped away.

'Troop, forward!' he shouted, and the whole party was tearing ahead.

Suddenly Centaine's gelding screamed with agony and reared under her. She was almost thrown from the saddle, but recovered her balance with a fine feat of horsemanship, and then the spare horses were whinnying and kicking and lashing out in agony. Blaine tried to turn out, but he was too late and his mount broke down under him, his spare horses, shrieking and bucking on their leads.

'Halt!' he screamed, turning desperately to try and stop Sergeant Hansmeyer's charge, signalling him with both arms. 'Halt! Troop, halt!' The Sergeant reacted swiftly, swinging his mount to block the troopers who followed him, and they came up short in a tangle of milling, trampling horses, the dust swirling over them in a fine mist.

Centaine sprang down from the saddle and checked her gelding's front legs, they were both sound and she lifted a rear hoof and stared in disbelief. A burr of rusted iron was stuck to the frog of the gelding's hoof and dark blood was already pouring from the wound it had inflicted, mingling into a muddy paste with the fine desert dust.

Gingerly Centaine took hold of the metal rose and tried to pull it away, but it was buried deeply and the gelding trembled with the pain. She tugged and twisted, carefully avoiding the protruding spikes, and at last the horrible thing came free in her hand, wet with the gelding's blood. She straightened and looked across at Blaine. He also had been busy with his own mount's feet and held two of the bloody irons in his hands.

'Horse irons,' Blaine told her. 'I haven't seen the cruel damned things since the war.' They were crudely forged, shaped like the ubiquitous devil thorns of the African veld, four pointed stars aligned so that one point was always standing upright. Three inches of sharp iron that would cripple man or beast, or would slash the tyres of a following vehicle.

Centaine looked around and saw that the earth all around where she stood was strewn with the wicked spikes. Dust had been lightly brushed over them to conceal them from casual observation but had in no way reduced their effectiveness.

Quickly she stooped again to the task of ridding all three of her horses of the spikes. The gelding had picked them up in both rear hooves and the spare horses had three and two hooves damaged. She plucked the iron spikes from their flesh and hurled them away angrily.

Sergeant Hansmeyer had dismounted his troopers and they came up to assist her and Blaine, stepping cautiously for the spikes would readily penetrate the soles of their boots. They cleared a narrow corridor through which the horses

could be led back to safe ground, but all six of them had been brutally mained. They hobbled slowly and painfully, reluctant to touch the earth with their damaged hooves.

'Six of them,' Blaine whispered bitterly. 'Wait until I get my hands on that bastard.' He drew the .303 rifle from the scabbard on his saddle and ordered Hansmeyer, 'Put our saddles onto two of your spare horses. Top up all the water bottles from those on the crippled horse. Have two of your troopers mark a path around the area of the horse irons. Move it quickly! We can't waste a minute.'

Centaine left them and went forward, cautiously circling around the booby-trapped patch of earth. She reached the black japanned despatch case which had deceived her and picked it up. The lid flapped open, the lock smashed by Lothar's bullet, and she turned the case upside down. It was empty. She let it drop and looked back.

Blaine's men had worked swiftly. Their saddles had been transferred to undamaged horses. They had chosen a black gelding for her and Sergeant Hansmeyer was leading it. The whole troop was circling out in single file, leaning out of the sadle to check for any more horse irons in their path. She knew that from now on they would not be able to relax for a moment, for she knew that Lothar would not have laid all his spikes. They would find more along the spoor.

Hansmeyer came up beside her. 'We are ready to go, ma'am.' He handed her the reins to the fresh horse and she mounted, then they all looked back.

Blaine stood with the Lee Enfield rifle on his hip, and with his back turned to them faced the line of six crippled horse. He seemed to be praying, or perhaps he was merely steeling himself, but his head was bowed.

He lifted it slowly and threw the butt of the rifle to his shoulder. He fired without lowering the rifle, his right hand flicking the bolt back and forth, and the shots crashing out in rapid succession, blending into a long-drawn-out drumroll of sound. The horses fell on top of one another, in a twitching, jerking pile. He turned away then, and even at that distance Centaine glimpsed his expression.

She found she was weeping. The tears poured down her face, and she could not stop them. Blaine rode up beside her. He glanced at her, and when he saw her tears, he stared straight ahead, letting her get over it.

'We have lost nearly an hour,' he said. 'Troop forward!'

Twice more before nightfall the Bushman stopped the column and they had to pick their way cautiously around a scattering of the wicked spikes. Each time it cost them precious minutes.

'We are losing ground,' Blaine estimated. 'They heard the rifle shots and they are alerted. They know they have got fresh horses waiting somewhere ahead. They are pushing harder – much harder than we dare.'

* * *

The country changed with dramatic suddenness as they emerged from the wastes of Bushmanland into the gently wooded more benevolent Kavango area.

Along the undulating ridges of the ancient compacted dunes grew tall trees, combretum the lovely bush willow, and albizia with its fine feathery foliage,

and stands of young mopani between them. The shallow valleys were covered with fine desert grasses whose silver and pink seed heads brushed their stirrup irons as they rode through.

The water was not far below the surface here and all Nature seemed to respond to its presence. For the first time since leaving the mission at Kalkrand, they saw large game, zebra and red-golden impala, and they knew that the water-hole for which they were riding could be only a few miles ahead for these animals would drink daily.

It was not too soon for all the horses were used up and weak, struggling onwards beneath the weight of their riders. A few inches remained in the water bottles, seeming to mock their thirst with hollow gurgles at each pace.

Lothar De La Rey could not remain in the saddle unaided. Swart Hendrick rode on one side of him and his bastard son Klein Boy on the other. They supported him when sudden bouts of delirium overcame him and he laughed and ranted and would have slipped from the saddle and tumbled to earth. Manfred trailed behind them, watching his father anxiously, but too exhausted and thirsty to assist him.

They struggled up another rise in the endless succession of consolidated dunes, and Swart Hendrick stood in the stirrups and peered down into the gentle basin ahead of them, barely daring to hope that they had been able to ride directly to their destination through the trackless land where every vista mirrored the previous one and the one that followed. All they had to steer by was the sun and the instinct of the desert creature.

Then his spirits soared, for ahead of them there were the tall grey mopani trunks nurtured into giants by the water over which they stood and the four great umbrella acacia exactly as they had been imprinted in his memory. Between their trunks Hendrick caught the soft sheen of standing water.

The horses managed a last jolting trot down the slope and through the trees, and then out over the bare clay that surrounded the shrunken puddle of water in the centre.

The water was the colour of *café au lait*, not ten paces across at the widest point nor deeper than a man's knee. Around it the hoofprints and pad marks of dozens of various types of wild animals – from the tiny multiple V scratches of quail and francolin to the huge round prints of a bull elephant the size of dustbin lids – had been sculpted into the black clay and then baked by the sun as hard as concrete.

Hendrick and Klein Boy drove their mounts into the centre of the pool and then flung themselves face down into the lukewarm muddy water, snorting and gasping and laughing wildly as they scooped it into their mouths.

Manfred helped his father to dismount at the edge, and then ran to scoop a hatful and bring it to Lothar where he had collapsed into a sitting position, supporting himself on his own knees.

Lothar drank greedily, choking and coughing as the water went down the wrong way. His face was flushed and swollen, his eyes fever-bright and the poison in his blood burning him up.

Swart Hendrick waded to the side, his boots squelching and water pouring from his sodden clothing, still grinning – until a thought struck him and he stopped. The grin was gone from his thick black lips and he glared about him.

'Nobody here,' he grunted. 'Buffalo and Legs – where are they?' He broke into a run, spraying water at each pace as he headed for the primitive hut that stood in the shade of the nearest umbrella acacia.

It was empty and derelict. The charcoal of the camp-fire was scattered widely; the freshest signs were days – no, weeks old. He raged through the forest, and at last came back to Lothar. Between them Klein Boy and Manfred had helped Lothar into the shade and he lay back against the trunk of the acacia.

'They've deserted.' Lothar anticipated Hendrick's report. 'I should have known. Ten horses, worth fifty pounds each. It was too much temptation.' The rest and the water seemed to have strengthened him; he was lucid again.

'They must have run away within days of us leaving them.' Hendrick sank down beside him. 'Surely they have taken the horses and sold them to the Portuguese, then gone home to their wives.'

'Promise me that when you see them again you will kill them slowly, Hendrick, very slowly.'

'I dream of how I will do it,' Hendrick whispered. 'First I will make them eat their own manhoods, I will cut them off with a blunt knife and I will feed them to them in small pieces.'

They were both silent, staring at the small group of their four horses which stood at the pool's edge. Their bellies were distended with water but their heads were hanging pathetically, noses almost touching the baked clay.

'Seventy miles to the river, seventy miles at least.' Lothar broke the silence, and he began to unwrap the filthy rags that covered his arm.

The swelling was grotesque. His hand was the size and shape of a ripe melon. The fingers stuck stiffly out of the blue ball of flesh. The swelling carried up the forearm to the elbow, trebling the girth of his lower limb, and the skin had burst open and clear lymph leaked out of the tears. The bite wounds were deep, slimy, yellow pits, the edges flared open like the petals of a flower, and the smell of infection was sweet and thick as oil in Lothar's own nostrils and throat, disgusting him.

Above the elbow the swelling was not so intense, but there were livid scarlet lines beneath the skin running right up to Lothar's shoulder. He reached up and gently explored the swollen glands in his armpit. They were hard as musket balls buried in his flesh.

'Gangrene,' he told himself, and he realized now that the carbolic acid solution with which he had orginally cleansed the bite wounds had aggravated the condition. 'Too strong,' he muttered. 'Too strong solution.' It had destroyed the capillary vessels around the wound, preparing the way for the gangrene that had followed. 'The hand should come off.' He faced the fact at last, and for a moment he even considered attempting the operation himself. He imagined starting at the elbow joint and cutting – '

'I can't do it,' he decided. 'I can't even think of it. I have to go on as far as the gangrene will let me, for Manie's sake.' He looked up at the boy.

'I need bandages.' He tried to make his voice firm and reassuring, but it came out as a raven's croak, and the boy started and tore his eyes from the ravaged limb.

Lothar dusted the suppurating wounds with carbolic crystals – all that he had – and bound them up with strips of blanket. They had used up all their extra clothing for bandages.

'How far is she behind us, Henny?' he asked, as he knotted the bandage.

'We have won time,' Hendrick guessed. 'They must be saving their horses. But look at ours.'

One of the animals had lain down at the edge of the water, the sign of capitulation.

'Five or six hours behind us.' And it was seventy miles to the river, with no guarantee that the pursuers would honour the border and not pursue them across. Lothar did not have to voice those doubts; they were all too aware of them.

'Manfred,' he whispered. 'Bring the diamonds.' The boy placed the canvas haversack beside Lothar and he unpacked it carefully.

There were twenty-eight of the small brown cartridge paper packages with their red wax seals. Lothar separated them into four piles, seven packages in each.

'Equal shares,' he said. 'We cannot value each package, so we will cut them four ways and give the youngest first pick.' He looked across at Hendrick. 'Agreed?'

Swart Hendrick understood that the sharing of the booty was at last an admission that not all of them were going to reach the river. Hendrick lowered his eyes from Lothar's face. He and this golden-haired, white-skinned devil had been together since the far-off time of their youth. He had never considered what held them together. He felt a deep, unwavering antagonism and distrust towards all white men except this one. They had dared so much, seen so much, shared so much. He did not think of it as love or as friendship. Yet the thought of the parting which lay just ahead filled him with a devastating despair, as though a little death awaited him.

'Agreed,' he said, in the deep resonant tone, like the chime of a bass bell, and he looked up at the white boy. The man and the boy were one unit in Hendrick's mind. What he felt for the father was also for the son.

'Choose, Manie,' he ordered.

'I don't know.' Manfred put both hands behind his back, reluctant to touch one of the piles.

'Do it,' snapped his father, and obediently he reached out and touched the nearest pile.

'Pick them up,' Lothar ordered, and then looked at the black youth. 'Choose, Klein Boy.'

There were two piles left, and Lothar grinned through cracked lips. 'How old are you, Henny?'

'As old as the burned mountain, as young as the first flower of spring,' the Ovambo said, and they both laughed.

'If I had a diamond for every time we have laughed together,' Hendrick thought, 'I would be the richest man in the world.' And it required an effort to keep the smile on his face. 'You must be younger than I am,' he spoke aloud. 'For I have always had to care for you like a nursemaid. Choose!'

Lothar shoved his chosen pile across to Manfred. 'Put it in the haversack,' he told him, and Manfred packed their share of the booty into the canvas bag and strapped it closed while the two black men filled the pockets of their tunics with their packages.

'Now fill the water bottles. It's only seventy miles to the river,' Lothar said.

When they were ready to leave Hendrick stooped to help Lothar to his feet, but he struck Hendrick's hand away irritably and used the trunk of the acacia to push himself upright.

One of the horses could not rise and they left it lying at the water's edge. Another broke down within the first mile, but the other two limped on gamely. Neither of them could any longer support the full weight of a man, but one

carried the water bottles and Lothar used the other as a crutch. He staggered along beside it with his good arm draped over its neck.

The other three men took it in turns to lead the horses, and they trudged on determinedly northwards. Sometimes Lothar laughed without reason and sang in a strong, clear voice, carrying the tune so beautifully that Manfred felt a buoyant rush of relief. But then the singing quavered and his voice broke and cracked. He shouted and raved and pleaded with the fever phantoms that crowded about him, and Manfred ran back to him and circled his waist with a helping arm and Lothar quieted down.

'You are a good boy, Manie,' he whispered. 'You've always been a good boy. We are going to have a wonderful life from now on. A fine school for you, you will become a young gentleman – we'll go to Berlin together, the opera – '

'Oh, Papa, don't talk. Save your strength, Papa.' And Lothar subsided once more into an oppressive silence, toiling on mechanically with his boots dragging and scuffing, and only the labouring horse and his son's strong young arm preventing him from crashing face forward onto the hot Kalahari sands.

Far ahead of them the first of the granite kopjes showed above the sparse heat-blighted forest. It was round as a pearl and the smooth rock glowed silver grey in the sunlight.

* * *

Centaine stopped her horse on the crest of the rise and looked down into the basin of land beyond. She recognized the tall trees from the top branches of which, many years, before, she had glimpsed her first wild African elephant, and a little of the childlike wonder of that moment had remained with her over all that time. Then she saw the water, and all else was forgotten. It was not easy to control the horses once they had smelled it. She had heard of desert travellers dying of thirst at the water-hole when they allowed their cattle and horse to rush ahead and trample the water into thick mud. But Blaine and his sergeant were experienced men and controlled them firmly.

As soon as the horses had been watered and picketed, Centaine pulled off her boots and waded fully dressed into the pool, ducking under the surface to soak her clothing and her hair and revelling at the chill of the muddy water.

At the far end of the pool Blaine had stripped to his breeches and was knee-deep, scooping water over his head. Centaine studied him surreptitiously. It was the first time she had seen him bare-chested, and his body hair was thick and dark and springing, sparkling with water droplets. There was a small black mole below the nipple of his right breast, which for no good reason intrigued her, otherwise his body was without blemish; his skin had the sheen of polished marble, like the Michelangelo statue of David, and his muscles were flat and hard-looking. The sun had stained a dark brown V below his throat and his arms were brown up to the distinct lines that his shirtsleeves had left; beyond that his skin was the pale ivory that she found so attractive that she had to look away from it.

As she came up to him he hurriedly pulled on his shirt again, and the water soaked through it in darker patches. His modesty made her smile.

'De La Rey found no spare horses here,' she told him, and he looked puzzled. 'Are you sure?'

'Kwi says that there were two men waiting here with many horses but that they left many days ago. He cannot count beyond the ten fingers on his hand, it was longer than that. Yes, I am sure Lothar De La Rey found no fresh horses.'

Blaine smoothed his wet hair straight back with both hands. 'Then my guess is that something has gone wrong with his plans. He would never have used up his horses like that unless he was expecting to find remounts.'

'Kwi says they have gone ahead on foot. They are leading their remaining horses, and the horses are obviously too weak to carry a man.' She broke off as Kwi called shrilly from the edge of the forst and she and Blaine hurried over to join him.

'They are desperate,' Blaine said, as they saw the pile of abandoned equipment beneath the acacia tree. 'Saddles and canned food, blankets and billy cans.' He turned over the pile with his feet. 'They've even dumped ammunition – and, yes, by God, the last of those damned horse irons.' The small wooden case lay on its side with the last few pounds of the vicious iron spikes spilling from it. 'They have stripped down, and they are making one last desperate run to reach the river.'

'Look here, Blaine,' Centaine called to him, and he went to her and examined the small pile of soiled bandages that lay at her feet.

'His condition is worsening,' Centaine murmured, but strangely there was no gloating in her voice, no triumph in her eyes. 'I think he is a dying man, Blaine.'

Unaccountably he felt the need to commiserate with her, to console her. 'If we can get him to a doctor – ' he broke off, the impulse was ludicrous. They were hunting a vicious criminal who, Blaine knew, would not hesitate to shoot him down at the first opportunity.

'Sergeant Hansmeyer,' he called harshly. 'See the men fed and the horses watered again before we leave in an hour.' He turned back to Centaine and saw with relief that she had rallied.

'An hour is not enough – let's see we use every minute of it.'

They sat together in the shade. Neither of them had eaten much; the heat and their fatigue had destroyed their appetite. Blaine took a cheroot from his leather case and then changed his mind. He slipped it back into the case and dropped the case into the pocket of his tunic.

'When I first met you I thought that you were brilliant and adamant and beautiful as one of your own diamonds,' he said.

'And now?' she asked.

'I have seen you weep for maimed horses, and I have sensed in you a deep compassion for a man who has done you cruel injury,' he replied. 'When we left Kalkrand I was in love with you. I suppose I was in love with you from the first hour I met you. I couldn't help that, but now I also like you and respect you.'

'Is that a different thing from love?'

'It is a very different thing from *being* in love,' he affirmed, and they were silent for a while before she tried to explain.

'Blaine, I have been alone for a long time with a small child to protect and to plan for. When I came to this land as a girl, I served a hard, unrelenting apprenticeship in this desert. I learned that there was nobody I could rely upon but myself, no way to survive but through my own strength and determination. That hasn't altered. I still have nobody but myself on whom I can rely. Isn't that so, Blaine?'

'I wish it were not.' He did not attempt to avoid her gaze but looked back at her candidly. 'I wish – '

He broke off and she finished the statement for him. 'But, you have Isabella and your girls.'

He nodded. 'Yes, they cannot fend for themselves.'

'And I can – isn't that right, Blaine?'

'Don't be bitter with me, please. I did not seek this. I have never made you any promises.'

'I'm sorry.' She was immediately contrite. 'You are right. You have never promised me anything.' She glanced at her watch. 'Our little hour is up,' she said, and rose in a single lithe movement to her feet.

'I shall just have to go on being strong and hard,' she said. 'But never tax me with it again, please Blaine. Never again.'

* * *

They had been forced to abandon five of their own horses since leaving the water-hole of the elephant, and Blaine was alternating between walking and riding in an attempt to save the remaining animals. They rode for half an hour and then dismounted and led for the next half hour.

Only the bushmen were unaffected by the thirst and fatigue and heat, and they chafed at the halting and torturous pace they were force to adopt.

'The only consolation is that De La Rey is doing even worse then we are.' From the spoor they could read that the fugitives, reduced to a single horse between them, were making even slower progress. 'And it's still thirty miles or more to the river.' Blaine checked his watch. 'Time to walk again, I'm afraid.'

Centaine groaned softly as she swung down from the saddle. She ached in every muscle, and the tendons of her hamstrings and calves felt like twisted wire strands.

They trudged forward and every pace required a conscious effort. Centaine's tongue filled her mouth, thick and leathery, and the mucous membrane of her throat and nostrils was swollen and painful so that it was difficult to breath. She tried to collect her saliva and hold it in her mouth, but it was gummy and sour, serving only to make her thirst more poignant.

She had forgotten what it was like to be truly thirsty, and the soft sloshing sound of the water bottles on the saddle of the horse she was leading became a torment. She could think of nothing but when they would next be allowed to drink. She kept glancing at her wristwatch, convincing herself that it had stopped, and she had forgotten to wind it, that at any moment Blaine would lift his arm to halt the column and they could unscrew the stoppers on the water bottles.

Nobody spoke from choice. All orders were terse and monosyllabic, every word an effort.

'I won't be the first to give in,' Centaine decided grimly, and then she was alarmed that the thought had even occurred to her. 'Nobody will give in. We have to catch them before the river and the river is not far ahead.'

She found she was focusing only on the earth at her feet, losing interest in her surroundings, and she knew that was a dangerous sign, the first small surrender. She forced herself to look up. Blaine was ahead of her. She had

fallen back in those few paces, and she made a huge effort and dragged her horse forward until she was side by side with him again. Immediately she felt heartened, she had won another victory over her body's frailty.

Blaine smiled at her, but she saw that it had cost him an effort also. 'Those kopjes are not marked on the map,' he said.

She had not noticed them, but now she looked up and a mile ahead saw their smooth bald granite heads raised above the forest. She had never been this far north; it was new territory for her.

'I don't think this country has ever been surveyed,' she whispered, and then cleared her throat and spoke more clearly. 'Only the river itself has been mapped.'

'We will drink when we reach the foot of the nearest hill,' he promised her.

'A carrot for the donkey,' she murmured, and he grinned.

'Think about the river. That is a garden full of carrots.' And they relapsed into silence; the Bushmen led them directly towards the hills. At the base of the granite cone they found the last of Lothar De La Rey's horses.

It lay on its side, but it lifted its head as they walked up to it. Blaine's mare whickered softly, and the downed animal tried to reply but the effort was to much. It dropped its head flat against the earth and its short hampered breathing raised tiny wisps of dust that swirled around its nostrils. The Bushmen circled the dying animal and then conferred excitedly. Kwi ran a short way towards the grey side of the kopje and looked up.

They all followed his example, staring up the steep rounded expanse of granite. It was two or three hundred feet high. The surface was not as smooth as it had appeared at a distance. They were deep cracks, some lateral, others running vertically from the foot to the summit, and the granite was flaking away in the 'onion peel' effect caused by heat expansion and contraction. This left small sharp edged steps which would give footholds and make it possible for a man to reach the top, though it would be an exposed and potentially dangerous climb.

On the summit a cluster of perfectly round boulders, each the size of a large dwelling house, formed a symmetrical crown. The whole was one of those natural compositions so artful and contrived that it seemed to have been conceived and executed by human engineers. Centaine was strongly reminded of the dolmens which she had visited as a child in France, or of one of those ancient Mayan temples in the South American jungles which she had seen illustrated.

Blaine had left her side and led his mount towards the foot of the granite cliff, and something on the crest of the kopje caught Centaine's eye. It was a flicker of movement in the shadow beneath one of the crowning boulders on the summit, and she shouted a warning.

'Blaine, be careful! On the top – ' He was standing at his horse's head with the reins over his shoulder, staring upwards. But before he could respond to her warning there was a thud as though a sack of wheat had been dropped on a stone floor. Centaine did not recognize the sound as a high-velocity bullet striking living flesh until Blaine's horse staggered, its front legs collapsed and it dropped heavily, dragging Blaine with it.

Centaine was stunned until she heard the whiplash crack of the Mauser from the summit of the kopje and she realized that the bullet had reached them before the sound.

All around her the troopers were shouting and wrestling with their panicking

horses, and Centaine spun and vaulted for the saddle of her own mount. With one hand on the pommel and without touching the stirrup irons she was up, dragging the horse's head around.

'Blaine, I'm coming,' she screamed. He had scrambled to his feet beside the carcass of his horse, and she rode for him. 'Grab my stirrup,' she called, and the Mausers up on the hill were cracking bullets amongst them. She saw Sergeant Hansmeyer's horse shot dead beneath him and he pitched headlong from the saddle.

Blaine ran to meet her and seized her dangling stirrup. She turned the horse and heeled him into a full gallop, pumping the reins heading back for the sparse cover of the mopani two hundred yards behind them.

Blaine was swinging on the stirrup leather, his feet skimming the ground, making giant strides as he kept level with her.

'Are you all right?' she yelled.

'Keep going!' His voice strained at the effort and she looked back under her arm. The gunfire still crackled and snapped around them. One of the troopers turned back to help Sergeant Hansmeyer, but as he reached him a bullet hit his horse in the head and it crashed over and flung the trooper sprawling to earth.

'They are picking off the horses!' Centaine cried, as she realized that hers was the only animal still unscathed. All the others were down, killed with a single shot in the head for each of them. It was superb marksmanship, for the men on the summit were firing downhill at a range of one hundred and fifty paces or more.

Ahead of her Centaine saw a shallow ravine that she had not noticed before. There was a tangle of fallen dead mopani branches upon the nearest bank, a natural palisade, and she rode for it, forcing her winded horse down the bank in a scrambling leap and then immediately springing down and seizing his head to control him.

Blaine had been dragged off his feet and had rolled down the bank, but he pulled himself up. 'I walked into that ambush like a greenhorn,' he snarled, angry at himself. 'Too bloody tired to think straight.' He jerked the rifle out of the scabbard on Centaine's saddle and climbed quickly to the lip of the bank.

Ahead of him the dead horses lay below the steep smooth slope of the kopje, and Sergeant Hansmeyer and his troopers were dodging and jinking as they sprinted back for the cover of the ravine. Mauser-fire crackled, kicking up spouts of yellow dust about their feet, and they winced and ducked at the implosion of air in their eardrums as passing shot whipped about their heads.

Magically the Bushmen had disappeared, like little brown leprechauns, at the first shot. Centaine knew they would not see them again. Already they were on their way back to join their clan at O'chee Pan.

Blaine pushed up the rear sight of the Lee Enfield to four hundred yards and aimed for the crest of the kopje, where a feather of drifting blue gunsmoke betrayed the hidden gunmen. He fired as fast as he could work the bolt, spraying bullets to cover the fleeing troopers, watching white chips of granite burst from the skyline of the kopje as the raking fire withered away. He snatched a clip of ammunition from his bandolier and pressed the brass cartridges into the open breech of the hot rifle, slammed the bolt shut and flung the weapon to his shoulder, and poured fire up at the marksmen on the crest of the kopje.

One by one Hansmeyer and his troopers reached the ravine and tumbled into it, sweating and panting wildly. With grim satisfaction Blaine noticed that each

of them had carried his rifle with him, and they wore their bandoliers strapped across their chests, seventy-five rounds a man.

'They shot the horses in the head but never touched a man.' Hansmeyer's breathing whistled in his throat as he struggled with the words.

'They never fired a shot near me,' Centaine blurted. Lothar must have taken great care not to endanger her. She realized with a tremor just how easily he could have put a bullet into the back of her skull as she fled.

Blaine was reloading the Lee Enfield, but he looked up and smiled humourlessly. 'The fellow is no idiot. He knows that he has shot his bolt, and he is not looking to add murder to the long list of the charges against him.' He looked at Hansmeyer. 'How many men on the kopje?' he demanded.

'I don't know,' Hansmeyer answered. 'But there is more than one. The rate of fire was too much for one man, and I heard shots overlapping.'

'All right, let's find out how many there are.' Blaine beckoned Centaine and Hansmeyer up beside him and explained.

Centaine took his binoculars and moved down the ravine until she was well out on the flank and below a dense tuft of grass which grew on the lip of the ravine. She used the tuft as a screen and raised her head until she could make out the summit of the kopje. She focused the binoculars and called. 'Ready!'

Blaine had his helmet on the ramrod of his rifle, and he lifted it and Hansmeyer fired two shots into the air to draw the attention of the marksmen on the kopje.

Almost immediately the answering fusillade crackled from the hilltop. More than one shot fired simultaneously, and dust kicked off the lip of the ravine inches from the khaki helmet while ricochet howled away over the mopani trees.

'Two or three,' Hansmeyer called.

'Three,' Centaine confirmed, lowering the binoculars as she ducked down. I saw three heads.'

'Good.' Blaine nodded. 'We've got them then, just a matter of time.'

'Blaine.' Centaine loosened the strap of her water bottle from the saddle. 'That's all we have got.' She shook the bottle, and it was less than a quarter full. They all stared at it, and involuntarily Blaine licked his lips.

'We will be able to recover the other bottles, just as soon as it's dark,' he assured them, and then briskly, 'Sergeant, take two troopers with you, try and work your way around the other side of the kopje. Make sure nobody leaves by the back door.

* * *

Lothar De La Rey sat propped against one of the huge round granite boulders at the top of the kopje. He sat in the shade, with the Mauser across his lap. He was bare-headed and his long golden hair blew softly across his forehead.

He stared out towards the south, across the plain and the scattered mopani forest, in the direction from which the relentless pursuit would come. The climb up the sheer granite wall had taxed him severely and he was not yet recovered from it.

'Leave me one water bottle,' he ordered and Hendrick placed it beside him.

'I have filled it from those,' Hendrick indicated the pile of discarded, empty water bottles. 'And we have a full bottle to see us as far as the river.'

'Good.' Lothar nodded and checked the other equipment that was laid out beside him on the granite slab.

There were four hand grenades – the old 'potato masher' type with a wooden handle. They had lain in the cache with the horse irons and other equipment for almost twenty years and he could not rely upon them.

Klein Boy had left his rifle and his bandolier of Mauser ammunition with the grenades. So Lothar had two rifles and 150 rounds – more than enough, if the grenades worked. If they didn't it wouldn't matter anyway.

'All right,' Lothar said quietly. 'I have everything I need. You can go.'

Hendrick turned his cannonball of a head to peer into the south. They were on a grandstand, high above the world, and the sweep of their horizon was twenty miles or more, but there was as yet no sign of pursuit.

Hendrick started to rise to his feet, and then paused. He squinted into the heat haze and glare. 'Dust!' he said. It was still five miles away, a pale haze above the trees.

'Yes.' Lothar had seen it minutes before. 'It could be a herd of zebra, or a willy willy, but I wouldn't bet my share of the loot on it. Move out now.'

Hendrick did not obey immediately. He stared into the white man's sapphire-yellow eyes.

Hendrick had not argued nor protested when Lothar had explained what they must do. It was right, it was logical. They had always left their wounded, often with just a pistol at hand, for when the pain or the hyenas closed in. And yet, this time Hendrick felt the need to say something, but there were no words that could match the enormity of the moment. He knew he was leaving a part of his own life upon this sunblasted rock.

'I will look after the boy,' he said simply, and Lothar nodded.

'I want to talk to Manie.' He licked his dry, cracked lips and shivered briefly with the heat of the poison in his blood. 'Wait for him at the bottom. It will take only a minute.'

'Come.' Hendrick jerked his head, and Klein Boy stood up beside him. Together they moved with the swiftness of hunting panthers to the cliff, and Klein Boy slipped over the edge. Hendrick paused and looked back. He raised his right hand.

'Stay in peace,' he said simply.

'Go in peace, old friend,' Lothar murmured. He had never called him friend before and Hendrick flinched at the word. Then he turned his head so Lothar could not see his eyes, and a moment later he was gone.

Lothar stared at him for long seconds, then shook himself lightly, driving back the self-pity and the sickly sentiment and the fever mists which threatened to close in and unman him completely.

'Manfred,' he said, and the boy started. He had been sitting as close as he dared to his father, watching his face, hanging on every word, every gesture he made.

'Pa,' he whispered. 'I don't want to go. I don't want to leave you. I don't want to be without you.'

Lothar made an impatient gesture, hardening his features to hide the softness in him. 'You will do as I tell you.'

'Pa – '

'You have never let me down before, Manie. I have been proud of you. Don't spoil it for me now. Don't let me find out that my son is a coward – '

'I'm not a coward!'

'Then you will do what you have to do,' he said harshly, and before Manfred could protest again he ordered, 'Bring me the haversack.'

Lothar placed the bag between his feet and with his good hand unbuckled the flap. He took one of the packages from it and tore open the heavy brown paper with his teeth. He spilled the stones into a small pile on the granite beside him and then spread them. He picked out ten of the biggest and whitest gems.

'Take off your jacket,' he ordered, and when Manfred handed the garment to him Lothar pierced a tiny hole in the lining with his clasp knife.

'These stones will be worth thousands of pounds. Enough to see you grown and educated,' he said, as he stuffed them one at a time into the lining of the jacket with his forefinger.

'But these others – there are too many, too heavy, too bulky to hide. Dangerous for you to carry them with you, a death warrant. He pushed himself to his feet with an effort. 'Come!'

He led Manfred amongst the cluster of huge boulders, bracing himself against the rock to keep himself from falling while Manfred supported him from the other side.

'Here!' He grunted and lowered himself to his knees, Manfred squatting down beside him. At their feet the granite cap was cracked through as though split with a chisel. At the top the crack was only as wide as two handspans, but it was deep, they could not see the bottom of it though they peered down thirty feet or more. The crack narrowed gradually as it descended and the depths of it were lost in shadow.

Lothar dangled the haversack of diamonds over the aperture. 'Mark this place,' he whispered. 'Look back often when you go northwards so that you will remember this hill. The stones will be waiting for you when you need them.'

Lothar opened his fingers and the haversack dropped into the crack. They heard the canvas scraping against the sides of the granite cleft as it fell, and then silence as it jammed deep down in the narrow throat of the crack.

Side by side they peered down, and they could just make out the lighter colour and the contrasting texture of the canvas thirty feet down, but it would escape even the concentrated scrutiny of anyone who did not know exactly where to look for it.

'That is my legacy to you, Manie,' Lothar whispered, and crawled back from the aperture. 'All right, Hendrick is waiting for you. It is time for you to go. Go quickly now.'

He wanted to embrace his son for the last time, to kiss his eyes and his lips and press him to his heart, but he knew it would undo them both. If they clung to each other now, they could never bring themselves to part.

'Go!' he ordered, and Manfred sobbed and flung himself at his father.

'I want to stay with you,' he cried.

Lothar caught his wrist and held him at arm's length.

'Do you want me to be ashamed.' he snarled. 'Is that how you want me to remember you, snivelling like a girl?'

'Pa, don't sent me away, please. Let me stay.'

Lothar drew back, released his grip on Manfred's wrist and immediately whipped his open palm across his face and then swung back with his knuckles.

The double slap knocked Manfred onto his haunches, leaving livid red blotches on his pale cheeks, and a tiny serpent of bright blood crawled from his nostril down over his upper lip. He stared at Lothar with shocked and incredulous eyes.

'Get out of here,' Lothar hissed at him, summoning all his courage and resolve to make his voice scornful and his expression savage. 'I won't have a blubbering little ninny hanging around my neck. Get out of here before I take the strap to you!'

Manfred scrambled to his feet and backed away, still staring with horrified disbelief at his father.

'Go on! Get away!' Lothar's expression never wavered, and his voice was angry and disdainful and unrelenting. 'Get out of here!'

Manfred turned and stumbled to the edge of the cliff. There he turned once more and held out his hands. 'Pa! Please don't – '

'Go, damn you. Go!' The boy scrambled over the edge, and the sounds of his clumsy descent dwindled into silence.

Only then Lothar let his shoulders droop, and he sobbed once, then suddenly he was weeping silently, his whole body shaking.

'It's the fever,' he told himself. 'The fever has weakened me.' But the image of his son's face, golden and beautiful and destroyed with grief, still filled his mind and he felt something tearing in his chest, an unbearable physical pain. 'Forgive me, my son,' he whispered through his tears. 'There was no other way to save you. Forgive me, I beg you.'

* * *

Lothar must have relapsed into unconsciousness, for he awoke with a start and could not remember where he was or how he had got there. Then the smell of his arm, sick and disgusting, brought it back to him, and he crawled to the edge of the cliff and looked out towards the south. He saw his pursuers then for the first time, and even at the distance of a mile or more he recognized the two wraithlike little figures that danced ahead of the column of horsemen.

'Bushmen,' he whispered. Now he understood how they had come so swiftly. 'She has put her tame Bushmen onto me.' He realized then that there had never been any chance of throwing them off the spoor; all that time Lothar had used in covering their sign and in anti-tracking subterfuges had been wasted. The Bushmen had followed them with barely a check over the worst going and most treacherous tracking terrain.

Then he looked beyond the trackers and counted the number of men coming against him. 'Seven,' he whispered, and his eyes narrowed as he tried to pick out a smaller feminine figure amongst them, but they were dismounted leading their horses and the intervening mopani obscured his vision.

He transferred all his attention from the approaching horsemen to his own preparations. His only concern now was to delay the pursuit as long as possible, and to convince the pursuers that all of his band were still together here upon the summit. Every hour he could win for them would give Hendrick and Manie just that much more chance of escape.

It was slow and awkward working with one hand, but he jammed Klein Boy's rifle into a niche of the granite with the muzzle pointing down towards the

plain. He looped a strap from one of the water bottles over the trigger and led the other end to his chosen shooting stance in the shadows, protected by a flare of the granite ledge.

He had to pause for a minute to rest, for his vision was starring and breaking up into patches of blackness, and his legs felt too weak to support his weight. He peeped over the edge and the horsemen were much closer, on the point of emerging from the mopani forest into the open ground. Now he recognized Centaine, slim and boyish in her riding-breeches, and he could even make out the bright yellow speck of the scarf around her throat.

Despite the fever heat and the darkness in his head, despite his desperate circumstances, he still found a bitter-sweet admiration for her. 'By God, she never gives up,' he muttered. 'She'll follow me over the other side to the frontiers of hell.'

He crawled to the pile of discarded water bottles and dragging them after him, arranged them in three separate piles along the lip of the ledge, and he knotted the leather straps together so that he could agitate all the piles simultaneously with a single twitch of the strap in his hand.

'Nothing else I can do,' he whispered, 'except shoot straight.' But his head was throbbing and his vision danced with the hot mirage of his fever. Thirst was an agony in his throat and his body was a furnace.

He unscrewed the stopper on the water bottle and drank, carefully controlling himself, sipping and holding it in his mouth before swallowing. Immediately he felt better, and his vision firmed. He closed the water bottle and placed it beside him with the spare ammunition clips. Then he folded his jacket into a cushion on the lip of granite in front of him and laid the Mauser on top of it. The pursuers had reached the foot of the kopje and were clustered about his abandoned horse.

Lothar held up his good hand in front of his eyes with fingers extended. There was no tremor, it was steady as the rock on which he lay and he cuddled the butt of the Mauser in under his chin.

'The horses,' he reminded himself. 'They can't follow Manie without horses – ' and he drew a long breath, held it, and shot Blaine Malcomess' chestnut mare in the centre of the white blaze.

As the echoes of the shot still bounced from the cliffs of the surrounding hills, Lothar flicked the bolt of the Mauser and fired again, but this time he jerked the strap attached to the other rifle and the report of the two shots overlapped. The double report would deceive even an experienced soldier into believing there was more than one man on the summit.

Strangely, in this moment of deadly endeavour, the fever had receded. Lothar's vision was bright and clear, the sights of the Mauser starkly outlined against each target and his gun hand steady and precise as he swung the rifle from one horse to the next and sent each one crashing to earth with a head shot. Now they were all down except one: Centaine's mount.

He picked Centaine up in the field of his gunsight. She was galloping back towards the mopani, lying flat over her horse's neck, her elbows pumping, a man hanging from her stirrup, and Lothar lifted his forefinger from the curve of the trigger. It was an instinctive reaction; he could not bring himself to send a bullet anywhere near her.

Instead he swung the barrel away from her. The riders of the downed horses, all four of them, were straggling away towards the mopani. Their thin cries of panic carried to the summit. They were easy marks; he could have knocked

them down with a single bullet for each, but instead he made it a game to see how close he could come without touching one of them. They ducked and cavorted as the Mauser fire whipped around them. It was comical, hilarious. He was laughing as he worked the bolt, and suddenly he heard the wild hysterical quality of his laughter ringing hollowly in his own skull and he bit it off. 'I'm losing my head,' he thought. 'Got to last it out.'

The last of the running men disappeared into the forest and he found himself shaking and sweating with reaction.

'Got to be ready,' he encouraged himself. 'Got to think. Can't stop now. Can't let go.'

He crawled to the second rifle and reloaded it, then rolled back to his shooting stance in the shadow of the summit boulders.

'Now they are going to try and mark me,' he guessed. 'They'll draw fire and watch for – '

He saw the helmet being offered invitingly above the lip of the ravine at the edge of the forest and grinned. That was a hoary old trick; even the red-necked pommy soldiers had learned not to fall for it as far back as the opening years of the Boer War. It was almost insulting that they should try to entice him with it now.

'All right then!' he taunted them. 'We'll see who foxes who!'

He fired both rifles simultaneously, and a moment later jerked the straps attached to the piles of empty water bottles. At that range the movement of the round felt-covered bottles would show against the skyline just like the heads of hidden riflemen.

'Now they will send men to circle the hill,' he guessed, and watched for movement amongst the trees on his flanks, the Mauser ready, blinking his eyes rapidly to clear them.

'Five hours until dark,' he told himself. 'Hendrick and Manie will be at the river by dawn tomorrow. Got to hold them until then.'

He saw a flash of movement out on the right flank: men crouching and running forward in shorts bursts, outflanking the kopje, and he aimed for the trunks over their heads. Mauser fire whiplashed and bark exploded from the mopani, leaving wet white wounds on the standing timber.

'Keep your heads down, *myne heeren*!'

Lothar was laughing again, hysterical, delirious cackles. He forced himself to stop it, and immediately the image of Manie's face appeared before him, the beautiful topaz eyes swimming with tears and the flash of blood on his upper lip.

'My son,' he lamented. 'Oh God, how will I live without you!'

Even then he would not accept that he was dying, but blackness filled his skull and his head dropped forward onto the filthy pus-stained bandage that swaddled his arm. The stench of his own decaying flesh became part of the delirious nightmares which continued to torment him even in unconsciousness.

He came back to reality gradually, and he was aware that the sunlight had mellowed and the terrible heat had passed. There was a tiny breeze fanning the hilltop and he panted for the cooler air, sucking it gratefully into his lungs. Then he became aware of his thirst and his hand shook as he reached for the water bottle; it required an enormous effort to remove the stopper and lift it to his lips. One gulp and the bottle slipped from his grip and precious water splashed the front of his shirt and glugged from the bottle, pooling on the rock, evaporating almost immediately. He had lost fully a pint before he could retrieve

the bottle and the loss made him want to weep. Carefully he screwed the stopper closed, then lifted his head and listened.

There were men on the hill. He heard the distinct crunch of a steel-shod boot biting into a granite foothold and he reached for one of the 'potato masher' grenades. With the Mauser over his shoulder he crawled back from the edge and used the rock to pull himself to his feet. He could not stand unassisted, and he had to lean his way around the boulder. He crept forward cautiously with the grenade ready.

The summit was clear; they must still be climbing the cliff. He held his breath and listened with all his being. He heard it again, close at hand, the scrape and slide of cloth against granite and a sharp involuntary inhalation of breath, a gasp of effort as somebody missed and then retrieved a foothold just below the summit.

'They are coming up from behind,' he told himself as though explaining to a backward child. Every thought required an effort. 'Seven-second delay on the fuse of the grenade.' He stared down at the clumsy weapon that he held by its wooden handle. 'Too long. They are very close.'

He lifted the grenade and tried to pull the firing-pin. It had corroded and was firmly stuck. He grunted and heaved at it and the pin came away. He heard the primer click and he began to count.

'A thousand and one, a thousand and two – ' And at the fifth second he stooped and rolled the grenade over the edge. Out of sight, but close by, someone shouted an urgent warning.

'Christ! It's a grenade!' And Lothar laughed wildly.

'Eat it, you jackals of the English!' He heard them sliding and slipping as they tried to escape and he braced himself for the explosion, but instead he heard only the clatter and rattle of the grenade as it bounced and dropped down the slope.

'Misfire!' He stopped laughing. 'Oh damn it to hell.'

Then abruptly, but belatedly, the grenade exploded, far down the cliff. A crash of sound followed by the rattle and whine of shrapnel on the rock, and a man cried out.

Lothar fell on his knees and crawled to the edge. He looked over. There were three khaki-uniformed men on the cliff, sliding and scrambling downwards. He propped the Mauser on the lip and fired rapidly. His bullets left lead smears on the rock close beside the terrified troopers. They dropped the last few feet and started back towards the trees. One of them was hurt, hit by shrapnel; his companions supported him on each side and dragged him away.

Lothar lay exhausted by the effort for almost an hour before he could drag himself back to the south side of the summit. He looked down at the dead horses lying in the sun. Already their bellies were swelling, but the water bottles were still strapped to their saddles. 'The water is the magnet,' he whispered. 'By now they will be really thirsty. They will come for the water next.'

At first he thought the darkness was only in his mind again, but when he rolled his head and looked into the west he saw the last orange flash of the sunset in the sky. Before his eyes it faded and the sudden African night was upon them.

He lay and listened for them to try to reach the water, and he wondered as he had so often before at the mystic sounds of the African night, the gentle muted orchestra of insect and bird, the piping of the hunting bats flitting around the dome of rock and out on the plain the plaintive yip of jackal and the occasional

outlandish grunting bark of the nocturnal honey badger. Lothar had to try to discount these distractions and listen for manmade sounds in the darkness directly below the cliff.

It was only the clink of a stirrup iron that alerted him, and he tossed the grenade with a full swing of his arm out over the abyss. The heavy crump of the explosion blew a puff of air into his face, and by the sudden flare of flame he saw far below the dark figures standing over the dead horse. He made out two of them, though he could not be certain there were not others, and he tossed the second grenade.

In the brief burst of orange light he saw them racing back towards the trees; they ran so lightly that they could not have been burdened by water bottles.

'Sweat it out,' he taunted them, but he had only the one remaining grenade. He held it to his chest as though it were some rare treasure. 'Must be ready when they come again. Can't let them get the water.' He was talking aloud, and he knew it was a sign of his delirium. Every time he felt the swimming dizziness he lifted his head and tried to focus on the stars.

'Got to hold out,' he told himself seriously. 'If I can only keep them here until noon tomorrow.' He tried to make the calculations of time and distance but it was too much for him. 'Must be eight hours since Hendrick and Manie left. They will keep going all night. They haven't got me to hold them back. They can make the river before dawn. If only I can hold them another eight hours they will get clear away – ' But the weariness and the fever overwhelmed him and he cradled his forehead in the curve of his elbow.

'Lothar!' It was his imagination, he knew that, but then his name was called again. 'Lothar!' And he lifted his head and shivered with the cold of the night and the memories that her voice summoned up.

He opened his mouth and then closed it. He would not reply, would give nothing away. But he listened avidly for Centaine Courtney to call again.

'Lothar, we have a wounded man.' He judged that she was at the edge of the forest. He could imagine her, determined and brave, that small firm chin lifted, those dark eyes.

'Why do I still love you?' he whispered.

'We must have water for him.' Strange how clearly her voice carried. He could pick out the inflection of her French accent and somehow he found that touching. It brought tears to his eyes.

'Lothar! I am coming out to fetch the water.'

Her voice was closer, stronger – clearly she had left the shelter of the trees.

'I'm alone, Lothar.' She must be halfway across the open ground.

'Go back!' He tried to shout, but it was a mumble. 'I warned you. I have to do it.' He fumbled for the grenade. 'Can't let you take the water – for Manie's sake. I have to do it.'

He hooked his finger through the firing ring of the grenade.

'I have reached the first horse,' she called. 'I am taking the bottle. Just one bottle, Lothar.'

She was in his power. She was standing at the foot of the cliff. It wouldn't need a long throw. All he had to do was roll the grenade over the edge and it would fly out like a toboggan along the curve of the cliff and land at her feet.

He imagined the flash of the explosion, that sweet flesh that had cradled his, and harboured his son, torn and rent by razor-edged shrapnel. He thought how much he hated her – and realized that he loved her as much, and the tears in his eyes blinded him.

'I'm going back now, Lothar. I have one bottle,' she called, and he heard in her voice gratitude and an acknowledgement of the bond between them that no deed, no passage of time could sever. She spoke again, dropping her voice so it reached him as a faint whisper.

'May God forgive you, Lothar De La Rey.' And then no more.

Those gentle words wounded him as deeply as any he had ever heard from her. There was a finality to them that he found unbearable, and he dropped his head onto his arm to smother the cry of despair which rose in his throat, and the darkness rustled in his head like the wings of a black vulture as he felt himself, falling, falling, falling.

* * *

'This one is dead,' Blaine Malcomess said quietly, standing over the prostrate figure. They had climbed the cliff at two places in the darkness; then in the dawn they had carried the summit in a concerted rush only to find it undefended. 'Where are the others?'

Sergeant Hansmeyer hurried out of the shadowy cluster of boulders. 'There is no one else on the hill, sir. They must have got clean away.'

'Blaine!' Centaine called urgently. 'Where are you? What is happening?' He had insisted that she remain at the foot of the kopje until they had captured the summit. He had not yet signalled her to come up, but here she was, only a minute behind their attack.

'Over here,' he snapped. And then, as she ran towards him, 'You disobeyed an order, madam.'

She ignored the accusation. 'Where are they?' She broke off as she saw the body. 'Oh God, it's Lothar.' She went down beside him.

'So this is De La Rey. Well, he's dead, I'm afraid,' Blaine told her.

'Where are the others?' Centaine looked up at him anxiously. She had been both dreading and anticipating finding Lothar's bastard; she still tried to avoid using the boy's name, even to herself.

'Not here.' Blaine shook his head. 'Given us the slip. De La Rey fooled us and put up a good rearguard delay. They have got clear away. They'll be across the river by now.'

Manfred. Centaine capitulated and thought of him by name. Manfred, my son. And her disappointment and sense of loss was so strong that it shocked her. She had wanted him to be there. To see him at last. She looked down at his father, and other emotions, long buried and suppressed, rose in her.

Lothar lay with his face cradled in the crook of his elbow. The other arm, bound up in strips of stained blanket, was outflung. She touched his neck below the ear, feeling for the carotid artery, and exclaimed immediately she felt the fever heat of his skin.

'He's still alive.'

'Are you sure?' Blaine squatted beside her. Between them they rolled Lothar onto his back, and they saw the grenade lying under him.

'You were right,' Blaine said softly. 'He did have another grenade. He could have killed you last night.'

Centaine shivered as she stared down at Lothar's face. He was no longer

beautiful and golden and brave. The fever had ruined him, his features had collapsed like those of a corpse and he was shrunken and grey.

'He is badly dehydrated,' she said. 'Is there water left in that bottle?' While Blaine dribbled water into his mouth, Centaine unwrapped the festering rags from his arm.

'Blood poisoning.' She recognized the livid lines beneath the skin and the stench of his rotting flesh. 'That arm will have to come off.' Though her voice was steady and businesslike, she was appalled at the damage she had wrought. It seemed impossible that a single bite could have caused that. Her teeth were one of her good features and she was proud of them, always kept them clean and white and cared for. That arm looked at though it had been savaged by one of the carrion eaters, by a hyena or a leopard.

'There is a Portuguese Roman Catholic mission at Cuangar on the river,' Blaine said. 'But he'll be lucky if we can get him there alive. With all but one of the horses dead, we'll be lucky to make it as far as the river ourselves.' He stood up. 'Sergeant, send one of your men to fetch the first-aid kit and then have the rest of them search every inch of this hilltop. A million pounds' worth of diamonds are missing.'

Hansmeyer saluted and hurried away, rapping out orders at his troopers.

Blaine sank down beside Centaine. 'While we are waiting for the medical kit, I suppose we had better search his clothing and equipment in the off-chance that he kept any of the stolen diamonds with him.'

'It's an off-chance all right,' Centaine agreed with bitter resignation. 'The diamonds are almost certainly with his son and that big black Ovambo ruffian of his. And without our Bushmen trackers – ' She shrugged.

Blaine spread Lothar's dusty stained tunic on the rock and began examining the seams, while Centaine bathed Lothar's injured arm and then bound it up with clean white bandages from the medical kit.

'Nothing, sir.' Hansmeyer reported back. 'We've gone over every inch of this rock, every nook and cranny.'

'Very well, Sergeant. Now we have to get this beggar off the kopje without letting him fall and break his neck.'

'Not that he doesn't deserve it.'

Blaine grinned. 'He does deserve it. But we don't want to do the hangman out of his five guineas, do we now, Sergeant?'

They were ready to move out within the hour. Lothar De La Rey was strapped into a drag litter of mopani saplings behind their single remaining horse, and the wounded trooper, the grenade shrapnel still in his back and shoulder, rode up in Centaine's saddle.

Centaine lingered on at the foot of the kopje after the column had started northwards towards the river once more, and Blaine came back to stand beside her.

He took her hand and she sighed and leaned lightly against his shoulder. 'Oh, Blaine, for me so much has ended here in this Godforsaken wilderness, on this sun-blasted lump of rock.'

'I think I can understand how much the loss of the diamonds means.'

'Do you, Blaine? I don't think so. I don't think even I can take it in yet. Everything has changed – even my hatred for Lothar – '

'There is still a chance we will recover the stones.'

'No, Blaine. You and I both know there is no chance. The diamonds are gone.'

He did not attempt to deny it, did not offer false comfort.

'I have lost it all, everything I ever worked for – for me and my son. It's all gone.'

'I didn't realize – ' he broke off and looked down at her with pity and deep concern. 'I understood it would be a hard blow, but everything? Is it that bad?'

'Yes, Blaine,' she said simply. 'Everything. Not all at once, of course, but now the whole edifice will start to crumble and I will struggle to shore it up. I will borrow and beg and plead for time, but the foundation is gone from under me. A million pounds, Blaine, it's an enormous sum of money. I will stave off the inevitable for a few months, a year perhaps, but it will go faster and faster, like a house of cards, and at the end it will come crashing down around me.'

'Centaine, I am not a poor man,' he began. 'I could help you – ' She reached up and laid her forefinger on his lips.

'There is one thing I would ask from you,' she whispered. 'Not money – but in the days ahead, I will need some comfort. Not often, just when it gets very bad.'

'I will be there whenever you need me, Centaine. I promise you that. You have only to call.'

'Oh, Blaine.' She turned to him. 'If only!'

'Yes, Centaine – if only.' And he took her in his arms. There was no guilt nor fear, even the terrible threat of ruin and destitution that hung over her seemed to recede when she was in his arms.

'I wouldn't even mind being poor again, if only I had you beside me always,' she whispered, and he could not reply. In desperation he bowed his head over her and stopped her lips with his mouth.

* * *

The Portuguese priest doctor at Cuangar Mission took off Lothar De La Rey's arm two inches below the elbow. He operated by the bright flat white of the Petromax lantern, and Centaine stood at his side, sweating behind the surgical mask, responding to the doctor's requests in French, trying to prevent herself freezing in horror at the rasping of the bone saw and the suffocating stench of chloroform and gangrene that filled the daub and thatch hut that served as an operating theatre. When it was over, she slipped away to the earthpit lavatory and vomited up her revulsion and pity. Alone in the mission hut that had been allocated to her, under the billowing ghostly mosquito net, she could still taste it in the back of her throat. The gangrene smell seemed to have impregnated her skin and lingered in her hair. She prayed that she might never smell it again, nor ever be forced to live through another hour as harrowing as watching the man she had once loved shorn of a limb, turned into a cripple before her eyes.

The prayer was in vain, for at noon the following day the priest doctor murmured regretfully, '*Désolé, mais j'ai manqué l'infection. Il faut couper encore une fois* – I am sorry, but I have missed the infection. It is necessary to cut again.'

The second time, because she now knew what to expect, seemed even worse than the first. She had to press her fingernails into the palms of her hands to prevent herself fainting as the priest took up the gleaming silver saw and cut

through the exposed bone of Lothar's humerus only inches below the great joint of the shoulder. For three days afterwards Lothar lay in a pale coma, seeming already to have passed the division between life and death.

'I cannot say.' The priest shrugged away her anxious plea for reassurance. 'It is up to the good Lord now.'

Then on the evening of the third day when she entered his hut, the sapphire yellow eyes swivelled towards her in their deep coloured sockets, and she saw recognition flare for an instant before Lothar's eyelids dropped down over them.

However, it was two days more before the priest allowed Blaine Malcomess to enter the hut. Blaine cautioned Lothar and placed him under formal arrest.

'My sergeant will have complete charge of you until you are passed fit to travel by Father Paulus. At that time you will be brought by boat downriver to the border post at Runtu under strict guard, and from there by road to Windhoek where you will stand your trial.'

Lothar lay against the bolster, pale and skeletal thin. His stump, wrapped in a turban of gauze bandage, the end stained yellow with iodine, looked like a penquin's wing. He stared at Blaine expressionlessly.

'Now, De La Rey, you don't need me to tell you that you will be a lucky man to escape the gallows. But you will give yourself a fighting chance of leniency if you tell us where you have hidden the diamonds or what you have done with them.'

He waited for almost a minute, and it was difficult not to be ruffled by that flat yellow stare with which Lothar regarded him.

'Do you understand what I'm trying to tell you, De La Rey?' he broke the silence, and Lothar rolled his head away, stared out of the paneless window of the hut down towards the riverbank.

'I think you know that I am administrator of the territory. I have power to review your sentence: my recommendation for clemency would almost certainly be acceded to by the minister of justice. Don't be a fool, man. Give up the diamonds. They are no use to you where you are going, and I will guarantee you your life in return.'

Lothar closed his eyes.

'Very well, De La Rey. We understand each other then. Don't expect any mercy from me.' He called Sergeant Hansmeyer into the hut. 'Sergeant, the prisoner has no privileges, none at all. He will be under guard day and night, twenty-four hours a day, until you hand him over to the appropriate authority in Windhoek. You will be directly responsible to me. You understand?'

'Yes, sir.' Hansmeyer drew himself to attention.

'Look after him, Hansmeyer. I want this one. I want him badly.'

Blaine strode out of the hut, down to where Centaine sat alone under the open-sided thatched *setengi* on the riverbank. He dropped into the camp chair beside hers and lit a cheroot. He inhaled the smoke, held it a moment and then blew it out forcefully and angrily.

'The man is intransigent,' he said. 'I offered him my personal guarantee of leniency in exchange for your diamonds. He didn't even deign to reply. I don't have the authority to offer him a free pardon but, believe me, if I did I wouldn't hesitate. As it is there is nothing more I can do.' He drew on the cheroot again and glared out across the wide green river. 'I swear he will pay for what he has done to you – pay in full measure.'

'Blaine.' She laid her hand lightly on his muscular brown forearm. 'Spite is too petty an emotion for a man of your stature.'

He glanced sideways and, despite his rancour, he smiled. 'Don't credit me with too much nobility, madam. I am many things, but not a saint.'

He looked boyish when he grinned like that, except that his green eyes took on a wicked slant and his ears stuck out at the most endearing angle.

'Oh la, sir, it might be amusing to test the limits of your nobility and sanctity – one day.'

He chuckled with delight. 'What a shameless but interesting proposal.' And then he became serious again. 'Centaine, you know that I should never have come on this expedition. At this moment my duties are being sadly neglected, and I will certainly have incurred the justified wrath of my superiors in Pretoria. I must get back to my office just as soon as I can. I have arranged with Father Paulus for canoes and paddlers to take us downriver to the border post at Runtu. I hope we will be able to requisition a police truck from there. Hansmeyer and his troopers will stay on to guard De La Rey and bring him in as soon as he is fit enough to travel.'

Centaine nodded. 'Yes, I also have to get back and start picking up the pieces, papering over the cracks.'

'We can leave first light tomorrow.'

'Blaine, I would like to speak to Lothar – to De La Rey, before we leave.' When he hesitated, she went on persuasively: 'A few minutes alone with him, please Blaine. It's important to me.'

* * *

Centaine paused in the doorway of the hut while her eyes adjusted to the gloom.

Lothar was sitting up, bare to the waist, a cheap trade blanket spread over his legs. His body was thin and pale; the infection had burned the flesh off his bones and his ribs were a gaunt rack.

'Sergeant Hansmeyer, will you leave us alone for a minute?' Centaine asked, and she stood aside.

As he passed her, Hansmeyer said quietly, 'I'll be within call, Mrs Courtney.'

In the silence that followed, Centaine and Lothar stared at each other, and it was she who gave in and spoke first.

'If you set out to ruin me, then you have succeeded,' she said, and he wriggled the stub of his missing arm, a gesture which was at once both pathetic and obscene.

'Who has ruined whom, Centaine?' he asked, and she dropped her eyes.

'Won't you give me back at least a part of what you have stolen from me?' she asked. 'For the sake of what we shared once long ago?'

He did not reply, but instead lifted his hand and touched the ancient puckered scar on his chest. She winced, for it was she who had fired that shot from the Luger pistol at the time of her disillusion and revulsion.

'The boy has the diamonds, hasn't he?' she asked. 'Your – ' she was about to say, 'Your bastard?' but she changed it: 'Your son?'

Lothar remained silent and she went on impulsively: 'Manfred, our son.'

'I never thought I'd hear you say that.' He could not disguise the pleasure in his tone. 'Will you remember he is our son, conceived in love, when you are tempted to destroy him also?'

'Why should you think I would do that?'

'I know you, Centaine,' he said.

'No.' She shook her head vehemently. 'You do not know me.'

'If he stands in your way, you will destroy him,' he said, flatly.

'Do you truly believe that?' She stared at him. 'Do you really believe that I am so ruthless, so vindictive, that I would take my revenge on my own son?'

'You have never acknowledged him as that.'

'I have now. You have heard me do it more than once in the last few minutes.'

'Are you promising me that you will not harm him?'

'I do not have to promise you, Lothar De La Rey. I am merely saying it. I will not harm Manfred.'

'And naturally you expect something from me in return,' he demanded, leaning forward. He was breathing with difficulty, sweating with the effort of fighting off his physical weakness. His sweat had a rank and sour smell in the gloomy confines of the hut.

'Would you offer me anything in return?' she asked quietly.

'No,' he said. 'Nothing!' And he sank back against the bolster, exhausted but defiant. 'Now let me hear you withdraw your promise.'

'I made no promise,' she said quietly. 'But, I repeat, Manfred, our son, is safe from me. I will never deliberately do anything to harm him. I do not give you the same assurance, however.'

She turned and called. 'Thank you, Sergeant, we have finished our business.' And she stooped to leave.

'Centaine – ' he cried weakly, and he wanted to tell her, 'Your diamonds are in the cleft on the summit of the hill.' But when she turned back he bit down on the words and said only, 'Goodbye, Centaine. It is finished at last.'

* * *

The Okavango is one of Africa's most beautiful rivers. It rises in the highlands of the Angolan plateau above 4,000 feet and flows south and east, a wide deep torrent of green water that it seems must reach the ocean, so swift and determined is its flow. However, it is a land-locked river, debouching first into the mis-named Okavango Swamps, a vast area of lucid lagoons and papyrus banks, studded with islets on which graceful ivory nut palms and great wild figs stand tall. Beyond that the river emerges again but shrivelled and weakened as it enters the desolation of the Kalahari Desert and disappears for ever beneath those eternal sands.

This section of the river that Centaine and Blaine set out upon was that above the swamps where the river was at its grandest. Their craft was a native *mukoro*, a dugout canoe fashioned from a single treetrunk over twenty feet long, rounded but not perfectly straight.

'The owl and the pussy cat put to sea in a beautiful banana-shaped boat,' quoth Blaine, and Centaine laughed a little apprehensively until she saw how masterfully their paddlers handled the misshapen craft.

They were two amiable coal-black giants of the river tribe. They had the balance of gymnasts and their bodies were forged and hardened to Grecian perfection by a lifetime of wielding their paddles and their long punting poles.

They stood at the stern and bows, singing their melodious work chant and trimming their narrow unstable craft with a relaxed, almost instinctive ease.

Amidships Blaine and Centaine lolled on cushions of rawhide stuffed with the fluffy heads of the papyrus reeds. The narrow beam forced them to sit in tandem, with Blaine in the lead, his Lee Enfield rifle across his lap ready to discourage the close approach of any of the numerous hippopotami which infested the river. 'The most dangerous animal in Africa by far,' he told Centaine.

'What about lions and elephants and poisonous snakes?' she challenged.

'The old hippo gets two humans for every one killed by all the other species put together.'

This was Centaine's first venture into these parts. She was a creature of the desert, unacquainted with the river or the swamps, unfamiliar with the boundless life they supported. Blaine, on the other hand, knew the river well. He had first been ordered here when serving with General Smuts' expeditionary force in 1915 and had since returned often to hunt and study the wildlife of the region. He seemed to recognize every animal and bird and plant, and he had a hundred stories, both true and apocryphal, with which to amuse her.

The mood of the river changed constantly; at places it narrowed and raced through rock-lined gaps and the long canoe flew like a lance upon it. The paddlers directed it past outcrops of fanged rock upon which the current humped up and split, and with delicate touches of the paddles took them through the creaming whirlpools beyond and into the next flying stretch where the surface was moulded like green Venetian glass into standing waves by its own speed and momentum. Centaine whooped breathlessly, half in terror and half in exhilaration, like a child on a roller coaster. Then they emerged onto broad shallow stretches, the flow broken by islands and sandbanks and bordered by wide flood plains on which grazed herds of wild buffalo, massive indolent-seeming beasts, black as hell and crusted with dried mud, great bossed horns drooping mournfully over their trumpet-shaped ears, standing belly-deep in the flood plains, lifting their black drooling muzzles in comical curiosity to watch them pass.

'Oh Blaine! What are those? I've never seen them before.'

'Lechwe. This is as far south as you will find them.'

There were vast herds of these robust water antelope with coarse wiry red coats, the rams standing as tall as a man's chest and carrying long gracefully recurved horns. The hornless ewes were fluffy as children's toys. So dense were the herds that when they fled from the human presence they churned the water until it sounded like the thunderous passage of a steam locomotive heard at a distance.

On nearly every tall tree along the river's banks were posted pairs of fish eagles, their white heads shining in the sunlight. They threw back their heads, belling out their throats to chant their weird yelping call as the *mukoro* glided past.

On the white sandbanks the long saurian shapes of the crocodiles were silhouetted, ugly and evil as they lifted themselves on their stubby deformed legs and waddled swiftly to the water's edge, then slipping away below the surface, only the twin knobs of their scaly eyebrows still showing.

In the shallows clusters of smooth rounded boulders, dark grey edged with baby pink, caught Centaine's attention, but she did not recognize them until Blaine warned:

'Watch them!' and the paddlers sheered off as one of the huge boulders moved, raising a head the size of a beer keg, gaping red, the mighty jaws lined with tusks of yellow ivory, and it bellowed at them with the deep sardonical laughter of a demented god.

Blaine shifted the rifle slightly. 'Don't be taken in by that jovial haw haw haw – he isn't really amused,' he told Centaine as he worked the bolt and pushed a cartridge into the breech.

As he spoke the bull hippo charged at them through the shallows, breaking the water into white foam with his elephantine bounds, blaring his hoarse menacing laughter, his jaws gaping, clashing the long curved yellow ivories whose razor edges could scythe the thick fibrous papyrus stems, or crush in the frail sides of a *mukoro*, or cut a swimming man into two pieces with equal ease.

The *mukoro* drove forward under the long powerful thrusts of the two oarsmen, but the hippopotamus gained on them rapidly and Blaine sprang to his feet, balancing in the unstable craft. He lifted the rifle to his shoulder and fired so rapidly that the reports blended together, and Centaine flinched at the whiplash of gunfire over her head and looked back, expecting to see the bullets strike on the great fleshy grey head and blood spurt from between those glassy pink-shot little eyes. But Blaine had aimed inches over the beast's forehead. The bristly ears twitched and fluttered like sunbirds' wings to the shock of passing shot, and the bull broke his charge and came up short, just his head showing above the surface, blinking rapidly with comical astonishment. The *mukoro* pulled swiftly away, and the bull submerged in a huge swirl of green water as if to cover his embarrassment at his own ineffectual performance.

'Are you all right, Centaine?' Blaine lowered the rifle.

'That was a little frosty.' She tried to keep her voice level with only partial success.

'Not as bad as it seemed – sound and fury, not too much of the deadly intent.' He smiled at her.

'I'm glad you didn't kill him.'

'Not much point in turning the old boy into four tons of rotting carrion and making twenty widows of his fat wives.'

'Is that why he chased us – protecting his females?'

'Probably, but you can never tell with wild animals. Perhaps one of his cows is calving, or he has unpleasant memories of human hunters, or perhaps he just felt plain bolshy today.'

His coolness in crisis had impressed her almost as much as his humanity in sparing the threatening beast.

'Only schoolgirls worship their heroes,' she reminded herself firmly as the canoe sped onwards, and then found herself studying the breadth of Blaine's shoulders and the way he held his head upon them. His dark hair was cut short down the back of his neck, and his neck was strong but not bulled, pleasingly proportioned and smooth, only his ears were too large, and the tips were pink where the sunlight seemed to shine through them. She felt an almost irresistible urge to lean forward and kiss the soft skin just behind where they jutted out, but she controlled herself with a giggle.

He turned and demanded with a smile, 'What's so funny?'

'A girl always feels weak and giggly after Prince Charming saves her from a fire-breathing dragon.'

'Mythical creatures, dragons.'

'Don't scoff,' she chided him. 'Anything is possible here, even dragons and

princes. This is never-never land. Santa Claus and the good fairy are waiting just around the next bend.'

'You are just a little bit crazy, do you know that?'

'Yes, I know that,' she nodded. 'And I think I should warn you, it's both contagious and infectious.'

'Your warning comes too late.' He shook his head sadly. 'I think I've caught it already.'

'Good,' she said, and giving in to her whim, she leaned forward and kissed that soft spot behind his ear.

He shivered theatrically. 'Now look what you've done.' He turned again and showed her the gooseflesh standing in little pimples on his forearms. 'You must promise never to do that again. It's too dangerous.'

'Like you, I never make promises.' She saw the quick shadow of regret and guilt in his eyes and cursed herself to alluding to his lack of commitment to her and thereby spoiling the mood.

'Oh, Blaine, look at those birds. Surely they aren't real are they? It proves me right, this is never-never land.' She tried to retrieve the mood.

They were drifting past a high bank of red clay bright as a blood orange that was perforated by thousands of perfectly round apertures, and a living swirling cloud of marvellously coloured birds hung over the bank, darting in and out of the myriad entrances to their nesting burrows.

'Carmine bee-eaters,' Blaine told her, sharing her wonder at the glory of the flashing darts of flaming pink and turquoise blue, with their long delicately streaming tail feathers and pointed wingtips sharp as stilettos. 'They are so unearthly, I am beginning to believe you,' he said. 'Perhaps we have indeed passed through the mirror.'

They spoke little after that, but somehow their silences seemed to bring them even closer. They only touched once more when Centaine laid her hand, palm open, along the side of his neck, and for a moment he covered her hand with his own, a gentle fleeting exchange.

Then Blaine spoke briefly to the leading oarsman.

'What is it, Blaine?' she asked.

'I told him to find a good place to camp for the night.'

'Isn't it still very early?' She glanced at the sun.

'Yes.' He turned and smiled at her, almost sheepishly. 'But then I'm trying for the record trip between Cuangar and Runtu.'

'The record?'

'Slowest journey ever.'

Blaine chose one of the large islands. The white sandbar folded upon itself to form a secret lagoon, clear and green and screened by tall waving papyrus. While the two paddlers piled driftwood for the fire and cut papyrus fronds to thatch night shelters for them, Blaine picked up his rifle.

'Where are you going?' Centaine asked.

'See if I can get a buck for dinner.'

'Oh, Blaine, please don't kill anything, not today. Not this special day.'

'Aren't you tired of bully beef?'

'Please,' she insisted and he set his rifle aside with a smile and a rueful shake of his head and went to make sure than the huts were ready and the mosquito nets rigged over each separate bed. Satisfied, Blaine dismissed the paddlers and they climbed into the *mukoro*.

'Where are they off to?' Centaine demanded as they poled out into the current.

'I told them to camp on the mainland,' Blaine answered, and they each looked away, suddenly awkward and shy and intensely aware of their isolation as they stared after the departing canoe.

Centaine turned and walked back to the camp. She knelt beside her saddle bags, which were her only luggage, and without looking up told him, 'I haven't bathed since last night. I'm going to swim in the lagoon.' She had a bar of yellow soap in her hand.

'Do you have a last message for the folks back home?'

'What do you mean?'

'This is the Okavango river, Centaine. The crocodiles here gobble little girls as hors d'oeuvres.'

'You could stand guard with the rifle – '

'Delighted to oblige.'

' – and with your eyes closed!'

'Rather defeats the object, doesn't it?'

He scouted the edge of the lagoon and found shallow water below an outcropping of black water-polished rock where the bottom was white sand and an approaching crocodile would show clearly, and he sat on the highest pinnacle of rock with the Lee Enfield loaded and the safety-catch off.

'You are on your honour not to peek,' she warned, standing on the beach below him, and he concentrated on a flock of spur-wing geese flogging their heavy wings as they passed across the lowering sun, but acutely aware of the rustle of her falling clothing.

He heard the water ripple, and her little gasp and then, 'All right, now you can watch for crocodiles.'

She was sitting on the sandy bottom, just her head above the surface, her back towards him and her hair scraped up and tied on top of her head.

'It's heavenly, so cool and refreshing.' She smiled over her shoulder, and he could see the gleam of her white flesh through the green water and he thought he might not be able to bear the pain of his wanting. He knew that she was deliberately provoking him, but he could neither resist her not steel himself against her wiles.

Isabella Malcomess had been thrown from her horse almost five years previously, and since then they had not know each other as man and woman. They had attempted it only once, but he could not bear to think about the agony and humiliation they had both suffered at their failure.

He had a healthy lusty body and a huge appetite for living. It had taken all his strength and determination to discipline himself to this unnatural monastic existence. He had succeeded at last, so that he was now unprepared for the savage escape of all those fettered desires and instincts.

'Eyes closed again,' she called gaily. 'I'm going to stand and work up some suds.'

He was unable to reply; he only just contained the groan that came up his throat, and he stared down fixedly at the rifle in his lap.

Centaine screamed on a wild rising note of terror. 'Blaine!'

He was on his feet in that instant. Centaine was standing thigh deep, the green water just lapping the deep cleft of her small round buttocks, the naked swell of her hips narrowing into a tiny waist. Her exquistively sculpted back and shoulders were stiff with horror.

The crocodile was coming in from deep water with slashing sweeps of its long cockscombed tail, a bow wave spreading back from its hideous armoured snout in a sharp arrowhead of ripples. The reptile was almost as long as the *mukoro*, twenty feet from its nose to the tip of its crested tail.

'Run, Centaine, run!' he bellowed, and she whirled and floundered back towards him. But the reptile was moving as swiftly as a horse at full gallop, the water breaking into a roiling wake behind it, and Centaine was blocking Blaine's aim, running directly back towards him.

Blaine sprang down from the rock and waded knee-deep into the water to meet her, his rifle held at high port across his chest.

'Down!' he shouted at her. 'Fall flat!' And she responded instantly diving forward at full length, and he fired over her back, a snap shot for the huge reptile was almost upon her.

The bullet cracked against the armoured scales of its hideous skull. The crocodile arched it back, exploding out of the water, drenching Blaine and covering Centaine in a breaking wave of foam. It stood on its massive tail, its dwarfed forelegs clawing desperately, its creamy belly chequered with symmetrical patterns of scales, the long angular snout pointed to the sky, and with a bellow it collapsed over backwards.

Blaine dragged Centaine to her feet and with one arm around her backed towards the beach, pointing the rifle like a pistol with his free hand. The crocodile was in monstrous convulsions, its primitive brain damaged by the bullet. It rolled and thrashed in uncontrolled erratic circles, snapping its jaws so that the jagged yellow teeth clashed like a steel gate slamming in a high wind.

Blaine thrust Centaine behind him and with both hands lifted the rifle. His bullets rang against the scaly head, tearing away chunks of flesh and bone, and the reptile's tail fluttered and lashed weakly. It dived over the edge of the shallow sandbank into the dark green beyond, came up in one last swirl and then was gone.

Centaine was shaking with terror, her teeth chattering so she could hardly speak. 'Horrible, oh what an awful monster!' and she threw herself against his chest, and clung to him. 'Oh Blaine, I was terrified.' Her face was pressed to his chest so that her voice was blurred.

'It's all right now.' He tried to calm her. 'Easy, my darling, it's all over. It's gone.' He propped the rifle against the rock and enfolded her in his arms.

He was stroking her and soothing her, at first without passion, as he would have gentled one of his own daughters when she woke from a nightmare screaming for him; then he became acutely aware of the silkiness of her bare wet skin under his hands. He could feel every plane of her back, the smooth curves of muscle on each side of her spine, and he could not prevent himself tracing with his fingertips the ridge of her spine. It felt like a string of polished beads beneath her skin; he followed it down until it disappeared into the divide of her small hard bottom.

She was quiet now, only breathing in little choking gasps, but at his touch she curled her spine like a cat, inclining her pelvis towards him, and he seized one of her buttocks in each hand and pulled her to him. She did not resist, but her whole body thrust forward to meet his. 'Blaine.' She said his name and lifted her face.

He kissed her savagely, with the anger of a man of honour who knows he can no longer keep his vows, and they locked together breathing each other's

breath, their tongues twisting together, kneading, pressing, so deep that they threatened to choke each other with their fervour.

She pulled away. 'Now,' she stammered. 'It has to be now,' and he lifted her in his arms like a child and ran with her, back through the clinging white sand to the thatched shelter, and he fell onto his knees beside the mattress of papyrus fronds and lowered her gently onto the blanket that covered it.

'I want to look at you,' he blurted, pulling back onto his haunches, but she squirmed up and reached for him.

'Later – I can't wait – please, Blaine. Oh God, do it now.' She was tearing at the buttons on his shirt front, clumsy with haste, desperate with haste.

He ripped off his sodden shirt and threw it away, and she was kissing him again, smothering his mouth, while both of them fumbled with his belt buckle, getting in each other's way, wildly laughing and gasping, bumping their noses together, bruising their lips between their teeth.

'Oh God, hurry – Blaine.'

He tore away from her and hopped on one leg as he tried to rid himself of his wet clinging breeches. He looked awkward and ungainly and he almost toppled over into the soft white sand in his haste. And she laughed wildly, breathlessly – he was so funny and beautiful and ridiculous and she wanted him so, and if he took a second longer something inside her would burst and she knew she would die.

'Oh please, Blaine – quickly come to me.'

Then at last he was naked as she was and as he came over her she seized his shoulder with one hand and fell backwards, pulling him with her, spreading her knees and lifting them high, with the other hand groping for him, finding him and guiding him.

'Oh Blaine, you're so – oh yes, like that, I can't – I want to scream.'

'Scream!' He encouraged her as he plunged and rocked and thrust above her. 'There is no one to hear you. Scream for both of us!'

And she opened her mouth wide and gave vent to all her loneliness and wanting and incredulous joy in a rising crescendo that he joined at the end, roaring wildly with her in the most complete and devastating moment of her existence.

Afterwards she wept silently against his bare chest and he was puzzled and compassionate and concerned.

'I was too rough – forgive me! I did not mean to hurt you.'

She shook her head and gulped back her tears. 'No, you never hurt me, it was the most beautiful – '

'Then why do you cry?'

'Because everything that is good seems so fleeting, the more wonderful it is, the sooner it is past, while the wretched vile times seem to last for ever.'

'Don't think like that, my little one.'

'I don't know how I will go on living without you. It was hell before, but this will only make it a thousand times worse.'

'I don't know where I will find the strength to walk away from you,' he whispered in agreement. 'It will be the hardest thing I ever have to do in my life.'

'How much longer do we have?'

'Another day – then we will be at Rundu.'

'When I was a little girl my father gave me a brooch of amber with an insect

embedded in it. I wish we could preserve this moment like that, capture it eternally in the precious amber of our love.'

* * *

Their parting was a gradual process, not a merciful guillotine stroke, but over the following days a slow intrusion of events and people that prised them apart so that they must suffer the smallest tear, each new wrench, in all its detailed agony.

From the morning they reached the border post at Rundu and went ashore to meet the police sergeant who was in command, they seemed constantly to be with strangers, always on their guard so that every glance that passed between them, every word or stolen caress, made them more dreadfully aware of impending separation. Only when the dusty police truck carried them down the last hills into Windhoek was the torturous process completed.

The world awaited them: Isabella, lovely and tragic in her wheelchair, and her daughters bubbling with laughter, mischievous and enchanting as elves, competing for Blaine's embraces; the superintendent of police and the territorial secretary and droves of petty officials and reporters and photographers; Twentyman-Jones and Abe Abrahams, Sir Garry and Lady Courtney, who had hurried up from their estate at Ladyburg the moment they heard of the robbery, and piles of messages of concern and congratulation, telegrams from the prime minister and from the *Ou Baas*, General Smuts, and from a hundred friends and business associates.

Yet Centaine felt detached from the hubbub. She watched it all through a screen of gossamer which muted sound and shape and gave it a dreamlike quality as though half of her was far away, drifting upon a beautiful green river, making love in the warm soft night while the mosquitoes whined outside the protective net, walking hand in hand with the man she loved, a tall strong gentle man with soft green eyes, the hands of a pianist and lovely sticky-out ears.

From her railway coach she telephoned Shasa and tried to sound enthusiastic about the fact that he was now the captain of his cricket eleven and about his mathematics marks which had at last taken an upward turn.

'I don't know when I will be back at Weltevreden, *chéri*. I have so many things to see to. We never recovered the diamonds, I'm afraid. There will have to be talks with the bank and I'll have to make new arrangements. No, of course not, silly boy! Of course we aren't poor, not yet, but a million pounds is a lot of money to lose, and then there will be the trial. Yes, he is an awful man, Shasa – but I don't know if they will hang him. Good Lord, no! They won't let us watch – '

Twice that first day of their separation she telephoned the residency in the forlorn hope that Blaine would answer, but it was a woman, either a secretary or Isabella, and each time she hung up without speaking.

They met again at the administrator's office the next day. Blaine had called a press conference and there was a crowd of journalists and photographers packed into the ante-chamber. Once again Isabella was there in her wheelchair, with Blaine attentive and dutiful and unbearably handsome behind her. It took all Centaine's acting ability to shake hands in a friendly fashion, and then to joke

lightly with the members of the press, even posing with Blaine for the photographs, and at no time to allow herself to moon at him. But afterwards as she drove herself back to the offices of the Courtney Mining and Finance Company, she had to pull off into a side road and sit quietly for a while to compose herself. There had been no opportunity for a single private exchange with Blaine.

Abe was waiting for her the moment she walked in through the front doors and he followed her up the stairs and into her office. 'Centaine, you are late. They have been waiting in the boardroom for almost an hour. I can't say with any great display of patience either.'

'Let them wait!' she told him with bravado she did not feel. 'They had better get accustomed to it.' The bank was her single largest creditor.

'The loss of the stones has frightened ten different shades of yellow out of them, Centaine.'

The bank directors had been demanding this meeting since the minute they heard she had arrived back in town.

'Where is Dr Twentyman-Jones?'

'He is in there with them, pouring oil on the troubled waters.' Abe laid a thick folder in front of her. 'Here are the schedules of the interest repayments.'

She glanced at them. She already knew them by heart. She could recite dates and amounts and rates. She had already prepared her strategy in detail but it was all dreamy and unreal, like a children's game.

'Anything new that I should know about before we go into the lions' den?' she asked.

'A long cable from Lloyds of London. They have repudiated the claim. No armed escort.'

Centaine nodded. 'We expected that. Will we take them to court? What do you advise?'

'I am talking silks opinion on that, but my own feeling is that it will be a waste of time and money.'

'Anything else?'

'De Beers,' he said. 'A message from Sir Ernest Oppenheimer himself.'

'Sniffing around already, is he?' She sighed, trying to make herself care, but she thought of Blaine instead. She saw him bending over the wheelchair. She pushed the image from her mind and concentrated on what Abe was telling her.

'Sir Ernest is coming up from Kimberley. He will be arriving in Windhoek on Thursday.'

'By some lucky chance,' she smiled cynically.

'He requests a meeting at your earliest convenience.'

'He has a nose like a hyena and the eyesight of a vulture,' Centaine said. 'He can smell blood and pick out a dying animal from a hundred leagues.'

'He is after the H'ani Mine, Centaine. He has been lusting after the H'ani for thirteen years.'

'They are all after the H'ani, Abe. The bank, Sir Ernest, all the predators. By God, they'll have to fight me for it.'

They stood up and Abe asked, 'Are you ready?'

Centaine glanced at herself in the mirror over the mantel, touched her hair, wet her lips with the tip of her tongue, and suddenly it all clicked into crisp focus again. She was going into battle, her mind cleared, her wits sharpened and she smiled a bright, confident, patronizing smile at herself. She was ready again.

'Let's go!' she said, and as they marched into the long boardroom with its stinkwood table and the six huge magically lyrical Pierneef murals of the desert places decorating the walls, she lifted her chin and her eyes sparkled with assumed confidence.

'Do forgive me, gentlemen,' she cried lightly, attacking immediately with the full force of her personality and sexual allure and watching them wilt before it, 'but I assure that you now have me, and my full attention, for as long as you want me.'

Deep inside her there was still that empty aching place which Blaine had filled for a few fleeting moments, but it was buttressed and fortified, she was impregnable once again, and as she took the leather upholstered chair at the head of the table she recited silently to herself like a mantra: 'The H'ani belongs to me – no one shall take it from me.'

* * *

Manfred De La Rey moved as swiftly through the darkness as the two grown men who led him northwards. The humiliation and pain of his father's dismissal had invoked within him a new defiance and steely determination. His father had called him a blubbering ninny.

'But I am a man now,' he told himself, striding onwards after the dark figure of Swart Hendrick. 'I will never cry again. I am a man, and I will prove it every day I live. I will prove it to you, Pa. If you are watching over me still, you will never have to be ashamed of me again.'

Then he thought of his father alone and dying upon the hilltop, and his grief was overwhelming. Despite his resolution, his tears rose to swamp him and it took all his strength and his will to thrust them down.

'I am a man now.' He fixed his mind upon it, and indeed he stood as tall as a man, almost as tall as Hendrick, and his long legs thrust him forward tirelessly. 'I will make you proud of me, Papa. I swear it. I swear it before God.'

He neither slackened his pace nor uttered a single complaint throughout the long night, and the sun was clear of the treetops when they reached the river.

As soon as they had drunk Hendrick had them up again and moving northwards. They travelled in a series of loops, swinging away from the river during the day, hiding out in the dry mopani, and then turning back to slake their thirst and follow the riverbank all the hours of darkness.

It was twelve of these nights of hard marching before Hendrick judged them clear of any pursuit.

'When will we cross the river, Hennie?' Manfred asked.

'Never,' Swart Hendrick told him.

'But it was my father's plan to cross to the Portuguese, to Alves De Santos the ivory trader, and then to travel to Luanda.'

'That was your father's plan,' Hendrick agreed. 'But your father is not with us. There is no place for a strange black man in the north. The Portuguese are even harder than the Germans or the English or the Boers. They will cheat us out of our diamonds, and beat us like dogs and send us to work on their labour gangs. No, Manie, we are going back – back to Ovamboland and our brothers of the tribe, where everyone is a friend and we can live like men and not animals.'

'The police will find us,' Manie argued.

'No man saw us. Your father made certain of that.'

'But they know you were my father's friend. They will come for you.'

Hendrick grinned. 'In Ovamboland my name is not Hendrick, and a thousand witnesses will swear I was always in my kraal and knew no white robber. To the white police all black men look the same, and I have a brother, a clever brother, who will know how and where to sell our diamonds for us. With these stones I can buy two hundred fine cattle and ten fat wives. No, Manie, we are going home.'

'And what will happen to me, Hendrick? I cannot go with you to the kraals of the Ovambo.'

'There is a place and a plan for you.' Hendrick placed his arm around the white boy's shoulders, a paternal gesture. 'Your father has entrusted you to me. You do not have to fear. I will see you safe before I leave you.'

'When you go, Hendrick, I will be alone. I will have nothing.' And the black man could not answer him. He dropped his arm and spoke brusquely. 'It is time to march again; a long, hard road lies ahead of us.'

They left the river that night and turned back towards the southwest, skirting the terrible wastes of Bushmanland, keeping to the gentler, better watered lands, striking a more leisurely pace but still avoiding all habitation or human contact until, on the twentieth day after leaving Lothar De La Rey on his fatal hilltop, they followed a wooded ridge through well-pastured country and at last in the dusk looked down on a sprawling Ovambo village.

The conical huts of thatch were built in haphazard clusters of four or five, each surrounded by an enclosure of woven grass matting, and these were grouped around the big central cattle kraal with its palisade of poles set into the earth. The smell of woodsmoke drifted up to them on pale blue wisps, and it mingled with the ammoniacal scent of cattle dung and the floury smell of maize cakes baking on the coals. The cries of children's laughter and the voices of the women were melodious as wild bird calls. They picked out the gaudy flashes of the skirts of bright trade cotton as the women came up in single file from the water-hole with brimming clay pots balanced gracefully upon their heads.

However, they made no move to approach the village. Instead they lay concealed upon the ridge, watching for strangers or any sign of the unusual, even the smallest hint of danger, Hendrick and Klein Boy quietly discussing each movement they spotted, each sound that carried up from the village until Manfred grew impatient.

'Why are we waiting, Hennie?'

'Only the stupid young gemsbok rushes eagerly into the pitfall,' Hendrick grunted. 'We will go down when we are certain.'

In the middle of the afternoon a small black urchin drove a herd of goats up the slope. He was stark naked except for the slingshot hanging around his neck, and Hendrick whistled softly.

The child started and stared at their hiding-place fearfully. Then, when Hendrick whistled again, he crept towards them cautiously. Suddenly he crinkled into a grin too big and white for his grubby face and rushed straight at Hendrick.

Hendrick laughed and lifted him onto his hip, and the child gabbled at him in ecstatic excitement.

'This is my son,' Hendrick told Manie, and then he questioned the child and listened to his piping replies with attention.

'There are no strangers in the village,' he grunted. 'The police were here, asking for me, but they have gone.'

Still carrying the child, he led them down the hill towards the largest of the clusters of huts, and he stooped through the opening in the matting fence. The yard was bare and swept, the circle of huts facing inwards. There were four women working in a group, all of them wearing only loincloths of coloured trade cotton; they rocked on the balls of their feets, singing softly in chorus, stamping and crushing the raw dried maize in tall wooden mortars, their bare breasts jerking and quivering with each stroke of the long poles they wielded as pestles in time to their chant.

One of the women shrieked when she saw Hendrick and rushed to him. She was an ancient crone, wrinkled and toothless, her pate covered with pure white wool. She dropped on her knees and hugged Hendrick's thick powerful legs, crooning with happiness.

'My mother,' said Hendrick, and lifted her to her feet. Then they were surrounded by a swarm of delighted chattering women, but after a few minutes Hendrick quieted them and shooed them away.

'You are luck, Manie,' he grunted, with a sparkle in his eyes. 'You will be allowed only one wife.'

At the entrance to the farthest hut the only man in the kraal sat on a low carved stool. He had kept completely aloof from the screeching excitement, and now Hendrick crossed to him. He was much younger than Hendrick, with paler, almost honey-coloured skin. However, his muscle had been forged and tempered by hard physical labour, and there was a confidence about him, that of a man who has striven and succeeded. He had also an air of grace, and fine intelligent features with a Nilotic cast like those of a young pharaoh. Surprisingly he held a thick battered book in his lap, a copy of Macaulay's *History of England*.

He greeted Hendrick with calm reserve, but their mutual affection was apparent to the white boy watching them.

'This is my clever young brother, same father, but different mothers. He speaks Afrikaans and much better English than even I do, and he reads books. His English name is Moses.'

'I see you, Moses.' Manie felt awkward under the penetrating scrutiny of those dark eyes.

'I see you, little white boy.'

'Do not call me "boy", Manie said hotly. 'I am not a "boy".'

The men exchanged glances and smiled. 'Moses is a boss-boy on the H'ani Diamond Mine,' Hendrick explained in placatory fashion, but the tall Ovambo shook his head and replied in the vernacular.

'No longer, Big Brother. I was sacked over a month ago. So I sit here in the sun drinking beer and reading and thinking, performing all those onerous tasks which are a man's duty.' They laughed together, and Moses clapped his hands and called to the women imperiously.

'Bring beer – do you not see how my brother thirsts?'

For Hendrick it was good to divest himself of his western European clothing and dress again in the comfortable loincloth, to let himself drift back into the pace of village life. It was good to savour the tart effervescent sorghum beer, thick as gruel and cool in the clay pots, and to talk quietly of cattle and game, of crops and rain, of acquaintances and friends and relatives, of deaths and

births and matings. It was a long leisurely time before they came circumspectly to the pressing issues which had to be discussed.

'Yes,' Moses nodded. 'The police were here. Two dogs of the white men in Windhoek who should be ashamed to have betrayed their own tribe. They were not dressed in uniform, but still they had the stink of police upon them. They stayed many days, asking questions about a man called Swart Hendrick – smiling and friendly at first, then angry and threatening. They beat a few of the women, your mother – ' He saw Hendrick stiffen and his jaw clench and went on quickly, 'She is old but tough. She has been beaten before; our father was a strict man. Despite the blows, she did not know Swart Hendrick, nobody knew Swart Hendrick, and the police dogs went away.'

'They will return,' said Hendrick, and his half-brother nodded.

'Yes. The white men never forget. Five years, ten years. They hanged a man in Pretoria for killing a man twenty-five years before. They will return.'

They drank in turn from the pot of beer, sipping with relish and then passing the black pot from hand to hand.

'So there was talk of a great robbery of diamonds on the road from the H'ani, and they mentioned the name of the white devil with whom you have always ridden and fought, with whom you went out on the big green to catch fish. They say that you were with him at the taking of the diamonds, and that they will hang you on a rope when they find you.'

Hendrick chuckled and counterattacked. 'I also have heard stories of a fellow who is neither unknown nor unrelated to me. I have heard he is well versed in the disposal of stolen diamonds. That all the stones taken from the H'ani Mine pass through his hands.'

'Now who could have told you such vile lies?' Moses smiled faintly, and Hendrick gestured to Klein Boy. He brought a rawhide bag from its hiding place and placed it in front of his father. Hendrick opened the flap and, one at a time, lifted out the small packages of brown cartridge paper and laid them on the hard bare earth of the yard – fourteen in a row.

His brother took up the first package and with his sheath knife split the wax seal. 'This is the mark of the H'ani Mine,' he remarked, and carefully unfolded the paper. His expression did not change as he examined the contents. He placed the package aside and opened the next. He did not speak until he had opened all fourteen, and studied them. Then he said softly, 'Death. There is death here. A hundred deaths, a thousand deaths.'

'Can you sell them for us?' Hendrick asked, and Moses shook his head.

'I have never seen such stones, so many together. To try to sell these all at once would bring disaster and death upon us all. I must think upon this, but in the meantime we dare not keep these deadly stones in the kraal.'

The next morning in the dawn the three of them – Hendrick and Moses and Klein Boy – left the village together and climbed to the crest of the ridge where they found the leadwood tree that Hendrick remembered from the days when he roamed here as a naked herdboy. There was a hollow in the trunk, thirty feet above the ground, which had been the nesting hole of a pair of eagle owls.

While the others stood guard, Klein Boy climbed to the nesting hole, carrying the rawhide bag.

* * *

It was many days more before Moses gave his carefully considered summation.

'My brother, you and I are no longer of this life or this place. Already I have seen the first restlessness in you. I have seen you look out to the horizon with the expression of a man who longs to breast them. This life, so sweet at first, palls swiftly. The taste of beer goes flat on the tongue, and a man thinks of the brave things he has done, and the braver things which wait for him still somewhere out there.'

Hendrick smiled. 'You are a man of many skills, my brother, even that of looking into a man's head and reading his secret thoughts.'

'We cannot stay here. The death stones are too dangerous to keep here, too dangerous to sell.'

Hendrick nodded. 'I am listening,' he said.

'There are things which I have to do. Things which I believe are in my destiny, and of which I have never spoken, not even to you.'

'Speak of them now.'

'I speak of the art which the white men call politics and from which we as black men are excluded.'

Hendrick made a dismissive scornful gesture. 'You read too many books. There is no profit or reward in that business. Leave it to the white men.'

'You are wrong, my brother. In that art lie treasures which make your little white stones seem paltry. No, do not scoff.'

Hendrick opened his mouth and then closed it slowly. He had not truly thought about this before, but the young man facing him had a powerful presence, a quivering intensity which stirred and excited him although he did not understand fully the implication of his words.

'My brother, I have decided. We will leave here. It is too small for us.'

Hendrick nodded. The thought did not disturb him. He had been a nomad all his life, and he was ready to move on again.

'Not only this kraal, my brother. We will leave this land.'

'Leave this land!' Hendrick started up and then sank back on his stool.

'We have to do this. This land is too small for us and the stones.'

'Where will we go?'

His brother held up his hand. 'We will discuss that soon, but first you must rid us of this white child you have brought amongst us. He is even more dangerous than the stones. He will bring the white police down upon us even more swiftly. When you have done that, my brother, we will be ready to go on to do what we have to do.'

Swart Hendrick was a man of great strength, both physical and mental. He feared very little, would attempt anything and suffer much for what he wanted, but always he had followed someone else. Always there had been a man even fiercer and more fearless than he to lead him.

'We will do as you say, my brother,' he agreed, and he knew instinctively that he had found someone to replace the man he had left to die upon a rock in the desert.

* * *

'I will wait here until the sun rises tomorrow,' Swart Hendrick told the white boy. 'If you do not return by then, I will know you are safe.'

'Will I see you again, Hennie?' Manie asked wistfully, and Hendrick hesitated on the brink of empty promise.

'I think that our feet will be on different paths from now on, Manie.' He reached out and placed a hand on Manfred's shoulder. 'But I shall think of you often – and, who knows, one day the paths may come together again.' He squeezed the boy's shoulder and he noticed that it was sheathed in muscle, like that of a man full grown. 'Go in peace, and be a man like your father was.'

He pushed Manfred away lightly, but the white boy lingered. 'Hendrick,' he whispered, 'there are many things I want to say to you – but I do not have the words.'

'Go,' Hendrick said. 'We both know. It does not have to be spoken of. Go, Manie.'

Manfred picked up his pack and blanket roll and stepped out of the undergrowth onto the dusty rutted road. He started down towards the village, towards the spire of the church which he recognized somehow as a symbol of a new existence, that at once both beckoned and repelled him.

At the bend in the road he looked back. There was no sign of the big Ovambo, and he turned and trudged down the main street towards the church at the far end.

Without conscious decision he turned from the main street down a side opening and approached the pastory along the sanitary lane as he had done on the last visit with his father. The narrow lane was hedged with fleshy moroto plants, and he whiffed the sanitary buckets behind the little sliding doors of the outhouses that backed onto the lane. He hesitated at the back gate of the pastory and then lifted the latch and started at a snail's pace up the long pathway.

Halfway along the path he was stopped by a bellow, and he stared about him apprehensively. There was another roar and a loud voice lifted in exhortation or acrimonious argument. It came from a ramshackle building at the bottom of the yard, a large woodshed perhaps.

Manfred sidled down towards the shed and peered around the jamb of the door. The interior was dark but as his eyes adjusted Manfred saw that it was a toolroom, with an anvil and forge at one end and tools hanging on the walls. The earthen floor was bare and in the centre of it knelt Tromp Bierman, the trumpet of God.

He was wearing dark suit trousers and a white shirt with the white tie of his office. His suit jacket hung on a pair of blacksmith's tongs above the anvil. Tromp Bierman's bushy beard was pointed to the roof and his eyes were closed, his arms lifted in an attitude of surrender or supplication; but his tone was far from submissive.

'Oh Lord God of Israel, I call upon you most urgently to give answer to your servant's prayers for guidance in this matter. How can I perform your will if I do not know what it is? I am only a humble instrument, I dare not take this decision alone. Look down, oh Lord God, have pity on my ignorance and stupidity and make known your intentions – '

Tromp broke off suddenly and opened his eyes. The great shaggy leonine head turned, and the eyes, like those of an Old Testament prophet, burned into Manfred's soul.

Hastily Manfred snatched the shapeless sweatstained hat from his head and held it with both hands to his chest.

'I have come back, *Oom*,' he said. 'Just like you said I must.'

Tromp stared at him ferociously. He saw a sturdy lad, broad-shouldered and

with powerful shapely limbs, a head of dusty golden curls and contrasting eyebrows black as coal dust over strange topaz-coloured eyes. He tried to see beyond the pale surface of those eyes and was aware of an aura of determination and lucid intelligence that surrounded the youth.

'Come here,' he ordered, and Manfred dropped his pack and went to him. Tromp seized him by the hand and dragged him down.

'Kneel, *Jong*, get down on your knees and give thanks to your Maker. Praise the Lord God of your fathers that he has heard my supplications on your behalf.'

Dutifully Manfred closed his eyes and clasped his hand.

'Oh Lord, forgive your servant's importunity in bringing to your notice such other trivial matters, when in fact you were occupied with more dire affairs. We thank you for delivering into our care this young person, whom we shall temper and hone into a sword. A mighty blade that shall strike down the Philistine, a weapon that shall be wielded to your glory, in the just and righteous cause of your chosen people, the Afrikaner *Volk*.' He prodded Manfred with a forefinger like a pruning shear.

'Amen!' Manfred gasped at the pain.

'We will glorify and praise you all the days of our life, O Lord, and we beg of you to bestow upon this chosen son of our people the fortitude and the determination – '

The prayer, punctuated by Manfred's fervent 'Amens' lasted until Manfred's knees ached and he was dizzy with fatigue and hunger. Then suddenly Tromp hauled him to his feet and marched him up to the path to the kitchen door.

'Mevrou,' the trumpet of God sounded. 'Where are you, woman?'

Trudi Bierman rushed breathlessly into the kitchen at the summons and then stopped aghast, staring at the boy in ragged, filthy clothing.

'My kitchen,' she wailed. 'My beautiful clean kitchen. I have just waxed the floor.'

'The Lord God has sent this *Jong* to us,' Tromp intoned. 'We will take him into our home. He will eat at our table, he will be as one of our own.'

'But he is filthy as a kaffir.'

'Then wash him, woman, wash him.'

At that moment a girl slipped timidly through the doorway behind the matronly figure of Trudi Bierman and then stiffened like a frightened fawn as she saw Manfred.

Manfred barely recognized Sarah. She had filled out, firm well-scrubbed flesh covered her elbows, which had so recently been bony lumps on sticklike arms. Her once pale cheeks were apple pink, the eyes that had been lacklustre were clear and bright, her blonde hair, brushed until it shone, was plaited into twin pigtails and pinned on top of her head, and she wore long modest but spotless skirts to her ankles.

She let out a cry and rushed at Manfred with arms outstretched, but Trudi Bierman seized her from behind and shook her soundly.

'You lazy wicked girl. I left you to finish your sums. Back you go this instant.' She pushed her roughly from the room and turned back to Manfred, her arms folded and her mouth pursed.

'You are disgusting,' she told him. 'Your hair is long as a girl's. Those clothes – ' Her expression hardened even more fearsomely. 'And we are Christian folk in this house. We'll have none of your father's godless wild ways, do you understand.'

'I'm hungry, Aunt Trudi.'

'You'll eat when everybody else eats, and not before you are clean.' She looked at her husband. '*Menheer*, will you show the boy how to build a fire in the hotwater geyser?'

She stood in the doorway of the tiny bathroom and remorselessly supervised his ablutions, brushing aside all his attempts at modesty and his protests at the temperature of the water, and when he faltered, taking the bar of blue mottled soap herself and scrubbing his most tender and intimate creases and folds.

Then with only a skimpy red towel about his waist she led him by the ear down the back steps and sat him on a fruit box. She armed herself with a pair of sheep shears and Manfred's blond hair fell about his shoulders like wheat before the scythe. When he ran his hand over his scalp it was stubbly and bristly and the back of his neck and the skin behind his ears felt cool and draughty.

Trudi Bierman gathered up his discarded clothing with a pantomine of distaste and opened the furnace of the geyser. Manfred was only just in time to rescue his jacket, and when she saw his expression as he backed away from her, holding the garment behind his back and surreptitiously fingering the small lumps in the lining she shrugged.

'Very well – perhaps with a wash and a few patches. In the meantime I'll find you some of the dominie's old things.'

Trudi Bierman took Manfred's appetite as a personal challenge to her kitchen and her culinary skills. She kept heaping his plate even before he had finished, standing over him with a ladle in one hand and the handle of the stewpot in the other. When at last he fell back satiated, she went to fetch the milk tart from the pantry with a victorious gleam in her eye.

As strangers in the family, Manfred and Sarah were allocated the lowliest seats in the centre of the table, the two plump, pudding-faced, blonde Bierman daughters sitting above them.

Sarah picked at her food so lightly that she earned Trudi Bierman's ire. 'I didn't cook good food for you to fiddle with, young lady. You'll sit here as long as it takes you to clean your plate, spinach and all – even if that takes all night.' And Sarah chewed mechanically, never taking her eyes from Manfred's face.

It was the first time that Manfred had paid for a meal with two graces, before and after, and each of them seemed interminable. He was nodding and swaying in his chair when Tromp Bierman startled him fully awake with an 'Amen' like a salvo of artillery.

The pastory was already groaning at the seams with Sarah and the Bierman offspring. There was no place for Manfred, so he was allocated a corner of the toolshed at the bottom of the yard. Aunt Trudi had turned a packing case on end to act as a cupboard for his few cast-off items of clothing and there was a iron bed with a hard lumpy coir mattress and a faded old curtain hung on a string to screen his sleeping corner.

'Don't waste the candle,' Aunt Trudi cautioned him from the doorway of the toolshed. 'You will only get a new one on the first day of each month. We are thrifty folk here. None of your father's extravagances, thank you!'

Manfred pulled the thin grey blanket over his head to protect his naked scalp from the chill. It was the first time in his life that he had had a bed and room of his own and he revelled in the sensation, sniffing the aroma of axle grease and paraffin and the dead coals in the forge as he fell asleep.

He woke to a light touch on his cheek and cried out; confused images rushed

out of the darkness to terrify him. He had dreamed of his father's hand, reeking of gangrene, that had reached across from the far side of the grave and he struggled up from under the blanket.

'Manie, Manie. It's me.' Sarah's voice was as terrified as his own cry had been. She was silhouetted by the moonlight through the single uncurtained window, thin and shivering in a white nightdress, her hair brushed out and hanging to her shoulders in a silvery cloud.

'What are you doing here?' he mumbled. 'You mustn't come here. You must go. If they find you here they will – ' he broke off. He was not sure what the consequences would be, but he knew instinctively that they would be severe. This strange but pleasant new sense of security and belonging would be shattered.

'I've been so unhappy.' He could tell by her voice that she was crying. 'Ever since you went away. The girls are so cruel – they call me *vuilgoed*, "trash". They tease me because I can't read and do sums the way they can and because I speak funny. I've cried every night since you went away.'

Manfred's heart went out to her, and despite his nervousness at being discovered, he reached out for her and drew her down onto the bed. 'I'm here now. I'll look after you, Sarie,' he whispered. 'I won't let them tease you any more.'

She sobbed against his neck, and he told her sternly, 'I don't want any more crying, Sarie. You aren't a baby any more. You must be brave.'

'I was crying because I was happy,' she sniffed.

'No more crying – not even when you are happy,' he ordered. 'Do you understand?' And she nodded furiously, and made a little choking sound as she brought her tears under control.

'I've thought about you every day,' she whispered. 'I prayed to God to bring you back like you promised. Can I get into bed with you, Manie? I'm cold.'

'No,' he said firmly. 'You must go back, before they catch you here.'

'Just for a moment,' she pleaded and before he could protest she had wriggled around, lifted the blanket and slipped under the corner.

She wrapped herself around him. The nightdress was thin and worn, her body cold and shivery, and he could not bring himself to chase her out.

'Five minutes,' he muttered. 'Then you have to go.'

Swiftly the heat flowed back into her small body, and her hair was soft against his face and smelt good, like the fur of an unweaned kitten, milky and warm. She made him feel old and important, and he stroked her hair with a paternal proprietary feeling.

'Do you think God answers our prayers?' she asked softly. 'I prayed the hardest I know how, and here you are, just like I asked.' She was silent a moment. 'But it took a long time and a lot of prayers.

'I don't know about prayers,' he admitted. 'My pa never prayed much. He never taught me how.'

'Well, you better get used to it now,' she warned him. 'In this house, everybody prays all the time.'

When she at last crept out of the toolshed back to the big house, she left a warm patch on the mattress, and a warmer place in his heart.

* * *

It was still dark when Manfred was roused by a blast from the Trumpet of God in person.

'Ten seconds and then you get a bucket of cold water, *Jong*.' And Uncle Tromp led him, shivering and covered in goosebumps, to the trough beside the stables.

'Cold water is the best cure for the sins of the young flesh, *Jong*,' Uncle Tromp told him with relish. 'You will muck out the stables and curry the pony before breakfast, do you hear?'

The day was a dizzying succession of labour and prayer, the household chores sandwiched between long sessions of school work and even longer sessions on their knees, while either Uncle Tromp or Aunt Trudi exhorted God to step up their performance or visit them with all kinds of retribution.

Yet by the end of the first week Manfred had subtly but permanently rearranged the pecking order amongst the younger members of the household. He had quelled the Bierman girls' first furtive but concerted attempts at mockery with a steady implacable stare from his yellow eyes, and they retreated in twittering consternation.

Over the school books it was different. His cousins were all dedicated scholars, with the benefit of a lifetime of enforced study. As Manfred grimly applied himself to the tome on German grammar and Melckes' *Mathematics for Secondary Schools*, their smug self-satisfied smiles at his floudering replies to Aunt Trudi's catechism were all the incentive he needed.

'I'll show them,' he promised himself, and he was so committed to the task of catching and overhauling his cousins that it was days before he became aware of how the Bierman girls were victimizing little Sarah. Their cruelty was refined and secretive; a jibe, a name, a mocking face; calculated exclusion from their games and laughter; sabotage of her domestic chores, a soot stain on garments Sarah had just ironed, rumpled linen on a bed she had just made, grease marks on dishes, she had washed; and vicious grins when Sarah was chastized for laziness and negligence by Aunt Trudi, who was only too pleased to perform this godly duty with the back of a hairbrush.

Manfred caught each of the Bierman girls alone. Held them by the pigtails and looked into their eyes from a range of a few inches while he spoke in a soft measured voice that hissed with passion and ended ' – and don't run and tell tales to your mother, either'. Their deliberate cruelty ended with dramatic suddenness, and under Manfred's protection Sarah was left severely alone.

At the end of that first week, after the fifth church service of a long, tedious Sunday, one of the cousins appeared in the doorway of the toolshed where Manfred was stretched on his bed with his German grammar.

'My pa wants to see you in his study.' And the messenger wrung one hand in a parody of looming disaster.

Manfred soused his short-cropped hair under the tap and tried to brush it flat in the splinter of mirror wedged above his bed. It immediately sprang up again in damp spikes and he gave up the effort and hurried to answer the summons.

He had never been allowed into the front rooms of the pastory. They were sacrosanct, and of these the dominie's study was the holy of holies. He knew from warnings, repeated by his cousins with morbid relish, that a summons to this room was always associated with punishment and pain. He trembled on the threshold, knowing that Sarah's nightly visits to the toolshed had been discovered, and he started wildly at the bellow that answered his timid knock, then pushed the door open slowly and stepped inside.

Uncle Tromp stood behind the sombre stinkwood desk, leaning on clenched fists that were placed in the centre of the blotter. 'Come in, *Jong*. Shut the door. Don't just stand there!' he roared and dropped heavily into his chair.

Manfred stood before him, trying to form the words of repentance and atonement, but before he could utter them, Uncle Tromp spoke again.

'Well, *Jong*, I have had reports of you from your aunt.' His tone was at odds with his ferocious expression. 'She tells me that your education has been sadly neglected, but that you are willing and seem to be applying yourself.' Manfred sagged with relief so intense that he had difficulty following the long exhortation that followed. 'We are the underdogs, *Jong*. We are the victims of oppression and Milnerism.' Manfred knew about Lord Milner from his father; the notorious English governor and opponent of Afrikanderdom under whose decree all children who spoke the Afrikaans language in school were forced to wear a dunce's cap with the legend 'I am a donkey – I spoke Dutch' inscribed upon it. 'There is only one way that we can overcome our enemies, *Jong*. We have to become cleverer and stronger and more ruthless than they are.'

The Trumpet of God became so absorbed by his own words, that he lifted his gaze to the elaborate patterns of the fancy plastered ceiling and his eyes glazed with a mixture of religious and political fanaticism, leaving Manfred free to glance around him furtively at the over-furnished room.

Bookshelves covered three walls, all of them stacked with religious and serious tomes. John Calvin and the authors of the Presbyterian form of church government predominated, though there were works of history and philosophy, law and biography, dictionaries and encyclopaedia and shelves of hymns and collected sermons in High Dutch, German and English.

The fourth wall, directly behind Uncle Tromp's desk, carried a gallery of photographs, stern ancestors in Sunday finery in the top row and then, below them, devout congregations or learned members of synod, all featuring amongst them the unmistakable likeness of Tromp Bierman – a gradually maturing and ageing succession of Tromps, from cleanshaven and bright-eyed youth to bearded leonine maturity in the front row.

Then, quite incongruously and startlingly, a framed and yellowing photograph, in the largest of them all and situated in the most prominent position, depicting a young man stripped to the waist, wearing full-length tights, and about his middle a magnificent belt, gleaming with engraved silver buckles and medallions.

The man in the photograph was Tromp Bierman aged no more than twenty-five, cleanshaven, his hair parted in the middle and plastered flat with brilliantine, his powerful body marvellously muscled, his clenched fists held before him, crouching in the classic stance of the pugilist. A small table in front of him held a treasure of glittering cups and sporting trophies. The young man smiled out of the photograph, strikingly handsome, and in Manfred's eyes, impossibly dashing and romantic.

'You are a boxer,' he blurted out, unable to contain his wonder and admiration, and the Trumpet of God was cut off in mid-blast. The great shaggy head lowered, the eyes blinking as they readjusted to reality and then swivelling to follow Manfred's gaze.

'Not just a boxer,' said Uncle Tromp. 'But a champion. Light heavyweight champion of the Union of South Africa.' He looked back and saw the expression on Manfred's face, and his own expression warmed and melted with remembrance and gratification.

'Did you win all those cups – and that belt?'

'I surely did, *Jong*. I smote the Philistines hip and thigh. I struck them down in their multitudes.

'Did you only fight Philistines, Uncle Tromp?'

'They were all Philistines, *Jong*. As soon as they stepped into the ring with me they became Philistines and I fell upon them without mercy, like the hammer and the sword of the Almighty.' Tromp Bierman lifted his clenched fists in front of him and shot out a swift tattoo of punches, firing them across the desk, stopping each blow only inches from Manfred's nose.

'I made my living with these fists, *Jong*. All comers at ten pounds a time. I fought Mike Williams and put him down in the sixth, the great Mike Williams himself.' He grunted as he weaved and boxed in his chair 'Ha! Ha! Left! Right! Left! I even thrashed the black Jephta, and I took the title from Jack Lalor in 1916. I can still hear the cheers now as Lalor hit the canvas. Sweet, my *Jong*, so very sweet – ' he broke off, and replaced his hands in his lap, his expression becoming dignified and stern once again. 'Then your Aunt Trudi and the Lord God of Israel called me from the ring to more important work.' And the gleam of battle lust faded regretfully from Uncle Tromp's eyes.

'Boxing and being champion – that would be the most important thing for me,' Manfred breathed, and Tromp's gaze focused thoughtfully upon him. He looked him over carefully from the top of his cropped head to his large but well-proportioned feet in battered velskoen.

'You want to learn to fight?' He dropped his voice, and glanced at the door, a conspiratorial gesture.

Manfred could not answer; his throat was closed with excitement, but he nodded vigorously and Uncle Tromp went on in his normal piercing tones.

'Your Aunt Trudi doesn't approve of brawling. Quite right too! Fisticuffs are for hooligans. Put the thought from your mind, *Jong*. Think on higher planes.' He shook his head so vigorously that his beard was disarranged, it took that effort to dislodge the notion from his own head, and he combed his beard with his fingers as he went on.

'To return to what I was saying. Your aunt and I think it best that you drop the name De La Rey for the time being. You shall adopt the name Bierman until the notoriety of your father's trial fades. There has already been too much mention of that name in the newspapers, those organs of Lucifer. Your aunt is quite right in not allowing them into this house. There will be a great hoo-ha once the trial of your father begins in Windhoek next month. It could bring shame and disgrace on you and this family.'

'My father's trial?' Manfred stared at him without comprehension. 'But my father is dead'

'Dead? Is that what you thought?' Tromp stood up and came around the desk. 'Forgive me, *Jong*.' He placed both his huge hands on Manfred's shoulders. 'I have caused you unnecessary suffering by not speaking of this earlier. Your father is not dead. He has been captured by the police, and he will stand trial for his life at the Supreme Court in Windhoek on the twentieth of next month.'

He steadied Manfred as the boy reeled at the impact of the words and then went on with a gentle rumble. 'Now you understand why we want you to change your name, *Jong*.'

* * *

Sarah had hurried through her ironing and sneaked out of the house. She was perched now on top of the woodpile with her knees drawn up under her chin, hugging her legs with both arms as she watched Manfred at work. She loved to watch him with the axe. It was a long two-handed axe, with a red-painted head and a bright edge to the blade. Manie sharpened it on the whetstone until he could shave the fine gold hair off the back of his hand with it.

He had taken off his shirt and given it to her to hold. His chest and back were all shiny with sweat. She liked the way he smelled when he sweated, like newly baked bread, or like a sun-warm fig just picked from the tree.

Manfred laid another log in the cradle and stood back. He spat on the palms of his hands. He always did that and she involuntarily worked up a ball of spit in her own mouth in sympathy. Then he hefted the long axe and she tensed herself.

'Five times table,' he ordered, and swung the axe in a long looping blow. It hummed faintly over his head as he brought it down. The bright blade buried itself in the log with a clunk and at the same instant Manie gave a sharp explosive grunt of effort.

'Five ones are five,' she recited in time to the swinging axe.

'Five twos are ten.' Manie grunted and a white wedge of wood flew as high as his head.

'Five threes are fifteen.' The axe head spun a bright circle in the yellow light of the lowering sun, and Sarah chanted shrilly as the wood chips pelted down like hail.

The log dropped from the cradle in two pieces just as Sarah cried, 'Five tens are fifty.' Manie stepped back and leaned on the axe handle, and grinned at her.

'Very good, Sarie, not a single mistake.'

She preened with pleasure – and then stared over his shoulder, her expression suddenly stricken and guilty. She leapt down from the woodpile and in a swirl of skirts scampered back up the path to the house.

Manie turned quickly. Uncle Tromp was leaning again the corner of the toolshed watching him.

'I'm sorry, Uncle Tromp.' He ducked his head. 'I know she shouldn't be here, but I just can't send her away.'

Uncle Tromp pushed himself away from the wall and came slowly to where Manfred stood. He moved like a great bear with long arms dangling, and he circled Manfred slowly, examining him with a small distracted frown creasing his forehead.

Manfred squirmed self-consciously, and Uncle Tromp prodded his gut with a large painful finger.

'How old are you, *Jong*?'

Manfred told him and Uncle Tromp nodded. 'Three years to full growth. You'll class light-heavy, I'd say, unless you make a spurt at the end and go full heavyweight.'

Manfred felt his skin prickle at the unfamiliar but somehow tremendously exciting terms, and Uncle Tromp left him and went to the woodpile. Deliberately he stripped off the dark jacket of his suit and folded it neatly. He laid it on the woodpile and then unknotted his white minister's tie and laid that meticulously on top of his jacket. He came back to Manfred rolling up the sleeves of his white shirt.

'So you want to be a boxer?' he asked, and Manfred nodded, unable to speak.

'Put the axe away.' Manfred buried the blade in the chopping stump and faced his uncle again. Uncle Tromp held up his open right hand, palm towards Manfred.

'Hit it!' he said. Manfred clenched his fist and made a tentative round-arm swing.

'You aren't knitting socks, *Jong*, you aren't kneading bread. What are you, a man or a kitchen maid? Hit it, man. Hit it! That's better, don't swing it around the back of your head, shoot it out! Harder! Harder! That's more like it. Now your left, that's it! Left! Right! Left!'

Uncle Tromp was holding up both hands now, swaying and dancing in front of him, and Manfred followed him eagerly, socking alternate fists into the big open palms.

'All right.' Tromp dropped his hands. 'Now hit me. Hit me in the face. Go on, hard as you can. Right on the button. Let's see you knock me on my back.'

Manfred dropped his hands and stepped back.

'I can't do that, Uncle Tromp,' he protested.

'Can't do what, *Jong*? What can't you do?'

'I couldn't hit you. It wouldn't be right. It wouldn't be respectful.'

'So we are talking respect now, not boxing. We are talking powder puffs and ladies' gloves, are we?' Uncle Tromp roared. 'I thought you wanted to fight. I thought you wanted to be a man and now I find a snot-nosed whining baby.' He changed his voice to a cracked falsetto. 'It wouldn't be right, Uncle Tromp, it wouldn't be respectful,' he mimicked.

Suddenly his right hand shot out and the open palm cracked against Manfred's cheek, a stinging slap that left the scarlet imprint of fingers on his skin.

'You're not respectful, *Jong*. You're yellow. That's what you are, a yellow-bellied whimpering little boy. You're not a man! You'll never be a fighter!'

The other huge paw blurred with speed, coming so fast and unexpectedly that Manfred barely saw it. The pain of the blow filled his eyes with tears.

'We'll have to find a skirt for you, girlie, a yellow skirt.'

Uncle Tromp was watching him carefully, watching his eyes, praying silently for it to happen as he poured withering contempt on the sturdy youth who retreated, bewildered and uncertain. He followed and struck again, cutting Manfred's lower lip, splitting the soft skin against his teeth, leaving a smear of blood down his chin.

'Come on!' he exhorted silently, behind the jeering flood of insults. 'Come on, please, come on!'

Then with a great explosion of joy that filled his chest to bursting, he saw it happen. Manfred dropped his chin, and his eyes changed. Suddenly they glowed with a cold yellow light, implacable as the stare of a lion in the moment before it launches its charge, and the youth came at him.

Though he had been waiting for it, expecting it, praying for it, still the speed and savagery of the attack caught Uncle Tromp off-balance. Only the old fighter's instinct saved him, and he deflected that first murderous assault, sensing the power in the fists that grazed his temple and ruffled his beard as they passed, and for the first few desperate seconds there was no time for thought. All his wits and attention were needed to stay on his feet and keep the cold, ferocious animal he had created at bay.

Then experience and ringcraft, long forgotten, reasserted themselves, and he ducked and dodged and danced easily just beyond the boy's reach, deflecting

the wild punches, watching objectively as though he sat in a ringside seat, assessing with rising delight the way in which the untutored youth used either fist with equal power and dexterity.

'A natural two-handed puncher! He doesn't favour his right, and he gets his shoulders behind every punch without being taught how,' he exulted.

Then he looked again at the eyes and felt a chill of awe at what he had loosed upon the world.

'He's a killer.' He recognized it. 'He has the instinct of the leopard who kills for the taste of blood and the simple joy of it. He no longer sees me. He sees only the prey before him.'

That knowledge had distracted him. He caught a right-hander on his upper arm and it jarred the teeth in his jaws and the bones of his ankles. He knew it would bruise him from the shoulder to the elbow, and his breath burned in his throat. His legs were turned to lead. He could feel his heart drumming against his ribs. Twenty-two years since he had been in the ring; twenty-two years of Trudi's cooking and his most vigorous exercise undertaken either at his desk or in the pulpit, while the youth before him was like a machine, boring in remorselessly, both fists swinging, those yellow eyes fixed upon him in a murderous myopic stare.

Uncle Tromp gathered himself, waited for the opening as Manfred swung right-handed, and then he counter-punched with his left, always his best, the same blow that had dropped black Jephta in the third, and it went in with that beautiful little click of bone against bone.

Manfred dropped to his knees, stunned, the killing yellow light fading from his eyes to be replaced by a dull bemused look, as though awakening from a trance.

'That's it, *Jong*.' The Trumpet of God's fine note was reduced to a breathy gasp. 'Down on your knees and give thanks to your Maker.' Uncle Tromp lowered his bulk beside Manfred and placed a thick arm around his shoulders. He raised his face and his unsteady voice to heaven. 'Almighty God, we give You thanks for the strong body with which You have endowed Your young servant. We give You thanks also for his natural left – while realizing that it will need a lot of hard work – and we humbly beseech You to look favourably upon our efforts to instil in him even the rudiments of footwork. His right hand is a blessing directly from You, for which we will always be eternally grateful, though he will have to learn not to telegraph it five days in advance of the punch.'

Manfred was still shaking his head and rubbing his jaw, but he responded to the probing thumb in his ribs with a fervent 'Amen'.

'We will begin roadwork immediately, O Lord, while we set up a ring in the toolshed in which to learn the ropes, and we humbly beseech Your blessing on our enterprize and Your co-operation in keeping it from coming to the notice of Your servant's partner in holy matrimony, Trudi Bierman.'

* * *

Most afternoons, under the pretext of visiting one of his parishioners, Uncle Tromp would put the pony in the trap and drive out of the front gate with a flourish, waving to his wife on the front stoep. Manfred would be waiting at the

clump of camel-thorn trees beside the main Windhoek road, already barefoot and tripped to khaki shorts, and he would trot out and fall in beside the trap as Uncle Tromp shook the fat pony into a canter.

'Five miles today, *Jong* – down to the river bridge and back, and we'll do it a bit faster than yesterday.'

The gloves that Uncle Tromp had smuggled down from the trunk in the loft were cracked with age, but they patched them with woodglue and the first time he laced them onto Manfred's hands he watched while the lad lifted them to his nose and sniffed them.

'The smell of leather and sweat and blood, *Jong*. Fill your nostrils with it. You'll live with it from now on.'

Manfred punched the tattered old gloves together, and for a moment that flat yellow light glowed in his eyes again, then he grinned.

'They feel good,' he said.

'Nothing feels better,' Uncle Tromp agreed, and led him to the heavy canvas kitbag filled with river sand that hung from the rafters in the corner of the toolshed.

'To begin with I want to see that left hand do some work. It's like a wild horse; we have to break it and train it, teach it not to waste strength and effort. It has to learn to do our bidding, not flap around in the air.'

They built the ring together, quarter-full size for the toolshed would take no more, and they sank the corner poles deep in the earthen floor and cemented them in. Then they stretched a sheet of canvas over the floor. The canvas and the cement had been commandeered from one of Uncle Tromp's wealthy parishioners, 'For the glory of God and the *Volk*,' an appeal that could not be lightly dismissed.

Sarah, sworn to secrecy by the most solemn and dreadful oath that Manfred and Uncle Tromp could concoct between them, was allowed to watch the ringwork, even though she was a thoroughly partisan audience and cheered shrilly and shamelessly for the younger participant.

After two of these sessions, which left Uncle Tromp unmarked but blowing like a steam engine, he shook his head ruefully. 'It's no use, *Jong*, either we have to find you another sparring partner, or I'll have to start training again myself.'

Thereafter the pony was left tethered in the camel-thorn clump and Uncle Tromp grunted and gasped beside Manfred on the long runs, while the sweat fell from his beard like the first rains of summer.

However, his protuberant gut shrivelled miraculously, and soon from under the layers of soft fat that covered his shoulders and chest the outline of hard muscle reappeared. Gradually they stepped up the rounds from two to four minutes with Sarah, elected official timekeeper, measuring each round with Uncle Tromp's cheap silver pocket watch which made up for its dubious accuracy by its size.

It was almost a month before Uncle Tromp could say to himself though he would never have dreamed of saying it to Manfred, 'He is starting to look like a boxer now.' Instead he said: 'Now I want speed. I want you to be fast as a mamba – brave as a ratel.'

The mamba was the most dreaded of all Africa's serpents. It could grow as thick as a man's wrist and reach twenty feet in length. Its venom could inflict death on a fully grown man in four minutes, an excruciating death. The mamba

was so swift that it could overhaul a galloping horse, and the strike was so swift as to cheat the eye.

'Fast as a mamba – brave a a ratel,' Uncle Tromp repeated, as he would a hundred, a thousand times in the years ahead.

The ratel was the African honey badger, a small animal with a loose but thick tough skin that could defy the bite of a mastiff or the fangs of a leopard, a massive flattened skull from which the heaviest club bounced harmlessly, and the heart of a lion, the courage of a giant. Normally mild and forbearing, it would fearlessly attack the largest adversary the instant that it was provoked. Legend had it that the ratel possessed an instinct for the groin and that it would rush in and rip the testicles out of any male animal, man or bull buffalo or lion who threatened it.

'I've got something to show you, *Jong*.' Uncle Tromp led Manfred to the big wooden chest against the back wall of the toolshed and opened the lid. 'It's for you. I ordered it by mail order from Cape Town. It arrived on the train yesterday.'

He placed the tangle of leather and rubber in Manfred's arms.

'What is it, Uncle Tromp?'

'Come, I'll show you.'

Within minutes Uncle Tromp had rigged the complicated contraption.

'Well, what do you think, *Jong*?' He stood back, beaming hugely through his beard.

'It's the best present anyone has ever given me, Uncle Tromp. But what is it?'

'You call yourself a boxer and you don't know a speed bag when you see one!'

'A speed bag! It must have cost a lot of money.'

'It did, *Jong*, but don't tell your Aunt Trudi.'

'What do we do with it?'

'This is what we do!' cried Uncle Tromp, and he started the bag rattling against the frame in a rapid staccato rhythm, using both fists taking the ball on the bounce, keeping it going unerringly until at last he stepped back panting.

'Speed, *Jong*, fast as a mamba.'

Faced with Uncle Tromp's generosity and enthusiasm, Manfred had to gather all his courage to speak the words that had been burning his tongue all these weeks.

He waited until the last possible moment of the last possible day before blurting out. 'I have to go away, Uncle Tromp,' and he watched in agony the disappointment and disbelief flood over the craggy bearded face that he had come so swiftly and naturally to love.

'Go away? You want to leave my house?' Uncle Tromp stopped short in the dust of the Windhoek road and wiped the sweat from his face with the threadbare towel draped around his neck. 'Why, *Jong*, why?'

'My pa,' Manfred answered. 'My pa's trial starts in three days' time. I have to be there, Uncle Tromp. I have to go, but I will come back. I swear I will come back, just as soon as I can.'

Uncle Tromp turned from him and began to run again, pounding down the long straight road, the dust puffing from under his bearlike feet at each pace, and Manfred sprinted up beside him. Neither of them spoke again until they reached the clump of trees where the pony trap was hitched.

Oom Tromp climbed up into the driver's seat and picked up the reins. He looked down at Manfred standing beside the front wheel.

'I wish *Jong*, that I had a son of my own to show me such loyalty,' he rumbled softly, and shook the pony into a trot.

The following evening, long after dinner and the evening prayers, Manfred lay on his bed, the candle on the shelf above his head carefully screened so that not a glimmer could alert Aunt Trudi to his extravagance. He was reading Goethe, his father's favourite author. It wasn't easy. His German had improved vastly. On two days a week Aunt Trudi insisted that no other language was spoken in the household, and she initiated erudite discussion at the dinner-table in which all members of the family were expected – nay, forced, to participate. Still Goethe wasn't a romp, and Manfred was concentrating so fiercely on his convoluted use of verbs that he didn't know Uncle Tromp was in the room until his shadow fell across the bed and the book was lifted from his hand.

'You will ruin your eyes, *Jong*.'

Manfred sat up quickly and swung his legs off the bed while Uncle Tromp sank down beside him.

For a few moments the old man leafed through the book. Then he spoke without looking up. 'Rautenbach is going in to Windhoek tomorrow in his T-model Ford. He is taking in a hundred turkeys to market, but he will have room for you on the back. You'll have to put up with flying feathers and turkey shit, but it's cheaper than the train.'

'Thank you, Uncle Tromp.'

'There is an old widow in town, devout and decent – also a very good cook. She'll take you in. I've written to her.' He drew a sheet of notepaper from his pocket and placed it in Manfred's lap. The single sheet was folded and sealed with a blob of red wax, a back country minister's stipend could not encompass the luxury of envelopes.

'Thank you, Uncle Tromp.' Manfred could think of nothing else to say. He wanted to fling his arms round that thick bearlike neck and lay his cheek against the coarse grey-shot beard, but he controlled himself.

'There may be other expenses,' Uncle Tromp gruffed. 'I don't know how you will get back here. Anyway – ' He groped in his pocket, seized Manfred's wrist with the other hand, and pressed something into his open palm.

Manfred looked down at the two bright half-crown coins in his hand and shook his head slowly.

'Uncle Tromp – '

'Say nothing, *Jong* – especially not to your your Aunt Trudi.' Uncle Tromp began to stand, but Manfred caught his sleeve.

'Uncle Tromp. I can pay you back – for this and all the other things.'

'I know you will, *Jong*. You will pay me back a thousand times, in pride and joy one day.'

'No, no, not one day. Now. I can pay you back now.'

Manfred sprang eagerly from the bed and ran to the upended packing case standing on four bricks that was his wardrobe. He knelt and thrust his arm into the space below the box and brought out a yellow tobacco bag. He hurried back to where Uncle Tromp sat on the iron bed, pulling open the drawstring of the small pouch, his hands shaking with excitement and eagerness to please.

'Here, Uncle Tromp, open your hand.'

Smiling indulgently Uncle Tromp held out his huge paw, the back of it covered with coarse black curls, the fingers thick as good farmer's sausages.

'What have you here, *Jong*?' he demanded jovially, and then the smile froze as Manfred spilled a cascade of glittering stones into his hand.

'Diamonds, Uncle Tromp,' Manfred whispered. 'Enough to make you a rich man. Enough to buy you anything you need.'

'Where did you get these, *Jong*?' Uncle Tromp's voice was calm and dispassionate. 'How did you come by these?'

'My pa – my father. He put them into the lining of my jacket. He said they were for me, to pay for my education and my upbringing, to pay for all the things that he wanted to do for me but had never been able.'

'So!' said Uncle Tromp softly. 'It is all true then, all of what the newspapers say. It isn't just English lies. Your father is a brigand and a robber.' The huge hand clenched into a fist over the glittering treasure. 'And you were with him, *Jong*. You must have been there when he did these terrible things that they accuse him of, that they will try and condemn him for. Were you with him, *Jong*? Answer me!' His voice was rising like a storm wind, and now he let out a bellow. 'Did you commit this great evil with him, *Jong*?' The other hand shot out and seized the front of Manfred's shirt. He pulled Manfred's face to within inches of his own jutting beard. 'Confess to me, *Jong*. Tell it all to me, every last scrap of evil. Were you with him when your father attacked this Englishwoman and robbed her?'

'No! No!' Manfred shook his head wildly. 'It's not true. My father wouldn't do a thing like that. They were our diamonds. He explained it to me. He went to get back what was rightfully ours.'

'Were you with him when he did this thing, *Jong*? Tell me the truth,' Uncle Tromp interrupted him with another roar. 'Tell me, were you with him?'

'No, Uncle Tromp. He went alone. And when he came back he was hurt. His hand – his wrist – '

'Thank you, Lord!' Uncle Tromp looked upwards with relief. 'Forgive him for he knew not what he did, O Lord. He was led into sin by an evil man.'

'My father isn't evil,' Manfred protested. 'He was cheated out of what was truly his.'

'Silence, *Jong*.' *Oom* Tromp rose to his full height, splendid and awesome as a biblical prophet. 'Your words are an offence in the sight of God. You will make retribution here and now.'

He dragged Manfred across the toolroom and pushed him in front of the black iron anvil.

'Thou shalt not steal. That is the very word of God.' He placed one of the diamonds in the centre of the anvil. 'These stones are the ill-begotten fruits of a terrible evil.' He reached to the rack beside him and brought down a four-pound sledgehammer. 'They must be destroyed.' His thrust the hammer into Manfred's hands.

'Pray for forgiveness, *Jong*. Beg the Lord for his charity and forgiveness – and strike!'

Manfred stood with the hammer in his hands, holding it at high port across his chest, staring at the diamond on the anvil.

'Strike, *Jong*! Break that cursed thing or be for ever cursed by it,' roared Uncle Tromp. 'Strike, in the name of God. Rid yourself of the guilt and the shame.'

Slowly Manfred raised the hammer on high and then paused. He turned and looked at the fierce old man.

'Strike swiftly,' roared Uncle Tromp. 'Now!' And Manfred swung, the same

fluid, looping, overhead blow with which he chopped wood, and he grunted with effort as the head of the hammer rang on the anvil.

Manfred lifted the hammer slowly. The diamond was crushed to white powder, finer than sugar, but still the vestiges of its fire and beauty remained as each minute crystal caught and magnified the candlelight; and when Uncle Tromp brushed the diamond dust from the anvil top with his open hand it fell in a luminous rainbow cloud to the earthen floor.

Uncle Tromp laid another fiery stone upon the anvil, a fortune such as few men could amass in ten years of unremitting labour, and stood back.

'Strike!' he cried, and the hammer hissed as it turned in the air and the anvil rang like a great gong. The precious dust was brushed aside and another stone laid in its place.

'Strike!' roared the Trumpet of God, and Manfred worked with the hammer, grunting and sobbing in his throat with each fateful blow until at last Uncle Tromp cried:

'Praised be the name of the Lord. It is done!' And he fell on his knees, dragging Manfred down with him, and side by side they knelt before the anvil as though it were an alter and the white diamond dust coated their knees as they prayed.

'Oh Lord Jesus, look upon this act of penance with favour. Thou who gave up Thy life for our redemption, forgive Thy young servant whose ignorance and childishness has led him into grievous sin.'

It was after midnight and the candle was guttering in a puddle of its own wax before Uncle Tromp rose from his knees and pulled Manfred up with him.

'Go to your bed now, *Jong*. We have done all we can to save your soul for the time being.'

He watched while Manfred undressed and slipped under the grey blanket. Then he asked quietly: 'If I forbade you to go to Windhoek in the morning, would you obey me?'

'My father,' whispered Manfred.

'Answer me, *Jong*, would you obey me?'

'I don't know, Uncle Tromp, but I don't think I could. My pa – '

'You have so much to repent already. It would not do to add the sin of disobedience to your load. Therefore, I place no such restriction upon you. You must do what loyalty and your conscience dictate. But for your own sake and mine, when you reach Windhoek, use the name of Bierman not De La Rey, *Jong*, do you hear me?'

* * *

'Judgement today! I make a rule never to predict the outcome of any piece of legislation or judicial process,' Abe Abrahams announced from his chair facing Centaine Courtney's desk. 'However, today I break my own rule. I predict that the man will get the rope. No question about it.'

'How can you be that certain, Abe?' Centaine asked quietly, and Abe looked at her with covert admiration for a moment before replying. She was wearing a simple low-waisted dress which would justify its expense only by its exquisite cut and the fineness of the silk jersey material. It showed off her fashionable small bosom and boyishly slim hips as she stood against the french windows.

The bright white African sunlight behind her formed a nimbus about her head, and it took an effort to look away from her and to concentrate on the burning cheroot which he held up to enumerate his points.

'Firstly, the small matter of guilt. Nobody, not even the defence, has made any serious attempt to suggest anything other than he is guilty as all hell. Guilty in intention and execution, guilty of planning it in detail and carrying it out as planned, guilty of all manner of aggravating circumstances, including attacking and robbing a military remount depot, firing on the police and wounding one of them with a grenade. The defence has as good as admitted their only hope will be to pull some arcane technical rabbit from the legal hat to impress His Lordship, a hope which so far has not materialized.'

Centaine sighed. She had spent two days in the witness stand. Though she had remained calm and unshakable in the face of the most rigorous and aggressive cross-examination, she was exhausted by it, and haunted by a sense of culpability, of having driven Lothar to that desperate criminal folly, and now guilty of heading the pack that was pulling him down and would soon rend him with all the vindictiveness that the law allowed.

'Secondly,' Abe waved the cheroot, 'the man's record. During the war he was a traitor and a rebel with a price on his head, a desperado with a long string of violent crimes to his discredit.'

'He was pardoned for his wartime crimes,' Centaine pointed out. 'A full pardon signed by the prime minister and the minister of justice.'

'Still, they will count against him.' Abe wagged his head knowingly. 'Even the pardon will make it worse for him: biting the hand of mercy, flouting the dignity of the law. The judge won't like that, believe me.'

Abe inspected the end of the cheroot. It was burning evenly with a firm inch of grey ash and he nodded approvingly. 'Thirdly,' he went on, 'the man has shown no remorse, not a jot nor a shred of it. He has refused to tell anybody what he did with the filthy loot.'

He broke off as he saw Centaine's distress at the mention of the missing diamonds, and continued hurriedly: 'Fourthly, the emotional aspects of the crime, attacking a lady of the highest standing in the community.' He grinned suddenly. 'A helpless female so unable to defend herself that she bit his arm off.' She frowned and he became serious again. 'Your own courage and integrity will count heavily against him, your dignity in the witness box. You have seen the newspapers: Joan of Arc and Florence Nightingale in one person, the veiled suggestion that his attack upon you might have been more dastardly and beastly than modesty will allow you to tell. The judge will want to reward you with the man's head on a platter.

She looked at her wristwatch. 'The court will reconvene in forty minutes. We should go up the hill.'

Abe stood up immediately. 'I love to watch the law in operation, the dignified and measured pace of it, the trappings and ritual of it, the slow grinding of evidence, the sorting of the chaff from the wheat – '

'Not now, Abe,' she stopped him as she adjusted her hat in the mirror above the mantel, draping the black veil over one eye, setting the small brim at an elegant angle and then picking up her crocodile-skin handbag and tucking it under her arm. 'Without any further oratory from you, let's go and see this awful thing through.'

They drove up the hill in Abe's Ford. The press was waiting for them in front of the courthouse, thrusting their cameras into the open window of the

Ford and blinding Centaine with bursting flash bulbs. She shielded her eyes with her handbag but the moment she stepped out of the automobile they were around her in a pack, yelling their questions.

'What will you feel if they hang him?'

'What about the diamonds. Can your company survive without them, Mrs Courtney?'

'Do you think they'll do a deal for the diamonds?'

'What are your feelings?'

Abe ran interference for her, barging his way through the crowd, dragging her by the wrist into the comparative quiet of the courthouse.

'Wait here for me, Abe,' she ordered, and slipped away down the passageway, weaving through the crowd that was waiting for the doors of the main courtroom to open. Heads turned to watch her and a buzz of comment followed her down the passage, but she ignored it and turned the corner towards the ladies' toilets. The office set aside for the defence was directly opposite the ladies' room and Centaine glance around to make sure she was unobserved, then turned to that door, tapped upon it sharply, pushed it open and stepped inside. She shut the door behind her and, as the defence counsel looked up, she said: 'Excuse this intrusion, gentlemen, but I must speak to you.'

Abe was still waiting where she had left him when Centaine returned only minutes later.

'Colonel Malcomess is here,' he told her, and all her other preoccupations were forgotten for the moment.

'Where is he?' she demanded eagerly. She had not seen Blaine since the second day of the trial when he had given his evidence in that ringing tenor lilt that raised the fine hair on the back of Centaine's neck, evidence that was all the more damning for its balanced unemotional presentation. The defence had tried to trip him on his description of the shooting of the horses and the grenade attack, but had swiftly sensed that he would provide little for their comfort and let him leave the stand after a few futile minutes of cross-examination. Since then Centaine had looked for him unavailingly each day.

'Where is he?' she repeated.

'He has gone in already,' Abe replied, and Centaine saw that while she had been away the ushers had opened the double doors to the main courtroom.

'Charlie is holding seats for us. No need to join the scrum.' Abe took her arm and eased her through the moving crowd. The ushers recognized her and helped clear the aisle for her to reach the seats in the third row that Abe's assistant was holding for them.

Centaine was covertly searching through the bustle for Blaine's tall form, and she started when the press of bodies opened for a moment and she saw him on the opposite side of the aisle. He was searching also and saw her a moment later; his reaction was as sharp as hers had been. They stared at each other from a few yards that seemed to Centaine to be an abyss wide as an ocean; neither of them smiled as they held each other's eyes. Then the crowd in the aisle intervened once again, and she lost sight of him. She sank down in the seat beside Abe and made a little show of searching in her handbag to give herself time to recover her composure.

'Here he is,' Abe exclaimed, and for a moment she thought he was referring to Blaine. Then she saw that the warders were bringing Lothar De Lay Rey through from the cells.

Although she had seen him in the dock for every one of the last five days, she

was still not hardened to the change in him. Today he wore a faded blue workman's shirt and dark slacks. The clothes seemed too large for him, and one sleeve was pinned up loosely over his stump. He shuffled like an old man and one of the warders had to help him up the steps into the dock.

His hair was completely white now, even his thick dark eyebrows were laced with silver. He was impossibly thin and his skin had a greyish lifeless look; it hung in little loose folds under his jaw and on his scrawny neck. His tan had faded to the yellowish colour of old putty.

As he sank onto the bench in the dock, he lifted his head and searched the gallery of the court. There was a pathetic anxiety in his expression as he ran his eyes swiftly over the packed benches. Then Centaine saw the little flare of joy in his eyes and his masked smile as he found what he was seeking. She had watched this scene enacted every morning for five days, and she twisted in her seat and looked up at the gallery behind her. But from where she sat the angle was wrong. She could not see who or what had attracted Lothar's attention.

'Silence in court,' the usher called and there was a shuffling and scrabbling as the body of the court came to its feet and Judge Hawthorne led his two assessors to their seats. He was a silver-haired little man with a benign expression and lively sparkling eyes behind his pince-nez. He looked more like a schoolmaster than the hanging judge that Abe said he was.

Neither he nor his assessors wore wigs or the colourful robes of the English courts. Roman Dutch law was more sombre in its trappings. They wore simple black gowns and white swallow-tailed neckties, and the three of them conferred quietly, inclining their heads together while the body of the court settled down and the coughing and throat-clearing and foot-shuffling abated. Then Judge Hawthorne looked up and went through the formality of convening the court and the charge sheet was read once again.

Now an expectant hush fell over the courtroom. The reporters leaned forward with their notebooks poised; even the barristers in the front row of benches were silenced and stilled. Lothar was expressionless but deathly pale as he watched the judge's face.

Judge Hawthorne was concentrating on his notes, heightening the tension with subtle showmanship until it was barely supportable. Then he looked up brightly and launched without preliminaries into the delivery of his summation and judgement.

First he detailed each of the charges, beginning with the most serious: three counts of attempted murder, two of assault with intent to inflict grievous bodily harm, one of armed robbery. There were twenty-six charges in all and it took almost twenty minutes for the judge to cover each of them.

'The prosecution has presented all these charges in an orderly and convincing manner.'

The red-faced prosecutor preened at the compliment and Centaine felt an unreasonable irritation at this petty vanity.

'This court was particularly impressed with the evidence of the main prosecution witness. His Excellency the Administrator's testimony was a great help to me and my assessors. We were most fortunate in having a witness of this calibre to relate the details of the pursuit and arrest of the accused, from which arise some of the most serious charges in this case.' The judge looked up from his notes directly at Blaine Malcomess. 'I wish to record the most favourable impression that Colonel Malcomess made upon this court, and we have accepted his evidence without reservation.'

From where she was sitting Centaine could see the back of Blaine's head. The tips of his large ears turned pink as the judge looked at him, and Centaine felt a rush of tenderness as she noticed. His embarrassment was somehow endearing and touching.

Then the judge looked at her.

'The other prosecution witness who conducted herself impeccably and whose evidence was unimpeachable, was Mrs Centaine Courtney. The court is fully aware of the great hardship with which Mrs Courtney has been inflicted and the courage which she has displayed, not only in this courtroom. Once again, we were most fortunate to have the benefit of her evidence in assisting us to reach our verdict.'

While the judge was speaking, Lothar De La Rey turned his head and looked at Centaine steadily. Those pale accusing eyes disconcerted her and she dropped her own gaze to the handbag in her lap to avoid them.

'In contrast, the defence was able to call only one witness, and that was the accused himself. After due consideration, we are of the opinion that much of the accused's evidence was unacceptable. The witness's attitude was at all times hostile and unco-operative. In particular we reject the witness's assertion that the offences were committed single-handed, and that he had no accomplices in their commission. Here the evidence of Colonel Malcomess, of Mrs Courtney and of the police troopers is unequivocal and collaborative.'

Lothar De La Rey turned his head slowly in the judge's direction once more and stared at him with that flat, hostile expression which had so antagonized Judge Hawthorne over the five long days of the trial, and the judge returned his gaze levelly as he went on.

'Thus we have considered all the facts and the evidence presented to us and are unanimous in our verdict. On all twenty-six charges we find the accused, Lother De La Rey, guilty as charged.'

Lothar neither flinched not blinked, but there was a concerted gasp from the body of the court, followed immediately by a buzz of comment. Three of the reporters leapt up and scampered from the courtroom, and Abe nodded smugly beside Centaine.

'I told you, the rope,' he murmured. 'He will swing, for sure.' The ushers were attempting to restore order. The judge came to their assistance.

He rapped his gavel sharply and raised his voice. 'I will not hesitate to have this court cleared – ' he warned, and once again a hush settled over the courtroom.

'Before passing sentence, I will listen to any submissions in mitigation that the defence may wish to put to the bench.' Judge Hawthorne inclined his head towards the young barrister charged with the defence, who immediately rose to his feet.

Lothar De La Rey was destitute and unable to afford his own defence. Mr Reginald Osmond had been appointed by the court to defend him. Despite his youth and inexperience – it was his first defence on a capital charge – Osmond had thus far acquitted himself as well as could have been expected, given the hopeless circumstances of his client's case. His cross-examination had been spirited and nimble, if ineffectual, and he had not allowed the prosecution to make any gratuitous gains.

'If it please my lord, I should like to call a witness to give evidence in mitigation.'

'Come now, Mr Osmond, surely you don't intend to introduce a witness at this stage? Do you have precedents for this?' The judge frowned.

'I respectfully commend your lordship to the matter of the Crown versus Van der Spuy 1923 and to the Crown versus Alexander 1914.'

The judge conferred for a few moments with his assessors and then looked up with a stagy sigh of exasperation. 'Very well, Mr Osmond, I am going to allow you your witness.'

'Thank you, my lord.' Mr Osmond was so overcome with his own success that he stuttered a little as he blurted eagerly: 'I call Mrs Centaine de Thiry Courtney to the stand.'

This time here was a stunned silence. Even Judge Hawthorne fell back in his tall carved chair before a buzz of surprise and delight and anticipation swept through the court. The press were standing to get a view of Centaine as she rose and from the gallery a voice called: 'Put the noose around the bastard's neck, luv!'

Judge Hawthorne recovered swiftly and his eyes flashed behind his pince-nez as he glared up at the gallery, trying to identify the wag.

'I will not tolerate a further outburst. There are severe penalties for contempt of court,' he snapped, and even the journalists sat down again hurriedly and, chastened, applied themselves to their notepads.

The usher handed Centaine into the witness stand then swore her in while every man in the room, including those on the bench, watched, most of them in open admiration, but a few, including Blaine and Abraham Abrahams, with puzzlement and perturbation.

Mr Osmond stood to open his examination, his voice pitched low with nervous respect.

'Mrs Courtney, will you please tell the court how long you have known the accused – ' he corrected himself hurriedly, for now Lothar De La Rey was no longer merely accused, he had been convicted. ' – the prisoner.'

'I have known Lothar De La Rey for nearly fourteen years.' Centaine looked across the room at the stooped grey figure in the dock.

'Would you be good enough to describe, in your own words, the circumstances of your first meeting.'

'It was in 1919. I was lost in the desert. I had been a castaway on the Skeleton Coast after the sinking of the *Protea Castle*. For a year and a half I had been wandering in the Kalahari desert with a small group of San Bushmen.' All of them knew the story. At the time it had been a sensation, but now Centaine's narrative, related in her French accent, brought it all vividly to life.

She conjured up the desolation and misery, the fearful hardships and loneliness that she had endured, and the room was deathly quiet. Even Judge Hawthorne was hunched down in his chair, supporting his chin on his clenched fist, absolutely still as he listened. They were all with her as she struggled through the clinging sand of the Kalahari, dressed in the skins of wild animals, her infant son on her hip, following the tracks of a horse, a shod horse, the first sign of civilized man that she had encountered in all those desperate months.

They chilled with her and shared her despair as the African night fell across the desert and her chances of succour receded; they willed her onwards, through the darkness, seeking the glow of a camp-fire far ahead, then started in horror as she described the sinister shape, dark with menace, that suddenly confronted her, and flinched as though they also had heard the roar of a hungry lion close at hand.

Her audience gasped and stirred as she described her fight for her life and the life of her infant; the way the circling lion drove her up into the highest branches of a tall mopani and then climbed up towards her like a cat after a sparrow. Centaine described the sound of its hot panting breath in the darkness and at last the shooting agony as the long yellow claws hooked into the flesh of her leg and she was drawn inexorably from her perch.

She could not go on, and Mr Osmond prompted her gently. 'Was it at this stage that Lothar De La Rey intervened?'

Centaine roused herself. 'I'm sorry. It all came back to me – '

'Please, Mrs Courtney, do not tax yourself.' Judge Hawthorne rushed to her aid. 'I will recess the court if you need time – '

'No, no, my lord. You are very kind, but that won't be necessary.' She squared her shoulders and faced them again. 'Yes, that was when Lothar De La Rey came up. He had been camped close at hand, and was alerted by the roars of the animal. He shot the lion dead while it was in the act of savaging me.'

'He saved your life, Mrs Courtney.'

'He saved me from a dreadful death, and he saved my child with me.'

Mr Osmond bowed his head in silence, letting the court savour the full drama of the moment, then he asked gently: 'What happened after that, madam?'

'I was concussed by my fall from the tree; the wound in my leg mortified. I was unconscious for many days, unable to care for myself or my son.'

'What was the prisoner's reaction to this?'

'He cared for me. He dressed my wounds. Tended every need of mine and of my child.'

'He saved your life a second time?'

'Yes.' She nodded. 'He saved me once again.'

'Now, Mrs Courtney. The years passed. You became a wealthy lady, a millionairess?'

Centaine was silent, and Osmond went on. 'Then one day three years ago the prisoner approached you for financial assistance for his fishing and canning enterprise. Is that correct?'

'He approached my company, Courtney Mining and Finance, for a loan,' she said, and Osmond led her through the series of events up to the time that she had closed down Lothar's canning factory.

'So, Mrs Courtney, would you say that Lothar De La Rey had reason to believe that he had been unfairly treated, if not deliberately ruined by your action?'

Centaine hesitated. 'My actions were at all times based on sound business principles. However, I would readily concede that from Lothar De La Rey's standpoint, it could have seemed that my actions were deliberate.'

'At the time, did he accuse you of attempting to destroy him?'

She looked down at her hands and whispered something.

'I am sorry, Mrs Courtney. I must ask you to repeat that.'

And she flared at him, her voice cracking with strain. 'Yes, damn it. He said that I was doing it to destroy him.'

'Mr Osmond!' The judge sat up straight, his expression severe. 'I must insist that you treat your witness in a more considerate fashion.' He sank back in his seat, clearly moved by Centaine's recital, and then raised his voice again. 'I will recess the court for fifteen minutes to allow Mrs Courtney time to recover herself.'

When they reconvened, Centaine entered the witness stand again and sat

quietly while the formalities were completed and Mr Osmond prepared to continue his examination.

From the third row Blaine Malcomess smiled at her encouragingly, and she knew that if she did not look away from him every single person in the courtoom would be aware of her feelings. She forced herself to break contact with his eyes and instead looked up at the gallery above his head.

It was an idle glance. She had forgotten the way in which Lothar De La Rey searched the gallery each morning, but now she was seeing it from the same angle as he did from the dock. And suddenly her eyes flicked to the furthest corner of the gallery, drawn irresistibly by another set of eyes, by the intensity of a glowering gaze that was fastened upon her, and she started and then swayed in her seat, giddy with shock, for she had stared once again into Lothar's eyes: Lothar's eyes as they had been when first she met him, yellow as topaz, fierce and bright, with dark brows arched over them – young eyes, unforgettable, unforgotten eyes. But the eyes were not set in Lothar's face, for Lothar sat across the courtroom from her, bowed and broken and grey. This face was young, strong and full of hatred, and she knew, she knew with a mother's sure instinct. She had never seen her younger son – at her insistence, he had been taken away, wet from the womb, at the very moment of birth, and she had turned her head away so as not to see his squirming naked body. But now she knew him, and it was as though the very core of her existence, the womb which had contained him, ached at this glimpse of his face, and she had to cover her mouth to prevent herself crying out with the pain of it.

'Mrs Courtney! Mrs Courtney!' The judge was calling her, his tone quickening with alarm, and she forced herself to turn her head towards him.

'Are you all right, Mrs Courtney?' Are you feeling well enough to continue?'

'Thank you, my lord, I am quite well.' Her voice seemed to come from a great distance, and it took all her willpower not to look back at the youth in the gallery – at her son, Manfred.

'Very well, Mr Osmond. You may proceed.'

It required an enormous effort of will for Centaine to concentrate on the questions as Osmond led her once more over the robbery and the struggle in the dry riverbed.

'So then, Mrs Courtney, he did not lay a finger upon you until you attempted to reach the shotgun?'

'No. He did not touch me until then.'

'You have already told us that you had the shotgun in your hand and were attempting to reload the weapon.'

'That is correct.'

'Would you have used the weapon if you had succeeded in reloading it?'

'Yes.'

'Can you tell us, Mrs Courtney, would you have shot to kill?'

'I object, my lord!' The prosecutor sprang angrily to his feet. 'That question is hypothetical.'

'Mrs Courtney, you do not have to answer that question, if you do not choose,' Judge Hawthorne told her.

'I will answer.' Centaine said clearly. 'Yes, I would have killed him.'

'Do you think the prisoner knew that?'

'My lord, I object. The witness cannot possibly know.'

Before the judge could rule, Centaine said clearly, 'He knew me, he knew me well. He knew I would kill him if I had the chance.'

The pent-up emotion of the courtroom exploded in ghoulish relish and it was almost a minute before quiet could be restored. In the confusion Centaine looked up at the corner of the high gallery again. It had taken all her self-control not to do so before.

The corner seat was empty. Manfred had gone, and she felt confused by his desertion. Osmond was questioning her again, and she turned to him vaguely.

'I'm sorry. Will you repeat that, please?'

'I asked, Mrs Courtney, if the prisoner's assault on you, as you stood there with the shotgun in your hands intent on killing him – '

'My lord, I object. The witness was intent only on defending herself and her property,' the prosecutor howled.

'You'll have to rephrase that question, Mr Osmond.'

'Very well, my lord. Mrs Courtney, was the force that the prisoner used against you inconsistent with that needed to disarm you?'

'I'm sorry.' Centaine could not concentrate. She wanted to search the gallery again. 'I don't understand the question.'

'Did the prisoner use more force than that necessary to disarm you and prevent you shooting him?'

'No. He simply pulled the shotgun away from me.'

'And later when you had bitten his wrist. When you had buried your teeth in his flesh, inflicting a wound that later would result in the amputation of his arm, did he strike you or inflict any other injury upon you in retaliation?'

'No.'

'The pain must have been intense, and yet he did not use undue force upon you?'

'No.' She shook her head. 'He was – ' Centaine searched for the word, ' – he was strangely considerate, almost gentle.'

'I see. And before he left you, did the prisoner make sure that you had sufficient water for survival? And did he give you advice concerning your well-being?'

'He checked that I had sufficient spare water, and he advised me to stay with the wrecked vehicle until I was rescued.'

'Now, Mrs Courtney,' Osmond hesitated delicately. 'There has been speculation in the press that the prisoner might have made some form of indecent assault – '

Centaine interrupted him furiously. 'That suggestion is repugnant and totally false.'

'Thank you, madam. I have only one more question. You knew the prisoner well. You accompanied him while he was hunting to provide meat for you and your child once he had rescued you. You saw him shoot?'

'I did.'

'In your opinion, if the prisoner had wanted to kill you or Colonel Malcomess, or any of the police officers pursuing him, could he have done so?'

'Lothar De La Rey is one of the finest marksmen I have ever known. He could have killed all of us on more than one occasion.'

'I have no further questions, my lord.'

Judge Hawthorne wrote at length on the notepad before him and then tapped his pencil thoughtfully upon the desk for another few seconds before he looked up at the prosecutor.

'Do you wish to cross-examine the witness?'

The presecutor came to his feet scowling sulkily. 'I have no further questions for Mrs Courtney.'

He sat down again, folded his arms and stared angrily at the revolving punkah fan on the ceiling.

'Mrs Courtney, the court is grateful to you for your further evidence. You may now return to your seat.'

Centaine was so intent on searching the gallery for her son that she tripped on the steps at the foot of the tiers of benches and both Blaine and Abe jumped up to help her. Abe reached her first and Blaine sank back into his seat as Abe led Centaine to hers.

'Abe,' she whispered urgently. 'There was a lad in the gallery while I was giving evidence. Blond, around thirteen years old, though he looks more like seventeen. His name is Manfred – Manfred De La Rey. Find him. I want to speak to him.'

'Now?' Abe looked surprised.

'Right now.'

'The submission in mitigation. I'll miss it.'

'Go!' she snapped. 'Find him.' And Abe jumped up, bowed to the bench and hurried out of the courtroom just as Mr Reginald Osmond rose to his feet once again.

Osmond spoke with passion and sincerity, using Centaine's evidence to full advantage, repeating her exact words: '"He saved me from a dreadful death, and he saved my child with me."' Osmond paused significantly and then went on. 'The prisioner believed that he deserved the gratitude and generosity of Mrs Courtney. He placed himself in her power by borrowing money from her, and he came to believe – mistakenly, but genuinely – that his trust in her had been betrayed.' His eloquent plea for mercy went on for almost half an hour, but Centaine found herself thinking of Manfred rather than the plight of his father. The look which the boy had levelled at her from the gallery troubled her deeply. The hatred in it had been a palpable thing and it resuscitated her sense of guilt, a guilt which she believed she had buried so many years before.

'He will be alone now. He will need help,' she thought. 'I have to find him. I have to try and make it up to him in some way.'

She realized then why she had so steadfastly denied the boy over all these years, why she had thought of him only as 'Lothar's bastard', why she had gone to extreme lengths to avoid any contact with him. Her instinct had been correct. Just a single glimpse of his face and all the defences which she had built up so carefully came tumbling down, all the natural feelings of a mother which she had buried so deeply were revived to overwhelm her.

'Find him for me, Abe,' she whispered, and then realized that Reginald Osmond had completed his submission with a final plea: 'Lothar De La Rey felt that he had been grieviously wronged. As a result, he committed a series of crimes which were abhorrent and indefensible. However, my lord, many of his actions prove that he was a decent and compassionate man, caught up in stormy emotions and events too powerful for him to resist. His sentence must be severe. Society demands that much. But I appeal to your lordship to show a little of the same Christian compassion that Mrs Courtney has displayed here today, and to refrain from visiting upon this hapless man, who has already lost one of his limbs, the extreme penalty of the law.'

He sat down in a silence that lasted for many long seconds, until Judge Hawthorne looked up from the reverie into which he had sunk.

'Thank you, Mr Osmond. This court will recess and reconvene at two o'clock this afternoon, at which time we will impose sentence.'

Centaine hurried from the courtroom, searching eagerly for Abe or for another glimpse of her son. She found Abe on the front steps of the courthouse, in deep conversation with one of the police guards. But he broke off and came to her immediately.

'Did you find him?' she demanded anxiously.

'I'm sorry, Centaine. No sign of anyone of that description.'

'I want the boy found and brought to me, Abe. Use as many men as you need. I don't care what it costs. Search the town. Do everything possible to find him. He must be staying somewhere.'

'All right, Centaine. I'll get on to it right away. You say his name is Manfred De La Rey – then he will be related to the prisoner?'

'His son,' she said.

'I see.' Abe looked at her thoughtfully. 'May I ask why you want him so desperately, Centaine? And what you are going to do with him when you find him?'

'No, you may not ask. Just find him.'

'Why do I want him?' she repeated Abe's question to herself wonderingly. 'Why do I want him after all these years?' And the answer was simple and self-evident. 'Because he is my son.'

'And what will I do with him if I find him? He is poisoned against me. He hates me. I saw that in his eyes. He does not know who I really am. I saw that also. So what will I do when I meet him face to face,' and she answered herself as simply: 'I don't know, I just do not know.'

* * *

The maximum penalty provided by law for the first three offences on the prisoner's charge sheet is death by hanging,' said Judge Hawthorne. 'The prisoner has been found guilty of these and the further offences with which he has been charged. In the normal course of events this court would have had no hesitation in inflicting that supreme penalty upon him. However, we have been given pause by the extraordinary evidence of an extraordinary lady. The submissions made voluntarily by Mrs Centaine de Thiry Courtney are all the more remarkable for the fact that she has suffered most grievously at the prisoner's hands – physically, emotionally and materially – and also for the fact that her admissions might be construed by small-minded and mean persons as invidious to Mrs Courtney herself.

'In twenty-three years' service on the bench I have never been privileged to witness such a noble and magnanimous performance in any courtroom, and our own deliberations must, by necessity, be tempered by Mrs Courtney's example.' Judge Hawthorne bowed slightly towards where Centaine sat, then took the pince-nez from his nose and looked at Lothar De La Rey.

'The prisoner will rise,' he said.

'Lothar De La Rey, you have been found guilty of all the various charges brought against you by the Crown, and for purpose of sentence, these will be taken as one. It is, therefore, the sentence of this court that you be imprisoned at hard labour for the rest of your natural life.'

For the first time since the beginning of the trial, Lothar De La Rey showed emotion. He recoiled from the judge's words. His face began to work, his lips trembling, one eyelid twitched uncontrollably and he lifted his remaining hand, palm up, in appeal towards the dark-robed figure on the bench.

'Kill me, rather.' A wild heart-cry. 'Hang me rather than lock me up like an animal – '

The warders hurried to him, seized him from either side and led him shaking and calling out piteously from the dock, while a hush of sympathy held the whole room. Even the judge was affected, his features set and grim as he stood up and slowly led his assessors from the room. Centaine remained sitting, staring at the empty dock as the subdued crowd filed out of the double doors like mourners leaving a funeral.

'Kill me, rather!' She knew that plea would stay with her for the rest of her life. She bowed her head and covered her eyes with her hands. In the eye of her mind she saw Lothar as he had been when she first met him, hard and lean as one of the red Kalahari lions, with pale eyes that looked to far horizons shaded blue by distance, a creature of those great spaces washed with white sunlight. And she thought of him now, locked in a tiny cell, deprived for the rest of his life of the sun and the desert wind.

'Oh Lothar,' she cried in the depths of her soul. 'How could something once so good and beautiful have ended like this? We have destroyed each other, and destroyed also the child that we conceived in that fine noon of our love.'

She opened her eyes again. The courtroom had emptied and she thought she was alone until she sensed a presence near her and she turned quickly and Blaine Malcomess was there.

'Now I know how right it was to love you,' he said softly. He stood behind her, his head bowed over her, and she looked up at him and felt the terrible regret and sorrow begin to lift.

Blaine took her hand that lay along the back of the bench and held it between both of his. 'I have been struggling with myself all these last days since we parted, trying to find the strength never to see you again. I almost succeeded. But you changed it all by what you did today. Honour and duty and all those other things no longer mean anything to me when I look at you now. You are part of me, I have to be with you.'

'When?'

'As soon as possible,' he said.

'Blaine, in my short life I have done so much damage to others, inflicted so much cruelty and pain. No more. I also cannot live without you, but nothing else must be destroyed by our love. I want all of you, but I will accept less – to protect your family.'

'It will be hard, perhaps impossible,' he warned her softly. 'But I accept your conditions. We must not inflict pain on others. Yet I want you so much – '

'I know,' she whispered, and stood up to face him. 'Hold me, Blaine, just for a moment.'

Abe Abrahams was searching for Centaine through the empty passages of the courthouse. He reached the double doors of the courtroom and pushed one leaf open quietly.

Centaine and Blaine Malcomess stood in the aisle between the tiers of oak benches. They were in each other's arms, oblivious to anything around them, and he stared for a moment without comprehension, then softly closed

the door again and stood guard before it, wracked by fear and happiness for her.

'You deserve love,' he whispered. 'Pray God, this man can give it to you.'

* * *

'Eden must have been like this,' Centaine thought. 'And Eve must have felt the way I do today.'

She drove slower than her usual frantic pace. Although her heart cried out for haste, she denied it to make the anticipation keener.

'I have been without sight of him for five whole months,' she whispered. 'Five minutes longer will only make it sweeter when at last I am in his arms again.'

Despite Blaine's assurances and best intentions, the conditions that Centaine had placed upon them had prevailed. They had not been alone together since those stolen moments in the empty courtroom. During most of that time they had been separated by hundreds of miles, Blaine shackled by his duties in Windhoek, Centaine at Weltevreden, fighting desperately day and night for the survival of her financial empire which was now in its death throes, stricken by the loss of the diamond shipment, no part of which had ever been recovered. In her mind she compared it to the hunting arrow of O'wa, the little yellow Bushman: a tiny reed, frail and feather-light, but tipped with virulent poison which not the greatest game of the African veld could withstand. It weakened and slowly paralysed the quarry, which first reeled and swayed on its feet, then dropped and lay panting, unable to rise, waiting for the cold lead of death to seep through the great veins and arteries or for the swift mercy stroke of the hunter.

'That is where I am now, down and paralysed, while the hunters close in on me.'

All these months she had fought with all her heart and all her strength, but now she was tired – tired to every last fibre of muscle and mind, sick tired to her bones. She looked up at the rearview mirror above her head and hardly recognized the image that stared back at her with stricken eyes, dark with the heavy mascara of fatigue and despair. Her cheekbones seemed to gleam through the pale skin, and there were chiselled lines of exhaustion at the corners of her mouth.

'But today I will set despair aside. I won't think about it – again, not for a minute. Instead I will think of Blaine and this magical display that nature has laid out for me.'

She had left Weltevreden at dawn and was now one hundred and twenty miles north of Cape Town, driving through the vast treeless plains of Namaqualand, heading down to where the green Benguela current caressed Africa's rocky western shores, but she was not yet in sight of the ocean.

The rains had come late this year, delaying the spring explosion of growth, so that although it was only weeks before Christmas, the veld was ablaze with its royal show of colour. For most of the year these plains were dun and windswept, sparsely populated and uninviting. But now the undulating expanses were clothed in an unbroken mantel so bright and vividly coloured that it confused and tricked the eye. Wild blooms of fifty different varieties and as

many hues covered the earth in banks and flocks and stands, massed together with their own kind so that they resembled a divine patchwork quilt, so bright that they seemed to burn with an incandescent light that was reflected from the very heavens and the eye ached with so much colour.

Closer at hand the earthen road, rough and winding, was the only reference point in this splendid chaos, and even it was soon obliterated by flowers. The twin tracks were separated by a dense growth of wild blooms that filled the middle ridge between them and swept the underside of the old Ford with a soft rushing sound like the water of a mountain stream as Centaine drove slowly up another gentle undulation and stopped abruptly at the top. She switched off the engine.

The ocean lay before her, its green expanse flecked with brilliant white and lapped by this other ocean of blazing blooms. Through the open window the sea wind ruffled Centaine's hair and caused the fields of wild flowers to nod and sway in unison, keeping time to the swells of ocean beyond.

She felt the care and terrible strain of those last months recede in the face of so much vibrant beauty, and she laughed spontaneously at the joy of it and shaded her eyes from the glare of orange and red and sulphur-yellow flower banks and searched the seashore eagerly.

'It's a shack,' Blaine had warned her in his last letter. 'Two rooms and no running water, an earth latrine and an open hearth. But I have spent my holidays there since a child and I love it. I have shared it with nobody else since my father's death. I go there alone whenever I can. You will be the first.' And he had drawn a map of the road to it.

She picked it out immediately, standing on the edge of the ocean, perched upon the horn of rock where the shallow bay turned. The thatched roof had blackened with age but the thick adobe walls were whitewashed as bright as the foam that curled out on the green sea, and a wisp of smoke smeared towards her from the chimney.

Beyond the building she saw movement and picked out a tiny human shape on the rocks at the edge of the sea, and suddenly she was desperate with haste.

The engine would not fire, though she cranked the starter until the battery faltered.

'*Merde!* And *double merde*!' It was an old vehicle, used and abused by one of her under-managers on the estate until she had commandeered it to replace the ruined Daimler, and now its failure was an unwelcome reminder of her financial straits, so different from when she had driven a new daffodil-yellow Daimler every year.

She let off the handbrake and let the Ford trundle down the slope, gathering speed until she jumped the clutch and the engine started with a shudder and roar of blue smoke and she flew down the hill and parked behind the whitewashed shack.

She ran out onto the black rocks above the water and the swaying beds of black-stemmed kelp that danced to the scend of the sea, and she waved and shouted, her voice puny on the wind and the rumble of the ocean but he looked up and saw her and came at a run, jumping from rock to slippery wet rock.

He wore only a pair of khaki shorts, and he carried a bunch of live rock lobsters in one hand. His hair had grown since last she had seen him. It was damp and curly with sea salt, and he was laughing, his mouth open and his big teeth flashing whitely and he had grown a moustache. She wasn't sure whether

she liked that, but the thought was lost in the tumult of her own emotions and she ran to meet him and flung herself against his bare chest.

'Oh Blaine,' she sobbed. 'Oh God, how I've missed you.' Then she lifted her mouth to him. His face was wet with seaspray and it was salty on his lips. His moustache pricked. She had been right first time, she didn't like it – but then he lifted her high and was running with her towards the shack, and she held him tightly with both arms around his neck, bouncing in his arms, jolted by his long strides, and laughing breathlessly with her own fierce need of him.

* * *

Blaine sat on a three-legged stool in front of the open hearth on which a fire of milkwood burned and perfumed the air with its fragrant incense. Centaine stood before him, working up a lather in the china shaving mug with his badger-hair brush, while Blaine complained.

'It took five months to grow – and I was so proud of it.' He twirled the ends of his moustache for the last time. 'It's so dashing, don't you think?'

'No,' said Centaine firmly. 'I do not. I'd prefer to be kissed by a porcupine.' She bent over him and lathered both sides of his upper lip with a thick foam, and then stood back and surveyed her handiwork with a critical eye.

Perched on the stool Blaine was still stark naked from their love-making, and suddenly Centaine grinned wickedly. Before he could fathom her intentions or move to protect himself, she had stepped forward again and daubed his most intimate extremity with a white blob of lather from the brush.

He looked down at himself, appalled. 'Him too?' he demanded.

'That would be cutting off my nose to spite my own face,' she giggled. 'or something like that.' Then she put her head on one side and gave her considered opinion. 'The little devil looks a lot better with a moustache than you do.'

'Careful with that adjective "little",' he admonished her, and reached for his towel. 'Come along, old fellow, you don't have to put up with this disrespect.' He wrapped the towel around his waist and Centaine nodded.

'That's better. Now I can concentrate on the job without distraction,' and she took up the cut-throat razor that lay ready on the table-top and stropped it on the leather with quick practised strokes.

'Where did you learn that? I am beginning to feel jealous.'

'My papa,' she explained. 'I always trimmed his moustaches. Now hold still!'

She took the tip of his large nose between thumb and forefinger and lifted it.

'For what we are about to receive – ' Blaine's voice was muffled by her grip on his nose. He closed his eyes and winced as the steel rustled over his upper lip, and a few moments later Centaine stepped back and wiped the lather and hair from the blade, laid the razor aside and came back to dry his upper lip and then stroke the smooth skin with her fingertip.

'It looks better; it feels better,' she told him. 'But there is still the final test.' And she kissed him.

'Hmmmm!' She murmured her approval, and then still without breaking the kiss she wriggled round and sat on his lap.

It went on for a long time until she broke away and looked down. The towel had slipped. 'I say, here comes the little moustached devil again, obviously

spoiling for trouble.' She reached down and gently wiped away the last traces of lather from the tip.

'You see! Even he looks a lot better cleanshaven.'

Blaine stood up with her in his arms. 'I think it is time, woman, that you learned the hard way that you can get away with just so much and then we must establish who is the boss around here.' And he carried her to the bunk against the far wall.

Much later they sat side by side cross-legged on the bunk with a single brightly coloured Basuto blanket draped over their bare shoulders, leaning together and watching the fire shadows flicker along the rough plastered walls, listening to the wind off the ocean soughing around the eaves of the thatched roof in the darkness outside, cupping their hands around steaming mugs of fish soup.

'One of my specialities,' Blaine had boasted, and it was thick with chunks of fresh galjoen fish and lobster that he had caught that day. 'Wonderful powers of rejuvenation for those suffering from over-exertion.'

Blaine recharged the mugs twice, for they were both ravenous, and then Centaine went to the fire, her naked body gleaming in the ruddy glow of the firelight, to bring him a smouldering twig to light his cheroot. When it was burning evenly, she climbed under the blanket again and snuggled against him.

'Did you ever find that young boy you were looking for?' he asked lazily. 'Abe Abrahams came to me for help, you know.'

He was unaware how the question had affected her, for she controlled the reflex stiffening of her body and simply shook her head. 'No. He disappeared.'

'He was Lothar De La Rey's son. I deduced that.'

'Yes,' she agreed. 'I was worried about him. He must have been deserted and alone after his father's sentence.'

'I'll keep looking for him,' Blaine promised. 'And let you know if anything comes up.' He stroked her hair. 'You are a kind person,' he murmured. 'There was no reason why you should concern yourself with the boy.'

They were silent again, but reference to the outside world had broken the spell and started a trail of thought that was unpleasant but had to be followed to the end.

'How is Isabella?' she asked, and felt the muscles of his chest tighten and swell beneath her cheek, but he inhaled a puff from the cheroot before he answered.

'Her condition is deteriorating. Atrophy of the nerves of her lower body. Ulceration. She has been in Groote Schuur hospital since Monday. The ulcers at the base of her spine will not heal.'

'I'm sorry, Blaine.'

'That is how I have managed to get away these few days. The girls are with their grandmother.'

'That makes me feel awful.'

'I would feel worse if I couldn't see you,' he replied.

'Blaine, we must keep to our resolution. We must never hurt her or the girls.'

He was silent again, then abruptly he flicked the stub of the cheroot across the room into the fire. 'It looks as though she will have to go to England. There is a surgeon at Guy's Hospital who has performed miracles.'

'When?' Her heart felt like a cannonball in her chest, suffocating her with its weight.

'Before Christmas. It depends on the tests they are doing now.'

'You will have to go with her, of course.'

'That would mean resigning as administrator and damaging my chances – ' he broke off; he had never discussed his ambitions with her.

'Your chances of a place in a future cabinet and possibly one day the premiership,' she finished for him.

He stirred, taking her face between his hands and turning it gently so he could look into her eyes. 'You knew?' he asked, and Centaine nodded.

'Do you think that cruel of me?' he asked. 'That I could let Isabella go on her own, for my selfish ambitions?'

'No,' she said seriously. 'I know about ambition.'

'I offered,' he said, while unquiet shadows clouded the green of his eyes. 'Isabella would not accept it. She insisted that I stay here.' He laid her head back against his chest and stroked the hair back from her temple. 'She is an extraordinary person – such courage. The pain is almost unceasing now. She cannot sleep without laudanum, and always more pain and more laudanum.'

'It makes me feel so guilty, Blaine, but no matter what, I am glad for the opportunity to be with you. I am taking nothing from her.'

But that was not true, and she knew it. She lay awake long after he was asleep. She lay with her ear pressed to his chest and listened to his heart and the slow filling and emptying of his lungs.

When she woke he was dressed in the old pair of khaki shorts and taking down a bamboo fishing rod with an old Scarborough reel from the rack on the wall above the hearth. 'Breakfast in twenty minutes,' he promised, leaving her cuddled down in the bunk, but he was back before then carrying a gleaming gunmetal and silver fish almost as long as his arm. He arranged it on a grid over the embers and then came to her and pulled the blanket off.

'Swim!' he grinned sadistically, and she screamed.

'You are crazy. It's freezing! I'll die of pneumonia.' She protested as wildly all the way down to the deep rock-lined pool in which he dunked her.

The water was clear as air and so cold that when they clambered out their bodies glowed bright pink all over and her nipples were standing out as hard and dark as ripe olives. But the icy water had honed their appetites and they sprinkled lemon juice on the hot succulent white flesh of the Galjoen and wolfed it down with chunks of brown bread and salty yellow farm butter.

Satiated at last they sat back and Blaine looked at her. She wore only one of his navy blue roll-necked fisherman's jerseys but the hem reached almost to her knees. She had piled her damp unruly tangle of hair on top of her head and tied it there with a yellow ribbon.

'We could go for a walk,' he suggested. 'Or – '

She thought about that for a few seconds and then decided. 'I rather think I'll settle for the "or".'

'Your wish, madam, is my command,' he replied courteously, and stood over her to lift the heavy jersey off over her head.

In the middle of the morning he lay flat on his back on the bunk while Centaine was propped on an elbow above him, tickling his lips and closed eyelids with a feather that she had plucked from the seam of one of the pillows.

'Blaine,' she said softly. 'I am selling Weltevreden.'

He opened his eyes, caught her wrist and sat up quickly. 'Selling?' he demanded. 'Why?'

'I have to,' she answered simply. 'The estate, the house and everything in it.'

'But why, my darling? I know how much it means to you. Why sell it?'

'Yes, Weltevreden means a great deal to me,' she agreed. 'But the H'ani Mine means more. If I sell the estate, there is just a chance, a very small chance, that I will be able to save the mine.'

'I didn't know,' he said gently. 'I had no idea things were that bad.'

'How could you know, my love?' She caressed his face. 'Nobody else does.'

But I don't understand. The H'ani Mine – surely it is making profits sufficient – '

'No, Blaine. Nobody is buying diamonds nowadays. Nobody is buying anything any more. This depression, this terrible depression! Our quota has been slashed. The prices we are being paid for our stones are less than half of what they were five years ago. The H'ani Mine is not quite breaking even. It is losing a small amount every month. But if I can hold on until the economy of the world turns around – ' she broke off. 'The only chance I have of doing that is by selling Weltevreden. That is all I have left to sell. That way I might be able to hold on until the middle of next year, and surely this terrible depression must be over by then!'

'Yes, of course it will!' he agreed readily, and then after a pause. 'I have some money, Centaine – '

She laid her fingers on his lips, smiled sadly and shook her head.

He lifted her hand away from his mouth and insisted. 'If you love me then you must let me help you.'

'Our bargain, Blaine,' she reminded him. 'Nobody else must be hurt. That money belongs to Isabella and the girls.'

'It belongs to me,' he said. 'And if I choose – '

'Blaine! Blaine!' she stopped him. 'A million pounds might save me now – a million pounds! Do you have that much? Any lesser amount would be wasted, simply disappear into the bottomless pit of my debts.'

'He shook his head slowly. 'So much?' Then he admitted regretfully, 'No. I don't have a third part of that, Centaine.'

'Then we will not speak of it again,' she told him firmly. 'Now show me how to catch crayfish for dinner. I don't want to talk of anything unpleasant for the rest of our time together. There will be plenty of time for ugliness when I get home.'

On their last afternoon they climbed the slope behind the shack, wading hand in hand through the bright banks of wild blooms. The pollen painted their legs the colour of saffron and the bees rose in noisy swarms as they disturbed them, then resettled as they passed on.

'Look, Blaine, see how every flower turns its head to follow the sun as it moves across the sky. I am like one of them, and you are my sun, my love.'

They wandered along the slope, and Blaine plucked the choicest blooms and plaited them into a crown. He placed it on her head. 'I crown you Queen of my heart,' he intoned, and though he smiled when he said it, his eyes were serious.

They made love lying on the mattress of wild flowers, crushing the stems and leaves beneath them, enveloped in the herby aroma of their juices and the perfume of their blooms, and afterwards Centaine asked him as she lay in his arms, 'Do you know what I'm going to do?'

'Tell me,' he invited, his voice drowsy from their loving.

'I'm going to give them something to talk about,' she said. 'A year from now they may say, "Centaine Courtney went out," but they'll have to add, "but she went out in style."'

'What do you propose?'

'Instead of the usual Christmas high jinks, I'm going to throw a bash to end all bashes! Open house at Weltevreden for a week, champagne and dancing every night.'

'It will also throw the creditors off the scent for a while longer,' he grinned at her. 'But I don't suppose you had thought of that, had you? You devious little vixen.'

'That's not the only reason. It will give us an excuse to be together in public. You will be there, won't you?'

'That depends.' He was serious again, and they both knew it depended on Isabella, but he did not say it. 'I'd have to find a pretty good excuse.'

'I'll give you an excuse,' she said excitedly. 'I'll make it a polo week – a twenty-goal tournament. I'll invite teams from all over the country, all the top players. You are the national captain. You could not reasonably refuse, could you?'

'I don't see how,' he agreed. 'Talk about devious!' And he shook his head in admiration.

'It will give you a chance to meet Shasa. I told you he had been pestering me ever since he heard that I knew you.'

'That I'd enjoy.'

'You will have to put up with a bit of hero-worship.'

'You could invite a few junior teams,' Blaine suggested. 'Give them a tournament of their own. I'd like to watch your son ride.'

'Oh, Blaine! What a wonderful idea!' She clapped her hands excitedly. 'My poor darling. It will probably be Shasa's last chance to ride his own ponies. Of course, I will have to sell them when I sell Weltevreden.' The shadows were in her eyes again for a moment, but then she rallied and her eyes sparkled. 'But as I said, we'll go out in style.'

* * *

Shasa's team, the Weltevreden Invitation, under 16 years, had won through to the final round of the junior league, mostly by virtue of their handicap allowance. Shasa was the only plus player. Of the other three members of the team, two were scratch handicaps and the third was a minus one.

However, they had finally come up against the Natal Juniors, four of the top youngsters, all of them two- and three-goal players except their captain. Max Theunissen had only made the age limit by a few months. He was rated five goals, the best in Africa for his age, with height and weight in the saddle, a good eye and a powerful wrist. He used all these advantages to the full, adopting a hard driving style of play.

Shasa was the next best rated player in the country, at four goals, but he lacked the older boy's weight and strength. Max was backed by his strong team-mates, and all Shasa's skill and determination were not sufficient to prevent his team crumbling under the onslaught, leaving Shasa virtually unaided to try and stem the rout.

In five chukkas Max had pounded in nine goals against Shasa's best efforts in defence, wiping out the Weltevreden team's handicap start, so that on handicap the teams were all square as they came in to change ponies for the last chukka.

Shasa flung himself out of the saddle, his face flushed with exertion and

frustration and anger and shouted at his chief groom. 'Abel you didn't tighten the girth properly.'

The coloured groom bobbed his head nervously. 'You checked it, Master Shasa.'

'Don't answer back, man.' But he wasn't even looking at Abel. He was glaring across the field at the Natal pony lines where Max Theunissen was surrounded by a cluster of his admirers. 'I'll ride Tiger Shark for this chukka,' he shouted at Abel over his shoulder.

'You said Plum Pudding,' Abel protested.

'And now I say Tiger Shark. Change the saddles and check the bandages on his forelegs.'

Plum Pudding was a small pony, getting a little on in years – and round in the middle – but still with an uncanny instinct to judge the run of the ball and set Shasa up for the shot. The two of them had developed a marvellous rapport. However, as befitted his advancing years, Plum Pudding was becoming cautious. He no longer enjoyed a heavy ride off and flinched from putting his plump shoulder to that of another pony at full gallop. Shasa had seen that at the other lines Max Theunissen had called for his black stallion, Nemesis. On this pony he had terrorized the junior league over the past four days, riding so cunningly close to foul play that the umpires had difficulty bringing him to book; he had succeeded in frightening most of the young lighter riders off the line even when they had the right of way, and riding off those who had the courage to stand up to him with such sadistic vigour that there had been two or three close calls – even one accident, when little Tubby Vermeulen from the Transvaal had been brought down so heavily that he had broken his wrist and dislocated his shoulder.

'Come on, Abel, don't just stand there. Get the saddle on Tiger Shark,' Tiger Shark was a young bay stallion with only a year's schooling behind him, an ugly animal with a hammer head and immensely powerful shoulders which gave him a hump-backed appearance. His temperament was equally unattractive. He kicked and bit without provocation or warning, was sometimes almost unmanageable, and he had a vicious aggressive streak that seemed to rejoice in the command to barge in for the ride off; he had never yet flinched from heavy contact. In any other circumstance Shasa would have stayed with Plum Pudding, but Max had saddled Nemesis and Shasa could guess what was coming.

The shaft of his stick had cracked in the final seconds of the last chukka and he unwound the strap from his wrist and threw it on the ground and called across to his number two as he went to the wagon for a replacement.

'Bunty, you must come up faster and move inside for my cross. Don't keep falling back, man.' Shasa broke off, becoming aware of the hectoring tone of his own voice as he realized that Colonel Blaine Malcomess, the national captain and Shasa's particular demi-god, was watching him. He had come up silently and was now leaning against the rear wheel of the wagon, one ankle crossed over the other, his arms folded over his chest, the wide-brimmed Panama hat canted over one eye and an enigmatic half-smile on his wide mouth. Shasa was sure that it showed disapproval and he tried to smooth over his scowl.

'Hello, sir. We're taking a bit of drubbing, I'm afraid,' and he forced a rueful and unconvincing smile. No matter what they taught you at Bishops, he didn't like losing, not one little bit.

Far from being censorious of Shasa's bad temper, Blaine was delighted with

it. The will to win was the single most important asset, and not only on the polo ground. He had not been sure that Shasa Courtney had it; for a person of his age he covered up very well. Offering a beautiful but urbane face to his elders, deferring attentively to them with the old-fashioned manners drummed into him by his mother and his school, and remaining at all times difficult to fathom.

However, Blaine had been watching him carefully over the last four days. He had seen that Shasa had a strong natural seat on a horse, a marvellous eye and a fluid stroke hinging on a powerful wrist. He was fearless and full of dash, which often meant he was penalized for cutting across the line and for other dangerous play. But Blaine knew that with experience he would learn to disguise his hard play and not make it so apparent to the umpires.

The other requirements for a top international-class player were great stamina, which would come with age, dedicated application and experience. This last item was so vitally important that a player only reached the high noon of his career at forty years or later. Blaine himself was only just peaking and could look forward to another ten years at the top.

Shasa Courtney had promise, and now Blaine had seen in him the will to win and his bitter anger at the thought of defeat. He smiled as he remembered his own reply when at that age his father had told him: 'Blaine, you must learn to be a better loser.' He had replied from the benefit of all sixteen years of acquired wisdom, 'Yes, sir, but I don't intend to get in enough practice to become really good at it.'

Blaine stifled the smile and spoke softly. 'Shasa, can we have a word, please?'

'Of course, sir.' Shasa hurried to his summons, pulling off his hard cap respectfully.

'You're letting Max rattle you,' Blaine said quietly. 'You've been using your noggin up to now. In the first four chukkas you held them to four goals, but in the last chukka Max knocked in five.'

'Yes, sir.' Shasa scowled again unconsciously.

'Think, lad. What has changed?'

Shasa shook his head and then blinked as it dawned on him. 'He's pulling me across onto his offside.'

'Right,' Blaine nodded. 'He's taking you on his strong side. Nobody has had a go at him from his other side, not once in five days. Change sides with Bunty and come at him on the nearside; come in steeply and barge him hard – just once. Something tells me young Max isn't going to like his own medicine. I think only one dose will be necessary. Nobody has yet seen the true colour of Master Theunissen's liver. My guess is that it has a streak of yellow in it!'

'You mean – foul him, sir?' Shasa stared at him wonderingly. All his life he had been coached in the games of young gentlemen. This was the first time he had received this type of advice.

'Perish the thought!' Blaine winked at him. 'Let's just learn to be good losers, shall we?'

They had established this peculiar accord from the moment Centaine had first introduced them. Of course Blaine's reputation had made it easier for him; he had Shasa's respect and admiration before they had even met and, given Blaine's experience as an officer and politician in the art of bending others to his will, it had been a simple matter for him to make the most of his advantage with one so inexperienced and gullible.

Besides that, Blaine had truly and deeply wanted it to be good between them. Not only for the reason that Shasa was the son of the woman he loved, but

because the boy was comely and charismatic, because he was quick-witted and had proved himself fearless and dedicated – and because Blaine did not have, and knew he never would have, a son of his own.

'Stick with him, Shasa, and play him at his own game,' he ended his advice, and Shasa smiled, his face radiant with pleasure and determination.

'Thank you, sir.' He clapped his hard hat on his head and strode away, the shaft of his mallet over his shoulder, the back of his white breeches stained brown with dubbin from the saddle and the sweat drying in salty white crystals between the shoulders of his bright yellow jersey.

'Bunty, we are changing sides,' he called, and when Abel led Tiger Shark up, Shasa punched his shoulder lightly. 'You are right, you old thunder, I did check the girth myself.' He made a show of doing it again, and Abel grinned delightedly when Shasa looked up from the girth buckle and told him, 'Now you can't blame me again.' Without touching the stirrups he swung up onto Tiger Shark's back.

Blaine pushed himself away from the wagon wheel and sauntered back towards the grandstand, his eyes instinctively sweeping the throng for the bright yellow of Centaine's hat.

She was in a circle of males. Blaine recognized Sir Garry Courtney and General Smuts amongst them, together with three influential men, a banker, a cabinet minister in the Hertzog government and Max Theunissen's father.

'A pretty average sort of bunch for Madame Courtney.' Blaine winced at the jealous pang he could not harden himself to accept.

Centaine's invitations had been sent out not only to the best players in the country but to all the most influential and important men in every other field: politicians, academics, great landowners and mining magnates, businessmen and newspaper editors, even a few artists and writers.

The château of Weltevreden was unable to house them all and she had taken over every room at the neighbouring Alphen Hotel, once also part of the Cloete family estate, to accommodate the overflow. Together with all her local guests, there were well over two hundred from out of town. She had chartered a special train to bring down the up-country contingent and their ponies, and for five days the entertainment had been continous.

Junior league polo in the mornings, an *al fresco* banquet at lunch time, senior polo in the afternoon, followed by an elaborate buffet dinner and all-night dancing.

Half a dozen bands played in relays, providing non-stop music through the days and nights. In between there were cabaret turns and fashion shows, a charity sale of art and rare wines, another sale of yearling thoroughbreds, a *concours d'élégance* for motor vehicles and lady drivers, a treasure hunt, a fancy-dress evening, tennis, croquet and bridge tournaments, show-jumping, a motor cyclist on a wall of death, Punch and Judy for the children and a team of professional nannies to keep the little ones occupied.

'And I am the only one who knows what it is all about.' Blaine looked up the stand at her. 'It's crazy and in a way immoral. It's no longer her money to spend. But I love her for her courage in the midst of misfortune.'

Centaine sensed him watching and her head turned quickly to him. For a moment they stared at each other, the distance between them not muting the intensity of their gaze, then she turned back to General Smuts and laughed gaily at what he was saying.

Blaine longed to go to her, just to be near to her, just to smell her perfume

and listen to that husky voice with its touch of French accent, but instead he strode determinedly across the front of the stand to where Isabella sat in her wheelchair. This was the first day that Isabella had felt strong enough to attend the tournament and Centaine had arranged for a special ramp to be built to allow her wheelchair to reach the first tier of seats in the stand for a view of the field.

Isbella's silver-haired mother sat on one side of her and she was surrounded by four of her close girl friends and their husbands; but her two daughters came streaking down from the stand as soon as they saw Blaine, holding up their skirts to the knees with one hand and cramming their wide-brimmed beribboned straw hats onto their heads with the other while they gabbled shrilly for his attention and then hopped along on each side of him, clinging to his hands and dragging him up to his seat beside Isabella.

Dutifully Blaine kissed the pale silky cheek that Isabella offered him. The skin was cool, and he caught a whiff of laudanum on her breath. The pupils of her large eyes were dilated from the drug, giving them a touchingly vulnerable look.

'I missed you, darling,' she whispered, and it was the truth.

The moment Blaine had left her, she had looked around desperately to find Centaine Courtney, her torment only easing a little when she saw Centaine surrounded by admirers higher in the stand.

'I had to chat to the boy,' Blaine excused himself. 'Are you feeling better?'

'Thank you. The laudanum is working now.' She smiled up at him, so tragic and brave that he stooped once more and kissed her forehead. Then as he straightened he glanced guiltily in Centaine's direction, hoping that she had not noticed that spontaneous gesture of tenderness; but she was watching him, and she looked away quickly.

'Papa, the teams are coming out.' Tara tugged him down into his seat. 'Come on, Weltevreden,' she shrieked, and Blaine could concentrate on the match rather than his own dilemma.

Changing sides Shasa led his team past the grandstand, cantering easily down the sideline, standing in the stirrups to adjust the chinstraps of his cap and searching for Blaine in the stand. They caught each other's eye and Shasa grinned as Blaine gave him a laconic thumbs up. Then he dropped back into the saddle and swung Tiger Shark around to face the Natal team as they rode out in their white breeches and caps, black boots and black short-sleeved shirts, looking tough and expert.

Max Theunissen frowned as he realized that Shasa had changed sides, and he circled out and flashed a hand signal to his number two on the far side of the field and then came back around again just as the umpire trotted to the centre and dropped the white bamboo root ball.

The last chukka opened with a confused scrappy mêlée, with hacked shots missing and the ball trampled and rolling under the ponies' hooves. Then it popped clear and Bunty leaned out of the saddle and hit his first good shot of the match, a high forehand drive that lofted well up-field and his pony went after it instinctively, bearing Bunty along on the line whether he liked it or not.

It was Bunty's shot, so he had the right of way and his pony came in perfectly to set him up, but Max Theunissen wheeled Nemesis and the black stallion was at full gallop within two strides. Max's father had not paid £1,000 for nothing, and the big powerful horse came down on Bunty like an avalanche.

Bunty looked over his shoulder and Shasa saw him blanch.

'Your line, Bunty,' Shasa screamed to encourage him. 'Stay on it!' But at the same time he saw Max deliberately press his toe into the back of the stallion's gleaming shoulder, and Nemesis altered his angle. It was a dangerous and menacing attack, and if Bunty had stood up to it, it would have been a blatant foul. But these tactics of terror worked yet again and Bunty sawed his pony's head frantically and broke away, giving up the line. Max swept onto it triumphantly, gathering himself and leaning out of the saddle, lifting his stick high in the foreswing and concentrating all his attention on the white ball that jumped and kicked over the turf directly ahead of him, setting up to take it on the backhand.

He had overlooked Shasa on his nearside, and was unprepared for the blazing burst of speed with which Tiger Shark responded to the drive of Shasa's heels as he came in at a legitimate angle for the ride off.

Neither of them had struck the ball last; it was therefore fair ball, each of them with equal right way. But as they came together, both horses at full gallop, Tiger Shark just a head behind the big black stallion, Shasa gave him the toe signal behind the shoulder and Tiger Shark responded joyously. He changed angle sharply and barged with all the power of his great misshapen shoulders. The collision was so unexpectedly violent that Shasa was almost unseated himself and was thrown up onto Tiger Shark's neck.

However, Blaine had been right, it was Max Theunissen's weak side, the one he had so assiduously protected all along, and Tiger Shark had timed the exploitation of his weakness perfectly. Nemesis reeled away and stumbled, his head going down between his front knees, and Max Theunissen was airborne, thrown high over his pony's head, somersaulting in mid-air but with the reins still in his hands, and for a terrible panicky moment Shasa knew he had killed him.

Then with an agility born of fear and natural athletic ability, Max switched around like a cat in the air and landed awkwardly, heavily but on his feet on the turf. For a few moments he was still too terrified and shocked to speak, and Shasa hauled himself back into the saddle and got Tiger Shark in hand as the whistles of the two umpires shrilled from both sides of the field. Max Theunissen started to scream hysterically.

'He fouled me, a deliberate foul. He crossed my line. I could have been killed.' Max was white and shaking, droplets of spittle flying from his quivering lips, and he was jumping up and down on the same spot like a petulant child, wild with frustration and fright.

The umpires were conferring in the middle of the field, and Shasa had a impulse to try and influence them with his own protestations of innocence, but good sense prevailed and he turned Tiger Shark back with all the dignity he could assemble, looking straight ahead, ignoring the roar of the crowd, but sensing that the roar was more an appreciation of justice, a bully caught in his own snare, than the expression of outraged sense of sportsmanship.

The umpires could not agree. They turned and trotted across the field to speak to the referee who came down from the grandstand to meet them.

'Good shot, Shas!' Bunty rode up to him. 'That will give the beggar something to write home about.'

'They might send me off, Bunty,' Shasa replied.

'You never crossed his line,' Bunty defended him hotly. 'I saw it all.'

But the fire in Shasa's blood was cooling and suddenly he thought what his grandfather would say, and even more unpleasant how his mother would react

if he were sent off in front of her guests, bringing disgrace to their house. He looked nervously across at the stands, but it was too far to make out the expression on Blaine Malcomess' face. High in the stand he saw the yellow fleck of his mother's hat, and to his fevered eye it seemed to be set at a disapproving angle – but now the umpires were cantering back, one of them coming directly towards Shasa and reining in before him, his expression severe.

'Mr Courtney!'

'Sir!' Shasa straightened in the saddle, ready for the worst.

'This is a formal warning, sir. You are officially warned for dangerous play.'

'I acknowledge your warning, sir.' Shasa tried to match his expression to the forbidding countenance of the umpire, but his heart was singing. He had got away with it.

'Play on, Mr Courtney,' said the umpire, and just before he turned away, Shasa saw the twinkle in his eye.

There were three minutes left in the final chukka as Max rode down to drive the ball deeply into their territory with his penalty shot; but there to pick it up was Shasa's number three and he hit a wobbling, bouncing ball out to the left field.

'Good oh, Stuffs!' Shasa was delighted. Thus far Stuffs Goodman had done nothing to distinguish himself. The relentless Natal attack had dispirited him, and more than once he had been the victim of Max Theunissen's robust play. This was the first time Stuffs had completed a pass and Shasa moved in to receive, then took the ball up field. But Bunty was hanging back again, and without support Shasa's attack was ridden down by a phalanx of Natal riders and the game reverted to an untidy mêlée while the seconds ticked away. The umpire blew up the mêlée and gave the shot to Natal.

'Dashed if we aren't going to hold them to a draw.' Bunty looked at his wristwatch and called across to Shasa as they fell back to receive the next Natal shot.

'Draw isn't ruddy good enough,' Shasa retorted furiously. 'We've got to win.' It was bravado, of course. They hadn't seriously attacked the Natal goal in five chukkas. But Bunty's limited ambitions angered Shasa, and Max Theunissen had definitely faded since his spill, no sign of his old dash and fire, and twice he had fallen back avoiding contact when Shasa brought the ball up field, leaving it to his backs to challenge.

'Only half a minute left!' Despite Shasa's boast, Bunty looked delighted at the term upon their sufferings, but at that moment the ball came to him hard and straight. He missed it and before he could turn the Natal attack swept past him and there was only Stuffs Goodman between them and the goal. As Shasa raced back to try and support him, his heart sank. It was all over. It was too much to hope that Stuffs could hit two clean shots in succession, but despite Shasa's misgivings, Stuffs came in, right into the heart of the Natal attack, white-faced and terrified but game, and he made a wild swing at the ball which never came within two feet of it. But his pony was a crafty old stager, clearly exasperated at the standard of his rider's play, and he trampled down the ball, and kicked it clear, right into Bunty's line. Bunty hit another corker, and chased it up field; but the Natal right back was there, driving in furiously, and the two of them ended up in another untidy waltz, swinging around each other, leaning out and hacking wildly, typical junior league play, neither man strong enough, or with sufficient experience to get another attack under way. The

muddle gave both teams time to reorganize themselves and the opposing captains were howling at their men for the ball.

'Let me have it, Bunty!' On the left side of the field Shasa was standing in the stirrups, and Tiger Shark was prancing sideways with nervous anticipation, watching the ball with eyes rolling until the whites showed.

'Here, Digger, here!' howled Max, lying back deep but ready to race up when the ball came clear.

Then Bunty hit his third and last scorcher of the day, right in the sweet spot of the hardwood mallet head, but the ball flew only a few feet before it hit the fore hoof of the Natal back's pony and rebounded under Bunty's stirrups, kicking back into the Weltevreden deep field, right out in the open.

Shasa had anticipated almost instantly and sent Tiger Shark away. He tapped the ball to change its direction and then wheeled Tiger Shark so sharply that the pony went down on his haunches.

'Ha!' Shasa put his heels in and the pony launched himself into full stride with the ball dribbling along just ahead of him.

Shasa leaned out, concentrating all his attention on the little white ball as it popped and flicked erratically, and he got the head of his mallet to it again, putting top spin on the ball so that it came under control and flew low across the turf, aimed at the Natal goal two hundred yards ahead.

Tiger Shark followed it beautifully, easing out to precisely the right distance for Shasa to get a full shot at it. Plum Pudding couldn't have judged it better, and Shasa hit it again with a neat click of wood on wood, and the ball skipped obediently ahead of him. He looked up over the ball and there was the Natal goal dead ahead, only one hundred and fifty yards away, and a kind of savage joy filled him as he realized that instead of merely holding Natal to the draw, they really did have a chance to win.

'Ha!' he called to Tiger Shark, 'Ha!' And the big animal plunged forward under him. At the same moment Max Theunissen on Nemesis wheeled onto the line ahead and rode directly at him.

'Down the throat,' was the term that described this most hazardous of all interception angles. On two powerful and swift animals they were charging each other down the throat; the roar from the grandstand faded into a horrified hush, and the spectators rose to their feet in unison.

Shasa had only once before witnessed a head-on collision between two big horses at full gallop. That had been at the trials before the Argentinian test match the previous year. He had been in the top row of the stand and he had heard the bones break clearly from there. One of the riders had burst his spleen and died later in hospital; the other had broken both legs. Afterwards they had shot the ponies as they lay in the middle of the field.

'My line!' he yelled at Max Theunissen as they swept towards each other.

'Damn you, Courtney!' Max yelled back defiantly. He had regained his courage, and he glared at Shasa over his pony's head; Shasa saw in his eyes that he was going to force the collision and he shifted slightly in the saddle. Tiger Shark felt it and flinched. They were going to give way – and then without warning Shasa was overwhelmed by the berserker's deadly passion.

Even from the stand Blaine Malcomess sensed it. He recognized that what had seized Shasa was not ordinary courage, rather it was a type of madness – the same madness that had once drive Blaine himself out into no man's land, alone with only a grenade in his hand, straight into the winking red eyes of the German Maxim guns.

He saw Shasa check Tiger Shark's turn and instead force him the opposite way, heading him directly at the black stallion, moving across the line of the ball in a deliberate challenge. It seemed that time slowed for Shasa. His vision was suddenly concentrated to brilliant clarity; he could see the wet pink mucous membrane deep in the flared nostrils of the great stallion in front of him; he could define each minute bubble in the froth that foamed from the corners of his mouth around the snaffle irons, each stiff black bristle in the charcoal velvet of his muzzle, each blood vessel in the lacework that covered the bloodshot corners of the stallion's eyes and each individual lash that surrounded them.

Shasa looked over the black stallion's head into Max's face. It was contorted with fury. He saw the tiny blisters of sweat on Max's chin, and the gap between his square white incisors as his lips were drawn back in a rictus of determination, and he looked into Max's brown eyes and held their gaze.

It was too late, Shasa judged; they had left it too late to avoid the collision, and as he thought it he saw the sudden shock in Max's face, saw his lips crumple and the flesh of his cheeks frost over with terror and watched him jerk back in the saddle and drag Nemesis' head around, pulling him off the line, breaking away right, only just in time.

Shasa swept past him, brushing him aside almost contemptuously, and with the passion still upon him he rose in the stirrups and struck the ball hard and true, driving it between the centre of the posts.

Blaine was still on his feet in the stand as the teams came in, and Shasa was flushed with triumph looking up at him for approbation, and though Blaine gave him only an airy wave and friendly smile, he was almost as exultant as Shasa.

'By God, the lad has the makings,' he told himself. 'He really has got it.' And he sat down again beside Isabella. She saw his expression; she knew him so well. She knew how desperately he had wanted a son – and the reason for his interest in the boy. It made her feel inadequate and useless and angry.

'That child is reckless and irresponsible.' She could not help herself, even though she knew that her censure would have the opposite effect on Blaine. 'He doesn't give a fig for anybody else, but then the Courtneys have always been like that.'

'Some people call it guts,' Blaine murmured.

'An ugly word for an ugly trait.' She knew she was being shrewish; she knew there was a limit to his forebearance, but she could not help this self-destructive urge to try and hurt him. 'He is like his mother – ' and she saw the anger snap in Blaine's eyes as he rose to his feet, cutting her off.

'I'll see if I can get you some lunch, my dear.' He strode away, and she wanted to cry after him.

'I'm sorry – it was only because I love you so!'

Isabella ate no red meat, for it seemed to aggravate her condition, so Blaine was contemplating the display of prawns and crayfish, clams and mussels and fish which formed the centrepiece of the buffet, a pyramid taller than his head, such a veritable work of art that it seemed sacrilegious to make the first inroad upon it. He was not alone in his reluctance; the display was surrounded by an admiring cluster of guests exclaiming with delight and admiration so that Blaine was not aware of Centaine's approach until she spoke just behind his shoulder.

'Whatever did you say to my son, Colonel, that turned him into a savage?' And he turned quickly, trying to cover the guilty delight that he felt at her

closeness. 'Oh yes, I saw you talking to him before the last chukka,' she went on.

'Man talk, I'm afraid, not for tender ears.'

She laughed softly. 'Whatever it was, it worked. Thank you, Blaine.'

'No need for that – the lad did it himself. That last goal was as plucky an effort as I've seen in a long time. He is going to be good – very good indeed.'

'Do you know what I thought as I watched it?' she asked softly, and he shook his head, leaning closer for her reply.

'I thought *Berlin*,' she told him softly, and he was perplexed for a moment. Then it dawned upon him.

Berlin 1936. The Olympic Games, and he laughed. She must be joking. From junior league to the seniors was the distance to the moon and the stars. Then he saw her expression and he stopped laughing.

'You really are serious!' He stared at her.

'Of course, I won't be able to afford to keep his ponies. But his grandfather loves to watch him play. He will help, and if he had the advice and encouragement of a really top man – ' She gave a graceful little shrug, and it was a moment before he could recover from his astonishment sufficiently to reply.

'You never fail to amaze me. Is there nothing you won't reach for?' Then he saw the sudden, sly, lascivious gleam in her eye, and he went on hurriedly, 'I withdraw the question, madam.' For a moment they looked at each other with the veil stripped aside, their eyes and their love naked for anyone to see. Then Centaine broke the contact.

'General Smuts has been asking for you.' She changed direction again in that disconcerting mercurial fashion of hers. 'We are sitting under the oaks behind the stand. Why don't you and your wife join us there?' She turned away from him and the throng of her guests opened before her.

Blaine wheeled Isabella slowly across the smooth carpet of mown Kikuyu grass towards the group under the oaks. The weather had blessed Centaine's tournament; the sky was heron's-egg blue with a silver burst of cloud hanging stationary over the peak of Muizenberg and another thick mattress laid over the massif of Table Mountain, that standing cloud known as 'the table cloth'.

It was windy, of course. It was always windy in December, but Weltevreden was tucked into a protected corner of the Constantia valley; passing overhead, the south-easter frou-froued the top leaves of the oaks, barely flickering at the women's skirts, but alleviating what would have been oppressive heat, and sweetening the air to earn its nickname 'the Cape doctor'.

When she saw Blaine coming, Centaine waved the white-jacketed waiter aside and poured champagne with her own hand and brought the glass to Isabella.

'Thank, you, no,' Isabella rebuffed her sweetly, and for a moment Centaine was at a loss, standing before the wheelchair with the scorned crystal glass in her hand.

Then Blaine rescued her. 'If it's going begging, Mrs Courtney.' He took the glass from her, and she smiled quick gratitude, while the others made room for the wheelchair in the circle and the chairman of the Standard Bank, sitting beside Centaine, took up his monologue where it had been interrupted.

'That fellow Hoover and his damned policy of interventionism, he didn't only destroy the economy of the United States but ruined us all in the process. If he had left it alone we'd all be out of this depression by now, but what do we have instead – over five thousand American banks bust this year, unemployment

up to twenty-eight millions, trade with Europe at a standstill, the currency of the world in the process of debasement. He has forced one country after another off the gold standard, even Britain has succumbed. We are one of the very few countries that have been able to maintain the gold standard, and believe me it's beginning to hurt. It makes the South African pound expensive, makes our exports expensive, it makes our gold expensive to bring to the surface and God alone knows how long we can hold out.' He glanced across the circle at General Smuts. 'What do you think, *Ou Baas*, how long can we stay on gold?'

And the *Ou Baas* chuckled until his white goatee waggled and his blue eyes sparkled. 'My dear Alfred, you mustn't ask me. I'm a botanist not an economist.' His laughter was infectious, for they all knew that his was one of the most brilliant minds in any field, that this tumultuous twentieth century had so far spewed forth; that he had urged Hertzog to follow Britain's example when she left the gold standard; that he had dined with John Maynard Keynes, the economist of the age, on his last visit to Oxford; and that the two of them corresponded regularly.

'Then you must look at my roses, *Ou Baas*, rather than the gold question,' Centaine ordered. She had judged the mood of her guests and sensed that such heavy discussion was making them uncomfortable. Day to day they had to live with the unpleasant reality of a world tottering on the financial brink and they escaped from it now with relief.

The conversation became light and trivial, but with a superficial sparkle like that of the champagne in the long-stemmed tulip glasses. Centaine led the banter and laugher, but beneath it was that empty feeling of impending disaster, the insistent aching knowledge that all this was ending, that it was unreal as a dream, that this was the last echo of the past as she was carried forward into a future full of menace and uncertainty, a future over which she would no longer have control.

Blaine looked over her shoulder and clapped lightly, and her other guests joined in a splatter of condescending adult applause.

'Hail the conquering hero – ' somebody laughed, and Centaine turned in her seat. Shasa was standing behind her, dressed in flannels and blazer, his hair wet from the shower and the marks left by the comb still sharply furrowed through it. He was smiling with just the right degree of modesty.

'Oh *chéri*, I'm so proud of you.' Centaine jumped up and kissed him impulsively and now he blushed with real embarrassment.

'I say, Mater, let's not go all French now,' he remonstrated, and he was so beautiful that she wanted to hug him. But she restrained herself and signalled the waiter to bring Shasa a glass of champagne. He glanced at her quizzically; he was usually restricted to lager, and not more than a pint of that either.

'Special occasion.' She squeezed his arm, and Blaine raised his glass.

'Gentlemen, I give you the famous victory of the Weltevreden juniors.'

'Oh, I say,' Shasa protested. 'We had nine goals start.' But they all drank, and Sir Garry made a place for Shasa beside him.

'Come and sit here, my boy, and tell us how it feels to be champions.'

'Please excuse me, Grandpater, but I have to be with the chaps. We are planning a surprise for later.'

'A surprise?' Centaine sat up. She had lived through some of Shasa's surprise turns. The amateur fireworks show during which the old barn had gone up in a most spectacular but unintended display together with the five acres of

plantation behind it was only one of his more memorable efforts. 'What surprise, *chéri*?'

'If I tell you, it won't be a surprise, Mater. But we are going to clear the field just before the prize-giving – I thought I'd let you know.' He gulped the last of the champagne. 'Have to run, Mater. See you later.' She held out a hand to restrain him, but he was already on his way back towards the grandstand where the other members of the victorious Weltevreden Invitation team were eagerly waiting for him. They piled into Shasa's old Ford and went roaring up the long driveway towards the château. She watched them with trepidation until they were out of sight, and when she looked back Blaine and General Smuts had also left the circle and were strolling away amongst the oaks, their heads inclined towards each other talking earnestly. She watched them surreptitiously. They made an interesting and ill-assorted couple, the spry little white-bearded statesman and the tall handsome warrior and lawyer. Their conversation was obviously engrossing, and they were oblivious to all else as they promenaded slowly back and forth, just out of earshot from where Centaine sat.

'When are you returning to Windhoek, Blaine?'

'My wife sails for Southampton in two weeks' time. I will return immediately the mail boat leaves.'

'Can you stay over?' General Smuts asked. 'Stay until the New Year? I am expecting developments.'

'May I have an inkling what they are?' Blaine asked.

'I want you back in the House,' Smuts evaded the direct question for the moment. 'I know it will involve sacrifice, Blaine. You are doing an excellent job in Windhoek and building up personal prestige and bargaining power. I am asking you to sacrifice that by resigning the administratorship and contesting the Gardens by-election for the South Africa Party.'

Blaine did not reply. The sacrifice that the *Ou Baas* was asking for was onerous.

The Gardens was a marginal seat. There was a real risk of losing it to the Hertzog party and even with a victory he would gain only a seat on the opposition benches, a heavy price to pay for the loss of the administratorship.

'We are in opposition, *Ou Baas*,' he said simply, and General Smuts struck at the Kikuyu grass with his cane as he pondered his reply.

'Blaine. This is for you only. I must have your word on that.'

'Of course.'

'If you trust me now, you will have a ministry within six months.' Blaine looked incredulous and Smuts stopped in front of him. 'I see I will have to tell you more.' He drew a breath. 'Coalition, Blaine. Hertzog and I are working out a Coalition cabinet. It looks certain and we will announce it in March next year, three months away. I will be taking Justice and it looks as though I will be able to appoint four of my own ministers. You are on my list.'

'I see.' Blaine tried to take it in. The news was stupendous. Smuts was offering him what he had always wanted, a place in the cabinet.

'I don't understand, *Ou Baas*. Why should Hertzog be prepared to negotiate with us now?'

'He knows that he has lost the confidence of the nation and that his own party is becoming unmanageable. His cabinet has become arrogant, if not downright lawless. It is engaging in descretionary rule.'

'Yes, yes, *Ou Baas*. But surely this is our opportunity! Look to this last month alone, look to the by-election at Germiston and the results of the

Transvaal provincial elections. We won both decisively. If we can force a general election now, we will win. We don't have to form a coalition with the Nationalists. We could win as the South Africa Party on our own terms.'

The old general was silent for a few moments, his grey beard sunk into his chest and his expression grave. 'You may be right, Blaine. We might win now, but not on our own showing. The vote would go against Hertzog, not for us. A party victory now would be barren and sterile. We could not justify forcing a general election for the national welfare. It would be party political profiteering and I want no part of that.'

Blaine could not reply. Suddenly he felt humbled to be in the confidence of such a man. A man so truly great and good that he would unhesitatingly turn his back on the opportunity of profit from his country's agony.

'These are desperate times, Blaine.' Smuts was speaking softly. 'Storm clouds are gathering all around us. We need a united people. We need a strong coalition cabinet, not a parliament split by party differences. Our economy is tottering on the brink, the gold-mining industry is in jeopardy. At present costs, many of the older mines are already closing down. Others will follow, and when they do it will mean the end of the South Africa that we know and love. In addition to that, the price of wool and diamonds, our other major exports, have crashed.'

Blaine nodded soberly. All these factors were the basis of nationwide concern.

'I don't have to emphasize the findings of the Wage Commission,' Smuts went on. 'One fifth of our white population has been plunged by drought and primitive farming methods into abject poverty, twenty per cent of our productive lands have been ruined by erosion and abuse, probably permanently.'

'The poor whites,' Blaine murmured, 'a great mass of itinerant beggars and starvelings, unemployed and untrained, without skills, without hope.'

'Then we have our blacks, split by twenty tribal divisions, flocking in from the rural districts in search of the good life, *die lekkerlewe*, and swelling the ranks of the unemployed, finding instead of the good life, crime and illicit liquor and prostitution, building up a pervading discontent, conceiving a fine contempt for our laws and discovering for the first time the sweet attractions of political power.'

'That is a problem we haven't even begun to address or attempt to understand,' Blaine agreed. 'Let us pray our children and our grandchildren do not curse us for our neglect.'

'Let us pray, indeed,' Smuts echoed. 'And while we do so, let us look beyond our own borders for a moment, to the chaos which engulfs the rest of the world.' He stabbed at the earth with his cane to mark each point as he made it.' 'In America the system of credit has collapsed and trade with Europe and the rest of the world has come to a standstill. Armies of the poor and dispossessed roam aimlessly across the continent.' He stabbed the point of the cane into the turf. 'In Germany the Weimar Republic is collapsing after ruining the economy. One hundred and fifty billion Weimar marks to one of the old gold marks, wiping out the nation's savings. Now from the ashes has risen a new dictatorship, founded in blood and violence, which has upon it the stench of immense evil.' He struck the earth again, angrily. 'In Russia a ravening monster is murdering millions of his own countrymen. Japan is in the throes of anarchy. The military have run riot cutting down the nation's elected rulers, seizing Manchuria and slaughtering the unfortunate inhabitants by the hundreds of thousands, threatening to walk out of the League of Nations when the rest of

the world protests.' Once again the cane hissed as he slashed at the lush Kikuyu grass. 'There has been a run on the Bank of England, Great Britain forced off the Gold Standard, and from the vault of history the ancient curse of anti-Semitism has escaped once more and stalks the civilized world.' Smuts stopped and faced Blaine squarely. 'Everywhere we turn there is disaster and mortal danger. I will not attempt to profit from it and in so doing divide this suffering land. No, Blaine, coalition and co-operation, not conflict.'

'How did it all go wrong so swiftly, *Ou Baas*?' Blaine asked softly. 'It seems just yesterday that we were prosperous and happy.'

'In South Africa a man can be filled with hope at dawn and sick with despair by noon.' Smuts was silent for a moment, and then he roused himself.

'I need you, Blaine. Do you want time to think about it?'

Blaine shook his head. 'No need. You can count on me, *Ou Baas*.'

'I knew I could.'

Blaine looked beyond him to where Centaine sat under the oaks and tried to hide his jubilation and to suppress the sense of shame that underlaid it, shame that unlike this saintly little man before him he was to profit from the agony of his country and the civilized world, shame that only now, out of despair and hardship, he would achieve his cherished ambition of cabinet rank. Added to that he would be returning to the Cape, coming in from the desert lands to this lush and beautiful place, coming in to where Centaine Courtney was.

Then his gaze flicked to the thin pale woman in the wheelchair, her beauty fading under the onslaught of pain and drugs, and his guilt and shame balanced almost perfectly his jubilation.

But Smuts was speaking again.

'I will be staying on here as a guest at Weltevreden for the next four days, Blaine. Sir Garry has bullied me into agreeing to allow him to write my biography and I will be working with him on the first draft. At the same time I will be conducting a series of secret meetings with Barry Hertzog to agree the final details of the coalition. This is an ideal place for us to talk and I would be obliged if you could keep yourself available. I will almost certainly be calling upon you.'

'Of course.' With an effort Blaine set his own emotions aside. 'I will be here as long as you need me. Do you want me to submit my resignation to the administrator's office?'

'Draft the letter,' Smuts agreed. 'I will explain your reasons to Hertzog and you can hand it to him in person.'

Blaine glanced at his watch and the old general said quickly, 'Yes, you will have to prepare for your match. This frivolity in the midst of such dire events is rather like fiddling while Rome burns, but one must keep up appearances. I have even agreed to present the prizes. Centaine Courtney is a persuasive lady. So I hope we will meet later – at the prize-giving when I hand you the cup.'

It was a close thing, but the Cape 'A' team, led by Blaine Malcomess, held off the most determined efforts of the Transvaal 'A' in the final match of the tournament to win by three goals. Immediately afterwards all the teams gathered at the foot of the grandstand where the array of silver cups was set out on the prize table but there was an awkward pause in the proceedings. One team was missing: the junior champions.

'Where is Shasa?' Centaine demanded in a low but furious voice of Cyril Slaine, who was the tournament organizer.

He flapped his hands and looked helpless. 'He promised me he would be here.'

'If this is his surprise – ' With an effort Centaine hid her anger behind a gracious smile for the benefit of her interested guests. 'Well, that is it. We begin without them.' She took her place on the front tier of the stand beside the general and held up both hands for attention.

'General Smuts, ladies and gentlemen, honoured guests and dear friends.' She faltered and looked around uncertainly, her voice overlaid by the drone in the air, a sound that rose steadily in volume, becoming a roar, and every face in the crowd was lifted to the sky, searching, some puzzled, others amused or uneasy. Then suddenly over the oaks at the far end of the polo field flashed the wings of a low-flying aircraft. Centaine recognized it as a Puss-Moth, a small single-engined machine. It banked steeply towards the grandstand and came straight at them, no more than head high as it raced across the field. Then, when it seemed it would fly straight into the crowded stand, the nose lifted sharply and it roared over their heads as half the spectators ducked instinctively and a woman screamed.

In the moment that it flashed over her, Centaine saw Shasa's laughing face in the side window of the aircraft's cabin, and the flicker of his hand as he waved, and instantly she was transported back over the years, through time and space.

The face was no longer Shasa's but that of Michael Courtney, his father. In her mind the machine was no longer blue and streamlined but had assumed the gaunt old-fashioned lines, the double deck of wings and wire riggings and the open cockpit and daubed yellow paintwork of a wartime scoutplane.

It banked around in a wide circle, appearing once more over the tops of the oaks, and she stood rigid with shock and her soul was riven by a silent scream of anguish as she watched again the shot-riddled yellow scoutplane trying to clear the great beech trees below the château of Mort Homme, its engine stuttering and missing.

'Michael!' She screamed his name in her head and it was like a blinding flash of agony as once again she watched his mortally wounded machine hit the top branches of the tall copper beech and cartwheel, wing over wing, as it fell out of the air and struck the earth to collapse in a welter of broken struts and canvas. Again she saw the flames bloom like beautiful poisonous flowers and leap high from the shattered machine, and the dark smoke roll across the lawns towards her, and the body of the man in the open cockpit twist and writhe and blacken as the orange flames sucked upwards and the heat danced in glassy mirage and greasy black smoke and filled her ears with drumming thunder.

'Michael!' Her jaws were locked closed, her teeth aching at the pressure, and her lips were rimmed with the ice of horror so that the name could not escape from between them.

Then miraculously the image faded, and she saw instead the small blue machine settle sedately onto the green turf of the polo field, its tail dropping onto the skid, the engine beat dwindling to a polite burbling murmur as it swung around at the far end of the field and then taxied back towards the stand, the wings rocking slightly. It stopped below them and the engine cut out with a final hiccough of blue smoke from the exhausts.

The doors on each side of the cabin were flung open and out tumbled Shasa Courtney and his three grinning team-mates. It amazed her that they had all crammed into that tiny cockpit.

'Surprise, everybody!' they howled. 'Surprise! Surprise!' And there was

laughter and applause and whistles and catcalls from the stand. An aircraft was still a marvellous novelty, able to attract the attention of even such a sophisticated gathering as this. Probably not more than one in five of them had ever flown in one, and this unexpected and noisy arrival had created an excited laughing mood so that the applause and comment was loud and raucous as Shasa led his team to the prize table to accept the silver cup from General Smuts.

The pilot of the blue aircraft climbed out of the left-hand door, a stocky bald-headed figure, and Centaine glared at him venomously. She had not known that Jock Murphy included flying among his assorted accomplishments, but she determined that he would rue this prank. She had always done all she could to discourage Shasa's interest in aircraft and flying, but it had been difficult. Shasa kept a photograph of his father in flying gear beside his bed and a replica of the SE5a fighter plane hung from the ceiling of his bedroom; over the last few years his questions about flying and his father's military feats had become more insistent and purposeful. She should have been warned by this, of course, but she had been so preoccupied and it had never occurred to her that he might take to flying without consulting her. Looking back, she realized that she had been deliberately ignoring the possibility, deliberately avoiding thinking about it, and now the shock was all the more unpleasant.

With the silver cup in his hands Shasa ended his short acceptance speech with the specific assurance:

'Finally, ladies and gentlemen, you might have thought that Jock Murphy was flying the Puss-Moth. He was not! He wasn't even touching the controls – were you?' He looked across at the bald-headed instructor, who shook his head in collaboration. 'There you are!' Shasa gloated. 'You see, I have decided that I am going to be a flyer, just like my dad.'

Centaine did not join in the clapping and laughter.

* * *

As suddenly as they had arrived and transformed the life of Weltevreden the hundreds of guests had gone, leaving only the ruined turf of the polo ground, the litter and the mountains of empty champagne bottles and piles of dirty linen in the laundry. Centaine was left also with a feeling of anticlimax. Her last flourish had been made, the last shot in her arsenal fired, and on the Saturday the mail ship docked in Table Bay and brought them an invited but unwelcome visitor.

'Damn fellow reminds me of an undertaker standing in for a tax collector,' Sir Garry huffed and took General Smuts off to the gunroom which he always used as a study when he visited Weltevreden. The two of them were immersed in the initial consultations for the biography and did not appear again until lunchtime.

The visitor came down to breakfast just as Centaine and Shasa arrived back from their early morning gallop, rosy-cheeked and starving. He was examining the hallmarks on the silver cutlery as they entered the dining-room arm in arm through the double doors, laughing at one of Shasa's sallies. However, the mood was instantly shattered and Centaine bit her lip and sobered when she saw him.

'May I introduce my son, Michael Shasa Courtney. Shasa, this is Mr Davenport from London.'

'How do you do, sir. Welcome to Weltevreden.'

Davenport looked at Shasa with the same appraising stare with which he had been examining the silver.

'It means "well satisfied",' Shasa explained. 'From the Dutch, you know – *Weltevreden*.'

'Mr Davenport is from Sotheby's, Shasa.' Centaine filled the awkward pause. 'He has come to advise me on some of our paintings and furniture.'

'Oh, jolly good,' Shasa enthused. 'Have you seen this, sir?' Shasa pointed out the landscape in soft oils above the sideboard. 'It's my mother's favourite. Painted on the estate where she was born. Mort Homme near Arras.'

Davenport adjusted his steel-framed spectacles and leaned over the sideboard for a closer view so that his considerable stomach drooped into the salver of fried eggs and left a greasy splotch on his waistcoat.

'Signed 1875,' he said sombrely. 'His best period.'

'It's by a chap called Sisley,' Shasa volunteered helpfully. 'Alfred Sisley. He is quite a well-known artist, isn't he, Mater?'

'*Chéri*, I think Mr Davenport knows who Alfred Sisley is.' But Davenport wasn't listening.

'We could get five hundred pounds,' he muttered, and pulled a notebook from his inner pocket to make an entry. A fine dusting of dandruff descended from his lank locks at the movement and sprinkled the shoulders of his dark suit.

'Five hundred?' Centaine demanded unhappily. 'I paid considerably more than that for it.' She poured a cup of coffee, she had never taken to these huge English breakfasts, and carried it to the head of the table.

'That is as maybe, Mrs Courtney. We had a better example of his work on auction only last month. "L'Ecluse de Marly" and it didn't reach the very modest reserve we placed on it. Buyer's market, I'm afraid, very much a buyer's market.'

'Oh don't worry, sir.' Shasa piled eggs onto his plate and crowned them with a wreath of crispy bacon. 'It's not for sale. My mother would never sell it, would you, Mater?'

Davenport ignored him and carried his own plate to the vacant seat beside Centaine.

'Now, the Van Gogh in the front salon is another matter,' he told her as he launched into the smoked kippers with more enthusiasm than he had shown for anything since his arrival. With his mouth full he read from his notebook.

'Green and violet wheatfield; furrows lead the eye to gold haloes around the huge orb of the rising sun high in the picture.' He closed the book. 'There is quite a vogue for Van Gogh in America, even in this soft market. Can't tell whether it will last, of course, can't stand him myself, but I will have the picture photographed and send copies to a dozen of our most important clients in the United States. I think we can bank on four to five thousand pounds.'

Shasa had laid down his knife and fork and was staring from Davenport to his mother with a puzzled and troubled expression.

'I think we should talk about this later, Mr Davenport,' Centaine intervened hurriedly. 'I have set aside the rest of the day for you. But let us enjoy our breakfast now.'

The rest of the meal passed in silence, but when Shasa pushed his plate away, half finished, Centaine rose with him. 'Where are you going, *chéri*?'

'The stables. The blacksmith is reshoeing two of my ponies.'

'I'll walk down with you.'

They took the path along the bottom wall of the Huguenot vineyard, where Centaine's best wine grapes were grown, and around the back of the old slave quarters. Both of them were silent, Shasa waiting for her to speak, and Centaine trying to find the words to tell him. Of course, there was no gentle way of saying it and she had delayed too long already. Her procrastination had only made it more difficult for her now.

At the gate of the stable yard she took his arm and turned him into the plantation. 'That man,' she began, and then broke off and started again. 'Sotheby's is the foremost firm of auctioneers in the world. They specialize in works of art.'

'I know,' he smiled condescendingly. 'I'm not a complete ignoramus, Mater.'

She drew him down onto the oak bench that stood at the edge of the spring. Sweet crystal water burbled out of a tiny rocky grotto and splashed down amongst ferns and green moss-covered boulders into the brick-lined pool at their feet. The trout in the pool, as long and as thick as Shasa's forearm, came nosing up to their feet, swirling hopefully for their feed.

'Shasa, *chéri*. He has come here to sell Weltevreden for us.' She said it clearly and loudly, and immediately the enormity of it came down upon her with the brutal force of a falling oak tree, and she sat numb and broken beside him, feeling herself shrinking and shrivelling, giving in at last to despair.

'You mean the paintings?' Shasa asked carefully.

'Not just the paintings, the furniture, the carpets and the silver.' She had to stop to draw breath and control the trembling of her lips. 'The château, the estate, your ponies, everything.'

He was staring at her, unable to comprehend it. He had lived at Weltevreden since he was four years old, as far back as he could remember.

'Shasa, we have lost it all. I have tried since the robbery to hold it together. I was not able to do it. It's gone, Shasa. We are selling Weltevreden to pay off our debts. There will be nothing left after that.' Her voice was cracking again, and she touched her lips to still them before she went on. 'We aren't rich any more, Shasa. It's all gone. We are ruined, completely ruined.' She stared at him, waiting for him to revile her, waiting for him to break as she was about to break, but instead he reached for her and after a moment the stiffness went out of her shoulders and she sagged against him and clung to him for comfort.

'We are poor, Shasa – ' and she sensed him struggling to take it in, trying to find the words to express his confused feelings.

'You know, Mater,' he said at last, 'I know some poor people. Some of the boys at school – their parents are pretty hard-up, and they don't seem to mind too much. Most of them are jolly good chaps. It might not be too bad, once we get used to being poor.'

'I'll never get used to it,' she whispered fiercely. 'I will hate it, every moment of it.'

'And so will I,' he said as fiercely. 'If only I were old enough – if only I could help you.'

She left Shasa at the blacksmith's shop and returned slowly, stopping often to chat with her coloured folk, the women coming to the stable doors of the cottages with their babies on their hips to greet her, the men straightening up

from their labours, grinning with pleasure for they had become her family; to part with them would be more painful even than giving up her carefully accumulated treasures. At the corner of the vineyard she climbed over the stone wall and wandered between the rows of lovingly pruned vines on which the bunches of new grapes already hung weightily, green and hard as musket balls, floury with bloom, and she reached up and took them in her cupped hands as though it was a gesture of farewell and found that she was weeping. She had been able to contain her tears while she had been with Shasa, but now she was alone, her grief and desolation overwhelmed her and she stood amongst her vines and wept.

Despair drained her and eroded her resolve. She had worked so hard, had been alone so long, and now in ultimate failure she was tired, so tired that her bones ached and she knew that she did not have the strength to start all over again. She knew she was beaten and that from now on her life would be a sad and sorry thing, a grinding daily struggle to maintain her pride while she was reduced to the position of a mendicant. For dearly as she loved Garry Courtney, it would be his charity on which she must rely from now on and her whole being quailed at the prospect. For the very first time in her life she could find neither the will nor the courage to go on.

It would be so good to lie down and close her eyes; a strong desire came upon her, the longing for peace and silence.

'I wish it was all over. That there was nothing, no more striving and worrying and hoping.'

The longing for peace became irresistible, filled her soul, obsessed her so that as she left the vineyard and entered the lane she quickened her step. 'It will be like sleeping – sleeping with no dreams.' She saw herself lying on a satin pillow, eyes closed, tranquil and calm.

She was still in breeches and riding-boots, so should could lengthen her stride. As she crossed the lawns she was running, and she flung open the french doors to her study and, panting wildly, ran to her desk and tore open the drawer.

The pistols had been a gift from Sir Garry. They were in a fitted case of royal blue pigskin with her name engraved on a brass plaque on the lid. They were a matched pair, hand-made by Beretta of Italy for a lady, engraved with exquisite gold inlay and the mother-of-pearl butts were set with small diamonds from the H'ani Mine.

She selected one of the weapons and broke it open. Every chamber was loaded, and she snapped it closed and cocked the hammer. Her hands were steady and her breathing had eased. She felt very calm and detached as she lifted the pistol, placed the muzzle to her temple and took up the slack in the trigger with her forefinger.

She seemed to be standing outside herself, looking on almost without emotion other than a faint remorse at the waste and a gentle sense of pity for herself.

'Poor Centaine,' she thought. 'What an awful way for it all to end.' And she looked across the room at the gilt-framed mirror. There were tall vases set on each side of the glass filled with fresh long-stemmed yellow roses from the gardens, so that her image was framed within blooms as though she were laid out in her coffin and her face was pale as death.

'I look like a corpse.' She said it aloud, and at the words her longing for oblivion changed instantly to a sickening self-disgust. She lowered the pistol

and stared at her image in the mirror, and saw the hot coals of anger begin to burn in her cheeks.

'No, *merde*!' she almost shrieked at herself. 'You don't get out of it that easily.' She opened the pistol and spilled the brass-cased cartridges onto the carpet, threw the weapon onto the blotter and strode from the room.

The coloured maids heard the heels of her riding-boots cracking on the marble treads of the circular staircase and lined up at the door to her suite, smiling happily and bobbing their curtseys.

'Lily, you lazy child, haven't you run my bath yet?' Centaine demanded, and the two maids rolled their eyes at each other. Then Lily scampered for the bathroom in a convincing pantomine of obedience and duty while the pretty little second maid followed Centaine to her dressing-room picking up the clothing that she deliberately dropped on the floor as she went.

'Gladys, you go and make sure Lily runs it deep and hot,' she ordered, and the two of them were standing expectantly beside the huge marble tub as Centaine came through in a yellow silk robe and tested the water with one finger.

'Lily, do you want to make soup out of me?' she demanded, and Lily grinned happily. The water was exactly the right temperature and Centaine's question was acknowledgement of that, a private joke between them. Lily had the bath crystals ready and sprinkled a careful measure on the steaming water.

'Here, give it to me,' Centaine ordered, and emptied half the jar into the bath. 'No more half measures.' Centaine watched the bubbles foam up over the rim of the tub and slide onto the marble floor with a perverse satisfaction, and the two maids dissolved into giggles at this craziness and fled from the room as Centaine threw off the robe and, gasping with the exquisite agony of the heat, settled chin deep in the foaming water. As she lay there, the image of the pearl-handled pistol reformed in her mind but she drove it forecfully away.

'One thing you have never been, Centaine Courtney, is a coward,' she told herself; and when she returned to her dressing-room she selected a dress of gay summer colours and she was smiling as she came down the stairs.

Davenport and Cyril Slaine were waiting for her.

'This is going to take a long time, gentlemen. Let us begin.'

Every single item in the huge mansion had to be numbered and described, the value estimated, the more important pieces photographed and everything entered laboriously in the draft catalogue. All this had to be completed before Davenport went back to England on the mail boat in ten days' time. He would return in three months to conduct the actual sale.

When the time came for Davenport to leave, Centaine surprised them all when she announced her intention of accompanying him around the mountain to the mail ship dock, a duty which would normally have fallen to Cyril.

The sailing of the mail ship was one of the exciting events of the Cape Town social calendar, and the liner swarmed with passengers and the dozens of guests who had come to wish them *bon voyage*.

At the first class entry port Centaine checked the passenger list and found the entry under 'M':

Malcomess, Mrs I. Cabin A 16
Malcomess, Miss T. Cabin A 17
Malcomess, Miss M. Cabin A 17

Blaine's family was sailing as planned. By agreement she had not seen him since the last day of the polo tournament, and surreptitiously she searched for him now through the smoking saloons and lounges of the liner's first class section.

She could not find him and realized that he was probably in Isabella's suite. The idea of their intimate seclusion galled her and she wanted desperately to go up to Cabin A 16 on the boat deck on the pretext of saying farewell to Isabella, but really to prevent Blaine being alone with her for another minute. Instead she sat in the main lounge and watched Mr Davenport demolishing pink gins, while she smiled and nodded at her acquaintances and exchanged banalities with those friends who paraded through the liner's public cabins determined to see and be seen.

She noted with grim satisfaction the warmth and respect of the greetings and attentions showered upon her. It was clear that the wild extravagance of the polo tournament had served its purpose and allayed suspicions of her financial straits. As yet no rumours had been set free to ravage her position and reputation.

That would change soon, she realized, and the thought made her angry in advance. She deliberately snubbed one of the Cape's most determined aspiring hostesses, publicly refusing her obsequious invitation and noting sardonically how the small cruelty increased the woman's respect. But all the time that she was playing these complicated social games, Centaine was gazing over their heads, looking for Blaine.

The liner's siren blared the final warning and the ship's officers, resplendent in white tropical rig, passed amongst them with the polite instruction: 'This vessel is sailing in fifteen minutes. Will all those who are not passengers kindly go ashore immediately.'

Centaine shook hands with Mr Davenport and joined the procession down the steep gangway to the dockside. There she lingered in the jovial press of visitors, staring up the liner's tall side and trying to pick out Isabella or her daughters from the passengers who lined the rail of the boat deck.

Gaily coloured paper streamers fluttered in the south-easter as they were thrown down from the high decks and seized by eager hands on the quayside, joining the vessel to land with a myriad frail umbilical cords – and suddenly Centaine recognized Blaine's eldest daughter. At this distance Tara was looking very grown-up and pretty in a dark dress and with her hair fashionably bobbed. Beside her, her sister had stuck her head through the railings and was furiously waving a pink handkerchief at someone on the dock below.

Centaine shaded her eyes and made out the figure in the wheelchair behind the two girls. Isabella was sitting with her face in shadow, and to Centaine she seemed suddenly to be the final harbinger of tragedy, an inimical force sent to plague her and deny her happiness.

'Oh God, how I wish that she were easy to hate,' she whispered, and her eyes followed the direction in which the two children were waving and she began to edge her way through the crowd.

Then she saw him. He had climbed up onto the carriage of one of the giant loading cranes. He was dressed in a cream-coloured tropical suit with his green and blue regimental tie and a wide-brimmed white Panama hat which he had taken from his head and was waving at his daughters high above him. The south-easter had tumbled his dark hair onto his forehead, and his teeth were very big and white against the dark mahogany of his tanned face.

Centaine withdrew into the crowd, from where she could watch him secretly.

'He is the one thing I will not lose.' The thought gave her comfort. 'I will always have him, after Weltevreden and the H'ani have been taken away.' And then suddenly a hideous doubt assailed her. 'Is that truly so?' She tried to close her mind to it, but the doubt slipped through. 'Does he love me, or does he love what I am? Will he still love me when I an just an ordinary woman, without wealth, without position, with nothing but another man's child?' And the doubt filled her head with darkness and sickened her physically, so that when Blaine lifted his fingers to his lips and blew a kiss up towards the slim, pale, blanket-draped figure in the wheelchair her jealousy struck again with gale force, and she stared at Blaine's face, torturing herself with his expression of affection and concern for his wife, feeling herself totally excluded and superfluous.

Slowly the gap between the liner and the quay opened. The ship's band on the promenade deck struck up 'God be with you till we meet again'; the bright paper streamers parted one by one and floated down, twisting and turning, falling like her ill-fated dreams and hopes to lie sodden and disintegrating in the murky waters of the harbour. The ship's sirens boomed farewell, and the steam tugs bustled in to take charge and work her out through the narrow entrance of the breakwater. Under her own steam the huge white vessel gathered speed; a bow wave curled at her forefoot and she turned majestically into the north-west to clear Robben Island.

Around Centaine the crowds were drifting away, and within minutes she was alone on the dockside. Above her Blaine still stood on the carriage of the crane, shading his eyes with the Panama hat, staring out across Table Bay for a last glimpse of the tall ship. There was no laughter now, no smile upon that wide mouth that she loved so dearly. He was supporting such a burden of sorrow that perforce she shared it with him, and it blended with her own doubts until the weight of it was unbearable and she wanted to turn and run from it. Then suddenly he lowered the hat and turned and looked down at her.

She felt guilty that she had spied upon him in this unguarded and private moment, and his own expression hardened into something that she could not fathom. Was it resentment or something worse? She never knew for the moment passed. He jumped down from the carriage, landing lightly and gracefully for such a big man, and came slowly to where she waited in the shade of the crane, settling the hat back on his head and shading his eyes with the brim so that she could not be certain what they contained; and she was afraid as she had never been before as he stood before her.

'When can we be alone?' he asked quietly. 'For I cannot wait another minute longer to be with you.'

All her fears, all her doubts, fell away and left her feeling bright and vibrant as a young girl again, almost light-headed with happiness.

'He loves me still,' her heart sang. 'He will always love me.'

* * *

General James Barry Munnik Hertzog came out to Weltevreden in a closed car which bore no mark or insignia of his high office. He was an old comrade in arms of Jan Christian Smuts. Both of them had fought with great distinction against the British during the South African War, and they had both taken a

part in the peace negotiations at Vereeniging that ended that conflict. After that they had served together on the national convention that led to the Union of South Africa, and they had both been in the first cabinet of Louis Botha's government.

Since then their ways had diverged, Hertzog taking the narrow view with his 'South Africa first' doctrine while Jan Smuts was the international statesman who had masterminded the formation of the British Commonwealth and had taken a leading part in the birth of the League of Nations.

Hertzog was militantly Afrikaner, and had secured for Afrikaans equal rights with English as an official language. His 'Two Streams' policy opposed the absorption of his own *Volk* into a greater South Africa, and in 1931 he had forced Britain to recognize in the Statute of Westminster the equality of the dominions of the empire, including the right of secession from the Commonwealth.

Tall and austere in appearance, he cut a formidable figure as he strode into the library of Weltevreden which Centaine had placed indefinitely at their disposal, and Jan Smuts rose from his seat at the long green-baize covered table and came to meet him.

'So!' Hertzog snorted as he shook hands. 'We may not have as much time for discussion and manoeuvre as we had hoped.'

General Smuts glanced down the table at Blaine Malcomess and Deneys Reitz, his confidants and two of his nominees for the new cabinet, but none of them spoke while Hertzog and Nicolaas Havenga, the Nationalist minister of finance, settled themselves on the opposite side of the long table. At seventeen years of age Havenga had ridden with Hertzog on commando against the British, acting as his secretary, and since then they had been inseparable. Havenga had held his present cabinet rank since Hertzog's Nationalists had come to power in 1924.

'Are we safe here?' he asked now, glancing suspiciously at the double brass-bound mahogany doors at the far end of the library and then sweeping his gaze around the shelves which rose to the ornately plastered ceiling and were filled with Centaine's collection of books, all bound in Morocco leather and embossed with gold leaf.

'Quite safe,' Smuts assured him. 'We may speak openly without the least fear of being overheard. I give you my personal assurance.'

Havenga looked at his master for further assurance and when the prime minister nodded he spoke with apparent reluctance.

'Tielman Roos has resigned from the Appellate Division,' he announced, and sat back in his seat. It was unnecessary for him to elaborate. Tielman Roos was one of the country's best known and most colourful characters. 'The Lion of the North' was his nickname and he had been one of Hertzog's most loyal supporters. When the Nationalists came to power, he had been minister of justice and deputy premier. It had seemed that he was destined to be Hertzog's successor, the heir apparent, but then failing health and disagreement over the issue of South Africa's adherence to the gold standard had intervened. He had retired from politics and accepted an appointment to the Appellate Division of the Supreme Court.

'Health?' Jan Smuts asked.

'No, the gold standard,' Havenga said gravely. 'He intends coming out against our remaining upon the standard.'

'His influence is enormous,' Blaine exclaimed.

'We cannot let him throw doubt upon our policies,' Hertzog agreed. 'A declaration from Roos now could be disastrous. It must be our first priority to agree upon our joint policy on gold. We must be in a position either to oppose or pre-empt his position. It is vitally important that we offer a united front.' He looked directly at Smuts.

'I agree,' Smuts answered. 'We must not allow our new coalition to be discredited before we have even come into existence.'

'This is a crisis,' Havenga interjected. 'We must handle it as such. May we have your views, *Ou Baas*?'

'You know my views,' Smuts told them. 'You will recall that I urged you to follow Great Britain's example when she went off the gold standard. I don't wish to throw that in your faces now, but I haven't altered my view since then.'

'Please go over your reasons again, *Ou Baas*.'

'At the time I predicted that there would be a flight from the South African gold pound into sterling. Bad money always drives out good money, and I was right. That happened,' Smuts stated simply, and the men opposite looked uncomfortable. 'The resulting loss of capital has crippled our industry and sent tens of thousands of our workers to swell the ranks of the unemployed.'

'There are millions of unemployed in Britain herself,' Havenga pointed out irritably.

'Our refusal to go off gold aggravated unemployment. It has endangered our gold-mining industry. It has sent prices for our diamonds and wool crashing. It has deepened the depression to this tragic level where we now find ourselves.'

'If we go off the gold standard at this late stage, what will be the benefit to the country?'

'First and by far the most important, it will rejuvenate our gold-mining industry. If the South African pounds falls to parity with sterling, and that is what should happen immediately, it will mean that the mines will receive seven pounds for an ounce of gold instead of the present four. Almost double. The mines that have closed down will re-open. The others will expand. New mines will open providing work for tens of thousands, whites and blacks, and capital will flow back into this country. It will be the turning point. We will be back on the road to prosperity.'

The arguments for and against were thrown back and forth, Blaine and Reitz supporting the old general, and gradually the two men opposite retreated before their logic until a little after noon Barry Hertzog said suddenly:

'The timing. There will be pandemonium in the stock exchange. There are only three trading days before Christmas. We must delay any announcement until then, do it only when the exchange is closed.' The atmosphere in the library seemed palpable. With Hertzog's statement, Blaine realized that Smuts had finally carried the argument. South Africa would be off gold before the stock exchange re-opened in the new year. He felt a marvellous sense of elation, of achievement. The first act of this new coalition was to set a term to the country's protracted economic agony, a promise of return to prosperity and hope.

'I still have sufficient influence with Tielman to prevail upon him to delay his announcement until the markets close.' Hertzog was still speaking, but it was only the details that remained to be agreed upon and that evening, as Blaine shook hands with the others in front of the white gables of Weltevreden and went to where his Ford was parked beneath the oaks, he was filled with a sense of destiny.

It was this that had attracted him into the political arena, this knowledge that he could help to change the world. For Blaine this was the ultimate use of power, to wield it like a bright sword against the demons that plagued his people and his land.

'I have become a part of history,' he thought, and the elation stayed with him as he drove out through the magnificent Anreith gates of Weltevreden, the last in the small convoy of vehicles.

Deliberately he let the prime minister's car, followed by the Plymouth that Deneys Reitz was driving, pull even further ahead and then disappear into the bends that snaked up Wynberg Hill. Only then he pulled off onto the verge and sat for a few minutes with the engine idling, watching the rearview mirror to make certain that he was not observed.

Then he put the Ford in gear again and swung a U-turn across the road. He turned off the main road before he reached the Anreith gates, into a lane that skirted the boundary of Weltevreden, and within minutes he was once more on Centaine's land, coming in through one of the back lanes, hidden from the château and the main building by a plantation of pines.

He parked the Ford amongst the trees and set off along the path, breaking into a run as he saw the whitewashed walls of the cottage ahead of him gleaming in the golden rays of the setting sun. It was exactly as she had described to him.

He paused in the doorway, Centaine had not heard him. She was kneeling before the open hearth, blowing on the smoky flames that were rising from the pile of pinecones she had set as kindling for fire. For a while he watched her from the doorway, delighted to be able to observe her while she was still unaware of him. She had removed her shoes and the soles of her bare feet were pink and smooth, her ankles slim, her calves firm and strong from riding and walking, the backs of her knees dimpled. He had never noticed that before and the dimples touched him. He was moved by the deep tenderness that until now he had felt only for his own daughters, and he made a small sound in his throat.

Centaine turned, springing to her feet the instant she saw him. 'I thought you weren't coming.' She rushed to him, holding up her face to him, her eyes shining, and then after a long time she broke off the kiss and still in his arms studied his face.

'You are tired,' she said.

'It has been a long day.'

'Come.' Holding his hand she led him to the chair beside the hearth. Before he sat, she slipped the jacket off his shoulders and stood on tiptoe to loosen his necktie.

'I've always wanted to do that for you,' she murmured, and hung his jacket in the small yellow-wood cupboard before she went to the centre table and poured whisky into a tumbler, squirted soda onto it from the siphon and brought it to him.

'Is that right?' she asked anxiously, and he sipped and nodded.

'Perfect.' He looked around the cottage, taking in the bunches of cut flowers in the vases, the gleam of new wax on the floors and simple solid furniture.

'Very nice,' he said.

'I worked all day to have it ready for you,' Centaine looked up from the cheroot that she was preparing. 'Anna used to live here, until she married Sir Garry. Nobody else has used it since then. Nobody comes here. It's our place now, Blaine.' She brought the cheroot to him, lit a taper in the fire and held it for him until it was burning evenly. Then she placed one of the leather cushions

at his feet and settled upon it, leaning her folded arms on his knee and watching his face in the light of the flames.

'How long can you stay?'

'Well – ' he looked thoughtful. 'How long do you want me? An hour? Two? Longer?' and Centaine squirmed with pleasure and clasped his knees tightly.

'The whole night,' she gloated. 'The whole glorious night!'

She had brought down a basket from the kitchen at Weltevreden. They dined on cold roast beef and turkey and drank the wines from her own vineyards. Afterwards she peeled the big yellow Hanepoort grapes and popped them into his mouth one at a time, kissing his lips lightly between each morsel.

'The grapes are sweet,' he smiled, 'but I prefer the kisses.'

'Fortunately, sir, there is no shortage of either.'

Centaine brewed coffee on the open hearth and they drank it sprawled together on the rug in front of the fire, watching the flames, neither of them speaking, but Blaine stroked the fine hairs at her temples and at the nape of her neck with his fingertips until slowly the tranquil mood hardened and he ran his fingers down her spine and she trembled and rose to her feet.

'Where are you going?' he demanded.

'Finish your cheroot,' she told him. 'Then come and find out.'

When he followed her into the small bedroom she was sitting in the centre of the low bed.

He had never seen her in a nightdress before. It was of pale lemon satin and the lace at the neck and cuffs was the colour of old ivory that glowed in the candlelight.

'You are beautiful,' he said.

'You make me feel beautiful,' she said gravely, and held out both hands to him.

Tonight their loving, in constrast to the other urgent wildly driven nights, was measured and slow, almost stately. She had not realized that he had learned so much about her body and its special needs. Calmly and skilfully he ministered to them and her trust in him was complete; gently he swept away her last reservations and bore her beyond a sense of self, his body deep in hers and she enfolding him and blending with him so that their very blood seemed to mingle and his pulse beat in time to her heart. It was his breath that filled her lungs, his thoughts that gleamed and glimmered through her brain, and she heard her own words echo in his eardrums:

'I love you, my darling, oh God, how I love you.'

And his voice replied, crying through the cavern of her own throat, his voice upon her lips, 'I love you. I love you.'

And they were one.

* * *

He woke before her and the sunbirds were twittering in the bright orange-coloured blooms of the tacoma shrubs outside the cottage window. A beam of sunlight had found a chink in the curtains and it cut through the air above his head like the blade of a golden rapier.

Slowly, very slowly, so as not to disturb her, he turned his head and studied her face. She had thrown aside her pillow and her cheek was pressed to the

mattress, her lips almost touching his shoulder, one arm thrown out over his chest.

Her eyes were closed, and there was a delicate pattern of blue veins beneath the soft translucent skin of the lids. Her breathing was so gentle that for a moment he was alarmed, then she frowned softly in her sleep and his alarm gave way to concern as he saw the tiny arrowheads of strain and worry that had been chiselled at the corners of her eyes and mouth during these last months.

'My poor darling.' His lips formed the words without sound, and slowly the splendid mood of the previous night washed away like sand before the incoming tide of harsh reality.

'My poor brave darling.' He had not known grief like this since he stood beside his father's open grave. 'If only there was something I could do to help you, now in this time of your need.' And as he said it the thought occurred to him, and he started so violently that Centaine felt it and rolled away from him in her sleep, frowning again, the corner of her eyelid twitching, and muttered something that he could not understand and then was still.

Blaine lay rigid beside her, every muscle in his body under stress, his fists clenched at his sides, his jaws biting down hard, appalled at himself, angry and frightened that he had even been capable of thinking that thought. His eyes were wide open now. He stared at the bright coin of sunlight on the opposite wall but did not see it, for he was a man on the torturer's rack, the rack of a terrible temptation.

'Honour – ' the words blazed in his mind, 'honour and duty.' He groaned silently as on the other side of his brain another word burned as fiercely: 'love'.

The woman who lay beside him had set no price upon her love. She had made no terms, no bargains, but had simply given without asking in return. Rather than demanding she had given him quittance; it was she who had insisted that no other person should be hurt by their happiness. Freely she had heaped upon him all the sweets of her love without asking the smallest price, not the gold band and vows of marriage, not even promises or assurances, and he had offered nothing. Until this moment there had been nothing for him to give her in repayment.

On the other hand he had been singled out by a great and good man who had placed unquestioning trust in him. Honour and duty on one hand – love on the other. This time there was no escape from the lash of his conscience. Who would he betray, the man he revered or the woman he loved? He could not lie still another moment and stealthily he lifted the sheet. Centaine's eyelids fluttered; she made a little mewling sound and then settled deeper into sleep.

The previous evening she had laid out a new razor and toothbrush on the washstand in the bathroom for him, and this little thoughtfulness goaded him further. The agony of indecision scourged him as he shaved and dressed.

He tiptoed back into the bedroom and stood beside the bed.

'I could walk away,' he thought. 'She will never know of my treachery.' And then he wondered at his choice of word. Was it treachery to keep intact his honour, to cleave to his duty? He forced the thought aside and made his decision.

He reached down and touched her eyelids. They fluttered open. She looked up at him, her pupils very black and big and unfocused. Then they contracted and she smiled, a comfortable sleepy contented smile.

'Darling,' she murmured, 'what time is it?'

'Centaine, are you awake?'

She sat up quickly, and exclaimed with dismay. 'Oh Blaine. You are dressed – so soon!'

'Listen to me, Centaine. This is very important. Are you listening?'

She nodded, blinking the last vestiges of sleep from her eyes, and stared at him solemnly.

'Centaine, we are going off gold,' he said, and his voice was harsh, rough with self-contempt and guilt. 'They made the decision yesterday, *Ou Baas* and Barry Hertzog. We'll be off gold by the time the markets re-open in the New Year.'

She stared at him blankly for a full five seconds and then suddenly it struck her and her eyes flared wide open, but then slowly the fire in them faded again.

'Oh God, my darling, what it must have cost you to tell me that,' she said, and her voice shook with compassion, for she understood his sense of honour and knew the depths of his duty. 'You do love me, Blaine. You do truly love me. I believe it now.'

Yet he was glaring at her. She had never seen such an expression on his face before. It was almost as though he hated her for what he had done. She couldn't bear that look, and she scrambled onto her knees in the centre of the rumpled bed and held out her arms in appeal.

'Blaine, I won't use it. I won't use what you have told me – ' and he snarled at her, his face contorted with guilt:

'That way you would let me make this sacrifice for nought.'

'Don't hate me for it, Blaine,' she pleaded, and the anger faded from his face.

'Hate you?' he asked sadly. 'No, Centaine, that I could never do.' He turned and strode from the room.

She wanted to run after him, to try and comfort him, but she knew that it was beyond even the power of her great love. She sensed that, like a wounded lion, he had to be alone, and she listened to his heavy footfalls receding down the path through the plantation outside her window.

* * *

Centaine sat at her desk at Weltevreden. She was alone, and in the centre of her desk stood the ivory and brass telephone.

She was afraid. What she was about to do would place her far beyond the laws of society and the courts. She was at the beginning of a journey into uncharted territory, a lonely dangerous journey which could end for her in disgrace and imprisonment.

The telephone rang and she started, and stared at the instrument fearfully. It rang again and she drew a deep breath and lifted the handset.

'Your call to Rabkin and Swales, Mrs Courtney,' her secretary told her. 'I have Mr Swales on the line.'

'Thank you, Nigel.' She heard the hollow tone of her voice and cleared her throat.

'Mrs Courtney,' She recognized Swales' voice. He was the senior partner in the firm of stockbrokers and she had dealt with him before. 'May I wish you the compliments of the festive season.'

'Thank you, Mr Swales.' Her voice was crisp and businesslike. 'I have a

buying order for you, Mr Swales. I'd like it filled before the market closes today.'

'Of course,' Swales assured her. 'We will complete it immediately.

'Please buy at best five hundred thousand East Rand Proprietary Mines,' she said, and there was an echoing silence in the earphones.

'Five hundred thousand, Mrs Courtney,' Swales repeated at last. 'ERPM are standing at twenty-two and six. That is almost six hundred thousand pounds.'

'Exactly,' Centaine agreed.

'Mrs Courtney – ' Swales stopped.

'Is there some problem, Mr Swales?'

'No, of course not. None at all. You caught me by surprise, that's all. Just the size of the order. I will get onto it right away.'

'I will post my cheque in full settlement just as soon as I receive your contract note for the purchase.' She paused, and then went on icily, 'Unless, of course, you require me to send you a deposit immediately.' She held her breath. Nowhere could she raise even the deposit that Swales was entitled to ask for.

'Oh dear, Mrs Courtney! I hope you didn't think – I must sincerely apologize for having led you to think that I might question your ability to pay. There is absolutely no hurry. We will post you the contract note in the usual way. Your credit with Rabkin and Swales is always good. I hope to confirm the purchase for you by tomorrow morning at the very latest. As you are no doubt aware, tomorrow is the final trading day before the Christmas recess.'

Her hands were shaking so violently that she had trouble setting the handset of the telephone on its hook.

'What have I done?' she whispered, and she knew the answer. She had committed a criminal act of fraud, the maximum penalty for which was ten years' imprisonment. She had just contracted a debt which she had no reasonable expectation of honouring. She was bankrupt, she knew she was bankrupt, and she had just taken on another half million pounds' obligation. She was taken with a fit of remorse and she reached for the telephone to cancel the order, but it rang before she touched it.

'Mrs Courtney, I have Mr Anderson of Hawkes and Giles on the line.'

'Put him on please, Nigel,' she ordered, and she was amazed that there was no tremor in her voice as she said, casually, 'Mr Anderson, I have a purchase order for you, please.'

By noon she had telephoned seven separate firms of stockbrokers in Johannesburg and placed orders for the purchase of gold-mining shares to the value of five and half million pounds. Then at last her nerve failed.

'Nigel, cancel the other two calls, please,' she said calmly, and ran to her private bathroom at the end of the passage with her hands over her mouth.

Just in time she fell to her knees in front of the white porcelain toilet bowl and vomitted into it a hard projectile stream, bringing up her terror and shame and guilt, heaving and retching until her stomach was empty and the muscles of her chest ached and her throat burned as though it had been scalded raw with acid.

* * *

Christmas Day had always been one of their very special days since Shasa was a child, but she awoke this morning in a sombre mood.

Still in their night clothes and dressing-gowns, she and Shasa exchanged their presents in her suite. He had hand painted a special card for her, and decorated it with pressed wild flowers. His present to her was François Mauriac's new novel *Noeud de Vipères* and he had inscribed on the flyleaf:

> No matter what, we still have
> each other
> Shasa

Her present to him was a leather flying helmet with goggles and he looked at her with amazement. She had made her opposition to flying very plain.

'Yes, *chéri*, if you want to learn to fly, I'll not stop you.'

'Can we afford it, Mater? I mean, you know – '

'You let me worry about that.'

'No, Mater.' He shook his head firmly. 'I'm not a child any more. From now on I am going to help you. I don't want anything that will make it more difficult for you – for us.'

She ran to him and embraced him quickly, pressing her cheek to his so that he could not see the shine of tears in her eyes.

'We are desert creatures. We will survive, my darling.'

But her moods swung wildly all the rest of the day as Centaine played the *grande dame*, the châtelaine of Weltevreden, welcoming the many callers at the estate, serving sherry and biscuits and exchanging gifts with them, laughing and charming, and then on the pretext of seeing to the servants hurrying away to lock herself in the mirrored study with the drawn curtains while she fought off the black moods, the doubts and the terrible crippling forebodings. Shasa seemed to understand, standing in her place when she fell out, suddenly mature and responsible, rallying to her aid as he had never been called upon to do before.

Just before noon one of their callers brought tidings which genuinely allowed Centaine to forget for a short time her own forebodings. The Rev Canon Birt was the headmaster of Bishops and he took Centaine and Shasa aside for a few moments.

'Mrs Courtney, you know what a name young Shasa has made for himself at Bishops. Unfortunately next year will be his last with us. We shall miss him. However, I am sure it will come as no surprise to you to hear that I have selected him to be head of school in the new term, or that the board of governors have endorsed my choice.'

'Not in front of the Head, Mater,' Shasa whispered, in an agony of embarrassment when Centaine embraced him joyously, but she deliberately kissed both his cheeks in the manner he designated 'French' and pretended to disparage.

'That is not all, Mrs Courtney.' Canon Birt beamed on this display of maternal pride. 'I have been asked by the board of governors to invite you to join them. You will be the first woman – ah, the first lady, ever to sit on the board.'

Centaine was on the point of accepting immediately, but then like the shadow of the executioner's axe the premonition of impending financial catastrophe dulled her vision and she hesitated.

'I know you are a very busy person – ' he was about to urge her.

'I am honoured, Headmaster,' she told him. 'But there are personal considerations. May I give you my reply in the new year?'

'Just as long as that is not an outright refusal – '

'No, I give you my assurance. If I can, I will.'

When the last caller had been packed off, Centaine could lead the family, including Sir Garry and Anna and the very closest family friends, down to the polo field for the next act in their traditional Weltevreden Christmas festival.

The entire coloured staff was assembled there, with their children and aged parents and the estate pensioners too old to work, and all the others who Centaine supported. Every one of them was dressed in their Sunday best, a marvellous assortment of styles and cuts and colours, the little girls with ribbons in their hair and the small boys for once with shoes on their feet.

The estate band, fiddles and concertinas and banjoes, welcomed Centaine, and the singing, the very voice of Africa, was melodious and beautiful. She had a gift for each of them, which she handed over with an envelope containing their Christmas bonus. Some of the older women, emboldened by their long service and sense of occasion, embraced her, and so precarious was Centaine's mood that these spontaneous gestures of affection made her weep again, which set the other women off.

It was swiftly becoming an orgy of sentiment and Shasa hastily signalled the band to strike up something lively. They chose 'Alabama', the old Cape Malay song that commemorated the cruise of the confederate raider to Cape waters when she captured the *Sea Bride* in Table Bay on 5 August, 1863.

> There comes the Alabama
> Daar dom die Alabama

Then Shasa supervised the drawing of the bung from the first keg of sweet estate wine, and almost immediately the tears dried and the mood became festive and gay.

Once the whole sheep on the spits were sizzling and dripping rich fat onto the coals, the second keg of wine had been broached, the dancing was losing all restraint and the younger couples were sneaking away into the vineyards, Centaine gathered the party from the big house and left them to it.

As they passed the Huguenot vineyard, they heard the giggling and scuffling amongst the vines behind the stone wall and Sir Garry remarked complacently: 'Shouldn't think Weltevreden is going to run short of labour in the foreseeable future. Sounds like a good crop being planted.'

'You are as shameless as they are,' Anna huffed, and then giggled herself just as breathlessly as the young girls in the vineyard as he squeezed her thick waist and whispered something in her ear.

That little intimacy lanced Centaine with a blade of loneliness, and she thought of Blaine and wanted to weep again. But Shasa seemed to sense her pain and took her hand and made her laugh with one of his silly jokes.

The family dinner was part of the tradition. Before they ate Shasa read aloud to them from the New Testament as he had every Christmas Day since his sixth birthday. Then he and Centaine distributed the pile of presents from under the tree, and the salon was filled with the rustle of paper and the ooh's and aah's of delight.

The dinner was roast turkeys and baron of beef followed by a rich black

Christmas pudding. Shasa found the lucky gold sovereign in his portion, as he did every year without suspecting that it had been carefully salted there by Centaine during the serving; and when at the end they all tottered away, satiated and heavy-eyed, to their separate bedrooms, Centaine slipped out of the french windows of her study and ran all the way down through the plantation and burst into the cottage.

Blaine was waiting for her and she ran to him. 'We should be together at Christmas and every other day.'

He stopped her from going on by kissing her, and she reviled herself for her silliness. When she pulled back in his arms, she was smiling brightly. 'I couldn't wrap your Christmas present. The shape is all wrong and the ribbon wouldn't stay on. You'll have to take it *au naturel*.'

'Where is it?'

'Follow me, sir, and it shall be delivered unto you.'

'Now that,' he said a little later, 'is by far the nicest present that anybody ever gave me, and so very useful too!'

* * *

There were no newspapers on New Year's Day, but Centaine listened to the news every hour on the radio. There was no mention of the gold standard or any other political issue on these bulletins. Blaine was away, occupied all day with meetings and discussions concerning his candidature of the coming parliamentary by-election at the Gardens. Shasa had gone as house guest to one of the neighbouring estates. She was alone with her fears and doubts.

She read until after midnight and then lay in the darkness, sleeping only fitfully and plagued by nightmares, starting awake and then drifting back into uneasy sleep.

Long before dawn she gave up the attempt to find rest and dressed in jodhpurs and riding-boots and her sheepskin coat. She saddled her favourite stallion and rode down in the darkness five miles to the railway station at Claremont to meet the early train from Cape Town.

She was waiting on the platform when the bundles of newspapers were thrown out of the goods van onto the concrete quay, and the small coloured newsboys swarmed over them, chattering and laughing as they divided up the bundles for delivery. Centaine tossed one of them a silver shilling and he hooted with glee when she waved away the change and eagerly unfolded the newspaper.

The headlines took up fully half the front page, and they rocked her on her feet.

SOUTH AFRICA ABANDONS GOLD STANDARD
HUGE BOOST FOR GOLD MINES

She scanned the columns below, barely able to take in any more, and then, still in a daze, rode back up the valley to Weltevreden. Only when she reached the Anreith gates did the full impact of it all dawn upon her. Weltevreden was still hers, it would always be hers, and she rose in the stirrups and shouted with joy, then urged her horse into a flying gallop, lifting him over the stone wall and racing down between the rows of vines.

She left him in his stall and ran all the way back to the château. She had to talk to someone – if only it could have been Blaine. But Sir Garry was in the dining-room; he was always first down for breakfast.

'Have you heard the news, my dear?' he cried excitedly the moment she entered. 'I heard it on the radio at six o'clock. We are off gold. Hertzog did it! By God, there will be a few fortunes made and lost this day! Anybody who is holding gold shares will double and treble their money. Oh, my dear, is something wrong?'

Centaine had collapsed into her chair at the head of the dining-room table.

'No, no.' She shook her head frantically. 'There is nothing wrong, not any more. Everything is all right – wonderfully, magnificently, stupendously all right.'

* * *

At lunchtime Blaine telephoned her at Weltevreden. He had never done so before. His voice sounded hollow and strange on the scratchy line. He did not announce himself but said simply: 'Five o'clock at the cottage.'

'Yes, I'll be there.' She wanted to say more but the line clicked dead.

She went down to the cottage an hour early with fresh flowers, clean crisply ironed linen for the bed and a bottle of Bollinger champagne, and she was waiting for him when he walked into the living-room.

'There are no words that can adequately express my gratitude,' she said.

'That is the way I want it, Centaine,' he told her seriously. 'No words! We will never talk about it again. I shall try to convince myself it never happened. Please promise me never to mention it, never again as long as we live and love each other.'

'I give you my solemn word,' she said, and then all her relief and joy came bubbling up and she kissed him, laughing. 'Won't you open the champagne?' And she raised the brimming glass when he handed it to her and gave him his own words back as a toast:

'For as long as we live and love each other, my darling.'

* * *

The Johannesburg Stock Exchange re-opened on January the second and in the first hour very little business could be conducted, for the floor was like a battlefield as the brokers literally tore at each other, screaming for attention. But by call-over the market had shaken itself out and settled at its new levels.

Swales of Rabkin and Swales was the first of her brokers to telephone Centaine. Like the market, his tone was buoyant and effervescent.

'My dear Mrs Courtney,' in the circumstances, Centaine was prepared to let that familiarity pass, 'my very dear Mrs Courtney, your timing has been almost miraculous. As you know, we were unfortunately unable to fill your entire purchase order. We were able to obtain only four hundred and forty thousand ERPMs at an average price of twenty-five shillings. The volume of your order pushed the price up two and six. However,' she could almost hear him puffing

himself up to make his announcement, 'however, I am delighted to be able to tell you that this morning ERPMs are trading at fifty-five shillings and still rising. I am looking forward to sixty shillings by the end of the week – '

'Sell them,' Centaine said quietly and heard him choke at the end of the line.

'If I may be permitted to offer a word of advice – '

'Sell them,' she repeated. 'Sell all of them.' And she hung up, staring out of the window as she tried to calculate her profits but the telephone rang again before she reached a total, and one after another her other brokers triumphantly reported on the contracts she had made. Then there was a call from Windhoek.

'Dr Twentyman-Jones, it's so good to hear your voice.' She had recognized him instantly.

'Well, Mrs Courtney, this is a pretty pickle,' Twentyman-Jones told her glumly. 'The H'ani Mine will be back in profit again now, even with the parsimonious quota De Beers is allowing us.'

'We've turned the corner,' Centaine enthused. 'We are out of the woods.'

'Many a slip 'twixt cup and lip.' Gloomily Twentyman-Jones capped cliché with cliché. 'Best not to count our chickens, Mrs Courtney.'

'Dr Twentyman-Jones, I love you.' Centaine laughed delightedly, and there was a shocked silence that echoed across a thousand miles of wire. 'I'll be there just as soon as I can get away from here. There is a lot for us to work on now.'

She hung up and went to look for Shasa. He was down at the stables chatting with his coloured grooms as they sat in the sun dubbining his polo harness and saddlery.

'*Chéri*, I am driving into Cape Town. Will you come with me?'

'What are you going all that way for, Mater?'

'It's a surprise.'

That was the one certain way to gain Shasa's full attention and he tossed the harness he was working on to Abel and sprang to his feet.

Her ebullient mood was infectious and they were laughing together as they walked into Porters Motors showroom on Strand Street. The sales manager came from his cubicle on the run.

'Mrs Courtney, we haven't seen you in far too long. May I wish you a happy and prosperous New Year.'

'It's off to a good start on both counts,' she smiled. 'Speaking of happiness, Mr Tims, how soon can you deliver my new Daimler?'

'It will be yellow, naturally?'

'With black piping, naturally!'

'And the usual fittings – the vanity, the cocktail cabinet?'

'All of them, Mr Tims.'

'I will cable our London office immeditely. Shall we say four months, Mrs Courtney?'

'Let us rather say three months, Mr Tims.'

Shasa could barely contain himself until they were on the pavments in front of the showroom.

'Mater, have you gone bonkers? We are paupers!'

'Well, *chéri*, let's be paupers with a little class and style.'

'Where are we going now?'

'The post office.' At the telegraph counter Centaine drafted a cable to Sotheby's in Bond Street.

> Sale no longer contemplated. Stop. Please cancel all preparations.

Then they went to lunch at the Mount Nelson Hotel.

* * *

Blaine had promised to meet her as early as he was able to escape from the meeting of the proposed new coalition cabinet. He was as good as his word, waiting for her in the pine forest, and when she saw his face her happiness shrivelled.

'What is it, Blaine?'

'Let's walk, Centaine. I've been indoors all day.'

They climbed the Karbonkelberg slopes behind the estate. At the summit they sat on a fallen log to watch the sunset and it was magnificent.

'This was the fairest Cape which we discovered in all our circumnavigation of the earth – ' she misquoted from Vasco da Gama's log, but Blaine did not correct her as she had hoped he might.

'Tell me, Blaine.' She took his arm and insisted, and he turned his face to her.

'Isabella,' he said sombrely.

'You have heard from her?' Her spirits sank deeper at the name.

'The doctors can do nothing for her. She will be returning on the next mail ship from Southampton.'

In silence the sun sank into the silver sea, taking the light from the world, and Centaine's soul was as dark.

'How ironic it is,' she whispered. 'Because of you I can have anything in this world except that which I most desire – you, my love.'

* * *

The women pounded the fresh millet grain in the wooden mortars into a coarse fluffy white meal and filled one of the leather sacks.

Carrying the sack, Swart Hendrick, followed by Moses his brother, left the kraal after the rise of the new moon and crept silently up the ridge in the night. While Hendrick stood guard, Moses climbed to the old eagle owl nest in the leadwood tree and brought down the cartridge paper packets.

They moved along the ridge until they were beyond all possible chance of observation from the village, and even then they very carefully screened the small fire that they built amonst the ironstone boulders. Hendrick broke open the packets and poured the gleaming stones into a small calabash gourd while Moses prepared the millet meal in another gourd, mixing it with water until it was a soft porridge.

Meticulously Hendrick burned the cartridge paper wrappings in the fire and stirred the ashes to powder with a stick. When it was done he nodded at his younger brother and Moses poured the dough over the coals. As it began to bubble Hendrick buried the diamonds in the unleavened dough.

Moses muttered ruefully as the millet cakes bubbled and hardened. It was almost an incantation. 'These are death stones. We will have no joy of them. The white men love them too dearly: they are the stones of death and madness.'

Hendrick ignored him and shaped the baking loaves, squinting his eyes against the smoke and smiling secretly to himself. When each round loaf was crisped brown on the underside he flipped it over and let it cook through until it was brick hard; then he lifted it off the fire and set it out to cool. Finally he repacked the crude thick loaves into the leather sack and they returned quietly to the sleeping village.

In the morning they left early and the women went with them the first mile of the journey, ululating mournfully and singing the song of farewell. When they fell behind neither of the men looked back. They trudged on towards the low brown horizon, carrying their bundles balanced on their heads. They did not think about it, but this little scene was acted out every single day in a thousand villages across the southern sub-continent.

Days later the two men, still on foot, reached the recruitment station. It was a single-roomed general-dealer's store, standing alone at a remote crossroad on the edge of the desert. The white trader augmented his precarious business by buying cattle hides from the surrounding nomadic tribes and by recruiting for 'Wenela'.

Wenela was the acronym for the Witwatersrand Native Labour Association, an ubiquitous sprawling enterprise which extended its tentacles into the vastness of the African wilderness. From the peaks of the Dragon Mountains in Basutoland to the swamps of the Zambezi and Chobe, from the thirstlands of the Kalahari to the rain forest of the high plateau of Nyasaland, it gathered up the trickle of black men and channelled them first into a stream and finally into a mighty river that ran endlessly to the fabulous goldfields of the Ridge of White Waters, the Witwatersrand of Transvaal.

The trader looked over these two new recruits in a perfunctory manner as they stood dumbly before him. Their faces were deliberately expressionless, their eyes blank, the only perfect defence of the black African in the presence of the white man.

'Name?' the trader demanded.

'Henry Tabaka.' Hendrick had chosen his new name to cover his relationship to Moses and to throw off any chance connection with Lothar De La Rey and the robbery.

'Name?' The trader looked at Moses.

'Moses Gama.' He pronounced it with a guttural 'G'.

'Have you worked on the mines before? Do you speak English?'

'Yes, *Baise*.' They were obsequious, and the trader grinned.

'Good! Very good! You will be rich men when you come home from *Goldi*. Plenty of wives. Plenty of jig-jig, hey?' He grinned lasciviously as he issued them each with a green Wenela card and a bus ticket. 'The bus will come soon. Wait outside,' he ordered, and promptly lost all interest in them. He had earned his guinea-a-head recruitment fee, good money easily made, and his obligation to the recruits was at an end.

They waited under the scraggy thorn tree at the side of the iron-roofed trading store for forty-eight hours before the railways bus came rattling and banging and blowing blue smoke across the dreary wastes.

It stopped briefly and they slung their meagre luggage up onto the roofrack that was already piled with calabashes and boxes and bundles, with trussed goats and cages of woven bark stuffed with live fowls. Then they climbed into the overloaded coach and squeezed onto one of the hard wooden benches. The bus bellowed and blustered on over the plains and the rows of black passengers,

wedged shoulder to shoulder, jolted and swayed in unison as it pitched and rolled over the rutted tracks.

Two days later the bus stopped outside the barbed-wire gates of the Wenela staging post on the outskirts of Windhoek, and most of the passengers, all young men, descended and stood looking about them aimlessly until a huge black overseer with brass plaques of authority on his arm and a long sjambok in his hand chivied them into line and led them through the gates.

The white station manager sat on the stoep of his office building, his boots propped on the half wall of the stoep and a black bottle of German lager at his elbow, fanning himself with his hat. One at a time, the black boss-boy pushed the new recruits in front of him for appraisal. He rejected only one, a skinny little runt of a man who barely had the strength to shuffle up to the verandah.

'That bastard is riddled with TB.' The manager took a gulp of his lager. 'Get rid of him. Send him back where he came from.'

When Hendrick stepped forward he straightened up in his thonged chair and set down the lager glass.

'What is your name, boy?' he asked.

'Tabaka.'

'Ha, you speak English.' The manager's eyes narrowed. He could pick out the troublemakers; that was his job. He could tell by their eyes, the gleam of intelligence and aggression in them. He could tell by the way they walked and carried their shoulders; this big strutting, sullen black was big trouble.

'You in trouble with the police, boy?' he asked again. 'You steal other man's cattle? You kill your brother perhaps – or jig-jig his wife, hey?'

Hendrick stared at him flatly.

'Answer me, boy.'

'No.'

'You call me *Baas* when you speak to me, do you understand?'

'Yes, *Baas*,' Hendrick said carefully, and the manager opened the police file that lay on the table beside him and thumbed through it slowly, suddenly looking up to catch any sign of guilt or apprehension on Hendrick's face. But he was wearing the African mask again, dumb, and resigned and inscrutable.

'Christ, they stink.' He threw the file back onto the table again. 'Take them away,' he told the black boss-boy, and he picked up his beer bottle and glass and went back into his office.

'You know better than that, my brother,' Moses whispered to him as they were marched away towards the line of thatched huts. 'When you meet a hungry white hyena, you do not put your hand in his mouth,' and Hendrick did not reply.

They were fortunate; the draft was almost full, three hundred black men already gathered in and waiting in the line of huts behind the barbed-wire fence. Some of them had been there ten days and it was time for the next stage of their journey, thus Hendrick and Moses were not forced to endure another interminable wait. That night three railway coaches were shunted onto the spur of line that ran beside the camp and the boss-boys roused them before dawn.

'Gather your belongings. *Shayile!* The hour has struck. The steamer waits to take you to *Goldi*, to the place of gold.'

They formed up in their ranks again and answered to the roll-call. Then they were marched to the waiting coaches.

Here there was another white man in charge. He was tall and sunbrowned, his khaki shirtsleeves rolled up high on his sinewy biceps and wisps of blond

hair hanging from under the shapeless black hat that was pulled low down on his forehead. His features were flat and Slavic, his teeth crooked and stained with tobacco smoke and his eyes were light misty blue; he smiled perpetually in a bland idiotic fashion and sucked at a cavity in one of his back teeth. He carried a sjambok on a thong from his wrist, and now and then, for no apparent reason, he flicked the tapered end of the hippohide whip against the bare legs of one of the men filing past him; it was a casual act born of disinterest and disdain rather than calculated cruelty, and though each stroke was feathery light, it stung like a hornet and the victim gasped and skipped and shot up the ladder into the coach with alacrity.

Henrick drew level with him and the foreman's lips drew back from his bad teeth as he smiled even more widely. The camp manager had pointed the big Ovambo out to him.

'A bad one,' he had warned him. 'Watch him. Don't let him get out of hand.' And now he used his wrist in the stroke that he aimed at the tender skin at the back of Hendrick's knee.

'*Che-cha*!' the overseer ordered. 'Hurry up!' And the lash popped as it wrapped around Hendrick's leg. It did not split the skin, the overseer was an expert, but it left a purple black welt on the dark velvety skin.

Hendrick stopped dead, the other leg lifted to the first rung of the boarding ladder, gripping the rail with his free hand, with the other hand balancing his bundle on his shoulder, and he turned his head slowly until he was staring into the overseer's pale blue eyes.

'Yes!' The overseer encouraged him softly, and for the first time there was a sparkle of interest in his eyes. He altered his stance subtly, coming onto the balls of his feet.

'Yes!' he repeated. He wanted to take this big black bastard, here in front of all the others. They were going to be five days in these coaches, five hot thirsty days during which tempers and nerves would be rubbed raw. He always liked to do it right at the beginning of the journey. It only needed one, and it would save a lot of trouble later if he made an example right here in the siding. That way all of them would know what to expect if they started anything, and in his experience they never did start anything after that.

'Come on, kaffir.' He dropped his voice even lower, making the insult more personal and intense. He enjoyed this part of his work, and he was very good at it. This cocky bastard would not be fit to travel when he had finished with him. He wouldn't be much use to anybody with four or five ribs stoved in, and perhaps a broken jaw.

Hendrick was too quick for him. He went up the ladder into the coach in a single bound, leaving the overseer on the siding, braced and poised for his attack with the sjambok held over-hand, ready to drive the point of the butt into Hendrick's throat as he charged.

Hendrick's move took him completely off balance so that when he aimed a hard cut of the lash at Hendrick's legs as he went up the ladder, he was too late by a full half second and the stroke hissed and died in air.

Following behind his brother, Moses saw the murderous expression on the white overseer's face as he passed. 'It is not yet ended,' he warned Hendrick as they placed their bundles on the overhead racks and settled on the hard wooden bench that ran the length of the coach. 'He will come after you again.'

In the middle of the morning the three coaches were pulled off the spur and coupled to the rear of a long train of goods carriages, and after another few

hours of shunting and jolting and false starts, they rumbled slowly up the hills and then ran southwards.

Late in the afternoon the train stopped for half an hour at a small siding and a food barrow was loaded into the leading coach. Under the pale eyes of the white overseer the two black boss-boys wheeled the barrow down the crowded coaches and each of the recruits was handed a small tin dish of white maize cake over which a dollop of bean stew had been spooned.

When they reached Swart Hendrick's seat, the white overseer shouldered the boss-boy aside and took the dish from his hands to serve Hendrick's portion himself.

'We must look after this kaffir,' he said loudly. 'We want him to be strong for his work at *Goldi*.' And he spooned an extra portion of bean stew into the dish and offered it to Hendrick.

'Here, kaffir.' But as Hendrick reached for the dish, he deliberately let it drop onto the floor. The hot stew splashed over Hendrick's feet and the overseer stepped into the mess of maize porridge and ground it under his boot. Then he stood back with one hand on the billy club in his belt and grinned.

'Hey, you clumsy black bugger, you only get one ration. If you want to eat it off the floor, that's up to you.'

He waited expectantly for Hendrick to react, and then grimaced with disappointment when Hendrick dropped his eyes, leaned forward and began to scrape the mashed cake into the dish with his fingers, then scooped a ball of it into his mouth and munched on it stolidly.

'You bloody niggers will eat anything, even your own dung,' he snarled and went on down the coach.

The windows of the coaches were barred, and the doors at both ends were locked and bolted from the outside. The overseer carried the ring of keys on his belt, carefully securing all doors behind him as he passed. From experience he knew that many of the recruits would begin to have misgivings as soon as the journey began, and driven by homesickness and increasing fear of the unknown, by the disturbing unfamiliarity of all about them, would begin to desert, some of them even leaping from the speeding coach. The overseer made his rounds every few hours, meticulously counting heads, even in the middle of the night, and he stood over Hendrick deliberately shining the beam of his lantern into his face, waking him every time he passed down the coach.

The overseer never tired of his efforts to provoke Hendrick. It had become a challenge, a contest between them. He knew it was there; he had seen it in Hendrick's eyes, just a flash of the violence and menace and power, and he was determined to bring it out, flush it into the open where he could crush it and destroy it.

'Patience, my brother,' Moses whispered to Hendrick. 'Hold your anger. Cherish it with care. Let it grow until it is full term, until you can put it to work for you.'

Hendrick was coming to rely more on his brother's advice and counsel with each day that passed. Moses was intelligent and persuasive, his tongue quick to choose the right word, and that special presence which he possessed made other men listen when he spoke.

Hendrick saw these special gifts of his demonstrated clearly in the days that followed. At first he spoke only to the men that sat near him in the hot crowded coach. He told them what it would be like at the place where they were going,

and how the white men would treat them, what would be expected of them and what the consequences would be if they disappointed their new employers.

The black faces around him were intent as they listened, and soon those further up the benches were craning to catch his words and calling softly. 'Speak, louder, Gama. Speak, that all of us may hear your words.'

Moses Gama raised his voice, a clear compelling baritone, and they listened with respect. 'There will be many black men at *Goldi*. More than you ever believed possible, Zulus and Xhosas and N'debeles and Swazis and Nyasas, fifty different tribes speaking so many languages that you have never heard before. Tribes as different from you as you are different from the white man. Some of them will be traditional blood enemies of our tribe, waiting and watching like hyenas for a chance to turn upon you and savage you. There will be times when you are deep in the earth, down there where it is always night, that you will be at the mercy of such men. To protect yourselves you must surround yourselves with men you can trust; you must place yourself under the protection of a strong leader; and in return for this protection you must give this chieftain your obedience and loyalty.' And very soon they came to recognize that Moses Gama was this strong leader. Within days he was the undisputed chieftain of all the men in coach three, and while he was talking to them and answering their queries, stilling their fears and misgivings, Moses was in his turn assessing their individual worth, watching and weighing each of them, selecting, evaluating and discarding. He began to rearrange the seating in the coach, ordering those whom he had chosen to move closer to his own seat in the centre, gathering around him the pick of the recruits. And immediately the men he had singled out gained prestige; they formed an élite praetorian guard around their new emperor.

Hendrick watched him doing it, manipulating the men around him, subjecting them to the force of his will and personality, and he was filled with admiration and pride for his younger brother, giving up his own last reservations and willingly according to him his full loyalty and love and obedience.

By association with Moses, Hendrick himself was accorded the respect and veneration of the other men in the coach. He was Moses' captain and henchman and they recognized him as such, and quite slowly it dawned upon Hendrick that in a few short days Moses Gama had forged himself an *impi*, a band of warriors on whom he could rely implicitly, and that he had done with with almost no apparent effort.

Sitting in the crowded coach that was already stinking like an animal cage with the rancid sweat of a hundred hot bodies and with the stench from the latrine cubicle, and mesmerized by the Messianic eyes and words of his own brother, Hendrick thought back to the other great black rulers who had emerged from the mists of African history, to lead first a tiny band, then a tribe and finally a vast horde of warriors across the continent, ravaging and plundering and laying waste.

He thought of Mantatisi and Chaka and Mzilikazi, of Shangaan and Angoni, and with a flash of clairvoyance he saw them at their beginnings, sitting like this at some remote camp-fire in the wilderness, surrounded by a small group of men, weaving the spell over them, capturing their imagination and spirit with a silken noose of words and ideas, inflaming them with dreams.

'I stand at the beginning of an enterprize which I do not yet understand,' he thought. 'All I have done up until this time was only my initiation, all the fighting and killing and striving was but a training. Now I am ready for the

endeavour, whatever it may be, and Moses Gama will lead me to it. I do not need to know what it is. It is sufficient only that I follow where it leads.'

And he was listening avidly as Moses spoke names he had never heard and expounded ideas that were new and strangely exciting.

'Lenin,' said Moses, 'not a man, but a god come down to earth.' And they thrilled to the tale of a land to the north where the tribes had united under this man-god Lenin, had smitten down a king and in doing so had become part of the godhead themselves.

They were enchanted and aroused as he told them of a war such as the earth had never seen before, and their atavistic battlelust scalded their veins and pumped up their hearts, hard and hot as the head of the fighting axe when it comes red and glowing from the ironsmith's forge. The 'revolution' Moses called this war, and as he explained it to them, they saw that they could be part of this glorious battle, they too could be slayers of kings and become part of the godhead.

The door at the head of the coach crashed back on its slide and the white overseer stepped through and stood with his hands on his hips, grinning mirthlessly at them, and they lowered their heads and stared at the floor, hooding and screening their eyes. But those sitting close to Moses, the chosen ones, the élite, they began to understand then where the battle would be fought and who were the kings that would be slain.

The white overseer sensed the charged atmosphere in the coach. It was thick as the odour of unwashed black bodies and the stink of the latrine in the corner of the coach; it was as electric as the air at noon in the suicide days of November just before the great rains break, and he searched quickly for Hendrick sitting in the centre of the coach.

'One rotten potato,' he thought bitterly, 'and the whole sackful is spoiled.' He touched the billy club in his belt. He had found out the difficult way that the lash of the sjambok was too long to wield effectively in the confines of the coaches. The billy was a stopper, fourteen inches of hard wood, the end drilled and filled with lead shot. He could break bone with it, crush in a skull to kill a man instantly if he needed to, or with a delicate alteration of the weight of the blow merely stun him. He was an artist with the billy club, as he was with the sjambok, but each had its place and time. It was the billy's time now, and he moved slowly down the coach, pretending to ignore Hendrick, examining the faces of each of the other men as he passed, seeing the new rebelliousness in their sullen faces and becoming more angry with the man who had made his task more difficult.

'I should have gone after him at the beginning,' he told himself bitterly. 'I've almost left it too late. Me, who loves the quiet life and the easy way. Well, we'll have to make the best of it now.'

He glanced casually at Hendrick as he passed, and then from the corner of his eye saw the big Ovambo relax slightly as he went on down the aisle between the seats.

'You are expecting it, my boy. You know it has to happen, and I'm not going to disappoint you.'

At the far door of the coach he paused, as if he had an afterthought, and he came back down the aisle slowly, grinning to himself. Now he stopped in front of Hendrick again, and sucked noisily at the cavity in his tooth.

'Look at me, kaffir,' he invited pleasantly and Hendrick lifted his chin and stared at him.

'Which is your *m'pahle*?' he asked. 'Which is your luggage?' and Hendrick was taken off-guard. He was acutely conscious of the treasure of diamonds in the rack above his head and now he glanced up at the leather sack instinctively.

'Good.' The white overseer lifted the sack off the rack and dropped it onto the floor in front Hendrick.

'Open it,' he ordered, still grinning, one hand on his hip the other on the handle of the billy.

'Come on.' The grin became cold and wolfish as Hendrick sat without moving. 'Open it, kaffir. Let's see what you are hiding.'

It had never failed him yet. Even the most docile of men would react to protect their belongings, no matter how worthless and insignificant.

Slowly Hendrick leaned forward and untied the neck of the leather sack. Then he straightened again and sat passively.

The white overseer stooped, seized the bottom of the sack and straightened up again, never taking his eyes off Hendrick's face. He shook the sack vigorously, spilling the contents onto the floor.

The blanket roll fell out first, and using the toe of his boot the overseer spread it open. There was a sheepskin gilet and other spare clothing in the roll, and a nine-inch knife in a leather sheath.

'Dangerous weapon,' said the overseer. 'You know that no dangerous weapons are allowed in the coaches.' He picked up the knife, pressed the blade into the niche of the window and snapped it off; then he tossed the two separate pieces out between the bars of the window behind Hendrick's head.

Hendrick did not move, although the overseer waited for almost a minute, staring at him provocatively. The only sound was the clackety-clack of the bogey over the cross ties of the steel lines and the faint huffing of the locomotive at the head of the train. None of the other black passengers was watching the small drama develop; they were all staring straight ahead of them, faces closed, eyes unseeing.

'What is this rubbish?' the overseer asked and touched one of the hard flat millet cakes with his toe, and though Hendrick did not move a muscle, the white man saw the first spark in those black smoky eyes.

'Yes,' he thought gleefully. 'That's it. Now he will move.' And he picked up a loaf and sniffed it thoughtfully.

'Kaffir bread,' he murmured. 'Not allowed. Company rules – no food allowed on the train.' And he turned the flat loaf on edge so that it would pass between the bars and he tossed it through the open window. The loaf bounced on the embankment below the racketing steel wheels and then shattered into fragments, and the overseer chuckled and stooped for the next loaf.

It snapped in Hendrick's head. He had held it in check too long and the loss of the diamonds drove him berserk. He went for the white man, launching himself out of the seat, but the overseer was ready for him. He straightened his right arm and drove the point of the billy club into Hendrick's throat. Then, as Hendrick fell back choking and clutching his throat, he whipped the club into the front of his skull, judging it finely, not a killing blow, and Hendrick's hand dropped from his damaged throat as he toppled forward. However, the overseer would not let him fall, and with his left hand shoved him back against the seat, holding him upright while he worked with the club.

It rang like an axe on wood as it bounced off the bone of Hendrick's skull, and it open the thin skin of his scalp and the blood sprang up in little ruby-bright fountains. The overseer hit him three times, measured calculated blows,

and then he thrust the point of the club into Hendrick's slack gaping mouth, snapping off both his incisor teeth level with the gums.

'Always mark them.' It was one of his maxims. 'Mark them so they don't forget.'

Only then did he release the unconscious man and let him topple, head first, into the centre of the aisle.

Instantly he whipped around and poised on his toes like a puff-adder cocking itself into the threatening 'S' of the strike. With the billy club ready in his right hand he stared down the shocked eyes of the black men around him. Quickly they dropped their gaze from his and the only movement was the jerking of their bodies in time to the swaying clatter of the coach beneath them.

Hendrick's blood was puddling under his head, and then running in little dark red snakes across the floor of the aisle. The overseer smiled again, looking down with an almost paternal expression at the recumbent figure. It had been a beautiful performance, quick and complete, exactly as he had planned it, and he had enjoyed it. The man at his feet was his own creation and he was proud of it.

He picked up the other millet loaves out of the blood puddle and one at a time tossed them out between the bars of the window. Finally he squatted over the man at his feet and on the back of his shirt carefully wiped the last traces of blood from his billy. Then he stood up, replaced the club in his belt and walked slowly down the aisle.

It was all right now. The mood had changed, the atmosphere was defused. There would be no more trouble. He had done his job, and done it well.

He went out onto the balcony of the coach, and smiling thinly, locked the sliding door behind him again.

The moment the door closed the men in the carriage came back to life. Moses gave his orders crisply and two of them lifted Hendrick back into his seat; another went to the water tank beside the latrine door, while Moses opened his own pack and brought out a stoppered buckhorn.

While they steadied Hendrick's lolling head, Moses poured a brown powder from the buckhorn into the wounds in his scalp. It was a mixture of ash and herbs, powdered finely, and he rubbed it into the open flesh with his finger. The bleeding stopped, and with a wet cloth he cleaned his brother's broken mouth. Then he cradled his unconscious head in his arms, and waited.

Moses had watched the conflict between his brother and the white man with almost clinical interest, deliberately restraining and directing Hendrick's reaction until the drama reached this explosive climax. His attachment to his brother was still tenuous. Their father had been a prosperous and lusty man and had brought all of his fifteen wives regularly to the child-bed. Moses had over thirty brothers and sisters. Towards very few of them he felt any special affection beyond vague tribal and family duty. Hendrick was many years his senior and had left the kraal when Moses was still a child. Since then the tales of his exploits had filtered back to him, and Hendrick's reputation had grown on these accounts of wild and desperate deeds. But tales are only tales until they are proven and reputations can be built on words and not deeds.

The testing time was at hand. Moses would consider the results of the test and upon them would depend their future relationship. He needed a hard man as his lieutenant, one of the steely men. Lenin had chosen Joseph Stalin. He would choose a man of steel also, a man like an axe, and with him as a weapon he would hack and shape his own plans out of the hard wood of the future. If

Hendrick failed the test Moses would toss him aside with as little compassion as he would an axe whose blade had shattered at the first stroke against the trunk of a tree.

Hendrick opened his eyes and looked at his brother with dilated pupils; he moaned and touched the open wounds on his scalp. He winced at the pain and his pupils shrank and focused, and the rage flamed in their depths as he struggled upright.

'The diamonds?' His voice was low and sibilant as the hiss of one of those deadly little horned adders of the desert.

'Gone,' Moses told him quietly.

'We must go back – find them.' But Moses shook his head.

'They are scattered like the seeds of the grass; there is no way to mark their fall. No, my brother, we are prisoners in this coach. We cannot go back. The diamonds are lost for ever.'

Hendrick sat quietly, with his tongue exploring his shattered mouth, running it over the jagged stumps of his front teeth, considering his brother's cold logic. Moses waited quietly. This time he would give no orders, point no direction, no matter how subtle. Hendrick must come to it of his own accord.

'You are right, my brother,' Hendrick said at last. 'The diamonds are gone. But I am going to kill the man that did this to us.'

Moses showed no emotion. He offered no encouragement. He merely waited.

'I will do it with cunning. I will find a way to kill him, and no man will ever know, except him and us.' Still Moses waited. So far Hendrick was taking the path that he had laid out for him. However, there was still something else he must do. He waited for it, and it came as he had hoped it would.

'Do you agree that I should kill this white dog, my brother?' He had asked for sanction from Moses Gama. He had acknowledged his liege lord, placed himself in his brother's hands, and Moses smiled and touched his brother's arm as though he were placing a mark, a brand of approval, upon him.

'Do it, my brother,' he ordered. If he failed, the white men would hang him on a rope; if he succeeded he would have proved himself an axe, a steely man.

Hendrick brooded darkly in his seat, not speaking for another hour. Occasionally massaging his temples when the throbbing pain of the blows threatened to burst his skull open. Then he rose and moved slowly down the coach examining each of the barred windows, shaking his head and muttering at the pain. He returned to his seat and sat there for a while, and then rose once again and shuffled down the aisle to the latrine cubicle.

He locked himself into the cubicle. There was an open hole in the deck and through it he could see the rushing blur of the stone embankment below the coach. Many of the men using the latrine had missed the hole, and the floor slopped with dark yellow urine and splattered faeces.

Hendrick turned his attention to the single unglazed window. The opening was covered with steel mesh in a wire frame which was screwed into a wooden frame at each corner and at the centre of each side.

He returned to his seat in the carriage and whispered to Moses, 'The white baboon took my knife. I need another.'

Moses asked no questions. It was part of the test. Hendrick must do it alone and, if he failed, accept the full consequences without expecting Moses to share them or attempt to aid him. He spoke quietly to the men around him, and within a few minutes a clasp knife was passed down the bench and slipped into Hendrick's hand.

He returned to the latrine and worked on the retaining screws of the wire frame, careful not to scratch the paintwork around them or leave any sign that they had been tampered with. He removed all eight screws, eased the frame from its seating and set it aside.

He waited until the tracks made a righthand bend, judging by the centrifugal force against his body as the coach turned under him, and then he glanced out of the open window. The train was turning away from him, the leading coaches and goods vans out of sight around the bend ahead, and he leaned out of the window and looked up.

There was a coaming along the edge of the roof of the coach. He reached up and ran his fingers over the ridge and found a handhold. He raised himself, putting his full weight upon it, hanging on his arms, only his feet still inside the latrine window, and the rest of his body suspended outside. He lifted his eyes to the level of the roof and memorized the slope and layout of the top of the coach, then he lowered himself again and ducked back into the latrine. He replaced the mesh over the window but turned the screws only finger tight, then went back to his seat in the coach.

In the early evening the white overseer and his two boss-boys came through the coach with the food barrow. When he reached Hendrick he smiled at him without rancour.

'You are beautiful now, kaffir. The black maids will love to kiss that mouth.' He turned and addressed the silent ranks of black men. 'If any of you want to be beautiful also, just let me know. I will do it for free.'

Just before dark the boss-boys came back to collect the empty dishes.

'Tomorrow night you will be at *Goldi*,' one of them told Hendrick. 'There is a white doctor there who will treat your wounds.' There was a hint of sympathy in his impassive black face. 'It was not wise of you to anger *Tshayela*, the striker. You have learned a hard lesson, friend. Remember it well, all of you.' He locked the door as he left the coach.

Hendrick gazed out of the windows at the sunset. In four days of travel the landscape had changed entirely as they had climbed up onto the plateau of the highveld. The grasslands were pale brown, seared by the black frosts of winter, the red earth gouged open with *dongas* of erosion and divided into geometrical camps with barbed-wire. The isolated homesteads seemed forlorn upon the open veld with the steel-framed windmills standing like gaunt sentinels over them, and the lean cattle were long-horned and parti-coloured, red and black and white.

Hendrick, who had lived his life in the unpeopled wilderness, found the fences cramping and restrictive. In this place you could never be out of sight of other men or their works, and the villages they passed were as sprawling and populous as Windhoek, the biggest town he had ever conceived of.

'Wait until you see *Goldi*,' Moses told him, as the darkness fell outside and the men around them settled down for the night, wrapping their blankets over their heads for the chill of the highveld blew in through the open windows.

Hendrick waited until the white overseer made his first round of the coaches, and when he shone the beam of his lantern into Hendrick's face made no attempt to feign sleep but blinked up at him blindly. The overseer passed on, locking the door as he left the coach.

Hendrick rose quietly in the seat. Opposite him Moses stirred in the darkness but did not speak, and Hendrick went down the aisle and locked himself in the latrine. Quickly he loosened the screws and worked the frame off its seating.

He set it against the bulkhead and leaned out of the window. The cold night air buffeted his head, and he slitted his eyes against the hot smuts that blew back from the coal-burning locomotive and stung his cheeks and forehead as he reached up and found his handholds on the ridge of the coaming.

He drew himself upwards smoothly, and then with a kick and a heave, flung the top half of his body over the edge of the roof and shot out one arm. He found a grip on the ventilator in the middle of the curved roof and pulled himself the rest of the way on his belly.

He lay for a while panting and with his eyes tightly closed until he got control of the pounding ache in his head. Then he raised himself to his knees and began crawling forward towards the leading edge of the roof.

The night sky was clear; the land was silver with starlight and blue with shadow, and the wind roared about his head. He rose to his feet and balanced against the lurch and sway of the coach. With his feet wide apart and his knees bent he moved forward. A premonition of danger made him look up and he saw the dark shape rush at him out of the darkness and he threw himself flat just as the steel arm of one of the railway water towers flashed over his head. A second later it would have decapitated him, and he shivered with the cold and the shock of near death. After a minute he gathered himself and crawled forward again, not raising his head more than a few inches until he reached the front edge of the roof.

He lay spreadeagled on his belly and cautiously peered over the edge. The balconies of the joining coaches were below him, the gap between the roof about the span of one of his arms. Directly under him the footplates articulated against each other as the train clattered through the curves of the line. Anybody moving from one coach to the next must pass below where Hendrick lay and he grunted with satisfaction and looked behind him.

One of the ventilator pots was just level with his feet as he lay outstretched. He crawled back, drawing the heavy leather belt from the top of his breeches, and buckled it around the ventilator, forming a loop into which he thrust one of his feet as far as the ankle.

Once again he stretched out on the roof, one foot securely anchored by the loop, and he reached down into the space between the coaches. He could just touch the banisters of the guard fence around the balcony. Electric bulbs in wire cages were fixed to the overhang of the balconies so the area below him was well lit.

He drew back and lay flat on the roof, only the top of his head and his eyes showing from below. But he knew that the lights would dazzle anybody who looked upwards into the gap between the roofs and he settled down to wait like a leopard in the tree over the water hole.

An hour passed and then another, but he judged the passage of time only by the slow rotation of the stars across the night sky. He was stiff and freezing cold as the wind thrashed his unprotected body, but he bore it stoically, never allowing himself to doze or lose concentration. Waiting was always a major part of the hunt, of the game of death, and he had played this game a hundred times before.

Suddenly, even over the rush of the train's passage and the rhythm of the cross ties, he heard the click of steel on steel and the rattle of keys in the lock of the door below him, and he gathered himself.

The man would step over the footplates as quickly as he could, not wanting

to be in that vulnerable and exposed position for a moment longer than was necessary to make the crossing, and Hendrick would have to be quicker still.

He heard the sliding door slam back against the jamb and the lock turn again, then an instant later the crown of the white overseer's hat appeared below him.

Instantly Hendrick shot his body forward and dropped as far as his waist into the gap between the coaches. Only the leather belt around his ankle anchored him. Lothar had taught him the double lock, and he whipped one arm around the white man's neck, and braced his other hand in the crook of his own elbow, catching the man's head in the vice of his arm, and jerked him off his feet.

The white man made a strangled cawing sound and droplets of spittle flew from his lips, sparkling in the electric light as Hendrick drew him upwards as though he were hoisted on the gallows tree.

The white man's hat fell from his head and flitted away into the night like a black bat, and he was kicking and twisting his body violently, clawing at the thick muscled arms that were locked around his neck, his long blond hair fluttering and tumbling in the night wind. Hendrick lifted him until their eyes were inches apart, and he smiled into his face, exposing the mangled black pit of his own mouth, his shattered front teeth still stained with clotted blood, and in the reflection of the balcony lights the white man recognized him. Hendrick saw the recognition flare in his pale dilated eyes.

'Yes, my friend,' he whispered. 'It is me, the kaffir.' He drew the man up another inch and wedged the back of his neck against the edge of the roof. Then very deliberately he put pressure on his spine at the base of his skull. The white man writhed and struggled like a fish on the barbs of the harpoon, but Hendrick held him easily, staring deep into his eyes, and bent his neck backwards, lifting with his forearm under the chin.

Hendrick felt the spine loading and locking at the pressure. It could give no more, and for a second longer he held him at the breaking point. Then with a jerk he pushed the man's chin up another inch and the spine snapped like a dry branch. The white man danced in the air, twitching and shuddering, and Hendrick watched the pale blue eyes glaze over, becoming opaque and lifeless, and over the rush of the wind he heard the soft spluttering release as his sphincter muscle relaxed and his bowels involuntarily voided.

Hendrick swung his dangling corpse like a pendulum and as it cleared the balcony rail he let it drop into the gap between the coaches, directly into the track of the racing wheels. It was sucked away by the spinning steel like a scrap of meat into the blades of a mincing machine.

He lay for a moment recovering his breath. He knew that the overseer's mutilated corpse would be smeared over half a mile of the railway tracks.

He untied his belt from the ventilator and buckled it around his waist, then he crawled back along the roof of the coach until he was directly above the latrine window. He lowered his feet over the sill and with a twist dropped into the cubicle. He replaced the mesh frame over the window and tightened the screws. He went back down the coach to his seat, and Moses Gama was watching him as he wrapped the blanket around his shoulders. He nodded at his brother and pulled the corner of the blanket over his head. Within minutes he was asleep.

He was awakened by the shouts of the boss-boys and the jolting of the coach as it was shunted off the main line. He saw the name of the small village where they had stopped painted on a white board on the platform: 'Vryburg', but it meant nothing to him.

Soon the platform and the coaches were invaded by blue uniformed railway police, and all the recruits were ordered out onto the platform. They lined up, shivering and sleepy under the floodlights, answered to the roll-call. Everyone was present.

Hendrick nudged his brother and with his chin pointed at the wheels and bogey below their coach. The hubs and axles were splattered with blood and tiny slivers and particles of raw red flesh and tissue.

All the following day the coaches stood in the siding while the police individually subjected each of the recruits to a hectoring interrogation in the station master's office. By mid-afternoon it was obvious that they were coming to accept that the overseer's death was accidental and were losing interest in the investigation. The evidence of the locked doors and barred windows was convincing and the testimony of the boss-boys and every one of the recruits was unanimous and unshakable.

In the late afternoon they were loaded back into the coaches and they rumbled on into the night, towards the fabulous Ridge of White Waters.

* * *

Hendrick woke to the excited chatter of the men around him, and when he shouldered his way to the crowded window the first thing he saw was a high mountain, so big that it blocked the sky to the north, a strange and wonderful mountain, glowing with a pearly yellow light in the early sun, a mountain with a perfectly flat top and symmetrical sloping sides.

'What kind of mountain is this?' Hendrick marvelled.

'A mountain taken from the belly of the earth,' Moses told him. 'That is a mine dump, my brother, a mountain built by men from the rock they dig up from below.'

Wherever Hendrick looked there were these flat-topped shining dumps scattered across the undulating grassland or standing along the skyline and near each of them stood tall giraffes of steel, long-necked and skeletal with giant wheels for heads, that spun endlessly against the pale highveld sky.

'Headgears,' Moses told him. 'Below each of those is a hole that reaches down into the guts of the world, into the rock bowels that hold the yellow *Goldi* for which the white men sweat and lie and cheat – and often kill.'

As the train ran on they saw wonder followed by wonder, taller buildings than they had ever believed possible, roads that ran like rivers of steel with growling vehicles, tall chimneys that filled the sky with black thunderclouds, and multitudes upon multitudes, human beings more numerous than the springbok migrations of the Kalahari, black men in silver helmets and knee-high rubber boots, regiments of them, marching towards the tall headgears or, as the shifts changed, wearily swarming back from the shafts splashed from head to foot with yellow mud. There were white men on the streets and platforms, white women in gaily coloured dresses with remote disdainful expressions, human beings in the windows of the buildings which crowded wall to red brick wall right to the verge of the railway tracks. It was too much, too huge and diffuse for them to assimilate at one time and they gaped and exclaimed and pressed to the windows of the coach.

'Where are the women?' Hendrick asked suddenly, and Moses smiled.

'Which women, brother?'

'The black women, the women of our tribe?'

'There are no women here, not the type of women you know. There are only the *Isifebi*, and they do it for gold. Everything here is for gold.'

Once again they were shunted off the main line into a fenced enclosure in which the long white barrack buildings stood in endless rows and the signboard above the gates read:

WITWATERSRAND NATIVE LABOUR ASSOCIATION
CENTRAL RAND INDUCTION CENTRE

From the coaches they were led to a long shed by a couple of grinning boss-boys and instructed to strip to the buff.

The lines of naked black men shuffled forward under the paternal eyes of the boss-boys, who treated them in a friendly jocular fashion.

'Some of you have brought your livestock with you,' they joked. 'Goats on your scalp, and cattle in your pubic hairs,' and dipping the paint brushes they wielded into buckets of bluebutter ointment, they plastered the heads and crotches of the recruits.

'Rub it in,' they ordered. 'We don't want your lice and crabs and itchy crawlies.' And the recruits entered into the spirit of the occasion and roared with laughter as they smeared each other with the sticky butter.

At the end of the shed they were each handed a small square of blue mottled carbolic soap.

'Your mothers may think you smell like the mimosa in flower, but even the goats shudder when you pass upwind.' The boss-boys laughed and shoved them under the hot showers.

The doctors were waiting for them when they emerged, scrubbed and still naked, and this time the medical examinations were exhaustive. Their chests were sounded and all their bodily apertures probed and scrutinized.

'What happened to your mouth, and your head?' one doctor demanded of Hendrick. 'No, don't tell me. I don't want to know.' He had seen injuries like these before. 'Those bloody animals in charge of the trains. All right, we will send you to the dentist to have those stumps pulled – too late to stitch the head, you'll have a couple of lovely scars! Apart from that, you are a beauty.' He slapped Hendrick's hard shiny black muscles. 'We'll put you down for underground work, and you'll get the underground bonus.'

They were issued grey overalls and hobnailed boots, and then given a gargantuan meal, as much as they could eat.

'It is not like I thought it would be.' Hendrick spooned stew into his mouth. 'Good food, white men who smile, no beatings – not like the train.'

'Brother, only a fool starves and beats his oxen – and these white men are not fools.'

One of the other Ovambo men took Moses' empty dish to the kitchen and returned with it refilled. It was no longer necessary for him to give orders for such menial services. His wants were taken care of by the men around him as if by birthright. Already the death of the white overseer, *Tshayela*, the striker, had been embroidered and built into a legend by many repetitions, reinforcing the stature and authority of Moses Gama and his lieutenant; men walked softly around them and inclined their heads respectfully when either Moses or Hendrick spoke directly to them.

At dawn the next morning they were roused from their bunks in the barrack rooms and after a huge breakfast of maize cake and *maas*, the thick clotted sour milk, they were led to the long iron-roofed classroom.

'Men of forty different tribes come from every corner of the land to *Goldi*, men speaking forty different languages, from Zulu to Tswana, from Herero to Basuto, and only one in a thousand of them understands a word of English or of Afrikaans,' Moses explained softly to his brother as the other men respectfully made room for them on one of the classroom benches. 'Now they will teach us the special language of *Goldi*, the tongue by which all men, whether black or white, and of whatever tribe, speak to each other here.'

A venerable old Zulu boss-boy, his pate covered with a cap of shining silver wool, was their instructor in the lingua franca of the gold mines, Fanakalo. The name was taken from its own vocabulary and meant literally 'like this, like that', the phrase that the recruits would have urged upon them frequently over the weeks ahead: Do it like this! Work like that! *Sebenza fanakalo!*'

The Zulu instructor on the raised dais was surrounded by all the accoutrements of the miner's trade, set out on display so that he could touch each item with his pointer and the recruits would chant the name of it in unison. Helmets and lanterns, hammers and picks, jumper bars and scrapers, safety rails and rigs – they would know them all intimately before they stood their first shift.

But now the old Zulu touched his own chest and said: '*Mina!*' Then pointed at his class and said: '*Wena!*'

And Moses led them in the chant: 'Me! You!'

'Head!' said the instructor and 'Arm!' and 'Leg!' He touched his own body and his pupils imitated him enthusiastically.

They worked at the language all that morning and then after lunch they were divided into groups of twenty and the group that included Moses and Hendrick was taken to another iron-roofed building similar to the language classroom. It differed only in its furnishings. Long trestle tables ran from wall to wall, and the person that welcomed them was a white man with peculiar bright ginger-coloured hair and moustache and green eyes. He was dressd in a long white coat like those the doctors had worn, and like them he was smiling and friendly, waving them to their places at the tables and speaking in English that only Moses and Hendrick understood, although they were careful not to make their understanding apparent and maintained a pantomime of perplexity and ignorance.

'All right you fellows. My name is Dr Marcus Archer and I am a psychologist. What we are going to do now is give you an aptitude test to see just what kind of work you are best suited to.' The white man smiled at them and then nodded to the boss-boy beside him, who translated:

'You do what *Bomvu*, the red one, tells you. That way we can find out just how stupid you are.'

The first test was a blockbuilding exercise which Marcus Archer had developed himself to test basic manual dexerity and awareness of mechanical shape. The multicoloured wooden blocks of various shapes had to be fitted into the frame on the table in front of each subject in the manner of an elementary jigsaw puzzle and the time allotted for completion was six minutes. The boss-boy explained the procedure and gave a demonstration and the recruits took their seats at the tables and Marcus Archer called: '*Enza!* Do it!' and started his stop watch.

Moses completed his puzzle in one minute six seconds. According to Dr

Archer's meticulous records, to date 116,816 had sat this particular test. Not one of them had completed it in under two and a half minutes. He left the dais and went down to Moses' table to check his assembly of the blocks. It was correct, and he nodded and studied Moses' expressionless features thoughtfully.

Of course, he had noticed Moses the moment he entered the room. He had never seen such a beautiful man in his life, either black or white and Dr Archer's preference was strongly for black skin. That was one of the main reasons he had come out to Africa five years before, for Dr Marcus Archer was a homosexual.

He had been in his third year at Magdalene College before he admitted this fact to himself, and the man who had introduced him to the bitter-sweet delights had at the same time stimulated his intellect with the wondrous new doctrines of Karl Marx and the subsequent refinements to that doctrine by Vladimir Ilyich Lenin. His lover had secrety enrolled him in the British Communist Party, and after he had left Cambridge introduced him to the comrades of Bloomsbury. However, the young Marcus had never felt entirely at home in intellectual London. He had lacked the spiked tongue, the ready acid wit and the feline cruelty, and after a short and highly unsatisfactory affair with Lytton Strachey, he had been given Lytton's notorious 'treatment' and ostracized from the group.

He had banished himself into the wilderness of Manchester University, to take up the new science of industrial psychology. In Manchester he had begun a long and lyrically happy liaison with a Jamaican trombone player and allowed his connections with the Party to fall into neglect. However, he was to learn that the Party never forgets its chosen ones, and at the age of thirty-one, when he had already made some small reputation for himself in his profession, but when his association with his Jamaican lover had ended acrimoniously and he was dejected and almost suicidal, the Party had reached out one of its tentacles and drawn him gently back into the fold.

They told him that there was an opening in his field with the South African Chamber of Mines working with African mine-workers. His penchant for black skin was by now an addiction. The infant South African Communist Party was in need of bolstering and the job was his if he wanted. It was implied that he had free choice in the matter, but the outcome was never in doubt and within a month he had sailed for Cape Town.

In the following five years he had done important pioneering work with the Chamber of Mines and had received both recognition and deep satisfaction from it. His connections with the party had been carefully concealed, but the covert work he had done in this area was even more important, and his commitment to the ideals of Marxism had grown stronger as he grew older and saw at first hand the inhumanities of class and racial discrimination, the terrible abyss that separated the poor and dispossessed black proletariat from the enormous wealth and privilege of the white *bourgeoisie*. He had found that in this rich and beautiful land all the gross ills of the human condition flourished as though in a hothouse, exaggerated until they were almost a caricature of evil.

Now Marcus Archer looked at this noble young man with the face of an Egyptian god and a skin of burnt honey, and he was filled with longing.

'You speak English, don't you?' he asked, and Moses nodded.

'Yes, I do,' he said softly, and Marcus Archer had to turn away and go back to his dais. His passion was impossible to disguise, and his fingers were

trembling as he took up a stick of chalk and wrote upon the blackboard, giving himself a respite to get his emotions under control.

The tests continued for the rest of the afternoon, the subjects gradually being sorted and channelled into their various grades and levels on the results. At the end only one remained in the main stream. Moses Gama had completed the progressively more difficult tests with the same aplomb as he had tackled the first, and Dr Archer realized that he had discovered a prodigy.

At five o'clock the session ended and thankfully the subjects trooped from the classroom; the last hour had taxed even the brightest amongst them. Moses alone had remained undaunted and as he filed past the desk Dr Archer said:

'Gama!' He had taken the name from the register. 'There is one more task I would like to attempt.'

He led Moses down the verandah to his office at the end.

'You can read and write, Gama?'

'Yes, Doctor.'

'It is a theory of mine that a man's handwriting can be studied to find the key to his personality,' Archer explained. 'And I would like you to write for me.'

They sat side by side at the desk, and Dr Archer set writing materials in front of Moses, chatting easily. 'This is a standard text I use.'

On the card he handed Moses was printed the nursery rhyme 'The Cat and the Fiddle'.

Moses dipped the pen and Archer leaned closer to watch. His writing was large and fluent, the characters formed with sharp peaks, forward sloping and definite. All the indictions of mental determination and ruthless energy were present.

Still studying the handwriting Archer casually laid his hand on Moses' thigh, intensely aware of the hard rubbery muscle beneath the velvety skin, and the nib spluttered as Moses started. Then his hand steadied and he went on writing. He finished, laid the pen down carefully, and for the first time looked directly into Marcus Archer's green eyes.

'Gama.' Marcus Archer's voice shook and his fingers tightened. 'You are much too intelligent to waste your time shovelling ore.' He paused and moved his hand slowly up Moses' leg.

Moses stared steadily into his eyes. His expression did not change, but he let his thighs fall slowly open, and Marcus Archer's heart was thumping wildly against his ribs.

'I want you to work as my personal assistant, Gama,' he whispered, and Moses considered the magnitude of this offer. He would have access to the files of every worker in the gold-mining industry; he would be protected and privileged, free to pass and enter where other black men were forbidden. The advantages were so numerous that he knew he could not grasp them all in so brief a moment. For the man who made the offer he felt almost nothing, neither revulsion nor desire, but he would have no compunction in paying the price he demanded. If the white man wished to be treated as a woman, then Moses would readily render him this service.

'Yes, Doctor, I would like to work for you,' he said.

* * *

On the last night in the barrack room of the induction centre, Moses called all his chosen lieutenants to him. They clustered around his bunk.

'Very soon you will go from here to the *Goldi*. Not all of you will go together for there are many mines along the Rand. Some of you will go down into the earth, others will work on the surface in the mills and the reduction plants. We will be separated for a while, but you will not forget that we are brothers. I, your elder brother, will not forget you. I have important work for you. I will seek you out, wherever you are, and you will be ready for me when I summon you.'

'*Eh he!*' they grunted in agreement and obedience. 'We are your younger brothers. We will listen for your voice.'

'You must know always that you are under my protection, that all trespasses against you will be revenged. You have seen what happens to those who give offence to our brotherhood.'

'We have seen it,' they murmured. 'We have seen it – and it is death.'

'It is death,' Moses confirmed. 'It is death also for any of the brotherhood who betray us. It is death for all traitors.'

'Death to all traitors.' They swayed together, coming once more under the mesmeric spell which Moses Gama wove about them.

'I have chosen a totem for our brotherhood,' Moses went on. 'I have chosen the buffalo for our totem for he is black and powerful and all men fear him. We are the Buffaloes.'

'We are the Buffaloes.' Already they were proud of the distinction. 'We are the black Buffaloes and all men will learn to fear us.'

'These are the signs, the secret signs by which we will recognize our own.'

He made the sign and then individually clasped their right hands in the fashion of the white man, but the grip was different, a double grip and turn of the second finger. 'Thus you will know your brothers when they come to you.'

They greeted each other in the darkened barracks, each of them shaking the hand of all the others in the new way, and it was a form of initiation into the brotherhood.

'You will hear from me soon. Until I call, you must do as the white man requires of you. You must work hard and learn. You must be ready for the call when it comes.' Moses sent them away to their bunks and he and Hendrick sat alone, their heads together, speaking in whispers.

'You have lost the little white stones,' Moses told him. 'By now the birds and the small beasts will have pecked the loaves and devoured the millet bread. The stones will be scattered and lost; the dust will cover them and the grass will grow over them. They are gone, my brother.'

'Yes. They are gone,' Hendrick lamented. 'After so much blood and striving, after all the hardships we endured, they have been scattered like seeds to the wind.'

'They were accursed,' Moses consoled him. 'From the moment I saw them I knew that they would bring only disaster and death. They are white man's toys. What could you have done with the white man's wealth? If you tried to spend it, if you tried to buy white man's things with it, you would instantly have been marked by the white police. They would have come for you immediately and there would have been a rope or a jail cell for you.'

Hendrick was silent, considering the truth of this. What could he have purchased with the stones? Black men could not own their own land. More than a hundred head of cattle and the local chieftain's envy would have been

aroused. He already had all the wives – and more – that he wished for, and black men did not drive in motor cars. Black men did not draw attention to themselves in any way, not if they were wise.

'No, my brother,' Moses told him softly. 'They were not for you. Thank the spirits of your ancestors that they were wrested from you and scattered back on the earth where they belong.'

Hendrick growled softly, 'Still it would have been good to have that treasure, to hold it in my hands, even secretly.'

'There are other treasures even more important than diamonds or white man's gold, my brother.'

'What are these treasures?' Hendrick asked.

'Follow me and I will lead you to them.'

'But tell me what they are,' Hendrick insisted.

'You will discover them in good time.' Moses smiled. 'But now, my brother, we must talk of first things; the treasures will follow later. Listen to me. *Bomvu*, the red one, my little doctor who likes to be used as a woman, *Bomvu* has allocated you to the *Goldi* called Central Rand Consolidated. It is one of the richest of the *Goldi*, with many deep shafts. You will go underground, and it is best if you make a name for yourself there. I have prevailed on *Bomvu* to send ten of our best men from the Buffaloes to CRC with you. These will be your *impi*, your chosen warriors. You must start with them, but you will build upon them, gathering around you the quick and strong and the fearless.'

'What must I do with these men?'

'Hold them in readiness. You will hear from me soon. Very soon.'

'What of the other Buffaloes?'

'*Bomvu* has sent them, at my suggestion, in groups of ten to each of the other *Goldi* along the Rand. Small groups of our men everywhere. They will grow, and soon we will be a great black herd of buffaloes which even the most savage lion will not dare to challenge.'

* * *

Swart Hendrick's initial descent in the earth was the first time in his life that he had been frightened witless, unable to speak or think, so terrified that he could not even scream or struggle against it.

The terror began when he was in the long line of black miners, each of them wearing black rubber gumboots and grey overalls, the unpainted silver helmets on their heads fitted with head lanterns. Hendrick shuffled forward in the press of bodies down the ramp between the poles of the crush, like cattle entering an abattoir, stopping and starting forward again. Suddenly he found himself at the head of the line, standing before the steel mesh gate that guarded the entrance to the shaft.

Beyond the mesh he could see the steel cables hanging into the shaft like pythons with shining scales, and over him towered the steel skeleton of the headgear. When he looked up he could see the huge wheels silhouetted against the sky a hundred feet above his head, spinning and stopping and reversing.

Suddenly the mesh gates crashed open and he was carried on the surge of black bodies into the cage beyond. They packed shoulder to shoulder, seventy men. The doors closed, the floor dropped under his feet and stopped again

immediately. He heard the tramp of feet over his head and looked up, realizing that the skip was a double decker and that another seventy men were being packed into the top compartment.

Again he heard the clash of closing mesh gates and he started as the telegraph shrilled, four long rings, the signal to descend, and the skip fell away under him – but this time accelerating so violently that his body seemed to come free and his feet lay only lightly on the steel floor plates. His belly was sucked up against his ribs and his terror was unleashed.

In the darkness the skip rocketed downwards, drumming and rattling and racing like an express train in a tunnel, and the terror went on and on, minute after minute, eternity after eternity. He felt himself suffocating, crushed by the thought of the enormous weight of rock above him, his ears popping and crackling at the pressure, a mile and then another mile straight down into the earth.

The skip stopped so abruptly that his knees buckled and he felt the flesh of his face sucked down from the bones of his skull, stretching like rubber. The gates crashed open and he was carried out into the main haulage, a cavern walled with glistening wet rock, filled with men, hundreds of men like rats in a sewer, streaming away into the endless tunnels that honeycombed the bowels of the world.

Everywhere there was water, glistening and shining in the flat glare of the electric light, running back in channels on each side of the haulage, squelching under his feet, hidden water drumming and rustling in the darkness or dripping from the jagged rock of the roof. The very air was heavy with water, humid and hot and claustrophobic so that it had a gelatinous texture, seeming to fill his eardrums and deafen him, trickling sluggishly into his lungs like treacle, and his terror lasted all that long march along the drive until they reached the stopes. Here the men split into their separate gangs and disappeared into the shadows.

The stopes were the vast open chambers from which the gold-bearing ore had already been excavated, the hanging wall above supported now by packed pillars of shoring timber, the footwall under them inclined upwards at an angle following the run of the reef.

The men of his gang trudging ahead of him led Hendrick to his station, and here under a bare electric bulb waited for the white shift boss, a burly Afrikaner flanked by his two boss-boys.

The station was a three-sided chamber in the rock, its number on the entrance. There was a long bench against the back wall of the station and a latrine, its open buckets screened by sheets of burlap.

The gang sat on the bench while the boss-boys called the roll, and then the white shift boss asked in Fanakalo, 'Where is the new hammer boy?' and Hendrick rose to his feet. Cronje, the shift boss, came to stand in front of him. Their eyes were on a level, both big men. The shift boss's nose was crooked, broken long ago in a forgotten brawl, and he examined Hendrick carefully. He saw the broken gap in his teeth and the scars upon his head and his respect was tentative and grudging. They were both hard, tough men, recognizing it in each other. Up there in the sunshine and sweet cool airs they were black man and white man. Down here in the earth they were simply men.

'You know the hammer?' Cronje asked in Fanakalo.

'I know it,' Hendrick replied in Afrikaans. He had practised working the hammer for two weeks in the surface training pits.

Cronje blinked and then grinned to acknowledge the use of his own language. 'I run the best gang of rock breakers on the CRC,' he said, still grinning. 'You will learn to break rock, my friend, or I will break your head and your arse instead. Do you understand?'

'I understand,' Hendrick grinned back at him, and Cronje raised his voice. 'All hammer boys here!'

They stood up from the bench – five of them, all big men like Hendrick. It took tremendous physical strength to handle the jack hammers. They were the élite of the rock-breaking gangs, earning almost double wages and bonus for footage, earning also immense prestige from lesser men.

Cronje wrote their names up on the blackboard under the electric bulb: Henry Tabaka at the bottom of the list and Zama, the big Zulu, at number one. When Zama stripped off his jacket and tossed it to his line boy, his great black muscles bulged and gleamed in the stark electric light.

'Ha!' He looked at Henrick. 'So we have a little Ovambo jackal come in yipping from the desert.' The men around him laughed obsequiously. Zama was top hammer on the section; everybody laughed when he made a joke.

'I thought that the Zulu baboon scratched his fleas only on the peaks of the Drakensberg so his voice can be heard afar,' Hendrick said quietly, and there was a shocked silence for a moment and then a guffaw of disbelieving laughter.

'All right, you two big talkers,' Cronje intervened, 'let's break some rock.' He led them from the station up the stope to the rockface where the gold reef was a narrow grey horizontal band in the jagged wall, dull and nondescript, without the faintest precious sparkle. The gold was locked away in it.

The roof was low; a man had to double over to reach the face; but the stope was wide, reaching away hundreds of metres into the darkness on either hand, and they could hear the other gangs out there along the rockface, their voices echoing and reverberating, their lanterns throwing weird shadows.

'Tabaka!' Cronje yelled. 'Here!' He had marked the shot holes to be drilled with splashes of white paint, indicating the inclination and depth of each hole.

The blast was a precise and calculated firing of gelignite charges. The outer holes would be charged with 'shapers' to form the hanging wall and foot wall of the stope they would fire first, while the pattern of inner shots fired a second later. These were the 'cutters' that would kick the ore back and clear it from the face.

'*Shaya*!' Cronje yelled at Hendrick. 'Hit it!' and lingered a second to watch as Hendrick stooped to drill.

It squatted on the rock floor in front of the face, an ungainly tool in the shape of a heavy machine-gun, with long pneumatic hoses attached to it and running back down the slope to the compressed air system in the main haulage.

Swiftly Hendrick fitted the twenty-foot-long steel jumper bit into the lug of the drill and then he and his line boy dragged the tool to the rockface. It took all the strength of both Hendrick and his assistant to lift the tool and position the point of the drill on the white paint mark for the first cut. Hendrick eased himself into position behind the tool, taking the full weight of it on his right shoulder. The line boy stepped back, and Hendrick opened the valve.

The din was stunning, a stuttering implosion of sound that drove in against the eardrums as compressed air at a pressure of 500 pounds a square inch roared into the drill and slammed the long steel bit into the rock.

Hendrick's entire body shuddered and shook to the drive of the tool against his shoulder but still he leaned his full weight against it. His head jumped on

the thick corded column of his neck so rapidly that his vision blurred, but he narrowed his eyes and aimed the point of the drill into the rock at the exact angle that the shift boss had called for. Water squirted down the hollow drill steel, bubbling out of the hole in a yellow mist, splattering into Hendrick's face.

The sweat burst from his black skin, running down his face as though he was standing under a cloudburst, mingling with the slimy mud pouring down his naked back and scattering like rain as his straining muscles fluttered and jumped to the impulse of the pounding steel drill at his shoulder.

Within minutes the entire surface of his body began to itch and burn. It was the hammer boys' affliction; his skin was being scrubbed back and forth a thousand times a minute by the violent shaking motion of the drill, and with each minute the agony became more intense. He tried to close his mind to it but still it felt as though a blowtorch was being played over his body.

The long steel drill sank slowly into the rock until it reached the depth marker painted on it and Hendrick closed the valve. There was no silence, for even though his hearing was dulled, as though his eardrums were filled with cotton wool, yet he could still hear the echoes of the drill thunder resounding against the roof of his skull.

The line boy ran forward, seized the jumper bit and helped him withdraw it from the first shot hole and reposition the tip on the second daubed paint mark. Once again Hendrick opened the valve and the din and the agony began again. However, gradually the itching burn of his body blurred into numbness and he felt disembodied as though cocaine had been injected under his skin.

So he stood to the rock all that shift, six hours without let or relief. When it ended and they trooped back from the face, splattered and coated with yellow mud from head to foot and weary beyond pain or feeling, even Zama the great black Zulu was reeling on his feet and his eyes were dull.

In the station Cronje wrote the total of work completed against their names on the blackboard. Zama had drilled sixteen patterns, Hendrick twelve and the next best man ten.

'*Hau!*' Zama muttered as they rode up to the surface in the crowded skip. 'On his very first shift the jackal is number two hammer.' And Hendrick had just enough strength to reply:

'And on his second shift the jackal will be top hammer.'

It never happened. Not once did he break more rock than the Zulu. But at the end of that first month as Hendrick sat in the company beer hall with the other Ovambos of the Buffalo totem gathered around him, the Zulu came to his table carrying two one-gallon jugs of the creamy effervescent millet beer that the company sold its men. It was thick as porridge, and just as nutritious, though only very mildly alcoholic.

Zama set a one-gallon jug down in front of Hendrick and said: 'We broke some rock together this month, hey, jackal?'

'And we'll break a lot more together next month, hey, baboon?'

And they both roared with laughter and raised the beer jugs in unison and drank them dry.

Zama was the first Zulu to become initiated into the brotherhood of the Buffaloes, not as natural as it sounded for tribal barriers, like mountain ranges, were difficult to cross.

* * *

It was three months before Hendrick saw his brother again, but by that time Hendrick had extended his influence throughout the entire compound of black mine workers at the CRC mine property. With Zama as his lieutenant, the Buffaloes now encompassed men from many different tribes, Zulus and Shangaans and Matabeles. The only criterion was that the new initiates should be hard reliable men, preferably with some influence over at least a section of the eight thousand odd black miners, and preferably also appointed by the mine administration to positions of authority on the property: clerks or boss-boys or company police.

Some of the men who were approached resisted the brotherhood's overtures. One of these, a senior Zulu boss-boy with thirty years' service and a misplaced sense of duty to his tribe and the company, fell into one of the ore chutes on the sixtieth level of the main haulage the day after he refused. His body was ground to a muddy paste by the tons of jagged rock that rumbled over it. It seemed that nobody had witnessed the accident.

One of the company police *indunas*, who also resisted the blandishments of the brotherhood, was found stabbed to death in his sentry box at the main gates to the property, while yet another was burned to death in the kitchens. Three Buffaloes witnessed this last unfortunate incident caused by the victim's own clumsiness and inattention and there were no more refusals.

When at last the messenger came from Moses, identifying himself with the secret sign and handclasp, he bore a summons to a meeting, and Hendrick was able to leave the mine property without check.

By government decree the black mine workers were strictly confined within the barbed-wire fences of the compounds. It was the opinion of both the Chamber of Mines and the Johannesburg city fathers that to let tens of thousands of single black males roam the goldfields at will would invite disaster. They had the salutary lesson of the Chinese before them. In 1904, almost fifty thousand Chinese coolies had been brought into South Africa to fill the huge shortage of unskilled labour for the gold mines. However, the Chinese were much too intelligent and restless to be confined to compounds and restricted to unskilled labour and they were highly organized in their secret tong societies. The result was a wave of lawlessness and terror that swept over the goldfields – rapine and robbery, gambling and drugs – so that in 1908, at huge cost, all the Chinese were rounded up and shipped home. The government was determined to avoid a repetition of this terror and the compound system was strictly enforced.

However, Hendrick passed through the gates of the CRC compound as though he were invisible. He crossed the open veld in the starlight until he found the overgrown track and followed it to the old abandoned shafthead. There, parked behind the deserted rusting corrugated iron shed, was a black Ford sedan and as Hendrick approached it cautiously the headlights were switched on, spotlighting Hendrick, and he froze.

Then the lights were switched off and Moses' voice called out of the darkness, 'I see you, my brother.'

They embraced impulsively and then Hendrick laughed. 'Ha! So you drive a motor car now, like a white man.'

'The motor car belongs to *Bomvu*.' Moses led him to it, and Hendrick sank back against the leather seat and sighed comfortably. 'This is better than walking.'

'Now tell me, Hendrick my brother. What has happened at CRC?' And

Moses listened without comment until Hendrick finished his long report. Then he nodded.

'You have understood my wants. It is exactly as I wished it. The brotherhood must take in men from all the tribes, not just the Ovambo. We must reach to each tribe, each property, every corner of the goldfields.'

'You have said all this before,' Hendrick growled, 'but you have never told me why, my brother. I trust you, but the men I have assembled, the *impi* you bid me build, they look to me, and they ask one question. They ask me why? What is the profit in this thing? What is there for us in the brotherhood?'

'And what do you answer them, my brother?'

'I tell them they must be patient.' Hendrick scowled. 'I do not know the answer, but I look wise as if I do. And if they nag me, like children – well, then I beat them like children.' Moses laughed delightedly, but Hendrick shook his head. 'Don't laugh, my brother, I can't go on beating them much longer.'

Moses clapped his shoulder. 'Nor will you have to much longer. But tell me now, Hendrick, what is it you have missed most in the months you have worked at CRC?'

Hendrick answered. 'The feeling of a woman under me.'

'That you shall have before the night is finished. And what else, my brother?'

'The fire of good liquor in my belly, not the weak slop from the company beerhall.'

'My brother,' Moses told him seriously, 'you have answered your own question. These are the things that you men will get from the brotherhood. These are the scraps we will throw our hunting dogs: women and liquor and, of course money, but for those of us at the head of the Buffaloes there will be more, much more.' He started the engine of the Ford.

The gold-bearing reefs of the Witwatersrand form a sprawling arc one hundred kilometres in length. The older properties such as East Daggafontein are in the eastern sector of the arc where the reef originally outcropped; the newer properties are in the west where the reef dips away sharply to great depth; but like Blyvooruitzicht, these deep mines are enormously rich. All the mines are laid out along this fabulous crescent, surrounded by the urban development which the gold wealth has attracted and fostered.

Moses drove the black Ford southwards, away from the mines and the white man's streets and buildings, and the road they followed quickly narrowed and deteriorated, its surface rutted and riven with pot holes and puddles from the last thunderstorm. It lost direction and began to meander, degenerating into a maze of lanes and tracks.

The street lights of the city were left behind them, but out here there was other illumination: the glow of hundreds of wood fires, their orange light muted by their own drifting smoke banks. There was one of these cooking fires in front of each of the shanties of tarpaper and old corrugated iron that crowded so closely that there were only narrow lanes between them, and there was amongst the shacks a feeling of the presence of many unseen people, as though an army were encamped out here in the open veld.

'Where are we?' Hendrick asked.

'We are in a city that no man acknowledges, a city of people who do not exist.'

Hendrick glimpsed their dark shapes as the Ford bumped and pitched over the rough track between the shanties and shacks and the headlights swung aimlessly back and forth illuminating little cameo scenes: a group of black

children stoning a pariah dog; a body lying beside the track drunk or dead; a woman squatting to urinate in the angle of one of the corrugated iron walls; two men locked in silent deadly combat; a family at one of the fires eating from tins of bully beef, their eyes huge and shining as they looked up startled into the headlights; and other dark shapes scurrying furtively away into the shadows – hundreds of them and the presence of thousands more sensed.

'This is Drake's Farm,' Moses told him. 'One of the squatter townships that surround the white man's *Goldi*.'

The odour of the amorphous sprawling aggregation of humanity was woodsmoke and sewage, old sweat on hot bodies and charred food on the open wood fires. It was the smell of garbage mouldering in the rain puddles and the nauseating sweetness of bloodsucking vermin in unwashed bedding.

'How many live here?'

'Five thousand, ten thousand. Nobody knows, nobody cares.' Moses stopped the Ford and switched off the headlights and the engine.

The silence afterwards was not truly silence; it was the murmur of multitudes like the sea heard at a distance, the mewling of infants, the barking of a cur dog, the sounds of a woman singing, of men cursing and talking and eating, of couples arguing shrilly or copulating, of people dying and defecating and snoring and gambling and drinking in the night.

Moses stepped out of the Ford and called imperatively into the darkness and half a dozen dark figures came scurrying from amongst the shacks. They were children, Hendrick realized, though their age and sex were obscure.

'Stand guard on my motor car,' Moses ordered, and tossed a small coin that twinkled in the firelight until one of the children snatched it from the air.

'Eh he! Baba!' they squeaked, and Moses led his brother amongst the shacks for a hundred yards and the sound of the women singing was louder, a thrilling evocative sound, and there was the buzz of many other voices and the sour smell of old stale alcohol and meat cooking on an open fire.

They had reached a long low building, a rough shed cobbled together from discarded material. Its wall were crooked and the outline of the roof was buckled and sway backed against the fireglow. Moses knocked upon the door and a lantern was flashed in his face before the door was thrown open.

'So my brother,' Moses took Hendrick's arm and drew him into the doorway. 'This is your first shebeen. Here you will have all that I promised you: women and liquor, your fill of both.'

The shed was packed with human beings, jammed so tightly that the far wall was lost in the fog of blue tobacco smoke and a man must shout to be heard a few feet away; the black faces shone with sweat and excitement. The men were miners, drinking and singing and laughing and groping the women. Some were very drunk and a few had fallen to the earth floor and lay in their own vomit. The women were of every tribe, all of their faces painted in the fashion of white women, dressed in flimsy gaudy dresses, singing and dancing and shaking their hips, picking out the men with money and tugging them away through the doors at the back of the shed.

Moses did not have to force his way through this jam of bodies. It opened almost miraculously before him, and many of the women called to him respectfully. Hendrick followed closely behind his brother and he was struck with admiration that Moses had been able to achieve this degree of recognition in the three short months since they had arrived on the Rand.

There was a guard at the door at the far end of the shebeen, an ugly scar-

faced ruffian, but he also recognized Moses and clapped his hands in greeting before he pulled aside the canvas screen to allow them to go through into the back room.

This room was less crowded, and there were tables and benches for the customers. The girls in here were still graced with youth, bright-eyed and fresh-faced. An enormous black woman was seated at a separate table in the corner. She had the serene round moon face of the high-bred Zulu but its contours were almost obscured by fat. Her dark amber skin was stretched tightly over this abundance; her belly hung down in a series of fleshy balconies onto her lap, and fat hung in great black dewlaps under her arms and formed bracelets around her wrists. On the table in front of her were neat stacks of coins, silver and copper, and wads of multi-coloured bank notes, and the girls were bringing her more to add to the piles each minute.

When she saw Moses her perfect white teeth shone like precious porcelain; she lumbered to her feet, her thighs so elephantine that she waddled with her feet wide apart as she came to him and greeted him as though he were a tribal chief, touching her forehead and clapping with respect.

'This is Mama Nginga,' Moses told Hendrick. 'She is the biggest shebeen keeper and whore mistress on Drake's Farm. Soon she will be the only one on Drake's Farm.'

Only then did Hendrick realize that he knew most of the men at the tables. They were Buffaloes who had travelled on the Wenela train and taken the initiation oath with him, and they greeted him with unfeigned delight and introduced him to the strangers in their midst.

'This is Henry Tabaka. He is the one of the legend. The man who slew *Tshayela*, the white overseer – ' and Hendrick noticed the immediate respect in the eyes of these new Buffaloes. They were men from the other mines along the reef, recruited by the original Buffaloes, and Hendrick saw that on the whole they had chosen well.

'My brother has not had a woman or a taste of good liquor in three months,' Moses told them as he seated himself at the head of the central table. 'Mama Nginga, we don't want your *skokiaan*. She makes it herself,' he told Hendrick in a loud aside, 'and she puts in carbide and methylated spirits and dead snakes and aborted babies to give it kick and flavour.'

Mama Nginga screeched with laughter. 'My *skokiaan* is famous from Fordsburg to Bapsfontein. Even some of the white men – the *mabuni* – come for it.'

'It's good enough for them,' Moses agreed, 'but not good enough for my brother.'

Mama Nginga sent one of the girls to them with a bottle of Cape brandy and Moses seized the young girl around the waist and held her easily. He pulled open the European-style blouse she wore, forcing out her big round breasts so that they shone like washed coal in the lamplight.

'This is where we start, my Buffaloes, a girl and a bottle,' he told them. 'There are fifty thousand lonely men at *Goldi* far from their wives, all of them hungry for sweet young flesh. There are fifty thousand men, thirsty from their work in the earth, and the white men forbid them to slake their thirst with this.' He shook the bottle of golden spirits. 'There are fifty thousand randy thirsty black men at *Goldi*, all with money in their pockets. The Buffaloes will give them what they want.' He pushed the girl into Hendrick's lap and she coiled herself about him with professionally simulated lust and thrust her shining black breasts into his face.

When the dawn broke over the sprawling shanty town of Drake's Farm, Moses and Hendrick picked their way down the reeking convoluted alleys to where they had left the Ford and the children were guarding it still, like jackals around the lion's kill. The brothers had sat all night in the back room of Mama Nginga's shebeen and the preliminary planning was at last done. Each of their lieutenants had been allotted areas and responsibilities.

'But there is still much work to be done, my brother,' Moses told Hendrick as he started the Ford. 'We have to find the liquor and the women. We will have to bring all the little shebeens and brothels like goats into our kraal, and there is only one way to do that.'

'I know how that has to be done,' Hendrick nodded. 'And we have an *impi* to do it.'

'And an *induna*, a general, to command that *impi*.' Moses glanced at Hendrick significantly. 'The time has come for you to leave CRC, my brother. All your time and your strength will be needed now. You will waste no more of your strength in the earth, breaking rock for a white man's pittance. From now on you will be breaking heads for power and great fortune.' He smiled thinly. 'You will never have to pine again for those little white stones of yours. I will give you more, much more.'

Marcus Archer arranged for Hendrick's contract at CRC to be cancelled and for him to be issued travel papers for one of the special trains that carried the returning miners who had worked out their ticket back to the reservations and the distant villages. But Hendrick never caught that train. Instead he disappeared from the white man's records and was absorbed into the shadowy halfworld of the townships.

Mama Nginga set aside one of the shanties at the back of her shebeen for his exclusive use, and one of her girls was always on hand to sweep and wash his laundry, to cook his food and warm his bed.

It was six days after his arrival at Drake's Farm that the Buffalo *impi* opened its campaign. The objective had been discussed and carefully explained by Hendrick and it was simple and clear-cut. They would make Drake's Farm their own citadel.

On the first night twelve of the opposition shebeens were burned to the ground. Their proprietors burned with them, as did those of their customers who were too drunk to crawl out of the flaming hovels. Drake's Farm was far outside the sector served by the white man's fire engines, so no attempt was made to fight the flames. Rather, the inhabitants of Drake's Farm gathered to watch the spectacle as though it was a circus arranged particularly for their entertainment. The children danced and shrilled in the firelight, and screeched with laughter as the bottles of spirits exploded like fireworks.

Nearly all the girls escaped from the flames. Those who had been at work when the fire began ran out naked, clutching their scanty clothing and weeping wildly at the loss of all their worldly possessions and savings. However, there were kindly concerned men to comfort them and lead them away to Mama Nginga's.

Within forty-eight hours the shebeens had been rebuilt on their ashes and the girls were back at work again. Their lot was much improved; they were well fed and clothed and they had their own Buffaloes to protect them from their customers, to make certain they were neither cheated nor abused. Of course, if they in turn shirked or tried to cheat, they were beaten soundly; but they

expected that, it made them feel part of the totem and replaced the father and brothers they had left in the reservations.

Hendrick allowed them to keep a fixed proportion of the fee they charged and made sure his men respected their right to it.

'Generosity breeds loyalty and firmness a loving heart,' he explained to his Buffaloes, and he extended his 'happy house' policy to embrace his customers and everybody else at Drake's Farm. The black miners coming into the township were as carefully protected as his girls were. In very short order the footpads, pickpockets, muggers and other smalltime entrepreneurs were routed out. The quality of the liquor improved. From now on all of it was brewed under Mama Nginga's personal supervision.

It was strong as a bull elephant, and bit like a rabid hyena, but it no longer turned men blind or destroyed their brains, and because it was manufactured in bulk, it was reasonably priced. A man could get falling-down drunk for two shillings or have a good clean girl for the same price.

Hendrick's men met every bus and train coming in from the country districts, bringing the young black girls who had run away from their villages and their tribe to reach the glitter of *Goldi*. They led the pretty ones back to Drake's Farm. When this source of supply became inadequate as the demand increased, Hendrick sent his men into the country districts and villages to recruit the girls at the source with sweet words and promises of pretty things.

The city fathers of Johannesburg and the police were fully aware of the unacknowledged halfworld of the townships that had grown up south of the goldfields but, daunted by the prospect of closing them down and finding alternative accommodation for thousands of vagrants and illegals, they turned a blind eye, appeasing their civic consciences by occasional raids, arrests and the wholesale imposition of fines. However, as the incidence of murder and robbery and other serious crime mysteriously abated at Drake's Farm and it became an area of comparative calm and order, so their condescension and forbearance became even more pragmatic. The police raids ceased, and the prosperity of the area increased as its reputation as a safe and convivial place to have fun spread amongst the tens of thousands of black mine workers along the Rand. When they had a pass to leave the compound, they would travel thirty and forty miles, by-passing other centres of entertainment to reach it.

However, there were still many hundreds of thousands of other potential customers who could never reach Drake's Farm, and Moses Gama turned his attention to these.

'They cannot come to us, so we must go to them.' He explained to Hendrick what must be done, and it was Hendrick who negotiated the piecemeal purchase of a fleet of second-hand delivery vans and employed a coloured mechanic to renovate them and keep them in running order.

Each evening convoys of these vehicles loaded with liquor and girls left Drake's Farm, journeying down the length of the goldfields to park at some secluded location close to the big mining properties, in a copse of trees, a valley between the mine dumps, or an abandoned shaft building. The guards at the gate of the mine workers' compound, who were all Buffaloes, made certain that the customers were allowed in and out, and now every member of the Buffalo totem could share in the good fortune of their clan.

'So, my brother, do you still miss your little white stones?' Moses asked after their first two years of operation from Drake's Farm.

'It was as you promised,' Hendrick chuckled. 'We have everything that a man could wish for now.'

'You are too easily satisfied,' Moses chided him.

'There is more?' Hendrick asked with interest.

'We have only just begun,' Moses told him.

'What is next, my brother?'

'Have you heard of a trade union?' Moses asked. 'Do you know what it is?'

Hendrick looked dubious, frowning as he thought about it. 'I know that the white men on the mines have trade unions, and the white men on the railways also. I have heard it spoken of, but I know very little about them. They are white men's business, no concern of the likes of us.'

'You are wrong, my brother,' Moses said quietly. 'The African Mine Workers Union is very much our concern. It is the reason why you and I came to *Goldi*.'

'I thought that we came for the money.'

'Fifty thousand union members each paying one shilling a week union dues – isn't that money?' Moses asked, and smiled as he watched his brother make the calculation. Avarice contorted his smile so that the broken gap in his teeth looked like a black mine pit.

'It is good money indeed!'

Moses had learned from his unsuccessful attempts to establish a mine workers' union at the H'ani Mine. The black miners were simple souls with not the least vestige of political awareness; they were separated by tribal loyalties; they did not consider themselves part of a single nation.

'Tribalism is the one great obstacle in our path,' Moses explained to Hendrick. 'If we were one people we would be like a black ocean, infinite in our power.'

'But we are not one people,' Hendrick pointed out. 'Any more than the white men are one people. A Zulu is as different from an Ovambo as a Scotsman is from a Russian Cossack or an Afrikaner from an Englishman.'

'Ha!' Moses smiled. 'I see you have been reading the books I gave you. When first we came to *Goldi* you had never heard of a Russian Cossack – '

'You have taught me much about men and the world they live in,' Hendrick agreed. 'Now teach me how you will make a Zulu call an Ovambo his brother. Tell me how we are to take the power that is held so firmly in the hands of the white man.'

'These things are possible. The Russian people were as diverse as we black people of Africa. They are Asiatics and Europeans, Tartars and Slavs, but under a great leader they have become a single nation and have overthrown a tyranny even more infamous than the one under which we suffer. The black people need a leader who knows what is good for them and will force them to it, even if ten thousand or a million die in achieving it.'

'A leader such as you, my brother?' Hendrick asked, and Moses smiled his remote enigmatic smile.

'The Mine Workers Union first,' he said. 'Like a child learning to walk, one step at a time. The people must be forced to do what is good for them in the long run even though at first it is painful.'

'I am not sure – ' Hendrick shook his great shaven round head on which the ridged scars stood proud like polished gems of black onyx. 'What is it we seek, my brother? Is it wealth or power?'

'We are fortunate,' Moses answered. 'You want wealth and I want power. The way I have chosen, each of us will get what he desires.'

Even with ruthless contingents of the Buffaloes on each of the mine properties the process of unionization was slow and frustrating. By necessity much of it had to be undertaken secretly, for the government's Industrial Conciliation Act placed severe limitations on black labour association and specifically prohibited collective bargaining by black workers. There was also opposition from the workers themselves, their natural suspicion and antagonism towards the new union shop stewards, all of them Buffaloes, all of them appointed and not elected; and the ordinary workers were reluctant to hand over part of their hard-earned wages to something they neither understood nor trusted.

However, with Dr Marcus Archer to advise and counsel them and with Hendrick's Buffaloes to push the cause forward, slowly the unionization of the workers on each of the various mine properties was accomplished. The miners' reluctance to part with their silver shillings was quelled. There were, of course, casualties, and some men died, but at last there were over twenty thousand dues-paying members of the African Mine Workers Union.

The Chamber of Mines, the association of mining interests, found itself presented with a *fait accompli*. The members were at first alarmed; their natural instinct was to destroy this cancer immeditely. However, the Chamber members were first and above all else businessmen, concerned with getting the yellow metal to the surface with as little fuss as possible and with paying regular dividends to their shareholders. They understood what havoc a labour battle could wreak amongst their interests, so they held their first cautious informal talks with the non-existent union and were most gratified to find the self-styled secretary general to be an intelligent articulate and reasonable person.

There was no trace of Bolshevik dialectic in his statements, and far from being radical and belligerent, he was co-operative and respectful in his address.

'He is a man we can work with,' they told each other. 'He seems to have influence. We've needed a spokesman for the workers and he seems a decent enough sort. We could have done a lot worse. We can manage this chap.' And sure enough, their very first meetings had excellent results and they were able to solve a few small vexing long-term problems to the satisfaction of the union and the profit of the mine owners.

After that the informal, unrecognized union had the Chamber's tacit acceptance, and when a problem arose with their labour the Chamber sent for Moses Gama and it was swiftly settled. Each time this happened, Moses' position became more securely entrenched. And, of course, there was never even a hint at strikes or any form of militancy on the union's part.

'Do you understand, my brothers?' Moses explained to the first meeting of his central committee of the African Mine Workers Union held in Mama Nginga's shebeen. 'If they come down upon us with their full strength while we are still weak, we will be destroyed for all time. This man Smuts is a devil, and he is truly the steel in the government's spear. He did not hesitate to send his troops with machine-guns against the white union strikers in 1922. What would he do to black strikers, my brothers? He would water the earth with our blood. No, we must lull them. Patience is the great strength of our people. We have a hundred years, while the white man lives only for the day. In time the black ants of the veld build mountains and devour the carcass of the elephant. Time is our weapon, and time is the white man's enemy. Patience, my brothers, and one day the white man will discover that we are not oxen to be yoked into the

traces of his wagon. He will discover rather that we are black-maned lions, fierce eaters of white flesh.'

* * *

'How swiftly the years have passed us by since we rode on *Tshayela's* train from the deserts of the west to the flat shining mountains of *Goldi*.' Hendrick watched the mine dumps on the skyline as Moses drove the old Ford through the sparse traffic of a Sunday morning. He drove sedately, not too slow not too fast, obeying the traffic rules, stopping well in advance of the changing traffic lights, those wonders of the technological age which had only been installed on the main routes within the last few months. Moses always drove like this.

'Never draw attention to yourself unnecessarily, my brother,' he advised Hendrick. 'Never give a white policeman an excuse to stop you. He hates you already for driving a motor car that he cannot afford himself. Never put yourself in his power.'

The road skirted the rolling fairways of the Johannesburg Country Club, oases of green in the brown veld, watered and groomed and mown until they were velvet green carpets on which the white golfers strolled in their foursomes followed by their barefooted caddies. Further back amongst the trees the white walls of the club house gleamed, and Moses slowed the Ford and turned at the bottom of the club property where the road crossed the tiny dry Sand Spruit river and the signpost said 'Rivonia Farm'.

They followed the unsurfaced road, and the dust raised by the Ford's wheels hung behind them in the still dry highveld air and then settled gently to powder the brittle frost-dried grass along the verges a bright theatrical red.

The road served a cluster of smallholdings, each of them five or ten acres in extent, and Dr Marcus Archer's property was the one at the end of the road. He made no attempt to farm the land, he had no chickens, horses or vegetable gardens such as the other smallholders kept. The single building was square and unpretentious, with a tattered thatched roof and wide verandah encompassing all four sides. It was screened from the road by a scraggly plantation of Australian blue gums.

There were four other vehicles parked under the gum trees, and Moses turned the Ford off the track and stopped the engine. 'Yes, my brother. The years have passed swiftly,' he agreed. 'They always do when men are intent on dire purposes, and the world is changing all around us. There are great events afoot. It is nineteen years since the revolution in Russia, and Trotsky has been exiled. Herr Hitler has occupied the Rhineland, and in Europe there is talk of war – a war that will destroy forever the curse of Capitalism and from which the revolution will emerge victorious.'

Hendrick laughed, the black gap in his teeth making it a grimace. 'These things do not concern us.'

'You are wrong again, my brother. They concern us beyond all else.'

'I do not understand them.'

'Then I will help you.' Moses touched his arm. 'Come, my brother. I am taking you now to the next step in your understanding of the world.' He opened the door of the Ford and Hendrick climbed down on his side and followed him towards the old house.

'It will be wise, my brother, if you keep your eyes and your ears open and your mouth closed,' Moses told him as they reached the steps at the front verandah. 'You will learn much that way.'

As they climbed the steps, Marcus Archer hurried out onto the verandah to greet them, his expression lighting with pleasure as he saw Moses, and he hurried to him and embraced him lovingly then, his arm still around Moses' waist, he turned to Hendrick.

'You will be Henny. We have spoken about you often.'

'I have met you before, Dr Archer, at the induction centre.'

'That was so long ago.' Marcus Archer shook his hand. 'And you must call me Marcus. You are a member of our family.' He glanced at Moses and his adoration was apparent. He reminded Hendrick of a young wife all agog with her new husband's virility.

Hendrick knew that Moses lived here at Rivonia Farm with Marcus and he felt no revulsion for the relationship. He understood how vitally important Marcus Archer's counsel and assistance had been in their successes over the years and approved the price that Moses paid for them. Hendrick himself had used men in the same fashion, never as a loving relationship but as a form of torture of a captured enemy. In his view there was no greater humiliation and degradation that one man could inflict upon another, yet he knew that in his brother's position he would not hesitate to use this strange red-haired little white man as he desire to be used.

'Moses has been very naughty in not bringing you to visit us sooner,' Marcus slapped Moses' arm playfully. 'There are so many interesting and important people here who you should have met ages ago. Come along now, let me introduce you.' He took Hendrick's arm and led him through to the kitchen.

It was a traditional farmhouse kitchen with stone-flagged floor, a black woodburning stove at the far end and bunches of onions, cured hams and polonies hanging from the hooks in the beams of the ceiling.

Eleven men were seated at the long yellow-wood table. Five of them were white, but the rest were black men, and their ages varied from callow youth to grey-haired sage. Marcus led Hendrick slowly down both sides of the table, introducing him to each in turn, beginning with the man at the head of the table.

'This is the Reverend John Dube, but you will have heard him called *Mafukuzela*,' and Hendrick felt an unaccustomed wave of awe.

'*Hau*, Baba!' he greeted the handsome old Zulu with vast respect. He knew that he was the political leader of the Zulu nation, that he was also the editor and founder of the *Illanga Lase Natal* newspaper, *The Sun of Natal* – but most importantly that he was president of the African National Congress, the only political organization that attempted to speak for all the black nations of the southern Africa continent.

'I know of you,' Dube told Hendrick quietly. 'You have done valuable work with the new trade union. You are welcome, my son.'

After John Dube, the other men in the room were of small interest to Hendrick, though there was one young black man who could not have been more than twenty years of age but who nevertheless impressed Hendrick with his dignity and powerful presence.

'This is our young lawyer – '

'Not yet! Not yet!' the young man protested.

'Our soon-to-be-lawyer,' Marcus Archer corrected himself. 'He is Nelson

Mandela, son of Chief Henry Mandela from the Transkei.' And as they shook hands in the white men's fashion that for Hendrick still felt awkward, he looked into the law student's eyes and thought: This is a young lion.'

The white men at the table made small impression on Hendrick. There were lawyers and a journalist, and a man who wrote books and poetry of which Hendrick had never heard, but the others treated his opinions with respect.

The only thing that Hendrick found remarkable about these whitemen was the courtesy which they accorded him. In a society in which a white man seldom acknowledged the existence of a black except to deliver an order, usually in brusque terms, it was unusual to encounter such concern and condescension. They shook Hendrick's hand without embarrassment, which was in itself strange, and made room for him at the table, poured wine for him from the same bottle and passed food to him on the same plate from which they had served themselves; and when they talked to him it was as an equal and they called him 'comrade' and 'brother'.

It seemed that Marcus Archer was a chef of repute, and he fussed over the woodburning stove producing dishes of food so minced and mixed and decorated and swimming in sauce that Hendrick could not tell either by inspection or taste whether they were fish or fowl or four-footed beast, but the others exclaimed and applauded and feasted voraciously.

Moses had advised Hendrick to keep his mouth filled with food rather than words, and to speak only when directly addressed and then in monosyllables, yet the others kept glancing at him with awe for he was an impressive figure in their midst: his head huge and heavy as a cannonball, the shining cicatrice lumped on his shaven pate and his gaze brooding and menacing.

The talk interested Hendrick very little but he feigned glowering attention as the others excitedly discussed the situation in Spain. The Popular Front Government, a coalition of Trotskyites, Socialists, left-wing Republicans and Communists, were threatened by an army mutiny under General Francisco Franco, and the company at Marcus Archer's luncheon table were filled with joyous outrage at this Fascist treachery. It seemed likely that it would plunge the Spanish nation into civil war and they all knew that only in the furnace of war could resolution be forged.

Two of the white men at the table, the poet and the journalist, declared their intention of leaving for Spain as soon as possible to join the struggle, and the other white men made no effort to disguise their envious admiration.

'You lucky devils. I would have gone like a shot but the Party wants me to remain here.'

There were many references to 'the Party' during the course of that long Sunday afternoon, and gradually the company turned its concerted attention on Hendrick as though it had been prearranged. Hendrick was relieved that Moses had insisted he read parts of *Das Kapital* and some of Lenin's works, in particular *What is to be Done?* and *On Dual Authority*. It was true that Hendrick had found them difficult to the point of pain and had followed them only imperfectly. However, Moses had gutted these works for him and presented him with the essentials of Marx's and Lenin's thoughts.

Now they were taking it in turns to talk directly at Hendrick, and he realized that he was being subjected to some sort of test. He glanced at Moses, and although his brother's expression did not change, he sensed that he was willing him consciously to a course of action. Was he trying to warn Hendrick to

remain silent? He was not certain, but at that moment Marcus Archer said clearly:

'Of course, the formation of a trade union amongst the black mine workers is in itself sufficient to assure the eventual triumph of the revolution – ' But his inflection posed a question, and he was watching Hendrick slyly, and Hendrick was not certain from where inspiration came.

'I do not agree,' he growled, and they were all silent, waiting expectantly. 'The history of the struggle bears witness that the workers unassisted will rise only as far as the idea of trade unionism, to combine their resources to fight the employers and the capitalist government. But it needs professional revolutionaries bound by complete loyalty to their ideals and by military-type discipline to carry the struggle to its ultimate victorious conclusion.'

It was almost a verbatim quotation from Lenin's *What is to be Done?* and Hendrick had spoke in English. Even Moses looked amazed by his achievement, while the others exchanged delighted smiles as Hendrick glowered around him and relapsed back into impressive monumental silence.

It was sufficient. He did not have to speak again. By nightfall, when the others traipsed out into the darkness calling farewells and thanks, climbed into their motor cars with slamming doors and roars of starting engines and drove away down the dusty track, Moses had achieved what he had aimed for in bringing his brother out to Rivonia Farm.

Hendrick had been sworn in as a full member of both the South African Communist Party and of the African National Congress.

* * *

Marcus Archer had set the guest bedroom aside for Hendrick. He lay in the narrow truckle bed listening to Moses and Marcus rutting in the main bedroom across the passage, and he was abruptly seized with the conviction that today the seeds of his destiny had been sown: that both the outer limits of his fortune and the time and manner of his own death had been determined in these last few hours. As he fell asleep, he was carried into the darkness on a wave of exultation and of dread.

Moses woke him while it was still dark and Marcus walked out to the Ford with them. The veld was white with frost; it crunched under their feet and had crusted on the windshield of the Ford.

Marcus shook hands with Hendrick. 'Forward, Comrade,' he said. 'The future belongs to us.' They left him standing in the frosty dark, staring after them.

Moses did not drive directly back into the city. Instead he parked the Ford below one of the high flat-topped mine dumps and he and Hendrick climbed the eroded dump side, five hundred feet almost sheer, and reached the top just as the rising sun cleared the horizon and turned the winter veld to pale gold.

'Now do you understand?' Moses asked as they stood shoulder to shoulder on the brink of the precipitous hillside, and suddenly like the sunrise itself Hendrick saw his brother's whole tremendous design.

'You want not a part of it,' he said softly, 'not even the greater part.' He spread his arms in a wide gesture that encompassed all below them from horizon

to horizon. 'You want it all. The whole land and everything in it.' And his voice was filled with wonder at the enormity of the vision.

Moses smiled. His brother had at last understood.

* * *

They climbed down the mine dump and went in silence to where the Ford was parked. In silence they drove towards Drake's Farm, for there were no words to describe what had happened, as there are no words adequately to describe birth or death. Only as they left the city limits and were forced to stop at one of the level crossings where the railway that served the mine properties crossed the main road, did the mundane world intrude once again.

A ragged black urchin, shivering in the frosty winter highveld morning, ran to the side window of the Ford and waved a folded newspaper at Moses through the glass. He rolled down the window, flipped the child a copper coin and placed the newspaper on the seat between them.

Hendrick frowned with interest and unfolded the news-sheet, holding it so they could both see the front page. The headlines were full column:

SOUTH AFRICAN TEAM CHOSEN FOR BERLIN OLYMPIC GAMES
THE NATION WISHES THEM GOOD LUCK

'I know that white boy,' Hendrick exclaimed, grinning gap-toothed as he recognized one of the photographs that accompanied the text.

'So do I,' Moses agreed, but they were looking at different young white faces in the long rows of individual pictures.

* * *

Of course, Manfred knew that Uncle Tromp kept the most extraordinary hours. Whenever Manfred's bladder woke him in the small dark hours and he dragged himself out of the toolshed and stumbled down the path to the outhouse against the moroto hedge he would look up and through sleep-blurred eyes see the lamplight burning in the window of Uncle Tromp's study.

Once, more wide awake than usual, Manfred left the path and crept through Aunt Trudi's cabbages to peer in over the sill. Uncle Tromp sat like a shaggy bear at his desk, his beard rumpled from constant tugging and combing with his thick fingers, wire-framed spectacles perched upon his great beak of a nose, muttering furiously to himself as he scribbled on the loose sheets of paper that were tumbled over the desktop like debris after a hurricane. Manfred had assumed he was working on one of his sermons, but had not thought it strange that his labours had continued night after night for almost two years.

Then one morning the coloured postman wheeled his bicycle up the dusty road, burdened by an enormous package wrapped in brown paper and blazoned with stamps and stickers and red sealing-wax. Aunt Trudi placed the mysterious package on the small hall table, and all the children found excuses to creep into

the hall and stare at it in awe, until at five o'clock Uncle Tromp drove up in his pony trap and the girls, led by Sarah, ran shrilling to meet him before he could dismount.

'There is a parcel for you, Papa.'

They crowded up behind him while Uncle Tromp made a show of examining the package and reading the label aloud. Then he took the pearl-handled penknife from the pocket of his waistcoat, deliberately tested the edge of the blade with his thumb, cut the strings binding the packet and carefully unwrapped the brown paper.

'Books!' sighed Sarah, and the girls all drooped with palpable disappointment and drifted away. Only Manfred lingered.

There were six thick copies of the same book, all identical, bound in red boards, the titles printed in fake gold leaf but still crisp and shining from the presses. And something in Uncle Tromp's manner and in the intent expression with which he watched Manfred as he waited for his reaction, alerted him to the unusual significance of this pile of books.

Manfred read the title of the top copy and found it long and awkward: *The Afrikaner: His Place in History and Africa*.

It was written in Afrikaans, the infant language still striving for recognition. Manfred found that unusual – all important scholarly works, even when written by Afrikaners, were in Dutch. He was about to remark upon this when his eyes moved down to the name of the author – and he started and gasped.

'Uncle Tromp!'

The old man chuckled with modest gratification.

'You wrote it!' Manfred's face lit with pride. 'You wrote a book.'

'*Ja, Jong* – even an old dog can learn new tricks.' Uncle Tromp swept up the pile in his arms and strode into his study. He placed the books in the centre of his desk and then looked around with astonishment to see that Manfred had followed him into the room.

'I'm sorry, Uncle Tromp.' Manfred realized his trespass. He had been in this room only once before in his life, and then only by special invitation. 'I didn't ask. May I come in, please, *Oom*?'

'Looks like you are in already.' Uncle Tromp tried to look stern. 'You might as well stay then.'

Manfred sidled up to the desk with his hands behind his back. In this house he had learned immense respect for the written word. He had been taught that books were the most precious of all men's treasures, the receptacles of his God-given genius.

'May I touch one of them?' he asked, and when Uncle Tromp nodded, he gingerly reached out and traced the author's name with his fingertip: 'The Reverend Tromp Bierman.'

Then he picked up the top copy, expecting at any moment the old man to bellow angrily at him. When it did not happen, he opened the book and stared at the small murky print on cheap spongy yellow paper.

'May I read it, please, Uncle Tromp?' he found himself begging, again expecting denial. But Uncle Tromp's expression turned softly bemused.

'You want to read it?' He blinked with mild surprise, and then chuckled. 'Well, I suppose that's why I wrote it – for people to read.'

Suddenly he grinned like a mischievous small boy and snatched the book from Manfred's hand. He sat down at his desk, placed his spectacles on his

nose, dipped his pen and scribbled on the flyleaf of the open book, re-read what he had written and then handed it to Manfred with a flourish:

'To Manfred De La Rey,
A young Afrikaner who will help make our people's place in history and Africa secure for all time.
Your affectionate
Uncle Tromp Bierman

Clutching the book to his chest, Manfred backed away to the door as though he feared it would be snatched from him again. 'Is it mine – is is truly for me?' he whispered.

And when Uncle Tromp nodded, 'Yes, *Jong*, it's yours,' he turned and fled from the room, forgetting in his haste to voice his thanks.

Manfred read the book in three successive nights, sitting up until long after midnight with a blanket over his shoulders, squinting in the flickering candlelight. It was five hundred pages of close print, larded with quotation from holy scripture, but it was written in strong simple language, not weighed down with adjectives or excessive description and it sang directly to Manfred's heart. He finished it bursting with pride for the courage and fortitude and piety of his people, and burning with anger for the cruel manner in which they had been persecuted and dispossessed by their enemies. He sat with the closed book in his lap, staring into the wavering shadows, living in full detail the wandering and suffering of his young nation, sharing the agony at the barricades when the black heathen hordes poured down upon them with war plumes tossing and the silver steel of the assegais drumming on rawhide shields like the surf of a gale-driven sea, sharing the wonder of voyaging out over the grassy ocean of the high continent into a beautiful wilderness unspoiled and unpeopled to take it as their own, finally sharing the bitter torment as the free land was wrested from them again by arrogant foreigners in their warlike legions and the final outrage of slavery, political and economic, was thrust upon them in their own land – the land that their fathers had won and in which they had been born.

As though the lad's rage had reached out and summoned him, Uncle Tromp came down the pathway, his footsteps crunching on the gravel, and stooped into the shed. He paused in the doorway, his eyes adjusting to the candlelight, and then he crossed to where Manfred crouched on the bed. The mattress sagged and squeaked as he lowered his bulk upon it.

They sat in silence for a full five minutes before Uncle Tromp asked, 'So, you managed to finish it then?'

Manfred had to shake himself back to the present. 'I think it is the most important book ever written,' he whispered. 'Just as important as the Bible.'

'That is blasphemy, *Jong*.' Uncle Tromp tried to look stern, but his gratification softened the line of his mouth and Manfred did not apologize.

Instead he went on eagerly, 'For the first time ever I know who I am – and why I am here.'

'Then my efforts have not been wasted,' Uncle Tromp murmured and they were silent again until the old man sighed. 'Writing a book is a lonely thing,' he mused. 'Like crying with all your heart into the night when there is nobody out there in the darkness, nobody to hear your cry, nobody to answer you.'

'I heard you, Uncle Tromp.'

'*Ja, Jong*, so you did – but only you.'

However, Uncle Tromp was wrong. There was other listeners out there in the darkness.

* * *

The arrival of a stranger in the village was an event; the arrival of three strangers together was without parallel or precedent and raised a storm of gossip and speculation that had the entire population in a fever of curiosity.

The strangers arrived from the south on the weekly mail train. Taciturn and granite-faced, dressed in severe dark broadcloth and carrying their own carpet bags, they crossed the road from the railway siding to the tiny iron-roofed boarding house run by the widow Vorster and were not seen again until Sunday morning when they emerged to stride down the rutted sidewalk, shoulder to shoulder, grim and devout, wearing the white neckties and black suits of deacons of the Dutch Reformed Church and carrying their black leatherbound prayer books under their right arms like sabres, ready to unsheath and wield upon Satan and all his works.

They stalked down the aisle and took the front pew beneath the pulpit as if by right, and the families who had sat on those benches for generations made no demur but quietly found places for themselves at the rear of the nave.

Rumours of the presence of the strangers – they had already been dubbed 'the three wise men' – had permeated to the remotest surrounding districts and even those who had not been inside the church in years, drawn by curiosity, now packed all the pews and even stood against the walls. It was a better turnout even than last Dingaan's Day, the Day of the Covenant with God in thankgiving for victory over the Zulu hordes and one of the most sacred occasions in the calendar of the Reformed Church.

The singing was impressive. Manfred stood beside Sarah and was so touched by the crystalline beauty of her sweet contralto that he was inspired to underscore it with his untrained but ringing tenor. Even under the deep hood of her traditional Voortrekker bonnet Sarah looked like an angel, golden blonde and lovely, her features shining with religious ecstasy. At fourteen years her womanhood was just breaking into tender uncertain bloom so that Manfred felt a strange breathlessness when he glanced at her over the hymn book they were sharing and she looked up and smiled at him with so much trust and adoration.

The hymn ended and the congregation settled down through a scraping of feet and muted coughing into a tense expectant silence. Uncle Tromp's sermons were renowned throughout South-West Africa, the best entertainment in the territory after the new moving-picture house in Windhoek which very few of them had dared to enter, and Uncle Tromp was in high fettle this day, provoked by the three sober-faced inscrutable gentlemen in the front row who had not even had the common decency to make a courtesy call at the pastory since arriving. He leaned his great gnarled fists on the rail of the pulpit and hunched over them like a prize fighter taking his guard, then he glanced down on his congregation with outraged contempt and they quailed before him with tremulous delight, knowing exactly what that expression presaged.

'Sinners!' Uncle Tromp let fly with a bellow that rang against the roof timbers and the three dark-suited strangers jumped in their seats as though a cannon

had been fired under them. 'The House of God is filled with unrepentant sinners – ' and Uncle Tromp was away; he flailed them with dreadful accusations, raking them with that special tone which Manfred thought of privately as 'the voice' and then lulling them with gentle sonorous passages and promises of salvation before again hurling threats of brimstone and damnation at them like fiery spears, until some of the women were weeping openly and there were hoarse spontaneous cries of 'Amen' and 'Praise the Lord' and 'Hallelujah' and in the end they went down trembling on their knees as he prayed for their very souls.

Afterwards they streamed out of the church with a sort of nervous relief, garrulous and gay as though they had just survived some deadly natural phenomenon such as earthquake or gale at sea. The three strangers were the last to leave, and at the door where Uncle Tromp waited to greet them they shook his hand and each of them spoke quietly and seriously to him in their turn.

Uncle Tromp listened to them gravely, then turned to consult briefly with Aunt Trudi before turning back to them.

'I would be honoured if you would enter my home and sit at my board.'

The four men paced in dignified procession up to the pastory, Aunt Trudi and the children following at a respectful distance. She muttered terse instructions to the girls as they walked and the minute they were out of public view they scampered away to open the drapes in the dining-room, which was only used on very special occasions, and to move the dinner setting from the kitchen to the heavy stinkwood dining-table that was Trudi's inheritance from her mother.

The three strangers did not allow their deep erudite discussion to interfere with their appreciation of Aunt Trudi's cooking, and at the bottom of the table the children ate in dutiful but goggle-eyed silence. Afterwards the men drank their coffee and smoked a pipe on the front step, the drone of their voices soporific in the midday heat, and then it was time to return to divine worship.

The text that Uncle Tromp had chosen for his second sermon was 'The Lord has made straight a path for you in the wilderness'. He delivered it with all his formidable rhetoric and power, but this time he included passages from his own book, assuring his congregation that the Lord had chosen them particularly as a people and set aside a place for them. It remained only for them to reclaim that place in this land that was their heritage. More than once Manfred saw the three grim-faced strangers sitting in the front pew glance at one another significantly as Uncle Tromp was speaking.

The strangers left on the southbound mail train on Monday morning, and for the days and weeks that followed a brittle sense of expectancy pervaded the pastory. Uncle Tromp, breaking his usual custom, took to waiting at the front gate to greet the postman each morning. Quickly he would peruse the packet of mail, and each day his disappointment became more obvious.

Three weeks passed before he gave up waiting for the postman. So he was in the toolshed with Manfred, drilling the Fitzsimmons shift into him, honing that savage left hand of Manfred's, when the letter finally arrived.

It was lying on the hall table when Uncle Tromp went up to the house to wash for supper, and Manfred, who had walked up with him, saw him blanch when he observed the seal of the high moderator of the church on the flap of the envelope. He snatched up the envelope and hurried into his study, slamming

the door in Manfred's face. The lock turned with a heavy clunk. Aunt Trudi had to wait supper almost twenty minutes before he emerged again, and his grace, full of praise and thanksgiving, was twice its usual length. Sarah rolled her eyes and squinted comically across the table at Manfred, and he cautioned her with a quick frown. At last Uncle Tromp roared 'Amen'. Yet he still did not take up his soupspoon but beamed down the length of the table at Aunt Trudi.

'My dear wife,' he said. 'You have been patient and uncomplaining all these years.'

Aunt Trudi blushed scarlet. 'Not in front of the children, *Meneer*,' she whispered, but Uncle Tromp's smile grew broader still.

They have given me Stellenbosch,' he told her, and the silence was complete. They stared at him incredulously. Every one of them understood what he was saying.

'Stellenbosch,' Uncle Tromp repeated, mouthing the word, rolling it over his tongue, gargling it in his throat as though it were the first taste of a rare and noble wine.

Stellenbosch was a small country town thirty miles from Cape Town. The buildings were gabled in the Dutch style, thatched and whitewashed, as dazzling as snow. The streets were broad and lined with the fine oaks that Governor Van Stel had ordered his burghers to plant back in the seventeenth century. Around the town the vineyards of the great château were laid out in a marvellous patchwork and the dark precipices of the mountains rose in a heaven-high backdrop beyond.

A small country town, pretty and picturesque, but it was also the very citadel of Afrikanerdom, enshrined in the university whose faculties were grouped beneath the green oaks and the protecting mountain barricades. It was the centre of Afrikaner intellectualism. Here their language had been forged and was still being crafted. Here their theologians pondered and debated. Tromp Bierman himself had studied beneath Stellenbosch's dreaming oaks. All the great men had trained here: Louis Botha, Hertzog, Jan Christian Smuts. No one who was not Stellenbosch had ever headed the government of the Union of South Africa. Very few who were not Stellenbosch men had even served in the cabinet. It was the Oxford and Cambridge of southern Africa, and they had given the parish to Tromp Bierman. It was an honour unsurpassed, and now the doors would open before him. He would sit at the centre; he would wield power, and the promise of greater power; he would become one of the movers, the innovators. Everything now became possible: the Council of the Synod, the moderatorship itself; none of these were beyond his grasp. Therre were no limits now, no borders nor boundaries. Everything was possible.

'It was the book,' Aunt Trudi breathed. 'I never thought. I never understood – '

'Yes, it was the book,' Uncle Tromp chuckled. 'And thirty years of hard work. We will have the big manse on Eikeboom Straat and a thousand a year. Each of the children will have a separate bedroom and a place at the university paid for by the church. I will preach to the mighty men of the land and our brightest young minds. I will be on the University Council. And you, my dear wife, will have professors and ministers of government at your table; their wives will be your companions – ' he broke off guiltily 'and now we will all pray. We will ask God for humility; we will ask him to save us from the

mortal sins of pride and avarice. Down everybody!' he roared. 'Down on your knees.'

The soup was cold before he allowed them up again.

* * *

They left two months later, after Uncle Tromp had handed over his duties to the young dominie fresh from the theology faculty of the university where the old man was now taking them.

It seemed that every man and woman and child from within a hundred miles was at the station to see them off. Manfred had not realized until that moment just how high was the affection and esteem in which the community held Uncle Tromp. The men all wore their church suits and each of them shook his hand, gruffly thanked him and wished him Godspeed. Some of the women wept and all of them brought gifts – they had baskets of jams and preserves, of milk tarts and *koeksisters*, bags of kudu biltong – and enough food to feed an army on the journey southwards.

Four days later the family changed trains at the central Cape Town railway station. There was barely time for them to troop out into Adderley Street and gape up at the legendary flat-topped massif of Table Mountain that towered over the city before they had to rush back and clamber aboard the coach for the much shorter leg of the journey across the Cape flats and through the sprawling vineyards towards the mountains.

The deacons of the church and half the congregation were on the platform at Stellenbosch station to welcome them, and the family discovered very swiftly that the pace of all their lives had changed dramatically.

From almost the first day, Manfred was totally immersed in preparations for the entrance examinations of the university. He studied from early morning until late every night for two months and then sat the examinations over a single painful week and lived through an even more painful week waiting for the results to be posted. He passed first in German language, third in mathematics and eighth overall, the habits of study he had learned over the years in the Bierman household now bearing full fruit, and was accepted into the faculty of law for the semester beginning at the end of January.

Aunt Trudi was strongly opposed to his leaving the manse and entering one of the university residences for men. As she pointed out, he had a fine room to himself now; the girls would miss him to the point of distraction – by implication she was included amongst those who would suffer – and even on Uncle Tromp's now princely stipend, the residence fees would be a burden on the family exchequer.

Uncle Tromp called upon the university registrar and made some financial arrangements which were never discussed in the family and then came down strongly on Manfred's side.

'Living in a house full of women will drive the boy mad in time. He should go where he can benefit from the company of other young men and from the full life of the university.'

So, on 25 January, Manfred eagerly presented himself at the imposing Cape Dutch style residence for gentlemen students, Rust en Vrede. The name translated as 'Rest and Peace', and within the first few minutes of arrival he

realized just how ironic was the choice for he was caught up in the barbaric ritual of freshman initiation.

His name was taken from him and he was given instead the sobriquet of *Poep*; which he shared with the nineteen other freshmen of the house. This translated freely as 'flatus'. He was forbidden to use the pronouns 'I' or 'me' but only 'this flatus', and he had to request permission not only of the senior men for every action but also of all inanimate objects he encountered in the residence. Thus he was obliged to utter endless inanities: 'Honourable door, this flatus wishes to pass through,' or 'Honourable toilet, this flatus wishes to sit upon you.'

Within the residence he and his fellow freshmen were not allowed normal means of perambulation but were made to walk backwards, even down stairs, at all times. They were held incommunicado from friends and family and in particular were most strenuously forbidden to talk to anybody of the opposite sex; if they were caught so much as looking in the general direction of a pretty girl a warning notice was hung around their necks and could not be removed even in the bath. 'Beware! Sex maniac at large.'

Their rooms were raided by the seniors every hour, on the hour, from six in the evening until six in the morning. All their bedding was piled in the middle of the floor and soaked with water, their books and possessions were swept from the shelves and turned out of the drawers and piled on the sodden blankets. The senior men performed this duty in shifts until the shivering freshmen took to sleeping on the bare tiles of the passage outside their bedrooms, leaving the chaos within to mould and fester. Whereupon the senior student, a lordly fourth-year honours man named Roelf Stander, held a formal house committee inspection of the rooms.

'You are the most disgusting cloud of flatus ever to disgrace this university,' he told them at the end of the inspection. 'You have one hour in which to make your rooms spotless and put them in perfect order, after which you will be taken on a route march as punishment for your slovenly attitude.'

It was midnight when Roelf Stander finally announced that he was satisfied with the condition of their bedrooms and they were prepared for the route march.

This involved stripping them to their underpants, placing a pillow case over their heads, tying them in Indian file with a rope around their necks and their hands strapped behind their backs and marching them through the streets of the sleeping town and out into the mountains. The chosen route was rough and stony and when one of them fell he brought down the freshmen in front and behind. At four in the morning they were led back into town on bleeding feet and with their throats chafed raw from the coarse hemp rope to find their rooms had been raided once again and that Roelf Stander's next inspection would take place at five o'clock. The first lecture of the university day began at seven. There was no time for breakfast.

All this came under the heading of good clean fun; the university authorities turned a blind eye upon the rites on the grounds that boys will be boys and that the initiation ritual was a 'university tradition', instilling a community spirit into the new arrivals.

However, in this climate of indulgence the bullies and sadists who lurk in any community took full advantage of the sanction accorded them. There were a few merciless beatings, and one freshman was tarred and feathered. Manfred had heard light talk of this punishment, but had not been able to imagine the

dreadful agony that it inflicted when the victim's skin was sealed and his scalp and body hair matted and coated with hot tar. The boy was hospitalized and never returned to the university, but the affair was hushed up completely.

Other freshmen dropped out in those first weeks, for the self-appointed guardians of the university tradition made no allowance for delicate physical or mental constitutions. One of the victims, an asthmatic, was judged guilty of insubordination by the seniors and was sentenced to formal drowning.

This sentence was carried out in the bathroom of the residence. The victim was pinioned by four hefty seniors and lowered headfirst into the toilet bowl of the lavatory. Two fifth-year medical students were present to monitor the victim's pulse and heartbeat during the punishment, but they had not made allowance for his asthma, and the drowning almost ended as the real thing. Only frantic efforts by the budding doctors and an intravenous injection of stimulant starting the boy's heart beating again; he left the university next day, like the other dropouts, never to return.

Manfred, despite his size and physique and good looks, which made him a natural target, was able to bridle his anger and check his tongue. He submitted stoically even to extreme provocation until in the second week of torment a note was pinned on the board in the residence common room:

> All flatus will report to the university gymnasium at 4 pm on Saturday to try out for the boxing squad.
> Signed: Roelf Stander
> Captain of Boxing

Each of the university residences specialized in some particular sport; one was the rugby football house, another was field and track; but Rust en Vrede's sport was boxing. This, together with the fact that it was Uncle Tromp's old house, was the reason why Manfred had applied for admission in the first place.

It was also the reason why the interest in the freshmen tryout was far beyond anything that Manfred had expected. At least three hundred spectators were assembled, and the seats around the ring were all filled by the time that Manfred and his fellow flatus arrived at the gymnasium. Marshalled by one of the senior men into a crocodile column, they were marched to the changing-rooms and given five minutes to change into tennis shoes, shorts and vests, then lined up against the lockers in order of height.

Roelf Stander strolled down the rank, glancing at the list in his hand and making the matchings. It was obvious that he had been studying them during the preceding weeks and grading their potential. Manfred, the tallest and sturdiest of all the freshmen, was at the end of the line, and Roelf Standeer stopped in front of him last.

'There is no other fart as loud and smelly as this one,' he announced, and then was silent for a moment as he studied Manfred. 'What do you weigh, Flatus?'

'This flatus is light heavyweight, sir,' and Roelf's eyes narrowed slightly. He had already singled Manfred out as the best prospect and now the technical jargon heartened him.

'Have you boxed before, Flatus?' he demanded, and then pulled a wry face at the disappointing reply.

'This flatus has never boxed a match, sir, but this flatus has had some practice.'

'Oh, all right, then! I am heavyweight. But as there is no one else to give you a match, I'll go a few rounds with you, if you promise to treat me lightly, Flatus.'

Roelf Stander was captain of the university squad, amateur provincial champion and one of South Africa's better propects for the team which would go to Berlin for the Olympic Games in 1936. It was a rich joke cracked by a senior student and everybody laughed slavishly. Even Roelf could not hide a grin at his own preposterous plea for mercy.

'All right, we'll begin with the flyweights,' he continued, and led them out into the gymnasium.

The freshmen were seated on a long bench at the back of the hall with an imperfect view of the ring over the heads of the more privileged spectators as Roelf and his assistants, all members of the boxing squad, put the gloves on the first trialists and led them down the aisle to the ring.

While this was going on Manfred became aware of somebody in the front row of seats standing and trying to catch his eye. He glanced around at the senior men who were in charge of them, but their attention was on the ring so for the first time he looked directly at the person in the crowd.

He had forgotten how pretty Sarah was, either that or she had blossomed in the weeks since he had last seen her. Her eyes sparkled and her cheeks were flushed with excitement as she waved a lace handkerchief and mouthed his name happily.

He kept his expression inscrutable, but lowered one eyelid at her in a furtive wink and she blew him a two-handed kiss and dropped back into her seat beside the mountainous bulk of Uncle Tromp.

'They have both come!' The knowledge cheered him enormously; until that moment he had not realized how lonely these last weeks had been. Uncle Tromp turned his head and grinned at him, his teeth very white in the frosted black bush of his beard; then he turned back to face the ring.

The first bout began: two game little flyweights going at each other in a flurry of blows, but one was outclassed and soon there was blood sprinkling the canvas. Roelf Stander stopped it in the second round and patted the loser on the back.

'Well done! No shame in losing.'

The other bouts followed, all of them spirited, the fighters obviously doing their very best, but apart from a promising middleweight, it was all very rough and unskilled. At last Manfred was the only one on the bench.

'All right, Flatus!' The senior laced his gloves and told him: 'Let's see what you can do.'

Manfred slipped the towel off his shoulders and stood up just as Roelf Stander climbed back into the ring from the changing-room end. He now wore the maroon vest and trunks piped with gold that were Varsity colours, and on his feet were expensive boots of glove leather laced high over the ankles. He held up both gloved hands to quieten the whistles and good-natured cheers.

'Ladies and Gentlemen. We do not have a match for our last trialist; no other freshman in his weight division. So if you will be kind enough to bear with me, I'm going to take him through his paces.'

The cheers broke out again, but now there were shouts of 'Go easy on him, Roelf,' and 'Don't kill the poor beggar!' Roelf waved his assurance of mercy at

them, concentrating on the section of seats filled with girls from the women's residences, and there were muted squeals and giggles and a tossing of permanently waved coiffures, for Roelf stood six feet, with a square jaw, white teeth and flashing dark eyes. His hair was thick and wavy and gleaming with Brylcreem, his sideburns dense and curling and his moustache dashing as a cavalier's.

As Manfred reached the front row of seats he could not restrain himself from glancing sideways at Sarah and Uncle Tromp. Sarah was hopping her bottom up and down on her seat, and she pressed her clenched fists to cheeks that were rosy with excitement.

'Get him, Manie,' she cried. '*Vat hom!*' and beside her Uncle Tromp nodded at him. 'Fast as a mamba, *Jong*! Brave as a ratel!' he rumbled so that only Manfred could hear; and Manfred lifted his chin and there was a new lightness in his feet as he ducked through the ropes into the ring.

One of the other seniors had taken over the duty of referee: 'In this corner at one hundred and eighty-five pounds the captain of Varsity and amateur heavyweight champion of the Cape of Good Hope – Roelf Stander! And in this corner at one hundred and seventy-three pounds a freshman – ' in deference to the delicate company, he did not use the full honorific, ' – Manfred De La Rey.' The timekeeper struck his gong and Roelf came out of his corner dancing lightly, ducking and wreaving, smiling thinly over his red leather gloves as they circled each other. Just out of striking distance, around they went, and then back the other way, and the smile left Roelf's lips and they tightened into a straight thin line. His light manner evaporated; he had not expected this.

There was no weak place in the guard of the man who faced him; his cropped golden head was lowered on muscled shoulders, and he moved on his feet like a cloud.

'He's a fighter!' Roelf's anger flared. 'He lied – he knows what he's doing.' He tried once more to command the centre of the ring, but was forced to turn out again as his adversary moved threateningly into his left.

As yet neither of them had thrown a punch, but the cheers of the crowd subsided. They sensed that they were watching something extraordinary; they saw Roelf's casual attitude change, saw deadly intent come into the way he was moving now; and those who knew him well saw the little lines of worry and perturbation at the corners of his mouth and eyes.

Roelf flicked out his left, a testing shot, and the other man did not even deign to duck; he turned it off his glove contemptuously, and Roelf's skin prickled with shock as he sensed the power in that fleeting contact and looked deeply into Manfred's eyes. It was a trick of his, establishing domination by eye contact.

This man's eyes were a strange light colour, like topaz or yellow sapphire, and Roelf remembered the eyes of a calf-killing leopard that his father had caught in a steel spring trap in the hills above the farm homestead. These were the same eyes, and now they altered, they burned with a cold golden light, implacable and inhuman.

It was not fear that clenched Roelf Stander's chest but rather a premonition of terrible danger. This was an animal in the ring with him. He could see the hunger in its eyes, a great killing hunger, and he struck out at it instinctively.

He used his left, his good hand, driving in hard at those pitiless yellow eyes. The blow died in the air and he tried desperately to recover, but his left elbow was raised, his flank was open for perhaps a hundredth part of a second, and

something exploded inside of him. He did not see the fist; he did not recognize it as a punch, for he had never been hit like that before. It felt as though it was inside him, bursting through his ribs, tearing out his viscera, imploding his lungs, driving the wind out of his throat in a hissing agony as he was flung backwards.

The ropes caught him in the small of the back and under the shoulder blades and hurled him forward again like a stone from a slingshot. Time seemed to slow down to a trickle; his vision was enhanced, magnified as though there was a drug in his blood, and this time he saw the fist; he had a weird flash of fantasy that it was not flesh and bone but black iron in that glove, and his flesh quailed. But he was powerless to avoid it and this time the shock was even greater – unbelievable, beyond his wildest imaginings. He felt something tear inside him and the bones of his legs melted like hot candlewax.

He wanted to scream at the agony of it, but even in his extremity he choked it off. He wanted to go down, to get down on the canvas before the fist came again, but the ropes held him up and his body seemed to shatter like crystal as the gloved hand crashed into him and the ropes flung him forward.

His hands dropped away from his face and he saw the fist coming yet again. It seemed to balloon before his eyes, filling his vision, but he did not feel it strike.

Roelf was moving into it with all his weight and his skull snapped back in whiplash against the tension of his spinal column and then dropped forward again and he went down on his face like a dead man and lay without a tremor of movement on the white canvas.

It was all over in seconds, the crowd sitting in stunned silence, Manfred still weaving and swaying over the prostrate figure that lay at his feet, his features contorted into a mask of savagery and that strange yellow light glowing in his eyes, not yet human, with the killing sickness still strong upon him.

Then in the crowd a woman screamed and instantly there was consternation and uproar. The men were up on their feet, chairs crashing over backwards, roaring in bewilderment and amazement and jubilation, rushing forward, clambering through the ropes, surrounding Manfred, pounding his back, others on their knees beside the maroon-and-gold-clad figure lying deathly still on the canvas, jabbering instructions at one another as they lifted him gingerly, one of them dabbing ineffectually at the blood; all of them stunned and shaken.

The women were pale-faced with shock, some of them still screaming with delicious horror, their eyes bright with excitation which was tinged with sexuality, craning to watch as Roelf Stander was lifted over the ropes and carried down the aisle, hanging limp as a corpse, his head lolling, blood running back from his slack mouth across his cheek into his gleaming hair – turning to watch Manfred as he was hustled along to the changing-rooms by a group of seniors. The women's faces betrayed fear and horror but some of their eyes smouldered with physical arousal, and one of them reached out to touch Manfred's shoulder as he passed.

Uncle Tromp took Sarah's arm to calm her, for she was capering and shrilling like a dervish, and led her out of the hall into the sunlight. She was still incoherent with excitement.

'He was wonderful – so quick, so beautiful. Oh, Uncle Tromp, I have never seen anything like that in my life. Isn't he wonderful?'

Uncle Tromp grunted but made no comment, listening to her chatter all the way back to the manse. Only when they climbed the front steps onto the wide

stoep did he stop and look back, as though to a place or a person that he was leaving with deep regret.

'His life has changed, and ours will change with him,' he murmured soberly. 'I pray Almighty God that none of us ever lives to regret what happened to us this day, for I am the one who brought this about.'

* * *

For three more days the ritual of initiation continued, and Manfred was still denied contact with anybody but his fellow freshmen. However, to them he had become a godlike figure, their very hope of salvation, and they crowded to him pathetically through the final humiliations and degradation to take strength and determination from him.

The last night was the worst. Blindfolded and denied sleep, forced to sit unflinching on a narrow beam, a galvanized bucket over their heads against which a senior would crack a club unexpectedly, the night seemed to last for ever. Then in the dawn the buckets and blindfolds were removed and Roelf Stander addressed them.

'Men!' he started, and they blinked with shock at being called that, for they were still in stupor from lack of sleep and half deafened by the blows on their buckets. 'Men!' Stander repeated. 'We are proud of you – you are the best damned bunch of freshers we've had in this house since I was a fresher myself. You took everything we could throw at you and never squealed or funked it. Welcome to Rust en Vrede; this is your house now, and we are your brothers.' And then the seniors were swarming around them, laughing and slapping their backs and embracing them.

'Come on, men! Down to the pub. We are buying the beer!' Roelf Stander bellowed and, a hundred strong, arms linked, singing the house song, they marched down to the old Drosdy Hotel and pounded on the locked door until the publican in defiance of licensing hours finally gave in and opened up for them.

Light-headed with sleeplessness and with a pint of lager in his belly, Manfred was grinning owlishly and hanging surreptitiously onto the bar counter to keep on his feet when he had a feeling that something was up. He turned quickly.

The crowd around him had opened, leaving a corridor down which Roelf Stander was stalking towards him, grim-faced and threatening. Manfred's pulse raced as he realized that this was to be their first confrontation since that in the ring three days before, and it was not going to be pleasant. He set down his empty tankard, shook his head to clear it and turned to face the other man, and they glowered at each other.

Roelf stopped in front of him, and the others, freshers and seniors, crowded close so as not to miss a single word. The suspense drew out for long seconds, nobody daring to breathe.

'Two things I want to do to you,' Roelf Stander growled, and then, as Manfred braced himself, he smiled, a flashing charming smile, and held out his right hand. 'First, I want to shake your hand, and second, I want to buy you a beer. By God, Manie, you punch like no man I've ever fought before.' There was a howl of laughter and the day dissolved into a haze of beer fumes and good fellowship.

That should have been the end of it, because even though formal initiation had ended and Manfred had been accepted into the Rust en Vrede fraternity, there was still a vast social divide between a fourth-year honours man, senior student and captain of boxing, and a freshman. However, the following evening, an hour before house dinner, there was a knock on Manie's door and Roelf sauntered in dressed in his academic gown and hood, dropped into the single armchair, crossed his ankles on top of Manie's desk and chatted easily about boxing and law studies and South-West Africa geography until the gong sounded, when he stood up.

'I'll wake you at five am tomorrow for roadwork. We've got an important match against the Ikeys in two weeks,' he announced, and then grinned at Manie's expression. 'Yes, Manie, you are on the squad.'

After that Roelf dropped in every evening before dinner, often with a black bottle of beer in the pocket of his gown which they shared out of tooth mugs, and each time their friendship became more relaxed and secure.

This was not lost on the other members of the house, both seniors and freshers, and Manie's status was enhanced. Two weeks later the match against the Ikey team was contested in four weight divisions and Manie donned the university colours for the first time. Ikeys was the nickname for the students at the University of Cape Town, the English-language university of the Cape and traditional rival of Stellenbosch, the Afrikaans-language university whose men were nicknamed Maties. So keen was the rivalry between them that Ikey supporters came out the thirty miles in busloads, dressed in their university colours, full of beer and rowdy enthusiasm, and packed out half the gymnasium, roaring their university songs at the Matie supporters on the other side of the hall.

Manie's opponent was Laurie King, an experienced lightheavy with good hands and a concrete jaw who had never been put down in forty amateur bouts. Almost nobody had ever heard of Manfred De La Rey, and those few who had now discounted his single victory as a lucky punch on an opponent who wasn't taking it seriously anyway.

Laurie King, however, had heard the story and he was taking it very seriously indeed. He kept off for most of the first round until the crowd started to boo with impatience. However, he had now studied Manfred and decided that, although he moved well, he wasn't as dangerous as he had been warned and that he could be taken with a left to the head. He went in to test this theory. The last thing he remembered was a pair of ferocious yellow eyes, burning like a Kalahari sun at midday into his face, and then the harsh canvas grazing the skin from his cheek as he slammed head first into the boards of the ring. He never remembered seeing the punch. Although the gong rang before he was counted out, Laurie King could not come out for the second round; his head was still rolling like a drunkard's. He had to be supported by his seconds back to the dressing-room.

In the front row Uncle Tromp roared like a wounded bull buffalo while beside him Sarah shrieked herself hoarse as tears of joy and excitement wet her lashes and shone upon her cheeks.

The next morning the boxing correspondent of the Afrikaans newspaper *Die Burger*, 'The Citizen', dubbed Manfred 'The Lion of the Kalahari' and mentioned that he was not only the great nephew of General Jacobus Hercules De La Rey, hero of the *Volk*, but also related to the Reverend Tromp Bierman, boxing champion, author, and the new dominie of Stellenbosch.

Roelf Stander and the entire boxing squad were waiting in the quadrangle when Manfred came out of his sociology lecture and they surrounded him.

'You've been holding out on us, Manie,' Roelf accused furiously. 'You never told us that your uncle is *the* Tromp Bierman. Sweet mercy, man, he was national champion for five years. He knocked out both Slater and Black Jephta!'

'Didn't I tell you?' Manie frowned thoughtfully. 'It must have slipped my mind.'

'Manie, you have to introduce us,' the vice-captain pleaded. 'We all want to meet him, please, man, please.'

'Do you think he would coach the team, Manie? Won't you ask him. Hell, if we had Tromp Bierman as coach – ' Roelf broke off, awed into silence by the thought.

'I tell you what,' Manie suggested. 'If you can get the whole boxing team to church on Sunday morning, I'm sure that my Aunt Trudi will invite us all to Sunday lunch. I tell you, gentlemen, you don't know what heaven is until you have tasted my Aunt Trudi's *koeksisters*.'

So scrubbed and shaven and Brylcreemed and buttoned into their Sunday-best suits, the university boxing squad took up a full pew of the church, and their responses and rendition of the hymns shook the roof timbers.

Aunt Trudi looked upon the occasion as a challenge to her culinary skills and she and the girls took all week to prepare the dinner. The guests, all lusty young men in peak physical condition, had existed on university fare for weeks, and they gazed in ravenous disbelief upon the banquet, trying valiantly to divide their attention between Uncle Tromp, who was in top form at the head of the long table recounting his most memorable fights, the tittering blushing daughters of the house who waited upon them and the groaning board piled with roasts and preserves and puddings.

At the end of the meal Roelf Stander, bloated like a python which had swallowed a gazelle, rose to make a speech of thanks on behalf of the team, and halfway through changed it into an impassioned plea to Uncle Tromp to accept the duties of honorary coach.

Uncle Tromp waved away the request with a jovial chortle as though it were totally unthinkable, but the entire team, including Manie, added their entreaties, whereupon he made a series of excuses, each one lamer than the preceding one, all of which were vociferously rebutted by the team in unison, until finally, with a heavy sigh of resignation and forbearance, he capitulated. Then while accepting their fervent gratitude and hearty handshakes, he at last broke down and beamed with unrestrained pleasure.

'I tell you, boys, you don't know what you've let yourselves in for. There are many words I don't understand at all. "I'm tired" and "I've had enough" are just some of them,' he warned.

After the evening service, Manie and Roelf walked back under the dark rustling oaks to Rust en Vrede and Roelf was uncharacteristically silent, not speaking until they had reached the main gates. Then his tone was reflective:

'Tell me, Manie, your cousin – how old is she?'

'Which one?' Manie asked without interest. 'The fat one is Gertrude and the one with pimples is Renata – '

'No! No, Manie, don't be a dog!' Roelf cut him short. 'The pretty one with blue eyes, the one with the silky gold hair. The one I'm going to marry.'

Manfred stopped dead and swung to face him, his head going down on his shoulders, his mouth twisting into a snarl.

'Never say that again!' His voice shook and he seized the front of Roelf's jacket. 'Don't ever talk dirty like that again. I warn you, you talk about Sarah like that again, and I'll kill you.'

Manfred's face was only inches from Roelf's. That terrible yellow glow, the killing rage, was in his eyes.

'Hey, Manie,' Roelf whispered hoarsely. 'What's wrong with you? I didn't say anything dirty. Are you mad? I would never insult Sarah.'

The yellow rage faded slowly from Manfred's eyes and he released his grip on Roelf's lapels. He shook his head as if to clear it, and his voice was bemused when he spoke again. 'She's only a baby. You shouldn't talk like that, man. She's only a little girl.'

'A baby?' Roelf chuckled uncertainly and straightened his jacket. 'Are you blind, Manie. She's not a baby. She is the most lovely – ' but Manfred flung away angrily and went storming through the gates into the house.

'So, my friend,' Roelf whispered, 'that's how it is!' He sighed and thrust his hands deeply into his pockets. And then he remembered how Sarah had looked at Manfred during the meal and how he had seen her lay her hand on the back of his neck, furtively and adoringly, as she leaned over him to take his empty plate, and he sighed again, overcome suddenly with a brooding sense of melancholy. 'There are a thousand pretty girls out there,' he told himself with an attempt to throw off the dark mood. 'All of them panting for Roelf Stander – ' and he shrugged and grinned lopsidedly and followed Manie into the house.

* * *

Manfred won his next twelve matches in an unbroken succession, all of them by knock-out, all of them within three rounds; and all the sports writers had by now adopted the name 'Lion of the Kalahari' in describing his feats.

'All right, *Jong*, win them while you can,' Uncle Tromp admonished. 'But just remember you aren't going to be young always, and in the long run it's not a man's muscles and fists that keep him on top. It's what's in his skull, *Jong*, and don't you ever forget it!' So Manfred threw himself as enthusiastically into his academic studies as he had into his training routine.

German was by now almost as natural to him as Afrikaans, and he was considerably more fluent in it than in English, which he spoke only reluctantly and with a heavy accent. He found the Roman Dutch Law satisfying in its logic and philosophy and read the Institutes of Justinian like literature; at the same time politics and sociology both fascinated him. He and Roelf debated and discussed them endlessly, cementing their own friendship in the process.

His boxing prowess had made him an instant celebrity on the Stellenbosch campus. Some of his professors treated him with special favour and condescension because of this, while others were at first deliberately antagonistic, acting as though he were a dunce until he proved that he was not.

'Perhaps our well-known pugilist will give us the benefit of his towering intellect and throw some light on the concept of National Bolshevism for us.' The speaker was the professor of Sociology and Politics, a tall austere intellectual with the piercing eyes of a mystic. Though he had been born in Holland his parents had brought him out to Africa at an early age, and Dr Hendrick Frensch Verwoerd was now one of the leading Afrikaans intellectuals and a champion of

his people's nationalist aspirations. He lectured first-year political students only once a semester, reserving most of his efforts for his faculty's honour students. Now he was smiling superciliously as Manfred rose slowly to his feet and composed his thoughts.

Dr Verwoerd waited for a few seconds and was about to wave him down again, the fellow was clearly a clod, when Manfred began his reply, speaking with carefully couched grammatical exactitude and in his newly acquired Stellenbosch accent which Roelf was helping him hone – the 'Oxford' accent of Afrikaans.

'As opposed to the revoluntionary ideology of conventional Bolshevism created under Lenin's leadership, National Bolshevism was originally a term used in Germany to describe a policy of resistance to the Treaty of Versailles – ' and Dr Verwoerd blinked and stopped smiling. The fellow had seen the trap from a mile off, separating the two concepts immediately.

'Can you tell us who was the innovator of the concept?' Dr Verwoerd demanded, a prickle of exasperation in his usual cool tones.

'I believe the idea was first put forward in 1919 by Karl Radek. His forum was an alliance of the pariah powers against the common Western enemies of Britain, France and the United States.'

The professor leaned forward like a falcon bating for its prey. 'In your view, sir, does it, or a similar doctrine, have any currency in the present politics of southern Africa?' They devoted all their attention to each other for the rest of the session, while Manfred's peers, relieved of all necessity to think, listened with varying degrees of mystification or boredom.

The following Saturday night, when Manfred won the university light heavyweight title in the packed gymnasium, Dr Verwoerd was sitting in the second row. It was the first time that he had been seen at any of the university's athletic tournaments, apart, of course, from the rugby football matches which no Afrikaner worthy of the name would have missed.

A few days later the professor sent for Manfred, ostensibly to discuss an essay that he had submitted on the history of liberalism, but their discussion ran for well over an hour and ranged widely. When it ended Dr Verwoerd stopped Manfred at the door. 'Here is a book that you might not have had an opportunity to look at.' He handed it across the desk. 'Keep it as long as you need, and let me know your views when you have finished with it.'

Manfred was in a hurry to get to his next lecture so he did not even read the title, and when he got back to his room he tossed it on his desk. Roelf was waiting to join him on their evening run and he had no chance to look at the book again until he had changed into his pyjamas late that night.

He picked it up from the desk and saw that he had already heard of it, and that it was in the original German. He did not put it down again until dawn was glimmering through the chinks of his curtains and the rock pigeons were cooing on the ledge outside of his window. Then he closed the book and re-read the title: *Mein Kampf* by Adolf Hitler.

He passed the rest of the day in a trance of almost religious revelation and hurried back to his room at lunchtime to read again. The author was speaking directly to him, addressing his German and Aryan bloodlines. He had the weird sensation that it had been written exclusively for him. Why else would Herr Hitler have included such marvellous passages as:

> It is considered as natural and honourable that a young man should learn to fence and proceed to fight duels right and left, but if he boxes, it is supposed to be vulgar! Why? There is no sport that

so much as this one promotes the spirit of attack, demanding lightning decisions, and trains the body in steel dexterity . . . but above all the young healthy body must also learn to suffer blows – it is not the function of the *Völkisch* state to breed a colony of peaceful aesthetes and physical degenerates . . . If our entire intellectual upper class had not been brought up so exclusively on upper-class etiquette; if instead they had learned boxing thoroughly, a German revolution of pimps, deserters and suchlike rabble would never have been possible . . .

Manfred shivered with a sense of foreknowledge when he saw his own hardly formulated attitudes to personal morality so clearly explained.

Parallel to the training of the body, a struggle against the poisoning of the soul must begin. Our whole public life today is a hot-house for sexual ideas and stimulations . . .

Manfred had himself suffered from these torments set like snares for the young and pure. He had been forced to struggle against the evil lustful clamour of his own body when he had been exposed to magazine and cinema posters – always written in English, that effete degenerate language which he was growing to hate – depicting half-naked females.

'You are right,' he muttered, turning the pages furiously. 'You are laying out the great truths for all of mankind. We must be pure and strong.'

Then his heart bounded as he saw set out in unequivocal language the other truths that he had only before heard lightly hinted at. He was transported back across the years to the hobo camp beside the railway tracks outside Windhoek, and saw again the tattered newspaper cartoon of Hoggenheimer driving the *Volk* into slavery. His outrage was consuming and he trembled with anger when he read:

With satanic joy in his face, the black-haired Jewish youth lurks in wait for the unsuspecting girl whom he defies with his blood, stealing her from her people.

In his imagination he saw Sarah's sweet pale body lying spreadeagled under the gross hairy carcass of Hoggenheimer and he was ready to kill.

Then the author lanced a vein of his Afrikaner blood so skilfully that Manfred's soul seemed almost to bleed upon the page.

It was and is the Jews who bring the negroes into the Rhineland, always with the same secret thought and clear aim ruining of the hated white race by the necessarily resulting bastardization . . .

He shuddered. '*Swartgevaar!* Black danger!' had been the rallying cry of his people over the centuries they had been in Africa, and his atavistic heart beat to that summons once again.

He finished the book shaken and exhausted as he had never been in the boxing ring. Although it was already late he went to find the man who had loaned it to him, and they talked eagerly and seriously until after midnight.

The next day the professor dropped an approving word to another in a high place: 'I have found one who I believe will be a valuable recruit, one with a good receptive mind who will soon have great infuence and standing amongst our young people.'

Manfred's name was laid before the high council of a secret society at its next conclave:

'One of our best young men at the university, the senior student of Rust en Vrede is close to him – '

'Have him recruited,' ordered the chairman of the council.

* * *

Five days a week Roelf and Manfred ran a training route through the mountains together, a hard route of steep gradients and rough footing. Five miles out they stopped to drink in the pool below a feathery white waterfall. Roelf watched Manfred kneel on the slippery wet rocks and scoop up a double handful of the clear cold water to pour it into his open mouth.

'He is a good choice,' he agreed silently with the decision of his superiors. The light vest and shorts that Manfred wore showed off his powerful but graceful body, and his lustrous coppery hair and fine features were compelling. But it was the gold topaz eyes that were the key to his personality. Even Roelf felt overshadowed by the younger man's developing confidence and assurance.

'I will be a strong leader, the type we need so desperately.'

Manfred sprang to his feet again, dashing the water from his mouth with his forearm.

'Come on, drag arse,' he laughed. 'Last one back home is a Bolshevik.'

But Roelf stopped him. 'Today I want to talk to you,' he admitted, and Manfred frowned.

'Hell, man, we do nothing but talk anyway. Why here?'

'Because here no one will overhear us. And you are wrong, Manie, some of us are doing more than just talking. We are preparing for action, hard fighting action, the kind of action you love so well.'

Manfred turned back towards him, immediately intrigued, and came to squat in front of him. 'Who? What action?' he demanded, and Roelf inclined his head.

'A secret élite of dedicated Afrikaners, the leaders of our people, men in top places, in government and education and the commercial life of the nation. That's who, Manie. And not only the leaders of today, Manie, the leaders of tomorrow also. Men like you and me, Manie – that's who.'

'A secret society?' Manfred swayed back on his heels.

'No, Manie, much more than that, a secret army ready to fight for our poor downtrodden people. Ready to die to restore our nation to greatness.'

Manfred felt the fine hairs on his arms and at the nape of his neck come erect as the thrill of it coursed through his veins. His response was immediate and unquestioning.

'Soldiers, Manie, the storm-troopers of our nation,' Roelf went on.

'Are you one of them, Roelf?' Manie demanded.

'Yes, Manie, I am one of them, and you also. You have attracted the attention of our supreme council. I have been asked to invite you to join us in our march to destiny, in our struggle to fulfil the manifest destiny of our people.'

'Who are our leaders? What is the name of this secret army?'

'You will know. You will be told everything after you have taken the oath of allegiance,' Roelf promised him, and reached out to seize his arm, pressing powerful fingers into Manie's thick rubber-hard biceps.

'Do you accept the call of duty?' he asked. 'Will you join us, Manfred De La Rey? Will you wear our uniform and fight in our ranks?'

Manfred's Dutch blood, suspicious and broodingly introspective, responded to his promise of clandestine intrigue, while his Germanic side longed for the order and authority of a society of fierce warriors, modern-day Teutonic knights, hard and unrelenting for God and Country. And though he was unaware of it, the streak of flamboyance and love of theatrics he had inherited from his French mother was drawn to the military pomp, uniforms and eagles, that Roelf seemed to offer him.

He reached out and seized Roelf's shoulder and they held each other in the clasp of comrades, staring deeply into each other's eyes.

'With all my heart,' Manfred said softly. 'I will join you with all my heart.'

* * *

The full moon stood high above the Stellenbosch mountains, silvering their sheer buttresses and plunging the gullies and ravines into deepest black. In the south the Great Cross stood high, but it was washed out into insignificance by the huge fiery cross that burned closer and fiercer at the head of the open forest glade. It was a natural amphitheatre, screened by the dense conifers that surrounded it, a secret place, hidden from curious or hostile eyes perfect for the purpose.

Beneath the fiery cross the ranks of storm-troopers were massed and their polished cross belts and buckles glinted in its light and in that of the burning torches each of them held high. There were not more than three hundred troopers present, for they were the elite, and their expressions were proud and solemn as they watched the tiny band of new recruits march out of the forest and down the slope of the glade to where the general waited to greet them.

Manfred De La Rey was the first of them to come to attention before the leaders. He wore the black shirt and riding-breeches, the high polished riding-boots of this secret band of knights, but his head was bare and his uniform unadorned except for the sheathed dagger on his belt.

The high commander stepped forward and stopped only a pace in front of Manfred. He was an imposing figure, a tall man with craggy weathered face and hard jutting jaw. Although thickened around the waist and big-bellied under his black shirt, he was a man in his prime, a black-maned lion in his pride and the aura of command and authority sat easily upon his broad shoulders.

Manfred recognized him immediately, for his was a face often reproduced in the political columns of the national newspaper. He was high in government, the administrator of one of the country's provinces, and his influence was deep and far-reaching.

'Manfred De La Rey,' the commander asked in a powerful voice, 'are you ready to take the blood oath?'

'I am,' Manfred replied clearly, and drew the silver dagger from his belt.

From the ranks behind him Roelf Stander, in full uniform, capped and booted and with the broken cross insignia on his right arm, stepped out and drew the pistol from his holster. He cocked the pistol and pressed the muzzle to Manfred's chest, aiming for the heart, and Manfred did not flinch. Roelf was

his sponsor. The pistol was symbolic of the fact that he would also be his executioner should Manfred ever betray the blood oath he was about to swear.

Ceremoniously the commander handed Manfred a sheet of stiff parchment. Its head was illuminated by the crest of the order: a stylized powderhorn like those used by the *Voortrekkers*, the pioneers of his people. Below it was printed the oath, and Manfred took it in one hand and with the other held the bared dagger pointed at his own heart to signify his willingness to lay down his life for the ideals of the brotherhood.

'Before Almighty God, and in the sight of my comrades,' he read aloud, 'I subject myself entirely to the dictates of my people's divinely ordained destiny. I swear to be faithful to the precepts of the *Ossewa Brandwag*, the sentinels of the Afrikaner wagon train, and to obey the orders of my superiors. On my life I swear a deadly oath of secrecy, that I will cherish and hold sacred the affairs and proceedings of the *Ossewa Brandwag*. I demand that if I should betray my comrades, my oath or my *Volk*, vengeance shall follow me to my traitor's grave. I call upon my comrades to hear my entreaty.

If I advance, follow me.
If I retreat, shoot me down.
If I die, avenge me.
So help me Almighty God!

And Manfred drew the silver blade across his wrist so that his blood sprang dark ruby in the torchlight, and he sprinkled the parchment with it.

The high commander stepped forward to embrace him, and behind him the black ranks erupted in a jubilant warlike roar of approval. At his side Roelf Stander returned the loaded pistol to its holster, his eyelids stinging with the nettles of proud tears. As the commander stepped back, Roelf rushed forward to take Manfred's right hand in his. 'My brother.' His whisper was choking. 'Now we are truly brothers.'

* * *

In mid-November Manfred sat his end-of-year examinations and passed third in a law class of 153.

Three days after the results were posted, the Stellenbosch boxing squad, led by its coach, left to take part in the Inter-Varsity Championships. This year the venue was the University of the Witwatersrand in Johannesburg, and boxers from the other universities of South Africa journeyed from every province and corner of the Union to take part.

The Stellenbosch team travelled up by train, and there was a cheering, singing crowd of students and faculty members to see them off at the railway station on their thousand-mile journey.

Uncle Tromp kissed his women farewell, beginning with Aunt Trudi and working his way down to Sarah, the youngest, at the end of the line, and Manfred followed him. He was wearing his colours blazer and straw basher and he was so tall and beautiful that Sarah could not bear it and she burst into tears as he stooped over her. She flung both arms around his neck and squeezed with all her strength.

'Come along, don't be a silly little duck,' Manfred gruffed in her ear, but his voice was rough with the strange unaccustomed tumult that the contact of her hot silky cheek against his provoked beneath his ribs.

'Oh, Manie, you are going so far away.' She tried to hide her tears in the angle of his neck. 'We have never been parted by such distance.'

'Come on, monkey. People are looking at you,' he chided her gently. 'Give me a kiss and I'll bring you back a present.'

'I don't want a present. I want you,' she sniffed, and then lifted her sweet face and placed her mouth over his. Her mouth seemed to melt in its own heat, and it was moist and sweet as a ripe apple.

The contact lasted only seconds, but Manfred was so intensely aware that she might have been naked in his arms and he was shaken with guilt and self-disgust at his body's swift betrayal and at the evil that seemed to smoke in his blood and burst like a sky rocket in his brain. He pulled away from her roughly, and her expression was bewildered and hurt, her arms still raised as he scrambled up the steps onto the balcony of the coach and joined the noisy banter and horseplay of his team mates.

As the train pulled out of the station she was standing a little apart from the other girls, and when they all turned and trooped away down the platform, Sarah lingered, staring after the train as it gathered speed and ran towards the mountains.

At last a bend in the tracks carried him out of sight of her, and as Manfred drew his head back into the carriage he saw that Roelf Stander was watching quizzically and now grinned and opened his mouth to speak, but Manfred flared at him furiously and guiltily:

'*Hou jou bek!* Hold your jaw, man!'

* * *

The Inter-Varsity Championships were held over ten days with five heats in each weight division; thus each contestant would fight every second day.

Manfred was seeded number two in his division, which meant that he would probably meet the holder of the champion's belt in the final round. The reigning champion was an engineering student who had just graduated from the Witwatersrand University. He was unbeaten in his career and had announced his intention of turning professional immediately after the Olympics for which he was considered a certain choice.

'The Lion of the Kalahari meets the sternest test of his meteoric career. Can he take the same sort of punishment that he deals out? This is the question everyone is asking, and which Ian Rushmore will answer for us if all goes as expected,' wrote the boxing correspondent of the *Rand Daily Mail*. 'There does not seem to be any contestant in the division who will be able to prevent De La Rey and Rushmore meeting on Saturday night, 20 December 1935. It will be Rushmore's right hand, made of granite and gelignite, against De La Rey's swarming battering two-handed style, and your correspondent would not miss the meeting for all the gold that lies beneath the streets of Johannesburg.'

Manfred won his first two bouts with insulting ease. His opponents, demoralized by his reputation, both dropped in the second round under the barrage of slashing red gloves, and the Wednesday was a rest day for Manfred.

He left the residence on the host university's campus before any of the others were up, missing breakfast to be in time for the early morning train from Johannesburg's Central Station. It was less than an hour's journey across the open grasslands.

He ate a frugal breakfast in the buffet of the Pretoria station and then started out on foot with a leaden reluctance in his gait.

Pretoria Central Prison was an ugly square building and the interior was as forbidding and depressing. Here all executions were carried out, and life imprisonments served.

Manfred went into the visitors' entrance, spoke to the unsmiling senior warder at the enquiries desk and filled in an application form.

He hesitated over the question, 'Relationship to prisoner', then boldly wrote 'Son'.

When he returned the form to the warder, the man read it through slowly and then looked up at him, studying him gravely and impersonally. 'He has not had a visitor, not one in all these years,' he said.

'I could not come before.' Manfred tried to excuse himself. 'There were reasons.'

'They all say that.' Then the warder's expression altered subtly. 'You are the boxer, aren't you?'

'That's right,' Manfred nodded, and then on an impulse he gave the secret recognition signal of the *OB* and the man's eyes flicked with surprise then dropped to the form in front of him.

'Very well, then. Have a seat. I'll call you when he is ready,' he said, and under cover of the counter top he gave Manfred the counter signal of the *Ossewa Brandwag*.

'Kill the *rooinek* bastard on Saturday night,' he whispered, and turned away. Manfred was amazed but elated to have proof of how widely the brotherhood had spread its arms to gather in the *Volk*.

Ten minutes later the warder led Manfred through to a green-painted cell with high barred windows, furnished only with a plain deal table and three straight-backed chairs. There was an old man sitting on one of the chairs, but he was a stranger and Manfred looked beyond him expectantly.

The stranger stood up slowly. He was bowed with age and hard work, his skin wrinkled and folded and spotted by the sun. His hair was thick and white as raw cotton, wisped over a scalp that was speckled like a plover's egg. His thin scraggy neck stuck out of the coarse calico prison uniform like a turtle's from the opening of its carapace, and his eyes were colourless, faded and red-rimmed and swimming with tears that gathered like dew on his lashes.

'Papa?' Manfred asked with disbelief as he saw the missing arm, and the old man began to weep silently. His shoulders shook and the tears broke over the reddened rims of his eyelids and slimed down his cheeks.

'Papa!' said Manfred, and outrage rose to choke him. 'What have they done to you?'

He rushed forward to embrace his father, trying to hide his face from the warder, trying to protect him, to cover his weakness and tears.

'Papa! Papa!' he repeated helplessly, patting the thin shoulders under the rough uniform, and he turned his head and looked back at the warder in silent appeal.

'I cannot leave you alone.' The man understood, but shook his head. 'It is the rule, more than my job is worth.'

'Please,' Manfred whispered.

'Do you give me your word, as a brother, that you will not try to help him escape?'

'My word as a brother!' Manfred answered.

'Ten minutes,' said the warder. 'I can give you no more.' He turned away, locking the green steel door as he left.

'Papa.' Manfred led the trembling old man back to the chair and knelt beside him.

Lothar De La Rey wiped his wet cheeks with his open palm and tried to smile, but it wavered and his voice quivered. 'Look at me, blubbering like an old woman. It was just the shock of seeing you again. I'm all right now. I'm fine. Let me look at you, let me just look at you for a moment.'

He drew back and stared into Manfred's face intently. 'What a man you have become – strong and well favoured, just like I was at your age.' He traced Manfred's features with his fingertips. His hand was cold and the skin was rough as sharkskin.

'I have read about you, my son. They allow us to have the newspapers. I have cut out everything about you and I keep them under my mattress. I'm proud, so proud. We all are, everybody in this place, even the narks.'

'Papa! How are they treating you?' Manfred cut him short.

'Fine, Manie, just fine.' Lothar looked down and his lips sagged with despair. 'It's just that – for ever is such a long time. So long, Manie, so very long, and sometimes I think about the desert, about the horizons that turn to distant smoke and the high blue sky.' He broke off and tried to smile. 'And I think about you every day – not a day that I don't pray to God, "Look after my son."'

'No, Papa – please,' Manfred pleaded. 'Don't! You will have me weeping too.' He pushed himself off his knees and pulled the other chair close to his father's. 'I've thought about you also, Papa, every day. I wanted to write to you. I spoke to Uncle Tromp, but he said it was best if – '

Lothar seized his hand to silence him. '*Ja*, Manie, it was best. Tromp Bierman is a wise man; he knows best.' He smiled more convincingly. 'How tall you have grown, and the colour of your hair – just like mine used to be. You will be all right, I know. What have you decided to do with your life? Tell me quickly. We have so little time.'

'I am studying law at Stellenbosch. I passed third in the first year.'

'That is wonderful, my son, and afterwards?'

'I am not sure, Papa, but I think I must fight for our nation. I think I have been called to the fight for justice for our people.'

'Politics?' Lothar asked, and when Manfred nodded, 'A hard road, full of turns and twists. I always preferred the straight road, with a horse under me and a rifle in my hand.' Then he chuckled sardonically. 'And look where that road has led me.'

'I will fight too, Papa. When the time is right, on a battleground of my own choosing.'

'Oh, my son. History is so cruel to our people. Sometimes I think with despair that we are doomed always to be the underdogs.'

'You are wrong!' Manfred's expression hardened and his voice crackled. 'Our day will come, is already dawning. We will not be the underdogs for much longer.' He wanted to tell his father, but then he remembered his blood oath and he was silent.

'Manie.' His father leaned closer, glancing around the cell like a conspirator

before he tugged at Manfred's sleeve. 'The diamonds – have you still got your diamonds?' he demanded, and immediately saw the answer in Manfred's face.

'What happened to them?' Lothar's distress was hard to watch. 'They were my legacy to you, all I could leave you. Where are they?'

'Uncle Tromp – he found them years ago. He said they were evil, the coin of the devil, and he made me destroy them.'

'Destroy them?' Lothar gaped at him.

'Break them on an anvil with a sledgehammer. Crush them to powder, all of them.'

Manfred watched his father's old fierce spirit flare up. Lothar leapt to his feet and raged around the cell. 'Tromp Bierman, if I could get my hand on you! You were always a stubborn sanctimonious hypocrite – ' He broke off and came back to his son.

'Manie, there are the others. Do you remember – the kopje, the hill in the desert? I left them there for you. You must go back.'

Manfred turned his head away. Over the years he had tried to drive the memory from his mind. It was evil, the memory of great evil, associated with terror and guilt and grief. He had tried to close his mind to that time in his life. It was long ago, and he had almost succeeded, but now at his father's words he tasted again the reek of gangrene in the back of his throat and saw the package of treasure slide down into the cleft in the granite.

'I have forgotten the way back, Papa. I could never find the way back.'

Lothar was pulling at his arm. 'Hendrick!' he babbled. 'Swart Hendrick! He knows – he can lead you.'

'Hendrick.' Manfred blinked. A name, half-forgotten, a fragment from his past; then suddenly and clearly an image of that great bald head, the black cannonball of a head, sprang into his mind. 'Hendrick,' he repeated. 'But he is gone. I don't know where. Gone back into the desert. I could never find him.'

'No! No! Manie, Hendrick is here, somewhere close here on the Witwatersrand. He is a big man now, a chief among his own people.'

'How do you know, Papa?'

'The grapevine! In here we hear everything. They come in from the outside, bringing news and messages. We hear everything. Hendrick sent word to me. He had not forgotten me. We were comrades. We rode ten thousand miles together and fought a hundred battles. He sent word to me, to set a place where I could find him if ever I escaped these damned walls.' Lothar leaned forward and seized his son's head, pulling it close, placing his lips to his ear, whispering urgently and then drawing back. 'You must go and find him there. He will lead you back to the granite hill below the Okavango river – and, oh sweet God, how I wish I could be there to ride into the desert with you again.'

There was the clink of keys in the lock and Lothar shook his son's arm desperately. 'Promise me you will go, Manie.'

'Papa, the stones are evil.'

'Promise me, my own son, promise me that I have not endured these captive years for nothing. Promise me you will go back for the stones.'

'I promise, Papa,' Manfred whispered, as the warder stepped into the cell.

'Time is up. I'm sorry.'

'Can I come and see my father again tomorrow?'

The warder shook his head. 'Only one visit a month.'

'I'll write to you, Papa.' He turned back to embrace Lothar. 'I'll write to you every week from now on.'

But Lothar nodded expressionlessly; his face had closed and his eyes were veiled. '*Ja*,' he nodded. 'You write to me sometime,' he agreed, and shuffled out of the cell.

Manfred stared at the closed green door until the warder touched his shoulder: 'Come along.' Manfred followed him to the visitors' entrance in a tangle of emotions. Only when he stepped out of the gates into the sunlight and looked up at the towering blue African sky of which his father had spoken so yearningly did one emotion emerge to swamp all the others.

It was rage, blind hopeless rage, and it grew stronger over the days that followed, seeming to climax as he marched down the aisle between the rows of screaming cheering spectators towards the brilliantly lighted ring of rope and canvas, dressed in shimmering silks with the crimson leather on his fists and bloody murder in his heart.

* * *

Centaine woke long before Blaine did; she grudged every second they wasted in sleep. It was still dark outside for the cottage was close under the precipice of the high table-topped mountain and screened from dawn's first glow by its bulk, though the birds in the tiny walled garden were already squeaking and chirping sleepily. She had ordered tacoma and honeysuckle to be trained over the stone walls to attract them, and on her orders the feeding-boxes were replenished every day by the gardener.

She had taken months to find the perfect cottage. It had to be discreetly enclosed, with covered parking for her Daimler and Blaine's new Bentley, both vehicles that attracted immediate attention. It had to be within ten minutes' walk of Parliament and Blaine's office in the wing of the imposing Herbert Baker building reserved for cabinet ministers. It had to have a view of the mountain, and must be set in one of the tiny lanes of an unfashionable suburb where none of their friends or business associates or fellow parliamentarians or enemies or members of the press were ever likely to stray. But above all it had to have that special feel.

When at last she walked into it she did not even see the stained and faded wallpaper or the threadbare carpets on the floor. She stood in the central room and smiled softly. 'Happy people have lived her. Yes, this is the one. I'll take it.'

She had registered the title deeds in one of her holding companies, but trusted no architect nor decorator with its renovation. She planned and executed the reconstruction entirely herself.

'It's got to be the most perfect love nest ever built.' She set her usual unattainable standard for herself and consulted with the builder and his carpenters and plumbers and painters every single morning while the work was in hand. They tore down the walls between the four tiny bedrooms and fashioned them into a single boudoir with french windows and shutters opening onto the enclosed garden with its high wall of yellow Table Mountain sandstone and the view of the grey mountain cliff beyond.

She built separate bathrooms for Blaine and herself, his finished in ruby-veined cream Italian marble with gold dolphin taps and fittings, hers like a Bedouin tent draped in rose silk.

The bed was a museum piece, Italian Renaissance workmanship inlaid with ivory and gold leaf. 'We can always play polo on it in the off-season,' Blaine remarked when first he saw it, and she placed her magnificent Turner, all sunlight and golden sea, so that it was in full view from the bed. She hung the Bonnard in the dining-room and lit it with a chandelier which was a shimmering inverted Christmas tree of crystal, and placed the choicest pieces of her collection of Queen Anne and Louis Quatorze silver on the sideboard.

She staffed the cottage with four permanent servants, including a valet for Blaine and a full-time gardener. The chef was a Malay who conjured up the most heavenly pilaffs and *boboties* and *rystafels* that Blaine, who had a spicy palate and was a connoisseur of curries, had ever tasted.

A flowerseller from her pitch outside the Groote Kerk near the parliament buildings had a contract to deliver huge bunches of yellow roses to the cottage each day, and Centaine stocked the small wine cellar with the noblest vintages from Weltevreden's own cavernous cellars and installed, at enormous expense, an electric walk-in cold room in the pantries to keep the hams and cheeses, the potted caviars and smoked Scotch salmon and other such necessities of life in prime condition.

Yet with all her loving attention to detail and lavish planning, they were lucky if they could spend a single night there in a month – although there were other stolen hours, garnered like diamonds, and hoarded by Centaine as though she were the stingiest of misers: a private luncheon when parliament recessed or a midnight interlude after the house had sat late; the occasional afternoon – and, oh sweet heavens, what afternoons – when his wife, Isabella, believed he was at polo practice or at a cabinet meeting.

Now Centaine rolled her head carefully on the lace pillow and looked at him. The dawn light was silvery through the shutters and his features seemed carved in ivory. She thought that he looked like a sleeping Roman Caesar, with that imperial nose and wide commanding mouth.

'In all but the ears,' she thought, and stifled a giggle. Strange how after three years his presence could make her still feel like a girl. She rose quietly, careful not to rock the mattress and disturb him, picked up her wrap from the couch and slipped through to her bathroom.

Swiftly she brushed her hair into thick dark plumes checking for grey and then, relieved, went on to clean her teeth and wash her eyes with the little blue glass bath of lotion until the whites were clear and sparkling. Then she creamed her face and wiped away the excess. Blaine liked her skin free of cosmetics. As she used her bidet she smiled again at Blaine's mock amazement when he had first seen it.

'Marvellous!' he had cried. 'A horse trough in the bathroom, how jolly useful!'

Sometimes he was so romantic he was almost French. She laughed with anticipation, snatched a fresh silk wrap from the wardrobe and ran through to the kitchen. The servants were all astir, bubbling with excitement because the master was here and they all adored Blaine.

'Did you get them, Hadji?' Centaine demanded, using the title of respect for one who has made the pilgrimage to Mecca, and the Malay chef grinned like a butter-yellow gnome under his tasselled red fez and proudly displayed the pair of thick juicy kippers.

'Come on the mail boat yesterday, madam,' he boasted.

'Hadji, you are a magician,' she applauded. Scotch kippers were Blaine's

favourite breakfast. 'You are going to do them his way, aren't you?' Blaine's way was simmered in milk, and Hadji looked pained at the impropriety of the question as he turned back to his stove.

For Centaine it was a marvellous game of make-believe, playing wife, pretending that Blaine truly belonged to her. So with a sharp eye she watched Miriam grind the coffee beans and Khalil finish sponging Blaine's grey pinstripe suit and begin to put a military gleam on his shoes before she left them and crept back into the darkened bedroom.

She felt quite breathless as she hovered beside the bed and studied his features. He still had that effect on her even after all this time.

'I am more faithful than any wife,' she gloated. 'More dutiful, more loving, more – '

His arm shot out so suddenly that she squealed with fright as he plucked her down beside him and flicked the sheet over her.

'You were awake all along,' she wailed. 'Oh, you awful man, I can never trust you.'

They could still, on occasion, drive each other into that mindless frenzy, those writhing sensual marathons that exploded at the end in a great burst of light and colour like the Turner on the wall before them. But more often it had become as it was this morning, a fortress of love, solid and impregnable. They left it with reluctance, coming apart slowly, lingeringly, as the day filled the room with gold and they heard the clink of Hadji's breakfast dishes on the terrace beyond the shutters.

She brought him his robe, full-length brocaded China silk, royal blue lined in crimson with a belt of embroidered seed pearls and velvet lapels. She had chosen it because it was so outlandish, so different from his usual severe style of dress.

'I wouldn't wear it in front of anybody else in the world,' he had told her, holding it gingerly at arm's length, when she presented it to him on his birthday.

'If you do, you'd better not let me catch you at it!' she warned, but after the first shock he had come to enjoy wearing it for her.

Hand in hand they went out onto the terrace and Hadji and Miriam beamed with delight and bowed them to their seats at the table in the morning sunlight.

With a rapid but steely survey, Centaine made sure everything was perfect, from the roses in the Lalique vase to the snowy linen and the Fabergé jug of silver gilt and crystal filled with freshly squeezed grapefuit juice, before she opened the morning paper and began to read to him.

Always in the same order: the headlines and then the parliamentary reports, waiting for him to comment on each, adding her own ideas, and then going on to the financial pages and stock exchange reports, and finally to the sports pages with special emphasis on any mention of polo.

'Oh, I see you spoke yesterday: "a forceful reply from the minister without portfolio", they say.'

And Blaine smiled as he lifted a filet off his kipper. 'Hardly forceful,' he demurred. '"Pissed off" better describes it.'

'What's this about secret societies?'

'A bit of a flap over these militant organizations, inspired it would seem by the charming Herr Hitler and his gang of political thugs.'

'Anything in it?' Centaine sipped at her coffee. She still couldn't get her stomach to accept these English breakfasts. 'You seem to have dismissed the

whole thing rather lightly.' Then she looked up at him with narrowing eyes. 'You were covering up, weren't you?' She knew him so well, and he grinned guiltily at her.

'Don't miss a thing, do you?'

'Can you tell me?'

'Shouldn't really.' He frowned, but she had never betrayed his trust. 'We are very worried indeed,' he admitted. 'In fact the *Ou Baas* considers it the most serious threat since the 1914 rebellion when De Wet called out his commandos to fight for the Kaiser. The whole thing is a political nettle, and a potential minefield.' He paused, and she knew there was more, but she waited quietly for him to make up his mind to tell her. 'All right,' he decided. 'The *Ou Baas* has ordered me to head a commission of enquiry – cabinet level and confidential – into the *Ossewa Brandwag*, which is the most extreme and flourishing of them all. Worse than the *Broederbond* even.'

'Why you, Blaine? It's a nasty one, isn't it?'

'Yes, it's a nasty one, and he picked me as a non-Afrikaner. The impartial judge.'

'Of course, I've heard of the *OB*. There has been talk for years but nobody seems to know much.'

'Extreme right-wing nationalists, anti-Semitic, anti-black, blaming all the ills of their world on perfidious albion, secret blood oaths and midnight rallies, a sort of Neanderthal boy scout movement with *Mein Kampf* as its inspiration.'

'I haven't yet read *Mein Kampf*. Everyone is talking about it. Is there an English or French translation?'

'Not officially published, but I have a Foreign Office translation. It's a rag-bag of nightmares and obscenities, a manual of naked aggression and bigotry. I would lend you my copy but it is appallingly bad literature and the sentiments would sicken you.'

'He may not be a great writer,' Centaine conceded. 'But, Blaine, whatever else he has done, Hitler has put Germany on its feet again after the disaster of the Weimar Republic. Germany is the only country in the world with full employment and a booming economy. My shares in Krupp and Farben have almost doubled in the last nine months.' She stopped as she saw his expression. 'Is something wrong, Blaine?'

He had laid his knife and fork down and was staring at her.

'You have shares in the German armaments industry?' he asked quietly, and she nodded.

'The best investment I have made since gold went off – ' She broke off; they had never mentioned that again.

'I have never asked you to do anything for me, have I?' he asked, and she considered that carefully.

'No, you haven't – ever.'

'Well, I'm asking you now. Sell your shares in German armaments.'

She looked puzzled. 'Why, Blaine?'

'Because it is like investing in the propagation of cancer, or like financing Genghis Khan's campaigns.'

She did not reply, but her expression went blank and her eyes went out of focus, crossing into a slightly myopic squint. The first time he had seen that happen he had been alarmed; it had taken him some time to realize that when she squinted like that she was involved in mental arithmetic, and it had fascinated him to see how quickly she made her calculations.

Her eyes flicked back into focus and she smiled agreement. 'On yesterday's prices, I'll show a profit of a hundred and twenty-six thousand pounds. It was time to sell anyway. I'll cable my London broker as soon as the post office opens.'

'Thank you, my love.' Blaine shook his head sorrowfully. 'But I do wish you'd made your profit somewhere else.'

'You may be misjudging the situation, *chéri*,' she suggested tactfully. 'Hitler may not be as bad as you think he is.'

'He doesn't have to be as bad as I think he is, Centaine. He only has to be as bad as he says he is in *Mein Kampf* to qualify for the chamber of horrors.' Blaine took a mouthful of his kipper and closed his eyes with mild ecstasy. She watched him with pleasure almost equal to his own. He swallowed, opened his eyes, and declared the subject closed with a wave of his fork.

'Enough horrors for such a splendid morning.' He smiled at her. 'Read me the sports pages, woman!'

Centaine rustled the pages portentously and then composed herself to read aloud, but suddenly the colour drained from her face and she swayed in her seat.

Blaine dropped his knife and fork with a clatter and jumped up to steady her. 'What is it, darling?' He was desperately alarmed and almost as pale as she was. She shrugged his hands away and stared at the open newspaper which trembled in her grip.

Blaine moved quickly behind her, and scanned the page over her shoulder. There was an article on the previous weekend's racing at Kenilworth. Centaine's entry, a good stallion named Bonheur, had lost the feature race by a short head, but that could not have occasioned her distress.

Then he saw that she was looking at the foot of the page and he followed her gaze to a quarter-column photograph of a boxer, in shorts and vest, facing the camera in a formal pose, bare fists raised and a grim expression on his handsome features. Centaine had never evinced the slightest interest in boxing, and Blaine was puzzled. He read the heading of the article which accompanied the photograph:

FEAST OF FISTICUFFS
CLASSY FIELD FOR INTER-VARSITY CHAMPIONSHIPS

which did nothing to alleviate his puzzlement. He glanced at the footnote beneath the photograph: 'The Lion of the Kalahari, Manfred De La Rey, the Challenger for the Inter-Varsity Light Heavyweight Belt. Hard pounding ahead.'

'Manfred De La Rey.' Blaine said the name softly, trying to remember where last he had heard it. Then his expression cleared and he squeezed Centaine's shoulders.

'Manfred De La Rey! The boy you were looking for in Windhoek. Is this him?'

Centaine did not look round, but she nodded jerkily.

'What is he to you, Centaine?'

She was shaken into an emotional turmoil; otherwise she might have answered differently. But now it was out before she could bite down on the words. 'He's my son. My bastard son.'

Blaine's hands dropped from her shoulders and she heard the sharp hissing intake of his breath.

'I must be mad!' Her reaction was immediate, and she thought, 'I should never had told him. Blaine will never understand. He'll never forgive me.'

She dared not look round at the shock and accusation she knew she would find in his face. She dropped her head and cupped her hands over her eyes.

'I've lost him,' she thought. 'Blaine is too upright, too virtuous to accept it.'

Then his hands touched her again, and they lifted her to her feet and turned her gently to face him.

'I love you,' he said simply, and her tears choked her and she flung herself against his chest and held him with all her strength.

'Oh Blaine, you are so good to me.'

'If you want to tell me about it, I'm here to help you. If you'd rather not talk, then I understand. There is just one thing – whatever it was, whatever you did, makes no difference to me and my feelings for you.'

'I want to tell you.' She fought back her tears of relief and looked up at him. 'I've never wanted to keep secrets from you. I've wanted to tell you for years now, but I am a coward.'

'You are many things, my love, but never a coward.' He seated her again and drew his own chair close so that he could hold her hand while she talked.

'Now tell me,' he commanded.

'It's such a long story, Blaine – and you have a cabinet meeting at nine.'

'Affairs of state can wait,' he said. 'Your happiness is the most important thing in the world.'

So she told him, from the time that Lothar De La Rey had rescued her to the discovery of the H'ani diamond mine and the birth of Manfred in the desert.

She held nothing back: her love for Lothar, the love of a lonely forsaken girl for her rescuer. She explained how it had changed to bitter hatred when she discovered that Lothar had murdered the old Bushman woman who was her foster mother, and how that hatred had focused on Lothar's child that she was carrying in her womb, and how she had refused even to look upon the newborn infant but had made the father take it from the childbed still wet from the act of birth.

'It was wicked,' she whispered. 'But I was confused and afraid, afraid of the rejection of the Courtney family if I brought a bastard amongst them. Oh, Blaine, I have regretted it ten thousand times – and hated myself as much as I hated Lothar De La Rey.'

'Do you want to go to Johannesburg to see him again?' Blaine asked. 'We could fly up to watch the championships.'

The idea startled Centaine. 'We?' she asked. '*We*, Blaine?'

'I couldn't let you go alone. Not to something so disturbing.'

'But can you get away? What about Isabella?'

'Your need is far more important now,' he told her simply. 'Do you want to go?'

'Oh yes, Blaine. Oh yes please.' She dabbed away the last tear with her lace table napkin, and he saw her mood shift. It always fascinated him how she could change moods as other women changed their hats.

Now she was crisp and quick and businesslike. 'I am expecting Shasa back from South-West later today. I'll ring Abe in Windhoek to find out what time they took off. If all is well, we can leave for Johannesburg tomorrow. What time, Blaine?'

'As early as you like,' he told her. 'This afternoon I will clear my desk and make my peace with the *Ou Baas*.'

'The weather should be fine this time of year – perhaps a few thunderstorms on the highveld.' She took his wrist and turned it to see his Rolex watch. '*Chéri*, you can still get to the cabinet meeting if you hurry.'

She went with him to the garage to see him off, still playing the dutiful wife, and kissed him through the open window of the Bentley.

'I'll ring your office as soon as Shasa arrives,' she murmured in his ear. 'I'll leave a message with Doris if you are still in the meeting.' Doris was Blaine's secretary, and one of the very few people in the world that knew about them.

As soon as he was gone, Centaine rushed back into the bedroom and picked up the phone. The line to Windhoek was noisy with crackles and hisses and Abe Abrahams sounded as though he were in Alaska.

'They left at first light, almost five hours ago,' he told her faintly. 'David is with him, of course.'

'What's the wind, Abe?'

'They should have a tail wind all the way. I'd say twenty or thirty miles an hour.'

'Thank you. I'll wait at the field for them.'

'That might be a little awkward.' Abe sounded hesitant. 'There was a lot of secrecy and deliberate vagueness when they got in from the mine yesterday evening, and I wasn't allowed to see them off from the airfield this morning. I think they might have company – if you will excuse the euphemism.'

As a reflex, Centaine frowned, though she truly could not find it in herself thoroughly to disapprove of Shasa's philanderings. She always excused him with: 'It's his de Thiry blood. He can't help himself,' feeling a covert touch of indulgent pride in her son's effortless successes with the opposite sex. Now she changed the subject.

'Thank you, Abe. I've signed the new Namaqualand leases so you can go ahead and draw up the contract.' They spoke business for five minutes more before Centaine hung up. She made three more calls, all business, then phoned her secretary at Weltevreden and dictated four letters and the cable to her London broker to 'Sell all Krupp and Farben at best'.

She hung up, sent for Hadji and Miriam and gave them instructions for the running of the cottage in her absence. Then she made a quick calculation. The Dragon Rapide, a beautiful blue and silver twin-engined aircraft which Shasa had prevailed on her to buy, could cruise at 150 knots, and with a tail wind of twenty miles an hour they should be at Youngsfield before noon.

'So we will see just how much Master Shasa's taste in women has improved recently.'

She went out to the Daimler and drove slowly around the shoulder of the mountain, below District Six, the colourful Malay quarter, its narrow lanes reverberating to the cries of the muezzin calling the faithful to prayer, the hoot of the fishsellers' horns declaring their wares and the birdlike cries of children, and past the hospital of Groote Schuur and the university which adjoined Cecil Rhodes' magnificent estate, his legacy to the nation.

'It must be the most beautiful situation of any university in the world,' she thought.

The colonnaded stone buildings were set against a backdrop of dark pines and the sheer sky-high cliff of the mountain, while on the meadows abutting them grazed small herds of plains animals, eland and wildebeest and zebra.

Sight of the university set her thinking about Shasa again. He had just completed his year, with a respectable second-class.

'I always suspect those who pass first class in everything,' Blaine had remarked when he heard Shasa's results. 'Most of them are too clever for their own good or the good of those around them. I prefer those lesser mortals for whom the achievement of excellence requires considerable effort.'

'You accuse me of spoiling him,' she had smiled. 'But you are always making excuses for Shasa yourself.'

'Being your son, my love, is not the easiest of tasks for a young man,' he had told her, making her bridle furiously.

'You think I am not good to him.'

'You are very good to him. As I have suggested, perhaps too good to him. It's just that you do not leave much for him. You are so successful, so dominant. You have done it all. What can he do to prove himself?'

'Blaine, I am not domineering.'

'I said dominant, Centaine, not domineering. The two are different. I love you because you are dominant. I would despise you if you were domineering.'

'Still I do not always understand this language of yours. I shall look it up in my dictionary.'

'Ask Shasa – English was his only first.' Blaine chuckled and then put his arm around her shoulders. 'You must slacken the rein a little, Centaine, give him space to make his own mistakes and enjoy his own triumphs. If he wants to hunt, even though you do not approve of killing animals that you cannot eat, the Courtneys have all been big-game hunters. Old General Courtney slew elephant in their hundreds and Shasa's father hunted; let the boy try his hand at it. That and polo are the only things you haven't done before him.'

'What about flying?' she challenged.

'I apologize – and flying.'

'Very well, I will let him go and murder beasts. But Blaine, tell me, will he make the polo team for the Olympics?'

'Frankly, my darling – no.'

'But he is good enough! You said so yourself.'

'Yes,' Blaine agreed. 'He is probably good enough. He has all the fire and dash, a marvellous eye and arm, but he lacks experience. If he were chosen he'd be the youngest international ever. However, I don't think he will be. I think Clive Ramsay has to get the ride at number two.'

She stared at him, and he stared back expressionlessly. He knew what she was thinking. As Captain, Blaine was one of the national selectors.

'David will be going to Berlin,' she had followed up.

'David Abrahams is the human version of a gazelle,' Blaine had pointed out reasonably. 'He has the fourth best time in the world for the two hundred metres and the third best for the four hundred. Young Shasa is competing against at least ten of the world's best horsemen for a place.'

'I would give anything in the world for Shasa to go to Berlin.'

'Very likely you would,' Blaine had agreed. She had built a new wing to the engineering faculty at the University of Cape Town, the Courtney Building, when it had finally been decided that Shasa would go there rather than to Oxford; yes, he knew no price was too high for her to pay.

'I assure you, my love, that I will make very certain – ' he paused, and she perked up expectantly ' – that I excuse myself from the room when, and if, Shasa's name ever comes up before the selectors.'

'He's so damned virtuous!' she exclaimed aloud now and beat her clenched fist on the steering-wheel of the Daimler with frustration, until a sudden vision of the ivory and gold inlaid bed stopped her and she grinned wickedly. 'Well, perhaps virtuous is not the correct word again.'

The airfield was deserted. She parked the Daimler beside the hangar, where Shasa would not see it from the air. Then she took the travelling rug from the boot and spread it under a tree on the edge of the wide grassy strip.

It was one of those lovely summer days, bright sunlight with only patches of cloud over the mountain, a sharp breeze ruffling the stone pines and taking the edge off the heat.

She settled down on the rug with Aldous Huxley's *Brave New World*, a book that she had been trying to finish for the last week, occasionally glancing up from the page to scan the northern sky.

* * *

David Abrahams was almost as enchanted with flying as he was with running. That was what had brought him and Shasa together in the beginning. Though Abe Abrahams had worked for Centaine and been one of her closest personal friends for almost all of David's lifetime, the two boys had really only noticed each other when they went up to university in the same year. Since then they had become inseparable and were founder members of the university flying club, for which Centaine had provided a Tiger Moth trainer.

David was studying law, and it was tacitly understood that when he qualified he would join his father in Windhoek, which meant naturally that he would become one of Centaine's people. She had observed the boy carefully over the years and found no vice in him, so she approved of his friendship with Shasa.

David was taller than his father, with a lean runner's body and an attractively ugly, humorous face, thick curly hair and a large beaky nose which he had inherited from Abe. His best features were his dark Semitic eyes and long sensitive hands, with which he was now manipulating the control column of the Dragon Rapide. He flew with an almost religious dedication, like a priest performing the ritual of some arcane religion. He treated the aircraft as though it were a beautiful living creature, whereas Shasa flew like an engineer – with understanding and great skill, but without David's mystic passion.

David brought that same passion to running and many of the other things in his existence. This was one of the reasons that Shasa loved him so dearly. He spiced Shasa's own life, enhanced the pleasure which Shasa derived from the things they did together. These past weeks might have been dull and anti-climactic without David.

With Centaine's blessing, withheld strenuously for almost a year and then mysteriously given at the last moment, the two of them had taken the Rapide and flown to the H'ani Mine the day after they had written their final examinations.

At the mine Dr Twentyman-Jones had arranged for two four-ton trucks to be waiting for them, fully equipped with camping equipment, camp staff, trackers, skinners and a cook. One of the company prospectors, a man thoroughly versed in the ways of the wild, in bushcraft and hunting big dangerous game, was in charge of the expedition.

Their destination was the Caprivi Strip, that remote ribbon of wilderness, between Angola and Bechuanaland. Entry to this area was severely restricted and hunting was forbidden except in exceptional circumstances. Enviously it was referred to by other sportsmen as the private hunting preserve of the cabinet ministers of the South African government. Blaine Malcomess had arranged entry permits and hunting licences for them.

Under the grizzled old prospector's quiet instruction and firm hand the two young men had come to a closer understanding of, and respect for, the wilderness and the fascinating spectrum of life it contained. In a few weeks he had taught them something of man's place in the fragile balance of nature and instilled in them the principles of ethical hunting.

'The death of each individual animal is sad but inevitable. However, the death of the forest or swamp or plain that supports the entire species is tragedy,' he explained. 'If the kings and noblemen of Europe had not been avid huntsmen, the stag and the boar and the bear would be extinct today. It was the huntsmen who saved the forest from the axe and the plough of the peasants.' And they listened attentively at the camp-fire as he explained. 'Men who hunt for love of the creatures they pursue will protect the breeding females and young from the poachers and save the forests from the goats and cattle. No, my young friends, Robin Hood was a dirty poacher. The sheriff of Nottingham was the real hero.'

So they spent enchanted days in the bush, leaving camp on foot while it was still dark and returning dog-weary after the sun had set. Each of them killed his lion, and experienced the hunter's sadness and elation at the deed, and came out determined to preserve that wild and beautiful country from the predations of unthinking, greedy men. And Shasa, blessed by the chance of birth with the promise of great wealth and influence, came to realize in some small measure how much of that responsibility could one day be his.

The women had been superfluous, as David had warned they would be. However, Shasa had insisted on bringing them, one for himself and one for David.

Shasa's choice was almost thirty years old. 'The best tunes are played on an old fiddle,' he assured David. She was also a divorcée. 'I never break in my own polo ponies.' She had big blue eyes, a ripe red mouth and a pneumatic figure, but was not burdened by an unnecessary amount of brain.

David nicknamed her 'Jumbo', 'Because,' he explained, 'she's so thick that two elephants could walk across her skull side by side.'

Shasa had prevailed upon Jumbo to bring a friend for David, and she had selected a tall dark lady, another divorcée, with trailing locks; her thin arms were loaded with bangles, her long neck with strings of beads. She affected an ivory cigarette-holder and had a smouldering intense gaze but spoke seldom – then usually to ask for another gin.

David dubbed her 'the Camel' for her insatiable thirst. However, the two of them turned out to be ideal, for while they delivered what was expected of them with vigour and expertise when called upon to do so, for the rest they were quite content to remain in camp all day, and in the evening demanded little attention and made no attempt to sabotage the conversation around the camp-fire by joining in.

'That was probably the most enjoyable holiday I will ever spend.' Shasa leaned back in the pilot's seat of the Rapide and stared dreamily ahead, content to let David, in the co-pilot's seat, do the flying. 'But it isn't over yet.' He

glanced at his wristwatch. 'Another hour before we reach Cape Town. Keep her on course,' he told David, and unfastened his safety-belt.

'Where are you going?' David demanded.

'I will not embarrass you by replying to that question, but do not be surprised when the Camel comes up to the cockpit to join you.'

'I really am worried about you.' David looked grave. 'You're going to rupture something if you go on like this.'

'Never felt stronger,' Shasa assured him as he wriggled out of the seat.

'Not you, dear boy, it's Jumbo I'm worried about.' David shook his head sadly, and Shasa chuckled, slapped his shoulder and ducked into the rear cabin.

The Camel looked up at him with that dark fanatical gaze and spilled a little gin and tonic down the front of her blouse, while Jumbo giggled and wriggled her fat little rump across the seat to make room for Shasa beside her.

He whispered in her ear and Jumbo looked bewildered, not an unusual expression for her.

'The Mile High Club – what in heaven's name is that?'

Shasa whispered again and she peered out of the side window at the earth below.

'Goodness! I didn't realize we were that high.'

'You get a special brooch when you become a member,' Shasa told her, 'made of gold and diamonds.' And Jumbo's interest flared.

'Oh goody! What kind of brooch?'

'A flying pussy cat, with gold wings and diamond eyes.'

'A pussy cat? Why a pussy – ' she broke off as understanding dawned in those china blue eyes. 'Shasa Courtney, you are awful!' She lowered her eyes and blinked demurely, and Shasa winked across the aisle at the Camel.

'I think Davie wants to talk to you.'

The Camel rose obediently, glass in hand, all her bangles and beads jangling as she wobbled from one side of the aisle to the other.

An hour later Shasa brought the Rapide in from the mountain side of the airstrip, and laid her down on the grass as though he were buttering hot toast. He swung her nose around before she had stopped, taxiing back towards the hangars. With a burst of the starboard engine, he brought her up onto the hard stand and cut the motors.

Only then did he notice the yellow Daimler parked in the shadow of the hangar with Centaine standing beside it.

'Oh for the love of Allah, Mater is here. Get those beauties flat on the floor!'

'Too late,' David groaned. 'Jumbo, bless her, is already waving at your mum through the porthole.'

Shasa steeled himself to his mother's wrath as Jumbo came giggling down the boarding ladder, supporting the Camel, whose legs had finally let her down.

Centaine said nothing, but she had a taxi waiting beside the Daimler. How she had known about the girls Shasa would never ask, but she waved the taxi forward and herded the unsteady pair into the back seat with an eye like a stockwhip.

'Get their luggage in the boot,' she ordered Shasa tersely, and the moment it was loaded, she nodded at the taxi-driver. 'Take them wherever they want to go.'

The Camel slumped owl-eyed in her seat, but Jumbo leaned out of the rear window waving and blowing kisses at Shasa until the taxi disappeared through

the gates of the airfield, and Shasa bowed his head and waited for his mother's icy sarcasm.

'Did you have a good trip, darling?' Centaine asked sweetly, holding up her face to be kissed, and the two girls were never mentioned again.

'Marvellous!' Shasa's kiss was full of gratitude and relief and genuine pleasure at being with her again, and he began to tell her all about it, but she cut him off.

'Later,' she said. 'Right now I want you to arrange for the Rapide to be refuelled and checked. We are flying up to Johannesburg tomorrow.'

* * *

In Johannesburg they stayed at the Carlton. Centaine owned thirty per cent of the equity in the hotel company, and the royal suite was at her disposal whenever she was in town.

The hotel would soon be in need of major renovation, but it occupied a prime position in the centre of Johannesburg. While she dressed for dinner, Centaine weighed the possibility of having the old building pulled down and redeveloping the site. She would have her architects prepare a report, she decided, as she put business out of her mind and devoted the rest of the evening and all her attention to Blaine.

Taking a silly chance of alerting the gossips, she and Blaine danced until two in the morning in the nightclub on the top floor of the hotel.

The next day Blaine had a full series of meetings at the Union Buildings in Pretoria, his excuse to Isabella for leaving Cape Town, so Centaine could spend the day with Shasa. In the morning there was a sale of yearlings at the showgrounds, but the prices were ridiculously high and they ended up without having bought a single animal. They lunched at the East African pavilion, where, more than the food, Centaine enjoyed the envious and speculative glances of the women at the surrounding tables.

In the afternoon they went to the zoo. Between feeding the monkeys and rowing on the lake, they discussed Shasa's plans for the future and she was delighted to learn that he had lost none of his determination to take up his duties and responsibilities with Courtney Mining and Finance as soon as he had obtained his Master's degree.

They arrived back at the Carlton with plenty of time to change for the boxing. Blaine, already in his dinner jacket, held a whisky and soda in his hand and he sprawled in one of the armchairs and watched Centaine complete her toilet. She enjoyed that. It was playing at being married again, and she called him to hook in her ear-rings and then paraded for his approval, pirouetting to spread her long skirts.

'I have never been to a boxing match before, Blaine. Aren't we terribly over-dressed?'

'I assure you that black tie is *de rigueur*.'

'Oh God, I'm so nervous. I don't know what I'm going to say to him, even if I get a chance – ' she broke off. 'You did manage to get tickets, didn't you?'

He showed them to her and smiled. 'Front row, and I have arranged for a car and driver.'

Shasa drifted into the suite with a white silk scarf draped casually over the

shoulders of his dinner jacket, and his black tie minutely and artfully asymmetrical so that it could never be mistaken for one of the modern clip-on monstrosities.

'He looks so magnificent.' Centaine's heart swelled at the sight of him. 'How ever am I going to preserve him from the harpies?'

He kissed her before going to the cabinet and pouring her customary glass of champagne.

'Can I freshen your whisky, sir?' he asked Blaine.

'Thanks, but one is my limit, Shasa,' Blaine declined, and Shasa poured himself a dry ginger-ale. That was one thing she didn't have to worry about, Centaine thought, liquor would never be one of Shasa's weaknesses.

'Well, Mater,' Shasa raised his glass, 'here's to your new-found interest in the gentlemanly art of boxing. Are you versed in the general objectives of the game?'

'I think two young men get into a ring and try to kill each other – is that right?'

'That, Centaine, is exactly right,' Blaine laughed. He never used an endearment in front of Shasa, and not for the first time she wondered what Shasa thought of her and Blaine. He must suspect, surely, but she had enough to worry about this evening without opening that dark door. She drank her champagne and then, gorgeous in diamonds and silks, on the arms of the two most important men in her world, she swept out to the waiting limousine.

The streets of the campus of the University of the Witwatersrand around the gymnasium were solid with parked vehicles and others moving nose to tail up the hill, while the sidewalks were packed with a jostling excited crowd of students and fight fans from the general public hurrying towards the hall, so their driver was forced to drop them off two hundred yards short of the entrance, and they joined the throng on foot.

The atmosphere in the hall was noisy and expectant, and as they took their reserved seats Centaine was relieved to see that everyone in the first three rows was wearing evening dress and that there were almost as many ladies as gentlemen in the crowd. She had had nightmares about being the only female in the hall.

She sat through the preliminary bouts, trying to appear interested in the lecture she was receiving from both Blaine and Shasa on the finer points of the contests, but the fighters in the lower weight divisions were so small and scrawny that they reminded her of underfed game cocks, and the flurry of action was fast enough to trick the eye. Besides, her mind and expectations were racing ahead to her first sight of the man she had come to see.

Another bout ended; the fighters, bruised and slick with sweat, climbed down from the ring, and an expectant hush fell on the hall, and heads began craning around towards the dressing-room.

Blaine checked his programme and murmured, 'This is it!'

Then a bloodthirsty roar went up from the mass of spectators.

'Here he comes.' Blaine touched her arm, but she found she could not turn her head.

'I wish I had never come,' she thought, and shrank down in her seat. 'I don't want him to see me.'

The light heavyweight challenger, Manfred De La Rey, came down to the ring first, attended by his coach and his two seconds, and the block of Stellenbosch students let out a roar and brandished their colour banners,

launching into the Varsity war cry. They were immediately answered by the Wits students opposite with cheers and jeers and stamping of feet. The pandemonium was painful to the eardrums as Manfred climbed up into the ring and did a little shuffling dance, holding his gloved hands above his head, the silk gown swinging from his shoulders like a cloak.

His hair had grown longer and unfashionably it was not dressed with Brylcreem, but rippled around his head like a gilded cloud as he moved. His jaw was strong, stopping just short of heaviness, and the bones in the forehead and cheek were prominent and cleanly chiselled, but his eyes dominated all his other features, pale and implacable as those of one of the big predatory cats, emphasized by his dark brows.

His shoulders were wide, descending in an inverted pyramid to his hips and the long clean lines of his legs, and his body had been pared of all fat and loose flesh, so that each individual muscle was visible beneath the skin.

Shasa stiffened in his seat as he recognized him. He chewed angrily, grinding his teeth together as he remembered the impact of those fists into his flesh and the suffocating slime of dead fish engulfing him as clearly as if the intervening years had never been.

'I know him, Mater,' he growled between clenched teeth. 'He is the one I fought on the jetty at Walvis Bay.' Centaine laid a hand on his arm to restrain him, but she did not look at him nor speak. Instead, she stole a single glance at Blaine's face, and what she saw distressed her.

Blaine's expression was grim, and she could feel the anger and the hurt in him. He might have been understanding and magnanimous a thousand miles from here, but with the living proof of her wantonness before him, he could only be thinking of the man who had made this bastard on her, and her acquiescence – nay, her joyous participation in the act. He was thinking of her body which should be his alone, used by a stranger, by an enemy against whom he had risked his life in battle.

'Oh God, why did I come?' She tortured herself, and then she felt something melt and change shape inside of her and knew the answer.

'Flesh of my flesh,' she thought. 'Blood of my blood.'

And she remembered the weight of him in her womb, and the spasm of burgeoning life deep within her, and all the instincts of motherhood welled and threatened to choke her, and the angry birth cry rang again in her head, deafening her.

'My son!' she almost cried aloud. 'My own son.'

The magnificent fighting man in the ring turned his head in her direction and saw her for the first time. He dropped his hands to his sides, and he lifted his chin and stared at her with such concentrated venom, with such bitter hatred in those yellow eyes that it was like the blow of a spiked mace in her unprotected face. Then Manfred De La Rey deliberately turned his back on her and strode to his corner.

The three of them, Blaine, Shasa and Centaine, sat rigid and silent in the midst of the roaring, chanting, heaving multitude. Not one of the three looked at the others, and only Centaine moved, twisting the corner of her sequined shawl in her lap and chewing on her lower lip to prevent it quivering.

The champion jumped up into the ring. Ian Rushmore was an inch shorter than Manfred, but broader and deeper in the chest, with long simian arms heavily muscled, and a neck so short and thick that his head seemed to ride

directly on his shoulders. Thick coarse black hair curled out of the top of his vest and he looked powerful and dangerous as a wild boar.

The bell rang and in the blood roar of the crowd the two fighters came together in the middle of the ring. Centaine gasped involuntarily at the thud of gloved fist on flesh and bone. Compared to the flickering blows of the lighter smaller men in the preceding bouts, this was like the meeting of gladiators.

She could not see any advantage between the two men as they wheeled and came together and their fists struck those terrible blows that bounced off solid guards of arms and gloves. Then they weaved and ducked and joined again while the crowd around her bellowed in a mindless frenzy.

As abruptly as it had begun, it ended, and the fighters separated and went back to the little groups of white-clad seconds who hovered over them, tending them lovingly, sponging and kneading their flesh, fanning and massaging and whispering to them.

Manfred took a mouthful from the bottle that his big black bearded coach held to his mouth. He sluiced it around his mouth and then turned and looked at Centaine again, singling her out of the crowd with those pale eyes, and deliberately spat the mouthful of water into the bucket at his feet without breaking his gaze. She knew that it was for her, he was spitting his anger at her. She quailed before his rage and she barely heard Blaine murmur beside her.

'I scored that round as a draw. De La Rey gave nothing away, and Rushmore is wary of him.'

Then the boxers were on their feet again, circling and jabbing and pumping leather-clad fists, grunting like labouring bulls at punches thrown and received, their bodies shining with the running sweat of their exertions and bright red patches glowing on their bodies where blows landed. It went on and on, and Centaine felt a sickness rising in her at the primeval savagery of it, at the sounds and smell and spectacle of violence and pain.

'Rushmore took that one,' Blaine said quietly, as the round ended, and she actually hated him for his calmness. She felt a clammy sweat break out on her face and her nausea threatened to overwhelm her as Blaine went on, 'De La Rey will have to end it in the next two rounds. If he doesn't, Rushmore is going to grind him down. He's getting more confident all the time.'

She wanted to jump to her feet and hurry out of the hall, but her legs would not function. Then the bell rang and the two men were out there again in the glare of the floodlights, and she tried to look away but could not – so she stared in sick fascination and saw it happen, saw every vivid detail of it, and knew she would never forget it.

She saw the red leather glove blur as it tore through a tiny gap in the defending circle of arms, and she saw the other man's head snap as though it had reached the limit of the hangman's noose as his body fell through the trap. She saw each individual droplet of sweat burst from his sodden locks, as though a heavy stone had been flung in a deep pool, and the features below twisted grotesquely out of shape by the impact into a carnival mask of agony.

She heard the blow, the snap of something breaking, teeth or bone or sinew, and she screamed, but her scream was lost and swallowed up in the high surf sound that burst from a thousand throats around her, and she thrust her fingers into her own mouth as the blows kept coming, so fast that they dissolved before her eyes, so fast that the shocking thuds of impact blended like the sound of an eggbeater in thick cream, and flesh turned to red ruin beneath them. She went on screaming as she watched the terrible killing yellow rage in the eyes of the

son she had borne, watched him become a ravening murderous beast, and the man before him wilted and broke, and reeled away on boneless legs, and went down twisting as he fell and rolled onto his back, staring up at the overhead lights with blind eyes, snoring in the thick bright flood that throbbed from his crushed nose into his open mouth. Manfred De La Rey danced over him, still possessed by the killing rage, so that Centaine expected him to throw back his head and howl like a wolf, or throw himself upon the broken thing at his feet and rip the bleeding scalp from its head and brandish it high in obscene triumph.

'Take me away, Blaine,' she sobbed. 'Get me out of this place,' and his arms lifted her to her feet and carried her out into the night.

Behind her the blood roar faded, and she gulped down the cold sweet highveld air as though she had been rescued at the very point of drowning.

* * *

'The Lion of the Kalahari writes his own ticket to Berlin,' the headlines crowed, and Centaine shuddered with the memory, and dropped the newspaper over the edge of the bed and reached for the telephone.

'Shasa, how soon can we leave for home?' she demanded, as soon as his voice, blurred with sleep, sounded in her earpiece, and Blaine came through from the bathroom of the hotel suite with shaving lather on his cheeks.

'You have decided?' he asked as soon as she hung up.

'There is no point in even trying to speak to him,' she replied. 'You saw how he looked at me.'

'Perhaps there will be another time – ' he tried to comfort her. But he saw the despair in her eyes and he went to hold her.

* * *

David Abrahams improved his best time for the 200-metre sprint by almost a second on the first day of the Olympic trials. However, in reaction he did not do as well as expected on the second day when he could only just win his final heat in the 400 by half a metre. Still, his name was high on the list that was read out at the banquet and ball that closed the five days of the track and field trials, and Shasa, who was sitting beside him, was the first to shake his hand and pound him between the shoulder blades. David was going to Berlin.

* * *

Two weeks later the polo trials were held at the Inanda Club in Johannesburg and Shasa was selected for the 'B' team of 'possibles' against Blaine's 'A' team of 'probables' for the last match of the final day.

Sitting high in the grandstand, Centaine watched Shasa play one of the most inspired games of his career, but with despair in her heart knew that it was still

not good enough. Shasa never missed an interception, nor mishit a stroke during the first five chukkas, and once even took the ball out from under the nose of Blaine's pony with a display of audacious riding that brought every person in the grandstand to their feet. Still it was not good enough, she knew.

Clive Ramsay, Shasa's rival for the position of number two in the team that would go to Berlin, had played well all week. He was a man of forty-two years, with a record of solid achievement behind him, and he had seconded Blaine Malcomess in almost thirty international matches. His polo career was just reaching its peak, and Centaine knew that the selectors could not afford to drop him in favour of the younger, more dashing, probably more gifted, but certainly less experienced and therefore less reliable rider.

She could almost see them nodding their heads sagely, puffing their cigars and agreeing. 'Young Courtney will get his chance next time,' and she was hating them for it in advance – Blaine Malcomess included – when suddenly there was a howl from the crowd around her and she jumped to her feet with them.

Shasa, thank God, was out of it, galloping wide down the sideline ready to take the cross as his own number one, another thrusting young player, challenged Clive Ramsay in centre field.

It was probably not deliberate, more likely the consequence of a reckless urge to shine, but Shasa's team-mate fouled Clive Ramsay murderously on the interception, knocking his pony onto its knees and sending Clive somersaulting from the saddle onto the iron-hard ground. Later that afternoon X-ray examination confirmed a multiple fracture of Ramsay's femur which the orthopaedic surgeon was subsequently forced to open up and wire.

'No polo for at least a year,' he ordered, when Clive Ramsay came out of the anaesthetic.

So when the selectors went into conclave, Centaine waited anxiously, allowing herself renewed hope. As he had warned Centaine he would, Blaine Malcomess excused himself from the selectors' room when Shasa's name came up. But when he was called back in, the chairman grunted.

'Very well, young Courtney gets the ride in Clive's place.' And despite himself he felt a lift of elation and pride, Shasa Courtney was the closest he would ever get to having a son of his own.

As soon as he could, Blaine telephoned Centaine with the news. 'It won't be announced until Friday, but Shasa has got his ticket.'

Centaine was beside herself. 'Oh Blaine, darling, how will I contain myself until Friday?' she cried. 'Oh, won't it be fun going to Berlin together, the three of us! We can take the Daimler and drive across Europe. Shasa has never visited Mort Homme. We can spend a few days in Paris, and you can take me to dinner at Laserre. There is so much to arrange, but we can talk about it when I see you on Saturday.'

'Saturday?' He had forgotten, she could hear it in his voice.

'Sir Garry's birthday – the picnic on the mountain!' She sighed with exasperation. 'Oh Blaine, it's one of the few times in the year we can be together – legitimately!'

'Is it Sir Garry's birthday again so soon? What happened to the year?' he hedged.

'Oh, Blaine, you did forget,' she accused. 'You can't let me down. It will be a double celebration this year – the birthday, and Shasa's selection for the Games. Promise you will be there, Blaine.'

He hesitated an instant longer. He had already promised to take Isabella and the girls to her mother's home at Franschoek for the weekend.

'I promise, my sweeting, I'll be there.' She would never know what that promise would cost him, for Isabella would make him pay with exquisite refinements of cruelty for the broken pledge.

It was the drug which had wrought this change in Isabella, he kept assuring himself. Beneath it she was still the same sweet and gentle person he had married. It was the unremitting pain and the drug which had ravaged her so, and he tried to maintain his respect and affection for her.

He tried to remember her loveliness, as delicate and ethereal as the bloom on the petals of a new-blown rose, but that loveliness had long since disappeared and the petals of the rose had withered, and the smell of corruption was upon her. The sweet sickly smell of the drug exuded from every pore of her skin and the deep never-healing abscesses in her buttocks and at the base of her spine gave off an odour, faint but penetrating, that he had come to abhor. It made it difficult for him to be near her. The smell and the sight of her offended him but at the same time filled him with helpless pity and corrosive guilt at his infidelity to her.

She had wasted to a skeleton. There was no flesh on the bones of those frail legs, they looked like the legs of one of the wading water birds, perfectly straight and shapeless, distorted only by the lumpy knots of her knees and the useless disproportionately large feet at their extremities.

Her arms were just as thin, and the flesh had receded from the bones of her skull. Her lips had drawn back so that her teeth were prominent and exposed, and looked like those of a skull when she tried to smile or more often grimaced with anger, and her gums were pale, almost white.

Her skin also was pale as ricepaper, and as dry and lifeless, so thin and translucent that the veins of her hands and forehead showed through it in a blue tracery and her eyes were the only living things in her face. They had a malicious glitter in them now, as though she resented him for his healthy lusty body when her own was destroyed and useless.

'How can you, Blaine?' she asked the question with the same accusing high-pitched whine that she had used countless times before. 'You promised me, Blaine. God knows, I see little enough of you as it is. I've been looking forward to this weekend since – ' It went on and on, and he tried to shut it out, but he found himself thinking of her body again.

He had not seen her unclothed in almost seven years, then only a month previously he had walked into her dressing-room believing that she was in the gazebo in the garden where she spent most of her day, but she was laid out naked on the white sheet of the massage table with her uniformed day nurse working over her and the shock must have shown clearly on his face as the two women looked up at him, startled.

Every rib stood out of Isabella's narrow chest and her breasts were empty pouches of skin that drooped under her armpits. The dark bush of her pubic hair was incongruous and obscene in the bony basin of her pelvis below which those sticklike legs protruded at a disjointed angle, so shrunken that the gap between her thighs was wider than the span of his hands.

'Get out!' she had screamed at him, and he had torn his eyes from her and hurried from the room. 'Get out! Don't ever come in here again!'

Now her voice had the same ring to it. 'Go to your picnic then, if you must.

I know what a burden I am to you. I know you can't bear to spend more than a few minutes in my presence – '

He could not stand it any longer, and held up a hand to quieten her. 'You are right, my dear. It was selfish of me to even mention it. We won't speak of it again. Of course I will go with you.' He saw the vindictive sparkle of triumph in her eyes, and suddenly for the very first time he hated her, and before he could prevent himself, he thought, 'Why doesn't she die? It would be better for her and everybody about her if she were dead.' Instantly he was appalled at himself and guilt washed over him so that he went to her quickly and stooped over the wheelchair, took that cold bony hand in both of his and squeezed it gently as he kissed her on the lips.

'Forgive me, please,' he whispered – but unbidden the image of her in her coffin appeared to him. She lay there, beautiful and serene as she had once been, her hair once again thick and lustrous auburn spread on the white satin pillow. He shut his eyes tightly to try and drive the image away, but it persisted even when she clung to his hand.

'Oh, it will be such fun to be alone together for a while.' She prevented him pulling away. 'We have so few opportunities to talk any more. You spend so much time in Parliament, and when you aren't about your cabinet duties you are out on the polo field.'

'I see you every day, morning and evening.'

'Oh, I know, but we never talk. We haven't even discussed Berlin yet, and the time is running out.'

'Is there much we should discuss, my dear?' he asked carefully as he disengaged her grip and returned to his own chair on the opposite side of the gazebo.

'Of course there it, Blaine.' She smiled at him, exposing those pale gums behind shrunken lips. It gave her a cunning, almost ferrety, expression which he found disturbing. 'There are so many arrangements to make. When is the team leaving?'

'I may not travel with the team,' he told her carefully. 'I may leave a few weeks earlier and stop off in London and Paris for discussions with the British and French Governments before going on to Berlin.'

'Oh Blaine, we must still make the arrangements for me to go with you,' she said and he had to control his expression for she was watching him carefully.

'Yes,' he said. 'It will need careful planning.'

The idea was insupportable. How he longed to be with Centaine, to be able to get away from all pretence and fear of discovery. 'We shall have to be very certain, my dear, that travelling will not seriously impair your health further.'

'You don't want me with you, do you?' Her voice rose sharply.

'Of course – '

'It's a wonderful chance for you to get away from me, to escape from me.'

'Isabella, please calm yourself. You will do yourself – '

'Don't pretend you care about me – I've been a burden on you for nine years. I'm sure you wish me dead.'

'Isabella – ' He was shaken by the accuracy of the accusation.

'Oh, don't play the saint with me, Blaine Malcomess. I may be locked into this chair, but I see things and I hear things.'

'I don't wish to continue like this.' He stood up. 'We'll talk again once you have control – '

'Sit down!' she screeched at him. 'I won't have you running off to your

French whore as you always do!' He flinched as though she had struck him in the face, and she went on gloatingly, 'There, I've said it at last. Oh God, you'll never know how close I've been to saying it so many times. You'll never know how good it feels to say it – whore! Doxy!'

'If you continue, I will leave,' he warned.

'Harlot,' she said with relish. 'Slut! Jade!'

He turned on his heel and went down the steps of the gazebo two at a time.

'Blaine,' she screamed after him. 'Come back!'

He continued walking up towards the house, and her tone changed.

'Blaine, I'm sorry. I apologize. Please come back. Please!' and he could not refuse her. Reluctantly he turned back, and found that his hands were shaking with shock and anger. He thrust them into his pockets and stopped at the top of the steps.

'All right,' he said softly. 'It's true about Centaine Courtney. I love her. But it is also true that we have done everything in our power to prevent you being hurt or humiliated. So don't ever talk like that about her again. If she had allowed it, I would have gone to her years ago – and left you. May God forgive me, but I would have walked out on you! Only she kept me here, only she still keeps me here.'

She was chastened and shaken as he was, or so he thought, until she raised her eyes again and he saw she had feigned repentance merely to lure him back within range of her tongue. 'I know I cannot go to Berlin with you, Blaine. I have already asked Dr Joseph and he has forbidden it. He says the journey would kill me. However, I know what you are planning, you and that woman. I know you have used all your influence to get Shasa Courtney into the team merely to give her an excuse to be there. I know you are planning a wonderful illicit interlude, and I can't stop you going – '

He spread his hands in angry resignation. It was useless to protest and her voice rose again into that harrowing shrillness.

'Well, let me tell you this – it isn't going to be the honeymoon that the two of you think it is. I've told the girls, both Tara and Mathilda Janine, that they are going with you. I've told them already, and they are beside themselves with excitement. It will be up to you. Either you are heartless enough to disappoint your own daughters, or you will be playing baby-sitter and not Romeo in Berlin.' Her voice rose even higher, and the glitter of her eyes was vindictive. 'And I warn you! If you refuse to take them with you, Blaine Malcomess, I will tell them why. I call on God as my witness, I will tell them that their beloved daddy is a cheat and a liar, a libertine and a whoremaster!'

* * *

Although everybody, from the most knowledgeable sports writers to the lowliest fight fan, had confidently expected Manfred De La Rey to be on the boxing squad to go to Berlin, when the official announcement of the team was made and he was indeed the light heavyweight selection, but in addition Roelf Stander was the heavyweight choice and the Reverend Tromp Bierman was given the duties of official team coach, the entire town and university body of Stellenbosch erupted in spontaneous expressions of pride and delight.

There was a civic reception and parade through the streets of the town, while

at a mass meeting of the *Ossewa Brandwag* the commanding general held them up as an example of Afrikaner manhood and extolled their dedication and fighting skills.

'It is young men such as these who will lead our nation to its rightful place in this land,' he told them, and while the massed uniformed ranks gave the *OB* salute, the clenched right fist held across the chest, Manfred and Roelf had the badges of officer rank pinned to their tunics.

'For God and the *Volk*,' their high commander exhorted them, and Manfred had never before experienced such pride, such determination to honour the trust that had been placed in him.

Over the weeks that followed, the excitement continued to build up. There were fittings at the official team tailor for the gold and green blazers, white slacks and broad-brimmed Panama hats which made up the uniform in which they would march into the Olympic stadium. There were endless team briefings, covering every subject from German etiquette and polite behaviour to travel arrangements and profiles of the opponents whom they were likely to encounter on the way to the final.

Both Manfred and Roelf were interviewed by journalists from every magazine and newspaper in the country, and a half an hour on the nationally broadcast radio programme 'This is your Land' was devoted entirely to them.

Only one person seemed unaffected by the excitement.

'The weeks you are away will seem longer than my whole life,' Sarah told Manfred.

'Don't be a silly little duck,' he laughed at her. 'It will be all over before you know it, and I'll be back with a gold medal on my chest.'

'Don't call me a silly little duck,' she flashed at him, 'not ever again!'

He stopped laughing. 'You are right,' he said. 'You are worth more than that.'

Sarah had taken on herself the duties of timekeeper and second for Manfred's and Roelf's evening training runs. On flying bare feet she took short cuts up the hillside and through the forest to wait for them at prearranged spots with her stopwatch, borrowed from Uncle Tromp, a wet sponge and a flask of cold freshly squeezed orange juice to refresh them. As soon as they had sponged down, drunk and set off again she would race away, cutting over the crest of the hill or through the valley to wait for them at the next stage.

Two weeks before the sailing date, Roelf was forced to miss one of the evening runs when he was obliged to chair an extraordinary meeting of the students' representative council and Manfred made the run alone.

He took the long steep side of the Hartenbosch mountain at a full run, going with all his strength, flying up the slope with long elastic strides, lifting his gaze to the crest. Sarah was waiting for him there, and the low autumn sun was behind her, crowning her with gold and striking through the thin stuff of her skirts so that her legs were silhouetted and he could see every line and lovely angle of her body almost as though she were unclothed.

He pulled up involuntarily in full stride and stood staring up at her, his chest heaving and his heart pounding, not only from his exertions.

'She is beautiful.' He was amazed that he had never seen it before, and he walked up the last angle of the slope slowly, staring at her, confused by this sudden realization and by the hollow hunger, the need that he had kept suppressed, whose existence he had never admitted to himself but which now suddenly threatened to consume him.

She came to meet him the last few paces; barefoot she was so much smaller than he was and that seemed only to increase this terrible hunger. She held out the sponge to him, but when he made no move to take it from her, she stepped up close to him and reached up to wipe the sweat from his neck and shoulders.

'I dreamed last night we were back in the camp,' she whispered as she worked, swabbing his upper arms. 'Do you remember the camp beside the railway tracks, Manie?'

He nodded. His throat had closed, and he could not reply.

'I saw my ma lying in the grave. It was a terrible thing. Then it changed, Manie, it wasn't my ma any more, it was you. You were so pale and handsome, but I knew I had lost you – and I was so eaten by my own sorrow that I wanted to die also and be with you for ever.'

He reached out and took her in his arms and she sobbed and fell against him. Her body felt so cool and soft and compliant and her voice shook.

'Oh, Manie. I don't want to lose you. Please come back to me – without you I don't want to go on living.'

'I love you, Sarie.' His voice was hoarse and she jerked in his arms.

'Oh Manie.'

'I never realized it before,' he croaked.

'Oh Manie, I have always realized it. I loved you from the first minute of the first day, and I will love you until the last,' she cried, and turned her mouth up to his. 'Kiss me, Manie, kiss me or I will die.'

The touch of her mouth ignited something within him, and the fire and the smoke of it obscured reason and reality. Then they were under the pines beside the path, lying on a bed of soft needles, and the sultry autumn air was soft as silk upon his bare back, but not as soft as her body beneath his nor as hot as the liquid depths in which she engulfed him.

He did not understand what had happened until she cried out, in pain and intense joy, but by then it was too late and he found himself answering her cry, no longer able to draw back, carried along on a swirling tidal wave to a place he had never been before – nor had he even dreamed of its existence.

Reality and consciousness returned slowly from far away, and he drew away from her and stared at her in horror, pulling on his own clothing.

'What we have done is wicked beyond forgiveness – '

'No.' She shook her head vehemently and, still naked, reached for him. 'No, Manie, it's not wicked when two people love each other. How can it be wicked? It's a thing from God, beautiful and holy.'

The night before Manfred sailed for Europe with Uncle Tromp and the team, he slept in his old room at the Manse. When the old house was dark and quiet, Sarah crept down the passage. He had left his door unlatched. Nor did he protest as she let her nightdress fall and crept under the sheet beside him.

She stayed until the doves in the oaks outside the stoep began fluttering and softly cooing. Then she kissed him one last time and whispered:

'Now we belong to each other – for ever and always.'

* * *

It was only half an hour before sailing and Centaine's stateroom was so crowded that the stewards were forced to pass the champagne glasses over the heads of

the guests, and it required a major expedition to get from one side of the cabin to the other. The only one of Centaine's friends who was not present was Blaine Malcomess. They had decided not to advertise the fact that they were sailing on the same mail ship, and had agreed only to meet once they were clear of the harbour.

Both Abe Abrahams, bursting with pride, his arm hooked through David's, and Dr Twentyman-Jones, tall and lugubrious as a marabou stork, were in the party around Centaine. They had come all the way down from Windhoek to see her off. Naturally, Sir Garry and Anna were there, as were the *Ou Baas* General Smuts, and his little fluffy-haired wife with her steel-rimmed spectacles making her look like an advertisement for Mazzawattee tea.

In the far corner Shasa was surrounded by a bevy of young ladies, and was in the middle of a story that was being followed by shrieks of amusement and gasps of incredulous wonder, when suddenly he lost track of what he had been saying and stared out of the porthole beside him. Through it he had a view out onto the boat deck, and what had caught his attention was a glimpse of a girl's head as she passed.

He couldn't see her face, just the side and back of her head, a cascade of auburn curls set on a long slim neck, and a little ear sticking out of the curls at a jaunty angle. It was a fleeting glimpse only, but something about the angle and carriage of that head made him lose immediate interest in the females in front of him.

He went up on his toes, spilling champagne, and stuck his head through the porthole, but the girl had passed by and he only had a back view of her. She had an impossibly narrow waist but a cheeky little rump that switched from side to side and made her skirts wing rhythmically as she walked. Her calves were perfectly turned and her ankles slim and neat. She went round the corner with a last twitch of her bottom, leaving Shasa determined that he must get a look at her face.

'Excuse me, ladies.' His audience gave little cries of disappointment, but he eased himself neatly out of their circle and began working his way towards the door. But before he reached it, the sirens started their booming thunder of warning and the cry went up, 'Last call, ladies and gentlemen – all ashore, those who are going ashore,' and he knew he had run out of time.

'She was probably a dog – a backside like heaven and a face like hell – and she almost certainly isn't sailing, anyway,' he consoled himself. Then Dr Twentyman-Jones was shaking his hand and wishing him luck for the Games, and he tried to forget that bunch of auburn curls and concentrate on his social duties, but it wasn't all that easy.

Out on deck he looked for an auburn head going down the gangway, or in the crowd on the quayside, but Centaine was tugging at his arm as the gap between ship and land opened below them.

'Come, *chéri*, let's go and check the dining-room seating.'

'But you have been invited to the captain's table, Mater,' he protested. 'There was an invitation in the – '

'Yes, but you and David haven't,' she pointed out. 'Come along, David, let's go and find where they have put the two of you, and have it changed if it's not suitable.'

She was up to something, Shasa realized. Normally she would take the seating for granted, secure in the knowledge that her name was all the guarantee of preference that was necessary, but now she was insistent, and she had that

look in her eye which he knew so well, and which he called her 'Machiavellian sparkle'.

'Come along then,' he agreed indulgently, and the three of them went down the walnut-panelled staircase to the first class dining-room on the deck below.

At the foot of the stairs a small group of seasoned travellers were being affable to the head waiter; five-pound notes were disappearing like magic into that urbane gentleman's pocket, leaving no bulge, and names were being rubbed out and re-pencilled on the seating plan.

Standing a little apart from the group was a tall familiar figure that Shasa recognized instantly. Something about him, the expectant turn of his head towards the staircase, told Shasa he was waiting for someone, and his dazzling smile as he saw Centaine made it clear who that someone was.

'Good Lord, Mater,' Shasa exclaimed. 'I didn't realize Blaine was sailing today – I thought he would be going later with the others – ' he broke off. He had felt his mother's grip on his forearm tighten and the quick catch of her breath as she saw Blaine.

'They have arranged this,' he realized with a flare of amazement. 'That's what her excitement was.' And at last it dawned upon him. 'You never think it of your own mother, but they are lovers. All these years, and I never saw it.' The little things, insignificant at the time but now full of meaning, came crowding back. 'Blaine and the mater, damn me blind! Who would have thought it – ' and conflicting emotions assailed him. 'Of all the men in the world, I would have chosen him – ' In that moment he realized how much Blaine Malcomess had come to stand in the place of the father he had never known, but the thought was followed instantly by a flush of jealous and moral indignation. 'Blaine Malcomess, pillar of society and government, and Mater who is always frowning and shaking her head at me – the naughty little devils, they have been raving away for years without anybody suspecting!'

Blaine was coming towards them. 'Centaine, this is a surprise!'

Mater was laughing and holding out her right hand to him. 'Gracious me, Blaine Malcomess, I had no idea you were on board.'

Shasa thought wryly: 'What marvellous acting! You have had me and everybody fooled for years. The two of you make Clark Gable and Ingrid Bergman look like a pair of beginners!'

Then suddenly it didn't matter any more. The only thing that was important was that there were two girls following Blaine as he came towards Centaine.

'Centaine, I'm sure you remember my two daughters. This is Tara and this is Mathilda Janine – '

'Tara.' Silently Shasa sang the name in his head. 'Tara – what a lovely name.' It was the girl he had glimpsed on the boat deck, and she was only one hundred times more stunning that he had hoped she might be.

Tara. She was tall, only a few inches below his own six foot, but her legs were like willow wands and her waist was like a reed.

Tara. She had the face of a madonna, a serene oval, and her complexion was a mixture of cream and flower petals, almost too perfect, yet redeemed from insipid vacuity by the smoking chestnut hair, her father's wide strong mouth and her own eyes, resilient as grey steel and bright with intelligence and determination.

She greeted Centaine with the correct amount of deference and then turned to look directly at Shasa.

'Shasa, you too remember Tara,' Blaine told him. 'She came out to Weltevreden four years ago.'

Was this the same noisy little pest? Shasa stared at her – the one in short skirts with scabs on her bony knees who had embarrassed him with her boisterous and childish capers? He could not believe it was, and his voice caught in his throat.

'How good to see you again, Tara, after so long.'

'Remember, Tara Malcomess,' she cautioned herself. 'Be controlled and aloof.' She almost shivered with shame as she remembered how she had gambolled and fawned around him like a puppy begging to be patted. 'What a callow little beast, I was.' But she had been smitten by a crush so powerful at first sight of him that the pain of it still lingered even now.

However, she managed to display the right shade of indifference as she murmured, 'Oh have we met? I must have forgotten, forgive me.' She held out her hand. 'Well, it's pleasant to meet you again – Shasa?'

'Yes, Shasa,' he agreed, and he took the hand as though it were a holy talisman. 'Why haven't we met again since then?' he asked himself, and immediately he saw the answer. 'It was deliberate. Blaine and Mater made damn sure that we never met again in case it complicated their own little arrangement. They did not want Tara reporting back to her mama.' But he was too happy to be angry with them now.

'Have you made your table reservations?' he asked, without relinquishing her hand.

'Daddy is sitting at the captain's table,' Tara pouted lovingly at her father. 'And we are to be left all alone.'

'The four of us could sit together,' Shasa suggested quickly. 'Let's go and talk to the *Maître*.' Blaine and Centaine exchanged relieved glances – it was all going exactly as they had planned, with one twist they had not foreseen.

Mathilda Janine had blushed as she shook hands with David Abrahams. Of the two sisters, she was the ugly duckling for she had inherited not only her father's wide mouth but his large nose and prominent ears as well, and her hair was not auburn but ginger carrot.

'But he's got a big nose too,' she thought defiantly, as she studied David, and then her thoughts went off on a tangent. 'If Tara tells him I'm only sixteen I'll just die!'

The voyage was a tempest of emotions, full of delights and surprises and frustrations and agonies for all of them. During the fourteen days of the passage to Southampton Blaine and Centaine saw very little of the four youngsters, meeting them for a cocktail beside the ship's pool before lunch and for a duty dance after dinner, David and Shasa each taking a turn at whirling Centaine around the floor while Blaine did the same to his daughters. Then there would be a quick exchange of glances between the four young people and they would make their elaborate excuses before all disappearing down into the tourist class where the real fun was, leaving Blaine and Centaine to their staid pleasures on the upper decks.

Tara in a one-piece bathing costume of lime green was the most magnificent sight Shasa had ever laid eyes upon. Her breasts under the clinging material were the shape of unripe pears and when she came from the pool with water streaming down those long elegant limbs, he could make out the dimple of her navel through the cloth and the hard little marbles of her nipples, and it took all his control to prevent himself groaning out loud.

Mathilda Janine and David discovered a mutual zany and irreverent sense of humour, and kept each other in convulsions of laughter most of the time. Mathilda Janine was up at four-thirty each morning, no matter how late they had got to bed, to give David raucous encouragement as he made his fifty circuits of the boat deck.

'He moves like a panther,' she told herself. 'Long and smooth and graceful.' And she had to think up fifty new witticisms each morning to shout at him as he went bounding past her. They chased each other around the pool and wrestled ecstatically below the surface once they had managed to fall in locked in each other's arms, but, apart from a furtive pecking kiss at the door of the cabin that Mathilda Janine shared with Tara, neither of them even considered carrying it any further. Although David had benefited from his brief relationship with the Camel, it never occurred to him to indulge in the same acrobatics with someone as special at Matty.

Shasa on the other hand suffered under no such inhibitions. He was vastly more sexually experienced than David, and once he had recovered from the initial awe of Tara's beauty, he launched an insidious but determined assault on the fortress of her virginity. However, his rewards were even less spectacular than David's.

It took him almost a week to work up to the stage of intimacy where Tara would allow him to spread suntan oil on her back and shoulders. In the small hours of the morning when the lights on the dance floor were dimmed for the last dance and the band played the sugary romantic 'Poinciana', she laid her velvet-soft cheek against his, but when he tried to press his lower body against her at the cabin door she held him off with both hands on his chest and gave him that low tantalizing laugh.

'The silly little witch is totally frigid,' Shasa told his reflection in the shaving mirror. 'She probably has an iceberg in her knickers.' Thought of those regions made him shiver with frustration, and he resolved to break off the chase. He thought of the five or six other females on board, not all of them young, who had looked at him with unmistakable invitation in their eyes. 'I could have any or all of them instead of panting along behind Miss Tin Knickers – ' But an hour later he was partnering her in the mixed doubles deck quoit championships, or smoothing suntan oil on that flawless finely muscled back with fingers that trembled with agonized desire, or trying to keep level with her in a discussion of the merits and demerits of the government's plans to disenfranchise the coloured voters of the Cape Province.

He had discovered with some dismay that Tara Malcomess had a highly developed political conscience, and that even though it was vaguely understood between him and Mater that Shasa would one day go into politics and parliament, his grasp of and interest in the complex problems of the country was not of the same calibre as Tara's. She held views that were almost as disturbing to him as her physical attractions.

'I believe, as Daddy does, that far from taking the vote away from the few black people who have it, we should be giving it to all of them.'

'All of them!' Shasa was appalled. 'You don't really believe that, do you?'

'Of course I do. Not all at once, but on a civilization basis, government by those who have proved fit to govern. Give the vote to all those who have the right standards of education and responsibility. In two generations every man and woman, black or white, could be on the roll.

Shasa shuddered at the thought, his own aspirations to a seat in the house would not survive that – but this was probably the least radical of her opinions.

'How can we prevent people from owning land in their own country or from selling their labour in the best market, or prohibit them from collective bargaining?'

Trade unions were the tools of Lenin and the devil. That was a fact Shasa had taken in with his mother's milk.

'She's a bolshy – but, God, what a beautiful bolshy!' he thought, and pulled her to her feet to break the unpalatable lecture. 'Come on, let's go for a swim.'

'He's an ignorant fascist,' she thought furiously, but when she saw the way the other women looked at him from behind their sunglasses, she wanted to claw their eyes out of their faces, and at night in her bunk when she thought about the touch of his hands on her bare back, and the feel of him against her on the dance floor, she blushed in the darkness at the fantasies that filled her head.

'If I just let it start – just the barest beginning, I know I won't be able to stop him, I won't even want to stop him – ' and she steeled herself against him. 'Controlled and aloof,' she repeated, like a charm against the treacherous wiles of her own body.

* * *

By some extraordinary coincidence it just so happened that Blaine Malcomess had shipped his Bentley in the hold, alongside Centaine's Daimler.

'We could drive to Berlin in convoy,' Centaine exclaimed as though the idea had just occurred to her, and there was clamorous acceptance of the idea from the four younger members of the party, and immediate jockeying and lobbying for seats in the two vehicles. Centaine and Blaine, protesting mildly, allowed themselves to be allocated the Bentley while the others, driven by Shasa, would follow in the Daimler.

From Le Havre they drove the dusty roads of north-western France, through the towns that still had the ring of terror in their names, Amiens and Arras. The green grass had covered the muddy battlefields where Blaine had fought, but the fields of white crosses were bright as daisies in the sunlight.

'May God grant that mankind never has to live through that again,' Blaine murmured, and Centaine reached across and took his hand.

In the little village of Mort Homme they parked in front of the *auberge* in the main street, and when Centaine walked in through the front door to enquire for lodgings, Madame behind the desk recognized her instantly and screeched with excitement.

'*Henri, viens vite! C'est Mademoiselle de Thiry du Château* – ' and she rushed to embrace Centaine and buss her on both cheeks.

A travelling salesman was ousted, and the best rooms put at their disposal; a little explanation was needed when Centaine and Blaine asked for separate accommodation, but the meal they were served that night was exquisitely nostalgic for Centaine, with all the specialities – terrines and truffles and *tartes* – with the wine of the region, while Madame stood beside the table and gave Centaine all the gossip, the deaths and births, the marriages and elopements and liaisons of the last nineteen years.

In the early morning Centaine and Shasa left the others sleeping, and drove up to the château. It was rubble and black scorched walls, pierced with empty windows and shell holes, overgrown and desolate, and Centaine stood in the ruins and wept for her father who had burned with the great house rather than abandon it to the advancing Germans.

After the war the estate had been sold off to pay for the debts that the old man had accumulated over a lifetime of good living and hard drinking. It was now owned by Hennessy, the great cognac firm; the old man would have enjoyed that little irony, Centaine smiled at the thought.

Together they climbed the hillock beyond the ruined château and from the crest Centaine pointed out the orchard and plantation that marked the old wartime airfield.

'That is where your father's squadron was stationed, on the edge of the orchard. I waited here every morning for the squadron to take off, and I would wave them away to battle.'

'They flew SE5a's didn't they?'

'Only later. At first it was the old Sopwiths.' She was looking up at the sky. 'Your father's machine was painted bright yellow. I called him *le petit jaune*, the little yellow one – I can see him now in his flying helmet. He used to lift the goggles so I could see his eyes as he flew past me. Oh Shasa, how noble and gay and young he was, a young eagle going up into the blue.'

They descended the hillock and drove slowly back between the vineyards. Centaine asked Shasa to stop beside a small stone-walled barn at the corner of North Field. He watched her, puzzled, as she stood for a few minutes in the doorway of the thatched building and then came back to the Daimler with a faint smile on her lips and a soft glow in her eyes.

She saw his enquiring look and told him, 'Your father and I used to meet here.' In a clairvoyant insight Shasa realized that in this rickety old building in a foreign land he had been conceived. The strangeness of this knowledge remained with him as they drove back towards the *auberge*.

At the entrance to the village in front of the little church with its green copper spire, they stopped again and went into the cemetery. Michael Courtney's grave was at the far end, beneath a yew tree. Centaine had ordered the headstone from Africa but had never seen it before. A marble eagle, perched on a tattered battle standard, was on the point of flight, with wings spread. Shasa thought it was a little too flamboyant for a memorial to the dead.

They stood side by side and read the inscription:

SACRED TO THE MEMORY OF
CAPTAIN MICHAEL COURTNEY RFC
KILLED IN ACTION 19 APRIL 1917.
GREATER LOVE HATH NO MAN.

Weeds had grown up around the headstone, and they knelt together and tidied the grave. Then they stood at the foot of it, their heads bowed.

Shasa had expected to be profoundly moved by his father's grave, but instead he felt remote and untouched. The man beneath the headstone had become clay long before he was born. He had felt closer to Michael Courtney six thousand miles from here when he had slept in his bed, worn his old thornproof tweed jacket, handled his Purdey shotgun and his fishing-rods, or used his gold-nibbed pen and his platinum and onyx dress studs.

They went back along the path to the church and found the village priest in the vestry. He was a young man, not much older than Shasa, and Centaine was disappointed for his youth seemed to her a break in her tenuous link to Michael and the past. However, she wrote out two large cheques, one for the repairs to the church's copper spire, and the other to pay for fresh flowers to be placed on Michael's grave each Sunday in perpetuity, and they went back to the Daimler with the priest's fervent benedictions following them.

The following day they all drove on to Paris; Centaine had wired ahead for accommodation at the Ritz in the Place Vendôme.

Blaine and Centaine had a full round of engagements – meetings, luncheons and dinner – with various members of the French government, so the four younger members of the party were left to their own devices and they very soon discovered that Paris was the city of romance and excitement.

They rode to the first *étage* of the Eiffel Tower in one of the creaking elevators and then raced each other up the open steel staircase to the very top and 'oohed' and 'aahed' at the city spread below them. They strolled with arms linked along the footpath on the riverbank and under the fabulous bridges of the Seine. With her baby box Brownie, Tara photographed them on the steps of Montmartre with the Sacré Coeur as a backdrop; they drank coffee and ate croissants in the sidewalk cafés and lunched at the Café de la Paix, dined at La Coupole and saw *La Traviata* at the Opéra.

At midnight when the girls had said goodnight to Centaine and their father and retired demurely and dutifully to their room, Shasa and David smuggled them out over the balcony and they went dancing in the *boites* on the Left Bank or sat listening to jazz in the cellars of Montparnasse, where they discovered a black trombone player who blew a horn that made your spine curl and a little brasserie where you could eat snails and wild strawberries at three in the morning.

In the last dawn, as they crept down the corridor to get the girls back to their room, they heard familiar voices in the elevator cage as it came up to their floor, and only just in time the four of them dived down the staircase and lay in a heap on the first landing, the girls stuffing handkerchiefs into their mouths to stifle their giggles, while just above them Blaine and Centaine, resplendent in full evening dress and oblivious of their presence, left the elevator and arm in arm strolled down the passage towards Centaine's suite.

They left Paris with regret and reached the German border in high spirits. They presented their passports to the French *douaniers* and were waved through to the German side with typical Gallic panache. They left the Bentley and Daimler parked at the barrier and trooped into the German border post where they were struck immediately by the difference in attitude between the two groups of officials.

The two German officers were meticulously turned out, their leather polished to a gloss, their caps set at the exact regulation angle and the black swastikas in a field of crimson and white on their left arms. From the wall behind their desk, a framed portrait of the Führer, stern and moustashed, glowered down upon them.

Blaine laid the sheaf of passports on the desk top in front of them with a friendly *'Guten Tag, mein Herr'*, and stood chatting to Centaine while one of the officials went through the passports one at a time, comparing each of the holders to his or her photograph and then stamping the visa with the black eagle and swastika device, before going to the next document.

Dave Abrahams' passport was at the bottom of the pile, and when the officer came to it, he paused and re-read the front cover and then pedantically turned and perused every single page in the document, looking up at David again and scrutinizing his features after each page. After a few minutes of this the group around David fell silent and began exchanging puzzled glances.

'I think something is wrong, Blaine,' Centaine said quietly, and he went back to the desk.

'Problem?' Blaine asked, and the official answered him in stilted but correct English.

'Abrahams, it is a Jewish name, no?'

Blaine flushed with irritation, but before he could reply David stepped up to the desk beside him. 'It's a Jewish name, yes!' he said quietly, and the official nodded thoughtfully, tapping the passport with his forefinger.

'You admit you are Jewish?'

'I am Jewish,' David replied in the same level tone.

'It is not written in your passport that you are Jewish,' the customs officer pointed out.

'Should it be?' David asked. The officer shrugged, then asked, 'You wish to enter Germany – and you are Jewish?'

'I wish to enter Germany to take part in the Olympic Games, to which I have been invited by the German Government.'

'Ah! You are an Olympic athlete – a Jewish Olympic athlete?'

'No, I am a South African Olympic athlete. Is my visa in order?'

The official did not reply to the question. 'Wait here, please.' He went through the rear door, carrying David's passport with him.

They heard him speaking to someone in the back office, and they all looked at Tara. She was the only one in the party who understood a little German, she had studied the language for her matriculation examinations and passed it on the Higher Grade.

'What is he saying?' Blaine asked.

'They are talking too fast – a lot about "Jews" and "Olympics",' Tara answered, then the rear door opened and the original official came back with a plump rosy-faced man who was clearly his superior, for his uniform and his manner were grander.

'Who is Abrahams?' he demanded.

'I am.'

'You are a Jew? You admit you are a Jew?'

'Yes, I am a Jew. I have said so many times. Is there something wrong with my visa?'

'You will wait, please.' This time all three officials retired to the rear office, once more taking David's passport with them. They heard the tinkle of a telephone bell, and then the senior officer's voice, loud and obsequious.

'What's going on?' They looked to Tara.

'He's talking to somebody in Berlin,' Tara told them. 'He's explaining about David.'

The one-sided conversation in the next room ended with '*Jawohl*, *mein Kapitän*,' repeated four times, each time louder, and then a shouted '*Heil Hitler!*' and the tinkle of the telephone.

The three officials filed back into the front office. The rosy-faced superior stamped David's passport and handed it to him with a flourish.

'Welcome to the Third Reich!' he declared, and flung his right hand up, palm open, and extended towards them, and shouted, '*Heil Hitler!*'

Mathilda Janine burst into nervous giggles, 'Isn't he a lark!' Blaine seized her arm and marched her out of the office.

So they drove into Germany, all of them silent and subdued.

They found lodgings in the first roadside inn, and contrary to her usual custom, Centaine accepted them without first inspecting the beds, the plumbing and the kitchens. After dinner nobody wanted to play cards or explore the village and they were in bed before ten o'clock.

However, by breakfast time they had recovered their high spirits, and Mathilda Janine had them laughing with a poem she had composed in honour of the extraordinary feats that her father, Shasa and David were about to perform in the Games ahead of them.

Their good humour increased during the day's easy journey through the beautiful German countryside, the villages and hilltop castles right out of the pages of Hans Andersen fairy tales, the forests of pine trees in dark contrast to the open meadows and the tumbling rivers crossed by arched bridges of stone. Along the way they saw groups of young people in national dress, the boys in lederhosen and feathered loden hats, the girls in *dirndls*, who waved and called greetings as the two big motor cars sped past.

They lunched in an inn full of people and music and laughter, on a haunch of wild boar with roast potatoes and apples and drank a Moselle with the taste of the grape and sunshine in its pale greenish depths.

'Everybody is so happy and prosperous-looking,' Shasa remarked as he glanced around the crowded room.

'The only country in the world with no unemployment and no poor,' Centaine agreed, but Blaine tasted his wine and said nothing.

That afternoon they entered the northern plain on the approach to Berlin, and Shasa, who was leading, swung the Daimler off onto the verge so suddenly that David grabbed for the dashboard and the girls in the back squeaked with alarm.

Shasa jumped out, leaving the engine still running, shouting, 'David! David! Just look at them – aren't they the most beautiful things you have ever seen.' The others piled out beside him and stared up at the sky, while Blaine pulled the Bentley in behind the Daimler and he and Centaine climbed out to join them, shading their eyes against the slanting sun.

There was an airfield adjoining the highway. The hangar buildings were painted silver and the windsock waved its long white arm in the small breeze. A stick of three fighter aircraft turned out of the sun, coming around in formation to line up for the strip. They were sleek as sharks, their bellies and lower wings painted sky blue, their upper surfaces speckled with camouflage and the boss of their propellers bright yellow.

'What are they?' Blaine called across to the two young pilots, and they answered as one:

'109s.'

'Messerschmitts.'

The machine-gun snouts bristled from the leading edges of the wings, and the eyes of the cannon peered malevolently from the centre of the spinning propeller bosses.

'What I'd give to fly one of those!'

'An arm – '

'And a leg – '

'And my hope of salvation!'

The three fighters changed formation into line astern and descended towards the airfield.

'They say that they can do 350 mph, straight and level – '

'Oh sweet! Oh sweet! Look at them fly!'

The girls were infected by their excitement, and they clapped and laughed, as the war machines passed low over their heads and touched down on the airstrip only a few hundred yards beyond.

'It would be worth going to war, just to get a shot at flying something like that,' Shasa exulted, and Blaine turned back to the Bentley to hide his sudden anger at the remark.

Centaine slid into the seat beside him and they drove in silence for five minutes before she said: 'He's so young and foolish sometimes – I'm sorry, Blaine, I know how he upset you.'

He sighed. 'We were the same. We called it "a great game" and thought it was going to be the glory of a lifetime that would make us men and heroes. Nobody told us about the ripped guts and the terror and how dead men smell on the fifth day in the sun.'

'It won't happen again,' Centaine said, fiercely. 'Please don't let it happen again!' In her mind's eye she saw once again the burning aircraft, with the body of the man she loved, blackening and twisting and crisping; then the face was no longer Michael's but that of his only son, and Shasa's beautiful face burst open like a sausage held too close to the flames and the sweet young life juices burst from it.

'Please stop the car, Blaine,' she whispered. 'I think I am going to be ill.'

* * *

With hard driving they could have reached Berlin that night, but in one of the smaller towns that they were passing through the streets were decorated for some sort of celebration, and Centaine asked and was told that it was the festival of the local patron saint.

'Oh Blaine, let's stay over,' she cried, and they joined in the festival.

That afternoon there was a procession. An effigy of the saint was paraded through the narrow cobbled streets, and a band followed it, with angelic little blond girls in national dress, and small boys in uniform.

'Those are the Hitler Youth,' Blaine explained. 'Something like old Baden-Powell's Boy Scouts, but with a much stronger emphasis on German national aspirations and patriotism.'

After the parade there was torchlit dancing in the town square, and barrows serving foaming tankards of beer or glasses of Sekt, the German equivalent of champagne, and serving-girls with lace aprons and cheeks like ripe apples carrying overflowing platters of rich food, pigs' trotters and veal, smoked mackerel and cheeses.

They found a table at the corner of the square, and the revellers at the neighbouring tables called greetings and merry banter to them; and they drank beer and danced and beat time to the 'oom-pa-pa' band with their beer mugs.

Then quite abruptly the atmosphere changed. The laughter around them

became brittle and forced, and there was a wariness in the faces and eyes of revellers at the adjacent tables; the band began to play too loudly and the dancers became feverish in their exertions.

Four men had entered the square. They wore brown uniforms with cross-straps over the chest and the ubiquitous swastika arm-bands. Their brown cloth caps with rounded peaks were pulled low and their leather chin straps were down. Each of them carried a small wooden collection box with a slot in the lid and they spread out and went to each of the tables.

Everybody made a donation, but as they pushed their coins into the slot of the box, they avoided looking at the brown-uniformed collectors. Their laughter was forced and nervous, and they looked into their tankards or at their own hands until the collectors had passed on to the next table, when they exchanged relieved glances.

'Who are these people?' Centaine asked innocently, making no attempt to hide her interest.

'They are the SA,' Blaine replied. 'Storm troopers, the bully boys of the National Socialist Party. Look at that one.' The trooper he had chosen had the bland heavy face of a peasant, dull and brutal. 'Is it not remarkable that there are always people to do this type of work – the need finds the man. Let us pray that his is not the face of the new Germany.'

The storm trooper had noticed their unconcealed interest and he came directly to their table with that menacing deliberate swagger.

'Papers!' he said.

'He wants our papers,' Tara translated, and Blaine handed over his passport.

'Ah! Foreign tourists.' The storm trooper's manner changed. He smiled ingratiatingly and handed back Blaine's passport with a few pleasant words.

'He says, welcome to the paradise of National Socialist Germany,' Tara translated, and Blaine nodded.

'He says, you will see how the German people are now happy and proud – and something else that I didn't catch.'

'Tell him we hope that they will always be happy and proud.' The trooper beamed and clicked the heels of his jackboots as he sprang to attention.

'*Heil Hitler!*' He gave the Nazi salute, and Mathilda Janine dissolved into helpless giggles.

'I can't help it,' she gasped as Blaine gave her a sharp look and a shake of the head. 'It just slays me when they do that.'

The storm troopers left the square, and they could feel the tension ease; the band slackened its frenetic beat and the dancers slowed down. People looked directly at one another and smiled naturally.

That night Centaine pulled the fat goose-down duvet up around her ears and snuggled into the curve of Blaine's arm.

'Have you noticed,' she asked, 'how the people here seemed caught between feverish laughter and nervous tears?'

Blaine was silent for a while and then he grunted. 'There is a smell in the air that troubles me – it seems to me that it is the stench of some deadly plague,' and he shuddered slightly and drew her closer to him.

* * *

With the Daimler leading, they streamed down the wide white autobahn into the suburbs of the German capital.

'So much water, so many canals and so many trees.'

'The city's built on a series of canals,' Tara explained. 'Rivers trapped between the old terminal moraines that lie east to west – '

'How is it you always know everything?' Shasa interrupted her, a touch of real exasperation under his teasing tone.

'Unlike some I could name, I am actually literate, you know,' she flashed back, and David winced theatrically.

'Ouch, that hurt, and it wasn't even aimed at me.'

'Very well, little Miss Know-it-all,' Shasa challenged. 'If you are so clever, what does that sign say?' He pointed ahead to a large white signboard beside the autobahn.

The lettering was in black, and Tara read it aloud.

'It says: "Jews! Keep straight on! This road will take you back to Jerusalem, where you belong!"'

As she realized what she had said, she flushed with embarrassment and leaned forward to touch David's shoulder over the back of his seat.

'Oh David, I'm so sorry. I should never have uttered such rot!'

David sat straight, staring ahead through the windscreen, and then after a few seconds he gave a thin little smile.

'Welcome to Berlin,' he whispered. 'The centre of Aryan civilization.'

* * *

'Welcome to Berlin! Welcome to Berlin!' The train that had brought them across half of Europe slid into the station, clouds of steam hissing from the vacuum brakes and the cries of greetings almost drowned by the beat of the band playing a rousing martial air.

'Welcome to Berlin!' The waiting crowd surged forward at the moment their coach came to a standstill, and Manfred De La Rey stepped down from the balcony to be surrounded by well-wishers, smiling happy faces and friendly handclasps, laughing girls and wreaths of flowers, shouted questions and popping flash bulbs.

The other athletes, all dressed like him in green blazers with gold piping, white slacks and shoes and Panama hats, were also surrounded and mobbed and it was some minutes before a loud voice rose above the hubbub.

'Attention, please! May I have your attention.' The band beat out a ruffle of drums while a tall man in a dark uniform and steel-rimmed spectacles stepped forward.

'First of all let me offer you the warm greetings of the Führer and the German people, and we welcome you to these the eleventh Olympic Games of the modern era. We know that you will represent the spirit and courage of the South African nation, and we wish you all success and many, many medals.' Amidst clapping and laughing, the speaker held up his hands. 'There are motor vehicles waiting to take you to your quarters in the Olympic village, where you will find all preparations have been made to make your stay with us both memorable and enjoyable. Now it is my pleasant duty to introduce the young lady who will be your guide and your interpreter over the next few weeks.' He

beckoned to somebody in the crowd, and a young woman stepped out into the space beside him and turned to face the band of athletes. There was a collective sigh and hum of appreciation.

'This is Heidi Kramer.' She was tall and strong, but unmistakably feminine, with hips and bosom like an hour-glass, yet touched with a dancer's grace and a gymnast's poise. Her hair was the colour of the Kalahari dawn, Manfred thought, and her teeth when she smiled were perfect, their edges minutely serrated and translucent as fine bone china, but her eyes were beyond description, bluer and clearer than the high African sky at noon, and he knew without any hesitation that she was the most magnificent woman he had ever seen. At the thought he made a silent guilty apology to Sarah – but compared to this German Valkyrie, Sarah was a sweet little tabby cat beside a female leopard in her prime.

'Now Heidi will arrange for your baggage to be collected and will get you all seated in the limousines. From now on if there is anything you need, ask Heidi! She is your big sister and your stepmother.'

They laughed and whistled and cheered and Heidi, smiling and charming but quick and efficient, took over. Within minutes their baggage had been whisked away by a band of uniformed porters and she led them down the long glass-domed platform to the magnificent entrance portals of the railway station where a line of black Mercedes limousines was waiting for them.

Manfred, Uncle Tromp and Roelf Stander climbed into the back seat of one of them, and the driver was just about to pull away when Heidi waved to him and came running back along the kerb. She wore high heels and they threw tension on her calf muscles, emphasizing their lovely lines and the fine delicacy of her ankles. Neither Sarah nor any of the girls Manfred knew at home wore high heels.

Heidi opened the front passenger door and stuck her head into the Mercedes. 'You gentlemen will object if I ride with you, yes?' she asked with that radiant smile, and they all protested vigorously, even Uncle Tromp joining in.

'No! No! Please come in.'

She slipped into the seat beside the driver, slammed the door, and immediately wriggled round so that she was facing them, with her arms folded along the back of her seat.

'I am so excited to meet you,' she told them in her accented English. 'I have read so much about Africa, the animals and the Zulus, and one day I will travel there. You must promise to tell me all about your beautiful country, and I will tell you all about my beautiful Germany.'

They agreed enthusiastically, and she looked directly at Uncle Tromp.

'Now, let me guess. You will be the Reverend Tromp Bierman, the team boxing coach?' she asked, and Uncle Tromp beamed.

'How clever of you.'

'I have seen your photograph,' she admitted. 'How could I forget such a magnificent beard?' Uncle Tromp looked highly gratified. 'But you must tell me who the others are.'

'This is Roelf Stander, our heavyweight boxer,' Uncle Tromp introduced them. 'And this is Manfred De La Rey, our light heavyweight.'

Manfred was certain that she reacted to his name, a lift to one corner of her mouth and slight narrowing of the eyes; then she was smiling again. 'We will all be good friends,' she said, and Manfred replied in German.

'My people, the Afrikaners, have always been the loyal friends of the German people.'

'Oh, your German is perfect,' she exclaimed with delight in the same language. 'Where did you learn to speak like a true German?'

'My paternal grandmother and my mother were both pure-blooded Germans.'

'Then you will find much to interest you in our country.' She switched back to English and began to lecture, pointing out the sights of the city as the line of black Mercedes, Olympic pennants fluttering on the bonnets, sped through the streets.

'This is the famous Unter den Linden, the street we Berliners love so dearly.' It was broad and magnificent with linden trees growing down the promenade that divided the double carriageway. 'The street is a mile long. That is the royal palace behind us, and there ahead of us is the Brandenburg Tor.' The tall colonnades of the monument were decked with enormous banners that hung from the quadriga charioteer group of figures on the summit to the ground far below; the crimson swastika flanked by the multi-coloured rings of the Olympic symbol billowed and heaved in the light breeze.

'That is the state opera house,' Heidi turned to point through the side window. 'It was built in 1741 – ' She was entertaining and informative.

'See how the people of Berlin welcome you,' she cried, with that gay brittle enthusiasm which seemed to characterize all the citizens of National Socialist Germany. 'Look! Look!'

Berlin was a city of flags and banners. From every public building, department store, apartment block and private dwelling the flags fluttered and waved, swastikas and the Olympic rings, thousands upon tens of thousands.

When they came at last to the apartment block in the Olympic village that had been set aside for them, an honour guard of the Hitler Youth with burning torches waited to welcome them, and another band drawn up on the sidewalk broke into 'The Voice of South Africa', the national anthem.

Inside the building Heidi issued each of them with a booklet filled with coloured coupons by which every last detail of their personal arrangements were organized, from their room and the bed on which they would sleep, and the buses that would carry them to and from the Olympic complex, to the changing rooms and the numbers of the lockers that they had been allocated at the stadium.

'Here in this house you will have your own chef and dining-hall. Food will be prepared to your own preference, with due regard to any special diets or tastes. There is a doctor and a dentist available at any hour. Drycleaning and laundry, radios and telephones, a private masseur for the team, a secretary with a typewriter – ' It had all been arranged, and they were amazed by the precise, meticulous planning.

'Please find your rooms, your luggage is already there waiting for you. Unpack and relax. Tomorrow morning I will take you on the bus for a tour of the *Reichssportfeld*, the Olympic complex. It is ten miles from here, so we will leave immediately after breakfast at eight-thirty am. In the meantime, if there is anything – anything at all – that you want, you have only to ask me.'

'I know what I'd like to ask her for,' one of the weight-lifters whispered, rolling his eyes, and Manfred clenched his fists with anger at the impertinence, even though Heidi had not heard it.

'Until tomorrow,' she called gaily, and went through to the kitchens to talk to the chef.

'Now that is what I call a woman!' Uncle Tromp growled. 'I give thanks that I am a man of the cloth, old and happily married, and beyond all the temptations of Eve.' There were cries of mock commiserations for Uncle Tromp was by this time everybody's uncle. 'All right!' He was suddenly stern. 'Running shoes, all you lazy young dogs. A quick ten miles before supper, please!'

Heidi was waiting for them when they came down to breakfast, gay and bright and smiling, answering their questions, distributing mail from home, sorting out a dozen small problems quickly and without fuss, and then when they had eaten, taking them off in a group to the bus station.

Most of the athletes from the other countries were in residence, and the village was bustling and full of tense excitement, men and women in sporting attire running through the streets, calling to each other in a multiplicity of tongues, their superb physical condition showing in their bright young faces and in every movement that they made. When they came to the stadium, the size of it awed them all. A huge complex of halls, gymnasiums and covered swimming-pools surrounded the oval track and field theatre. The banks of seating seemed to reach away for ever, and the Olympic altar at the far end of the unlit tripod torch gave a sense of religious solemnity to this temple devoted to the worship of the human body.

It took the morning for them to see it all, and they had a hundred questions between them. Heidi answered them all, but more than once Manfred found her walking beside him, and when they spoke German together it gave them a sense of intimacy, even in the crowd. It was not his imagination alone, for Roelf had noticed the special attention Manfred was receiving.

'How are you enjoying your German lessons?' he asked innocently at lunch, and when Manfred snarled at him he grinned unrepentantly.

* * *

Their hosts had arranged sparring partners from the local boxing clubs, and over the days that followed, Uncle Tromp drove them hard towards the pinnacle of their training.

Manfred tore at his opponents, slamming punches into the thick padding that covered their midriffs and heads, so that even with that protection none of them lasted more than a round or two before calling for quarter; and when Manfred went back to his corner and looked around it was usually to find Heidi Kramer watching from somewhere near at hand, a flush on her flawless neck, a strange intent look in those impossibly blue eyes, her lips slightly parted and the tip of her pink tongue held between sharp white teeth.

However, it was only after four days of training that he found himself alone with her. He had finished a hard session in the gymnasium and after showering and changing into grey slacks and a Varsity sweater, he went out through the front entrance of the stadium. He had almost reached the bus station when she called his name and ran to catch up with him.

'I am also going back to the village. I have to talk to the chef – may I ride the bus with you?' She must have been waiting for him and he felt flattered and a little nervous.

She had a free, hip-swinging walk, and her hair swayed around her head like

a sheet of golden silk when she looked up at him as they walked down to the bus station.

'I have been watching the boxers from the other countries,' she said, 'especially the light heavyweights, and I have also been watching you.'

'Yes.' He frowned to cover his embarrassment. 'I saw you.'

'You have nobody to fear, except the American.'

'Cyrus Lomax,' he nodded. 'Yes, *Ring Magazine* rates him the best amateur light heavyweight in the world. Uncle Tromp has been watching him also. He agrees that he is very good. Very strong, and being a nigger, he will have a skull like solid ivory.'

'He is the only one you will have to beat for the gold,' she agreed. *The gold* – the sound of it on her lips had a music that quickened his pulse. 'And I will be there cheering for you.'

'Thank you, Heidi.'

They boarded the bus, and when the men in the other seats glanced at Heidi with admiration, he felt proud to have her at his side.

'My uncle is a great follower of boxing. He thinks as I do, that you have a good chance of beating the American negro. He would like very much to meet you.'

'It is kind of your uncle.'

'He is having a small reception at his home this evening. He asks me to invite you.'

'You know that is not possible,' he shook his head. 'My training schedule – '

'My uncle is an important and very influential man,' she insisted, holding her head on one side and smiling appealingly up at him. 'It will be very early. I promise you will be home before nine o'clock.' She saw him hesitate and went on, 'It will make my uncle – and me – very happy.'

'I have an uncle also, Uncle Tromp – '

'If I get your Uncle Tromp's permission, will you promise to come?'

Heidi was waiting at the Mercedes at the front door of their house in the village at seven o'clock, as she had arranged. The driver held the rear door open for him and Manfred slid onto the leather seat beside her.

She smiled at him. 'You look very handsome, Manfred.'

She had plaited her blonde hair into two thick gleaming ropes and piled them on top of her head. Her shoulders and the upper slopes of her stately bosom were bare, and snowy perfection. Her blue taffeta cocktail dress matched the colour of her eyes perfectly.

'You are beautiful,' he said with wonder in his tone. He had never paid a compliment to a woman before, but this was a mere statement of fact. She lowered her eyes, a touchingly modest gesture from someone who must be accustomed to male adulation.

'To the Rupertstrasse,' she ordered the driver.

They drove slowly down the Kurfürstendamm, watching the throngs of merry-makers on the brightly lit sidewalks, then the Mercedes accelerated as they entered the quieter streets of the westerly section of the Grünewald district. This was the millionaires' village on the western outskirts of the sprawling city, and Manfred relaxed and settled back against the leather upholstery and turned to the lovely woman beside him. She was talking seriously, asking him questions about himself and his family, and about his country. Quickly he realized that she had a much better knowledge of South Africa than he could have expected, and he wondered how she had acquired it.

She knew the history of war and conflict and rebellion, the struggle of his people against the barbarous black tribes, and then the subjugation of the Afrikaner by the British, and the terrible threats to their existence as a people.

'The English,' she said, and there was a knife-edge of bitterness in her tone. 'They are everywhere, bringing war and suffering with them – Africa, India, my own Germany. We too have been oppressed and persecuted. If it were not for our beloved Führer, we should still be staggering under the yoke of the Jew and the English.'

'Yes, he is a great man, your Führer,' Manfred agreed and then he quoted: 'What we must fight for is to safeguard the existence and reproduction of our race and our people, the sustenance of our children and the purity of our blood, the freedom and independence of the fatherland, so that our people may mature for the fulfilment of the mission allotted it by the creator of the universe.'

'*Mein Kampf*,' she exclaimed. 'You can quote the words of the Führer!' They had passed a significant milestone in their relationship, Manfred realized.

'With those words he has captured everything that I feel and believe,' he said. 'He is a great man, head of a great nation.'

The house in the Rupertstrasse was set back from the road in large gardens on the bank of one of the beautiful Havel Lakes. There were a dozen chauffeured limousines parked in the driveway, most of them with swastika pennants on their bonnets and uniformed chauffeurs waiting behind the wheels. All the windows of the large house were lit and there was the sound of music and voices and laughter as their own chauffeur let them out of the Mercedes under the portico.

Manfred offered Heidi his arm and they went in through the open front doors, crossed a lobby of black and white chequered marble slabs and panelled walls decorated with a forest of stag antlers, and paused in the doorway of the large reception room beyond. The room was already filled with guests. Most of the men were in dashing uniforms that glittered with the insignia of rank and regiment, while the women were elegant in silks and velvets, with shoulders bare and hair bobbed in the latest style.

The laughter and conversation subsided as they turned to examine the newcomers, and there were interested and calculating appraisals, for Manfred and Heidi made a strikingly handsome couple. Then the conversation picked up again.

'There is Uncle Sigmund,' Heidi exclaimed, and drew Manfred into the room towards the tall uniformed figure who came to meet them.

'Heidi, my dear.' He stooped over Heidi's hand as he kissed it. 'You grow more beautiful each time I see you.'

'Manfred, this is my uncle, Colonel Sigmund Boldt. Uncle Sigmund, may I present Herr Manfred De La Rey, the South African boxer.'

Colonel Boldt shook hands with Manfred. He had pure white hair scraped severely back from the thin face of an academic, with good bone structure and a narrow aristocratic nose.

'Heidi tells me that you are of German extraction?' He wore a black uniform with silver death's head insignia on the lapels; and one eyelid drooped, while the eye itself watered uncontrollably and he dabbed at it with the fine linen handkerchief he held in his right hand.

'That is true, Colonel. I have very strong ties to your country,' Manfred replied.

'Ah, you speak excellent German.' The colonel took his arm. 'There are

many people here this evening who will want to meet you, but first tell me, what do you think of the black American boxer, Cyrus Lomax? And what will be your tactics when you meet him?'

With discreet social grace, either Heidi or Colonel Boldt were always on hand to steer him from one group of guests to the next, and the wine waiter brought him a glass of mineral water when he refused the champagne that was offered.

However, they left him longer than usual with one guest whom Heidi had introduced as General Zoller, a tall Prussian officer in field grey uniform with an iron cross at the throat who, despite a rather undistinguished and forgettable face with pale sickly features, proved to have a sharp incisive intelligence. He questioned Manfred minutely on the politics and conditions in South Africa, particularly as to the feelings of the average Afrikaner towards their ties to Great Britian and the Empire.

While they spoke, General Zoller chain-smoked a series of thin cigarettes wrapped in yellow paper with a strong herbal odour, and every now and again he wheezed with asthma. Manfred quickly found that he was sympathetic and had an encyclopaedic grasp of African affairs; the time passed very quickly before Heidi came across the room and touched his arm.

'Excuse me, General Zoller, but I have promised the boxing coach that I will have his star back before nine o'clock.'

'I have enjoyed meeting you, young man.' The general shook Manfred's hand. 'Our countries should be good friends.'

Manfred assured him, 'I will do all in my power to bring that about.'

'Good luck for the Games, Herr de La Rey.'

In the Mercedes again Heidi remarked, 'My uncle liked you very much, and so did many of his friends – General Zoller for one.'

'I enjoyed the evening.'

'Do you like music, Manfred?'

He was a little surprised by the question. 'I enjoy some music, but I am no expert.'

'Wagner?'

'Yes, I like Wagner very much.'

'Uncle Sigmund has given me two tickets to the Berlin Philharmonic Orchestra for next Friday. The young conductor Herbert von Karajan is performing a programme of Wagner. I know you will be fighting your first bout that afternoon, but afterwards we could celebrate.' She hesitated, and then she went on quickly, 'Forgive me, you think me forward, but I assure you – '

'No, no. I would be greatly honoured to accompany you – whether I win or lose.'

'You will win,' she said simply. 'I know you will.'

She dropped him in front of the team house, and waited until he had gone in before she ordered the driver, 'Back to the Rupertstrasse.'

When she got back to the colonel's house most of the other guests were leaving. She waited quietly until he came back from seeing the last of them away and, with an inclination of his silver hair, ordered her to follow him. His treatment of her had altered completely, it was now brusque and superior.

He crossed to the unobtrusive oak door at the far end of the room and went in ahead of her. Heidi entered and closed the door behind her softly, then drew herself to attention and stood waiting. Colonel Boldt left her standing while he poured two balloon glasses of cognac and took one to General Zoller where he

sat in the wingbacked chair beside the log fire in the stone fireplace, puffing at one of his herbal cigarettes, with an open file on his knees.

'So, Fräulein,' Colonel Boldt sank into the leather chair and waved Heidi towards the couch, 'sit down. You may relax in your "uncle's" house.'

She smiled politely but sat stiff-backed on the edge of the couch and Colonel Boldt turned back to the general.

'May I ask the general's opinion of the subject?'

'There seems to be a grey area surrounding the subject's mother. Is it confirmed that his mother was a German, as he claims?'

'I am afraid we do not have confirmation on that. We can establish no proof of his mother's nationality, although I have made exhaustive enquiries amongst our people in South West Africa. The general belief is that she died at childbirth in the African wilderness. However, on his father's side there is definite documented proof that his grandmother was German and that his father fought most valiantly for the Kaiser's army, in Africa.'

'Yes, I see that,' the General said testily, and looked up at Heidi. 'What sentiments has he expressed to you, Fräulein?'

'He is very proud of his German blood, and he looks upon himself as the natural ally of the German people. He is a great admirer of the Führer and can quote at length from *Mein Kampf*.'

The general coughed and wheezed and lit another cigarette with a taper from the fire before turning all his attention back to the red file with the eagle and swastika emblem on the front cover. The others waited quietly for almost ten minutes before he looked up at Heidi.

'What relationship have you established with the subject, Fräulein?'

'On Colonel Boldt's orders, I have made myself agreeable and friendly towards him. I have in small ways conveyed my interest as a woman towards him. I have shown him that I am knowledgeable and interested in the art of boxing, and that I know a great deal about the problems of his fatherland.'

'Fräulein Kramer is one of my best operatives,' Colonel Boldt explained. 'She has been given a thorough grounding in the history of South Africa and the sport of boxing by our department.' The general nodded. 'Proceed, Fräulein,' he ordered, and Heidi went on.

'I have conveyed to him my sympathy for his people's political aspirations and made it clear that I am his friend, with the possibility of more than that.'

'There has been no sexual intimacy between you?'

'No, my General. I judge that the subject would be offended if I were to proceed too rapidly. As we know from his file, he comes from a strict Calvinist religious background. Besides which, I have not received orders from Colonel Boldt to initiate sexual advances.'

'Good,' the general nodded. 'This is a matter of major importance. The Führer himself is aware of our operation. He considers, as I do, that the southern tip of Africa has enormous tactical and strategic importance in our plans for global expansion. It guards the sea routes to India and the East, and in the event that the Suez Canal is denied to our shipping, it is the only route available. In addition, it is a treasure house of raw material vital to our military preparations – chrome, diamonds, the platinum group minerals. With this in mind, and after my meeting with the subject, I am of the firm belief that we must proceed. Therefore, the operation now has full departmental sanction and a "red" rating.'

'Very good, my General.'

'The code name for the operation will be "White Sword" – *Das Weisse Schwart.*'

'*Jawohl*, my General.'

'Fräulein Kramer, you are now assigned exclusively to this operation. You will, at the first opportunity, initiate sexual intimacy with the subject in such a way as not to alarm nor offend him, but rather to strengthen our hold over his allegiance.'

'Very well, my General.'

'In due course it may be necessary for you to enter into a form of marriage with the subject. Is there any reason why you could not do so, if required?'

Heidi did not hesitate. 'None, my General. You can rely on my duty and loyalty entirely. I will do whatever is required of me.'

'Very good, Fräulein.' General Zoller coughed and hunted noisily for breath, and his voice was still rough as he went on, 'Now, Colonel, it will suit our purpose if the subject is a winner of a gold medal at these Games. It will give him a great deal of prestige in his home country, apart from the ideological aspect of a white Aryan triumphing over a person of an inferior black race.'

'I understand, my General.'

'There is not a serious German contender for the light heavyweight title, is there?'

'No, my General, the subject is the only serious white contender. We can make certain that all matches which the subject fights are refereed and judged by members of the Party who are under the control of our department. Naturally, we cannot effect the decision in the case of a knock-out, but – '

'Naturally, Boldt, but you will do all in your power, and Fräulein Kramer will report daily to Colonel Boldt on her progress with the subject.'

* * *

Both the Courtney and Malcomess clans had descended upon the luxurious Bristol Hotel rather than the Olympic village, though David Abrahams had bowed to the dictates of the athletics coach and moved into the apartment house with his team mates, so that Shasa saw little of him during the days of hard training leading up to the opening of the Games.

Mathilda Janine prevailed on Tara to accompany her to most of the field athletic training, in return for equal timeshares of her company at the polo fields, so the two girls spent most of their time dashing from the vast Olympic complex across Berlin to the equestrian centre at high speed, the only rate of progress with which Tara seemed able to conduct her father's green Bentley.

The brief lay-off from training, combined with the imminence of the Games themselves, seemed to have sharpened David's running rather than harmed it. He returned some excellent times during those five days and courageously resisted Mathilda Janine's suggestion that he should sneak out for 'just an hour or two' in the evenings.

'You are in with a chance, Davie,' his coach told him, checking the stopwatch after his last run before the official opening ceremony. 'Just concentrate it all now and you'll have a bit of tin to take home with you.'

Both Shasa and Blaine were delighted with the ponies that their German hosts had provided. Like everything else in the equestrian centre, the grooms,

stabling and equipment were all without fault, and under Blaine's iron control, the team settled down to concentrated practice and were soon once more a cohesive phalanx of horsemen.

Between their own long sessions on the practice field, they watched and judged the other teams whom they would have to meet. The Americans, expense not considered, had brought their own mounts across the Atlantic. The Argentinians had gone one better and brought their grooms as well, in flat-brimmed gaucho hats and leather breeches decorated with silver studs.

'Those are the two to beat,' Blaine warned them. 'But the Germans are surprisingly good – and the Brits, as always, will be slogging away at it.'

'We can flatten any of them,' Shasa gave the team the benefit of his vast experience, 'with a little luck.'

Tara was the only one who took the boast seriously, as from the stand she watched him tear down the side field, sitting tall in the saddle, a beautiful young centaur, lean and lithe, white teeth flashing against the dark tan of his face.

'He's so big-headed and cock-sure,' she lamented. 'If only I could just ignore him. If only life wasn't just so *flat* when he's not around.'

* * *

By nine o'clock on the morning of 1 August 1936, the vast Olympic stadium, the largest in the world, was packed with over one hundred thousand human beings.

The turf of the central isle had been groomed into an emerald velvet sheet, and ruled with the stark white lanes and circles that marked out the venue for the field events. The running track around the periphery was of brick-red cinders. High above it rose the 'Tribune of Honour', the reviewing stand for the traditional march-past of the athletes. At the far end of the stadium was the Olympic altar with its tripod torch still cold.

Outside the entrance to the stadium stretched the Maifeld, its open acres of space containing the high bell tower with the legend: '*Ich rufe die Jugend der Welt* – I summon the youth of the world.' And the massed echelons of athletes were drawn up to face down the long boulevard of the Kaiserdamm, renamed for the solemn occasion the Via Triumphalis. High above the field floated the giant airship, the *Hindenburg*, towing behind it the banner of the Olympics, the five great linked circles.

From afar a faint susurration rose on the cool still morning air. Slowly it grew louder, closer. A long procession of open four-door Mercedes tourers was approaching down the Via Triumphalis, chromework gleaming like mirrors, passing between the closed ranks of fifty thousand brown-uniformed storm troopers who lined both sides of the way, holding back a dense throng of humanity, ten and twenty deep, who roared with adulation as the leading vehicle passed them and threw their right arms high in the Nazi salute.

The cavalcade drew to a halt before the legion of athletes and from the leading Mercedes Adolf Hitler stepped down. He wore the plain brown shirt, breeches and jackboots of a storm trooper. Rather than rending him inconspicuous, this sombre unadorned dress seemed rather to distinguish him in the mass of

brilliant uniforms, gold lace, bearskins and stars and ribbons that followed him between the ranks of athletes towards the marathon gate of the stadium.

'So that is the wild man,' Blaine Malcomess thought as Hitler strolled by, not five paces from where he stood. He was precisely as Blaine had seen him portrayed a thousand times, the dark hair combed forward, the small square moustache. But Blaine was unprepared for the intense Messianic gaze that rested upon him for a fleeting part of a second, then passed on. He found that the hair on his forearms had come erect and prickled electrically, for he had just looked into the eyes of an Old Testament prophet – or a madman.

Following close behind Adolf Hitler were all his favourites: Goebbels wore a light summer suit, but Goering was portly and resplendent in the sky-blue full-dress of a *Luftwaffe* marshal and he saluted the athletes casually with his gold baton as he went by. At that moment the great bronze bell high above the Maifeld began to toll, summoning the youth of the world to assembly.

Hitler and his entourage passed out of sight, entering the tunnel beneath the stands, and a few minutes later a great fanfare of trumpets, magnified a hundred times by the banks of loudspeakers, crashed over the field and a massed choir burst into *Deutschland über alles*. The ranks of athletes began to move off, wheeling into their positions for the entry parade.

As they emerged from the gloom of the tunnel into the sunlit arena, Shasa exchanged a glance with David marching beside him. They grinned at each other in shared excitement as the great waves of sound, amplified music from the bands and the choir singing the Olympic hymn and the cheering of one hundred thousand spectators, poured over them. Then they looked ahead, chins up, arms swinging, and stepped out to the grandeur of Richard Strauss's music.

In the rank ahead of Shasa, Manfred De La Rey stepped out as boldly, but his eyes were focused on the brown-clad figure far ahead in the front rank of the Tribune of Honour and surrounded by princes and kins. As they came level, he wanted to fling up his right arm and shout, '*Heil Hitler*!' but he had to restrain himself. After lengthy discussion and argument, the counsel of Blaine Malcomess and the other English speakers in the team had prevailed. Instead of the German salute the team members merely snapped their heads around in the 'eyes right' salute as they came level. A low whistle and stamp of disapproval from the largely German spectators followed them. Manfred's eyes burned with tears of shame at the insult he had been forced to offer the great man on the high dais.

His anger stayed with him during the rest of the amazing festivities that followed: the lighting of the Olympic torch and the offical speech of opening by the Führer, the sky filled with the white wings of fifty thousand doves released together, the flags of the nations raised simultaneously around the rim of the stadium, the displays of swaying gymnasts and dancers, the searchlights and the fireworks and the music and the fly-past by squadrons of Marshal Goerings *Luftwaffe* that filled and darkened the sky with their thunder.

* * *

Blaine and Centaine dined alone that evening in her suite at the Bristol and both of them were suffering from an anti-climactic weariness after the day's excitements.

'What a show they put on for the world!' Centaine remarked. 'I don't think any of us expected this.'

'We should have,' Blaine replied, 'after their experience in arranging the Nuremberg rallies, the Nazis are the grand masters of pageantry. Not even the ancient Romans developed the seductive appeal of public spectacle to this refinement.'

'I loved it,' Centaine agreed.

'It was pagan and idolatrous, and blatant propaganda – Herr Hitler selling Nazi Germany and his new race of supermen to the world. But, yes, I have to agree with you, it was unfortunately jolly good fun, with an ominous touch of menace and evil to it that made it even more enjoyable.'

'Blaine, you are a hard-nosed old cynic.'

'My only real virtue,' he conceded, and then changed the subject. 'They have posted the draw for the first-round matches. We are fortunate not to have drawn either the Argentinians or the Yanks.'

* * *

They had drawn the Australians, and their hopes of an easy win were dashed almost immediately for the Aussies galloped in like charging cavalry from the first whistle, driving both Blaine and Shasa back in desperate defence, and they kept up that unrelenting attack through the first three hard-ridden chukkas, never allowing Blaine's team to gather themselves.

Shasa kept the curb on his own instincts, which were to ride and shine alone, and placed himself completely under the control of his captain, responding instantly to Blaine's calls to 'cut left' or 'cover the fall' or 'break back', drawing from Blaine the only thing which he lacked himself, experience. Now in these desperate minutes the bond of understanding and trust between them, which had taken so long to forge, was tested almost to breaking point, but in the end it held and halfway through the fourth chukka, Blaine grunted as he passed close to his young number two.

'They've shot their bolt, Shasa. Let's see now if they can take what they've been handing out.'

Shasa took Blaine's next high cross shot at full stretch, standing in his stirrups to pull it down out of the air, and then to drive it far up field, drawing off the Aussie backs before sending it back inside in a lazy dropping parabola to fall under the nose of Blaine's racing pony. That was the turning-point, and in the end they rode in on lathered ponies and jumped down from the saddle to pound each other between the shoulder blades, laughing with a triumph touched by a shade of disbelief at their own achievement.

Triumph turned to gloom when they heard that they would meet the Argentinians in the second round.

* * *

David Abrahams ran a disappointing race in his first head of the 400-metre dash, coming in fourth and missing the cut. Mathilda Janine refused dinner

and went up to bed early that night, but two days later she was bubbling and deliriously excited when David won his head in the 200 metres and went through to the semi-finals.

* * *

Manfred De La Rey's first opponent was the Frenchman, Maurice Artois, unranked in his division.

'Fast as a mamba – brave as a ratel,' Uncle Tromp whispered to Manfred at the gong.

Heidi Kramer was sitting beside Colonel Boldt in the fourth row, and she shivered with unexpected excitement as she watched Manfred leave his corner and come out into the centre. He moved like a cat.

Up to this time it had taken much effort for her to feign an interest in the sport. She had found the sounds and odours and sights associated with it all repellent – the stench of rancid sweat on canvas and leather, the animal grunting and the slogging of padded fists into flesh, the blood and sweat and flying spittle offended her fastidious nature. Now in this company of well-dressed and cultivated spectators, clad herself in fresh silk and lace, perfumed and serene, she found the contrast of violence and savagery before her frightening but at the same time stirring.

Manfred De La Rey, the quiet stern young man, humourless and grave, slightly gauche in unaccustomed clothing and ill at ease in sophisticated company, had been transformed into a magnificent wild beast, and the primeval ferocity he seemed to exude, the blaze of those yellow eyes under the black brows as he slashed the Frenchman's face into a distorted bleeding mask and then drove him down onto his knees in the centre of the sheet of spotless white canvas, excited her perversely so that she found she was clenching her thighs tightly together and her groin was hotly melting and dampening the expensive crêpe-de-chine skirt under her.

That excitement persisted as she sat beside Manfred in the stalls of the state opera house that evening while Wagner's heroic Teutonic music filled the auditorium with thrilling sound. She moved slightly in her seat until her bare upper arm touched Manfred's. She felt him start, begin to pull away, then catch himself. The contact between them was gossamer-light but both of them were intensely aware of it.

Once again Colonel Boldt had placed the Mercedes at her disposal for the evening. The driver was waiting for them when they came down the front steps of the opera house. As they settled into the back seat, she saw Manfred wince slightly.

'What is it?' she asked quickly.

'It is nothing.'

She touched his shoulder with firm strong fingers. 'Here – does it hurt?'

'A stiffness in the muscle – it will be all right tomorrow.'

'Hans, take us to my apartment in the Hansa,' she ordered the driver, and Manfred glanced at her, perturbed.

'Mutti has passed down to me one of her special secrets. It is an embrocation made with wild ferns, and truly magical.'

'It is not necessary – ' he protested.

'My apartment is on the way back to the Olympic village. It will not take long and Hans can drop you back home afterwards.'

She had been uncertain as to how she would get him alone without alarming him, but now he accepted her suggestion without further comment. He was silent for the rest of the drive and she could sense the tension in him, though she made no attempt to touch him again.

Manfred was thinking of Sarah, trying to form the image of her face in his mind but it was blurred, a sweet and insipid blur. He wanted to order Hans to drive directly back to the village, but he could not find the will to do so. He knew what they were doing was incorrect – to be alone with a young attractive woman – and he tried to convince himself that it was innocent, but then he remembered the touch of her arm against him and he stiffened.

'It does hurt?' she misinterpreted the movement.

'Just a little,' he whispered, and his voice caught.

It was always most difficult after he had fought. For many hours after the match he was strung up and nervously sensitive, and it was then that his body was likely to play Satan's tricks upon him. He could feel it happening now, and his mortification and guilt forced hot blood up into his face. What would this pure clean German virgin think of him if she guessed at that obscene and wicked tumescence? He opened his mouth to tell her he would not go with her, but she was leaning forward in the seat.

'Thank you, Hans. Drop us here on the corner and you can wait down the block.' She was out of the car and crossing the sidewalk, and he had no option but to follow her.

It was half dark in the entrance lobby of the building.

'I'm sorry, Manfred, I am on the top floor and there is no elevator.'

The climb allowed him to regain control of himself, and she let him into a small one-roomed flat.

'This is my palace,' she smiled apologetically. 'Flats are so difficult to find in Berlin these days.' She gestured to the bed. 'Sit there, Manfred.'

She slipped off the jacket she wore over her white blouse, and stood on tiptoe to hang it in the cupboard. Her breasts swung forward heavily as she lifted her pale smooth arms.

Manfred looked away. There was a shelf of books on one wall; he saw a set of Goethe's works and remembered how he had been his father's favourite author. Think of anything, he told himself, anything but those big pointed breasts under the thin white cloth.

She had gone through to the little bathroom and he heard running water and the clink of glass. Then she came back with a small green bottle in her hands and stood in front of him smiling.

'You must take off your coat and your shirt,' she said, and he could not reply. He had not thought of that.

'That is not proper, Heidi.'

She laughed softly, a throaty little sound, and through the laughter she murmured, 'Don't be shy, Manfred. Just think of me as a nurse.' Gently she lifted the coat off his shoulders, helping him out of it. Her breasts swung forward again and almost brushed against his face before she stepped back and hung his coat over the back of the single chair and then, a few seconds later, folded his shirt on top of it. She had warmed the bottle in the basin and the lotion was instantly soothing on his skin, her fingers cunning and strong.

'Relax,' she whispered. 'There, I can feel it. It's all hard and knotted. Relax,

let the pain just wash away.' Gently she drew his head forward. 'Lean against me, Manfred. Yes, like that.'

She was standing in front of him and she thrust her hips forward so that his forehead was pressed against her lower torso. Her belly was soft and warm and her voice hypnotic, he felt waves of pleasure spreading out from the contact of her kneading fingers.

'You are so hard and strong, Manfred, so white and hard and beautiful – ' It was moments before he realized what she had said, but her fingers were stroking and caressing, and all rational thought ebbed out of his mind. He was conscious only of the hands and the murmured endearments and praise, then he was aware of something else, a warm musky odour wafted up from her belly against which his face was pressed. Though he did not recognize it as the smell of a healthy young woman physically aroused and ripe for love, yet his own reaction to it was instinctive and no longer to be denied.

'Heidi,' his voice shook wildly. 'I love you. Forgive me, God, but I love you so.'

'Yes, *mein Schatz*, I know,' she whispered. 'And I love you also.'

She pushed him back gently upon the bed and standing over him began slowly to unbutton the front of the white blouse. As she came over him, her big silky white breasts, tipped with ruby, were the most beautiful things he had ever seen.

'I love you,' he cried so many times during that night, each time in a different voice of wonder and awe and ecstasy, for the things she did with him and for him surpassed all his imaginings.

⋆ ⋆ ⋆

For the first day of the finals of the track and field events, Shasa had managed to finagle team tickets for the girls, but the seats were high in the north stand. Mathilda Janine had borrowed Shasa's binoculars and was anxiously scanning the great arena far below them.

'I can't see him,' she wailed.

'He's not out yet,' Shasa reassured her. 'They are running the hundred metres first – ' But he was as strung out as she was. In the semi-final heat of the 200-metre dash, David Abrahams had run second to the great American athlete Jesse Owens, 'the Ebony Antelope', and so had secured his place in the final event.

'I'm so nervous I think I am going to have a fit of the vapours,' Mathilda Janine gasped without lowering the binoculars; on Shasa's other side Tara was as agitated, but for different reasons.

'It's outrageous,' she said, so vehemently that Shasa turned to her surprised.

'What is?'

'Haven't you been listening to a word?'

'I'm sorry, you know David will be coming out at any moment – ' He was drowned out by a deafening thunder of applause and the banks of spectators rose to their feet as the finalists in the hundred-metre dash sprang from the blocks and sped down their lanes; as they crossed the finish line, the quality of the sound changed, groans mixed with the ovation for the winner.

'There!' Tara caught Shasa's arm. 'Listen to them.'

Near them in the crowd a voice called, 'Another American negro wins.' And closer still, 'The Americans should be ashamed to let the black animals wear their colours.'

'These bigots are disgusting.' Tara glared around her, trying to identify the speakers in the sea of faces that surrounded them and when she failed turned back to Shasa. 'The Germans are threatening to disallow all medals won by what they call the inferior races, the blacks and the Jews,' she said in a loud voice. 'They are disgusting.'

'Cool down,' Shasa whispered.

'Don't you care?' Tara challenged him. 'David is a Jew.'

'Of course I care,' he said quietly, glancing around in embarrassment. 'But do shut up, Tara, there's a brick.'

'I think – ' Tara's voice rose in direct response to Shasa's appeal, but Mathilda Janine screamed even more piercingly.

'There he is – there's David!'

With relief Shasa sprang to his feet. 'There he is – go it, Davie boy. Run like a hairy springbok!'

The finalists for the 200-metre dash had clustered at the far end of the arena and were jogging on the spot, windmilling their arms and going through their warm-up routines.

'Isn't David just indescribable?' Mathilda Janine demanded.

'I think that describes him perfectly,' Shasa agreed, and she punched his arm.

'You know what I mean.'

Then the group of athletes spread out to their blocks and the starter stepped forward. Once more silence descended on the vast arena, and the runners were crouched down, frozen in a rigour of concentration.

The pistol fired, at this distance a pop of sound, and the athletes hurled themselves forward; in a perfect line, long legs flashing, arms pumping high, they sped away on a rising wave of sound, and the line lost its perfection, bulged in the centre, a lean dark panther of a man pulled out ahead and the roar of the crowd became articulate.

'Je-Se O-wens!' repeated in a soaring chant, while the dark man flashed over the finish line pulling a bunch of other runners behind him.

'What happened?' Mathilda Janine screamed.

'Jesse Owens won,' Shasa shouted to make himself heard in the uproar.

'I know that – but David, what happened to David?'

'I don't know. I couldn't see. It was all so close.'

They waited in a fever until the loudspeakers boomed their stentorian command.

'*Achtung! Achtung!*' and they heard the names in the jumble of German.

'Jesse Owens, Carter Brown – ' and then, stunningly, 'David Abrahams.'

Mathilda Janine shrieked. 'Catch me, I'm going to faint. David got the bronze!'

She was still shrieking, and hopping up and down on the spot, tears of wild joy running unheeded down her cheeks and dripping off her chin, while on the green field below a thin gangling figure in shorts and running vest climbed up onto the inferior step of the victors' pyramid and bowed his head as the ribbon with the bronze medal dangling from it was draped around his neck.

The four of them began their celebration that evening in the salon of Centaine's suite at the Bristol. Blaine made a short speech of congratulation

while David stood in the middle of the floor looking bashful and self-conscious as they toasted him in champagne. Because it was for David, Shasa drank the whole glass of the magnificent 1929 Bollinger that Centaine provided for the occasion.

He drank another full glass of Sekt at the Café am Ku-damm, on the corner of the Kurfürstendamm just down the street from the hotel and then the four of them linked arms and set off down Berlin's notorious fun street. All the signs of decadence that the Nazis had banned – the Coca-Cola bottles on the sidewalk tables, and the strains of jazz from the café bands, the movie posters of Clark Gable and Myrna Loy – were once more in evidence, allowed back under special dispensation for the duration of the Olympics only.

They stopped at another café, and this time Shasa ordered a schnapps.

'Slow down,' David whispered to him, he knew Shasa seldom drank alcohol, and then never more than a single glass of wine or beer.

'Davie my boy, it's not every day that an old mate of mine wins an Olympic medal.' He was flushed under his tan and his eyes had a feverish glitter.

'Well, I for one refuse to carry you home,' David warned.

They went on down the Ku-damm and Shasa had the girls in fits of giggles at his nonsense humour.

'Ach so, meine lieblings, dis is de famousa Kranzlers coffee house, no? We will enter and drink a leetle champagne, yes?'

'That's Italian, not German,' Tara pointed out. 'And I think you are sloshed.'

'Sloshed is a foul word on fair lips,' Shasa told her, and marched her into the elegant coffee shop.

'Not more champagne, Shasa,' David protested.

'My dear boy, you don't suggest I should drink everlasting life to you in beer, now do you?' Shasa snapped his fingers to summon the waitress and she poured four tulip glasses of the seething yellow wine.

They were all four laughing and chattering so that for some seconds none of them was aware of the sudden tense silence that had descended on the crowded coffee shop.

'Oh dear,' Tara murmured. 'Here come the cavalry.'

Six brown-uniformed storm troopers had entered the room. They had obviously been to some ceremony or function of their regiment, for two of them carried furled banners. It was just as obvious that they had already been drinking; their attitude was bellicose and swaggering, and some of the other customers of the coffee shop hurriedly gathered their hats and coats, paid their bills and left the room.

The six troopers came strutting across to the vacant table next to where the four of them were sitting, and ordered tankards of beer from the waitress. The owner of the coffee shop, anxious to avoid trouble, came to their table, and greeted them obsequiously. They talked for a short while. Then the proprietor took his leave of them by standing at attention and giving the Nazi salute. Immediately the six storm troopers jumped to their feet and returned the salute, cracking the heels of their jackboots together and shouting, '*Heil Hitler!*'

Mathilda Janine, who had drunk at least one full glass of champagne, let out a shriek of laughter and dissolved into helpless giggles, and the full attention of all the troopers was instantly focused upon her.

'Shut up, Matty,' David implored, but that only made it worse. Mathilda Janine rolled her eyes and went scarlet in the face with the effort of trying to contain her giggles, but in the end they exploded out of her with a wild snorting

whoop and the storm troopers exchanged glances and then moved across in a bunch and stood shoulder to shoulder surrounding their table.

The leader, a hefty middle-aged sergeant, said something and Tara answered in schoolgirl German.

'Ah,' said the sergeant in heavily accented English, 'you are English.'

'My sister is very young and silly.' Tara glared at Mathilda Janine who let out another muffled snort through her handkerchief.

'They are English,' said the sergeant, an explanation of all madness, and would have turned away, but one of the younger troopers had been staring at David.

Now he asked in passable English, 'You are the runner? You are the winner of the bronze medal. David Abrahams.'

David looked bashful and nodded.

'You are David Abrahams, the Jew runner.' The trooper enlarged on the theme, and David's face went pale and set. The two English-speaking storm troopers explained to the others, the word *Juden* was repeated, and then they all stared at David with hostile faces and fists clenched on their hips as the sergeant asked loudly, 'Are not the English and Americans ashamed to let the Jews and the negroes win their medals for them?'

Before they could answer Shasa had risen to his feet, smiling politely.

'I say, you chaps are barking up the wrong tree. He isn't a Jew at all, he's a Zulu.'

'How is this possible?' The sergeant looked puzzled. 'Zulus are black.'

'Wrong again, old chap. Zulus are born white. They only go black when they've been left out in the sun. We've always kept this one in the shade.'

'You are joking,' accused the sergeant.

'Of course I am choking!' Shasa imitated his pronunciation. 'Wouldn't you be, looking at what I'm looking at?'

'Shasa, for goodness sake sit down,' David told him. 'There is going to be trouble.' But Shasa was inebriated with champagne and his own wit and he tapped the sergeant on the chest.

'Actually, my dear fellow, if you are looking for Jews, I am the only Jew here.'

'You are both Jews?' the sergeant demanded, narrowing his eyes threateningly.

'Don't be a clot. I've explained already – he's the Zulu and I'm the Jew.'

'That is a lie,' said the sergeant.

By this time the entire clientele of the coffee shop was listening to this exchange with full attention, and for those who did not understand English their companions were translating.

Shasa was encouraged by all this attention, and reckless with champagne. 'I see I shall have to prove my case to you. Therefore to convince you that I am privy to all the age-old secrets of Judiasm, I will reveal one of our best-kept secrets to you. Have you ever wondered what we do with that little piece the rabbi snips off the end of us?'

'Shut up, Shasa,' said David.

'What is he talking about?' Mathilda Janine asked with interest.

'Shasa Courtney, don't be disgusting,' said Tara.

'*Bitte*?' said the storm trooper, looking uneasy, but the other customers of the coffee house were grinning with anticipation. Bawdy humour was common

currency on the Ku-damm and they were revelling in the unaccustomed discomfiture of the storm troopers.

'Very well, I shall tell you.' Shasa ignored David and Tara. 'We pack them in salt, like kippers, and send them off to Jerusalem. There in the sacred grove of the Mount of Olives on the day of the Passover, the chief rabbi plants them in rows and makes a magic sign over them and a miracle takes place – a miracle! They begin to grow.' Shasa made a gesture to describe the growing. 'Higher and higher, they grow.' The storm troopers watched his hand rise with mystified expressions. 'Then do you know what happens?' Shasa asked and the sergeant shook his head involuntarily.

'When they have grown into really big thick *schmucks*, we send them to Berlin where they join the Nazi storm troopers.'

They gaped at him, not believing what they had heard and Shasa ended his recital, 'And they teach them to say – ' he sprang to attention and raised his right hand '*Heil* – what is that fellow's name again?'

The sergeant let out a bellow and swung a wild right-handed punch. Shasa ducked, but unsteady with champagne he lost his balance and went down with a crash pulling the tablecloth with him, and the glasses shattered. The champagne bottle rolled across the floor, spurting wine, and two storm troopers jumped on top of Shasa and rained punches on his head and upper body.

David leaped up to go to his assistance, and a storm trooper grabbed his arms from behind. David wrenched his right arm free, swung round and belted a beautiful right-hander into the trooper's nose. The man howled and released David to clutch his injured organ, but instantly two other troopers seized David from behind and twisted his arms up behind his back.

'Leave him alone,' screamed Mathilda Janine and with a flying leap landed on the shoulders of one of the troopers. She knocked his cap over his eyes and grabbed a double handful of his hair. 'Leave David, you pig!' She tugged at his hair with all her strength and the trooper spun in a circle trying to dislodge her.

Women were screaming, and furniture was shattering. The proprietor stood in the doorway of his kitchen, wringing his hands, his face working pitifully.

'Shasa Courtney,' Tara yelled furiously. 'You are behaving like a hooligan. Stop this immediately.'

Shasa was half buried under a pile of brown uniforms and swinging fists and made no audible reply. The storm troopers had been taken by surprise, but now they rallied swiftly. Street fighting was their game.

Mathilda was dislodged with a heave of broad brown-shirted shoulders and sent flying into the corner. Three troopers jerked Shasa to his feet, arms twisted up behind his back, and hustled him towards the kitchen door. David received the same treatment, a trooper on each of his arms. The one with the injured nose following close behind, bleeding down his shirt front and cursing bitterly.

The proprietor stood aside hurriedly, and they ran Shasa and David through the kitchens, scattering chefs and serving maids, and out into the alley behind the coffee house, knocking over the garbage cans as Shasa struggled ineffectually.

None of the storm troopers spoke. There was no need to give orders. They were professionals engaged in the sport they loved. Expertly they pinned the two victims to the brick wall of the alley, while a trooper went to work on each of them, switching punches from face to body and back to the face, grunting like pigs at the trough in time to the rhythm of their blows.

Mathilda Janine had followed them out and again she tried to rush to David's

defence, but a casual shove sent her reeling back, tripping and falling amongst the garbage cans, and the trooper returned to his task.

Tara was in the kitchen shouting angrily at the café proprietor. 'Call the police, this instant. Do you hear, call the police. They are killing two innocent people out there.'

But the proprietor made a helpless gesture. 'No use, Fräulein. The police will not come.'

Shasa doubled over and they let him fall. Then all three of them started in with the boot. The steel-shod jackboots crashed into his belly and back and flanks.

The storm trooper working on David was sweating and panting with exertion. Now he stepped back, measured the shot carefully, and sent a final upper cut smashing into David's dangling head. It took David full in the mouth and his head jerked backwards, cracking against the brickwork and they let him collapse, face down onto the paving stones.

David lay slack and unmoving, making no effort to avoid the boots that smashed into his inert body, and the storm troopers tired of the sport. It was no fun to kick somebody who was not writhing and doubling up and screaming for mercy. Swiftly they gathered up their caps and banners and in a group trotted away, past the two police constables who were standing at the mouth of the alley trying to look disinterested.

Mathilda Janine dropped on her knees beside David and lifted his battered head into her lap.

'Speak to me, Davie,' she wailed, and Tara came out of the kitchen with a wet dishcloth and stooped over Shasa, trying not to show her anxiety.

It was some minutes before there were signs of life from the victims. Then Shasa sat up and put his head between his knees, shaking it groggily. David pulled himself up on one elbow, and spat out a tooth in a drool of blood-stained spittle.

'Are you all right, Davie my boy?' Shasa asked through crushed lips.

'Shasa, don't ever come to my rescue again,' David croaked. 'Next time you'll get me killed.'

Mathilda Janine helped them to their feet, but now that Shasa had revived, Tara was bleak and disapproving.

'That was the most despicable display I have ever seen, Shasa Courtney. You were obscene and rowdy, and you asked for everything that you got.'

'That's a bit hard, old girl,' Shasa protested, and he and David leaned heavily on each other as they limped down the alley. One of the constables waiting at the corner snarled at them as they passed.

'What did he say?' Shasa asked Tara.

'He says, quite rightly,' she translated frostily, 'that next time you will be arrested for public violence.'

As the two of them made their painful way back down the Ku-damm, bloodied and battered, Mathilda Janine hovering close at hand and Tara marching a dozen paces ahead of them, trying to disassociate herself, they drew the quick horrified glances of passers-by who looked away immediately and then hurried on.

As the four of them rode up in the elevator of the Bristol, Mathilda Janine asked thoughtfully, 'That story of yours, Shasa, you know about growing things on the Mount of Olives. I didn't understand it. Tell me, what is a *schmuck*?'

David and Shasa doubled over with agonized mirth, clutching their injuries.

'Please, Matty, don't say anything more,' David pleaded. 'It hurts so when I laugh.'

Tara turned on her sternly. 'You just wait until I tell Daddy about your part in all this, young lady. He is going to be livid.' She was right, he was, but not as furious as Centaine Courtney.

It turned out that Shasa had broken four ribs and a collar bone and ever afterwards he maintained that his absence from the team accounted for the Argentinian victory over them by ten goals to four in the polo quarter-finals two days later. Apart from two missing teeth, David's injuries were superficial contusions, sprains and lacerations.

'Not too much harm done,' Centaine conceded at last. 'At least there will be no publicity – one of those horrid little newspaper men writing gloating spiteful articles.' She was wrong. Amongst the clientele at the Kranzler coffee house had been the South African correspondent for Reuters, and his article was picked up by the South African *Jewish Times*. It played heavily upon Shasa Courtney's part in defending his Jewish friend, the bronze medalist sprinter, and when they finally got back to Cape town, Shasa found himself a minor celebrity. Both Shasa and David were asked to speak at a luncheon of the Friends of Zion.

'The law of unforeseen consequence,' Blaine pointed out to Centaine.

'How many Jewish voters do you suppose there are on the rolls?' Centaine squinted slightly as she calculated, and Blaine chuckled.

'You truly are incorrigible, my sweeting.'

* * *

The boxing hall in the great complex of the *Reichssportfeld* was filled to capacity for the final bout in the light heavyweight division, and there were ranks of brown-uniformed storm troopers lining each side of the aisle from the dressing-rooms, forming an honour guard for the contenders as they came down to the ring.

'We thought it might be necessary to have them,' Colonel Boldt explained to Heidi Kramer as they sat in their ringside seats, and he glanced significantly at the four judges. All of them were Germans, all members of the party, and it had taken some delicate negotiation and trading on Colonel Boldt's part to arrange it so.

Manfred De La Rey was the first contender to enter the ring. He wore green silk shorts and a green vest with the springbok emblem on his chest and his hair was freshly cropped into a golden stubble. He swept a quick glance around the ringside seats as he clasped both gloved fists over his head to acknowledge the tremendous burst of applause that greeted him. The German sporting public had accepted him as one of their heroes; this evening he was the champion of white racial supremacy.

He picked out Heidi Kramer almost immediately, for he knew where to expect her, but he did not smile. She looked back at him as seriously, but he felt the strength flow into his body, absorbed from her presence. Then suddenly his gaze switched away from her, and he scowled, rage mingling with the strength of his love.

That woman was here. He always thought of Centaine Courtney as 'that

woman'. She sat only three seats away from his beloved Heidi. Her dense dark plume of hair was unmistakable, and she wore yellow silk and diamonds, elegant and poised; he hated her so strongly that he could taste it in his mouth, like gall and alum.

'Why does she always come to hound me?' he wondered. She had been there in the crowd more than once during the other matches he had fought, and always that tall arrogant man, with large nose and ears, sat beside her.

Centaine was watching him with that disconcerting enigmatic expression in her dark eyes that he had come to recognize so well. He turned his back on her deliberately, trying to convey the full force of his contempt and hatred, and watched Cyrus Lomax climb into the ring across from where he stood.

The American had a well-muscled body the colour of milk chocolate, but his magnificent head was all African, like one of those antique bronze castings of an Ashanti prince, with deep-domed brow and wide-spaced eyes, thick lips sculpted into the shape of an Assyrian war bow, and a broad flat nose. He wore the red, white and blue stars and stripes on his chest and there was an air of menace about him.

'This is the worst you will ever meet,' Uncle Tromp had warned Manfred. 'If you can beat him, you can beat them all.'

The referee called them to the centre of the ring and announced them and the crowd roared at Manfred's name. He felt strong and indomitable as he went back to his corner. Uncle Tromp smeared Vaseline on his cheeks and eyebrows and slipped the red gumshield into his mouth.

He slapped Manfred's shoulder, an open-handed stinging blow that was like the goad to the bull and he hissed in his ear.

'Fast as a mamba! Brave as a ratel!' Manfred nodded, mouthing the bulky rubber shield, and went out to the chime of the gong, into the hot white glare of the lights. The American came to meet him, stalking him like a dark panther.

They fought matched and equal, they fought close and hard, blows with the power to maim and stun slipping by just a shade wide, sensing each other's intention with almost supernatural concentration and shifting the head, pulling back, ducking, using the spring of the ropes, blocking with forearm and glove and elbows, neither ever quite connecting but both of them hostile and quick and dangerous.

The gong tolled the rounds – five, six and seven – Manfred had never been forced to fight this long. Always his victories had come swiftly, ending in that sudden barrage of blows that smashed his opponent into the canvas. However, the hard training that Uncle Tromp had imposed upon him had given him long wind, and toughened his legs and arms. He felt strong and invulnerable still, and he knew it had to come soon. He had only to wait it out. The American was tiring. His punches no longer snapped with quite the same velocity. The mistake must come and Manfred waited for it, containing his passionate hunger to see the American's blood.

It came halfway through the seventh round.

The American threw one of those straight hissing lefts, and not even seeing, sensing it with animal instinct, Manfred reared back pulling in his chin and the blow brushed his face but stopped short.

Manfred was poised on the balls of his feet, with his weight back but ready to move forward, his right arm was cocked, the fist clenched like a blacksmith's hammer, and the American was a hundredth part of a second slow on the recovery. Seven hard rounds had tired him and he dragged a fraction, and his

right side was open. Manfred could not see the opening, it was too minute, too fleeting, but again that instinct triggered him and experience guided his arm; he knew by the set of the American's shoulders, the angle of his arm and the cock of his head where the opening was.

It was too quick for conscious decision, and the punch was already launched before he could think but the decision was made instinctively and it was to end it in one. Not his usual two-handed, swarming battering finish, but the single stroke, decisive and irretrievable, that would end it all.

It began in the great elastic muscles of his calves and thighs, accelerating like a stone in the swing of a slingshot through the twist of his pelvis and spine and shoulders, all of it channelled into his right arm like a wide roaring river trapped in a narrow canyon; it went through the American's guard and burst into the side of his dark head with a force that made Manfred's teeth clash together in his own skull. It was everything he had, all his training and experience, all his strength, all his guts and his heart and every finely tuned muscle was behind that blow, and it landed solid and cleanly.

Manfred felt it go. He felt the bones of his right hand break, snapping and crackling like dry twigs, and the pain was a white electric thing that flared back up his arm and filled his head with flames. But in the pain was triumph and soaring joy for he knew it was over. He knew he had won.

The flames of agony cleared from his vision and he looked to see the American crumpled on the canvas at his feet, but the wild soaring of his heart stopped and turned to a plunging stone of despair. Cyrus Lomax was still on his feet. He was hurt and staggering, his eyes dull and sightless, his legs filled with cotton waste and his skull with molten lead, tottering on the very brink, but he was still on his feet.

'Kill him!' screamed the crowd. 'Kill him!'

Manfred could see how little it needed, just one more with the right hand, for the American was out on his feet – just one more. But there was no more, nothing left. The right hand was gone.

The American was reeling about drunkenly, bouncing off the ropes, knees sagging and then by some immense effort of will recovering again.

'The left hand.' Manfred summoned it all, everything that remained. 'I've got to take him with the left.' And through his own agony he went after him again.

He threw the left hand, going for the head, but the American smothered it with an uncoordinated forward lunge, and he threw both arms around Manfred's shoulders and clinched him, clinging to him like a drowning man. Manfred tried to throw him off and the crowd noise was a berserk thunder, the referee shouting above it 'Break! Break!' but the American held on just long enough.

When the referee got them apart, Cyrus Lomax's eyes were sighted and focused; and he backed away in front of Manfred's desperate efforts to land with the left hand – and the bell rang.

'What is it, Manie?' Uncle Tromp seized him and guided him to his corner. 'You had him beaten. What went wrong?'

'My right,' Manfred mumbled through the pain, and Uncle Tromp touched it, just above the wrist and Manfred almost screamed. The hand was ballooning, the swelling spreading up the arm even as they stared at it.

'I'm throwing in the towel,' Uncle Tromp whispered. 'You can't fight with that hand!'

Manfred snarled at him, 'No!' His eyes were fierce and yellow as he looked across the ring to where they were working on the dazed American, cold compresses and sal volatile, slapping his cheeks, talking to him, talking him round.

The bell rang for the start of the eighth round and Manfred went out and saw with despair the new strength and coordination with which the American was moving. He was still afraid and uncertain, backing off, waiting for Manfred's attack, but getting stronger every minute, obviously puzzled at first by Manfred's failure to use the right hand again, and then realization dawning in his eyes.

'You all gone,' he growled in Manfred's ear in the next clinch. 'No right hand, white boy. I'm going to eat you up now!' His punches started hurting, and Manfred began to back away. His left eye was closing up and he could taste the coppery salt of blood in his mouth.

The American shot out a hard straight left-hander, and instinctively Manfred blocked with his right, catching the blow on his glove; the pain was so intense that blackness shaded his vision and the earth tipped up under him, and the next time he was afraid to block with the right and the American's punch got through and slammed into his injured eye. He could feel the swelling hanging on his face like a bloated blood-sucking tick, a fat purple grape that closed the eye completely and the bell rang to end the eighth round.

'Two more rounds,' Uncle Tromp whispered to him, compressing the swollen eye with an ice-pack. 'Can you see it out, Manie?' Manfred nodded and went out to the gong for the ninth and the American came eagerly to meet him – too eagerly, for he dropped his right hand for the big punch and Manfred beat him to it, slamming in a hard left-hander that jolted Lomax back on his heels.

If he had had the use of his right hand Manfred could have taken him yet again, following up in that raging cross storm of blows that no opponent could survive, but the right was maimed and useless, and Lomax ducked away, backing off, recovering and circling in again, working on Manfred's eyes, trying to cut it open and with the last punch of the round he succeeded. He slashed the fat purple sac that closed the eye with a glancing left, catching it with the inside of the glove, ripping it open with the cross hatching of the laces, and it burst. A sheet of blood poured down Manfred's face and splashed over his chest.

Before the referee could hold them up to examine the damage, the gong sounded and Manfred staggered back to his corner as Uncle Tromp rushed out to meet him.

'I'm going to stop it,' he whispered fiercely as he examined the terrible wound. 'You can't fight with that – you could lose the eye.'

'If you stop it now,' Manfred told him, 'I will never forgive you.' His voice was low, but the fire in his yellow eyes warned Tromp Bierman that he meant every word. The old man grunted. He cleaned the wound, and applied a styptic pencil. The referee came to examine the eye, turning Manfred's face to the light.

'Can you go on?' he asked quietly.

'For the *Volk* and the Führer,' Manfred answered him softly, and the referee nodded.

'You are a brave man!' he said and signalled for the fight to continue.

That last round was an eternity of agony, the American's blows sledge-hammered Manfred's body, laying bruises on top of deep seeping bruises, each

of them sapping Manfred further, reducing his ability to protect himself from the blows that followed.

Each breath was fresh agony as it stretched the torn muscles and ligaments of his chest and burned the soft tissue of his lungs. The pain in his right hand flowed up his arm and mingled with the pain of each new blow, and darkness lapped the vision of his single remaining eye so that he could not see the punches coming. The agony roared like a rushing wind in his eardrums, but still he stayed on his feet. Lomax pounded him, smashing his face to raw meat, and still he stayed on his feet.

The crowd was outraged, their blood lust turned to pity and then to horror. They were shouting for the referee to stop this atrocity, but still Manfred stayed on his feet, making pathetic fumbling efforts to punch back with his left hand, and the blows kept crashing into his blind face and broken body.

At last, too late – much too late, the gong rang to end it and Manfred De La Rey was still on his feet. He stood in the centre of the ring, swaying from side to side, unable to see, unable to feel, unable to find his way back to his own corner, and Uncle Tromp ran out to him and embraced him tenderly. Uncle Tromp was weeping, tears running shamelessly into his beard as he led Manfred back.

'My poor Manie,' he whispered. 'I should never have let you. I should have stopped it.'

On the opposite side of the ring Cyrus Lomax was surrounded by a crowd of well-wishers. They laughed and slapped his back, and Lomax did a weary little dance of triumph, waiting for the judges to confirm his victory, but shooting troubled glances across the ring at the man he had destroyed. As soon as the announcement was made he would go to him, to express his admiration for such a show of raw courage.

'*Achtung! Achtung!*' The referee had the judges' cards in one hand and the microphone in the other. His voice boomed over the loudspeakers. 'Ladies and gentlemen. The winner of the Olympic Gold Medal on points is – Manfred De La Rey of South Africa.'

There was a tense incredulous silence in the vast hall that lasted for three beats of Manfred's racing heart, and then a storm of protest, a roar of outrage and anger, of booing and foot-stamping. Cyrus Lomax was rushing around the ring like a madman, shaking the ropes, shouting at the judges, dancing with dismay, and hundreds of spectators were trying to climb into the ring to stage an impromptu demonstration against the decision.

Colonel Boldt nodded at somebody near the back of the hall and the squads of brown-shirted storm troopers moved quickly down the aisles and surrounded the ring, driving back the angry mob and clearing a corridor to the dressing-rooms down which Manfred was hustled.

Over the loudspeaker the referee was attempting to justify the decision. 'Judge Krauser scored five rounds to De La Rey, one round drawn and four rounds to Lomax – ' but nobody was listening to him, and the uproar almost drowned out the full volume of the loudspeakers.

* * *

'The woman must be five or six years older than you are,' Uncle Tromp said carefully, choosing his words. They were walking in the Tegel Gardens and autumn's first chill was in the air.

'She is three years older than I am,' Manfred replied. 'But that makes no difference, Uncle Tromp. All that matters is that I love her and she loves me.' His right hand was still in plaster and he carried it in a sling.

'Manie, you are not yet twenty-one years of age – you cannot marry without the permission of your guardian.'

'You are my guardian,' Manfred pointed out, turning his head to watch him steadily with that disconcerting topaz-yellow gaze and Uncle Tromp dropped his eyes.

'How will you support your wife?' he asked.

'The Reich's Department of Culture has granted me a scholarship to finish my law degree here in Berlin. Heidi has a good job in the Ministry of Information and an apartment, and I will box professionally to earn enough to live on until I can begin my career as a lawyer. Then we will return to South Africa.'

'You have planned it all,' Uncle Tromp sighed, and Manfred nodded; his eyebrow was still knotted with crusty black scab, and he would be scarred for life. He touched the injury now as he asked, 'You will not deny me your permission, will you, Uncle Tromp? We will marry before you leave to go home – and we both want you to be the one to marry us.'

'I am flattered.' Uncle Tromp looked distraught. He knew this lad – how stubborn he was once he had set on a course. To argue further would merely confirm his decision.

'You are a father to me,' Manfred said simply. 'And yet more than a father. Your blessing would be a gift without price.'

'Manie! Manie!' said Uncle Tromp. 'You are the son I never had – I want only what is best for you. What can I say to persuade you to wait a little – not to rush into this thing.'

'There is nothing which will dissuade me.'

'Manie, think of your Aunt Trudi – '

'I know she would want me to be happy,' Manfred cut in.

'Yes, I know she would. But, Manie, think also of little Sarah – '

'What of her?' Manfred's eyes went fierce and cold and he thrust out his jaw, defiant with his own guilt.

'Sarah loves you, Manie. She has always loved you – even I have been able to see that.'

'Sarah is my sister, and I love her. I love her with a brother's love. I love Heidi with the love of a man, and she loves me as a woman loves.'

'I think you are wrong, Manie. I have always thought that you and Sarah – '

'Enough, Uncle Tromp. I don't want to hear any more. I will marry Heidi – I hope with your permission and blessing. Will you make those your wedding gifts to us, please, Uncle Tromp?'

And the old man nodded heavily, sadly. 'I give you both my permission and my blessing, my son – and I will marry you with a joyous heart.'

* * *

Heidi and Manfred were married on the bank of the Havel Lake in the garden of Colonel Sigmund Boldt's home in the Grünewald. It was a golden afternoon in early September with the leaves turning yellow and red at the first touch of autumn. To be there both Uncle Tromp and Roelf Stander had stayed over when the Olympic teams scattered for home, and Roelf stood up with Manfred as his best man while Uncle Tromp conducted the simple ceremony.

Heidi was an orphan so Sigmund Boldt gave her away, and there were a dozen or so of Heidi's friends – most of them her superiors and colleagues in the Ministry of Propaganda and Information – but there were others, her cousins and more distant relatives in the black dress uniforms of the élite SS divisions, or the blue of the *Luftwaffe* or the field grey of the *Wehrmacht*, and pretty girls, some of them in the traditional peasant-style *dirndls* of which the Nazi Party so strongly approved.

After a short and simple Calvinistic ceremony that Uncle Tromp conducted, there was an *al fresco* wedding banquet provided by Colonel Boldt, under the trees, with a four-piece band wearing Tyrolean hats and lederhosen. They played the popular Party-approved music of the day, alternating with traditional country airs, and the guests danced on the temporary wooden floor which had been laid over the lawn.

Manfred was so absorbed with the lovely new wife in his arms that he did not notice the sudden excitement amongst the other guests, or the way that Colonel Boldt hurried to greet the small party that was coming down from the house, until suddenly the band broke into the stirring marching song of the Nazi Party, the Horst Wessel song.

All the wedding guests were on their feet, standing rigidly to attention, and though he was puzzled, Manfred stopped dancing and stood to attention with Heidi at his side. As the small party of new arrivals stepped onto the temporary wooden dance floor, all the guests raised their arms in the Nazi salute and cried together, '*Heil Hitler!*' Only then did Manfred realize what was happening, the incredible honour that he and Heidi were being accorded.

The man coming towards him wore a white jacket buttoned high at the throat with the simple Iron Cross for valour its only decoration. His face was pale, square and strong; his dark hair was brushed forward over his high forehead, and there was a small clipped moustache under the large well-shaped nose. It was not an extraordinary face, but the eyes were like no others Manfred had ever seen, they seared his soul with their penetrating intensity, they reached to his heart and made him a slave for ever.

His right hand was still encased in plaster as he held the Nazi salute and Adolf Hitler smiled and nodded. 'I have heard that you are a friend of Germany, Herr De La Rey,' he said.

'I am of German blood, a true friend and your most ardent admirer. I can find no words to describe the great but humble honour I feel in your presence.'

'I congratulate you on your courageous victory over the American negro.' Adolf Hitler held out his hand. 'And I congratulate you also on your marriage to one of the lovely daughters of the Reich.' Manfred took the Führer's hand in his own undamaged left hand and he was trembling and filled with awe by the significance of the moment. 'I wish you great joy,' Hitler continued, 'and may your marriage forge iron links between yourself and the German people.'

The Führer's hand was cool and dry, the strong yet elegant hand of an artist, and Manfred's emotions welled up to choke him. 'Always, my Führer, the links between us will last for ever.'

Adolf Hitler nodded once more, shook hands with Heidi, smiled at her joyous tears, and then he was leaving as suddenly as he had arrived, with a word and smile for a few of the most important guests.

'I never dreamed – ' whispered Heidi, clinging to Manfred's arm. 'My happiness is complete.'

'That is greatness,' Manfred said, watching him go. 'That is true greatness. It is hard to think he is mere mortal – and not a god.'

* * *

Sarah Bester pedalled down the main street of the little village of Stellenbosch, weaving through the light traffic, smiling and waving at anybody she recognized on the sidewalks. Her school books were strapped on the carrier behind the saddle of her bicycle. The skirt of her gymslip billowed up almost as high as her knees, and she had to keep clutching at her school hat.

That morning her class had been given the results of the previous term's work and she was bursting with the need to tell Aunt Trudi that she had pulled up from fifth to second place. The headmistress had noted on her school report, 'Well done, Sarah, keep up the good work.' It was her last year, in October she would be seventeen and she would write her matriculation the next month.

Manie would be so proud of her. It was his inspiration and encouragement which had done so much to make her one of the top girls in the school. She started to think about him now, daydreaming as she pedalled along under the oaks. He had been away so long, but soon he would be home; then she would tell him and it would all be all right. She wouldn't have to worry and cry alone at night. Manie would be back – strong, kind, loving Manie would make it all right again.

She thought of being married to him, cooking his breakfast, washing his shirts, darning his socks, walking to church at his side, calling him *Meneer* the way Aunt Trudi called Uncle Tromp, lying beside him every night, waking beside him every morning and seeing his beautiful blond head on the pillow beside her, and she knew there was nothing else in all the world she wanted.

'Only Manie,' she whispered. 'Always and only Manie. His is all I have ever had, all I have ever longed for.'

Ahead of her she saw the postman at the gate of the manse and she jumped down off the bicycle and called, 'Have you got anything for us, Mr Grobler?'

The postman grinned at her and took a buff-coloured envelope from his leather purse.

'A telegram,' he told her importantly. 'A telegram from overseas – but it's not for you, little one, it's for your aunt.'

'I'll sign for it!' Sarah scribbled in his receipt book, propped her bicycle at the gate of the manse and flew up the front steps.

'Aunt Trudi!' she screamed. 'A telegram! Where are you?'

She smelt cooking odours, and knew where to look.

'It's a telegram!' Sarah rushed into the kitchen. Aunt Trudi was standing over the long yellow-wood table with the rolling-pin in her hands, flour to her elbows and wisps of silver-blonde hair tickling her nose so that she blew at them as she straightened. She was glowing moistly from the heat of the kitchen range, and great pots of peach and fig jam bubbled over the flames.

'Goodness me! What a to-do! You must learn to act like a lady, Sarie, you are not a child – '

'A telegram! Look, a real telegram! It's the first we've ever had.'

Even Aunt Trudi was impressed. She reached for it and then paused.

'My hands are covered with flour. Open it, Sarie.'

Sarah tore open the envelope. 'Shall I read it out?' she demanded.

'Yes. Yes, read it – who is it from?'

'It's from Uncle Tromp – he signs it "Your dutiful husband Tromp Bierman".'

'Silly old man! He has paid for four unnecessary words,' Aunt Trudi grumbled. 'Read what he says.'

'He says, "I have to inform you that Manfred was – "' Sarah's voice trailed off into silence and her bright expectant expression crumbled as she stared at the sheet in her hands.

'Go on, child,' Aunt Trudi urged her. 'Read it out.'

Sarah began again, her voice small and whispery. '"I have to inform you that Manfred was today married to a German girl named Heidi Kramer. He plans to study at the University of Berlin and will not be returning home with me. I am sure you wish him happiness as I do. Your dutiful husband Tromp Bierman."'

Sarah lifted her eyes from the form and they stared at each other.

'I cannot believe – ' Aunt Trudi breathed. 'Not our Manfred. He wouldn't – he couldn't desert us.' Then she noticed Sarah's face. The child had gone grey as the ashes in the fireplace.

'Oh, my little Sarie.' Aunt Trudi's plump features collapsed with compassion and shared agony and she reached for the girl, but Sarah let the telegram flutter from her fingers to the kitchen floor and whirled and raced from the kitchen.

She snatched up her bicycle from the gate and stepped up into the saddle. She stood up on the pedals so as to drive harder, and her legs pumped to the beat of her heart. Her hat flew off her head and dangled down her back, suspended on the elastic around her neck. Her eyes were wide and dry, her face still grey with shock, as she raced out of the village, turning up past the old Lanzerac estate, heading instinctively for the mountains.

When the track became too steep and rough she dropped the bicycle and went on upwards on foot, through the pine forest until she reached the first crest. There she stumbled off the track and threw herself full length on the damp bed of pine needles, on the exact spot where she had given her love and her body and her soul to Manfred.

Once she had recovered her breath after the hard run up the mountainside, she lay quietly, neither sobbing nor weeping, merely pressing her face into the curve of her own arm. As the afternoon wore on, so the wind veered into the north west and the clouds gathered on the high peaks above where Sarah lay. At dusk it began to rain, and the darkness came on prematurely. The air turned icy, and the wind whimpered in the pines, shaking down droplets onto her prostrate body until her gymslip was soaked through. She never lifted her head, but lay and shivered like a lost puppy and her heart cried out in the darkness.

'Manfred, Manfred, where did you go to? Why did I have to lose you?'

A little before morning broke, one of the search parties from the village, which had scoured the mountainsides all night, stumbled upon her and they carried her down the mountainside.

'It's pneumonia, Mevrou Bierman,' the doctor told Aunt Trudi when she

called him to the manse for the second time that next night. 'You are going to have to fight for her life – she doesn't seem to want to fight herself.'

Aunt Trudi would not allow them to take Sarah to the new town hospital. She nursed the girl herself, tending her day and night in the small back bedroom, sponging the sweat and heat from her body while the fever mounted, sitting beside the bed and holding her hot hand through the crisis, not leaving her even when it had broken and Sarah lay pale and wasted with the flesh melted off her face so that her features were bony and gaunt and her lacklustre eyes too large for the bruised cavities into which they had sunk.

On the sixth day, when Sarah was able to sit up and drink a little soup without Aunt Trudi's assistance, the doctor made his final call and behind the closed bedroom door gave Sarah a detailed examination. Afterwards he found Aunt Trudi in the kitchen and spoke to her quietly and seriously. Once he had left the manse Aunt Trudi went back to the bedroom and sat beside the bed, in the same chair on which she had conducted her long vigil.

'Sarah.' She took the girl's thin hand. It was light and frail and cold. 'When did you last have your courses?' she asked.

Sarah stared at her without replying for long seconds, and then for the first time she began to weep. Slow, almost viscous tears welled up from the depths of those haunted bruised eyes and her thin shoulders shook silently.

'Oh, my little girl.' Aunt Trudi reached for her and held her to the bulky pillow of her bosom. 'My poor little girl – who did this to you?'

Sarah wept silently and Aunt Trudi stroked her hair. 'You must tell me – ' Suddenly the gentling hand froze on Sarah's head in midstroke, as understanding crashed in upon her.

'Manie – it was Manie!'

It was not a question, but the confirmation was immediate as a painful sob came exploding up out of Sarah's tortured chest.

'Oh Sarie – oh my poor little Sarie.'

Involuntarily Aunt Trudi turned her head towards a small framed photograph which stood on the table beside the sick girl's bed. It was a studio photograph of Manfred De La Rey in boxer's shorts and vest, crouched in the classic pugilist's pose with the silver championship belt around his waist. The inscription read, 'To little Sarie. From your big brother, Manie.'

'What a terrible thing!' Aunt Trudi breathed. 'What will we do now?'

The following afternoon while Aunt Trudi was in the kitchen, larding a leg of venison which was a gift from one of the parishioners, Sarah came in on bare feet.

'You should not be out of bed, Sarie,' Aunt Trudi told her sternly, then was silent as Sarah did not even glance in her direction.

The thin white cotton nightdress hung loosely on her wasted frame, and she had to steady herself on the back of a kitchen chair for she was weak from her sick bed.

Then she gathered herself and crossed like a sleepwalker to the kitchen range. With the tongs she lifted the round black cast-iron cover off the firebox, and orange points of flame flickered through the opening. Only then did Aunt Trudi realize that Sarah had the photograph of Manfred in her hand. She had removed it from the frame and she held it up in front of her eyes and studied it for a few seconds. Then dropped it into the opening of the firebox.

Rapidly the square of cardboard curled and blackened. The image upon it faded to ghostly grey and then was obscured by flames. With the points of the

fire-tongs Sarah stabbed at the scrap of soft ash that remained, crushing and pounding it to powder. Even then she went on striking the irons into the flames with unnecessary force, until there was nothing left. Then she replaced the cast-iron cover over the firebox and dropped the tongs. She swayed on her feet and might have toppled forward onto the hot stove, but Aunt Trudi caught her and steered her to a kitchen chair.

Sarah sat staring across the kitchen at the stove for many minutes before she spoke.

'I hate him,' she said softly, and Aunt Trudi bowed her head over the haunch of vension to hide her eyes.

'We have to talk, Sarie,' she said softly. 'We have to decide what to do.'

'I know what to do,' Sarah said and the tone chilled Aunt Trudi. It was not the voice of a bright sweet child, but that of a woman hardened and embittered and coldly angry with what life had offered her.

Eleven days later Roelf Stander returned to Stellenbosch, and six weeks later he and Sarah were married in the Dutch Reformed Church. Sarah's son was born on the 16th March 1937. It was a difficult birth, for the infant was big-boned and she was small-hipped and her body still not fully recovered from the pneumonia.

Roelf was allowed into the delivery room immediately after the birth. He stood over the cot staring down at the mottled swollen face of the newborn infant.

'Do you hate him, Roelf?' she asked from the bed. Sarah's hair was sodden with sweat and she was drawn and exhausted. Roelf was silent for a few moments while he considered the question. Then he shook his head.

'He is part of you,' he said. 'I could never hate anything that is you.'

She held out her hand to him, and he came to stand beside the bed and took it.

'You are a kind person. I will be a good wife to you, Roelf. I promise you that.'

* * *

'I know exactly what you are going to say, Daddy.' Mathilda Janine sat opposite Blaine in his panelled ministerial office in the Parliament building.

'You do, do you?' Blaine asked. 'Then let's hear from you exactly what I'm going to say.'

'Firstly,' Mathilda Janine held up her index finger, 'you are going to say that David Abrahams is a fine young man, a brilliant law student and a sportsman of international reputation who won one of the only two medals which this country was awarded at the Berlin Olympics. You are then about to say that he is gentle, considerate and kind, that he has a marvellous sense of humour and dances beautifully, that he is handsome in a funny sort of way and would make any girl a wonderful husband. Then you will say "but" and look grave.'

'I was going to say all that, was I?' Blaine shook his head with wonder. 'All right. Now I say "but" and look grave. Please continue for me, Matty.'

'But, you say gravely, he is Jewish. You will notice the inflexion, and now you look not only grave but significantly grave.'

'This puts a certain amount of strain on my facial muscles – significantly grave. Very well, continue.'

'My darling Daddy would not be so callow as to add, "Don't get me wrong, Matty, some of my best friends are Jews." You would never be as gauche as that, would you?'

'Never.' Blaine tried not to grin, even though he was still seriously worried by the proposition. He could never resist the impishness of his plain carrot-headed but beloved youngest daughter. 'I would never say that.'

'"But," you would say, "mixed marriages are very difficult, Matty. Marriage is a hard business without complicating it by different religions and customs and ways of life."'

'How wise of me,' Blaine nodded. 'And how would you reply?'

'I would tell you that for the past year I have been taking instruction with Rabbi Jacobs and by the end of next month I will be a Jewess.'

Blaine winced. 'You have never kept anything from me before, Matty.'

'I told Mummy.'

'I see.'

She smiled cheerily, still trying to make a game of it. 'Then you would say, "But, Matty, you are still a baby."'

'And you would reply, "I will be eighteen next birthday."'

'And you would look gruff and say, "What are David's prospects?"'

'And you would tell me, "David starts work with Courtney Mining and Finance at the end of the year with a salary of two thousand a year."'

'How did you know that?' Matty was stunned. 'David only told me – ' She broke off as she realized what his source had been and she fidgeted in her seat. Her father's relationship with Centaine Courtney troubled her more than she could ever tell him.

'Do you love him, Matty?'

'Yes, Daddy. With all my heart.'

'And you have already obtained your mother's permission – that I can be sure of.' Over the years both Mathilda Janine and Tara had become adept at playing Isabella and Blaine off against each other.

Mathilda Janine nodded guiltily, and Blaine selected a cheroot from the humidor on his desk. While he prepared it, he frowned thoughtfully.

'It's not a thing to go into lightly, Matty.'

'I am not going into it lightly. I've known David two years.'

'I always thought you might make a career – '

'I am, Daddy. My career is going to be making David happy and giving him lots and lots of babies.'

He lit the cheroot and grumbled, 'Well then, you'd better send your David to see me. I want to warn him what will happen to him if he doesn't look after my little girl.'

Mathilda Janine shot round the desk, dumped herself into his lap and flung both arms around his neck. 'You are the most wonderful father any girl ever had!'

'When I give in to you!' he qualified the compliment, and she hugged him until her arms and his neck ached.

* * *

Shasa and David flew up to Windhoek in the Rapide to fetch Abe Abrahams and his wife down for the wedding. The rest of David's family and most of his friends, including Dr Twentyman-Jones, came down by train. Together with the friends and family of Mathilda Janine Malcomess this made up a multitude that filled the great synagogue in the Gardens suburb to capacity.

David would dearly have liked Shasa to act as his best man. However, it had taken some delicate persuasion to get the strictly orthodox Rabbi Jacobs to perform the ceremony for a bride who had clearly converted to the Faith for the express purpose of marriage rather than out of purely religious commitment. David could not therefore try to smuggle a gentile best man into the *schul*, and Shasa had to be content with the position of pole-holder at one corner of the *huppah* canopy. However, Shasa made a hilariously funny speech at the reception which Blaine gave at the house in Newlands Avenue, with David as the butt of his wit.

The wedding reception provided Shasa with an opportunity to effect one of his periodic reconciliations with Tara Malcomess. Their relationship over the two years since the Berlin Olympics had been storm and sunny weather alternating so rapidly that even the two protagonists themselves were not always certain as to how matters stood between them at any given time.

They managed to occupy opposing grounds on almost every issue; though politics was their favourite subject of dissension, the plight of the poor and oppressed in a land where there were plenty of both of these classes was another perennial winner.

Tara could usually find plenty to say about the insensitivity of the privileged rich white ruling classes, and the iniquity of a system which enabled a young man, whose only proven distinctions were a beautiful face and a rich and indulgent mother, to number amongst his playthings fifteen polo ponies, an SS Jaguar in British racing green with the special three and a half litre engine, and a De Havilland Tiger Moth biplane, while thousands of black children had their little bellies bloated with malnutrition and their legs bowed and deformed by rickets.

These subjects did not exhaust their genius at finding contentious issues. Tara had strong views on so-called 'sportsmen' who went out into the veld armed with high-powered rifles to blast the innocent and beautiful animals and birds; nor did she approve of the obvious relish with which some witless young men regarded the slow but inexorable approach of war clouds for the promise of excitement that they seemed to offer. She was scornful of anyone who was satisfied with a second-class degree when it was apparent that with just a little application they could have finished an expensive education, denied to tens of thousands of others, with a *cum laude* degree in engineering.

On the other hand, Shasa thought it sacrilege that a girl who had the face and body of a goddess should try to disguise these facts in an attempt to be taken for a daughter of the proletariat. Nor did he approve of this same young woman spending most of her waking hours either in study, or in the slums and shanty towns that had sprung up on the Cape Flats, dishing out to snot-nosed piccaninnies free soup the ingredients of which she had helped obtain by standing on street corners with a beggar's box.

He especially did not like the medical students and newly qualified young doctors, bolsheviks one and all, with whom she spent so much time in her capacity as an unpaid and untrained nurse in the volunteer clinics, tending unwashed and highly infectious brown and black patients suffering from

tuberculosis, syphilis, infant dysentery, scabies, the secondary effects of chronic alcoholism and all the other unlovely consequences of poverty and ignorance.

'St Francis of Assisi was lucky he didn't have you to compete with – you'd have made him look like Attila the Hun.'

He found her friends boring in their serious singlemindedness, and ostentatious in their left-wing beards and shoddy dress.

'They just lack any style or class, Tara. I mean, how can you bear to walk in the street with one of them?'

'Their style is the style of the future, and their class is the class of all humanity.'

'Now you are even talking like one of them, for cat's sake!'

However, these differences were mild and without real substance when compared to their truly monumental disagreement on the subject of Tara Malcomess' chastity and virginity.

'For God's sake, Tara, Queen Victoria has been dead for thirty-seven years. This is the twentieth century.'

'Thank you for the history lesson, Shasa Courtney, but if you try to get your hand into my bloomers again I am going to break your arm in three separate and distinct places.'

'What you have got in there isn't so bloody special. There are plenty of other young ladies – '

'"Ladies" is an euphemism, but let that pass. I suggest that in the future you confine your attentions to them and leave me alone.'

'That is the only sensible suggestion you have made all evening,' Shasa told her in an icy fury of frustration and started the Jaguar sports car with a thunder of exhausts and superchargers that echoed through the pine forests and startled all the other couples parked in the darkness about the pseudo-Greek temple that was the memorial to Cecil John Rhodes.

They drove down the winding mountain road at a savage pace, and Shasa skidded the big sports car to a halt in the gravel in front of the double mahogany doors of the Malcomess home.

'Don't bother to hold the door for me,' Tara said coldly, and slammed it so hard that he flinched.

That had been two months before, and there hadn't been a day since then that Shasa hadn't thought of her. When he was sweating in the heat of the great pit of the H'ani Mine or poring over a contract with Abe Abrahams in the Windhoek office or watching the muddy brown waters of the Orange river being transformed into sheets of silver by the spinning overhead sprinklers of the irrigation equipment, Tara's image would pop uninvited into his mind.

He tried to erase it by flying the Tiger Moth so low that the landing wheels raised puffs of dust from the surface of the Kalahari, or by absorbing himself in precise and intricate aerobatic evolutions, the spin and barrel roll and stall turn, but as soon as he landed Tara's memory was waiting for him.

He hunted the red-maned Kalahari lions in the desert wilderness beyond the mystic hills of the H'ani, or immersed himself in the multifarious affairs of the Courtney companies, studying under his mother, watching her methods and absorbing her thinking, until she trusted him sufficiently to put him in control of some of the smaller subsidiaries.

He played the game of polo with almost angry dedication, pushing himself and the horses under him to the outer limits, and brought the same single-minded determination to the pursuit and seduction of a daunting procession of

women – young and not so young, plain and pretty, married and single, more and less experienced – but when he saw Tara Malcomess again he had the strange hollow feeling that he had only been half alive during those months of separation.

For her sister's wedding, Tara had put aside the pretentiously drab uniform of the left-wing intellectual, and as a bridesmaid she was dressed in grey silk with a blue sheen to it which, beautiful as it was, could not quite match the steely grey of her eyes. She had changed her hairstyle, cutting it short; the thick smoky curls formed a neat cap around her head, leaving the back of her long neck bare, and this seemed to emphasize her height and the length and perfection of her limbs.

They looked at each other for a moment across the length of the crowded marquee, and it seemed to Shasa that lightning had flashed across the tent; for an instant he knew that she had missed him as much and thought about him as often. Then she nodded politely and turned her full attention back to the man beside her.

Shasa had met him once before. His name was Hubert Langley and he was one of Tara's bleeding-heart brigade. He wore a shabby tweed jacket with leather elbow patches when most of the other male guests were in morning dress. He was an inch shorter than Tara, with steel-rimmed spectacles and prematurely thinning blond hair. His beard was the colour and texture of the plumage of a day-old chicken, and he lectured in Sociology at the university.

Tara had once confided in Shasa. 'Huey is actually a card-carrying member of the Communist Party, isn't that remarkable?' Her voice was awed. 'He is totally committed and he has an absolutely brilliant mind.'

'One might call him a shining jewel in a greasy and grubby setting,' Shasa remarked, thereby precipitating another of their periodic estrangements.

Now he watched as Huey laid one of his freckled paws on Tara's unblemished forearm, and when he touched Tara's cheek with his wispy moustaches and whispered one of the gems from that absolutely brilliant mind into her pink shell-like ear, Shasa realized that slow strangulation was too good for him.

He sauntered across the tent to intervene and Tara greeted him coolly, perfectly hiding the fact that her pulse was thumping loudly in her ears. She hadn't realized how intensely she had missed him until she watched him making his speech, urbane and self-assured, amusing and so infuriatingly good-looking.

'However, we are not climbing the same old merry-go-round again,' she warned herself, and put up all her defences as he took the chair on the other side of her and smiled at her and teased her lightly while looking at her with open admiration, which was so hard to resist. They had shared so much together, friends and places and fun and fights, and he knew exactly how to tickle her sense of humour. She realized that once she started to laugh it was all over, and she held out against it, but he worked on her defences with skill and perfect timing, adroitly breaking them down as swiftly as she set them up, until at last she surrendered with a tinkle of laughter which she could no longer contain, and he followed up swiftly, cutting her out from Huey's side.

From the balcony Mathilda Janine singled out her elder sister and tossed her bouquet directly at her. Tara made no effort to catch it but Shasa snatched it out of the air and handed it to Tara with a bow, while the other wedding guests applauded and looked knowing.

As soon as David and Matty had departed, dragging a bunch of old shoes and tin cans behind David's old bull-nosed Morris, Shasa worked Tara out of the

marquee and spirited her away in the Jaguar. He didn't make the mistake of taking her back up the mountain to the Rhodes memorial, scene of their last historic battle. Instead he drove out to Hout Bay and parked on the top of the precipitous cliffs. While the sun set in a silent bomb-burst of orange and red into the sombre green Atlantic, they fell upon each other in a frenzy of reconciliation.

Tara's body was divided into two zones by an invisible but distinct line around her waist. On occasions of extreme goodwill such as this, the area above the line was, after a suitable show of resistance, made available to him. However, the area south of the line was inviolate, a restriction that left them both strung up with nervous tension when in the dawn they finally reluctantly parted with one last lingering kiss at Tara's front door.

This latest reconciliation lasted four months which was a new record for them, and after preparing an emotional balance-sheet on which the many advantages of bachelorhood were overbalanced by one single weighty consideration – 'I cannot live without her', Shasa formally proposed marriage to Tara Malcomess and was devastated by her reply.

'Don't be silly, Shasa, apart from a sort of vulgar animal attraction, you and I have absolutely nothing in common.'

'That is the most utter bilge, Tara,' he protested. 'We come from the same backgrounds, we speak the same language, laugh at the same jokes – '

'But Shasa you don't care.'

'You know that I plan to enter Parliament.'

'That is a career decision, not a thing of the heart, that isn't caring for the poor and the needy and the helpless.'

'I care for the poor – '

'You care for Shasa Courtney, that's who you really care for.' Her voice rasped like a stiletto drawn from its sheath. 'For you the poor is anybody who can afford to run only five polo ponies.'

'Your papa had fifteen nags in training at the last count,' he pointed out tartly.

'You leave my father out of this,' she flashed at him. 'Daddy has done more for the black and brown people of this country – '

He held up both hands to stop her. 'Come on, Tara! You know I am Blaine Malcomess's most ardent admirer. I was not trying to insult him, I was simply trying to get you to marry me.'

'It's no good, Shasa. It's one of my unshakable convictions that the vast wealth of this land must be redistributed, removed from the hands of the Courtneys and the Oppenheimers and given – '

'That's Hubert Langley speaking, not Tara Malcomess. Your little Commie pal should think of generating new wealth rather than divvying up the old. When you take everything we have, the Courtneys and the Oppenheimers, and share it out equally, there would be enough for a square meal for everybody, twenty-four hours later we would all be starving again, the Courtneys and the Oppenheimers included.'

'There you are!' She was triumphant. 'You are quite happy to see everybody starve but yourself.'

He gasped at the injustice, and rallied to launch a full-scale counterattack, but just in time he saw the steely grey battle light in her eyes and checked himself.

'If you and I were married,' he made his voice humble, 'you could influence me, persuade me to your way of thinking – '

She had been poised for one of their marvellously exhilarating shouting matches, now she looked slightly crestfallen.

'You crafty little capitalist!' she said. 'That's not fighting fair.'

'I don't want to fight with you, my dear girl. In fact, what I want to do with you is diametrically the opposite of fighting.'

Despite herself, she giggled. 'That's another thing I have against you, you carry your mind around in your underpants.'

'You still haven't answered my question: will you marry me?'

'I have an essay to hand in by nine o'clock tomorrow morning, and I am on duty at the clinic from six o'clock this evening. Please take me home now, Shasa.'

'Yes or no?' he demanded.

'Perhaps,' she said, 'but only after I detect a vast improvement in your social conscience, and certainly not before I have obtained my master's degree.'

'That's another two years.'

'Eighteen months,' she corrected him. 'And even then it's not a promise, it's only a big fat "perhaps".'

'I don't know if I can wait that long.'

'Then bye-bye, Shasa Courtney.'

They never extended their record beyond four months, for three days later Shasa received a phone call. He was at a meeting with his mother and the new winemaker that Centaine had recently brought out to Weltevreden from France. They were discussing the designs for the labels on the latest vintage of Cabernet Sauvignon when Centaine's secretary came through to her office.

'There is a phone call for you, Master Shasa.'

'I can't come now. Take a message and I'll call back.' Shasa did not even look up from the display of labels on Centaine's desk.

'It's Miss Tara, and she says it's urgent.'

Shasa glanced sheepishly at Centaine. It was one of her strict maxims that business came first, and did not mix with any of his social or sporting activities, but this time she gave him a nod.

'I won't be a minute.' He hurried out and was back within seconds.

'What on earth is it?' Centaine stood up quickly when she saw his face.

'Tara,' he said. 'It's Tara.'

'Is she all right?'

'She's in jail.'

* * *

In December of the year 1838 on a tributary of the Buffalo river, the Zulu King Dingaan had sent his impis of warriors armed with rawhide shield and assegai against the circle of wagons of the Voortrekkers, the ancestors of the Afrikaner people.

The wheels of the wagons were bound together with trek-chains and the spaces between them blocked with thorn branches. The Voortrekkers stood to the barricade with their long muzzle loaders, all of them veterans of a dozen such battles, brave men and the finest marksmen in the world.

They shot down the Zulu hordes, choking the river from bank to bank with dead men and turning its waters crimson, so that for ever after it was known as Blood river.

On that day the might of the Zulu empire was shattered, and the Voortrekker leaders, standing bare-headed on the battlefield, made a covenant with God to celebrate the anniversary of the victory with religious service and thanksgiving for all time.

This day had become the most holy date in the Calvinistic Afrikaner calendar after the day of Christ's birth. It celebrated all their aspirations as a people, it commemorated their sufferings and honoured their heroes and their forefathers.

Thus the hundredth anniversary of the battle had peculiar significance for the Afrikaners and during the protracted celebrations the leader of the Nationalist Party declared, 'We must make South Africa safe for the white man. It is shameful that white men are forced to live and work beside lesser breeds; coloured blood is bad blood and we must be protected from it. We need a second great victory if white civilization is to be saved.'

Over the months that followed, Dr Malan and his Nationalist Party introduced a series of racially orientated bills to the House. These ranged from making mixed marriages a crime, to the physical segregation of the whites from men of colour, whether Asiatic or African, and disenfranchising all coloured persons who already had the vote while ensuring that those who did not have it, remained without it. Up until the middle of 1939 Hertzog and Smuts had managed to head off or defeat these proposals.

The South African census distinguished between the various racial groups, 'the Cape-coloured and other mixed breeds'. These were not, as one might believe, the progeny of white settlers and indigenous tribes, but were rather the remnants of the Khoisan tribes, the Hottentots and Bushmen and Damaras, together with descendants of Asiatic slaves who had been brought out to the Cape of Good Hope in the ships of the Dutch East India Company.

Taken together they were an attractive people, useful and productive members of a complex society. They tended to be small-boned and light-skinned with almond eyes in faintly oriental features. They were cheerful, clever and quick-witted, fond of pageant and carnival and music, dextrous and willing workers, good Christians or devout Muslims. They had been civilized in Western European fashion for centuries and had lived in close and amiable association with the whites since the days of slavery.

The Cape was their stronghold and they were better off than most other coloured groups. They had the vote, albeit on a separate roll from the whites, and many of them, as skilled craftsmen and small traders, had achieved a standard of living and affluence surpassing that of many of their white neighbours. However, the majority of them were domestic servants or urban labourers surviving just above or below subsistence level. These people now became the subject of Dr Daniel Malan's attempts to enforce segregation in the Cape as well as every other corner of the land.

Hertzog and Smuts were fully aware that many of their own followers sympathized with the Nationalists, and that to oppose them rigidly might easily bring down the delicate coalition of their United Party. Reluctantly they put together a counter-proposal, for residential segregation, which would disrupt the delicate social balance as little as possible and which, while making law a situation which already existed, would appease their own party and cut the ground from under the Nationalist opposition's feet.

'We aim to peg the present position,' General Jan Smuts explained, and a week after this explanation a large orderly crowd of coloured people, joined by many liberal whites, gathered in the Greenmarket Square in the centre of Cape Town peaceably to protest against the proposed legislation.

Other organizations, the South African Communist Party and the African National Congress, the Trotsky National Liberation League and the African Peoples Organization, scented blood in the air and their members swelled the ranks of the gathering, while in the front row centre, right under the hastily erected speakers' stand, auburn hair shining and grey-blue eyes flashing with righteous ardour, stood Tara Malcomess. At her side, but slightly below her level, was Hubert Langley, backed by a group of Huey's Sociology students from the university. They stared up at the speaker, enthralled and enchanted.

'This fellow is very good,' Hubert whispered. 'I wonder why we have never heard of him before.'

'He is from the Transvaal,' one of his students had overheard and leaned across to explain. 'One of the top men in the African National Congress on the Witwatersrand.'

Hubert nodded. 'Do you know his name?'

'Gama – Moses Gama. Moses, the name suits him – the one to lead his people out of captivity.'

Tara thought that she had seldom seen a finer-looking man, black or white. He was tall and lean, with the face of a young pharaoh – intelligent, noble and fierce.

'We live in time of sorrow and great danger,' Moses Gama's voice had a range and timbre that made Tara shiver involuntarily. 'A time that was foreseen in the Book of Proverbs.' He paused and then spread his hands in an eloquent gesture as he quoted. 'There is a generation, whose teeth are as swords, and their jaw teeth as knives to devour the poor from the earth, and the needy from among men.'

'That's magnificent!' Tara shivered again.

'My friends, we are the poor and the needy. When each of us stands alone we are weak – alone we are the prey for those with teeth like swords. But together we can be strong. If we stand together, we can resist them.'

Tara joined in the applause, clapping until the palms of her hands were numb, and the speaker stood calmly waiting for silence. Then he went on, 'The world is like a great pot of oil slowly heating. When it boils over there will be turmoil and steam and it will feed the fire beneath it. The flames will fly up to the sky and afterwards nothing will be the same again. The world we know will be altered for ever, and only one thing is certain, as certain as the rise of tomorrow's sun. The future belongs to the people, and Africa belongs to the Africans.'

Tara found she was weeping hysterically as she clapped and screamed her adulation. After Moses Gama, the other speakers were dull and halting and she was angry with their ineptitude, but when she looked for him in the crowd Moses Gama had disappeared.

'A man like him dare not stay too long in one place,' Hubert explained. 'They have to move like the will-o'-the-wisp to keep ahead of the police. A general never fights in the front line. They are too valuable to the revolution to be used as cannon-fodder. Lenin only returned to Russia after the fighting was over. But we will hear of Moses Gama again – mark my words.'

Around them the crowd was being marshalled to form up into a procession

behind a band, a fifteen-piece marching band – any gathering was an excuse for the Cape-coloured people to make music, and in ranks four and five abreast the demonstration began to snake out of the square. The band played 'Alabama', setting a festive mood, and the crowd was laughing and singing; it seemed a parade rather than a demonstration.

'We will be peaceful and orderly,' the organizers re-inforced their previous orders, passing them down the column. 'No trouble – we want no trouble with the police. We are going to march to the Parliament building and hand a petition to the prime minister.'

There were two or three thousand in the procession, more than they had hoped for. Tara marched in the fifth rank just behind Dr Goollam Gool and his daughter Cissie and the other coloured leaders.

With the band leading them, they turned into Adderley Street, the main city thoroughfare. As they marched up towards the Parliament building, the ranks of the procession were swelled by the idlers and the curious, so that as their leaders attempted to turn into Parliament Lane, they were followed by a column of five thousand, a quarter of a mile long, almost half of whom were there for the fun and the excitement, rather than from any political motives.

At the entrance to Parliament Lane a small detachment of police was waiting for them. The road had been barricaded, and there were more police armed with batons and sjamboks, those long black whips of hippohide, being held in reserve further up the road in front of the fence of cast-iron palings which protected the Parliament building.

The procession came to a ragged halt at the police barrier and Dr Gool signalled the band to silence, then went forward to parley with the white police inspector commanding the detail while the photographers and reporters from local newspapers crowded around them to record the negotiations.

'I wish to present a petition to the prime minister on behalf of the coloured people of the Cape Province,' Dr Gool began.

'Dr Gool, you are conducting an unlawful assembly and I must ask you to get your people to disperse,' the police inspector countered. None of his men had been issued with firearms and the atmosphere was almost friendly. One of the trumpet-players blew a loud raspberry and the inspector smiled at the insult and wagged his finger like a schoolmaster at the culprit; the crowd laughed. This was the kind of paternal treatment which everybody understood.

Dr Gool and the inspector haggled and argued in a good-natured fashion, undeterred by pleasantries from the wags in the crowd, until finally a parliamentary messenger was sent for. Dr Gool handed him the petition and then returned to address the procession.

By this time many of the idlers had lost interest and drifted away; only the original nucleus of the procession remained.

'My friends, our petition has been conveyed to the prime minster,' Dr Gool told them. 'We have achieved our object and we can now rely on General Hertzog, as a good man and a friend of the people, to do the just thing. I have promised the police we will all go home quietly now, and that there will be no trouble.'

'We have been insulted,' Hubert Langley called out loudly. 'They will not even deign to speak to us.'

'Make them listen to us,' another voice called and there was loud agreement and equally loud dissent. The procession began to lose its orderly form and to heave and sway.

'Please! My friends – ' Dr Gool's voice was almost drowned in the uproar, and the police inspector called an order and the reserves moved down the street and formed up behind the barricade, batons at the ready, facing the head of the procession.

For some minutes the mood was ugly and confused, and then the coloured leaders prevailed and the procession began to break up and disperse – except for a hard core of three or four hundred. All of these were young, many of them students, both black and white, and Tara was one of the few females amongst them.

The police moved foward and firmly herded them away from the barricade, but spontaneously they re-formed into a smaller but more cohesive band and began marching back towards District Six, the almost exclusively coloured area of the city which abutted onto the central commercial area, but whose diffuse and indistinct boundaries would be one of the subjects of the proposed legislation physically to segregate the racial groups.

The younger, more aggressive marchers linked arms and began to chant and sing, and the police detachments shadowed them, firmly frustrating their efforts to turn back into the central area of the city, shepherding them towards their own areas.

'Africa for the Africans,' they chanted as they marched.

'We are all the same colour under the skin.'

'Bread and freedom.'

Then Hubert Langley's students became more lyrical and picked up the ancient refrain of the oppressed that he had taught them:

> When Adam delved and Eve span
> Who was then the gentleman?

The band began to play the more modern protest:

'Mine eyes have seen the glory of the coming of the Lord.' And after that they launched into: '*Nkosi sikelela Africa* – God Save Africa.'

As they entered the narrow lanes and higgledy-piggledy alleys of District Six, the street gangs emerged to watch with interest, and then to join the fun. In the crowded streets were those with personal scores to settle, and there were also the blatantly criminal and opportunistic gang members.

A half brick came sailing in a high arc out of the packed ranks and crashed through the plate-glass window front of one of the white general dealers, a man notorious for over-charging and restricting credit. The crowd was galvanized, a woman screamed, men began to howl like wolves in a pack.

Somebody reached through the jagged hole in the shop window and grabbed an armful of men's suits. Further down the street another window went with a shattering of glass shards, and the police grouped more tightly and moved forward.

Tara was trying desperately to help restore order, pleading with the laughing looters as they stampeded into the shops, but she was shoved aside and almost knocked down and trampled underfoot.

'Go home, whitey,' one of the gang members shouted in her face. 'We don't want you here.' Then he ducked into the doorway of the shop and picked up a new Singer sewing-machine in his arms.

'Stop it!' Tara met him as he came back through the door of the shop. 'Put it back. You are spoiling everything. Don't you see that's what they want you to

do?' She beat her clenched fists on the man's chest, and he recoiled before her fury. However, the lane was jammed with humanity, looters, gang members, ordinary citizens and political protesters, confused and angry and afraid. From the end of the lane the police charged in a phalanx; batons rising and falling, sjamboks swinging, they began to sweep the mob down the street.

Tara ran out of the looted store just at the moment when a large constable in dark blue uniform was laying on his baton with a will, his target a skinny little Malay tailor who had scampered out of his shop to try to retrieve a bolt of looted cloth.

The constable hit the tailor with a full swing of the baton, crushing his red pillbox fez, and when the little man dropped on the paving stones, stooped over him to aim another blow at his head. Tara launched herself at the policeman. It was a reflex action, like a lioness protecting one of her cubs. The policeman was bent forward, his back to her, and Tara took him off balance. He went down sprawling, but Tara had a death grip on his baton and the wrist-strap parted.

Suddenly she found herself armed and triumphant with the blue jacketed enemy of the proletariat, minions of the bourgeoisie, before her.

She had come in behind the rank of advancing police as they passed the shop, and their backs were turned to her. The thuds of the swinging batons and the terrified squeals of the victims infuriated her. There were the poor and the needy and the oppressed and here were the oppressors – and here also with raised baton was Tara Malcomess.

* * *

Normally it would have taken Shasa little over half an hour to drive the Jaguar from the Anreith gates of Weltevreden to the charge office in Victoria Street. This afternoon it took him almost an hour and a good deal of fast talking.

The police had cordoned off the area from Observatory Main Road right to the old fort on the extreme south end of the Grand Parade. An ominous shroud of black smoke hung over District Six and drifted out over Table Bay and the police at the roadblocks were tense and on edge.

'You can't go in there, sir,' a sergeant flagged down the Jaguar. 'Nobody is allowed in there. Those black bastards are throwing bricks and burning everything in sight.'

'Sergeant, I have just had a message. My fiancée is in there and she needs me. She's in terrible trouble – you have to let me go to her.'

'Orders, sir, I'm sorry.' There were half a dozen constables at the barricade, four of them coloured municipal police.

'Sergeant, what would you do if it were *your* wife or mother who needed you?'

The sergeant glanced around him sheepishly. 'I tell you what I'll do, sir. My men are going to open the roadblock for one minute and we are going to turn our backs. I never saw you and I don't know nothing about you.'

The streets were deserted but littered with debris, loose stones and bricks and broken glass that crunched under the tyres of the Jaguar. Shasa drove fast, appalled at the destruction he saw around him, slitting his eyes against the drifts of smoke that obscured his vision every few hundred yards. Once or twice he saw figures lurking in the alleys, or watching from the upper windows of the

undamaged buildings, but nobody attempted to stop him or attack him. Nevertheless, it was with intense relief that he reached the police station in Victoria Road, and the protection of the hastily marshalled police riot squads.

'Tara Malcomess.' The sergeant at the front desk of the charge office recognized the name immediately. 'Yes, you could say that we know about her! After all, it took four of my men to carry her in here.'

'What are the charges, Sergeant?'

'Let me see – ' He consulted the charge sheet. 'So far we have only got attending an unlawful assembly, wilful destruction of property, inciting to violence, using abusive and threatening language, obstructing the police in the execution of their duty, assaulting a policeman and/or policemen, common assault, assault with an offensive weapon and/or assault with intent.'

'I will put up her bail.'

'That, sir, will cost a pretty penny, I should say.'

'Her father is Colonel Malcomess, the cabinet minister.'

'Well, why didn't you say so before? Please wait here, sir.'

Tara had a blackened eye and her blouse was torn; her auburn hair stood up in tangled disarray as she peered out at Shasa between the bars of her cell.

'What about Huey?' she demanded.

'Huey can cook in Hades for all I care.'

'Then I'm going to cook with him,' Tara declared truculently. 'I'm not leaving here without him.'

Shasa recognized the obstinate set of her madonnalike features, and sighed. So it cost him one hundred pounds – fifty for Tara and fifty for Huey.

'I'll be damned if I will give him a lift though,' Shasa declared. 'Fifty quid is enough for any little bolshevik. He can walk back to his kennel from here.'

Tara climbed into the front seat of the Jaguar and folded her arms defiantly. Neither of them spoke as Shasa gunned the motor and pulled away with unnecessary violence, burning blue smoke off the back tyres.

Instead of heading back towards the affluent white southern suburbs, he sent the Jaguar roaring up the lower slopes of Devil's Peak and parked at one of the viewpoints overlooking the smoking and damaged buildings of District Six.

'What are you doing?' she demanded, as he switched off the engine.

'Don't you want to have a look at your handiwork?' he asked coldly. 'Surely you are proud of what you have achieved.'

She shifted uneasily in her seat. 'That wasn't us,' she muttered. 'That was the *skollie* boys and the gangsters.'

'My dear Tara, that is how revolution is supposed to work. The criminal elements are encouraged to destroy the existing system, to break down the rule of law and order, and then the leaders step in and restore order again by shooting the revolutionaries. Haven't you studied the teachings of your idol Lenin?'

'It was the fault of the police – '

'Yes, it's always the fault of the police – that's also part of Lenin's plan.'

'It isn't like that – '

'Shut up,' he snapped at her. 'Just for once shut up and listen to me. Up to now I've put up with your Joan of Arc act. It was silly and naive but I tolerated it because I loved you. But when you start burning down people's homes and throwing bricks and bombs, then I don't think it's so funny any more.'

'Don't you dare condescend to me,' she flared.

'Look, Tara, look down there at the smoke and flames. Those are the people

you pretend to care for, those are the people who you say you want to help. Those are their homes and livelihoods that you have put the torch to.'

'I didn't think – '

'No, you certainly didn't think. But I am going to tell you something now and you'd better remember it. If you try to destroy this land I love and make its people suffer, then you become my enemy and I will fight you to the death.'

She was silent for a long time, her head turned away from him and then at last she said softly, 'Will you take me home, please?'

He took the long way home over Kloof Nek and along the Atlantic coast, circling around the far side of Table Mountain to avoid the riot-torn areas and they never spoke again until he parked at last in front of the Malcomess home in Newlands.

'Perhaps you are right,' Tara said. 'Perhaps we really are enemies.' She climbed out of the Jaguar and stood looking down at him as he sat behind the wheel in the open cockpit.

'Goodbye Shasa,' she said softly, sadly, and went into the house.

'Goodbye, Tara,' he whispered. 'Goodbye, my beloved enemy.'

* * *

All the Courtneys were gathered in the front room of Weltevreden.

Sir Garrick and Anna sat on the long sofa which was covered with striped Regency patterned damask. They had come down from Natal for Sir Garry's birthday, and the week before they had all climbed Table Mountain for the traditional birthday picnic. It had been a merry occasion and the *Ou Baas*, General Jan Christian Smuts, had been with them, as he nearly always was.

Sir Garry and Lady Anna had planned to return home a few days previously, but then the ghastly news of the German invasion of Poland had broken and they had stayed on at Weltevreden. It was only right that the family should be together in these desperate days.

The two of them held hands like young lovers as they sat close together. Since his last birthday, Sir Garry had grown a small silver goatee beard, perhaps in unconscious imitation of his old friend General Smuts. It increased his scholarly mien and added a little touch of distinction to his pale aesthetic features. He leaned slightly forward on the sofa, inclined towards his wife but with his attention on the radio cabinet over which Shasa Courtney was fussing, twiddling the tuning knobs and frowning at the crackle and whine of static.

'The BBC is on the forty-one-metre band,' Centaine told him sharply and glanced at her diamond-studded wristwatch. 'Do be quick, *chéri*, or we will miss the transmission.'

'Ah!' Shasa smiled as the static cleared and the chimes of Big Ben rang out clearly. As they died away the announcer spoke.

'Twelve hundred hours Greenwich Mean Time and in place of the news we are broadcasting a statement by Mr Neville Chamberlain the prime minister – '

'Turn it up, *chéri*,' Centaine ordered anxiously, and the fateful words, measured and grave, boomed into the elegant room.

They listened to it all in complete silence. Sir Garry's beard quivered, and he took the steel-rimmed spectacles off his nose and absentmindedly chewed on one of the side frames. Beside him Anna wriggled forward onto the edge of the

sofa, her thick thighs spread under their own weight; her face slowly turned a deeper shade of brick and her grip on her husband's hand tightened as she stared at the radio in its mahogany cabinet.

Centaine sat in the tall wingbacked chair beside the huge stone fireplace. She looked like a young girl in a white summer dress with a wide yellow ribbon around her slim waist. She was thirty-nine years old, but there was not yet a single threat of silver in the dense dark curls of her hair and her skin was clear, the faint crow's feet at the corners of her eyes smoothed almost entirely by expensive oils and creams. She leaned an elbow on the arm of the chair, and while with one finger she touched her cheek, she never took her eyes off her son.

Shasa paced the long room, moving from the radio cabinet in its niche between the long flowered curtains, across the highly polished parquet floor with its scattering of oriental carpets until he reached the grand concert piano that stood against the main wall of bookcases at the far end of the room, then turning and coming back with quick restless paces, his hands clasped behind his back, his head bowed in concentration.

She thought how he looked so much like his father. Though Michael had been older and not quite so handsome, yet they had the same quality of grace. She remembered how she had believed Michael to be immortal, a young god, and she felt the terror enter her soul again – that same helpless crippling terror – as she heard the words of war echo through this beautiful home that she had built as a fortress against the world.

'We are never safe – there is no refuge,' she thought. 'It is coming again, and I cannot save those I love. Shasa and Blaine – they will both go and I cannot keep them from it. Last time it was Michael and Papa, this time it's Shasa and Blaine – and, oh God, I hate it. I hate war and I hate the evil men who make it. Please God spare us this time. You took Michael and Papa, please spare Shasa and Blaine. They are all I have – please don't take them from me.'

The deep slow voice spoke into the room, and Shasa froze in the centre of the floor, turning his head to stare over his shoulder at the radio as the voice said:

'And so, it is with the deepest regret that I have to inform you that a state of war now exists between Great Britain and Germany.'

The transmission ended and was replaced by the slow sad strains of chamber music.

'Turn it off, *chéri,*' Centaine said softly, and there was complete silence in the room.

Nobody moved for many seconds. Then abruptly Centaine rose to her feet. She was smiling gaily as she linked her arm through Shasa's.

'Lunch is ready everybody,' she cried lightly. 'In such lovely weather we will eat on the terrace. Shasa will open a bottle of champagne, and I have managed to get the first oysters of the season.'

She kept up a bright and cheery monologue until they were all seated at the table and the wine glasses were filled and then suddenly her act collapsed, and she turned to Sir Garry with a tortured expression.

'We won't have to go in, will we Papa? General Hertzog promised he would keep us out. He says it's an English war. We won't have to send our men again – not this time, will we Papa?'

Sir Garry reached across and took her hand. 'You and I know what the price was last time – ' his voice choked off and he could not mention Michael's name.

After a moment he gathered himself. 'I wish I could give you comfort, my dear. I wish I could say what you want to hear.'

'It's not fair,' said Centaine miserably. 'It just isn't fair.'

'No, I agree it isn't fair. However, there is a monstrous tyranny abroad, a great evil which will swallow us and our world if we do not resist it.'

Centaine sprang up from the table and ran into the house. Shasa rose quickly to follow her, but Sir Garry restrained him with a hand on his arm, and ten minutes later Centaine came out again. She had washed her face and refreshed her make-up and she was smiling, but there was a feverish glitter in her eyes as she took her place at the head of the table.

'We are all going to be gay,' she laughed. 'That's an order. No brooding, no morbid thoughts or words – we are all going to be happy – ' she broke off and the laughter wobbled. She had been about to say, 'for it may be the last time we will all be happy together ever again.'

* * *

On 4 September 1939, the day after Great Britain and France had declared war on Nazi Germany, General Barry Hertzog rose to address the Parliament of the Union of South Africa.

'It is my sad and painful duty to inform the house that the cabinet of the Government is divided on the question of this country's position in the state of war that exists at present between Britain and France on the one hand and Germany on the other hand.' He paused and replaced his spectacles to scrutinize the faces of the men who sat beside him on the government front benches, and then went on gravely.

'It my firm belief that the ultimatum given to Germany by the British Government concerning the occupation of Poland by the German *Wehrmacht* is not binding upon this country, nor does the German occupation of Poland constitute a threat to the security of the Union of South Africa – ' A great roar of approval went up from the opposition benches and Dr Daniel Malan, froglike and bespectacled, smiled benignly, while on the government benches Smuts and his supporters registered their protest as loudly.

'It is rather a local matter between Germany and Poland,' Hertzog went on, 'and it gives this country no cause to join in the declaration of war. Accordingly I propose that South Africa remain neutral; that it cede the naval base at Simonstown to Britain, but in all other respects continue its present relationship with all the belligerents as if no war were being waged.'

The ageing prime minister was a fluent and persuasive speaker and as he continued enlarging his case for neutrality, Blaine Malcomess on the front bench of the government side was covertly watching the reaction of the Smuts supporters around him.

He knew which of them were as firmly committed as himself and the *Ou Baas* to stand by Britain, and which of them were wavering and uncertain. As Hertzog continued speaking, he sensed the swing of emotions towards the old general's side, and with a sense of disbelief and rising shame he foresaw the ignominious decision that the House was about to take. His anger rose to keep pace with his shame.

General Hertzog was still speaking, and Blaine was now only listening with

half an ear as he scribbled a note to pass across to the *Ou Baas*, when abruptly his full attention flashed back to what the prime minister was saying.

'Finally, coming to the ethics of the German invasion of Poland, a case could very well be made out for the justification of this action if it were taken into consideration that the security of the German state – '

Blaine felt his spirits soar, and he sensed rather than saw the sudden shock and revulsion of feeling amongst those who had begun to waver towards the side of neutrality.

'He has gone too far,' Blaine wrote on a fresh sheet of his notepad. 'He is defending Hitler's aggression. We have won.'

He tore the sheet from the pad and handed it to General Smuts, who read it and nodded slightly, and rose to his feet to put the other side of the argument.

'Britain is our friend, our oldest and our best friend. We must stand by her to the end,' he said in his high-pitched voice, rolling his r's in his distinctive Malmesbury bray.

'Far from being a local dispute, the Polish invasion has consquences that reach far beyond Danzig and the corridor, into the hearts and souls of free men in every corner of the globe.'

When, at last, the motion, for war or neutrality, was put to the vote, Dr Malan's Nationalists voted as a block for neutrality, and one third of Hertzog's own party, together with three of his cabinet ministers, followed his lead.

However, Smuts and his own men – Reitz and Malcomess and Stuttaford and the others – carried the day and by the slim margin of eighty votes to sixty-seven, South Africa declared war on Nazi Germany.

In a last desperate bid to thwart the declaration, General Hertzog called for dissolution of Parliament and a general election, but the governor-general, Sir Patrick Duncan, refused the request and instead accepted the old general's resignation and invited General Jan Christian Smuts to form a new government and take the nation to war.

* * *

'The *Ou Baas* won't let me go,' Blaine said bitterly, and Centaine ran to him across the bedroom of their cottage and stood on tiptoe to embrace him.

'Oh thank God, Blaine my darling. I prayed and prayed and He answered me. I couldn't bear to lose you both. Not you and Shasa – I could never have survived it.'

'I'm not proud that I will stay at home while others go.'

'You have fought once, bravely, unselfishly,' she told him. 'You are a thousand times more valuable here than lying dead on a battlefield in a foreign land.'

'The *Ou Baas* has convinced me of that,' he sighed. With an arm around her waist he led her through to the sitting-room, and she knew that tonight for once they would not make love. His distress was too great. She knew that tonight he wanted only to talk, and it was her duty to listen to him while he poured out his doubts and fears and regrets.

They came out in a jumble, without logical sequence, and she sat close to him so he could touch her merely by stretching out a hand as she listened quietly.

'Our position is so precarious – how can we wage a war when we command a majority of only thirteen votes in the House, while against us we have a solid opposition who hate the *Ou Baas* and what they call his English war? They will fight us every step of the way, while the people also are deeply divided against us. We have within our own borders an enemy as vicious as the Nazis, the *Ossewa Brandwag* and the Black Shirts and the Grey Shirts, the *Deutsche Bund* in South West Africa, enemies within and without.'

She poured him another whisky and soda and brought him the Stuart crystal tumbler. It was his second drink that evening and she had never before seen him take more than one.

'Pirow has betrayed us. He is one of them now, but for all those years he has been in a position of trust.' Oswald Pirow had been the Minister of Defence under the Hertzog government. 'We gave him a defence budget of fifty-six million and a brief to build up an effective modern army, but instead he treacherously gave us a paper army. We believed his reports and his assurances, but now that he has gone we find ourselves without modern weapons, a handful of obsolete tanks and venerable aircraft and an army of fewer than fifteen hundred in the permanent force. Pirow refused to arm the nation for a war which he and Hertzog were determined we would never fight.'

The night wore on but both of them were too strung up to think of sleeping, and when he refused a third whisky she went through to the kitchen to make a pot of coffee and he followed her. He stood behind her with his arms around her waist while they waited for the water to come to the boil.

'General Smuts has given me the Interior Ministry in the new cabinet. One of the reasons he chose me was that I have already chaired the commission of enquiry into the *Ossewa Brandwag* and the other subversive organizations. It will be one of my major concerns to suppress their efforts to disrupt our preparations for war. The *Ou Baas* himself has taken the Ministry of Defence, and he has already promised Britain an army of fifty thousand volunteers ready to fight anywhere in Africa.'

They took the coffee tray through to the sitting-room and as Centaine poured, the telephone rang, shrill and shocking in the silent cottage. She started and spilled steaming coffee over the tray.

'What time is it, Blaine?'

'Ten minutes to one.'

'I won't answer it – let it ring,' Centaine shook her head, staring at the insistent instrument, but he stood up.

'Only Doris knows I'm here,' he said. 'I had to let her know in case – ' He didn't have to explain further. Doris was his secretary, the only one in their confidence, and of course she had to know where to find him. Centaine picked up the telephone.

'Mrs Courtney speaking.' She listened for a moment. 'Yes, Doris, he is here.' She handed the telephone to Blaine and turned away. He listened for a few moments, then said quietly, 'Thank you, Doris, I'll be there in twenty minutes.' He hung up and looked up at Centaine.

'I'm sorry, Centaine.'

'I'll fetch your coat.'

She held it for him and he slipped his arms into the sleeves and turned to face her, buttoning it as he said, 'It's Isabella.' He saw her surprise and went on, 'The doctor is with her. They need me. Doris wouldn't say more, but it sounds serious.'

After Blaine had gone, she took the coffee pot and cups through to the kitchen, and rinsed them in the sink. Seldom had she felt so lonely. The cottage was silent and cold and she knew she could not sleep. She went back into the lounge and put a gramophone record on the turntable. It was an aria from Verdi's *Aida*, always one of her favourites, and as she sat and listened to it the memories it aroused came stealing back out of the past – Michael and Mort Homme and the other long-ago war – and her melancholy swamped her.

She slept at last, sitting in the armchair with her legs curled up under her, and the telephone woke her with a start. She reached for it before she was properly awake.

'Blaine!' She recognized his voice instantly. 'What time is it?'

'It's four o'clock – a few minutes after.'

'Is something wrong, Blaine?' She came fully awake.

'Isabella,' he said. 'She is asking for you.'

'For me?' Centaine was confused.

'She wants you to come here.'

'I can't, Blaine. That's not possible, you know that.'

'She's dying, Centaine. The doctor says she won't last out the day.'

'Oh God, Blaine, I'm so sorry.' And with wonder at herself, she realized she truly was. 'Poor Isabella – '

'Will you come?'

'Do you want me to, Blaine?'

'It is her last request. If we refuse it, our guilt will be so much harder to bear.'

'I'll come,' she said and hung up.

She took only a few minutes to bathe her face and change and put on light make-up. She drove through the almost deserted streets, and Blaine's big gabled home was the only one in Newlands Avenue with lights burning.

He met her at the mahogany double front doors and he did not embrace her, but said simply, 'Thank you, Centaine.' Only then she saw his daughter standing in the hall behind him.

'Hello, Tara,' she greeted her. The girl had been weeping. Her big grey eyes were puffy and swollen and rimmed with red, and her face was so pale that her dark auburn hair seemed to burn like a bush fire. 'I'm so sorry to hear about your mother.'

'No, you aren't.' Tara stared at her with a flat hostile expression which suddenly wavered and cracked. She sobbed and ran down the passageway. A door slammed in the back of the house.

'She's very upset,' Blaine said. 'I apologize for her.'

'I understand,' Centaine answered. 'I deserve at least part of that.'

He shook his head to deny it, but said simply, 'Please come with me.'

They climbed the circular staircase side by side and Centaine asked softly, 'What is it, Blaine?'

'A degeneration of the spine and nervous system, a process that has been going on slowly over the years. Now there is pneumonia, and she can no longer resist.'

'Pain?' Centaine asked.

'Yes,' he replied. 'She has always had pain, more than the average person could bear.'

They went down the wide carpeted passageway and Blaine tapped on the door at the end and then opened it.

'Come in, please.'

The room was large and furnished in cool restful greens and blues. The curtains were closed and a night lamp burned on the bedside table. The man standing beside the bed was clearly a doctor. Blaine led Centaine to the four-poster bed and though she had tried to prepare herself, still she started when she saw the figure that lay upon the banked pillows.

She remembered Isabella Malcomess' serene and gentle beauty. Now a death's head stared at her from sunken eye-sockets, and the fixed grin of yellowish teeth, the rictus of shrunken lips, was somehow obscene. The effect was heightened by the contrast of thick auburn hair which formed a cloud about the ravaged head.

'It was kind of you to come.' Centaine had to lean closer to the bed to hear the thin voice.

'I came as soon as I heard you wanted me.'

The doctor intervened quietly. 'You may stay only a few minutes – Mrs Malcomess must rest.' But Isabella fluttered her hand impatiently, and Centaine saw that it was a bird's claw of fragile bones covered with skin the colour of tallow and a ropy network of blue veins.

'I wish to speak in private,' she whispered. 'Please leave us, Doctor.'

Blaine leaned over her to adjust the pillows under her head.

'Please don't tire yourself, dear,' he said, and his gentleness towards the dying woman gave Centaine a jealous pang she could not suppress.

Blaine and the doctor left quietly, and closed the door with a click of the latch. They were alone together for the first time. Centaine was overcome by the sense of unreality. For so many years this woman had bulked large in her life, her very existence had meant that Centaine had to suffer all the vile emotions from guilt to jealousy, from anger to hatred. But now that she stood beside her deathbed, they had all evaporated. All she felt was a vast sense of pity.

'Come nearer, Centaine,' Isabella whispered, beckoning her with another feeble flutter of her wasted hand. 'Talking is such an effort.'

Impulsively Centaine went down on her knees beside the bed so that their eyes were only inches apart. She felt a terrible need to repent for all the unhappiness she had caused and to ask for Isabella's forgiveness, but Isabella spoke first.

'I told Blaine that I wanted to make my peace with you, Centaine. I told him I understood that the two of you had not been able to help falling in love, and that I realized you had tried to spare me as much as possible. I told him I knew that you were never vindictive, and that although you could have taken him away, you never inflicted that final humiliation upon me, that although I was no longer a woman, you allowed me to retain the last shreds of my dignity.'

Centaine felt the pity flood her soul and fill her eyes. She wanted to take this frail dying creature in her arms and hold her, but something in Isabella's eyes prevented her, it was a fierce proud light and Centaine simply bowed her head and remained silent.

'I told Blaine that you had filled his life with the happiness I could not give him, but despite that and because of your generosity, I was still able to keep part of him for myself.'

'Oh, Isabella, I don't know how to tell you – ' Centaine's voice choked and Isabella gestured her to silence.

She seemed to be gathering herself for some enormous effort. A faint flush of

colour came back into her cheeks and the fierce light in her eyes flared up. Her breath quickened and when she spoke again her voice was stronger, harsher.

'I told him all these things to persuade him to bring you here. If he had guessed what I truly intended, he would not have allowed you to come.' She raised her head from the pillow and her voice became a serpent's hiss.

'Now I can tell you how deeply I have hated you every waking hour of every long year, how my hatred kept me alive this long so that I could prevent you from having him as your husband, and now that I am dying that hatred is magnified a hundred times – ' she broke off and panted for breath, as Centaine recoiled before her glare. She realized that Isabella was a woman driven to madness by the agony she had endured, by the long corrosion of hatred and jealousy.

'If a dying woman's curse has any force,' Isabella spoke again, 'then I curse you, Centaine Courtney, with my last breath. May you experience the same torture you have inflicted upon me, may you know pain as I have known it. The day you stand before the altar with my husband I will reach out to you from beyond the grave – '

'No!' Centaine stumbled to her feet, and backed towards the door. 'Stop it! Please, stop it!'

Isabella laughed, a shrill and taunting sound. 'I curse you, and let my curse blight your adulterous passion. I curse every minute the two of you spend together when I have gone. I curse whatever seed he places in your womb, I curse each kiss and touch – I curse you and I curse your brat. I curse all your issue. An eye for an eye, Centaine Courtney. Heed my words – an eye for an eye!'

Centaine ran across the room and flung herself against the door. Throwing it open, she ran down the passage. Blaine was coming up the staircase at a run. He tried to hold her, but she tore herself from his grasp and rushed out through the front doors to where the Daimler was parked.

She had been driving for many hours, driving fast with the accelerator pressed to the floorboards, keeping the great seven-litre engine at a long sustained bellow, sending a tall pale column of dust into the sky behind her, before she consciously realized she was going back into the desert, back to the dreaming mystical hills that the little Bushmen called 'The Place of all Life'.

* * *

It was two months before Centaine came back out of the Kalahari Desert. For all that time she had thwarted Blaine's efforts to contact her, refusing to reply to the letters he wrote or the telephone calls he made to both Abe Abrahams and Dr Twentyman-Jones.

She read the death notices for Isabella Malcomess in the obituary columns of the newspapers which reached the H'ani Mine only weeks after publication, but they served to increase her feeling of isolation and the brooding premonition of disaster and tragedy which Isabella's death curse had left with her.

She returned to Weltevreden in the end only at Shasa's insistence. When she arrived her hair was floury with dust from the long journey and she was darkly tanned by the Kalahari sun, but tired and dispirited still.

Shasa must have received her telegram and been expecting her. He must

have heard the Daimler's motor as she came up the avenue to the château, but he was not on the front steps to meet her, and she realized why when she went into her study. He turned from the window from where he had watched her arrival and now he crossed the room to meet her. He was in uniform.

She stopped in the doorway, and an icy stillness froze her. She watched him come towards her – and in her memory she was carried back down the years and across space to another meeting with a tall and impossibly handsome young man in the same khaki tunic, with the polished belt and Sam Browne cross-strap, the peaked cap set at a jaunty angle, and the airman's wings on his chest.

'Thank God, you've come, Mater,' Shasa greeted her. 'I had to see you before I left.'

'When?' she breathed the question, terrified to hear the answer. 'When do you go?'

'Tomorrow.'

'Where? Where are they sending you?'

'First we go to Roberts Heights,' that was the airforce training base in the Transvaal, 'for conversion to fighters, and after that wherever they send us. Wish me luck, Mater.'

She saw that he wore orange flashes on the epaulettes of his tunic, the insignia of those who had volunteered to fight beyond the country's borders.

'Yes, my darling, I wish you luck,' she said, and knew that her heart would break to see him go.

* * *

The roar of the Rolls-Royce Merlin engine filled his head even through the earphones of the radio telephone that Shasa wore over his leather flying helmet. The cockpit canopy of the Hawker Hurricane fighter aircraft was open, so the slipstream buffeted his head, but it gave him an uninterrupted view of the blue African sky around him. The three fighters flew in a loose arrowhead formation. The dun-coloured desert camouflage could not disguise their beautiful deadly lines.

Shasa led the flight. His promotion had been rapid. Command came naturally to him, he had learned that lesson well from Centaine Courtney. It had taken only eighteen months for him to reach the rank of squadron leader.

He flew in a short-sleeved khaki tunic, khaki shorts and with velskoen on his bare feet, for the summer heat of Abyssinia was brutal. Around his waist was belted a Webley service revolver, an archaic weapon for the pilot of modern pursuit aricraft, but all of them had taken to wearing sidearms since the intelligence section had circulated those obscene photographs. One of the motorized recce units had overrun a village in the mountains and found the remains of two South African pilots who had been forced down and captured by the Abyssinian irregulars – the *shufta*, wild hill bandits. The pilots had been given to the women of the village. They had first been emasculated, then flayed with hot irons and disembowelled so skilfully that they were still living as their viscera was drawn from them. Finally, their jaws had been wedged open with thorn branches and the women had urinated into their open mouths until they drowned. So all pilots carried sidearms now, to defend themselves first, and to make certain they were never captured alive.

Today the air was clear and bright under a cloudless azure sky, and visibility was unlimited. Below and ahead stretched the rugged Abyssinian highlands, precipitous Ambas, the huge table-topped mountains, the dark deep gorges between, desert and rock, dry and sun-bleached to the dun colour of an old lion's scarred hide.

The three fighters bored upwards, striving for height. They had scrambled from the dusty forward airstrip at Yirga Alem only minutes before, in response to a faint but desperate appeal over the field radio from the advancing infantry, and Shasa wheeled the flight onto the northern heading and picked out the thin pale thread of the road winding through the mountains far below them.

Immediately he resumed the fighter pilot's scan, his head pivoting and turning, eyes darting and flicking, never allowed to fix and focus short, up and around and down in a regular never-ceasing motion – and he saw them first.

They were tiny specks, a cloud of black midges against the aching blue.

'Popeye flight, this is leader. Tally ho!' he said into the microphone of his radio telephone. 'Eleven o'clock high! Ten plus – and they look like Capronis. Buster! Buster!' 'Buster' was the order to go to full throttle.

'I have them,' Dave Abrahams answered immediately. It was extraordinary that they had been able to keep together, from the training days at Roberts Heights through all the vagaries of the East African campaign, until now they were fighting with Dan Pienaar's South African Corps, driving the Duke of Aosta's Italians back through the mountains towards Addis Adaba.

Shasa glanced across at him. David had brought his Hurricane up on Shasa's starboard wingtip. He also had his canopy open, and they flashed a grin across at each other. David's large peaky nose had been burned raw and pink by the sun, and the straps of his helmet hung unbuckled under his chin. It was a good feeling to have him on his wing. Then both of them closed their canopies in preparation for the attack and looked ahead. Shasa brought the flight around into a gentle turn, climbing up into the sun, the classic fighter tactics.

The distant midges resolved swiftly into the familiar silhouettes of three-engined Caproni bombers. Shasa counted twelve, four sticks of three. They were going for the crossroads at Kerene again, where the South African advance was bottled into the pass between the soaring walls of the high Ambas, and at that moment Shasa saw the bombs drop away from below the leading bombers.

Still under full throttle, the Rolls-Royce engines screamed in protest as they climbed out, turning into the sun that blinded the Italian gunners. Shasa winged over and went down into the attack.

He could see the bomb-bursts now, tiny fountains of pale dust, spurting up around the crossroads, falling amongst the antlike column of vehicles in the gut of the hills. Those poor bastards down there were taking a pounding, and as they tore down the sky the second flight of Capronis released their bombloads. The fat grey eggs, finned at one end, went down with a deceptively slow wobbling motion, and Shasa twisted his head around in one last sweep of the heavens, squinting into the sun, checking that the Italian fighters were not waiting up there, lying in ambush; but the sky was unsullied blue, and he switched his full attention back to his gunsight.

He picked out the leading Caproni in the third flight, hoping his attack would spoil the bomb-layer's aim, and he touched left rudder and rotated the Hurricane's nose downwards a hair's breadth until the silver and blue Caproni swam gently in the rose of his gunsight.

Six hundred yards and he held his fire. He could see the insignia of the fasces

on the fuselage, the bundled rods and axe of imperial Rome. The heads of the two pilots in the cockpit were inclined earthwards, watching for the fall of the bombs. The twin machine-guns in the revolving power turret were trained aft.

Five hundred yards. He could see the head and shoulders of the turret gunner. The back of his helmet was towards Shasa. He had not yet spotted the three deadly machines screaming down onto his starboard quarter.

Four hundred yards – so close that Shasa could see the scorching of fumes around the exhaust ports of the Caproni's engines, and the gunner still was unaware.

Three hundred yards. The bomb bay of the Caproni began to open under swollen belly, pregnant with death. Now Shasa could make out the rows of rivet heads along the silver fuselage and on the wide blue wings. He settled his grip on the joystick between his knees and slipped the safety-lock on the firing button, readying the eight Browning machine-guns in his wings.

Two hundred yards. He played the rudder bars with his toes and the gunsight drifted over the Caproni's fuselage. He stared through it, frowning slightly with concentration, his lower lip caught between his front teeth. Suddenly a line of bright fiery phosphorescent beads strung across the nose of his Hurricane. The gunner of the second Caproni had spotted him at last, and fired a warning burst across his nose.

One hundred yards. The gunner and both pilots in the leading Caproni, alerted by the burst of fire, had looked around and seen him. The turret gunner was traversing frantically trying to bring his guns to bear. Through the gunsight Shasa could see his white face, contorted with terror.

Eighty yards. Still frowning, Shasa pressed hard down with his thumb on the firing-button. The Hurricane shuddered and slowed to the recoil of eight Brownings, and Shasa was thrown gently forward against his shoulder straps by the deceleration. Bright streams of tracer, sparkling like electricity, hosed into the Caproni, and Shasa watched the strike of shot, directing it with quick subtle touches of his controls.

The Italian gunner never fired his turret guns. The Perspex canopy disintegrated around him and concentrated fire tore him to shreds. Half his head and one of his arms were pulled off like those of a careless child's rag doll, and went spinning and bouncing away in the propeller wash. Instantly Shasa switched his aim, picking up the silver coin of the spinning propeller and the vulnerable wing root of the Caproni in his sights. The crisp silhouette of the wing dissolved like wax in a candleflame. Glycerine and fuel vapour poured from the motor in liquid sheets, and the whole wing pivoted slowly backwards on its root, and then tore away and spun off, a dead leaf in the slipstream. The bomber flipped over on its back and went down in a flat inverted spiral, unbalanced by the missing wing, weaving irregular zigzag patterns of smoke and vapour and flame down the sky, and Shasa turned all his attention to the next formation of bombers.

He brought his Hurricane round still under full throttle, and he pulled his turn so tightly that the blood drained away from his brain and his vision turned grey and shadowy. He tensed his belly muscles and clenched his jaw to resist the drainage of blood, and levelled out on a head-on course with the next Caproni in line.

The two aircraft raced together with terrifying speed. The nose of the Caproni swelled miraculously to fill all Shasa's vision, and he fired into it at pointblank range and then pulled up his nose and they flashed past each other so close that

he felt the bump and jar of the bomber's slipstream. He came round again, hard and furiously, breaking up the Italian formations, scattering them across the sky, turning and diving and firing until with that abruptness that is so much part of aerial combat, they were all gone.

He was alone in an enormously blue and empty sky and he was sweating with adrenalin reaction. His grip on the control column was so tight that it hurt his knuckles. He throttled back and checked his fuel guage. Those desperate minutes at full throttle had burned over half a tankful.

'Popeye flight, this is leader. Come in all units.' He spoke into his microphone and the response was immediate.

'Leader, this is three!' That was the third Hurricane, with young Le Roux at the controls. 'I'm down to quarter of a tank.'

'All right, three return independently to base,' Shasa ordered. And then he called again. 'Popeye two, this is leader. Do you read me?'

Shasa was searching the sky around him, trying to pick up David's aircraft, feeling the first prickle of anxiety.

'Come in, Popeye two,' he repeated, and looked down, searching for smoke rising from a wrecked aircraft in the broken brown land below. Then his pulse jumped as David's voice came in clearly through his headphones.

'Leader, this is two, I have damage.'

'David, where the hell are you?'

'Approximately ten miles east of Kerene crossroads, at eight thousand feet.'

Shasa glanced into the easterly quarter and almost instantly picked out a thin grey line being swiftly drawn above the blue horizon towards the south. It looked like a feather.

'David, I see smoke in your area. Are you on fire?'

'Affirmative. I have an engine fire.'

'I'm coming, David, hold on!'

Shasa flung the Hurricane's wing up in a steep turn and rammed the throttle open to its stop.

David was a little below him, and he went screaming down the sky.

'David, how bad is it?'

'Roast turkey,' David said laconically, and ahead of him Shasa made out the burning Hurricane.

David had his stricken machine in a steep side slip, so that the flames were not streaming back over the cockpit canopy but were being blown out to one side. He was going down fast, trying to build up speed to the critical point when the fire would be starved of oxygen and would extinguish itself spontaneously.

Shasa bore down on him and then eased back his own speed and kept slightly above and two hundred yards off. He could see the bullet holes in the other machine's engine cowling and wing. One of the Italian gunners had got in a good burst at David. The paintwork was blackening and blistering back down the Hurricane's fuselage, almost as far as the cockpit, and David was struggling with the Perspex canopy, trying to open it.

'A jammed canopy and David will cook,' Shasa thought, but at that moment the canopy came free and slid back easily and David looked across at him. The air around his head was distorted by the shimmering heat of invisible flames and a brown patch appeared on the sleeve of David's tunic as the Khaki cotton scorched.

'No good! I'm hitting the silk, Shasa.' He saw David's lips move and his

voice echoed in Shasa's earphones, but before he could reply, David pulled the helmet from his head and released his shoulder-straps. He lifted one hand in a farewell salute, and then turned the burning Hurricane onto its back and fell out of the open cockpit.

He went down with arms and legs spread in an untidy sprawling starfish, beginning to turn like a cartwheel until suddenly a cascade of silk burst from his parachute pack, bloomed into a glistening snowy flower over him and he was jerked backwards, his fall broken, and he drifted away towards the parched, dung-coloured earth five thousand feet below, the light breeze carrying his parachute away towards the south.

Shasa throttled his Hurricane back until he was losing height at the same rate as the descending parachute, and he circled David slowly, keeping two or three hundred yards separation from his dangling body, craning his head over the side of his open cockpit, trying to estimate where David would land, and then glancing anxiously at the fuel guage on his instrument panel. The needle hovered just above the red line.

David's burning Hurricane smashed into the dusty plain below the soaring Ambas and exploded in a quick dragon's breath of smoke, and Shasa surveyed the ground. Directly below were ridges of iron grey which peaked into cones of darker rock. Between the ridges were stony hollows, rough as a crocodile's skin, and then, just beyond the last ridge, a softer smoother valley; as they descended he made out the regular furrows of primitive cultivation on the gentle slopes of the valley. David would come down on or very close to the final ridge.

Shasa's eyes narrowed. Human habitation! There was a tiny group of thatched huts at the end of the valey, and for a moment his spirits rose. Then he remembered the photographs – those mutilated and desecrated lumps of human flesh, and his jaw clenched as he looked across at David, swaying and swinging on the parachute shrouds.

He banked the Hurricane away, turning and dropping down towards the valley, and he levelled out at fifty feet above the ground, and flew back between the rock ridges up the shallow valley. He roared over the rude fields of cultivation, scraggly stalks of sorghum standing in ragged lines, stunted and browned by the drought, and then ahead of him he saw human figures.

A group of men were running down the valley from the village, twenty or more figures in long dirty grey robes that flapped around their bare black legs as they ran. Their hair was teased up into fuzzy dark bushes, and all of them were armed, some with modern carbines probably looted from the battlefield, others with the long muzzle-loading jezails.

As the Hurricane roared low over their heads, three or four of them stopped running and threw their rifles to their shoulders, pointing them up at Shasa. He saw the flash of black powder smoke as their fired, but he did not feel the bullets hit his aircraft.

Shasa needed no further evidence of their hostile intentions. The armed men were streaming along the bottom of the ridge, waving their rifles, racing to intercept the tiny figure on the floating parachute.

Shasa dropped down again, lined up the running group and at five hundred yards, opened up with the eight Brownings. Sheets of tracer and dust flew up around the group of robed figures in a raging storm, and he saw four or five of them picked up and flung down again by the hail of machine-gun fire.

Then he was forced to climb out to miss the hills at the head of the valley,

and as he came around once more he saw that the *shufta* had regrouped and were once again running to intercept David who was at less than a thousand feet now. It was clear that he would fall on the slope of the ridge.

Shasa dropped in for a second attack, but this time the *shufta* scattered before the approaching Hurricane and from the cover of the rocks they turned a furious fusillade on Shasa as he roared over their heads. His own machine-gun fire threw up clouds of dust and rock fragments, but did little execution.

He climbed up and levelled out, swivelling his head to watch David land. The parachute drifted over the ridge, missing it by only a few feet, then it hit the down-draught of the back slope and dropped sharply.

He saw David land heavily and tumble head over heels, bumping across the rocky slope until the parachute jerked him to his feet again. He struggled with the tangled shrouds and the billowing folds of silk, sawing and tipping it, spilling air from it until the parachute collapsed in a silvery heap and David threw off the harness.

He stood and stared down the slope towards the band of running howling *shufta* and Shasa saw him unbuckle the flap of his holster and draw his service pistol, then shade his eyes and look up at the circling Hurricane.

Shasa dropped down almost to his level, and as he passed he pointed urgently down the slope. David stared up at him without comprehension. He looked very small and abandoned on the desert hillside, and Shasa was close enough to see the resignation on his face as he waved farewell to Shasa and turned to face the savage band coming up to take him.

Shasa fired another burst at the *shufta* as he roared towards them, and again they scattered for cover. They were still half a mile from David; he had delayed them for precious seconds. He put the Hurricane into a maximum-rate turn, his wingtip brushing the thorn scrub of the ridge as he came around, and the instant he levelled out he let down his undercarriage. With landing-wheels hanging he roared back over the spot where David stood and repeated his urgent signal, pointing down into the valley.

He saw the understanding lighten David's face. He turned and ran down the slope with long bounding strides, so that he seemed to float above the dark rocks, skimming them lightly.

Shasa turned at the bottom end of the valley and lined up on the roughly ploughed strip of land at the foot of the slope. He saw that David was already halfway down and that the *shufta* were trying to head him off – but then he needed all his wits for the touch down.

At the last moment he pulled on full flap and held the Hurricane off, letting her float in, bleeding off speed – back, back, back with the stick. Two feet off the ploughed earth she stalled and dropped in with a crash, bounced and hit again, and bounced, caught a wheel in the rough and her tail went up. She almost nosed in, then checked and ran out, kicking and jolting, throwing Shasa cruelly against his shoulder-straps.

He was down. He had given himself even odds on getting her down without breaking her, but here he was down and David had almost reached the bottom of the ridge.

David wasn't going to make it, he realized almost immediately. Four of the stongest runners amongst the *shufta* had pulled ahead, and they were going to cut David off before he reached the ploughed land. The other *shufta* had stopped and were shooting at long range. Shasa saw bullets kick up little dust

feathers along the slope, some of them fell frighteningly close to David's racing form.

Shasa turned the Hurricane, standing on one rudder to force her wheels over the rough furrows. When her nose was pointed directly at the four leading *shufta*, he gave the Hurricane a burst of full throttle and her tail lifted. For a moment she was level and her Brownings could bear. He fired a full burst, and a tornado of shot swept across the field, scything down the dry sorghum stalks and catching the group of running men, blowing two of them into sodden bundles of red rags, spinning a third in a giddy little *danse macabre* veiled by the curtain of flying dust. The remaining bandit threw himself flat to the earth, and the Hurricane's tail dropped back onto the tail wheel. The machine-guns could no longer bear.

David was only a few hundred yards away now, coming on fast, his long legs flying and Shasa swung the Hurricane to point back down the valley. The down slope would add speed to their take-off run.

Shasa leaned out of the cockpit.

'Come on, Davie,' he yelled. 'Gold medal this time, boyo!'

Something hit the cowling just in front of the canopy with a metallic twang and then went screaming off in ricochet, leaving a silver smear through the paintwork. Shasa looked back. The *shufta* were into the edge of the field, running forward, then stopping to kneel and fire. Another bullet cracked past his head, forcing him to flinch and duck.

'Come on, Davie.' He could hear David's panting breath above the idling beat of the Rolls-Royce engine, and a bullet slapped into the wing, punching a neat round hole through the fabric.

'Come on, Davie.' Sweat had stained David's tunic and greased his flushed face. He reached the Hurricane and jumped up onto the wing. The aircraft dipped under his weight.

'On my lap,' Shasa yelled. 'Get in!' David scrambled in on top of him, grunting for breath.

'I can't see ahead,' Shasa shouted. 'You take the stick and the throttle – I'll work the rudders.'

He felt David's hands on the joystick and the throttle lever, and relinquished both of them. The engine beat quickened and the Hurricane began to roll forward.

'A touch of left rudder,' David called, his voice broken and rough with fatigue, and Shasa pushed on an inch of left rudder.

In a gale of sound and dust the Rolls-Royce engine built up to full power, and they were bumping and bouncing over the field, steering an erratic course as Shasa worked the rudders blindly, over-correcting to David's instructions.

Shasa could not see ahead. David was crushing him down in the seat and totally obscuring his forward vision. He twisted his head and looked over the edge of the cockpit, watching the ground begin to blur past him as their speed built up, responding quickly to David's calls for left or right rudder. The dry sorghum stalks whipped against the leading edges of the wings; the sound they made was almost as ugly as the snap and flute of bullets passing close. All the remaining *shufta* were still firing at them, but the range was opening rapidly.

The Hurricane hit a hump in the field and it kicked them into the air. The jolting and thudding ceased abruptly and they were airborne, climbing away.

'We made it!' Shasa shouted, amazed at their achievement, and as the words left his lips something hit him in the face.

The bullet was a piece of hammered-iron pot-leg, as long and thick as a man's thumb. It had been fired from a 1779 Tower musket by a handful of black powder. It struck the metal frame of the canopy beside Shasa's head, and the pot leg mushroomed and tumbled as it ricocheted. Spinning, it smashed into the side of Shasa's face, its velocity sharply reduced by the impact on the frame. Striking side-on, it did not penetrate the brain.

Shasa did not even lose consciousness. It felt as though he had been hit in the outer corner of his left eye with a full swing of a hammer. His head was knocked across so that it struck the opposite side of the canopy.

He felt the supra-orbital margin of the frontal bone of his skull shatter, and hot blood drenched his eye and tatters of his own skin and flesh hung down over his face like a curtain.

'David!' he screamed. 'I'm hit! I can't see!'

David twisted around and looked back at Shasa's face and he cried out in horror. Blood was spurting and dribbling and splashing, blown by the slipstream into pink veils that spattered into David's face.

'I can't see,' Shasa kept repeating. His face was raw meat running red. 'I can't see, oh God Davie, I can't see.'

David pulled the silk scarf from around his own neck and pushed it into one of Shasa's groping hands.

'Try and stop the bleeding,' he shouted above the roar of the engine, and Shasa bundled the scarf and pressed it into the hideously ragged wound, while David gave all his attention to getting them home, keeping low, skimming the wild brown hills.

It took them fifteen minutes back to the airstrip at Yirga Alem and they came in at treetop level. David slammed the Hurricane onto the dustry strip and taxied tail up to the waiting field ambulance that he had called for from the air.

They lifted Shasa out of the blood-spattered cockpit. Then David and a medical orderly half-carried, half-led him, stumbling like a blind man to the ambulance. Within fifteen minutes Shasa was anaesthetized and laid out on the operating table in the hospital tent and an airforce doctor was working over him.

When he came round from the anaesthetic, all was dark.

He lifted his hand and touched his face. It was swathed in bandages, and panic rose in him.

'David!' he tried to scream, but it came out in a drunken slur from the chloroform.

'All right, Shasa, I'm here.' The voice was close by and he groped for him.

'Davie! Davie!'

'It's all right, Shasa, it's all going to be just fine.'

Shasa found his hand and clung to it. 'I can't see. I'm blind.'

'The bandages, that's all,' David assured him. 'The doctor is delighted with you.'

'You're not lying to me, David?' Shasa pleaded. 'Tell me I'm not blind.'

'You are not blind,' David whispered, but mercifully Shasa could not see his face as he said it. Shasa's desperate grip relaxed slowly, and after a minute the painkillers took effect and he drifted back into unconsciousness.

David sat beside his cot all that night; even in darkness the tent was hot as an oven. He wiped the glistening sweat from Shasa's neck and chest, and held his hand when he whimpered in his sleep and muttered, 'Mater? Are you there, Mater?'

After midnight the doctor ordered David to leave him and get some rest, but David refused.

'I have to be here when he wakes – I have to be the one to tell him. I owe him that much at least.'

Outside the tent the jackals yipped at the dawn, and then the first glow struck through the canvas, Shasa woke again, and asked immediately, 'David?'

'I'm here, Shasa.'

'It hurts like hell, David, but you told me it's going to be all right. I remember that, you did tell me, didn't you?'

'Yes, that's what I said.'

'We'll be flying together soon, won't we, Davie boy? The old team, Courtney and Abrahams back in business?'

He waited for the reply, but when it did not come Shasa's tone changed. 'I'm not blind, am I? We will be flying again?'

'You are not blind,' David said softly. 'But you won't be flying again. You're going home, Shasa.'

'Tell me!' Shasa ordered. 'Don't try and spare me, that will only make it worse.'

'All right, I'll tell you straight. The bullet burst your left eyeball. The doctor had to remove it.'

Shasa lifted his hand and touched the left side of his face disbelievingly.

'You will still have full vision in the right eye, but you won't be flying Hurricanes again. I'm sorry, Shasa.'

'Yes,' Shasa whispered. 'So am I.'

David came to visit him again that evening. 'The CO has put you up for the DFC. You'll get it, for sure.'

'That's charming of him,' Shasa said. 'Bloody charming.' And they were silent for a while, then David spoke again.

'You saved my life, Shasa.'

'Oh shut up, Davie, don't be a bore.'

'They are flying you down to the coast tomorrow morning in the transport Dakota. You'll be in Cape Town for Christmas. Give Matty and the baby a kiss for me, you lucky sod.'

'I'd change places any day,' Shasa told him. 'But we'll give you one hell of a party when you come home.'

'Is there anything I can do for you – anything you need?' David asked as he stood up.

'As a matter of fact, there is. Do you think you could get your hands on a bottle of whisky for me, Davie?'

* * *

The commander of the submarine straightened up from the eye-piece of the telescope and nodded to Manfred De La Rey.

'Look, please!' he said, and Manfred took his place at the telescope, pressing his forehead against the rubber pad and staring into the lens.

They were lying two miles offshore and on the surface it was late evening. The sun was setting behind the land.

'Do you recognize the landmarks?' the U-boat commander asked in German

and Manfred did not answer immediately, for he found it difficult to speak. His emotions were too strong.

Five years, five long years since he had set eyes on this beloved coast, and his joy was abundant. He knew that he could never be truly happy anywhere but in his Africa.

However, the intervening years had not been unhappy. There had always been Heidi, and in this last year his son, Lothar, named after his own father. The two of them had formed the pivot of his existence. And there had also been his work – two tasks running side by side, each of them demanding and utterly fulfilling.

His law studies had culminated in a Master's degree in Roman Dutch Law and International Law at the University of Berlin.

There had also been his military preparations. Sometimes these had kept him from his new family for months at a time, but now he was a highly trained and dedicated operative of the German *Abwehr*. He had acquired unusual and diverse skills. He had become a radio operator, and an expert in explosives and small arms; he had made ten parachute jumps, five of these in darkness, and he could pilot a light aircraft; he was versed in cipher and coding, he was a deadly marksman with rifle or sidearms, an exponent of unarmed combat, a trained assassin, both body and mind honed to a razor's edge of preparedness. He had learned the art of persuasive public speaking and rhetoric, and had studied the political and military structures of South Africa until he knew all the vulnerable areas and how to exploit them. He was now ready in every way that he and his masters could foresee for the task that lay ahead of him. Not one man in a million, he knew, would ever have an opportunity such as he was being given – the opportunity to mould history and to turn the detestable order of the world upon its head. Greatness had been thrust upon him, and he knew himself equal to that challenge.

'Yes,' he replied in German to the U-boat commander, 'I recognize the landmarks.'

He had spent one happy, carefree summer holiday on this sparsely populated stretch of the south-eastern coast of Africa. Here Roelf Stander's family owned five thousand hectares, and five miles of this foreshore.

Manfred and Roelf had fished from that rocky headland, pulling the big silver kabeljou from the creaming green surf that broke over the black boulders. They had climbed that low range of hills to hunt the speckled bushbuck amongst the flowering ericas and magnificent blooms of the wild protea shrubs. In that quiet cove with its rind of smooth yellow sand they had swum naked, and afterwards lain on the beach to discuss the future and fantasize about their own particular roles in it. There below the hills, gleaming in the last rays of the sun, stood the whitewashed walls of the small holiday cottage in which they had lived.

'Yes,' he repeated. 'This is the rendezvous.'

'We will wait for the agreed time,' the U-boat commander said, and gave the order to lower the periscope.

Still two miles offshore, the submarine lay twenty metres below the surface, suspended in the dark waters with its engines stopped, while above it the sun sank below the horizon and night fell over the African mainland. Manfred went down the narrow passageway to the tiny cubicle he shared with two of the U-boat's junior officers and began his final preparations for landing.

In the weeks since they had left Bremerhaven, he had come to hate this

sinister craft. He hated the cramped quarters and the close intimate proximity of other men, he hated the motion and the ceaseless vibration of the engines. He had never become accustomed to the knowledge that he was locked in an iron box deep under the cold oceanic waters, and he hated the stink of diesel and oil and the reek of the other men trapped down here with him. He longed with all his soul for the clean night air in his lungs and the hot African sun on his face.

Quickly he stripped off the white rollneck jersey and the navy blue peajacket and dressed instead in the worn and shapeless clothing of a country Afrikaner, a *bywoner* or poor white squatter. He was still darkly tanned from his training in the mountains and he had allowed his hair to grow out over his collar and his beard to become thick and curly, adding many years to his age. He looked at himself now in the small mirror on the bulkhead above his bunk.

'They will never recognize me,' he said aloud. 'Not even my own family.'

He had dyed his hair and beard black, the same colour as his eyebrows, and his nose was thickened and twisted. It had never set properly after the American Cyrus Lomax had broken it in the Olympic final, and one eyebrow was lumpy and scarred. He looked entirely different from the young, clean-cut, blond athlete who had sailed from Africa five years before. He pulled the stained felt hat low over his eyes and nodded at his image with satisfaction, then turned from the mirror and went down on his knees to reach the equipment that had been stowed beneath his bunk.

It was packed in rubber waterproofed containers and sealed with tape. He checked off each numbered package on his list, and a German seaman carried them away and stacked them at the foot of the ladder in the submarine's conning tower.

Manfred checked his watch. There was just time for a quick meal and then he would be ready. The bosun called him from the galley, and with a mouth still full of bread and sausage, Manfred hurried to the U-boat's control room.

'There are lights ashore.' The captain stood up from the periscope and gestured Manfred to take his place.

It was fully dark on the surface and through the lens Manfred picked out immediately the three beacon fires, one on each horn of the headlands and one on the sheltered beach.

'That is the correct recognition signal, Captain.' He straightened up and nodded. 'We should surface now and make the reply.'

To the thunder and crackle of compressed air purging and diving tanks, the U-boat rose up like Leviathan through the dark depths and burst out through the surface.

While the submarine still wallowed in her own froth, the captain and Manfred climbed the ladder and went out onto the bridge. The night air was cool and sweet, and Manfred drew deep breaths of it as he peered through his binoculars at the black loom of the shore.

The captain gave a quiet order to the signals yeoman, and he worked the handle of the Addis lamp, clattering out quick beams of yellow light across the dark silver-flecked ocean, spelling out the Morse letters 'W S', the abbreviation of 'White Sword'. After a short pause one of the beacon fires on the headland was snuffed out, and a few minutes later the second fire was extinguished, leaving only the one on the beach still burning.

'That is the correct response,' Manfred grunted. 'Please have my equipment brought on deck, Captain.'

They waited almost half an hour until out of the darkness close at hand a voice hailed them.

'White Sword?'

'Come alongside,' Manfred called back in Afrikaans, and a small open fishing-boat crept towards them on its long oars.

Quickly Manfred shook hands with the U-boat captain and gave him the Nazi salute, '*Heil Hitler*!'

Then he scrambled down onto the lower deck. The moment the wooden hull of the fishing-boat touched, Manfred leapt lightly across and balanced easily on the central thwart.

The rower in the forward seat rose to greet him.

'Manie, is that you?'

'Roelf!' Manfred embraced him briefly. 'It's good to see you! Let's get my equipment aboard.'

The rubber canisters were swung across by the U-boat's deck crew and stowed in the bottom of the fishing-boat, and at once they pushed off. Manfred took the oar beside Roelf and they gave way swiftly, then rested on their oars to watch the black submarine shark below the surface and disappear in a rash of white water.

Once again they began pulling towards the shore, and Manfred asked softly, 'Who are the others?' He indicated the three other oarsmen with his chin.

'All our people – local farmers from the district. I've known them since I was a child. They are completely trustworthy.'

They did not speak again until they had run the boat in through the low surf to the beach, dragged it up the sand and hidden it amongst the salt bush.

'I will fetch the truck,' Roelf muttered, and a few minutes later the yellow headlights came down the rough track to the beach. Roelf parked the battered green four-tonner beside the fishing-boat.

The three farmers helped them transfer Manfred's equipment to the back of the truck and cover the canisters with bales of dried lucerne and a tattered old tarpaulin. Then they climbed up on top of the load while Manfred took the passenger seat in the cab.

'Tell me all the news of my family, first,' Manfred burst out. 'We have plenty of time for business later.'

'Uncle Tromp is just the same, What a sermon that man can preach! Sarie and I go every Sunday – '

'How is Sarah?' Manfred demanded. 'And the baby?'

'You are out of date,' Roelf laughed. 'Three babies now. Two boys and a little girl of three months. You'll meet them all soon.'

One at a time they dropped the other men off along the winding dirt road with a word of thanks and a quick handshake, until at last they were alone. A few miles further on they reached the main coastal road near the village of Riversdale, and turned westwards towards Cape Town two hundred miles away, and ran on through the night, stopping only to refuel the truck at the little town of Swellendam and to spell each other at the wheel of the truck.

Four hours later they crossed the mountains and went down the steep narrow pass to the wide littoral. They stopped again a few miles outside Stellenbosch, at one of the co-operative winery companies. Although it was three o'clock in the morning, the manager was waiting for them and he helped them unload the rubber canisters and carry them down into the cellar.

'This is Sakkie Van Vuuren,' Roelf introduced the manager. 'He is a good friend, and he has prepared a safe place for your equipment.'

He led them to the rear of the cellar, to the last row of wooden casks. These were massive oak containers each holding a thousand gallons of immature red wine, but the manager thumped the palm of his hand against one of them and when it gave out a hollow sound, he smiled.

'I did the work myself,' he said and opened the front of the cask. It was hinged like a door and the cask beyond was empty. 'Nobody will ever find the goods here.'

They packed the rubber canisters into the cask and closed the hinged lid. It was indistinguishable from any other of the massive wine-filled casks in the row.

'We will be ready to move when the time is ripe,' the winemaker told Manfred. 'When will it be?'

'Soon, my friend,' Manfred promised him. 'Very soon,' and he and Roelf drove on into the village of Stellenbosch.

'It's good to be home.'

'You will only stay here tonight, Manie,' Roelf told him. 'Even with your new black beard and broken nose, you are too well-known. You will be recognized.'

He parked the truck in the yard of a secondhand car dealer down near the railway tracks and left the key under the floor mat. Then the two of them walked the last mile, through the deserted streets to Roelf's home, a cottage in a row of small thatched cottages. Roelf let them in through the back door into the kitchen, and a familiar figure rose up from his seat at the kitchen table to greet them.

'Uncle Tromp!' Manfred cried. The old man held open his arms, and Manfred ran into his embrace.

'What a terrible ruffian you are with that beard,' Uncle Tromp laughed. 'And I see the American did a permanent job on your nose.'

Manfred looked over Uncle Tromp's shoulder and there was a woman standing in the doorway of the kitchen. That was what misled him – a woman, not a girl. Her face was marked by a kind of sad wisdom, and her expression was pinched and without joy.

'Sarah?' Manfred left Uncle Tromp and went towards her. 'How are you, my little sister?'

'I was never your little sister, Manfred,' she said. 'But I am very well, thank you.' Sarah made no effort to embrace him and Manfred was clearly disturbed by the coolness of her welcome.

'Are you happy, Sarah?'

'I have a fine man and three beautiful babies,' she said, and looked at Roelf.

'You will be hungry now,' she told him. 'Sit down. You can talk while I make your breakfast.'

The three men seated themselves at the kitchen table and every once in a while Manfred glanced surreptitiously at Sarah as she worked over the stove, and his expression was troubled, ridden by old memories and guilt. Then he gathered himself and concentrated once more on what the others were saying.

'The news is all good – the British smashed and broken at Dunkirk, France has fallen and the Netherlands. The German U-boats are winning the battle of the Atlantic and even the Italians are victorious in North Africa – '

'I did not know you were one of us, Uncle Tromp,' Manfred cut in on the discussion.

'Yes, my son. I am a patriot as you are. The *Ossewa Brandwag* is forty thousand strong now. Forty thousand picked men in positions of power and authority, while Jannie Smuts has sent one hundred and sixty thousand of the English-lovers with their little orange tabs on their shoulders out of the country. He has put himself at our mercy.'

'Our leaders know of your arrival, Manie,' Roelf told him. 'They know that you bring a message from the Führer himself, and they are eager to meet you.'

'Will you arrange a meeting,' Manfred asked, 'as soon as possible? There is much work to do. Glorious work to do.'

Sarah Stander stood quietly at the kitchen stove, breaking eggs into the frying pan, turning the chops under the grill. She did not look round or draw attention to herself, but she thought:

'You have come to bring sadness and suffering into my life again, Manfred De La Rey. With your every word and look and gesture you open the wounds I thought had healed. You have come to destroy what little life has left me. Roelf will follow you blindly into folly. You come to threaten my husband and my babies – ' And her hatred of him was made stronger and more venomous as it fed on the corpse of the love that he had murdered.

* * *

Manfred travelled alone. There was no control of personal movement, there were no roadblocks, police searches or demands for identification papers. South Africa was so far from the main war centres that there were not even significant shortages of consumer goods, apart from petrol rationing and a ban on the milling of white flour, therefore no need for ration books or other documentation existed.

Carrying a small valise, Manfred merely purchased a second-class railway ticket for Bloemfontein, the capital town of the Orange Free State province, and he shared a compartment with five other travellers on the five hundred mile journey.

Ironically, the meeting to subvert the elected government of the nation took place in the provincial government building at the foot of Artillery Hill. When Manfred entered the imposing administrator's office, he was reminded how wide was the influence of their secret organization.

The commander of the *OB* came to meet him at the door. He had changed little since he had administered the blood-oath to Manfred in that midnight torchlit ceremony. Still paunchy and craggy-featured, he was now dressed in a sombre double-breasted civilian suit. He greeted Manfred warmly, clasping his hand and patting his shoulder, smiling broadly.

'I have been expecting you, brother, but first let me congratulate you on your achievements since last we met, and the magnificent work you have accomplished so far.'

He led Manfred into the room and introduced him to the five other men seated at the long table.

'All of us have taken the blood-oath. You may speak freely,' he told Manfred who knew now that he was addressing the highest council of the brotherhood.

He sat at the bottom of the table facing the commander and gathered his thoughts for a moment before beginning. 'Gentlemen, I bring you personal greetings from the Führer of the German people, Adolf Hitler. He has asked me to assure you of the close friendship that has always existed between the Afrikaner and the German nation, and to tell you that he is ready to support us in every possible way in our struggle to win back what is rightfully ours, to regain for the Afrikaner the land that belongs to him by right of birth and conquest.' Manfred spoke forcefully and logically. He had prepared this address with the help of experts of the German propaganda department and had rehearsed it until his delivery was perfect; he could judge his success by the rapt expressions of the men listening to him.

'The Führer is fully aware that this country has been stripped of almost all men of military age who have sympathy with the Smuts government and the British. Almost one hundred and sixty thousand men have been sent north to serve beyond our borders. This makes the task easier.'

'Smuts has called in all weapons in private hands,' one of the men interrupted him. 'He had taken the sporting rifles and shotguns, even the memorial cannons from the town squares. There will be no rising without weapons.'

'You have seen to the centre of the problem,' Manfred agreed. 'To succeed we need money and weapons. We will get those.'

'The Germans will send them to us?'

'No,' Manfred shook his head. 'This has been considered and rejected. The distance is too great, the difficulty of landing great quantities of arms on an inhospitable coast is not acceptable and the ports are well guarded. However, immediately we have control of the ports, supplies of heavy arms will be rushed to us by U-boats of the German navy, and in return we will throw open our harbours to the German U-boats. We will deny the Cape route to the British.'

'Then where will we get the arms we need for the rising?'

'From Jannie Smuts,' Manfred told them, and they stirred uncomfortably and glanced at one another doubtfully.

'With your approval, naturally, I will recruit and train a small élite striking force of our *stormjagters*. We will raid the government arms and ammunition dumps and seize what we need – the same with money. We will take it from the banks.'

The enormity of the concept, the boldness and sweep of it, amazed them. They stared in silence and Manfred went on.

'We will act swiftly and ruthlessly, seize the arms and distribute them. Then at a given signal we will rise, forty thousand patriots, to seize all the reins of power, the police and the army, the communications system, the railways, the harbours. In all of these we have our people already in place. All of it will be done at the prearranged signal.'

'What will that signal be?' asked the commander of the *OB*.

'It will be something that will turn the entire country on its head – something staggering, but it is too early to speak of it. It is necessary only to say that the signal has been chosen and the man who will give the signal.' Manfred looked at him steadily, seriously. 'I will have that honour. I have trained for the task, and I will do it alone and unaided. After that it will only remain for you to take up the reins, to swing our support to the side of the victorious German army, and to lead our people to the greatness that has been denied them by our enemies.'

He was silent then as he studied their expressions, and he saw the patriotic fervour on their faces and the new light in their eyes.

'Gentlemen, do I have your approval to proceed?' he asked, and the commander looked at each of them in turn, and received a curt nod of the head.

He turned back to Manfred. 'You have our approval and our blessing. I will see that you have the support and assistance of every single member of the brotherhood.'

'Thank you, gentlemen,' Manfred said quietly. 'And now if I may give you the words of Adolf Hitler himself from the great book of *Mein Kampf*, "Almighty God, bless our arms when the time is ripe. Be just as Thou has always been. Judge now whether we be deserving of freedom. Lord, bless our battle."'

'Amen!' they cried, leaping to their feet and giving the *OB* salute of clenched fist across the chest. 'Amen!'

* * *

The green Jaguar was parked in the open, beside the road where it skirted the top of the cliff. The vehicle looked abandoned, as though it had stood here for days and weeks.

Blaine Malcomess parked his Bentley behind it and walked to the cliff's edge. He had never been here before, but Centaine had described the cove to him and how to find the pathway. He leaned out now and looked down the cliff. It was very steep but not sheer; he could make out the path zigzagging down three hundred feet to Smitswinkel Bay, and at the bottom he saw the roofs of three or four rude huts strung out along the curve of the bay, just as Centaine had described.

He shrugged out of his jacket and threw it onto the front seat of the Bentley. The climb down the pathway would be warm work. He locked the door of the car and set off down the cliff path. He had come, not only because Centaine had pleaded with him to do so, but because of his own affection and pride and sense of responsibility towards Shasa Courtney.

At various times in the past he had anticipated that Shasa would be either his stepson or his son-in-law. As he climbed down the pathway he felt again the deep regret – no, more than regret, the deep sorrow – that neither expectation had been fulfilled thus far.

He and Centaine had not married, and Isabella had been dead for almost three years now. He remembered how Centaine had fled from him on the night Isabella died, and how for many months afterwards she had avoided him, frustrating all his efforts to find her. Something terrible had happened that night at Isabella's deathbed. Even after they had been reconciled, Centaine would never talk about it, never even hint at what had taken place between her and the dying woman. He hated himself for having put Centaine in Isabella's power. He should never have trusted her, for the damage she had done had never healed. It had taken almost a year of patience and gentleness from Blaine before Centaine had recovered from it sufficiently to take up again the role of lover and protectress which she had so revelled in before.

However, she would not even discuss with him the subject of marriage, and became agitated and overwrought when he tried to insist. It was almost as if Isabella were still alive, as if she could from her long-cold grave assert some

malevolent power over them. There was nothing in life he wanted more than to have Centaine Courtney as his lawful wife, his wife in the eyes of God and all the world, but he was coming to doubt it would ever be so.

'Please Blaine, don't ask me now. I cannot – I just cannot talk about it. No, I can't tell you why. We have been so happy just the way we are for so many years. I can't take the chance of ruining that happiness.'

'I am asking you to be my wife. I'm asking you to confirm and cement our love, not to ruin it.'

'Please, Blaine. Leave it now. Not now.'

'When, Centaine, tell me when?'

'I don't know. I honestly don't know, my darling. I only know I love you so.'

Then there was Shasa and Tara. They were like two lost souls groping for each other in darkness. He knew how desperately they needed each other, he had recognized it from the very beginning, and how close they had come to linking hands. But always they failed to make that last vital contact, and drifted, pining, apart. There seemed to be no reason for it, other than pride and pigheadedness, and without each other they were diminishing, neither of them able to fulfil their great promise, to take full advantage of all the rare blessings that had been bestowed upon them at birth.

Two beautiful, talented young people, full of strength and energy, frittering it all away in a search for something that never existed, wasting it on impossible dreams or burning it up in despair and despondency.

'I cannot let it happen,' he told himself with determination. 'Even if they hate me for it, I have to prevent it.'

He reached the foot of the path and paused to look around. He did not need to rest, for although the descent had been arduous and although he was almost fifty years old, he was harder and fitter than most men fifteen years younger.

Smitswinkel Bay was enclosed by a crescent of tall cliffs; only its far end was open to the wider expanse of False Bay. Protected on all sides, the water was lake-calm and so clear he could follow the stems of the kelp plants down thirty feet to where they were anchored on the bottom. It was a delightful hidden place and he took a few moments longer to appreciate its tranquil beauty.

There were four shacks built mostly of driftwood, each of them widely separated from the others, perched upon the rocks above the narrow beach. Three were deserted, their windows boarded up. The last one in the line was the one he wanted, and he set off along the beach towards it.

As he drew closer he saw the windows were open, but the curtains, faded and rotted by salt air, were drawn. There were crayfish nets hanging over the railing of the stoep and a pair of oars and a cane fishing-rod propped against one wall. A dinghy was drawn up on the beach above the highwater mark.

Blaine climbed the short flight of stone steps and crossed the stoep to the front door. It was open and he stepped into the single room.

The small Devon stove on the far wall was cold, and a frying pan stood on it, greasy with congealed leftovers. Dirty plates and mugs cluttered the central table, and a column of black ants was climbing one leg to reach them. The wooden floor of the shack was unswept, gritty with beach sand. There were two bunks set against the side wall, opposite the window. The bar boards of the upper bunk were without a mattress, but in the lower bunk was a jumble of grey blankets and a hard coir mattress with a stained and torn cover. On top of it all lay Shasa Courtney.

It was a few minutes before noon and he was still asleep. An almost empty

bottle of whisky and a tumbler stood on the sandy floor within reach of Shasa's dangling arm. He wore only a pair of old rugby shorts and his body was burned to the colour of oiled mahogany, a dark beachcomber's tan; and the hair on his arms was sunbleached to gold, but on his chest it remained dark and curly. It was obvious that he had not shaved in many days and his hair was long and unkempt on the dirty pillow. Yet the deep tan covered all the more obvious signs of debauchery.

He slept quietly, no sign on his face of the turmoil which must have driven him from Weltevreden to this squalid shack. He was still in all respects but one a magnificent-looking young man – that was why the left eye was even more shocking. The top ridge of the eye-socket was depressed on the outside corner where the bone had shattered; the scar through his dark eyebrow was shiny white and ridged. The empty eye-socket was sunken, and the eyelids drooped apart, exposing wet red tissue in the gap between his thick dark lashes.

It was impossible to look on the hideous injury without feeling pity, and it took Blaine a few seconds to steel himself to what he had to do.

'Shasa!' He made his voice harsh. Shasa groaned softly and the lid of his empty eye twitched.

'Wake up, man.' Blaine went to the bunk and shook his shoulder. 'Wake up. We've got some talking to do.'

'Go away,' Shasa mumbled, not yet awake. 'Go away and leave me alone.'

'Wake up, damn you!'

Shasa's good eye flickered open and he peered up at Blaine blearily. His eye focused and his expression altered.

'What the hell are you doing here?' He rolled his head away, hiding the bad eye as he groped amongst the tangled bedclothes until he found a scrap of black cloth on a black elastic band. With his face still averted, he fitted the patch over the damaged eye and looped the band over his head before he turned back to look at Blaine again. The eye-patch gave him a piratical panache, and in some perverse way highlighted his good looks.

'Got to pump ship,' he blurted and tottered out onto the stoep.

While he was away Blaine dusted one of the stools and set it against the wall. He sat down on it, leaned back and lit one of his long black cheroots.

Shasa came back into the shack, pulling up the front of his rugby shorts, and sat down on the edge of the bunk, holding his head with both hands. 'My mouth tastes like a polecat pissed in it,' he muttered, and he reached down for the bottle between his feet and poured what remained of the whisky into the glass, licked the last drop from the neck and trundled the empty bottle across the floor in the general direction of the overflowing garbage bucket beside the stove.

He picked up the glass. 'Offer you one?' he asked, and Blaine shook his head. Shasa looked at him over the rim.

'That look on your face can mean only one of two things,' Shasa told him. 'Either you have just smelled a fart or you don't approve of me.'

'I take it the coarse language is a recent accomplishment, like your new drinking habits. I congratulate you on both. They suit your new image.'

'Bugger you, Blaine Malcomess!' Shasa retorted defiantly, and raised the glass to his lips. He swished the whisky through his teeth, rinsing his mouth with it. Then he swallowed and shuddered as the raw spirit went down his throat and he exhaled the fumes noisily.

'Mater sent you,' he said flatly.

'She told me where I could find you, but she didn't send me.'

'Same thing,' Shasa said, and held the glass to his lips, letting the last drop run onto his tongue. 'She wants me back, digging diamonds out of the dirt, picking grapes, growing cotton, pushing paper – damn it, she just doesn't understand.'

'She understands much more than you give her credit for.'

'Out there men are fighting. David and my other mates. They are in the sky – and I am down here in the dirt, a cripple, grovelling in the dirt.'

'You chose the dirt.' Blaine looked around the filthy shack scornfully. 'And you are doing the whining and grovelling.'

'You'd better get the hell out of here, sir,' Shasa told him. 'Before I lose my temper.'

'A pleasure, I assure you.' Blaine stood up. 'I misjudged you. I came to offer you a job, an important war job, but I can see that you are not man enough for it.' He crossed to the door of the cottage and paused. 'I was going to issue an invitation as well, an invitation to a party on Friday night. Tara is going to announce her engagement to marry Hubert Langley. I thought it might amuse you – but forget it.'

He went out with his long determined stride and after a few seconds Shasa followed him out onto the stoep and watched him climb the cliff path. Blaine never looked back once, and when he disappeared over the top, Shasa felt suddenly abandoned and bereft.

He had not until that moment realized how large Blaine Malcomess bulked in his life. How much he had relied on Blaine's good counsel and experience, both on and off the polo field.

'I wanted to be like him so much,' he said aloud. 'And now I never will be.' He touched the black patch over his eye.

'Why me?' He gave the eternal cry of the loser. 'Why me?' And he sank down onto the top step and stared out over the calm green waters to the entrance of the bay.

Slowly the full impact of Blaine's words sank home. He thought about the job he had offered, an important war job – then he thought about Tara and Hubert Langley. Tara – he saw her grey eyes and smoking red hair, and self-pity washed over him in a cold dark wave.

Listlessly he stood up and went into the shack. He opened the cupboard above the sink. There was a single bottle of Haig left. 'What happened to the others?' he asked himself. 'Mice?'

He cracked the cap on the bottle, and looked for a glass. They were all dirty, piled in the sink. He lifted the bottle to his lips, and the fumes made his eye smart. He lowered the bottle before he drank and stared at it. His stomach heaved and he was filled with sudden revulsion, both physical and emotional.

He tipped the bottle over the sink, and watched the golden liquid chug and spurt into the drainhole. When it was gone, once it was too late, his need for it returned strongly and he was seized by dismay. His throat felt parched and sore and the hand that held the empty bottle began to shake. The desire for oblivion ached in every joint of his bones, and his eye burned so that he had to blink it clear.

He hurled the bottle against the wall of the shack and ran out into the sunshine, down the steps to the beach. He stripped off the eye-patch and his rugby shorts and dived into the cold green water and struck out in a hard overarm crawl. By the time he reached the entrance to the cove, every muscle

ached and his breathing scorched his lungs. He turned and without slackening the tempo of his stroke headed back to the beach. As soon as his feet touched bottom he turned again, and swam out to the headland, back and forth he ploughed, hour after hour, until he was so exhausted that he could not lift an arm clear of the surface and he was forced to struggle back the last hundred yards in a painful side-stroke.

He crawled up the beach, fell face down on the wet sand and lay like a dead man. It was the middle of the afternoon before he had recovered the energy to push himself upright and limp up to the shack.

He stood in the doorway and looked around at the mess he had created. Then he took the broom from behind the door and went to work. It was late afternoon before he had finished. The only think he could do nothing about was the dirty bed linen. He bundled the soiled blankets with his dirty clothes for the dhobi wallah at Weltevreden to launder. Then he drew a kettle of fresh water from the rainwater tank beside the back door and heated it over the stove.

He shaved carefully, dressed in the cleanest shirt and slacks he could find and adjusted the patch over his eye. He locked the shack and hid the key; then, carrying the bundle of dirty laundry he climbed the pathway to the top. His Jaguar was dusty and streaked with sea salt. The battery was flat and he had to run it down the hill and start it on the fly.

Centaine was in her study, seated at her desk, poring over a pile of documents. She sprang to her feet when he came in and would have rushed to him, but with an obvious effort she restrained herself.

'Hello, *chéri*, you look so well. I was worried about you – it's been so long. Five weeks.'

The patch over his eye still horrified her. Every time she saw it she remembered Isabella Malcomess' last words to her:

'An eye for any eye, Centaine Courtney. Heed my words – an eye for an eye.'

As soon as she had herself under control again she went calmly to meet him and lifted her face for his kiss.

'I'm glad you are home again, *chéri*.'

'Blaime Malcomess has offered me a job, a war job. I'm thinking of taking it.'

'I am sure it is important,' Centaine nodded. 'I am happy for you. I can hold the fort here until you are ready to return.'

'I am sure you can, Mater,' he grinned wryly. 'After all you have been doing pretty well for the last twenty-two years – holding the fort.'

* * *

The long line of goods trucks drawn by a double coupling of steam locomotives climbed the last slope of the pass. On the steep gradient, the locomotives were sending bright silver columns of steam spurting from their valves, and the Hex river mountains echoed to the roar of their straining boilers.

With a final effort they crested the head of the pass and burst out onto the high plateau of the open karoo; gathering speed dramatically they thundered away across the flatlands and the line of closed trucks snaked after them.

Forty miles beyond the head of the pass the train slowed and then trundled

to a halt in the shunting yards of the intermediate railway junction of Touws river.

The relief crews were waiting in the stationmaster's office and they greeted the incoming crews with a little light banter and then climbed aboard to take their places on the footplates. The leading locomotive was uncoupled and shunted onto a side spur. It was no longer needed, the rest of the run, a thousand miles northwards to the goldfields of the Witwatersrand, was across comparatively flat land. The second locomotive would return down the mountain pass to link up with the next goods train and assist it up the steep gradients.

The incoming crews, carrying their lunch pails and overcoats, set off down the lane towards the row of railway cottages, relieved to be home in time for a hot bath and dinner. Only one of the drivers lingered on the platform and watched the goods train pull out of the siding, gathering speed swiftly as it headed northwards.

He counted the trucks as they passed him, verifying his previous count. Numbers twelve and thirteen were closed trucks, painted silver to distinguish them and to deflect the heat of the sun's rays. On the side of each was blazoned a crimson cross, and in letters six feet tall that ran the full length of each truck, the warning: 'EXPLOSIVES.' They had each been loaded at the Somerset West factory of African Explosives and Chemical Industries with twenty tons of gelignite consigned to the gold mines of the Anglo American Group.

As the guard's van passed him the driver sauntered into the stationmaster's office. The stationmaster was still at the far end of the platform, his pillbox cap on his furled flags of red and green under his arm. The driver lifted the telephone off its bracket on the wall and spun the handle.

'Central,' he said into the voice-piece, speaking in Afrikaans, 'give me Matjiesfontein eleven sixteen.'

He waited while the operator made the connection. 'You are through. Go ahead.' But the driver waited for the click of the operator going off the line before he said,

'Van Niekerk here.'

'This is White Sword.' The reply, though he had been expecting it, made the hair on the back of his neck prickle.

'She is running twenty-three minutes late. She left here two minutes ago. The trucks are numbers twelve and thirteen.'

'Well done.'

Manfred De La Rey replaced the telephone and checked his wrist-watch before he smiled at the two women who watched him apprehensively across the farmhouse kitchen.

'Thank you, *Mevrou*,' he addressed the older of the two. 'We are grateful for your help. No trouble will come to you out of this, I give you my word.'

'Trouble is an old acquaintance, *Meneer*,' the proud old woman replied. 'In ninety-nine the *rooinekke* burned my farm and killed my husband.'

Manfred had parked the motorcycle behind the barn. He started it and rode back down the track a mile or so until he joined the main road. He turned north, and a few miles further on he was riding parallel to the railway line. At the base of a rocky hill the lines and the road diverged. The railway tracks climbed the shoulder of the hill and then disappeared behind it.

Manfred stopped the motorcycle and checked that the road was clear, ahead and behind, then he turned off onto another farmtrack, and followed the railway

tracks around the back of the hill. Again he stopped, propped the bike on its foot rest, and checked the locale.

They were far enough from the widow's farmhouse not to attach suspicion to the old woman. The hill hid this section of the tracks from the main road, but the road was close enough to offer a swift escape route in either direction. The gradient would slow the approaching locomotive to almost walking pace. He had watched while other goods trains passed the spot.

He turned the cycle off the road, following the tracks of other wheels that had flattened the grass. In the first fold of the land, hidden in a cluster of thorn trees, the trucks were parked. Four of them – a three-tonner, two four-tonners and a big brown Bedford ten-tonner. Getting fuel rationing coupons to fill their tanks had been difficult.

It was a mere hundred paces to the railway line from where the trucks stood and his men were waiting beside them, resting, lying in the grass, but they scrambled up as the motorcycle bumped and puttered over the fold of ground and they crowded around him eagerly. Roelf Stander was at their head.

'She'll be here at nine-thirty.' Manfred told him. 'The trucks are twelve and thirteen. Work that out.'

One of his band was a railway man, and he made the calculations of distance between the locomotive and the explosive trucks. Roelf and Manfred left the others hidden and went out onto the line to mark out the distances. Manfred wanted to stop the goods train so that the two laden trucks were directly opposite the waiting vehicles in the clump of thorn trees.

They paced it out from this point and Manfred set the charges under the fish plates in a joint of the tracks. Then he and Roelf went back and laid the red warning flares, using the railwayman's calculations of speed and distance as a guide.

It was dark by the time they had finished, so they could proceed to the next step. They moved the men out into their positions. They were all young, picked for their size and physical strength. They were dressed in rough clothing of dark colours and armed with a motley collection of weapons that had survived the call-in by the Smuts government – shotguns and old Lee Enfields and Mannlichers from other long-ago wars. Only Roelf and Manfred were armed with modern German Lugers, part of the contents of the rubber canisters from the U-boat.

Manfred took charge of the smaller group while Roelf waited with the work party that would unload the trucks, and they settled down in darkness to wait.

Manfred heard it first, the distant susurration in the night, still far off, and he roused them with three sharp blasts on his whistle. Then he armed the battery box and connected the wires to the brass screw terminals. The huge Cyclops eye of the approaching locomotive glared across the plain below the hill. The waiting men adjusted their face masks and lay hidden in the grassy ditch beside the railway line.

The beat of the locomotive engine slowed and became deeper as it ran onto the slope. It climbed laboriously, running past the first group of waiting men, and then it hit the first of the warning flares. The flare ignited with a sharp crack and lit the veld for fifty yards around with red flickering light.

Manfred heard the metallic squeal of brakes, and he relaxed slightly. The driver was acting reflexively, it would not be necessary to blow out the tracks. The second flare ignited, shooting out long tongues of red flame from under the

driving wheels, but by now the locomotive was pulling up sharply, brakes grinding metal on metal and steam flying from the emergency vacuum tubes in screaming white jets.

While it was still moving, Manfred leapt onto the footplates, and thrust the Luger into the astonished faces of the driver and his fireman.

'Shut her down! Switch off the headlight!' he yelled through his mask. 'Then get down from the cab!'

With the brakes locked, the railwaymen scrambled down and lifted their hands high. They were immediately searched and trussed up. Manfred ran back down the train, and by the time he reached the explosives trucks, Roelf's men had already forced the doors and the wooden cases of gelignite were being handed along a human chain to be loaded into the first lorry.

'What about the guard at the rear of the train?' Manfred asked.

'We have got him tied up,' Roelf answered, and Manfred ran back to the head of the train. Swiftly he defused and lifted the explosive charges he had laid, delighted that it had not been necessary to fire them. By the time he got back, the first lorry was fully loaded with cases of explosives.

'Take her away!' Roelf yelled, and one of his men climbed into the cab, started the engine and with lights extinguished, drove it away.

The second vehicle reversed up to the explosives trucks and they began to load it.

Manfred checked his watch. 'Twelve minutes,' he muttered. They were ahead of schedule.

The driver, the guard and the fireman were tied securely and locked in the guard's van while the loading of explosives went on smoothly and swiftly.

'All finished,' Roelf shouted 'We can't load any more.'

'Forty-eight minutes,' Manfred told him. 'Well done. All right, move out everybody!'

'What about you?'

'Go!' Manfred ordered. 'I'll look after myself.'

He watched the Bedford truck pull away and waited until it reached the farm road and switched on its headlights. The sound of its engine dwindled. He was alone. If Roelf or the others had known what he intended to do now, they might have baulked and tried to prevent it.

Manfred climbed into the open door of the explosives truck. It was half filled with the white wooden cases. They had only been able to carry away a part of the load, while the second truck had not been touched. There were still at least twenty-five tons of explosive remaining on board.

He set the timing device with a delay of fifteen minutes and placed it in the gap between the stacked cases and the steel side of the truck, pushing it far back where it could not be readily seen. Then he jumped down to the ground and ran forward to the locomotive. None of the three men locked in the caboose of the guard's van were members of the *Ossewa Brandwag*. Left alive they would be certain to give damaging evidence to the police. He felt little pity for them. They were casualties of war.

He climbed into the cab of the locomotive and disengaged the wheel brakes; then he opened the throttle gradually. The wheels spun, then found purchase and the train jolted forward with the couplings clanking. It began to pull away jerkily up the slope.

Manfred eased the throttle open to the halfway notch and locked it there. Then he jumped down to the ground, and watched the trucks rumble past

where he stood. They were gaining speed gradually. When the caboose passed, he walked back down the tracks to the clump of thorn trees, and sat astride the seat of the motorcycle.

He waited impatiently, glancing at his watch every few minutes.

The explosion, when at last it came, was a brief orange flare, like sheet lightning over the northern horizon, followed after a long pause by the puff of the shockwave against his face and a sound like distant surf breaking on a rocky shore.

Manfred kick-started the motorcycle and drove southwards into the night.

It was a good beginning, he thought, but there was so much still to do.

* * *

Blaine looked up as Shasa entered his office and hesitated in the doorway. He was neatly dressed in airforce uniform, medal ribbons on his chest, DFC and Africa Star, and the badges of rank on his shoulders.

'Morning, Shasa,' Blaine nodded bleakly. 'Ten o'clock. May I offer you a whisky?'

Shasa winced. 'I came to apologize for my behaviour the other day, sir. It was inexcusable.'

'Sit down.' Blaine pointed at the buttoned leather armchair against the bookcase. 'We all act like blithering idiots at some time in our lives. The trick is to know when you are doing it. Apology accepted.'

Shasa sat down and crossed his legs, then uncrossed them. 'You mentioned a job, sir?'

Blaine nodded and stood up. He moved to the window and stood staring down into the gardens. An old woman was feeding the pigeons from a paper bag. He watched her as he made his final decision. Was he letting his concern for Centaine Courtney and her son cloud his sense of duty? What he had in mind was critical to the welfare of the state. Was Shasa too young and inexperienced for the task? he wondered. But he had gone over this many times already, and he turned back to his desk.

He picked up a plain unmarked black folder. 'This is highly classified,' he said as he weighed the folder in his right hand. 'A most secret and sensitive report and appreciation.' He handed it to Shasa. 'It is not to leave this office. Read it here. I have a meeting with Field Marshal Smuts.' He pulled back his sleeve and glanced at his watch. 'I will be back in an hour. We'll talk again then.'

He was longer than an hour, and when he returned Shasa was still reading. He looked up at Blaine from the armchair with the open folder in his hands, and his expression was troubled and grave.

'What do you make of it?' Blaine asked.

'Of course, I have heard of the *OB*,' Shasa replied. 'But I had no idea it was anything like this. It's a secret army, sir, right in our midst. If it were ever to be fully mobilized against us – ' he shook his head, trying to find the words. 'A revolution, a civil war, while most of our own fighting men are up north.'

'They have begun to move,' Blaine said softly. 'Until now they have been procrastinating, in typical Afrikaner style, squabbling amongst themselves, but

something has happened recently to give them new purpose – ' he broke off, thought for a moment, then went on. 'It goes without saying, Shasa, that nothing we discuss must be repeated to anybody, not even closest family.'

'Of course, sir.' Shasa looked aggrieved.

'You read about the explosion of a dynamite train on the Touws river line two weeks ago?'

'Yes, sir, a frightful accident. The driver and his crew went up with it.'

'We have new evidence. We don't believe it was an accident. The crew were all in the guard's van, and there are indications that at least one of them was bound hand and foot. We believe that a large quantity of explosives was hijacked from the train, and afterwards the remainder was detonated to cover the theft.'

Shasa whistled softly.

'I believe this was merely a beginning. I believe that a new phase has begun and that it is going to escalate swiftly from now onwards. As I said, something has happened to trigger it – we have to find out what it is and crush it.'

'How can I help, sir?'

'This thing is big – nationwide. I have to keep close contact with the police chiefs of each of the various provinces together with military intelligence. The entire operation must be closely co-ordinated. I need a personal assistant, a liaison officer. I'm offering you the job.'

'I'm honoured, sir, but I can't see why you have chosen me. There must be dozens of other better qualified – '

'We know each other well, Shasa,' Blaine interrupted him. 'We have worked together over many years. We make a good team. I trust you. I know you have both brains and guts. I don't need a policeman. I need someone who understands my thinking and who I know will follow my orders implicitly.' Suddenly Blaine grinned. 'Besides which, you need a job. Am I right?'

'You are right, sir. Thank you.'

'You are on convalescent leave at the moment, but I will have you seconded from the airforce to the Department of the Interior immediately. You will keep your rank and pay as squadron leader, but you will report directly to me from now on.'

'I understand, sir.'

'Shasa, have you flown since you lost your eye?' He came right out and spoke about the eye without evasion. Nobody, not even Mater, had done that. Shasa's regard for him was reinforced.

'No, sir,' he said.

'Pity. You may be required to move around the country pretty damned quickly.' He watched Shasa's face, saw his jaw clench determinedly.

'It's only a matter of judging distance accurately,' Shasa muttered. 'Just practice.' Blaine felt a glow of gratification.

'Try hitting a polo ball again,' he suggested off-handedly. 'Good practice in developing judgement – but let's discuss more serious business now. The police officer in overall charge of the investigation is Chief Inspector Louis Nel, here at the Cape Town Central Station. I'll introduce you. He's a first-rate chap, you'll like him.'

They talked and planned for another hour before Blaine dismissed him. 'That's enough for you to get on with. Report back to me here at eight-thirty tomorrow morning.' But when Shasa reached the door he stopped him.

'By the way, Shasa, Friday night. The invitation is still open. Eight o'clock. Black tie or mess kit. Try and make it, won't you?'

* * *

Sarah Stander lay alone in the brass-framed bed in the darkness. The older children were sleeping in the next room. The baby in the cot beside her snuffled contentedly in her sleep.

The town hall clock struck four o'clock. She had listened to it chime every hour since midnight. She thought she would go through to the other room to make sure the children were covered – little Petrus always kicked off his blankets – but at that moment she heard the kitchen door open stealthily and she went rigid and held her breath to listen.

She heard Roelf come through and begin undressing in the bathroom, the double thump-thump as he dropped his boots, then a little later the bedroom door creaked and the bed tipped under his weight. She pretended to be sleeping. It was the first time he had ever stayed out this late. He had changed so much since Manfred had returned.

She lay unsleeping in the darkness and thought, 'He is the bringer of trouble. He will destroy us all. I hate you, Manfred De La Rey.'

Beside her she knew Roelf was not sleeping either. He was restless and strung up. The hours passed slowly, and she forced herself to lie still. Then the baby whimpered and she took her into the bed and gave her one of her breasts. Sarah's milk had always been strong and good, and the baby drank and burped and dropped back to sleep. She returned her to the cot, and the moment she slipped back under the sheet Roelf reached for her. Neither of them spoke, and she steeled herself to accept him. She hated this. It was never like it had been on those well-remembered occasions with Manfred. However, tonight Roelf was different. He mounted her quickly, almost brutally, and ended swiftly with a hoarse wild cry and he fell off her into a deep sleep. She lay and listened to him snore.

At breakfast she asked him quietly, 'Where were you last night?'

Instantly he was angry. 'Hold your mouth, woman,' he shouted at her, using the word *bek*, the mouth of an animal not a human being. 'You are not my keeper.'

'You are involved in some dangerous foolishness.' She ignored the warning. 'You have three little ones, Roelf. You cannot afford stupidity – '

'Enough, woman!' he yelled at her. 'This is man's business. You keep out of it.'

Without another word he left for the university, where he was a lecturer in the law faculty. She knew that in ten years he could have the chair, if only he didn't get into trouble before that.

After she had cleaned the house and made the beds, she put the children into the big double pram and pushed them down the sidewalk towards the centre of the village. She stopped once to talk with one of the other university wives, and again to buy sugar suckers for the two big children. Then, as she was paying for the candy, she noticed the headlines of the newspapers piled on the counter.

'I'll take a *Burger* as well.' She crossed the road and sat on a park bench while

she read the story of the explosion of the goods train somewhere in the karoo. Then she folded the paper neatly and sat thinking.

Roelf had left after lunch the previous day. The explosion had occurred at a little before ten-thirty p.m. She worked out times and distances, and slowly a cold crippling dismay made her belly cramp. She put the children back in the pram and crossed to the post office. She parked the pram beside the glass telephone booth where she could keep an eye on it.

'Central, please give me the main police station in Cape Town.'

'Hold the line.'

Suddenly the enormity of what she was about to do broke in upon her. How could she turn Manfred De La Rey over to the police without betraying her own husband to them at the same time – and yet she knew it was her duty to stop Roelf doing these terrible things that must lead to disaster. It was her duty to her husband and to her babies.

'This is Cape Town central police station. May I help you?'

'Yes,' Sarah stuttered, and then, 'No, I'm sorry. It doesn't matter. It isn't important.' She hung up, ran out of the booth and wheeled the pram determinedly back towards the cottage. She sat at the kitchen table and wept softly, bewildered and alone and uncertain. Then after a while she wiped her eyes on her apron and made herself a cup of coffee.

* * *

Shasa parked the Jaguar across the road from Blaine Malcomess' home, but he did not get out at once. He sat and considered what he was about to attempt.

'Probably make an idiot of myself again,' he thought, and tilted the rearview mirror so that he could see himself in it. He ran a comb through his hair and adjusted the eye-patch carefully. Then he climbed out.

Vehicles were parked bumper to bumper down both sides of Newlands Avenue. It was a big party, two or three hundred guests, but then Blaine Malcomess was a big man and his daughter's engagement an important event.

Shasa crossed the road. The front doors were wide open, but still it was difficult to get into the house. Even the lobby was crowded, and the party was in full swing. A coloured band was belting out 'The Lambeth Walk' and Shasa could see into the lounge where the dancers were prancing around merrily. He pushed his way through to the bar. Even Blaine Malcomess couldn't offer whisky, it just wasn't obtainable any longer. Nowadays it was considered patriotic to drink Cape brandy, but Shasa ordered a ginger ale.

'My drinking days have come and gone,' he thought wryly and, glass in hand, eased his way through the packed rooms, shaking hands with old friends, kissing the cheeks of the women, many of whom he had at one time or another kissed with more purpose.

'So good to see you back, Shasa.' They tried not to notice the black eye-patch, and after a few seconds he moved on, searching for her.

She was in the dining-room with the coloured chef and two maids, supervising the final touches to the elaborate buffet dinner.

She looked up and saw him and froze. She was wearing a filmy light evening dress the colour of ash of roses, and her hair was down to her shoulders. He

had forgotten how her eyes could shine like mother-of-pearl, grey mother-of-pearl.

She made a gesture dismissing the servants, and he went slowly to meet her.

'Hello, Tara, I'm back,' he said.

'Yes, I heard. You've been back five weeks. I thought you might – ', she stopped and studied his face. 'I heard you were decorated,' she touched the ribbon on his chest. 'And that you were wounded.'

She studied his face frankly, not avoiding looking at his left eye. Then she smiled. 'It makes you look very dashing.'

'It doesn't make me feel dashing.'

'I can sense that,' she nodded. 'You have changed.'

'Do you think so?'

'Yes, you aren't so – ' she shook her head, irritated that she could not find the precise word. 'Not so brash, so cocksure.'

'I want to talk to you,' he said. 'Seriously.'

'All right,' she nodded. 'What is it?'

'Not here,' he said. 'Not with all these people.'

'Tomorrow?'

'Tomorrow will be too late. Come with me now.'

'Shasa, are you mad? This is my party – my engagement party.'

'I'll bring the Jag around to the tradesmen's entrance,' he said. 'You'll need a wrap, it's cold out.'

He parked the Jag close in against the wall. This was where they used to conduct those long lingering farewells. He switched off the headlights. He knew she would not come, but nevertheless, he waited.

His surprise was genuine, his relief intense when she pulled open the door and slid into the passenger's seat. She had changed into slacks and a rollneck sweater. She wasn't going back to the party.

'Drive!' she said. 'Get away from here.'

They were silent for a while, and he glanced at her every time a street lamp lit the interior. She was looking straight ahead, smiling faintly, and at last she spoke.

'You never needed anything or anyone before. That was the one thing I couldn't stand about you.'

He did not reply.

'I think you need me now. I sensed it the very moment I saw you again. You truly need me at last.'

He was silent, words seemed superfluous. Instead he reached across and took her hand.

'I'm ready for you now, Shasa,' she said. 'Take me somewhere we can be alone, entirely alone.'

There was enough moon to light the pathway. She clung to him for support and they laughed breathlessly with excitement and stopped halfway down the cliff to kiss.

He let them into the shack and lit the paraffin lamp. With relief Shasa saw that the servants from Weltevreden had followed his orders. There was fresh linen on the bunk, and the floor had been polished.

Tara stood in the centre of the floor, her hands clasped protectively in front of her, her eyes huge and luminous in the lamplight, and she began to tremble when he took her in his arms.

'Shasa, please be gentle,' she whispered. 'I'm so scared.'

He was patient and very gentle, but she had no yardstick by which to recognize how immensely skilled and certain he was. She only knew that he seemed to sense each nuance of change in her feelings, anticipating each response of her body so that she felt no shame at her nakedness, and all her other fears and doubts dissolved swiftly under his tender hands and soft loving lips. At last she found herself running ahead of him, learning swiftly to guide and encourage him with subtle little movements and small gasps and cries of approval.

So that at the end she gazed up at him with wonder, and whispered, huskily, 'I never thought – I never dreamed it would be like that. Oh, Shasa, I'm so glad you came back to me.'

* * *

The Fordsburg branch of the Standard Bank serviced all the gold mines in the Central Rand complex. All the wages of the tens of thousands of weekly paid black mine workers were drawn from this branch and the senior accountant was a member of the *OB*.

His name was Willem De Kok, a small pasty-faced runt of a man with myopic misty eyes behind thick lenses, but his looks were deceptive. Within a few minutes of their meeting Manfred De La Rey found he had a quick mind, a complete dedication to the cause and almost too much courage for his small body.

'The money comes in on Thursday afternoon, between five and six o'clock. They use an armoured car and there is a police escort on motorcycles. This isn't the time to do it. There would almost certainly be shooting.'

'I understand,' Manfred nodded. 'Before you go on, please tell us how much money is usually transferred.'

'Between fifty thousand and seventy thousand pounds – except on the last Thursday of each month, when we make provision for the monthly paid workers on the mine properties. Then it will be closer to a hundred thousand. In addition there is always our ordinary cash float of approximately twenty-five thousand.'

They were gathered in the home of one of the mine officials of the Crown Deep gold mines. The same man had recruited the local *stormjagters* for the operation. He was a big red-faced man named Lourens, with the look of a heavy drinker. Manfred was not entirely happy with him; although so far he had found no real cause for his mistrust, he felt the man would be unreliable under stress.

'Thank you, Meneer De Kok, please go on.'

'The bank manager, Mr Cartwright, opens the back door of the building and the money is brought in. Of course, at this time in the afternoon the bank is closed to normal business. Mr Cartwright and I, together with our two senior tellers, count the money and issue a receipt. It is then deposited in the vault and locked up for the night. I have one key and half of the combination. Mr Cartwright keeps the other key and has the other half of the combination.'

'That would be the time,' Manfred anticipated. 'After the police escort has left, but before the vault is locked.'

'That is a possibility,' De Kok nodded. 'However, at that time it will still be

light. Many people on the streets. Mr Cartwright is a difficult man – many things could go wrong. Man I tell you how I would arrange it, if I were in command?'

'Thank you, Meneer De Kok. I'm glad of your assistance.'

* * *

It was ten minutes before midnight when Mr Peter Cartwright left the Freemason hall at the end of the meeting. He was the master of the lodge and he was still wearing his apron over his dinner jacket. He always parked his Morris in the lane behind the hall, but tonight as he sat in the driver's seat and fumbled with the ignition key, something hard was pressed into the back of his neck and a cold voice said quietly, 'This is a pistol, Mr Cartwright. If you do not do exactly as you are told, you will be shot in the back of the head. Drive to the bank, please.'

Terrified for his life and following the instructions of the two masked men in the back seat of the Morris, Peter Cartwright drove to the bank building and parked the Morris near the back door. There had been a spate of bank robberies over the last few months, at least four on the Witwatersrand and during one of them a bank guard had been shot dead. Cartwright was in no doubt as to the danger of his position or the ruthlessness of his captors

As soon as he climbed out of the Morris, they closed on each side of him, pinning his arms and hustling him to the back door of the bank. One of them tapped upon it with the butt of his pistol and to Cartwright's astonishment it opened immediately. Only when he was inside did he realize how the robbers had gained access. His senior accountant Willem De Kok was already there, in pyjamas and dressing-gown, his hair tousled and his face slack and ashen with terror. He had obviously been dragged from his bed.

'I'm sorry, Mr Cartwright,' he blubbered. 'They forced me.'

'Pull yourself together, man,' Cartwright snapped at him, his own fear making him brusque – then his expression changed as he saw the two women: De Kok's fat little wife and his own beloved Mary in hair curlers and pink full-length dressing gown with artificial pink roses down the front.

'Peter,' she wailed. 'Oh Peter, don't let them do anything.'

'Stop that, Mary. Don't let them see you like that.'

Cartwright looked around at his captors. There were six of them, including the two who had waylaid him, but his training in character judgement enabled him to pick out the leader almost immediately, a tall, powerfully built man with a dense black beard curling out from under his cloth face-mask, and above the mask a pair of strangely pale eyes, like those of one of the big predatory cats. His fear turned to real terror when he looked into those yellow eyes, for he sensed that there was no compassion in them.

'Open the vault,' the man said. His English was heavily accented.

'I don't have the key,' Cartwright said, and the man with yellow eyes seized Mary Cartwright by the wrist and forced her to her knees.

'You wouldn't dare,' Cartwright blustered, and the man placed the muzzle of his pistol to Mary's temple.

'My wife is going to have a baby,' Cartwright said.

'Then you will want to spare her any further unpleasantness.'

'Open it for them, Peter. Let them have it. It's not our money,' Mary screamed. 'It's the bank's. Give it to them.' And she began to urinate in little spurts that soaked through the skirts of her dressing-gown.

Cartwright went to the green Chatwood steel door of the vault and drew his watch chain from his fob pocket with the key dangling on the end of it. Anger and humiliation seethed in him as he tumbled the combination and turned the key. He stood back while De Kok came forward to do the same. Then, while all their attention was on the vault door as it swung open, he glanced across at his desk. He kept the pistol in the top right-hand drawer. It was a .455 service Webley and there was always a round under the hammer. By now his outrage at the treatment of his wife outweighed his terror.

'Get the money!' the leader with the pale eyes ordered and three of the robbers, carrying canvas kit bags, hurried into the vault.

'My wife,' Cartwright said, 'I must see to her.' Nobody interfered as he lifted her to her feet and helped her to the desk. Tenderly he settled her into the chair, keeping up a flow of reassurance that covered the soft scrape as he opened the drawer.

He lifted the pistol and slipped it into the pocket of his masonic apron.

Then he backed away, leaving his wife at the desk. He had both hands raised to shoulder level in an attitude of surrender as he rejoined De Kok against the far wall. Both women were out of the line of his fire, but he waited until the three robbers re-emerged from the vault, each of them lugging a kitbag stuffed with wads of banknotes. Again all attention was on those bulging canvas bags, and Cartwright reached into the pocket of his white leather apron, brought out the pistol and his first shot crashed across the room in a long spurt of blue gunsmoke. He kept firing as the Luger bullets smashed into his body, and he was flung back against the wall. He fired until the hammer of the Webley snapped down on a spent cartridge, but his last bullet had gone into the concrete floor between his feet, and he was dead as he slumped down the bullet-pocked wall and huddled at the foot of it, with his blood puddling under him.

SHOOT-OUT AT RAND BANK
TWO DEAD
ROBBERY LINKED TO OB

The letters *OB* caught Sarah Stander's eye on the placard outside the news-stand. She went in and bought candy for the children, as she always did, and then, as an apparent afterthought, she took a copy of the newspaper.

She crossed to the park and while the two toddlers romped on the lawn and she absently rocked the pram with her foot to keep the baby quiet, she read the front-page article avidly.

Mr Peter Cartwright, the manager of a bank in Fordsburg, was last night shot dead while attempting to prevent a robbery at the bank's premises. One of the robbers was also shot dead, while a second man was seriously wounded and taken into custody by the police.

First estimates are that the four remaining robbers fled with cash in excess of £100,000.

A police spokesman said this morning that preliminary interrogation of the wounded robber had established definite involvement by members of the *Ossewa Brandwag* in the outrage.

The Minister of the Interior, Colonel Blaine Malcomess, announced from his office in the House of Parliament in Cape Town that he had ordered an enquiry into the subversive activities of the *OB* and that any member of the public with information to offer should contact the nearest police

station or telephone the following numbers: Johannesburg 78114, Cape Town 42444. The minister gave the assurance that all information would be treated in the strictest confidence.

She sat for almost an hour, trying to reach a decision, torn between loyalty to her family and her patriotic duty to her own people. She was confused, terribly confused. Was it right to blow up trains and rob banks and kill innocent people in the name of freedom and justice? Would she be a traitoress if she tried to save her husband and her babies? And what about those other innocents who were certain to die if Manfred De La Rey were allowed to continue? She could readily imagine the strife and chaos that would result if the entire country were to be plunged into civil war. She looked at the newspaper again and memorized the telephone number.

She stood up, called the children and wheeled the pram across the road. As she reached the far sidewalk and started towards the post office, she noticed old Mr Oberholster, the postmaster, watching her from the window of his office. She knew that he was one of them, she had seen him in *OB* uniform when he came to the cottage to pick Roelf up for one of their meetings.

Immediately she felt panicky with guilt. All telephone calls went through the post office exchange. Oberholster might easily listen in on her conversation, or the operator might recognize her voice. She turned away and pushed the pram down towards the butcher as though that had originally been her intention. She bought two pounds of pork chops, Roelf's favourite dinner, and hurried back to the cottage, eager to be off the street, to be alone so she could think.

As she let herself in the kitchen she heard men's voices in the front room that Roelf used as a study. He was back early from the university today, and then her pulse quickened as she heard Manfred's voice. She felt guilty and disloyal that he could still have that effect upon her. Manfred had not been to the cottage for almost three weeks, and she realized that she had missed him and thought about him almost every day with feelings that oscillated from bitter hatred and resentment to tremulous physical arousal.

She began to prepare dinner for Roelf and the children, but the men's voices carried quite clearly from the front room. Occasionally Sarah paused to listen, and once she heard Manie say, 'While I was in Jo'burg – ' So he had been in Johannesburg. The bank robbery had taken place the night before last – time enough since then for him to come down by road or on the mail train. She thought about the two men who had been killed. She had read in the paper that the bank manager had a pregnant wife and two small children. She wondered how the woman felt now, with her husband gone, and three little ones to care for.

Then she was distracted by the men's voices again, and she paused to listen. What she heard filled her with foreboding.

'Where will this thing end?' she brooded. 'Oh I wish they would stop. I wish Manie would go away and leave us alone – ' But the thought of that filled her with a sense of hopelessness.

* * *

Shasa flew down alone from Witwatersrand in the Rapide and landed at Youngsfield after dark. He drove directly from the airfield to Blaine's home in Newlands Avenue.

Tara opened the door to him, her face lighting when she realized it was him. 'Oh, darling, I missed you!' They kissed rapturously until Blaine's voice made them start apart.

'Look here, Shasa, I don't like to interrupt anything important, but when you can spare a moment I'd like to hear your report.'

Tara was blushing furiously. 'Daddy, you were spying on us!'

'Public display, my dear. No spying necessary. Come along, Shasa.' He led the way to his study and waved Shasa to a chair.

'Drink?'

'I'd like a ginger ale, sir.'

'How are the mighty fallen!' Blaine poured a little of his hoarded whisky for himself and handed Shasa the ginger ale. 'Now what is it that you couldn't talk about on the telephone?'

'We just might have had a bit of luck at last, sir.' On Blaine's orders Shasa had flown up to Johannesburg as soon as the Fordsburg bank robbery had been linked to the *Ossewa Brandwag*. He had been at Marshall Square, the headquarters of the CID, while the captured bank robber was being interrogated. 'As you know, the fellow is an official on the Crown Mines. Thys Lourens is his name, and sure enough he was on our list of known *OB* members. Not one of the big fish, however, but quite a formidable-looking chap, although I'd expect him to be a bit of a boozer. I told the police inspector that you wanted answers – '

'No rough stuff.' Blaine frowned.

'No, sir. It wasn't necessary. Lourens wasn't as tough as he looked. We only had to point out that the penalty for armed robbery and accessory to murder was the gallows, but that we were prepared to do a deal and he started to gush. I gave you most of what he told us when I telephoned you this morning.'

'Yes. Go on.'

'Then he gave us the names of the other men involved in the robbery, that is, three of them. We were able to make the arrests before I left Johannesburg. However, the leader of the gang was a man he had only met three days before the robbery. He did not know his name, or where we could find him.'

'Did he give you a description?'

'Yes. Big man, black hair and beard, crooked nose, scar over one eye – a pretty detailed description, but he gave us something else which may be vital.'

'What is that?'

'A code name. The leader is known only as *Die Wit Swaard*, the White Sword, and they were ordered to co-operate with him from the very top level of the *stormjagters*.'

'White Sword,' Blaine mused. 'Sounds like something out of *Boys' Own Paper*.'

'Unfortunately not so childish,' Shasa went on. 'I impressed upon the inspector in charge that the code name and the description must be withheld until he had orders from you personally.'

'Good.' Blaine sipped his drink, pleased that his trust in Shasa Courtney had been so soon vindicated. 'White Sword – I wonder if this is the trigger we have been looking for, the catalyst that has at last brought the *OB* to the point of action.'

'It could very well be, sir. All the arrested members of the gang are obviously very much in awe of the man. He was clearly the force behind the entire thing, and he has disappeared completely. There is no trace of the missing money – incidentally, we have established that it is over one hundred and twenty-seven thousand pounds.'

'A tidy sum,' Blaine murmured, 'and we must presume that it has gone into the war chest of the *OB*, probably along with the gelignite from the railway hijacking.'

'As far as this code name goes, sir, I would like to suggest that we continue to keep it from the press and everybody not directly concerned with the investigation.'

'I agree. However, let me hear your reasons – see if they are the same as mine.'

'Firstly, we don't want to alert the quarry. We don't want him to know that we are on his track.'

Blaine nodded. 'Quite so.'

'The other reason is that it will confirm the reliability of any informant who uses the code name.'

'I don't follow you,' Blaine frowned.

'Your appeal to the public for assistance has resulted in a flood of telephone calls, but unfortunately most of them are bogus. If we let the code name become general knowledge, they'll all be using it.'

'I see. Use of the code name will establish the callers' credentials.'

'That's it, sir.'

'All right then, we'll keep it under the hat for the time being. Is there anything else?'

'Not at present.'

'Then let me tell you what has happened here while you were away. I have met the prime minister and we have decided to declare the *OB* a political organization. All civil servants, including the police and the army, will be obliged to resign their membership immediately.'

'That won't alter their sympathies,' Shasa pointed out.

'Of course not,' Blaine agreed. 'We will still have something like forty or fifty per cent of the country against us and for Nazi Germany.'

'It can't go on like this, sir. You and the *Ou Baas* will have to force a showdown.'

'Yes, we know that. As soon as our investigations are complete, as soon as we have a pretty comprehensive list of the ringleaders, we will swoop.'

'Arrest them?' Shasa was startled.

'Yes. They will be interned for the duration of the war as enemies of the state.'

Shasa whistled softly. 'Pretty drastic, sir. That could lead to real trouble.'

'That is why we have to scoop them all in the net at one time – we cannot afford to miss any of them.' Blaine stood up. 'I can see you are exhausted, Shasa, and I am sure there are a few things that Mademoiselle Tara has to say to you. I'll expect you at my office at eight-thirty sharp tomorrow morning.' They moved to the study door and Blaine added as an afterthought, 'By the way, your grandfather, Sir Garry, arrived at Weltevreden this morning.'

'He has come down for his birthday,' Shasa smiled. 'I look forward to seeing him. I hope you and Field Marshal Smuts will be coming to the birthday picnic as usual.'

'Wouldn't miss it for the world!' Blaine opened the study door, and across the lobby Tara was hovering innocently, pretending to be selecting a book from the shelves in the library.

Blaine grinned, 'Tara, you let Shasa get some sleep tonight, do you hear me? I refuse to work with a zombie tomorrow.'

* * *

The meeting in Blaine's office the following morning lasted longer than either of them expected, and later moved down the passageway to the prime minister's office where Field Marshal Smuts personally questioned Shasa. His questions were so searching that Shasa felt drained by the effort of keeping pace with the *Ou Baas*' mercurial mind. He escaped with relief, Smuts's admonition following him.

'We want this fellow "White Sword" whoever he is, and we want him before he can do any more damage. Get that message across to everybody involved.'

'Yes, sir.'

'And I want those lists on my desk before the weekend. We must have these fellows locked up and out of harm's way.'

It was mid-morning before Shasa arrived at CID headquarters and parked the Jaguar in the reserved bay that had been set aside for him.

The special operations room had been set up in one of the extensive basement areas. There was a constable on duty at the door and Shasa signed the register. Entry was restricted to persons on the list. Many of the police force were known *OB* members, or sympathizers. Inspector Louis Nel had chosen his team with extreme care.

He was a balding, taciturn man whose age and job classification had prevented him from volunteering for overseas military service, a fact that he bitterly resented. However, Shasa had soon discovered that he was an easy man to like and respect, though a difficult one to please. They had quickly established a working rapport.

Nel was in his shirt-sleeves, a cigarette dangling from his lips as he talked into the telephone, but he covered the mouthpiece and summoned Shasa with an imperious wave.

'Where the hell have you been? I was going to send out a search party,' he reprimanded him. 'Sit down. I want to talk to you.'

Shasa perched on the corner of his desk while the inspector continued his telephone call, and he stared through the window into the busy operations room. Inspector Nel had been allocated eight detectives and a bevy of female stenographers. The room was full of cigarette smoke and the clatter of typewriters as they worked. One of the other telephones on the inspector's desk rang, and he glanced up at Shasa. 'Take that – damned switchboard keeps putting everything through to me.'

Shasa picked up the receiver. 'Good morning, this is CID headquarters. May I help you?' he said, and when there was silence, he repeated it in Afrikaans.

'Hello, I want to talk to somebody – ' the caller was a woman, a young woman and very agitated, she was speaking Afrikaans, and her voice was breathless and uncertain. 'In the paper they said you wanted to know about the *Ossewa Brandwag*. I want to talk to somebody.'

'My name is Courtney,' Shasa said in Afrikaans. 'Squadron-Leader Courtney. I am grateful that you want to assist the police. You can tell me everything.' He tried to make his voice warm and reassuring. He could sense that the woman was afraid, perhaps on the point of changing her mind and ringing off. 'Take your time. I'm here to listen to you.'

'Are you the police?'

'Yes, madam. Would you like to give me your name?'

'No! I won't tell you – '

He realized his mistake. 'That's perfectly all right. You don't have to give your name,' he told her quickly, and there was a long silence. He could hear her breathing.

'Take your time,' he repeated gently. 'You just tell me what you want to.'

'They are stealing guns.' The woman's voice sank to a whisper.

'Can you tell me what guns?' Shasa asked carefully.

'From the gun factory in Pretoria, the railway workshop.' Shasa sat up straighter and held the telephone receiver with both hands. Almost all the military arms and munitions manufacture was being undertaken in the railway workshops in Pretoria. It was the only establishment with the heavy equipment, highspeed lathes and steam presses, capable of turning out barrels and blocks for rifles and machine-guns. The cartridge cases for the munitions were being stamped out at the Pretoria Mint, but they were despatched to the railway workshops for final processing.

'What you are saying is important,' he told her carefully. 'Can you tell me how they are stealing the guns?'

'They are putting scrap iron in the cases, and stealing the guns,' the woman whispered.

'Can you tell me who is doing this, please? Do you know who is responsible?'

'I don't know the people in the workshop, but the one who is in charge. I know who he is.'

'We must know his name,' Shasa told her persuasively, but she was silent. He could sense that she was struggling with herself, and that if he pushed her now he would lose her.

'Do you want to tell me who he is?' he asked. 'Just take your time.'

'His name – ' the woman hesitated, was silent a moment longer, and then she blurted our, 'they call him *Wit Swaard* – White Sword.'

Shasa felt his skin crawl as though it were infested with vermin, and his heart seemed to check, miss a beat, then race away wildly.

'What did you say?'

'White Sword – his name is White Sword,' the woman repeated and there was a crackle and click as the connection was broken.

'Hello! Hello!' Shasa shouted into the receiver. 'Are you there? Don't hang up!' But the hiss of static on the empty line mocked him.

* * *

Shasa stood beside Blaine Malcomess' desk while he made the call to the commissioner of police at Marshall Square in Johannesburg.

'As soon as you have the search warrant you are to close the workshops. No one allowed to enter or leave. I have already spoken to the military commander

of the Transvaal. He and his quartermaster-general will give you full co-operation. I want you to begin to search right away, open all the weapons cases in the stores and check every item against the factory production sheets. I will be flying up, leaving immediately. Please have a police car meet me at Roberts Heights airfield at – ' he glanced at Shasa for a time, ' – five o'clock this evening. In the meantime, I want you to impress utter secrecy on all your men involved in the search. One other thing, Commissioner, please select only men who you are satisfied are not members of any subversive organizations, particularly the *Ossewa Brandwag*.'

Shasa drove them out to Youngsfield in the Jaguar and as they parked behind the hangar Blaine unfolded his long legs and climbed out of the sportscar.

'Well, at least the most gruelling part of the journey is over with,' he remarked.

There was a police inspector waiting for them on the hard stand below the Roberts Heights control tower as Shasa taxied the Rapide in and cut the engines. He came forward to meet them as Blaine and Shasa came down the landing steps.

'How is the investigation going?' Blaine demanded immediately after they had shaken hands. 'What have you found so far?'

'Nothing, Minister.' The inspector shook his head. 'We have checked over six hundred cases of rifles. It's a time-consuming job. But so far everything seems to be in order.'

'How many cases in the stores?'

'Nine hundred and eighty.'

'So you have checked over half.' Blaine shook his head. 'Let's go and have a look anyway.'

He settled his hat on his head and buttoned his overcoat to the neck for there was a cold wind sweeping across the airstrip, bringing memories of the snows of the Drakensberg mountains, and the highveld grass was bleached silvery by the frosts of late winter. He and Shasa climbed into the back seat of the black police Packard and neither of them spoke on the short journey into the centre of Pretoria.

At the gates to the railway workshops there was a double guard of police and military personnel. They checked the occupants of the Packard carefully, not visibly impressed by Blaine's status.

The chief inspector in charge of the investigation was in the office of the workshop manager and his report had little to add to what they already knew. They had so far been unable to find any irregularity in the production or packaging of weapons.

'Give me the tour,' Blaine ordered grimly, and the entire party – Blaine, Shasa, the chief inspector and the workshop manager – went out on to the main production floor.

'Workshop' was hardly a correct description of the large factory that they entered. Originally built to service and repair the rolling stock of the state-owned railway, it had been expanded and modernized until it was capable of building its own locomotives from scratch. Now the long production line along which they picked their way was turning out armoured cars for the desert war in North Africa.

The working of the factory had not been halted by the police investigation and the cavernous sheds roofed with corrugated iron echoed to the thunder of the steam presses and the cacophony of the lathes and turret head drills.

'How many men do you employ?' Blaine had to shout to make himself heard in the uproar.

'Almost three thousand altogether – we are working three shifts now. Wartime production.'

The manager took them through the furthest building.

'This is where we turn out the small arms,' he shouted. 'Or rather the metal parts. Barrel and blocks. The woodwork is manufactured by outside contractors.'

'Show us the finished articles and the packing,' Blaine ordered. 'That's where the trouble is, if there is trouble.'

After assembly and checking, the completed rifles, British Long Service No. 4 Mark I in .303 calibre, were greased and wrapped in yellow grease-proof paper, then packed in the long WD green wooden cases, ten rifles to a case. Finally the cases were loaded onto steel pallets and trundled through to the despatch stores.

When they entered the despatch stores, there were a dozen uniformed police constables working with at least fifty factory employees in blue overalls. Each case was being taken down from the tall stacks and opened by one of the constables, then the wrapped rifles were taken out and counted, repacked and the case lids relocked. The checked cases were being stacked at the far end of the storehouse, and Shasa saw immediately that only about fifty cases remained to be opened and inspected.

The chief storekeeper hurried across from his desk and challenged Blaine indignantly. 'I don't know who you are – but if you are the bloody fool who ordered this, you need your arse kicked. We have lost a day's production. There is a goods train at the siding and a convoy waiting in Durban harbour to take these weapons to our boys up north.'

Shasa left the group and went across to watch the working constables. 'No luck?' he asked one of them.

'We're wasting our time,' the man grunted without looking up, and Shasa silently reviled himself. A day's war production lost because of him, it was a dire responsibility and his sense of despondency increased as he stood and watched the remaining cases opened, checked and resealed.

The constables assembled at the door of the stores and the overalled factory employees went out through the tall sliding doors to resume their posts on the production line. The police inspector came back to where they stood in a small disconsolate group.

'Nothing, Minister. I'm sorry.'

'We had to do it,' Blaine said, glancing at Shasa. 'Nobody is to blame.'

'Too bloody true somebody is to blame,' the chief storeman broke in truculently. 'Now that you've had your fun, can I get on with loading the rest of the shipment?'

Shasa stared at him. There was something about the man's behaviour that set off a little warning tingle down his spine – the blustering defensive manner, the shiftiness of his gaze.

'Of course,' he thought. 'If there was a switch, this is where it would take place, and this fellow would be in it to his neck.' His mind was starting to slough off the inertia of disappointment and anti-climax.

'All right,' Blaine agreed. 'It was a wild-goose chase. You can get on with your work.'

'Hold on, sir,' Shasa intervened quietly, and he turned back to the storeman. 'How many railway trucks have you loaded already?'

There it was again – the shift of the man's eyes, the slight hesitation. He was going to lie. Then he glanced involuntarily at the sheaf of papers in the clipboard that lay on his desk beside the doors that led out onto the loading bays.

Shasa crossed quickly to the desk and picked up the sheaf of loading manifest. 'Three trucks have already been loaded,' he read from the manifest. 'Which are they?'

'They have been shunted away,' the storeman muttered sulkily.

'Then let's have them shunted back here right away,' Blaine intervened briskly.

Blaine and Shasa stood together under the arc lamps on the concrete loading quay while the first of the closed railway goods trucks was unlocked and the sliding door opened. The interior of the truck was loaded to the roof with green rifle cases.

'If they are here, they will be at the bottom of the load,' Shasa suggested. 'Whoever is responsible would get rid of the evidence as soon as possible. He'd make damned sure they were the first cases loaded.'

'Get down to the bottom cases,' Blaine ordered sharply, and the top cases were carried out and stacked on the quay.

'Right!' Blaine pointed to the back of the truck. 'Get that case out and open it.'

The lid came up and the constable let it fall to the concrete floor with a clatter.

'Sir!' he exclaimed. 'Look at this.'

Blaine stepped up beside him and stared down into the open box, and then he loooked up again quickly.

The chief storekeeper was hurrying across the floor of the shed towards the doors at the far end.

'Arrest that man!' Blaine shouted urgently, and two constables ran forward and seized him. He was struggling angrily as they dragged him out onto the loading quay.

Blaine turned to Shasa, his expression grim and his eyes flinty. 'Well, my boy, I hope you are satisfied. You've given us a mountain of work and a lot of sleepless nights ahead,' he said.

* * *

Fifteen grave men sat around the long polished stinkwood table in the panelled cabinet office and listened silently as Blaine Malcomess made his report.

'There is no way of establishing with any certainty exactly how many weapons are missing. Two other large shipments have been sent out since the first of the month and as yet neither of these has reached its destination in Cairo. They are still in transit, but we must expect that weapons are missing from both shipments. I estimate that some two thousand rifles together with a million and a half rounds of ammunition.'

The men around the table stirred uneasily, but nobody spoke.

'This is alarming, of course. However, the truly disturbing aspect of the

business is the theft of some thirty to fifty Vickers machine-guns from the same source.'

'This is incredible,' Denys Reitz muttered. 'That is enough to launch a nationwide rebellion. It could be 1914 all over again. We must make sure no word of this gets out. It will cause panic.'

'We should also consider,' Blaine went on, 'the tons of explosives hijacked in the karoo. Those would almost certainly be used to disrupt communications and prevent deployment of our limited military strength. If there was to be a rebellion – '

'Please tell us, Blaine,' the prime minister held up a finger. 'Firstly, do we have any indication of when we can expect them to come out into the open and attempt their *coup d'état*?'

'No, Prime Minister. The best I can do is an estimate based on our probable discovery of the weapons theft. They must have realized that the theft would be discovered as soon as the first consignment reached Cairo, and almost certainly they plan to move before that time.'

'When would the shipment have reached Cairo?'

'Two weeks from now approximately.'

'So we must expect that they will make the attempt within days, rather than weeks?'

'I'm afraid so, Prime Minister.'

'My next question, Blaine. How complete is your investigation? Do you have a full list of the ringleaders of *OB* and the *stormjagters*?'

'Not a full list, we have only about six hundred names so far. I think it includes almost all their key men – but, of course, we can't have any way of being sure of that.'

'Thank you, Blaine.' The prime minister tugged throughtfully at his small silver goatee beard. His expression was almost serene, his blue eyes calm and unworried. They all waited for him to speak again.

'How sensitive are the names on the list?' he asked.

'There is the administrator of the Orange Free State.'

'Yes, we know about him.'

'Twelve members of Parliament, including one former cabinet minister.'

'Parliamentary privilege,' Field-Marshal Smuts murmured. 'We can't touch them.'

'Then there are church leaders, at least four high-ranking army officers, top civil servants, one assistant police commissioner.' Blaine read the list through, and by the time he had finished, the prime minister had already made up his mind.

'We can't afford to wait,' he said. 'With the exception of the members of parliament, I want detention and internment orders prepared for all the others on the list of suspects. I'll sign them as soon as they are drafted. In the meantime I want you to plan the simultaneous arrests of all of them, and make provision for their incarceration.'

'There are the concentration camps built for Italian prisoners of war at Baviaanspoort and Pietermaritzburg,' Blaine pointed out.

'Good,' Field-Marshal Smuts agreed. 'I want these men all safely behind barbed-wire as soon as possible. And I want the missing weapons and explosives found, and found quickly.'

* * *

'We cannot afford to wait,' Manfred De La Rey said carefully. 'Every hour is dangerous, every day brings us closer to the brink, a week could spell disaster.'

'We are not ready. We need time,' one of the other men in the first-class railway compartment cut in. There were eight men, including Manfred, in the compartment. They had boarded the southbound express separately at different stops over the last two hundred miles. The conductor of the train was a sympathizer, and there were *stormjagters* in the corridors outside the compartment, acting as sentries. Nobody could reach them or eavesdrop on their conversation.

'You promised us another ten days in which to complete the final preparations.'

'We haven't got ten days, man. Haven't you listened to what I am telling you?'

'It can't be done,' the man repeated stubbornly.

'It can be done,' Manfred raised his voice. 'It has to be done!'

The administrator intervened sternly. 'Enough of that, gentlemen. Let's keep the fighting for our enemies.'

With an obvious effort Manfred moderated his tone. 'I apologize for my outburst. However, I repeat that we have no time to spare. The removal of the weapons from the railway workshops has been discovered, ten of our men there have been arrested. One of our men at Marshall Square has told us that they have received detention orders for over two hundred of our senior members and that these are to be served on Sunday – that is four days from now.'

'We are aware of all that,' the administrator intervened again. 'What we must do now is decide whether we can afford to put the entire plan forward – or if it should be abandoned. I will listen to each of your opinons and then we will vote. We shall stand by the majority decision. Let us hear first from Brigadier Koopman.'

They all looked to the army general. He was in civilian clothing but his military bearing was unmistakable. He spread a large-scale map on the fold-down table, and used it to illustrate his report in a professionally dispassionate voice. First he set out the order of battle of the army, and the dispositions of the troops, aircraft and armoured cars that remained in the country and then went on, 'So you see that the two main troop concentrations are at the infantry training barracks at Roberts Heights and at Durban awaiting shipment for overseas duty. With almost one hundred and sixty thousand outside the country, these do not amount to more than five thousand men. There are no modern aircraft, other than the fifty Harvard trainers. This makes it feasible to immobilize the troops at their present positions at least for the first few crucial days that it will take to seize control. This can be achieved by destroying all major road and railway bridges, partcularly those over the Vaal river, the Orange river and the Umzindusi river.'

He went on talking for another ten minutes, and then summed up, 'We have our men placed in positions of command, right up to the general staff, and they will be able to cushion us from any forthright action by the army. After that they will arrest and hold the Smuts men on the general staff and bring the army in on our side to support the new republican government.'

One after another the other men present made their reports. Manfred was last to speak.

'Gentlemen,' he began. 'Within the last twelve hours I have been in direct radio contact with the German *Abwehr* through their representative in

Portuguese Angola. He has relayed to us the assurances of the German High Command and of the Führer himself. The German submarine supply vessel *Altmark* is at present within three hundred nautical miles of Cape Town carrying over five hundred tons of armaments. She awaits only the signal to steam to our aid.' He spoke quitely but persuasively, and he sensed the mood swing in his favour.

When he finished there was a short but profound silence and then the administrator said, 'We have all the facts before us now. We must make the decision. It is this. Before the government can arrest and imprison us and the other legitimate leaders of the *Volk*, we put into effect the plan. We rise and depose the present government and take the power into our own hands to put our nation back on the course to freedom and justice. I will ask each of you in turn – do you say "Yes" or do you say "No"?'

'*Ja,*' said the first man.

'*Ek stem ja.* I say yes.'

'*Ek stem ook ja,* I also say yes.'

At the end the administrator summed up for them. 'We are all agreed – there is not one of us against the enterprise.' He paused and looked at Manfred De La Rey. 'You have told us of the signal to launch the rising. Something that will turn the country on its head. Can you tell us now what that signal will be?'

'The signal will be the assissination of the traitor Jan Christian Smuts,' Manfred said.

They stared at him in silence. It was clear that even though they anticipated something momentous, none of them had expected this.

'The details of this political execution have been carefully planned,' Manfred went on to assure them. 'Three different contingency plans were drawn up in Berlin, each for a different date, depending on the dictates of circumstances. The first plan, the earliest date, suits our present purpose exactly. Smuts will be executed this coming Saturday. Three days from now – the day before the detention orders are served on our leaders.'

The silence drew out a minute longer, then the administrator asked, 'Where? How will it be done?'

'You do not need to know that. I will do what is necessary, alone and unaided. It will be up to you to act quickly and forcibly as soon as the news of Smuts' death is released. You must step into the void he leaves and seize the reins of power.'

'Let it be so,' said the administrator quietly. 'We will be ready for the moment when it comes, and may God bless our battle.'

Of the eight men in the compartment, only Manfred remained aboard when the express pulled out of Bloemfontein station and began its long run southwards towards Cape Town.

* * *

'I have a permit to keep a firearm on the estate,' Sakkie Van Vuuren, the winery manager, told Manfred. 'We use it to shoot the baboons that come down from the mountains to raid the vineyards and orchards.'

He led the way down the steps into the cool gloom of the cellars.

'Anybody who hears a few shots coming from the mountains will take no

notice of them – but if you are challenged, tell them you are employed by the estate and refer them to me.' He opened the false front of the wine cask and stood back while Manfred knelt and opened one of the waterproof canisters.

First he lifted out the radio transmitter and connected the new batteries which Van Vuuren had procured for him. The radio was fitted into a canvas rucksack and was readily portable.

He opened the second canister and brought out the rifle case. In it was a sniper's model 987 Mauser, with that superb action which permitted such high breech pressure levels that the velocity of the 173 grain bullet could be pushed up over 25000 feet per second. There were fifty rounds of the 7 × 57mm ammunition which had been specially hand-loaded by one of the expert technicians at *Deutsche Waffen und Munitionsfabrik*, and the telescopic sight was by Zeiss. Manfred fitted the telescopic sight to the rifle and filled the magazine. The rest of the ammunition he repacked and then stowed the canisters away in the false-fronted cask.

Van Vuuren drove him up into one of the valleys of the Hottentots Holland mountains in his battered old Ford half-tonner, and when the track at last petered out, left him there and drove back down the rocky winding trail.

Manfred watched him out of sight and then hefted his pack and rifle and began to climb upwards. He had plenty of time, there was no need to hurry, but the hard physical exertion gave him pleasure and he went up with long elastic strides, revelling in the flood of sweat on his face and body.

He crossed the first range of the foothills, went down into the wooded valley and then climbed again to one of the main peaks beyond. Near the crest he stopped and set up the radio, stringing his aerials from the tops of two cripplewood trees and orientating them carefully towards the north.

Then he settled down with his back to a boulder and ate the sandwiches that little Sarah had made for him. The contact time with the *Abwehr* agent in Luanda, the capital of Portuguese Angola, was 1500 hours Greenwich Mean Time, and he had almost an hour to wait.

After he had eaten he took the Mauser in his lap and handled it lovingly, refamiliarizing himself with the weapon's feel and balance, working the bolt action, bringing the butt to his shoulder and sighting through the lens of the telescope at objects down the slope.

In Germany he had practised endlessly with this same rifle, and he knew that at any range up to three hundred metres he could choose in which eye he would shoot a man. However, it was essential that he check the rifle to make absolutely certain that the sights were still true. He needed a target as close to that of a human form as possible, but he could find nothing suitable from where he sat. He laid the rifle carefully aside, checked his wristwatch and transferred his attention to the radio.

He set up the Morse key and turned to the page in his notebook on which he had already reduced the message to code. He flexed his fingers and began to send, tapping the brass key with a fluid rapid movement, aware that the operator at Luanda far in the north would recognize his style and would accept that rather than his code name as proof of his identity.

'Eagle Base, this is White Sword.' On the fourth call he was answered. The signal in his headphones was strong and clear.

'Go ahead, White Sword.'

'Confirm plan one in force. Repeat plan one. Acknowledge.'

There was no need for a long message that could increase the chances of

being traced or intercepted. Everything had been arranged with Teutonic attention to detail before he left Berlin.

'Understand plan one. Good luck. Over and out from Eagle Base.'

'Over and out White Sword.'

He rolled the aerial wires, repacked the transmitter, and was about to swing it on his shoulder when an explosive barking cough echoed along the cliffs and Manfred sank down flat behind the rock and reached for the Mauser. The wind favoured him and he settled down to wait.

He lay for almost half an hour without moving, still and intent scanning the valley floor below, before he saw the first movement amongst the jumbled lichen-covered rocks and stunted protea bushes.

The baboons were moving in their usual foraging order, with half a dozen young males in the van, the females and young in the centre, and three huge grey patriarchal males in the rearguard. The infants were slung upside down below their mothers' bellies, clinging with tiny paws to the thick coarse belly fur and peering out with pink hairless faces. The larger youngsters rode like jockeys perched on the backs of their dams. The three fighting bulls at the rear of the troop followed them, swaggering arrogantly, knuckling the ground as they moved forward on four legs, their heads held high, almost doglike, their muzzles long and pointed, their eyes close-set and bright.

Manfred chose the largest of the three apes and watched him through the lens of the sight. He let him come up on the slope until he was only three hundred metres from where he lay.

The bull baboon suddenly loped forward and with an agile bound reached the top of a grey boulder the size of a small cottage. He sat there, perched on his hindquarters, resting his elbows on his knees, almost human in his pose, and he opened his jaws in a cavernous yawn. His fangs were pointed and yellow and as long as a man's forefinger.

Carefully Manfred took up the slack in the rear trigger until he felt the hair trigger engage with an almost inaudible click, then he settled the cross hairs of the telescopic sight on the baboon's forehead, and held his aim for the hundredth part of a second. He touched the front trigger, while he still concentrated fixedly on the baboon's sloping furry forehead and the rifle slammed back into his shoulder. The shot crashed out across the valley. The echoes rang back from the cliffs in a descending roll of thunder.

The bull baboon somersaulted backwards from his seat on the boulder, and the rest of the troop fled back down the slope in screaming panic.

Manfred stood up, hoisted the pack onto his shoulders and picked his way down the slope. He found the ape's carcass huddled at the base of the rock. It still twitched and quivered in reflex but the top of the animal's skull was missing. It had been cut away as though by an axe stroke at the level of the eyes and bright blood welled up through the base of the brain pan and dribbled over the rocks.

Manfred rolled the carcass over with his foot and nodded with satisfaction. The special hollow-tipped bullet would decapitate a man just as neatly, and the rifle had held true to within a finger's breadth at three hundred metres.

'Now I am as ready as I will ever be,' Manfred murmured and went down the mountain.

* * *

Shasa had not been home to Weltevreden, nor had he seen Tara since he and Blaine had flown home from Pretoria in the Rapide after the discovery of the stolen weapons.

He had not left CID headquarters during that time. He ate at the police canteen and snatched a few hours's sleep in the dormitory that had been set up on the floor above the operations room. The rest of the time he had been engrossed entirely in the preparations for the planned police swoop.

There were almost a hundred and fifty suspects to be dealt with in Cape Province alone, and for each the warrant had to be drawn, the expected whereabouts of subjects charted, the police officers delegated to make each separate arrest.

Sunday had been selected deliberately for almost all of the subjects were devout Calvinists, members of the Dutch Reformed Church, and would attend divine service that morning. Their whereabouts could be anticipated with a high degree of certainty and they would in all probability be unsuspecting, in a religious frame of mine, and not in the mood to offer any resistance to the arresting officers.

It was midday Friday before Shasa remembered that his grandfather's birthday picnic was the following day and he rang Centaine at Weltevreden from the police operations room.

'Oh *chéri*, that is terrible news, Sir Garry will be so disappointed. He has asked for you every day since he arrived – and we are all so looking forward to seeing you.'

'I'm sorry, Mater.'

'Can't you get away to join us – even for an hour?'

'That's just not possible. Believe me, Mater, I am as disappointed as anyone.'

'You don't have to come up the mountain, Shasa. Just drink a glass of champagne with us at Weltevreden before we leave. You can go back immediately and do whatever it is you are doing that is so important. For my sake, *chéri*, won't you try?'

She sensed that he was wavering. 'Blaine and Field-Marshal Smuts will be here. They have both promised. If you come at eight o'clock, just to wish your grandfather a happy birthday, I promise you can leave again before eight-thirty.'

'Oh, all right, Mater,' he capitulated, and grinned into the telephone. 'Don't you find it boring always to get your own way?'

'It is something I have learned to bear, *chéri*,' she laughed back at him. 'Until tomorrow.'

'Until tomorrow,' he agreed.

'I love you, *chéri*'

'I love you too, Mater.'

He hung up, feeling guilty at having given in to her, and was about to ring Tara to tell her that he wouldn't be able to escort her to the picnic when one of the sergeants across the room called him.

'Squadron Leader Courtney, this call is for you.'

'Who is it?'

'She didn't say, it's a woman,' and Shasa smiled as he crossed the room. Tara had anticipated him and called him first.

'Hello, is that you Tara?' he said into the mouthpiece, and there was silence except for the soft sound of somebody breathing nervously. His nerves snapped

tight, and he lowered his voice, trying to make it friendly and encouraging as he switched into Afrikaans.

'This is Squadron Leader Courtney speaking. Is that the lady I spoke to before?'

'*Ja*. It is me.' He recognized her voice, young, breathless and afraid.

'I am very grateful to you. What you have done has saved many lives – the lives of innocent people.'

'I saw nothing about the guns in the newspapers,' the woman whispered.

'You can be proud of what you have done,' he told her, and then on inspiration added, 'Many people would have died, perhaps even women and little children.'

The words 'little children' seemed to decide her and she blurted out, 'There is still great danger. They are planning something terrible, White Sword is going to do something. Soon, very soon. I heard him say that it will be the signal, and it will turn the nation on its head – '

'Can you tell me what it is?' Shasa asked, trying not to frighten her, keeping his voice low and reassuring. 'What is this thing he plans?'

'I don't know. I only know it will be very soon.'

'Can you find out what it is?'

'I don't know – I can try.'

'For the sake of everybody, the women and little children, will you try to find out what it is?'

'Yes, I will try.'

'I will be here at this telephone – ' then suddenly he remembered his promise to Centaine ' – or at this other number – ' and he gave her the number at Weltevreden. 'Try here first, and the other number if I am not here.'

'I understand.'

'Can you tell me who White Sword is?' He took a calculated risk. 'Do you know his real name?' Immediately the connection crackled and was broken. She had hung up. He lowered the telephone and stared at it. He sensed that he had frightened her off for good with that last question, and dismay overwhelmed him.

'Something that will turn the nation on its head.' Her words haunted him, and he was filled with an ominous sense of impending disaster.

* * *

Manfred drove sedately along the De Waal Drive past the university buildings. It was past midnight, and the streets were almost deserted except for a few Friday-night revellers wending their unsteady way homeward. The car he was driving was a nondescript little Morris and the rifle was in the boot under a tattered piece of tarpaulin. He was dressed in a railwayman's blue overalls over which he wore a thick fisherman's jersey and a heavy greatcoat.

He was moving into position now to avoid the danger of being seen on the mountain during daylight carrying a rifle. On a weekend the slopes of Table Mountain were favoured by hikers and rock climbers, birdwatchers and picnickers, boy scouts and lovers.

He passed the forestry station and turned into Rhodes Avenue, then followed the road up past the Kirstenbosch Botanical Gardens with the bulk of the

mountain blotting out half the starry night sky. The road wound around the bottom slopes through the dark forests. Before he reached the Constantia Nek pass he slowed down, and checked in his rearview mirror to make certain there was no vehicle following him. Then he switched off his headlights and turned off sharply onto the forestry track.

He drove at a walking pace, keeping in low gear until he reached the forestry gate. Then he stopped and, leaving the engine idling, went to the gate and tried his key in the lock. Roelf had given him the key and assured him that the forester was a friend. It turned easily, and Manfred drove the Morris through and closed the gate behind him. He hooked the staple of the padlock through the chain, but did not lock it.

He was on the bottom stretch of the bridle path now and drove on up the narrow track as it ascended the slope in a series of tight hairpins. He passed the contour path that girdled the mountain three hundred metres above sea level. A mile further on, just below the summit he reversed the Morris off the bridle path so that it was out of sight of a casual hiker. From the boot he took the Mauser and wrapped it carefully in a light tarpaulin. Then he locked the doors of the Morris and went back down towards the contour path carrying the rifle across his shoulder. He used his flashlight as little as possible and then only for quick glimpses of the pathway, shielding the beam with his body.

Within twenty minutes he intercepted the pathway that climbed directly up Skeleton Gorge and he flashed his light onto the square concrete signpost and read the legend printed on it.

SMUTS TRACK

The concrete block resembled a tombstone rather than a signpost and he smiled grimly at the appropriateness of the name upon it. The old field-marshal had made this ascent the most famous of all routes to the summit.

Manfred climbed quickly, without resting, 1200 feet up Skeleton Gorge until he came up past Breakfast Rock over the crest, onto the tableland. Here he paused for a moment to look back. Far below him the Constantia valley huddled in the night, lit by only a star dusting of lights. He turned his back upon it and began his final preparations. He had scouted the site two days previously, and he had chosen the stance from which he would fire and paced out the exact range from there to the point on the pathway where a man would become visible as he came out onto the summit.

Now he moved into his stance. It was a hollow between two boulders, lightly screened by mountain scrub. He spread the tarpaulin over the low wiry bracken and then lay full length upon it, flattening the plants into a comfortable mattress under him.

He wriggled into firing position, cradled the butt of the Mauser into his cheek and aimed at the head of the pathway 250 metres away. Through the Zeiss lens he could make out the individual branches of the bush that grew beside the path starkly silhouetted against the soft glow of light from the valley beyond.

He laid the weapon on the tarpaulin in front of him, ready for instant use. Then he pulled the colour of the greatcoat up around his ears and huddled down. It was going to be a long cold wait, and to pass the time he reviewed all the planning that had led him to this place, and the odds that tomorrow morning, at a little before or a little after ten-thirty, his quarry would come up the path that bore his name and step into the cross hairs of the Zeiss scope.

The dossier on Jan Christian Smuts meticulously assembled by the*Abwehr* in Berlin, which he had studied so avidly, had shown that for the last ten years, on every anniversary of this date, the field-marshal had kept this arrangement with an old friend, and now the fate of a nation depended on him doing so once again.

* * *

Shasa drove through the Anreith gates and up the long driveway to the château. There were a dozen motor cars parked in front of Weltevreden, Blaine's Bentley amongst them. He parked the Jag beside it and checked his wristwatch. It was ten minutes past eight o'clock. He was late and Mater was going to be huffed, she was an absolute stickler for punctuality.

She surprised him again by springing up from the long table in the dining-room and running to embrace him. The entire party of twenty was assembled for one of Weltevreden's celebrated breakfasts. The buffet sideboard groaned under the weight of silver and food. The servants in their long white *Kanzas* and red pillbox fezes burst into beaming grins when they saw Shasa and a welcoming buzz of pleasure went up from the guests seated at the stinkwood table.

They were all there, everybody Shasa loved – Grandpater Garry at the head of the table, sprightly as a pixie; Anna beside him, her red face creasing into an infinity of smiles like a friendly bulldog; Blaine; Tara, as lovely as this spring morning; Matty, all freckles and carroty red hair; the *Ou Baas*; and of course Mater. Only David was missing.

Shasa went to each of them in turn, laughing and exchanging banter, embracing and shaking hands and kissing. There were whoops and whistles when he pecked Tara's blushing cheek. He handed Grandpater Garry his present and stood beside him as he unwrapped the specially bound first editions of *Burchell's Travels* and exclaimed with delight. He shook hands with the *Ou Baas* respectfully and glowed with pleasure at his quiet commendation, 'Good work you are doing, *Kêrel*.' Finally he exchanged a quick word with Blaine before loading his plate at the sideboard and taking the chair between Tara and Mater.

He refused the champagne – 'I've got work to do today' – and played with Tara's foot under the table while he joined in the hilarity that resounded around the long table.

Too soon they were all rising and the women went to get their coats while the men went out to the cars and made certain that the rugs and picnic baskets were loaded.

'I'm sorry you can't come with us, Shasa.' Grandpater Garry took him aside. 'I hoped we could have a chat, but I've heard from Blaine how important your work is.'

'I'll try and get back here tomorrow night. The pressure should be off by then.'

'I won't go back to Natal until we've been able to spend a little time together. You are the one to carry on the Courtney name, my one and only grandson.'

Shasa felt a rush of deep affection for this wise and gentle old man; in some

strange way the fact that they had both suffered mutilation, Sir Garry's leg and Shasa's eye, seemed to have forged an even stronger bond between them.

'It's years since I have been up to visit you and Anna at Theuniskraal,' Shasa burst out impulsively. 'May I come and spend a couple of weeks with you?'

'Nothing would give us greater pleasure,' Sir Garry hugged him, and at that moment Field-Marshal Smuts came across.

'Still talking, old Garry, do you ever stop? Come alone now, we have a mountain to climb, and the last one to the top gets sent to an old-age home.'

The old friends smiled at each other. They could have been brothers, both slight of build but wiry and dapper, both with little goatee beards and disreputable old hats upon their heads.

'Forward!' Sir Garry brandished his cane, linked his arm through the field-marshal's and led him to the back seat of Centaine's yellow Daimler.

The Daimler led the procession, followed by Blaine's Bentley and Tara blew Shasa a kiss as it passed. He stood on the front steps of Weltevreden and it was very quiet after they had all gone.

He turned back into the house and went upstairs to his own room, selected a batch of clean shirts, socks and underpants from his drawers and stuffed them into a grip.

On the way downstairs he turned aside, went into Centaine's study and picked up the telephone. One of the duty sergeants in the operations room at CID headquarters answered.

'Hello, Sergeant. Have there been any messages for me?'

'Hold on, sir, I'll have a look.' He was back in a few seconds. 'Only one, sir, ten minutes ago. A woman – wouldn't leave her name.'

'Thank you, Sergeant,' Shasa hung up quickly. He found that his hand was trembling and his breath had shortened. *A woman – wouldn't leave her name*. It had to be her. Why hadn't she called him here? She had the number.

He stood over the phone, willing it to ring. Nothing happened. After five minutes he began to pace the floor – moving restlessly between the wide french windows and the huge ormolu Louis Quatorze desk, watching the silent telephone. He was undecided, should he go back to CID headquarters in case she called there again, but what if she came through here? Should he ring the sergeant – but that would block the line.

'Come on!' he pleaded. 'Come on!' He glanced at his wristwatch – thirty-five minutes he had wasted in indecision.

'I'll have to pack it up. Can't stand here all day.'

He went to the desk. He reached for the instrument, but before he could touch it, it rang. He hadn't been ready for it, the sound raked his nerves shrilly, and he snatched it up.

'Squadron Leader Courtney,' he spoke in Afrikaans. 'Is that you, *Mevrou*?'

'I forgot the number – I had to go back to the house to fetch it,' she said. Her voice was rough with exertion, she had been running. 'I couldn't call before – there were people, my husband – ' she broke off. She had said too much.

'That is all right. Don't worry, everything is all right.'

'No,' she said. 'It's terrible what they are going to do. It's just terrible.'

'Do you want to tell me?'

'They are going to kill the field-marshal – '

'The field-marshal?'

'The *Ou Baas* – Field-Marshal Smuts.'

He could not speak for a moment, and then he rallied. 'Do you know when they plan to do it?'

'Today. They will shoot him today.'

'That's not possible – ' he did not want to believe it. 'The *Ou Baas* has gone up Table Mountain today. He's on a picnic with – '

'Yes! Yes!' The woman was sobbing. 'On the mountain. White Sword is waiting for him on the mountain.'

'Oh my God!' Shasa whispered. He felt as though he were paralysed. His legs were filled with concrete and a great weight crushed his lungs so that for a moment he could not breathe.

'You are a brave woman,' he said. 'Thank you for what you have done.'

He dropped the telephone onto its cradle and snatched open the drawer of Centaine's desk. The gold-engraved Beretta pistols were in their presentation case. He lifted one of them out of its nest of green baize and checked the load. There were six in the magazine and an extra magazine in a separate slot in the case. He thrust the pistol into his belt and the magazine into his pocket and turned for the door.

The pistol was useless at anything further than pointblank range, but the hunting rifles were locked in the cabinet in the gunroom, the ammunition was kept separately, his key was in the Jag – it would take precious minutes to fetch it, open the cabinet, unchain his 9.3 Mannlicher, find the ammunition – he could not afford the time. The picnic party had a start of nearly forty minutes on him. They might be halfway up the mountain by now. All the people he loved were there – and an assassin was waiting for them.

He sprinted down the steps and sprang into the open cockpit of the Jag. She started with a roar; he spun her in a tight circle, gravel spraying from under the back tyres, and went down the long drive with the needle climbing quickly to the eighty mph notch. He went out through the Anreith gates, and into the narrow curves and dips as the road skirted the base of the mountain. More than once he nearly ran out of road as the Jag snarled and screeched through the turns, but it was fully fifteen minutes before he snaked her in through the gates of Kirstenbosch Botanical Gardens and at last pulled into the parking area behind the curator's office. The other vehicles were there, parked in a straggling line, the Daimler and the Bentley and Denys Reitz's Packard, but the parking area was deserted.

He took one quick look up the mountain that towered 2000 feet above him. He could make out the path as it climbed out of the forest and zigzagged up the gut of Skeleton Gorge, passing the pimple of Breakfast Rock on the skyline and then crossing the rim onto the tableland.

There was a line of moving specks on the pathway, just emerging from the forest. The *Ou Baas* and Grandpater were setting their usual furious pace, proving to each other how fit they were, and as he shaded his eyes he recognized Mater's yellow dress, and Tara's turquoise skirt, just tiny flecks of colour against the grey and green wall of the mountain. They were trailing far behind the leaders.

He began to run. He took the first easy slope at a trot, pacing himself. He reached the 300-metre contour path and paused beside the concrete signpost to draw a few long breaths. He surveyed the track ahead.

It went up very steeply from here, jigging through the forest, following the bank of the stream, a series of uneven rocky steps. He went at it fast, but his town shoes had thin leather soles and gave him little purchase. He was panting

wildly and his shirt was soaked through with sweat as he came out of the forest. Still almost 1000 feet to the top, but he saw immediately that he had gained on the picnic party.

They were strung out down the pathway. The two figures leading were Grandpater and the *Ou Baas* – at this distance it was impossible to distinguish between them, but that was Blaine a few paces behind them. He would be hanging back so as not to force the older men to a pace beyond their strength. The rest of the party were in groups and singles, taking up half the slope, with the women far in the rear.

He drew a deep breath and shouted. The women paused and looked back down the slope.

'Stop!' he yelled with all his lung power. 'Stop!'

One of the women waved – it was probably Matty – then they began to climb again. They had not recognized him, nor had they understood the command to stop. They had taken him for another friendly hiker. He was wasting time, the leaders were just under the crest of the summit.

Shasa began to climb with all his strength, leaping over the uneven footing, forcing himself to ignore the burning of his lungs and the numbing exhaustion of his legs, driving himself upwards by sheer force of will.

Tara looked back when he was only ten feet below her.

'Shasa!' she cried, delighted but surprised. 'What are you doing – '

He brushed past her. 'Can't stop,' he grunted, and went on up, passing Anna and then Mater.

'What is it, Shasa?'

'Later!' There was no wind for words, his whole existence was in his agonized legs, and the sweat poured into his eye, blurring his vision.

He saw the leaders make the last short traverse before going over the top, and he stopped and tried to shout again. It came out as an agonized wheeze, and as he watched Grandpater and the *Ou Baas* disappeared over the crest of the slope with Blaine only twenty paces behind them.

The shot was dulled by distance, but even so Shasa recognized the sharp distinctive crack of a Mauser.

From somewhere he found new strength and he flew at the slope, leaping from rock to rock. The single shot seemed to echo and re-echo through his head, and he heard somebody shouting, or perhaps it was only the wild sobbing of his breath and the thunder of his blood in his own eardrums.

* * *

Manfred De La Rey lay all that night in his hide. At sunrise he stood up and swung his arms, squatted and twisted to loosen his muscles and banish the chill that had soaked through the overcoat into his bones. He moved a few paces back and emptied his bladder.

Then he stripped off the overcoat and the jersey – both had been bought from a second-hand clothes dealer on the Parade. They were unmarked and could never be traced to him. He bundled them and stuffed them under a rock. Then he settled back in his hide, stretched out on the tarpaulin. A few blades of grass were obscuring his line of fire and he broke them off and aimed at the head of the path.

His aim was clear and uninterrupted. He worked a cartridge from the magazine into the breech of the Mauser, checking it visually as it slid home, and he locked the bolt down.

Once more he took his aim, and this time he curled his finger round the rear trigger and carefully set the hair trigger with that crisp satisfying little click. Then he pushed the safety-catch over with his thumb and laid the rifle on the tarpaulin in front of him.

He froze into immobility. Patient as a leopard in a tree above a water-hole, only his yellow eyes alive, he let the hours drift by, never for an instant relaxing his vigil.

When it happened, it happened with the abruptness that might have taken another watcher by surprise. There was no warning, no sound of footsteps or voices. The range was too long for that. Suddenly a human figure appeared on the head of the path, silhouetted against the blue of the sky.

Manfred was ready for it. He lifted the rifle to his shoulder with a single fluid movement and his eye went naturally to the aperture of the lens. He did not have to pan the telescopic sight, the image of the man appeared instantly in his field of vision, enlarged and crisply focused.

It was an old man, with thin and narrow shoulders, wearing an open-neck white shirt and a Panama hat that was yellow with age. His silver goatee beard sparkled in the bright spring sunshine. The unwavering cross hairs of the telescope were already perfectly aligned on the exact centre of his narrow chest, a hand's breadth below the vee of his open shirt. No fancy head shot, Manfred had decided, take him through the heart.

He touched the hair trigger and the Mauser clapped in his eardrums, and the butt drove back into his shoulder.

He saw the bullet strike. It flapped the loose white shirt against the skinny old chest and Manfred's vision was so heightened that he even saw the bullet exit. It flew out of the old man's back as a long pink tail of blood and living tissue like a flamingo's feather, and as the frail body was plucked out of sight into the grass, the cloud of blood persisted, hanging in the clear morning air for the thousandth part of a second before it settled.

Manfred rolled to his feet and started to run. He had plotted every yard of his escape route back to the Morris, and a savage elation gave strength to his legs and speed to his feet.

Behind him somebody shouted, a plaintive bewildered sound, but Manfred did not check or look back.

* * *

Shasa came over the crest at a full run. The two men were kneeling beside the body that lay in the grass at the side of the track. They looked up at Shasa, both their faces stricken.

Shasa took one look at the body as it lay face down. The bullet must have been a dum-dum to inflict such a massive exit wound. It had carved a hole through the chest cavity into which he could have thrust both his fists.

There was no hope. He was dead. He hardened himself. There would be time for grief later. Now was the time for vengeance.

'Did you see who did it?' he gasped.

'Yes.' Blaine jumped to his feet. 'I got a glimpse of him. He cut back around Oudekraal Kop,' he said, 'dressed in blue.'

Shasa knew this side of the mountain intimately, every path and cliff, every gorge and gully between Constantia Nek and the Saddle.

The killer had turned around the foot of the kop – he had a start of less than two minutes.

'The bridle path,' Shasa gasped. 'He is heading for the bridle path. I'll try and cut him off at the top of Nursery Ravine.' he started to run again, back towards Breakfast Rock.

'Shasa, be careful!' Blaine yelled after him. 'He has the rifle with him – I saw it.'

The bridle path was the only way a vehicle could reach the table-land, Shasa reasoned as he ran, and this had been so carefully planned that the killer must have an escape vehicle. It had to be parked somewhere on the bridle path.

The footpath made a wide loop around Oudekraal Kop, then came back to the edge and ran along the cliff top past the head of Nursery Ravine until it intersected the bridle path half a mile farther on. There was another rough, little-used path that cut this side of the Kop, along the cliff top. The beginning was difficult to find and a mistake would lead into a dead end against the precipice – but if he found it he could cut a quarter of a mile off the route.

He found the path and turned off onto it. At two places the track was overgrown and he had to struggle through interlaced branches, at another spot at the edge the track had washed away. He had to back up and take a run at it, jumping over the gap with five hundred feet of open drop below him. He landed on his knees, clawed himself to his feet and kept running.

He burst out unexpectedly into the main footpath and collided at full tilt with the blue-overalled killer coming in the opposite direction.

He had a fleeting impression of the man's size and the breadth of his shoulders, and then they were down together, locked chest to chest, grappling savagely, rolling down the slope of the path. The impact had knocked the rifle out of the killer's hand, but Shasa felt the springy hardness and the bulk of his muscle, and the first evidence of the man's strength shocked him. He knew instantly that he was outmatched. Against his fiercest resistance the man rolled him onto his back and came up on top of him, straddling him.

Their faces were inches apart. The man had a thick dark curling beard that was sodden with sweat, his nose was twisted and his brows were dense and black, but it was the eyes that struck terror into Shasa. They were yellow and somehow dreadfully familiar. However, they galvanized Shasa, transforming his terror into superhuman strength.

He wrenched one arm free and rolled the killer over far enough to yank the Beretta pistol from his own belt. He had not loaded a cartridge into the chamber, but he struck upwards with the short barrel, smashing it into the man's temple, and he heard the steel crack on the bone of the skull.

The man's grip slackened and he fell back. Shasa wriggled to his knees, fumbling to load the Beretta. With a metallic snicker the slide pushed a cartridge into the chamber, and he lifted the barrel. He had not realized how close they had rolled to the clifftop. He was kneeling on the very brink, and as he tried to steady his aim on that bearded head, the killer jack-knifed his body and drove both feet into Shasa's chest.

Shasa was hurled backwards. The pistol fired but the shot went straight into the air, and he found himself falling free as he went over the edge of the cliff.

He had a glimpse down the precipice; there was open drop for hundreds of feet, but he fell less than ten of those before he wedged behind a pine sapling that had found foothold in a cleft of the rock.

He hung against the cliff face, his legs dangling free, winded and dazed, and he looked up. The killer's head appeared over the edge of the cliff, those strange yellow eyes glared at him for an instant and then disappeared. Shasa heard his boots scrabble on the pathway, and then the unmistakable sound of a rifle bolt being loaded and cocked.

'He is going to finish me off,' he thought, and only then realized that he still had the Beretta in his right hand.

Desperately he hooked his left elbow over the pine sapling and pointed the Beretta up at the rim of the cliff above his head.

Once more the killer's head and shoulders appeared against the sky, and he was swinging the long barrel of the Mauser downwards; but the weapon was awkward to point at this angle and Shasa fired an instant before it could bear. He heard the light bullet of the pistol strike against flesh, and the killer grunted and disappeared from view. A moment afterwards he heard someone else shout from a distance, and recognized Blaine's voice.

Then the killer's running footsteps moved swiftly away as he set off along the path once more, and a minute later Blaine looked down at Shasa from the clifftop.

'Hold on!' Blaine's face was flushed with exertion and his voice unsteady. He pulled the thick leather belt from his trouser top and buckled it into a loop.

Lying flat on his belly at the top of the cliff, he lowered the looped belt and Shasa hooked his arm through it. Even though Blaine was a powerful man with abnormal arm and chest development from polo practice, they struggled for minutes before he could drag Shasa over the top of the cliff.

They lay together for a few moments; and then Shasa pulled himself unsteadily to his feet and staggered off along the pathway in pursuit of the fugitive. Within a dozen paces Blaine pulled ahead of him, running strongly and his example spurred Shasa. He kept up, and Blaine gasped over his shoulder.

'Blood!' He pointed to the wet red speckles on the flat stone in the pathway. 'You hit him!'

They came out onto the wide bridle path, and started down, running shoulder to shoulder now, helped by the gradient of the descent, but they had not reached the first hairpin bend when they heard an engine start in the forest below.

'He's got a car!' Blaine panted as the engine whined into a crescendo, then the sound of it receded swiftly. They pulled up and listened to it dwindle into silence. Shasa's legs could hold him up no longer. He sank into a heap in the middle of the road.

There was a telephone at the Cecilia Forestry Station and Shasa got through to Inspector Nel at CID headquarters and gave him a description of the killer.

'You'll have to move fast. The man has obviously got his escape planned.'

The mountain club kept a lightweight stretcher at the forestry station, for this mountain took many human lives each year. The forester gave them six of his black labourers to carry it, and accompanied them back up the bridle path and along the mountain rim to the head of Skeleton Gorge.

The women were there, Centaine and Anna were in tears, clinging to each other for comfort. They had spread one of the rugs over the dead man.

Shasa knelt beside the body and lifted the corner of the rug. In death Sir Garry Courtney's features had fallen in, so that his nose was arched and beaky, his closed eyelids were in deep cavities, but there was about him a gentle dignity so that he resembled the death mask of a fragile Caesar.

Shasa kissed his forehead and the skin was cool and velvety smooth against his lips.

When he stood up, Field-Marshal Smuts laid a hand of comfort on his shoulder. 'I'm sorry, my boy,' the old field-marshal said. 'That bullet was meant for me.'

* * *

Manfred De La Rey pulled off the road, steering with one hand. He did not leave the driver's seat of the Morris, and he kept the engine running while he unbuttoned the front of his overalls.

The bullet had entered just below and in front of his armpit, punching into the thick pad of the pectoral muscle and it had angled upwards. He could find no exit wound, the bullet was still lodged in his body, and when he groped gently around the back of his own shoulder, he found a swelling that was so tender that he almost screamed involuntarily as he touched it.

The bullet was lying just under the skin, but it did not appear to have penetraded the chest cavity. He wadded his handkerchief over the wound in his armpit and buttoned the overalls. He checked his watch. It was a few minutes before eleven o'clock, just twenty-three minutes since he had fired the shot that would set his people free.

A sense of passionate soaring triumph overrode the pain of his wound. He pulled back onto the road and drove sedately around the base of the mountain, down the main road and through Woodstock. At the gates of the railway yards he showed his pass to the gatekeeper and went through to park the Morris outside the restrooms for off-duty firemen and engine drivers.

He left the Mauser under the seat of the Morris. Both the weapon and the vehicle would be taken care of. He crossed quickly to the back door of the restroom and they were waiting for him inside.

Roelf leapt to his feet anxiously as he saw the blood on the blue overalls.

'Are you all right? What happened?'

'Smuts is dead,' Manfred said, and his savage joy was transmitted to them. They did not cheer or speak, but stood quietly, savouring the moment on which history would hinge.

Roelf broke the silence after a few seconds. 'You are hurt.'

While one of the *stormjagters* went out and drove the Morris away, Roelf helped Manfred strip off his soiled overalls. There was very little blood now, but the flesh around the wound was swollen and bruised. The bullet-hole itself was a black puncture that wept watery pink lymph. Roelf dressed and bound it up with bandages from a railway first-aid kit.

Because Manfred had very little use of his left arm, Roelf lathered the black beard and shaved it off with a straight razor for him. With the beard gone Manfred was years younger, handsome and clean-cut once again, but pale from loss of blood and the weakness of his wound. They helped him into a clean pair of overalls and Roelf set the fireman's cap on his head.

'We will meet again soon,' Roelf told him. 'And I am proud to be your friend. From now on glory will follow you all the days of your life.'

The engine driver came forward. 'We must go,' he said. Roelf and Manfred shook hands and then Manfred turned away and followed the driver out of the restroom and down the platform to the waiting locomotive.

The police stopped the northbound goods train at Worcester Station. They opened and searched all the trucks and a constable climbed into the cab of the locomotive and searched that also.

'What is the trouble?' the engine driver demanded.

'There has been a murder. Some bigwig was shot on Table Mountain this morning. We've got a description of the killer. There are police roadblocks on all the roads and we are searching every motor vehicle and ship and train – '

'Who was killed?' Manfred asked, and the constable shrugged.

'I don't know, my friend, but judging by the fuss it's somebody important.' He climbed down from the cab, and a few minutes later the signals changed to green and they rolled out of the station heading north.

By the time they reached Bloemfontein, Manfred's shoulder had swollen into a hard purple hump and the pain was insupportable. He sat hunched in a corner of the cab, moaning softly, teetering on the brink of consciousness, the rustle of dark wings filled his head.

Roelf had telephoned ahead, and there were friends to meet him and smuggle him out of the Bloemfontein railway yards.

'Where are we going?'

'A doctor,' they told him, and reality broke up into a patchwork of darkness and pain.

He was aware of the choking reek of chloroform, and when he woke he was in a bed in a sunny but monastically furnished room. The shoulder was bound up in crisp white bandages, and despite the lingering nausea of the anaesthetic, he felt whole again.

There was a man sitting in the chair beside the window, and as soon as he realized Manfred was awake, he came to him.

'How do you feel?'

'Not too bad. Has it happened – the rising? Have our people seized power?'

The man looked at him strangely. 'You do not know?' he asked.

'I only know that we have succeeded – ' Manfred began, but the man fetched a newspaper and laid it on the bed. He stood beside Manfred as he read the headlines:

ASSASSINATION ON TABLE MOUNTAIN
OB BLAMED FOR KILLING OF PROMINENT HISTORIAN
SMUTS ORDERS ARREST AND INTERNMENT OF 600

Manfred stared uncomprehendingly at the news-sheet, and the man told him, 'You killed the wrong man. Smuts has the excuse he wanted. All our leaders have been seized, and they are searching for you. There is a manhunt across the land. You cannot stay here. We expect the police to be here at any minute.'

Manfred was passed on and he left the city riding in the back of a truck under a load of stinking dry hides. The *Ossewa Brandwag* had been decimated by the arrests, and those members remaining at liberty were shaken and afraid, all of them running for cover. None of them wanted to take the risk of harbouring the fugitive. He was passed on again and again.

The plan had seen no further ahead than the assassination and successful revolt, after which Manfred would have emerged as a *Volk* hero and taken his rightful place in the councils of the republican government. Now it was run and hide, sick and weak, a price of five thousand pounds on his head. Nobody wanted him; he was a dangerous risk and they passed him on as quickly as they could find someone else to take him.

In the published lists of those arrested and interned in the government crackdown, he found many named he knew, and with dismay he read Roelf's name, and that of the Reverend Tromp Bierman amongst them. He wondered how Sarah, Aunt Trudi and the girls would fare now, but he found it difficult to think or concentrate, for despair had unmanned him, and he knew the terror of a hunted and wounded animal.

It took eight days to make the journey to Johannesburg. He had not deliberately set out for the Witwatersrand, but circumstances and the whim of his helpers led him that way. By rail and truck and, later, when the wound began to heal and his strength returned, at night and on foot across the open veld, he at last reached the city.

He had an address, his last contact with the brotherhood and he took the tramcar from the main railway station along the Braamfontein ridge and watched the street numbers as they passed.

The number he needed was 36. It was one in a row of semi-detached cottages, and he started to rise to leave the tramcar at the next stop. Then he saw the blue police uniform in the doorway of number 36 and he sank down in his seat again and rode the tramcar to its terminus.

He left it there and went into a Greek café across the road. He ordered a cup of coffee, paying for it with his last few coins, and sipped it slowly, hunched over the cup, trying to think.

He had avoided a dozen police roadblocks and searches in these last eight days, but he sensed that he had exhausted his luck. There was no hiding-place open to him any longer. The road led from here on to the gallows.

He stared out of the greasy plate-glass window of the café and the street sign across the road caught his eye. Something stirred in his memory, but it eluded his first efforts to grasp it. Then suddenly he felt the lift of his spirits and another weak glimmer of hope.

He left the café and followed the road whose name he had recognized. The area deteriorated quickly into a slum of shanties and hovels and he saw no more white faces on the rutted unmade street. The black faces at the windows or in the reeking alleyways watched him impassively across that unfathomable void which separates the races in Africa.

He found what he was looking for. It was a small general dealer's store crowded with black shoppers, noisy and laughing, the women with their babies strapped upon their backs, bargaining across the counter for sugar and soap, paraffin and salt, but the hubbub descended into silence when a white man entered the shop, and they gave way for him respectfully, not looking directly at him.

The proprietor was an elderly Zulu with a fluffy beard of white wool, dressed in a baggy Western-style suit. He left the black woman he was serving and came to Manfred, inclining his head deferentially to listen to Manfred's request.

'Come with me, *Nkosi*.' He led Manfred through to the storeroom at the back of the shop.

'You will have to wait,' he said, 'perhaps a long time,' and he left him there.

Manfred slumped down on a pile of sugar sacks. He was hungry and exhausted and the shoulder was starting to throb again. He fell asleep and was roused by a hand on his shoulder and a deep voice in his ear.

'How did you know where to look for me?'

Manfred struggled to his feet. 'My father told me where to find you,' he answered. 'Hello, Swart Hendrick.'

'It has been many years, little Manie.' The big Ovambo grinned at him through the black gap of missing teeth; his head, laced with scars, was black and shiny as a cannonball. 'Many years, but I never doubted we would meet again. Never once in all those years. The gods of the wilderness have bound us together, little Manie. I knew you would come.'

* * *

The two men sat alone in the back room of Swart Hendrick's house. It was one of the few brick-built dwellings in the shanty town of Drake's Farm. However, the bricks were unbaked and the building was not so ostentatious as to stand out from the hovels that crowded close around it. Swart Hendrick had long ago learned not to draw the attention of the white police to his wealth.

In the front room the women were cooking and working, while the children bawled or shouted with laughter round their feet. As befitted his station in life, Swart Hendrick had six town wives who lived together in an amiable symbiotic relationship. The possessive jealousy of monogamistic Western women was totally alien to them. Senior wives took a major part in the selection of the junior wives and gained considerable presige from the multiplicity, nor did they resent the maintenance sent to the country wives and their offspring or their spouse's periodic visits to the country kraal to add to the number of those offspring. They considered themselves all part of one family. When the children from the country were old enough to be sent into the city for the furtherance of their eduction and fortune, they found themselves with many fostermothers and could expect the same love and discipline as they had received in the kraal.

The smaller children had the run of the house and one of them crawled mother-naked into Swart Hendrick's lap as he sat on his carved stool, the sign of rank of a tribal chieftain. Although he was deep in discussion with Manfred, he fondled the little one casually, as he would a favourite puppy, and when the beer pot was empty, he clapped his hands and one of the junior wives, the pretty moon-faced Zulu or the nubile Basuto with breasts as round and hard as ostrich eggs, would bring in a new pot and kneel before Hendrick to present it to him.

'So, little Manie, we have spoken of everything, and said all that is to be said, and we come back to the same problem.' Swart Hendrick lifted the beer pot and swallowed a mouthful of the thick white bubbling gruel. He smacked his lips, then wiped the half moon of beer from his upper lip with the back of his forearm and handed the pot across to Manfred. 'That problem is this. At every railway station and on every road the white police are searching for you. They have even offered a price for you – and what a price, little Manie. They will give five thousand pounds for you. How many cattle and women could a man buy with that amount of money?' He broke off to consider the question and shook his head in wonder at the answer. 'You ask me to help you to leave

Johannesburg and to cross the great river in the north. What would the white police do if they caught me? Would they hang me on the same tree as they hang you – or would they only send me to break rocks in the prison of *Ou Baas* Smuts and King Georgy?' Swart Hundrick sighed theatrically. 'It is a heavy question, little Manie. Can you give me an answer?'

'You have been as a father to me, Hennie,' Manfred said quietly. 'Does a father leave his son for the hyena and the vultures?'

'If I am your father, little Manie, why then is your face white and mine black?' Hendrick smiled. 'There are no debts between us, they were all paid long ago.'

'My father and you were brothers.'

'How many summers have burned since those days,' Hendrick mourned the passage of time with a sorrowful shake of his head. 'And how the world and all those in it have changed.'

'There is one thing that never changes – not even over the years, Hennie.'

'What is that, oh child with a white face who claims my paternity?'

'A diamond, my black father. A diamond never changes.'

Hendrick nodded. 'Let us speak then of a diamond.'

'Not one diamond,' Manfred said. 'Many diamonds, a bagful of diamonds that lie in a faraway place that only you and I know of.'

* * *

'The risks are great,' Hendrick told his brother. 'And doubt lurks in my mind like a man-eating lion lying in thick bush. Perhaps the diamonds are where the white boy says they are, but the lion of doubt still waits for me. The father was a devious man, hard and without mercy – I sense that the son has grown to be like the father. He speaks of friendship between us, but I no longer feel the warmth in him.'

Moses Gama stared into the fire; his eyes were dark and inscrutable. 'He tried to kill Smuts,' he mused aloud. 'He is of the hard Boers like those of old, the ones that slaughtered our people at Blood river and shattered the power of the great chiefs. They have been defeated this time, as they were in 1914, but they have not been destroyed. They will rise to fight again, these hard Boers, when this white men's war across the sea ends, they will call out their impis and carry the battle to Smuts and his party once again. It is the way of the white man – and I have studied his history – that when peace comes, they often reject those who fought hardest during the battle. I sense that in the next conflict the whites will reject Smuts and that the hard Boers will triumph – and this white boy is one of them.'

'You are right, my brother,' Hendrick nodded. 'I had not looked that far into the future. He is the enemy of our people. If he and his kind come to power then we will learn a bitter lesson in slavery. I must deliver him to the vengeance of those who seek after him.'

Moses Gama raised his noble head and looked across the fire at his elder brother.

'It is the weakness of the multitudes that they cannot see the horizon – their gaze is fixed only as far ahead as their bellies or their genitals,' Moses said. 'You

have admitted to that weakness – why, my brother, do you not seek to rise above it? Why do you not raise your eyes and look to the future?'

'I do not understand.'

'The greatest danger to our people is their own patience and passivity. We are a great herd of cattle under the hand of a cunning herdsman. He keeps us quiescent with a paternal despotism, and most of us, knowing no better, are lulled into an acceptance which we mistake for contentment. Yet the herdsman milks us and at his pleasure eats our flesh. He is our enemy, for the slavery in which he holds us is so insidious that it's impossible to goad the herd to rebel against it.'

'If he is our enemy, what of these others that you call the hard Boers?' Hendrick was perplexed. 'Are they not a fiercer enemy?'

'Upon them will depend the ultimate freedom of our people. They are men without subtlety and artifice. Not for them the smile and kind word that disguises the brutal act. They are angry men filled with fear and hatred. They hate the Indians and the Jews, they hate the English, but most of all they hate and fear the black tribes, for we are many and they are few. They hate and fear us because they have what is rightly ours, and they will not be able to conceal their hatred. When they come to power, they will teach our people the true meaning of slavery. By their oppressions, they will transform the tribes from a herd of complacent cattle into a great stampede of enraged wild buffalo before whose strength nothing can stand. We must pray for this white boy of yours and all he stands for. The future of our people depends upon him.'

Hendrick sat for a long time staring into the fire, and then slowly raised his great bald head and looked at his brother with awe.

'I sometimes think, son of my father, that you are the wisest man of all our tribe,' he whispered.

* * *

Swart Hendrick sent for a *sangoma*, a tribal medicine man. He made a poultice for Manfred's shoulder that when applied, hot and evil-smelling, proved highly efficacious and within ten days Manfred was fit to travel again.

The same *sangoma* provided a herbal dye for Manfred's skin which darkened it to the exact hue of one of the northern tribes. The eyes, Manfred's yellow eyes, were not a serious handicap. Amongst the black mine workers who had worked out their Wenela contract and were returning home, there were certain symbols which confirmed their status as sophisticated men of the world, tin trunks to hold the treasures they had acquired, the pink post office savings books filled with the little numbers of their accumulated wealth, the silver metal mine helmets which they were allowed to retain and which would be worn with pride everywhere from the peaks of Basutoland to the equatorial forests, and lastly a pair of sunglasses.

Manfred's travel papers were issued by one of Hendrick's Buffaloes, a clerk in the pay office of ERPM, and they were totally authentic. He wore his dark sunglasses when he boarded the Wenela rain and his skin was dyed the same hue as the black workers who surrounded him closely. All these men were Hendrick's Buffaloes, and they kept him protected in their midst.

He found it strange but reassuring that the few white officials that he

encountered in the long slow journey back to South West Africa, seldom looked at him directly. Because he was black, their gaze seemed to slide by his face without touching it.

Manfred and Hendrick left the train at Okahandja and with a group of other workers climbed onto the bus for the final hot dusty miles to Hendrick's kraal. Two days later they set out again, this time on foot, heading north and east into the burning wilderness.

There had been good rains during the previous season and they found water in many of the pans in the southern Kavango and it was two weeks before they saw the kopjes humped like a caravan of camels out of the blue heat haze along the desert horizon.

Manfred realized as they tramped towards the hills how alien he was in this desert. Hendrick and his father had belonged here, but since childhood Manfred had lived in towns and cities. He would never have been able to find his way back without Hendrick's guidance; indeed he would not have survived more than a few days in this harsh and unforgiving land without the big Ovambo.

The kopje that Hendrick led Manfred towards seemed identical to all the others. It was only when they scaled the steep granite side and stood upon the summit, that the memories came crowding back. Perhaps they had been deliberately suppressed, but now they emerged again in stark detail. Manfred could almost see his father's features ravaged by fever and smell again the stench of gangrene from his rotting flesh. He remembered with fresh agony the harsh words of rejection with which his father had driven him to safety, but he closed his mind to the ache of them.

Unerringly he went to the crack that split the granite dome and knelt over it, but his heart sank when he peered down and could distinguish nothing in the deep shadows that contrasted with the sunlight and its reflections from the rock around him.

'So they have gone, these famous diamonds,' Hendrick chuckled cynically when he saw Manfred's dismay. 'Perhaps the jackals have eaten them.'

Manfred ignored him and from his pack brought out a roll of fishing-line. He tied the lead sinker and the stout treble fish hook to the end and lowered it into the crack. Patiently he worked, jigging the hook along the depth of the crack while Hendrick squatted in the small strip of shade under the summit boulders and watched him without offering encouragement.

The hook snagged something deep in the crack, and cautiously Manfred applied pressure on the line. It held and he took a twist around his wrist and pulled upwards with gradually increasing strength. Something gave, and then the hook pulled free. He drew the line in hand over hand. One point of the treble hook had opened under the strain, but there was a shred of rotted canvas still attached to the barb.

He bent the tine of the hook back into shape and lowered it once again into the crack. He plumbed the depths, working each inch from side to side and up and down. Another half hour of work and he felt the hook snag again.

This time the weight stayed on it, and he eased the line in, an inch at a time. He heard something scraping on the rough granite, then slowly a shapeless lumpy bundle came into view deep down. He lifted it slowly, holding his breath as it came up the last few feet. Then as he swung it clear, the canvas of the old rucksack burst open and a cascade of glittering white stones spilled onto the granite top around him.

They divided the diamonds into two equal piles as they had agreed, and drew

lots for the first choice. Hendrick won and made his selection. Manfred poured his share into the empty tobacco pouch he had brought for the purpose.

'You told the truth, little Manie,' Hendrick admitted. 'I was wrong to doubt you.'

The following evening they reached the river and slept side by side beside the fire. In the morning they rolled their blankets and faced each other.

'Goodbye, Hennie. Perhaps the road will bring us together again.'

'I have told you, little Manie, that the gods of the wilderness have linked us together. We will meet again, that I am certain of.'

'I look forward to that day.'

'The gods alone will decide whether we meet again as father and son, as brothers – or as deadly enemies,' Hendrick said and slung his pack over his shoulder. Without looking back he walked away into the southern desert.

Manfred watched him out of sight, then he turned and followed the bank of the river into the north-west. That evening he came upon a village of the river people. Two of the young men in their dugout canoe ferried him across to the Portuguese side. Three weeks later Manfred reached Luanda, capital of the Portuguese colony, and rang the bell on the wrought-iron gates of the German consulate.

He waited in Luanda three weeks for orders from the German *Abwehr* in Berlin, and slowly it dawned upon him that the delay was deliberate. He had failed in the task they had set him, and in Nazi Germany failure was unforgivable.

He sold one of the smallest diamonds from his hoard at a fraction of its real value and waited out his punishment. Each morning he called at the German consulate and the military attaché turned him away with barely concealed contempt.

'No orders yet, Herr De La Rey. You must be patient.'

Manfred spent most of his days in one of the water-front cafés and his nights in his cheap lodgings, endlessly going over each detail of his failure, or thinking about Uncle Tromp and Roelf in the concentration camp, or about Heidi and the child in Berlin.

His orders came at last. He was issued a German diplomatic passport and he sailed on a Portuguese freighter as far as the Canary Islands. From there he flew on a civilian Junkers aircraft with Spanish markings to Lisbon.

In Lisbon he encountered the same deliberate contempt. He was dismissed casually to find his own lodgings and await those orders which seemed never to come. He wrote personal letters to Colonel Sigmund Boldt and to Heidi. Although the consulate attaché assured him that these had gone out in the diplomatic bag to Berlin, he received no reply.

He sold another small diamond and rented pleasant spacious lodgings in an old building on the bank of the Tagus river, passing the long idle days in reading, study and writing. He began work on two literary projects simultaneously, a political history of southern Africa and an autobiography, both for his own edification and with no intention of ever publishing. He learned Portuguese, taking lessons from a retired schoolmaster who lived in the same building. He kept up a rigorous physical training schedule, as though he were still boxing professionally, and he came to know all the secondhand book stores of the city where he purchased every law book he could find and read them in German, English and Portuguese. But still the time hung heavily on his hands

and he chafed at his inability to take part in the conflict that raged around the globe.

The conflict swung against the Axis powers. The United States of America had entered the war and Flying Fortresses were bombing the cities of Germany. Manfred read of the terrible conflagration that had destroyed Cologne and he wrote again to Heidi for perhaps the hundredth time since he had arrived in Portugal.

Three weeks later, on one of his regular calls at the German consulate, the military attaché handed him an envelope and with a surge of joy he recognized Heidi's handwriting upon it. It told him that she had received none of his previous letters and had come to believe that he was dead. She expressed her wonder and thankfulness at his survival and sent him a snapshot of herself and little Lothar. In the photograph he saw that she had put on a little weight, but in a stately manner she was even more handsome than when last he had seen her – and in a little over three years his son had grown into a sturdy youngster with a head of blond curls and features that showed promise of strength as well as beauty. The photograph was black and white and did not show the colour of his eyes. Manfred's longing for them both threatened to consume him. He wrote Heidi a long passionate letter explaining his circumstances and urging her to make all possible efforts to procure a travel pass and to join him with the child in Lisbon. Without being specific, he was able to let her know that he was financially able to take care of them, and that he had plans for a future that included them both.

* * *

Heidi De La Rey lay awake and listened to the bombers. They had come on three successive nights. The centre of the city was devastated, the opera house and the railway station totally destroyed, and from the information which she had access to in the Department of Propaganda, she knew of the Allied successes in France and Russia, she knew the truth of the hundred thousand German troops captured by the Russians at Minsk.

Beside her Colonel Sigmund Boldt slept restlessly, rolling over and grunting so she was even more disturbed by him than by the distant American bombers. He had reason to worry, she thought. All of them were worried since the abortive attempt to assassinate the Führer. She had seen the films of the execution of the traitors, every minute detail of their agony as they hung on the meat hooks, and General Zoller had been one of them.

Sigmund Boldt had not been one of the conspirators, she was certain of that, but he was close enough to the plot to be caught up in the tidal wave that flowed from it. Heidi had been his mistress for almost a year now, but she had begun to notice the first signs of his waning interest in her, and she knew that his days of influence and power were numbered. Soon she would be alone again, without special food rations for herself and little Lothar.

She listened to the bombers. The raid was over, and the sound of their motors dwindled away to a mosquito hum, but they would be back. In the silence after their departure, she thought about Manfred and the letters he had written to which she had never replied. He was in Lisbon, and in Portugal there were no bombers.

She spoke to Sigmund the next day at breakfast. 'It is only little Lothar I am thinking of,' she explained, and she thought she saw a glimmer of relief in his expression. Perhaps he had already been calculating how he could be rid of her without a fuss. That afternoon she wrote to Manfred, care of the German Consulate in Lisbon, and she enclosed a photograph of herself and Lothar.

Colonel Sigmund Boldt moved quickly. He still had influence and power in the department sufficient for him to procure her travel pass and documents within a week, and he drove her out to Tempelhot airport in the black Mercedes and kissed her goodbye at the foot of the boarding ladder of the Junkers transport aircraft.

Three days later Sigmund Boldt was arrested in his home in Grünewald and a week later he died under interrogation in his cell at the Gestapo headquarters, still protesting his innocence.

* * *

Little Lothar De La Rey caught his first glimpse of Africa peering between the rails of the Portuguese freighter as it steamed into Table Bay. He stood between his father and mother, holding their hands and chuckling with delight at the steam tugs that came bustling out to welcome their ship.

The war had ended two years ago, but Manfred had taken extraordinary precautions before bringing his family to Africa. First he had written to Uncle Tromp who had been released from internment at the end of the war, and from him learned all the family and political news. Aunt Trudi was well and both the girls were married now. Roelf had been released at the same time as Uncle Tromp and had returned to his job at the university. He and Sarah were happy and well and expecting another addition to their family before the year's end.

Politically the news was promising. Although the *Ossewa Brandwag* and the other para-military organizations had been discredited and disbanded, their members had been absorbed into the National Party under Dr Daniel Malan, and the Party was rejuvenated and strengthened by their numbers. Afrikaner unity had never been more solid, and the dedication of the massive Voortrekker monument on a kopje above Pretoria had rallied the *Volk* so that even many of those who had joined Smuts' army and fought in North Africa and Italy were flocking to the cause.

A backlash was developing against Smuts and his United Party. The feeling was that he placed the interests of the British Commonwealth, which he had done so much to bring into being, before the interests of South Africa.

Furthermore, Smuts had made a political misjudgement by inviting the British Royal Family to visit the country, and their presence had served to polarize public feelings between the English-speaking jingoists and the Afrikaners. Even many of those who had been Smuts men were offended by the visit.

Doctor Hendrik Frensch Verwoerd who had left his teaching post at Stellenbosch University to become editor of *Die Vanderland* allowed only one reference to the royal visit in his newspaper. He warned his readers that there might be some disruption of traffic in Johannesburg owing to the presence of foreign visitors in the city.

On the occasion of the loyal address at the opening of the South African

Parliament, Dr Daniel Malan and all his Nationalist members had absented themselves from the House in protest.

Uncle Tromp ended his letter, 'So we have come through the storm strengthened and purified as a *Volk*, and more determined than ever in our endeavours. There are great days ahead, Manie. Come home. We need men like you.'

Still Manfred did not move immediately. First he wrote to Uncle Tromp again. In veiled terms he asked what the position was with regard to a white sword he had left behind, and after delay he received assurance that nobody knew anything about his sword. Discreet enquiries through friends in the police force had elicited the information that although the dossier on the missing sword was still open, it was no longer under active investigation and nobody knew its whereabouts or to whom it belonged. It must be assumed that it would never be found.

Leaving Heidi and the boy in Lisbon, Manfred travelled by train to Zürich where he sold the remainder of the diamonds. In the post-war euphoria prices were high, and he was able to deposit almost £200,000 in a numbered account with Crédit Suisse.

When they reached Cape Town the family went ashore without attracting attention, although as an Olympic gold medallist Manfred could have found himself the centre of a great deal of publicity if he had wished. Quietly he felt his way, visiting old friends, former *OB* members and political allies, making certain that there were no nasty surprises in store for him before he gave his first interview to the *Burger* newspaper. To them he explained how he had passed the war in neutral Portugal because he had declined to fight for either side, but now he had returned to the land of his birth to make whatever contribution he could to political progress towards what was every Afrikaner's dream, a Republic of South Africa, free from the dictates of any foreign power.

He had said all the right things, and was an Olympic gold medallist in a land where athletic prowess was venerated. He was handsome and clever and devout, with an attractive wife and son. He still had friends in high places and the number of those friends was increasing each day.

He purchased a partnership in a prosperous Stellenbosch law firm. The senior partner was an attorney named Van Schoor, very active in politics and a luminary of the Nationalist Party. He sponsored Manfred's entry into the Party.

Manfred devoted himself to the affairs of Van Schoor and De La Rey and just as single-mindedly to those of the Cape Nationalist Party. He showed great skills as an organizer and as a fund-raiser, and by the end of 1947 he was a member of the *Broederbond*.

The *Broederbond*, or brotherhood, was another secret society of Afrikaners. It had not replaced the defunct *Ossewa Brandwag*, but had existed concurrently, and often in competition with it. Unlike the *OB* it was not flamboyant and overtly militant, there were no uniforms or torchlit rallies.

It worked quietly in small groups in the homes and offices of powerful and influential men for membership was only bestowed upon the brightest and the best. It considered its members to be an elite of super-Afrikaners, whose end object was the formation of an Afrikaner Republic. Like the disbanded *OB*, the secrecy surrounding it was iron-clad. Unlike the *OB*, a member must be much more than merely a pure-blooded Afrikaner. He must be a leader of men, or at the very least a potential leader, and an invitation to join the brotherhood held

within it the promise of high political preference and favour in the future Republic.

Manfred's first rewards of membership came almost immediately, for when the campaign for the general election of 1948 opened, Manfred De La Rey was nominated as the official Nationalist candidate for the marginal seat of Hottentots Holland.

Two years previously, in a by-election, the seat had been won for Smuts' United Party by a young war-hero from a rich English-speaking Cape family. As the incumbent, Shasa Courtney had been nominated by the United Party as their candidate to contest the general election.

Manfred De La Rey had been offered a safer seat but he had deliberately chosen Hottentots Holland. He wanted the opportunity to meet Shasa Courtney again. He recalled vividly their first meeting on the fish jetty at Walvis Bay. Since then their destinies seemed to have been inextricably bound together in a knot of Gordian complexity, and Manfred sensed that he had to face this adversary one more time and unravel that knot.

To prepare himself for the campaign as well as to satisfy his brooding enmity towards them, Manfred began an investigation of the Courtney family, in particular Shasa and his mother Mrs Centaine de Thiry Courtney. Almost immediately he found areas of mystery in the woman's past, and these grew deeper as his investigations continued. Finally he was sufficiently encouraged to employ a Parisian firm of private investigators to examine in detail Centaine's family background and her origins.

On his regular monthly visit to his father in Pretoria Central Prison, he brought up the Courtney name and begged the frail old man to tell him everything he knew about them.

When the campaign opened, Manfred knew that his investigations had given him an important advantage, and he threw himself into the rough and tumble of a South African election with gusto and determination.

* * *

Centaine de Thiry Courtney stood on the top of Table Mountain, a little apart from the rest of the party. Since Sir Garry's murder the mountain always saddened her, even when she looked at it from the windows of her study at Weltevreden. This was the first time that she had been on the summit since the tragic day, and she was here only because she could not refuse Blaine's invitation to act as his official partner. 'And, of course, I am still enough of a snob to relish the idea of being introduced to the king and queen of England!' She was truthful with herself.

The *Ou Baas* was chatting to King George, pointing out the landmarks with his cane. He was wearing his old Panama hat and baggy slacks, and Centaine felt a pang at his resemblance to Sir Garry. She turned away.

Blaine was with the small group around the royal princesses. He was telling a story and Margaret Rose laughed delightedly. 'How pretty she is,' Centaine thought. 'What a complexion, a royal English rose.' The princess turned and said something to one of the other young men. Centaine had been introduced to him earlier; he was an airforce officer as Shasa was, a handsome fellow with a fine sensitive face, she thought, and then her female instincts were alerted as

she caught the secret glance the couple exchanged. It was unmistakable, and Centaine felt that little lift of her spirits she always enjoyed when she saw two young people in love.

It was followed almost immediately by a return of her sombre mood. Thinking of love and young lovers, she studied Blaine. He was unaware of her gaze, relaxed and charming, but there was silver in his hair, shining silver wings above those sticky-out ears she loved so well, and there were deep creases in his tanned face, around the eyes and at the corners of his mouth and his big aquiline nose. Still his body was hard and flat-bellied from riding and walking, but he was like the old lion, and with a further slide of her spirits she faced the fact that he was no longer in his prime. Instead he stood at the threshold of old age.

'Oh God,' she thought, 'even I will be forty-eight years old in a few months,' and she lifted her hand to touch her head. There was silver there also, but so artfully tinted that it seemed merely a bleaching of the African sun. There were other unpalatable truths that her mirror revealed to her in the privacy of her boudoir, before she hid them with the creams and powders and rouges.

'How much more time is there, my darling?' she asked sadly but silently. 'Yesterday we were young and immortal, but today I see at last that there is a term to all things.'

At that moment Blaine looked across at her, and she saw his quick concern as he noticed her expression. He murmured an apology to the others and came to her side.

'Why so serious on such a lovely day?' he smiled.

'I was thinking how shameless you are, Blaine Malcomess,' she answered, and his smile slipped.

'What is it, Centaine?'

'How can you blatantly parade your mistress before the crowned heads of Empire,' she demanded. 'I have no doubt it is a capital crime, you could have your head struck off on Tower Green!'

He stared at her for a moment, and then the grin came back, boyish and jubilant. 'My dear lady, there must be some way I can escape that fate. What if I were to change your status – from scarlet mistress to demure wife?'

She giggled. She very seldom did that, but when she did, he found it irresistible. 'What an extraordinary time and place to receive a proposal of marriage, and an even more extraordinary time and place to accept one.'

'What do you think their majesties would say if I were to kiss you here and now?' He leaned towards her and she leapt back startled.

'Crazy man, you just wait until I get you home,' she threatened. He took her arm and they went to join the company.

* * *

'Weltevreden is one of the loveliest homes in the Cape,' Blaine agreed. 'But it doesn't belong to me – and I want to carry my bride over the threshold of my own home.'

'We cannot live in Newlands House.' Centaine did not have to say more, and for a moment Isabella's ghost passed between them like a dark shadow.

'What about the cottage?' He laughed to banish Isabella's memory. 'It's got a magnificent bed, what else do we need?'

'We'll keep that,' she agreed. 'And every now and then we will slip away to revisit it.'

'Dirty weekends, good-oh!'

'You are vulgar, do you know that?'

'So where shall we live?'

'We will find a place. Our own special place.'

It was five hundred acres of mountain, beach and rocky coastline with a profusion of protea plants and grand views across Hout Bay and out to the cold green Atlantic.

The house was a huge rambling Victorian mansion, built at the turn of the century by one of the old mining magnates from the Witwatersrand, and in desperate need of the attention that Centaine proceeded to lavish upon it. However, she kept the name Rhodes Hill. For her one of its chief attractions was that a mere twenty minutes in the Daimler took her over the Constantia Nek pass and down to the vineyards of Weltevreden.

Shasa had taken over the chairmanship of Courtney Mining and Finance at the war's end, although Centaine kept a seat on the board and never missed a meeting. Now Shasa and Tara moved into the great château of Weltevreden that she had vacated, but Centaine visited there every weekend and sometimes more often. It gave her a pang when Tara rearranged the furniture that she had left and re-landscaped the front lawns and gardens, but with an effort she managed to hold her tongue.

Often these days she thought of the old Bushman couple who had rescued her from the sea and the desert, and then she would sing softly the praise song that O'wa had composed for the infant Shasa:

> His arrows will fly to the stars
> and when men speak his name
> it will be heard as far –
> And he will find good water,
> wherever he travels, he will find good water.

Although after all these years the clicks and tones of the San language tripped strangely on her tongue, she knew that the blessing of O'wa had borne fruit. That, and her own rigorous training had led Shasa to the good waters of life.

Gradually Shasa with the help of David Abrahams in Windhoek had instilled into the sprawling Courtney Mining and Finance Company a new spirit of youthful vigour and adventure. Although the old hands, Abe Abrahams and Twentyman-Jones, grumbled and shook their heads and although Centaine was occasionally forced to side with them and veto Shasa's wilder more risky projects, the company regained direction and increased in stature. Each time that Centaine examined the books or took her seat below her son at the boardroom table, there was less to complain about and more cause for self-congratulation. Even Dr Twentyman-Jones, that paragon of pessimists, had been heard to mutter, 'The boy has got a head on his shoulders.' And then appalled at his own lapse, he had added morosely, 'Mind you, it will take a full day's work for all of us to keep it there.'

When Shasa had been nominated as the United Party candidate for the parliamentary by-election of Hottentots Holland and had snatched a close-fought victory from his Nationalist opponent, Centaine saw all her ambitions

for him becoming reality. He would almost certainly be offered something more important after the next general electioon, perhaps the job as deputy minister of mines and industry. After that, a full seat in the cabinet, and beyond that? She let the idea of it send little thrills up her spine, but did not allow herself to dwell on it in case the thought brought ill-fortune on the actuality. Still it was possible. Her son was well favoured, even the eye-patch added to his individuality, he spoke amusingly and articulately, and he had the trick of making people listen and like him. He was rich and ambitious and clever – and he had herself and Tara behind him. It was possible and more than possible.

By some remarkable dialectic contortion Tara Malcomess Courtney had retained her social conscience intact while taking up the management of the Weltevreden household as though to the manner born.

It was typical that she retained her maiden name, and that she could rush from the elegant surroundings of Weltevreden to the slum clinics and feeding centres for the poor out on the Cape flats without missing a step, taking with her larger charitable donations than Shasa really liked to part with.

She threw herself into the duties of motherhood with equal abandon. Her first three efforts were all male, healthy and rumbustious. In order of seniority they were Sean, Garrick and Michael. With her fourth visit to the childbed she produced, with little effort and time wasted in labour, her masterpiece. This one Tara named after her own mother, Isabella, and from the moment he first picked her up and she puked a little sour clotted milk on his shoulder, Shasa was totally besotted with her.

Up to this time it was Tara's spirit and intriguing individuality that had kept Shasa from growing bored and responding to the subtle and less than subtle invitations that were showered on him by circling female predators.

Centaine, fully aware that Shasa's veins were charged with hot de Thiry blood, agonized that Tara seemed oblivious of the danger and dismissed her veiled warnings with offhand, 'Oh, Mater, Shasa isn't like that.' Centaine knew that was exactly the way he was. '*Mon Dieu*, he started at fourteen.' But she relaxed after the other woman finally entered his life in the shape of Isabella de Thiry Malcomess Courtney. It would have been so easy for a fatal slip to spoil it all, to dash the sweet cup from her lips just as she was able to savour it to the full, but now at last Centaine was secure.

She sat under the oaks beside the polo practice grounds of Weltevreden, a guest on the estate she had built up and cherished, but an honoured guest and well content. The coloured nannies had charge of the babies, Michael just a year and a bit and Isabella still at the breast.

Sean was out in the middle of the field. He sat on the pommel of Shasa's saddle, shrieking with excitement and delight, as his father ran the pony at a full gallop down between the far goal posts, brought him up short in a swirl of dust, pivoted and came back in a crescendo of hoof beats. Meanwhile Sean, secure in the circle of Shasa's left arm, urged him, 'Faster! faster, Papa! Go faster!'

On Centaine's knee Garrick bounced impatiently, 'Me!' he yelled. 'Now me!'

Shasa brought the pony in still at full gallop, then reined him down to a dead stop. He lifted Sean off the pommel against his best effort to stick like a bush tick. Garrick slipped off Centaine's lap and toddled to his father.

'Me, Daddy, my turn!'

Shasa leaned out of the saddle, swung the child up in front of him and they were off again at a gallop. It was a game of which they never tired; they had already exhausted two ponies since lunchtime.

There was the sound of a motor vehicle coming down from the château, and Centaine sprang to her feet involuntarily as she recognized the distinctive beat of the Bentley's engine. Then she composed herself and went to meet Blaine with a little more dignity than her eagerness dictated, but as he stepped out of the vehicle she saw his expression and she quickened her step.

'What is it, Blaine!' she demanded as he kissed her cheek. 'Is something wrong?'

'No, of course not,' he assured her. 'The Nationalists have announced their candidates for the Cape constituencies, that's all.'

'Who have they put up against you?' She was all attention now. 'Old Van Schoor again?'

'No, my dear, new blood. Someone you have probably never heard of, Dawid Van Niekerk.'

'Who have they nominated for Hottentots Holland?' When he hesitated, she was immediately insistent. 'Who is it, Blaine?'

He took her arm and began to walk her slowly back to join the family at the tea-table under the oaks.

'Life is a strange thing,' he said.

'Blaine Malcomess, I asked you for an answer, not a few gems of homespun philosophy. Who is it?'

'I'm sorry my dear,' he mumured regretfully. 'They have nominated Manfred De La Rey as their official party candidate.'

Centaine stopped dead, and she felt the blood drain from her face. Blaine tightened his grip on her arm to steady her as she swayed on her feet. Since the beginning of the war Centaine had heard or seen nothing of her second, unacknowledged son.

* * *

Shasa began his campaign with an open meeting in the Boy Scouts hall of Somerset West.

He and Tara drove out the thirty miles from Cape Town to this beautiful little village which nestled at the foot of Sir Lowry's Pass beneath the rugged barrier of the Hottentots Holland mountains. Tara insisted that they take her old Packard. She never felt comfortable in Shasa's new Rolls.

'How can you bear to drive around on four wheels that cost enough to clothe, educate and feed a hundred black children from the cradle to the grave?'

For once Shasa saw the practical wisdom of not flaunting his wealth in front of his constituents. Tara was really tremendous value for money, Shasa reflected. An aspiring politician could not ask for a better running mate – a mother of four lovely children, outspoken, holding strong opinions and possessing a natural shrewdness that anticipated the prejudices and fickle enthusiasm of the herd. She was also strikingly beautiful with all that smouldering auburn hair and a smile that could light up a dreary meeting, and despite

four childbirths in almost as many years, her figure was still marvellous, small waist, good hips – only her bosom had burgeoned.

'I'd back her in a showdown with Jane Russell – tit for tat she'd win by a length going away.' Shasa chuckled aloud, and she looked across at him.

'That's your dirty laugh,' she accused. 'Don't tell me what you are thinking. Let me hear your speech instead.'

He rehearsed it for her, with appropriate gestures and she made an occasional suggestion on content and delivery. 'I would pause longer there,' and 'look fierce and determined,' or, 'I wouldn't make too much of that bit about the Empire. Not really in fashion any more.'

Tara still drove furiously and the journey was soon over. There were larger-than-life posters of Shasa pasted at the entrance and the hall was gratifyingly full. All the seats were taken and there were even a dozen or so younger men standing at the back – they looked like students, Shasa doubted they were old enough to vote.

The local United Party organizer, a Party rosette on his lapel, introduced Shasa as a man who needed no introduction and extolled the fine work he had done for the constituency during his previous short term of office.

Then Shasa rose, tall and debonair in a dark blue suit that was not too new or fashionably cut, but with a crisp white shirt – only spivs wore coloured shirts – and an airforce tie to remind them of his war record. The eye-patch further emphasized what he had sacrificed for his country and his smile was charming and sincere.

'My friends – ' he began, and got no further. He was drowned out by a pandemonium of stamping and chanting and jeering. Shasa tried to make a joke of it, pretending to conduct the orchestrated abuse, but his smile became steadily less sincere as the uproar showed no signs of abating, instead becoming louder and more vindictive as the minutes passed. Finally he began to deliver his address, bellowing it out to be heard above the din.

There were about three hundred of them, taking up the entire back half of the hall, and they made clear their allegiance to the Nationalist Party and its candidate, waving Party banners that depicted the powder horn insignia and holding up posters of Manfred De La Rey's gravely handsome portrait.

After the first few minutes a number of the elderly and middle-aged voters in the front of the hall, sensing the violence that was coming, helped their wives from their seats and scuttled out of the side entrance to a renewed outburst of jeers.

Suddenly Tara Courtney leapt to her feet beside Shasa. Flushed with anger, her grey eyes hard and glittering as bayonets, she yelled at them, 'What kind of men are you? Is this fair? You call yourselves Christians? Where is your Christian charity? Give the man a chance!'

Her voice carried, and her furious beauty checked them. Their inherent sense of chivalry began to take effect, one or two of them sat down and grinned sheepishly, the noise began to abate, but a big dark-haired man leapt up from the audience and rallied them.

'*Kom kêrels*, come on, boys, let's see the *Soutie* back to England where he belongs.

Shasa knew the man, he was one of the local Party organizers. He had been on the Olympic team back in 1936 and had spent most of the war in an internment camp. He was a senior lecturer in Law at Stellenbosch University and Shasa challenged him in Afrikaans:

'Does Meneer Roelf Stander believe in the rule of law and the right of free speech?'

Before he could finish, the first missile was thrown. It came sailing in a high parabola from the back of the hall and burst on the table in front of Tara, a brown paper bag filled with dog turds, and immediately there was a bombardment of soft fruit and toilet rolls, dead chickens and rotten fish.

From the front of the hall the United Party supporters stood up and shouted for order, but Roelf Stander waved his men forward and joyously they surged up to give battle. Seats were overturned, and women screamed, men were shouting and swearing and wrestling and falling over one another.

'Keep close behind me,' Shasa told Tara. 'Hold onto my coat!' He fought his way towards the door, punching any man who stood in his way.

One of them went down before Shasa's right hook, and protested plaintively from the floor, 'Hey, man, I'm on your side,' but Shasa dragged Tara out of the side door and they ran to the Packard.

Neither of them spoke until Tara had them back on the main road, headlights pointing towards the dark bulk of Table Mountain. Then she asked. 'How many of them did you get?'

'Three of theirs – one of ours,' and they burst into nervously relieved laughter.

'It looks as though this is going to be a lot of fun.'

The election of 1948 was fought with increasing acrimony as across the land a realization began to dawn that the nation had reached some fateful crossroads.

The Smuts men were flabbergasted by the depth of feeling the Nationalists had managed to engender amongst the Afrikaner people, and they were totally unprepared for the almost military mobilization of all the forces at the command of the Nationalist Party.

There were few black voters and of all white South Africans the Afrikaners formed a small majority. Smuts had relied for his support upon the English-speaking electorate together with the moderate Afrikaner faction. As polling day drew closer, this moderate support was slowly seduced by the wave of Nationalistic hysteria, and the gloom of the United Party deepened.

* * *

Three days before polling day, Centaine was in her new garden, supervising the marking out and planting of a hundred additional yellow rose bushes when her secretary came hurrying down from the house.

'Mr Duggan is here, ma'am.'

Andrew Duggan was the editor of the *Cape Argus*, the English-language newspaper with the largest readership in the Cape. He was a good friend of Centaine's, a regular house guest, but still it was most inconsiderate of him to call unannounced. Centaine's hair was a bushy fright, despite her headscarf, and she was flushed and sweaty and without make-up.

'Tell him I'm not at home,' she ordered.

'Mr Duggan sends his apologies, but it's a matter of extreme urgency. He used the term "life and death", ma'am.'

'Oh, very well. Go tell him I will be with him in five minutes.'

She changed from slacks and sweater into a morning dress and made a few perfunctory dabs with a powder puff, then she sweapt into the front room where Andrew Duggan stood by the french doors looking out over the Atlantic. Her welcome to him was less than effusive, and she did not offer her cheek for him to kiss, a small token of her displeasure. Andrew was apologetic.

'I know how you feel, Centaine, this is damned cheeky of me barging in here, but I simply had to speak to you and I couldn't use the telephone. Tell me I am forgiven, please.'

She softened and smiled. 'You are forgiven and I'll give you a cup of tea to prove it.'

She poured the orange pekoe tea, brought the paper-thin Royal Doulton cup to him and sat beside him on the sofa.

'Life and death?' she asked.

'More correctly – life and birth.'

'You intrigue me. Please go on, Andy.'

'Centaine, I have received the most extraordinary allegations, supported by documents which appear on the surface to be genuine. If they are, then I shall be obliged to print the story. The allegation concerns you and your family, but especially you and Shasa. They are most damaging allegations – ' he trailed off and looked at her for permission to continue.

'Go on, please,' Centaine said with a calm she did not feel.

'Not to put too fine a point on it, Centaine, we have been told that your marriage to Blaine was your first and only marriage – ' Centaine felt the leaden weight of dismay crush down upon her ' – which, of course, means that Shasa is illegitimate.'

She held up her hand to stop him. 'Answer me one question. Your informant is the Nationalist Party candidate in the Hottentots Holland constituency or one of his agents. Is my guess correct?'

He bowed his head slightly in assent but said, 'We do not reveal our sources. It's not the policy of our newspaper.'

They were silent for a long while and Andrew Duggan studied her face. What an extraordinary woman she was, indomitable even in the face of catastrophe. It saddened him to think that he must be the one who would destroy her dream. He had guessed at her ambitions and empathized with them. Shasa Courtney had much value to give the nation.

'You have the documents, of course?' Centaine asked, and he shook his head.

'My informant is holding them against my firm undertaking to print the story before polling day.'

'Which you will give him?'

'If I cannot have something from you to refute the allegations, then I must print. It is material and in the public interest.'

'Give me until tomorrow morning,' she asked, and he hesitated. 'As a personal favour, please Andy.'

'Very well,' he agreed. 'I owe you that at least.' He stood up. 'I'm sorry, Centaine, I have taken too much of your time already.'

* * *

Immediately Andrew Duggan had left, Centaine went upstairs and bathed and changed. Within half an hour she was in the Daimler and heading for the town of Stellenbosch.

It was long after five when she parked in front of the law offices of Van Schoor and De La Rey, but the front door opened to her touch and she found one of the partners working late.

'Meneer De La Rey left a little early today. He took a brief home to work undisturbed.'

'My business is most urgent. Can you give me his home address?'

It was a pleasant but modest gabled house on an acre of ground on the banks of the river, adjoining the spreading Lanzerac estate. Somebody had taken a gread deal of care with the garden and it was filled with flowers even this late in the year, with the first snows of winter on the mountains.

A woman opened the door to Centaine, a big blonde woman with a heavily handsome head and a high full bosom. Her smile was reserved and she opened the door only halfway.

'I would like to speak to Meneer De la Rey,' Centaine told her in Afrikaans. 'Will you tell him Mrs Malcomess is here.'

'My husband is working. I do not like to disturb him – but come in, I will see if he will speak to you.'

She left Centaine in the front room with its flocked wallpaper of dark red, velvet curtains and heavy Teutonic furniture. Centaine was too keyed up to sit down. She stood in the centre of the floor and looked at the paintings on the fireplace wall without really seeing them, until she became aware of being observed herself.

She turned quickly and a child stood in the doorway, studying her with unblinking frankness. He was a lovely boy, probably seven or eight years old, with a head of blond curls but with incongruously dark eyes under dark brows.

The eyes were her own, she recognized them immediately. This was her grandchild – she knew it instinctively, and the shock of it made her tremble. They stared at each other.

Then she gathered herself and approached him slowly. She held out her hand and smiled.

'Hello,' she said. 'What is your name?'

'I am Lothar De La Rey,' he answered importantly. 'And I am nearly eight years old.'

'Lothar!' she thought, and the name brought all the memories and heartaches back to swamp her emotions. Still she managed to hold the smile.

'What a big fine boy – ' she began, and she had almost touched his cheek when the woman appeared in the door behind him.

'What are you doing here, Lothie?' she scolded. 'You have not finished your dinner. Back to the table this instant, do you hear?'

The child bolted from the room and the woman smiled at Centaine.

'I'm sorry. He is at the inquisitive age,' she apologized. 'My husband will see you, *Mevrou*. Plese come with me.'

Still shaken from her brief encounter with her grandchild, Centaine was unprepared for the additional shock of meeting her son face to face. He stood behind a desk that was strewn with documents and he glared at her with that disconcerting yellow gaze.

'I cannot tell you that you are welcome in this house, Mrs Malcomess.' He spoke in English. 'You are a blood enemy of my family and of mine.'

'That is not true.' Centaine found her voice was breathless, and she tried desperately to regain control.

Manfred made a dismissive gesture. 'You robbed and cheated my father, you crippled him, and through you he has spent half his life in prison. If you could see him now, an old man broken and discarded, you would not come here seeking favours from me.'

'Are you certain I came for a favour?' she asked, and he laughed bitterly.

'For what other reason? You have hounded me – from the day I first saw you in the courtroom at my father's trial. I have seen you watching me, following me, stalking me, like a hungry lioness. I know you seek to destroy me as you destroyed my father.'

'No!' She shook her head vehemently, but he went on remorselessly.

'Now you dare to come and beg my favour. I know what you want.' He pulled open the drawer of his desk and lifted out a file. He opened it and let the papers it contained spill upon the desktop. Amongst them she recognized French birth certificates and old newspaper clippings.

'Shall I read all these to you or will you read them yourself? What other proof do I need to show the world that you are a whore and your son a bastard?' he asked, and she flinched at the words.

'You have been very thorough,' she said softly.

'Yes,' he agreed. 'Very thorough. I have all the evidence – '

'No,' she contradicted him. 'Not all the evidence. You know about one bastard son of mine – but there is another bastard. I will tell you about my second bastard.'

For the first time he was uncertain, staring at her, at a loss for words. Then he shook his head.

'You are shameless,' he marvelled. 'You flaunt your sins before the world.'

'Not before the world,' she said. 'Only before the person they concern most. Only before you, Manfred De La Rey.'

'I do not understand.'

'Then I shall explain why I followed you – as you put it – hounded and stalked you like a lioness. It was not the way a lioness stalks her prey, it was the way a lioness follows her cub. You see, Manfred, you are my other son. I gave birth to you in the desert and Lothar took you away before I had seen your face. You are my son and Shasa is your half-brother. If he is a bastard, so are you. If you destroy him with that fact, you destroy yourself.'

'I do not believe you!' He recoiled from her. 'Lies! All lies! My mother was a German woman of noble birth. I have her photograph. There! Look there on the wall!'

Centaine glanced at it. 'That was Lothar's wife,' she agreed. 'She died almost two years before you were born.'

'No. It's not true. It cannot be true.'

'Ask your father, Manfred,' she said softly. 'Go to Windhoek. The date of that woman's death will be registered there.'

He saw it was true, and he slumped down into his chair and buried his face in his hands.

'If you are my mother – how can I hate you so bitterly?'

She went and stood over him. 'Not as bitterly as I have hated myself for renouncing and abandoning you.'

She bent and kissed his head. 'If only – ' she whispered. 'But now it is too late – far too late. As you have said, we are enemies. Separated by a void as wide as the ocean. Neither of us can ever cross it, but I do not hate you, Manfred, my son. I have never hated you.'

She left him slumped at his desk and walked slowly from the room.

* * *

At noon the following day Andrew Duggan telephoned her.

'My informant has retracted his allegations, Centaine. He tells me that the papers – all the papers connected to the case – have been burned. I think somebody got at him, Centaine, but I cannot for the life of me think who.'

* * *

On 25 May 1948, the day before polling for the general election, Manfred addressed a huge crowd in a Dutch Reform Church hall in Stellenbosch. All of them were staunch Nationalist supporters. No opposition was allowed to enter the hall, Roelf Stander and his action squad saw to that.

Yet when Manfred rose to speak, he also was prevented from doing so. The standing ovation that the crowd gave him kept him silent for fully five minutes. However, when it was over, they sat and listened in attentive silence as he gave them a vision of the future.

'Under Smuts this land of ours will become peopled by a coffee-coloured race of half-bred mongrels, the only white ones left will be the Jews – those same Jews who at this very moment in Palestine are murdering innocent British soldiers at every turn. As you well know, Smuts has hastened to recognize the new state of Israel. That is only to be expected. His paymasters are the Jewish owners of the gold mines – '

Now the crowd cried: '*Skande* – Scandal!' and he paused impressively before he went on.

'What we offer you instead is a plan, nay more than a plan – a vision, a bold and noble vision which will ensure the survival of the pure untainted bloodlines of our *Volk*. A vision that will at the same time protect all the other people of this land, the Cape coloured, the Indians, the black tribes. This grand concept has been drawn up by clever men working with dedication and without self-interest – men like Dr Theophilus Dönges and Dr Nicolaas Diederichs and Dr Hendrik Frensch Verwoerd – brilliant men every one of them.'

The crowd roared their agreement, and he sipped a glass of water and shuffled his notes until they quieted.

'It is an idealistic, carefully worked out and completely infallible concept that will allow all the different races to live in peace and dignity and prosperity and yet allow each of them to retain its separate identity and culture. For this reason we have named the policy 'Separateness'. That is our vision that will carry our land to greatness, a vision at which the world will wonder, an example to all men of good will everywhere. That is what we call *Apartheid*. That, my beloved people is the glorious mantle which we have prepared to place upon our

country. *Apartheid,* my dear friends, that is what we offer you, the shining vision of *Apartheid*.'

He could not speak for many minutes, but when there was silence he went on in a brisker more businesslike tone.

'Of course, it will first be necessary to disenfranchise those black and coloured people who are already registered on the voters' roll – '

When he ended an hour later they carried him on their shoulders from the hall.

* * *

Tara stood close beside Shasa as they waited for the electoral officers to finish counting the votes and announce the result in the Hottentots Holland constituency.

The hall was filled with an excited crowd. There was laughter and singing and horseplay. The Nationalist candidate was at the far side of the hall with his tall blonde wife beside him, surrounded by a restless overwrought knot of his supporters all sporting Nationalist rosettes.

One of the United Party organizers beckoned frantically at Shasa over the heads of the crowd, but he was chatting gaily to a bevy of female enthusiasts, and Tara slipped away to answer the summons. She came back only seconds later and when Shasa saw her face he broke off his conversation and went to meet her, forcing his way through the throng.

'What is it, darling? You look as though you have seen a ghost.'

'It's the *Ou Baas*,' she whispered. 'A telephone call from the Transvaal. Smuts has lost Standerton. The Nationalists have won it.'

'Oh God, no.' Shasa was appalled. 'The *Ou Baas* has held that seat for twenty-five years. They cannot discard him now.'

'The British discarded Winston Churchill,' Tara said. 'They don't want heroes any more.'

'It's a sign,' Shasa muttered. 'If Smuts goes, we all go with him.'

Ten minutes later the news was telephoned through. Colonel Blaine Malcomess had lost the Gardens by almost a thousand votes.

'A thousand votes – ' Shasa tried to accept it, 'but that's a swing of almost ten per cent. What happens now?'

The electoral officer climbed onto the stage at the end of the hall. He had the results in his hand, and the crowd fell silent but edged forward eagerly.

'Ladies and gentlemen, the results of the election for the constitution of Hottentots Holland,' he intoned. 'Manfred De La Rey, Nationalist Party: 3,126 votes. Shasa Courtney, United Party: 2,012 votes. Claude Sampson, Independent: 196 votes.'

Tara took Shasa's hand and they went out to where the Packard was parked. They sat side by side on the front seat, but Tara did not start the engine immediately. They were both shaken and confused.

'I just cannot believe it,' Tara whispered.

'I feel as though I am on a runaway train,' Shasa said. 'Heading into a long dark tunnel, no means of escape, no way of stopping it.' He sighed softly. 'Poor

old South Africa,' he murmured. 'God alone knows what the future holds for you.'

* * *

Moses Gama was surrounded by men. The small room with walls of galvanized corrugated iron was packed with them. They were his praetorian guard, and Swart Hendrick was chief amongst them.

The room was lit only by a smoky paraffin lamp, and the yellow flame highlighted Moses Gama's features.

'He is a lion among men,' Hendrick thought, reminded again of one of the old kings – of Chaka or Mzilikazi, those great black elephants. Thus must they have called the war chiefs to council, thus they must have ordered battle.

'Even now the hard Boers vaunt their victory across the land,' Moses Gama said. 'But I tell you, my children, and I tell you true that below the leaping flames of their pride and avarice lie the ashes of their own destruction. It will not be easy and it may be long. There will be hard work, bitter hard work and even bloody work – but tomorrow belongs to us.'

* * *

The new Deputy Minister of Justice left his office and went down the long corridor in the Union Buildings, that massive fortresslike complex designed and built by Sir Herbert Baker on a low Kopje overlooking the city of Pretoria. It was the administrative headquarters of the South African Government.

Outside it was dark, but there were lights burning in most of the offices. All of them were working late. Taking over the reins of power was an onerous business, but Manfred De La Rey revelled in every tedious detail of the task he had been given. He was sensible of the honour for which he had been selected. He was young, some said too young, for the post of deputy minister, but he would prove them wrong.

He knocked on the minister's door and opened it to the command, '*Kom binne* – enter!'

Charles Robberts 'Blackie' Swart was tall almost to the point of deformity with huge hands that now lay on the desk top in front of him.

'Manfred.' He smiled like a crack apearing in a granite slab. 'Here is the little present I promised you.' He picked up an envelope embossed with the crest of the Union of South Africa and handed it across the desk.

'I will never be able to express my gratitude, Minister.' Manfred took the envelope. 'I hope only to demonstrate it to you by my loyalty and hard work in the years ahead.'

Back in his own office Manfred opened the envelope and unfolded the document it contained. Slowly savouring each word of it, he read through the free pardon granted to one Lothar De La Rey, convicted of various crimes and sentenced to life imprisonment.

Manfred folded the document and slipped it back into its envelope. Tomorrow he would deliver the pardon to the prison government in person, and he

would be there to take his father's hand and lead him out into the sunshine again.

He stood up and went to his safe, tumbled the combination and swung open the heavy steel door. There were three files lying on the top shelf, and he took them down and laid them on his desk. One file was from military intelligence, the second from CID headquarters, the third from his own Department of Justice. It had taken time and careful planning to have all three on his desk and all record of their existence removed from the archive registers. They were the only existing files on 'White Sword'.

He took his time and read each one through carefully. It was long after midnight when he finished, but now he knew that nowhere in those files had any person made the connection between 'White Sword' and Manfred De La Rey, Olympic gold medallist and now Deputy Minister of Justice.

He picked up the three files and carried them through to the outer office where he switched on the shredding machine. As he fed each separate page into the shredder and watched the thin strips of paper come curling out the far side like spaghetti, he considered what he had learned from them.

'So there was a traitoress,' he murmured. 'I was betrayed. A woman, a young woman, speaking in Afrikaans. She knew everything, from the guns in Pretoria to the ambush on the mountain. There is only one young woman who knew all that.' There would be retribution in time, but Manfred was in no hurry – there were many scores to settle, many debts to pay.

When the last page of the reports was reduced to minute slivers, Manfred locked his office and went down to where the new black Ford sedan that went with his rank was parked.

He drove back to his sumptuous official residence in the elegant suburb of Waterkloof. As he went upstairs to the bedroom he was careful not to wake Heidi. She was pregnant again, and her sleep was precious.

He lay in the darkness unable to sleep himself. There was too much to think about, too much planning to do, and he smiled and thought, 'So at last the sword of power is in our hands – and we will see, with a vengeance, who are the underdogs now.'

Rage

I dedicate this book to my wife, Danielle

Hand in hand we have crossed the continents of this earth,
But none of them was as broad as my love for you.

Together we have voyaged on all the oceans,
But none was as deep as my love for you.

Tara Courtney had not worn white since her wedding day. Green was her favourite colour, for it best set off her thick chestnut hair.

However, the white dress she wore today made her feel like a bride again, tremulous and a little afraid but with a sense of joy and deep commitment. She had a touch of ivory lace at the cuffs and the high neckline, and had brushed her hair until it crackled with ruby lights in the bright Cape sunshine. Excitement had rouged her cheeks and although she had carried four children, her waist was slim as a virgin's. So the wide sash of funereal black that she wore over the shoulder was all the more incongruous: youth and beauty decked in the trappings of mourning. Despite her emotional turmoil, she stood with her hands clasped in front of her and her head bowed, silent and still.

She was only one of almost fifty women, all dressed in white, all draped with the black sashes, all in the same attitude of mourning, who stood at carefully spaced intervals along the pavement opposite the main entrance of the parliament buildings of the Union of South Africa.

Nearly all of the women were young matrons from Tara's own set, wealthy, privileged and bored by the undemanding tenor of their lives. Many of them had joined the protest for the excitement of defying established authority and outraging their peers. Some were seeking to regain the attentions of their husbands which after the first decade or so of marriage were jaded by familiarity and fixed more on business or golf and other extra marital activity. There was, however, a hard nucleus to the movement consisting mostly of the older women, but including a few of the younger ones like Tara and Molly Broadhurst. These were moved only by revulsion at injustice. Tara had tried to express her feelings at the press conference that morning when a woman reporter from the *Cape Argus* had demanded of her, 'Why are you doing this, Mrs Courtney?' and she had replied, 'Because I don't like bullies, and I don't like cheats.' For her that attitude was partially vindicated now.

'Here comes the big bad wolf,' the woman who stood five paces on Tara's right said softly. 'Brace up, girls!' Molly Broadhurst was one of the founders of the Black Sash, a small determined woman in her early thirties whom Tara greatly admired and strove to emulate.

A black Chevrolet with government licence plates had drawn up at the corner of Parliament Square and four men climbed out on to the pavement. One was a police photographer and he went to work immediately, moving quickly down the line of white-clad, black-draped women with his Hasselblad camera, photographing each of them. He was followed by two of the others brandishing notebooks. Though they were dressed in dark, ill-cut business suits, their clumpy black shoes were regulation police issue and their actions were brusque and businesslike as they passed down the ranks demanding and noting the names and addresses of each of the protesters. Tara, who was fast becoming

something of an expert, guessed that they probably ranked as sergeants in the special branch, but the fourth man she knew by name and by sight, as did most of the others.

He was dressed in a light grey summer suit with brown brogues, a plain maroon tie and a grey fedora hat. Though of average height and unremarkable features, his mouth was wide and friendly, his smile easy as he lifted his hat to Molly.

'Good morning, Mrs Broadhurst. You are early. The procession won't arrive for another hour yet.'

'Are you going to arrest us all again today, Inspector?' Molly demanded tartly.

'Perish the thought.' The inspector raised an eyebrow. 'It's a free country, you know.'

'You could have fooled me.'

'Naughty Mrs Broadhurst!' He shook his head. 'You are trying to provoke me.' His English was excellent, with only a faint trace of an Afrikaans accent.

'No, Inspector. We are protesting the blatant gerrymandering of this perverse government, the erosion of the rule of law, and the abrogation of the basic human rights of the majority of our fellow South Africans merely on the grounds of the colour of their skins.'

'I think, Mrs Broadhurst, you are repeating yourself. You told me all this last time we met.' The inspector chuckled. 'Next you'll actually be demanding that I arrest you again. Let's not spoil this grand occasion – '

'The opening of this parliament, dedicated as it is to injustice and oppression, is a cause for lament not celebration.'

The inspector tipped the brim of his hat, but beneath his flippant attitude was a real respect and perhaps even a little admiration.

'Carry on, Mrs Broadhurst,' he murmured. 'I'm sure we'll meet again soon,' and he sauntered on until he came opposite Tara.

'Good morning to you, Mrs Courtney.' He paused, and this time his admiration was unconcealed. 'What does your illustrious husband think of your treasonable behaviour?'

'Is it treason to oppose the excesses of the National Party and its legislation based on race and colour, Inspector?'

His gaze dropped for a moment to her bosom, large and yet finely shaped beneath the white lace, and then returned to her face.

'You are much too pretty for this nonsense,' he said. 'Leave it to the grey-headed old prunes. Go home where you belong and look after your babies.'

'Your masculine arrogance is insufferable, Inspector.' She flushed with anger, unaware that it heightened the looks he had just complimented.

'I wish all traitoresses looked the way you do. It would make my job a great deal more congenial. Thank you, Mrs Courtney.' He smiled infuriatingly and moved on.

'Don't let him rattle you, my dear,' Molly called softly. 'He's an expert at it. We are protesting passively. Remember Mahatma Gandhi.'

With an effort Tara controlled her anger, and reassumed the attitude of the penitent. On the pavement behind her the crowds of spectators began to gather. The rank of white-clad women became the object of curiosity and amusement, of some approbation and a great deal of hostility.

'Goddamn commies,' a middle-aged man growled at Tara. 'You want to hand the country over to a bunch of savages. You should be locked up, the whole lot

of you.' He was well dressed, and his speech cultivated. He even wore the small brass tin hat insignia in his lapel to signify that he had served with the volunteer forces during the war against fascism. His attitude was a reminder of just how much tacit support the ruling National party enjoyed even amongst the English-speaking white community.

Tara bit her lip and forced herself to remain silent, head bowed, even when the outburst earned a ragged ironical cheer from some of the coloured people in the growing crowd.

It was getting hot now, the sunshine had a flat Mediterranean brilliance, and though the mattress of cloud was building up above the great flat-topped bastion of Table Mountain, heralding the rise of the south-easter, the wind had not yet reached the city that crouched below it. By now the crowd was dense and noisy, and Tara was jostled, she suspected deliberately. She kept her composure and concentrated on the building across the road from where she stood.

Designed by Sir Herbert Baker, that paragon of Imperial architects, it was massive and imposing, red brick colonnaded in shimmering white – far from Tara's own modern taste, which inclined to uncluttered space and lines, to glass and light Scandinavian pine furnishing. The building seemed to epitomize all that was inflexible and out-dated from the past, all that Tara wanted to see torn down and discarded.

Her thoughts were broken by the rising hum of expectation from the crowd around her.

'Here they come,' Molly called, and the crowd surged and swayed and broke into cheers. There was the clatter of hooves on the hard-metalled roadway and the mounted police escort trotted up the avenue, pennants fluttering gaily at the tips of their lances, expert horsemen on matched chargers whose hides gleamed like burnished metal in the sunlight.

The open coaches rumbled along behind them. In the first of these rode the governor-general and the prime minister. There he was, Daniel Malan, champion of the Afrikaners, with his forbidding almost froglike features, a man whose only consideration and declared intent was to keep his *Volk* supreme in Africa for a thousand years, and no price was for him too high.

Tara stared at him with palpable hatred, for he embodied all that she found repellent in the government which now held sway over the land and the peoples which she loved so dearly. As the coach swept past where she stood, their eyes met for a fleeting moment and she tried to convey the strength of her feelings, but he glanced at her without a flicker of acknowledgement, not even a shadow of annoyance, in his brooding gaze. He had looked at her and had not seen her, and now her anger was tinged with despair.

'What must be done to make these people even listen?' she wondered, but now the dignitaries had dismounted from the carriages and were standing to attention during the playing of the national anthems. And though Tara did not know it then, it was the last time 'The King' would be played at the opening of a South African Parliament.

The band ended with a fanfare of trumpets and the cabinet ministers followed the governor-general and the prime minister through the massive front entrance doors. They were followed in turn by the opposition front-benchers. This was the moment Tara had been dreading, for her own close family now formed part of the procession. Next behind the leader of the opposition came Tara's own father with her stepmother on his arm. They made the most striking couple in the long procession, her father tall and dignified as a patriarchal lion, while on

his arm Centaine de Thiry Courtney-Malcomess was slim and graceful in a yellow silk dress that was perfect for the occasion, a jaunty brimless hat on her small neat head with a veil over one eye; she seemed not a year older than Tara herself, though everybody knew she had been named Centaine because she had been born on the first day of the twentieth century.

Tara thought she had escaped unnoticed, for none of them had known she intended joining the protest, but at the top of the broad staircase the procession was held up for a moment and before she entered the doorway Centaine turned deliberately and looked back. From her vantage point she could see over the heads of the escort and the other dignitaries in the procession, and from across the road she caught Tara's eye and held it for a moment. Although her expression did not alter, the strength of her disapproval was even at that range like a slap in Tara's face. For Centaine the honour, dignity and good name of the family were of paramount importance. She had warned Tara repeatedly about making a public spectacle of herself and flouting Centaine was a perilous business, for she was not only Tara's stepmother but her mother-in-law as well, and the doyenne of the Courtney family and fortune.

Halfway up the staircase behind her Shasa Courtney saw the direction and force of his mother's gaze, and turning quickly to follow it saw Tara, his wife, in the rank of black-sashed protestors. When she had told him that morning at breakfast that she would not be joining him at the opening ceremony, Shasa had barely looked up from the financial pages of the morning newspaper.

'Suit yourself, my dear. It will be a bit of a bore,' he had murmured. 'But I would like another cup of coffee, when you have a moment.'

Now when he recognized her, he smiled slightly, and shook his head in mock despair, as though she were a child discovered in some naughty prank, and then he turned away as the procession moved forward again.

He was almost impossibly handsome, and the black eye-patch gave him a debonair piratical look that most women found intriguing and challenging. Together they were renowned as the handsomest young couple in Cape Town society. Yet it was strange how the passage of a few short years had caused the flames of their love to sink into a puddle of grey ash.

'Suit yourself, my dear,' he had said, as he did so often these days.

The last back-benchers in the procession disappeared into the House, the mounted escort and empty carriages trotted away and the crowds began to break up. The demonstration was over.

'Are you coming, Tara?' Molly called, but Tara shook her head.

'Have to meet Shasa,' she said. 'See you on Friday afternoon.' Tara slipped the wide black sash off over her head, folded it and placed it in her handbag as she threaded her way through the dispersing crowd. She crossed the road.

She saw no irony in now presenting her parliamentary pass to the doorman at the visitors' entrance and entering the institution against whose actions she had been so vigorously protesting. She climbed the side staircase and looked into the visitors' gallery. It was packed with wives and important guests, and she looked over their heads down into the panelled chamber below to the rows of sombre-suited members on their green leather-covered benches, all involved in the impressive ritual of parliament. However, she knew that the speeches would be trivial, platitudinous and boring to the point of pain, and she had been standing in the street since early morning. She needed to visit the ladies room as a matter of extreme urgency.

She smiled at the usher and withdrew surreptitiously, then turned and

hurried away down the wide panelled corridor. When she had finished in the ladies room, she headed for her father's office, which she used as her own.

As she turned the corner she almost collided with a man coming in the opposite direction. She checked only just in time, and saw that he was a tall black man dressed in the uniform of a parliamentary servant. She would have passed on with a nod and a smile, when it occurred to her that a servant should not have been in this section of the building during the time when the House was in session, for the offices of the prime minister and the leader of the opposition were at the end of the corridor. Then again, although the servant carried a mop and pail, there was something about him that was neither menial nor servile and she looked sharply at his face.

She felt an electric tingle of recognition. It had been many years, but she could never forget that face – the features of an Egyptian pharaoh, noble and fierce, the dark eyes alive with intelligence. He was still one of the finest-looking men she had ever seen, and she remembered his voice, deep and thrilling so that the memory of it made her shiver slightly. She even remembered his words: 'There is a generation, whose teeth are as swords . . . to devour the poor from the earth.'

It was this man who had given her the first glimmer of understanding as to what it was like to be born black in South Africa. Her true commitment dated from that distant meeting. This man had changed her life with a few words.

She stopped, blocking his path, and tried to find some way to convey her feelings to him, but her throat had closed and she found she was trembling from the shock. The instant he knew he had been recognized, he changed, like a leopard coming on guard as it becomes aware of the hunters. Tara sensed she was in danger, for a sense of African cruelty invested him, but she was unafraid.

'I am a friend,' she said softly, and stood aside to let him pass. 'Our cause is the same.'

He did not move for a moment, but stared at her. She knew that he would never forget her again, his scrutiny seemed to set her skin on fire, and then he nodded.

'I know you,' he acknowledged, and once again his voice made her shiver, deep and melodious, filled with the rhythm and cadence of Africa. 'We will meet again.'

Then he passed on and without a backward glance disappeared around the corner of the panelled corridor. She stood staring after him, and her heart was pounding, her heart burned the back of her throat.

'Moses Gama,' she whispered his name aloud. 'Messiah and warrior of Africa – ' then she paused and shook her head. 'What are you doing here, in this of all places?'

The possibilities intrigued and stirred her, for now she knew with a deep instinct that the crusade was afoot, and she longed to be part of it. She wanted to do more than merely stand on a street corner with a black sash draped over her shoulder. She knew Moses Gama had only to crook his finger and she would follow him, she and ten million others.

'We will meet again,' he had promised, and she believed him.

Light with joy she went on down the passageway. She had her own key to her father's office and as she fitted it to the lock, her eyes were on a level with the brass plate:

COLONEL BLAINE MALCOMESS
DEPUTY LEADER OF THE OPPOSITION

With surprise she found that the lock was already opened, and she pushed the door wide and went in.

Centaine Courtney-Malcomess turned from the window beyond the desk to confront her. 'I have been waiting for you, young lady.' Centaine's French accent was an affectation that annoyed Tara. She has been back to France just once in thirty-five years, she thought, and lifted her chin defiantly.

'Don't toss your head at me, Tara *chérie*,' Centaine went on. 'When you act like a child, you must expect to be treated as a child.'

'No, Mater, you are wrong. I do not expect you to treat me as a child, not now or ever. I am a married woman of thirty-three years of age, the mother of four children and the mistress of my own establishment.'

Centaine sighed. 'All right,' she nodded. 'My concern made me ill-mannered, and I apologize. Let's not make this discussion any more difficult for each other than it already is.'

'I was not aware that we needed to discuss anything.'

'Sit down, Tara,' Centaine ordered, and Tara obeyed instinctively and then was annoyed with herself for doing so. Centaine took her father's chair behind the desk, and Tara resented that also – it was Daddy's chair and this woman had no right to it.

'You have just told me that you are a wife with four children,' Centaine spoke quietly. 'Would you not agree that you have a duty – '

'My children are well cared for,' Tara flared at her. 'You cannot accuse me of that.'

'And what about your husband and your marriage?'

'What about Shasa?' Tara was immediately defensive.

'You tell me,' Centaine invited.

'It's none of your business.'

'Oh, but it is,' Centaine contradicted her. 'I have devoted my entire life to Shasa. I plan for him to be one of the leaders of this nation.' She paused and a dreamy glaze covered her eyes for a moment, and she seemed to squint slightly. Tara had noticed that expression before, whenever Centaine was in deep thought, and now she wanted to break in upon it as brutally as she could.

'That's impossible and you know it.'

Centaine's eyes snapped back into focus and she glared at Tara. 'Nothing is impossible – not for me, not for us.'

'Oh yes it is,' Tara gloated. 'You know as well as I do that the Nationalists have gerrymandered the electorate, that they have even loaded the Senate with their own appointees. They are in power for ever. Never again will anyone who is not one of them, an Afrikaner Nationalist, ever be this country's leader, not until the revolution – and when that is over, the leader will be a black man,' Tara broke off and thought for an instant of Moses Gama.

'You are naïve,' Centaine snapped. 'You do not understand these things. Your talk of revolution is childish and irresponsible.'

'Have it your own way, Mater. But deep down you know it's so. Your darling Shasa will never fulfil your dream. Even he is beginning to sense the futility of being in opposition for ever. He is losing interest in the impossible. I wouldn't be surprised if he decides not to contest the next election, gives up the political aspirations that you have foisted on him and simply goes off to make himself another trillion pounds.'

'No,' Centaine shook her head. 'He won't give up. He is a fighter like I am.'

'He'll never be even a cabinet minister, let alone prime minister,' Tara stated flatly.

'If you believe that, then you are no wife for my son,' Centaine said.

'You said it,' Tara said softly. 'You said it, not me.'

'Oh, Tara, my dear, I am sorry.' Centaine reached across the desk but it was too broad for her to touch Tara's hand. 'Forgive me. I lost my temper. All this is so desperately important to me. I feel it so deeply, but I did not mean to antagonize you. I want only to help you – I am so worried about you and Shasa. I want to help, Tara. Won't you let me help you?'

'I don't see that we need help,' Tara lied sweetly. 'Shasa and I are perfectly happy. We have four lovely children – '

Centaine made an impatient gesture. 'Tara, you and I haven't always seen eye to eye. But I am your friend, I truly am. I want the best for you and Shasa and the little ones. Won't you let me help you?'

'How, Mater? By giving us money – you have already given us ten or twenty million – or is it thirty million pounds? I lose track sometimes.'

'Won't you let me share my experience with you? Won't you listen to my advice?'

'Yes, Mater, I'll listen. I don't promise to take it, but I'll listen to it.'

'Firstly, Tara dear, you must give up these crazy left-wing activities. You bring the whole family into disrepute. You make a spectacle of yourself, and therefore of us, by dressing up and standing on street corners. Apart from that, it is positively dangerous. The Suppression of Communism Act is now law. You could be declared a communist, and placed under a banning order. Just consider that, you would become a non-person, deprived of all human rights and dignity. Then there is Shasa's political career. What you do reflects on him.'

'Mater, I promised to listen,' Tara said stonily. 'But now I withdraw that promise. I know what I am doing.' She stood up and moved to the door where she paused and looked back. 'Did you ever think, Centaine Courtney-Malcomess, that my mother died of a broken heart, and it was your blatant adultery with my father that broke it for her? Yet you can sit there smugly and advise me how to conduct my life, so as not to disgrace you and your precious son.' She went out and closed the heavy teak door softly behind her.

* * *

Shasa Courtney lolled on the opposition front bench with his hands pushed deeply into his pockets, his legs thrust out and crossed at the ankles, and listened intently to the minister of police outlining the legislation which he intended bringing before the House during the current session.

The minister of police was the youngest member of the cabinet, a man of approximately the same age as Shasa, which was extraordinary. The Afrikaner revered age and mistrusted the inexperience and impetuosity of youth. The average age of the other members of the Nationalist cabinet could not be less than sixty-five years, Shasa reflected, and yet there was Manfred De La Rey standing before them, a mere stripling of less than forty years, setting out the general contents of the Criminal Law Amendment Bill which he would be proposing and shepherding through its various stages.

'He is asking for the right to declare a state of emergency which will put the police above the law, without appeal to the courts,' Blaine Malcomess grunted beside him, and Shasa nodded without looking at his father-in-law. Instead he was watching the man across the floor.

Manfred De La Rey was speaking in Afrikaans, as he usually did. His English was heavily accented and laboured, and he spoke it unwillingly, making only the barest gesture towards the bilingualism of the House. On the other hand, when speaking in his mother tongue, he was eloquent and persuasive, his oratorial attitudes and devices were so skilled as to seem entirely natural and more than once he raised a chuckle of exasperated admiration from the opposition benches and a chorus of '*Hoor, hoor!*' from his own party.

'The fellow has a damned cheek.' Blaine Malcomess shook his head. 'He is asking for the right to suspend the rule of law and impose a police state at the whim of the ruling party. We'll have to fight that tooth and nail.'

'My word!' Shasa agreed mildly, but he found himself envying the other man, and yet mysteriously drawn to him. It was strange how their two destinies seemed to be inexorably linked.

He had first met Manfred De La Rey twenty years ago, and for no apparent reason the two of them had flown at each other on the spot like young game cocks and fought a bloody bout of fisticuffs. Shasa grimaced at the way it had ended, the drubbing he had received still rankled even after all that time. Since then their paths had crossed and recrossed.

In 1936 they had both been on the national team that went to Adolf Hitler's Olympic Games in Berlin, but it had been Manfred De La Rey in the boxing ring who collected the only gold medal the team had won, while Shasa returned empty-handed. They had hotly and acrimoniously contested the same seat in the 1948 elections that had seen the National Party come sweeping to power, and again it was Manfred De La Rey who had won the seat and taken his place in parliament, while Shasa had to wait for a by-election in a safe United Party constituency to secure his own place on the opposition benches from which to confront his rival once again. Now Manfred was a minister, a position that Shasa coveted with all his heart, and with his undoubted brilliance and oratorical skills together with growing political acumen and a solid power base within the party, Manfred De La Rey's future must be unbounded.

Envy, admiration and furious antagonism – that was what Shasa Courtney felt as he listened to the man across the floor from him, and he studied him intently.

Manfred De La Rey still had a boxer's physique, wide shoulders and powerful neck, but he was thickening around the waist and his jawline was beginning to blur with flesh. He wasn't keeping himself in shape and hard muscle was turning flabby. Shasa glanced down at his own lean hips and greyhound belly with self-satisfaction and then concentrated again on his adversary.

Manfred De La Rey's nose was twisted and there was a gleaming white scar through one of his dark eyebrows, injuries he had received in the boxing ring. However, his eyes were a strange pale colour, like yellow topaz, implacable as the eyes of a cat and yet with the fire of his fine intellect in their depths. Like all the Nationalist cabinet ministers, with the exception of the prime minister himself, he was a highly educated and brilliant man, devout and dedicated, totally convinced of the divine right of his party and his *Volk*.

'They truly believe they are God's instruments on earth. That's what makes them so damned dangerous.' Shasa smiled grimly as Manfred finished speaking

and sat down to the roar of approval from his own side of the House. They were waving order papers, and the prime minister leaned across to pat Manfred's shoulder, while a dozen congratulatory notes were passed to him from the back benches.

Shasa used this distractiuon to murmur an excuse to his father-in-law. 'You won't need me for the rest of the day, but if you do, you'll know where to find me.' Then he stood up, bowed to the Speaker and, as unobtrusively as possible, headed for the exit. However, Shasa was six foot one inch tall and with the black patch over one eye and his dark waving hair and good looks, he drew more than a few speculative glances from the younger women in the visitors' gallery, and a hostile appraisal from the government benches.

Manfred De La Rey glanced up from the note he was reading as Shasa passed, and the look they exchanged was intent but enigmatic. Then Shasa was out of the chamber and he shrugged off his jacket and slung it over his shoulder, as he acknowledged the salute of the doorman and went out into the sunshine.

Shasa did not keep an office in the parliament building, for the seven-storied Centaine House, the headquarters of the Courtney Mining and Finance Co. Ltd., was just two minutes' walk across the gardens. As he strode along under the oaks he mentally changed hats, doffing his political topper for the businessman's Homburg. Shasa kept his life in separate compartments, and he had trained himself to concentrate on each in its turn, without ever allowing his energy to dissipate by spreading it too thinly.

By the time he crossed the road in front of St George's cathedral and went into the revolving glass front door of Centaine House, he was thinking of finance and mining, juggling figures and choices, weighing factual reports against his own instincts, and enjoying the game of money as hugely as he had the rituals and confrontations on the floor of the houses of parliament.

The two pretty girls at the reception desk in the entrance lobby with its marbled floors and columns burst into radiant smiles.

'Good afternoon, Mr Courtney,' they chorused, and he devastated them with his smile as he crossed to the lifts. His reaction to them was instinctive; he liked pretty females around him, although he would never touch one of his own people. Somehow that would have been incestuous, and unsporting for they would not have been able to refuse him, too much like shooting a sitting bird. Still the two young females at the desk sighed and rolled their eyes as the lift doors closed on him.

Janet, his secretary, had heard the lift and was waiting as the doors opened. She was more Shasa's type – mature and poised, groomed and efficient, and though she made little attempt to conceal her adoration, Shasa's self-imposed rules prevailed here also.

'What have we got, Janet?' he demanded, and as she followed him across the ante-chamber to his own office, she read off his appointments for the rest of the afternoon.

He went first to the ticker-tape in the corner and ran the closing prices through his fingers. Anglos had dropped two shillings, it was almost time to buy again.

'Ring Allen and put him off. I'm not ready for him yet,' he told Janet and went to his desk. 'Give me fifteen minutes and then get David Abrahams on the phone.'

As she left the room Shasa settled to the pile of telex sheets and urgent messages that she had left on his blotter. He worked swiftly through them,

undistracted by the magnificent view of Table Mountain through the window on the opposite wall, and when one of the phones rang he was ready for David.

'Hello, Davie, what's happening in Jo'burg?' It was a rhetorical question, he knew what was happening and what he was going to do about it. The daily reports and estimates were amongst the pile on his desk, but he listened carefully to David's résumé.

David was group managing-director. He had been with Shasa since varsity days and he was as close to Shasa as no other person, with the exception of Centaine, had come.

Although the H'ani diamond mine near Windhoek in the north was still the fountainhead of the company's prosperity, and had been for the thirty-two years since Centaine Courtney had discovered it, under Shasa's direction the company had expanded and diversified until he had been forced to move the executive headquarters from Windhoek to Johannesburg. Johannesburg was the commercial centre of the country and the move was inevitable, but Johannesburg was also a bleak, heartless and unattractive city. Centaine Courtney-Malcomess refused to leave the beautiful Cape of Good Hope to live there, so the company's financial and administrative headquarters remained in Cape Town. It was a clumsy and costly duplication, but Centaine always got her way. Moreover, it was convenient for Shasa to be so close to parliament and as he loved the Cape as much as she did, he did not try to change her mind.

Shasa and David spoke for ten minutes before Shasa said, 'Right, we can't decide on this on the phone. I'll come up to you.'

'When?'

'Tomorrow afternoon. Sean has a rugby match at ten in the morning. I can't miss it. I promised him.'

David was silent a moment as he considered the relative importance of a schoolboy's sporting achievement against the possible investment of something over ten million pounds in the development of the company's options on the new Orange Free State goldfields.

'Give me a ring before you take off,' David agreed with resignation. 'I'll meet you at the airfield myself.'

Shasa hung up and checked his wristwatch. He wanted to get back to Weltevreden in time to spend an hour with the children before their bath and dinner. He could finish his work after his own dinner. He began to pack the remaining papers on his desk into his black crocodile-skin Hermès briefcase, when Janet tapped on the inter-leading door and came into his office.

'I'm sorry, sir. This has just been delivered by hand. A parliamentary messenger, and he said it was very urgent.'

Shasa took the heavy-quality envelope from her. It was the type of expensive stationery reserved for use by members of the cabinet and the flap was embossed with the coat of arms of the Union, the quartered shield and rampant antelopes supporting it with the motto in the ribbon beneath *Ex Unitate Vires* – Strength through Unity.

'Thank you, Janet.' He broke the flap with his thumb and took out a single sheet of notepaper. It was headed: 'Office of the Minister of Police', and the message was handwritten in Afrikaans.

Dear Mr Courtney,

Knowing of your interest in hunting, an important personage has asked me to invite you to a

springbok hunt on his ranch over the coming weekend. There is an airstrip on the property and the coordinates are as follows: 28°32′S 26°16′E.

I can assure you of good sport and interesting company. Please let me know if you are able to attend.

Sincerely,

Manfred De La Rey.

Shasa grinned and whistled softly through his teeth as he went to the large-scale map on the wall and checked the coordinates. The note amounted to a summons, and he could guess at the identity of the important personage. He saw that the ranch was in the Orange Free State just south of the goldfields at Welkom, and it would mean only a minor detour off his return course from Johannesburg to reach it.

'I wonder what they are up to now,' he mused, and he felt a prickle of anticipation. It was the kind of mystery he thoroughly enjoyed, and he scribbled a reply on a sheet of his personal notepaper.

Thank you for your kind invitation to hunt with you this weekend. Please convey my acceptance to our host and I look forward to the hunting.

As he sealed the envelope he muttered, 'In fact, you'd have to nail both my feet to the ground to keep me away.'

* * *

In his green Jaguar SS sports car, Shasa drove through the massive white-painted gateway of Weltevreden. The pediment had been designed and executed in 1790 by Anton Anreith, the Dutch East India Company's architect and sculptor, and such an exquisite work of art was a fitting entrance to the estate.

Since Centaine had handed the estate over to him and gone to live with Blaine Malcomess on the far side of the Constantia Berg mountains, Shasa had lavished the same love and care upon Weltevreden as she had before. The name translated from the Dutch as 'Well Satisfied' and that was how Shasa felt as he slowed the Jaguar to a walking-pace, so as not to blow dust over the vineyards that flanked the road.

The harvest was in full swing, and the headscarves of the women working down the rows of shoulder-high vines were bright spots of colour that vied with the leaves of red and gold. They straightened up to smile and wave as Shasa passed, and the men, doubled under the overflowing baskets of red grapes, grinned at him also.

Young Sean was on one of the wagons in the centre of the field, walking the draught horses slowly, keeping pace with the harvest. The wagon was piled high with ripe grapes that glowed like rubies where the powdery bloom had been rubbed from their skin.

When he saw his father, Sean tossed the reins to the driver who had been tactfully supervising him, and leapt over the side of the wagon and paced down the rows of vines to intercept the green Jaguar. He was only eleven years old, but big for his age. He had inherited his mother's clear shining skin and Shasa's looks, and although his limbs were sturdy, he ran like an antelope, springy and

quick on his feet. Watching him Shasa felt that his heart might burst with pride.

Sean flung open the passenger door of the Jag and tumbled into the seat, where he abruptly recovered his dignity.

'Good evening, Papa,' he said, and Shasa put an arm around his shoulders and hugged him.

'Hello, sport. How did it go today?'

They drove down past the winery and the stables and Shasa parked in the converted barn where he kept his collection of a dozen vintage cars. The Jaguar had been a gift from Centaine and he favoured it even over the 1928 Phantom I Rolls Royce with Hooper coachwork beside which he parked it.

The other children had witnessed his arrival from the nursery windows and came pelting down across the lawns to meet him. Michael, the youngest boy was leading, with Garrick, his middle son, a good five lengths back. Less than a year separated each of the boys. Michael was the dreamer of the family, a fey child who at nine years of age could lose himself for hours in *Treasure Island* or spend an afternoon with his box of water-colours, lost to all else in the world. Shasa embraced him as affectionately as he had his eldest, and then Garrick came up, wheezing with asthma, pale-faced and skinny, with wispy hair that stuck up in spikes.

'Good afternoon, Papa,' he stuttered. He really was an ugly little brat, Shasa thought, and where the hell did he get them from, the asthma and the stutter?

'Hello, Garrick.' Shasa never called him 'son' or 'my boy' or 'sport' as he did the other two. It was always simply 'Garrick' and he patted the top of his head lightly. It never occurred to him to embrace the child, the little beggar still peed his bed and he was ten years old.

Shasa turned with relief to meet his daughter.

'Come on, my angel, come to your daddy!' And she flew into his arms and shrieked with rapture as he swung her high, then wrapped both arms around his neck and showered warm wet kisses on his face.

'What does my angel want to do now?' Shasa asked, without lowering her to earth.

'I wanna wide,' Isabella declared, and she was already wearing her new jodhpurs.

'Then wide we shall,' Shasa agreed. Whenever Tara accused him of encouraging her lisp, he protested, 'She's only a baby.'

'She's a calculating little vixen who knows exactly how to twist you around her little finger – and you let her do it.'

Now he swung her up on to his shoulders, and she sat astride his neck and took a handful of his hair to steady herself while she bounced up and down chanting, 'I love my daddy.'

'Come on, everybody,' Shasa ordered. 'We are going for a wide before dinner.'

Sean was too big and grown up to hold hands, but he kept jealously close to Shasa's right side; Michael was on his left clinging unashamedly to Shasa's hand, while Garrick trailed five paces behind looking up adoringly at his father.

'I came first in arithmetic today, Daddy,' Garrick said softly, but in all the shouting and laughter Shasa didn't hear him.

The grooms had the horses saddled up already, for the evening ride was a family ritual. In the saddle room Shasa slipped off his city shoes and changed them for old well-polished riding boots, before he lifted Isabella on to the back

of her plump little piebald Shetland. Then he went up into the saddle of his own stallion and took Isabella's lead rein from the groom.

'Company, forward – walk, march, trot!' He gave the cavalry command and pumped his hand over his head, a gesture which always reduced Isabella to squeals of delight, and they clattered out of the stableyard.

They made the familiar circuit of the estate, stopping to talk with any of the coloured boss-boys they met, and exchanging shouted greetings with the gangs of labourers trudging home from the vineyards. Sean discussed the harvest with his father in adult terms, sitting straight and important in the saddle, until Isabella, feeling left out, intervened and immediately Shasa leaned over to listen deferentially to what she had to tell him.

The boys ended the ride as always with a mad gallop across the polo fields and up the hill to the stables. Sean, riding like a centaur, was far ahead of the rest of them, Michael was too gentle to use the whip and Garrick bounced awkwardly in the saddle. Despite Shasa's drilling, his seat was atrocious with toes and elbows sticking out at odd angles.

'He rides like a sack of potatoes,' Shasa thought with irritation, following them at the sedate pace set by Isabella's portly Shetland on the lead rein. Shasa was an international polo player, and he took his middle son's maladroit seat as a personal affront.

Tara was in the kitchens overseeing the last-minute details for dinner, when they came trooping in. She looked up and greeted Shasa casually.

'Good day?' She was wearing those appalling trousers in faded blue denim which Shasa detested. He liked feminine women.

'Not bad,' he answered, trying to divest himself of Isabella who was still wrapped around his neck. He dislodged her and handed her over to Nanny.

'We are twelve for dinner.' Tara turned her attention back to the Malay chef who was standing by dutifully.

'Twelve?' Shasa asked sharply.

'I invited the Broadhursts at the last moment.'

'Oh God,' Shasa groaned.

'I wanted some stimulating conversation at the table for a change, not just horses and shooting and business.'

'Last time she came to dinner your and Molly's stimulating conversation broke the party up before nine o'clock.' Shasa glanced at his wristwatch. 'I'd better think about dressing.'

'Daddy, will you feed me?' Isabella called from the children's dining room beyond the kitchen.

'You are a big girl, angel,' he answered. 'You must learn to feed yourself.'

'I can feed myself – I just like it better when you do it. Please, Daddy, pretty please a trillion times.'

'A trillion?' Shasa asked. 'I am bid one trillion – any advance on a trillion?' but he went to her summons.

'You spoil her,' Tara said. 'She's becoming impossible.'

'I know,' said Shasa. 'You keep telling me.'

Shasa shaved quickly while his coloured valet laid out his dinner-jacket in the dressing-room and put the platinum and sapphire studs into his dress shirt. Despite Tara's vehement protests he always insisted on black tie for dinner.

'It's so stuffy and old-fashioned and snobby.'

'It's civilized,' he contradicted her.

When he was dressed, he crossed the wide corridor strewn with oriental

carpets, the walls hung with a gallery of Thomas Baines water-colours, tapped on Tara's door and went in to her invitation.

Tara had moved into this suite while she was carrying Isabella, and had stayed here. Last year she had redecorated it, removing the velvet drapes and George II and Louis XIV furniture, the Qum silk carpets and the magnificent oils by De Jon and Naudé, stripping the flocked wallpaper and sanding the golden patina off the yellow-wood floor until it looked like plain deal.

Now the walls were stark white with only a single enormous painting facing the bed; it was a monstrosity of geometrical shapes in primary colours in the style of Miró, but executed by an unknown art student at the Cape Town University Art School and of no value. To Shasa's mind paintings should be pleasing decorations but at the same time good long-term investments. This thing was neither.

The furniture Tara had chosen for her boudoir was made of angular stainless steel and glass, and there was very little of it. The bed was almost flat on the bare boards of the floor.

'It's Swedish decor,' she had explained.

'Send it back to Sweden,' he had advised her.

Now he perched on one of the steel chairs and lit a cigarette. She frowned at him in the mirror.

'Forgive me.' He stood up and went to flick the cigarette out of the window. 'I'll be working late after dinner,' he turned back to her, 'and I want to warn you before I forget that I'm flying up to Jo'burg tomorrow afternoon and I'll be away for a few days, maybe five or six.'

'Fine.' She pursed her lips as she applied her lipstick, a pale mauve shade that he disliked intensely.

'One other thing, Tara. Lord Littleton's bank is preparing to underwrite the share issue for our possible new development on the Orange Free State goldfields. I would take it as a personal favour if you and Molly could refrain from waving your black sashes in his face and from regaling him with merry tales of white injustice and bloody black revolution.'

'I can't speak for Molly, but I promise to be good.'

'Why don't you wear your diamonds tonight?' he changed the subject. 'They look so good on you.'

She hadn't worn the suite of yellow diamonds from the H'ani Mine since she had joined the Sash movement. They made her feel like Marie Antoinette.

'Not tonight,' she said. 'They are a little garish, it's really just a family dinner party.' She dusted her nose with the puff and looked at him in the mirror.

'Why don't you go down, dear. Your precious Lord Littleton will be arriving at any moment.'

'I just want to tuck Bella up first.' He came to stand behind her.

They stared at each other in the mirror, seriously.

'What happened to us, Tara?' he asked softly.

'I don't know what you, mean, dear,' she replied, but she looked down and adjusted the front of her dress carefully.

'I'll see you downstairs,' he said. 'Don't be too long, and do make a fuss of Littleton. He's important, and he likes the girlies.'

After he had closed the door Tara stared at it for a moment, then she repeated his question aloud. 'What happened to us, Shasa? It's quite simple really. I just grew up and lost patience with the trivialities with which you fill your life.'

On the way down she looked in at the children. Isabella was asleep with

teddy on top of her face. Tara saved her daughter from suffocation and went to the boys' rooms. Only Michael was still awake. He was reading.

'Lights out!' she ordered.

'Oh, Mater, just to the end of the chapter.'

'Out!'

'Just this page.'

'Out, I said!' And she kissed him lovingly.

At the head of the staircase she drew a deep breath like a diver on the high board, smiled brightly and went down into the blue drawing-room where the first guests were already sipping sherry.

Lord Littleton was much better value than she had expected – tall, silver-haired and benign.

'Do you shoot?' she asked at the first opportunity.

'Can't stand the sight of blood, me dear.'

'Do you ride?'

'Horses?' he snorted. 'Stupid bloody animals.'

'I think you and I are going to be good friends,' she said.

There were many rooms in Weltevreden that Tara disliked; the dining-room she actively hated with all those heads of long-dead animals that Shasa had massacred staring down from the walls with glass eyes. Tonight she took a chance and seated Molly on the other side of Littleton and within minutes Molly had him hooting with delighted laughter.

When they left the men with the port and Hauptmanns and went through to the ladies room, Molly pulled Tara aside, bubbling over with excitement.

'I've been dying to get you alone all evening,' she whispered. 'You'll never guess who is in the Cape at this very moment.'

'Tell me.'

'The secretary of the African National Congress – that's who. Moses Gama, that's who.'

Tara went very still and pale and stared at her.

'He's coming to our home to talk to a small group of us, Tara. I invited him, and he especially asked for you to be present. I didn't know you knew him.'

'I met him only once – ' she corrected herself, 'twice.'

'Can you come?' Molly insisted. 'It'll be best if Shasa does not know about it, you understand.'

'When?'

'Saturday evening, eight o'clock.'

'Shasa will be away and I'll be there,' Tara said. 'I wouldn't miss it for the world.'

* * *

Sean Courtney was the stalwart of the Western Province Preparatory School first fifteen, or Wet Pups, as the school was known. Quick and strong, he ran in four tries against the Rondebosch juniors and converted them himself, while his father and two younger brothers stood on the touchline and yelled encouragement.

After the final whistle blew Shasa lingered just long enough to congratulate his son, with an effort restraining himself from hugging the sweaty grinning

youngster with grass stains on his white shorts and a graze on one knee. A display like that in front of Sean's peers would have mortified him horribly. Instead they shook hands.

'Well played, sport. I'm proud of you,' he said. 'Sorry about this weekend, but I'll make it up to you.' And although the expression of regret was sincere, Shasa felt a buoyancy of his spirits as he drove out to the airfield at Youngsfield. Dicky, his erk, had the aircraft out of the hangar and ready for him on the hardstand.

Shasa climbed out of the Jaguar and stood with his hands in his pockets and the cigarette in the corner of his mouth, staring at the sleek machine with rapture.

It was a DH 98 Mosquito fighter bomber. Shasa had bought it at one of the RAF disposal sales at Biggin Hill and had it completely stripped and overhauled by De Havilland trained riggers. He had even had them re-glue the sandwich construction of the wooden bodywork with the new Araldite wonder glue. The original Rodux adhesives had proved unreliable under tropical conditions. Stripped of all armaments and military fittings, the Mosquito's already formidable performance had been considerably enhanced. Not even Courtney Mining could afford one of the new civilian jet-engined aircraft, but this was the next best thing.

The beautiful machine crouched on the hardstand like a falcon at bate, the twin Rolls Royce Merlin engines ready to roar into life and hurtle her into the blue. Blue was her colour, sky blue and silver; she shone in the bright Cape sunlight and on her fuselage where once the RAF roundel had been was now emblazoned the Courtney Company logo, a stylized silver diamond, its facets entwined with the Company's initials.

'How is the port number two magneto?' Shasa demanded of Dicky as he sauntered across in his oily overalls. The little man bridled.

'Ticking over like a sewing machine,' he answered. He loved the machine even more than Shasa did, and any imperfection, no matter how minor, wounded him deeply. When Shasa reported one, he took it very badly. He helped Shasa load his briefcase, overnight bag and guncase into the bomb bay which had been converted into a luggage compartment.

'All tanks are full,' he said, and stood aside looking superior as Shasa insisted on checking them visually, and then made a fuss of his walk-around inspection.

'She'll do,' Shasa agreed at last and could not resist stroking the wing, as though it were the limb of a lovely woman.

Shasa switched to oxygen at eleven thousand feet and levelled out at Angels twenty, grinning into his oxygen mask at the old airforce slang. He tuned her for cruise, carefully watching the exhaust gas temperatures and engine revs and then settled back to enjoy it.

Enjoy was too mild a term for it. Flying was an exultation of spirit and a fever in his blood. The immense lion-tawny continent drifted by beneath him, washed by a million suns and burned by the hot herb-scented Karoo winds, its ancient hide riven and wrinkled and scarred with donga and canyon and dried riverbed. Only up here, high above it, did Shasa truly realize how much he was a part of it, how deep was his love for it. Yet it was a hard land and cruel, and it bred hard men, black and white, and he knew that he was one of them. There is no place for weaklings here, he thought, only the strong can flourish.

Perhaps it was the pure oxygen he breathed, enhanced by the ecstasy of flight, but his mind seemed clearer up here. Issues that had been obscure

became lucid, uncertainties resolved, and the hours sped away as swiftly as the lovely machine streaked across the blue so that when he landed at Johannesburg's civilian airport he knew with certainty what had to be done. David Abrahams was waiting for him, lanky and skinny as ever, but he was balding a little and he had taken to wearing gold-rimmed spectacles which gave him a perpetually startled expression. Shasa jumped down off the wing of the Mosquito and they embraced happily. They were closer than brothers. Then David patted the aircraft's wing.

'When do I get to fly her again?' he asked wistfully. David had got a DFC in the western desert and a bar to it in Italy. He had been credited with nine kills and ended the war as a wing commander, while Shasa had been a mere squadron leader when he had lost his eye in Abyssinia and been invalided home.

'She's too good for you,' Shasa told him and slung his luggage into the back seat of David's Cadillac.

As David drove out through the airfield gates they exchanged family news. David was married to Mathilda Janine, Tara Courtney's younger sister, so David and Shasa were brothers-in-law. Shasa boasted about Sean and Isabella without mentioning his other two sons and then they went on to the real objects of their meeting.

These, in order of importance, were, first, the decision whether or not to exercise the option on the new Silver River mining prospect in the Orange Free State. Then there was the trouble with the company's chemical factory on the Natal coast. A local pressure group was kicking up a rumpus about poisoning the sea bed and reefs in the area where the factory was discharging effluent into the sea. And finally, there was David's crazy fixation, from which Shasa was finding it difficult to dislodge him, that they should spend something over a quarter of a million pounds on one of those new elephantine electric calculators.

'The Yanks did all the calculations for the atomic bomb with one of them,' David argued. 'And they call them computers, not calculators,' he corrected Shasa.

'Come on, Davie, what are we going to blow up?' Shasa protested. 'I'm not designing an A-bomb.'

'Anglo-American have one. It's the wave of the future, Shasa. We'd better be on it.'

'It's a quarter-million-pound wave, old son,' Shasa pointed out. 'Just when we need every penny for Silver River.'

'If we'd had one of these computers to analyse the geological drilling reports from Silver River, we'd have already saved ourselves almost the entire cost of the thing, and we'd be a lot more certain of our final decision than we are now.'

'How can a machine be better than a human brain?'

'Just come and have a look at it,' David pleaded. 'The university has just installed an IBM 701. I have arranged a demonstration for you this afternoon.'

'Okay, Davie,' Shasa capitulated. 'I'll look, but that doesn't mean I'm buying.'

The IBM supervisor in the basement of the engineering faculty building was no more than twenty-six years of age.

'They're all kids,' David explained. 'It's a young people's science.'

The supervisor shook hands with Shasa, and then removed her horn-rimmed spectacles. Suddenly Shasa's interest in electronic computers burgeoned. Her eyes were clear bright green and her hair was the colour of wild honey made

from mimosa blossom. She wore a green sweater of tight-fitting angora wool, and a tartan skirt which left her smooth tanned calves bare. It was immediately obvious that she was an expert, and she answered all Shasa's questions without hesitation in a tantalizing southern drawl.

'Marylee has a master's in electrical engineering from MIT,' David murmured, and Shasa's initial attraction was spiced with respect.

'It's so damned big,' he protested. 'It fills the entire basement. The ruddy thing is the size of a four-bedroomed house.'

'Cooling,' Marylee explained. 'The heat build-up is enormous. Most of the bulk is oil cooling baffles.'

'What are you processing at the moment?'

'Professor Dart's archaeological material from the Sterkfontein caves. We are correlating about two hundred thousand observations of his against over a million from the sites in East Africa.'

'How long will that take you?'

'We started the run twenty minutes ago, we'll finish it before we shut down at five o'clock.'

'That's in fifteen minutes,' Shasa chuckled. 'You're having me on!'

'I wouldn't mind,' she murmured speculatively, and when she smiled her mouth was wide and moist and kissable.

'You say you shut down at five?' he asked. 'When do you start up again?'

'Eight tomorrow morning.'

'And the machine stands idle overnight?'

Marylee glanced down the length of the basement. David was at the other end watching the print-out and the hum of the computer covered their voices.

'That's right. It will stand idle all tonight. Just like me.' Clearly she was a lady who knew exactly what she wanted, and how to get it. She looked at him directly, challengingly.

'We can't have that,' Shasa shook his head seriously. 'One thing my mummy taught me was "Waste not, want not". I know a place called the Stardust. The band is far beyond belief. I will wager a pound to a weekend in Paris that I can dance you until you plead for mercy.'

'It's a bet,' she agreed as seriously. 'But do you cheat?'

'Of course,' he answered. David was coming back and Shasa went on smoothly and professionally. 'What about running costs?'

'All in, including insurance and depreciation, a little under four thousand pounds a month,' she told him with a matching businesslike expression.

As they said goodbye and shook hands, she slipped a card into Shasa's palm. 'My address,' she murmured.

'Eight o'clock?' he asked.

'I'll be there,' she agreed.

In the Cadillac, Shasa lit a cigarette and blew a perfect smoke ring that exploded silently against the windscreen.

'Okay, Davie, contact the dean of engineering first thing tomorrow. Offer to hire that monster all its down time from five o'clock in the evening until eight the next morning, and weekends also. Offer him four thousand a month and point out that he'll get the use of it for free. We'll be paying all his costs.'

David turned to him with a startled expression and almost drove up on to the pavement, then corrected with a wild swing of the wheel.

'Why didn't I think of that?' he wondered when he had the Cadillac under control.

'You have to get up earlier,' Shasa grinned and went on, 'Once we know how much time we will need on the thing, we'll sublet the surplus time to a couple of other non-competitor companies who must be thinking about buying a computer themselves. That way we'll get our own usage free, and when IBM have improved the design and made the damned thing smaller, then we will buy our own.'

'Son of a gun.' David shook his head in awe. 'Son of a gun.' Then with sudden inspiration, 'I'll get young Marylee on our payroll – '

'No,' said Shasa sharply. 'Get someone else.'

David glanced at him again and his excitement faded. He knew his brother-in-law too well.

'You won't be taking up Matty's invitation to dinner this evening, will you?' he asked morosely.

'Not this evening,' Shasa agreed. 'Give her my love and apologies.'

'Just be careful. It's a small town and you are a marked man,' David warned as he dropped Shasa off at the Carlton Hotel where the company kept a permanent suite. 'Do you think you will be fit for work tomorrow?'

'Eight o'clock,' Shasa told him. 'Sharp!'

By mutual agreement the dance competition at the Stardust was declared a draw, and Shasa and Marylee got back to his Carlton suite a little after midnight.

Her body was young and smooth and hard and just before she drifted off to sleep with her thick honey-coloured hair spread on his bare chest, she whispered drowsily, 'Well, I guess that's about the only thing my IBM 701 can't do for me.'

Shasa was in the Courtney mining offices fifteen minutes before David the next morning. He liked to keep everybody on their toes. Their offices occupied the entire third floor of the Standard Bank building in Commissioner Street. Although Shasa owned a prime piece of real estate on the corner of Diagonal Street opposite the stock exchange and within yelling distance of Anglo American Corporation's head office, he hadn't yet got around to building on it; any spare money in the company always seemed to be earmarked for mining options or extensions or other income-producing enterprises.

The young blood on the Courtney executive board was judicially leavened with a few grey heads. Doctor Twentyman-Jones was still there, in an old-fashioned black alpaca jacket and string tie, hiding his affection for Shasa behind a mournful expression. He had run the very first prospect on the H'ani diamond mine for Centaine back in the early twenties and was one of the three most experienced and gifted mining consultants in southern Africa, which meant the world.

David's father Abraham Abrahams was still head of the legal section, perched up beside his son, bright and chirpy as a little silver sparrow. His files were piled high on the table in front of him, and he seldom had to refer to them. With half a dozen other newcomers whom Centaine and Shasa between them had hand-picked, it was a balanced and functional team.

'Let's talk about the Courtney chemical plant at Chaka's Bay first.' Shasa brought the meeting to order. 'How much meat is there in the beef against us, Abe?'

'We are running hot sulphuric acid into the sea at a rate of between eleven and sixteen tons per day at a concentration of one in ten thousand,' Abe Abrahams told him matter-of-factly. 'I've had an independent marine biologist

do a report on it for us.' He tapped the document. 'It isn't good. We have altered the pH for five miles along the coastline.'

'You haven't circulated this report?' Shasa asked sharply.

'What do you think?' Abe shook his head.

'All right, David. What will it cost us to modify the manufacturing procedure on the fertilizer division to dispose of the acid waste some other way?'

'There are two possible modifications,' David told him. 'The simplest and cheapest is trucking the effluent in tankers, but then we have to find another dumping ground. The ideal solution is recycling the acid.'

'Costs?'

'One hundred thousand pounds per annum for the tankers – one shot of almost three times that for the other way.'

'A year's profits down the drain,' Shasa said. 'That's not acceptable. Who is this Pearson woman that is heading up the protest? Can we reason with her?'

Abe shook his head. 'We have tried. She is holding the whole committee together. Without her they would crumble.'

'What is her position?'

'Her husband owns the local bakery.'

'Buy it,' said Shasa. 'If he won't sell, let him know discreetly that we will open another bakery in competition and subsidize its product. I want this Pearson woman far away and long ago. Any questions?' He looked down at the table. Everybody was busy making notes, nobody looked at him and he wanted to ask them reasonably, 'All right, gentlemen, are you prepared to spend three hundred thousand pounds to give a good home to the oysters and the sea urchins of Chaka's Bay?'

'No questions!' he nodded instead. 'All right, let's take on the big one now. Silver River.'

They all shifted in their seats, and there was simultaneous and nervous exhalation of breath.

'Gentlemen, we have all read and studied Dr Twentyman-Jones's geological report based on his drilling on the property. It is a superb piece of work, and I don't have to tell you, that it's the best opinion you'll get on Harley Street. Now I want to hear from each of you your own opinions as departmental heads. Can we start with you, Rupert?'

Rupert Horn was the junior member of the executive team. As treasurer and chief accountant he filled in the financial background.

'If we let the option lapse, we shall be writing off the two point three million that we have spent on exploration over the last eighteen months. If we take up the option it will mean an initial payment of four million on signature.'

'We can cover that from the rainy-day account,' Shasa intervened.

'We are holding four point three million in the provisional fund,' Rupert Horn agreed. 'We have it invested in Escom 7% Stock at present, but once we utilize that fund we will be in an extremely exposed position.'

One after the other, in ascending order of seniority, Shasa's managers gave their views as seen from their own departments, and David put it all together at the end.

'So it seems that we have twenty-six days remaining on the option, and four million to pay if we take it up. That is going to leave us bare-bummed, and facing development costs of three million pounds for the main shaft alone, plus

another five million for plant, interest and running costs to see us into the production phase, four years from now in 1956.' He stopped and they all watched intently while Shasa selected a cigarette and tapped it lightly on the lid of his gold case.

Shasa's expression was deadly serious. He knew better than any of them that the decision could destroy the company or take it up onto a new high plateau, and nobody could make that decision for him. He was up on the lonely pinnacle of command.

'We know there is gold down there,' he spoke at last. 'A thick rich reef of it. If we reach it, it will go on producing for the next fifty years. However, gold is standing at thirty-five dollars an ounce. The Americans have pegged it, they have threatened to keep the price there for all time. Thirty-five dollars an ounce – and it will cost us between twenty and twenty-five an ounce to go down that deep and bring it to the surface. A slim margin, gentlemen, much too slim.'

He lit the cigarette, and they all sighed and relaxed, at the same time disappointed and relieved. It would have been glorious to make the charge, but disastrous to have failed. Now they would never know. But Shasa hadn't finished. He blew a spinning smoke-ring down the length of the table, and went on.

'However, I don't think the Americans are going to be able to keep the lid on the gold price much longer. Their hatred of gold is emotional, not based on economic reality. I know, deep down in my guts, that the day is not far off when we will see gold at sixty dollars and one day, sooner than any of us think, it will be a hundred and fifty dollars – perhaps even two hundred!' They stirred with disbelief, and Twentyman-Jones looked as though he might break down and weep in the face of such wild optimism, but Shasa ignored him and turned to Abe Abrahams.

'Abe, at noon on the eighteenth of next month, twelve hours before the option expires, you will hand over a cheque for four million to the owners of Silver River farms, and take possession of the property in the name of a company to be formed.' Shasa turned to David. 'At the same time we will simultaneously open subscription lists on the Johannesburg and London stock exchanges for ten million £1 shares in the Silver River gold-mining property. You and Doctor Twentyman-Jones will start today drawing up the prospectus. Courtney Mining will register the property in the name of the new company in return for the balance of five million shares transferred into our name. We will also be responsible for the management and development.' Quickly, succinctly, Shasa laid out the structure, financing and management of the new company, and more than once these wily seasoned campaigners glanced up from their notepads in blatant admiration of some deft and unusual touch he added to the scheme.

'Is there anything I have left out?' Shasa asked at the end, and when they shook their heads, he grinned. David was reminded strongly of the movie he and Matty had taken the children to see the previous Saturday afternoon, *The Sea Hawk*, though the eye-patch made Shasa look even more piratical than Errol Flynn had done in the title role.

'The founder of our company, Madame Centaine de Thiry Courtney-Malcomess, has never approved of the consumption of alcohol in the boardroom. However – ' Still grinning, Shasa nodded at David, who went to open the main doors of the boardroom and a secretary wheeled in a trolley on which the rows of glasses clinked and the green bottles of Dom Perignon swished in

their silver ice-buckets. 'Old customs give way to new,' Shasa said, and drew the first cork with a discreet pop.

* * *

Shasa throttled back the Rolls Royce engines and the Mosquito sank down through the ribbons of scattered cirrus cloud, and the endless golden plains of the high African shield came up to meet her. Off to the west Shasa could just make out the clustered buildings of the mining town of Welkom, centre of the Orange Free State goldfields. Founded only a few years previously, when the vast Anglo American Corporation began opening up these fields, it was already a model town of over a hundred thousand persons.

Shasa unclipped his oxygen mask and let it dangle on his chest, as he leaned forward on his straps and peered ahead through the windshield ahead of the Mosquito's blue nose.

He picked out the tiny steel tower of the drilling rig almost lost in the immensity of the dusty plain, and using it as a landmark traced the gossamer thread of fences that enclosed the Silver River farms – eleven thousand acres, most of it bare and undeveloped. It was amazing that the geologists of the big mining houses had overlooked this little pocket, but then nobody could have reasonably expected the gold reef to spur off like that – that is, nobody but Twentyman-Jones and Shasa Courtney.

Yet the reef was as far beneath the earth as the Mosquito now circled above it. It seemed impossible that any human endeavour would be able to burrow down that deep, but already Shasa could see in his imagination the tall headgear of the Silver River main towering two hundred feet above the peak plain, with its shaft stabbing down a mile and more into the underground river of precious metal.

'And the Yanks can't hold out for ever – they will have to let gold go free,' he told himself.

He stood the Mosquito on one wing and on the instrument panel the gyro compass revolved smoothly. Shasa lifted the wing and she was precisely on her new heading of 125°.

'Fifteen minutes, with these winds,' he grunted, as he marked the large-scale map on his knee, and the fine exaltation of spirit stayed with him for the remainder of the flight until he saw the dark pencil-line of smoke rising into the still air dead ahead. They had put up a smoke beacon to guide him in.

There was a Dakota parked in front of the lonely galvanized iron-clad hangar at the end of the strip. The big aircraft had airforce markings. The runway was of rolled yellow clay, hard and smooth and the Mosquito settled to it with barely a jolt. It had taken endless practice to develop that sort of distance judgement after he had lost the eye.

Shasa slid back the canopy and taxied towards the hangar. There was a green Ford pick-up near the mast of the windsock, and a lone figure dressed in khaki shorts and shirt stood beside the smoke pot, fists clenched on his hips, watching Shasa taxi up and cut the engines. Then as Shasa jumped down, he stepped forward and offered his right hand, but his expression, solemn and reserved, was at odds with the welcoming gesture.

'Good afternoon, Minister.' Shasa was as unsmiling and their grip was hard

but brief. Then as Shasa looked deeply into Manfred De La Rey's pale eyes, he had a strange feeling of *déjà vu*, of having stared into those same eyes in desperate circumstances before. He had to shake his head slightly to be rid of it.

'I am glad for both our sakes that you were able to come. Can I help you with your bags?' Manfred De La Rey asked.

'Don't worry. I can manage.' Shasa went back to tie down and secure the Mosquito and fetch his luggage from the bomb bay, while Manfred doused the smoke pot.

'You brought your own rifle,' Manfred remarked. 'What is it?'

'Seven mm Remington magnum.' Shasa swung the luggage into the back of the truck and stepped up into the passenger door of the Ford.

'Perfect for this type of shooting,' Manfred approved as he started the truck. 'Long shots over flat ground.' He swung on to the track and they drove for a few minutes in silence.

'The prime minister could not come,' he said. 'He intended to be here, but he sent a letter for you. It confirms that I speak with his authority.'

'I'll accept that.' Shasa kept a straight face.

'The minister of finance is here, and the minister of agriculture is our host – this is his farm. One of the biggest in the Free State.'

'I am impressed.'

'Yes,' Manfred nodded. 'I think you will be.' He stared hard at Shasa. 'Is it not strange how you and I seem doomed always to confront each other?'

'It had crossed my mind,' Shasa admitted.

'Do you think there is some reason for it – something of which we are unaware?' Manfred insisted, and Shasa shrugged.

'I shouldn't think so – coincidence only.' The reply seemed to disappoint Manfred.

'Has your mother never spoken about me?'

Shasa looked startled. 'My mother! Good Lord, I don't think so. She may have mentioned you casually – why do you ask?'

Manfred seemed not to have heard, he looked ahead. 'There is the homestead,' he said, with a finality that closed the subject.

The track breasted the rim of a shallow valley and the homestead nestled below them. Here the water must be near the surface for the pasturage was lush and green and the skeletal steel towers of a dozen windmills were scattered down the valley. A plantation of eucalyptus trees surrounded the homestead, and beyond it stood substantial outbuildings, all freshly painted and in good repair. Twenty or more brand new tractors were lined up before one of the long garages, and there were flocks of fat sheep on the pastures. The plain beyond the homestead reaching almost to the horizon was already ploughed, thousands of acres of chocolate loam ready for sowing with maize seed. This was the heart land of Afrikanerdom, this was where the support of the National Party was solid and unwavering, and it was the only reason why under the Nationalists the electoral areas had been re-demarcated to swing the centres of power away from the urban concentrations of population to favour these rural constituencies. That was why the Nationalists would stay in power for ever, and Shasa grimaced sourly. Immediately Manfred glanced at him, but Shasa offered no explanation and they drove down to the homestead and parked in the farm yard.

There were a dozen men sitting at the long yellow-wood kitchen table, smoking and drinking coffee and chatting while the women hovered in

attendance. The men rose to welcome Shasa and he went down the table shaking hands with each of them and exchanging polite, if not effusive greetings.

Shasa knew every one of them. He had faced all of them across the floor of the house and had lashed most of them with his tongue, and in return had been attacked and vilified by each of them, but now they made room for him at the table and the hostess poured strong black coffee for him and placed a dish of sweet cakes and hard-baked rusks in front of him. They all treated him with that innate courtesy and hospitality that is the hallmark of the Afrikaner. Though they were dressed in rough hunting clothing and pretended to be bluff and simple farmers, they were in reality a group of shrewd and adroit politicians, amongst the richest and most powerful men in the land.

Shasa spoke their language perfectly, understood the most heavily veiled references and laughed at their private jokes, but he was not one of them. He was the *rooinek*, the traditional enemy, and subtly they had closed their ranks against him.

When he had drunk his coffee his host, the minister of agriculture, told him, 'I will show you to your room. You will want to change and unpack your rifle. We will hunt as soon as it is cooler.'

A little after four o'clock, they set out in a procession of pick-up trucks, the elder more important men riding in the cabs while the others stood in the open backs of the trucks. The cavalcade climbed out of the valley, skirted the ploughed lands and then sped out across the plains towards a line of low hills on the horizon.

They saw game now, small herds of springbok far out on the plain like a fine dusting of cinnamon powder on the pale earth, but the trucks raced on, slowing only as they reached the foot of the rocky hills. The lead truck stopped for a moment and two of the hunters jumped down and scrambled into a shallow donga.

'Good luck! Shoot straight,' they called to them as they passed and a few hundred yards farther the convoy stopped again to let another pair take up their positions.

Within half an hour all of the huntsmen had been hidden in an irregular extended line below the ragged range of hills. Manfred De La Rey and Shasa had been placed together in a cluster of broken grey rock, and they squatted down to wait with their rifles across their laps, staring out across the flats that were speckled with darker scrub.

The trucks, driven by the teenage sons of their host, headed out in a wide circle until they were merely specks against the pale glare of the horizon, each marked by the ostrich feather of dust it drew behind it. Then they turned back towards the hills, travelling more slowly, not much above walking pace, as they began to move the scattered herds of antelope ahead of them.

Shasa and Manfred had almost an hour to wait for the driven game to come within rifle shot, and they chatted in a desultory, seemingly aimless manner, at first touching only lightly on politics, but rather discussing their host, the minister of agriculture, and the other guests. Then quite subtly Manfred changed the direction of their talk and remarked on how little real difference existed between the policies and aspirations of the governing National Party and Shasa's own opposition United Party.

'If you examine it carefully, our differences are only those of style and degree. We both want to keep South Africa safe for the white man and for European civilization. We both know that for all of us *apartheid* is a matter of life and

death. Without it we will all drown in the black sea. Since the death of Smuts, your party has moved sharply towards our own thinking, and the leftists and liberals have begun to split away from you.'

Shasa was noncommittal, but the point was apt and painful. There were deep cracks appearing in his own party, and every day it became more apparent that they would never again form the government of this land. However, he was intrigued to know where Manfred De La Rey was leading. He had learned never to underestimate this adversary, and he sensed that he was being artfully prepared for the true purpose of this invitation. It was quite obvious that their host had manoeuvred to place them together, and that every other member of the party was privy to the business afoot. Shasa spoke little, conceding nothing, and waited with rising anticipation for the lurking beast to reveal its shape.

'You know that we have entrenched the language and culture of the English-speaking South Africans. There will never be any attempt to erode those rights – we look upon all English speakers of good will who consider themselves South Africans first as our brothers. Our destinies are linked with chains of steel – ' Manfred broke off, and lifted his binoculars to his eyes. 'They are moving in closer now,' he murmured. 'We had better get ready.' He lowered the binoculars and smiled carefully at Shasa. 'I have heard that you shoot well. I look forward to a demonstration.'

Shasa was disappointed. He had wanted to know where the carefully rehearsed recital had been heading, but now he hid his impatience behind that easy smile of his and opened the breech of the rifle across his lap.

'You are right in one thing, Minister,' he said. 'We are linked together with chains of steel. Let us hope the weight of them doesn't draw us all under.' He saw a strange flash in those topaz yellow eyes, of anger or triumph, he was not certain, and it lasted only an instant.

'I will fire only on a line from dead ahead towards the right,' Manfred said. 'You only in an arc to the left. Agreed?'

'Agreed,' Shasa nodded, although he felt a prickle of irritation at being out-manoeuvred so soon and so easily. Manfred had carefully placed himself to cover the right flank, the natural side for a right-handed marksman to swing.

'You will need the advantage,' Shasa thought grimly and asked aloud. 'I hear you also are a fine shot. What about a small wager on the bag?'

'I do not gamble,' Manfred replied easily. 'That is a device of the devil, but I will count the bag with interest,' and Shasa was reminded of just how puritanical was the extreme Calvinism that Manfred De La Rey practised.

Carefully Shasa loaded his rifle. He had hand-loaded his own cartridges for he never trusted mass-produced factory ammunition. The shiny brass cases were filled with a charge of Norma powder that would drive the Nosler Partition bullet at well over three thousand feet a second. The special construction of the bullet would ensure that it mushroomed perfectly on impact.

He worked the bolt and then raised the weapon to his shoulder and used the telescopic sight to scan the plain. The pick-up trucks were less than a mile away, gently weaving back and forth, to prevent the herds breaking back, keeping them moving slowly down towards the line of hills and the hunters hidden below them. Shasa blinked his eye rapidly to clear his vision, and he could make out each individual animal in the herds of antelope trotting ahead of the vehicles.

They were light as smoke, and they rippled like cloud shadow across the

plain. Trotting daintily with heads held high and with their horns shaped like perfect miniature lyres, they were graceful and indescribably lovely.

Without stereoscopic vision, Shasa had difficulty in judging distance, but he had developed the knack of defining relative size and added to this a kind of sixth sense that enabled him to pilot an aircraft, strike a polo ball, or shoot as well as any fully sighted person.

The nearest of the approaching antelope were almost at extreme range, when there was a crackle of rifle fire from farther down the line and immediately the herds exploded into silent airy flight. Each tiny creature danced and bounced on long legs no thicker than a man's thumb. Seeming no longer bounded by the dictates of gravity, every fluid leap blurring against the matching background of parched earth, they tumbled and shot into the mirage-quivering air in the spectacular display of aerobatics that gave them their name, and down each of their backs a frosty mane came erect and shone with their alarm.

It was more difficult than trying to bring down a rocketing grouse with a spreading pattern of shot, impossible to hold the darting ethereal shapes in the cross-hairs of the lens, fruitless to aim directly at the swift creatures – necessary rather to aim at the empty space where they would be a micro second later when the supersonic bullet reached them.

With some men shooting well is skill learned with much practice and concentration. With Shasa it was a talent that he had been born with. As he turned his upper body, the long barrel pointed exactly where he was looking and the cross hairs of the telescopic sight moved smoothly in the centre of his vision and settled on the nimble body of a racing antelope as it went bounding high in the air. Shasa was not conscious of squeezing the trigger, the rifle seemed to fire of its own accord and the recoil drove into his shoulder at precisely the correct instant.

The ram died in the air, turned over by the bullet so his snowy belly flashed in the sunlight, somersaulting to the impetus of the tiny metal capsule as it lanced his heart, and he fell and rolled horned head over dainty hooves as he hit the earth and lay still.

Shasa worked the bolt and picked up another running creature and the rifle fired again and the sharp stink of burned powder prickled his nostrils. He kept shooting until the barrel was hot enough to raise blisters and his eardrums ached to the crackle of shot.

Then the last of the herds were gone past them and over the hills behind them, and the gunfire died away. Shasa unloaded the cartridges that remained in his rifle and looked at Manfred De La Rey.

'Eight,' Manfred said, 'and two wounded.' It was amazing how those tiny creatures could carry away a misplaced bullet. They would have to follow them up. It was unthinkable to allow a wounded animal to suffer unnecessarily.

'Eight is a good score,' Shasa told him. 'You can be pleased with your shooting.'

'And you?' Manfred asked. 'How many?'

'Twelve,' Shasa answered expressionlessly.

'How many wounded?' Manfred hid his chagrin well enough.

'Oh.' Shasa smiled at last. 'I don't wound animals – I shoot where I aim.' That was enough. He did not have to rub in salt.

Shasa left him and walked out to the nearest carcass. The springbok lay on its side and in death the deep fold of skin along its back had opened and from it the snowy plume started erect. Shasa went down on one knee and stroked the

lovely plume. From the glands in the fold of skin had exuded reddish-brown musk, and Shasa parted the long plume and rubbed the secretion with his forefinger, then raised it to his face and inhaled the honey-scented aroma. It smelled more like a flower than an animal. Then the hunter's melancholy came upon him, and he mourned the beautiful little creature he had killed.

'Thank you for dying for me,' he whispered the ancient Bushman prayer that Centaine had taught him so long ago, and yet the sadness was pleasure, and deep inside him the atavistic urge of the hunter was for the moment replete.

* * *

In the cool of the evening the men gathered around the pits of glowing embers in front of the homestead. The *braaivleis*, or meat bake, was a ritual that followed the hunt; the men did the cooking while the women were relegated to the preparation of salads and pudding at the long trestle tables on the stoep. The game had been marinated or larded or made into spiced sausage, and the livers, kidneys and tripes were treated to jealously guarded recipes before they were laid upon the coals in the grilling pit, while the self-appointed chefs kept the heat of the fires from becoming oppressive with liberal draughts of *mampoer*, the pungent peach brandy.

A scratch band of coloured farm labourers belted out traditional country airs on banjo and concertina and some of the guests danced on the wide front stoep. A few of the younger women were very interesting, and Shasa eyed them thoughtfully. They were tanned and glowing with health and an unsophisticated sensuality that was made all the more appealing by the fact of their Calvinist upbringing. Their untouchability and probable virginity made them even more attractive to Shasa who enjoyed the chase as much as the kill.

However, there was too much at stake here to risk giving the slightest offence. He avoided the shy but calculating glances that some of them cast in his direction, and avoided just as scrupulously the savage peach brandy and filled his glass with ginger ale. He knew he would need all his wits before the night was ended.

When their appetites, sharpened on the hunting veld, had been blunted by the steaming platters piled with grilled venison, and the leftovers had been carried away delightedly to the servants' quarters, Shasa found himself sitting at the end of the long stoep farthest from the band. Manfred De La Rey was sitting opposite him, and the two other ministers of the government sprawled contentedly in their deep lounging chairs flanking him. Despite their relaxed attitudes, they watched him warily from the corners of their eyes.

'The main business is about to begin,' Shasa decided, and almost immediately Manfred stirred.

'I was telling Meneer Courtney that in many ways we are very close,' Manfred started quietly, and his colleagues nodded sagely. 'We all want to protect this land and preserve all that is fine and worthwhile in it.'

'God has chosen us as guardians – it is our duty to protect all its peoples, and make certain that the identity of each group and each separate culture is kept intact, and apart from the others.'

It was the party line, this notion of divine selection, and Shasa had heard it

all a hundred times before; so although he nodded and made small noncommittal sounds, he was becoming restless.

'There is still much to be done,' Manfred told him. 'After the next election we will have great labours ahead of us, we are the masons building a social edifice that will stand for a thousand years. A model society in which each group will have its place, and will not intrude upon the space of others, a broad and stable pyramid forming a unique society.' They were all silent then for a while, contemplating the beauty of the vision, and though Shasa kept his expression neutral, still he smiled inwardly at the apt metaphor of a pyramid. There was no doubt in any of their minds as to which group was divinely ordained to occupy the pinnacle.

'And yet there are enemies?' the minister of agriculture cued Manfred.

'There are enemies, within and without. They will become more vociferous and dangerous as the work goes ahead. The closer we come to success, the more avid they become to prevent us achieving it.'

'Already they are gathering.'

'Yes,' Manfred agreed. 'And even old and traditional friends are warning and threatening us. America, who should know better, racked by her own racial problems, the unnatural aspirations of the negroes they brought as slaves from Africa. Even Britain with her Mau Mau troubles in Kenya and the disintegration of her Indian Empire wishes to dictate to us and divert us from the course we know is right.'

'They believe us to be weak and vulnerable.'

'They already hint at an arms embargo, denying us the weapons to defend ourselves against the dark enemy that is gathering in the shadows.'

'They are right,' Manfred cut in brusquely. 'We are weak and militarily disorganized. We are at the mercy of their threats – '

'We have to change this,' the finance minister spoke harshly. 'We must make ourselves strong.'

'At the next budget the defence allocation will be fifty million pounds, while by the end of the decade it will be a billion.'

'We must put ourselves above their threats of sanction and boycott and embargo.'

'Strength through Unity, *Ex Unitate Vires*,' said Manfred De La Rey. 'And yet by tradition and preference, the Afrikaner people have been farmers and country folk. Because of the discrimination which was practised against us for a hundred years and more, we have been excluded from the marketplace of commerce and industry and we have not learned the skills which come so readily to our English-speaking countrymen.' Manfred paused, glanced at the other two, as if for approval, and then went on. 'What this country needs desperately is the wealth to make our vision come true. It is a massive undertaking for which we lack the skills. We need a special type of man.' They were all looking keenly at Shasa now. 'We need a man with the vigour of youth but the experience of age, a man with proven genius for finance and organization. We can find no member of our own party with those attributes.'

Shasa stared at them. What they were suggesting was outrageous. He had grown up in the shadow of Jan Christian Smuts and had a natural and unshakable allegiance to the party that Smuts, that great and good man, had founded. He opened his mouth to answer angrily, but Manfred De La Rey raised his hand to stop him.

'Hear me out,' he said. 'The person chosen for this patriotic work would be

immediately given a senior cabinet appointment which the prime minister would create specifically for him. He would become minister of mines and industry.'

Shasa closed his mouth slowly. How carefully they must have studied him, and how accurately they had analysed him and arrived at his price. The very foundations of his political beliefs and principles were shaken, and the walls cracked through. They had led him up into a high place and shown him the prize that was his for the taking.

* * *

At twenty thousand feet Shasa levelled the Mosquito and trimmed for cruise. He increased the flow of oxygen into his mask to sharpen his brain. He had four hours' flying time to Youngsfield, four hours to think it all out carefully, and he tried to divorce himself from the passions and emotions which still swept him along and attempted instead to reach his decision logically – but the excitement intruded upon his meditations. The prospect of wielding vast powers, building up an arsenal that would make his country supreme in Africa and a force in the world was awe-inspiring. That was power. The thought of it all made him slightly light-headed, for it was all there at last, everything he had ever dreamed of. He had only to reach out his hand and seize the moment. Yet what would be the cost in honour and pride – how would he explain to men who trusted him?

Then abruptly he thought of Blaine Malcomess, his mentor and adviser, the man who had stood in the place of his own father all these years. What would he think of this dreadful betrayal that Shasa was contemplating?

'I can do more good by joining them, Blaine,' he whispered into his mask. 'I can help change and moderate them from within more effectively than in opposition, for now I will have the power – ' but he knew he was prevaricating, and all else was dross.

It all came down to that one thing in the end, the power – and he knew that although Blaine Malcomess would never condone what he would see as treachery, there was one person who would understand and give him support and encouragement. For after all it was Centaine Courtney-Malcomess who had so carefully schooled her son in the acquisition and use of wealth and power.

'It could all come true, Mater. It could still happen, not exactly as we planned it, but it could still happen all the same.' Then a thought struck him, and a shadow passed across the bright light of his triumph.

He glanced down at the red folder that Manfred De La Rey, minister of police, had given him at the airstrip, just as he was about to climb up into the Mosquito, and which now lay on the co-pilot's seat beside him.

'There is only one problem we will have to deal with, if you accept our offer,' Manfred had said as he handed it over, 'and it is a serious problem. This is it.'

The folder contained a police special branch security report, and the name on the cover was:

TARA ISABELLA COURTNEY née MALCOMESS

Tara Courtney made her round of the children's wing, calling in at each of the bedrooms. Nanny was just tucking Isabella under her pink satin eiderdown, and the child let out a cry of delight when she saw Tara.

'Mummy, Mummy, teddy has been naughty. I'm going to make him sleep on the shelf with my other dolls.'

Tara sat on her daughter's bed and hugged her while they discussed teddy's misdemeanours. Isabella was pink and warm and smelled of soap. Her hair was silky against Tara's cheek and it took an effort for Tara to kiss her and stand up.

'Time to go to sleep, Bella baby.'

The moment the lights went out Isabella let out such a shriek that Tara was stricken with alarm.

'What is it, baby?' She snapped on the lights again and rushed back to the bed.

'I've forgiven teddy. He can sleep with me after all.'

The teddy-bear was ceremoniously reinstated in Isabella's favour and she took him in a loving half-nelson and stuck her other thumb in her mouth.

'When is my Daddy coming home?' she demanded drowsily around the thumb, but her eyes were closed and she was asleep before Tara reached the door.

Sean was sitting on Garrick's chest in the middle of the bedroom floor, tweaking the hair at his brother's temples with sadistic finesse. Tara separated them.

'Sean, you get back to your room this instant, do you hear me? I have warned you a thousand times about bullying your brothers. Your father is going to hear all about this when he gets home.'

Garrick snuffled up his tears and came wheezing to his elder brother's defence.

'We were only playing, Mater. He wasn't bullying me.' But she could hear that he was on the verge of another asthma attack. She wavered. She really should not go out, not with an attack threatening, but tonight was so important.

'I'll prepare his inhaler and tell Nanny to look in on him every hour until I get back,' she compromised.

Michael was reading, and barely looked up to receive her kiss. 'Lights out at nine o'clock. Promise me, darling.' She tried never to let it show, but he was always her favourite.

'I promise, Mater,' he murmured and under cover of the eiderdown carefully crossed his fingers.

On the way down the stairs she glanced at her wristwatch. It was five minutes before eight. She was going to be late, and she stifled her maternal feelings of guilt and fled out to her old Packard.

Shasa detested the Packard, taking its blotched sun-faded paintwork and its shabby stained upholstery as an affront to the family dignity. He had given her a new Aston Martin on her last birthday, but she left it in the garage. The Packard suited her Spartan image of herself as a caring liberal, and it blew a streamer of dirty smoke as she accelerated down the long driveway, taking a perverse pleasure in sending a pall of fine dust over Shasa's meticulously groomed vineyards. It was strange how even after all these years she felt herself a stranger at Weltevreden, and alien amongst its treasures and stuffy old-fashioned furnishings. If she lived here another fifty years it would never be her home, it was Centaine Courtney-Malcomess' home, the other woman's touch

and memory lingered in every room that Shasa would never allow her to redecorate.

She escaped through the great ostentatious Anreith gateway into the real world of suffering and injustice, where the oppressed masses wept and struggled and cried out for succour and where she felt useful and relevant, where in the company of other pilgrims she could march forward to meet a future full of challenge and change.

The Broadhursts' home was in the middle-class suburb of Pinelands, a modern ranch-type home with a flat roof and large picture windows, with ordinary functional mass-produced furniture and nylon wall-to-wall carpet. There were dog hairs on the chairs, well thumbed intellectual books piled in odd corners or left open on the dining-room table, children's toys abandoned in the passageways, and cheap reproductions of Picasso and Modigliani hanging askew on the walls marked with grubby little fingerprints. Tara felt comfortable and welcome here, mercifully released from the fastidious splendour of Weltevreden.

Molly Broadhurst rushed out to meet her as she parked the Packard. She was dressed in a marvellously flamboyant caftan.

'You're late!' She kissed Tara heartily and dragged her through the disorder of the lounge to the music room at the rear.

The music room was an afterthought stuck on to the end of the house without any aesthetic considerations and was filled now with Molly's guests who had been invited to hear Moses Gama. Tara's spirits soared as she looked around her, they were all vibrant creative people, all of them spirited and articulate, filled with the excitement of living with a fine sense of justice and outrage and rebellion.

This was the type of gathering that Weltevreden would never see. Firstly, black people were included, students from the black University of Fort Hare and the fledgling University of the Western Cape, teachers and lawyers and even a black doctor, all of them political activists who, although denied a voice or a vote in the white parliament, were beginning to cry out with a passion that must be heard. There was the editor of the black magazine *Drum* and the local correspondent of the *Sowetan*, named after that sprawling black township.

Just to mingle socially with blacks made her feel breathlessly daring.

The whites in the room were no less extraordinary. Some of them had been members of the Communist Party of South Africa before that organization had been disbanded a few years previously. There was a man called Harris who she had met before at Molly's house. He had fought with the Irgun in Israel against the British and the Arabs, a tall fierce man who inspired a delicious fear in Tara. Molly hinted that he was an expert in guerrilla warfare and sabotage, and certainly he was always travelling secretly around the country or slipping across the border into neighbouring states on mysterious business.

Talking earnestly to Molly's husband was another lawyer from Johannesburg, Bram Fischer, who specialized in defending black clients charged under the myriad laws that were designed to muzzle and disarm them and restrict their movements. Molly said that Bram was reorganizing the old Communist Party into underground cells, and Tara fantasized that she might one day be invited to join one of these cells.

In the same group was Marcus Archer, another ex-communist and an industrial psychologist from the Witwatersrand. He was responsible for the training of thousands of black workers for the goldmining industry, and Molly

said that he had helped to organize the black mineworkers' union. Molly had also whispered that he was a homosexual, and she had used an odd term for it that Tara had never heard before. 'He's gay, gay as a lark.' And because it was totally unacceptable to polite society, Tara found it fascinating.

'Oh God, Molly,' Tara whispered. 'This is so exciting. These are all real people, they make me feel as though I am truly living at last.'

'There he is.' Molly smiled at this outburst and dragged Tara with her through the press of bodies.

Moses Gama leaned against the far wall faced by a half circle of admirers, yet standing head and shoulders above them, and Molly pushed her way into the front row.

Tara found herself staring up at Moses Gama, and she thought that even in this brilliant company he stood out like a black panther in a pack of mangy alley cats. Though his head seemed carved from a block of black onyx, and his handsome Nilotic features were impassive, yet there was a force within him that seemed to fill all the room. It was like standing on the high slopes of a dark Vesuvius, knowing that at any instant it could boil over into cataclysmic eruption.

Moses Gama turned his head and looked at Tara. He did not smile, but a shadowy thing moved in the depths of his dark gaze.

'Mrs Courtney – I asked Molly to invite you.'

'Please don't call me that. My name is Tara.'

'We must talk later, Tara. Will you stay?'

She could not answer, she was too overcome at being singled out, but she nodded dumbly.

'If you are ready, Moses, we can begin,' Molly suggested, and taking him out of the group led him to the raised dais on which the piano stood.

'People! People! Your attention, please!' Molly clapped her hands, and the animated chatter died away. Everybody turned towards the dais. 'Moses Gama is one of the most talented and revered of the new generation of young black African leaders. He has been a member of the African National Congress since before the war, and a prime mover in the formation of the African Mineworkers' Union. Although the black trade unions are not officially recognized by the government of the day, yet the secret union of mineworkers is one of the most representative and powerful of all black associations, with more than a hundred thousand paid-up members. In 1950 Moses Gama was elected Secretary of the ANC, and he has worked tirelessly, selflessly and highly effectively in making the heart cry of our black citizens heard, even though they are denied a voice in their own destiny. For a short while Moses Gama was an appointed member of the government's Natives' Representative Council, that infamous attempt to appease black political aspirations, but it was he who resigned with the now celebrated remark, "I have been speaking into a toy telephone, with nobody listening at the other end."'

There was a burst of laughter and applause from the room, and then Molly turned to Moses Gama.

'I know that you have nothing to tell us that will comfort and soothe us – but, Moses Gama, in this room there are many hearts that beat with yours and are prepared to bleed with yours.'

Tara applauded until the palms of her hands were numb, and then leaned forward to listen eagerly as Moses Gama moved to the front of the dais.

He was dressed in a neat blue suit and a dark blue tie with a white shirt.

Strangely, he was the most formally dressed man in a room full of baggy woollen sweaters and old tweed sports coats with leather patches on the elbows and gravy stains on the lapels. His suit was severely cut, draped elegantly from wide athletic shoulders, but he imparted to it a panache that made it seem that he wore the leopard-skin cloak of royalty and the blue heron feathers in his close-cropped mat of hair. His voice was deep and thrilling.

'My friends, there is one single ideal to which I cling with all my heart, and which I will defend with my very life, and that is that every African has a primary, inherent and inalienable right to the Africa which is his continent and his only motherland,' Moses Gama began, and Tara listened, enchanted, as he detailed how that inherent right had been denied the black man for three hundred years, and how in these last few years since the Nationalist government had come to power, those denials were becoming formally entrenched in a monumental edifice of laws and ordinances and proclamations which was the policy of *apartheid* in practice.

'We have all heard it said that the whole concept of *apartheid* is so grotesque, so obviously lunatic, that it can never work. But I warn you, my friends, that the men who have conceived this crazy scheme are so fanatical, so obdurate, so convinced of their divine guidance, that they will force it to work. Already they have created a vast army of petty civil servants to administer this madness, and they have behind them the full resources of a land rich in gold and minerals. I warn you that they will not hesitate to squander that wealth in building up this ideological Frankenstein of theirs. There is no price in material wealth and human suffering that is too high for them to contemplate.'

Moses Gama paused and looked down upon them, and it seemed to Tara that he personally felt every last agony of his people, and was filled with suffering beyond that which mortal men could bear.

'Unless they are opposed, my friends, they will create of this lovely land a desolation and an abomination; a land devoid of compassion, of justice, a land materially and spiritually bankrupt.'

Moses Gama spread his arms. 'These men call those of us who defy them traitors. Well, my friends, I call any man who does not oppose them a traitor – a traitor to Africa.'

He was silent then, glaring this accusation at them, and they were struck dumb for a moment, before they began to cheer him. Only Tara remained still in the uproar, staring at him; she had no voice, and she was shivering as though there was malaria in her blood.

Moses' head sank until his chin was on his chest, and they thought he had finished. Then he raised that magnificent head again and spread his arms.

'Oppose them? How do we oppose them? I reply to you – we oppose them with all our strength and all our resolve and with all our hearts. If no price is too high for them to pay, then no price is too high for us. I tell you, my friends, there is nothing – ' He paused for emphasis ' – *nothing* I would not do to further the struggle. I am prepared both to die and to kill for it.'

The room was silent in the face of such deadly resolve. For those of them who were practitioners of elegant, socialist dialectic, the effete intellectuals, such a declaration was menacing and disquieting, it had the sound of breaking bones in it and the stench of fresh-spilled blood.

'We are ready to make a beginning, my friends, and already our plans are far advanced. Starting in a few months' time we will conduct a nationwide campaign of defiance against these monstrous *apartheid* laws. We will burn the passes

which we are ordered by act of parliament to carry, the hated *dompas* which is akin to the star that the Jews were forced to wear, the document that marks us as racial inferiors. We will make a bonfire of them and the smoke of their burning will sting and offend the nostrils of the civilized world. We will sit in the whites-only restaurants and cinemas, we will ride in the whites-only coaches of the railways, and swim from the whites-only beaches. We will cry out to the fascist police, "Come! Arrest us." And in our thousands we will overflow the white man's jails and block his law courts with our multitudes until the whole giant apparatus of *apartheid* breaks down under the strain.'

Tara lingered afterwards as he had asked her to, and when Molly had seen most of her guests leave, she came and took Tara's arm. 'Will you risk my spaghetti Bolognaise, Tara dear? As you know, I'm the worst cook in Africa, but you are a brave girl.'

Only a half dozen of the guests had been invited to remain for a late dinner and they sat out on the patio. The mosquitoes whined around their heads and every once in a while a shift of the wind brought a sulphurous whiff from the sewerage works across the Black River. It did not seem to spoil their appetites and they tucked into Molly's notorious spaghetti Bolognaise and washed it down with tumblers of cheap red wine. Tara found it a relief from the elaborate meals that were served at Weltevreden, accompanied always by the quasi-religious ceremony of tasting wines that cost a working man's monthly wage for the bottle. Here food and wine were merely fuel to power the mind and tongue, not for gloating over.

Tara sat beside Moses Gama. Although his appetite was hearty, he hardly touched the tumbler of wine. His table manners were African. He ate noisily with an open mouth, but strangely this did not offend Tara in the least. Somehow it confirmed his differentness, marked him as a man of his own people.

At first Moses gave most of his attention to the other guests, replying to the questions and comments that were called down the table to him. Then gradually he concentrated on Tara, at first including her in his general conversation, and at last, when he had finished eating, turning in his chair to face her fully and lowering his voice to exclude the others.

'I know your family,' he told her. 'Know them well, Mrs Centaine Courtney and more especially your husband, Shasa Courtney.'

Tara was startled. 'I have never heard them speak of you.'

'Why would they do so? In their eyes I was never important. They would have forgotten me long ago.'

'Where did you know them and when?'

'Twenty years ago. Your husband was still a child. I was a boss-boy, a supervisor on the H'ani diamond mine in South West Africa.'

'The H'ani,' Tara nodded. 'Yes, the fountainhead of the Courtney fortune.'

'Shasa Courtney was sent by his mother to learn the workings of the mine. He and I were together for a few weeks, working side by side – ' Moses broke off and smiled. 'We got along well, as well as a black man and a little white *baas* ever could, I suppose. We talked a great deal, and he gave me a book. Macaulay's *History of England*. I still have it. I recall how some of the things I said puzzled and disturbed him. He told me once, "Moses, that is politics. Blacks don't take part in politics. That's white men's business."' Moses chuckled at the memory, but Tara frowned.

'I can hear him say it,' she agreed. 'He hasn't changed much in twenty years,' and Moses stopped laughing.

'Your husband has become a powerful man. He has great wealth and influence.'

Tara shrugged. 'What good is power and wealth unless it is used with wisdom and compassion.'

'You have compassion, Tara,' he said softly. 'Even if I did not know of the work that you do for my people, I would sense it in you.

Tara lowered her eyes from his smouldering regard.

'Wisdom.' His voice sank even lower. 'I think you have that also. It was wise not to speak of our last meeting in front of others.'

Tara's head came up and she stared at him. In the evening's excitement she had almost forgotten their encounter in the forbidden corridors of parliament.

'Why?' she whispered. 'Why were you there?'

'One day I may tell you,' he replied. 'When we have become friends.'

'We are friends,' she said, and he nodded.

'Yes, I think we are friends, but friendships have to be tried and proven. Now, tell me about your work, Tara.'

'It's so very little that I am able to do – ' and she told him about the clinic and the feeding scheme for the children and the old people, unconscious of her own enthusiasm and animation until he smiled again.

'I was right, you do have compassion, Tara, enormous compassion. I would like to see this work. Is it possible?'

'Oh, would you come – that would be marvellous!'

Molly brought him out to the clinic the following afternoon.

The clinic was on the southern edge of the black township of Nyanga – the name meant 'dawn' in the Xhosa language, but was hardly apt. Like most black townships it comprised row upon row of identical brick cottages with asbestos sheet roofs separated by dusty lanes; although aesthetically ugly and uninspiring, the accommodation was adequate and offered reticulated water, mains sewerage and electricity. However, beyond the township proper, in the bushy dune country of the Cape Flats, had sprung up a shanty town that housed the overflow of black migrants from the impoverished rural areas, and Tara's clinic found its main clientele amongst these wretches.

Proudly Tara led Moses and Molly around the small building.

'Being the weekend, none of our volunteer doctors are here today,' she explained and Moses stopped to chat with the black nurses and with some of the mothers waiting patiently with their small children in the yard.

Afterwards she made coffee for all three of them in her tiny office and when Moses asked how the clinic was financed, Tara told him vaguely.

'Oh, we get a grant from the local provincial government – ' but Molly Blackhurst cut in.

'Don't let her fool you – most of the running costs come out of her own pocket.'

'I cheat my husband on the housekeeping,' Tara laughed, dismissing it lightly.

'Would it be possible for us to drive around the squatter slums? I'd like to see them.' Moses looked at Molly, but she bit her lip and glanced at her wristwatch.

'Oh, damn, I have to get back,' and Tara intervened quickly.

'Don't worry, Molly. I can drive Moses around. You get on back and I will drop him off at your house later this evening.'

In the old Packard they bumped over the sandy tracks amongst the overgrown dunes, where the Port Jackson willow had been cleared to make way for hutments of rusty corrugated iron and cardboard and tattered plastic sheeting. Now and then they stopped and walked amongst the shanties. The south-easter was roaring in off the bay, filling the air with a mist of dust. They leaned against it as they walked.

The people knew Tara and smiled and called greetings to her as she passed, and the children ran to meet her and danced around her begging for the cheap boiled sweets she kept in her pocket.

'Where do they get water?' Moses asked, and she showed him how the older children had banded old oil drums with discarded car tyres. They filled the drums at a communal water tap at the boundary of the official township a mile away, and rolled the drums back to their hovels.

'They cut the Port Jackson willow for fuel,' Tara told him. 'But in winter the children are always full of colds and flu and pneumonia. You don't have to ask about sewerage – ' she sniffed at the thick odour of the shallow toilet pits, screened with strips of old burlap.

It was half dark when Tara parked the Packard at the back door of the clinic and switched off the engine. They sat quietly for a few minutes.

'What we have seen is no worse than a hundred other shanty towns, places where I have lived most of my life,' Moses said.

'I am sorry.'

'Why do you apologize?' Moses asked.

'I don't know, I just feel guilty.' She knew how inadequate it sounded and she opened the door of the Packard.

'There are some papers I must get from my office. I won't be a minute, and then I will drive you back to Molly's house.'

The clinic was deserted. The two nurses had locked up and gone home an hour before. Tara let herself in with her own key and went through the single consulting room to her own office. She glanced at herself in the mirror above the washstand in the corner as she washed her hands. She was flushed and her eyes sparkled. She was so accustomed to the squalor of the squatter camps that it had not depressed her as it once had; instead she felt tingling alive and strangely elated.

She stuffed the folder of correspondence and bills into her leather sling bag and locked the drawer of her desk, made sure the plug of the electric kettle was pulled out of the wall-socket and that the windows were closed, then switched off the lights and hurried out into the consulting room. She stopped with surprise. Moses Gama had followed her into the building and was sitting on the white draped examination bed against the far wall.

'Oh,' she recovered. 'Sorry I took so long – '

He shook his head, then stood up and crossed the tiled floor. He stopped, facing her. She felt awkward and uncertain as he studied her face solemnly.

'You are a remarkable woman,' he said in a deep quiet voice that she had not heard him use before. 'I have never met another white woman like you.'

She could think of no reply, and he went on softly, 'You are rich and privileged. You are gifted with everything that your life can offer you, and yet you come here. To this poverty and misery.'

He reached out and touched her arm. His palm and the inside of his fingers

were a pale rose colour, contrasting vividly with the back of his hand and his dark muscular forearm, and his skin felt cool. She wondered if it were really so, or if her own skin was hot. She felt hot, she felt a furnace glow deep within her. She looked down at his hand on her smooth pale arm. She had never been touched by a black man before, not deliberately, not lingeringly like this.

She let the strap of the sling bag slide off her shoulder and it fell to the tiled floor with a thud. She had been holding her own hands clasped in front of her hips in an instinctively defensive gesture but now she let them fall to her sides, and almost without conscious volition arched her back and pushed her lower body towards him. At the same time she raised her head and looked squarely into his eyes. Her lips parted and her breathing quickened. She saw it reflected in his own eyes and she said,

'Yes.'

He stroked her arm, up from the elbow to the shoulder, and she shuddered and closed her eyes. He touched her left breast and she did not pull away. His hand closed around her, she felt it fill his grip, and her flesh hardened, her nipple swelled and thrust out into his palm and he squeezed her. The feeling was so intense it was almost painful and she gasped as it rippled down her spine spreading like wavelets when a stone is thrown into a quiet pool.

Her arousal was so abrupt that she was unprepared. She had never considered herself a sensual person. Shasa was the only man she had ever known and it took all his skill and patience to quicken her body, but now at a touch her bones went soft with desire and her loins melted like wax in the flame and she could not breathe, so strong was her need of this man.

'The door,' she blurted. 'Lock the door.'

Then she saw that he had already barred the door, and she was grateful for it, for she felt that she could not have brooked the delay. He picked her up quickly and carried her to the bed. The sheet that covered it was spotless and so crisply starched that it crackled softly under her weight.

He was so huge that he terrified her, and though she had borne four children, she felt as though she was being split asunder as his blackness filled her, and then the terror passed to be replaced by a strange sense of sanctity. She was the sacrificial lamb, with this act she was redeeming all the sins of her own race, all the trespasses that they had committed against his people down the centuries; she was wiping away the guilt that had been her stigma since as far back as she could remember.

When at the end he lay heavy upon her with his breathing roaring in her ears and the last wild convulsions racking his great black muscles, she clung to him with a joyous gratitude. For he had, at one and the same time, set her free from guilt and made her his slave for ever.

* * *

Subdued by the sadness of after love, and by the certain knowledge that her world was for ever altered, Tara was silent on the drive back to Molly's home. She parked a block before she reached it, and keeping the engine running she turned to examine his face in the reflection of the street lights.

'When will I see you again?' she asked the question that countless women in her position had asked before her.

'Do you wish to see me again?'

'More than anything else in my life.' She did not at that moment even think of her children. He was the only thing in her existence.

'It will be dangerous.'

'I know.'

'The penalties if we are discovered – disgrace, ostracism, imprisonment. Your life would be destroyed.'

'My life was a sham,' she said softly. 'Its destruction would be no great loss.'

He studied her features carefully, searching for insincerity. At last he was satisfied.

'I will send for you, when it is safe.'

'I will come immediately, whenever you call.'

'I must leave you now. Take me back.'

She parked at the side of Molly's house, in the shadow where they could not be observed from the road.

'Now the subterfuge and dissembling begins,' she thought calmly. 'I was right. It will never be the same again.'

He made no attempt to embrace her, it was not the African way. He stared at her, the whites of his eyes gleaming like ivory in the half dark.

'You realize that when you choose me you choose the struggle?' he asked.

'Yes, I know that.'

'You have become a warrior and you, and your wants, even your life are of no consequence. If you have to die for the struggle, I will not lift my hand to save you.'

She nodded. 'Yes, I know that.' The nobility of the concept filled her chest and made it difficult for her to breathe so her voice was laboured as she whispered, 'Greater love hath no man – I will make any sacrifice you ask of me.'

* * *

Moses went to the guest bedroom which Molly had allocated to him, and as he washed his face in the basin Marcus Archer slipped into the room without knocking, closed the door and leaned against it, watching Moses in the mirror.

'Well?' he asked at last, as though he was reluctant to hear the answer.

'Just as we planned it.' Moses dried his face on a clean towel.

'I hate the silly little bitch,' Marcus said softly.

'We agreed it was necessary.' Moses selected a fresh shirt from the valise on his bed.

'I know we agreed,' Marcus said. 'It was my suggestion, if you remember, but I do not have to like her for it.'

'She is an instrument. It is folly to let your personal feelings intrude.'

Marcus Archer nodded. In the end he hoped he could act like a true revolutionary, one of the steely hard men which the struggle needed, but his feelings for this man, Moses Gama, were stronger than all his political convictions.

He knew that it was completely one-sided. Over the years Moses Gama had used him as clinically and as calculatingly as he now planned to use the Courtney woman. His vast sexual appeal was to Moses Gama merely another

weapon in his arsenal, another means of manipulating people. He could use it on men or women, young or old, no matter how attractive or unappealing, and Marcus admired him for the ability, and at the same time was devasted by it.

'We leave for the Witwatersrand tomorrow,' he said, as he pushed himself away from the door, for the moment controlling his jealousy. 'I have made the arrangements.'

'So soon?' Moses asked.

'I have made the arrangements. We will travel by car.'

It was one of the problems which dogged their work. It was difficult for a black man to travel about the huge sub-continent, liable as he was at any time to demands to show his *dompas* and to interrogation when the authority realized that he was far from the domicile shown on the pass without apparent reason, or that the pass had not been stamped by an employer.

Moses' association with Marcus and the nominal employment he provided with the Chamber of Mines gave him valuable cover when it was necessary to travel, but they always needed couriers. That was one of the functions that Tara Courtney would perform. In addition she was by birth and by marriage highly placed, and the information she could provide would be of the greatest value in the planning. Later, after she had proved herself, there would be other, more dangerous work.

* * *

In the end, Shasa Courtney realized, it was his mother's advice that would tip the fine balance and decide whether he accepted or rejected the offer that had been made to him during the springbok hunt on the open plains of the Orange Free State.

Shasa would have been the first to despise any other man of his age who was still firmly enmeshed in the maternal apron strings, but he never considered that this applied to him. The fact that Centaine Courtney-Malcomess was his mother was merely incidental. What influenced him was that she was the shrewdest financial and political brain he had access to; she was also his business partner and his only true confidante. To make such an important decision without consulting her never even occurred to him.

He waited a week after his return to Cape Town to let his own feelings distil out, and for an opportunity to have Centaine alone, for he was in no doubt as to what his stepfather's reaction would be to the proposal. Blaine Malcomess was the opposition representative on the parliamentary sub-committee examining the proposed establishment of an oil-from-coal project, part of the government's long-term plan to reduce the country's reliance on imported crude oil. The committee was going to take evidence on site, and for once Centaine was not accompanying her husband. That was the opportunity Shasa needed.

It was less than an hour's drive from Weltevreden, across the Constantia Nek pass and down the other side of the mountains to the Atlantic seaboard where the home that Centaine had made for Blaine stood on five hundred acres of wild protea-covered mountainside that dropped steeply down to rocky headlands and white beaches. The original house, Rhodes Hill, had been built during Queen Victoria's reign by one of the old mining magnates from the Rand, but Centaine had stripped the interior and refurbished it completely.

She was waiting for Shasa on the verandah when he parked the Jaguar, and ran up the steps to embrace her.

'You're getting too thin,' she scolded him fondly. She had guessed from his telephone call that he wanted a serious discussion, and they had their own traditions. Centaine was dressed in an open-neck cotton blouse and slacks with comfortable hiking boots, and without discussing it she took his arm and they set out along the path that skirted her rose gardens and climbed the untended hillside.

The last part of the ascent was steep and the path rough, but Centaine took it without pause and came out on the summit ahead of him. Her breathing was hardly altered, and within a minute had returned to normal. 'She keeps herself in wonderful condition, Heaven alone knows what she spends on health cures and potions, and she exercises like a professional athlete,' Shasa thought as he grinned down at her proudly. He placed an arm around her small firm waist.

'Isn't it beautiful?' Centaine leaned lightly against him and looked out over the cold green Benguela current, as it swirled, decked in lacy foam, around Africa's heel, which like a medieval knight was spurred and armoured with black rock. 'This is one of my favourite places.'

'Whoever would have guessed it,' Shasa murmured, and led her to the flat lichen-covered rock that was her seat.

She perched up on it, hugging her knes and he sprawled on the bed of moss below her. They were both silent for a few moments, and Shasa wondered how often they had sat like this at this special place of hers, and how many heavy decisions they had taken here.

'Do you remember Manfred De La Rey?' he asked suddenly, but he was unprepared for her reaction. She started and looked down at him, colour draining from her cheeks, with an expression he could not fathom.

'Is something wrong, Mater?' He began to rise, but she gestured at him to remain seated.

'Why do you ask about him?' she demanded, but he did not reply directly.

'Isn't it strange how our paths seem to cross with his family? Ever since his father rescued us, when I was an infant and we were castaways living with the Bushmen in the Kalahari.'

'We needn't go over all that again,' Centaine stopped him, and her tone was brusque. Shasa realized he had been tactless. Manfred's father had robbed the H'ani Mine of almost a million pounds' worth of diamonds, an act of vengeance for fancied wrongs that he had convinced himself Centaine had inflicted on him. For that crime he had served almost fifteen years of a life sentence for robbery, and had been pardoned only when the Nationalist government had come to power in 1948. At the same time the Nationalists had pardoned many other Afrikaners serving sentences for treason and sabotage and armed robbery, convicted by the Smuts' government when they had attempted to disrupt the country's war effort against Nazi Germany. However, the stolen diamonds had never been recovered, and their loss had almost destroyed the fortune that Centaine Courtney had built up with so much labour, sacrifice and heartache.

'Why do you mention Manfred De la Rey?' she repeated her question.

'I had an invitation from him to a meeting. A clandestine meeting – all very cloak and dagger.'

'Did you go?'

He nodded slowly. 'We met at a farm in the Free State, and there were two other cabinet ministers present.'

'Did you speak to Manfred alone?' she asked, and the tone of the question, the fact that she used his Christian name, caught Shasa's attention. Then he remembered the unexpected question that Manfred De La Rey had put to him.

'Has your mother ever spoken about me?' he had asked, and faced by Centaine's present reaction to his name, the question took on a new significance.

'Yes, Mater, I spoke to him alone.'

'Did he mention me?' Centaine demanded, and Shasa gave a little chuckle of puzzlement.

'He asked the same question – whether you ever spoke about him. Why are the two of you so interested in each other?'

Centaine's expression turned bleak, and he saw her close her mind to him. It was a mystery he would not solve by pursuing it openly, he would have to stalk it.

'They made me a proposition.' And he saw her interest reawaken.

'Manfred? A proposition? Tell me.'

'They want me to cross the floor.'

She nodded slowly, showing little surprise and not immediately rejecting the idea. He knew that if Blaine were here it would have been different. Blaine's sense of honour, his rigid principles, would have left no room for manoeuvre. Blaine was a Smuts man, heart and blood, and even though the old field-marshal had died of a broken heart soon after the Nationalists unseated him and took over the reins of power, still Blaine was for ever true to the old man's memory.

'I can guess why they want you,' Centaine said slowly. 'They need a top financial brain, an organizer and a businessman. It's the one thing they lack in their cabinet.'

He nodded. She had seen it instantly, and his enormous respect for her was confirmed yet again.

'What price are they willing to pay?' she demanded.

'A cabinet appointment – minister of mines and industry.'

He saw her eyes go out of focus, and cross in a myopic stare as she gazed out to sea. He knew what that expression meant. Centaine was calculating, juggling with the future, and he waited patiently until her eyes snapped back into focus.

'Can you see any reason for refusing?' she asked.

'How about my political principles?'

'How do they differ from theirs?'

'I am not an Afrikaner.'

'That might be to your advantage. You will be their token Englishman. That will give you a special status. You will have a freer rein. They will be more reluctant to fire you than if you were one of their own.'

'I don't agree with their native policy, this *apartheid* thing of theirs, it's just financially unsound.'

'Good Lord, Shasa. You don't believe in equal political rights for blacks, do you? Not even Jannie Smuts wanted that. You don't want another Chaka ruling us, black judges and a black police force working for a black dicator?' She shuddered. 'We'd get pretty short shrift from them.'

'No, Mater, of course not. But this *apartheid* thing is merely a device for grabbing the whole pie. We have to give them a slice of it, we can't hog it all. That's a certain recipe for eventual bloody revolution.'

'Very well, *chéri*. If you are in the cabinet, you can see to it that they get a fair crack of the whip.'

He looked dubious, and made a side-show of selecting a cigarette from his gold case and lighting it.

'You have a special talent, Shasa,' Centaine went on persuasively. 'It's your duty to use it for the good of all.'

Still he hesitated, he wanted her to declare herself fully. He had to know if she wanted this as much as he did.

'We can be honest with each other, *chéri*. This is what we have worked towards since you were a child. Take this job and do it well, after that who knows what else may follow.'

They were both silent then, they knew what they hoped would follow. They could not help themselves, it was their nature always to strive towards the highest pinnacle.

'What about Blaine?' Shasa said at last. 'How will he take it? I don't look forward to telling him.'

'I'll do that,' she promised. 'But you will have to tell Tara.'

'Tara,' he sighed. 'Now that will be a problem.'

They were silent again, until Centaine asked, 'How will you do it? If you cross the floor it will expose you to a blaze of hostile publicity.'

So it was agreed without further words, only the means remained to be discussed.

'At the next general election I will simply campaign in different colours,' Shasa said. 'They will give me a safe seat.'

'So we have a little time to arrange the details then.'

They discussed them for another hour, planning with all the meticulous attention that had made them such a formidably successful team over the years, until Shasa looked up at her.

'Thank you,' he said simply. 'What would I ever do without you! You are tougher and cleverer than any man I know.'

'Get away with you,' she smiled. 'You know how I hate praise.' They both laughed at that absurdity.

'I'll walk you down, Mater.' But she shook her head.

'I've still got some thinking to do. Leave me here.'

She watched him go down the hill and her love and pride was so intense as to almost suffocate her.

'He is everything I ever wanted in a son, and he has fulfilled all my expectations a thousand times over. Thank you, my son, thank you for the joy you have always given me.'

Then abruptly the words 'my son' triggered another reaction, and her mind darted back to the earlier part of their conversation.

'Do you remember Manfred De La Rey?' Shasa had asked her, but he could never know what the answer to that must be.

'Can a woman ever forget the child she bears?' she whispered the reply aloud, but her words were lost on the wind and on the sound of the green surf breaking on the rocky shore below the hill.

* * *

Every pew of the church was filled. The women's bonnets were colourful as a field of wild Namaqua daisies in the springtime, while the men's suits were

sombre and severe. All their faces were upturned towards the magnificent carved pulpit of polished black stinkwood in which stood the most reverend Tromp Bierman, moderator of the Dutch Reformed Church of South Africa.

Manfred De La Rey considered once again how much Uncle Tromp had aged in the years since the war. He had never fully recovered from the pneumonia he had contracted in the concentration camp at Koffiefontein, where that English-lover Jannie Smuts had incarcerated him with hundreds of patriotic Afrikaners for the duration of the English war with Germany.

Uncle Tromp's beard was snow white now, even more spectacular than the curly black bush it once had been. The hair on his head, also white, had been close cropped to conceal its sparsity and it glittered like powdered glass on the high-domed pate, but his eyes were full of fire as he glowered at his congregation, and his voice that had earned him the sobriquet 'The Trumpet of God' had lost none of its power and rolled like a cannonade against the high-arched ceiling of the nave.

Uncle Tromp could still pack the pews, and Manfred nodded soberly but proudly as the thunderous outpouring burst over his head. He was not really listening to the words, merely enjoying the sense of continuity that filled him; the world was a safe good place when Uncle Tromp was in the pulpit. Then a man could trust in the God of the *Volk* which he evoked with so much certainty, and believe in the divine intervention which directed his life.

Manfred De La Rey sat in the front pew at the right side of the nave nearest the aisle. It was the most prestigious position in the congregation, and rightly so for Manfred was the most powerful and important man in the church. The pew was reserved for him and his family, and their names were gold-leafed on the hymn books that lay beside each seat.

Heidi, his wife, was a magnificent woman, tall and strong, her bare forearms below the puff sleeves were smooth and firm, her bosom large and shapely, her neck long and her thick golden hair plaited into ropes that were twisted up under the wide-brimmed black hat. Manfred had met her in Berlin when he had been the gold medallist light heavyweight boxer at the Olympic Games in 1936, and Adolf Hitler himself had attended their wedding. They had been separated during the war years, but afterwards Manfred had brought her out to Africa with their son, little Lothar.

Lother was almost twelve years old now, a fine strong boy, blond as his mother, and upright as his father. He sat very straight in the family pew, his hair neatly slicked down with Brylcreem and the stiff white collar biting into his neck. Like his father, he would be an athlete, but he had chosen the game of rugby at which to excel. His three younger sisters, blond and pretty in a fresh-faced healthy way, sat beyond him, their faces framed by the hoods of their traditional *voortrekker* bonnets and full-length skirts reaching to their ankles. Manfred liked them to wear national dress on Sundays.

Uncle Tromp ended with a salvo that thrilled his flock with the threat of hell-fire, and they rose to sing the final hymn. Sharing the hymn book with Heidi, Manfred examined her handsome Germanic features. She was a wife to be proud of, a good housekeeper and mother, a fine companion whom he could trust and confide in, and a glittering ornament to his political career. A woman like this could stand beside any man, even the prime minister of a powerful and prosperous nation. He let himself dwell on that secret thought. Yet everything was possible, he was a young man, the youngest by far in the cabinet, and he had never made a political mistake. Even his wartime activities gave him credit

and prestige with his peers, although few people outside the inner circle knew of the full role he had played in the militant anti-British pro-Nazi secret army of the *Ossewa Brandwag*.

Already they were whispering that he was the coming man, and it was evident in the huge respect that was shown him as the service ended and the congregation left the church. Manfred stood, with Heidi beside him, on the lawns outside the church while one after another important and influential men came up to deliver social invitations, to ask a favour, to congratulate him on his speech introducing the new Criminal Law Amendment Bill in the House, or simply to pay their respects. It was almost twenty minutes before he was able to leave the church grounds.

The family walked home. It was only two blocks under the green oaks that lined the streets of Stellenbosch, the small university town which was the citadel of Afrikaner intellectualism and culture. The three girls walked ahead, Lothar followed them and Manfred with Heidi on his arm brought up the rear, stopping every few paces to acknowledge a greeting or exchange a few words with a neighbour or a friend or one of Manfred's constituents.

Manfred had purchased the house when they had arrived back from Germany after the war. Although it stood in a small garden, almost facing on to the street, it was a large house with spacious high-ceilinged rooms that suited the family well. Manfred had never seen any reason to change it, and he felt comfortable with Heidi's formal Teutonic furnishings. Now Heidi and the girls rushed through to help the servants in the kitchen, and Manfred went around the side of the house to the garage. He never used his official chauffeur-driven limousine at weekends, and he brought out his personal Chevrolet sedan and drove to fetch his father for the family Sunday luncheon.

The old man seldom attended church, especially when the Reverend Tromp Bierman was preaching. Lothar De La Rey lived alone on the smallholding that Manfred had bought for him on the outskirts of the town at the foot of the Helshoogte Pass. He was out in the peach orchard pottering with his beehives and Manfred paused by the gate to watch him with a mixture of pity and deep affection.

Lothar De La Rey had once been tall and straight as the grandson who now bore his name, but the arthritis he had contracted during the years in Pretoria Central Prison had bowed and twisted his body and turned his single remaining hand to a grotesque claw. His left arm was amputated above the elbow, too high to fit an artificial limb. He had lost it during the robbery that led to his imprisonment. He was dressed in dirty blue dungarees, with a stained brown hat on his head, the brim drooped over his eyes. One sleeve of the dungaree was pinned back.

Manfred opened the gate and went down into the peach orchard where the old man was stooping over one of the wooden hives.

'Good morning, Pa,' Manfred said softly 'You aren't ready yet.'

His father straightened up and stared at him vaguely, and then started with surprise.

'Manie! Is it Sunday again already?'

'Come along, Pa. Let's get you, tidied up. Heidi is cooking a roast of pork – you know how you love pork.'

He took the old man's hand, and led him unprotestingly up to the cottage.

'It's a mess, Pa.' Manfred looked around the tiny bedroom with distaste. The

bed had obviously been slept in repeatedly without being remade, soiled clothing was strewn on the floor and used plates and mugs stood on the bedside table. 'What happened to the new maid Heidi found for you?'

'I didn't like her, cheeky brown devil,' Lothar muttered. 'Stealing the sugar, drinking my brandy. I fired her.'

Manfred went to the cupboard and found a clean white shirt. He helped the old man undress.

'When did you last bath, Pa?' he asked gently.

'Hey?' Lothar peered at him.

'It doesn't matter.' Manfred buttoned his father's shirt. 'Heidi will find another maid for you. You must try and keep her longer than a week this time.'

It wasn't the old man's fault, Manfred reminded himself. It was the prison that had affected his mind. He had been a proud free man, a soldier and huntsman, a creature of the wild Kalahari Desert. You cannot cage a wild animal. Heidi had wanted to have the old man to live with them, and Manfred felt guilty that he had refused. It would have meant buying a larger home, but that was the least of it. Manfred could not afford to have Lothar dressed like a coloured labourer wandering vaguely around the house, coming into his study uninvited when he had important visitors with him, slobbering his food and making inane statements at the dinner table when he was entertaining. No, it was better for all of them, the old man especially, that he lived apart. Heidi would find another maid to take care of him, but he felt corrosive guilt as he took Lothar's arm and led him out to the Chevrolet.

He drove slowly, almost at a walking pace, steeling himself to do what he had been unable to do during the years since Lother had been pardoned and freed from prison at Manfred's instigation.

'Do you remember how it was in the old days, Pa? When we fished together at Walvis Bay?' he asked, and the old man's eyes shone. The distant past was more real to him than the present, and he reminisced happily, without hesitation recalling incidents and the names of people and places from long ago.

'Tell me about my mother, Pa,' Manfred invited at last, and he hated himself for leading the old man into such a carefully prepared trap.

'Your mother was a beautiful woman,' Lothar nodded happily, repeating what he had told Manfred so many times since childhood. 'She had hair the colour of the desert dunes, with the early sun shining on them. A fine woman of noble German birth.'

'Pa,' Manfred said softly. 'You aren't telling me the truth, are you?' He spoke as though to a naughty child. 'The woman you call my mother, the woman who was your wife, died years before I was born. I have a copy of the death certificate signed by the English doctor in the concentration camp. She died of diphtheria, the white sore throat.'

He could not look at his father as he said it, but stared ahead through the windscreen, until he heard a soft choking sound beside him and with alarm turned quickly. Lothar was weeping, tears slid down his withered old cheeks.

'I'm sorry, Pa.' Manfred pulled the Chevrolet off the road and switched off the engine. 'I shouldn't have said that.' He pulled a white handkerchief from his pocket and handed it to his father.

Lothar wiped his face slowly, but his hand was steady, and his wandering mind seemed to have been concentrated by the shock.

'How long have you know that she was your real mother?' he asked, and his

voice was firm and sure. Manfred's soul quailed, he had hoped to hear his father deny it.

'She came to see me when first I stood for parliament. She blackmailed me, for her other son's sake. I had him in my power. She threatened to expose the fact that I was her bastard son and destroy my candidacy if I acted against her other son. She dared me to ask you if it was not true, but I could not bring myself to do it.'

'It's true,' Lothar nodded. 'I'm sorry, my son. I lied to you only to protect you.'

'I know.' Manfred reached across and took the bony hand as the old man went on.

'When I found her in the desert, she was so young and helpless – and beautiful. I was young and lonely – it was just the two of us, and her infant, alone together in the desert. We fell in love.'

'You don't have to explain,' Manfred told him, but Lothar seemed not to hear him.

'One night two wild Bushmen came into our camp. I thought they were marauders, come to steal our horses and oxen. I followed them, and caught up with them at dawn. I shot them down before I was within range of their poison arrows. It was the way we dealt with those dangerous little yellow animals in those days.'

'Yes, Pa, I know.' Manfred had read the history of his people's conflict with and extermination of the Bushmen tribes.

'I did not know it then, but she had lived with these same two little Bushmen before I found her. They had helped her survive the desert and tended her when she gave birth to her first child. She had come to love them, she even called them "old grandfather" and "old grandmother".' He shook his head wonderingly, still unable to comprehend this relationship of a white woman with savages. 'I did not know it, and I shot them without realizing what they meant to her. Her love for me changed to bitter hatred. I know now that her love could not have been very deep, perhaps it was only loneliness and gratitude and not love at all. After that she hated me, and the hatred extended to my child that she was carrying in her womb. To you, Manie. She made me take you away the moment you were born. She hated us both so deeply that she wanted never to set eyes on you. I cared for you after that.'

'You were my father and my mother.' Manfred bowed his head, ashamed and angry that he had forced the old man to relive those tragically cruel events. 'What you have told me explains so much that I could never understand.'

'*Ja*.' Lothar wiped fresh tears away with the white handkerchief. 'She hated me, but you see I still loved her. No matter how cruelly she treated me, I was obsessed with her. That was the reason why I committed the folly of the robbery. It was a madness and it cost me this arm.' He held up the empty sleeve. 'And my freedom. She is a hard woman. A woman without mercy. She will not hesitate to destroy anything or anybody who stands in her way. She is your mother, but be careful of her, Manie. Her hatred is a terrible thing.' The old man reached across and seized his son's arm, shaking it in his agitation. 'You must have nothing to do with her, Manie. She will destroy you as she has destroyed me. Promise me you will never have anything to do with her or her family.'

'I'm sorry, Pa,' Manfred shook his head. 'I am already tied to her through her son,' he hesitated to give voice to the next words, 'to my brother, to my

half-brother Shasa Courtney. It seems, Papa, that our bloodlines and our destinies are so closely tangled together that we can never be free of each other.'

'Oh, my son, my son,' Lothar De La Rey lamented. 'Be careful – please be careful.'

Manfred reached for the ignition key to start the engine, but paused before he touched it.

'Tell me, Pa. How do you feel for this woman now – for my mother?'

Lothar was silent for a moment before he answered. 'I hate her almost as much as I still love her.'

'It is strange that we can love and hate at the same time.' Manfred shook his head slightly with wonder. 'I hate her for what she has done to you. I hate her for all the things she stands for, and yet her blood calls to mine. At the end, when all else is put aside, Centaine Courtney is my mother and Shasa Courtney is my brother. Love or hatred – which will prevail, Papa?'

'I wish I could tell you, my son,' Lothar whispered miserably. 'I can only repeat what I have already told you. Be careful of them, Manie. Mother and son, they are dangerous adversaries.'

* * *

For almost twenty years Marcus Archer had owned the old farmhouse at Rivonia. He had purchased the five-acre smallholding before the area became fashionable. Now the fairways and greens of the Johannesburg Country Club, the most exclusive private club on the Witwatersrand, backed right up against Marcus' boundary. The trustees of the Country Club had offered him fifteen times his original purchase price, over £100,000, but Marcus steadfastly refused to sell.

On all the other large plots that comprised the Rivonia Estate, the prosperous new owners – entrepreneurs and stockbrokers and successful doctors – had built large pretentious homes, most of them in the low sprawling ranch house style which was the rage, or with pink clay tile roofs, imaginative copies of Mexican *haciendas* or Mediterranean villas, and they had surrounded the main buildings with paddocks and stables, with tennis courts and swimming-pools and wide lawns that the winter highveld frosts burned the colour of cured tobacco leaves.

Marcus Archer had re-thatched the roof of the old farmhouse, whitewashed the walls, and planted frangipani and bougainvillaea and other flowering shrubs and let the grounds grow wild and unkempt, so that even from its own boundary fence the house was completely screened.

Although the area was now very much a bastion of the wealthy white elite, the Country Club employed a large staff of waiters and kitchen helpers and groundsmen and golf caddies, so black faces were not remarkable, as they might have been on the streets of some of the other wealthy white suburbs. Marcus's friends and political allies could come and go without arousing unwelcome interest. So Puck's Hill, as Marcus had recently renamed his farmhouse, gradually became the rallying ground for some of the most active of the African Nationalist movements, the leaders of black consciousness and their white compatriots, the remnants of the defunct Communist Party.

It was only natural, therefore, that Puck's Hill was chosen as the headquarters

for the final planning and co-ordination of the black disobedience campaign that was about to begin. However, it was not a unified group that came together under Marcus Archer's roof, for although their stated final objective was the same, their separate visions of the future differed widely.

Firstly, there was the old guard of the African National Congress headed by Dr Xuma. They were the conservatives, committed to plodding negotiation with white civil servants within the unyielding established system.

'You people have been doing that since 1912 when the ANC was formed,' Nelson Mandela glared at him. 'It is time to move on to confrontation, to force our will upon the Boers.'

Nelson Mandela was a young lawyer, practising on the Witwatersrand in partnership with another activist named Oliver Tambo. Together they were making a strong challenge for the leadership of the young Turks in the Congress hierarchy.

'It is time for us to move on to direct action.' Nelson Mandela leaned forward in his chair and looked down the long kitchen table. The kitchen was the largest room in Puck's Hill, and all their meetings were held in it. 'We have drawn up a programme of boycott and strike and civil disobedience.' Mandela was speaking in English, and Moses Gama sitting near the end of the table watched him impassively, but all the time his mind was racing ahead of the speaker, assessing and evaluating. He as much as any of them present was aware of the undertones in the room. There was not a single black man present who did not cherish, somewhere in his soul, the dream of one day leading all the others, of one day being hailed as the paramount chief of all southern Africa.

Yet the fact that Mandela spoke in English pointed up the single most poignant fact that they had to face: they were all different. Mandela was a Tembu, Xuma was a Zulu, Moses Gama himself was an Ovambo, and there were half a dozen other tribes represented in the room.

'It would be a hundred times easier if we blacks were all one people,' Moses thought, and then despite himself he glanced uneasily at the Zulus, sitting together as a group across the table. They were the majority, not only in this room, but in the country as a whole. What if they somehow formed an alliance with the whites? – It was a disquieting thought, but he put it firmly aside. The Zulus were the proudest, most independent of the warrior tribes. Before the white man came, they had conquered all their neighbouring peoples and held them subjugated. The Zulu King Chaka had called them his dogs. Because of their multitudes and their warrior tradition, it was almost certain that the first black president of South Africa would be a Zulu, or someone with very close ties to the Zulu nation. Ties of marriage – not for the first time, Moses thought about that possibility with narrowed eyes, it was time he married anyway. He was almost forty-five years of age. A Zulu maiden of royal blood? He stored the idea for future consideration, and concentrated once again on what Nelson Mandela was saying.

The man had charisma and presence, and he was articulate and persuasive, a rival – a very dangerous rival. Moses recognized that fact as he had often before. They were all rivals. However, the Youth League of the ANC was Nelson Mandela's power base, the hotheads, young men burning for action, and even now Mandela was proposing caution, tempering his call for action with reservations.

'There must be no gratuitous violence,' he was saying. 'No damage to private property, no danger to human life – ' and although Moses Gama nodded wisely,

he wondered how much appeal that would have with the rank and file of the Youth League. Would they not prefer the offer of a bloody and glorious victory? That was something else to be considered.

'We must show our people the way, we must demonstrate that we are all one in this enterprise,' Mandela was saying now, and Moses Gama smiled inwardly. The total membership of the ANC was seven thousand, while his secret union of mineworkers numbered almost ten times that figure. It would be as well to remind Mandela and the rest of them of his overwhelming support amongst the best paid and most strategically placed of all the black population. Moses turned slightly and looked at the man who sat beside him, and felt an untoward pang of affection. Hendrick Tabaka had been beside him like this for twenty years.

Swart Hendrick was a big man, as tall as Moses but wider across the shoulder, and heavier around the middle, with thick muscled limbs. His head was round and bald as a cannonball and laced with scars from ancient fights and battles. His front teeth were missing, and Moses remembered how the white man who had done that to him had died.

He was Moses' half-brother, son the same father, a chief of the Ovambo, but of a different mother. He was the one man in all the world whom Moses trusted, a trust not lightly given but earned over all of those twenty years. He was the only black man in his room who was not a rival, but was instead both comrade and loyal servant. Swart Hendrick nodded at him unsmilingly and Moses realized that Nelson Mandela had finished speaking and that they were all watching him, waiting for him to reply. He rose slowly to his feet, aware of the impression he was making, and he could see the respect in their expressions. Even his enemies in the room could not entirely conceal the awe which he inspired.

'Comrades,' he began. 'My brothers. I have listened to what my good brother Nelson Mandela has said and I agree with every word of it. There are just a few points which I feel I must add – ' and he spoke for nearly an hour.

Firstly he proposed to them a detailed plan to call a series of wildcat strikes in the mines where the labour force was controlled by his unions.

'The strikes will be in sympathy with the defiance campaign, but we will not call a general strike which would give the Boers an excuse for heavy-handed action. We will bring out only a few mines at any one time, and then only for a limited period, before going back to work, just enough to thoroughly disrupt gold production and to exasperate management. We will nip at their heels like a terrier harassing a lion, ready to spring away the instant he turns. But it will be a warning. It will let them realize our strength, and what would happen if we called a general strike.'

He saw how they were impressed with his planning, and when he asked for a vote to confirm his proposal, he was given unanimous approval. It was another small victory, another addition to his prestige and influence within the group.

'In addition to the strike action, I would like to propose a boycott of all white-owned business on the Witwatersrand for the duration of the defiance campaign. The people will be allowed to buy their necessities of life from shops owned and run by black businessmen only.'

Hendrick Tabaka owned over fifty large general dealer stores in the black townships along the gold reef, and Moses Gama was his sleeping partner. He saw the others at the table baulk at the suggestion, and Mandela objected.

'It will cause undue hardship amongst our people,' he said. 'Many of them live in areas where they can trade only with white stores.'

'Then they must travel to areas where there are black-owned businesses, and it will do our people no harm to learn that the struggle demands sacrifices from all of us,' Moses answered him quietly.

'A boycott such as you propose would be impossible to enforce,' Mandela insisted, and this time Hendrick Tabaka replied to the objection.

'We will use the Buffaloes to make sure the people obey,' he growled, and now the more conservative members of the Council looked positively unhappy.

The Buffaloes were the union enforcers. Hendrick Tabaka was their commander and they had a reputation for swift, ruthless action. They were too close to being a private political army for the peace of mind of some of the other men in the room, and Moses Gama frowned slightly. It had been a mistake for Hendrick to mention his Buffaloes at all. Moses hid his chagrin when the vote to declare a boycott of white dealers on the Witwatersrand and enforce it strictly was defeated. It was a victory for Mandela and his moderates. So far the score was even, but Moses was not finished yet.

'There is one other matter I would like to bring up before we adjourn. I would like to consider what lies beyond the defiance campaign. What action do we take if the campaign is crushed by ruthless white police action, and followed by an onslaught on the black leaders and the promulgation of even more draconian laws of domination?' he asked. 'Will our response always be mild and subservient, will we always take off our caps and mutter "Yes, my white *baas*! No, my white *baas*"?'

He paused, and studied the others, seeing the disquiet he had expected in the faces of old Xuma and the conservatives, but he had not spoken for them. At the far end of the table there were two young men, still in their early twenties. They were observers from the executive of the Youth League of the ANC and Moses knew them both to be militants longing for fierce action. What he was about to say now was for them, and he knew they would take his words back to the other young warriors. It could begin the erosion of Nelson Mandela's support amongst the youth, and the transference of that support to a leader who was prepared to give them the blood and fire for which they hungered.

'I propose the formation of a military wing of the ANC,' Moses said, 'a fighting force of trained men, ready to die for the struggle. Let us call this army *Umkhonto we Sizwe*, the Spear of the Nation. Let us forge the spear secretly. Let us hone its edge to razor-sharpness, keeping it hidden, but always ready to strike.' He used that deep thrilling tone of his, and he saw the two young men at the end of the table stir eagerly and their faces begin to glow with expectation. 'Let us choose our brightest and fiercest young men, and from them form the impis as our forefathers did.' He paused, and his expression became scornful. 'There are old men amongst us, and they are wise. I respect their grey hairs and their experience. But remember, comrades, the future belongs to the young. There is a time for fine words, and we have heard them spoken at our councils – often, too often. There is a time also for action, bold action and that is the world of the young.'

When at last Moses Gama sat down again he saw that he had moved them all deeply, each in his separate way. Old Xuma was shaking his grey pate, and his lips quivered. He knew his day had passed. Nelson Mandela and Oliver Tambo watched him impassively, but he saw the fury in their hearts beamed through their eyes. The battle lines had been drawn, and they had recognized their enemy. Yet, most important of all, he saw the expressions on the faces of the

two Youth Leaguers. It was the look of men who had found a new star to follow.

* * *

'Since when have you conceived such a burning interest in archaeological anthropology?' Shasa Courtney asked as he shook out the pages of the *Cape Times*, and turned from the financial section to the sports pages at the rear.

'It was one of my majors,' Tara pointed out reasonably. 'May I pour you another cup of coffee?'

'Thank you, my dear.' He sipped the coffee before he spoke again. 'How long do you intend being away?'

'Professor Dart will be giving a series of four lectures on successive evenings, covering all the excavations from his original discovery of the Taung skull, right up to the present time. He has been able to correlate the whole mass of material with one of these new electronic computers.'

Behind his newspaper Shasa smiled reflectively as he remembered Marylee from MIT and her IBM 701. He wouldn't mind another visit to Johannesburg himself in the near future.

'It's absolutely riveting stuff,' Tara was saying, 'and it all fits in with the new discoveries at Sterkfontein and Makapansgat. It really does seem that southern Africa was the true cradle of mankind, and that *Australopithecus* is our direct ancestor.'

'So you will be away for at least four days?' Shasa interrupted. 'What about the children?'

'I have spoken to your mother. She will be happy to come across and stay at Weltevreden while I am away.'

'I won't be able to join you,' Shasa pointed out. 'The third reading of the new Criminal Law Amendment Bill is coming up, and all hands are needed in the House. I could have flown you up in the Mosquito – now you'll have to take the commercial flight on the Viscount.'

'What a pity,' Tara sighed. 'You would have enjoyed it. Professor Dart is a fascinating speaker.'

'You'll stay at the Carlton suite, of course. It's standing empty.'

'Molly has arranged for me to stay with a friend of hers at Rivolnia.'

'One of her Bolshies, I presume.' Shasa frowned slightly. 'Try not to get yourself arrested again.' He had been waiting for an opportunity to talk about her political activities and he lowered the newspaper and looked at her thoughtfully, then realized it was not the correct moment and merely nodded. 'Your grass orphans and your widower will try to bumble along without you for a few days.'

'With your mother and sixteen servants at hand, I have no doubt you will survive,' she told him crisply, letting her irritation show through for an instant.

Marcus Archer met her at the airport. He was affable and amusing and while they listened to a Mozart programme on the car radio as they drove out to Rivonia, Marcus discussed the composer's life and works. He knew much more about music than she did, but although she listened to his dissertation with pleasure and attention, she was nevertheless aware of his enmity. It was well concealed, but flashed out in a barbed remark or a spiced glance. He never

mentioned Moses Gama's name, and nor did she. Molly had said he was a homosexual, the first she had ever encountered to her certain knowledge, and she wondered if they all hated women.

Puck's Hill was a delight, with its shaggy thatch and unkempt grounds, so different from Weltevreden's carefully manicured splendour.

'You'll find him at the end of the front stoep,' Marcus said, as he parked under one of the bluegums at the rear of the house. It was the first time he had referred to Moses, but even then he did not use his name. He wandered away and left her standing.

She had not known how to dress, though she imagined that he would not approve of slacks. So she had chosen a long loose skirt made of cheap but colourful trade print that she had purchased in Swaziland, and with it wore a simple green cotton blouse with sandals on her feet. Again, she had not been sure whether she should wear make-up, and she had compromised with a pale pink lipstick and just a touch of mascara. She thought she looked well enough in the mirror of the women's room at the airport as she combed her dense chestnut curls, but was suddenly stricken by the thought that he would find her pale skin insipid and unattractive.

Now standing alone in the sunshine, she was once again attacked by doubts and that terrible sense of inadequacy. If Marcus had been there, she would have begged him to drive her back to the airport, but he had disappeared and so she summoned up all her courage and walked slowly around the side of the whitewashed house.

She paused at the corner and looked down the long covered verandah. Moses Gama was sitting at a table at the far end with his back to her. The table was piled with books and writing materials. He was wearing a casual white shirt with open neck that contrasted with the marvellous anthracite of his skin. His head was bowed and he was writing rapidly on a block of notepaper.

Timidly she stepped up on the verandah and although her approach was noiseless, he sensed her presence and turned abruptly when she was half-way down the verandah. He did not smile, but she thought she saw pleasure in his gaze as he stood up and came to meet her. He did not attempt to embrace her, or kiss her, and she was pleased, for it confirmed his differentness. Instead he led her to the second chair placed beside his table, and seated her in it.

'Are you well?' he asked. 'Are your children well?' The innate African courtesy, always the enquiry and then the offer of refreshment, 'Let me give you a cup of tea.' He poured from the tray already set on his cluttered desk, and she sipped with pleasure.

'Thank you for coming,' he said.

'I came as soon as I received your message from Molly, as I promised I would.'

'Will you always keep your promises to me?'

'Always,' she answered with simple sincerity, and he studied her face.

'Yes,' he nodded. 'I think you will.'

She could hold his gaze no longer, for it seemed to sear her soul and lay it bare. She looked down at the table top, at the closely written sheets of his handwriting.

'A manifesto,' he said, following her gaze. 'A blueprint for the future.'

He selected half a dozen sheets and handed them to her. She set aside her tea cup and took them from his hand, shivering slightly as their fingers touched. His skin was cool – that was one of the things that she remembered.

She read the sheets, her attention becoming fastened upon them more firmly the more she read, and when she finished them, she lifted her eyes to his face again.

'You have a poetry in your choice of words that makes the truth shine more luminously,' she whispered.

They sat on the cool verandah, while outside the brilliant high-veld sun threw shadows black and crisp as paper cut-outs beneath the trees and the noonday swooned in the heat, and they talked.

There were no trivialities in their discussion, everything he said was thrilling and cogent, and he seemed to inspire her for her replies and her own observations she knew were measured and lucid and she saw she had aroused and held his interest. She no longer was aware of her small vanities of dress and cosmetics, all that mattered now were the words that they exchanged and the cocoon they wove out of them. With a start she realized that the day had slipped away unnoticed and the short African twilight was upon them. Marcus came to fetch her and show her to her sparsely furnished bedroom.

'We will leave for the museum in twenty minutes,' he told her.

In the lecture theatre of the Transvaal museum the three of them sat near the back. There were half a dozen other blacks in the crowded audience, but Marcus sat between the two of them. A black man beside a white woman would have excited interest, and certain hostility. Tara found it difficult to concentrate on the eminent professor's address, and though she glanced in his direction only once or twice, it was Moses Gama who occupied all her thoughts.

Back at Puck's Hill they sat late in the cavernous kitchen, while Marcus hovered over the Aga stove, joining in their conversation while he produced a meal that even in her preoccupation Tara realized was as good as anything that had ever come out of the kitchens of Weltevreden.

It was after midnight when Marcus stood up abruptly.

'I will see you in the morning,' he said, and the look he gave Tara was once again spiced with venom. She could not understand how she had offended him, but soon it did not matter for Moses took her hand.

'Come,' he said softly, and she thought her legs might not support her weight.

Long afterwards she lay pressed to him, her body bathed in sweat and her nerves still spasming and twitching uncontrollably.

'Never,' she whispered, when she could speak again. 'I have never known anyone like you. You teach me things about myself that I never suspected. You are a magician, Moses Gama. How do you know so much about a woman?'

He chuckled softly. 'You know we are entitled to many wives. If a man cannot keep them all happy at the same time, then his life becomes a torment. He has to learn.'

'Do you have many wives?' she asked.

'Not yet,' he answered. 'But one day – '

'I will hate every one of them.'

'You disappoint me,' he said. 'Sexual jealousy is a silly European emotion. If I were to detect it in you, I would despise you.'

'Please,' she said quietly, 'never despise me.'

'Then never give me reason, woman,' he commanded, and she knew she was his to command.

* * *

She realized that the first day and night with him, spent alone and uninterrupted, was exceptional. She realized also that he must have set the time aside for her, and it must have been difficult to do so for there were others, hundreds of others, demanding his attention.

He was like one of the ancient African kings holding tribal court on the verandah of the old house. There were always men and women waiting patiently under the bluegum trees in the yard for their turn to speak to him. They were of all types and ages, from simple uneducated folk newly arrived from the reserves in the country to sophisticated lawyers and businessmen in dark suits arriving at Puck's Hill in their own automobiles.

They had one thing in common only – the deference and respect they showed Moses Gama. Some of them clapped their hands in the traditional greeting and called him *Baba* or *Nkosi*, father or lord, others shook his hand in the European manner, but Moses greeted each of them in their own dialect. 'He must speak twenty languages,' Tara wondered.

Mostly he allowed Tara to sit quietly beside his table and he explained her presence with a quiet word.

'She is a friend – you may speak.'

However, twice he asked her to leave while he spoke to his more important visitors and once when a great black bull of a man, bald and scarred and gap-toothed, arrived in a shiny new Ford sedan, he excused them.

'This is Hendrick Tabaka, my brother,' he said, and the two of them left the verandah and strolled side by side in the sunlit garden just out of earshot of where Tara sat.

What she saw during those days impressed her immensely and confirmed her feelings of reverence for this man. Everything he did, every word he uttered marked him as different, and the respect and adulation showered upon him by his fellow Africans proved that they also recognized that he was the giant of the future.

Tara felt awed that he had selected her for special attention, and yet already saddened by that certain knowledge that she could never have for herself alone any part of him. He belonged to his people, and she must be grateful for the precious grains of his time which she could glean for herself.

Even the evenings that followed, unlike that first evening, were crowded with people and events. Until long after midnight they sat at the table in the kitchen, sometimes as many as twenty of them at one time, smoking and laughing and eating and talking. Such talk, such ideas that lit the gloomy room and shimmered like angels' wings in the air around their heads. Then later, in the quiet dark hours, they made love and she felt as though her body no longer belonged to her but that he had taken it for his own, and devoured it like some darkly beloved predator.

She must have met a hundred new faces in those three short days and nights, and though some of them were hazy and made little lasting impression, it seemed as though she had become a member of a large diffuse new family, and because of the patronage of Moses Gama, she was immediately accepted and accorded complete unquestioning trust by both black and white.

On the last evening before her return to the dream world at Weltevreden, there was a guest beside her at the kitchen table to whom Tara took an instant unqualified liking. She was a young woman, at least ten years junior to Tara, barely into her twenties, but with an unusual maturity for one so young.

'My name is Victoria Dinizulu,' she introduced herself. 'My friends call me Vicky. I know you are Mrs Courtney.'

'Tara,' Tara corrected her quickly. Nobody had used her surname since she had left Cape Town and it sounded a jarring note in her own ears.

The girl smiled shyly in acknowledgement. She had the serene beauty of a black madonna, the classic moon face of the high-bred Zulu with hugh almond eyes and full lips, her skin the colour of dark amber, her hair plaited into an intricate pattern of tiny curls over her skull.

'Are you related to the Courtneys of Zululand?' she asked Tara. 'Old General Sean Courtney and Sir Garrick Courtney of Theuniskraal, near Ladyburg?'

'Yes.' Tara tried not to show the shock she felt at the mention of those names. 'Sir Garrick was my husband's grandfather. My own sons are named Sean and Garrick after them. Why do you ask, Vicky? Do you know the family well?'

'Oh yes, Mrs Courtney – Tara.' When she smiled, the Zulu girl's face seemed to glow like a dark moon. 'Long ago, during the last century, my grandfather fought at General Sean Courtney's side in the Zulu wars against Cetewayo who stole the kingship of Zululand from my family. It was my grandfather, Mbejane, who should have been king. Instead he became General Courtney's servant.'

'Mbejane!' Tara cried. 'Oh yes. Sir Garrick Courtney wrote about him in his *History of Zululand*. He was Sean Courtney's faithful retainer until his death. I remember they came up here to the goldfields of the reef together and later went on to what is now Rhodesia, hunting ivory.'

'You know all about that!' Vicky laughed with pleasure. 'My father used to tell me the same stories when I was a little girl. My father still lives near Theuniskraal. After my grandfather, Mbejane Dinizulu, died my father took his place as the old general's body servant. He even went to France with the general in 1916 and worked for him until the general was murdered. In his will the general left him a section of Theuniskraal for his lifetime and a pension of a thousand pounds a year. They are a fine family, the Courtneys. My old father still weeps whenever he mentions the general's name – ' Vicky broke off and shook her head, suddenly perplexed and saddened. 'Life must have been so simple in those days, my grandfather and my father were hereditary chieftains and yet they were satisfied to spend their lives subservient to a white man, and strangely they loved that man and he, in his way, seemed to love them. I wonder sometimes if theirs was not the better way – '

'Do not even think that,' Tara almost hissed at her. 'The Courtneys have always been heartless robber barons, plundering and exploiting your people. Right and justice are on the side of your struggle. Never entertain the slightest doubt of that.'

'You are right,' Vicky agreed firmly. 'But sometimes it's nice to think of the friendship of the general and my grandfather. Perhaps one day we could be friends again, equal friends, both sides stronger for the friendship.'

'With every new oppression, and every new law passed, the prospect fades,' Tara said grimly, 'and I become more ashamed of my race.'

'I don't want to be sad and intense tonight, Tara. Let's talk about happy things. You said you have sons, Sean and Garrick, named after their ancestors. Tell me about them, please.'

However, the thought of the children and Shasa and Weltevreden made Tara feel guilty and uncomfortable, and as soon as she could she changed the subject again.

'Now tell me about yourself, Vicky,' she insisted. 'What are you doing in Johannesburg, so far from Zululand?'

'I work at Baragwanath Hospital,' Vicky told her.

Tara knew that was one of the largest hospitals in the world, certainly the largest in the southern hemisphere, with 2400 beds and over 2000 nurses and doctors, most of them black, for the hospital catered exclusively for black patients. All hospitals, like schools and transport and most other public facilities, were strictly segregated by law, true to the grand concept of *apartheid*.

Vicky Dinizulu was so modest about her own achievements that Tara had to draw out of her the fact that she was a qualified theatre sister.

'But you are so young, Vicky,' she protested.

'There are others younger,' the Zulu girl laughed. Her laughter had a pleasing musical lilt.

'She really is a lovely child,' Tara thought, smiling in sympathy, and then corrected herself. 'No, not a child – a clever and competent young woman.'

So Tara told her about her clinic at Nyanga, and the problems of malnutrition and ignorance and poverty they encountered, and Vicky related some of her experiences and the solutions they had found to the terrible challenges that faced them in caring for the physical well-being of a peasant population trying to adapt to an urban existence.

'Oh, I have enjoyed talking to you,' Vicky blurted out at last. 'I don't know when I have ever spoken to a white woman like this before. So natural and relaxed and,' she hesitated, 'just like an elder sister or a dear friend.'

'A dear friend. Yes, I like that,' Tara agreed. 'And Puck's Hill is probably one of the few places in the whole of this country where we could meet and talk like this.'

Involuntarily both of them looked up towards the head of the long kitchen table. Moses Gama was watching them intently, and Tara felt her stomach flop over like a stranded fish. For a few moments there, she had been totally engrossed with the Zulu girl, but now her feelings for Moses Gama flooded back at full ebb. She forgot Vicky, until the girl spoke quietly beside her.

'He is a great man – our hope for the future.'

Tara glanced at her sideways. Vicky Dinizulu's face glowed with hero worship as she smiled shyly at Moses Gama, and jealousy struck Tara such a sickening blow in the pit of her stomach, that for a moment she believed she was going to be physically ill.

The jealousy and terror of imminent separation persisted even after Tara was alone with Moses that night. When he made love to her she wanted to hold him within her for all eternity, knowing that this was the only time that he truly belonged to her. Too soon she felt the great dam burst and flood her and she cried out, pleading for it never to end, but her cry was incoherent and without sense, and then he was gone from within her and she was desolated.

She thought he had fallen asleep, and she lay and listened to his quiet breathing, holding him in the circle of her arms, but he was awake and he spoke suddenly, startling her.

'You were speaking to Victoria Dinizulu,' he said, and it took an effort for her to cast her mind back to the early part of the evening. 'What did you think of her?' he persisted.

'She is a lovely young woman. Intelligent and obviously dedicated. I like her very much.' She tried to be objective, but the sick jealous feeling was there deep in her belly.

'I had her invited,' Moses said. 'It was the first time I have met her.'

Tara wanted to ask, 'Why? – Why did you invite her?' But she remained silent, dreading the reply. She knew her instincts had been correct.

'She is of the royal house of Zulu,' he said softly.

'Yes. She told me,' Tara whispered.

'She is well favoured, as I was told she was, and her mother had many sons. They breed many sons in the Dinizulu line. She will make a good wife.'

'Wife?' Tara breathed. She had not expected that.

'I need the alliance with the Zulus, they are the largest and most powerful tribe. I will begin the negotiations with her family immediately. I will send Hendrick to Ladyburg to see her father and make the arrangements. It will be difficult, he is one of the old school, dead set against mixed tribal marriages. It must be a wedding that will impress the tribe, and Hendrick will convince the old man of the widsom of it.'

'But, but,' Tara found she was stuttering. 'You hardly know the girl. You spoke barely a dozen words to her all evening.'

'What does that have to do with it?' His tone was genuinely puzzled, and he rolled away from her and switched on the bedside light, dazzling her.

'Look at me!' he commanded, taking her by the chin and lifting her face to the light, studying it for a moment and then removing his fingers as though he had touched something loathsome. 'I have misjudged you,' he said scornfully. 'I believed that you were an exceptional person. A true revolutionary, a dedicated friend of the black people of this land, ready to make any sacrifice. Instead I find a weak, jealous woman, riddled with bourgeois white prejudices.'

The mattress tipped under her as Moses stood up. He towered over the bed.

'I have been wasting my time,' he said, gathering his clothing, and still naked turned towards the door.

Tara threw herself across the room and clung to him, barring his way to the door.

'I'm sorry. I didn't mean it. Forgive me. Please forgive me,' she pleaded with him, and he stood cold and aloof and silent. She began to weep, her tears muffling her voice, until she was no longer making sense.

Slowly she slid down with her arms still encircling him, until she was on her knees hugging his legs.

'Please,' she sobbed. 'I will do anything. Just don't leave me. I will do anything, everything you tell me to do – only just don't send me away like this.'

'Get up,' he said at last, and when she stood before him like a penitent, he said softly, 'You have one more chance. Just one. Do you understand?' and she nodded wildly, still choking on her sobs, unable to answer him. She reached out hesitantly and when he did not pull away, took his hand and led him back to the bed.

As he mounted her again, he knew that at last she was ready, completely prepared. She would do anything and everything he commanded.

* * *

In the dawn she came awake to find him leaning over her staring into her face and immediately she relived the night's terror, the dreadful fear of his scorn and rejection. She felt weak and trembly, her tears very close, but he took her

calmly and made love to her with a gentle consideration that reassured her and left her feeling whole and vital again. Then he spoke to her quietly.

'I am going to put my trust in you,' he told her, and her gratitude was so strong it left her breathless. 'I am going to accept you as one of us, one of the inner circle.'

She nodded, but could not speak, staring into his fierce black eyes.

'You know how we have conducted the struggle thus far,' he said, 'we have played by the white man's rules, but he made those rules, and he designed them so we could never win. Petitions and delegations, commissions of enquiry and representations – but in the end there are always more laws made against us, governing every facet of our lives, how we work, where we live, where we are allowed to travel, or eat or sleep or love – ' he broke off with an exclamation of scorn. 'The time is coming when we will rewrite the rule book. First, the defiance campaign when we will deliberately flout the mass of laws which bind us, and after that – ' Now his expression was savage. 'And after that the struggle will go on and become a great battle.'

She was silent beside him, studying his face.

'I believe there comes a time when a man confronted by great evil must take up the spear and become a warrior. He must rise up and strike it down.' He was watching her, waiting for a reply.

'Yes,' she nodded. 'You are right.'

'These are words, ideas, Tara,' he told her. 'But what of action? Are you ready for action?'

She nodded. 'I am ready.'

'Blood, Tara, not words. Killing and maiming and burning. Tearing down and destroying. Can you face that, Tara?'

She was appalled, facing the reality at last, not merely the dizzy rhetoric. In her imagination she saw the flames roaring up through the great roof of Weltevreden and blood splashed on the walls shining wetly in the sunlight, while in the courtyard lay the broken bodies of children, of her own children, and she was on the very point of rejecting the images when he spoke again.

'Destroying what is evil, Tara, so that we may rebuild a good and just society.' His voice was low and compelling, it thrilled like a drug through her veins and the cruel images faded, she looked beyond them to the paradise, the earthly paradise they would build together.

'I am ready,' she said, and there was not a trace of a quaver in her voice.

There was an hour before Marcus would take her to the airport to catch the Viscount flight back to Cape Town. They sat at his table on the verandah, just the two of them, and Moses explained to her in detail what must be done.

'*Umkhonto we Sizwe*,' he told her. 'The Spear of the Nation.' The name shimmered and rang like polished steel in her brain.

'Firstly, you must withdraw from all overt liberal activities. You must abandon your clinic – '

'My clinic!' she exclaimed. 'Oh Moses, my poor little ones, what will they do – ' she broke off as she saw his expression.

'You care for the physical needs of a hundred,' he said. 'I'm concerned for the welfare of twenty million. Tell me which is more important.'

'You are right,' she whispered. 'Forgive me.'

'You will use the excuse of the defiance campaign to make a statement of your disillusion with the freedom movement and to announce your resignation from the Black Sash.'

'Oh dear, what will Molly say?'

'Molly knows,' he assured her. 'Molly knows why you are doing it. She will help you in every way. Of course, the police special branch will continue to keep you under observation for a while, but when you give them nothing more for their files, they will lose interest and drop you.'

She nodded. 'I understand.'

'You must take more interest in your husband's political activities, cultivate his parliamentary associates. Your own father is the deputy leader of the opposition, with access to the government ministers. You must become our eyes and ears.'

'Yes, I can do all that.'

'Later, there will be other tasks for you. Many difficult and some even dangerous. Would you risk your life for the struggle, Tara?'

'For you, Moses Gama, I would do more. I would willingly lay down that life for you,' she replied, and when he saw that she meant it, he nodded with deep satisfaction.

'We will meet whenever we can,' he promised her. 'Whenever it is safe to do so.' And then he gave her the salute which would become the rallying cry of the defiance campaign, '*Mayibuye! Afrika!*'

And she replied, '*Mayibuye! Afrika!* Africa, let it persist!'

* * *

'I am an adulteress,' Tara thought, as she had each morning as she sat at the breakfast table during all the weeks that had passed since she had arrived back from Johannesburg. 'I am an adulteress.' And she thought it must show, like a brand upon her forehead for all the world to see. Yet Shasa had greeted her cheerfully on her return, apologizing for sending a driver to meet her at the airport and not coming in person, asking her if she had enjoyed her illicit interlude with *Australopithecus*. 'Thought you might have gone for someone a little younger. I mean a million years old is just a little long in the tooth, isn't it?' And since then their relationship had continued unaltered.

The children, with the exception of Michael, seemed not to have missed her at all. Centaine had run the household in her absence with her usual iron fist in a candy-flavoured glove and after they had greeted Tara with dutiful but offhand kisses, the children were full of what Nana had done and said, and Tara was painfully aware that she had neglected to bring any presents for them.

Only Michael was different. For the first few days he would not let her out of his sight, but traipsed around behind her, even insisting on spending his precious Saturday afternoon with her at the clinic while his two brothers went off to Newlands Rugby Ground with Shasa to watch Western Province playing the visiting All Blacks team from New Zealand.

Michael's company helped alleviate a little of the pain of making the first arrangements to close down the clinic. She had to ask her three black nursing sisters to start looking for other jobs. 'Of course, you'll be paid your salaries until you find other positions, and I will help you all I can – ' But still she had to suffer the reproach in their eyes.

Now, almost a month later, she sat at Weltevreden's laden breakfast table on a Sunday morning in the dappled shade beneath the trellised vines of the

terrace, while the servants in crisp white uniform fussed about then. Shasa read aloud extracts from the *Sunday Times* to which none of them listened, Sean and Garrick wrangled acrimoniously over who was the best full-back in the world, and Isabella clamoured for her daddy's attention. Michael was giving her a detailed account of the plot of the book he was reading, and she felt like an impostor, an actress playing a role for which she had not rehearsed her lines.

Shasa finally crumpled his newspaper and dropped it beside his chair, acceding to Isabella's request to 'Take me on your lap, Daddy!' ignoring Tara's ritual protest and demanded:

'All right, everybody, this meeting will come to order and address the serious question of what we are all going to do with this Sunday.' This precipitated a near riot which Isabella punctuated with shrill cries of 'Picnic! Picnic!' and finally picnic it was, after Shasa has used his casting vote in his daughter's favour.

Tara tried to excuse herself, but Michael was so close to tears that she relented and they all rode out together, with the servants and the picnic baskets following them in the little two-wheeled dog cart. Of course they could have gone by car, but the ride was half the fun.

Shasa had had the pool below the waterfall bricked out to make a natural swimming-pool and had built a thatched summer house on the bank. The great attraction was the long slide down the glassy smooth rock of the waterfall on a red rubber inner tube, and the plunge over the final sheer drop into the green pool below, the entire journey accompanied by howls and shrieks of glee. It was sport that never palled and it kept the children busy all morning.

Shasa and Tara, in their bathing-suits, lolled on the grassy bank, basking in the hot bright sunlight. They used to come here often in the first days of their marriage, even before the pool was bricked and the summer house built. In fact Tara was certain that more than one of the children had been conceived on this grassy bank. Some of the warm feelings from those days persisted. Shasa opened a bottle of Riesling, and they were both more relaxed and friendly towards each other than they had been for years.

Shasa sensed his opportunity, fished the wine bottle out of the ice bucket and refilled Tara's glass before he said, 'My dear, I have something to tell you that is of great importance to both of us and may quite substantially change our lives.'

'He has found another woman,' she thought, half in dread, half in relief, so that she did not at first understand what he was telling her. Then suddenly the enormity of it crashed in upon her. Shasa was going to join them, he was going across to the Boers. He was throwing in his lot with the band of the most evil men that Africa had ever spawned. Those supreme architects of misery and suffering and oppression.

'I believe that I am being offered the opportunity to use my talents and my financial gift for the greater good of this land and its people,' he was saying, and she twirled the stem of the wineglass between her fingers and stared down into the pale golden liquid, not daring to lift her eyes and look at him in case he saw what she was thinking.

'I have considered it from every angle, and I have discussed it with Mater. I think I have a duty to the country, to the family and to myself. I believe that I have to do it, Tara.'

It was a terrible thing to feel the last blighted fruits of her love for him shrivel and fall away, and then almost instantly she felt free and light, the burden was

gone and in its place came a rush of contrary emotion. It was so powerful that she could not put a name to it for a moment, and then she knew it was hatred.

She wondered that she had ever felt guilty on his account, she wondered even that she could ever have loved him. His voice droned on justifying himself, attempting to excuse the inexcusable, and still she knew she dared not look up at him lest he see it in her eyes. She felt an almost irresistible need to scream at him, 'You are callous, selfish, evil, as they are!' and physically to attack him, to claw at his single eye with her nails, and it took all her power to sit still and quiet. She remembered what Moses had told her, and she clung to his words. They seemed the only sane things in all this madness.

Shasa finished the explanation that he had so carefully prepared for her, and then waited for her reply. She sat on the plaid rug in the sun with her legs curled up under her, staring into the glass in her hands, and he looked at her as he had not done for years and saw that she was still beautiful. Her body was smooth and lightly tanned, her hair sparkled with ruby lights in the sun, and her big breasts that had always enchanted him, seemed to have filled out again. He found himself attracted by her and excited as he had not been for a long time and he reached out gently and touched her cheek.

'Talk to me,' he invited. 'Tell me what you think about it.' And she lifted her chin and stared at him. For an instant he was chilled by her gaze, for it was as inscrutable and merciless as the stare of a lioness, but then Tara smiled slightly and shrugged, and he thought that he had been mistaken, it was not hatred he had seen in her eyes.

'You have decided already, Shasa. Why do you need my approval? I have never been able to prevent you doing anything you wanted to do before. Why would I presume to do that now?'

He was amazed and relieved, he had anticipated a bitter battle.

'I wanted you to know why,' he said. 'I want you to know that we both want the same thing – prosperity and dignity for everybody in this land. That is why we have different ways of trying to achieve it, and I believe that my way is more effective.'

'I repeat, why do you need my approval?'

'I need your co-operation,' he corrected her. 'For in a way this opportunity depends on you.'

'How?' she asked, and looked away from him to where the children were splashing and cavorting. Only Garrick was not in the water. Sean had ducked him, and now he sat shivering on the edge of the pool. His thin weedy body was blue with cold. He was fighting for breath, the rack of his ribs sticking out of his chest as he coughed and wheezed.

'Garry,' she called sharply. 'That's enough. Dry yourself and put on our jersey.'

'Oh, Ma,' he gasped a protest, and she flared at him.

'Do it this instant.' And when he went reluctantly to the summerhouse she turned back to Shasa.

'You want my co-operation?' She felt totally in control of herself. She would not let him see how she felt towards him and his monstrous intention. 'Tell me what you want me to do.'

'It will come as no surprise to you to hear that BOSS, the Bureau of State Security, has quite an extensive file on you.'

'In view of the fact that they have arrested me three times,' Tara smiled again, a tight humourless grimace, 'you are right, I'm not surprised.'

'Well, my dear, what it boils down to is that it would be impossible for me to hold cabinet rank while you were still raising Cain and committing mayhem with your sisters in the Black Sash.'

'You want me to give up my political work? But what about my record? I mean, I am an old hardened jailbird, you know.'

'Fortunately the security police regard you with a certain amused indulgence. I have seen a copy of your file. The assessment is that you are a dilettante, naïve and impressionable, and easily swayed by your more vicious associates.'

That insult was difficult to bear. Tara jumped to her feet and strode around the edge of the pool, seized Isabella by the wrist and dragged her from the pool.

'That's enough for you also, young lady.' She ignored Isabella's howls of protest and stripped off her bathing costume.

'You're hurting me,' Isabella wailed as Tara scrubbed her sodden hair with a rough dry towel and then wrapped her in it.

Isabella ran to her father, still snivelling and tripping over the tails of the towel.

'Mommy won't let me swim.' She crawled into his lap.

'Life is full of injustice.' Shasa hugged her, and she gave one last convulsive sob and then cuddled her damp curls against his shoulder.

'All right, I am an ineffectual dilettante.' Tara flopped down on the rug again. She had regained her composure and sat cross-legged facing him. 'But what if I refuse to give up? What if I continue to follow the dictates of my conscience?'

'Tara, don't try and force a confrontation,' he said softly.

'You always get what you want, don't you, Shasa?' She was goading him, but he shook his head, refusing the challenge.

'I want to discuss this logically and calmly,' he said, but she could not prevent herself flouting him, for the insult rankled.

'I would get the children – you must know that, your clever lawyers must have warned you of that.'

'God damn it, Tara, you know that's not what I had in mind,' Shasa said coldly, but he hugged the child closer and Isabella reached up and touched his chin.

'You are all scratchy,' she murmured happily, unaware of the tension. 'But I still love you, my daddy.'

'Yes, my angel, I love you also,' he said, and then to Tara, 'I wasn't threatening you.'

'Not yet,' she qualified. 'But that comes next, if I know you – and I should.'

'Can't we discuss this sensibly?'

'It's not necessary,' Tara capitulated suddenly. 'I had already made up my mind. I had already seen the futility of our little protests. I have known for some time that it was a waste of my life. I know I have neglected the children and during this last visit to Johannesburg I decided that I should take up my studies again and leave politics to the professionals. I had already decided to resign from the Sash and close down the clinic or hand it over to somebody else.'

He stared at her in amazement. He distrusted any victory too easily won.

'What do you want in return?' he asked.

'I want to go back to university and take a Ph.D. in archaeology,' she said crisply. 'And I want completely freedom to travel and pursue my studies.'

'You have a bargain,' he agreed readily, not even attempting to conceal his relief. 'You keep your nose clean politically, and you can go where and when

you want.' And then despite himself his eyes dropped back to her breasts. He was right, they had filed out beautifully and bulged from the thin silken cups of her bikini. He felt a quick hot need of her.

She saw that look on his face. She knew it well, and she was revolted by it. After what he had just told her, after the insults he casually offered her, after his betrayal of that which she held sacred and dear, she knew she could never take him again. She pulled up the top of her bikini and reached for her robe.

Shasa was delighted with their bargain, and though he seldom drank more than a glassful, this afternoon he finished the rest of the Riesling while he and the boys cooked their lunch on the barbecue pit.

Sean took his duties as assistant chef seriously. Only one or two of the chops landed up in the dirt, but as Sean explained to his younger brothers, 'Those are yours, and if you don't let your teeth touch, then you won't even feel the grit.'

At the table in the summer-house Isabella helped Tara prepare the salads, dousing herself liberally with French dressing in the process, and when they sat down to eat Shasa had the children shrieking with laughter at his stories. Only Tara sat aloof from the general hilarity.

When the children were given permission to leave the table with the injunction not to swim again for an hour while their food digested, Tara asked him quietly. 'What time are you leaving tomorrow?'

'Early,' he replied. 'I have to be in Johannesburg before lunch. Lord Littleton is arriving on the Comet from London. I want to be there to meet him.'

'How long will you be away this time?'

'After the launching David and I will be going on tour,' he replied. He had wanted her to attend the launching party which would celebrate and publicize the opening of the subscription lists for shares in the new Silver River mine. She had found an excuse but she noticed that he did not repeat the invitation now.

'So you'll be gone about ten days?' Every quarter Shasa and David made a tour of all the company's operations, from the new chemical factory at Chaka's Bay, and the paper pulp mills in the eastern Transvaal to the H'ani Diamond Mine in the Kalahari Desert, which was the company's flagship.

'Perhaps a little longer,' Shasa demurred. 'I'll be in Johannesburg at least four days,' and he thought happily of Marylee from MIT and her IBM 701.

* * *

David Abrahams had persuaded Shasa to hand the Silver River launching over to one of those public relations consultants, a breed that had recently sprung up but which Shasa viewed with suspicion. Despite his original misgiving he was now reluctantly prepared to concede that it wasn't such a bad idea as he had first believed, even though it was going to cost over five thousand pounds.

They had flown out the editors of the London *Financial Times* and the *Wall Street Journal*, with their wives, and afterwards would be taking them on for five days in the Kruger National Park with all expenses paid. All the local press and radio journalists were invited and as an unexpected bonus the television team that had come out from New York to do a series called 'Focus on Africa' for North American Broadcasting Studios had also accepted an invitation to attend the launching party.

In the entrance lobby of the Courtney Mining Co. offices they had set up a twenty-five-foot-high working replica of the mine headgear that would be erected above the Silver River main, and had surrounded it with an enormous display of wild proteas designed and executed by the same team which had won a gold medal at the Chelsea Flower Show in London the previous year. Appreciating that journalism is thirsty work, David had laid in one hundred cases of Moët & Chandon, although Shasa had vetoed the idea of a vintage *cru*.

'Even non-vintage is too damn good for them.' Shasa did not have a lofty view of the profession of journalism.

David had also hired the chorus line from the Royal Swazi Spa to provide a floor-show. The promise of a flash of bared bosom would be almost as big a draw as the champagne; to the South African censors the female nipple was every bit as dangerous as Karl Marx's Communist Manifesto.

On arrival every guest was handed a presentation pack which contained a glossy colour brochure, a certificate made out in his or her name for one £1 share in the Silver River Mining Co. and a genuine miniature bar of twenty-two carat South African gold, stamped with the company logo. David had sought Reserve Bank authority to have these bars struck by the South African mint, and at almost thirty dollars each they had been a major part of the advertising budget, but the excitement they created and the subsequent publicity fully justified the expense.

Shasa made his address before the Moët & Chandon could soften the wits of his guests or the floor-show distract them. Speaking in public was something that Shasa had always enjoyed. Neither the fusillade of camera flashes nor the sultry brilliance of the arc lights set up by the NABS televison camera team detracted from his enjoyment this evening.

Silver River was one of the major achievements of his career to date. He alone had recognized the chance that the gold reef spurred at depth from the main run at the Orange Free State series, and personally he had negotiated the drilling options. Only when the diamond drills had finally intercepted the narrow black band of the gold-bearing carbon leader almost a mile and a half below the surface of the arid plain had Shasa's decision been vindicated. The strike was rich beyond even his expectations, running at over twenty-six penny-weights of pure gold to the ton of reef.

Tonight was Shasa's night. It was his particular gift that he was able to extract from everything he did the last ounce of enjoyment, and he stood in the arc lights tall and debonair in his immaculately tailored evening dress, the black eye-patch giving him a rakish and dangerous air, so obviously at ease and in control of himself and the company he commanded, that he carried them all along with him effortlessly.

They laughed and applauded at the right places, and they listened with fascinated attention as he explained the scale of the investment that was called for and how it would help to strengthen the bonds of kinship that tied South Africa so securely to England and the British Commonwealth of Nations, and set up new lines of friendship with the investors of the United States of America from where he hoped almost thirty per cent of the necessary capital for the project would come.

When he ended to prolonged applause, Lord Littleton, as head of the underwriting bank, stood up to reply. He was lean and silver-haired, his evening dress, just that touch archaic in cut, with wide cuffs to the trousers, as if to underline his aristocratic scorn of fashion. He told them of his bank's

strong relationship with Courtney Mining and the intense interest that this new company had aroused in the City of London.

'From the very beginning we at Littleton Bank were pretty damned certain that we were going to earn our underwriting fees very easily. We knew that there would be very few unsubscribed shares for us to take up. So it gives me a deal of pleasure to stand before you here this evening and say, I told you so.' There was a buzz of comment and speculation which he raised a hand to silence. 'I am going to tell you something that not even Mr Shasa Courtney knows yet, and which I only learned an hour ago.' He reached into his pocket and brought out a telex flimsy which he waved at them.

'As you are aware, the subscription lists for shares in Silver River Mining opened this morning at 10 a.m. London time, two hours behind South African time. When my bank closed a few hours ago, they sent me this telex.' He placed gold-rimmed reading glasses on his nose. 'I quote: "Please convey congratulations to Mr Courtney and Courtney Mining and Finance as promoters of Silver River Gold-Mining Co. Stop as of 4 pm London time today the Silver River issue was oversubscribed by four times Ends Littleton Bank."'

David Abrahams seized Shasa's hand, the first to congratulate him. In the roar of applause they grinned at each other happily, until Shasa broke away and jumped down off the dais.

Centaine Courtney-Malcomess was in the first row of his audience and she sprang lightly to her feet to meet him. She was dressed in a sheath of gold lamé and wearing her full suite of diamonds, each stone carefully picked from thirty years' production of the H'ani Mine. Slim and glittering and lovely, she went to meet her son.

'Now we have it all, Mater,' he whispered as he hugged her.

'No, *chéri* we'll never have it all,' she whispered back. 'That would be dull. There is always something more to strive for.'

Blaine Malcomess was waiting to congratulate him, and Shasa turned to him with an arm still around Centaine's waist.

'Big night, Shasa.' Blaine took his hand. 'You deserve it all.'

'Thank you, sir.'

'What a pity Tara couldn't be here,' Blaine went on.

'I wanted her to come.' Shasa was immediately defensive. 'But as you know she decided she couldn't leave the children again so soon.'

The crowd surged around them, and they were laughing and replying to congratulations, but Shasa saw the public relations director hovering and eased his way through to her.

'Well, Mrs Anstey, you have done us proud.' He smiled at her with all his charm. She was tall and rather bony but with silky blond hair that hung in a thick curtain over her bare shoulders.

'I always try to give full satisfaction.' Jill Anstey hooded her eyes and pouted slightly to give the remark an ambiguous slant. They had been teasing each other ever since they had met the previous day. 'But I'm afraid I have some more work for you, Mr Courtney. Will you bear with me just once more?'

'As often as you wish, Mrs Anstey.' Shasa played the game out, and she placed her hand on his forearm to lead him away, squeezing just a little more than was necessary.

'The television people from NABS want to do a five-minute interview with you, for inclusion in their "Africa in Focus" series. It could be a wonderful chance to speak directly to fifty million Americans.'

The TV team was setting up their equipment in the boardroom; the lights and cameras were being trained on the far end of the long room, where Centaine's portrait by Annigoni, hung on the stinkwood panelling. There were three men in the camera crew, all young and casually dressed but clearly highly professional and competent, and with them was a girl.

'Who will do the interview?' Shasa asked, glancing around curiously.

'That's the director,' Jill Anstey said. 'And she'll talk to you.' It took him a moment to realize that she meant the girl, then he saw that without seeming to do so, the girl was directing the set-up, indicating a camera angle or a lighting change with a word or a gesture.

'She's just a child,' Shasa protested.

'Twenty-five and smart as a bunch of monkeys,' Jill Anstey warned him. 'Don't let the little-girl look fool you. She's a professional and a strong comer with a big following in the States. She did that incredible series of interviews with Jomo Kenyatta, the Mau Mau terrorist, not to mention the "Heartbreak Ridge" story in Korea. They say she'll get an Emmy for it.'

South Africa did not have a TV network, but Shasa had seen 'Heartbreak Ridge' on BBC television during his last stay in London. It was a gritty, totally absorbing commentary on the Korean war, and Shasa found it hard to believe that this child had done that. She turned now and came directly to him, holding out her hand, frank and friendly, a fresh-faced *ingénue*.

'Hello, Mr Courtney, I'm Kitty Godolphin.' She had an enchanting southern accent and there were fine golden freckles across her cheeks and her small pert nose, but then he saw that she had good bone structure and interesting planes to her face that would render her highly photogenic.

'Mr Courtney,' she said. 'You speak so well, I couldn't resist trying to get a little more of you on film. I hope I haven't put you out too much.' She smiled at him, a sweet engaging smile, but he looked beyond it into eyes as hard as any diamonds from the H'ani Mine, eyes that were bright with a sharp cynical intelligence and ruthless ambition. That was unexpected and intriguing.

'Here's a show that will be worth the entrance fee,' he thought and glanced down. Her breasts were small, smaller than he usually chose, but they were unsupported and he could see their shape beneath her blouse. They were exquisite.

She led him to the leather chairs she had arranged to face each other under the lights.

'If you would sit on this side we'll get right into it. I'll do my introduction later. I don't want to keep you any longer than I have to.'

'As long as you like.'

'Oh, I know that you have a room full of important guests.' She glanced at her crew and one of them gave her a thumbs-up. She looked back at Shasa. 'The American public knows very little about South Africa,' she explained. 'What I am trying to do is capture a cross-section of your society and figure out how it all works. I will introduce you as a politician, mining tycoon and financier, and tell them about this fabulous new gold-mine of yours. Then we'll cut to you. Okay?'

'Okay!' He smiled easily. 'Let her roll.'

The clapper loader snapped the board in front of Shasa's face, somebody said 'Sound?' and somebody else replied 'Rolling' and then 'Action'.

'Mr Shasa Courtney, you have just told a meeting of your shareholders that your new gold-mine will probably be one of the five richest in South Africa,

which makes it one of the richest in the world. Can you tell our viewers just how much of that fabulous wealth will be going back to people from which it was stolen in the first place?' she asked with breathtaking candour. 'And I am, of course, referring to the black tribes who once owned the land.'

Shasa was off-balance for only the moment that it took him to realize that he was in a fight. Then he responded easily.

'The black tribes who once owned the land on which the Silver River mine is situated were slaughtered, to the last man, woman and child, back in the 1820s by the impis of Kings Chaka and Mzilikazi, those two benevolent Zulu monarchs who between them managed to reduce the population of southern Africa by fifty per cent,' he told her. 'When the white settlers moved northwards, they came upon a land denuded of all human life. The land they staked was open, they stole it from nobody. I bought the mineral rights from people who had clear undisputed title to it.' He saw the glint of respect in her eyes, but she was as quick as he had been. She had lost a point but was ready to play the next.

'Historical facts are interesting, of course, but let's return to the present. Tell me, if you had been a man of colour, Mr Courtney, say black or an Asiatic businessman, would you have been allowed to purchase the concessions to the Silver River mine?'

'That's a hypothetical question, Miss Godolphin.'

'I don't think so – ' she cut off his escape. 'Am I wrong in thinking that the Group Areas Act recently promulgated by the parliament of which you are a sitting member, prevents non-white individuals and companies owned by blacks from purchasing land or mineral rights anywhere in their own land?'

'I voted against that legislation,' Shasa said grimly. 'But yes, the Group Areas Act would have prevented a coloured person acquiring the rights in the Silver River mine,' he conceded. Too clever to labour a point well taken, she moved on swiftly.

'How many black people does the Courtney Mining and Finance Company employ in its numerous enterprises?' she asked with that sweet open smile.

'Altogether through eighteen subsidiary companies, we provide work for some two thousand whites and thirty thousand blacks.'

'That is a marvellous achievement, and must make you very proud, Mr Courtney.' She was breathlessly girlish. 'And how many blacks do you have sitting on the boards of those eighteen companies?'

Again he had been wrong-footed, and he avoided the question. 'We make a point of paying well above the going rate for the job, and the other benefits we provide to our employees – ' Kitty nodded brightly, letting him finish, quite happy that she could edit out all this extraneous material, but the moment he paused, she came in again:

'So there are no black directors on the Courtney companies' boards. Can you tell us how many black departmental managers you have appointed?'

Once long ago, hunting buffalo in the forests along the Zambezi river, Shasa had been attacked by a heat-maddened swarm of the big black African honey-bees. There had been no defence against them, and he had only escaped at last by diving into the crocodile-infested Zambezi river. He felt that same sense of angry helplessness now, as she buzzed around his head, effortlessly avoiding his attempts to swat her down and darting out to sting painfully almost at will.

'Thirty thousand black men working for you, and not a single director or manager amongst them!' she marvelled ingenuously. 'Can you suggest why that might be?'

'We have a predominantly tribal black society in this country and they come to the cities unskilled and untrained – '

'Oh, don't you have training programmes?'

Shasa accepted the opening. 'The Courtney group has a massive training programme. Last year alone we spent two and a half million pounds on employee education and job training?'

'How long has this programme been in operation, Mr Courtney?'

'Seven years, ever since I became chairman.'

'And in seven years, after all that money spent on education, not one black of all those thousands has been promoted to managerial status? Is that because you have not found a single capable black, or is it because your job reservation policy and your strict colour bar prevent any black, no matter how good – '

He was driven back inexorably until in anger he went on the defensive. 'If you are looking for racial discrimination, why didn't you stay in America?' he asked her, smiling icily. 'I'm sure your own Martin Luther King would be able to help you more than I can.'

'There is bigotry in my country,' she nodded. 'We understand that, and we are changing it, educating our people and outlawing its practice, but from what I have seen, you are indoctrinating your children in this policy you call *apartheid* and enshrining it in a monumental fortress of laws like your Group Areas Act and your Population Registration Act which seeks to classify all men by the colour of their skin alone.'

'We differentiate,' Shasa conceded, 'but that does not mean that we discriminate.'

'That's a catchy slogan, Mr Courtney, but not original. I have already heard it from your minister of Bantu affairs, Dr Hendrik Frensch Verwoerd. However, I suggest to you that you do discriminate. If a man is denied the right to vote or to own land merely because his skin is dark, that in my book is discrimination.'

And before he could respond, she had switched again.

'How many black people do you number amongst your personal friends?' she asked engagingly, and the question transported Shasa instantly back across the years. He remembered as a lad standing his first shifts on the H'ani Mine and the man who had been his friend. The black boss-boy in charge of the weathering grounds on which the newly mined blue ore from the pit was laid out to soften and crumble to the point at which it could be carted to the mill.

He hadn't thought about him for years, yet he remembered his name without effort, Moses Gama, and he saw him in his mind's eye, tall and broad-shouldered, handsome as a young pharaoh with skin that glowed like old amber in the sunlight as they toiled side by side. He remembered their long rambling discussions, how they had read and argued together, drawn together by some unusual bond of the spirit. Shasa had lent him Macaulay's *History of England*, and when Moses Gama was fired from the H'ani Mine on the instigation of Centaine Courtney as a direct result of the unacceptably intimate friendly relationship between them, Shasa had asked him to keep the book. Now he felt again a faint echo of the sense of deprivation he had experienced at the time of their enforced parting.

'I have only a handful of personal friends,' he told her now. 'Ten thousand acquaintances, but only a very few friends – ' He held up the fingers of his right hand. 'No more than that, and none of them happen to be black. Though once I had a black man as a friend, and I grieved when our ways parted.'

With the sure instinct which made her supreme in her craft, Kitty Godolphin recognized that he had given her a perfect peg on which to hang the interview.

'Once I had a black man as a friend,' she repeated softly. 'And I grieved when our ways parted. Thank you, Mr Courtney.' She turned to her camera man. 'Okay, Hank, cut it and get the studio to print it tonight.'

She stood up quickly and Shasa towered over her.

'That was excellent. There is a great deal of material there we can use,' she enthused. 'I am really grateful for your co-operation.'

Smiling urbanely Shasa leaned close to her. 'You are a devious little bitch, aren't you?' he said softly. 'A face like an angel and a heart of hell. You know it isn't like you made it sound, and you don't care. As long as you get a good story, you don't give a damn whether it's true or not or who it hurts, do you?'

Shasa turned from her and strode out of the boardroom. The floor-show had started and he went to the table at which Centaine and Blaine Malcomess were sitting, but the night had been spoiled for him.

He sat and glowered at the swirling dancers, not really seeing their long naked limbs and gleaming flesh but thinking furiously of Kitty Godolphin instead. Danger exicted him, that was why he hunted lion and buffalo and flew his own Tiger Moth and played polo. Kitty Godolphin was dangerous. He was always attracted to intelligent and competent women, with strong personalities – and this one was devastatingly competent and made of pure silk and steel.

He thought about that lovely innocent face and childlike smile and the hard gleam of her eyes, and his fury was compounded by his desire to subjugate her, emotionally and physically, and the fact that he knew it would be difficult made the thought all the more obsessive. He found that he was physically aroused and that increased his anger.

He glanced up suddenly, and from across the room Jill Anstey, the public relations director, was watching him. The coloured lights played on the Slavic planes of her face and glinted on the platinum sheet of her hair. She slanted her eyes at him and ran the tip of her tongue over her lower lip.

'All right,' he thought. 'I have to take it out on somebody and you will do.' He inclined his head slightly, and Jill Anstey nodded and slipped out of the door behind her. Shasa murmured an apology to Centaine, then stood up and moved through the pounding music and semi-darkness towards the door through which Jill Anstey had disappeared.

Shasa got back to the Carlton Hotel at nine o'clock in the morning. Still in black tie and dinner jacket, he avoided the lobby and went up the back stairs from the underground garage. Centaine and Blaine were in the company suite, and Shasa had the smaller suite across the passage. He dreaded meeting either of them dressed as he was at this time in the morning, but he was lucky and got into his lounge uninterrupted.

Somebody had slipped an envelope under his door and he picked it up without particular interest, until he saw the Killarney Film Studios crest on the flap. Kitty Godolphin was working out of that studio and he grinned and split the flap with his thumbnail.

Dear Mr Courtney,

The rushes are just great – you look better than Errol Flynn on film. If you want to see them, call me at the studio.

Kitty Godolphin

His anger had cooled and he was amused by her cheek, and though he had a full day ahead – lunch with Lord Littleton and meetings all afternoon – he called the studio.

'You just caught me,' Kitty told him. 'I was on my way out. You want to see the rushes? Okay, can you get up here at six this evening?'

She was smiling that sweet childlike smile and mocking him with a malicious green sparkle in her eyes as she came down to the reception desk of the studio to shake his hand and lead him to her hired projection room in the complex.

'I knew I could rely on your masculine vanity to get you up here,' she assured him.

Her film crew were sprawled untidily over the front row of seats in the projection room, smoking Camels and drinking Cokes, but Hank, the camera man, had the film clip in the projector ready to run, and they watched it through in silence.

When the lights went up again, Shasa turned to Kitty and conceded.

'You are good – you made me look a real prick most of the time. And, of course, you can always lose the parts where I held my own on the cutting-room floor.'

'You don't like it?' she grinned, wrinkling her small nose so the freckles on it gleamed like tiny gold coins.

'You are a bushwhacker, shooting from cover, and I'm out there with my back wide open.'

'If you accuse me of faking it,' she challenged him, 'how about you taking me and showing me the way it really is. Show me the Courtney mines and factories and let me film them!'

So that was why she had called him. He smiled to himself, but asked, 'Have you got ten days?'

'I've got as long as it takes,' she assured him.

'All right, let's start with dinner tonight.'

'Great!' she enthused, and then turned to her crew. '*Mazeltov*, boys, Mr Courtney is standing us all dinner.'

'That's not exactly what I had in mind,' he murmured.

'Do tell?' She gave him her innocent little girl look.

Kitty Godolphin was a rewarding companion. Her interest in everything he said or showed her was flattering and unfeigned. She watched his eyes or his lips as he spoke, and often leaned so close to listen that he could feel her breath on his face, but she never actually touched him.

For Shasa her appeal was heightened by her personal cleanliness. In the days they spent together, hot dusty days in the desert of the far west or in the eastern forests, tramping through pulp mills or fertilizer factories, watching the bulldozers strip the overburden from the coal deposits in billowing clouds of dust, or baking in the depths of the great excavation of the H'ani Mine, Kitty was always fresh-faced and cool-looking. Even in the dust her eyes were clear and her small even teeth sparkled. When or where she had an opportunity to rinse her clothes he could never decide, but they were always clean and crisp and her breath when she leaned to him was always sweet.

She was a professional. That impressed Shasa also. She would go to any lengths to get the film footage she wanted, taking no account of fatigue or personal danger. He had to forbid her riding on the outside of the mine cage on the H'ani main incline shaft to film the drop into the pit, but she went back later, while he was in a meeting with his mine manger, and got exactly what she

wanted and then smiled away his fury when he found out. Her crew treated her with an ambivalence that amused Shasa. They held her in fond affection and were immensely protective of her, as though they were her elder brothers, and their pride in her achievements was unconcealed. However, at the same time they were much in awe of her ruthless search for excellence, to which they knew she would sacrifice them and anything else that got in her way. Her temper, although not often displayed, was merciless and vitriolic and when she gave an order, no matter how quietly or how sweet the smile that accompanied it, they jumped.

Shasa was also affected by the deep feelings which she had conceived for Africa, its land and its people.

'I thought America was the most beautiful country in all the world,' she said quietly one evening as they watched the sun set behind the great desolate mountains of the western deserts. 'But when I look at this, I have to wonder.'

Her curiosity took her into the compounds where the Courtney Company employees were housed, and she spent hours talking to the workers and their wives, filming it all, the questions and answers of black miners and white overseers and shift bosses, their homes and the food they ate, their recreations and their worship, and at the end Shasa asked her, 'So how do you like the way I oppress them?'

'They live well,' she conceded.

'And they are happy,' he pushed her. 'Admit it. I hid nothing from you. They are happy.'

'They are happy like children,' she agreed. 'As long as they look up to you like big daddy. But just how long do you think you can keep fooling them? How long is it going to be before they look at you in your beautiful airplane flying back to parliament to make a few more laws for them to obey and say to themselves, "Hey man! I'd like to try that also"?'

'For three hundred years under white government the people of this land have woven a social fabric which has held us all together. It works, and I would hate to see it torn asunder without knowing what will replace it.'

'How about democracy for a start?' she suggested. 'That's not a bad thing to replace it with – you know, *the will of the majority must prevail*!'

'You left out the best bit,' he flashed back at her. '*The interests of the minority must be safeguarded*. That doesn't work in Africa. The African knows and understands one principle: winner takes all – and let the minority go to the wall. That's what will happen to the white settlers in Kenya if the British capitulate to the Mau Mau killers.'

So they wrangled and sparred during the long hours of flying which took them over the enormous distances of the African continent. From one destination to the next, Shasa and Kitty went ahead in the Mosquito, and the helmet and oxygen mask were too large for her and made her appear even younger and more girlish. David Abrahams piloted the slower and more commodious company De Havilland Dove, the camera equipment and the crew flying with him, and even though most of Shasa's time on the ground was spent in meetings with his managers and administrative staff, there was still much time that he could devote to the seduction of Kitty Godolphin.

Shasa was not accustomed to prolonged resistance from any female who warranted his concentrated attention. There might be a token flight, but always with coy glances over the shoulder, and usually they chose to hide from him in

the nearest bedroom, absentmindedly forgetting to turn the key in the lock, and he expected it to go very much the same way with Kitty Godolphin.

Getting into her blue jeans was his first priority; convincing her that Africa was different from America and that they were doing the best job they could came second by a long way. At the end of the ten days he had succeeded in neither endeavour. Both Kitty's political convictions and her virtue remained intact.

Kitty's interest in him, however wide-eyed and intense, was totally impersonal and professional, and she gave the same attention to an Ovambo witchdoctor demonstrating how he cured abdominal cancer with a poultice of porcupine dung, or a muscled and tattooed white shift-boss explaining to her that a black worker should never be punched in the stomach as their spleens were always enlarged from malaria and could easily rupture – hitting them in the head was all right, he explained, because the African skull was solid bone anyway and you couldn't inflict serious damage that way.

'Mary Maria!' Kitty breathed. 'That was worth the trip in itself!'

So on the eleventh day of their odyssey, they flew out of the vastness of the Kalahari Desert from the remote H'ani Diamond Mine on its mystic and brooding range of hills, into the town of Windhoek, capital of the old German colony of South West Africa which had been mandated to South Africa at the Treaty of Versailles. It was a quaint little town, the German influence still very obvious in the architecture and the way of life of the inhabitants. Set in the hilly uplands above the arid littoral, the climate was pleasant and the Kaiserhof Hotel, where Shasa kept another permanent suite, offered many of the creature comforts that they had lacked during the previous ten days.

Shasa and David spent the afternoon with their senior staff in the local office of the Courtney Company, which before its move to Johannesburg had been the head office, but which was still responsible for the logistics of the H'ani Mine. Kitty and her team, never wasting a moment, filmed the German colonial buildings and monuments and the picturesque Herero women on the streets. In 1904 this tribe of warriors had engaged the German administration in their worst colonial war which finally left eighty thousand Hereroes dead of famine and battle out of a total population of a hundred thousand. They were tall and magnificent-looking people and the women wore full-length Victorian skirts in butterfly colours and tall matching headdresses. Kitty was delighted with them, and late that afternoon came back to the hotel in ebullient mood.

Shasa had planned carefully, and had left David at the Courtney Company offices to finish the meeting. He was waiting to invite Kitty and her team through to the beer garden of the hotel where a traditional oom-pa-pa band in Lederhosen and alpine hats was belting out a medley of German drinking songs. The locally brewed Hansa Pilsner was every bit as good as the original of the Munich beerhalls, with a clear golden colour and thick creamy head. Shasa ordered the largest tankards, and Kitty drank level with her crew.

The mood turned festive until Shasa drew Kitty aside and under cover of the band told her quietly, 'I don't know how to break this to you, Kitty, but this will be our last evening together. I had my secretary book seats on the commercial flight for you and your boys to fly back to Johannesburg tomorrow morning.'

Kitty stared at him aghast. 'I don't understand. I thought we were flying down to your diamond concessions in the *Sperrgebiet*.' She pronounced it 'Spear Beat' in her enchanting accent. 'That was going to be the main act.'

'*Sperrgebiet* means "Forbidden Area",' Shasa told her sadly. 'And it means just that, Kitty, forbidden. Nobody goes in there without a permit from the goverment inspector of mines.

'But I thought you had arranged a permit for us,' she protested.

'I tried. I telexed our local office to arrange it. The application was denied. The Government doesn't want you in there, I'm afraid.'

'But why not?'

'There must be something going on in there that they don't want you to see or film,' he shrugged, and she was silent but he saw the play of fierce emotion across her innocent features and her eyes blazed green with anger and determination. He had early on discovered that the infallible means of making anything irresistibly attractive was to deny it to Kitty Godolphin. He knew that now she would lie, cheat or sell her soul to get into the *Sperrgebiet*.

'You could smuggle us in,' she suggested.

He shook his head. 'Not worth the risk. We might get away with it, but if I were caught it could mean a fine of £100,000 or five years in the slammer.'

She laid her hand on his arm, the first time she had deliberately touched him. 'Please, Shasa. I want so badly to film it.'

He shook his head sorrowfully. 'I'm sorry, Kitty, can't be done, I'm afraid,' and he stood up. 'Got to go up and change for dinner. You can break it to your crew while I'm away. Your flight back to Jo'burg leaves ten o'clock tomorrow.'

It was obvious at the dinner-table that she hadn't warned her crew of the change of plans, for they were still jovial and garrulous with good German beer.

For once Kitty took no part in the conversation, and she sat morosely at the end of the table, nibbling without interest at the hearty Teutonic fare and occasionally darting a sulky glance at Shasa. David skipped coffee to go and make his nightly phone call to Matty and the children, and Hank and his crew had been told of a local night spot with hot music and even hotter hostesses.

'Ten days with no feminine company except the boss,' Hank complained. 'My nerves need soothing.'

'Remember where you are,' Shasa warned him. 'In this country black velvet is royal game.'

'Some of the poontang I've seen today would be worth five years' hard labour,' Hank leered.

'Did you know that we have a South African version of Russian roulette?' Shasa asked him. 'What you do is take a coloured girl into a telephone booth. Then you phone the police flying squad and see who comes first.'

Kitty was the only one who didn't laugh, and Shasa stood up. 'I've got some papers to go over. We'll save the farewells until breakfast.'

In his suite he shaved and showered quickly, then slipped on a silk dressing-gown. As he went through to check that there was ice in the bar, there was a light tap on the door of the suite.

Kitty stood on the threshold looking tragic.

'Am I disturbing you?'

'No, of course not.' He held the door open and she crossed the lounge and stood staring out of the window.

'Can I get you a night-cap?' Shasa asked.

'What are you drinking?' she asked.

'A rusty nail.'

'I'll have one also – whatever it is.'

While he mixed Drambuie and malt whisky, she said, 'I came to thank you

for everything you've done for me these last ten days. It's going to be hard to say goodbye.'

He carried the glasses across to where she stood in the middle of the floor, but when he reached her she took both glasses from him and placed them on the coffee table. Then she stood on tiptoe, slid both arms around his neck and turned her face up for his kiss.

Her lips were soft and sweet as warm chocolate, and slowly she pushed her tongue deeply into his mouth. When at last their mouths parted with a little wet sucking sound, he stooped and hooked an arm around the back of her knees and lifted her against his chest. She clung to him, pressing her face against his throat as he carried her through to the bedroom.

She had the lean hips and flat belly of a boy, and her buttocks were white and round and hard as a pair of ostrich eggs. Like her face, her body seemed childlike and immature except for those tight little pear-shaped breasts and the startling burst of thick dark hair at the base of her belly, but when he touched her there he found to his surprise that it was fine as silk and soft as smoke.

Her love-making was so artful as to seem totally uncontrived and spontaneous. She had the trick of telling him exactly what he was doing to her in the coarsest barnyard terms, and the obscenities on that soft innocent-looking mouth were shockingly erotic. She took him to those heights that he had seldom scaled before, and left him completely satiated.

In the dawn glow she snuggled against him and whispered, 'I don't know how I am going to be able to bear being parted from you after this.'

He could see her face in the wall mirror across the room, although she was unaware of his scrutiny. 'Damn it – I can't let you go,' he whispered back. 'I don't care what it costs I'm taking you down to the *Sperrgebiet* with me.'

In the mirror he watched her smile, a complacent and smug little smile. He had been correct, Kitty Godolphin used her sexual favours like trumps in a game of bridge.

At the airport her crew were packing their equipment into the Dove under David Abrahams' supervision when Shasa and Kitty drove up in the second company car, and Kitty jumped out and went to David.

'How are you going to work it, Davie?' she asked, and he looked puzzled.

'I don't understand the question.'

'You'll have to fake the flight plan, won't you?' Kitty insisted. Still mystified, David glanced at Shasa. Shasa shrugged and Kitty became exasperated.

'You know very well what I mean. How are you going to cover the fact that we are going into the *Sperrgebiet* without permits?'

'Without permits?' David echoed, and fished a handful of documents out of the zip pocket of his leather flying-jacket. 'Here are the permits. They were issued a week ago – all kosher and correct.'

Kitty wheeled and glared speechlessly at Shasa, but he refused to meet her eyes and instead ambled off to make his walk-around check of the Mosquito.

They didn't speak to each other again until Shasa had the Mosquito at twenty thousand feet, flying straight and level, then Kitty said into his earphones, 'You son of a bitch.' Her voice shook with fury.

'Kitty, my darling.' He turned and smiled at her over the oxygen mask, his single eye glinting happily. 'We both got what we wanted, and had a lot of fun in the process. What are you so mad about?'

She turned her face away and stared down at the magnificent lion-coloured mountains of the *Khama's Hochtland*. He left her to sulk. Some minutes later

he heard an unusual stuttering sound in his headset, and he frowned and leaned forward to adjust the radio. Then, from the corner of his eye he saw that Kitty was hunched up in the seat shaking uncontrollably and that the stuttering sound was coming from her.

He touched her shoulder and she turned her face to him, it was swollen and crimson with suppressed laughter and tears of mirth were squeezing out of the corners of her eyes with the pressure. She couldn't hold it any longer, and she let out a snort.

'You crafty bastard,' she sobbed. 'Oh, you tricky monster – ' and then she became incoherent as laughter overwhelmed her.

A long time later she wiped away her tears. 'We are going to get on just fine together, you and me,' she declared. 'Our minds work the same way.'

'Our bodies don't do too badly either,' he pointed out, and she unclipped her oxygen mask and leaned across to offer him her mouth again. Her tongue was sinuous and slippery as an eel.

* * *

Their time in the desert together passed too swiftly for Shasa, for since they had become lovers he found her a constant joy to be with. Her quick and curious mind stimulated his own, and through her observant eyes he saw old familiar things afresh.

Together they watched and filmed the elephantine yellow caterpillar tractors ripping the elevated terraces that had once been the ocean bed. He explained to Kitty how in the time when the crust of the earth was soft and the molten magma still burst through to the surface, the diamonds, conceived at great depth and heat and pressure, were carried up with this sulphurous outpouring.

In the endless rains of those ancient times the great rivers scoured the earth, running down to the sea, washing the diamonds down with them, until they collected in the pockets and irregularities of the seabed closest to the river mouth. As the emerging continent shrugged and shifted, so the old seabed was lifted above the surface. The rivers had long ago dried up or been diverted, and sediment covered the elevated terraces, concealing the diamond-bearing pockets. It had taken the genius of Twentyman-Jones to work out the old river courses. Using aerial photography and an inherent sixth sense, he had pinpointed the ancient terraces.

Kitty and her team filmed the process by which the sand and rubble churned up by the dozer blades was screened and sieved, and finally dry-blown with great multi-bladed fans, until only the precious stones – one part in tens of millions – remained.

In the desert nights the mine hutments, lacking air-conditioning, were too hot for sleep. Shasa made a nest of blankets out amongst the dunes, and with the faint peppery smell of the desert in their nostrils, they made love under a blaze of stars.

On their last day Shasa commandeered one of the company jeeps and they drove out into a land of red dunes, the highest in all the world, sculptured by the incessant winds off the cold Benguela Current, their ridges crested like living reptiles as they writhed high against the pale desert sky.

Shasa pointed out to Kitty a herd of gemsbok, each antelope large as a pony,

but with a marvellously patterned face mask of black and white and slender horns, straight and long as they were tall, that were the original unicorn of the fable. They were beautiful beasts, so adapted to their harsh country that they need never drink from surface water, but could survive only on the moisture they obtained from the silvery sun-scorched grasses. They watched them dissolve magically into the heat mirage, turning to squirming black tadpoles on the horizon before they disappeared.

'I was born here. Somewhere in these deserts,' Shasa told her as they stood hand in hand on the crest of one of the dunes and looked down a thousand feet to where they had left the jeep in the gut of the sand mountains.

He told her how Centaine had carried him in her womb through this terrible terrain, lost and abandoned, with only two little Bushmen as her guides and companions, and how the Bushwoman, for whom the H'ani Mine was named, acted as midwife at his birth and named him Shasa – 'Good Water' – after the most precious substance in her world.

The beauty and the grandeur affected them both so they drew close together in the solitude, and by the end of the day Shasa was sure that he truly loved her and that he wanted to spend the rest of his life with her.

Together they watched the sun sink towards the red dunes and the sky turned to a screen of hot hammered bronze, dented with flecks of blue cloud as though by blows from a celestial blacksmith's hammer. As the sky cooled, the colours chameleoned into puce and orange and lofty purples until the sun sank behind the dunes – and at the instant it disappeared, a miracle occurred.

They both gasped in wonder as in a silent explosion the entire heavens flared into electric green. It lasted only as long as they held their breath, but in that time the sky was as green as the ocean depths or the ice in the gaping cracks of a high mountain glacier. Then it faded swiftly into the drab gun-metal of dusk, and Kitty turned to him with a silent question in her eyes.

'We saw it together,' Shasa said softly. 'The Bushmen call it the Green Python. A man can live a lifetime in the desert without seeing it. I have never witnessed it, not until this moment.'

'What does it mean?' Kitty asked.

'The Bushmen say it is the most fortuitous of all good omens.' He reached out and took her hand. 'They say that those who see the Green Python will be specially blessed – and we saw it together.'

In the fading light they went down the slip face of the dune to where Shasa had parked the jeep. They sank almost knee-deep in the fluffy sun-warm sand, and laughing they clung to each other for support.

When they reached the jeep, Shasa took her by the shoulders, turned her to face him and told her, 'I don't want it to end, Kitty. Come with me. Marry me. I'll give you everything that life has to offer.'

She threw back her head to laugh in his face. 'Don't be daft, Shasa Courtney. What I want from life isn't yours to give,' she told him. 'This was fun, but it wasn't reality. We can be good friends for as long as you want, but our feet are set on different paths, and we aren't going in the same direction.'

The next day when they landed at Windhoek airport, a telegram addressed to her was pinned to the board in the crew room. Kitty read it swiftly. When she looked up she wasn't seeing Shasa any longer.

'There is another story breaking,' she said. 'I have to go.'

'When will I see you again?' Shasa asked, and she looked at him as though he were a complete stranger.

'I don't know,' she said, and she and her crew were on the commercial flight that left for Johannesburg an hour later.

* * *

Shasa was angry and humiliated. He had never offered to divorce Tara for any other woman – had never even contemplated it – and Kitty had laughed at him.

There were well-explored avenues down which he knew he could cure his anger, one was the hunt. For Shasa nothing else existed in the world when the hunter's passion thrilled in his blood, when a bull buffalo, big as a mountain and black as hell, came thundering down upon him, bloody saliva drooling from its raised muzzle, the polished points of its curved horns glinting, and murder in its small piglike eyes. However, this was the rainy season and the hunting grounds in the north would be muggy wet and malarial, and the grass high above a man's head. He could not hunt so he turned to his other sure panacea, the pursuit of wealth.

Money held endless fascination for Shasa. Without that obsessive attraction he could not have accumulated such a vast store of it, for that required a devotion and dedication that few men are capable of. Those that lack it console themselves with old platitudes about it not buying happiness and being the root of all evil. As an adept, Shasa knew that money was neither good nor evil, but simply amoral. He knew that money had no conscience, but that it contained the most powerful potential for both good and evil. It was the man who possessed it who made the ultimate choice between them, and that choice was called power.

Even when he had believed himself to be totally absorbed with Kitty Godolphin, his instinct had been in play. Almost subconsciously he had noticed those tiny white specks way out on the green Benguela Current of the Atlantic. Kitty Godolphin had not been gone from his life for an hour before he stormed into the offices of Courtney Mining and Finance in Windhoek's main street and started demanding figures and documents, making telephone calls, summoning lawyers and accountants, calling in favours from men in high places in government, despatching his minions to search the archives of the registrar and the local newspapers, assembling the tools of his trade, facts, figures and influence, and then losing himself happily in them, like an opium-eater with his pipe.

It was another five days before he was ready to bring it all together, and make the final weighing up. He had kept David Abrahams with him, for David was an excellent sounding-board in a situation like this one, and Shasa liked to bounce ideas off him and catch the returns.

'So this is what it looks like,' Shasa began the summing up. There were five of them in the boardroom, sitting under the magnificent Pierneef murals that Centaine had commissioned when the artist was in his prime, Shasa and David, the local manager and secretary of Courtney Mining, and the German lawyer based in Windhoek whom Shasa kept on permanent retainer.

'It looks like we have been asleep on our feet. In the last three years an industry has sprung up under our noses, an industry that last year alone netted twenty million pounds, four times the profits of the H'ani Mine, and we have let it happen.'

He glowered cyclops-eyed at his local manager for an explanation.

'We were aware of the recommencement of the fishing industry at Walvis Bay,' that unfortunate gentleman sought to explain. 'The explanation for pilchard trawling licences was gazetted, but I didn't think that fishing would match up with our other activities.'

'With due respect, Frank, that's the kind of decision I like to make myself. It's your job to pass on all information, of whatever nature, to me.' It was said quietly, but the three local men had no illusions as to the severity of the reprimand and they bowed their heads over their notepads. There was silence for ten seconds while Shasa let them suffer.

'Right, Frank,' Shasa ordered him. 'Tell us now what you should have told us four or five years ago.'

'Well, Mr Courtney, the pilchard-fishing industry was started in the early 1930s at Walvis Bay and although initially successful, it was overtaken by the depression, and with the primitive trawling methods of those days was unable to survive. The factories closed down and became derelict.'

As Frank spoke, Shasa's mind went back to his childhood. He remembered his first visit to Walvis Bay and blinked with the realization that it had been twenty years ago. He and Centaine had driven down in her daffodil-coloured Daimler to call in the loan she had made to De La Rey's canning and fishing company and to close down the factory. Those were the desperate years of the depression when the Courtney companies had survived only through his mother's pluck and determination – and ruthlessness.

He remembered how Lothar De La Rey, Manfred's father, had pleaded with his mother for an extension of the loan. When his trawlers lay against the wharf, loaded to the gunwales with their catch of silver pilchards, and the sheriff of the court, on Centaine's orders, had put his seals on the factory doors.

That was the day he had first met Manfred De La Rey. Manfred had been a bare-footed, cropped-head hulk of a lad, bigger and stronger than Shasa, burned dark by the sun, dressed in a navy-blue fisherman's jersey and khaki shorts that were smeared with dried fish-slime, while Shasa had worn immaculate grey slacks, white open neck shirt and a college sweater with polished black shoes on his feet.

Two boys from different worlds, they had come face to face on the main fish wharf and their hostility had been instantaneous, their hackles rising like dogs, and within minutes, gibes and insults had turned to blows and they had flown at each other furiously, punching and wrestling down the wharf while the coloured trawlermen had egged them on delightedly. He remembered clearly even after all this time Manfred De La Rey's pale ferocious eyes glaring into his as they fell from the wharf on to the slippery, stinking cargo of dead pilchards, and he felt again the dreadful humiliation as Manfred had forced his head deeply into the quagmire of cold dead fish and he had begun to drown in their slime.

He jerked his mind back to the present, to hear his manager saying, 'So the position is now that the government has issued four factory licenses to catch and process pilchards at Walvis Bay. The department of fisheries allocates an annual quota to each of the licensees, which is presently two hundred thousand tons.' Shasa contemplated the enormous profit potential of those quantities of fish. According to their published accounts, each of those four factories had averaged two million pounds profit in the last fiscal year. He knew he could improve on that, probably double it, but it didn't look as though he was going to get the chance.

'Approaches to both the Fisheries Department, and to higher authority – ' Shasa had taken the administrator of the territory himself to dinner, 'have elicited the firm fact that no further licences will be issued. The only way to enter the industry would be to buy out one of the licensees.' Shasa smiled sardonically for he had already sounded out two of the companies. The owner of the first one had told Shasa in movingly eloquent terms to commit an unnatural sexual act on himself and the other had quoted a figure at which he might be prepared to negotiate which ended with a string of zeros that reached to the horizon. Despite his gloomy expression, it was the kind of situation in which Shasa revelled, seemingly hopeless, and yet with the promise of enormous rewards if he could find his way around the obstacles.

'I want a detailed breakdown of balance sheets on all four companies,' he ordered. 'Does anybody know the director of fisheries?'

'Yes, but he's straight up and down,' Frank warned him, knowing how Shasa's mind worked. 'His fists are tight closed, and if we try to slip him a little gifty, he'll raise a stink they'll smell in the high court in Bloemfontein.'

'Besides which the issue of licences is outside his jurisdiction,' the company secretary agreed with him. 'They are granted exclusively by the ministry in Pretoria, and there won't be any more. Four is the limit. That is the decision of the minister himself.'

Five more days Shasa remained in Windhoek, covering every possible lead or chance with a total dedication to detail that was one of his strengths, but at the end of that time he was no closer to owning a factory licence at Walvis Bay than he had been when he had first spotted the little white trawlers out on the green ocean. The only thing he had achieved was to forget that malignant little sprite, Kitty Godolphin, for ten whole days.

However, when at last he admitted to himself that there was nothing more to be gained by staying on in Windhoek and he climbed into the pilot's seat of the Mosquito, Kitty Godolphin's memory mocked him from the empty seat beside him. On impulse, instead of laying a course direct to Cape Town, he detoured westwards, heading for the coast and Walvis Bay, determined to have one long look at the site before finally abandoning the idea.

There was something else beside Kitty's memory that plagued him as the Mosquito dropped down the escarpment towards the sea. It was a burr of doubt, a prickle of discomfort that he had overlooked something important in his investigations.

He saw the ocean ahead, wreathed in tendrils of fog where the cold current brushed the land. The high dunes writhed together like a nest of razor-backed vipers, the colour of ripe wheat and copper, and he banked the Mosquito and followed the endless beaches upon which the surf broke in regular snowy lines until he saw the horn of the bay spike into the restless ocean and the lighthouse on Pelican Point winked at him through the fog banks.

He throttled back the Rolls Royce Merlins and went down, brushing the tops of the scattered fog banks and in the gaps he saw the trawler fleet at work. They were close in to the land, on the edge of the current line. Some of the boats had their nets full, and he saw the silver treasure glittering through the water as the trawlermen raised it slowly to the surface, while over them hung a shimmering white panoply of seabirds greedy for the feast.

Then a mile away he picked out another boat hunting, cutting a foaming arabesque with its wake as it stalked yet another pilchard shoal.

Shasa pulled on flap and banked the Mosquito steeply, turning above the

trawler to watch the hunt develop. He saw the shoal, a dark shadow as though a thousand gallons of ink had been spilled into the green waters, and he was amazed by its size, a hundred acres of solid fish, each individual no longer than his hand, but in their multitudes dwarfing leviathan.

'Millions of tons in one shoal,' he whispered. As he translated it into terms of wealth, the acquisitive passion flared up in him again. He watched the trawler beneath him throw its net around a tiny part of the gigantic shoal, and then he levelled out and flew at a hundred feet, skimming the fog banks, towards the maw of the bay. There were the four factory buildings, standing on the edge of the water, each with its own jetty thrusting out into the shallow waters, and black smoke billowing from the chimney stacks of the furnaces.

'Which one belonged to old De La Rey?' he wondered. On which of those flimsy structures had he fought with Manfred and ended with his ears and nose and mouth filled with fish slime? He grinned ruefully at the memory.

'But surely it was farther north,' he puzzled, trying to cast his mind back twenty years. 'It wasn't down here so close to the hook of the bay.' He banked the Mosquito and flew back parallel to the beach, and then a mile ahead he saw the line of palings, rotted and black, running in an irregular line out into the waters of the bay, and on the beach the roofless old ruins of the factory.

'It's still there,' he realized, and instantly his skin prickled with excitement. 'It's still there, deserted and forgotten all these years.' He knew then what he had overlooked.

He made two more passes, so low that the blast of his propellers raised a miniature sandstorm from the tops of the dunes. On the seaward wall of the derelict factory whose corrugated iron covering was gnawed and streaked with red rust, he could still make out the faded lettering: SOUTH WEST AFRICAN CANNING AND FISHING CO. LTD.

He pushed on throttle and lifted the Mosquito's nose into a gentle climbing turn, bringing her out of the turn on course for Windhoek. Cape Town and his promise to his sons and Isabella to be home before the weekend were forgotten. David Abrahams had flown the Dove back to Johannesburg, leaving a few minutes before Shasa that morning, so there was nobody in Windhoek whom Shasa would trust to conduct the search. He went down to the registrar of deeds himself and an hour before the deed office closed for the weekend he found what he was looking for.

The licence to capture and process pilchards and all other pelagic fish was dated 20 September 1929 and signed by the administrator of the territory. It was made out in favour of one Lothar De La Rey of Windhoek, and there was no term of expiry. It was good now and for all time.

Shasa stroked the crackling, yellowing document, smoothing out the crumples in it lovingly, admiring the crimson revenue stamps and the administrator's fading signature. Here in these musty drawers it had lain for over twenty years – and he tried to put a value on this scrap of paper. A million pounds, certainly – five million pounds, perhaps. He chuckled triumphantly and took it to the deeds clerk to have a notorized copy made.

'It will cost you a pretty penny, sir,' the clerk sniffed. 'Ten and six for the copy and two pounds for the attestation.'

'It's a high price,' Shasa agreed, 'but I can just afford it.'

* * *

Lothar De La Rey came bounding up the wet black rocks, surefooted as a mountain goat, dressed only in a pair of black woollen bathing trunks. In one hand he carried a light fishing rod and in the other he held the trace on the end of which a small silver fish fluttered.

'I've got one, Pa,' he called excitedly, and Manfred De La Rey roused himself. He had been lost in thought; even on this, one of his rare vacations, his mind was still concentrated on the work of his ministry.

'Well done, Lothie.' He stood up and picked up the heavy bamboo surf rod that lay beside him. He watched his son gently unhook the small bait fish and hand it to him. He took it from him. It was cold and firm and slippery, and when he pressed the sharp point of his large hook through the flesh, the tiny dorsal fin along its back came erect and its struggles were frantic.

'Man, no old kob will be able to resist that,' Manfred held the live bait up for his son to admire. 'It looks so good, I could eat it myself.' He picked up the heavy rod.

For a minute he watched the surf break on the rocks below them, and then timing his moment he ran down to the edge, moving lightly for such a big man. The foam sucked at his ankles as he poised, and then swung the bamboo rod in a full whipping action. The cast was long and high, the live bait sparkled as it spun a parabola in the sunlight and then hit the green water a hundred yards out, beyond the first line of breakers.

Manfred ran back as the next wave dashed head-high at him. With the rod over his shoulder and line still streaming from the big Scarborough reel he beat the angry white surf and regained his seat high up on the rocks.

He thrust the butt of the rod into a crack in the rocks and jammed his old stained felt hat against the reel to hold it. Then he settled down on his cushion with his back to the rock and his son beside him.

'Good kob water,' he grunted. The sea was discoloured and cloudy, like home-made ginger beer, the perfect conditions for the quarry they were seeking.

'I promised Ma we would bring her a fish for pickling,' Lothar said.

'Never count your kob before it's in the pickle barrel,' Manfred counselled, and the boy laughed.

Manfred never touched him in front of others, not even in front of his mother and the girls, but he remembered the enormous pleasure it had given him when he was Lothar's age to have his own father's embrace, and so at times when they were alone together like this he would let his true feelings show. He let his arm slip down off the rock and fall around the boy's shoulders and Lother froze with joy and for a minute did not dare to breathe. Then slowly he leaned closer to his father and in silence they watched the tip of the long rod nod in rhythm to the ocean.

'And so, Lothie, have you decided what you want to do with your life when you leave Paul Roos?' Paul Roos was the leading Afrikaans medium school in the Cape Province, the South African equivalent of Eton or Harrow for Afrikaners.

'Pa, I've been thinking,' Lothar was serious. 'I don't want to do law like you did, and I think medicine will be too difficult.'

Manfred nodded resignedly. He had come to terms with the fact that Lothar was not academically brilliant, but just a good average student. It was in all the other fields that he excelled. Already it was clear that his powers of leadership, his determination and courage, and his athletic prowess were all exceptional.

'I want to join the police,' the boy said hesitantly. 'When I finish at Paul Roos, I want to go to the police academy in Pretoria.'

Manfred sat quietly, trying to hide his surprise. It was probably the last thing he would have thought of himself.

At last he said. '*Ja*, why not! You'd do well there.' He nodded. 'It's a good life, a life of service to your country and your *Volk*.' The more he thought about it, the more he realized that Lothar was making a perfect choice – and of course, the fact that his father was minister of police wouldn't hurt the boy's career either. He hoped he would stick to it. '*Ja*,' he repeated, 'I like it.'

'Pa, I wanted to ask you – ' Lothar started, and the tip of the rod jerked, bounced straight, and then arced over boldly. Manfred's old hat was thrown clear of the spinning reel as the line hissed from it in a blur.

Father and son leapt to their feet and Manfred seized the heavy bamboo and leaned back against it to set the hook.

'It's a monster,' he shouted, as he felt the weight of the fish, and the flow of line never checked, even when he thrust the palm of the leather mitten he wore against the flange of the reel to brake it. Within seconds blue smoke burned from the friction reel and leather glove.

When it seemed that the last few turns of line would be stripped from the spindle of the reel, the fish stopped, and two hundred yards out there under the smoky grey waters it shook its head doggedly so the rod butt kicked against Manfred's belly.

With Lothar dancing at his side, howling encouragement and advice, Manfred winched in the fish, pumping the rod to recover a few turns of line at a time, until the reel was almost full again and he expected to see the quarry thrashing in the surf below the rocks. Then suddenly the fish made another long heavy run, and he had to begin the laborious back-straining task all over again.

At last they saw it, deep in the water below the rocks, its side shining like a great mirror as it caught the sun. With the rod bent taut as a longbow, Manfred forced it up until it flapped ponderously, washing back and forth in the suck and thrust of the waves, gleaming in marvellous iridescent shades of rose and pearl, its great jaws gaping with exhaustion.

'The gaff!' Manfred shouted. 'Now, Lothie, now!' and the boy sprang down to the water's edge with the long pole in his hands and buried the point of the gaff hook into the fish's shoulder, just behind the gills. A flush of blood stained the waters pink, and then Manfred threw down his rod and jumped down to help Lothar with the gaff pole.

Between them they dragged the fish, flapping and thumping, up the rocks above the high-water mark.

'He's a hundred pounds if he's an ounce,' Lothar exulted. 'Ma and the girls will be up till midnight pickling this one.'

Lothar carried the rods and the fishing box while Manfred slung the fish over his shoulder, a short loop of rope through its gills, and they trudged back around the curve of white beach. On the rocks of the next headland, Manfred lowered the fish for a few minutes to rest. Once he had been Olympic light heavyweight champion but he had fleshed out since those days, his belly was softening and spreading and his breath was short.

'Too much time behind my desk,' he thought ruefully, and sank down on a black boulder. As he mopped his face he looked around him.

This place always gave him pleasure. It grieved him that he could find so little time in his busy life to come here. In their old student days he and Roelf

Stander, his best friend, had fished and hunted on this wild unspoiled stretch of coast. It had belonged to Roelf's family for a hundred years, and Roelf would never have sold the smallest piece of it to anybody but Manfred.

In the end he had sold Manfred a hundred acres for one pound. 'I don't want to get rich on an old friend,' he had laughed away Manfred's offer of a thousand. 'Just let us have a clause in the contract of sale that I have a right of first option to buy it back at the same price at your death or whenever you want to sell.'

There beyond the headland on which they sat was the cottage that he and Heidi had built, white stucco walls and thatch, the only sign of human habitation. Roelf's own holiday house was hidden beyond the next headland, but within easy walking distance so they could be together whenever both families were on holiday at the same time.

There were so many memories here. He looked out to sea. That was where the German U-boat had surfaced when it had brought him back in the early days of the war. Roelf had been on the beach, waiting for him, and had rowed out in the darkness to fetch him and his equipment ashore. What mad exciting days those had been, the danger and the fighting, as they had struggled to raise the Afrikaner *Volk* in rebellion against the English-lover Jan Christian Smuts, and to declare South Africa a republic under the protection of Nazi Germany – and how very close they had come to success.

He smiled and his eyes glowed at the memory. He wished he could tell the boy about it. Lothie would understand. Young as he was, he would understand the Afrikaner dream of republic and he would be proud. However that was a story that could never be told. Manfred's attempt to assassinate Jan Smuts and precipitate the rebellion had failed. He had been forced to fly the country, and to languish for the rest of the war in a far-off land, while Roelf and the other patriots had been branded traitors and hustled into Jannie Smuts' internment camps, humiliated and reviled until the war ended.

How it had all changed. Now they were the lords of this land, although nobody outside the inner circle knew the part that Manfred De La Rey had played in those dangerous years. They were the overlords, and once again the dream of republic burned brightly, like a flame on the altar of Afrikaner aspirations.

His thoughts were broken up by the roar of a low-flying aircraft overhead, and Manfred looked up. It was a sleek blue and silver machine, turning away steeply to line up for the airstrip that lay just beyond the first line of hills. The airstrip had been built by the public works department when Manfred had achieved full ministerial rank. It was essential that he was in close contact with his department at all times, and from that landing-field an airforce plane could fetch him within hours if he were needed in an emergency.

Manfred recognized this machine and knew who was flying it, but frowned with annoyance as he stood up and hefted the huge carcass of the fish again. He treasured the isolation of this place, and fiercely resented any unwarranted intrusion. He and Lothar set off on the last leg of the long haul back to the cottage.

Heidi and the girls saw them coming, and ran down the dunes to meet them and then surrounded Manfred, laughing and squealing their congratulations. He plodded up the soft dunes, with the girls skipping beside him, and hung the fish on the scaffold outside the kitchen door. While Heidi went to fetch her Kodak camera, Manfred stripped off his shirt which was stained with fish blood

and stooped to the tap of the rainwater tank and washed the blood from his hand and the salt from his face.

As he straightened up again, with water dripping from his hair and running down his bare chest, he was abruptly aware of the presence of a stranger.

'Get me a towel, Ruda,' he snapped, and his eldest daughter ran to his bidding.

'I was not expecting you.' Manfred glowered at Shasa Courtney. 'My family and I like to be alone here.'

'Forgive me. I know I am intruding.' Shasa's shoes were floury with dust. It was a mile walk from the airstrip. 'I am sure you will understand when I explain that my business is urgent and private.'

Manfred scrubbed his face with the towel while he mastered his annoyance, and then, when Heidi came out with the camera in her hand, he introduced her gruffly.

Within minutes Shasa had charmed both Heidi and the girls into smiles, but Lothar stood behind his father and only came forward reluctantly to shake hands. He had learned from his father to be suspicious of Englishmen.

'What a tremendous kob,' Shasa admired the fish on the scaffold. 'One of the biggest I have seen in years. You don't often get them that size any more. Where did you catch it?'

Shasa insisted on taking the photographs of the whole family grouped around the fish. Manfred was still bare-chested, and Shasa noticed the old bluish puckered scar in the side of his chest. It looked like a gunshot wound, but there had been a war and many men bore scars of that nature now. Thinking of war wounds, he adjusted his own eye-patch self-consciously as he handed the camera back to Heidi.

'You will stay to lunch, *Meneer*?' she asked demurely.

'I don't want to be a nuisance.'

'You are welcome.' She was a handsome woman, with a large high bosom and wide fruitful hips. Her hair was dense and golden blond, and she wore it in a thick plaited rope that hung almost to her waist, but Shasa saw Manfred De La Rey's expression and quickly transferred all his attention back to him.

'My wife is right. You are welcome.' Manfred's natural Afrikaner duty of hospitality left him no choice. 'Come, we will go to the front stoep until the women call for us to eat.'

Manfred fetched two bottles of beer from the ice-chest and they sat in deckchairs, side by side, and looked out over the dunes to the wind-flecked blue of the Indian Ocean.

'Do you remember where we first met, you and I?' Shasa broke the silence.

'*Ja*,' Manfred nodded. 'I remember very well.'

'I was back there two days ago.'

'Walvis Bay?'

'Yes. To the canning factory, the jetty where we fought,' Shasa hesitated, 'where you thumped me, and pushed my head into a mess of dead fish.'

Manfred smiled with satisfaction at the memory. '*Ja*, I remember.'

Shasa had to control his temper carefully. It still rankled and the man's smugness infuriated him, but the memory of his childhood victory had softened Manfred's mood as Shasa had intended it should.

'Strange how we were enemies then, and now we are allies,' Shasa persisted, and let him think about that for a while before he went on. 'I have most carefully considered the offer you made to me. Although it is difficult for a man

to change sides, and many people will put the worst construction on my motives, I now see that it is my duty to my country to do what you suggest and to employ what talent I have for the good of the nation.'

'So you will accept the prime minister's offer?'

'Yes, you may tell the prime minister that I will join the government, but in my own time and my own way. I will not cross the floor of the House, but as soon as parliament is dissolved for the coming elections, I will resign from the United Party to stand for the National Party.'

'Good,' Manfred nodded. 'That is the honourable way.'

But there was no honourable way, Shasa realized, and was silent for a moment before he went on.

'I am grateful for your part in this, *Meneer*. I know that you have been instrumental in affording me this opportunity. In view of what has happened between our families, it is an extraordinary gesture you have made.'

'There was nothing personal in my decision.' Manfred shook his head. 'It was simply a case of the best man for the job. I have not forgotten what your family has done to mine – and I never will.'

'I will not forget either,' Shasa said softly. 'I have inherited guilt – rightly or wrongly, I will never be sure. However, I would like to make some reparation to your father.'

'How would you do that, *Meneer*?' Manfred asked stiffly. 'How would you compensate a man for the loss of his arm and for all those years spent in prison? How will you pay a man for the damage to his soul that captivity has inflicted?'

'I can never full compensate him,' Shasa agreed. 'However, suddenly and unexpectedly I have been given the opportunity to restore to your father a large part of that which was taken from him.'

'Go on,' Manfred invited. 'I am listening.'

'Your father was issued a fishing licence in 1929. I have searched the records. That licence is still valid.'

'What would the old man do with a fishing licence now? You don't understand – he is physically and mentally ruined.'

'The fishing industry out of Walvis Bay has revived and is booming. The number of licences has been severly limited. Your father's licence is worth a great deal of money.'

He saw the shift in Manfred's eyes, the little sparks of interest swiftly screened.

'You think my father should sell it?' he asked heavily. 'And by any chance would you be interested in buying it?' He smiled sarcastically.

Shasa nodded. 'Yes, of course I'd like to buy it, but that might not be best for your father.' Manfred's smile withered, he hadn't expected that.

'What else could he do with it?'

'We could re-open the factory and work the licence together as partners. Your father puts up the licence, and I put up the capital and my business skills. Within a year or two, your father's share will almost certainly be worth a million pounds.'

Shasa watched him carefully as he said it. This was more, much more than a business offer. It was a testing. Shasa wanted to reach beyond the man's granite crust, that monumental armour of puritanical righteousness. He wanted to probe for weaknesses, to find any chinks that he could exploit later.

'A million pounds,' he repeated. 'Perhaps even a great deal more.' And he saw the sparks in the other man's fierce pale eyes again, just for an instant, the

little yellow sparks of greed. The man was human after all. 'I can deal with him now,' Shasa thought, and to cover his relief he lifted his briefcase from the floor beside his deckchair and opened it on his lap.

'I have worked out a rough agreement – ' he took out a sheaf of typed blue foolscap sheets ' – you could show it to your father, discuss it with him.'

Manfred took the sheets from him. '*Ja*, I will see him when I return home next week.'

'There is one small problem,' Shasa admitted. 'This licence was issued a long time ago. The government department may wish to repudiate it. It is their policy to allow only four licences – '

Manfred looked up from the contract. 'That will be no problem,' Manfred said, and Shasa lifted his beer tankard to hide his smile. They had just shared their first secret. Manfred De La Rey was going to use his influence for personal gain. Like a lost virginity, the next time would be easier.

Shasa had realized from the beginning that he would be an outsider in a cabinet of Afrikaner Nationalists. He desperately needed a trustworthy ally amongst them, and if that ally could be linked to him by shared financial blessings and a few off-colour secrets, then his loyalty would be secured. Shasa had just achieved this, with the promise of vast profits to himself to sweeten the bargain. A good day's work, he thought, as he closed the briefcase with a snap.

'Very good, *Meneer*. I'm grateful to you for having given me your time. Now I will leave you to enjoy what remains of your holiday undisturbed.'

Manfred looked up. '*Meneer*, my wife is preparing lunch for us. She will be very unhappy if you leave so soon.' At last his smile was genial. 'And this evening I will have a few good friends visit me for a *braaivleis*, a barbecue. There are plenty of spare beds. Stay the night. You can leave early tomorrow morning.'

'You are very kind.' Shasa sank back in his chair. The feeling between them had changed, but Shasa's intuition warned him there were hidden depths in their relationship which still had to be plumbed, and as he smiled into Manfred De La Rey's topaz-coloured eyes, he felt a sudden small chill, a cold wind through a chink in his memory. Those eyes haunted him. He was trying to remember something. It remained obscure but somehow strangely menacing. Could it have been from their childhood fight? he wondered. But he did not think so. The memory was closer than that, and more threatening. He almost grasped it, and then Manfred looked down at the contract again, almost as though he had sensed what Shasa was searching for, and the shape of the memory slipped away beyond Shasa's grasp.

Heidi De La Rey came out on to the verandah in her apron, but she had changed out of her faded old skirt and twisted her plaited hair up on top of her head.

'Lunch is ready – and I do hope you eat fish, Meneer Courtney.'

Shasa set out to charm the family during lunch. Heidi and the girls were easy. The boy Lothar was different, suspicious and withdrawn. However, Shasa had three sons of his own, and he drew him out with stories of flying and hunting big game, until despite himself the boy's eyes shone with interest and admiration.

When they rose from the table, Manfred nodded grudgingly. '*Ja, Meneer*, I must remember never to underestimate you.'

That evening a small group comprising a man and a woman and four children

came straggling over the dunes from the south, and Manfred's children rushed out to meet them and lead them up on to the verandah of the cottage.

Shasa stayed in the background throughout the noisy greetings of the two families. Theirs was obviously a close relationship of long standing.

Of course, Shasa recognized the head of the family. He was a big man, even heavier in build than Manfred De La Rey. Like him, he had also been a member of the boxing team that had participated in the Berlin Olympic Games of 1936. He had been a senior lecturer in law at Stellenbosch University, but had recently resigned to become a junior partner in the firm of Van Schoor, De La Rey and Stander, the firm in which Manfred De La Rey had become the senior partner after the death of old Van Schoor some years before.

Apart from his law practice, Roelf Stander acted as Manfred's chief party organizer and had managed Manfred's 1948 campaign for him. Although not himself a member of parliament, he was a leg man of the National Party and Shasa knew that he was almost certainly a member of the *Broederbond*, the Brotherhood, that clandestine society of elite Afrikaners.

When Manfred De La Rey began to introduce them, Shasa saw that Roelf Stander recognized him and looked a little sheepish.

'I hope you aren't going to throw eggs at me again, Meneer Stander,' Shasa challenged him, and Roelf chuckled.

'Only if you make another bad speech, Meneer Courtney.'

During the 1948 election, in which Shasa had been defeated by Manfred De La Rey, this man had organized the gang of bully boys who had broken up Shasa's election meetings. Though Shasa was smiling now, his resentment was almost as fierce as it had been at the time. It had always been standard Nationalist tactics to break up the meetings of their opponents. Manfred De La Rey sensed the hostile feelings between them.

'We will soon be on the same side,' he said, as he stepped between them placatingly and placed a hand on each of their arms. 'Let me find a beer for both of you and we'll drink to letting bygones be bygones.'

The two of them turned away and quickly Shasa scrutinized Roelf Stander's wife. She was thin, almost to the point of starvation, and there was an air of resignation and weariness about her, so it took a moment for even Shasa's trained eye to see how pretty she must once have been, and how attractive she still was. She was returning his scrutiny, but dropped her eyes the moment they met Shasa's single eye.

Heidi De La Rey had not missed the exchange and now she took the woman's arm and led her forward.

'Meneer Courtney, this is my dear friend Sarah Stander.'

'*Aangename kennis*,' Shasa bowed slightly. 'Pleasant meeting, *Mevrou*.'

'How do you do, Squadron Leader,' the woman replied quietly, and Shasa blinked. He had not used his rank since the war. It was, of course, poor form to do so.

'Have we met?' he asked, for once off-balance and the woman shook her head quickly and turned to Heidi to speak about the children. Shasa was unable to pursue the matter, for at that moment Manfred handed him a beer and the three men carried their tankards down off the stoep to watch Lothar and Standers' eldest boy, Jakobus, build the fire for the barbecue. Though the masculine conversation was informed and their views interesting – both Manfred and Roelf Stander were educated and highly intelligent men – Shasa found his thoughts returning to the thin pale woman who had used his airforce rank. He

wished for the opportunity to speak to her alone, but realized that was unlikely and dangerous. He knew very well how protective and jealous the Afrikaners were of their women, and how easy it would be to precipitate an ugly and damaging incident. So he kept away from Sarah Stander, but for the rest of the evening observed her carefully, and so gradually became aware of undercurrents of emotion in the relationships of the two families. The two men seemed very close and it was obvious that their friendship was of long standing, but with the women it was different. They were just too kind and considerate and appreciative of each other, the certain indications of deep-seated female antagonism. Shasa stored that revelation, for human relationships and weaknesses were essential tools of his trade, but it was only later in the evening that he made two other important discoveries.

He intercepted an unguarded look that Sarah Stander directed at Manfred De La Rey while he was laughing with her husband, and Shasa recognized it instantly as a look of hatred, but that particularly corrosive type of hatred that a woman can conceive for a man whom she once loved. That hatred explained for Shasa the weariness and resignation that had almost ruined Sarah Stander's beauty. It explained also the resentment that the two women felt for each other. Heidi De La Rey must realize that Sarah had once loved her husband, and that beneath the hatred she probably still did. The play of feelings and emotions fascinated Shasa, he had learned so much of value and had achieved so much in a single day that he was well satisfied by the time Roelf Stander called his family together.

'It's almost midnight, come on, everybody. We have a long walk home.'

Each of them had brought a flashlight, and there was a flurry of farewells, the girls and women exchanging kisses, while first Roelf Stander and then his son Jakobus came to shake Shasa's hand.

'Goodbye,' Jakobus said, with the innate good manners and respect for elders that every Afrikaner child is taught from birth. 'I would also like to hunt a black-maned lion one day.'

He was a tall well-favoured lad, two or three years older than Lothar; he had been as fascinated as Lothar by Shasa's hunting stories but there was something familiar about him that had niggled Shasa all evening. Lothar stood beside his friend, smiling politely, and suddenly it dawned on Shasa. The boys had the same eyes, the pale cat-eyes of the De La Reys. For a moment he was at a loss to explain it, and then it all fell into place. The hatred he had observed in Sarah Stander was explained. Manfred De La Rey was the father of her son.

Shasa stood beside Manfred on the top stair of the stoep and they watched the Stander family climb the dunes, the beams of their flashlights darting about erratically and the shrill voices of the children dwindling into the night, and he wondered if he could ever piece together the clues he had gleaned this evening and discover the full extent of Manfred De La Rey's vulnerability. One day it might be vital to do so.

It would be easy enough discreetly to search the records for the marriage date of Sarah Stander and compare it to the birth date of her eldest son, but how would he ever coax from her the true significance of her use of his military rank. She had called him 'Squadron Leader'. She knew him, that was certain, but how and where? Shasa smiled. He enjoyed a good mystery, Agatha Christie was one of his favourite authors. He would work on it.

* * *

Shasa woke with the grey of dawn lining the curtains over his bed, and a pair of bokmakierie shrikes singing one of their complicated duets from the scrub of the dunes. He stripped off the pyjamas Manfred had lent him and shrugged on the bathrobe, before he crept from the silent cottage and went down to the beach.

He swam naked, slashing over-arm through the cold green water and ducking under the successive lines of breaking white surf until he was clear; then he swam slowly parallel to the beach but five hundred yards off. The chances of shark attack were remote, but the possibility spiced his enjoyment. When it was time to go in he caught a breaking wave and rode it into the beach, and waded ashore, laughing with exhilaration and the joy of life.

He mounted quietly to the stoep of the cottage, not wanting to disturb the family, but a movement from the far end stopped him. Manfred sat in one of the deckchairs with a book in his hands. He was already shaved and dressed.

'Good morning, *Meneer*,' Shasa greeted him. 'Are you going fishing again today?'

'It's Sunday,' Manfred reminded him. 'I don't fish on a Sunday.'

'Ah, yes.' Shasa wondered why he felt guilty for having enjoyed his swim, then recognized the antique leather-covered black book that Manfred was holding.

'The Bible,' he remarked, and Manfred nodded.

'*Ja*, I read a few pages before I begin each day, but on Sunday or when I have a particular problem to face, I like to read a full chapter.'

'I wonder how many chapters you read before you screwed your best friend's wife,' Shasa thought, but said aloud, 'Yes, the Book is a great comfort,' and tried not to feel a hypocrite as he went through to dress.

Heidi laid an enormous breakfast, everything from steak to pickled fish, but Shasa ate an apple and drank a cup of coffee before he excused himself.

'The forecast on the radio is for rain later. I want to get back to Cape Town before the weather closes in.'

'I will walk up to the airstrip with you.' Manfred stood up quickly.

Neither of them spoke until the track reached the ridge, and then Manfred asked suddenly, 'Your mother – how is she?'

'She is well. She always is, and she never seems to age.' Shasa watched his face, as he went on, 'You always ask about her. When last did you see her?'

'She is a remarkable woman,' Manfred said stolidly, avoiding the question.

'I have tried to make up in some way for the damage she has done your family,' Shasa persisted, and Manfred seemed not to have heard. Instead he stopped in the middle of the track, as if to admire the view, but his breathing was ragged. Shasa had set a fast pace up the hill.

'He's out of condition,' Shasa gloated. His own breathing was unruffled, and his body lean and hard.

'It's beautiful,' Manfred said, and only when he made a gesture that swept the wide horizon, did Shasa realize that he was talking about the land. He looked and saw that from the ocean to the blue mountains of the Langeberge inland, it was indeed beautiful.

'And the Lord said unto him, "This is the land which I sware unto Abraham, unto Isaac and unto Jacob, saying, I will give it unto thy seed",' Manfred quoted softly. 'The Lord has given it to us, and it is our sacred duty to keep it for our children. Nothing else is important compared to that duty.'

Shasa was silent. He had no argument with that sentiment, although the expression of it was embarrassingly theatrical.

'We have been given a paradise. We must resist with our lives all efforts to despoil it, or to change it,' Manfred went on. 'And there are many who will attempt just that. They are gathering against us already. In the days ahead we will need strong men.'

Again Shasa was silent, but now his agreement was tinged with scepticism. Manfred turned to him.

'I see you smile,' he said seriously. 'You see no threat to what we have built up here on the tip of Africa?'

'As you have said, this land is a paradise. Who would want to change it?' Shasa asked.

'How many Africans do you employ, *Meneer*?' Manfred seemed to change course.

'Almost thirty thousand altogether,' Shasa frowned with puzzlement.

'Then you will soon learn the poignancy of my warning,' Manfred grunted. 'There is a new generation of trouble-makers who have grown up amongst the native people. These are the bringers of darkness. They have no respect for the old orders of society which our forefathers so carefully built up and which have served us so faithfully so long. No, they want to tear all that down. As the Marxist monsters destroyed the social fabric of Russia, so they seek to destroy all that the white man has built up in Africa.'

Shasa's tone was disparaging as he replied. 'The vast bulk of our black peoples are happy and law-abiding. They are disciplined and accustomed to authority, their own tribal laws are every bit as strict and circumscribing as the laws we impose. How many agitators are there amongst them, and how great is their influence? Not many and not much, would be my guess.'

'The world has changed more in the short time since the end of the war than it ever did in the hundred years before that.' Manfred had recovered his breath now, and he spoke forcefully and eloquently in his own language. 'The tribal laws which governed our black peoples are eroded as they leave the rural areas and flock to the cities in search of the sweet life. There they learn all the white man's vices, and they are ripened for the heresies of the bringers of darkness. The respect that they have for the white man and his government could easily turn to contempt, especially if they detect any weakness in us. The black man respects strength and despises weakness, and it is the plan of this new breed of black agitators to test our weaknesses and expose them.'

'How do you know this?' Shasa asked and then immediately was angry with himself. He did not usually deal in banal questions, but Manfred answered seriously.

'We have a comprehensive system of informers amongst the blacks, it is the only way a police force can do its job efficiently. We know that they are planning a massive campaign of defiance of the law, especially those laws that have ben introduced in the last few years – the Group Areas Act and the Population Registration Act and the pass laws, the laws necessary to protect our complicated society from the evils of racial integration and miscegenation.'

'What form will this campaign take?'

'Deliberate disobedience, flouting of the law, boycotts of white businesses and wild-cat strikes in mining and industry.'

Shasa frowned as he made his calculation. The campaign would directly

threaten his companies. 'Sabotage?' he asked. 'Destruction of property – are they planning that?'

Manfred shook his head. 'It seems not. The agitators are divided amongst themselves. They even include some whites, some of the old comrades from the communist party. There are a few amongst them who favour violent action and sabotage, but apparently the majority are prepared to go only as far as peaceful protest – for the moment.'

Shasa sighed with relief, and Manfred shook his head. 'Do not be too complacent, *Meneer*. If we fail to prevent them, if we show weakness now, then it will escalate against us. Look what is happening in Kenya and Malaya.'

'Why do you not simply round up the ringleaders now, before it happens?'

'We do not have such powers,' Manfred pointed out.

'Then you should damned well be given them.'

'*Ja*, we need them to do our job, and soon we will have them. But in the meantime we must let the snake put its head out of the hole before we chop it off.'

'When will the trouble begin?' Shasa demanded. 'I must make my arrangements to deal with the strikes and disturbances – '

'That is one thing we are not certain of, we do not think the ANC itself has as yet decided – '

'The ANC,' Shasa interjected. 'But surely they aren't behind this? They have been around for forty years or so, and they are dedicated to peaceful negotiations. The leaders are decent men.'

'They were,' Manfred corrected him. 'But the old leaders have been superseded by younger more dangerous men. Men like Mandela and Tambo and others even more evil. As I said before, times change – we must change with them.'

'I had not realized that the threat was so real.'

'Few people do,' Manfred agreed. 'But I assure you *Meneer*, that there is a nest of snakes breeding in our little paradise.'

They walked on in silence, down to the clay-surfaced airstrip where Shasa's blue and silver Mosquito stood. While Shasa climbed into the cockpit and readied the machine for flight, Manfred stood quietly at the wingtip watching him. After Shasa had completed all his checks, he came back to Manfred.

'There is one certain way to defeat this enemy,' Shasa said. 'This new militant ANC.'

'What is that, *Meneer*?'

'To pre-empt their position. Take away from our black people the cause of complaint,' Shasa said.

Manfred was silent, but he stared at Shasa with those implacable yellow eyes. Then Manfred asked, picking his words carefully, 'Are you suggesting that we give the natives political rights, *Meneer*?' Do you think that we should give in to the parrot cry of "One man, one vote" – is that what you believe, *Meneer*?' On Shasa's reply rested all Manfred's plans. He wondered if he could have been so wrong in his selection. Any man who believed that could never be a member of the National Party, let alone bear the responsibility of cabinet rank. His relief was intense as Shasa dismissed the idea contemptuously.

'Good Lord, no! That would be the end of us and white civilization in the land. Blacks don't need votes, they need a slice of the pie. We must encourage the emergence of a black middle class, they will be our buffer against the

revolutionaries. I never saw a man yet with a full belly and a full wallet who wanted to change things.'

Manfred chuckled. 'That's good, I like it. You are correct, *Meneer*. We need massive wealth to pay for our concept of *apartheid*. It will be expensive, we accept that. That is why we have chosen you. We look to you to find the money to pay for our future.'

Shasa held out his hand and Manfred took it. 'On a personal level, *Meneer*, I am pleased to hear that your wife has taken notice of whatever you said to her. Reports from my special branch indicate that she has given up her liberal left wing associations and is no longer taking any part in political protests.'

'I convinced her how futile they were,' Shasa smiled. 'She has decided to become an archaeologist instead of a Bolshevik.'

They laughed together, and Shasa climbed back into the cockpit. The engines started with a stuttering roar and a mist of blue smoke blew from the exhaust ports, clearing quickly. Shasa lifted a hand in salute and closed the canopy.

Manfred watched him taxi down to the end of the strip then come thundering back, and hurtle aloft in a flash of silver and blue. He shaded his eyes to watch the Mosquito bank away towards the south, and he felt again that strange almost mystic bond of blood and destiny to the man under the perspex canopy as Shasa waved in farewell. Though they had fought and hated each other, their separate people were bound together by a similar bond and at the same time held apart by religion and language and political beliefs.

'We are brothers, you and I,' he thought. 'And beyond the hatred lie the dictates of survival. If you join us, then other Englishmen may follow you, and neither of us can survive alone. Afrikaner and Englishman, we are so bound together that if one goes down, we both drown in the black ocean.'

* * *

'Garrick has to wear glasses,' Tara said, and poured fresh coffee into Shasa's cup.

'Glasses?' He looked up from his newspaper. 'What do you mean glasses?'

'I mean eye glasses – spectacles. I took him to the optician while you were away. He is shortsighted.'

'But nobody in our family has ever worn glasses.' Shasa looked down the breakfast table at his son, and Garrick lowered his head guiltily. Until that moment he had not realized that he had disgraced the entire family. He had believed the humiliation of spectacles was his alone.

'Glasses.' Shasa's scorn was undisguised. 'While you are having him fitted with glasses, you might as well get them to fit a cork in the end of his whistle to stop him wetting his bed also.'

Sean let out a guffaw and dug his elbow into his brother's ribs, and Garrick was stung into self-defence. 'Gee, Dad, I haven't wet my bed since last Easter,' he declared furiously, red-faced with embarrassment and close to tears of humiliation.

Sean made circles with his thumbs and forefingers and peered through them at his brother.

'We will have to call you "Owly Wet Sheets",' he suggested, and as usual Michael came to his brother's defence.

'Owls are wise,' he pointed out reasonably. 'That's why Garry came top in his class this term. Where did you come in yours, Sean?' and Sean glared at him wordlessly. Michael always had a mild but stinging retort.

'All right, gentlemen.' Shasa returned to his newspaper. 'No bloodshed at the breakfast table, please.'

Isabella had been out of the limelight for long enough. Her father had given far too much of his attention to her brothers, and she hadn't yet received her dues. Her father had arrived home late the previous evening, long after she was in bed, and the traditional ceremony of home-coming had not been fully enacted. Certainly he had kissed and pampered her and told her how beautiful she was, but one vital aspect had been neglected, and though she knew it was bad manners to ask, she had contained herself long enough.

'Didn't you even bwing me a pwesent?' she piped, and Shasa lowered his newspaper again.

'A pwesent? Now what on earth is a pwesent?'

'Don't be a silly-billy, Daddy – you know what it is.'

'Bella, you know you mustn't beg for presents,' Tara chided.

'If I don't tell him, Daddy might just forget,' Isabella pointed out reasonably, and made her special angel face at Shasa.

'My goodness gracious me.' Shasa snapped his fingers. 'I did almost forget!' And Isabella hopped her lace-clad bottom up and down on her high stool with excitement.

'You did! You did bring me one!'

'Finish your porridge first,' Tara insisted, and Isabella's spoon clanked industriously on china as she devoured the last of it and scraped the plate clean.

They all trooped through from the breakfast room to Shasha's study.

'I'm the likklest one. I get my pwesent first.' Isabella made up the rules of life as she went along.

'All right, likklest one. Step to the front line, please.'

Her face a masterpiece of concentration, Isabella stripped away the wrappings of her gift.

'A doll!' she squeaked and showered kisses upon its bland china face. 'Her name is Oleander, and I love her already.' Isabella was the owner of what was probably one of the world's definitive collections of dolls, but all additions were rapturously received.

When Sean and Garry were handed their long packages, they went still with awe. They knew what they were – they had both of them pleaded long and eloquently for this moment and now that it had arrived, they were reluctant to touch their gifts in case they disappeared in a puff of smoke. Michael hid his disappointment bravely; he had hoped for a book, so secretly he empathized with his mother when she cried with exasperation, 'Oh, Shasa, you haven't given them guns?'

All three rifles were identical. They were Winchester repeaters in .22 calibre, light enough for the boys to handle.

'This is the best present anybody ever gave me.' Sean lifted his weapon out of the cardboard box and stroked the walnut stock lovingly.

'Me, too.' Garrick still couldn't bring himself to touch his. He knelt over the open package in the middle of the study floor, staring raptly at the weapon it contained.

'It's super, Dad,' said Michael, holding his rifle awkwardly and his smile was unconvincing.

'Don't use that word, Mickey,' Tara snapped. 'It's so American and vulgar.' But she was angry with Shasa, not Michael.

'Look.' Garry touched his rifle for the first time. 'My name – it's got my own name on it.' He stroked the engraving on the barrel with his fingertip, then looked up at his father with myopic adoration.

'I wish you'd brought them anything but guns,' Tara burst out. 'I asked you not to, Shasa. I hate them.'

'Well, my dear, they must have rifles if they are coming on a hunting safari with me.'

'A safari!' Sean shouted gleefully. 'When?'

'It's time you learned about the bush and the animals.' Shasa put his arm around Sean's shoulders. 'You can't live in Africa without knowing the difference between a scaly anteater and a chacma baboon.'

Garry snatched up his new rifle and went to stand as close to his father's side as he could, so that Shasa could also put his other arm around his shoulders – if he wanted to. However, Shasa was talking to Sean.

'We'll go up to south west in the June hols, take a couple of trucks from the H'ani Mine and drive through the desert until we reach the Okavango Swamps.

'Shasa, I don't know how you can teach your own children to kill those beautiful animals. I really don't understand it,' Tara said bitterly.

'Hunting is a man's thing,' Shasa agreed. 'You don't have to understand – you don't even have to watch.'

'Can I come, Dad?' Garry asked diffidently, and Shasa glanced at him.

'You'll have to polish up your new specs, so you can see what you're shooting at.' Then he relented. 'Of course you are coming, Garry,' and then he looked across at Michael, standing beside his mother. 'What about you, Mickey? Are you interested?'

Michael glanced apologetically at his mother before he replied softly. 'Gee, thanks Dad. It should be fun.'

'Your enthusiasm is touching,' Shasa grunted and then, 'Very well, gentlemen, all the rifles locked in the gun room, please. Nobody touches them again without my permission and my supervision. We'll have our first shooting practice this evening when I get back home.'

Shasa made a point of getting back to Weltevreden with two hours of daylight in hand, and he took the boys down to the range he had built over which to sight in his own hunting rifles. It was beyond the vineyards and far enough from the stables not to disturb the horses or any of the other livestock.

Sean with the co-ordination of a born athlete, was a natural shot. The rifle seemed immediately an extension of his body, and within minutes he had mastered the art of controlling his breathing and letting the shot squeeze away without effort. Michael was nearly as good, but his interest wasn't really in it and he lost concentration quickly.

Garry tried so hard that he was trembling, and his face was screwed up with effort. The horn-rimmed spectacles which Tara had fetched from the optician that morning kept sliding down his nose and misting over as he aimed, and it took ten shots for him finally to get one on the target.

'You don't have to pull the trigger so hard, Garry,' Shasa told him with resignation. 'It won't make the bullet go any further or any faster, I assure you.'

It was almost dark when the four of them got back to the house, and Shasa led them down to the gun room and showed them how to clean their weapons before locking them away.

'Sean and Mickey are ready to have a crack at the pigeons,' Shasa announced, as they trooped upstairs to change for dinner. 'Garry, you will need a little more practice, a pigeon is more likely to die of old age than one of your bullets.'

Sean shouted with laughter. 'Kill them with old age, Garry.'

Michael did not join in. He was imagining one of the lovely blue and pink rock pigeons that nested on the ledge outside his bedroom window, dying in a drift of loose feathers, splattering ruby drops as it fluttered to earth. It made him feel physically sick, but he knew his father expected it of him.

That evening as usual the children came one at a time to say goodnight to Shasa as he was tying his black bow tie. Isabella was first.

'I'm not going to sleep a wink until you come home tonight, Daddy,' she warned him. 'I'm just going to lie all by myself in the dark.'

Sean came next. 'You are the best Dad in the world,' he said as they shook hands. Kissing was for sissies.

'Will you let me have that in writing?' Shasa asked solemnly.

It was Michael who was always the most difficult to answer. 'Dad, do animals and birds hurt a lot when you shoot them?'

'Not if you learn to shoot straight,' Shasa assured him. 'But, Mickey, you have too much imagination. You can't go through life worrying about animals and other people all the time.'

'Why not, Dad?' Michael asked softly, and Shasa glanced at his wristwatch to cover his exasperation.

'We have to be at Kelvin Grove by eight. Do you mind if we go into that some other time, Mickey?'

Garrick came last. He stood shyly in the doorway of Shasa's dressing-room, but his voice shook with determination as he announced, 'I'm going to learn to be a crack shot, like Sean. You'll be proud of me one day, Dad. I promise you.'

Garrick left his parents' wing and crossed to the nursery. Nanny stopped him at Isabella's door.

'She's asleep already, Master Garry.'

In Michael's room they discussed the promised safari, but Mickey's attention kept wandering back to the book in his hands, and after a few minutes Garry left him to it.

He looked into Sean's room cautiously, ready to take flight if his elder brother showed any signs of becoming playful. One of Sean's favourite expressions of fraternal affection was known as a chestnut and consisted of a painful knuckling of Garry's prominent ribcage. However, this evening Sean was hanging backwards over his bed, heels propped on the wall and the back of his head almost touching the floor, a Superman comic book held at arm's length above his face.

'Goodnight, Sean,' Garry said.

'Shazam!' said Sean without lowering the comic book.

Garrick retreated thankfully to his own room and locked the door. Then he went to stand before the mirror and regard the reflection of his new horn-rimmed spectacles.

'I hate them,' he whispered bitterly, and when he removed them they left red indentations on the ridge of his nose. He went down on his knees, removed the skirting board under the built-in wardrobe and reached into the secret recess beyond. Nobody, not even Sean, had discovered this hiding place.

Carefully he withdrew the precious package. It had cost him eight weeks of his accumulated pocket money, but was worth every penny. It had arrived in a

plain wrapper with a personal letter from Mr Charles Atlas himself. 'Dear Garrick,' the letter had begun, and Garry had been overcome with the great man's condescension.

He laid out the course on his bed and stripped to his pyjama pants as he revised the lessons.

'Dynamic tension,' he whispered aloud, and he took up his stance before the mirror. As he began the sequence of exercises he kept time with the soft chant of, 'More and more in every way, I'm getting better every day.'

When he finished he was sweating heavily but he made an arm and studied it minutely.

'They *are* bigger,' he tried to put aside his doubts as he poked the little walnut of muscle that popped out of his straining biceps, 'they really are!'

He stowed the course back in its hidy-hole and replaced the skirting board. Then he took his raincoat from the wardrobe and spread it on the bare boards.

Garrick had read with admiration how Frederick Selous, the famous African hunter, had toughened himself as a boy by sleeping uncovered on the floor in winter. He switched out the light and settled down on the raincoat. It was going to be a long uncomfortable night, he knew from experience, already the floor boards were like iron, but the raincoat would prevent Sean detecting any nocturnal spillage when he made his morning inspection, and Garrick was certain that his asthma had improved since he had stopped sleeping on a soft mattress with a warm eiderdown over him.

'I'm getting better every day,' he whispered, closing his eyes tightly and willing himself to ignore the cold and the hardness of the floor. 'And then one day Dad will be proud of me – just like he is of Sean.'

* * *

'I thought your speech this evening was very good, even for you,' Tara told him, and Shasa glanced at her in surprise. She had not paid him a compliment for a long time now.

'Thank you, my dear.'

'I sometimes forget what a gifted person you are,' she went on. 'It's just that you make it seem so easy and natural.' He was so moved that he might have reached across to caress her, but she was leaning away from him and the Hooper coachwork of the Rolls was too wide for him to reach her.

'I must say, you look absolutely stunning this evening,' he compromised with a matching compliment, but as he had expected, she dismissed it with a grimace.

'Are you really going to take the boys on safari?'

'My dear, we have to let them make up their own minds about life. Sean will love it, but I'm not too sure about Mickey.' Shasa replied, and she noticed that he hadn't mentioned Garrick.

'Well, if you are determined, then I'm going to take advantage of the boys' absence. I have been invited to join the archaeological dig at the Sundi caves.'

'But you are a novice,' he was surprised. 'That's an important site. Why would they invite you?'

'Because I offered to contribute two thousand pounds to the cost of the dig, that's why.'

'I see, this is straight blackmail.' He chuckled sardonically as he saw the reason for her flattery. 'All right, it's a deal. I'll give you a cheque tomorrow. How long will you be away?'

'I'm not sure.' But she thought, 'as long as I can be close to Moses Gama.'

The site at Sundi Caves was only an hour's drive from the house at Rivonia. She reached under the fur coat and touched her stomach. It would begin to show soon – she had to find excuses to keep away from the eyes of the family. Her father and Shasa would not notice, she was sure of that, but Centaine de Thiry Courtney-Malcomess had eyes like a hawk.

'I presume that my mother has agreed to care for Isabella while you are away,' Shasa was saying, and while she nodded, her heart was singing.

'Moses, I'm coming back to you – both of us are coming back, to you, my darling.'

* * *

Whenever Moses Gama came to Drake's Farm it was like a king returning to his own realm after a successful crusade. Within minutes of his arrival, the word was flashed almost telepathically through the vast sprawling black township, and a sense of expectancy hung over it, as palpable as the smoke from ten thousand cooking fires.

Moses usually arrived with his half brother, Hendrick Tabaka, in the butcher's delivery van. Hendrick owned a chain of a dozen butcher shops in the black townships along the Witwatersrand, so the signwriting on the side of the van was authentic. In sky blue and crimson, it declared:

PHUZA MUHLE BUTCHERY
BEST MEAT AT BEST PRICES

From the vernacular 'Phuza Muhle' translated as 'Eat Well' and the van provided a perfect cover for Hendrick Tabaka wherever he went. Whether he was genuinely delivering slaughtered carcasses to his butcheries or goods to his general dealer stores, or was engaged in less conventional business: the distribution of illicitly brewed liquor, the notorious *skokiaan* or township dynamite, or ferrying his girls to their places of business nearer the compounds that housed the thousands of black contract workers of the gold-mines so that they could briefly assist them in relieving their monastic existence, or whether he was on the business of the African Mineworkers Union, that close-knit and powerful brotherhood whose existence the white government refused to acknowledge – the blue and red van was the perfect vehicle. When he was at the wheel, Hendrick wore a peaked driver's cap and a khaki tunic with cheap brass buttons. He drove sedately and with meticulous attention to all the rules of the road, so that in twenty years he had never been stopped by the police.

When he drove the van into Drake's Farm, with Moses Gama sitting in the passenger seat beside him, they were entering their own stronghold. This was where they had established themselves when together they had arrived from the wastelands of the Kalahari twenty years before. Although they were sons of the same father, they had been different in almost every way. Moses had been

young and tall and marvellously handsome, while Hendrick was years older, a great bull of a man with a bald, scarred head and gapped and broken teeth.

Moses was clever and quick, self-educated to a high standard, charismatic and a leader of men, while Hendrick was the faithful lieutenant, accepting his younger brother's authority and carrying out his orders swiftly and ruthlessly. Though Moses Gama had conceived the idea of building up a business empire, it was Hendrick who had made the dream a reality. Once he was shown what to do, Hendrick Tabaka was as much a bulldog in tenacity as he was in appearance.

For Hendrick, what they had built between them, the business enterprises both illicit and legitimate, the trade union and its private army of enforcers known and dreaded throughout the compounds where the mineworkers lived and through the black townships as 'The Buffaloes', all these were an end in themselves. But for Moses Gama it was different. What they had achieved thus far was only the first stage on his quest for something so much greater that although he had explained it many times to Hendrick, his brother could not truly grasp the enormity of Moses Gama's vision.

In the twenty years since they had arrived here, Drake's Farm had changed entirely. In those early days it had been a small squatters' encampment, hanging like a parasite tick on the body of the huge complex of gold-mines that made up the central Witwatersrand. It had been a collection of squalid hovels, built of scrap lumber and wattle poles and old iron sheets, flattened paraffin cans and tarpaper on the bleak open veld, a place of open drains and cesspools, lacking reticulated water or electricity, without schools or clinics or police protection, not even recognized as human habitation by the white city fathers in Johannesburg's town hall.

It was only after the war that the Transvaal Divisional Council had decided to recognize reality and to expropriate the land from the absentee landowners. They had declared the entire three thousand acres an official township set aside for black occupation under the Group Areas Act. They had retained the original name, Drake's Farm, for its picturesque connotations to old Johannesburg, unlike the more mundane origin of the nearby Soweto, which was merely an acronym for South Western Townships. Soweto already housed over half a million blacks, while Drake's Farm was home to less than half that number.

The authorities had fenced off the new township and covered the greater part of it with monotonous lines of small three-roomed cottages, each identical except for the number stencilled on the cement brick front wall. Crowded close together and separated by narrow lanes with dusty untarred surfaces, the flat roofs in galvanized corrugated iron shone like ten thousand mirrors in the brilliant highveld sunlight.

In the centre of the township were the administrative buildings where, under a handful of white municipal supervisors, the black clerks collected the rents and regulated the basic services of reticulated water and refuse removal. Beyond this Orwellian vision of bleak and soulless order, lay the original section of Drake's Farm, its hovels and shebeens and whorehouses – and it was here that Hendrick Tabaka still lived.

As he drove the delivery van slowly through the new section of the township, the people came out of their cottages to watch them pass. They were mostly women and children, for the men left each morning early, commuting to their employment in the city and returning only after nightfall. When they recognized Moses, the women clapped and ululated shrilly, the greeting for a tribal chief,

and the children ran beside the van, dancing and laughing with excitement at being so close to the great man.

They drove slowly past the cemetery where the untidy mounds of earth were like a vast mole run. On some of the mounds crudely wrought crosses had been set while on the others raggedy flags fluttered in the wind and offerings of food and broken household utensils and weirdly carved totems had been placed to placate the spirits, Christian symbols side by side with those of the animists and witch-worshippers. They went down into the old township, into the higgledy-piggledy lanes, where the stalls of the witchdoctors stood side by side with those offering food and trade cloth and used clothes and stolen radios. Where the chickens and pigs rooted in the muddy ruts of the road and naked toddlers with only a string of beads around their fat little tummies defecated between the stalls and the young whores strutted their wares and the stink and the noise were wondrous.

This was a world no white men ever entered, and where even the black municipal police came only on invitation and under sufferance. It was Hendrick Tabaka's world, where his wives kept nine houses for him in the centre of the old quarter. They were sturdy well-built houses of burned brick, but the exteriors were left deliberately shabby and uncared for, so they blended into the general squalor. Hendrick had learned long ago not to draw attention to himself and his material possessions. Each of his nine wives had her own home, built in a circle around Hendrick's slightly more imposing house, and he had not limited himself to women of his own Ovambo tribe. His wives were Pondo and Xhosa and Fingo and Basuto, but not Zulu. Hendrick would never trust a Zulu in his bed.

They all came out to greet him and his famous brother as Hendrick parked the van in the lean-to at the back of his own house. The obeisances of the women and their soft clapping of respect ushered the men into the living-room of Hendrick's house where two plush chairs covered with tanned leopard skins were set like thrones at the far end. When the brothers were seated the two youngest wives brought pitchers of millet beer, freshly brewed, thick as gruel, tart and effervescent and cold from the paraffin refrigerator, and when they had refreshed themselves, Hendrick's sons came in to greet their father and pay their respects to their uncle.

The sons were many, for Hendrick Tabaka was a lusty man and bred all his wives regularly each year. However, not all his elder sons were present today. Those of them whom Hendrick considered unworthy had been sent back to the country to tend the herds of cattle and goats that were part of Hendrick's wealth. The more promising boys worked in the butchery shops, the general dealers or the shebeens, while two of them, those especially gifted with intelligence, were law students at Fort Hare, the black university in the little town of Alice in the eastern Cape.

Only Hendrick's younger boys were here to kneel respectfully before him, and of these were two whom Moses Gama looked upon with particular pleasure. They were the twin sons of one of Hendrick's Xhosa wives, a woman of unusual accomplishments. Apart from being a dutiful wife and a breeder of sons, she was an accomplished dancer and singer, an amusing story-teller, a person of shrewd common sense and intelligence, and a noted *sangoma*, a healer and occult doctor with sometimes uncanny powers of prescience and divination. Her twins had inherited most of her gifts together with their father's robust physique and some of their uncle Moses' fine feaures.

At their birth, Hendrick had asked Moses to name them, and he had chosen their names from his treasured copy of Macaulay's *History of England*. Of all his nephews they were his favourites, and he smiled now as they knelt before them. They were already thirteen years old, Moses realized.

'I see you, Wellington Tabaka,' he greeted first the one and then the other. 'I see you, Raleigh Tabaka.'

They were not identical twins. Wellington was the taller lad, lighter-skinned, toffee-coloured against Raleigh's mulberry-stain black. His features had the same Nilotic cast as Moses' own, while Raleigh was more negroid, flat-nosed and thick-lipped, his body heavier and squatter.

'What books have you read since we last met?' Moses changed into English, forcing them to reply in the same language. 'Words are spears, they are weapons with which to defend yourself and with which to attack your enemies. English words have the sharpest blades, without them you will be warriors disarmed,' he had explained to them, and now he listened attentively to their halting replies in that language.

However, he noted the improvements in their command of the language and remarked on it. 'It is still not good enough, but you will learn to speak it better at Waterford,' and both boys looked uncomfortable. Moses had arranged for them to write the entrance examination for this elite multi-racial school across the border in the independent black kingdom of Swaziland, and the twins had both passed and been accepted and now were dreading the day not far away when they would be uprooted from this comfortable familiar world of theirs and packed off into the unknown. In South Africa all education was strictly segregated, and it was the declared policy of the minister of Bantu affairs, Dr Hendrick Verwoerd, not to educate black children to the point of discontentment. He had told parliament quite frankly that education for blacks should not conflict with the government policy of *apartheid* and should not be of such a standard as to evoke in the black pupil expectations which could never be fulfilled. The annual expenditure by the state on each white pupil was £60 while that on a black student was £9 per annum. Those black parents who could afford it, the chiefs and small businessmen, sent their children out of the country to be educated, and Waterford was a favourite choice.

The twins escaped from the daunting presence of their father and uncle with relief, but their mother was waiting for them in the yard beside the blue and crimson van, and with a sharp inclination of her head ordered them into her own parlour.

The room was a sorceress's lair from which the twins were usually barred, and now they crept in with even more trepidation than they had entered their father's house. Against the far wall stood their mother's gods and goddesses carved in native woods and dressed in feathers and skins and beads, with eyes of ivory and mother-of-pearl, and bared teeth of dog and baboon. They were a terrifying assembly, and the twins shivered and dared not look directly upon them.

Before the family idols were arranged offerings of food and small coins, and from the other walls hung all the gruesome accoutrements of their mother's craft, gourds and clay pots of ointments and medicines, bundles of dried herbs, snake skins and mummified iguana lizards, bones and baboon skulls, glass jars of hippopotamus and lion fat, musk of crocodile, and other nameless substances which festered and bubbled and stank so foully that it made their teeth ache in their jaws.

'You wore the charms I gave you?' Kuzawa, their mother, asked. She was incongruously handsome in the midst of her unholy and hideous tools and medicines, full-faced and glossy-skinned with very white teeth and liquid gazelle eyes. Her limbs were long and gleamed with secret and magical ointments and her breasts under the necklaces of ivory beads and charms were big and firm as wild Kalahari melons.

In response to her question, the twins nodded vehemently, too overcome to speak, and unbuttoned their shirts. The charms were hung around their necks, each on a thin leather thong. They were the horns of the little grey duiker, the open ends sealed with gum arabic, and Kuzawa had taken all the twelve years of their lives to assemble the magical potion that was contained in each of them. It was made up of samples of all the bodily excretions of Hendrick Tabaka, the father of the twins, his faeces and urine, his spittle and nasal mucus, his sweat and his semen, the wax from his ears, and the blood from his veins, his tears and his vomit. With these, Kuzawa had mixed the dried skin from the soles of his feet, the clippings of his nails, the shavings of his beard and his pate and pubes, the lashes of his eyes plucked in his sleep, and the crusted scabs and pus from his wounds. Then she had added herbs and fats of wonderful efficacy, and spoken the words of power over them and finally, to make the charm infallible, she had paid a vast sum to one of the grave-robbers who specialized in such procurements to bring her the liver of an infant drowned at birth by its own mother.

All these ingredients she had sealed in the two little duiker horns, and the twins were never allowed into their father's presence except that they wore them hung around their necks. Now Kuzawa retrieved the two charms from her sons. They were far too precious to leave in the children's possession. She smiled as she weighed them in the smooth pink palms of her delicately shaped hands. They had been worth all the expense and the patience and meticulous application of her skills to create.

'Did your father smile when he saw you?' she asked.

'He smiled like the rise of the sun,' Raleigh replied, and Kuzawa nodded happily.

'And were his words kind, did he make enquiry of you fondly?' she insisted.

'When he spoke to us he purred like a lion at meat,' Wellington whispered, still intimidated by his surroundings. 'And he asked us how we fared at school, and he commended us when we told him.'

'It is the charms that have ensured his favour,' Kuzawa smiled contentedly. 'As long as you wear them, your father will prefer you over all his other children.'

She took the two little buckhorns and went to kneel before the central carved figure in the array of idols, a fearsome image with a headdress of lion's mane that housed the spirit of her dead grandfather.

'Guard them well, oh venerable ancestor,' she whispered, as she hung them around the neck of the image. 'Keep their powers strong until they are needed once again.'

They were safer there than in the deepest vault of the white man's banks. No human being, and only the most powerful of the dark ones, would dare challenge her grandfather's spirit for possession of the charms, for he was the ultimate guardian.

Now she turned back to the twins, took their hands and led them out of her lair into the family kitchen next door, putting aside the mantle of the witch and

assuming that of the loving mother as she passed through the door and closed it behind her.

She fed the twins, bowls piled with fluffy white maize meal and butter beans and stew swimming with delicious fat, food that befitted the family of a rich and powerful man. And while they ate, she tended them lovingly, questioning and chaffing them, pressing more food upon them, her dark eyes glowing with pride, and finally reluctantly letting them go.

They fled from her, delirious with excitement, into the narrow fetid lanes of the old quarter. Here they were entirely at their ease. The men and women smiled and called greetings and pleasantries as they passed and laughed delightedly at their repartee for they were the favourites of all, and their father was Hendrick Tabaka.

Old Mama Nginga, fat and silver-haired, sitting at the front door of the shebeen that she ran for Hendrick, shouted after them, 'Where are you going, my little ones?'

'On secret business we cannot discuss,' Wellington shouted back, and Raleigh added:

'But next year our secret business will be with you, old mama. We will drink all your *skokiaan* and stab all your girls.'

Mama Nginga wobbled with delight, and the girls sitting in the windows shrieked with laughter. 'He is the cub of the lion, that one,' they told each other.

As they scurried through the lanes, they called out and from the hovels and the shanties of the old quarter and from the new brick cottages that the white government had built, their comrades hurried out to join them. Some of them carried long bundles, carefully wrapped and bound up with rawhide thongs.

At the far end of the township the high fence had been cut, the gap concealed from casual scrutiny by a clump of scrub. The boys climbed through the gap and in the plantation of bluegums beyond, they gathered in an excited jabbering cluster and stripped off the shabby western European clothing they wore. They were uncircumcised, their penises although beginning to develop were still surmounted by the little wrinkled caps of skin. In a few years' time they would all of them go into the initiation class and endure the ordeal of the isolation and hardship, and the agony of the blade together. This, even more than their tribal blood, bound them together; all their lives they would be comrades of the circumcision knife.

They set aside their clothing carefully – any losses would have to be accounted for to angry parents – and then naked, they gathered around the precious rolls and watched impatiently as they were opened by their acknowledged captains Wellington and Raleigh Tabaka, and each of them were issued with the uniform of the Xhosa warrior – not the true regalia, the cow-tails and rattles and headdress – those were for circumcised *amadoda* only. These were childish replicas, merely skins of dogs and cats, the strays and pariahs of the township, but they donned them as proudly as if they were genuine, and bound their upper arms and thighs and foreheads with strips of fur, and then took up their weapons.

Again these were not the warriors' long-bladed assegais, but were merely the traditional fighting-sticks. However, even in the hands of these children the long limber staves were formidable weapons. With a stick in each hand they were immediately transformed into shrieking demons. They brandished and swung the staves, using a practised wrist action that made them hiss and sing

and whistle, they rattled them together, crossing them to form a guard against which the blows of their peers clattered, and they leapt and cavorted and danced, aiming blows at each other, until Raleigh Tabaka blew a sharp fluting command on his buckhorn whistle, and they fell in behind him in a compact, disciplined column.

He led them away. In a swaying stylized trot, fighting-sticks held high, singing and humming the battle chants of their tribe, they left the plantation and went out into the open undulating veld. The grass was knee-high and brown, and the chocolate red earth showed through it in raw patches. The ground fell away gently to a narrow stream, its rocky bed enclosed by steep banks and then climbed again to meet the pale sapphire of the highveld sky.

Even as they started down the long slope, the clean sweep of the far skyline was interrupted, a long line of waving headdresses showed above it, and then another band of lads appeared, clad like them in loincloths of skin, legs and arms and torsos bare. Carrying their fighting-sticks high, they paused along the crest, and as they saw each other, both bands gave tongue like hounds taking the scent.

'Zulu jackals,' howled Raleigh Tabaka, and his hatred was so intense that a fine sheen of sweat burst out upon his brow. For as long and as far back as his tribal memory reached, this had been the enemy; his hatred was in his blood, deep and atavistic. History did not record how often this scene had been repeated, how many thousands of times over the centuries armed impis of Xhosa and Zulu had faced each other thus; all that was remembered was the heat of the battle and the blood and the hatred.

Raleigh Tabaka leapt as high as the shoulder of his brother beside him, and screamed wildly, his treacherous voice breaking into a girlish squeak at the end.

'I am thirsty. Give me Zulu blood to drink!' and his warriors leapt and screamed.

'Give us Zulu blood!'

The threats and insults and challenges were flung back at them from the opposite ridge, carried to them on the wind. Then spontaneously both impis started down, singing and prancing into the shallow valley, until from the steep red banks they faced each other across the narrow streambed, and their captains strode forward to exchange more insults.

The Zulu *induna* was a lad the same age as the twins. He attended the same class as they did in the government secondary school in the township. His name was Joseph Dinizulu, and he was as tall as Wellington and as broad across the chest as Raleigh. His name and his strutting arrogance reminding the world that he was a princeling of the royal house of Zulu.

'Hey, you eaters of hyena dung,' he called. 'We smelt you from a thousand paces against the wind. The smell of Xhosa makes even the vultures puke.'

Raleigh leapt high, turning in the air and lifting the skirts of his loincloth to expose his buttocks. 'I cleanse the air of the Zulu stench with a good clean fart!' he shouted. 'Sniff that, you jackal-lovers,' and he blew a raspberry so loud and long that the Zulus facing him hissed murderously and rattled their fighting-sticks.

'Your fathers were women, your mothers were monkeys,' Joseph Dinizulu cried, scratching his own armpits. 'Your grandfathers were baboons,' he imitated a simian lollop, 'and your grandmothers were – ' Raleigh interrupted this recital of his ancestral line with a blast on the buckhorn whistle and leapt from the bank into the streambed. He landed on his feet, light as a cat, and

with a bound was across. He went up the far bank so fast that Joseph Dinizulu, who had expected the exchange of pleasantries to last a little longer, fell back before his onslaught.

A dozen of the other Xhosa lads had responded to his whistle and followed him across, and Raleigh's furious attack had won a bridgehead for them on the far bank. They bunched up behind him with sticks hissing and singing, and drove into the centre of the opposing impi. The battle lust was on Raleigh Tabaka. He was invincible, his arms tireless, his hands and wrists so cunning that his sticks seemed to have separate life, finding the weak places in the guards of the Zulus who opposed him, thudding on flesh, cracking on bone, cutting open skin so that soon their sticks shone wet with blood and little droplets of it flew in the sunlight.

It seemed nothing could touch him, until abruptly something crashed into his ribs just below his raised right arm, and he gasped with pain and the sudden awareness of his own humanity. For a minute there he had been a warrior god, but suddenly he was a small boy, almost at the end of his strength, hurting very badly, and so tired that he could not mouth another challenge while before him danced Joseph Dinizulu, who seemed to have grown six inches in as many seconds. Again his fighting-stick whistled in, aimed at Raleigh's head, and only with a desperate defence he deflected it. Raleigh fell back a pace and looked around him.

He should have known better than to attack a Zulu so boldly. They were the most treacherous and sly of all adversaries, and the stratagem of encirclement was always their master-stroke. Chaka Zulu, the mad dog who had founded this tribe of wolves, had called the manoeuvre 'the Horns of the Bull'. The horns surrounded the enemy while the chest crushed him to death.

Joseph Dinizulu had not fallen back out of fear or surprise, it was his instinctive cunning, and Raleigh had led his dozen stalwarts into the Zulu trap. They were alone, none of the others had followed them across the stream. Over the heads of the encircling Zulus he could see them on the far bank, and Wellington Tabaka, his twin brother, stood at their head, silent and immobile.

'Wellington!' he screamed, his voice breaking with exhaustion and terror. 'Help us! We have the Zulu dog by the testicles. Come across and stab him in the chest!'

That was all he had time for. Joseph Dinizulu was on him again and each stroke of his seemed more powerful than the last. Raleigh's chest was agony, and then another blow crashed through his guard and caught him across the shoulder, paralysing his right arm to the fingertips, and the stick flew from his grasp.

'Wellington!' he screamed again. 'Help us!' and all around him his men were going down, some of them beaten to their knees, others simply dropping their sticks and cowering in the dust, screaming for mercy while the Zulu boys crowded in with their sticks rising and falling, the blows flogging into soft flesh, the Zulu war cries rising in jubilant chorus like hounds crowding in to rend the hares.

'Wellington!' He had one last glimpse of his brother across the stream and then a blow caught him on the forehead just above his eye, and he felt the skin split as warm blood poured down his face. Just before it blinded him he caught a last glimpse of Joseph Dinizulu's face, crazy with blood lust, and then his legs collapsed under him and he flopped face-first into the dirt, while the blows still thudded across his back and shoulders.

He must have lost consciousness for a moment, for when he rolled on to his side and wiped the blood from his eyes with the back of his hand, he saw that the Zulus had crossed the stream in a phalanx and that the remnants of his impi were racing away in wild panic towards the bluegum plantation pursued by Dinizulu's men.

He tried to push himself upright, but his senses reeled and darkness filled his head, as he toppled once again. When next he came to, he was surrounded by Zulus, jeering and mocking, covering him with insults. This time he managed to sit up, but then the tumult around him quieted and was replaced by an expectant hush. He looked up and Joseph Dinizulu pushed his way through the ranks and sneered down at him.

'Bark, Xhosa dog,' he ordered. 'Let us hear you bark and whine for mercy.'

Groggy, but defiant, Raleigh shook his head, and pain flared under his skull at the movement.

Joseph Dinizulu placed a bare foot on his chest and shoved hard. He was too weak to resist and he toppled over on his back. Joseph stood over him, and lifted the front of his loincloth. With his other hand he drew back his foreskin exposing the pink glans, and he directed a hissing stream of urine into Raleigh's face.

'Drink that, you Xhosa dog,' he laughed. It was hot and ammoniacal and burned like acid in the open wound on his scalp – and Raleigh's rage and humiliation and hatred filled all his soul.

* * *

'My brother, it is only very seldom that I try to dissuade you from something on which you have set your mind,' Hendrick Tabaka sat on the leopard-skin covering of his chair, leaning forward earnestly with his elbows on his knees. 'It is not the marriage in itself, you know how I have always urged you to take a wife, many wives, and get yourself sons – it is not the idea of a wife I disapprove of, it is this Zulu baggage that makes me lie awake at night. There are ten million other nubile young women in this land – why must you choose a Zulu? I would rather you took a black mamba into your bed.'

Moses Gama chuckled softly. 'Your concern for me proves your love.' Then he became serious. 'Zulu is the largest tribe in southern Africa. Numbers alone would make them important, but add to that their aggressive and warlike spirit, and you will see that nothing will change in this land without Zulu. If I can form an alliance with that tribe, then all the dreams I have dreamed need not be in vain.'

Hendrick sighed, and grunted and shook his head.

'Come Hendrick, you have spoken with them. Have you not?' Moses insisted, and reluctantly Hendrick nodded.

'I sat four days at the kraal of Sangane Dinizulu, son of Mbejane who was the son of Gubi, who was the son of Dingaan, who was the brother of Chaka Zulu himself. He deems himself a prince of Zulu, which he is at pains to point out means "The Heavens" and he lives in grand style on the land that his old master, General Sean Courtney, left him on the hills above Ladyburg, where he keeps many wives and three hundred head of fat cattle.'

'All this I know, my brother,' Moses interrupted. 'Tell me about the girl.'

Hendrick frowned. He liked to begin a story at the beginning and work through it, sparing no detail, until he reached the end.

'The girl,' he repeated. 'That old Zulu rogue whines that she is the moon of his night and the sun of his day, no daughter has ever been loved as he loves her – and he could never allow her to marry any man but a Zulu chief.' Hendrick sighed. 'Day after day I heard the virtues of this Zulu she-jackal recounted, how beautiful she is, how talented, how she is a nurse at the government hospital, how she comes from a long line of son-bearing wives – ' Hendrick broke off and spat with disgust. 'It took three days before he mentioned what had been on his mind from the first minute – the *lobola*, the bride price,' and Hendrick threw up his hands in a gesture of exasperation. 'All Zulus are thieves and dung-eaters.'

'How much?' Moses asked with a smile. 'How much did he need to compensate him for a marriage outside the tribe?'

'Five hundred head of prime cattle, all cows in calf, none older than three years,' Hendrick scowled with outrage. 'All Zulus are thieves and he claims to be a prince, which makes him a prince of thieves.'

'Naturally you agreed to his first price?' Moses asked.

'Naturally I argued for two more days.'

'The final price?'

'Two hundred head,' Hendrick sighed. 'Forgive me, my brother. I tried, but the old dog of a Zulu was like a rock. It was his very lowest price for the moon of his night.'

Moses Gama leaned back in his chair, and thought about it. It was an enormous price. Prime cattle were worth £50 the head, but unlike his brother, Moses Gama had no yen for money other than as a means to procure an end.

'Ten thousand pounds?' he asked softly. 'Do we have that much?'

'It will hurt. I will ache for a year as though I have been whipped with a sjambok,' Hendrick grumbled. 'Do you realize just how much else a man could buy with ten thousand pounds, my brother? I could get you at least ten Xhosa maidens, pretty as sugar birds and plump as guinea fowl, each with her maidenhead attested by the most reliable midwife – '

'Ten Xhosa maidens would not bring the Zulu people within my reach,' Moses cut him off. 'I need Victoria Dinizulu.'

'The *lobola* is not the only price demanded,' Hendrick told him. 'There is more.'

'What else?'

'The girl is a Christian. If you take her, there will be no others. She will be your only wife, my brother, and listen to a man who has paid for wisdom in the heavy coin of experience. Three wives are the very minimum a man needs for contentment. Three wives are so busy competing with one another for their husband's favour, that a man can relax. Two wives are better than one. However, a single wife, a one and only wife, can sour the food in your belly and frost your hair with silver. Let this Zulu wench go to someone who deserves her, another Zulu.'

'Tell her father that we will pay the price he asks and that we agree to his terms. Tell him also that if he is a prince, then we expect him to provide a marriage feast that befits a princess. We expect a marriage that will be the talk of Zululand from the Drakensberg Mountains to the ocean. I want every chieftain and elder of the tribe there to see me wed, I want every counseller and

induna, I want the king of the Zulus himself to come and when they are all assembled, I will speak to them.'

'You might as well talk to a troop of baboons. A Zulu is too proud and too full of hatred to listen to sense.'

'You are wrong, Hendrick Tabaka.' Moses laid his hand on his brother's arm. 'We are not proud enough, nor do we hate enough. What pride we do have, the little hatred that we do have, is misspent and ill-directed. We waste it on each other, on other black men. If all the tribes of this land took all their pride and all their hatred and turned it on the white oppressor – then how could he resist us? This is what I will talk about when I speak at my wedding feast. This is what I have to teach the people. It is for this that we are forging *Umkhonto we Sizwe*, the Spear of the Nation.'

They were silent awhile. The depth of his brother's vision, the terrible power of his commitment, always awed Hendrick.

'It will be as you wish,' he agreed at last. 'When do you wish the wedding to take place?'

'On the full moon of mid-winter.' Moses did not hesitate. 'That will be the week before our campaign of defiance begins.'

Again they were silent, until Moses roused himself. 'It is settled then. Is there anything else we should discuss before we take the evening meal?'

'Nothing.' Hendrick rose to his feet and was about to call his women to bring their food, when he remembered. 'Ah. There is one other thing. The white woman, the woman who was with you at Rivonia – do you know the one?'

Moses nodded. 'Yes, the Courtney woman.'

'That is the one. She has sent a message. She wishes to see you again.'

'Where is she?'

'She is close by, at a place called Sundi Caves. She has left a telephone number for you. She says it is an important matter.'

Moses Gama was clearly annoyed. 'I told her not to try and contact me,' he said. 'I warned her of the dangers.' He stood up and paced the floor. 'Unless she learns discipline and self-control, she will be of no value to the struggle. White women are like that, spoiled and disobedient and self-indulgent. She must be trained – '

Moses broke off and went to the window. Something in the yard had caught his attention, and he called out sharply.

'Wellington! Raleigh! Come here, both of you.'

A few seconds later the two boys shuffled self-consciously into the room and stood just inside the door, hanging their heads guiltily.

'Raleigh, what has happened to you?' Hendrick demanded angrily. The twins had changed their furs and loincloths for their ordinary clothing, but the gash in Raleigh's forehead was still weeping through the wad of grubby rags he had strapped on it. There were speckles of blood on his shirt, and the swelling had closed one eye.

'*Baba!*' Wellington started to explain. 'It was not our fault. We were set upon by the Zulus.' And Raleigh darted a look of contempt at him before he contradicted his twin.

'We arranged a faction fight with them. It went well, until some of us ran away and left the others,' Raleigh raised his hand to his injured head. 'There are cowards even amongst the Xhosa,' he said, and again glanced at his twin. Wellington stood silent.

'Next time fight harder and show more cunning,' Hendrick Tabaka dismissed

them and when they scurried from the room he turned to Moses. 'Do you see, my brother. Even with the children, what hope do you have of changing it?'

'The hope is with the children,' Moses told him. 'Like monkeys, you can train them to do anything. It is the old ones who are difficult to change.'

* * *

Tara Courtney parked her shabby old Packard on the edge of the mountain drive and stood for a few seconds looking down on the city of Cape Town spread below her. The south-easter was whipping the waters of Table Bay to cream.

She left the car and walked slowly along the verge, pretending to admire the flush of wild flowers which painted the rocky slope above her. At the head of the slope the grey rock bastion of the mountain rose sheer to the heavens, and she stopped walking and tilted her head back to look up at it. The clouds were driving over the top, creating the illusion that the wall of rock was falling.

Once again she darted a glance along the road up which she had driven. It was still empty. She was not being followed. The police must have finally lost interest in her. It was weeks since last she had been aware of being tailed.

Her aimless behaviour altered and she returned to the Packard and took a small picnic basket from the boot, then she walked quickly back to the concrete building that housed the lower cable station. She ran up the stairs and paid for a return ticket just as the attendant opened the doors at the end of the waiting room, and the small party of other passengers trooped out to the gondola and crowded into it.

The crimson car started with a jerk and they rose swiftly, dangling below the silvery thread of the cable. The other passengers were exclaiming with delight as the spreading panorama of ocean and rock and city opened below them, and Tara inspected them surreptitiously. Within a few minutes she was convinced that none of them were plain-clothes members of the special branch and she relaxed and turned her attention to the magnificent view.

The gondola was climbing steeply, rising almost vertically up the face of the cliff. The rock had weathered into almost geometrical cubes, so that they seemed to be the ancient building blocks of a giant's castle. They passed a party of rock-climbers roped together inching their way hand over hand up the sheer face. Tara imagined being out there, clinging to the rock with the empty drop sucking at her heels, and vertigo made her sway dizzily. She had to clutch the handrail to steady herself, and when the gondola docked at the top station on the brink of the thousand-foot-high cliff, she escaped from it thankfully.

In the little tearoom, built to resemble an alpine chalet, Molly was waiting for her at one of the tables and she jumped up when she saw her friend.

Tara rushed to her and embraced her. 'Oh Molly, my dear dear Molly, I have missed you so.'

After a few moments they drew apart, slightly embarrassed by their own display and the smiles of the other teashop customers.

'I don't want to sit still,' Tara told her. 'I'm just bursting with excitement. Come on, let's walk. I've brought some sandwiches and a Thermos.'

They left the tearoom and wandered along the path that skirted the precipice.

In mid-week there were very few hikers on the mountain, and before they had gone a hundred yards they were alone.

'Tell me about all my old friends in the Black Sash,' Tara ordered. 'I want to know everything you have been doing. How is Derek and how are the children? Who is running my clinic now? Have you been there recently? Oh, I so miss it all, all of you.'

'Steady on,' Molly laughed. 'One question at a time – ' and she began to give Tara all the news. It took time, and while they chatted, they found a picnic spot and sat with their legs dangling over the cliff, drinking hot tea from the Thermos, and with scraps of bread feeding the fluffy little hyrax, the rock rabbits that crept out of the crevices and cracks of the cliff.

At last they exhausted their stocks of news and gossip, and sat in companionable silence. Tara broke it at last.

'Molly, I'm going to have another baby.'

'Ah ha!' Molly giggled. 'So that's what has been keeping you busy.' She glanced at Tara's stomach.

'It doesn't show yet. Are you certain?'

'Oh, for Pete's sake, Molly. I'm hardly the simpering virgin, you know. Give me credit for the four I have already! Of course I'm certain.'

'When is it due?'

'January next year.'

'Shasa will be pleased. He dotes on the kids. In fact, apart from money, they are the only things I've ever seen Shasa Courtney sentimental about. Have you told him yet?'

Tara shook her head. 'No. You are the only one I've told. I came to you first.'

'I'm flattered. I wish you both joy.' Then she paused as she noticed Tara's expression and studied her more seriously.

'For Shasa there will be little joy in it, I'm afraid,' Tara said softly. 'It's not Shasa's baby.'

'Good Lord, Tara! You of all people – ' then she broke off, and thought about it. 'I'm going to ask another silly question, Tara darling, but how do you know it isn't Shasa's effort?'

'Shasa and I – we don't – well, you know – we haven't been man and wife since – oh, not for ages.'

'I see.' Despite her affection and friendship, Molly's eyes sparkled with interest. This was intriguing. 'But, Tara love, that isn't the end of the world. Rush home now and get Shasa's pants off. Men are such clots, dates don't mean much to them, and if he does start counting, you can always bribe the doctor to tell him it's a prem.'

'No, Molly, listen to me. If ever he saw the infant, he would know.'

'I don't understand.'

'Molly, I am carrying Moses Gama's baby.'

'Sweet Christ!' Molly whispered.

The strength of Molly's reaction brought home to Tara the full gravity of the predicament in which she found herself.

Molly was a militant liberal, as colour-blind as Tara was herself, and yet Molly was stunned by the idea of a white woman bearing a black man's infant. In this country miscegenation was as nothing compared to the social outrage it would engender. She would become an outcast and a pariah.

'Oh dear,' Molly moderated her language. 'Oh dear, oh dear! My poor Tara, what a mess you are in. Does Moses know?'

'Not yet, but I hope to see him soon and I'll tell him.'

'You will have to get rid of it, of course. I have an address in Lourenço Marques. There is a Portuguese doctor there. We sent one of our girls from the orphange to him. He's expensive, but clean and good, not like some dirty old crone in a back room with a knitting needle.'

'Oh Molly, how could you think that of me? How could you believe I would murder my own baby?'

'You are going to keep it?' Molly gaped at her.

'Of course.'

'But, my dear, it will be – '

'Coloured,' Tara finished for her. 'Yes, I know, probably *café au lait* in colour and with crispy black hair and I will love it with all my heart. Just as I love the father.'

'I don't see how – '

'That's why I came to you.'

'I'll do whatever you want – just tell me what that is.'

'I want you, to find me a coloured couple. Good decent people, preferably with children of their own, who will take care of the infant for me until I can arrange to take it myself. Of course, they will have all the money they need and more – ' her voice trailed off and she stared at Molly imploringly.

Molly considered for a minute. 'I think I know the right couple. They are both school-teachers, and they have four of their own, all girls. They'll do it for me – but, Tara, how are you going to hide it? It will begin to show soon, you were huge with Isabella. Shasa might not notice, he's so busy looking into his cheque book, but your mother-in-law is an absolute tartar. You couldn't get anything by her.'

'I've already made plans to cover that. I have convinced Shasa that I have conceived a burning interest in archaeology to replace my political activities and I've got a job on the dig at Sundi Caves with the American archaeologist, Professor Marion Hurst, you know.'

'Yes, I've read two of her books.'

'I've told Shasa that I will only be away for two months, but once I'm out of sight I'll just keep postponing my return. Centaine will look after the children, I've arranged that also, she loves doing it and, the Lord knows, the kids will benefit from it. She's a much better disciplinarian than I am. They'll be perfectly behaved angels by the time my beloved mother-in-law is finished with them.'

'You'll miss them,' Molly stated, and Tara nodded.

'Yes, of course, I shall miss them, but it's only another six months to go.'

'Where will you have the child?' Molly persisted.

'I don't know. I can't go to a recognized hospital or nursing home. Oh God, could you imagine the fuss if I produced a little brown bundle on their clean whites-only sheets, in their lovely clean whites-only maternity hospital. Anyway, there is plenty of time to arrange all that later. The first thing is to get away to Sundi, away from Centaine Courtney-Malcomess' malevolent eye.'

'Why Sundi, Tara, what made you choose Sundi?'

'Because I will be near Moses.'

'Is it that important?' Molly stared at her mercilessly. 'Do you feel like that

about him? It wasn't just a little experiment, just a little kinky fun to find out what it is really like with one of them?'

Tara shook her head.

'Are you sure, Tara? I mean I've had the same urge occasionally. I suppose it's natural to be curious, but I've never been caught at it.'

'Molly, I love him. If he asked me, I would lay down my life for him without a qualm.'

'My poor sweet Tara.' Tears started in Molly's eyes, and she reached out with both arms. They hugged desperately and Molly whispered, 'He is far beyond your reach, my darling. You can never, never have him.'

'If I can have a little piece of him, for even a little while. That will be enough for me.'

* * *

Moses Gama parked the crimson and blue butchery van in front of the visitors' bay and switched off the engine. In front of him stretched lawns on which a single small sprinkler was trying to atone for all the frosts and drought of the highveld winter, but the Kikuyu grass was seared and lifeless. Beyond the lawn was the long double-storied block of the Baragwanath nurses' home.

A small group of black nurses came up the pathway from the main hospital. They were in crisp white uniform, neat and efficient-looking, but when they drew level with the van and saw Moses at the wheel, they dissolved into giggles, hiding their mouths with their hands in the instinctive gesture of subservience to the male.

'Young woman, I wish to speak to you.' Moses leaned out for the window of the van. 'Yes, you!' The chosen nurse was almost overcome wth shyness. Her friends teased her as she approached Moses and paused timidly five paces from him.

'Do you know Sister Victoria Dinizulu?'

'*Eh he!*' the nurse affirmed.

'Where is she?'

'She is coming now. She is on the day shift with me.' The nurse looked around her for escape, and instead picked out Victoria in the middle of the second group of white-clad figures coming up the path. 'There she is. Victoria! Come quickly!' the girl cried, and then fled, taking the steps up into the nurses' home two at a time. Victoria recognized him, and with a word to her friends, left them and cut across the dry brown lawns, coming directly to him. Moses climbed out of the van, and she looked up at him.

'I'm sorry. There was a terrible bus accident, we were working in theatre until the last case was attended to. I have kept you waiting.'

Moses nodded. 'It's not important. We have plenty of time still.'

'It will take me only a few minutes to change into street clothes,' she smiled up at him. Her teeth were perfect, so white that they seemed almost translucent and her skin had the lustre of health and youth. 'I am so pleased to see you again – but I do have a very big bone to pick with you.' They were speaking English, and although hers was accented, she seemed confident in the language with a choice of words which matched his own fluency.

'Good,' he smiled gravely. 'We will have your bone for dinner – which will save me money.'

She laughed, a fine throaty chuckle. 'Don't go away, I will be back.' She turned and went into the nurses' home, and he watched her with pleasure as she climbed the steps. Her waist was so narrow that it accentuated the swell of her buttocks under the white uniform. Although her bosom was small, she was full-bottomed and broad-hipped; she would carry a child with ease. That kind of body was the model of Nguni beauty, and Moses was strongly reminded of the photographs he had seen of the Venus de Milo. Her carriage was erect, her neck long and straight, and although her hips swayed as though she danced to a distant music, her head and shoulders never moved. It was obvious that as a child she had taken her turn with the other young girls at carrying the brimming clay pots up from the water-hole, balancing the pot on her head without spilling a drop. That was how the Zulu girls acquired that marvellously regal posture.

With her round madonna face and huge dark eyes, she was one of the handsomest women he had ever seen, and while he waited, leaning against the bonnet of the van, he pondered how each race had its ideal of feminine beauty, and how widely they differed. That led him to think of Tara Courtney, with her huge round breasts and narrow boyish hips, her long chestnut hair and soft insipid white skin. Moses grimaced, faintly repelled by the image, and yet both women were crucial to his ambitions, and his sensual response to them – attraction or revulsion – was completely irrelevant. All that mattered was their utility.

Victoria came back down the steps ten minutes later. She was wearing a vivid crimson dress. Bright colours suited her, they set off that glossy dark skin. She slid into the passenger's seat of the van beside him, and glanced at the cheap gold-plated watch on her wrist. 'Eleven minutes sixteen seconds. You cannot really complain,' she announced, and he smiled and started the engine.

'Now let us pick your thighbone of a dinosaur,' he suggested.

'Tyrannosaurus Rex,' she corrected him. 'The most ferocious of the dinosaurs. But, no, we'll keep that for dinner as you suggested.'

Her banter amused him. It was unusual for an unmarried black girl to be so forthcoming and self-assured. Then he remembered her training and her life here at one of the world's largest and busiest hospitals. This wasn't a little country girl, empty-headed and giggling, and as if to make the point, Victoria fell into an easy discussion of General Dwight Eisenhower's prospects for election to the White House, and how that would affect the American civil rights struggle – and ultimately their own struggle here in Africa.

While they talked, the sun began to set and the city, with all its fine buildings and parks, fell behind them, until abruptly they entered the half world of Soweto township where half a million black people lived. The dusk was thick with the smell of wood-smoke from the cooking fires, and it turned the sunset a diabolical red, the colour of blood and oranges. The narrow unmade sidewalks were crowded with black commuters, each of them carrying a parcel or a shopping bag, all hurrying in the same direction, back to their homes after a long day that had begun before the sun with a tortuous journey by bus or train to their places of work in the outer world, and that now ended in darkness with the reverse journey which fatigue made even longer and more tedious.

The van slowed as the streets became more crowded, and then some of them recognized Moses and ran ahead of them, clearing the way.

'Moses Gama! It's Moses Gama, let him pass!' And as they went by, some of them shouted greetings.

'I see you, *Nkosi*.'

'I see you, *Baba*!' They called him father and lord.

When they reached the community centre which abutted the administration buildings, the huge hall was overflowing, and they were forced to leave the van and go on foot for the last hundred yards.

However, the Buffaloes were there to escort them. Hendrick Tabaka's enforcers pushed a way through the solid pack of humanity, tempering this show of force with smiles and jokes so the crowd made way for them without resentment.

'It is Moses Gama, let him pass,' and Victoria hung on to his arm and laughed with the excitement of it.

As they went in through the main doors of the hall, she glanced up and saw the name above the door: H. F. VERWOERD COMMUNITY HALL.

It was fast becoming a custom for the Nationalist government to name all state buildings, airports, dams and other public works after political luminaries and mediocrities, but there was an unusual irony in naming the community hall of the largest black township after the white architect of the laws which they had gathered here to protest. Hendrik Frensch Verwoerd was the minister of Bantu affairs, and the principal architect of *apartheid*.

Inside the hall, the noise was thunderous. A permit to use the hall for a political rally would have been denied by the township administration, so officially this had been billed and advertised as a rock 'n' roll concert by a band that gloried in the name of 'The Marmalade Mambas'.

They were on the stage now, four of them dressed in tight-fitting sequined suits that glittered in the flashing coloured lights. A bank of amplifiers sent the music crashing over the packed audience, like an aerial bombardment, and the dancers screamed back at them, swaying and writhing to the rhythm like a single monstrous organism.

The Buffaloes opened a path for them across the dance floor and the dancers recognized Moses and shouted greetings, trying to touch him as he passed. Then the band became aware of his presence and broke off in the middle of the wild driving beat to give him a trumpet fanfare and a roll of drums.

Dozens of willing hands helped Moses up on to the stage, while Victoria remained below with her head at the level of his knees, trapped in the press of bodies that pressed forward to see and to hear Moses Gama. The band leader attempted to introduce him but even the power of the electronic amplifiers could not lift his voice above the tumultuous welcome that they gave Moses. From four thousand throats a savage sustained roar rose and went on and on without diminution. It broke over Moses Gama like a wild sea driven by a winter gale, and like a rock he stood unmoved by it.

Then he lifted his arms, and the sound died away swiftly until a suppressed and aching silence hung over that great press of humanity, and into that silence Moses Gama roared.

'*Amandla!* Power!'

As a single voice they roared back at him, '*Amandla!*'

He shouted again, in that deep thrilling voice that rang against the rafters and reached into the depths of their hearts.

'*Mayibuye!*'

They bellowed the reply back at him.

'*Afrika!* Let Africa persist.'

And then they were silent again, expectant and wound up with excitement and tension, as Moses Gama began to speak.

'Let us talk of Africa,' he said.

'Let us talk of a rich and fruitful land with tiny barren pockets on which our people are forced to live.

'Let us speak of the children without schools and the mothers without hope.

'Let us speak of taxes and passes.

'Let us speak of famine and sickness.

'Let us speak of those who labour in the harsh sunlight, and in the depths of the dark earth.

'Let us speak of those who live in the compounds far from their families.

'Let us speak of hunger and tears and the hard laws of the Boers.'

For an hour he held them in his hands, and they listened in silence except for the groans and involuntary gasps of anguish, and the occasional growl of anger, and at the end Victoria found she was weeping. The tears flowed freely and unashamedly down her beautiful upturned moon face.

When Moses finished, he dropped his arms and lowered his chin upon his chest, exhausted and shaken by his own passion and a vast silence fell upon them. They were too moved to shout or to applaud.

In the silence Victoria suddenly flung herself on to the stage and faced them.

'*Nkosi sikelel' iAfrika*,' she sang.

'God save Africa,' and immediately the band picked up the refrain, while from the body of the hall their magnificent African voices soared in haunting chorus. Moses Gama stepped up beside her and took her hand in his, and their voices blended.

At the end it took them almost twenty minutes to escape from the hall, their way was blocked by the thousands who wanted the experience to last, to touch them and to hear their voices and to be a part of the struggle.

In the course of one short evening the beautiful Zulu girl in the flaming crimson dress had become part of the almost mystic legend that surrounded Moses Gama. Those who were fortunate enough to be there that evening would tell those who had not, how she had looked like a queen as she stood and sang before them, a queen that befitted the tall black emperor at her side.

'I have never experienced anything like that,' Vicky told him, when at last they were alone again, and the little blue and crimson van was humming back along the main highway towards Johannesburg. 'The love they bear you is so powerful – ' she broke off. 'I just can't describe it.'

'Sometimes it frightens me,' he agreed. 'They place such a heavy responsibility upon me.'

'I don't believe you know what fear is,' she said.

'I do.' He shook his head. 'I know it better than most.' And then he changed the subject. 'What time is it? We must find something to eat before curfew.'

'It's only nine o'clock.' Victoria looked surprised as she turned the dial of her wristwatch to catch the light of a street lamp. 'I thought it would be much later. I seem to have lived a lifetime in one short evening.'

Ahead of them a neon sign flickered: 'DOLLS' HOUSE DRIVE-IN. Tasty Eats.' Moses slowed and turned the van into the parking lot. He left Vicky for a few minutes to go to the counter of the replica dolls' house, then he returned with hamburgers and coffee in two paper mugs.

'Ah, that's good!' she mumbled through a mouthful of hamburger. 'I didn't realize I was so hungry.'

'Now what about the bone you threaten me with?' Moses asked, and he spoke in fluent Zulu.

'You speak Zulu!' She was amazed. 'I didn't know. When did you learn?' she demanded in the same language.

'I speak many languages,' he told her. 'If I want to reach all the people, there is no other way.' And he smiled. 'However, young woman, you don't change the subject so easily. Tell me about this bone.'

'Oh, I feel so stupid talking about it now, after all we have shared this evening – ' she hesitated. 'I was going to ask you why you sent your brother to speak to my father before you had said anything to me. I'm not a country girl of the kraals, you know. I am a modern woman with a mind of her own.'

'Victoria, we should not discard the old traditions in our struggle for liberation. What I did was out of respect for you and for your father. I am sorry if it offended you.'

'I was a little ruffled,' she admitted.

'Will it help at all if I ask you now?' he smiled. 'You can still refuse. Before we go any further, think very deeply. If you marry me, you marry the cause. Our marriage will be part of the struggle of our people, and the road before us will be hard and dangerous, with never an end in sight.'

'I do not need to think,' she said softly. 'Tonight when I stood there before our people with your hand in mine, I knew that was the reason why I was born.'

He took both her hands in his and drew her gently towards him, but before their mouths could touch, the harsh white beam of a powerful spotlight shone into their faces. Startled, they drew apart, shielding their eyes with raised hands.

'Hey, what is this?' Moses exclaimed.

'Police!' a voice answered from the darkness beyond the open side window. 'Get out both of you!'

They climbed out of the van, and Moses went around the bonnet to stand beside Victoria. He saw that while they had been engrossed with each other, a police pick-up had entered the parking lot and parked beside the restaurant building. Now four blue-uniformed constables with flashlights were checking the occupants of all the parked vehicles in the lot.

'Let me see your passes, both of you.' The constable in front of him was still shining the light in his eyes, but beyond it Moses could make out that he was very young.

Moses reached into his inner pocket, while Victoria searched in her purse, and they handed their pass booklets to the constable. He turned the beam of the flashlight on them and studied them minutely.

'It's almost curfew,' he said in Afrikaans, as he handed them back. 'You Bantu should be in your own locations at this time of night.'

'There is still an hour and a half until curfew,' Victoria replied sharply, and the constable's expression hardened.

'Don't take that tone with me, maid.' That term of address was insulting and again he shone the flashlight in her face. 'Just because you've got shoes on your feet and rouge on your face, doesn't mean you are a white woman. Just remember that.'

Moses took Victoria's arm and firmly steered her back to the van. 'We are

leaving right away, officer,' he said placatingly, and once they were both in the van, he told Victoria, 'You will accomplish nothing by getting us both arrested. That is just a callow little white boy with more authority than he knows how to handle.'

'Forgive me,' she said. 'I just get so angry. What were they looking for anyway?'

'They were looking for white men with black girls, their Immorality Act to keep their precious white blood pure. Half their police force spends its time trying to peer into other people's bedrooms.' He started the van and turned into the highway.

Neither of them spoke again until he parked in front of the Baragwanath nurses' home.'

'I hope we will not be interrupted again,' Moses said quietly, and placing an arm around her shoulders turned her gently to face him.

Although she had seen how it was done on the cinema screen, and although the other girls in the hostel endlessly discussed what they referred to as 'Hollywood style', Victoria had never kissed a man. It was not part of Zulu custom or tradition. So she lifted her face to him with a mixture of trepidation and breathless expectation, and was amazed at the warmth and softness of his mouth. Swiftly the stiffness and tension went out of her neck and shoulders and she seemed to mould herself to him.

* * *

The work at Sundi Caves was even more interesting than Tara Courtney had expected it to be, and she adapted rapidly to the leisurely pace and life and intellectually stimulating companionship of the small specialist team of which she was now a part.

Tara shared a tent with two young students from the University of the Witwatersrand, and she found with mild surprise that the close proximity of other women in such spartan accomodation did not bother her. They were up long before dawn to escape the heat in the middle of the day, and after a quick and frugal breakfast, Professor Hurst led them up to the site and allocated the day's labours. They rested and ate the main meal at noon, and then as the day cooled, they returned to the site and worked on until the light faded. After that they had only enough energy for a hot shower, a light meal and the narrow camp beds.

The site was in a deep kloof. The rocky sides dropped steeply two hundred feet to the narrow riverbed in the gut. The vegetation in the protected and sun-warmed valley was tropical, quite alien to that on the exposed grasslands that were scoured by wind and winter frosts. Tall candelabra aloes grew on the upper slopes, while farther down it became even denser, and there were tree ferns and cycads, and huge strangler figs with bark like elephant hide, grey and wrinkled.

The caves themselves were a series of commodious open galleries that ran with the exposed strata. They were ideal for habitation by primitive man, located high up the slope and protected from the prevailing winds yet with a wide view across the plain on to which the kloof debouched. They were close to water and readily defensible against all marauders, and the depth of the midden

and accumulated detritus on the floor of the caves attested to the ages over which they had been occupied.

The roofs of the caves were darkened with the smoke of countless cooking fires and the inner walls were decorated with the engravings and childlike paintings of the ancient San peoples and their predecessors. All the signs of a major site with the presence of very early hominids were evident, and although the dig was still in its early stages and they had penetrated only the upper levels, spirits and optimism were high and the whole feeling on the dig was of a close-knit community of persons bound by a common interest co-operating selflessly on a project of outstanding importance.

Tara particularly liked Marion Hurst, the American professor in charge of the excavations. She was a woman in her early fifties, with cropped grey hair, and a skin burned to the colour and consistency of saddle-leather by the suns of Arabia and Africa. They had become firm friends even before Tara discovered that she was married to a negro professor of anthropology at Cornell. That knowledge made their relationship secure, and relieved Tara of the necessity of any subterfuge.

One night she sat late with Marion in the shed they were using as a laboratory, and suddenly Tara found herself telling her about Moses Gama and her impossible love, even about the child she was carrying. The elder woman's sympathy was immediate and sincere.

'What iniquitous social order can keep people from loving others – of course, I knew all about these laws before I came here. That is why Tom stayed at home. Despite my personal feelings, the work here was just too important to pass up. However, you have my promise that I will do anything in my power to help the two of you.'

Yet Tara had been on the dig for five weeks without having heard from Moses Gama. She had written him a dozen letters and telephoned the Rivonia number, and the other number in Drake's Farm township. Moses was never there, and never responded to her urgent messages.

At last she could stand it no longer, and she borrowed Marion's pick-up truck and went into the city, almost an hour's drive with the first half of the journey over clay roads that were rutted and bumpy and finally over wide black-top highways in a solid stream of heavy traffic, coming up from the coalfields at Witbank.

She parked the pick-up under the bluegum trees at the back of Puck's Hill land and was suddenly afraid to see him again, terrified that it had all changed and he would send her away. It took all her courage to leave the cab of the pick-up and go around the big unkempt house to the front verandah.

At the far end there was a man sitting at the desk and her heart soared and then as swiftly plunged as he turned and saw her and stood up. It was Marcus Archer. He came down the long verandah towards her, and his smile was spiteful and vinegary.

'Surprise!' he said. 'The last person I expected to see.'

'Hello, Marcus. I was looking for Moses.'

'I know who you are looking for, dearie.'

'Is he here?'

Marcus shook his head. 'I haven't seen him for almost two weeks.'

'I have written and telephoned – he doesn't reply. I was worried.'

'Perhaps he doesn't reply, because he doesn't want to see you.'

'Why do you dislike me so, Marcus?'

'Oh my dear, whatever gave you that idea?' Marcus smiled archly.

'I'm sorry to have bothered you.' She began to turn away and then paused. Her expression hardened. 'Will you give him a message, when you see him?'

Marcus inclined his head, and for the first time she noticed the grey hairs in his ginger sideburns and the wrinkles in the corners of his eyes. He was much older than she had thought.

'Will you tell Moses that I came to find him, and that nothing has changed. That I meant every word I said.'

'Very well, dearie. I'll tell him.'

Tara went down the steps, but when she reached the bottom, he called after her.

'Tara.' And she looked up. He leaned on the railing of the verandah. 'You'll never have him. You know that, don't you? He will keep you only as long as he needs you. Then he will cast you aside. He will never belong to you.'

'Nor to you either, Marcus Archer,' she said softly, and he recoiled from her. 'He belongs to neither of us. He belongs to Africa and his people.' And she saw the desolation in his eyes. It gave her no satisfaction, and she went slowly back to the pick-up and drove away.

* * *

At Level Six in the main gallery of the Sundi Caves they exposed an extensive deposit of clay pottery fragments. There were no intact artefacts, and it was obviously a dumping site for the ancient potters. Nevertheless, the discovery was of crucial importance in dating the levels for the pottery was of a very early type.

Marion Hurst was excited by the find, and transmitted her excitement to all of them. By this time Tara had been promoted from the heavy work of grubbing in the dirt at the bottom of the trenches. She had displayed a natural aptitude for the puzzle game of fitting the fragments of bone and pottery together in their original form, and she now worked in the long prefabricated shed under Marion Hurst's direct supervision and was making herself an invaluable member of the team.

Tara found that while she was absorbed with the fragments, she could suppress the ache of longing and the turmoil of uncertainty and guilt. She knew that her neglect of her children and her family was unforgivable. Once a week she telephoned Rhodes Hill and spoke to her father and Centaine and Isabella. The child seemed quite content, and in a strangely selfish way Tara resented the fact that she seemed not to pine for her mother but was accepting her grandmother as a happy substitute. Centaine was friendly and made no criticism of her continued absence, but Blaine Malcomess, her beloved father, was as usual bluntly outspoken.

'I don't know what you are trying to run away from, Tara, but believe me it never works. Your place is here with your husband and your children. Enough of this nonsense now. You know your duty, however unpleasant you may find it – it's still your duty.'

Of course, Shasa and the boys would soon be returning from their grand safari, and then she could procrastinate no longer. She would have to make a decision, and she was not even certain of the alternatives. Sometimes in the

night, in those silent small hours when human energy and spirits are at their lowest ebb, she even considered following Molly's advice and aborting the child from her womb and turning her back on Moses, going back to the seductive and destructively soft life of Weltevreden.

'Oh, Moses, if only I could see you again. Just to speak to you for a few hours – then I would know what to do.'

She found herself withdrawing from the company of the other workers on the excavation. The cheerful carefree attitude of the two university students she shared her tent with began to irritate her. Their conversation was so naïve and childlike, even the music they played endlessly on a portable tape recorder was so loud and uncouth that it rasped her nerves.

With Marion's blessing she purchased a small tent of her own and erected it near the laboratory where she worked, so that when the others took their noonday siesta, she could slip back to her work bench and forget all her insoluble problems in the totally absorbing task of fitting together the shattered scraps. Their antiquity seemed to soothe her and make the problems of the present seem trivial and unimportant.

It was here, at her bench, in the middle of a hot somnolent highveld afternoon, that the light from the open doorway was blocked suddenly, and she looked up frowning, wiping back the sweaty wisps of hair from her forehead with the back of her hand, and then her mouth went dry and her heart seemed to freeze for a long moment and then race wildly.

The sunlight was behind him, so his was a tall silhouette, broad-shouldered, slim-hipped and regal. She sobbed and sprang up from the bench and flew to him, wrapping her arms around his chest and pressing her face to his heart so that she could feel it beat against her cheek. She could not speak, and his voice was deep and gentle above her.

'I have been cruel to you. I should have come to you sooner.'

'No,' she whispered. 'It doesn't matter. Now that you are here, nothing else matters.'

He stayed only one night, and Marion Hurst protected them from the other members of the expedition so that they were alone in her small tent, isolated from the world and its turmoil. Tara did not sleep that night, each moment was far too precious to waste.

In the dawn he said to her. 'I must go again soon. There is something that you must do for me.'

'Anything!' she whispered.

'Our campaign of defiance begins soon. There will be terrible risk and sacrifice by thousands of our people, but for their sacrifice to be worth while it must be brought to the attention of the world.'

'What can I do?' she asked.

'By a most fortunate coincidence, there is an American television team in the country at this very moment. They are making a series called "Africa on Focus".'

'Yes, I know about them. They interviewed – ' she broke off. She didn't want to mention Shasa, not now, not during this treasured interlude.

'They interviewed your husband,' he finished for her. 'Yes, I know. However, they have almost finished filming and I have heard that they plan to return to the United States within the next few days. We need them here. We need them to film and record our struggle. They must show it to the world –

the spirit of our people, the indomitable will to rise above oppression and inhumanity.'

'How can I help?'

'I cannot reach the producer of this service on my own. I need a go-between. We have to prevent them leaving. We have to make certain they are here to film the defiance when it begins. You must speak to the woman in charge of the filming. Her name is Godolphin, Kitty Godolphin, and she will be staying at the Sunnyside Hotel in Johannesburg for the next three days.'

'I will go to her today.'

'Tell her that the time is not yet agreed – but when it is, I will let her know, and she must be there with her camera.'

'I will see that she is,' Tara promised, and he rolled her gently on to her back and made love to her again. It seemed impossible, but for Tara every time was better than the last, and when he left her and rose from the campbed, she felt weak and soft and warm as molten wax.

'Moses,' she said softly, and he paused in buttoning the pale blue open-neck shirt.

'What is it?' he asked softly.

She had to tell him about the child she was carrying. She sat up, letting the rumpled sheet fall to her waist and her breasts, already heavy with her pregnancy, were dappled with tiny blue veins beneath the ivory smooth skin.

'Moses,' she repeated stupidly, trying to find the courage to say it, and he came to her.

'Tell me,' he commanded, and her courage failed her. She could not tell him, the risk that it would drive him away was too great.

'I just wanted to tell you how grateful I am that you have given me this opportunity to be of service to the struggle.'

* * *

It was much easier to contact Kitty Godolphin than she had expected it to be. She borrowed Marion's pick-up and drove five miles to the nearest village, and telephoned from the public booth in the little single-roomed post office. The operator in the Sunnyside Hotel put her through to the room, and a firm young voice with a Louisiana lilt said, 'Kitty Godolphin. Who is it please?'

'I'd rather not give my name, Miss Godolphin. But I would like to meet you as soon as possible. I have a story for you, an important and dramatic story.'

'When and where do you want to meet?'

'It will take me two hours to reach your hotel.'

'I'll be waiting for you,' said Kitty Godolphin, and it was as easy as that.

Tara checked with Reception and the girl at the desk phoned through to Miss Godolphin's suite and then told her to go up.

A young girl, slim and pretty, in a tartan shirt and blue jeans opened the door to Tara's ring.

'Hello, is Miss Godolphin in? She's expecting me.'

The girl looked her over carefully, taking in her khaki bush skirt and mosquito boots, her tanned arms and face and the scarf tied around her thick auburn hair.

'I'm Kitty Godolphin,' said the girl, and Tara could not hide her surprise.

'Okay, don't tell me. You expected an old bag. Come on in and tell me who you are.'

In the lounge Tara removed her sunglasses and faced her.

'My name is Tara Courtney. I understand you know my husband. Shasa Courtney, Chairman of Courtney Mining and Finance.'

She saw the shift in the other woman's expression, and the sudden hard gleam in those eyes that she had thought were frank and innocent.

'I meet a lot of people in my business, Mrs Courtney.'

Tara had not expected the hostility, and hurriedly she tried to forestall it.

'I'm sure you do – '

'Did you want to talk to me about your husband, lady? I don't have a lot of time to waste.' Kitty looked pointedly at her wristwatch. It was a man's Rolex and she wore it on the inside of her wrist like a soldier.

'No, I'm sorry. I didn't mean to give you that impression. I have come here on behalf of someone else, someone who is unable to come to you himself.'

'Why not?' Kitty asked sharply, and Tara readjusted her early estimate of her. Despite her childlike appearance, she was as tough and sharp as any man Tara had ever met.

'Because he is being watched by the police special branch, and because what he is planning is dangerous and illegal.' Tara saw instantly that she had said the right things and had aroused the newswoman's instinct.

'Sit down, Mrs Courtney. Do you want some coffee?' She picked up the house phone and ordered from room service, then turned back to Tara.

'Now tell me. Who is this mysterious person?'

'You probably have never heard of him, but soon the whole world will know his name,' Tara said. 'It's Moses Gama.'

'Moses Gama, hell!' Kitty Godolphin exclaimed. 'For six weeks now I've been trying to catch up with him. I was beginning to think he was just a rumour, and that he didn't really exist. A scarlet pimpernel.'

'He exists,' Tara assured her.

'Can you get me an interview with him?' Kitty demanded, so anxious that she leaned across and grasped Tara's wrist impulsively. 'He's an Emmy score, that one. He is the one person in South Africa I really want to talk to.'

'I can do a whole lot better than that,' Tara promised her.

* * *

Shasa Courtney was determined that his sons would not grow up believing that the affluent white suburbs of Cape Town and Johannesburg were all of Africa. This safari was to show them the old Africa, primeval and eternal, and to establish for them a firm link with their history and their ancestors, to engender in them a sense of pride in what they were and in those who had gone before them.

He had set aside six whole weeks, the full period of the boys' school holidays, for this venture, and that had taken a great deal of planning and considerable heart-searching. The affairs of the company were so many-faceted and complex that he did not like leaving them, even in such capable hands as those of David Abrahams. The shaft-sinking at Silver River was going ahead apace, and they were down almost a thousand feet already while work on the plant was also far

advanced. Apart from that, the first six pilchard trawlers for the factory at Walvis Bay were due for delivery in three weeks' time, and the canning plant was on the water from the suppliers in the United Kingdom. There was so much happening, so many problems that could demand his immediate decision.

Centaine was, of course, always on hand for David to consult with, but of late she had withdrawn more and more from the running of the company, and there were many eventualities that might arise that could only be dealt with by Shasa personally. Shasa weighed up the chances of this happening against what was necessary, in his view, for his sons' education and understanding of their place in Africa and their inherited duties and responsibilities, and decided he had to risk it. As a last resort he arranged a strict itinerary for the safari, of which both Centaine and David had a copy, so that they would know exactly where he was during every day of his absence, and a radio contact would be maintained with the H'ani Mine so that an aircraft could reach any of his camps in the deep bush within four or five hours.

'If you do call me out, then the reason had better be ironclad,' Shasa warned David grimly. 'This is probably the only time in our lives that the boys and I will be able to do this.'

They left from the H'ani Mine the last week in May. Shasa had taken the boys out of school a few days early, which in itself was enough to put everybody in the right mood and ensure a splendid beginning. He had commandeered four of the mine's trucks and made up a full team of safari boys, including drivers, camp servants, skinners, trackers, gunbearers and the chef from the H'ani Mine Club. Of course, Shasa's own personal hunting vehicle was always kept in the mine workshops, tuned to perfection and ready to go at any time. It was an ex-army jeep which had been customized and modified by the mine engineers without regard to expense. It had everything from long-range fuel tanks and gun racks to a shortwave radio set, and the seats were upholstered in genuine zebra skin while the paintwork was an artistic creation in bush camouflage. Proudly the boys clipped their Winchester .22 repeaters into the gun rack beside Shasa's big .375 Holland and Holland magnum, and dressed in their new khaki bush jackets, scrambled into their seats in the jeep. As was the right of the eldest, Sean sat up front beside his father, with Michael and Garry in the open back.

'Anybody want to change his mind and stay at home?' Shasa asked as he started the jeep, and they took the question seriously, shaking their heads in unison, eyes shining and faces pale with excitement, too overcome to speak.

'Here we go then,' Shasa said and they drove down the hill from the mine offices with the convoy of four trucks following them.

The uniformed mine guards opened the main gates and gave them a flashy salute, grinning widely as the jeep passed, and behind them the camp boys on the backs of the open trucks started to sing one of the traditional safari songs.

Weep, oh you women, tonight you sleep alone
The long road calls us and we must go –

Their voices rose and fell to the eternal rhythm of Africa, full of its promise and mystery, echoing its grandeur and its savagery, setting the mood for the magical adventure into which Shasa took his sons.

They drove hard those first two days to get beyond the areas which had been

spoiled by men's too frequent intrusions with rifle and four-wheel drive vehicle, where the veld was almost bare of large game and those animals that they did see were in small herds that were running as soon as they heard the first hum of the jeep engine and were merely tiny specks in their own dust by the time they spotted them.

Sadly Shasa realized how much had changed since his earliest memory of this country. He had been Sean's age then and the herds of springbok and gemsbok had been on every side, great herds, trusting and confiding. There had been giraffe and lion, and small bands of Bushmen, those fascinating little yellow pygmies of the desert. Now, however, wild men and beast had all retreated before the inexorable advance of civilization deeper and deeper into the wilderness. Even now, Shasa could look ahead to the day when there would be no more wilderness, no more retreat for the wild things, when the roads and the railway lines would criss-cross the land and the endless villages and kraals would stand in the desolation they had created. The time when the trees were all cut down for firewood, and the grass was eaten to the roots by the goats and the top soil turned to dust and blew on the wind. The vision filled him with sadness and a sense of despair, and he had to make a conscious effort to throw it off so as not to spoil the experience for his sons.

'I owe them this glimpse of the past. They must know a little of the Africa that once was, before it has all gone, so that they will understand something of its glory.' And he smiled and told them the stories, reaching back in his memory to bring out for them all his own experiences, and then going back farther, to what he had learned from his own mother, and from his grandfather, trying to make clear to them the extent and depth of their family's involvement with this land, and they sat late around the camp fire that first night, listening avidly until, despite themselves, their eyelids drooped and their heads began to nod.

On they went, driving hard all day over rutted tracks, through desert scrub and grassland and then through mopani forest, not yet stopping to hunt, eating the food they had brought with them from the mine, though that night the servants muttered about fresh meat.

On the third day they left the rudimentary road they had been following since dawn. It was nothing more than a double track of tyres that had last been used months before, but now Shasa let it swing away towards the east and they went on northwards, breaking fresh ground, weaving through the open forest until abruptly they came out on the banks of a river, not one of the great African rivers like the Kavango, but one of its tributaries. Still, it was fifty feet wide, but green and deep, a formidable barrier that would have turned back any hunting safari before them that had come this far north.

Two weeks previously Shasa had reconnoitred this entire area from the air, flying the Mosquito low over the tree tops so that he could count the animals in each herd of game, and judge the size of the ivory tusks that each elephant carried. He had marked this branch of the river on his large-scale map, and had navigated the convoy back to this exact spot. He recognized it by the oxbow bend of the banks and the giant makuyu trees on the opposite side, with a fish eagle nest in the upper branches.

They camped another two days on the southern river bank while every member of the safari, including the three boys and the fat Herero chef, helped to build the bridge. They cut the mopani poles in the forest, thick as a fat woman's thigh and forty feet long, and dragged them up with the jeep. Shasa

kept guard against crocodiles, standing high on the bank with the .375 magnum under his arm while his naked gangs floated the poles out into the centre of the river and set them into the mud of the bottom. Then they lashed the cross-ties to them with ropes of mopani bark that still wept glutinous sap, red as blood.

When at last the bridge was complete, they unloaded the vehicles to lighten them, and one at a time Shasa drove them out on to the rickety structure. It swayed and creaked and rocked under them, but at last he had the jeep and all four trucks on the far bank.

'Now the safari truly begins,' he told the boys. They had entered a pocket of country, protected by its remoteness and its natural barriers of forest and river from men's over-exploitation, and from the air Shasa had seen the herds of buffalo thick as domestic cattle and the clouds of white egrets hovering over them.

That night he told the boys stories about the old elephant hunters – 'Karamojo' Bell, and Frederick Selous and Sean Courtney their own ancestor, Shasa's great-uncle and namesake of his eldest son.

'They were tough men, all of them, incredible shots and natural athletes. They had to be to survive the hardships and the tropical disease. When he was a young man, Sean Courtney hunted on foot in the tsetse-fly belt of the Zambezi valley where the temperature reaches 115° at noon, and he could run forty miles in a day after the big tuskers. His eye was so sharp he could actually see the flight of his bullet.' The boys listened with total fascination, pleading with him to continue whenever he paused, until at last he told them, 'That's enough. You have to be up early tomorrow. Five o'clock in the morning. We are going to hunt for the first time.'

In the dark they drove slowly along the northern bank of the river in the open jeep, all of them bundled up against the cold for the frost lay thick in the open vleis and crunched under the jeep's tyres. In the first feeble light of dawn they found where a herd of buffalo had drunk during the night and then gone back into the heavy bush.

They left the jeep on the river bank, and stripped off their padded anoraks. Then Shasa put his two Ovambo trackers to the spoor and they followed the herd on foot. As they moved silently and swiftly through the dense second-growth mopani thickets, Shasa explained it all to the boys, speaking in a whisper and relying on hand signals to point out the different hoof prints of old bull and cow and calf, or to draw their attention to other smaller but equally fascinating animals and birds and insects in the forest around them.

A little before noon they finally came up with the herd. Over a hundred of the huge cow-like beasts, with their trumpet-shaped ears and the drooping horns that gave them such a lugubrious air. Most of them were lying in the mopani shade, ruminating quietly, although one or two of the herd bulls were dozing on their feet. The only movement was the lazy flick of their tails as the stinging flies swarmed over their flanks.

Shasa showed the boys how to work in close. Using the breeze and every stick of cover, freezing whenever one of the great horned heads swung in their direction, he took them within thirty feet of the biggest of the bulls. They could smell him, the hot rank bovine reek of him, and they could hear his breathing puffing through his wet drooling muzzle, hear his teeth grinding on his cud, so close they could see the bald patches of age on his shoulders and rump and the

balls of dried mud from the wallow that clung in the stiff black hairs of his back and belly.

While they held their breaths in delicious terror and watched in total fascination, Shasa slowly raised the heavy rifle and aimed into the bull's thick neck, just forward of his massive shoulder.

'Bang!' he shouted, and the great bull plunged forward wildly, crashing into the screen of thick mopani, and Shasa gathered his sons and drew them into the shelter of one of the grey tree trunks, keeping his arms around them while on all sides the panicking herd galloped, huge black shapes thundering by, the calves bawling and the old bulls grunting.

The sounds of their flight dwindled away into the forest though the dust of their passage hung misty in the air around them, and Shasa was laughing with the joy of it as he let his arms fall from their shoulders.

'Why did you do that?' Sean demanded furiously, turning his face up to his father. 'You could have shot him easily – why didn't you kill him?'

'We didn't come out here to kill,' Shasa explained. 'We came here to hunt.'

'But – ' Sean's outrage turned to bewilderment ' – but what's the difference?'

'Ah! That's what you have to learn. That bull was a big one, but not big enough, and we have all the meat we need, so I let him go. That's lesson number one. Now, for lesson number two – none of you is going to kill anything until you know all about that animal, understand its habits and life cycle, and learn to respect it and hold it in high esteem. Then and only then.'

In camp that evening he gave them each two books, which he had had bound in leather with their own names on the cover: Roberts' *Mammals of South Africa* and his *Birds of South Africa*.

'I brought these especially for you, and I want you to study them,' he ordered. Sean looked appalled, he hated books and studying, but both Garry and Mickey hurried to their tent to begin the task.

Over the days that followed he questioned them on every animal and bird they saw. At first the questions were elementary, but he made them progressively more difficult and soon they could quote the biological names and give him full details of sizes and body weights of males and females, their calls and behaviour patterns, distribution and breeding, down to the smallest detail. Set an example by his younger brothers, even Sean mastered the difficult Latin names.

However, it was ten days before they were allowed to fire a shot – and then it was only bird-hunting. Under strict supervision, they were allowed to hunt the fat brown francolin and speckled guinea fowl with their strange waxen yellow helmets in the scrub along the river. Then they had to clean and dress their kill and help the Herero chef to prepare and cook it.

'It's the best meal I've ever eaten,' Sean declared, and his brothers agreed with him enthusiastically through full mouths.

The next morning Shasa told them, 'We need fresh meat for the men.' In camp there were thirty mouths to feed, all with an enormous appetite for fresh meat. 'All right, Sean, what is the scientific name for impala?'

Aepyceros Melampus,' Sean gabbled eagerly. 'The Afrikaners call it *rooibok* and it weighs between 130 and 160 pounds.'

'That will do,' Shasa laughed. 'Go and get your rifle.'

In a patch of whistling thorn near the river, they found a solitary old ram, an outcast from the breeding herd. He had been mauled by a leopard and was limping badly on one foreleg, but he had a fine pair of lyre-shaped horns. Sean

stalked the lovely red brown antelope just as Shasa had taught him, using the river bank and the wind to get within easy shot, even with the light rifle. However, when the boy knelt and raised the Winchester to his shoulder, Shasa slipped the safety-catch of his heavy weapon, ready to render the *coup de grâce*, if it was needed.

The impala dropped instantly, shot through the neck, dead before it heard the shot, and Shasa went to join his son at the kill.

As they shook hands, Shasa recognized in Sean the deep atavistic passion of the hunter. In some contemporary men that urge had cooled or been suppressed – in others it still burned brightly. Shasa and his eldest son were of that ilk, and now Shasa stooped and dipped his forefinger in the bright warm blood that trickled from the tiny wound in the ram's neck and then he traced his finger across Sean's forehead and down each cheek.

'Now you are blooded,' he said, and he wondered when that ceremony had first been performed, when the first man had painted his son's face with the blood of his first kill, and he knew instinctively that it had been back before recorded time, back when they still dressed in skins and lived in caves.

'Now you are a hunter,' he said, and his heart warmed to his son's proud and solemn expression. This was not a moment for laughter and chatter, it was something deep and significant, something beyond mere words. Sean had sensed that Shasa was proud of him.

The following day they drew lots and it was Michael's turn to kill. Again Shasa wanted a solitary impala ram, so as not to alarm the breeding herd, but an animal with a good pair of horns as a trophy for the boy. It took them almost all that day of hunting before they found the right one.

Shasa and his two brothers watched from a distance as Michael made his stalk. It was a more difficult situation than Sean had been presented with, open grassland and a few scattered flat-top acacia thorns, but Michael made a stealthy approach on hands and knees, until he reached a low ant heap from which to make his shot.

Michael rose slowly and lifted the light rifle. The ram was still unaware, grazing head down thirty paces off, broadside on and offering the perfect shot for either spine or heart. Shasa was ready with the Holland and Holland to back him, should he wound the impala. Michael held his aim, and the seconds drew out. The ram raised its head and looked around warily, but Michael was absolutely still, the rifle to his shoulder, and the ram looked past him, not seeing him. Then it moved away unhurriedly, stopping once to crop a few mouthfuls. It disappeared into a clump of taller grass and without having fired, Michael slowly lowered his rifle.

Sean jumped to his feet, ready to rush out and challenge his brother, but Shasa restrained him with a hand on his shoulder. 'You and Garry go and wait for us back at the jeep,' he said.

Shasa walked out to where Michael was sitting on the ant heap with the unfired Winchester held across his lap. He sat down beside Michael and lit a cigarette. Neither of them said anything for almost ten minutes and then Michael whispered, 'He looked straight at me – and he had the most beautiful eyes.'

Shasa dropped the butt of his cigarette and ground it out under his heel. They were silent again, and then Michael blurted, 'Do I really *have* to kill something, Dad? Please don't make me.'

'No, Mickey,' Shasa put his arm around his shoulders. 'You don't have to

kill anything. And in a different sort of way, I'm just as proud of you as I am of Sean.'

* * *

Then it was Garrick's turn. Again it was a solitary ram with a beautiful head of wide-curved horns and the stalk was through scattered bush and waist-high grass.

His spectacles glinting determinedly, Garry began his stalk under Shasa's patient supervision. However, he was still a long way out of range of the ram, when there was a squawk and Garry disappeared into the earth. Only a small cloud of dust marked the spot where he had been. The impala raced away into the forest, and Shasa and the two boys ran out to where Garry had last been seen. They were guided by muffled cries of distress, and a disturbance in the grass. Only Garry's legs were still above ground kicking helplessly in the air. Shasa seized them and heaved Garry out of the deep round hole in which he was wedged from the waist.

It was the entrance to an antbear burrow. Intent on his stalk, Garry had tripped over his own bootlace and tumbled headlong into the hole. The lenses of his spectacles were thick with dust and he had skinned his cheek and torn his bushjacket. These injuries were insignificant when compared to the damage to his pride. In the next three days Garry made as many attempts to stalk. All of these were detected by his intended victim, long before he was within gunshot. Each time as he watched the antelope dash away, Garry's dejection was more abject and Sean's derision more raucous.

'Next time we will do it together,' Shasa consoled him, and the following day he coached Garry quietly through the stalk, carrying the rifle for him, pointing out the obstacles over which Garry would have tripped, and leading him the last ten yards by the hand until they were in a good position for the shot. Then he handed him the loaded rifle.

'In the neck,' he whispered. 'You can't miss.'

The ram had the best trophy horns they had seen yet, and he was twenty-five yards away. Garry lifted the rifle and peered through spectacles that were misted with the heat of excitement and his hands began to shake uncontrollably.

Watching Garry's face screwed up with tension, and seeing the erratic circles that the rifle barrel was describing, Shasa recognized the classic symptoms of 'buck fever' and reached out to prevent Garry firing. He was too late, and the ram jumped at the sharp crack of the shot, and then looked around with a puzzled expression. Neither Shasa nor the animal, and least of all Garry, knew where the bullet had gone.

'Garry!' Shasa tried to prevent him, but he fired again as wildly, and a puff of dust flicked from the earth half-way between them and the ram.

The impala went up into the air in a fluid and graceful leap, a flash of silken cinnamon-coloured skin and a glint of sweeping horns and then it was bounding away on those long delicate legs, so lightly it seemed not to touch the earth.

They walked back to the jeep in silence, Garry trailing a few paces behind his father, and his elder brother greeted him with a peal of merry laughter.

'Next time throw your specs at him, Garry.'

'I think you need a little more practice before you have another go at it,'

Shasa told him tactfully. 'But don't worry. Buck fever is something that can attack anyone – even the oldest and most experienced.'

* * *

They moved camp, going deeper into the little Eden they had discovered. Now every day they came across elephant droppings, knee-high piles of fibrous yellow lumps the size of tennis balls, full of chewed bark and twigs and the stones of wild fruit in which the baboons and red-cheeked francolin delved delightedly for titbits.

Shasa showed the boys how to thrust a finger into the pile of dung to test for body heat and judge its freshness, and how to read the huge round pad-marks in the dust. To differentiate between bull and cow, between front and rear foot, to tell the direction of travel and to estimate the age of the animal. 'The tread is worn off the feet of the old ones – smooth as an old car tyre.'

Then, at last, they picked up the spoor of a huge old bull elephant, with smooth pad-marks the size of garbage-bin lids, and they left the jeep and followed him on foot for two days, sleeping on the spoor, eating the hard rations they carried. In the late afternoon of the second day, they caught up with the bull. He was in almost impenetrable jess bush through which they crept on hands and knees, and they were almost within touching distance when they made out the loom of the colossal grey body through the interlaced branches. Eleven foot high at the shoulder, he was grey as a storm cloud, and his belly rumbled like distant thunder. One at a time Shasa took the boys up closer to have a good look at him, and then they retreated out of the jess bush and left the outcast to his eternal wanderings.

'Why didn't you shoot him, Dad?' Garry stuttered. 'After following all that way?'

'Didn't you see? One tusk was broken off at the tip and despite his bulk, the other tusk was pretty small.'

They limped back over the miles on feet that were covered in blisters, and it took two rest days in camp for the boys to recover from a march that had been beyond their strength.

Often during the nights they were awakened and lay in their narrow camp beds, thrilling to the shrieking cries of the hyena scavenging the garbage dump beside the lean-to kitchen. They were accompanied by the soprano yelping bark of the little dog-like jackals. The boys learned to recognize all these and the other sounds of the night – the birds such as the night jar and the dikkop, the smaller mammals, the night ape, the genet and the civet, and the insects and reptiles that squealed and hummed and croaked in the reeds of the waterhole.

They bathed infrequently, in matters of hygiene Shasa was more-easy going than their mother and a thousand times more so than their grandmother, and they ate the delicious concoctions that the Herero chef dreamed up for them with plenty of sugar and condensed milk. School was far away and they were happy as they had ever been with their father's complete and undivided attention and his wonderful stories and instruction.

'We haven't seen any signs of lions yet,' Shasa remarked at breakfast one morning. 'That's unusual. There are plenty of buffalo about, and the big cats usually keep close to the herds.'

Mention of lions gave the boys delightful cold shivers, and it was as though Shasa's words had conjured up the beast.

That afternoon as the jeep bumped and weaved slowly through the long grass avoiding antbear holes and fallen logs, they came out on the edge of a long dry vlei, one of those grassy depressions of the African bush that during the rainy season become shallow lakes and at other times are treacherous swamps where the vehicle can easily bog down, or in the driest months are smooth treeless expanses resembling a well-kept polo ground. Shasa stopped the jeep in the tree line and searched the far side of the vlei, panning his binoculars slowly to pick up any game standing amongst the shadows of the tall grey mopani trees on the far side.

'Only a couple of bat-eared foxes,' he remarked, and passed the binoculars to the boys. They laughed at the antics of these quaint little animals, as they hunted grasshoppers in the short green grass in the centre of the vlei.

'Hey, Dad!' Sean's tone changed. 'There is a big old baboon in the top of that tree.' He passed the binoculars back to his father.

'No,' Shasa said, without lowering the glasses. 'That's not a baboon. It's a human being!'

He spoke in the vernacular to the two Ovambo trackers in the back of the jeep, and there was a quick but heated discussion, everybody taking differing views.

'All right, let's go and take a look.' He drove the jeep out into the open vlei, and before they were half-way across there was no longer any doubt. In the top branches of a high mopani crouched a child, a little black girl dressed only in a loin cloth of cheap blue trade cotton.

'She's all alone,' Shasa exclaimed. 'Out here, fifty miles from the nearest village.'

Shasa sent the jeep roaring across the few hundred yards then pulled up in a rolling cloud of dust and ran to the base of the mopani. He shouted up at the almost naked child. 'Come down!' and gestured to reinforce the command that she would certainly not understand. She neither moved nor raised her head from the branch on which she lay.

Shasa looked around him quickly. At the base of the tree lay a blanket roll which had been ripped open, the threadbare blankets had been shredded and torn. A skin bag had also been ripped and the dry maize meal it contained had poured into the dust, there was a black three-legged pot lying on its side, a crude axe with the blade rough forged from a piece of scrap mild steel, and the shaft of a spear snapped off at the back of the head, but the point was missing.

A little farther off were scattered a few rags on which blood stains had dried black as tar, and some other objects which were covered by a living cloak of big shimmering iridescent flies. As Shasa approached, the flies rose in a buzzing cloud, revealing the pathetic remains on which they had been feasting. There were two pairs of human hands and feet, gnawed off at the wrists and ankles, and then – horribly – the heads. A man and a woman, their necks chewed through and the exposed vertebrae crushed by great fangs. Both heads were intact, although the mouths and nostrils and empty eyesockets were filled with the white rice pudding of eggs laid by the swarming flies. The grass was flattened over a wide area, crusted with dried blood, and the trodden dust was patterned with the unmistakable pug-marks of a fully grown male lion.

'The lion always leaves the head and hands and feet,' his Ovambo tracker said in a matter-of-fact voice, and Shasa nodded and turned to warn the boys to

stay in the car. He was too late. They had followed him and were studying the grisly relics with varied expressions – Sean with ghoulish relish, Michael with nauseated horror and Garry with intense clinical interest.

Swiftly Shasa covered the severed heads with the torn blankets. He smelt that they were already in an advanced state of decomposition: they must have lain here many days. Then above again he turned his attention to the child in the branches high above them, calling urgently to her.

'She is dead,' said his tracker. 'These people have been dead four days at least. The little one has been in the tree all that time. She is surely dead.'

Shasa would not accept that. He removed his boots and safari jacket and climbed into the mopani. He went up cautiously, testing each hand-hold and every branch before committing his weight to it. To a height of ten feet above the ground the bark of the tree had been lacerated by claws. When the child was directly above him, almost within reach, Shasa called softly in Ovambo and then in Zulu.

'Hey, little one, can you hear me?'

There was no movement and he saw that her limbs were thin as sticks, and her skin ash-grey with that peculiar dusty look that in the African presages death. Shasa eased himself up the last few feet and reached up to touch her leg. The skin was warm, and he felt an unaccountable rush of relief. He had expected the soft cold touch of death. However, the child was unconscious and her dehydrated body was light as a bird as Shasa gently loosened her grip on the branch and lifted her against his chest. He climbed down slowly, shielding her from any jarring or rough movement and when he reached the ground carried her to the jeep and laid her in the shade.

The first-aid kit contained a comprehensive collection of medical equipment. Long ago, Shasa had been forced to minister to one of his gunbearers mauled by a wounded buffalo and after that he never hunted without the kit, and he had learned to use all of it.

Swiftly he prepared a drip set and probed for the vein in the child's arm. The vein had collapsed, her pulse was weak and erratic, and he had to try again in the foot. This time he got the canula in and administered a full bag of Ringers lactate, and while it was flowing he added ten ccs of glucose solution to it. Only then did he attempt to make the child take water orally, and her swallowing reflex was still evident. A few drops at a time he got a full cup down her throat, and she showed the first signs of life, whimpering and stirring restlessly.

As he worked, he gave orders to his trackers over his shoulder. 'Take the spade, bury those people deep. It is strange that the hyena haven't found them yet, but make sure they don't do so later.'

One of the trackers held the child on his lap during the rough journey back to camp, protecting her from the jolts and heavy bumps. As soon as they arrived, Shasa strung the aerial of the short-wave radio to the highest tree in the grove, and after an hour of frustration finally made contact, not with the H'ani Mine, but with one of the Courtney Company's geological exploration units that was a hundred miles closer. Even then the contact was faint and scratchy and intermittent, but with many repetitions he got them to relay a message to the mine. They were to send an aircraft, with mine doctor, to the landing strip at the police post at Rundu as soon as possible.

By this time, the little girl was conscious and talking to the Ovambo trackers in a weak piping voice that reminded Shasa of the chirping of a nesting sparrow. She was speaking an obscure dialect of one of the river people from Angola in

the north, but the Ovambo was married to a woman of her tribe and could translate for Shasa. The story she told was harrowing.

She and her parents had been on a journey to see her grandparents at the river village of Shakawe in the south, a trek on foot of hundreds of miles. Carrying all their wordly possessions, they had taken a short cut through this remote and deserted country when they had become aware that a lion was dogging them, following them through the forest – at first keeping its distance and then closing in.

Her father, an intrepid hunter, had realized the futility of stopping and trying to build some sort of shelter or of taking to the trees where the beast would besiege them. Instead he had tried to keep the lion off by shouting and clapping while he hurried to reach the river and the sanctuary of one of the fishing villages.

The child described the final attack when the animal, its thick ruff of black mane erect, had rushed in at the family, grunting and roaring. Her mother had only time enough to push the girl into the lowest branch of the mopani before the lion was on them. Her father had stood gallantly to meet it, and thrust his long spear into its chest, but the spear had snapped and the lion leapt upon him and tore out his bowels with a single swipe of curved yellow claws. Then it had sprung at the mother as she was attempting to climb into the mopani and hooked its claws into her back and dragged her down.

In her small birdlike voice the child described how the lion had eaten the corpses of her parents, down to the heads and feet and hands, while she watched from the upper branches. It had taken two days over the grisly feast, at intervals pausing to lick the spear wound on its shoulder. On the third day it had attempted to reach the child, ripping at the trunk of the mopani and roaring horribly. At last it had given up and wandered away into the forest, limping heavily with the wound. Even then the child had been too terrified to leave her perch and she had clung there until at last she had passed out with exhaustion and grief, exposure and fear.

While she was relating all this, the camp servants were refuelling the jeep and preparing supplies for the journey to Rundu. Shasa left as soon as this was done, taking the boys with him. He would not leave them in the camp while there was a wounded man-eating lion roaming in the vicinity.

They drove through the night, recrossing their jerry-built bridge and retracing their tracks until the following morning they intersected the main Rundu road, and that afternoon they finally arrived, dusty and exhausted, at the airstrip. The blue and silver Mosquito that Shasa had left at H'ani Mine was parked in the shade of the trees at the edge of the strip and the company pilot and the doctor were squatting under the wing, waiting patiently.

Shasa gave the child into the doctor's care, and went quickly through the pile of urgent documents and messages that the pilot had brought with him. He scribbled out orders and replies to these, and a long letter of instruction to David Abrahams. She would receive first-rate medical attention at the mine hospital, and Shasa would decide what to do with the little orphan once she was fully recovered.

The return to the safari camp was more leisurely than the outward journey, and over the next few days the excitement of the lion adventure was forgotten in the other absorbing concerns of safari life, not least of which was the business of Garry's first kill. Bad luck now combined with his lack of coordination and poor marksmanship to cheat him of this experience that he hungered for more

than any other, while on the other hand Sean succeeded in providing meat for the camp at every attempt.

'What we are going to do is practise a little more on the pigeons,' Shasa decided, after one of Garry's least successful outings. In the evenings the flocks of fat green pigeons came flighting in to feast on the wild figs in the grove beside the waterhole.

Shasa took the boys down as soon as the sun lost its heat, and placed them in the hides they had built of saplings and dried grass, each hide far enough from the next and carefully sited so that there was no danger of a careless shot causing an accident. This afternoon Shasa put Sean into a hide at the near end of the glade, with Michael, who had once again declined to take an active part in the sport, to keep him company and pick up the fallen birds for him.

Then Shasa and Garry set off together for the far side of the grove. Shasa was leading with Garry following him as the game path twisted between the thick yellow trunks of the figs. Their bark was yellow and scaly as the skin of a giant reptile, and the bunches of figs grew directly on the trunks rather than on the tips of the branches. Beneath the trees the undergrowth was tangled and thick, and the game path was so twisted that they could see only a short distance ahead. The light was poor this late in the afternoon, with the branches meeting overhead.

Shasa came around another turn and the lion was in the game path, walking straight towards him only fifty paces away. In the instant he saw it, Shasa realized that it was the man-eater. It was a huge beast, the biggest he had ever seen in a lifetime of hunting. It stood higher than his waist, and its mane was coal-black, long and shaggy and dense, shading to blue grey down the beast's flanks and back.

It was an old lion, its flat face criss-crossed with scars. Its mouth was gaping, panting with pain as it limped towards him, and he saw that the spear wound in the shoulder had mortified, the raw flesh crimson as a rose petal and the fur around the wound wet and slicked down where the lion had been licking it. The flies swarmed to the wound, irritating and stinging, and the lion was in a vicious mood, sick with age and pain. It lifted its dark and shaggy head and Shasa looked into the pale yellow eyes and saw the agony and blind rage they contained.

'Garry!' he said urgently. 'Walk backwards! Don't run, but get out of here,' and without looking around he swung the sling of the rifle off his shoulder.

The lion dropped into a crouch, its long tail with the black bush of hair at the tip lashed back and forth like a metronome, as it gathered itself for the charge, and its yellow eyes fastened on Shasa, a focus for all its rage.

Shasa knew there would be time for only a single shot, for it would cover the ground between them in a blazing blur of speed. The light was too bad and the range was too far for that single shot to be conclusive, he would let it come in to where there could be no doubt, and the big 300-grain soft-nosed bullet from the Holland and Holland would shatter its skull and blow its brains to a mush.

The lion launched into its charge, keeping low to the earth, snaking in and grunting as it came, gut-shaking bursts of sound through the gaping jaws lined with long yellow fangs. Shasa braced himself and brought up the rifle, but before he could fire, there was the sharp crack of the little Winchester beside him and the lion collapsed in the middle of his charge, going down head first and cartwheeling, flopping over on its back to expose the soft butter-yellow fur of its belly, its limbs stretching and relaxing, the long curved talons in its huge

paws slowly retracting into the pads, the pink tongue lolling out of its open jaws, and the rage dying out of those pale yellow eyes. From the tiny bullet hole between its eyes a thin serpent of blood crawled down to dribble from its brow into the dirt beneath it.

In astonishment Shasa lowered his rifle and looked round. Beside him stood Garry, his head at the level of Shasa's lowest rib, the little Winchester still at his shoulder, his face set and deadly pale, and his spectacles glinting in the gloom beneath the trees.

'You killed it,' Shasa said stupidly. 'You stood your ground and killed it.'

Shasa walked forward slowly and stooped over the carcass of the man-eater. He shook his head in amazement, and then looked back at his son. Garry had not yet lowered the rifle, but he was beginning now to tremble with delayed terror. Shasa dipped his finger into the blood that dribbled from the wound in the man-eater's forehead, then walked back to where Garry stood. He painted the ritual stripes on the boy's forehead and cheeks.

'Now you are a man and I'm proud of you,' he said. Slowly the colour flushed back into Garry's cheeks and his lips stopped trembling, and then his face began to glow. It was an expression of such pride and unutterable joy that Shasa felt his throat close up and tears sting his eyelids.

Every servant came from the camp to view the man-eater and to hear Shasa describe the details of the hunt. Then, by the light of the lanterns, they carried the carcass back. While the skinners went to work, the men sang the song of the hunter in Garry's honour.

Sean was torn between incredulous admiration and deepest envy of his brother, while Michael was fulsome in his praises. Garry refused to wash the dried lion's blood from his face when at last, well after midnight, Shasa finally ordered them to bed. At breakfast he still wore the crusted stripes of blood on his beaming grubby face and Michael read aloud the heroic poem he had written in Garry's honour. It began:

> With lungs to blast the skies with sound
> And breath hot as the blacksmith's forge
> Eyes as yellow as the moon's full round
> And the lust on human flesh to gorge –

Shasa hid a smile at the laboured rhyming, and at the end applauded as loudly as the rest of them. After breakfast they all trooped out to watch the skinners dressing out the lion-skin, pegging it fur side down in the shade, scraping away the yellow subcutaneous fat and rubbing in coarse salt and alum.

'Well, I still think it died of a heart attack,' Sean could suppress his envy no longer, and Garry rounded on him furiously.

'We all know what a clever dick you are. But when you shoot *your* first lion, then you can come and talk to me, smarty pants. All you are good for is a few little old impala!'

It was a long speech, delivered in white heat, and Garry never stumbled nor stuttered once. It was the first time Shasa had seen him stand up to Sean's casual bullying, and he waited for Sean to assert his authority. For seconds it hung in the balance, he could see Sean weighing it up, deciding whether to tweak the spikes of hair at Garry's temple or to give him a chestnut down the ribs. He could see also that Garry was ready for it, his fists clenched and his lips set in a pale determined line. Suddenly Sean grinned that charming smile.

'Only kidding,' he announced airily, and turned back to admire the tiny bullet-hole in the skull. 'Wow! Right between the eyes!' It was a peace offering.

Garry looked bemused and uncertain. It was the first time that he had forced Sean to back down, and he wasn't able immediately to grasp that he had succeeded.

Shasa stepped up and put his arm around Garry's shoulders. 'Do you know what I'm going to do, champ? I'm going to have the head fully mounted for the wall in your room, with eyes and everything,' he said.

For the first time, Shasa was aware that Garry had developed hard little muscles in his shoulders and upper arm. He had always thought him a runt. Perhaps he had never truly looked at the child before.

* * *

Then suddenly it was over, and the servants were breaking camp and packing the tents and beds on to the trucks, and appallingly the prospect of the return to Weltevreden and school loomed ahead of them. Shasa tried to keep their spirits jaunty with stories and songs on the long drive back to H'ani Mine but with every mile the boys were more dejected.

On the last day when the hills which the Bushmen call the 'Place of All Life' floated on the horizon ahead of them, detached from the earth by the shimmering heat mirage, Shasa asked, 'Have you gentlemen decided what you are going to do when you leave school?' It was an attempt to cheer them up, more than a serious enquiry. 'What about you, Sean?'

'I want to do what we have been doing. I want to be a hunter, an elephant hunter like great-grand-uncle Sean.'

'Splendid!' Shasa agreed. 'Only problem I can see is that you are at least sixty years too late.

'Well then,' said Sean, 'I'll be a soldier – I like shooting things.'

A shadow passed behind Shasa's eyes before he looked at Michael.

'What about you, Mickey?'

'I want to be a writer. I will work as a newspaper reporter and in my spare time I'll write poetry and great books.'

'You'll starve to death, Mickey,' Shasa laughed, and then he swivelled around to Garry who was leaning over the back of the driving seat.

'What about you, champ?'

'I'm going to do what you do, Dad.'

'And what is it I do?' Shasa demanded with interest.

'You are the chairman of Courtney Mining and Finance, and you tell everybody else what to do. That's what I want to be one day, chairman of Courtney Mining and Finance.'

Shasa stopped smiling and was silent for a moment, studying the child's determined expression, then he said lightly, 'Well then, it looks as though it's up to you and me to support the elephant hunter and the poet.' And he ran his hand over Garry's already unruly hair. It no longer required any effort to make an affectionate gesture towards his ugly duckling.

* * *

They came singing across the rolling grasslands of Zululand, and they were one hundred strong. All of them were members of the Buffaloes and Hendrick Tabaka had carefully picked them for this special honour guard. They were the best, and all of them were dressed in tribal regalia, feathers and furs and monkey-skin capes, kilts of cow-tails. They carried only fighting-sticks, for the strictest tradition forbade metal weapons of any kind on this day.

At the head of the column Moses Gama and Hendrick Tabaka trotted. They also had set aside their European clothing for the occasion, and of all their men they alone wore leopard-skin cloaks, as was their noble right. Half a mile behind them rose the dust of the cattle herd. This was the *lobola*, the marriage price, two hundred head of prime beasts, as had been agreed. The herd-boys were all of them sons of the leading warriors who had ridden in the cattle trucks with their charges during the three-hundred-mile journey from the Witwatersrand. In charge of the herd-boys were Wellington and Raleigh Tabaka and they had detrained the herd at Ladyburg railway station. Like their father, they had discarded their western-style clothing for the occasion and were dressed in loincloths, and armed with their fighting-sticks, and they danced and called to the cattle, keeping them in a tight bunch, both of them excited and filled with self-importance by the task they had been allotted.

Ahead of them rose the high escarpment beyond the little town of Ladyburg. The slopes were covered with dark forests of black wattle and all of it was Courtney land, from where the waterfall smoked with spray in the sunlight around the great curve of hills. All ten thousand acres of it belonged to Lady Anna Courtney, the relict of Sir Garrick Courtney and to Storm Anders, who was the daughter of General Sean Courtney. However, beyond the waterfall lay a hundred choice acres of land which had been left to Sangane Dinizulu in terms of the will of General Sean Courtney, for he had been a faithful and beloved retainer of the Courtney family as had his father Mbejane Dinizulu before him.

The road descended the escarpment in a series of hairpin bends, and when Moses Gama shaded his eyes and stared ahead, he saw another band of warriors coming down to meet them. They were many more in number, perhaps five hundred strong. Like Moses' party they were dressed in full regimentals, with plumes of fur and feathers on their heads and war rattles on their wrists and ankles. The two parties halted at the foot of the escarpment, and from a hundred paces faced each other, though still they sang and stamped and brandished their weapons.

The shields of the Zulus were matched, selected from dappled cowhides of white and chocolate brown, and the brows of the warriors that carried them were bound with strips of the same dappled hide while their kilts and their plumes were cow-tails of purest white. They made a daunting and warlike show, all big men, their bodies gleaming with sweat in the sunlight, their eyes bloodshot with dust and excitement and the pots of millet beer they had already downed.

Facing them Moses felt his nerves crawl with a trace of the terror that these men had for two hundred years inspired in all the other tribes of Africa, and to suppress it he stamped and sang as loudly as his Buffaloes who pressed closely around him. On this his wedding day, Moses Gama had put aside all the manners and mores of the west, and slipped back easily into his African origins and his heart pumped and thrilled to the rhythms and the pulse of this harsh continent.

From the Zulu ranks opposite him sprang a champion, a magnificent figure of a man with the strip of leopard skin around his brow that declared his royal origins. He was one of Victoria Dinizulu's elder brothers, and Moses knew he was a qualified lawyer with a large practice at Eshowe, the Zululand capital, but today he was all African, fierce and threatening as he swirled in the *giya*, the challenge dance.

He leapt and spun and shouted his own praises and those of his family, daring the world, challenging the men who faced him, while behind him his comrades drummed with their sticks on the rawhide shields, and the sound was like distant thunder, the last sound that a million victims had ever heard, the death-knell of Swazi and Xhosa, of Boer and Briton in the days when the impis of Chaka and Dingaan and Cetewayo had swept across the land, from Isandhlawana, the Hill of the Little Hand, where seven hundred British infantry were cut down in one of the worst military reverses that England had ever suffered in Africa, to the 'Palace of Weeping' which the Boers named 'Weenen' for their grief for the women and children who died to that same dreadful drum roll when the impis came swarming down across the Tugela river, to a thousand other nameless and forgotten killing grounds where the lesser tribes had perished before the men of Zulu.

At last the Zulu champion staggered back into the ranks, streaked with sweat and dust, his chest heaving and froth upon his lips, and now it was Moses' turn to *giya*, and he danced out from amongst his Buffaloes, and leapt shoulder-high with his leopard-skins swirling around him. His limbs shone like coal freshly cut from the face, and his eyes and teeth were white as mirrors flashing in the sunlight. His voice rang from the escarpment, magnified by the echoes, and though the men facing him could not understand the words, the force and meaning of them was clear, his haughty disdain evident in every gesture. They growled and pressed forward, while his own Buffaloes were goaded by his example, their blood coming to the boil, ready to rush forward and join battle with their traditional foe, ready to perpetuate the bloody vendetta that had already run a hundred years.

At the very last moment, when violence and inevitable death were only a heartbeat away, and rage was as thick in the air as the static electricity of the wildest summer thunderstorm, Moses Gama stopped dancing abruptly, posing like a heroic statue before them – and so great was the force of his personality, so striking his presence, that the drumming of shields and the growl of battle rage died away.

Into the silence Moses Gama called in the Zulu language. 'I bring the marriage price!' and he held his stick aloft, a signal to the herdboys who followed the marriage party.

Lowing and bawling, adding their dust to the dust of the dancers, the herd was driven forward and immediately the mood of the Zulus changed. For a thousand years, since they had come down from the far north, following the tsetse-fly-free corridors down the continent with their herds, the Nguni peoples from which the Zulu tribe would emerge under the black emperor Chaka, had been cattle men. Their animals were their wealth and their treasure. They loved cattle as other men love women and children. Almost from the day they could walk unaided, the boys tended the herds, living with them in the veld from dawn to dusk of every day, establishing with them a bond and almost mystic communion, protecting them from predators with their very lives, talking to them and handling them and coming to know them completely. It was said that

King Chaka knew every individual beast in his royal herds, and that out of a hundred thousand head he would know immediately if one were missing and would ask for it with a complete description, and not hesitate to order his executioners with their knobkerries to dash out the brains of even the youngest herd-boy if there was even a suspicion of his negligence.

So it was a committee of strict and expert judges who put aside the dancing and posturing and boasting, and instead applied themselves to the serious business of appraising the bride price. Each animal was dragged from the herd, and amid a buzz of comment and speculation and argument, was minutely examined. Its limbs and trunk were palpated by dozens of hands simultaneously, its jaws were forced open to expose the teeth and tongue, its head twisted so that its ears and nostrils could be peered into, its udders stroked and weighed in the palm, is tail lifted to estimate its calf-bearing history and potential. Then finally, almost reluctantly, each animal was declared acceptable by old Sangane Dinizulu himself, the father of the bride. No matter how hard they tried, they could find no grounds for rejecting a single animal. The Ovambo and the Xhosa love their cattle every bit as much as the Zulu, and are as expert in their judgement. Moses and Hendrick had exercised all their skills in making their selection, for pride and honour were at stake.

It took many hours for every one of the two hundred animals to be examined while the bridegroom's party, still keeping aloof from the Zulus, squatted in the short grass on the side of the road, pretending indifference to the proceedings. The sun was hot and the dust aggravated the men's thirst, but no refreshment was offered while the scrutiny went on.

Then at last Sangane Dinizulu, his silver pate shining in the sun, but his body still upright and regal, called his herd-boys. Joseph Dinizulu came forward. As the senior herdsman, the old man gave the herd into his care. Although his exhortations were severe and he scowled most ferociously, the old man's affection for his youngest son was ill-concealed, as was his delight at the quality of the stock which made up the marriage price. So when he turned and for the first time greeted his future son-in-law, he was having great difficulty in suppressing his smiles, they kept shooting out like beams of sunlight through cloud holes and were just as swiftly extinguished.

With dignity he embraced Moses Gama, and though he was a tall man, he had to reach up to do so. Then he stepped back and clapped his hands, calling to the small party of young women who were sitting a little way off.

Now they rose and helped each other to settle the enormous clay pots of beer upon each other's heads. Then they formed a line and came forward, singing and undulating their hips, although their heads remained steady and not a drop slopped over the rims of the pots. They were all unmarried girls, none of them wore the high clay headdress or the matron's leather cloak, and above their short beaded skirts their bodies were oiled and stark naked so their pert young breasts joggled and bounced to the rhythm of the song of welcome and the wedding guests murmured and smiled appreciatively. Although deep down old Sangane Dinizulu disapproved of marriage outside the tribe of Zulu, the *lobola* had been good and his future son-in-law was, by all accounts, a man of stature and importance. None could reasonably object to suitors of this calibre, and as there might be others like him in the bridegroom's party, Sangane wasn't loath to show off his wares.

The girls knelt in front of the guests, hanging their heads and averting their eyes shyly. Giggling in response to the knowing looks and sly sallies of the men,

they proffered the brimming beer-pots, and then withdrew swinging their hips so their skirts swirled up and pert young buttocks peeked provocatively from beneath them.

The beer-pots were so heavy that they required both hands to lift, and when they were lowered, there were thick white moustaches on the upper lips of the guests. Noisily they licked them away and the laughter became more relaxed and friendly.

When the beer-pots were empty, Sangane Dinizulu stood before them and made a short speech of welcome. Then they formed up again and started up the road that climbed the escarpment, but now Zulu ran shoulder to shoulder with Ovambo and Xhosa. Moses Gama had never believed he would see that happen. It was a beginning, he thought, a fine beginning, but there remained to be scaled a range of endeavour as high as the peaks of the Drakensberg mountains which rose out of the blue distances before them as they topped the escarpment.

Sangane Dinizulu had set the pace up the slope, although he must be all of seventy years of age, and now he led the cavalcade of men and animals down to his kraal. It was sited in a grassy slope above the river. The huts of his many wives were arranged in a circle, beehives of smooth thatch each with an entrance so low that a man must stoop to enter. In the centre of the circle was the old man's hut. It also was a perfect beehive, but much grander than the others, and the thatch had been plaited into intricate patterns. It was the home of the chieftain of Zulu, a son of the heavens.

On the grassy slope was assembled a multitude, a thousand or more of the most important men of the tribe with all their senior wives. Many of them had travelled for days to be here, and they squatted in clumps and clusters down the slope, each chieftain surrounded by his own retainers.

When the bridegroom's party came over the crest, they rose as one man, shouting their greetings and drumming their shields, and Sangane Dinizulu led them down to the entrance of the kraal where he paused and spread his arms for silence. The wedding guests settled down again comfortably in the grass. Only the chieftains sat on their carved stools of office, and while the young girls carried the beer-pots amongst them, Sangane Dinizulu made his wedding speech.

First he related the history of the tribe, and particularly of his own clan of Dinizulu. He recited their battle honours and the valiant deeds of his ancestors. These were many and it took a long time, but the guests were well content for the black beer-pots were replenished as swiftly as they were emptied, and although the old ones knew the history of the tribe as intimately as did Sangane Dinizulu, its repetition gave them endless satisfaction, as though it were an anchor in the restless sea of life. As long as the history and the customs persisted, the tribe was secure.

At last Sangane Dinizulu was done, and in a voice that was hoarse and scratchy, he ended. 'There are those amongst you who have queried the wisdom of a daughter of Zulu marrying with a man of another tribe. I respect these views, for I also have been consumed by doubts and have pondered long and seriously.'

Now the older heads in the congregation were nodding, and a few hostile glances were shot at the bridegroom's party, but Sangane Dinizulu went on.

'I had these same doubts when my daughter asked my permission to leave the hut of her mother and journey to *goldi*, the place of gold, and to work in the great hospital at Baragwanath. Now I am persuaded that what she has done was

right and proper. She is a daughter of which an old man can be proud. She is a woman of the future.'

He faced his peers calmly and resolutely, seeing the doubt in their eyes, but ignoring it.

'The man who will be her husband is not of Zulu – but he also is a man of the future. Most of you have heard his name. You know him as a man of force and power. I am persuaded that by giving him my daughter in marriage I am once again doing what is right – for my daughter and for the tribe.'

When the old man sat down on his stool they were silent, serious and withdrawn, and they looked uneasily towards the bridegroom where he squatted at the head of his party.

Moses Gama rose to his feet, and strode up the slope from where he could look down upon them. He was silhouetted against the sky, his height was emphasized and the royal leopard skin declared his lineage.

'Oh people of Zulu, I greet you.' That deep thrilling voice reached to everyone of them, carrying clearly in the silence, and they stirred and murmured with surprise as they realized that he was speaking fluent Zulu.

'I have come to take one of the most comely daughters of your tribe, but as part of the marriage price I bring you a dream and a promise,' he began, and they were attentive but puzzled. Slowly the mood changed as he went on to set out his vision for them, a unification of the tribes and a sloughing off of the white domination under which they had existed for three hundred years. The older men became more and more uneasy as they listened, they shook their heads and exchanged angry glances, some of them muttered aloud, an unusual discourtesy towards an important guest, but what he was suggesting was a destruction of the old ways, a denial of the customs and orders of society which had held together the fabric of their lives. In its place he was offering something strange and untested, a world turned upside down, a chaos in which old values and proven codes were discarded with nothing to replace them except with words – and like all old men, they were afraid to change.

With the younger men it was different. They listened, and his words warmed them like the flames of the camp fire in the frosty winter night. One of them listened more intently than all the rest. Joseph Dinizulu was not yet fourteen years of age, but the blood of great Chaka charged his veins and pumped up his heart. These words, strange at first, began to sing in his head like one of the old fighting chants, and his breath came quicker as he heard Moses Gama end his bridal speech.

'So, people of Zulu, I come to give you back the land of your fathers. I come to give you the promise that once again a black man will rule in Africa, and that as surely as tomorrow's sun will rise, the future belongs to us.'

All of a sudden Joseph Dinizulu was struck by a sense of destiny.

'A black man will rule in Africa.'

For Joseph Denizulu, as for many others there that day, the world would never be the same again.

* * *

Victoria Dinizulu waited in her mother's hut. She sat on the earthen floor with a tanned kaross of hyrax fur under her. She wore the traditional dress of a Zulu

bride. The beadwork had been sewn by her mother and her sisters, intricate and beautiful, each pattern carrying a hidden message. There were strings of coloured beads around her wrists and her ankles, and necklaces of beads were plaited into her hair and draped around her waist. In one respect only did her costume differ from that of the traditional Zulu bride: her breasts were covered, as they had been since puberty when she had been baptized into the Anglican Church. She wore a blouse of striped silk in gay colours which complemented the rest of her costume.

As she sat in the centre of the hut, she listened intently to the voice of her bridegroom from without. It carried clearly to her, though she had to shush the others girls when they whispered and giggled. Every word struck her with the force of an arrow, and she felt her love and duty for the man who uttered them swell until they threatened to choke her.

The interior of the hut was gloomy as an ancient cathedral for there were no windows, and the air was hazy with wood smoke that uncoiled lazily from the central fire and rose to the small hole in the summit of the belled roof. The cathedral atmosphere enhanced her mood of reverence, and when the voice of Moses Gama ceased, the silence seemed to enter her heart. No cheers or shouted agreement followed his speech. The men of Zulu were silent and disturbed by it. Victoria could feel it even where she sat in the darkened hut.

'It is time now,' her mother whispered, and lifted her to her feet. 'Go with God,' she whispered, for her mother was a Christian and had introduced her to that religion.

'Be a good wife to this man,' she instructed, and led her to the entrance of the hut.

She stepped outside, into the dazzling sunlight. This was the moment for which the guests had been waiting, and when they saw how beautiful she was, they roared like bulls and drummed their shields. Her father came to greet her and lead her to the carved ebony stool at the entrance of the kraal, so that the *cimeza* ceremony could begin.

The *cimeza* was the 'closing of the eyes' and Victoria sat with her eyes tightly closed as the representatives of the various clans came forward one at a time to place their gift before her. Only then was Victoria allowed to open her eyes and exclaim in wonder at the generosity of the givers. There were gifts of pots and blankets and ornaments, marvellously woven beadwork, and envelopes of money.

Shrewdly old Sangane calculated the value of each as he stood behind her stool, and he was grinning with satisfaction when at last he gave the signal to his son Joseph to drive in the feast. He had set aside twelve fat steers for the slaughter, a gesture that proved him to be even more generous than the bearers of the wedding gifts, but then he was a great man and head of a noble clan. The chosen warriors came forward to slaughter the steers, and their mournful death bellows and the rank smell of fresh blood in the dust soon gave way to the aroma from the cooking fires that drifted blue smoke across the hillside.

At a gesture from old Sangane Moses Gama strode up the slope to the entrance of the kraal and Victoria rose to her feet to meet him. They faced each other and once again a silence fell. The guests were awed by this couple, the groom so tall and commanding, the bride beautiful and nubile.

Involuntarily they craned forward as Victoria unclipped the *ucu* string of beads from around her waist. This was the symbol of her virginity, and she knelt before Moses and, with both hands cupped in the formal and polite

gesture, she offered him the beads. As he accepted her and her gift, a great shout went up from the guests. It was done, Moses Gama was her husband and her master at last.

Now the feasting and the beer-drinking could begin in earnest, and the raw red meat was heaped upon the coals and snatched off again barely singed, while the beer-pots passed from hand to hand and the young girls went swinging from the slope bearing fresh pots upon their heads.

Suddenly there was an uproar and a band of plumed warriors came dashing up the slope towards where Victoria sat at the kraal entrance. They were her brothers and half-brothers and nephews, even Joseph Dinizulu was amongst them, and they shouted their war cries as they came to rescue their sister from this stranger who would take her from their midst.

However, the Buffaloes were ready for them, and with Hendrick at their head and sticks whistling and hissing, they rushed in to prevent the abduction. The women wailed and ululated and the fighting-sticks clattered and whacked on flesh, and the warriors howled and circled and charged at each other in a fine mist of dust.

It was for this that all metal weapons were strictly banned from the ceremony, for the fighting, which was at first playful, soon heated up and blood dripped and bones cracked before the abductors allowed themselves to be driven off. The blood was staunched with a handful of dust clapped on the wound, and both victors and vanquished had worked up a fine thirst and shouted to the girls to bring more beer. The uproar subsided for only a few minutes to be resumed almost immediately as from the top of the slope came the rumble of motor cars.

The children raced up the hill and began to clap and sing as two big motor cars appeared over the brow and came bumping slowly over the rough track that led to the kraal.

In the leading vehicle was a large white woman, with a red face as lined and craggy as that of a bulldog, and a wide-brimmed old-fashioned hat on her head from under which grey hair curled untidily.

'Who is she?' Moses demanded.

'Lady Anna Courtney,' Victoria exclaimed. 'She was the one who encouraged me to leave here and go into the world.'

Impulsively Victoria ran forward to meet the vehicle, and when Lady Anna descended ponderously, she embraced her.

'So, my child, you have come back to us.' Lady Anna's accent was still thick, though she had lived thirty-five years in Africa.

'Not for long.' Victoria laughed and Lady Anna looked at her fondly. Once the child had served in the big house as one of her house maids, until her bright beauty and intelligence had convinced Lady Anna that she was superior to such menial work.

'Where is this man who is taking you away?' she demanded, and Victoria took her hand.

'First you must greet my father, then I will introduce you to my husband.'

From the second motor car a middle-aged couple climbed down to be enthusiastically greeted by the crowd that pressed forward around them. The man was tall and dapper, with the bearing of a soldier. He was tanned by the sun and his eyes had the far-away look of the outdoor man. He twirled his moustaches and took his wife on his arm. She was almost as tall and even

slimmer than he was, and despite the streaks of grey in her hair, she was still an unusually handsome woman.

Sangane Dinizulu came to greet him.

'I see you, Jamela!' His dignity was somewhat tempered by a happy grin of welcome, and Colonel Mark Anders answered him in perfectly colloquial Zulu.

'I see you, old man.' The term was one of respect. 'May all your cattle and all your wives grow fat and sleek.'

Sangane turned to his wife Storm, who was the daughter of old General Sean Courtney. 'I see you, *Nkosikazi*, you bring honour to my kraal.' The bond between the two families was like steel. It went back to another century and had been tested a thousand times.

'Oh, Sangane, I am so happy for you this day – and for Victoria.' Storm left her husband and went quickly to embrace the Zulu girl.

'I wish you joy and many fine sons, Vicky,' she told her, and Victoria answered.

'I owe you and your family so much, *Nkosikazi*. I will never be able to repay you.'

'Don't ever try,' Storm told her with mock severity. 'I feel as though my own daughter is getting married today. Introduce us to your husband, Vicky.'

Now Moses Gama came towards them, and when Storm greeted him in Zulu, he replied gravely in English, 'How do you do, Mrs Anders, Victoria has spoken of you and your family very often.'

When at last he turned to Mark Anders, he proffered his right hand.

'How do you do, Colonel?' Moses asked, and a wry smile flitted across his lips as he saw the white man hesitate momentarily before accepting the handshake. It was unusual for men to greet each other thus across the dividing line of colour, and despite his fluency in the language and his pretended affection for the Zulu people, Moses recognized this man.

Colonel Mark Anders was an anachronism, a son of the English Queen Victoria, a soldier who had fought in two world wars, and the warden of Chaka's Gate National Park which he had saved from the poachers and despoilers by dedication and sheer bloody-mindedness, and made into one of Africa's most celebrated wild-life sanctuaries. He loved the wild animals of Africa with a kind of paternal passion, protecting and cherishing them, and to only a slightly less degree his attitude towards the black tribes, especially the Zulus, was the same, paternalistic and condescending. By this definition he was the mortal enemy of Moses Gama, and as they looked into each other's eyes, they both recognized this fact.

'I have heard the lion roar from afar,' Mark Anders said in Zulu. 'Now I meet the beast face to face.'

'I have heard of you as well, Colonel,' Moses replied, pointedly speaking English.

'Victoria is a gentle child,' Mark Anders persisted in his use of Zulu. 'We all hope you will not teach her your fierce ways.'

'She will be a dutiful wife,' Moses said in English. 'She will do what I ask of her, I am sure.'

Storm had been following the exchange, sensing the innate hostility between the two men and now she intervened smoothly.

'If you are ready, Moses, we can all go down to Theuniskraal for the ceremony.'

Victoria and her mother had insisted on a Christian ceremony to reinforce

the traditional tribal wedding. Now Sangane and most of the other guests who were pagan and ancestor-worshippers, remained at the kraal, while the diminished bridal party crowded into the two motor vehicles.

Theuniskraal was the home of Lady Anna Courtney and the original seat of the Courtney family. It stood amongst its sprawling lawns and unruly gardens of palms and bougainvillaea and pride of India trees at the foot of the Ladyburg escarpment. It was a rambling old building of oddly assorted architectual styles, and beyond the gardens stretched endless fields of sugar cane, that dipped and undulated to the breeze like the swells of the ocean.

The wedding party trooped into the house to change into garb more suitable than beads and furs and feathers for the second ceremony while Lady Anna and the family went to greet the Anglican priest in the marquee that had been set up on the front lawn.

When the bridegroom and his attendants came out on to the lawns half an hour later, they wore dark lounge suits and Victoria's elder brother, who had pranced and swirled his plumes in the *giya* just a few hours before, now wore his Law Association tie in an impeccable Windsor knot and aviator-style dark glasses against the glare of Theuniskraal's whitewashed walls, as he chatted affably with the Courtney family, while they waited for the bride.

Victoria's mother was decked out in one of Lady Anna's cast-off caftans, for the two ladies were of similar build, and she was already sampling the fare that was laid out on the long trestle table in the marquee. Colonel Mark Anders and the Anglican priest stood a little aside from the main group; men of the same generation, they both found the proceedings disquieting and unnatural. It had taken all Storm's powers to persuade the priest to perform the ceremony, and then he had only agreed on condition that the wedding was not held in his own church in the village where his conservative white congregation might take offence.

'Damned if we weren't all a sight better off in the old days when everybody knew their place instead of trying to ape their betters,' Mark Anders grumbled, and the priest nodded.

'No sense in looking for trouble – ' He broke off as Victoria came out on to the wide verandah. Storm Anders had helped her select her full-length white satin wedding dress with a wreath of tiny red tea roses holding the long veil in place around her brow. The contrast of red and white against her dark and glossy skin was striking and her joy was infectious. Even Mark Anders forgot his misgivings for the moment, as Lady Anna at the piano struck up the wedding march.

* * *

At her father's kraal, Victoria's family had built a magnificent new hut for her nuptial night. Her brothers and half-brothers had cut the wattle saplings and the trunk for the central post and plaited the stripped green branches into the shape of the beehive. Then her mother and sisters and half-sisters had done the women's work of thatching, carefully combing the long grass stems and lacing the crisp bundles on to the wattle framework, packing and trimming and weaving them until the finished structure was smooth and symmetrical and the brushed grass stems shone like polished brass.

Everything the hut contained was new, from the three-legged pot to the lamp and the blankets and the magnificent kaross of hyrax and monkeyskins which was the gift of Victoria's sisters, lovingly tanned and sewn by them into a veritable work of art.

At the cooking fire in the centre of the hut Victoria worked alone, preparing the first meal for her husband, while she listened to the shouted laughter of the guests outside in the night. The millet beer was mild. However, the women had brewed hundreds of gallons and the guests had been drinking since early morning.

Now she heard the bridegroom's party approaching the hut. There was singing and loud suggestive advice, cries of encouragement and rude exhortations to duty and then Moses Gama stooped through the entrance. He straightened and stood tall over her, his head brushing the curved roof and outside the voices of his comrades retreated and dwindled.

Still kneeling, Victoria sat back on her heels and looked up at him. Now at last she had discarded her western clothing and wore for the last time the short beaded skirt of the virgin. In the soft ruddy light of the fire her naked upper body had the dark patina of antique amber.

'You are very beautiful,' he said, for she was the very essence of Nguni womanhood. He came to her and took her hands and lifted her to her feet.

'I have prepared food for you,' she whispered huskily.

'There will be time later to eat.'

He led her to the piled kaross and she stood submissively while he untied the thong of her apron and then lifted her in his arms and laid her on the bed of soft fur.

As a girl she had played the games with the boys in the reed banks beside the waterhole, and out on the open grassy veld where she had gone with the other girls to gather firewood conveniently close to where the cattle were being herded. These games of touching and exploring, of rubbing and fondling, right up to the forbidden act of intromission, were sanctioned by tribal custom and smiled at by the elders, but none of them had fully prepared her for the power and skill of this man, or for the sheer magnificence of him. He reached deeply into her body and touched her very soul so that much later in the night she clung to him and whispered.

'Now I am more than just your wife, I am your slave to the end of my days.'

In the dawn her joy was blighted, and though her lovely moon face remained serene, she wept within when he told her, 'There will only be one more night – on the road back to Johannesburg. Then I must leave you.'

'For how long?' she asked.

'Until my work is done,' he replied, then his expression softened and he stroked her face. 'You knew that it must be so. I warned you that when you married me, you were marrying the struggle.'

'You warned me,' she agreed in a husky whisper. 'But there was no way that I could guess at the agony of your leaving.'

* * *

They rose early the following morning. Moses had acquired a second-hand Buick, old and shabby enough not to excite interest or envy, but one of

Hendrick Tabaka's expert mechanics had overhauled the engine and tightened the suspension, leaving the exterior untouched. In it they would return to Johannesburg.

Though the sun had not yet risen, the entire kraal was astir, and Victoria's sisters had prepared breakfast for them. After they had eaten came the hard part of taking leave of her family. She knelt before her father.

'Go in peace, my daughter,' he told her fondly. 'We will think of you often. Bring your sons to visit us.'

Victoria's mother wept and keened as though it were a funeral, not a wedding, and Victoria could not comfort her although she embraced her and protested her love and duty until the other daughters took her away.

Then there were all her stepmothers and her half-brothers and half-sisters, and the uncles and aunts and cousins who had come from the farthest reaches of Zululand. Victoria had to make her farewells to all of them, though some partings were more poignant than others. One of these was her goodbye to Joseph Dinizulu, her favourite of all her relatives. Although he was a half-brother and seven years younger than she was, a special bond had always existed between them. The two of them were the brightest and most gifted of their generation in the family, and because Joseph lived at Drake's Farm with one of the elder brothers, they had been able to continue their friendship.

However, Joseph would not be returning to the Witwatersrand. He had written the entrance exams and been accepted by the exclusive multi-racial school, Waterford, in Swaziland, and Lady Anna Courtney would be paying his school fees. Ironically, this was the same school to which Hendrick Tabaka was sending his sons, Wellington and Raleigh. There would be opportunity for their rivalry to flourish.

'Promise me you will work hard, Joseph,' Vicky said. 'Learning makes a man strong.'

'I will be strong,' Joseph assured her. The elation that Moses Gama's speech had aroused in him still persisted. 'Can I come and visit you and your husband, Vicky? He is a man, the kind of man I will want to be one day.'

Vicky told Moses what the child had said. They were alone in the old Buick, all the wedding gifts and Vicky's possessions filling the boot and piled in the back seat, and they were leaving that great littoral amphitheatre of Natal, going up over the tail of the Drakensberg range on to the high veld of the Transvaal.

'The children are the future,' Moses nodded, staring ahead at the steep blue serpent of road that climbed the escarpment, past the green hill of Majuba where the Boers had thrashed the British in the first of many battles with them. 'The old men are beyond hope. You saw them at the wedding, how they kicked and baulked like unbroken oxen when I tried to show them the way – but the children, ah the children!' He smiled. 'They are like fresh clean sheets of paper. You can write on them what you will. The old men are stone-hard and impermeable, and the children are clay, eager clay waiting for the shaping hands of the potter.' He held up one of his hands. It was long and shapely, the hand of a surgeon or an artist and the palm was a delicate shade of pink, smooth and not calloused by labour. 'Children lack any sense of morality, they are without fear, and death is beyond their conception. These are all things they acquire later, by the teaching of their elders. They make perfect soldiers for they question nothing and it takes no great physical strength to pull a trigger. If an enemy strikes them down they become the perfect martyrs. The bleeding corpse of a child strikes horror and remorse into even the hardest heart. Yes,

the children are our key to the future. Your Christ knew it when he said "Suffer the little children to come unto me.".'

Victoria twisted on the leather bench seat of the Buick and stared at him.

'Your words are cruel and blasphemous,' she whispered, torn by her love for him and her instinctive rejection of what he had just said.

'And your reaction proves their truth,' he said.

'But – ' she paused, reluctant to ask, and fearful to hear his reply, 'but you are saying that we should use our children – ' She broke off, and an image of the paediatric section of the hospital came into her mind. She had spent the happiest months of all her training among the little ones. 'Are you suggesting that you would use the children in the front line of the struggle – as soldiers?'

'If a child cannot grow up a free man, then he might as well die as a child,' Moses Gama said. 'Victoria, you have heard me say this before. It is time now that you learn to believe it. There is nothing I would not do, no price I would not pay, for our victory. If I have to see a thousand little children dead so that a hundred thousand more may live to grow up free men, then for me the bargain is a fair one.'

Then, for the very first time in her life, Victoria Dinizulu was truly afraid.

* * *

That night they stayed at Hendrick Tabaka's house in Drake's Farm Township, and it was well after midnight before they could go to the small bedroom that had been set aside for them because there were many who demanded Moses' attention, men from the Buffaloes and the Mineworkers' Union, a messenger from the council of the ANC and a dozen petitioners and supplicants who came quietly as jackals to the lion when the word flashed through the township that Moses Gama had returned.

At all these meetings Victoria was present, although she never spoke and sat quietly in a corner of the room. At first the men were surprised and puzzled, darting quick glances across at her and reluctant to come to their business until Moses pressed them. None of them was accustomed to having women present when serious matters were discussed. However, none of them could bring themselves to protest, until the ANC messenger came into the room. He was invested with all the power and importance of the council he represented, and so he was the first to speak about Victoria's presence.

'There is a woman here,' he said.

'Yes,' Moses nodded. 'But not just a woman, she is my wife.'

'It is not fitting,' said the messenger. 'It is not the custom. This is men's business.'

'It is our purpose and our aim to tear down and burn the old customs and to build up the new. In that endeavour we will need the help of all our people. Not just the men, but the women and children also.'

There was a long silence while the messenger fidgeted under Moses' dark unrelenting stare.

'The woman can remain,' he capitulated at last.

'Yes,' Moses nodded. 'My wife will remain.'

Later in the darkness of their bedroom, in the narrowness of the single bed,

Victoria pressed closed to him, the soft plastic curves of her body conforming to his hardness and she said:

'You have honoured me by making me a part of your struggle. Like the children, I want to be a soldier. I have thought about it and I have discovered what I can do.'

'Tell me,' he invited.

'The women. I can organize the women. I can begin with the nurses of the hospital, and then the other women – all of them. We must take our part in the struggle beside the men.'

His arms tightened around her. 'You are a lioness,' he said. 'A beautiful Zulu lioness.'

'I can feel your heartbeat,' she whispered, 'and my own heart beats in exact time to it.'

In the morning Moses drove her to the nurses' home at the hospital. She stood at the top of the steps and did not go into the building. He watched her in the rear-view mirror as he drove away and she was still standing there when he turned into the traffic, heading back towards Johannesburg and the suburb of Rivonia.

He was one of the first to arrive at Puck's Hill that morning to attend the council meeting to which the previous night's messenger had summoned him.

Marcus Archer met Moses on the verandah, and his smile was vitriolic as he greeted him. 'They say a man is incomplete until he marries – and only then is he finished.'

There were two men already seated at the long table in the kitchen which had always been used as their council chamber. They were both white men.

Bram Fischer was the scion of an eminent Afrikaner family whose father had been a judge-president of the Orange Free State. Though he was an expert on mining law, and a QC at the Johannesburg bar, he had also been a member of the old Communist Party and was a member of the ANC, and lately his practice had become almost entirely the defence of those accused under the racial laws that the Nationalist government had enacted since 1948. Although he was a charming and erudite man with a real concern for his countrymen of all races, Moses was wary of him. He was a starry-eyed believer in the eventual miraculous triumph of good over evil, and firmly opposed the formation of *Umkhonto we Sizwe*, the military branch of the ANC. His pacifist influence on the rest of the Congress set a brake on Moses' aspirations.

The other white man was Joe Cicero, a Lithuanian immigrant. Moses could guess why he had come to Africa – and who had sent him. He was one of the eagles, fierce hearted as Moses was himself, and an ally when the need for direct and even violent action was discussed. Moses went to sit beside him, across the table from Fischer. He would need Joe Cicero's support this day.

Marcus Archer, who loved to cook, set a plate of devilled kidneys and *oeufs ranchero* in front of him, but before Moses had finished his breakfast, the others began to arrive. Nelson Mandela and his faithful ally Tambo, arrived together, followed quickly by Walter Sisulu and Mbeki and the others, until the long table was crowded and cluttered with papers and dirty plates, with coffee cups and ashtrays which were soon overflowing with crushed cigarette butts.

The air was thick with tobacco smoke and Marcus's cooking aromas, and the talk was charged and serious as they tried to decide and agree exactly what were the objects of the defiance campaign.

'We have to stir the awareness of our people, to shake them out of their dumb

cowlike acceptance of oppression.' Mandela put the premier proposition, and across from him Moses leaned forward.

'More important, we must awaken the conscience of the rest of the world, for that is the direction from which our ultimate salvation will come.'

'Our own people – ' Mandela began, but Moses interrupted him.

'Our own people are powerless without weapons and training. The forces of oppression ranged against us are too powerful. We cannot triumph without arms.'

'You reject the way of the peace then?' Mandela asked. 'You presuppose that freedom can only be won at the point of the gun?'

'The revolution must be tempered and made strong in the blood of the masses,' Moses affirmed. 'That is always the way.'

'Gentlemen! Gentlemen!' Bram Fischer held up his hand to stop them. 'Let us return to the main body of the discussion. We agree that by our campaign of defiance we hope to stir our own people out of their lethargy and to attract the attention of the rest of the world. Those are our two main objects. Let us now decide on our secondary objects.'

'To establish the ANC as the only true vehicle of liberation,' Moses suggested. 'At present we have less than seven thousand members, but by the end of the campaign we should aim to have enrolled one hundred thousand more.' To this there was general agreement, even Mandela and Tambo nodded and when the vote was taken it was unanimous and they could go on to discuss the details of the campaign.

It was a massive undertaking, for it was planned that the campaign should be nationwide and that it should be conducted simultaneously in every one of the main centres of the Union of South Africa so as to place the utmost strain on the resources of the government and to test the response of the forces of law and order.

'We must fill their goals until they burst. We must offer ourselves up for arrest in our thousands until the machinery of tyranny breaks down under the strain,' Mandela told them.

For three more days they sat in the kitchen at Puck's Hill, working out and agreeing every minute detail, preparing the lists of names and places, putting together the timetable of action, the logistics of transport and communication, establishing the lines of control from the central committee down through the provincial headquarters of the movement, and ultimately to the regional cadres in every black township and location.

It was an onerous task but at last there was only one detail left to decide – the day on which it would begin. Now they all looked to Albert Luthuli at the head of the table and he did not hesitate.

'June the twenty-sixth,' he said, and when there was a murmur of agreement, he went on, 'So be it then. We all know our tasks.' And he gave them the salute of upraised thumbs. '*Amandla!* Power! *Ngawethu!*'

When Moses went out to where the old Buick was parked beneath the gum trees, the sunset was filling the western sky with furnace colours of hot orange and smouldering red, and Joe Cicero was waiting for him. He leaned against the silver trunk of one of the bluegum trees, with his arms folded over his broad chest, a bearlike figure, short and squat and powerful.

He straightened up as Moses came towards him.

'Can you give me a lift in to Braamfontein, comrade?' he asked, and Moses opened the door of the Buick for him, and they drove in silence for ten minutes

before Joe said quietly, 'It is strange that you and I have never spoken privately.' His accent was elusive, but the planes of his pale face above the dark fringe of beard were flat and Slavic and his eyes were dark as tar pools.

'Why is it so strange?' Moses asked.

'We share common views,' Joe replied. 'We are both true sons of the revolution.'

'Are you certain of that?'

'I am certain,' Joe nodded. 'I have studied you and listened to you with approval and admiration. I believe that you are one of the steely men that the revolution needs, comrade.'

Moses did not reply. He kept his eyes on the road, and his expression impassive, letting the silence draw out, forcing the other man to break it.

'What are your feelings towards mother Russia?' Joe asked softly at last, and Moses considered the question.

'Russia has never had colonies in Africa,' Moses answered carefully. 'I know that she gives support to the struggle in Malaya and Algeria and Kenya. I believe she is a true ally of the oppressed peoples of this world.'

Joe smiled and lit another Springbok cigarette from the flat maroon and white pack. He was a chain-smoker and his stubby fingers were stained dark brown.

'The road to freedom is steep and rocky,' he murmured. 'And the revolution is never secure. The proletariat must be protected from itself by the revolutionary guards.'

'Yes,' Moses agreed. 'I have read the works of both Marx and Lenin.'

'Then I was correct,' Joe Cicero murmured. 'You are a believer. We should be friends – good friends. There are difficult days ahead and there will be a need for steely men.' He reached over the back seat and picked up his attaché case. 'You can let me out at the central railway station, comrade,' he said.

* * *

It had been fully dark for two hours by the time Moses reached the camp in the gorge below the Sundi Caves and parked the Buick behind the Nissen hut that was the expedition's office and laboratory, and he went up the path to Tara Courtney's tent, stepping softly so as not to alarm her. He saw her silhouette against the canvas side. She was lying on her stretcher bed reading by the light of the petromax lantern, and he saw her start as he scratched on the canvas.

'Don't be afraid,' he called softly. 'It's me.'

And her reply was low but quivering with joy. 'Oh God, I thought you'd never come.'

She was in a frenzy for him. Her other pregnancies had always left her feeling nauseous and bloated, and the thought of sexual contact during that time had been repugnant. But now, even though she was over three months pregnant, her wanting was a kind of madness. Moses seemed to sense her need, but did not try to match it. He lay naked upon his back on the stretcher, and he was like a pinnacle of black granite. Tara hurled herself upon him to impale herself. She was sobbing and uttering little cries and yelps. At once both clumsy and adroit, her body, not yet swollen by the child within her, thrashed and churned above him as he lay quiescent and unmoving, and she went on beyond physical endurance, beyond the limits of flesh, insatiable and desperate for him, until

exhaustion at last overcame her and she rolled off him and lay panting weakly, her chestnut hair darkened by her own sweat and plastered to her forehead and neck, and there was a thin pink colouring of blood on the front of her thighs, so wild had been her passion.

Moses drew the sheet over her and held her until she had stopped shaking and her breathing had quietened, and then he said, 'It will begin soon – the date has been agreed.'

Tara was so transported that for a while she did not understand, and she shook her head stupidly.

'June the twenty-sixth,' Moses said. 'Across the land, in every city, all at the same time. Tomorrow I will be going to Port Elizabeth in the eastern Cape to command the campaign there.'

That was hundreds of miles from Johannesburg, and she had come to be near him. With the melancholy of after-love upon her, Tara felt cheated and abused. She wanted to protest but with an effort checked herself.

'How long will you be away?'

'Weeks.'

'Oh Moses!' she began, and then warned by his quick frown, she relapsed into silence.

'The American woman – the Godolphin woman. Have you contacted her? Without publicity the value of our efforts will be halved.'

'Yes.' Tara paused. She had been on the point of telling him that it was all arranged, that Kitty Godolphin would meet him any time he wanted, but she stopped herself. Instead of handing her over to Moses and standing aside, here was her chance to stay close to him.

'Yes, I have spoken to her. We met at her hotel, she is eager to meet you but she is out of town at the moment, in Swaziland.'

'That is no good,' Moses muttered. 'I had hoped to see her before I left.'

'I could bring her down to Port Elizabeth,' Tara cut in eagerly. 'She will be back in a day or two and I will bring her to you.'

'Can you get away from here?' he asked dubiously.

'Yes, of course. I will bring the television people down to you in my own car.'

Moses grunted uncertainly, and was silent while he thought about it, and then he nodded.

'Very well. I will explain how you will be able to contact me when you get there. I will be in the township of New Brighton, just outside the city.'

'Can I be with you, Moses? Can I stay with you?'

'You know that is impossible.' He was irritated by her persistence. 'No whites are allowed in the township without a pass.'

'The television team will not be able to help you much if we are kept out of the township,' Tara said quickly. 'We should be close to you to be of any use to the struggle.' Cunningly she had linked herself to Kitty Godolphin, and she held her breath as he thought about it.

'Perhaps,' he nodded, and she exhaled softly. He had accepted it. 'Yes. There might be a way. There is a mission hospital run by German nuns in the township. They are friends. You could stay there. I will arrange it.'

She tried not to let him see her triumph. She would be with him, that was all that was important. It was madness, but though her body was bruised and sore, already she wanted him again. It was not physical lust, it was more than that. It

was the only way she could possess him, even for a few fleeting minutes. When she had him locked in her body, he belonged to her alone.

* * *

Tara was puzzled by Kitty Godolphin's attitude towards her. She was accustomed to people, both men and women, responding immediately to her own warm personality and good looks. Kitty was different, from the very beginning there had been a cold-eyed reserve and an innate hostility in her. Very swiftly Tara had seen beyond the angelic little-girl image that Kitty so carefully projected, but even after she had recognized the tough and ruthless person beneath, she could find no logical reason for the woman's attitude. After all, Tara was offering her an important assignment, and Kitty was examining the gift as though it were a live scorpion.

'I don't understand,' she protested, her voice and eyes snapping. 'You told me we could do the interview here in Johannesburg. Now you want me to traipse off into the deep sticks somewhere.'

'Moses Gama has to be there. Something important is about to take place – '

'What is so important?' Kitty demanded, fists on her lean denim-clad hips. 'What we agreed was important also.'

Most people, from leading politicians and international stars of sport and entertainment down to the lowest nonentity, were ready to risk slipping a spinal disc in their eagerness to appear for even the briefest moment on the little square screen. It was Kitty Godolphin's right, a semi-divine right, to decide who would be accorded that opportunity and who would be denied it. Moses Gama's cavalier behaviour was insulting. He had been chosen, and instead of displaying the gratitude which was Kitty Godolphin's due, he was setting conditions.

'Just what is so important that he cannot make the effort of common courtesy?' she repeated.

'I'm sorry, Miss Godolphin, I can't tell you that.'

'Well then, I'm sorry also, Mrs Courtney, but you tell Moses Gama from me that he can go straight to hell without passing GO and without collecting his hundred dollars.'

'You aren't serious!' Tara hadn't expected that.

'I have never been more serious in my life.' Kitty rolled her wrist to look at her Rolex. 'Now, if you will excuse me, I have more important matters to attend to.'

'All right,' Tara gave in at once. 'I will risk it. I'll tell you what is going to happen – ' Tara paused while she considered the consequences, and then asked, 'You will keep it to yourself, what I am about to tell you?'

'Darling, if there is a good story in it, they wouldn't get it out of me with thumbscrew and hot irons – that is, not until I splash it across the screen myself.'

Tara told her in a rush of words, getting it out quickly before she could change her mind. 'It will be a chance to film him at work, to see him with his people, to watch him defying the forces of oppression and bigotry.'

She saw Kitty hesitating and knew that she had to think quickly.

'However, I should warn you, there may be danger. The confrontation could turn to violence and even bloodshed,' she said, and she had got it exactly right.

'Hank!' Kitty Godolphin shouted through to the lounge of her suite where the camera crew were strewn over the furniture like the survivors of a bomb blast, listening at full volume of the radio to the new rock 'n' roll sensation warning them to keep off his blue suede shoes.

'Hank!' Kitty raised her voice above Presley's. 'Get the cameras packed. We are going to a place called Port Elizabeth. If we can find where the hell it is.'

They drove through the night in Tara's Packard, and the suspension sagged under the weight of bodies and camera equipment. In his travels around the country Hank had discovered that cannabis grew as a weed around most of the villages in the reserves of Zululand and the Transkei. In an environment that the plant found agreeable, it reached the size of a small tree. Only a few of the older generation of black tribesmen smoked the dried leaves, and although it was proscribed as a noxious plant and listed as a dangerous drug, its use was so localized and restricted to the more primitive blacks in the remote areas – for no white person or educated African would lower himself to smoke it – that the authorities made little effort to prevent its cultivation and sale. Hank had found an endless supply of what he declared to be 'pure gold' for the payment of pennies.

'Man, a sack of this stuff on the streets of Los Angeles would fetch a hundred thousand dollars,' he murmured contentedly as he lit a hand-rolled cigarette and settled down on the back seat of the Packard. The heavy incense of the leaves filled the interior, and after a few draws Hank passed the cigarette to Kitty in the front seat. Kitty drew on the butt deeply and held the smoke in her lungs, as long as she was able, before blowing it out in a pale streamer against the windscreen. Then she offered the butt to Tara.

'I don't smoke tobacco,' Tara told her politely, and they all laughed.

'That ain't baccy, sweetheart,' Hank told her.

'What is it?'

'You call it *dagga* here.'

'*Dagga.*' Tara was shocked. She remembered that Centaine had fired one of her houseboys who smoked it.

'He dropped my Rosenthal tureen, the one that belonged to Czar Nicholas,' Centaine had complained. 'Once they start on that stuff they become totally useless.'

'No thanks,' Tara said quickly, and thought how angry Shasa would be if he knew that she had been offered it. That thought gave her pause and she changed her mind. 'Oh, all right.' She took the butt, steering the Packard with one hand. 'What do I do?'

'Just suck it in and hold it down,' Kitty advised, 'and ride the glow.'

The smoke scratched her throat and burned her lungs, but the thought of Shasa's outrage gave her determination. She fought the urge to cough and held it down.

Slowly she felt herself relaxing, and a mild glow of euphoria made her body seem air-tight and cleansed her mind. All the agonies of her soul became trivial and fell behind her.

'I feel good,' she murmured, and when they laughed, she laughed with them and drove on into the night.

In the early morning before it was fully light, they reached the coast, skirting

the bay of Algoa where the Indian Ocean took a deep bite out of the continent, and the green waters were chopped to a white froth by the wind.

'Where do we go from here?' Kitty asked.

'The black township of New Brighton,' Tara told her. 'There is a mission run by German nuns, a teaching and nursing order, the sisters of St Magdalene. They are expecting us. We aren't really allowed to stay in the township, but they have arranged it.'

Sister Nunziata was a handsome blond woman, not much older than forty years. She had a clear scrubbed-looking skin and her manner was brisk and efficient. She wore the light grey cotton habit of the order, and a white shoulder-length veil.

'Mrs Courtney, I have been expecting you. Our mutual friend will be here later this morning. You will want to bathe and rest.' She led them to the cells that had been set aside for them and apologized for the simple comforts they contained. Kitty and Tara shared a cell. The floor was bare cement, the only decoration was a crucifix on the whitewashed wall, and the springs of the iron bedsteads were covered with thin hard coir mattresses.

'She's just great,' Kitty enthused. 'I must get her on film. Nuns always make good footage.'

As soon as they had bathed and unpacked their equipment, Kitty had her crew out filming. She recorded a good interview with Sister Nunziata, her German accent lent interest to her statements, and then they filmed the black children in the schoolyard and the out-patients waiting outside the clinic.

Tara was awed by the girl's energy, her quick mind and glib tongue, and her eye for angle and subject as she directed the shooting. It made Tara feel superfluous, and her own lack of talent and creative skill irked her. She found herself resenting the other girl for having pointed up her inadequacies so graphically.

Then everything else was irrelevant. A nondescript old Buick sedan pulled into the mission yard and a tall figure climbed out and came towards them. Moses Gama wore a light blue open-neck shirt, the short sleeves exposed the sleek muscle in his upper arms and neck, and his tailored blue slacks were belted around his narrow waist. Tara didn't have to say anything, they all knew immediately who he was as Kitty Godolphin breathed softly beside her, 'My God, he is beautiful as a black panther.'

Tara's resentment of her flared into seething hatred. She wanted to rush to Moses and embrace him so that Kitty might know he was hers, but instead she stood dumbly while he stopped in front of Kitty and held out his right hand.

'Miss Godolphin? At last,' he said, and his voice brought out a rush of goose-bumps on Tara's arms.

The rest of the day was spent in reconnaisance and the filming of more background material, this time with Moses as the central figure in each shot. The new Brighton township was typical of the South African urban locations, rows of identical low-cost housing laid out in geometric squares of narrow roads, some of them paved and others rutted and filled with muddy puddles in which the pre-school children and toddlers, many of them naked or dressed only in ragged shorts, played raucously.

Kitty filmed Moses picking his way around the puddles, squatting to talk to the children, lifting a marvellously photogenic little black cherub in his arms and wiping his snotty nose.

'That's great stuff,' Kitty enthused. 'He's going to look magnificent on film.'

The children followed Moses, laughing and skipping behind him as though he were the Pied Piper, and the women attracted by the commotion came out of the squalid little cottages. When they recognized Moses and saw the cameras, they began to ululate and dance. They were natural actresses and completely without inhibition, and Kitty was everywhere, calling for shots and unusual camera angles, clearly delighted by the footage she was getting.

In the late afternoon the working men began to arrive back in the township by bus and train. Most of them were production-line workers in the vehicle assembly plants of Ford and General Motors, or factory-workers in the tyre companies of Goodyear and Firestone, for Port Elizabeth and its satellite town of Uitenhage formed the centre of the country's motor vehicle industry.

Moses walked the narrow streets with the camera following him, and he stopped to talk to the returning workers, while the camera recorded their complaints and problems, most of which were the practical everyday worries of making ends meet while remaining within the narrow lines demarcated by the forest of racial laws. Kitty could edit most of that out, but every one of them mentioned the 'show on demand' clause of the pass laws as the thing they hated and feared most. In every little vignette they filmed Moses Gama was the central heroic figure.

'By the time I've finished with him, he will be as famous as Martin Luther King,' Kitty enthused.

They joined the nuns for their frugal evening meal, and afterwards Kitty Godolphin was still not satisfied. Outside one of the cottages near the mission a family was cooking on an open fire, and Kitty had Moses join them, hunched over the fire in the night with the flames lighting his face, adding drama to his already massive presence as she filmed him while he spoke. In the background one of the women was singing a lullaby to the infant at her breast, and there were the murmurous sounds of the location, the soft cries of the children and the distant yapping of pariah dogs.

Moses Gama's words were poignant and moving, spoken in that deep thrilling voice, as he described the agony of his land and his people, so that Tara, listening to him in the darkness, found tears running down her face.

In the morning Kitty left her team at the mission, and without the camera the three of them, Kitty and Tara and Moses, drove in the Buick to the railway station that served the township and watched the black commuters swarm like hiving bees through the station entrance marked NON WHITES – NIE BLANKES, crowding on to the platform reserved for blacks, and as soon as the train pulled in, flooding into the coaches set aside for them.

Through the other entrance, marked WHITES ONLY – BLANKES ALLEENLIK, a few white officials and others who had business in the township sauntered and unhurriedly entered the first-class coaches at the rear of the train where they sat on green leather-covered seats and gazed out through glass at the black swarm on the opposite platform with detached expressions as though they were viewing creatures of another species.

'I've got to try and get that,' Kitty murmured. 'I've got to get that reaction on film.' She was busily scribbling notes in her pad, sketching rough maps of the station layout and marking in camera sites and angles.

Before noon Moses excused himself. 'I have to meet the local organizers and make the final plans for tomorrow,' and he drove away in the Buick.

Tara took Kitty and the team down to the seaside at St George's Strand, and they filmed the bathers on the beaches lying under the signboards BLANKES

ALLEENLIK – WHITES ONLY. School was out and tanned young people, the girls in bikinis and the boys with short haircuts and frank open faces lolled on the white sand, or played beach games and surfed the rolling green waves.

When Kitty asked them, 'How would you feel if black people came to swim here?' some of them giggled nervously at a question they had never considered before:

'They aren't allowed to come here – they've got their own beaches.'

And at least one was indignant. 'They can't come here and look at our girls in bathing-costumes.' He was a beefy young man with sea-salt caked in his sun-streaked hair and skin peeling from his sun-burned nose.

'But wouldn't you look at the black girls in their bathing costumes?' Kitty asked innocently.

'*Sis* man!' said the surfer, his handsome tanned features contorted with utter disgust at the suggestion.

'It's just too good to be true!' Kitty marvelled at her own fortune. 'I'll cut that in with some footage I've got of a beautiful black dancer in a Soweto night club.'

On the way back to the mission Kitty asked Tara to stop at the New Brighton railway station once again, for a final reconnaisance. They left the cameras in the Packard and two white-uniformed railway constables watched them with idle interest as they wandered around the almost deserted platforms that during the rush hours swarmed wih thousands of black commuters. Quietly Kitty pointed out to her team the locations she had chosen earlier, and explained to them what shots she would be striving for.

That night Moses joined them for the evening meal in the mission refectory, and though the conversation was light and cheerful, there was a hint of tension in their laughter. When Moses left, Tara went out with him to where the Buick was parked in the darkness behind the mission clinic.

'I want to be with you tonight,' she told him pathetically. 'I feel so alone without you.'

'That is not possible.'

'It's dark – we could go for a drive to the beach,' she pleaded.

'The police patrols are looking for just that sort of thing,' Moses told her. 'You would see yourself in the *Sunday Times* next weekend.'

'Make love to me here, please Moses,' and he was angry.

'Your selfishness is that of a spoilt child – you think only of yourself and your own desires, even now when we are on the threshold of great events, you would take risks that could bring us down.'

Tara lay awake most of the night and listened to Kitty's peaceful breathing in the iron bed across the cell.

She fell asleep just before dawn, and awoke feeling nauseous and heavy, when Kitty leapt gaily out of bed in her pink striped pyjamas, eager for the day.

'June twenty-sixth,' she cried. 'The big day at last!'

None of them took more than a cup of coffee for an early breakfast. Tara felt too sick and the others were too keyed up. Hank had checked his equipment the previous night, but now he went over it again before he loaded it into the Packard and they drove down to the railway station.

It was gloomy and a few street lights were still burning while under them the hordes of black commuters hurried. However, by the time they reached the station the first rays of the sun struck the entrance and the light was perfect for filming. Tara noticed that a pair of police Black Maria vans were parked outside

the main entrance and instead of the two young constables who had been on duty the previous day, there were eight railway policemen in a group under the station clock. They were in blue uniform with black peaked caps and holstered sidearms on their polished leather Sam Browne belts. They all carried riot batons.

'They have been warned,' Tara exclaimed as she parked across the street from the two vans. 'They are expecting trouble – just look at them.'

Kitty had twisted around and was giving last-minute instructions to Hank in the back seat, but when Tara glanced at her to assess her reaction to the waiting police, something about Kitty's expression and her inability to meet Tara's eyes made her pause.

'Kitty?' she insisted. 'These policemen. You don't seem – ' she broke off as she remembered something. The previous afternoon on the way to the beach, Kitty had asked her to stop outside the Humewood post office because she wanted to send a telegram. However, from across the road looking through the post office window, Tara had seen her slip into one of the glass telephone booths. It had puzzled her at the time.

'You!' she gasped. 'It was you who warned the police!'

'Listen, darling,' Kitty snapped at her. 'These people want to get themselves arrested. That's the whole point. And I want film of them getting arrested. I did it for all our sakes – ' she broke off and cocked her head. 'Listen!' she cried. 'Here they come!'

Faintly on the dawn there was the sound of singing, hundreds of voices together, and the group of policemen in the station entrance stirred and looked around apprehensively.

'Okay, Hank,' Kitty snapped. 'Let's go!'

They jumped out of the Packard, and hurried to the positions they had chosen, lugging their equipment.

The senior police officer with gold braid on his cap was a captain. Tara knew enough of police rank insignia from first-hand experience. He gave an order to his constables. Two of them began to cross the road towards the camera team.

'Shoot, Hank. Keep shooting!' Tara heard Kitty's voice, and the singing was louder now. The beautifully haunting refrain of *Nkosi Sikelel' iAfrika* carried by a thousand African voices made Tara shiver.

The two constables were halfway across the road when the first rank of protestors marched around the nearest row of shops and cottages and hurriedly the police captain called his constables back to his side.

They were twenty abreast, arms linked, filling the road from pavement to pavement, singing as they came on, and behind them followed a solid column of black humanity. Some of them were dressed in business suits, others in tattered cast-off clothing, some were silver-haired and others were in their teens. In the centre of the front rank, taller than the men around him, bare-headed and straight-backed as a soldier, marched Moses Gama.

Hank ran into the street with his sound technician following him. With the camera on his shoulder, he retreated in front of Moses, capturing him on film, the sound man recording his voice as it soared in the anthem, full and magnificent, the very voice of Africa and his features were lit with an almost religious fervour.

Hurriedly the police captain was drawing his men up across the whites-only entrance, and they were hefting their batons nervously, pale-faced in the early sunlight. The head of the column wheeled across the road and began to climb

the steps, and the police captain stepped forward and spread his arms to halt them. Moses Gama held up one hand. The column came to a jerking shuffling halt, and the singing died away.

The police captain was a tall man with a pleasantly lined face. Tara could see him over their heads, and he was smiling. That was the thing that struck Tara. Faced with a thousand black protesters, he was still smiling.

'Come on now,' he raised his voice, like a schoolmaster addressing an unruly class. 'You know you can't do this, it's just nonsense, man. You are acting like a bunch of skollies, and I know you are good people.' He was still smiling as he picked a few of the leaders out of the front ranks. 'Mr Dhlovu and Mr Khandela – you are on the management committee, shame on you!' He waggled his finger, and the men he had spoken to hung their heads and grinned shamefacedly. The whole atmosphere of the march had begun to change. Here was the father figure, stern but benevolent, and they were the children, mischievous but at the bottom good-hearted and dutiful.

'Off you go, all of you. Go home and don't be silly now,' the captain called, and the column wavered. From the back ranks there was laughter, and a few of those who had been reluctant to join the march began to slip away. Behind the captain his constables were grinning with relief, and the crowd began to jostle as it broke up.

'Good Christ!' Kitty swore bitterly. 'It's all a goddamned anti-climax. I have wasted my time – '

Then on to the top steps of the railway station a tall figure stepped out of the ranks and his voice rang out over them, silencing them and freezing them where they stood. The laughter and the smiles died away.

'My people,' Moses Gama cried, 'this is your land. In it you have God's right to live in peace and dignity. This building belongs to all who live here – it is your right to enter, as much as any other person's that lives here. I am going in – who will follow me?'

A ragged, uncertain chorus of support came from the front ranks and Moses turned to face the police captain.

'We are going in, Captain. Arrest us or stand aside.'

At that moment a train, filled with black commuters, pulled into the platform and they hung out of the windows of a coach and cheered and stamped.

'*Nkosi Sikelel' iAfrika!*' sang Moses Gama, and with his head held high he marched under the warning sign WHITES ONLY.

'You are breaking the law,' the captain raised his voice. 'Arrest that man.' And the thin rank of constables moved forward to obey.

Instantly a roar went up from the crowd behind him. 'Arrest me! Arrest me too!' And they surged forward, picking Moses up with them as though he were a surfer on a wave.

'Arrest me!' they chanted. 'Malan! Malan! Come and arrest us!'

The crowd burst through the entrance, and the white police constables were carried with them, struggling ineffectually in the press of bodies.

'Arrest me!' It had become a roar. '*Amandla! Amandla!*'

The captain was fighting to keep his feet, shouting to rally his men, but his voice was drowned out in the chant of, 'Power! Power!' The captain's cap was knocked over his eyes and he was shoved backwards on to the platform. Hank, the cameraman, was in the midst of it, holding his Arriflex high and shooting out of hand. Around him the white faces of the constables bobbed like flotsam

in a wild torrent of humanity. From the coaches the black passengers swarmed out to meet and mingle with the mob, and a single voice called out.

'*Jee!*' the battle cry that can drive an Nguni warrior into the berserker's passion, and '*Jee!*' a hundred voices answered him and '*Jee!*' again. There was the crash of breaking glass, one of the coach windows exploded as a shoulder thrust into it and '*Jee!*' they sang.

One of the white constables lost his footing and went sprawling backwards. Immediately he was trampled under foot and he screamed like a rabbit in a snare.

'*Jee!*' sang the men, transformed into warriors, the veneer of western manners stripped away, and another window smashed. By now the platform was choked with a struggling mass of humanity. From the cab of the locomotive, the mob dragged the terrified engine-driver and his fireman. They jostled them, ringing them in.

'*Jee!*' they chanted, bouncing at the knees, working themselves up into the killing madness. Their eyes were glazing and engorging with blood, their faces turning into shining black masks.

'*Jee!*' they sang. '*Jee!*' and Moses Gama sang with them. Let the others call for restraint and passive resistance to the enemy, but all that was forgotten and now Moses Gama's blood seethed with all his pent-up hatred and '*Jee!*' he cried, and his skin crawled and itched with atavistic fury and his fighting heart swelled to fill his chest.

The police captain, still on his feet, had been driven back against the wall of the station-master's office. One epaulette had been torn from the shoulder of his uniform and he had lost his cap. There was a fleck of blood at the corner of his moustache where an elbow had struck him in the mouth, and he was struggling with the flap of the holster on his belt.

'Kill!' shouted a voice. '*Bulala!*' and it was taken up. Black hands clutched at the police captain's lapels, and he drew the service revolver from its holster and tried to raise it, but the crowd was packed too densely around him. He fired blindly from the hip.

The shot was a great blurt of sound, and somebody yelled with shock and pain, and the crowd around the captain backed away, leaving a young black man in an army surplus greatcoat kneeling at his feet, moaning and clutching his stomach.

The captain, white-faced and panting, lifted the revolver and fired again into the air.

'Form up on me!' he shouted in a voice hoarse and breaking with terror and exertion. Another of his men was down on his knees, submerged in the milling crowd, but he managed to clear his revolver from its holster and he fired point-blank, emptying the chamber into the press around him.

Then they were running, blocking the entrance, jamming in it as they sought to escape the gunfire, and all the police constables were firing, some on their knees, all of them dishevelled and terrified, and the bullets told in the mass of bodies with loud, meaty thumps, like a housewife beating the dust from a hanging carpet. The air was thick with the smell of gunsmoke and dust and blood, of sweat and unwashed bodies and terror.

They were screaming and pushing, fighting their way out into the street again, leaving their fallen comrades crumpled on the platform in seeping puddles of blood, or crawling desperately after them dragging bullet-shattered limbs.

And the little group of policemen were running to help each other to their feet, bruised and bloodied in torn uniforms. They gathered up the engine-driver and his fireman and, staggering, supporting each other, drawn revolvers still in their hands, they crossed the platform stepping over the bodies and the puddles of blood and hurried down the steps to the two parked vans.

Across the road the crowd had reassembled and they screamed and shook their fists and chanted as the policemen scrambled into the vehicles and drove away at speed, and then the crowd swarmed into the roadway and hurled stones and abuse at the departing vans.

Tara had watched it all from the parked Packard, and now she sat paralysed with horror, listening to the animal growl of the crowd penetrated by the cries and groans of the wounded.

Moses Gama ran to her and shouted into the open window, 'Go and fetch Sister Nunziata. Tell her we need all the help we can get.'

Tara nodded dumbly and started the engine. Across the road she could see Kitty and Hank still filming. Hank was kneeling beside a wounded man, shooting into his tortured face, panning down on to the pool of blood in which he lay.

Tara pulled away, and the crowd in the road tried to stop her. Black faces, swollen with anger, mouthed at her through the Packard's windows and they beat with their fists on the roof, but she sounded her horn and kept driving.

'I have to get a doctor,' she shouted at them. 'Let me pass, let me through.'

She got through them, and when she looked in the rear-view mirror, she saw that in frustration and fury they were stoning the railway station, ripping up the pavement and hurling heavy slabs through the windows. She saw a white face at one of the windows, and felt a pang for the station-master and his staff. They had barricaded themselves in the ticket-office.

The crowd outside the building was solid, and as she drove towards the mission she passed a flood of black men and women rushing to join it. The women were ululating wildly, a sound that maddened their menfolk. Some of them ran into the road to try and stop Tara, but she jammed her palm down on the horn ring and swerved around them. She glanced up into her driving-mirror and one of them picked up a rock from the side of the road and hurled it after the car. The rock crashed against the metal of the cab and bounced away.

At the mission hospital they had heard the sound of gunfire and the roar of the mob. Sister Nunziata, the white doctor, and her helpers, were anxiously waiting on the verandah and Tara shouted up at her.

'You must come quickly to the station, Sister, the police have shot and wounded people – I think some of them are dead.'

They must have been expecting the call, for they had their medical bags on the verandah with them. While Tara backed and turned the Packard, Sister Nunziata and the doctor ran down the steps, carrying their black bags. They clambered into the cab of the mission's small blue Ford pick-up and turned towards the gate, cutting in front of Tara's Packard. Tara followed them, but by the time she had turned the Packard and driven out through the gates, the little blue pick-up was a hundred yards ahead of her. It turned the corner into the station road and even above the engine-beat Tara heard the roar of the mob.

When she swung through the corner the Ford was stopped only fifty paces ahead of her. It was completely surrounded by the crowd. The road from side to side was packed with screaming black men and women. Tara could not hear the words, there was no sense to their fury, it was incoherent and deafening.

They were concentrating on the Ford, and took no notice of Tara in the Packard.

Those nearest to the Ford were beating on the metal cab, and rocking the vehicle on its suspension. The side door opened and Sister Nunziata stood on the running board, a little higher than the heads of the howling mob that pushed closely around her. She was trying to speak to them, holding up her hands and pleading with them to let her through to take care of the wounded.

Suddenly a stone was thrown. It arced up out of the crowd and hit the nun on the side of her head. She reeled as she stood, and there was a bright flash of blood on her white veil. Stunned, she raised her hand to her cheek and it came away bloody.

The sight of blood enraged them. A forest of black arms reached up to Sister Nunziata and dragged her down from the vehicle. For a while they fought over her, dragging her in the road and worrying her like a pack of hounds with the fox. Then suddenly Tara saw the flash of a knife, and sitting in the Packard she screamed and thrust her fingers into her mouth to silence herself.

The old crone who wielded the knife was a *sangoma*, a witchdoctor, and around her neck she wore the necklace of bones and feathers and animal skulls that were her insignia. The knife in her right hand had a handle of rhino horn and the hand-forged blade was nine inches long and wickedly curved. Four men caught the nun and threw her across the engine bonnet of the Ford while the old woman hopped up beside her. The men held Sister Nunziata pinioned, face up, while the crowd began to chant wildly, and the *sangoma* stooped over her.

With a single stroke of the curved blade she cut through the nun's grey habit and split her belly open from groin to rib cage. While Sister Nunziata writhed in the grip of the men who held her, the crone thrust her hand and naked arm into the wound. Tara watched in disbelief as she brought out something wet and glistening and purple, a soft amorphous thing. It was done so swiftly, so expertly, that for seconds Tara did not realize that it was Sister Nunziata's liver that the crone held in her bloody hands.

With a slash of the curved blade, the *sangoma* cut a lump from the still living organ and hopped to her feet. Balancing on the curved bonnet of the Ford she faced the crowd.

'I eat our white enemy,' she screeched, 'and thus I take his strength.' And the mob roared, a terrible sound, as the old woman thrust the purple lump into her toothless mouth and chewed upon it. She hacked another piece off the liver, and still chewing with open mouth, she threw it to the crowd below her.

'Eat your enemy!' she shrilled, and they fought for the bloody scraps like dogs.

'Be strong! Eat the liver of the hated ones!'

She threw them more and Tara covered her eyes and heaved convulsively. Acid vomit shot up her throat and she swallowed it down painfully.

Abruptly the driver's door of the Packard beside her was jerked open and rough hands seized Tara. She was dragged out into the road. The blood roar of the crowd deafened her, but terror armed her with superhuman strength, and she tore herself free of the clutching hands.

She was at the edge of the mob, and the attention of most of them was entirely on the ghastly drama around the Ford. The crowd had set the vehicle alight. Sister Nunziata's mutilated body lay on the bonnet like a sacrifice on a burning altar, while trapped in the cab, the doctor thrashed around and beat at the

flames with his bare hands, and the crowd chanted and danced around him like children around the bonfire on Guy Fawkes night.

For that instant Tara was free, but there were men around her, shouting and reaching for her, their faces bestial, their eyes glazed and insensate. No longer human, they were driven into that killing madness in which there was no reason nor mercy. Swift as a bird Tara ducked under the outstretched arms and darted away. She found that she had broken out of the mob, and in front of her was a plot of wasteland strewn with old rusted car bodies and rubbish. She fled across it and behind her she heard her pursuers baying like a pack of hunting dogs.

At the end of the open land a sagging barbed-wire fence blocked her way, and she glanced back over her shoulder. A group of men still followed her, and two of them had outdistanced the others. They were both big and powerful-looking, running strongly on bare feet, their faces contorted in a cruel rictus of excitement. They came on silently.

Tara stooped into the space between the strands of wire. She was almost through when she felt the barbs catching the flesh of her back, and pain arrested her. For a moment she struggled desperately, feeling her skin tear as she fought to free herself and blood trickled down her flanks – and then they seized her.

Now they shouted with wild laughter as they dragged her back through the fence, the barbs ripping at her clothing and her flesh. Her legs collapsed under her, and she pleaded with them.

'Please don't hurt me. I'm going to have a baby – '

They dragged her back across the waste plot, half on her knees, twisting and pleading in their grip – and then she saw the *sangoma* coming to meet them, hopping and capering like an ancient baboon, cackling through her toothless mouth, her bones and beads rattling around her scrawny neck and the curved knife in her blood-caked fingers.

Tara began to scream, and she felt her urine squirt uncontrollably down her legs. 'Please! Please don't!' she raved and terror was an icy blackness of her mind and body that crushed her to earth, and she closed her eyes and steeled herself to the stinging kiss of the blade.

Then in the mindless animal roar of the crowd, above the old crone's shrill laughter, there was another voice, a great lion's roar of anger and command that stilled all other sound. Tara opened her eyes and Moses Gama stood over her, a towering colossus, and his voice alone stopped them and drove them back. He lifted her in his arms and held her like a child. The crowd around the Packard opened before him as he carried her to it and placed her on the front seat and then slid behind the wheel.

As he started the engine and swung the Packard away in a hard U-turn, the black smoke from the burning van poured over them and obscured the windscreen for a moment, and Tara smelled Sister Nunziata's flesh roasting.

This time she could not control herself and she flopped forward, her head between her knees, and vomited on the floor of the Packard.

* * *

Manfred De La Rey had taken the chair at the top of the long table in the operations rooms in the basement of Marshall Square. He had come across from his own office suite in the Union Buildings in Pretoria to police headquarters at

the centre of the storm, where he could be at hand to consider, with his senior officers, each fresh despatch as it came in from the police provincial HQs around the country.

The entire wall facing Manfred's seat was a large-scale map of the subcontinent. Working in front of it were two junior police officers. They were placing magnetic markers on the map. Each of the small black discs had a name printed upon it and represented one of the almost five hundred ANC officials and organizers that had been so far identified by the intelligence department.

The discs were clustered most thickly along the great crescent of the Witwatersrand in the centre of the continent, although others were scattered across the entire map as the physical whereabouts of each person was confirmed by the police reports that were coming in every few seconds.

Amongst the rash of black markers were a very few red discs, less than fifty in all. These represented the known members of the central committee of the African National Congress.

Some of the names were those of Europeans: Harris, Marks, Fischer, and some were Asians like Naicker and Nana Sita, but the majority were African. Tambo and Sisulu and Mandela – they were all there. Mandela's red disc was placed on the city of Johannesburg, while Moroka was in the Eastern Cape and Albert Luthuli was in Zululand.

Manfred De La Rey was stony-faced as he stared at the map, and the senior police officers seated around him studiously avoided catching his eye or even looking directly at him. Manfred had a reputation of being the strongman of the cabinet. His colleagues privately referred to him as 'Panga Man' after the heavy chopping knife that was used in the cane fields, and was the favourite weapon of the Mau Mau in Kenya.

Manfred looked the part. He was a big man. The hands that lay on the table before him were still, there was no fidgeting of nervousness or uncertainty, and they were big hard hands. His face was becoming craggy now, and his jowls and thick neck heightened the sense of power that emanated from him. His men were afraid of him.

'How many more?' he asked suddenly, and the colonel sitting opposite him, a man with the medal ribbons of valour on his chest, started like a schoolboy and quickly consulted his list.

'Four more to find – Mbeki, Mtolo, Mhlaba and Gama.' He read out the names on his list that remained unticked, and Manfred De La Rey relapsed into silence.

Despite his brooding stillness and forbidding expression, Manfred was pleased with the day's work. It was not yet noon on the first day and already they had pinpointed the whereabouts of most of the ringleaders. Altogether the ANC had planned the entire campaign with quite extraordinary precision and had exhibited unusual thoroughness and foresight in its execution, Manfred reflected. He had not expected them to be so efficient, the African was notoriously lackadaisical and happy-go-lucky – but then they had the advice and assistance of their white communist comrades. The protests and demonstrations and strikes were widespread and effective. Manfred grunted aloud and the officers at the table looked up apprehensively, but dropped their eyes hurriedly when he frowned.

Manfred returned to his thoughts. No, not bad for a bunch of kaffirs, even with a few white men to help them. Yet their naivety and amateurishness showed in their almost total lack of security and secrecy. They had blabbed as

though they were at a beer-drink. Full of their own importance they had boasted of their plans and made little effort to conceal the identities of the leaders and cover their movements. The police informers had had little difficulty in picking up the information.

There were, of course, exceptions and Manfred scowled as he considered the lists of leaders still unaccounted for. One name pricked like a burr, Moses Gama. He had made a study of the man's file. After Mandela, he was probably the most dangerous of them all.

'We must have him,' he told himself. 'We must get those two, Mandela and Gama.' And now he spoke aloud, barking the question: 'Where is Mandela?'

'At the moment he is addressing a meeting in the community hall at Drake's Farm township,' the colonel answered promptly, glancing up at the red marker on the map. 'He will be followed when he leaves, until we are ready to make the arrests.'

'No word of Gama yet?' Manfred asked impatiently, and the officer shook his head.

'Not yet, Minister, he was last seen here on the Witwatersrand nine days ago. He might have gone underground. We may have to move without him.'

'No,' Manfred snapped. 'I want him. I want Moses Gama.'

Manfred relapsed into silence, brooding and intense. He knew that he was caught in the cross-currents of history. He could feel the good winds blowing at his back, set fair to carry him away on his course. He knew also that at any moment those winds might drop, and the ebb of his tide might set in. It was dangerous – mortally dangerous but still he waited. His father and his ancestors had all been huntsmen. They had hunted the elephant and lion and he had heard them speak of the patience and the waiting that was part of the hunt. Now Manfred was a hunter as they had been, but his quarry, though every bit as dangerous, was infinitely more cunning.

He had set his snares with all the skill at his command. The banning orders, five hundred of them, were already made out. The men and women to whom they were addressed would be driven out from society into the wilderness. Prohibited from attending a gathering of more than three persons, physically confined to a single magisterial district, prohibited also from publishing a single written word and prevented from having their spoken word published by anyone else, their treacherous and treasonable voices would be effectively gagged. That was how he would deal with the lesser enemy, the smaller game of this hunt.

For the others, the fifty big game, the dangerous ones, he had other weapons ready. The warrants of arrest had been drawn up and the charges framed. Amongst them were high treason and furthering the aims of international communism, conspiracy to overthrow the government by violent revolution, incitement to public violence – and these, if proven, led directly to the gallows tree. Complete success was there, almost within his grasp, but at any moment it could be snatched away.

At that moment a voice was raised so loudly in the operations room beyond the cubicle windows that they all looked up. Even Manfred swung his head towards the sound and narrowed his pale eyes. The officer who had spoken was sitting with his back to the window holding the telephone receiver to his ear, and scribbling on the notepad on the desk in front of him. Now he slammed the receiver back on to its bracket, ripped the top sheet off the pad and hurried into the map room.

'What is it?' demanded the super.

'We've got him, sir.' The man's voice was shrill with excitement. 'We've got Moses Gama. He is in Port Elizabeth. Less than two hours ago he was at the head of a riot at the New Brighton railway station. The police were attacked, and were forced to open fire in self-defence. At least seven people have been killed, one of them a nun. She was horribly mutilated – there is even an unconfirmed report that she was cannibalized – and her body has been burned.'

'Are they sure it was him?' Manfred asked.

'No doubt, Minister. He was positively identified by an informer who knows him personally and the police captain has identified him by file and photograph.'

'All right,' Manfred De La Rey said. 'Now we can move.' He looked down at the commissioner of police at the far end of the long table. 'Do it, please, Commissioner,' he said, and picked up his dark fedora hat from the table. 'Report to me the moment you have them all locked up.'

He rode up in the lift to ground level and his chauffeur-driven limousine was waiting to take him back to his office in the Union Buildings. As he settled back against the leather-padded rear seat and the limousine pulled away, he smiled for the first time that morning.

'A nun,' he said aloud. 'And they ate her!' He shook his head with satisfaction. 'Let the bleeding hearts of the world read that and know what kind of savages we are dealing with.'

He felt the good winds of his fortune freshen, bearing him away towards those places which only recently he had allowed himself to dream of.

* * *

When they got back to the mission, Moses helped Tara out of the Packard. She was still pale and shaking like a woman with malaria. Her clothing was ripped and soiled with blood and dirt, and she could hardly stand unaided.

Kitty Godolphin and her camera crew had escaped the wrath of the mob by running across the railway tracks and hiding in a storm-water drain, then working their way in a wide circle back to the mission.

'We've got to get out of here,' Kitty yelled at Tara as she came out on to the verandah and saw Moses helping her up the steps. 'I've got the most incredible footage of my life. I can't trust it to anybody else. I want to get on the Pan Am flight from Jo'burg tomorrow morning and take the undeveloped cans to New York myself.' She was so excited that her voice shook wildly, and like Tara her denim jeans were torn and dusty. However, she was already packed and ready to leave, carrying the red canvas tote bag that was all her luggage.

'Did you film the nun?' Moses demanded. 'Did you film them killing Sister Nunziata?'

'Sure did, sweetheart!' Hank grinned. He was close behind Kitty. 'Got it all.'

'How many cans did you shoot?' Moses insisted.

'Four.' Hank was so excited he could not stand still. He was bouncing on his toes and snapping his fingers.

'Did you get the police shooting?'

'All of it, sweetheart, all of it.'

'Where is the film of the nun?' Moses demanded.

'Still in the camera.' Hank slapped the Arriflex that hung by his side. 'It's all

here, baby. I had just changed film when they grabbed the nun and ripped her up.'

Moses left Tara leaning against the column of the verandah, and crossed to where Hank stood. He moved so casually that none of them realized what he was about to do. Kitty was still talking.

'If we leave right away, we can be in Jo'burg by tomorrow morning. The Pan Am flight leaves at 11.30 – '

Moses had reached Hank's side. He seized the heavy camera, twisting the carrying strap so that Hank was pulled up on his toes helplessly, and he unclipped the round magazine of film from its seat on top of the camera body. Then he turned and smashed the magazine against the brick column of the verandah.

Kitty realized what he was doing and she flew at him like an angry cat, clawing for his eyes with her nails. 'My film,' she screeched. 'God damn you to hell, that's my film.'

Moses shoved her so violently that she collided with Hank, taking him off balance and they fell over each other, sprawling together on the verandah floor.

Moses hit the magazine again and this time the can burst open. The ribbon of glistening celluloid spilled out and cascaded over the retaining wall.

'You've ruined it,' Kitty screamed, coming to her feet and charging at him.

Moses tossed the empty can away, and caught Kitty's wrists, lifting her bodily off the ground and holding her effortlessly, though she struggled and kicked him.

'You have the film of police brutality, the murder of innocent blacks,' he said. 'The rest of it you were not meant to witness. I will not let you show that to the world.' He pushed her away. 'You may take the Packard.'

Kitty glared at him, massaging her wrists where the skin was red from his grip and she spat like a cat.

'I won't forget that – one day you will pay for that, Moses Gama.' Her malignancy was chilling.

'Go,' Moses commanded. 'You have a plane to catch.'

For a moment she hesitated, and then she whirled, picked up her tote bag.

'Come on, Hank,' she called, and she ran down the stairs to the Packard and sprang into the driver's seat.

'You cock-sucking bastard,' Hank hissed at Moses as he passed. 'That was the best stuff I ever scored.'

'You've still got three cans,' Moses said softly. 'Be grateful for that.'

Moses watched them drive away in the Packard and then turned to Tara.

'We must move very fast now – the police will act at once. We have to get out of the township before they cordon it off. I am a marked man – we have to get clear.'

'What do you want me to do?' Tara asked.

'Come, I'll explain later,' Moses said and hustled her towards the Buick. 'First, we must get clear.'

* * *

Tara gave the salesman a cheque and waited in the tiny cubicle of his office that stank of cheap cigar smoke while he phoned her bank in Cape Town.

There was a crumpled newspaper on the cluttered desk, and she picked it up and read it avidly.

SEVEN DEAD IN P.E. RIOTS
NATIONWIDE DISTURBANCES
500 ACTIVISTS BANNED
MANDELA ARRESTED

Almost the entire newspaper was devoted to the defiance campaign and its consequences. At the bottom of the page, under the lurid accounts of the killing and the cannibalization of Sister Nunziata, there were accounts of the action taken by the ANC in other sectors of the country. Thousands had been arrested, and there were photographs of protesters being loaded into police vans, grinning cheerfully and giving the thumbs-up sign that had become the protester's salute.

The inner page of the newspaper gave the lists of almost five hundred persons who had been banned, and explained the consequences of the banning orders – how they effectively terminated the public life of the victim.

There was also the much shorter list of persons who had been arrested for high treason and furthering the aims of the communist party, and Tara bit her lip when she saw Moses Gama's name. The police spokesman must have anticipated his arrest, but it was proof that the precautions Moses was taking were wise. High treason was a capital offence, and she had a mental picture of Moses, his head hooded, twisting and kicking from the gallows crossbeam. She shuddered and thrust the image aside, concentrating on the rest of the newspaper.

There were photographs, most of them murky and indistinct, of the leaders of the ANC, and she smiled humourlessly as she realized that these were the first fruits of the campaign. Up to this moment, not one in a hundred white South Africans had ever heard of Moses Gama, Nelson Mandela, or any of the other leaders, but now they had come bursting in on the national conscience. The world suddenly knew who they were.

The middle pages were mostly filled with public reaction to the campaign and to the government's counter measures. It was too soon for the foreign reactions, but local opinion seemed almost unanimous: condemnation of the barbaric murder of Sister Nunziata, and high praise for police courage and the swift action of the minister of police in crushing the communist-inspired plot.

The editor wrote:

> We have not always been able to commend the actions and utterances of the Minister of Police. However, the need finds the man and we are thankful this day that a man of courage and strength stands between us and the forces of anarchy –

Tara's reading was interrupted by the used car salesman. He bustled back into the tiny office to fawn on Tara and to gush.

'My dear Mrs Courtney, you must forgive me. I had in idea who you were, or I would never have subjected you to the humiliation of querying your cheque.'

He ushered her out to the yard, bowing and grinning ingratiatingly, and held open the door of the 1951-model black Cadillac for which Tara had just given her cheque for almost a thousand pounds.

Tara drove down the hill and parked on the Donkin overlooking the sea. The military and naval outfitters were only half a block down the main street and

from their stocks she picked out a chauffeur's cap with a glossy patent-leather peak and a dove-grey tunic with brass buttons in Moses' size which the assistant packed in a brown paper bag.

Back in the new Cadillac she drove slowly down to the main railway station and parked opposite the entrance. She left the key in the ignition and slipped back into the seat. Within five minutes Moses came out. He was dressed in grubby blue overalls and the police constable at the railway entrance did not even glance at him. Moses sauntered down the sidewalk and as he drew level with the Cadillac, Tara passed the paper bag through the open window.

Within ten minutes Moses was back, the overalls discarded, wearing the chauffeur's cap and smart new tunic over his dark slacks and black shoes. He climbed into the driver's seat and started the engine.

'You were right. There is a warrant out for your arrest,' she said softly.

'How do you know?'

'There is a newspaper on the seat.' She had folded it open at the report on his arrest. He read it swiftly, and then eased the Cadillac out into the traffic stream.

'What are you going to do, Moses? Will you give yourself up and stand trial?'

'The courtroom would be a platform from which to speak to the world,' he mused.

'And if you were convicted, the gallows would be an even more riveting pulpit,' she pointed out acidly, and he smiled at her in the rear-view mirror.

'We need martyrs – every cause must have martyrs.'

'My God, Moses, how can you speak like that? Every cause needs a leader. There are many who would make fine martyrs, but very few who can lead.'

He drove in silence for a while and then he said firmly, 'We will go to Johannesburg. I must talk to the others before I decide.'

'Most of the others have been arrested,' Tara pointed out.

'Not all.' He shook his head. 'I must talk to those who have escaped. How much money do you have?'

She opened her handbag and counted the notes she had in her purse.

'Over a hundred pounds.'

'More than enough,' he nodded. 'Be prepared to play the grand lady when the police stop us.'

They ran into the first road-block on the outskirts of the city at the Swartkops bridge. There was a line of cars and heavy vehicles and they moved forward slowly, stopping and starting, until two police constables signalled them over and a young police warrant officer came to the passenger window.

'Good afternoon, *Mevrou*.' He touched his cap. 'May we look in the boot of your car?'

'What is this about, officer?'

'The troubles, madam. We are looking for the trouble-makers who killed the nun and ate her.'

Tara leaned forward and spoke sharply to Moses. 'Open the boot for the policeman, Stephen.' And Moses climbed out and held the lid open while the constables made a cursory search. None of them looked at his face, the chauffeur's uniform had rendered him miraculously invisible.

'Thank you, lady.'

The warrant officer waved them through and Moses murmured. 'That was most unflattering. I thought I was a celebrity now.'

It was a long and arduous drive from the coast, but Moses drove sedately,

careful not to give anyone an excuse to stop them and question them more carefully.

As he drove he tuned the Cadillac's wireless for the South African Broadcasting Corporation's hourly news bulletin. The reception was intermittent as the terrain varied, but they picked up one exciting item.

The Soviet Union supported her by allies had demanded an urgent debate in the United Nations General Assembly on the situation in the country. This was the first time the UN had ever shown an interest in South Africa. For that alone all their sacrifice had been worthwhile. However, the rest of the news was disquieting. Over eight thousand protesters had been arrested and all the leaders banned or picked up, and a spokesman for the minister of police assured the country that the situation was firmly under control.

They drove on until after dark when they stopped at one of the small Orange Free State hotels that catered mainly for commercial travellers. When Tara asked for board and lodging for her chauffeur, the request was taken as matter of course because all the travellers employed coloured drivers and Moses was sent around the back to the servants' quarters in the hotel yard.

After the plain and unappetizing fare in the hotel dining-room, Tara telephoned Weltevreden, and Sean answered on the second ring. They had returned from their hunting safari with Shasa the previous day, and were garrulous and excited. Each of the boys spoke to her in turn, so she was treated to three separate accounts of how Garrick had shot a man-eating lion. Then Isabella came on the line, and her sweet childish lisp tugged at Tara's heart, making her feel dreadfully guilty at her lack of maternal duty. Yet none of the children, Isabella included, seemed to have missed her in the least, Isabella was just as long-winded as her brothers in recounting all the things that she and Nana had done together, and the new dress that Nana had bought her and the doll that grandpa Blaine had brought back from England especially for her. None of them asked her how she was and when she was coming home to Weltevreden.

Shasa came on the line last, distant but friendly. 'We are all having a wonderful time – Garry shot a lion – '

'Oh God, Shasa, don't you tell me about it, I've already had three accounts of the poor beast's death.'

Within a few minutes they had run out of things to say to each other. 'Well then, old thing, take care of yourself. I see the uglies are cutting up rather rough on the Rand, but De La Rey has it well in hand,' Shasa ended. 'Don't get caught up in any unpleasantness.'

'I won't,' she promised. 'Now I'll let you go in to dinner.' Shasa liked to dine at eight o'clock sharp and it was four minutes before the hour. She knew he was already dressed and checking his watch. When she hung up she realized he hadn't asked her where she was, what she was doing or when she was coming home.

'Saved me from having to lie,' she consoled herself.

From her bedroom she could look over the hotel yard, and the lights were on in the servants' quarters. Suddenly she was overwhelmed with loneliness. It was so chilling, that she seriously thought about creeping across the yard to be with him. It took an effort of will to thrust that madness aside, and instead she picked up the telephone again and asked the operator for the number at Puck's Hill.

A servant, with a marked African accent, answered and Tara's heart sank. It

was vital that they find out whether the Rivonia house was still safe. They could be going into a police trap.

'Is Nkosi Marcus there?' she demanded.

'Nkosi Marcus no here, he go away, missus,' the servant told her. 'You Missus Tara?'

'Yes! Yes!' Although she did not remember a servant, he must have recognized her voice, and she was about to go on when Marcus Archer spoke in his normal voice.

'Forgive me, my dear, for the music-hall impression, but the sky has fallen in here. Everybody is in a panic – the pigs have moved much quicker than anybody expected. Joe and I are the only ones to survive, as far as I know. How is our good friend, have they got him?'

'He's safe. Can we come to Puck's Hill?'

'So far it seems as though they have overlooked us here, but do be careful, won't you? There are road-blocks everywhere.'

Tara slept very little and was up before dawn to begin the last leg of the journey. The hotel chef had made her a packet of corned beef sandwiches and a thermos of hot tea, so they breakfasted as they drove. Any stop would increase their chances of discovery and arrest, and except to refuel, they kept going and crossed the Vaal river before noon.

Tara had been seeking the right moment to tell Moses ever since she had returned to the Transvaal to be near him, but now she knew that there would never be a right moment and that within hours they would be at Puck's Hill. After that nothing was certain except that there would be confusion and great danger for all of them.

'Moses,' she addressed the back of his head in a resolute voice, 'I can't keep it from you any longer. I have to tell you now. I am bearing your child.'

She saw his head flinch slightly and then those dark mesmeric eyes were glowering at her in the driver's mirror.

'What will you do?' he asked. He had not asked if she was certain nor had he queried his paternity of the child. That was typical of him – and yet he had accepted no responsibility either. 'What will you do?'

'I am not sure yet. I will find a way to have it.'

'You must get rid of it.'

'No,' she cried vehemently. 'Never. He's mine. I will take care of him.'

He did not remark on her choice of the masculine pronoun.

'The child will be half-caste,' he told her. 'Are you prepared for that?'

'I will find a way,' she insisted.

'I cannot help you – not at all,' he went on remorselessly. 'You understand that.'

'Yes, you can,' she answered. 'You can tell me that you are pleased that I am carrying your son – and that you will love him, as I love his father.'

'Love?' he said. 'That is not an African word. There is no word for love in my vocabulary.'

'Oh, Moses, that is not true. You love your people.'

'I love them as a people entire, not as individuals. I would sacrifice any of them for the good of the whole.'

'But our son, Moses. Something precious that we have made between us – don't you feel anything at all for him?'

She watched his eyes in the mirror and saw the pain in them.

'Yes,' he admitted. 'Of course, I do. Yet I dare not acknowledge it. I must lock such feelings away lest they weaken my resolve and destroy us all.'

'Then I will love him for both of us,' she said softly.

As Marcus Archer had warned Tara, there were more road-blocks. As they drew closer to the great industrial and mining complex of the Witwatersrand, they were stopped three times, the last at Halfway House, but each time the chauffeur's uniform and Tara's white face and haughty manner protected him.

Tara had expected Johannesburg to be like a city under siege, but the road-blocks and the news posters on the street corners were the only indications of something unusual afoot. The headgear wheels of the mines they passed were spinning busily, and beyond the perimeter fences they saw the black miners in gumboots and shiny hard hats flocking to the shaft heads.

When they passed through downtown Johannesburg, the city streets were crowded as usual with shoppers of all races and their faces were cheerful and relaxed. Tara was disappointed. She was not sure what she had expected, but at least she had hoped for some visible sign that the people were on the march.

'You cannot expect too much,' Moses told her when she lamented that nothing had changed. 'The forces against us are obdurate as granite, and the resources they command are limitless. Yet it is a beginning – our first faltering step on the road to liberation.'

They drove past Puck's Hill slowly. It seemed deserted, and at least there were no signs of police activity. Moses parked the Cadillac in the wattle plantation at the back of the Country Club and left Tara while he went back on foot to make absolutely certain they were not running into a police trap.

He was back within half an hour. 'It's safe. Marcus is there,' he told her as he started the Cadillac and drove back.

Marcus was waiting for them on the verandah. He looked tired and worn, and he had aged dramatically in the short time since Tara had last seen him.

He led them into the long kitchen, and went back to the stove on which he was preparing a meal for them, and while he worked he told them everything that had happened in their absence.

'The police reaction was so massive and immediate that it must have been carefully prepared. We expected a delay while they caught up with the situation and gathered themselves. We expected to be able to exploit that delay, and call upon the masses to join us in the defiance campaign until it gathered its own momentum and became irresistible, but they were ready for us. There are not more than a dozen of the leaders at large now, Moses is one of the lucky ones, and without leaders the campaign is already beginning to grind to a halt.'

He glanced at Tara with a vindictive sparkle in his eye before he went on.

'However, there are still some pockets of resistance – our little Victoria is doing sterling work. She has organized the nurses at Baragwanath and brought them out as part of the campaign. She won't keep that up much longer – she'll be arrested or banned pretty damn soon, you can bet on that.'

'Vicky is a brave woman,' Moses agreed. 'She knows the risks, and she takes them willingly.'

He looked straight at Tara as he said it, as if daring her to voice her jealousy. She knew of his marriage, of course, but she had never spoken of it. She knew what the consequences would be, and now she dropped her eyes, unable to meet his challenge.

'We have underestimated this man De La Rey,' Moses said. 'He is a formidable opponent. We have achieved very little of what we hoped for.'

'Still, the United Nations is debating our plight,' Tara said quietly without looking up again.

'Debating,' Moses agreed scornfully. 'But it requires only a single veto from America or Britain or France, and no action will be taken. They will talk and talk while my people suffer.'

'Our people,' Marcus chided him. 'Our people, Moses.'

'My people,' Moses contradicted him harshly. 'The others are all in prison. I am the only leader who remains. They are my people.' There was silence in the kitchen, except for the scrape of utensils on the plates as they ate, but Marcus was frowning and it was he who broke the silence.

'So what happens now?' he asked. 'Where will you go? You cannot stay here, the police may swoop at any moment. Where will you go?'

'Drake's Farm?' Moses mused.

'No.' Marcus shook his head. 'They know you too well there. The moment you arrive the whole township will know and there are police informers everywhere. It will be the same as turning yourself in at the nearest police station.'

They were silent again until Moses asked, 'Where is Joe Cicero? Have they taken him?'

'No,' Marcus answered. 'He has gone underground.'

'Can you contact him?'

'We have an arrangement. He will ring me here – if not tonight, then tomorrow.'

Moses looked across the table at Tara. 'Can I come with you to the expedition base at Sundi Caves? It's the only safe place I can think of at the moment.' And Tara's spirits bounded. She would have him for a little longer still.

Tara explained to Marion Hurst, not attempting to conceal Moses' identity nor the fact that he was a fugitive, and she was not surprised by the American woman's response.

'It's like Martin Luther King coming and asking me for sanctuary,' she declared. 'Of course, I'll do whatever I can to help.'

As a cover, Marion gave Moses a job in the pottery section of the warehouse under the name of Stephen Khama, and he was absorbed immediately into the company of the expedition. Without asking questions the other members, both black and white, gathered around to shield him.

Despite Marcus Archer's assurances, it was almost a week before he was able to contact Joe Cicero, and another day before he could arrange for them to meet. The hardest possible way they had learned not to underestimate the vigilance of the police, while Joe Cicero had always been secretive and professional. Nobody was certain where he lived or how he maintained himself, his comings and goings were unannounced and unpredictable.

'I have always thought him to be theatrical and over-careful, but now I see the wisdom behind it,' Moses told Tara as they drove into the city. Moses was once more dressed in his chauffeur's uniform. 'From now on we must learn from the professionals, for those ranged against us are the hardest of professionals.'

Joe Cicero came out of the entrance of the Johannesburg railway station as Moses stopped the Cadillac for the red light at the pedestrian crossing, and he slipped unobtrusively into the back seat beside Tara. Moses pulled away, heading out in the direction of Doornfontein.

'I congratulate you on still being at large,' Joe told Moses wryly, as he lit a

fresh cigarette from the butt of the last and glanced sideways at Tara. 'You are Tara Courtney,' and smiled at her surprise. 'What is your part in all this?'

'She is a friend,' Moses spoke for her. 'She is committed to us. You may speak freely in front of her.'

'I never speak freely,' Joe murmured. 'Only an idiot does that.' They were all silent then until Joe asked suddenly, 'And so, my friend, do you still believe that the revolution can be won without blood? Are you still one of the pacifists who would play the game by the rules that the oppressor makes and changes at will?'

'I have never been a pacifist,' Moses' voice rumbled. 'I have always been a warrior.'

'I rejoice to hear you say it, for it confirms what I have always believed.' Joe smiled a sly and inscrutable smile behind the fringe of dark beard. 'If I did not, I would not be sitting here now.' Then his tone altered. 'Make a U-turn here and take the Krugersdorp road!' he ordered.

The three of them were silent while Joe turned to scrutinize the following traffic. After a minute he seemed satisfied and relaxed in the back seat. Moses drove out of the built-up areas into the open grassy veld. The traffic around them thinned, and abruptly Joe Cicero leaned forward and pointed ahead to an empty lay-by on the side of the road.

'Pull in there,' he ordered, and as Moses parked the Cadillac he opened the door beside him. As he stepped out he jerked his head. 'Come!'

When Tara opened her own door to join them, Joe snapped. 'No, not you! Stay here!'

With Moses at his side he walked through the stand of scraggly black wattle into the open veld beyond, out of sight of the road.

'I told you the woman is trustworthy,' Moses said, and Joe shrugged.

'Perhaps. I do not take chances until it is necessary to do so.' And then he changed direction. 'I asked you, once what you thought of Mother Russia?'

'And I replied that she was a friend of the oppressed peoples of the world.'

'She wishes to be your friend also,' Joe said simply.

'Do you mean me personally – Moses Gama?'

'Yes, you personally – Moses Gama.'

'How do you know this?'

'There are men in Moscow who have watched you carefully for many years. What they have seen they approve of. They offer you the hand of friendship.'

'I ask you again. How do you know this?'

'I am a colonel in the Russian KGB. I have been ordered to tell you this.'

Moses stared at him. It was moving so fast that he needed a respite to catch up.

'What does this offer of friendship entail?' he asked cautiously, buying time in which to think, and Joe Cicero nodded approvingly.

'It is good you ask the terms of our friendship. It confirms our estimate of you. That you are a careful man. You will be given the answer to that in due course. In the meantime be content with the fact that we have singled you out above all others.'

'Very well,' Moses agreed. 'But tell me why I have been chosen. There are other good men – Mandela is one of them.'

'Mandela was considered, but we do not believe he has the steel. We detect a softness in him. Our psychologists believe that he will flinch from the hard and bloody work of the revolution. We know also that he does not have the same

high regard for Mother Russia that you do. He has even called her the new oppressor, the colonialist of the twentieth century.'

'What about the others?' Moses asked.

'There are no others,' Joe told him flatly. 'It was either you or Mandela. It is you. That is the decision.'

'They want my answer now?' Moses stared into the tar pits of his eyes, but they had a strangely lifeless dullness in them and Joe Cicero shook his head.

'They want to meet you, talk to you, make sure you understand the bargain. Then you will be trained and groomed for the task ahead.'

'Where will this meeting take place?'

Joe smiled and shrugged. 'In Moscow – where else?' And Moses did not let his amazement show on his face, though his hands clenched into fists at his sides.

'Moscow! How will I get there?'

'It has been arranged,' Joe assured him, and Moses lifted his head and stared at the tall thunderheads that rose in silver and blue splendour along the horizon. He was lost in thought for many minutes.

He felt his spirits grow light and take wing up towards those soaring thunder clouds. It had come – the moment for which he had worked and waited a lifetime. Destiny had cleared the field of all his rivals, and he had been chosen.

Like a victor's laurel they were offering a land and a crown.

'I will meet them,' he agreed softly.

'You will leave in two days' time. It will take me that long to make the final arrangements. In the meantime keep out of sight, do not attempt to take leave of any friends, do not tell anybody you are going – not even the Courtney woman or your new wife. I will get a message to you through Marcus Archer and if he is arrested before then, I will contact you at the expedition base at Sundi Caves. Professor Hurst is a sympathizer.' Joe dropped the butt of his cigarette and while he ground it under his heel, he lit another. 'Now we will go back to the car.'

* * *

Victoria Gama stood at the top end of the sloping lawns of the Baragwanath nurses' home. She was still dressed in her uniform with the badges of a nursing sister sparkling on her tunic, but she looked very young and self-conscious as she faced the hundred or so off-duty nurses who were gathered on the lawns below her. The white matron had refused permission for them to meet in the dining-hall, so they were standing out under a sky full of towering thunderheads.

'My sisters!' She held out her hands towards them. 'We have a duty to our patients – to those in pain, to those suffering and dying, to those who turn to us in trust. However, I believe that we have a higher duty and more sacred commitment to all our people who for three hundred years have suffered under a fierce and unrelenting oppression – '

Victoria seemed to gather confidence as she spoke, and her sweet young voice had a music and rhythm that caught their attention. She had always been popular with the other nurses, and her winning personality, her capacity for hard work and her unselfish attitude had seen her emerge, not only as one of

the most senior nursing staff for her age, but also as an example and a trend-setter amongst the younger nurses. There were women ten and fifteen years older than she was, who listened now to her with attention and who applauded her when she paused for breath. Their applause and approval bolstered Victoria and her voice took on a sharper tone.

'Across the land our leaders, in actions rather than pale words, are showing the oppressors that we will no longer remain passive and acquiescent. They are crying to the world for justice and humanity. What kind of women will we be if we stand aside and refuse to join them? How can we ignore the fact that our leaders are being arrested and harassed by the infernal laws – '

There was a stir in the crowd of uniformed nurses, and the faces which had been lifted towards Victoria turned away and the expressions of rapt concentration changed to consternation. From the edges of the crowd one or two of the nurses broke away and scuttled back up the steps of the nurses' home.

Three police vans had driven up to the gates, and the white matron and two of her senior staff had hurried out to confer with the police captain in charge of the contingent as he alighted from the leading vehicle. The matron's white tunic and skirt contrasted with the blue of the police uniforms, and she was pointing at Victoria and talking animatedly to the captain.

Victoria's voice faltered, and despite her resolve, she was afraid. It was an instinctive and corrosive fear. From her earliest remembered childhood the blue police uniforms had been symbols of unquestionable might and authority. To defy them now went against all her instincts and the teaching of her father and all her elders.

'Do not challenge the white man,' they had taught her. 'For his wrath is more terrible than the summer fires that consume the veld. None can stand before it.'

Then she remembered Moses Gama, and her voice firmed; she beat down her fear and cried aloud, 'Look at yourselves, my sisters. See how you tremble and cast your eyes down at the sight of the oppressor. He has not yet spoken nor raised a hand to you, but you have become little children!'

The police captain left the group at the gate and came to the edge of the lawn. There he paused and raised a bull-horn to his lips.

'This is an illegal gathering on state-owned property.' His voice was magnified and distorted. 'You have five minutes to disperse and return to your quarters.' He raised his arm and ostentatiously checked his wristwatch. 'If you have not done so in that time – '

The nurses were scattering already, scampering away, not waiting for the officer to complete his warning, and Victoria found herself alone on the wide lawn. She wanted to run and hide also, but she thought about Moses Gama and her pride would not let her move.

The police officer lowered his loud-hailer and turned back to the white matron. They conferred again, and the officer showed her a sheaf of paper which he took from his despatch case. The matron nodded and they both looked at Victoria again. Alone now, she still stood at the top of the lawn. Pride and fear held her rigid. She stood stiffly, unable to move as the police captain marched across to where she stood.

'Victoria Dinizulu?' he asked her in a normal conversational voice, so different from the hoarse booming of the loud-hailer.

Victoria nodded, and then remembered. 'No,' she denied. 'I am Victoria Gama.' The police officer looked confused. He was very fair-skinned with a fine blond moustache. 'I was told you were Victoria Dinizulu – there has been a

mess-up,' he muttered, and then he blushed with embarrassment and immediately Victoria felt sorry for him.

'I got married,' she explained. 'My maiden name was Victoria Dinizulu, but now I am Victoria Gama.'

'Oh, I see.' The captain looked relieved, and glanced down at the document in his hand. 'It's made out to Victoria Dinizulu. I suppose it's still all right though.' He was uncertain again.

'It's not your fault,' Victoria consoled him. 'The wrong name, I mean. They can't blame you. You couldn't have known.'

'No, you're right.' The captain perked up visibly. 'It's not my fault. I'll just serve it on you anyway. They can sort it out back at HQ.'

'What is it?' Victoria asked curiously.

'It's a banning order,' the captain explained. He showed it to her. 'It's signed by the minister of the police. I have to read it to you, then you have to sign it,' he explained and then looked contrite. 'I'm sorry, it's my duty.'

'That is all right.' Vicky smiled at him. 'You have to do your duty.'

He looked down at the document again and began to read aloud:

TO VICTORIA THANDELA DINIZULU

Notice in terms of Section 9(i) of the Internal Security Act 1950 (Act 44 of 1950). Whereas I, Manfred De La Rey, Minister of Police, am satisfied that you are engaged in activities which endanger or are calculated to endanger the maintenance of public order –

The captain stumbled over the more complicated legal phraseology and mispronounced some of the English words. Vicky corrected him helpfully. The banning document was four typewritten pages, and the policeman reached the end of it with patent relief.

'You have to sign here.' He offered her the document.

'I don't have a pen.'

'Here, use mine.'

'Thank you,' said Victoria. 'You are very kind.'

She signed her name in the space provided and as she handed him back his pen, she had ceased to be a complete person. Her banning order prohibited her from being in the company of more than two other persons at any one time, except in the course of her daily work, of addressing any gathering or preparing any written article for publication. It confined her physically to the magisterial area of Johannesburg and required that she remain under house arrest for twelve hours of the day and also that she report daily to her local police station.

'I'm sorry,' the police captain repeated, as he screwed the top back on his pen. 'You seem a decent girl.'

'It's your job,' Victoria smiled back at him. 'Don't feel bad about it.'

Over the following days Victoria retreated into the strange half-world of isolation. During working hours she found that her peers and superiors avoided her, as though she were a carrier of plague. The matron moved her out of the room that she shared with two other nursing sisters and she was given a small single room on the unpopular southern side of the hostel which never received the sun in winter. In this room her meals were served to her on a tray as she was prohibited from using the dining-hall when more than two other persons were present. Each evening after coming off shift she made the two-mile walk down to the police station to sign the register, but this soon became a pleasant outing rather than a penance. She was able to smile and greet the people she

passed on the street for they did not know she was a non-person and she enjoyed even that fleeting human contact.

Alone in her room she listened to her portable radio and read the books that Moses had given her, and thought about him. More than once she heard his name on the radio. Apparently a controversial film had been shown on the NABS television channel in the United States which had created a furore across the continent. It seemed that South Africa, which for most Americans was a territory remote as the moon and a thousand times less important, was suddenly a political topic. In the film Moses Gama had figured largely, and such was his presence and stature that he had been accepted abroad as the central figure in the African struggle. In the United Nations debate which had followed the television film, nearly every one of the speakers had referred to Moses Gama. Although the motion in the General Assembly calling for the condemnation of South Africa's racial discrimination had been vetoed in the Security Council by Great Britain, the debate had sent a ripple across the world and a cold shiver down the spine of the white government in the country.

South Africa had no television network, but on her portable radio Victoria listened to a pungent edition of 'Current Affairs' on the state-controlled South African Broadcasting Corporation in which the campaign of defiance was described as the action of a radical minority, and Moses Gama was vilified as a communist-inspired revolutionary criminal who was still at large, although a warrant had been issued for his arrest on a charge of high treason.

Cut off from all other sympathetic human contact, Victoria found herself pining for him with such desperate longing that she cried herself to sleep in her lonely room each night.

On the tenth day of her banning she was returning from her daily report to the police station, keeping to the edge of the pavement in that sensual gliding walk that the Nguni woman practises from childhood when she carries every load, from faggots of firewood to five-gallon clay pots of water, balanced upon her head. A light delivery van slowed down as it approached her from behind, and began to keep pace with her.

Victoria was accustomed to extravagant male attention, for she was the very essence of Nguni female beauty, and when the driver of the vehicle whistled softly, she did not glance in his direction but lifted her chin an inch and assumed a haughty expression.

The driver whistled again, more demandingly, and from the corner of her eye she saw the van was blue with the sign EXPRESS DRY CLEANERS – SIX HOUR SERVICE painted on the side. The driver was a big man, and although his cap was pulled low over his eyes, she sensed he was attractive and masterful. Despite herself her hips began to swing as she strode on, and her large perfectly round buttocks oscillated like the cheeks of a chipmunk chewing a nut.

'Victoria!' Her name was hissed, and the voice was unmistakable. She stopped dead and swung round to face him.

'You!' she whispered, and then glanced around her frantically. For the moment the sidewalk was clear and only light traffic moved down the highway between rows of tall bluegum trees. Her eyes flashed back to his face, almost hungrily, and she whispered, 'Oh Moses, I didn't think you'd come.'

He leaned across the front seat of the van and opened the door nearest her, and she rushed across and threw herself into the moving van.

'Get down,' he ordered, and she crouched below the dashboard while he slammed the door closed and accelerated away.

'I couldn't believe it was you. I still don't – this van, where did you get it? Oh Moses, you'll never know how much – I heard your name on the radio, many times – so much has happened – ' She found that she was gabbling almost hysterically. It had been so long since she had been able to talk freely, and it was as though the painful abscess of loneliness and longing had burst and all the poison was draining in the rush of words.

She began to tell him about the nurses' strike and the banning, and how Albertina Sisulu had contacted her and there was going to be a march by a hundred thousand women, to the government buildings at Pretoria, and she was going to defy her banning order to join the march.

'I want you to be proud of me. I want to be part of the struggle, for that is the only way I can truly be a part of you.'

Moses Gama drove in silence, smiling a little as he listened to her chatter. He wore blue overalls with the legend 'Express Dry Cleaners' embroidered across his back and the rear of the van was filled with racks of clothing that smelled strongly of cleaning solvent. She knew he had borrowed the van from Hendrick Tabaka.

After a few minutes Moses slowed the van and then turned off sharply on to a spur road which swiftly deteriorated into a rutted track, and then petered out entirely. He bumped the last few yards over tussocks of grass and then parked behind a ruined and roofless building, the windows from which the frames had been ripped out were like the eyes of a skull. Victoria straightened up from under the dashboard.

'I have heard about the nurses' strike and your banning,' he said softly as he switched off the engine. 'And yes, I am proud of you. Very good. You are a wife fit for a chief.'

She hung her head shyly, and the pleasure his words gave her was almost unbearable. She had not truly realized how much she loved him while they had been separated, and now the full force of it rushed back upon her.

'And you are a chief,' she said. 'No, more than that – you are a king.'

'Victoria, I do not have much time,' he said. 'I should not have come here at all – '

'I would have shrivelled up if you had not – my soul was drought-stricken – ' she burst out, but he laid his hand on her arm to still her.

'Listen to me, Victoria. I have come to tell you that I am going away. I have come to charge you to be strong while I am away.'

'Oh, my husband!' In her agitation she lapsed into Zulu. 'Where are you going?'

'I can tell you only that it is to a distant land.'

'Can I not journey by your side?' she pleaded.

'No.'

'Then I will send my heart to be your travelling companion, while the husk of me remains here to await your return. When will you come back, my husband?'

'I do not know, but it will be a long time.'

'For me every minute that you are gone will become a weary day,' she told him quietly, and he raised his hand and stroked her face gently.

'If there is anything you need you must go to Hendrick Tabaka. He is my brother, and I have placed you in his care.'

She nodded, unable to speak.

'There is only one thing I can tell you now. When I return I will take the world we know and turn it on its head. Nothing will ever be the same again.'

'I believe you,' she said simply.

'I must go now,' he told her. 'Our time together has come to an end.'

'My husband,' she murmured, casting down her eyes again. 'Let me be a wife to you one last time, for the nights are so long and cold when you are not beside me.'

He took a roll of canvas from the back of the van and spread it on the grass beside the parked van. Her naked body was set off by the white cloth as she lay upon it like a figure cast in dark bronze thrown down upon the snow.

At the end when he had spent and lay weak as a child upon her, she clasped his head tenderly to the soft warm swell of her bosom and she whispered to him, 'No matter how far and how long you travel, my love will burn away time and distance and I will be beside you, my husband.'

* * *

Tara was waiting for him, with the lantern lit, lying awake in the cottage tent when Moses returned to the camp. She sat up as he came through the fly. The blanket fell to her waist and she was naked. Her breasts were big and white and laced with tiny bluish veins around the swollen nipples – so different from those of the woman he had just left.

'Where have you been?' she demanded.

He ignored the question as he began to undress.

'You have been to see her, haven't you? Joe ordered you not to.'

Now he looked at her scornfully, and then deliberately re-buttoned the front of his overalls as he moved to leave the tent again.

'I'm sorry, Moses,' she cried, instantly terrified by the thought of his going. 'I didn't mean it, please stay. I won't talk like that again. I swear it, my darling. Please forgive me. I was upset, I have had such a terrible dream – ' she threw aside the blanket and came up on her knees, reaching out both hands towards him. 'Please!' she entreated. 'Please come to me.'

For long seconds he stared at her and then began once more to unbutton his overalls. She clung to him desperately as he came into the bed.

'Oh Moses – I had such a dream. I dreamed of Sister Nunziata again. Oh God, the look on their faces as they ate her flesh. They were like wolves, their mouths red and running with her blood. It was the most horrific thing, beyond my imagination. It made me want to despair for all the world.'

'No,' he said. His voice was low but it reverberated through her body as though she were the sounding box of a violin trembling to the power of the strings. 'No!' he said. 'It was beauty – stark beauty, shorn of all but the truth. What you witnessed was the rage of the people, and it was a holy thing. Before that I merely hoped, but after witnessing that I could truly believe. It was a consecration of our victory. They ate the flesh and drank the blood as you Christians do to seal a pact with history. When you have seen that sacred rage you have to believe in our eventual triumph.'

He sighed, his great muscular chest heaved in the circle of her arms and then he went to sleep. It was something to which she could never grow accustomed,

the way he could sleep as though he had closed a door in his mind. She was left bereft and afraid, for she knew what lay ahead for her.

Joe Cicero came for Moses in the night. Moses had dressed like one of a thousand other contract workers from the gold-mines in a surplus army greatcoat and woollen balaclava helmet that covered most of his face. He had no luggage, as Joe had instructed him, and when the ramshackle Ford pick-up parked across the road from them had flashed its lights once, Moses slipped out of the Cadillac and swiftly crossed it. He did not say goodbye to Tara, they had taken their farewells long ago and he did not look back to where she sat forlornly behind the wheel of the Cadillac.

As soon as Moses climbed into the rear of the Ford, it pulled away. The tail lights dwindled and were lost around the first curve of the road, and Tara was smoothered by such a crushing load of despair that she did not believe she could survive it.

* * *

François Afrika was the headmaster of the Mannenberg coloured school on the Cape Flats. He was a little over forty years old, a plump and serious man with a *café au lait* complexion and thick very curly hair which he parted in the middle and plastered flat with Vaseline.

His wife Miriam was plump also, but much shorter and younger than he. She had taught history and English at the Mannenberg junior school until the headmaster had married her, and she had given him four children, all daughters. Miriam was president of the local chapter of the Women's Institute which she used as a convenient cover for her political activities. She had been arrested during the defiance campaign, but when that petered out she had not been charged and had been released under a banning order. Three months later, when the furore had died away completely, her banning order had not been renewed.

Molly Broadhurst had known her since before she had married François, and the couple were frequent visitors at Molly's home. Behind her thick spectacles Miriam wore a perpetual chubby smile. Her home in the grounds of the junior school was clean as an operating theatre with crocheted antimacassars on the heavy maroon easy chairs, and a mirrorlike shine on the floors. Her daughters were always beautifully dressed with coloured ribbons in their pigtails and like Miriam were chubby and contented, a consequence of Miriam's cookery rather than her genes.

Tara met Miriam for the first time at Molly's home. Tara had come down by train from the expedition base at Sundi Caves two weeks before her baby was due. She had booked a private coupé compartment and kept the door locked the entire journey to avoid being recognized. Molly had met her at Paarl station, for she had not wanted to risk being seen at the main Cape Town terminus. Shasa and her family still believed that she was working with Professor Hurst.

Miriam was all that Tara had hoped for, all that Molly had promised her, although she was not prepared for the maternity dress.

'You are pregnant also?' she demanded as they shook hands, and Miriam patted her stomach shyly.

'It's a cushion, Miss Tara, I couldn't just pop a baby out of nowhere, could

I? I started with just a small lump as soon as Molly told me, and I've built it up slowly.'

Tara realized what inconvenience she had put her to, and now she embraced her impulsively. 'Oh, I can never tell you how grateful I am. Please don't call me Miss Tara. I'm your friend and plain Tara will do very well.'

'I'll look after your baby like it's my own, I promise you,' Miriam told her, and then saw Tara's expression and hastily qualified her assurance. 'But he will always be yours, Tara. You can come and see him whenever, and one day if you are able to take him – well, François and I won't stand in your way.'

'You are even nicer than Molly told me!' Tara hugged her. 'Come, I want to show you the clothes I've brought for our baby.'

'Oh, they are all blue,' Miriam exclaimed. 'You are so sure you are going to have a boy?'

'No question about it – I'm sure.'

'So was I,' Miriam chuckled. 'And look at me now – all girls! Though it's not too bad, they are good girls and they are all expecting this one to be a boy,' she patted her padded abdomen, 'and I know they are going to spoil him something terrible.'

Tara's baby was born in Molly Broadhurst's guest room. Doctor Chetty Abrahamji who deliverd it was an old friend of Molly's and had been a secret member of the Communist Party, one of its few Hindu members.

As soon as Tara went into labour, Molly telephoned Miriam Afrika, and she arrived with bag and bulging tummy and went in directly to see Tara.

'I'm so glad we have started at last,' she cried. 'I must admit that although it was a difficult pregnancy, it will be my quickest and easiest delivery.' She reached up under her own skirt and with a flourish produced the cushion. Tara laughed with her and then broke off as the next contraction seized her.

'Ouch!' she whispered. 'I wish mine was that easy. This one feels like a giant.'

Molly and Miriam took turns, sitting beside her and holding her hand when the contractions hit her, and the doctor stood at the foot of the bed exhorting her to, 'Push! Push!' By noon the following day Tara was exhausted, panting and racked, her hair sodden with sweat as though she had plunged into the sea.

'It's no good,' the doctor said softly. 'We'll have to move you, into hospital and do a Caesar.'

'No! No!' Tara struggled up on an elbow, fierce with determination. 'Give me one more chance.'

When the next contraction came she bore down on it with such force that every muscle in her body locked and she thought the sinews in her loins must snap like rubber bands. Nothing happened, it was jammed solid, and she could feel the blockage like a great log stuck inside her.

'More!' Molly whispered in her ear. 'Harder – once more for the baby,' Tara bore down again with the strength of desperation and then screamed as she felt her flesh tear like tissue paper. There was a hot slippery rush between her thighs and relief so intense that her scream changed to a long drawn-out cry of joy, that joined with her infant's birth cry.

'Is it a boy?' she gasped, trying to sit up. 'Tell me – tell me quickly!'

'Yes,' Molly reassured her. 'It's a boy – just look at his whistle. Long as my finger. There's no doubt about that – he's a boy all right,' and Tara laughed out aloud.

He weighed nine and a half pounds with a head that was covered with pitch

black hair, thick and curly as the fleece of an Astrakhan lamb. He was the colour of hot toffee, and he had Moses Gama's fine Nilotic features. Tara had never seen anything so beautiful in all her life, none of her other babies had been anything like this.

'Let me hold him,' she croaked, hoarse with the terrible effort of his birth, and they placed the child still wet and slippery in her arms.

'I want to feed him,' she whispered. 'I must give him his first suck – then he will be mine for ever.' She squeezed out her nipple and pressed it between his lips and he fastened on it, snuffling and kicking spasmodically with pleasure.

'What is his name, Tara?' Miriam Afrika asked.

'We'll call him Benjamin,' Tara said. 'Benjamin Afrika. I like that – he is truly of Africa.'

Tara stayed with the infant five days. When finally she had to relinquish him, and Miriam drove away with him in her little Morris Minor, Tara felt as though part of her soul had been hacked away by the crudest surgery. If Molly had not been there to help her through, Tara knew she could not have borne it. As it was Molly had something for her.

'I've been saving it until now,' she told Tara. 'I knew how you would feel when you had to give up your baby. This will cheer you up a little.' She handed Tara an envelope, and Tara examined the handwritten address. 'I don't recognize the writing.' She looked mystified.

'I received it by a special courier – open it up. Go on!' Molly ordered impatiently, and Tara obeyed. There were four sheets of cheap writing paper. Tara turned the last sheet and as she read the signature her expression altered.

'Moses!' she cried. Oh I can't believe it – after all these months. I had given up hope. I didn't even recognize his handwriting.' Tara clutched the letter to her breast.

'He wasn't allowed to write, Tara dear. He has been in a very strict training camp. He disobeyed orders and took a grave risk to get this note out to you.' Molly went to the door. 'I'll leave you in peace to read it. I know it will make up a little for your loss.'

Even after Molly had left her alone, Tara was reluctant to begin reading. She wanted to savour the pleasure of anticipation, but at last she could deny herself no longer.

Tara, my dearest,

I think of you every day in this place, where the work is hard and demanding, and I wonder about you and our baby. Perhaps it has already been born, I do not know, and I wonder often if it is a boy or a little girl.

Although what I am doing is of the greatest importance for all of us – for the people of Africa, as well as for you and me – yet I find myself longing for you. The thought of you comes to me unexpectedly in the night and in the day and it is like a knife in my chest.

Tara could not read on, her eyes were awash with tears.

'Oh Moses,' she bit her lip to prevent herself blubbering, 'I never knew you could feel like that for me.' She wiped her eyes with the back of her hand.

When I left you, I did not know where I was going, nor what awaited me here. Now everything is clear, and I know what the difficult tasks are that lie ahead of us. I know also that I will need your help. You will not refuse me, my wife? I call you 'wife' because that is how I feel towards you, now that you are carrying our child.

It was difficult for Tara to take it in. She had never expected him to give her this kind of recognition and she felt humbled by it.

'There is nothing that I could ever refuse you,' she whispered aloud, and her eyes raced down the sheet. She turned it over quickly and Moses had written:

Once before I told you how valuable it would be if you used your family connections to keep us informed of affairs of state. Since then this has become more imperative. Your husband, Shasa Courtney, is going over to the side of the neo-fascist oppressors. Although this fills you with hatred and contempt for him, yet it is a boon we could not have expected or prayed for. Our information is that he has been promised a place in the cabinet of that barbarous regime. If you were in his confidence, it would afford us a direct inside view and knowledge of all their plans and intentions. This would be so valuable that it would be impossible to put a price upon it.

'No,' she whispered, shaking her head, sensing what was coming, and it took courage for her to read on.

I ask you, for the sake of our land and our love, that when the child has been born and you are recovered from the birth, that you return to your husband's home at Weltevreden, ask his forgiveness for your absence, tell him that you cannot live without him and his children, and do all in your power to ingratiate yourself with him and to earn his confidence once more.

'I cannot do it,' Tara whispered, and then she thought of the children, and especially of Michael, and she felt herself wavering. 'Oh Moses, you don't know what you are asking of me.' She covered her eyes with her hand. 'Please don't make me do it. I have only just won my freedom – don't force me to give it up again.' But the letter went on remorselessly:

Every one of us will be called upon to make sacrifice in the struggle that lies ahead. Some of us may be required to lay down our very lives and I could well be one of those –

'No, not you, my darling, please not you!'

However, for the loyal and true comrades there will be rewards, immediate rewards in addition to the ultimate victory of the struggle and the final liberation. If you can bring yourself to do as I ask you, then my friends here will arrange for you and me to be together – not where we have to hide our love, but in a free and foreign land where, for a happy interlude, we can enjoy our love to the utmost. Can you imagine that, my darling? Being able to spend the days and nights together, to walk in the streets hand in hand, to dine together in public and laugh openly together, to stand up unafraid and say what we think aloud, to kiss and do all the silly adorable things that lovers do, and to hold the child of our love between us –

It was too painful, she could not go on. When Molly found her weeping bitterly, she sat on the bed beside her and took her in her arms.

'What is it, Tara dear, tell me, tell old Molly.'

'I have to go back to Weltevreden,' she sobbed. 'Oh God, Molly, I thought I was rid of that place for ever, and now I have to go back.'

* * *

Tara's request for a formal meeting to discuss their matrimonial arrangements threw Shasa into a state of utmost consternation. He had been well enough satisfied by the informal understanding between them, by which he had

complete freedom of action and control of the children, together with the respectability and protection of the marriage form. He had been happy to pay without comment the bills that Tara forwarded to him, and to see that her generous allowance was paid into her bank account promptly on the first of each month. He had even made good the occasional shortfall when the bank manager telephoned him to report that Tara had overdrawn. On one occasion there was a cheque made out to a second-hand motor dealer, for almost a thousand pounds. Shasa did not query it. Whatever it was, it was a bargain as far as he was concerned.

Now it looked as if all this was coming to an end, and Shasa immediately called a meeting of his principal advisors in the boardroom of Centaine House. Centaine herself was in the chair and Abraham Abrahams had flown down from Johannesburg, bringing with him the senior partner of a firm of renowned but very expensive divorce lawyers.

Centaine took over immediately. 'Let us consider the worst possible case,' she told him crisply. 'Tara will want the children and she'll want a settlement, plus a living allowance for herself and each of the children.' She glanced at Abe who nodded his silver head, which set the rest of the legal counsel nodding like mandarin dolls, looking grave and learned, and secretly counting their fees, Shasa thought wryly.

'Damn it, the woman deserted me! I'll go to hell before I give her my children.'

'She will claim that you made it impossible for her to remain in the conjugal home,' Abe said, and then when he saw Shasa's thunderous expression, tried to soothe him. 'You must remember, Shasa, that she will probably be taking the best available legal advice herself.'

'Damned shyster lawyers!' said Shasa bitterly, and his counsel looked pained, but Shasa did not apologize nor qualify. 'I've already warned her I won't give her a divorce. My political career is at a very delicate stage. I cannot afford the scandal. Very soon I'll be contesting a general election.'

'You may not be able to refuse,' Abe murmured. 'Not if she has good grounds.'

'She hasn't any,' said Shasa virtuously. 'I've always been the considerate and generous husband.'

'Your generosity is famous,' Abe murmured drily. 'There is many an attractive young lady who could give you a testimonial on that score.'

'Really Abe,' Centaine intervened. 'Shasa has always kept out of trouble with women – '

'Centaine, my dear. We are dealing with facts here – not maternal illusions. I am not a private detective and Shasa's private life is none of my concern. However, completely disinterested as I am, I am able to cite you at least six occasions in the last few years when Shasa has given Tara ample grounds – '

Shasa was making frantic signals down the table to shut Abe up, but Centaine leaned forward with an interested expression.

'Go ahead, Abe,' she ordered. 'Start citing!'

'In January two years ago the leading lady in the touring production of the musical *Oklahoma*,' Abe began, and Shasa sank down in his chair and covered his eyes as though in prayer. 'A few weeks later the left-winger, ironically, in the visiting British women's hockey team.' So far Abe was avoiding mentioning names, but now he went on. 'Then there was the female TV producer from North American Broadcasting Studios, pert little vixen with a name like a fish

– no a dolphin, that's it, Kitty Godolphin. Do you want me to go on? There are a few more, but as I have said already, I'm not a private investigator. You can be sure that Tara will get herself a good one, and Shasa makes very little effort to cover his tracks.'

'That will do, Abe,' Centaine stopped him, and considered her son with disapproval and a certain grudging admiration.

'It's the de Thiry blood,' she thought. 'The family curse. Poor Shasa.' But she said sternly, 'It looks as though we do have a problem after all,' and she turned to the divorce lawyer.

'Let us accept that Tara has grounds of infidelity. What is the worst judgement we might expect against us?'

'It's very difficult, Mrs Courtney – '

'I'm not going to hold you to it,' Centaine told him brusquely. 'You don't have to equivocate. Just give me the worst case.'

'She could get custody, especially of the two younger children, and a large settlement.'

'How much?' Shasa demanded.

'Considering your circumstances, it could be – ' the lawyer hesitated delicately ' – a million pounds, plus the trimmings, a house and allowance and a few other lesser items.'

Shasa sat up very straight in his chair. He whistled softly and then murmured. 'That is really taking seriously something that was merely poked in fun,' he said, and nobody laughed.

So Shasa took pains preparing for the reunion with Tara. He studied the advice which Abe and the other lawyers had drawn up for him, and had his tactics firmly established. He knew what to say and what to avoid. He was to make no admissions and no promises, particularly regarding the children.

For the venue he chose the pool at the foot of the Constantia Berg, hoping that Tara would associate it with the happy hours they had spent there. He had his chef prepare an exquisite picnic hamper which contained all Tara's favourite delicacies, and he chose half a dozen bottles of his best wines from the cellar.

He took especial care with his appearance. He had his hair trimmed and picked out a new black silk eye-patch from the drawer that he kept full of them. He wore the after-shave she had given him and the cream-coloured wild silk suit which she had once remarked on favourably, with his airforce scarf in the open neck of his blue shirt.

All the children were packed off to Rhodes Hill, into Centaine's care for the weekend, and he sent the chauffeur in the Rolls to fetch Tara from Molly Broadhurst's home where she was staying. The chauffeur brought her directly up to the pool and Shasa opened the door for her, and was surprised when she offered him her cheek for her kiss.

'You look so well, my dear,' he told her, and it was not entirely untrue. She had lost a lot of weight, her waist was once again wasped in and her bosom was magnificent. Despite the gravity of the moment Shasa felt his loins stir as he looked down that cleavage.

'Down boy!' he admonished himself silently and looked away, concentrating on her face. Her skin had cleared, the rings below her eyes were barely discernible and her hair had been washed and set. Obviously she had taken the same pains with her appearance as he had.

'Where are the children?' she demanded immediately. 'Mater has them – so we could talk without interruption.'

'How are they, Shasa?'

'They are all just fine. Couldn't be better.' He wanted there to be no special pleading on that score.'

'I do miss them terribly,' she said. The remark was ominous, and he did not reply. Instead he led her to the summer-house and settled her on the couch facing the waterfall.

'It's so beautiful here.' She looked around her. 'It is my favourite spot on all of Weltevreden.' She took the wineglass he handed her.

'Better days!' He gave her the toast. They clinked glasses and drank.

Then she set her glass down on the marble table-top and Shasa steeled himself to receive the opening shot of the engagement.

'I want to come back home,' she said, and he spilled white wine down the front of his silk suit, and then dabbed at it with the handkerchief from his breast pocket to give himself time to recover his balance.

In a perverse way he had been looking forward to the bargaining. He was a businessman, supremely confident in his ability to get the best trade. Furthermore, he had already adjusted to the idea of becoming a bachelor once more, and was beginning to look forward to the delights of that state, even if it cost him a million pounds. He felt the prickle of disappointment.

'I don't understand,' he said carefully.

'I miss the children. I want to be with them – and yet I don't want to take them away from you. They need a father as much as a mother.'

It was too easy. There had to be more than that, Shasa's bargaining instincts were sure.

'I have tried living alone,' she went on. 'And I don't like it. I want to come back.'

'So we just pick it up again where we dropped it?' he asked carefully, but she shook her head.

'That's impossible, we both know that.' She prevented further questions with a raised hand. 'Let me tell you what I want. I want to have all the benefits of my old life, access to my children, the prestige that goes with the name Courtney and the money not to have to stint – '

'You were always scornful of the position and the money before.' He could not prevent the jibe, but she took no offence.

'I have never had to do without it before,' she said simply. 'However, I want to be able to go away for a while when it becomes too much for me here – but I will not embarrass you politically or in any other way.' She paused. 'That's all of it.'

'And what do I get in return?' he asked.

'A mother for your children, and a public wife. I will preside at your dinner-parties, and make myself agreeable to your associates, I will even help you with your political electioneering, I used to be very good at that.'

'I thought that my politics disgusted you.'

'They do – but I will never let it show.'

'What about my conjugal rights, as they are delicately referred to by the lawyers?'

'No.' She shook her head. 'That will only complicate our relationship.' She thought of Moses. She could never be unfaithful to him, even if he had ordered it. 'No, but I have no objection to you going elsewhere. You have always been reasonably discreet. I know you will continue to be.'

He looked at her bosom and felt a twinge of regret, but the bargain she was

offering amazed him. He had everything he wanted, and had saved himself a million pounds into the bargain.

'Is that all?' he asked. 'Are you sure?'

'Unless you can think of anything else we should discuss.'

He shook his head. 'Shall we shake hands on it – and open a bottle of the Widow?'

She smiled at him over the rim of her glass to conceal what she truly felt for him and his world, and she made a vow as she sipped the tingling yellow wine.

'You will pay, Shasa Courtney, you will pay for your bargain much more than you ever dreamed.'

* * *

For over a decade Tara had been the mistress of Weltevreden, so there was nothing difficult or alien in taking up that role again, except that now more than ever she felt that she was acting a part in a tedious and unconvincing play.

There were some differences, however. The guest list had altered subtly, and now included most of the top Nationalist politicians and party organizers, and more often than before the conversation at the dinner-table was in Afrikaans rather than English. Tara's knowledge of Afrikaans was adequate, it was after all a very simple language with a grammar so uncomplicated that the verbs were not even conjugated and much of the vocabulary was taken directly from English. However, she had some difficulty with the guttural inflections, and most of the time smiled sweetly and remained silent. She found that by doing so her presence was soon overlooked and she heard much more than she would have had she joined in the conversation.

A frequent visitor to Weltevreden now was the minister of police, Manfred De La Rey, and Tara found it ironical that she was expected to feed and entertain the one man who to her epitomized all that was evil and cruel in the oppressive regime that she hated with all her being. It was like sitting down to a meal with a man-eating leopard, even his eyes were pale and cruel as those of a great predatory cat.

Strangely, she found that despite her loathing, the man fascinated her. It surprised her to find, once she had got over the initial shock of his presence, that he had a fine brain. Of course it was common knowledge that he had been a brilliant student in the law faculty of Stellenbosch University, and before standing for parliament, he had built up a highly successful law practice in his own right. She knew also that no man who was not essentially brilliant was included in the Nationalist cabinet, yet his intelligence was sinister and ominous. She found herself listening to the most heinous concepts expressed with such logic and eloquent conviction that she had to shake herself out of his mesmeric influence, like a bird trying to break the spell of the cobra's swaying dance.

Manfred De La Rey's relationship with the Courtney family was another enigma to her. It was part of family lore how his father had robbed the H'ani Mine of a million pounds of diamonds, and how Blaine, her own father, and Centaine, before she was Blaine's wife, had pursued him into the desert and after a fierce battle captured him. Manfred's father had served fifteen years of a

life sentence before being released under the amnesty that the Nationalists had granted to so many Afrikaner prisoners when they came to power in 1948.

The two families should have been bitter enemies, and indeed Tara detected definite traces of that hatred in the occasional tone of a remark and unguarded look that Manfred De La Rey and Shasa directed at each other, and there was a peculiarly brittle and artificial quality to the overtly friendly façade they showed, as though at any moment it might be stripped away and they would fly at each other's throats like fighting dogs.

On the other hand, Tara knew that Manfred was the one who had enticed Shasa into forsaking the ailing United Party and joining the Nationalists with the promise of ministerial rank, and that Shasa had made the De La Reys, father and son, major shareholders and directors in the new fish canning company at Walvis Bay, a company which looked set to turn half a million pounds of profit in its very first year of operation.

The mystery of their relationship was made even more intriguing by Centaine. On the second occasion that Shasa invited Manfred De La Rey and his wife to dine at Weltevreden, Centaine had telephoned her a few days beforehand, and asked her bluntly if she and Blaine might join the party.

Although Tara had determined to see as little of Centaine as possible, and to do all in her power to reduce Centaine's influence over the children and the general running of the estate, Tara had been so taken aback by the direct request that she had not been able to think of an excuse.

'Of course, Mater,' she had agreed with false enthusiasm. 'I would have invited you and Daddy anyway, but I thought you might have found the evening tedious, and I know Daddy cannot abide De La Rey – '

'Whatever gave you that idea, Tara?' Centaine asked tartly. 'They are on opposite sides of the house, but Blaine has a healthy respect for De La Rey, and he concedes that De La Rey certainly handled the troubles firmly enough. His police did a magnificent job in clamping down on the ringleaders and preventing serious disruptions and further loss of life.'

Furious words filled Tara's mouth and she wanted to hurl them at her mother-in-law, but she gritted her teeth and took a deep breath, before she said sweetly, 'Well then, Mater, both Shasa and I will be looking forward to Friday night. Half past seven for eight, and naturally the men will be wearing black tie.'

'Naturally.'

It had been a surprisingly mellow evening, when the explosive elements seated around the same table were considered, but it was a strict rule of Shasa's that shop party politics were never discussed in Weltevreden's palatial dining-room. The men's conversation ranged from the projected All Blacks rugby tour to the recent angling capture of a six hundred pound blue fin tunny in False Bay, the first of its kind. Manfred De La Rey and Blaine were both keen anglers and were excited by the prospect of such a magnificent prize.

Centaine was unusually quiet during the meal. Tara had placed her beside Manfred, but she listened attentively to everything that he said and when they went through to the blue drawing-room at the end of the meal, she stayed close to Manfred, and the two of them were soon oblivious of everyone else, lost in rapt but low-voiced discussion.

Manfred's statuesque blond German wife, Heidi, had failed to enthral Tara with a long-winded complaint about the laziness and dishonesty of her coloured

servants, and Tara escaped as soon as she could and took another cognac to her father on the long blue velvet sofa, and then settled beside him.

'Centaine says that you admire De La Rey,' she said quietly, and they both looked across at the other couple on the far side of the room.

'He's a formidable piece of work,' Blaine grunted. 'Hard as iron and sharp as an axe. Do you know even his own colleagues call him "Panga Man"?'

'Why does he facinate Centaine so much? She rang me and demanded an invitation when she knew he would be here. She seems to have some sort of obsession with him. Why is that, Daddy, do you know?'

Blaine dropped his eyes and considered the firm grey ash on his cigar. What could he tell her? he wondered. He was one of probably only four people in the world who knew Manfred De La Rey was Centaine's bastard son. He remembered his own shock and horror when she had told him. Not even Shasa knew that he and Manfred were half-brothers, though Manfred knew, of course. Centaine had told him, when she used it as blackmail to prevent Manfred destroying Shasa's political career back in 1948.

It was all so complicated, and Blaine found himself disturbed as he had been so often over the years by the echoes of Centaine's follies and indiscretions before he had met her. Then he smiled ruefully. She was still a fiery and impetuous woman, and he wouldn't have it any other way.

'I think she is interested in anything that affects Shasa's career. It's only natural she should be, De La Rey is Shasa's sponsor. It's as simple as that, my dear.'

'Yes, De La Rey is his sponsor,' Tara agreed. 'But what do you think, Daddy, about Shasa's turn of political coats?'

Despite her resolution to remain calm, she had raised her voice in agitation and Shasa, who was in intimate conversation with the French ambassador's chic and bold-eyed young second wife, heard his name across the room and glanced up in her direction. Tara dropped her voice quickly.

'What do you think of it, Daddy? Weren't you simply appalled?'

'I was at first,' Blaine admitted. 'But then I discussed it with Centaine and Shasa came to see me. We thrashed it out between us, and I had my say – but in the end I came to see his point of view. I don't agree with it, but I respect it. He believes that he can do the greatest good – ' Tara heard her own father repeating all Shasa's trite and glib justifications and the sense of outrage overwhelmed her all over again. She found herself trembling with suppressed passion, and she wanted to scream out at them, Shasa and Centaine and her own father, but then she thought of Moses and the struggle and with an effort she was able to retain her self-control.

'I must remember everything,' she told herself. 'Everything that they say or do. Even the smallest detail might be of inestimable value to the struggle.'

So, faithfully she reported it all to Molly Broadhurst. She slipped away from Weltevreden at least once a week on the pretence of visiting her dressmaker or her hairdresser. She and Molly met only after Tara had taken elaborate precautions to make sure she was not followed. Her instructions were to cut all her left-wing connections and to refrain at all times from political or socialistic comments in the presence of others. Molly was her only contact with the real world of the struggle, and she treasured every minute of their time together.

Miriam Afrika was always able to bring the baby to be with her during these interludes, and Tara held him in her arms and fed him his bottle as she made her report to Molly. Everything about little Benjamin fascinated her from the

tight curls of crisp black hair that covered his scalp, through the exquisite softness and colour shading of his skin – honey and old ivory – down to the soles of his tiny feet which were the palest, clearest, coral pink.

Then on one of her visits Molly had another letter for her from Moses, and even the joy of holding Benjamin paled beside that of those written words.

The letter had been written in Addis Ababa, the capital of Ethiopia. Moses was there to address a meeting of the heads of the black African states at the express invitation of the Emperor Haile Selassie, and he described to her the warm welcome that he had been given, and the offers of support, moral, financial and military, that had been pledged to the struggle in Anzania – that was the new name for South Africa. It was the first time she had heard it, and when she repeated it aloud, the sound of it stirred a deep patriotic response in her that she had never felt before. She read the rest of Moses' letter:

> From here I will travel on to Algeria, where I will meet with Colonel Boumedienne, who is at this moment struggling against French imperialism, and whose great valour will surely bring freedom and happiness to his tragically oppressed land.
>
> After that I will fly to New York, and it seems certain that I will be allowed to put our case to the General Assembly of the United Nations. All this is exciting, but I have even better news that affects you and our baby Benjamin.
>
> If you continue the important work you are doing for the cause, our powerful friends are determined to give you a special reward. Some day the three of us – you and me and Benjamin – will be together in London. I cannot tell you how greatly I look forward to holding my son and to greeting you again.
>
> I will write to you as soon as I have more definite news. In the meantime I entreat you to continue your valuable work for the cause, in particular you should make every effort to see that your husband is elected to the government front benches at the elections next month. This will make your position and value to the struggle unique.

For days after receiving this letter Tara's mood was so light and gay that both Shasa and Centaine remarked on it, and took it as a sign that she had finally accepted her responsibilities as the mistress of Weltevreden, and was prepared to honour the agreement that she had made with Shasa.

* * *

When the prime minister announced the date of the general election, the country was immediately seized by the peculiar frenzy of excitement and intrigue which accompanies all major political activity in South Africa and the newspapers began their strident and partisan pronouncements.

Shasa's resignation from the United Party and his nomination as the Nationalist candidate for the constituency of South Boland was one of the highlights of the campaign. The English press castigated him, branding him a coward and a traitor, while the *Burger* and the *Transvaler*, those stalwarts of the Nationalist cause, hailed him as a far-seeing man of the future and looked forward to the day when all white South Africans, albeit under the firm hand of the National Party, marched shoulder to shoulder towards the golden republic which was the dream of all true South African patriots.

Kitty Godolphin had flown back from New York to cover the elections and to up-date her famous 'Focus on Africa' series that had won her another Emmy

and had made her one of the highest paid of the new generation of young, pretty and waspish television commentators.

Shasa's political defection was the headline story when she landed at Jan Smuts airport, and she telephoned him from the airport on his private line and got him in his office just as the board meeting he had been chairing broke up, and he was about to leave Centaine House to fly up to the H'ani Mine for his monthly inspection.

'Hi!' she said gaily. 'It's me.'

'You bitch.' He recognized her voice instantly. 'After what you did to me, I should kick your bottom, wearing hobnailed boots and taking a full swing, at that.'

'Oh, did you see it? Wasn't it good? I thought I captured you perfectly.'

'Yes, I saw it last month on BBC while I was in London. You made me look like a cross between Captain Bligh and Simon Legree, although more pompous than either and a lot less lovable.'

'That's what I said – I got you perfectly.'

'I don't know why I am talking to you,' he chuckled despite himself.

'Because you are lusting after my miraculously beautiful body,' she suggested.

'I'd be wiser to make advances to a nest of hornets.'

'We aren't talking wisdom here, buddy boy, we are talking lust. The two are not compatible.' And Shasa had a poignant vision of her slim body and her perfect little breasts, and he felt slightly breathless.

'Where are you?' he said.

'Johannesburg airport.'

'What are you doing this evening?' He made a quick calculation. He could postpone the H'ani Mine inspection, and it was four hours' flying time to Johannesburg in the Mosquito.

'I'm open to suggestions,' she told him, 'as long as the suggestions include an exclusive interview for NABS on your change of political status and your view of the up-coming elections and what they mean to the ordinary people of this country.'

'I should know better,' he said. 'But I'll be there in five hours. Don't go away.'

Shasa placed the receiver back on its cradle and stood for a moment wondering at himself. His change of plans would throw the entire company into consternation, for he had a tight schedule laid out for the weeks ahead, including the opening of his election campaign, but the woman had woven some sort of spell around him. Like a malignant sprite her memory had danced at the edge of his mind all these months, and now the thought of being with her filled him with that quivering expectation he had not known since he was a lad embarking on his very first sexual explorations.

The Mosquito was fuelled and parked on the hardstand ready for the flight to H'ani Mine. It took him ten minutes to calculate his new flight plan and file it with air traffic control and then he climbed up into the cockpit and, grinning like a schoolboy playing hookey, he cranked the Rolls Royce Merlin engines.

It was dusk when he landed, but a company car was waiting for him and he drove directly to the Carlton Hotel in the centre of Johannesburg. Kitty was in the lobby as he came in through the revolving doors. She was fresh-faced as a teenager, long-legged and narrow-hipped in blue jeans, and she came to him with childlike enthusiasm and wrapped both arms around his neck to kiss him.

Strangers in the lobby must have imagined Shasa was a father greeting his schoolgirl daughter, and they smiled indulgently.

'They let us into your suite,' she told him as she led him towards the elevator, skipping beside him to keep pace and hugging his arm in a pantomime of adoration. 'Hank has got his camera and lights set up already.'

'You aren't even giving me time to visit the heads,' Shasa protested, and she pulled a wry face.

'Let's get it over and done. Then we'll have more time for whatever you want to do afterwards.' She gave him a devilish grin, and he wagged his head in reluctant acquiescence.

It was deliberate, of course. Kitty was too professional to give him time to pull himself together and concentrate his mind. It was part of her technique to get her subject off-balance, while on the other hand, she had been carefully preparing her own notes and questions during the five hours since they had spoken on the telephone.

She had rearranged the furniture in his suite, making one corner into an intimate nook and Hank had lit it and was standing by with his Arriflex. Shasa shook hands with him and exchanged a friendly greeting while Kitty poured him a massive whisky from the liquor cabinet.

'Take your jacket off,' she instructed as she handed it to him. 'I want you relaxed and casual.' She led him to the two facing chairs and while he sipped his whisky she lulled him with an amusing account of the flight out which had been delayed by bad weather in London for eight hours. Then Hank gave her the signal and she said sweetly:

'Shasa Courtney, since the turn of this century your family has been a traditional ally of General Smuts. He was a personal friend of your grandfather, and your mother. He was a frequent guest in your house, and sponsored your own entry into the political arena. Now you have turned your back on the United Party which he led, and have deserted the fundamental principles of decency and fair play towards the coloured citizens of this country which were so much a part of General Smuts' philosophy. You have been called a deserter and a turncoat – and worse. Do you think that is a fair description, and if not, why not?'

The attack was so swift and savage that for a moment it checked him, but he had known what to expect, and he grinned. He knew he was going to enjoy this.

'General Smuts was a great man, but not quite as saintly towards the natives as you suppose. In all the time he was in power, their political status remained unchanged, and when they stepped out of line, he did not hesitate before sending in the troops and giving them a whiff of grape. Have you ever heard of the Bondelswart rebellion and the Bulhoek massacre?'

'You are suggesting that Smuts also oppressed the native people of this country?'

'No more than a strict headmaster oppresses his children. In the main, he never seriously addressed himself to the coloured question. He left that for a future generation to settle. We are that future generation.'

'All right, so what are you going to do about the black people of this country who outnumber you nearly four to one and have no political rights whatsoever in the land of their birth?'

'First, we will try to avoid the trap of simplistic thinking.'

'Can you explain that?' Kitty frowned. She didn't want him to wriggle out of

her grip by using vague terminology. 'Give us a concrete example of simplistic thinking.'

He nodded. 'You glibly use the terms black people and white people, dividing this population into two separate, if unequal, portions. That is dangerous. It might work in America. If all the American blacks were given white faces they would be simply Americans and think of themselves as that – '

'You are suggesting that this is not the case in Africa?'

'I am indeed,' Shasa agreed. 'If all the blacks in this country were given white faces, they would still think of themselves as Zulus and Xhosas and Vendas, and we would still be English and Afrikaners – very little would have altered.'

Kitty didn't like that, it was not what she wanted to tell her audiences.

'So, of course, you are ruling out the idea of a democracy in this country. You will never accept the policy of one man one vote, but will always aspire to white domination – '

Shasa cut in on her quickly. 'One man one vote would lead not to the black government you seem to foresee, but to a Zulu government, for the Zulus outnumber any other group. We would have a Zulu dictator, like good old King Chaka, and that would be a thrilling experience.'

'So what is your solution?' she demanded, hiding her irritation behind that little-girl smile. 'Is it white *baasskap*, white domination and savage oppression backed by an all-white army and police force – ?'

'I don't know the solution,' he cut her off. 'It's something we have to work towards, but I expect it will be a system in which every tribal group, whether it be black, brown or white, can maintain its identity and its territorial integrity.'

'What a noble concept,' she agreed. 'But tell me when, in the history of mankind, any group who enjoyed supreme political power over all others ever gave up that power without an armed struggle. Do you truly believe that South Africans will be the first?'

'We'll have to make our own history,' Shasa matched her honeyed smile. 'But in the meantime the material existence of the black people in this country is five or six better than any other on the African continent. More is spent on black education, black hospitals and black housing, per capita, than in any other African country.'

'How does the expenditure per capita on black education compare with expenditure on white education?' Kitty shot back at him. 'My information is that five times more is spent on the education of a white child, than on a black.'

'We will strive to correct that imbalance, as we build up the wealth of our nation, as the black peasant becomes more productive and makes more of a contribution to the taxation that pays for that education. At the moment the white section of the population pays ninety-five per cent of the taxes – '

That wasn't the way the interview was meant to go and Kitty headed him off smoothly.

'And just how and when will the black people be consulted in these changes? Is it fair to say that nearly all blacks, and certainly all the educated and skilled blacks who are the natural leaders, totally reject the present political system which allows one sixth of the population to decide the fate of the rest?'

They were still sparring when Hank lifted his head from the camera lens, and rolled his eyes.

'Out of film, Kitty, you told me twenty minutes tops. We have forty-five minutes in the can.'

'Okay, Hank. My fault. I didn't realize we had such a garrulous bigot on the

show.' She smiled at Shasa acidly. 'You can wrap it up, Hank, and I'll see you in the morning. Nine o'clock at the studio.' She turned to Shasa and they didn't even look up as Hank left the suite. 'So what did we decide?' she asked Shasa.

'That the problem is more complex than anybody, perhaps even we in government, realize.'

'Insoluble?' Kitty asked.

'Certainly – without delicacy and the utmost good will of everybody in the country, and our friends abroad.'

'Russia?' she teased him, and he shuddered.

'Britain,' he said.

'What about America?'

'No. Britain understands. America is too wrapped up in her own racial problems. They aren't interested in the dissolution of the British Empire. However, we have always stood by Britain – and now Britain will stand by us.'

'Your confidence in the gratitude of great nations is refreshing. However, I think you will find that in the next decade there will be an enormous rip-tide of concern over human rights emanating from the United States. At least I hope so – and North American Broadcasting Studios will be doing all in its power to build it up into a tidal wave.'

'Your job is to report reality, not to attempt to re-structure it,' Shasa told her. 'You are a reporter, not the God of judgement.'

'If you believe that, you, are naïve,' she smiled. 'We make and destroy kings.'

Shasa stared at her, as though he were seeing her for the first time. 'My God, you are in the power game, just like everybody else.'

'It's the only game in town, buddy boy.'

'You are amoral.'

'No more than you are.'

'Oh yes you are. We are prepared to make our decisions and live with the consequences. You wreak your destruction, then like a child with a broken toy, throw it aside and go on without a moment's remorse to some new cause that will sell more advertising time.'

He had made her angry. Her eyes slanted and narrowed into bright arrowheads and the freckles on her nose and cheeks glowed like specks of gold leaf. It roused him to see her come out from behind the screen, as hard and formidable as any adversary he had ever faced. He wanted to goad her further, to make her give way completely.

'You have made yourself the guru of southern Africa on US television for one reason only. Not for concern over the fate of the black masses, but quite simply because you smell blood and violence in the air. You have sensed that this is where the action will be next and you want to be the one who captures it on film –'

'You bastard,' she hissed at him. 'I want peace and justice.'

'Peace and justice don't make good footage, Kitty my love. You are here to record the killing and the screaming – and if it doesn't happen soon enough, well that is easily fixed – you'll give it a little shove.'

She was out of her chair now, facing him, and her lips were frosty with rage.

'For the last hour you have been spouting the most vicious racial poison, and now you accuse me of injustice. You call me an *agent provocateur* for the violence that is coming.'

He raised an eyebrow, giving her the taunting supercilious smile which had enraged his opponents across the floor of the House, and it was too much for

her to bear. She sprang at him, white-lipped and shaking with fury, and she clawed for his single mocking eye with both hands.

Shasa caught her wrists, and lifted her feet clear of the floor. She was shocked by his strength, but she lifted her knee sharply, driving for his groin. He turned slightly and caught the knee on the hard muscle of his thigh.

'Where did a nice girl learn a trick like that?' he asked, and twisted her arms behind her, took both her wrists in his left hand and then bowed over her. She pressed her lips together, and tried to turn her face away, but he found her mouth and while he kissed her, he opened her blouse and with his free hand took out her small breasts. Her nipples were standing out like ripe mulberries, she was as aroused as he was, but kicking and spitting with fury.

He swung her round and threw her face down over the thick padded arm of the buttoned leather chair, pinning her with a hand between her shoulder blades, and her bottom in the air. That's how they had administered the cane at Shasa's school, and now while she screamed and kicked he jerked the leather belt out of the loops of her jeans, and pulled her trousers and panties down as far as her ankles and stepped in close behind her. Her buttocks were white and round and they maddened him.

Though she fought and struggled without let-up, at the same time she lifted her hips slightly and arched her back to make it easier for him, and only when it happened did she stop fighting and push back hard against him, sobbing with the effort of keeping pace with him.

It was over very quickly for both of them, and she rolled over and pulled him down on to the chair and whispered raggedly into his mouth, 'Well, that's one hell of a way to settle an argument, I'll give you that much.'

Shasa ordered dinner served in the suite, grilled crayfish with a sauce Mornay, followed by a Chateaubriand, baked baby potatoes and fresh young asparagus. He sent the waiter away and served it himself for Kitty was clad only in one of the hotel's long towelling dressing gowns.

As he drew the cork on the bottle of Chambertin, he told her, 'I've put four days aside for us. In the last few weeks I have been fortunate enough to get my hands on fifty thousand acres of land across the Sabi river from the Kruger National Park. I've been after it for fifteen years. It belonged to the widow of one of the old Randlords and I had to wait for the old biddy to cross the great divide before it came on the market. It's marvellous unspoilt bush country, teeming with wild game, perfect place for a lost weekend, we'll fly down after breakfast tomorrow – nobody will know where we are.'

She laughed at him. 'You are out of your little mind, lover. I'm a working girl. At eleven o'clock tomorrow I've got an interview with the leader of the opposition, De Villiers Graaff, and I'm certainly not breezing off into the boondocks with you to stare at lions and tigers.'

'No tigers in Africa – you are the African expert, you should know that.' He was angry again. 'It's a case of false pretences. You got me all the way up here for nothing,' he accused.

'Nothing?' she chuckled again. 'You call that *nothing*?'

'I expected four days of it.'

'You overestimate the going price for an interview. All you get is the rest of the night, and then tomorrow it's back to work – for both of us.'

She was getting under his guard too often, Shasa realized. Last time he had proposed marriage to her, and the idea still had its appeal. She had moved him the way no woman had since he had first met Tara. It was partly her

unattainability that made her so desirable. Shasa was accustomed to getting what he wanted, even if it was a hard and heartless little vixen with a childlike face and body.

He watched her eat the rare steak with the same sensual gusto as she made love. She was sitting cross-legged on the front edge of her chair and the hem of her dressing-gown had ridden up high on her thighs. She saw the direction of his gaze but made no effort to cover herself.

'Eat up,' she grinned at him. 'One thing at a time, lover.'

* * *

Shasa was chary of Tara's offer to assist his election campaign, and for the first two meetings left her at Weltevreden and drove out alone over Sir Lowry's Pass and the mountains.

South Boland, his new constituency, was an area of rich land, between the mountains and the sea, on the Cape's eastern littoral. The voters were almost entirely of Afrikaner extraction, and their families had held the land for three hundred years. They were wealthy farmers of wheat and sheep, Calvinist and conservative, but not as rabidly republican and anti-English as their cousins of the interior, the Free Staters and the Transvalers.

They received Shasa's first speeches with caution, and applauded him politely at the end. His opponent, the United Party candidate, was a blood Smuts man, like Blaine, who had been the incumbent until 1948 when he lost it to the Nationalists. Yet he still had a base of support in the district amongst the men who had known Smuts and had gone 'up north' to fight the Axis.

After Shasa's second meeting, the local Nationalist organizers were looking worried and scared.

'We are losing ground,' one of them told Shasa. 'The wives are suspicious of a man who campaigns without his own wife. They want to have a look at her.'

'You see, Meener Courtney, you are a bit too good-looking. It's okay for the younger women who think you look like Errol Flynn, but the older women don't like it, and the men don't like the way the young women look at you. We have to show them you are a family man.'

'I'll bring my wife,' Shasa promised, but his spirits sank. What kind of impression would Tara create in this dour God-fearing community where many of the women still wore the *voortrekker* bonnets and the men believed a woman's place was either in the bed or in the kitchen?

'Another thing,' the chief party organizer went on tactfully. 'We need one of the top men, one of the cabinet ministers to stand up on the platform with you. You see, Meneer Courtney, the people are having difficulty believing that you are a *ware* Nationalist. What with the English name and your family history.'

'We need somebody to make me look respectable, you mean?' Shasa hid his smile, and they all looked relieved.

'*Ja*, man! That's it!'

'What if I could get Minister De La Rey to come out for the meeting on Friday – and my wife, of course?'

'Hell, man!' they enthused. 'Minister De La Rey is perfect. The people like the way he handled the trouble. He is a good strong man. If you get him to come to talk to them, we'll have no more problems.'

Tara accepted the invitation without comment, and by an exercise in self-restraint Shasa refrained from giving her advice on how to dress or conduct herself, and was delighted and grateful when she came on to the platform in the town hall of the little town of Caledon, dressed in a dark blue dress with her thick auburn hair neatly gathered into a bun behind her head.

Though pretty and smiling she was the picture of the good wife. Isabella sat up beside her with knee-length white socks and ribbons in her hair. A born actress, Isabella responded to the occasion by behaving like a candidate for holy orders. Shasa saw the organizers exchanging approving nods and relieved smiles.

Minister De La Rey, supported by his own blonde wife and large family, introduced Shasa with a fiery speech in which he made it very clear that the Nationalist government was not going to allow itself to be dictated to by foreign governments or communist agitators, especially not if these agitators were black as well as communist.

Manfred had a finely tuned style of oratory, and he thrust out his jaw and flashed those topaz-coloured eyes, he wagged his finger at them, and stood with arms defiantly akimbo when they stood up to applaud him at the end.

Shasa's style was different, relaxed and friendly, and when he tried his first joke, they responded with genuine amusement. He followed it with assurances that the government would increase the already generous subsidy for farm products, especially wool and wheat, and that they would at the same time foster local industry and explore new overseas markets for the country's raw materials, particularly wool and wheat. He ended by telling them that many English speakers were coming to realize that the salvation of the country lay in strong uncompromising government and predicted a substantial increase in the Nationalist majority.

This time there was no reservation in the tumultuous applause that followed his speech, and the votes of confidence in the government, the National Party and the Nationalist candidate for South Boland were all carried unanimously. The entire district, including the United Party supporters, turned up for the free barbecue on the local rugby grounds, to which Shasa invited them. Two whole oxen were roasted on the spit and were washed down with lakes of Castle beer and rivers of *mampoer*, the local peach brandy.

Tara sat with the women, looking meek and demure and speaking little, allowing the older women to develop pleasantly maternal feelings towards her, while Shasa circulated amongst their husbands, talking knowledgeably about such momentous subjects as scale on wheat and scab on sheep. The whole atmosphere was cosy and reassuring, and for the first time Shasa was able to appreciate the depth of planning by the party organizers, their dedication and commitment to the Nationalist cause, which resulted in this degree of mobilization of all its resources. The United Party could never match it, for the English speakers were complacent and lethargic when it came to politics. It was the old English fault of wanting never to appear to try too hard. Politics was a kind of sport and every gentleman knew that sport should be played only by amateurs.

'No wonder we lost control,' Shasa thought. 'These chaps are professionals, and we just couldn't match them' – and then he checked himself. These were his organizers now, no longer the enemy. He had become a part of this slick, highly tuned political machine, and the knowledge was a little daunting.

At last, with Tara at his side, Shasa made a round of goodnights with a party organizer steering him tactfully to each of the most important local dignitaries,

making sure that none of these was slighted, and everybody agreed that the family made a charming group.

They stayed overnight with the most prosperous of the local farmers, and the following morning, which was Sunday, attended the Dutch Reformed Church in the village. Shasa had not been in a church since Isabella was christened. He was not looking forward to it. This was another grand show, for Manfred De La Rey had prevailed upon his uncle, the Reverend Tromp Bierman, moderator of the church, to deliver the sermon. Uncle Tromp's sermons were famous throughout the Cape, and families thought nothing of travelling a hundred miles to listen to them.

'I never thought I would ever speak for a cursed *rooinek*,' he told Manfred. 'It is either advancing senility, or a sign of my great love for you, that I do so now.' Then he climbed into the pulpit, and with his great silver beard flashing like the surf of a stormy sea, he lashed the congregation with such force and fury that they quivered and squirmed with delicious terror for their souls.

At the end of the sermon, Uncle Tromp reduced the volume to remind them that there was an election coming up, and that a vote for the United Party was a vote for Satan himself. No matter how some of them felt about Englishmen, they weren't voting for a man here, they were voting for the party upon which the Almighty had bestowed his blessing and into whose hands he delivered the destiny of the *Volk*. He stopped just short of closing the gates of Heaven in the face of any of them who did not put their cross opposite the name of Courtney, but when he glared at them threateningly, there were few who felt inclined to take a chance on his continued forbearance.

'Well, my dear, I can't thank you enough for your help,' Shasa told Tara, as they drove home over the high mountain passes of the Hottentots Holland. 'From here on it looks like a cakewalk.'

'It was interesting to watch our political system in action,' Tara murmured. 'All the other jockeys got down off their mounts and shooed you in.'

Polling day in South Boland was merely an endorsement of certain victory, and when the voters were counted it appeared that Shasa had wooed across at least five hundred erstwhile United Party voters, and, much to the delight of the Nationalist hierarchy, increased the majority most handsomely. As the results came in from around the rest of the country, it became apparent that the trend was universal. For the first time ever, substantial numbers of English speakers were deserting Smuts' party. The Nationalists took 103 seats to the United Party's 53. The promise of strong uncompromising government was bearing good fruits.

At Rhodes Hill Centaine gave an elaborate dinner dance for 150 important guests to celebrate Shasa's appointment to the new cabinet.

As they swirled together around the dance floor to the strains of 'The Blue Danube', Centaine told Shasa, 'Once again we have done the right thing at the right time, *chéri*. It can still come true – all of it.' And she sang softly the praise song that the old Bushman had composed at Shasa's birth:

> 'His arrows will fly to the stars
> And when men speak his name
> It will be heard as far
> And wherever he goes, he will find good water.'

The clicking sounds of the Bushman language, like snapping twigs and

footsteps in mud, raised nostalgic memories from the distant time when they had been together in the Kalahari.

* * *

Shasa enjoyed the Houses of Parliament. They were like an exclusive men's club. He liked the grandeur of white columns and lofty halls, the exotic tiles on the floors, the panelling and the green leather-covered benches. He often paused in the labyrinth of corridors to admire the paintings and the sculpted busts of famous men, Merriman and Louis Botha, Cecil Rhodes and Leander Starr Jameson, heroes and rogues, statesmen and adventurers. They had made this country's history – and then he reminded himself.

'History is a river that never ends. Today is history, and I am here at the fountainhead,' and he imagined his own portrait hanging there with the others one day. 'I'll have it commissioned at once,' he thought. 'While I am still in my prime. For the time being I'll hang it at Weltevreden, but I'll put a clause in my will.'

As a minister, he now had his own office in the House, the same suite of rooms that had been used by Cecil Rhodes when he was prime minister of the old Cape parliament before the House had been enlarged and extended. Shasa redecorated and furnished it at his own expense. Thesens, the timber firm from Knysna, installed the panelling. It was indigenous wild olive, marvellously grained and with a satiny lustre. He hung four of his finest Pierneef landscapes on the panelling, with a Van Wouw bronze of a Bushman hunter standing on the table beneath them. Although he was determined to keep the artwork authentically African, the carpet was the choicest green Wilton and his desk Louis XIV.

It felt strange to enter the chamber for the first time to take his place on the government front bench, a mirror image of his usual view. He ignored the hostile glances of his erstwhile colleagues, smiling only at Blaine's expressionless wink and while the Speaker of the House read the prayer, he measured the men to whom he had transferred his allegiance.

His reflections were interrupted as the Speaker of the House ended the prayer, and across the floor De Villiers Graaff, the tall handsome leader of the opposition, rose to propose the traditional vote of no confidence, while the government members, smug and cocksure, still revelling in their heady election triumph, mocked him noisily with cries of '*Skande!* Scandal!' and '*Siestog*, man! Shame on you, man!'

Two days later Shasa rose to deliver his first speech from the government front benches and pandemonium seized the House. His former comrades howled their contempt, and waved their order papers at him, stamping their feet and whistling with outrage, while his newly adopted party roared encouragement and support.

Tall and elegant, smiling with scorn, switching easily from English to Afrikaans, Shasa gradually quietened the benches opposite him with his low key but riveting oratorical style, and once he had their attention he made them squirm uneasily as he dissected their party with an insider's surgical skill, then held up their weaknesses and blemishes for them to contemplate.

When he sat down he left them severely discomforted, and the prime minister

leaned forward in his seat to nod at him, an unprecedented public accolade, while most of the other ministers, even those northerners most hostile to his appointment, passed him notes of congratulation. Manfred De La Rey's note invited him to join a party of senior ministers for lunch in the member's dining room. It was an auspicious beginning.

Blaine Malcomess and Centaine came out to Weltevreden for the weekend. As usual the family spent all of Saturday afternoon at the polo field. Blaine had recently resigned as captain of the South African team.

'It's obscene for a man over sixty to still be playing,' he had explained his decision to Shasa.

'You are better than most of us youngsters of forty, Blaine, and you know it.'

'Wouldn't it be pleasant to keep the captaincy in the family?' Blaine suggested.

'I've only got one eye.'

'Oh tush, man. You hit the ball as sweetly as you ever did. It's simply a matter of practice and more practice.'

'I don't have the time for that,' Shasa protested.

'There is time for everything in life that you really want.'

So Blaine forced him to practise, but deep down he knew that Shasa had lost interest in ball games and would never captain the national team. Oh, certainly he still rode like a centaur, his arm was strong and true and he had the courage of a lion when he was roused, but these days it needed stronger medicine to get his blood racing.

'It's a strange paradox that a man gifted with too many talents can fritter them all away without developing a single one to its full.' At that thought Blaine looked from Shasa to his sons.

As always Sean and Garrick had joined in the practice uninvited, and though they could not come close to matching the furious pace and skill of their elders, they were acting as pick-up men and passers for them.

Sean rode as his father had at that age and it gave Blaine a nostalgic pang to watch him. The horse was a part of him, the accord between rider and mount was total, his stick work was natural and unforced, but he lost interest quickly and made sloppy little errors, was more interested in teasing his brother and showing off and making eyes at the young girls in the stand than in perfecting his style.

Garrick was the opposite of his elder brother. He rode with enough sunlight shining between the saddle-leather and his bum to dazzle a blind man. However, his concentration was absolute, and he scowled murderously at the ball through his spectacles, using his stick with all the grace of a labourer digging a trench, but it was surprising how often he got a solid strike and how the bamboo root ball flew when he did. Then Blaine was amazed by the sudden change in his physique. From the skinny little runt he had been not long before, he was almost grotesquely overdeveloped in shoulder and chest and upper arms for a child of his age. Yet when they went in for tea and dismounted, his still skinny legs gave him an unfortunate anthropoid appearance. When he removed his riding cap, his hair stuck up in unruly dark spikes, and while Sean sauntered across to make the girls giggle and blush, Garrick stayed close to his father. Again Blaine was surprised at how often Shasa spoke directly to the child, even demonstrating a fine point of grip by rearranging his fingers on the handle of the stick, and when he perfected it, Shasa punched his arm lightly and told him:

'That's it, champ. We'll get you into a green and gold jersey one day.'

Garrick's glow of satisfaction was touching to watch, and Blaine exchanged a glance with Centaine. Not long before, they had discussed Shasa's total lack of interest in the child, and the detrimental effect that it might have on him. Their fears for Garrick seemed to have been unfounded, Blaine conceded, it was the other two they should have been worrying about.

Michael was not riding today. He had hurt his wrist, a mysterious injury which although excruciatingly painful, showed no bruising nor swelling. It was astonishing how often that wrist, or his ankle or his knee, plagued him whenever there was the prospect of hard physical exercise in the offing. Blaine frowned as he glanced at him now, sitting beside Tara at the tea table under the oaks, both their heads bowed over a book of poetry. Neither of them had looked up once during all the shouting and galloping and ribald exchanges on the field. Blaine was a firm believer in the old adage that a young man should have a disciplined mind in a healthy body, and should be able to join robustly in the rough and tumble of life. He had spoken to Tara about him, but though she had promised to encourage Michael's participation in sport and games, Blaine had not noticed any evidence that she had done so.

There was a chorus of muted shrieks and giggles behind him, and Blaine glanced over his shoulder. Wherever Sean was these days there seemed always to be a flock of females. He attracted them the way a tree full of fruit brings a swarm of noisy mousebirds to it. Blaine had no idea who all these girls belonged to, some of them were the daughters of the estate managers and of Shasa's German wine-maker, the pretty blond child was the American consul's daughter and the two little dark ones were the French ambassador's, but the others were unknown – probably the offspring of the half dozen politicians and other members of the diplomatic corps who made up the usual guest-list for Saturday high tea at Weltevreden.

'Shouldn't really interfere,' Blaine grumbled to himself. 'But I think I'll have a word with Shasa. No good speaking to Tara. She's too soft by a long chalk.' Blaine glanced around and saw that Shasa had left the group at the tea table under the oaks and had moved down the pony lines. He was squatting with one of the grooms to examine the fore hock of his favourite pony, a powerful stallion he had named Kenyatta, because he was black and dangerous.

'Good opportunity,' Blaine grunted and went to join Shasa. They discussed taping the pony's leg, his only weak point, and then stood up.

'How's Sean making out at Bishops?' Blaine asked casually, and Shasa looked surprised.

'Tara been talking to you?' he asked. Sean had gone up to the senior school at the beginning of the year, after ending as head boy and captain of sport at his preparatory school.

'Having trouble?' Blaine asked.

'Going through a phase,' Shasa shrugged. 'He'll be all right. He has too much talent not to make good in the end.'

'What happened?'

'Nothing to worry about. He's become a bit of a rebel, and his grades have gone to hell. I gave him the sweet end of the riding-crop. Only language he speaks fluently. He'll be all right, Blaine, don't worry.'

'For some people it's all too easy,' Blaine remarked. 'They get into the habit of free-wheeling through life.' He saw Shasa bridle slightly, and realized he was

taking the remark personally. Good, he thought, let him – and he went on deliberately, 'You should know, Shasa. You have the same weakness.'

'I suppose you do have the right to speak to me like that. The only man in the world who does,' Shasa mused. 'But don't expect me to enjoy it, Blaine.'

'I expect young Sean cannot accept criticism either,' Blaine said. 'He's the one I wanted to talk about, not you. How did we end up discussing you? However, since we are, let an old dog give a few words of caution to both of you. Firstly, don't dismiss Sean's behaviour too lightly, you may just find yourself with a serious problem one day, if you don't check it now. Some people have to have constant stimulation or else they get bored. I think Sean might be one of those. They become addicted to excitement and danger. Watch him, Shasa.'

'Thank you, Blaine,' Shasa nodded, but he was not grateful.

'As for you, Shasa. You have been playing life like a game.'

'That's all it is, surely,' Shasa agreed.

'If you truly believe that, then you have no right to take on the responsibility of cabinet rank,' Blaine said softly. 'No, Shasa. You have made yourself responsibile for the welfare of sixteen million souls. It's no longer a game, but a sacred trust.'

They had stopped walking and turned to face each other.

'Think about that, Shasa,' Blaine said. 'I believe that there are dark and difficult days ahead, and you won't be playing for an increase in company dividends – you will be playing for the survival of a nation, and if you fail, it will mean the end of the world you know. You will not suffer alone – '

Blaine turned to Isabella as she ran to him.

'Grandpapa! Grandpapa!' she cried. 'I want to show you, the new pony daddy gave me,' and they both looked down at the beautiful child.

'No, Shasa, not you alone,' Blaine repeated, and took the child's hand.

'All right, Bella,' he said. 'Let's go down to the stables.'

* * *

Shasa had found that Blaine's words were like arrow-grass seeds. They scratched when they first attached themselves to your clothing, and then gradually worked themselves deeper until they penetrated the skin to cause real pain. Those words were still with him when he went into the cabinet room on Monday morning and took his place at the foot of the table, as befitted the most junior member of the gathering.

Before Blaine had spoken to him, Shasa had considered these meetings no more important than, say, a full board meeting of Courtney Mining and Finance. Naturally, he prepared himself as thoroughly, not only were his own notes exhaustive and cogent, but he had assembled full portfolios on every other member of the cabinet. Blaine had helped him with his work, and the results had been fed into the company computer and were kept up to the minute. After a lifetime in politics, Blaine was a skilled analyst and he had been able to trace in the tenuous and concealed lines of loyalty and commitment that bound this group of important men together.

At the broadest level every single one of them, apart from Shasa, was a member of the *Broederbond* – the Brotherhood – that invidious secret society of

eminent Afrikaners whose single object was to advance the interest of the Afrikaner above all others at every possible turn and at every level from that of national politics through business and the economy, on down to the levels of education and the civil service. No ousider could ever hope to fathom its ramifications, for it was protected by a curtain of silence which no Afrikaner dared to break. It united them all, no matter whether they were members of the Calvinist Dutch Reformed Church or of the even more extreme *Dopper* church, the Hervormde church which by Article No 3 of its charter had ordained that heaven was reserved exclusively for members of the white race. The *Broederbond* united even the southerners, the Cape Nationalists, and those hard men from the north.

As Shasa rearranged his thick sheaf of notes, which he would not need since they were already committed to memory, he glanced down the table and saw how the two opposing forces in the cabinet had arranged themselves like the grouping of an army. Shasa was quite obviously arrayed with the southerners under Dr Theophilus Dönges, one of the most senior men, who had been a member of the cabinet since Dr Malan brought the party to power in 1948. He was leader of the party in the Cape, and Manfred De La Rey was one of his men. However, they were the smaller and least influential of the two groups. The northerners comprised both the Transvalers and the Orange Free Staters, and amongst them were the most formidable politicians in the land.

Strangely, in this assembly of impressive men, Shasa's attention went to a man who had been a member of the Senate as long as Shasa had himself been a member of the lower house. Before his appointment to the Senate in 1948, Verwoerd had been the editor of *Die Transvaler*, and before that he had been a Professor at Stellenbosch University. Shasa knew that he had lectured to Manfred De La Rey when he was a student, and had exerted enormous influence upon him. However, they were in different camps now, Verwoerd was in the north. Since 1950 he had been Minister of Bantu Affairs, with godlike powers over the black population and had made his name synonymous with the ideal of racial segregation at all levels of society.

For a man with such a monumental reputation for racial intolerance, the architect of the great edifice of *apartheid* which was being erected with intricate interlocking laws that dictated every aspect of the lives of the country's millions of black people, his appearance and manner were a pleasant surprise. His smile was kindly, almost benign, and he was quiet spoken but persuasive as he rose to address the cabinet and explain with the aid of a specially prepared map of South Africa his plans for the rearrangement of black population densities.

Tall and slightly round-shouldered, with his curly hair beginning to turn to silver, there could be little doubt of his utmost sincerity and belief in the absolute rightness of his conclusions. Shasa found himself being carried along on the plausible flood of his logic. Although his voice was pitched a little too high, and the tense note of his monologue grated on the ear, he carried them all on the strength, not only of his total conviction, but also of his personality. Even his opponents were filled with awe at his debating ability.

Only one small detail worried Shasa, Verwoerd's blue eyes were slitted, as though he were always looking into the sun, and though they were surrounded by a complex web of laughter lines, they were cold eyes, the eyes of a machine-gunner staring over the sights of his weapon.

Blaine's words came back to Shasa as he sat at the polished stinkwood table.

'No, Shasa, it's not a game. You have made yourself responsible for the welfare of sixteen million souls. It's no longer a game, but a sacred trust.'

But he remained expressionless as Verwoerd ended his presentation. 'Not one of us here today doubts that South Africa is a white man's country. My proposals will see to it that within the reserves the natives will have some measure of autonomy. However, as to the country as a whole, and the European areas in particular, we the white people, are and shall remain the masters.'

There was a general murmur of agreement and approbation, and two of the others asked for clarification on minor points. There was no call to vote or to make any joint decision, for Verwoerd's lecture had been in the form of a report back from his department.

'I think that Doctor Henk has covered this subject fully – unless anybody else has a question, we can go on to the next matter on the agenda.' The prime minister looked down the table at Shasa. The agenda read:

ITEM TWO: Projection by the Hon. Minister for Mines and Industry on the capital requirements of the private industrial sector over the next ten years and the proposal of means to satisfy such requirements.

This morning would be the first time Shasa would address the full cabinet, and he hoped he would muster only a small portion of Verwoerd's aplomb and persuasion.

His nervousness faded as soon as he rose to speak, for he had prepared in depth and detail. He began with an assessment of the foreign capital needs of the economy over the next decade, 'to carry us through to the end of the 1960s,' and then set out to estimate the amounts available to them from their traditional markets within the British Commonwealth.

'As you see, this leaves us with a considerable shortfall, particularly in mining, the new oil from coal industry and the armaments sector. This is how I propose that shortfall should be met: in the first instance we have to look to the United States of America. That country is a potential source of capital that has barely been tapped – '

He held their attention completely as he described his department's plans to advertise the country as a prosperous market amongst the American business leaders, and to entice as many of them as he could to visit South Africa at the expense of his department. He also intended establishing associations with sympathetic and influential politicians and businessmen in the United States and the United Kingdom to promote the country's image, and to this end he had already contacted Lord Littleton, head of Littleton merchant banks, who had agreed to act as chairman of the British South Africa Club. A similar association, the American South Africa Club, would be formed in the United States.

Shasa was encouraged by the obviously favourable reception of his presentation to continue with a matter he had not intended raising.

'We have just heard from Dr Verwoerd the proposal to build up self-governing black states within the country. I don't wish to tackle the political aspects of this scheme, but as a businessman I feel that I am competent to bring to your attention the final cost, in financial rather than human terms, of putting this into practice.'

Shasa went on swiftly to outline the massive obstacles in logistics and lost productivity that would result.

'We will have to duplicate a number of times the basic structures of the state

in various parts of the country, and we must expect the bill for this to run into many billions of pounds. That money could more profitably be invested in wealth-producing undertakings – '

Across the table he saw Verwoerd's great charm ice over with a crust of hostility. Shasa knew he was autocratic and contemptuous of criticism, and he sensed that he was taking a risk by antagonizing a man who might one day wield ultimate power, but he went on doggedly.

'The proposal has another flaw. By decentralizing industry we will make it less effective and competitive. In a modern age when all countries are economically in competition with each other, we will be placing a handicap on ourselves.'

When he sat down he saw that though he might have convinced nobody, he had given them much to think about seriously and soberly, and when the meeting ended, one or two of the other ministers, most of them southerners, stayed to exchange a few words with him. Shasa sensed that he had enhanced his reputation and consolidated his place in the cabinet with that afternoon's work, and he drove back to Weltevreden feeling well pleased with himself.

He dropped his briefcase on the desk in his study and, hearing voices out on the terrace, went out into the late sunshine. The guest that Tara was entertaining was the headmaster of Bishops. Usually this worthy would summon the parents of recalcitrant pupils to appear before him as summarily as he did their offspring. This did not apply to the Courtney family. Centaine Courtney-Malcomess had been a governor of the school for almost thirty years, the only woman on the board. Her son had been head boy before the war and was now on the board with his mother, and both of them were major contributors to the College's coffers – amongst their gifts were the organ, the plate-glass windows in the new chapel, and the new kitchens to the main dining-hall. The headmaster had come to call upon Shasa, rather than the other way around. However, Tara was looking uneasy and stood up to greet Shasa with relief.

'Hello, Headmaster.' Shasa shook hands, but was not encouraged by the head's lugubrious expression.

'Headmaster wants to talk to you about Sean,' Tara explained. 'I think a man-to-man chat will be appropriate, so I will leave the two of you alone while I go and get a fresh pot of tea.'

She slipped away, and Shasa asked genially, 'Sun's over the yard arm. May I offer you a whisky, Headmaster?'

'No thank you, Mr Courtney.' That he had not used Shasa's Christian name was ominous, and Shasa adjusted his own expression to the correct degree of solemnity and took the chair beside him.

'Sean, hey? So what has that little hooligan been up to now?'

Tara opened the door to the dining-room quietly and crossed the floor to stand behind the drapes. She waited until the voices on the terrace were so intense and serious that she could be certain that Shasa would be there for the next hour at least. She turned quickly and left the dining-room, closing the door behind her, and went swiftly down the wide marble-tiled passageway, past the library and the gun room. The door to Shasa's study was unlocked, the only doors ever locked at Weltevreden were those to the wine cellar.

Shasa's briefcase stood in the middle of his desk. She opened it and saw the blue folder embossed with the coat of arms of the state which contained the typed minutes of that day's cabinet meeting. She knew that numbered copies

were made and distributed to each minister at the end of the weekly meetings, and she had expected to find it in his case.

She lifted it out, careful not to disarrange anything else in the crocodile-skin attaché case, and carried it to the table beside the french doors. The light was better here, and in addition, by glancing around the drapes, she could see down the terraced to where Shasa and the headmaster were still deep in conversation under the trellis of vines.

Quickly she arranged the blue sheets on the table, and then focused the tiny camera that she took from the pocket of her skirt. It was the size of a cigarette-lighter. She was still unaccustomed to the mechanism, and her hands were shaking with nervousness. It was the first time she had done this.

Molly had given her the camera at their last meeting, and explained that their friends were so pleased by the quality of the information she was providing that they wanted to make her job easier for her. Her fingers felt like pork sausages as she manipulated the tiny knobs and snapped each of the sheets twice, to cover herself against possible mistakes of exposure or focus. Then she slipped the camera back into her pocket, before stacking the sheets in their folder and replacing it carefully in Shasa's briefcase in exactly the same way she had found it.

She was so nervous that her bladder felt as though it might burst and she had to run down the passage to the downstairs toilet. She only just reached it in time. Five minutes later she carried the silver Queen Anne teapot out on to the terrace. Usually this would have annoyed Shasa who did not like her to usurp the servants' work, especially in front of guests. However, he was too engrossed in his discussion with the headmaster to notice.

'I find it difficult to believe that it is anything more than robust boyish spirits, Headmaster.' He was frowning as he sat forward in his chair, hands on his knees, to confront the schoolmaster.

'I have tried to look upon it that way.' The headmaster shook his head regretfully. 'In view of the special relationship that your family has to the school, I have been as lenient as I can be. However,' he paused meaningfully, 'we are not dealing simply with an isolated instance. Not simply one or two boyish pranks, but a state of mind, an entire behaviour pattern which is most alarming.' The headmaster broke off to accept the cup of tea that Tara passed across the table to him. 'Forgive me, Mrs Courtney, this is as painful to me as it must be to you.'

Tara said quietly, 'I can believe that. I know you look upon each of your boys as one of your own sons.' And she glanced at Shasa. 'My husband has been reluctant to come to terms with the problem.' She hid her smug satisfaction behind the sorrowful but brave little smile. Sean had always been Shasa's child, strong-willed and thoughtless of others. She had never understood nor accepted that cruel streak in him. She recalled his selfishness and lack of gratitude even before he could talk. As an infant when he had gorged himself at her breast, he would let her know he was satiated by biting her nipple with sufficient force to bruise her painfully. She had loved him, of course, but had found it hard to like him. As soon as he had learned to walk, he headed straight for his father, staggering after him like a puppy, and his first word had been 'Dada'. That hurt her, after she had carried him big and heavy in her belly and given him birth and suck, 'Dada'. Well, he was Shasa's child now and she sat back and watched him grapple with the problem, feeling a spiteful pleasure at his discomfort.

'He's a natural sportsman,' Shasa was saying, 'and a born leader. He has a good mind – I am convincd that he will pull himself together. I gave him a good thrashing after his school report at the end of last term, and I'll give him another this evening to get him in the right frame of mind.'

'With some boys the cane has no effect, or rather it has the opposite to the desired effect. Your Sean looks upon corporal punishment the way a soldier looks on his battle wounds, as a mark of his courage and fortitude.'

'I have always been against my husband beating the children,' Tara said, and Shasa flashed her a warning look, but the headmaster went on.

'I have also tried the cane on Sean, Mrs Courtney. He seems positively to welcome that punishment as though it affords him some special distinction.'

'But he is a good athlete,' Shasa repeated rather lamely.

'I see you choose, as I would, the term "athlete" rather than "sportsman",' the headmaster nodded. 'Sean is precocious and mature for his age. He is stronger than the other boys in his group and has no qualms in using his strength to win, not always in accordance with the rules of the game.' The headmaster looked at Shasa pointedly. 'He does have a good brain, but his school marks indicate that he is not prepared to use it in the classroom. Instead he applies his mind to less commendable enterprises.' The headmaster paused, sensing that this was not the moment to give a doting father concrete examples. He went on: 'He is also, as you have noted, a born leader. Unfortunately, he gathers about him the least desirable elements in the school, which he has formed into a gang with which he terrorizes the other boys, even those senior to him are afraid of him.'

'I find this difficult to accept.' Shasa was grim-faced.

'To be blunt, Mr Courtney: Sean seems to have a vindictive and vicious streak in him. I am, of course, looking for an improvement in him. However, if that is not soon forthcoming, I will have to make a serious decision over Sean's future at Bishops.'

'I had set my heart on him being head boy, as I was,' Shasa admitted, and the headmaster shook his head.

'Far from becoming head boy, Mr Courtney, unless Sean has pulled up his socks by the end of the year, I am, with the greatest reluctance, going to have to ask you to remove him from Bishops altogether.'

'My God!' Shasa breathed. 'You don't really mean that?'

'I'm sorry to say that I do.'

* * *

It was quite remarkable that Clare East had ever been employed by the headmaster of Bishops. The explanation was that the appointment was a temporary one, a mere six-month contract, to fill in after the unexpected resignation of the previous art master on the grounds of ill-health. The salary offered was such that it had attracted only two other applications, both patently unsuitable.

Clare had come to the interview with the headmaster dressed in clothes she had not worn for six years, not since she was twenty-one years of age. She had exhumed them from a forgotten cabin trunk for the occasion, a high-buttoned dress in drab green that conformed closely to the head's own ideas of suitable

apparel for a school-mistress. Her long black hair she had plaited and twisted up severely behind her head, and the portfolio of her painting she had chosen to show him, was composed of landscapes and seascapes and still lifes, subjects which had interested her at about the same time as she had bought the chaste woollen dress. At Bishops, art was not one of the main-stream subjects, but merely a catch-all for the pupils who showed little aptitude for the sciences.

Once Clare had charge of the art school, which was situated far enough from the main buildings as to offer her a certain freedom of behaviour, she reverted to her usual style of dress: wide loose skirts in vivid colours and flamboyant patterns, worn with Mexican-style blouses like those that Jane Russell had worn in *The Outlaw*. She had seen the movie five times while she was attending the London School of Arts, and modelled herself on Jane Russell, though of course Clare knew her own breasts were better than Russell's, just as big but higher and more pointed.

Her long hair she wore in a different style every day, and when she was teaching she always kicked off her sandals and strode around the art room barefooted, smoking thin black Portuguese cigarettes which one of her lovers brought her in packs of a thousand.

Sean had absolutely no interest in art. He had filtered down to this class by a process of natural rejection. Physics and chemistry demanded too much effort, and geography, the next lowest subject, was an even greater bore than paint-brushes.

Sean fell in love with Clare East the very moment that she walked into the art room. The first time she had paused at his easel to inspect the mess of colour he had smeared on his sheet of art paper, he realized that she was an inch shorter than he was, and when she reached up to correct one of his shaky outlines, he saw that she had not shaved her armpit. That bush of dark coarse hair glistening with sweat, induced the hardest and most painful erection he had ever experienced.

He tried to impress her with manly strutting behaviour, and when that failed, he used an oath in her presence that he usually reserved for one of his polo ponies. Clare East sent him to the head with a note and the head gave him four strokes of his heavy Malacca cane, accompanying the beating with a few words of counsel.

'You will have to learn, young man, WHACK, that I will not allow you to compound atrocious behaviour, WHACK, with foul language, WHACK, especially in the presence of a lady, WHACK.'

'Thank you very much Headmaster.' It was traditional to express gratitude for these ministrations, and to refrain from rubbing the injured area in the great man's presence. When Sean returned to the art room, his ardour, far from being cooled by the Malacca cane, was rather inflamed to unbearable proportions, but he realized he had to change tactics.

He discussed it with his henchman, Snotty Arbuthnot, and was only mildly discouraged by Snotty's advice. 'Forget it, man. Every fellow in school is whacking away thinking about Marsh Mallows – ' the nickname was a reference to Clare East's bosom, 'but Tug saw her at the movies with some chap at least thirty, with a moustache and his own car. They were smooching away like mad dogs in the back row. Why don't you go and see Poodle instead?'

Poodle was a sixteen-year-old from Rustenberg Girls' School, just across the railway line from Bishops. She was a young lady with a mission in life, to see as many boys across the borders of manhood as she could fit into her busy

afternoons. Though Sean had never spoken to her, she had been a spectator at every one of his recent cricket matches and she had sent a message to him through a mutual friend suggesting a meeting in the pine forest on Rondebosch Common.

'She looks like a poodle,' Sean dismissed the suggestion scornfully, and resigned himself to distant adoration of Clare East, until one day he was searching her desk for those black Portuguese cigarettes for which he had developed a taste. Love did not mean he could not steal from her. In a locked drawer which he picked with a paper clip, he came across a stiff cardboard folder tied with green ribbons. The folder contained over twenty pencil drawings of nude male models, all of them signed and dated by Clare East, and after the first jealous shock, Sean realized that each drawing was of a different subject with only one common feature. While the models' faces had been roughed in, their genitals had been depicted in minute and loving detail, and all of them were fully tumescent.

What Sean had discovered was Clare's collection of scalps, or an equivalent thereof. Clare East had strong tastes, but even more than garlic and red wine she needed men in her diet. This was so evident in the secret folder that all Sean's deflated hopes were once more revived, and that night he commissioned Michael, for the sum of five shillings, to paint a portrait of Claire East in Sean's art book.

Michael was in the junior art class and was able to make his studies for the portrait without the model's knowledge, and the completed work surpassed even Sean's expectations. He submitted the portrait and at the end of the following session Clare dismissed the class with a rider, 'Oh Sean, will you please remain behind?'

When the art room was cleared, she opened his art book at the painting of herself.

'Did you do this, Sean?' she asked. 'It really is very good.' The question was innocent enough, but the difference between the portrait and Sean's murky compositions was so evident that even he saw the danger of claiming authorship.

'I was going to tell you, I did it,' he admitted openly, 'but I can't lie to you, Miss East. I paid my brother to do it for me.'

'Why, Sean?'

'I suppose because I like you so much,' he mumbled, and to her surprise she saw that he was actually blushing. Clare was touched. Up to that time she had actively disliked this boy. He was brash and cocky and a disruptive influence in her class. She was certain that it was he who was stealing her cigarettes.

This unsuspected sensitivity surprised her, and suddenly she realized that his bumptious behaviour had been to attract her attention. She relented towards him, and over the following days and weeks she showed Sean that she had forgiven him by giving him small largesse – from a special smile to an extra few minutes of her time tidying up his creative efforts.

In return Sean began leaving gifts in her desk, thereby confirming her suspicion that he had been into it before. However, the theft of cigarettes stopped and she accepted the offerings of fruit and flowers without comment, just a smile and a nod as she passed his easel.

Then one Friday afternoon she opened her drawer and there lay a blue enamel box with 'Garrards' in gold lettering on the lid. She opened it with her back turned to the class, and she started uncontrollably and almost dropped the box as she realized that it contained a brooch of white gold. The centrepiece

was a large star sapphire, and even Clare, who was no judge of gems, realized that it was an exquisite stone. It was surrounded by small diamonds set in a star pattern. Clare experienced a giddy rush of avarice. The brooch must certainly be worth many hundreds of pounds, more money than she had ever had in her hand at one time, more than a year's salary at her present parsimonious rate of pay.

Sean had taken the piece from his mother's dressing-table and hidden it in the thatch of the saddle room behind the stables until the furore had died down. All the house servants had been interrogated, first by Shasa, who was outraged by this breach of faith. Nothing, apart from liquor, had ever been stolen by his employees before. When his own investigations ran into a dead end, Shasa called in the police. Fortunately for Sean, it transpired that one of the junior maids had previously served a six-month sentence for theft from an employer. She was obviously guilty and the Wynberg magistrate gave her eighteen months, her offence compounded by her obstinate refusal to return the stolen brooch. Since she was now over twenty-one years, the maid was sent to the Pollsmoor Women's Prison.

Sean had waited another ten days for the incident to be forgotten before presenting the gift to the object of his passion. Clare East was mightily tempted. She realized that the brooch must have been stolen, but on the other hand she was, as usual for her, in serious financial difficulty. This was the only reason she had taken on her present employment. She looked back with nostalgic regret on the idle days of eating and drinking and painting and making love which had led her into her present embarrassed circumstances. The brooch would solve it all. She had no scruples of conscience, but a terror of being convicted of theft. She knew that her free and creative soul would wither behind the bars of a women's prison.

Surreptitiously she returned the brooch to her desk drawer and for the rest of that art period she was distracted and withdrawn. She chain-smoked cigarettes and kept well clear of the rear of the art room, where Sean made a fine picture of innocence as he applied himself with unusual industry to his easel. She did not have to tell him to remain behind when the bell rang at the end of the period. He came to where she sat at her desk.

'Did you like it?' he asked softly, and she opened the drawer and placed the enamel box in the centre of the desk between them.

'I cannot accept it, Sean,' she said. 'You know that very well.' She didn't want to ask him where he had obtained it. She didn't want to know, and involuntarily she reached out to touch the box for the last time. The enamel surface felt like a new-laid egg, smooth and warm to the touch.

'It's all right,' Sean said quietly. 'Nobody knows. They think somebody else took it. It's quite safe.'

Had the child seen through her so easily? She stared at him. Was it one amoral soul recognizing another? It made her angry to be found out, to have her greed so exposed. She took her hand off the box and placed it in her lap.

She drew a breath, and steeled herself to repeat her refusal, but Sean stilled her by opening his art book and taking out three loose leaves. He placed them beside the blue enamel box, and she drew a hissing breath. They were her own drawings from her fun folder, signed by herself.

'I took these – sort of fair exchange,' Sean said, and she looked at him and truly saw him for the first time.

He was young in years only. In the museum in Athens she had been

enchanted by a marble statue of the great god Pan in his manifestation as a young boy. A beautiful child, but about him an ancient evil as enthralling as sin itself. Clare East was not a teacher by vocation, she felt no innate revulsion at the corruption of the young. It was simply that she had not thought of it before. With her hearty sexual appetite she had experienced almost everything else, including partners of her own sex, although those had been unsuccessful experiments long ago put behind her. Men she had known, in the biblical sense, in every possible variation of size and shape and colour. She took and discarded them with a kind of compulsive fervour, seeking always an elusive fulfilment which seemed to dance for ever just beyond her grasp. Often she was afraid, truly terrified, that she had reached the point of satiety, when her pleasure was irreparably blunted and jaded.

Now she was presented with a new and titillating perversion, enough to reawaken the lusty response that she had thought lost for ever. This child's loveliness contained a wickedness that left her breathless as she discovered it.

She had never been paid before, and this mannikin was offering her a prostitute's fee that was princely enough for a royal courtesan. She had never been blackmailed before, and he was threatening her with those unwise sketches. She knew what would happen if they ever fell into the hands of the school governors, and she did not doubt that he would carry out the unspoken threat. He had already hinted that he had placed blame for the theft of the sapphire brooch on an innocent party. Most tantalizing, she had never had a child before. She let her eyes run over him curiously. His skin was clear and firm, with the sweet gloss of youth on it. The hair on his forearms was silky, but his cheeks were bare. He was using a razor already, and he was taller than she was, a man's outline emerging from boyhood in his shoulders and narrow hips. His limbs were long and shapely, strange that she should never have noticed the muscle in his arms before. His eyes were green as emeralds, or of *crème de menthe* in a crystal glass and there were tiny flecks of brown and gold surrounding the pupils. She saw those pupils dilate slightly as she leaned forward, deliberately letting the top of her blouse gape open to expose the swell and cleavage of her breasts. Carefully she picked up the enamel box.

'Thank you, Sean,' she whispered hoarsely. 'It's a magnificent gift and I shall treasure it.'

Sean picked up the lewd sketches and slipped them into his art book, hostage to the unspoken pact between them.

'Thank you, Miss East.' His voice was as rough as hers. 'I am so glad you like it.'

It was so exciting to see his agitation that her own loins melted and she felt the familiar pressure build up swiftly in her lower body. With calculated cruelty she stood up, dismissing him to the exquisite torture of anticipation. Instinctively she knew that he had planned it all. No further effort would be required from her, the boy's genius would provide the means and the moment, and it was part of the excitement, waiting to see what he would do.

She did not have long to wait, and though she had expected something unusual, she was surprised by the note he left on her desk.

Dear Miss East,

My son, Sean, tells me that you are having difficulty in procuring suitable lodgings. I do understand how difficult this can be, particularly in the summer when the whole world seems to descend on our little peninsula.

As it happens, I have a furnished cottage on the estate, which at the present time is standing

empty. If you find it suitable, you are welcome to the use of it. The rental would be nominal. I should say a guinea a week would satisfy the estate bookkepper, and you would find the cottage secluded and quiet with the lovely view over the Constantia Berg and False Bay, which will appeal to the artist.

Sean speaks highly of your work, and I look forward to seeing examples of it.

Very sincerely,
Tara Courtney

Clare East was paying five guineas a week for a single squalid room beside the railway tracks at the back of Rondebosch station. When she sold the sapphire brooch for three hundred pounds, which she suspected was a fraction of its real value, Clare had been determined to pay off her accumulated debts. However, as with so many of her good intentions, she closed her mind to the impulse, and instead blew most of the money on a secondhand Morris Minor.

She drove out to Weltevreden the following Saturday morning. Some instinct warned her not to attempt to conceal her Bohemian inclinations, and she and Tara recognized kindred spirits at the very first meeting. Tara sent a driver and one of the estate lorries to fetch her few sticks of furniture and her pile of finished canvases, and personally helped her move into the cottage.

As they worked together, Clare showed Tara a few of the canvases, beginning with the landscape and seascapes. Tara's response was noncommittal, so once again, following her instinct, Clare stripped the cover off one of her abstracts, a cubist arrangement of blues and fiery reds, and held it up for Tara.

'Oh God, it's magnificent!' Tara murmured. 'So fierce and uncompromising. I love it.'

A few evenings later Tara came down the path through the pines, carrying a small basket. Clare was on the stoep of the cottage, sitting bare-footed and cross-legged on a leather cushion with a sketch-pad on her lap.

She looked up and grinned, 'I hoped you'd come,' and Tara flopped down beside her and took a bottle of Shasa's best estate wine, the fifteen-year-old vintage, out of the basket.

They chatted easily while Clare sketched, drinking the wine and watching the sunset over the mountains.

'It's good to find a friend,' Tara said impulsively. 'You can't imagine how lonely it is here sometimes.'

'With all the guests and visitors!' Clare chuckled at her.

'Those aren't real people,' Tara said. 'They are just talking dolls, stuffed with money and their own importance,' and she took a flat silver cigarette case out of the pocket of her skirt, and opened it. It contained rice papers and shredded yellow leaf.

'Do you?' she asked shyly.

'Darling, you have probably saved my life,' Clare exclaimed. 'Roll one for us this instant. I can't wait.'

They passed the joint back and forth, and in the course of their lazy conversation Clare remarked, 'I've been exploring. It's so beautiful here. A little earthly paradise.'

'Paradise can be an awful bore,' Tara smiled.

'I found a waterfall with a little summer-house.'

'That's the picnic spot. None of the servants are allowed there, so if you want to swim in the buff, you don't have to worry. Nobody is going to surprise you.'

Clare had not seen Sean on the estate since she moved into the cottage. She had expected him to come panting to the door on the very first day, and was

His entire body arched and convulsed and for a moment she thought he had gone too far, and she reached down and squeezed him hard and painfully to stop him.

Then as he broke away, shocked by her assault, she turned and swam swiftly to the bank, dragged herself from the pool and ran wet and naked to the summer-house. She snatched up her towel, wiped her face dry and, holding the towel in front of her, turned back to face him as he reached the door of the summer-house behind her. He stood flushed and angry in the doorway, and they stared at each other, both of them panting heavily.

Then slowly she lowered the towel and tossed it over the couch. Swinging her hips deliberately she went to where he stood.

'All right, Master Sean. We know you are worse than useless with a paint brush. Let's see if there isn't anything else we can teach you.'

* * *

He was like a blank canvas on which she could trace her own designs, no matter how bizarre.

There were things from which her other lovers had recoiled, and other acts that she had only imagined and never had the courage to suggest to a partner. At last she felt free of all constraint. It was as though he could read her intentions. She had only to start some new experiment, guide him just part of the way, and he picked it up with a greedy relish that astonished her and carried it through to a conclusion that she had not always fully foreseen, and which sometimes left her stunned.

His strength and confidence increased with every one of their meetings. For the first time she had found something that did not swiftly pall. Gradually her existence seemed to centre around the summer-house beside the pool, and she could not wait to reach it each evening. It required all her self-discipline to keep her hands off him in the art room. She could not trust herself to stand close to him, or to look at him directly during her classes.

Then he initiated a new series of dangerous games. He would remain behind after class, for just a few minutes. It had to be very quick, but risk of discovery enhanced the thrill for both of them.

Once the janitor came in as they were busy and it was so close, so exciting, that she thought she had experienced heart failure at the climax. Sean was standing erect behind her desk, and she was kneeling in front of him. He had taken a handful of her hair and twisted it, holding her face against his lower body.

'I am looking for Miss East,' the janitor said from the doorway. He was a pensioner, almost seventy years of age but out of vanity he refused to wear spectacles. 'Is she here?' he demanded, peering at Sean myopically.

'Hello, Mr Brownlee. Miss East has gone up to the staff common room already,' Sean told him coolly, holding Clare by her hair so she could not pull away from him. The janitor muttered unintelligibly and turned to leave the art room, when to Clare's horror Sean called him back.

'Oh, Mr Brownlee, can I give her a message for you?' he asked, and he and the janitor talked for almost a minute that seemed like all the ages, while she, screened by the desk, was forced to continue.

She knew then, when she paused to think about it, that she was in over her head. She had seen glimpses of the cruelty and violence in him and as the months passed, his physical strength increased with all the sudden blooming of desert grass after rain. The last garlands of puppy fat around his torso were replaced by hard muscle and it seemed that before her eyes his chest broadened and took on a covering of springing dark curls.

Though sometimes she still challenged and fought him, each time he subdued her with greater ease, and then he would force her to perform one of the tricks to which she had originally introduced him, but which he had embroidered with little sadistic twists of his own.

She developed a taste for these humiliations, and she began deliberately to provoke him, until at last she succeeded beyond her expectations. It was in her cottage – the first time they had met there because there was always the danger that Tara would drop in unexpectedly, but by now both of them were reckless.

Clare waited until he was fully ripe, his eyes glazing and his lips pulled back in a rictus of ecstasy, then she twisted and bucked, throwing him off her and she knelt before him and jeered with laughter.

He was angry, but she calmed him down. Then a few minutes later she did it again, and this time she squeezed him painfully, just as she had done that first evening at the pool.

Seconds later she lay dazed, only semi-conscious, sprawled half off the bed, both her eyes rapidly closing with plum-coloured swellings, her lips broken against her teeth, and blood dripping from her nose. Sean stood over her. His face was white as ice, the knuckles of his clenched fists grazed raw, still shaking with fury. He caught her by the tresses of her dark hair and knelt over her while he forced her to take him through her split and bleeding lips. After that there was no question but that he was her master.

Clare missed three days of school, while the worst of the swelling subsided and the bruises faded, and then wore dark sunglasses to her art class. When she passed Sean at his easel, she brushed herself against him like a cat, and he waited behind again after class.

Sean had gone long enough without boasting of his conquest, but Snotty Arbuthnot refused to believe him.

'You've got a screw loose if you think I swallow that,' he taunted. 'You think I'm as green as I'm cabbage-looking, man? You and Marsh Mallows – in your dreams you mean!'

Sean had one alternative to beating him up. 'Okay then, I'll prove it to you.'

'Boy, it had better be good.'

'It will be,' Sean assured him grimly.

The following Saturday afternoon he placed Snotty amongst the protea bushes at the head of the waterfall, and for good measure, lent him the binoculars that his grandmother had given him for his fourteenth birthday.

'Let's take the cushions off the couch,' he suggested to Clare when she came into the summer-house. 'We'll put them on the lawn, there on the bank. It will be warmer in the sun.' She agreed with alacrity.

Snotty Arbuthnot was still almost inarticulate when they met at the school gates the next day.

'Hell, man, I never dreamed that people did that. I mean, *unbelievable*, man! When she – you know – when she actually – well, I thought I was going to die on the spot.'

'Did I tell the truth?' Sean demanded. 'Or did I lie to you?'

'Man, it was super titanic. Boy, Sean, I was painting maps of Africa over my sheets all last night, I kid you not. Will you let me watch again – please, Sean, please?'

'Next time will cost you money,' Sean said. Even though performing to an audience had filled an exhibitionist need, Sean meant it as a refusal, but when Snotty asked without hesitation, 'How much, Sean? Just name your price!' Sean looked at him appraisingly.

It was Shasa's policy to keep his sons on very modest pocket-money, a policy that he had inherited from his own mother. 'They must learn the value of money,' was the family maxim.

Even Snotty whose father was only a surgeon received four times the pittance that was Sean's allowance. The protection racket that Sean ran amongst the juniors, an idea he had picked up from a George Raft movie at the Odeon, more than doubled his income. However, he was always lamentably short of hard cash, and Snotty could afford to pay.

'Two pounds,' Sean suggested. He knew that was exactly his weekly pocket money, but Snotty smiled radiantly. 'You're on, man!'

However, it was only when Snotty actually placed the two crumpled notes in Sean's fist the following Saturday morning that Sean realized the full financial potential.

There was very little chance of Clare realizing that she was on stage. The protea bushes were dense, the noise of the waterfall covered the sound of any involuntary gasps or sniggers, and anyway once she was started, Clare was deaf and blind to all else. Sean appointed Snotty his ticket salesman and organizer. The commission he received ensured Snotty's free admission to each Saturday performance. Reluctantly they decided to restrict admission to ten spectators at any one session, but even that meant a take of eighteen pounds every single week. It lasted almost three months, which was in itself a miracle, for after the first sell-out matinée, the entire senior school was agog.

The word-of-mouth publicity was so good that Snotty was able to demand cash with reservation, and even so his booking sheet was full as far ahead as the beginning of the hols and half the fellows were saving so frantically to try and come up with two pounds that sales at the school tuck shop fell off dramatically. Snotty was trying to get Sean to agree to a mid-week performance, or at least to an increase in the Saturday gate, when the first rumour reached the staff common room.

While passing the windows of one of the change rooms, the history teacher had overheard two satisfied customers discussing the previous Saturday's performance. The headmaster was unable to bring himself to take the report seriously. The whole idea was patently preposterous. Nevertheless, he knew it was his duty to have a discreet word with Miss East, if only to warn her of the revolting tittle-tattle that was circulating.

He went down to the art room after school, late on Friday afternoon, a most inopportune moment. Clare had by this time abandoned all sense of discretion, for her it had become almost a self-destructive frenzy. She and Sean were in the paint store at the back of the art school, and it was some seconds before either of them realized that the headmaster was in the room with them.

* * *

For Shasa everything seemed to happen at once. Sean's expulsion from Bishops was a bombshell that ripped through Weltevreden. When it happened, Shasa was in Johannesburg, and they had to call him out of a meeting with the representatives of the Chamber of Mines to receive the headmaster's telephone call. On the open line the headmaster would give no details, and Shasa flew back to Cape Town immediately and drove directly from the airfield to the school.

Flabbergasted and seething with anger at the stark details the headmaster gave him, Shasa sent the Jaguar roaring around the lower slopes of Table Mountain towards Weltevreden.

From the first he had not approved of the woman who Tara had installed in the cottage. She was all the things he despised, with her great sloppy breasts and silly pretensions which she thought made her *avant-garde* and artistic. Her paintings were atrocious, daubed primary colours and childish perspectives, and she tried to conceal her lack of talent and taste behind Portuguese cigarettes, sandals and skirts of blindingly vivid designs. He decided to deal with her first.

However, she had fled, leaving the cottage in slovenly disarray. Thwarted, Shasa took anger unabated up to the big house and shouted at Tara as he stormed into the hall.

'Where is the little blighter – I'm going to skin his backside for him.'

The other children, all three of them, were peeking over the railing from the second-floor gallery, in a fine fever of vicarious terror. Isabella's eyes were as enormous as one of Walt Disney's fawns.

Shasa saw them and roared up the stair well. 'Back to your own rooms, this instant. That goes for you as well, young lady.' And they ducked and scampered. As an afterthought Shasa bellowed after them, 'And tell that brother of yours I want to see him in the gun room immediately.'

The three of them raced each other down the passage of the nursery wing, each of them determined to be the bearer of the dreaded summons. The gun room was the family equivalent of Tower Green where all executions took place.

Garrick got there first, and pounded on Sean's locked door.

'Pater wants you immediately,' he yelled.

' – in the gun room – ' Michael joined in, and Isabella who had been left far behind at the start, piped up breathlessly, 'He's going to skin your backside!' She was flushed and trembling with eagerness, and she hoped desperately that Sean would show her his bottom after Daddy had carried out his threat. She couldn't imagine what it would look like, and she wondered if Daddy would have the skin made into a floor mat like the skins of the zebras and lions in the gun room. It was probably the most exciting thing that had ever happened in her life.

In the entrance hall Tara was attempting to calm Shasa. She had seen him in a comparable rage only two or three times during their marriage, always when he fancied the family honour or reputation had been compromised. Her efforts were in vain, for he turned on her with his single eye glittering.

'Damn you, woman. This is mostly your fault. It was you who insisted on bringing that whore to live on Weltevreden.'

As Shasa stormed off into the gun room, his voice carried clearly up the stairwell to where Sean was bracing himself to come down and face retribution. Up to that moment Sean had been so confused by the speed of events that he hadn't been thinking clearly. Now, as he descended the stairs, his mind was racing as he prepared his defence. He passed his mother, still standing in the

middle of the chessboard black and white marble squares of the entrance hall floor, and she gave him a strained smile of encouragement.

'I tried to help, darling,' she whispered. They had never been close, but now for once Shasa's rage made them allies.

'Thank you, Mater.'

He knocked on the gun-room door, and opened it cautiously when his father roared. He closed it carefully behind him and advanced to the centre of the lion skin where he halted and stood to attention.

Beatings at Weltevreden followed an established ritual. The riding crops were laid out on the baize gun table, five of them of various lengths, weights and stinging potential. He knew his father would make a show of selecting the correct one for the occasion, and that today it would almost certainly be the long whippy whalebone. Involuntarily he looked to the over-stuffed leather chair beside the fireplace over which he would be asked to drape himself, reaching over to grip the legs of the chair on the far side. His father was an international polo player with wrists like steel springs, his strokes made even the headmaster's seem like a powder puff.

Then deliberately Sean closed his mind against fear and lifted his chin to stare calmly at his father. Shasa was standing in front of the fireplace, hands clasped beside his back, rocking on the balls of his feet.

'You have been fired from Bishops,' he said.

Although the headmaster had not specifically mentioned this fact to Sean himself during his extended diatribe, the news did not come as a complete surprise.

'Yes, sir,' he said.

'I find it hard to believe what I have been told about you. It is true that you were making a spectacle of yourself with this – this woman?'

'Yes, sir.'

'That you were letting your friends watch you?'

'Yes, sir.'

'And charging them money for the privilege?'

'Yes, sir.'

'A pound a head?'

'No, sir.'

'What do you mean – no sir?'

'Two pounds a head, sir.'

'You are a Courtney – what you do reflects directly on every member of this family. Do you realize that?'

'Yes, sir.'

'Don't keep saying that. In the name of all that is holy, how could you do it?'

'She started it, sir. I would never have even thought of it without her.'

Shasa stared at him, and suddenly his rage evaporated. He remembered himself at almost exactly the same age, standing chastened before Centaine. She had not beaten him, but had sent him to a lysol bath and a humiliating medical examination. He remembered the girl, a saucy little harlot only a year or two older than he was, with a shock of sunbleached hair and a sly smile – and he almost smiled himself. She had teased and provoked him, leading him on into folly, and yet he felt a strange nostalgic glow. His first real woman – he might forget a hundred others but never that one.

Sean had seen the anger fade out of his father's eye, and sensed that now was the moment to exploit the change of mood.

'I realize that I have brought scandal on the family, and I know that I have to take my medicine – ' His father would like that, it was one of his sayings, 'Take your medicine like a man.' He saw the further softening of his father's regard. 'I know how stupid I have been, and before my punishment I would just like to say how sorry I am that I have made you ashamed of me.' This was not exactly true, and Sean instinctively knew it. His father was angry with him for being caught out, but deep down he was rather proud of his eldest son's now proven virility.

'The only excuse I have was that I couldn't help myself. She just drove me mad, sir. I couldn't think of anything else but – well, but what she wanted me to do with her.'

Shasa understood entirely. He was still having the same sort of problems at nearly forty – what was it that Centaine said? 'It's the de Thiry blood, we all have to live with it.' He coughed softly, moved by his son's honesty and openness. He was such a fine-looking boy, straight and tall and strong, so handsome and courageous, no wonder the woman had picked on him. He couldn't really be bad, Shasa thought, a bit of a devil perhaps, a little too cocksure, a little too eager for life – but not really bad. 'I mean, if boffing a pretty girl is mortal sin, there is no salvation for any of us,' he thought.

'I'm going to have to beat you, Sean,' he said aloud.

'Yes, sir, I know that.' Not a trace of fear, no whinning. No, damn it, he was a good boy. A son to be proud of.

Shasa went to the gun table and picked up the long whalebone crop, the most formidable weapon in his arsenal, and without being ordered to do so, Sean marched to the armchair and adopted the prescribed position. The first stroke hissed in the air and cracked against his flesh, then suddenly Shasa grunted with disgust and threw the crop on to the gun table.

'The stick is for children – you are no longer a child,' Shasa said. 'Stand up, man.'

Sean could hardly believe his luck. Although the single stroke had stung like a nest of scorpions, he kept an impassive face and made no effort to rub the seat of his pants.

'What are we going to do with you?' his father demanded, and Sean had the sense to remain silent.

'You have to finish matric,' Shasa stated flatly. 'We'll just have to find someone else to take you on.'

This was not as easy as Shasa had anticipated. He tried SACS and Rondebosch Boys and then Wynberg Boys. The headmasters knew about Sean Courtney. He was, for a short while, the best-known schoolboy in the Cape of Good Hope.

In the end he was accepted by Costello's Academy, a cram school that operated out of a dilapidated Victorian mansion on the other side of Rondebosch common, and was not particular about its admissions. Sean arrived for the first day and was gratified to find he was already a celebrity. Unlike the exclusive boys school which he had recenty left, there were girls in the classrooms and academic excellence and moral rectitude were not prerequisites for entrance to Costello's Academy.

Sean had found his spiritual home and he set about sorting out the most promising of his fellow scholars and organizing them into a gang which within a year was virtually running the cram school. His final selection included a half dozen of the most comely and accommodating young ladies on the academy's

roll. As both his father and erstwhile headmaster had noted, Sean was a born leader.

* * *

Manfred De La Rey stood to attention on the reviewing stand. He wore a severe dark pinstrip suit and a black Homburg hat, with a small spray of carnations and green fern in his buttonhole. This was the uniform of a Nationalist cabinet minister.

The police band was playimng a traditional country air '*Die Kaapse Nooi*' – 'The Cape Town girl', to a lively marching beat and the ranks of the police cadets stepped out vigorously, passing the stand with their FN rifles at the slope. As each platoon drew level with the dais, they gave Manfred the eyes right, and he returned the salute.

They made a grand show with their smart blue uniforms and sparkling brasswork catching the white highveld sunlight. These athletic young men, proud and eager, their perfect drill formations, their transparent dedication and patriotism filled Manfred de La Rey with a vast sense of pride.

Manfred stood to attention while the formations wheeled past him and then formed up in review order in the open parade ground facing the stand. The band played a final ruffle of drums and then fell silent. Resplendent in full dress uniform and decorations, the police general stepped to the microphone and in a few crisp sentences introduced the minister, then fell back relinquishing the microphone to Manfred.

Manfred had taken especial care with the preparation of his speech, but before he began he could not prevent himself from glancing aside to where Heidi sat in the front row of honoured guests. This was her day also, and she looked like a blond Valkyrie, her handsome Teutonic features set off by the wide-brimmed hat and its tall decoration of artificial roses. Few women would have the presence and stature to wear it without looking ridiculous, but on Heidi it was magnificent. She caught his eye and smiled at Manfred. 'What a woman,' he thought. 'She deserves to be First Lady in the land, and I will see that she is – one day. Perhaps sooner than she imagines.'

He turned back to the microphone and composed himself. He knew that he was a compelling orator, and he enjoyed the fact that thousands of eyes were concentrated upon him. He felt at ease up here on the dais, relaxed and in total control of himself and those below him.

'You have chosen a life of service to your *Volk* and to your country,' he began. He was speaking in Afrikaans and his reference to the *Volk* was quite natural. The intake of police recruits was almost exclusively from the Afrikaner section of the white community. Manfred De La Rey would not have had it any other way. It was desirable that control of the security forces should be vested solidly in the more responsible elements of the nation, those who understood most clearly the dangers and threats that faced them in the years ahead. Now he began to warn this dedicated body of young men of those dangers.

'It will require all our courage and fortitude to resist the dark forces which are arrayed against us. We must thank our Maker, the Lord God of our fathers, that in the covenant he made with our ancestors on the battlefield of Blood river he has guaranteed us his protection and guidance. It needs only that we remain

constant and true, trusting him, worshipping him, for the way always to be made smooth for our feet to follow.'

He ended his address with the act of faith that had lifted the Afrikaner out of poverty and oppression to his rightful place in the land:

Believe in your God.
Believe in your *Volk*.
Believe in yourself.

His voice, magnified a hundred times, boomed across the parade ground, and he truly felt the divine and benevolent presence very close to him as he looked out upon their shining faces.

Now came the presentation. Out on the field there were shouted orders and the blue ranks came to attention. A pair of officers stepped forward to flank Manfred and one of them carried a velvet-lined tray on which were laid out the medals and awards.

Reading from the list in his hands the second officer called the recipients forward. One at a time they left the ranks, marching briskly, to halt before the imposing figure of Manfred De La Rey. He shook hands with each of them, and then pinned the medals upon their chests.

Then came the moment, and Manfred felt his pride suffocating him. The last of the award-winners was marching towards him across the parade ground, and this one was the tallest and smartest and straightest of them all. In the front rank of guests, Heidi was weeping silently with joy, and she dabbed unashamedly at her tears with a lace handkerchief.

Lothar De La Rey came to a halt in front of his father and stood to rigid attention. Neither of them smiled, their expressions were stern; they stared into each other's eyes, but between them flowed such a current of feeling that made words or smiles redundant.

With an effort Manfred broke that silent rapport, and turned to the police colonel beside him. He offered the sword to Manfred, and the engraved scabbard glistened in silver and gold as Manfred took it from him and turned back to his son.

'The sword of honour,' he said. 'May you wear it with distinction,' and he stepped up to Lothar and attached the beautiful weapon to the blanched belt at his son's waist. They shook hands, both of them solemn still, but the brief grip they exchanged suppressed a lifetime of love and pride and filial duty.

They stood to attention, holding the salute, as the band played the national anthem:

From the blue of our heavens
From the depths of our seas –

And then the parade was breaking up, and young men were swarming forward to find their families in the throng, and there were excited female cries and laughter and long fervent embraces as they met.

Lothar De La Rey stood between his parents, with the sword hanging at his side, and while he shook the hands of an endless procession of well-wishers and made modest responses to their fulsome congratulations, neither Manfred nor Heidi could any longer contain their proud and happy smiles.

'Well done, Lothie!' One of Lothar's fellow cadets got through to him at last,

and the two lads grinned as they shook hands. 'No doubt about who was the best man.'

'I was lucky,' Lothar laughed self-deprecatingly, and changed the subject. 'Have you been told your posting yet, Hannes?'

'*Ja*, man. I'm being sent down to Natal, somewhere on the coast. How about you, perhaps we'll be together?'

'No such luck,' Lothar shook his head. 'They are sending me to some little station in the black townships near Vereeniging – a place called Sharpeville.'

'Sharpeville? Bad luck, man.' Hannes shook his head with mock sympathy. 'I've never heard of it.'

'Nor had I. Nobody has ever heard of it,' said Lothar with resignation. 'And nobody ever will.'

* * *

On 24 August 1958 the prime minister, Johannes Gerhardus Strijdom, 'Lion of the Waterberg', succumbed to heart disease. He had only been at the head of government for four years, but his passing left a wide gap in the granite cliffs of Afrikanerdom, and like termites whose nest has been damaged, they rushed to repair it.

Within hours of the announcement of the prime minister's death, Manfred De La Rey was in Shasa's office, accompanied by two of the senior Cape back-benchers of the National Party.

'We have to try and keep the northerners out,' he announced bluntly. 'We have to get our man in.'

Shasa nodded cautiously. He was still regarded by most of the party as an outsider in the cabinet. His influence in the coming election of a new leader would not be decisive, but he was ready to watch and learn as Manfred laid out their strategy for him.

'They have already made Verwoerd their candidate,' he said. 'All right, he has been in the Senate most of his career and has little experience as an MP, but his reputation is that of a strong man and a clever one. They like the way he has handled the blacks. He has made the name Verwoerd and the word *apartheid* mean the same thing. The people know that under him there will be no mixing of races, that South Africa will always belong to the white man.'

'*Ja*,' agreed one of the others. 'But he is so brutal. There are ways of doing things, ways of saying things that don't offend people. Our own man is strong also. Dönges introduced the Group Areas Bill and the Separate Representation of Voters bill – nobody can accuse him of being a *kafferboetie*, a nigger-lover. But he's got more style, more finesse.'

'The northerners don't want finesse. They don't want a genteel prime minister with sweet lips, they want a man of power, and Verwoerd is a talker, hell that man can talk and he's not afraid of work – and as we all know, anybody whom the English press hates so much can't be all bad.' They laughed, watching Shasa, waiting to see how he would take it. He was still an outsider, their tame *rooinek*, and he would not give them the satisfaction of seeing their raillery score. He smiled easily.

'Verwoerd is canny as an old bull baboon, and quick as a mamba. We'll have to work hard if we are to keep him out,' Shasa agreed.

They worked hard, all of them. Shasa was convinced that despite his record of introducing racially inspired legislation to the House, Dönges was the most moderate and altruistic of the three men who allowed themselves to be persuaded to stand as candidates for the highest office in the land.

As Dr Hendrick Verwoerd himself said, as he accepted nomination, 'When a man receives a desperate call from his people, he does not have the right to refuse.'

On 2 September 1958, the caucus of the National Party met to choose the new leader. The caucus was made up of 178 Nationalist members of parliament and Nationalist senators voting together, and Verwoerd's short term in parliament that had seemed at first to be a weakness, turned out to be an advantage. For years Hendrik Verwoerd had been the leader of the Senate, and had dominated the upper house by the strength of his personality and the powers of his oratory. The senators, docile and compliant, men whose ranks had been enlarged to enable the governing party to force through distasteful legislation, voted for Verwoerd as a block.

Dönges survived the first ballot in which 'Blackie' Swart, the Free State's candidate, was eliminated, but on the second ballot, a straight contest between Verwoerd and Dönges, the northerners closed their ranks and swept Verwoerd into the premiership by ninety-eight votes to seventy-five.

That evening when, as prime minister, Hendrik Frensch Verwoerd broadcast to the nation, he did not try to conceal the fact that his election had been the will of Almighty God. 'He it is who has ordained that I should lead the people of South Africa in this new period of their lives.'

Blaine and Centaine had driven across from Rhodes Hill. It was a family tradition to gather in this room to listen to important broadcasts. Here they had heard speeches and announcements that had shifted the world they knew on its axis: declarations of war and peace, the news of the evil mushroom clouds planted in the skies above Japanese cities, the death of kings and beloved rulers, the accession of a queen, to all these and others they had listened together in the blue drawing-room of Weltevreden.

Now they sat quietly as the high-pitched, nervously strained but articulate voice of the new prime minister came to them, jarring when he repeated platitudes and well-worn themes.

'No one need doubt for a single moment that it will always be my aim to uphold the democratic institutions of our country, for they are the most treasured possessions of western civilization,' Verwoerd told them, 'and the right of people with other convictions to express their views will be maintained.'

'Just as long as those views are passed by the government board of censors, the synod of the Dutch Reformed Church and the caucus of the National Party,' Blaine murmured, a sarcastic qualification for him, and Centaine nudged him.

'Do be quiet, Blaine, I want to listen.'

Verwoerd had moved on to another familiar subject, how the country's enemies had deliberately misconstrued his racial policies. It was not he who had coined the word *apartheid*, but other dedicated and brilliant minds had foreseen the necessity of allowing all the races of a complicated and fragmented society to develop towards their own separate potential. 'As the minister of Bantu affairs, since 1950 it has been my duty to give cohesion and substance to this policy, the only policy which will allow full opportunity for each and every group within its own racial community. In the years ahead, we will not deviate one inch from this course.'

Tara had been tapping her foot restlessly as she listened, but now she sprang to her feet. 'I'm sorry,' she blurted. 'I'm feeling a little queasy. I must get a breath of fresh air on the terrace – ' and she hurried from the room. Centaine glanced sharply at Shasa, but he smiled and shrugged, was about to make a light comment, when the voice on the radio riveted them all once more.

'I come now to one of the most, if not the most sacred ideal of our people,' the high-pitched voice filled the room, 'and that is the formation of the Republic. I know how many of the English-speaking South Africans listening to me tonight are filled with a sense of loyalty to the British Crown. I know also that this divided loyalty has prevented them from always dealing with the real issues on their merits. The ideal of monarchy has too often been a divisive factor in our midst, separating Afrikaners and English-speakers when they should have been united. In a de-colonizing world, the black man and his newly fledged nations are beginning to emerge as a threat to the South Africa we know and love. Afrikaner and Englishman can no longer afford to stand apart, but must now link arms as allies, secure and strong in the ideal of a new white republic.'

'My God,' Blaine breathed, 'that's a new line. It used always to be the Afrikaner Republic exclusively, and nobody took it seriously, least of all the Afrikaners. But this time he is serious, and he has started something that is going to raise a stink. I remember all too well the controversy over the flag, back in the 1920s. That will seem like a love feast compared to the idea of a republic – ' he broke off to listen as Verwoerd ended:

'Thus I give you my assurance that from now on the sacred ideal of Republic will be passionately pursued.'

When the prime minister finished speaking, Shasa crossed the room and switched off the radio; then he turned and stood with his hands thrust deeply into his pockets, and his shoulders hunched as he studied their faces. They were all of them subdued and shaken. For one hundred and fifty years the country had been British, and there was a pride and a vast sense of security in that state. Now it was to change, and they were afraid. Even Shasa felt strangely bereft and uncertain.

'He doesn't mean it. It's just another sop for his own people. They are always ranting about the republic,' Centaine said hopefully, but Blaine shook his head.

'We don't know this man very well yet. We only know what he wrote when he was editor of *Transvaler*, and we know with what vigour and determination he has set about segregating our society. There is one other thing we have learned about him. He is a man who means exactly what he says, and who will let nothing stand in his way.' He reached across and took Centaine's hand. 'No, my heart. You are wrong. He means it.'

They both looked up at Shasa, and Centaine asked for both of them, 'What will you do, *chéri*?'

'I am not sure that I will have any choice. They say he brooks no opposition, and I opposed him. I lobbied for Dönges. I may not be on the list when he announces his cabinet on Monday.'

'It will be hard to move to the back bench again,' Blaine remarked.

'Too hard,' Shasa nodded. 'And I will not do it.'

'Oh *chéri*,' Centaine cried. 'You would not resign your seat – after all we have sacrificed, after all our hard work and hopes.'

'We'll know on Monday,' Shasa shrugged, trying not to let them see how bitterly disappointed he was. He had held true power for too short a time, just

long enough to learn to enjoy the taste of it. He knew, furthermore, that there was so much he had to offer his country, so many of his efforts almost ready for harvesting. It would be hard to watch them wither and die with his own ambitions, before he had even tasted the first sweets, but Verwoerd would sack him from his cabinet. He could not doubt it for a moment.

'"If you can meet with triumph and disaster",' Centaine quoted, and then laughed gaily, with only the barest tremor in it. 'Now, *chéri*, let's open a bottle of champagne. It's the only way to treat these two imposters of Kipling'.'

Shasa entered his office in the House, and looked around it regretfully. It had been his for five years, and now he would have to pack up his books and paintings and furniture; the panelling and carpeting he would leave as a gift to the nation. He had hoped to make a larger bequest than that, and he grimaced and went to sit behind his desk for the last time and try to assess where he had erred and what he could have done if he had been allowed. The telephone on his desk rang, and he picked it up before his secretary in the outer office could reach it.

'This is the prime minister's secretary,' the voice told him, and for a moment he thought of the dead man and not his successor.

'The prime minister would like to see you as soon as is convenient.'

'I will come right away, of course,' Shasa replied, and as he replaced the receiver he thought, 'So he personally wants to have the pleasure of chopping me down.'

Verwoerd kept him waiting only ten minutes and then rose from behind his desk to apologize as Shasa entered his office. 'Forgive me. It has been a busy day,' and Shasa smiled at the understatement. His smile was not forced, for Verwoerd was displaying all his enormous charm, his voice soft and lulling, unlike the higher harsher tone of his public utterances, and he actually came around the desk and took Shasa's arm in an avuncular grip. 'But, of course, I had to speak to you, as I have spoken to all the members of my new cabinet.'

Shasa started so that his pulled his arm out of the other man's grip, and they turned to face each other.

'I am keeping the portfolio of Mines and Industry open, and of course there is no man better qualified for the job than you. I have liked your presentations to the old cabinet. You know what you are talking about.'

'I cannot pretend not to be surprised, Prime Minister,' Shasa told him quietly, and Verwoerd chuckled.

'It is good to be unpredictable at times.'

'Why?' Shasa asked. 'Why me?' Verwoerd cocked his head on the side, a characteristic gesture of interrogation, but Shasa insisted, 'I know you value straight talk, Prime Minister, so I will say it. You have no reason to like me or to consider me an ally.'

'That is true,' Verwoerd agreed. 'But I don't need sycophants. I have enough of those already. What I have considered is that the job you are doing is vital to the eventual well-being of our land, and that there is no one who could do it better. I am sure we will learn to work together.'

'Is that all, Prime Minister?'

'You have mentioned that I like to talk straight. Very well, that is not all. You probably heard me begin my premiership with an appeal for a drawing together of the two sections of our white population, an appeal to Boer and Briton to forget old worn-out antipathy and side by side to build the republic.

How would it look if with the next breath I fired the only Englishman in my government?'

They both laughed, and then Shasa shook his head. 'On the matter of the Republic I will oppose you,' he warned, and for a moment saw through a chink the cold and monolithic ego of a man who would never bow to the contrary view, and then the chink was closed and Verwoerd chuckled.

'Then I will have to convince you that you are wrong. In the meantime you will be my conscience – what is the name of the character in the Disney story?'

'Which one?'

'The story of the puppet – Pinocchio, is it? What was the name of the cricket?'

'Jiminy Cricket,' Shasa told him.

'Yes, in the meantime you will be my Jiminy Cricket. Do you accept the task?'

'We both know it is my duty, Prime Minister.' As Shasa said, he thought cynically, 'Isn't it remarkable that once ambition has dictated, duty so readily concurs?'

* * *

They were dining out that night, but Shasa went to Tara's room to tell her the news as soon as he had dressed.

She watched him in the mirror as he explained his reasons for accepting the appointment. Her expression was solemn but her voice had a brittle edge of contempt in it as she said, 'I am delighted for you. I know that is what you want, and I know that you will be so busy you will not even notice that I am gone.'

'Gone?' he demanded.

'Our bargain, Shasa. We agreed that I could go away for a while when I felt the need. Of course, I will return – that was also part of our bargain.'

He looked relieved. 'Where will you go – and for how long?'

'London,' she replied. 'And I should be away several months. I want to attend a course on archaeology at London University.' She tried to hide it from him, but she was wildly, deliriously excited. She had only heard from Molly that afternoon, just after the new cabinet had been announced. Molly had a message. Moses had at last sent for her, and she had already booked passage for Benjamin, Miriam and herself on the *Pendennis Castle* to Southampton. She would take the child to meet his father.

The mailship sailing was an exciting event in which the citizens of the mother city, of whatever station in life, could join gaily. The deck was crowded and noisy. Paper streamers joined the tall ship to the quayside with a web of colour that fluttered in the south-easter. A coon band on the dock vied with the ship's band high up on the promenade deck, and the old Cape favourite 'Alabama' was answered by 'God be with you till we meet again'.

Shasa was not there. He had flown up to Walvis Bay to deal with some unforeseen problem at the canning factory. Nor was Sean, he was writing exams at Costello's Academy, but Blaine and Centaine brought the other three children down to the docks to see Tara off on her voyage.

They stood in a small family group, surrounded by the crowd, each of them

holding a paper streamer and waving up at Tara on the first class 'A' deck. As the gap between the quay and the ship's side opened, the foghorns boomed, and the paper streamers parted and floated down to settle on the dark waters of the inner harbour. The tugs pushed the great bows around, until they lined up with the harbour entrance and under the stern the gigantic propeller chopped the water into foam and drove her out into Table Bay.

Tara ran lightly up the companionway to her stateroom. She had protested only mildly when Shasa had insisted that she cancel her original bookings in tourist and travel first class. 'My dear, there are bound to be people we know on board. What would they think of my wife travelling steerage?'

'Not steerage, Shasa – tourist.'

'Everything below "A" deck is steerage,' he had replied, and now she was glad of his snobbery for the stateroom was a private place where she could have Ben all to herself. It would have excited curiosity if she had been seen with a coloured child on the public deck. As Shasa had pointed out, there were watching eyes on board and the reports would have flown back to Shasa like homing pigeons. However, Miriam Afrika had good-naturedly agreed to wear a servant's livery and to act out the subterfuge of being Tara's maid during the voyage. Her husband had reluctantly let her go with Tara to England, despite the disruption to his own household. Tara had compensated him generously and Miriam had come aboard with the child registered as her own.

Tara hardly left her stateroom during the entire voyage, declining the captain's offer to join his table and shunning the cocktail parties and fancy-dress dance. She never tired of being with Moses' son, her love was a hunger that could never be appeased and even when, exhausted by her attentions, Benjamin fell asleep in his cot, Tara hovered over him constantly. 'I love you,' she whispered to him, 'best in the world after your Daddy,' and she did not think of the other children, not even Michael. She ordered all their meals to be sent up to her suite, and ate with Benjamin, almost jealously taking over his care from Miriam. Only late at night with the greatest reluctance did she let her carry the child away to the tourist cabin on the deck below.

The days sped by swiftly and, at last, holding Benjamin's hand she stepped off the gangplank to the boat train in Southampton docks for the ride up to London.

Again at Shasa's insistence, she had taken the suite at the Dorchester overlooking the park that the family always used, with a single room at the back for Miriam and the baby for which she requested a separate bill and paid in cash out of her own pocket so that Shasa would have no record of it on her bank statement.

There was a message from Moses waiting for her at the porter's desk when she registered. She recognized the handwriting. She opened the envelope the moment she entered the suite, and felt the cold slide of disappointment. He wrote very formally:

Dear Tara

I am sorry I was not able to meet you. However, it is necessary for me to attend important talks in Amsterdam with our friends. I will contact you immediately on my return.

Yours sincerely,
Moses Gama.

She was thrown into black despair by the tone of the letter and the dashing of her expectations. Without Miriam and the child she would have despaired.

However, they passed the waiting days in the parks and zoos, and in long walks along the river bank and through London's fascinating alleys and convoluted streets. She shopped for Benjamin at Marks and Spencer and C & A, avoiding Harrods and Selfridges, for those were Shasa's haunts.

Tara registered at the university for the course in African archaeology. She did not trust Shasa not to check that she had done so. In accordance with Shasa's other expectations she even dressed in her most demure twin set and pearls and took a cab up to Trafalgar Square to make a courtesy call on the high commissioner at South Africa House. She could not avoid his invitation to lunch and had to show a bright face during a meal whose menu and wine-list and fellow guests could have been taken straight from a similar gathering at Weltevreden. She listened to the editor of the *Daily Telegraph*, who sat beside her, but kept glancing out of the windows at Nelson's tall column, and longed to be as free as the cloud of pigeons that circled it. Her duty done, she escaped at last, only just in time to get back to the Dorchester and give Ben his bath.

She had bought him a plastic tugboat at Hamley's toy shop which was a great success, and Ben sat in the bath and chuckled with delight as the tugboat circled him.

Tara was laughing and drying her hands when Miriam came through from the lounge to the bathroom.

'There is somebody to see you, Tara.'

'Who is it?' Tara demanded without rising from where she knelt beside the bath.

'He wouldn't give his name.' Miriam kept a straight face. 'I will finish bathing Ben.'

Tara hesitated, she did not want to waste a minute away from her son. 'Oh all right,' she agreed, and with the towel in her hand she went through to the lounge, and stopped abruptly in the doorway.

The shock was so intense that her face drained of blood and she swayed giddily and had to snatch at the door jamb to steady herself.

'Moses,' she whispered, staring at him.

He wore a long tan-coloured trenchcoat, and the epauletted shoulders were spattered with rain drops. The coat seemed to accentuate his height and the breadth of his shoulders. She had forgotten the grandeur of his presence. He did not smile, but regarded her with that steady heart-checking stare of his.

'Moses,' she said again, and took a faltering step towards him. 'Oh God, you'll never know how slowly the years have passed since last I saw you.'

'Tara.' His voice thrilled every fibre of her being. 'My wife,' and he held out his arms to her.

She flew to him and he enfolded her and held her close. She pressed her face to his chest and clung to him, inhaling the rich masculine smell of his body, as warm and exciting as the herby smell of the African noonday. For many seconds neither of them moved or spoke except for the involuntary tremors that shook Tara's body and the little moaning sound she made in her throat.

Then gently he held her off and took her face between his hands and lifted it to look into her eyes.

'I have thought about you every day,' he said, and suddenly she was weeping. The tears streamed down her cheeks, and into the corners of her mouth, so that when he kissed her, their metallic salt mingled with the slick taste of his saliva.

Miriam brought Benjamin out to them, clean and dry and dressed in his new blue pyjamas. He regarded his father solemnly.

'I greet you, my son,' Moses whispered. 'May you grow as strong and beautiful as the land of your birth,' and Tara thought that her heart might stop with the pride and sheer joy of seeing them together for the first time.

Though the colour of their skin differed, Benjamin was caramel and chocolate cream while Moses was amber and African bronze, Tara could see the resemblance in the shape of their heads and the set of jaw and brow. They had the same wide-spaced eyes, the same noses and lips, and to her they were the two most beautiful beings in her existence.

* * *

Tara kept the suite at the Dorchester, for she knew that Shasa would contact her there and that any invitations from South Africa House or correspondence from the university would be addressed to her at the hotel. But she moved into Moses' flat off the Bayswater Road.

The flat belonged to the Ethiopian emperor, and was kept for the use of his diplomatic staff. However, Haile Selassie had placed it at Moses Gama's disposal for as long as he needed it. It was a large rambling apartment, with dark rooms and a strange mixture of furnishings, well-worn Western sofas and easy chairs, with hand-woven woollen Ethiopian rugs and wall hangings. The ornaments were African artefacts, carved ebony statuettes, crossed two-handed broadswords, bronze Somali shields and Coptic Christian crosses and icons, in native silver studded with semi-precious stones.

They slept on the floor, in the African manner, on thin hard mattresses filled with coir. Moses even used a small wooden head stool as a pillow, though Tara could not accustom herself to it. Benjamin slept with Miriam in the bedroom at the end of the passage.

Love-making was as naturally part of Moses Gama's life as eating or drinking or sleeping, and yet his skills and his consideration of her needs were an endless source of wonder and delight to her. She wanted more than anything else in life to bear him another child. She tried consciously to open the mouth of her womb, willing it to expand like a flower bud to accept his seed, and long after he had fallen asleep she lay with her thighs tightly crossed and her knees raised so as not to spill a precious drop, imagining herself a sponge for him, or a bellows to draw his substance up deeply into herself.

Yet the times they were alone were far too short for Tara, and it irked her that the flat seemed always filled with strangers. She hated to share Moses with them, wanting him all for herself. He understood this, and when she had been churlish and sulky in the presence of others, he reminded her sternly.

'I am the struggle, Tara. Nothing, nobody, comes ahead of that. Not even my own longings, not my life itself can come before my duty to the cause. If you take me, then you make that same sacrifice.'

To moderate the severity of his words, he lifted her in his arms and carried her to the mattress, and made love to her until she sobbed and rolled her head from side to side, delirious with the power and wonder of it, and then he told her, 'You have as much of me as any person will ever have. Accept that without complaint, and be grateful for it, for we never know when one of us may be called to sacrifice it all. Live now, Tara, live for our love this day, for there may never be a tomorrow.'

'Forgive me, Moses,' she whispered. 'I have been so small and petty. I will not disappoint you again.'

So she put aside her jealousy and joined in his work, and looked upon the men and women who came to the Bayswater Road no longer as strangers and interlopers, but as comrades – part of their life and the struggle. Then she could realize what a fascinating slice of humanity they represented. Most of them were Africans, tall Kikuyus from Kenya, Jomo Kenyatta's young men, the warriors of Mau Mau, once even the little man with a great heart and brain, Hastings Banda, spent an evening with them. There were Shonas and Shangaans from Rhodesia, Xhosas and Zulus from her own South Africa and even a few of Moses' own tribe from Ovamboland. They had formed a fledgling freedom association which they called South West African Peoples' Organization, and they wanted Moses' patronage, which he gave them willingly. Tara found it difficult to think of Moses as belonging to a single tribe, all of Africa was his fief, he spoke most of their separate languages and understood their specific fears and aspirations. If ever the word 'African' described one man, that man was Moses Gama.

There were others who came to the flat in Bayswater Road; Hindus and Moslems and men of the north lands, from Ethiopia and Sudan and Mediterranean Africa, some of them still living under colonial tyranny, others newly liberated and eager to help their suffering fellow Africans.

There were white men and women also, speaking in the accents of Liverpool and the north country, of the coal mines or the mills; and other white men and women whose English was halting and laboured, but whose hearts were fierce, patriots from Poland and East Germany and the Soviet bloc, some from Mother Russia herself. All had a common love of freedom and hatred of the oppressor.

From the unlimited letter of credit that Shasa had given her to his London bank, Tara filled the flat with good food and liquor, taking a vindictive pleasure in paying out Shasa's money for the very best fillet steak and choice lamb, for turbot and sole and lobster.

For the first time she derived pleasure from ordering Burgundies and clarets of the best vintages and noblest estates, about which she had listened to Shasa lecturing his dinner guests so pompously. She laughed delightedly when she watched the enemies of all Shasa stood for, the ones called the 'bringers of darkness', quaffing his wines as though they were Coca-Cola.

She had not prepared food for a long time, the chef at Weltevreden would have been mortified if she had attempted to do so, and now she enjoyed working with some of the other women in the kitchen. The Hindu wives showed her how to make wondrous curries and the Arab women prepared lamb in a dozen exciting ways, so that every meal was a feast and an adventure. From the impecunious students to the heads of revolutionary governments and the leaders in exile of captive nations, they came to talk and plan, to eat and drink and exchange ideas even more heady than the wines that Tara poured for them.

Always Moses Gama was at the centre of the excitement. His vast brooding presence seemed to inspire and direct their energies, and Tara realized that he was making bonds, forging loyalties and friendships to carry the struggle onwards to the next plateau. She was immensely proud of him, and humbly proud of her own small part in the grand enterprise. For the very first time in her life she felt useful and important. Until the present time she had spent her life in trivial and meaningless activity. By making her a part of his work, Moses

had made her a whole person at last. Impossible as it seemed, during those enchanted months her love for him was multiplied a hundredfold.

Sometimes they travelled together, when Moses was invited to speak to some important group, or to meet representatives of a foreign power. They went to Sheffield and Oxford to address elements from opposite ends of the political spectrum, the British Communist Party and the association of Conservative students. One weekend they flew to Paris to meet with officials from the French directorate of foreign affairs and a month later they even went to Moscow together. Tara travelled on her British passport and spent the days sightseeing with her Russian Intourist guide while Moses was closeted in secret talks in the offices of the fourth directorate overlooking the Gorky Prospekt.

When they returned to London, Moses and some of his exiled fellow South Africans organized a protest rally in Trafalgar Square directly opposite the imposing edifice of South Africa House, with its frieze of animal head sculptures and colonnaded front entrance. Tara could not join the demonstration, for Moses warned her that they would be photographed with telescopic lenses from the building, and forbade her to expose herself to the racist agents. She was far too valuable to the cause. Instead she struck upon a delightfully ironic twist, and telephoned the high commissioner. He invited her to lunch again. She watched from his own office, sitting in one of his easy chairs in the magnificent stinkwood-panelled room, while below her in the square Moses stood beneath a banner 'Apartheid is a crime against Humanity' and made a speech to five hundred demonstrators. Her only regret was that the wind and the traffic prevented her hearing his words. He repeated them to her that evening as they lay together on the hard mattress on the floor of their bedroom, and she thrilled to every single word.

One lovely English spring morning they walked arm in arm through Hyde Park, and Benjamin threw crumbs to the ducks in the Serpentine.

They watched the riders in Rotten Row, and admired the show of spring blooms in the gardens as they passed them on their way up to Speakers' Corner.

On the lawns the holiday crowds were taking advantage of the unseasonable sunshine, and many of the men were shirtless while the girls had pulled their skirts high on their thighs as they lolled on the grass. The lovers were entwined shamelessly, and Moses frowned. Public displays of this kind offended his African morality.

As they arrived at Speakers' Corner, they passed the militant homosexuals and Irish Republicans on their upturned milk crates and went to join the group of black speakers. Moses was instantly recognized, he had becomed a well-known figure in these circles, and half a dozen men and women hurried to meet him, all of them were coloured South African expatriates, and all of them were eager to give him the news.

'They have acquitted them – '

'They have set them all free – '

'Nokwe, Makgatho, Nelson Mandela – they are all free!'

'Judge Rumpff found every one of them not guilty of treason – '

Moses Gama stopped dead in his tracks and glowered at them as they surrounded him, dancing joyfully, and laughing in the pale English sunlight, these sons and daughters of Africa.

'I do not believe it,' Moses snarled angrily, and somebody shoved a crumpled copy of the *Observer* at him.

'Here! Read it! It's true.'

Moses snatched the newspaper from him. He read swiftly, scanning the front-page articles. His face was set and bleak, and then abruptly he thrust the paper into his pocket and shouldered his way out of the group. He strode away down the tarmac pathway, a tall brooding figure and Tara had to run with Benjamin to catch up with him.

'Moses, wait for us.'

He did not even glance at her, but his fury was evident in the set of his shoulders and the fixed snarl on his lips.

'What is it, Moses, what has made you so angry? We should rejoice that our friends are free. Please speak to me, Moses.'

'Don't you understand?' he demanded. 'Are you so witless that you do not see what has happened?'

'I don't – I'm sorry – '

'They have come out of this with enormous prestige, especially Mandela. I had thought that he would spend the rest of his life in prison, or better still, that they would have dropped him through the trap of the gallows.'

'Moses!' Tara was shocked. 'How can you speak like that? Nelson Mandela is your comrade.'

'Nelson Mandela is my rival to the death,' he told her flatly. 'There can only be one ruler in South Africa, either him or me.'

'I do not understand.'

'You understand very little, woman. It is not necessary that you should. All you must learn to do is obey me.'

She annoyed and irritated him with her perpetual moods and jealousies. He found it more difficult each day to accept her cloying adoration. Her soft pale flesh had begun to revolt him and each time it took more of an effort to feign passion. He longed for the day that he could be rid of her – but that day was not yet.

'I am sorry, Moses, if I have been stupid and made you angry.'

They walked on in silence, but when they came back to the Serpentine, Tara asked diffidently, 'What will you do now?'

'I have to lay claim to my rightful place as the leader of the people. I cannot allow Mandela to have a clear field.'

'What will you do?' she repeated.

'I must go back – back to South Africa.'

'Oh, no!' she gasped. 'You cannot do that. It is too dangerous, Moses. They will seize you the minute you set foot on South African soil.'

'No,' he shook his head. 'Not if I have your help. I will remain underground, but I will need you.'

'Of course. Whatever you want – but, my darling, what will you hope to achieve by taking such a dreadful risk?'

With an effort he put aside his anger, and looked down at her.

'Do you remember where we first met, the first time we spoke to each other?'

'In the corridors of the houses of parliament,' she answered promptly. 'I will never forget.'

He nodded. 'You asked me what I was doing there, and I replied that I would tell you one day. This is the day.'

He spoke for another hour, softly, persuasively, and as she listened her emotions rose and fell, alternating between a fierce joy and a pervading dread.

'Will you help me?' he asked at the end.

'Oh, I am so afraid for you.'

'Will you do it?'

'There is nothing I can deny you,' she whispered. 'Nothing.'

* * *

A week later Tara telephoned Centaine at Rhodes Hill and was surprised by the clarity of the connection. She spoke to each of the children in turn. Sean was monosyllabic and seemed relieved to surrender the telephone to Garry, who was solemn and pedantic, in his first year at business school. It was like talking to a little old man, and Garry's single topic of original news was the fact that his father had at last allowed him to start work part-time, as an office boy at Courtney Mining and Finance. 'Pater is paying me two pounds ten shillings a day,' he announced proudly. 'And soon I am to have my own office with my name on the door.'

When his turn came to speak to her, Michael read her a poem of his own, about the sea and the gulls. It was really very good, so her enthusiasm was genuine. 'I love you so much,' he whispered. 'Please come home soon.'

Isabella was petulant. 'What present are you going to bring me?' she demanded. 'Daddy bought me a gold locket with a real diamond – ' and Tara was guiltily relieved when her daughter passed the telephone back to Centaine.

'Don't worry about Bella,' Centaine soothed her. 'We've had a little confrontation and mademoiselle's feathers are a wee bit ruffled.'

'I want to buy a coming-home present for Shasa,' Tara told her. 'I have found the most gorgeous medieval altar that has been converted into a chest. I thought it would be just perfect for his cabinet office at the House. Won't you measure the length of the wall on the right of his desk, under the Pierneef paintings – I want to be certain it will fit in there.'

Centaine sounded a little puzzled. It was unusual for Tara to show any interest in antique furniture. 'Of course, I will measure it for you,' she agreed dubiously. 'But remember Shasa has very conservative tastes – I wouldn't choose anything too – ah – ' she hesitated delicately, not wanting to denigrate her daughter-in-law's taste, 'too obvious or flamboyant.'

'I'll phone you tomorrow evening.' Tara did not acknowledge the advice. 'You can read me the measurements then.'

Two days later Moses accompanied her when she returned to the antique dealer in Kensington High Street. Together they made meticulous measurements of both the exterior and interior of the altar. It was truly a splendid piece of work. The lid was inlaid with mosaic of semi-precious stones while effigies of the apostles guarded the four corners. They were carved in ivory and rare woods and decorated with gold leaf. The panels depicted scenes of Christ's agony, from the scourging to the crucifixion. Only after careful examination did Moses nod with satisfaction.

'Yes, it will do very well.' Tara gave the dealer a bank draft for six thousand pounds.

'Price is Shasa's yardstick of artistic value,' she explained to Moses while they waited for his friends to come and collect the piece. 'At six thousand pounds he won't be able to refuse to have it in his office.'

The dealer was reluctant to hand the chest over to the three young black men who arrived in an old van in response to Moses' summons.

'It is a very fragile piece of craftsmanship,' he protested. 'I would feel a lot happier if you entrusted the packing and shipping to a firm of experts. I can recommend – '

'Please don't worry,' Tara reassured him. 'I will accept full responsibility from now on.'

'It's such a beautiful thing,' the dealer said. 'I would simply curl up and die if it were even scratched.' He wrung his hands piteously as they carried it out and loaded it into the back of the van. A week later Tara flew back to Cape Town.

The day after the crate cleared Customs in Cape Town docks, Tara held a small, but select, surprise party in Shasa's cabinet office to present him with her gift. The prime minister was unable to attend, but three cabinet ministers came and with Blaine and Centaine and a dozen others crowded into Shasa's suite to drink Bollinger champagne and admire the gift.

Tara had removed the rosewood Georgian sofa table that had previously stood against the panelled wall, and replaced it with the chest. Shasa had some idea of what was in store. Centaine had dropped a discreet hint, and of course the charge had appeared on his latest statement from Lloyds Bank.

'Six thousand pounds!' Shasa had been appalled. 'That's the price of a new Rolls.' What on earth was the damned woman thinking of? It was ridiculous buying him extravagant gifts for which he paid himself; knowing Tara's tastes, he dreaded his first view of it.

It was covered by a Venetian lace cloth when Shasa entered his office, and he eyed it apprehensively as Tara said a few pretty words about how much she owed him, what a fine and generous husband and what a good father he was to her children.

Ceremoniously Tara lifted the lace cloth off the chest and there was an involuntary gasp of admiration from everyone in the room. The ivory figurines had mellowed to a soft buttery yellow and the gold leaf had the royal patina of age upon it. They crowded closer to examine it, and Shasa felt his unreasonable antipathy towards the gift cool swiftly. He would never have guessed that Tara could show such taste. Instead of the garish monstrosity he had expected, this was a truly great work of art, and if his instinct was correct, which it almost always was, it was also a first-class investment.

'I do hope you like it?' Tara asked him with unusual timidity.

'It's magnificent,' he told her heartily.

'You don't think it should be under the window?'

'I like it very well just where you put it,' he answered her, and then dropped his voice so nobody else could overhear. 'Sometimes you surprise me, my dear. I'm truly very touched by your thoughtfulness.'

'You too were kind and thoughtful to let me go to London,' she replied.

'I could skip the meeting this afternoon and get home early this evening,' he suggested, glancing down at her bosom.

'Oh, I wouldn't want you to do that,' she answered quickly, surprised by her own physical revulsion at the idea. 'I am certain to be exhausted by this afternoon. It's such a strain – '

'So our bargain still stands – to the letter?' he asked.

'I think that it is wiser that way,' she told him. 'Don't you?'

* * *

Moses flew from London directly to Delhi, and had a series of friendly meetings with Indira Gandhi, the president of the Indian Congress Party. She gave Moses the warmest encouragement and promises of help and recognition.

At Bombay he went on board a Liberian-registered tramp steamer with a Polish captain. Moses signed on as a deckhand for the voyage to Lourenço Marques in Portuguese Mozambique. The tramp called in at Victoria in the Seychelles Islands to discharge a cargo of rice and then sailed direct for Africa.

In the harbour of Lourenço Marques Moses said goodbye to the jovial Polish skipper and slipped ashore in the company of five members of the crew who were bound for the notorious red-light area of the seaport. His contact was waiting for him in a dingy night club. The man was a senior member of the underground freedom organization which was just beginning its armed struggle against Portuguese colonial rule.

They ate the huge juicy Mozambique prawns for which the club was famous, and drank the tart green wine of Portugal while they discussed the advancement of the struggle and promised each other the support and assistance of comrades.

When they had eaten, the agent nodded to one of the bar girls and she came to the table and after a few minutes of arch conversation took Moses' hand and led him through the rear door of the bar to her room at the end of the yard.

The agent joined them there after a few minutes and while the girl kept watch at the door, to warn them of a surprise raid by the colonial police, the man handed Moses the travel documents he had prepared for him, a small bundle of second-hand clothing, and sufficient escudos to see him across the border and as far as the Witwatersrand gold-mines.

The next afternoon Moses joined a group of a hundred or more labourers at the railway station. Mozambique was an important source of labour for the gold-mines, and the wages earned by her citizens made a large contribution to the economy. Authentically dressed and in possession of genuine papers, Moses was indistinguishable from any other in the shuffling line of workers and he went aboard the third-class railway coach without even a glance from the uninterested white Portuguese official.

They left the coast in the late afternoon, climbed out of the muggy tropical heat and entered the hilly forests of the lowveld to approach the border post of Komatipoort early the following morning. As the coach rumbled slowly over the low iron bridge, it seemed to Moses that they were crossing not a river but a great ocean. He was filled with a strange blend of dismay and joy, of dread and anticipation. He was coming home – and yet home was a prison for him and his people.

It was strange to hear Afrikaans spoken again, guttural and harsh, but made even more ugly to Moses' ear because it was the language of oppression. The officials here were not the indolent and slovenly Portuguese. Dauntingly brisk and efficient, they examined his papers with sharp eyes, and questioned him brusquely in that hated language. However, Moses had already masked himself in the protective veneer of the African. His face was expressionless and his eyes blank, just a black face among millions of black faces, and they passed him through.

Swart Hendrick did not recognize him when he slouched into the general dealer's store in Drake's Farm township. He was dressed in ill-fitting hand-me-downs and wore an old golfing cap pulled down over his eyes. Only when he straightened up to his full height and lifted the cap did Swart Hendrick start and exclaim in amazement, then seized his arm and, casting nervous glances

over his shoulder, hustled his brother through into the little cubicle at the back of the store that he used as an office.

'They are watching this place,' he whispered agitatedly. 'Is your head full of fever, that you walk in here in plain daylight?' Only when they were safely in the locked office and he had recovered from the shock, did he embrace Moses. 'A part of my heart has been missing, but is now restored.'

He shouted over the rhino board partition wall of his office, 'Raleigh, come here immediately, boy!' and his son came to peer in astonishment at his famous uncle and then kneel before him, lift one of Moses' feet and place it on his own head in the obeisance to a great chief. Smiling, Moses lifted him to his feet and embraced him, questioned him about his schooling and his studies and then let him respond to Swart Hendrick's order.

'Go to your mother. Tell her to prepare food. A whole chicken and plenty of maize meal porridge, and a gallon of strong tea with plenty of sugar. Your uncle is hungry.'

They stayed locked in Swart Hendrick's office until late that night, for there was much to discuss. Swart Hendrick made a full report of all their business enterprises, the state of the secret mineworkers' union, the organization of their Buffaloes, and then gave him all the news of their family and close friends.

When at last they left the office, and crossed to Swart Hendrick's house, he took Moses' arm and led him to the small bedroom which was always ready for his visits, and as he opened the door, Victoria rose from the low bed on which she had been sitting patiently. She came to him and, as the child had done, prostrated herself in front of him and placed his foot upon her head.

'You are my sun,' she whispered. 'Since you went away I have been in darkness.'

'I sent one of the Buffaloes to fetch her from the hospital,' Swart Hendrick explained.

'You did the right thing.' Moses stooped and lifted the Zulu girl to her feet, and she hung her head shyly.

'We will talk again in the morning.' Swart Hendrick closed the door quietly and Moses placed his forefinger under Vicky's chin and lifted it so he could look at her face.

She was even more beautiful than he remembered, an African madonna with a face like a dark moon. For a moment he thought of the woman he had left in London, and his senses cringed as he compared her humid white flesh, soft as putty, to this girl's glossy hide, firm and cool as polished onyx. His nostrils flared to her spicy African musk, so different from the other woman's thin sour odour which she tried to disguise with flowery perfumes. When Vicky looked up at him and smiled, the whites of her eyes and her perfect teeth were luminous and ivory bright in her lovely dark face.

When they had purged their first passion, they lay under the thick kaross of hyrax skins and talked the rest of the night away.

He listened to her boast of her exploits in his absence. She had marched to Pretoria with the other women to deliver a petition to the new minister of Bantu affairs, who had replaced Dr Verwoerd when he had become prime minister.

The march had never reached the Union Buildings. The police had intercepted it, and arrested the organizers. She had spent three days and nights in prison, and she related her humiliations with such humour, giggling as she repeated the *Alice in Wonderland* exchanges between the magistrate and herself, that Moses chuckled with her. In the end, the charges of attending an unlawful

assembly and incitement to public violence had been dropped, and Vicky and the other woman had been released.

'But I am a battle-trained warrior now,' she laughed. 'I have bloodied my spear, like the Zulus of old King Chaka.'

'I am proud of you,' he told her. 'But the true battle is only just beginning – ' and he told her a small part of what lay ahead for all of them, and in the yellow flickering light of the lantern, she watched his face avidly and her eyes shone.

Before they at last drifted off into sleep, the false dawn was framing the single small window, and Vicky murmured with her lips against his naked chest.

'How long will you stay this time, my lord?'

'Not as long as I wish I could.'

He stayed on three more days at Drake's Farm, and Vicky was with him every night.

Many visitors came when they heard that Moses Gama had returned and most of them were the fierce younger men of *Umkhonto we Sizwe*, the Spear of the Nation, the warriors eager for action.

Some of the older men of the Congress who came to talk with Moses left disturbed by what they had heard and even Swart Hendrick was worried. His brother had changed. He could not readily tell in what way he had changed, but the difference was there. Moses was more impatient and restless. The mundane details of business, and the day-to-day running of the Buffaloes and the trade union committees no longer seemed to hold his attention.

'It is as though he has fastened his eyes upon a distant hilltop, and cannot see anything in between. He speaks only of strange men in distant lands and what do they think or say that concerns us here?' he grumbled to the twins' mother, his only real confidante. 'He is scornful of the money we have made and saved, and says that after the revolution money will have no value. That everything will belong to the people – ' Swart Hendrick broke off to think for a moment of his stores and his shebeens, the bakeries and herds of cattle in the reservations which belonged to him, the money in the post office savings book and in the white man's bank, and the cash that he kept hidden in many secret places – some of it even buried under the floor upon which he now sat and drank the good beer brewed by his favourite wife. 'I am not sure that I wish all things to belong to the people,' he muttered thoughtfully. 'The people are cattle, lazy and stupid, what have they done to deserve the things for which I have worked so long and hard?'

'Perhaps it is a fever. Perhaps your great brother has a worm in his bowel,' his favourite wife suggested. 'I will make a *muti* for him that will clear his guts and his skull.' Swart Hendrick shook his head sadly. He was not at all certain that even one of his wife's devastating laxatives would drive the dark schemes from his brother's head.

Of course, long ago he had talked and dreamed strange and wild things with his brother. Moses had been young and that was the way of young men, but now the frosts of wisdom were upon Hendrick's head, and his belly was round and full, and he had many sons and herds of cattle. True he was not free – but then he was not sure what free really meant. He loved and feared his brother very much, but he was not sure that he wanted to risk all he had for a word of uncertain meaning.

'We must burn down and destroy the whole monstrous system,' his brother

said, and it occurred to Swart Hendrick that in the burning down might be included his stores and bakeries.

'We must goad the land, we must make it wild and ungovernable, like a great stallion, so that the oppressor is hurled to earth from its back,' his brother said, but Hendrick had an uncomfortable image of himself and his cosy existence taking that same painful toss.

'The rage of the people is a beautiful and sacred thing, we must let it run free,' Moses said, and Hendrick thought of the people running freely through his well-stocked premises. He had also witnessed the rage of the people in Durban during the Zulu rioting, and the very first concern of every man had been to provide himself with a new suit of clothing and a radio from the looted Indian stores.

'The police are the enemies of the people, they too will perish in the flames,' Moses said, and Hendrick remembered that when the faction fighting between the Zulus and the Xhosas had swept through Drake's Farm the previous November, it was the police who had separated them and prevented many more than forty dead. They had also saved his stores from being looted in the uproar. Now Hendrick wondered just who would prevent them killing each other after the police had been burned, and just what day-to-day existence would be like in the townships when each man made his own laws.

However, Swart Hendrick was ashamed of his treacherous relief when three days later Moses left Drake's Farm, and moved to the house at Rivonia. Indeed it was Swart Hendrick who had gently pointed out to his brother the danger of remaining when almost everybody in the township knew he had returned, and all day long there was a crowd of idlers in the street hoping for a glimpse of Moses Gama, the beloved leader. It was only a matter of time before the police heard about it through their informers.

* * *

The young warriors of *Umkhonto we Sizwe* willingly acted as Moses' scouts in the weeks that followed. They arranged the meetings, the small clandestine gatherings of the most fierce and bloody-minded amongst their own ranks. After Moses had spoken to them, the smouldering resentments which they felt towards the conservative and pacific leadership of the Congress was ready to burst into open rebellion.

Moses sought out and talked with some of the older members of Congress who, despite their age, were radical and impatient. He met secretly with the cell leaders of his own buffaloes without the knowledge of Hendrick Tabaka for he had sensed the change in his brother, the cooling of his political passions which had never boiled at the same white heat as Moses' own. For the first time in all the years he no longer trusted him entirely. Like an axe too long to use, Hendrick had lost the keen bright edge, and Moses knew that he must find another sharper weapon to replace him.

'The young ones must carry the battle forward,' he told Vicky Dinizulu. 'Raleigh, and yes, you also, Vicky. The struggle is passing into your hands.'

At each meeting he listened as long as he spoke, picking up the subtle shifts in the balance of power which had taken place in the years that he had been in foreign lands. It was only then that he realized how much ground he had lost,

how far he had fallen behind Mandela in the councils of the African National Congress and the imagination of the people.

'It was a serious error on my part to go underground and leave the country,' he mused. 'If only I had stayed to take my place in the dock beside Mandela and the others – '

'The risk was too great,' Vicky made excuse for him. 'If there had been another judgement – if any of the Boer judges other than Rumpff had tried them, they might have gone to the gallows and if you had gone with them the cause would have died upon the rope with all of you. You cannot die, my husband, for without you we are children without a father.'

Moses growled angrily. 'And yet, Mandela stood in the dock and made it a showcase for his own personality. Millions who had never heard his name before, saw his face daily in their newspapers and his words became part of the language.' Moses shook his head. 'Simple words: *Amandla* and *Ngawethu*, he said, and everyone in the land listened.'

'They know your name also, and your words, my lord.'

Moses glared at her. 'I do not want you to try to placate me, woman. We both know that while they were in prison during the trial – and I was in exile – they formally handed over the leadership to Mandela. Even old Luthuli gave his blessing, and since his acquittal Mandela has embarked on a new initiative. I know that he has been travelling around the country, in fifty different disguises, consolidating that leadership. I must confront him, and wrest the leadership back from him very soon, or it will be too late and I will be forgotten and left behind.'

'What will you do, my lord? How will you unseat him? He is riding high now – what can we do?'

'Mandela has a weakness – he is too soft, too placatory towards the Boers. I must exploit that weakness.' He said it quietly, but there was such a fierce light in his eyes that Victoria shivered involuntarily, and then with an effort closed her mind against the dark images his words had conjured up.

'He is my husband,' she told herself, fervently. 'He is my lord, and whatever he says or does is the truth and the right.'

* * *

The confrontation took place in the kitchen at Puck's Hill. Outside the sky was pregnant with leaden thunder clouds, dark as bruises that cast an unnatural gloom across the room and Marcus Archer switched on the electric lights that hung above the long table in their pseudo-antique brass fittings.

The thunder crashed like artillery and rolled heavily back and forth through the heavens. Outside the lightning flared in brilliant crackling white light and the rain poured from the eaves in a rippling silver curtain across the windows. They raised their voices against tumultuous nature so they were shouting at each other. They were the high command of *Umkhonto we Sizwe*, twelve men in all, all of them black except Joe Cicero and Marcus Archer – but only two of them counted, Moses Gama and Nelson Mandela. All the others were silent, relegated to the role of observers, while these two, like dominant black-maned lions, battled for the leadership of the pride.

'If I accept what you propose,' Nelson Mandela was standing, leaning

forward with clenched fists on the table top, 'we will forfeit the sympathy of the world.'

'You have already accepted the principle of armed revolt that I have urged upon you all these years.' Moses leaned back in the wooden kitchen chair, balancing on its two back legs with his arms folded across his chest. 'You have resisted my call to battle, and instead you have wasted our strength in feeble demonstrations of defiance which the Boers crush down contemptuously.'

'Our campaigns have united the people,' Mandela cried. He had grown a short dark beard since Moses had last seen him. It gave him the air of a true revolutionary, and Moses admitted to himself that Mandela was a fine-looking man, tall and strong and brimming with confidence, a formidable adversary.

'They have also given you a good look at the inside of the white man's gaol,' Moses told him contemptuously. 'The time for those childish games has passed. It is time to strike ferociously at the enemy's heart.'

'You know we have agreed.' Mandela was still standing. 'You know we have reluctantly agreed to the use of force – '

Now Moses leapt to his feet so violently that his chair was flung crashing against the wall behind him.

'Reluctantly!' He leaned across the table until his eyes were inches from Mandela's dark eyes. 'Yes, you are as reluctant as an old woman and timid as a virgin. What kind of violence is this you propose – dynamiting a few telegraph poles, blowing up a telephone exchange?' Moses's tone was withering with scorn. 'Next you will blow up a public shit house and expect the Boers to come cringing to you for terms. You are naïve, my friend, your eyes are full of stars and your head full of sunny dreams. These are hard men you are taking on and there is only one way you will get their attention. Make them bleed and rub their noses in the blood.'

'We will attack only inanimate targets,' Mandela said. 'There will be no taking of human life. We are not murderers.'

'We are warriors.' Moses dropped his voice, but that did not reduce its power. His words seemed to shimmer in the gloomy room. 'We are fighting for the freedom of our people. We cannot afford the scruples with which you seek to shackle us.'

The younger men at the foot of the table stirred with a restless eagerness, and Joe Cicero smiled slightly, but his eyes were fathomless and his smile was thin and cruel.

'Our violent acts should be symbolic,' Mandela tried to explain, but Moses rode over him.

'Symbols! We have no patience with symbolic acts. In Kenya the warriors of Mau Mau took the little children of the white settlers and held them up by their feet and chopped between their legs with razor-sharp pangas and threw the pieces into the pit toilets, and that is bringing the white men to the conference table. That is the type of symbol the white men understand.'

'We will never sink to such barbarism,' Nelson Mandela said firmly, and Moses leaned even closer to him, and their eyes locked. As they stared at each other, Moses was thinking swiftly. He had forced his opponent to make a stand, to commit himself irrevocably in front of the militants on the high command. Word of his refusal to engage in unlimited warfare would be swiftly passed to the Youth Leaguers and the young hawks, to the Buffaloes and the others who made up the foundation of Moses' personal support.

He would not push Mandela further now, that could only lose Moses some of

his gains. He would not give Mandela the opportunity to explain that he might be willing to use harder measures in the future. He had made Mandela appear a pacifist in the eyes of the militants, and in contrast had shown them his own fierce heart.

He drew back disdainfully from Nelson Mandela and he gave a soft scornful chuckle, as he glanced at the young men at the end of the table and shook his head as though he had given up on a dull and stubborn child.

Then he sat down, crossed his arms over his chest and let his chin sink forward on his chest. He took no further part in the conference, remaining a massive brooding presence, by his very silence mocking Mandela's proposals for limited acts of sabotage on government property.

He had given them fine words, but Moses Gama knew that they would need deeds before they all accepted him as the true leader.

'I will give them a deed – such a deed that will leave not a doubt in their hearts,' he thought, and his expression was grim and determined.

* * *

The motorcycle was a gift from his father. It was a huge Harley Davidson with a seat like a cowboy saddle and the gear shift was on the side of the silver tank. Sean was not quite sure why Shasa had given it to him. His final results at Costello's Academy didn't merit such paternal generosity. Perhaps Shasa was relieved that he had managed to scrape through at all, and on the other hand perhaps he felt that encouragement was what Sean needed now, or again it might merely be an expression of Shasa's guilt feelings towards his eldest son. Sean didn't care to consider it too closely. It was a magnificent machine, all chrome and enamel and red glass diamond reflectors, flamboyant enough to catch the eye of any young lady and Sean had wound it up well over the ton on the straight stretch of road beyond the airport.

Now, however, the engine was burbling softly between his knees, and as they reached the crest of the hill he switched off the headlight and then as gravity took the heavy machine, he cut the engine. They free-wheeled down silently in darkness, and there were no street lights in this elegant suburb. The plots of land around each grand home were the size of small farms.

Near the foot of the hill Sean swung the Harley Davidson off the road. They bumped through a shallow ditch into a clump of trees. They climbed off and Sean pulled the motorcycle up on to its kick stand.

'Okay?' he asked his companion. Rufus was not one of Sean's friends whom he could invite back to Weltevreden to meet the folks. Sean had only met him through their mutual love for motorcycles. He was smaller than Sean by at least four inches, and at first glance appeared to be a skinny runt of a lad with a grey complexion as though road grime and sump oil had soaked into his skin. He had nervously shy mannerisms, hanging his head and avoiding eye contact. It had taken some time for Sean to realize that Rufus's lean body was sinewy hard, that he was as quick and agile as a whippet, and that his whining voice and shifty eyes hid a sharp street-wise intelligence and a caustic irreverent wit. It had not taken long after that for him to be promoted to the rank of principal lieutenant in Sean's gang.

Since graduating without particular distinction from Costello's Academy, his

father had insisted that Sean enter articles with the object of one day becoming a member of the Institute of Chartered Accountants. The auditors of the Courtney Mining and Finance, Messrs Rifkin and Markovitch, had been prevailed upon, not without some misgivings on their part, to accept Sean as an articled clerk. This employment was not as dreary as Sean had at first imagined. He had no compunction in using the family name and his boundless charm to work himself into the plummiest audits, preferably of those companies which employed a large staff, and none of the senior partners had courage enough to report to Shasa Courtney that his favourite son was on a free ride. The Courtney account was worth almost a quarter of a million pounds annually.

Sean was never more than an hour late for work in the morning, his hangover or his lack of sleep hidden by gold-framed aviator's glasses and his brilliant smile. A little judicious rest during the morning and some light banter with the typists and female clerks would set him up for lunch at the Mount Nelson or Kelvin Grove which ended just in time for a swift return to the office to hand in an imaginative report to the senior partner, after which he was free for a game of squash or an hour's polo practice at Weltevreden.

He usually took dinner at home, it was cheaper than eating out, and although Shasa added substantially to the miserly salary paid by Messrs Rifkin and Markovitch, Sean was always in a financial crisis. After dinner he was free to shed his dinner jacket and black tie and change into a leather cycling jacket and steel-shod boots and then his other life beckoned, the life so different from his diurnal existence, a life of excitement and danger, full of colourful fascinating beings, of eager women and satisfying companions, of deliberate risks and wild adventures – like the one this evening.

Rufus unzipped his black leather jacket and grinned at him. 'Ready, willing and able, as the actress said to the bishop.' Under the jacket he wore a black roll-neck sweater, black trousers and on his head a black cloth cap.

They didn't have to discuss what they were about to do. They had worked together on the same kind of job four times already, and all the planning had been gone over in detail. However, Rufus's grin was pale and tense in the starlight beneath the trees. This was their most ambitious project yet. Sean felt the delicious blend of fear and excitement like raw spirit in his blood tingling and charging him.

This was what he did it for, this feeling, this indescribable euphoria with which danger always charged him. This was just the first tickle of it, it would grow stronger, more possessing, as the danger increased. He often wondered just how high he could go, there must be a zenith beyond which it was not possible to rise, but unlike the sexual climax which was intense but so fleeting, Sean knew he had not even approached the ultimate thrill of danger. He wondered what it would be like, killing a man with his bare hands? Killing a woman the same way – but doing it as she reached her own climax beneath him? The very idea of that always gave him an aching erection, but until those opportunities presented themselves, he would savour the lesser moments such as these.

'Nail?' Rufus asked, offering him his cigarette tin, but Sean shook his head. He wanted nothing to blunt his enjoyment, not nicotine nor alcohol, he wanted to experience the utmost enjoyment of every instant.

'Smoke half of it and then follow me,' he ordered, and slipped away amongst the trees.

He followed the footpath along the low bank of the stream and then crossed

at a shallow place, stepping lightly over the exposed rocks. The high diamond-mesh security fence was on the opposite bank, and he squatted below it. He didn't have to wait long. Within seconds a wolflike shape appeared out of the darkness beyond the fence, and the moment it saw him the German shepherd rushed at him, hurling itself against the heavy-gauge wire fence.

'Hey, Prince,' Sean said quietly, leaning toward the animal, showing not the least sign of fear. 'Come on, boy, you know me.'

The dog recognized him at last. It had only barked once, not creating enough of an uproar to alert the household, and now Sean gently pushed his fingers through the diamond mesh, talking softly and soothingly. The dog sniffed his hand and its long tail began to wave back and forth in friendly salutation. Sean had a way with all living creatures, not only humans. The dog licked his fingers.

Sean whistled softly and Rufus scrambled up the bank behind him. Immediately the German shepherd stiffened and the hair on its back came erect. It growled throatily and Sean whispered, 'Don't be a fool, Prince. Rufus is a friend.'

It took another five minutes for Sean to introduce the two of them, but at last in response to Sean's urging, Rufus gingerly put his fingers through the mesh and the dog sniffed them carefully and wagged his tail.

'I'll go over first,' Sean said, and swarmed up the high fence. There were three strands of barbed wire at the top, but Sean flicked his body over, feet first, arching his back like a gymnast. He dropped lightly to earth and the dog rose on its hind legs and placed its front paws on his chest. Sean fondled his head holding him while Rufus came over the barbed wire with even greater agility than Sean had.

'Let's go,' Sean whispered, and with the guard dog padding along beside them they went up towards the house, crouching as they ran and keeping to the shadow of the ornamental shrubs until they flattened against the wall, shrinking into the leafy ivy that covered the brickwork.

The house was a double-storied mansion, almost as imposing as Weltevreden. It belonged to another leading Cape family, close friends of the Courtneys. Mark Weston had been at school with Shasa and in the same engineering class at university. His wife, Marjorie, was a contemporary of Tara Courtney's. They had two teenage daughters, the elder of which Sean had deprived of her virginity the previous year, and then dropped without another phone call.

The seventeen-year-old child had suffered a nervous breakdown, refusing to eat, threatening suicide and weeping endlessly until she had to be taken out of school. Marjorie Weston had sent for Sean to try to remonstrate with him, and persuade him to let her daughter down gently. She had arranged the meeting without her daughter's knowledge, and while her husband was on one of his regular business trips to Johannesburg.

She took Sean to her sewing room on the ground floor and locked the door. It was Thursday afternoon, the servants' day off, and her younger daughter was at school while the eldest, Veronica, was in her bedroom upstairs palely pining.

Marjorie patted the sofa. 'Please come and sit next to me, Sean.' She was determined to keep the interview friendly. It was only when he was beside her that Marjorie realized how infernally goodlooking he was. Even more so than his father, and Marjorie had always had a strong fancy for Shasa Courtney.

She found that she was becoming a little breathless as she reasoned with Sean, but it was only when she placed her hand on his bare arm and felt the

elastic muscle under the smooth young skin that she realized what was happening.

Sean had the philanderer's sure and certain instinct, perhaps he had inherited it from her father. He hadn't really thought about Veronica's mother that way. God! She was as old as his mother. However, since Clare East he had always had a taste for older women, and Marjorie Weston was slim and athletic from swimming and tennis and meticulously tanned to disguise the crow's feet at the corners of her eyes and the first signs of crêping at her throat; and where Veronica was vacuous and simpering, her mother was poised and mature, but with the same mauve-blue eyes that had first attracted him to the daughter and an even more carefully groomed mane of thick tawny hair.

As Sean became aware of her excitement, the flush of blood beneath her tan, the agitated breathing that made her bosom beneath the angora jersey and pearls work like a bellows and the subtle change in her body odour that the average male would not have noticed, but which to Sean was like an invitation on an embossed card, he found his own arousal was spiced by the perversity of the situation.

'A double,' he thought. 'Mother and daughter – now that's something different.'

He didn't have to plot further, he let his infallible instinct guide him.

'You are much more attractive than your daughters could ever be – the main reason I broke off with Ronny was I couldn't bear being near you without being able to do this – ' and he leaned over her and kissed her with an open mouth.

Marjorie had believed herself to be in complete control of the situation right up until the moment she tasted his mouth. Neither of them spoke again until he was kneeling in front of her, holding her knees apart with both hands, and she was sprawled across the sofa with her pleated skirt rucked up around her waist. Then she panted brokenly, 'Oh Christ, I can't believe this is happening – I must be crazy.'

Now she sat at the foot of the stairs in her satin bathrobe. She was naked under the robe and every few seconds she shivered in a brief spasm. The night was warm, and the house was in darkness. The girls were asleep upstairs and Mark was away on one of his regular business trips. This was the first chance at an assignation there had been in almost two weeks and she was shivering with anticipation. She had switched off the burglar alarms at nine o'clock as they had arranged – Sean was almost half an hour late. Perhaps something had happened and he wasn't coming after all. She hugged herself and shivered miserably at the thought, then she heard the light tap on the glass of the french windows leading on to the swimming-pool patio, and she leapt to her feet and raced across the darkened room. She found she was panting as she fumbled with the latch.

Sean stepped into the room and seized her. He was so tall and powerful that she turned to putty in his arms. No man had ever kissed her like this, so masterfully and yet so skilfully. She sometimes wondered who had taught him and then was consumed by jealousy at the thought. Her need of him was so intense that waves of giddy vertigo washed over her and without his arms to support her she was certain she would have sagged to the floor. Then he tugged at the knot that secured the belt of her robe. It became undone and he thrust his hand into the opening. She shifted her weight, setting her feet wider apart so he could reach her more easily, and she gave a stifled gasp as she felt him slip his forefinger into her and she pushed hard against his hand.

'Lovely,' Sean chuckled in her ear. 'Like the Zambezi river in flood.'

'Shh,' she whispered. 'You'll wake the girls.' Marjorie liked to think of herself as genteel and refined, yet his crude words increased her excitation to a fever. 'Lock the door,' she ordered him, her voice thick and shaking. 'Let's go upstairs.'

He released her and turned to the door. He pressed it closed until the catch snapped and then turned the key and in the same instant reversed the movement, leaving it unlocked.

'All right.' He turned back to Marjorie. 'All set.'

They kissed again, and she ran her hands frantically down the front of his body, feeling the throbbing hardness through the thin cloth. It was she who broke away at last.

'Oh God, I can't wait any longer.' She took his hand and dragged him up the marble staircase. The girls' bedrooms were in the east wing and Marjorie locked the heavy mahogany door that secured the master suite. They were safe from discovery here, and at last she could let herself go completely.

Marjorie Weston had been married for over twenty years, and she had taken about the same number of lovers in that time. Some of them had merely been mad one-night frolics, others had been longer more permanent liaisons. One had lasted for almost all these twenty years, an erratic on-and-off arrangement, passionate interludes interspersed with long periods of denial. However, none of her other lovers had been able to match this stripling in beauty and performance, in physical endurance and in devilish inventiveness, not even Shasa Courtney who was that other long-term lover. The son had the same intuitive understanding of her needs. He knew when to be rough and cruel and when to be loving and gentle, but in other ways he outstripped his father. She had never been able to exhaust him or even to force him to falter, and he had a streak of genuine brutality and inherent evil in him that could terrify her at times. Added to that was the almost incestuous delight of taking the son after having had the father.

Tonight Sean did not disappoint her. While she was driving hard towards her first climax of the evening he suddenly reached out to the bedside table and lifted the telephone receiver.

'Ring your husband,' he ordered, and thrust the instrument into her hand.

'God, are you mad!' she gasped. 'What would I say to him?'

'Do it!' he said, and she realized that if she refused, he would slap her across the face. He had done that before.

Still holding him between her thighs, she twisted awkwardly and dialled the Carlton Hotel in Johannesburg. When the hotel operator answered, she said, 'I wish to speak to Mr Mark Weston in Suite 1750.'

'You are going through,' the operator said, and Mark answered on the third ring.

'Hello darling,' Marjorie said, and above her Sean began to move again. 'I couldn't sleep, so I thought I'd ring you. Sorry if I woke you.'

It became a contest with Sean trying to force her to gasp or cry out, while she attempted to maintain a casual conversation with Mark. When he succeeded and she gave a little involuntary squeal, Mark asked sharply, 'What was that?'

'I made myself a cup of Milo and it was too hot. I burned my lip.'

She could see how it was exciting Sean also. His face was no longer beautiful but swollen and flushed so that his features seemed coarsened, and in her she felt him swell and harden, filling her to bursting point, until she could control

herself no longer, and she broke off the telephone conversation abruptly. 'Goodnight, Mark, sleep well,' and slammed the receiver down on its cradle, just as the first scream came bursting up in her throat.

Afterwards they lay still, both of them regaining their breath, but when he tried to roll off her she tightened the grip of her legs and held him hard. She knew that if she could keep him from sliding out, within minutes he would be ready again.

Outside on the front lawn, the dog barked once. 'Is someone there?' she asked.

'No Prince is just being naughty,' Sean murmured, but he was listening intently, even though he knew that Rufus was too good to be heard, and they had planned every detail with care. Both he and Rufus knew exactly what they were after.

To commemorate the first month of their affair, Marjorie had bought Sean a set of Victorian dress studs and links in platinum and onyx and diamonds. She had invited him up to the house on a Thursday afternoon and led him through to Mark Weston's panelled study on the ground floor. While Sean watched, she checked the combination of the wall safe which was discreetly engraved on the corner of the silver-framed photograph of herself and the girls on Mark's desk, and then she had swung aside the false front of the section of the bookcase that concealed the safe and tumbled the combination of the lock.

She left the safe door ajar when she brought the gift to him. Sean had demonstrated his gratitude by pulling her skirts up and her peach-coloured satin bloomers down, then sitting her on the edge of her husband's desk, he lifted her knees and placed her feet on each corner of the leather-bound blotter. Then while he stood in front of her and made love to her, he evaluated the contents of the safe over her shoulders.

Sean had heard his father talk about Mark Weston's collection of British and South African gold coins. It was apparently one of the ten most important in private hands anywhere in the world. In addition to the dozen thick leather-bound albums which contained the collection, the middle shelf of the safe held the ledgers and cash books for the running of the estate and household, and a small gentleman's jewel box, while the top shelf was crammed with wads of pristine banknotes still in the bank wrappers and a large canvas bag stencilled 'Standard Bank Ltd' which obviously contained silver. There could not have been less than £5,000 in notes and coins in the safe.

Sean had explained to Rufus exactly where to look for the safe combination, how to open the false front of the bookcase and what to expect when he did.

The knowledge that Rufus was at work downstairs and the danger of possible discovery stimulated Sean so that at one point Marjorie blurted, 'You aren't human – you are a machine.'

He left her at last, lying in the big bed like a wax doll that had melted in the sun, her limbs soft and plastic, the thick mane of her hair darkened and sodden with her own sweat and her mouth smeared out of shape by exhausted passion. Her sleep was catatonic.

Sean was still pent up and excited. He looked into Mark Weston's study on the way out. The front of the bookcase was open, the safe door wide, the ledgers and cash books tumbled untidily on the floor, and the excitement came on him again in a thick musky wave and he found he was once more fully tumescent.

It was dangerous to remain in the house another minute, and the knowledge made his arousal unbearable. He looked up the marble staircase again and only

then did the idea come to him. Veronica's room was the second floor down the east wing passage. She might scream if he woke her suddenly, she might hate him so that she would scream when she recognized him, but on the other hand she might not. The risk was lunatic, and Sean grinned in the darkness and started back up the marble staircase.

A silver blade of moonlight pierced the curtains and fell on Veronica's pale hair that swirled across the pillow. Sean leaned over her and covered her mouth with his hand. She came awake struggling and terrified.

'It's me,' he whispered. 'Don't be afraid, Ronny. It's me.'

Her struggles stilled, the fear faded from her huge mauve eyes, and she reached up for him with both arms. He lifted his hand off her mouth and she said, 'Oh Sean, deep down I knew it. I knew you still loved me.'

Rufus was furious. 'I thought you had been caught,' he whined. 'What happened to you, man?'

'I was doing the hard work.' Sean kicked the Harley Davidson and it roared into life. As he turned back on to the road he felt the weight of the saddle bags pull the machine off balance, but he met her easily and straightened up.

'Slow down, man,' Rufus leaned forward from the pillion to caution him. 'You'll wake the whole valley.' And Sean laughed in the wild rush of wind, drunk with excitement, and they went up over the crest at a hundred miles an hour.

Sean parked the Harley Davidson on the Kraaifontein road and they scrambled down the bank and squatted in the dry culvert beneath the road. By the light of an electric torch they shared the booty.

'You said there would be five grand,' Rufus whined accusingly. 'Man, there isn't more than a hundred.'

'Old man Weston must have paid his slaves.' Sean chuckled carelessly as he split the small bundle of bank notes, and pushed the larger pile towards Rufus. 'You need it more than me, kid.'

The jewel box contained cuff-lins and studs, a diamond tie-pin that Sean judged to be fully five carats in weight, masonic medallions, Mark Weston's miniature decorations on a bar – he had won an MC at El Alamein and a string of campaign medals – a Pathek Philippe dress watch in gold and a handful of other personal items.

Rufus ran over them with an experienced eye. 'The watch is engraved, all the other stuff is too hot to move, too dangerous, man. We'll have to dump it.'

They opened the coin albums. Five of them were filled with sovereigns. 'Okay,' Rufus grunted. 'I can move that small stuff, but not these. They are red hot, burn your fingers.' With scorn he discarded the albums of heavy coins, the five-pound and five-guinea issues of Victoria and Elizabeth, Charles and the Georges.

After he dropped Rufus off at the illicit shebeen in the coloured District Six where Rufus had parked his own motorcycle, Sean rode out alone along the high winding road that skirts the sheer massif of Chapman's Peak. He parked the Harley on the edge of the cliff. The green Atlantic crashed against the rock five hundred feet below where he stood. One at a time Sean hurled the heavy gold coins out over the edge. He flicked them underhanded, so that they caught the dawn's uncertain light, and then were lost in the shadows of the cliff face as they fell, so he could not see them strike the surface of the water far below. When the last coin was gone, he tossed the empty albums after them and they fluttered as they caught the wind. Then he flung the gold wristwatch and the

diamond pin out into the void. He kept the medals for last. It gave him a vindictive satisfaction to have screwed Mark Weston's wife and daughter, and then to throw his medals into the sea.

When he mounted the Harley Davidson and turned it back down the steep winding road, he pushed the goggles up on to his forehead and let the wind beat into his face and rake his eyes so that the tears streamed back across his cheeks. He rode hard, putting the glistening machine over as he went into the turns so that the footrest struck a shower of sparks from the road surface.

'Not much profit for a night's work,' he told himself, and the wind tore the words from his lips. 'But the thrills, oh, the thrills!'

* * *

When all his best efforts to interest Sean and Michael in the planetary system of the Courtney companies had resulted in either lukewarm and deviously feigned enthusiasm or in outright disinterest, Shasa had gone through a series of emotions, beginning with puzzlement.

He tried hard to see how anyone, particularly a young man of superior intellect, and even more particularly a son of his, could find the whole complex interlinking of wealth and opportunity, of challenge and reward, less than fascinating. At first he thought that he was to blame, that he had not explained it sufficiently, that he had somehow taken their response for granted and had through his own omissions, failed to quicken their attention.

To Shasa it was the very stuff of life itself. His first waking thought each morning and his last before sleep each night, was for the welfare and sustenance of the company. So he tried again, more patiently, more exhaustively. It was like trying to explain colour to a blind man, and from puzzlement Shasa found himself becoming angry.

'Damn it, Mater,' he exploded, when he and Centaine were alone at her favourite place on the hillside above the Atlantic. 'They just don't seem to care.'

'What about Garry?' Centaine asked quietly.

'Oh Garry!' Shasa chuckled disparagingly. 'Every time I turn around I trip over him. He is like a puppy.'

'I see you have given him his own office on the third floor,' Centaine observed mildly.

'The old broom cupboard,' Shasa said. 'It was a joke really, but the little blighter took it seriously. I didn't have the heart – '

'He takes most things seriously, does young Garrick,' Centaine observed. 'He's the only one who does. He's quite a deep one.'

'Oh, come on, Mater! Garry?'

'He and I had a long chat the other day. You should do the same, it might surprise you. Did you know that he's in the top three in his year?'

'Yes, of course, I knew – but I mean, it's only his first year of business administration. One doesn't take that too seriously.'

'Doesn't one?' Centaine asked innocently, and Shasa was unusually silent for the next few minutes.

The following Friday Shasa looked into the cubbyhole at the end of the passage which served as Garry's office when he was temporarily employed by Courtney Mining during his college vacations. Garry leapt dutifully to his feet

when he recognized his father and he pushed his spectacles up on the bridge of his nose.

'Hello, champ, what are you up to?' Shasa asked, glancing down at the forms that covered the desk.

'It's a control,' Garry was caught in a cross-fire – awe at his father's sudden interest in what he was doing and desperation to retain his attention and to obtain his approval.

'Did you know that we spent over a hundred pounds on stationery last month alone?' He was so anxious to impress his father that he stuttered again, something he only did when he was overexcited.

'Take a deep breath, champ.' Shasa eased into the tiny room. There was just room for the two of them. 'Speak slowly, and tell me about it.'

One of Garry's official duties was to order and issue the office stationery. The shelves behind his desk were filled with sheaves of typing paper and boxes of envelopes.

'According to my estimates we should be able to cut that below eighty pounds. We could save twenty pounds a month.'

'Show me.' Shasa perched on the corner of the desk and applied his mind to the problem. He treated it with as much respect as if they were discussing the development of a new gold-mine.

'You are quite right,' Shasa approved his figures. 'You have full authority to put your new control system into practice.' Shasa stood up. 'Well done,' he said, and Garry glowed with gratification. Shasa turned to the door so the lad wouldn't see his expression of amusement, and then he paused and looked back.

'Oh, by the way, I'm flying up to Walvis Bay tomorrow. I'm meeting the architects and the engineers on site to discuss the extensions to the canning factory. Would you like to come along?'

Unable to trust his voice lest he stutter again, Garry nodded emphatically.

* * *

Shasa allowed Garry to fly. Garry had been granted his private pilot's licence two months previously, but he still needed a few hours for his twin-engine endorsement. A year older than Garry, Sean had been given his licence immediately he was eligible. Sean flew the way he rode and shot, naturally, gracefully, but carelessly. He was one of those pilots who flew by the grace of God and the seat of his pants. In contrast, Garry was painstaking and meticulous and therefore, Shasa admitted grudgingly, the better pilot. Garry filed a flight plan as though he was submitting a thesis for his doctorate, and his pre-flight checks went on so long that Shasa squirmed in the right-hand seat and only just contained himself from crying out, 'For God's sake, Garry, let's get on with it.'

Yet it was a mark of his trust that he allowed Garry to take the controls of the Mosquito at all. Shasa was prepared to take over at the first sign of trouble, but he was amply rewarded for his forbearance when he saw the sparkle of deep pleasure behind Garry's spectacles as he handled the lovely machine, lifting her up through the silver wreaths of cloud into a blue African sky where Shasa could share with him a rare feeling of total accord.

Once they arrived at Walvis Bay Shasa tended to forget that Garry was with

him. He had become accustomed to his middle son's close attendance, and though he did not really think of it, it was becoming familiar and comforting to have him there. Garry seemed to anticipate his smallest need, whether it was a light for his cigarette or a piece of scrap paper and pencil on which to illustrate an idea to the architect. Yet Garry was quiet and unobtrusive, not given to inane questions and bumptious or facetious remarks.

The cannery was fast becoming one of the big winners in the Courtney stable of companies. For three seasons they had captured their full quota of pilchards, and then there had been an unusual development. In a private meeting Manfred De La Rey had suggested to Shasa that if the company were to issue a further ten thousand bonus shares in the name of a nominee in Pretoria, the consequences might be very much to everybody's advantage. Taking Manfred on trust, Shasa had issued the shares as suggested, and within two months there had been a review of their quota by the government Department of Land and Fisheries and that quota had been almost doubled to the two hundred thousand tons of pilchard that they were now permitted to capture annually.

'For three hundred years the Afrikaners have been left out of business,' Shasa smiled cynically as he received the glad tidings. 'But they are catching on fast. They are in the race now, and not too fussy about how they win. The Jews and the English had better look to their business laurels, here come the Nats.' And he set about planning and financing the extension to the cannery.

It was late afternoon before Shasa finished with the architects, but at this season there were still a few hours of daylight remaining.

'How about a swim at Pelican Point?' Shasa suggested to Garry, and they took one of the cannery Land-Rovers and drove along the hard wet sand at the edge of the bay. The waters of the bay stank of sulphur and fish offal, but behind it the high golden dunes and arid mountains rose in desolate grandeur, while out over the protected and silken waters the flamingo flocks were such a brilliant pink as to seem improbable and theatrical. Shasa drove fast around the curve of the bay with the wind ruffling their hair.

'So what, if anything, did you learn today?'

'I learned that if you want other people to talk too freely, you keep quiet and look sceptical,' Garry answered, and Shasa glanced at his son with a startled expression. That had always been a deliberate technique of his, but Shasa had never expected anyone so young and inexperienced to see through it. 'Without saying anything, you made the architect admit that he really hasn't worked out a solution to siting the boiler room yet,' Garry went on. 'And even I could see that his present proposal is an expensive compromise.'

'Is that so?' It had taken Shasa a full day of discussion to reach the same conclusion, but he wasn't going to say so. 'What would you do then?'

'I don't know, Pater, not for sure,' Garry said. He had a pedantic manner of delivering an opinion which had at first irritated Shasa, but which now amused him, particularly as the opinions were usually worth listening to. 'But instead of simply sticking on another boiler, I would explore the possibility of installing the new Patterson process – '

'What do you know about the Patterson process?' Shasa demanded sharply. He had only heard about it himself very recently. Suddenly Shasa found himself arguing as though with an equal. Garry had read all the sales pamphlets and memorized the specifications and figures of the process, and had worked out for himself most of the advantages and disadvantages over the conventional method of preparation and canning.

They were still arguing as they rounded the sandy horn of the bay, and beyond the lighthouse the deserted beach, clean and white, stretched away in dwindling perspective to the horizon. Here the Atlantic waters were wild and green, cold and clean, foamy and effervescent with the rush of the surf.

They stripped off their clothes and, naked, swam out into the tumultuous seas, diving deep beneath each curling wave as it came hissing down upon them. At last they emerged, their bodies tinted blue with the cold, but laughing breathlessly with exhilaration.

As they stood beside the Land-Rover and towelled themselves, Shasa studied his son frankly. Even though sodden with salt water, Garry's hair stuck up in disorderly spikes and without his spectacles he had a bemused myopic look. His torso was massively developed, his chest was like a pickle barrel and he had grown such a coat of dark body hair that it almost obscured the ridges of muscle that covered his belly like chain mail.

'Looking at him, there is no way you would ever suspect that he was a Courtney. If I didn't know better, I would think that Tara had a litle fling on the side.' Shasa was certan that Tara might be capable of many things, but never infidelity or promiscuity. 'There is nothing about him of his ancestry,' he thought, and then looked further and grinned suddenly.

'Well at least, Garry, you have inherited one of the Courtney gifts. You've got a wanger on you that would make old General Courtney himself turn in his grave with envy.'

Hurriedly Garry covered himself with his towel and reached into the Land-Rover for his underpants, but secretly he was pleased. Up until now he had always regarded that portion of his anatomy with suspicion. It seemed to be an alien creature with a will and existence of its own, determined to embarrass and humiliate him at the most unexpected or inappropriate moments, like that unforgettable occasion when he was standing in front of the commerce class at business school giving his dissertation and the girls in the front row started giggling, or when he was forced to retreat in confusion from the typing-pool at Centaine House because of the alien's sudden but very apparent interest in the surroundings. However, if his father spoke respectfully of it, and the shade of the legendary general approved, then Garry was prepared to reconsider his own relationship with it and come to terms.

They flew on to the H'ani Mine the next morning. All three of the boys had done their stint at the H'ani. As indeed had Shasa so many years before, they had been required to work their way through every part of the mine's operation, from the drilling and blasting in the deep amphitheatre of the open pit, to the final separation rooms where at last the precious crystals were recovered from the crushed blue ground.

That forced labour had been more than sufficient for both Sean and Michael and neither of them had ever shown the least desire to return to the H'ani Mine again. Garry was the exception, he seemed to have developed the same love for these remote wild hills as both Shasa and Centaine shared. He asked to accompany his father here whenever Shasa's regular inspection tours were scheduled. In a few short years he had built up an expert knowledge of the mine's operation, and had at one time or another personally performed all of the tasks involved in the process of production. So on their last evening at the mine the two of them, Shasa and Garry, stood on the brink of the great pit and while the sun set over the desert behind them, they stared down into its shadowy depths.

'It's strange to think that it all came out of there,' Garry said softly.

'Everything that you and Nana have built up. It makes one feel somehow humble, like when I am in church.' He was silent for a long moment and then went on. 'I love this place. I wish we could stay longer.'

To hear his own feeling echoed like this, moved Shasa deeply. Of his three sons, this was the only one who understood, who seemed capable of sharing with him the almost religious awe that this massive excavation and the wealth it produced evoked in him. This was the fountainhead, and only Garry had recognized it.

He placed his arm around Garry's shoulders and tried to find words, but after a moment he simply said, 'I know how you feel, champ. But we have to get back home. I have to introduce my budget to the House on Monday.' It was not what he had wanted to say, but he sensed that Garry knew that, and as they picked their way down the rough pathway in the dusk, they were closer in spirit than they had ever been.

* * *

The budget for Shasa's ministry of mines and industry had been almost doubled this year, and he knew that the opposition were planning to give it a rough passage. They had never forgiven him for changing parties. So he was on his mettle as he rose to his feet and sought the Speaker's recognition, and then instinctively glanced up at the galleries.

Centaine was in the middle of the front row of the visitors' gallery. She was always there when she knew that either Shasa or Blaine was going to speak. She wore a small flat hat tilted forward over her eyes with a single yellow bird of paradise feather raked back at a jaunty angle, and she smiled and nodded encouragement as their eyes met.

Beside Centaine sat Tara. Now that was unusual. He couldn't remember when last she had come to listen to him.

'Our bargain doesn't include torture by boredom,' she had told him, but there she was looking surprisingly elegant in a dainty straw basher with a trailing pink ribbon around the crown and elbow-length white gloves. She touched the brim in a mocking salute, and Shasa lifted an eyebrow at her and then turned to the press gallery high above the Speaker's throne. The political correspondents from the English-speaking press were all there, pencils poised eagerly. Shasa was one of their favourite prey, but all their attacks seemed only to consolidate his position in the National Party, and by their pettiness and subjectivity point up the efficiency and effectiveness with which he ran his ministry.

He loved the rough and tumble of parliamentary debate, and his single eye sparkled with battle lust as he took up his familiar slouch, both hands in his pockets, and launched into his presentation.

They were at him immediately, yapping and snapping at his heels, interjecting with expressions of disbelief and outrage, calling out 'Shame on you, sir!' and 'Scandal!' and Shasa's grin infuriated them and goaded them to excesses which he brushed aside with casual contempt, holding his own easily and then gradually overwhelming them and turning their own ridicule back upon them, while around him his colleagues grinned with admiration and encouraged his more devastating sallies with cries of '*Hoor, hoor!* – Hear, hear!'

When the division was called, his party backed him solidly, and his budget was approved by the expected majority. It was a performance which had enhanced his stature and standing. He was no longer the junior member of the cabinet and Dr Verwoerd passed him a note.

'I was right to keep you on the team. Well done.'

In the front of the visitors' gallery Centaine caught his eye, and clasped both hands together in a boxer's victory flourish, yet somehow she made the gesture appear at once regal and ladylike. Shasa's smile faded as he realized that beside her Tara's seat was empty, she had left during the debate, and Shasa was surprised by his own feeling of disappointment. He would have liked her to witness his triumph.

The House was moving on to other business which did not concern him and on an impulse Shasa rose and left the chamber. He went up the wide staircase and down the long panelled passageway to his office suite. As he approached the front entrance to the suite, he checked suddenly and again on impulse at the corner of the passage and went down to the unobtrusive and unmarked doorway at the end.

This was the back door to his office, a convenient escape route from unwanted visitors which had been ordered by old Cecil John Rhodes himself as a by-pass of the front waiting-room, a means for special visitors to reach him and leave again unobserved. Shasa found it equally convenient. The prime minister used it occasionally, as did Manfred De La Rey, but the majority of other users were female, and their business with Shasa was seldom political.

Instead of rattling the key in the Yale lock, Shasa slipped it in silently and turned it gently, then pushed the door open sharply. On the inside the door was artfully blended into the panelling of his office and few people knew of its existence.

Tara was standing with her back to him, bending over the altar chest. She did not know the door existed. Except for the gift of the chest, she had taken little interest in the decoration and furbishment of his office. It was a few seconds before she sensed that she was not alone, and then her reaction was extravagant. She jumped back from the chest and whirled to face him, and as she recognized Shasa, instead of showing relief, she paled with agitation and began to explain breathlessly.

'I was just looking at it – it's such a magnificent piece of work. Quite beautiful, I had forgotten how beautiful – '

One thing Shasa realized immediately, she was as guilty as if she had been caught red-handed in some dreadful crime, but he could not imagine what had made her react that way. She was quite entitled to be in his office, she had her own key to the front door, and she had given him the chest – she could admire it whenever she chose.

He remained silent and fastened his eye upon her accusingly, hoping to trick her into over-explaining, but she left the chest and moved across to the window behind the desk.

'You were doing very well on the floor,' she said. She was still a little breathless, but her colour had returned and she was recovering her composure. 'You always put on such a good show.'

'Is that why you left?' he asked, as he closed the door and pointedly crossed the room to the chest.

'Oh you know how useless I am with figures, you quite lost me towards the end.'

Shasa studied the chest carefully. 'What was she up to?' he asked himself thoughtfully, but he could not see that anything was altered. The Van Wouw bronz sculpture of the Bushman was still in its place, so she could not have opened the lid.

'It's a marvellous piece,' he said, and stroked the effigy of St Luke at the corner.

'I had no idea there was a door in the panel.' Clearly Tara was trying to distract his attention from the chest, and her efforts merely piqued his curiosity. 'You gave me quite a turn.' Shasa refused to be led and ran his fingers over the inlaid lid.

'I should get Dr Findlay from the National Gallery to have a look at it,' Shasa mused. 'He's an expert on medieval and Renaissance religious art.'

'Oh, I promised Tricia I would let her know when you arrived.' Tara sounded almost desperate. 'She's got an important message for you.' She crossed quickly to the interleading door and opened it. 'Tricia, Mr Courtney's here now.' Shasa's secretary popped her head into the inner office.

'Do you know a Colonel Louis Nel?' she asked. 'He's been trying to get hold of you all morning.'

'Nel?' Shasa was still studying the chest. 'Nel? No, I don't think so.'

'He says he knows you, sir. He says you worked together during the war.'

'Oh, good Lord, yes!' She had Shasa's full attention now. 'It was so long ago – but, yes, I know him well. He wasn't a colonel then.'

'He's head of CID for the Cape of Good Hope now,' Tricia told him. 'And he wants you to telephone him as soon as you, can. He says it's very urgent, he actually said "life and death".'

'Life and death, hey,' Shasa grinned. 'That probably means he wants to borrow money. Get him on the blower, please Trish.'

He went to his desk, sat down and pulled the telephone towards him. He motioned Tara towards the couch, but she shook her head.

'I'm meeting Sally and Jenny for lunch,' and she sidled towards the door with a relieved expression. But he wasn't looking at her, he was staring out of the window over the oaks to the slopes of Signal Hill beyond, and he didn't even glance as she slipped out of the room and closed the door quietly behind her.

Louis Nel's call had transported Shasa back almost twenty years in time. 'Was it that long ago?' he wondered. 'Yes, it was. My God, how quickly the years have passed.'

Shasa had been a young squadron leader, invalided back from the campaign in Abyssinia where he had lost his eye fighting the Duke of Aosta's army on the drive up to Addis Ababa. At a loose end, certain that his life was ruined and that he was a cripple and a burden on his family and friends, Shasa had gone into seclusion and started drinking heavily and letting himself slip into careless despondency. It had been Blaine Malcomess who had sought him out and given him a scornful and painful tongue-lashing, and then offered him a job helping track down and break up the *Ossewa Brandwag*, the Sentinels of the Wagon Train, a secret society of militant nationalist Afrikaners who were virulently opposed to Field-Marshal Jan Christian Smuts' pro-British war efforts.

Shasa had worked in co-operation with Louis Nel, establishing the identity of the leading members of the pro-Nazi conspiracy and preparing the warrants for their arrest and internment. His investigations of the *Ossewa Brandwag*'s activities had put him in contact with a mysteriousu informer, a woman who

had contacted him only by telephone and who took every precaution to conceal her identity. To this day Shasa did not know who she had been, or indeed if she were still alive.

This informer had revealed to him the *OB* theft of weapons from the government arms and munitions factory in Pretoria, and enabled them to deal a major blow to the subversive organization. Then the same informer had warned Shasa of the White Sword conspiracy. This was an audacious plot to assassinate Field-Marshal Smuts, and in the ensuing confusion to seize control of the armed forces, declare South Africa a republic, and throw in their lot with Adolf Hitler and the Axis powers.

Shasa had been able to foil the plot at the very last minute, but only by the most desperate efforts, and at the cost of his own grandfather's life. Sir Garrick Courtney had been shot by the assassin in mistaken identity, for the old man had physically resembled his good and dear friend, Field-Marshal Smuts.

Shasa had not thought about those dangerous days for many years. Now every detail came back vividly. He lived it all again as he waited for the telephone on his desk to ring; the reckless climb up the sheer side of Table Mountain as he tried to catch his grandfather and the Field-Marshal before they could reach the summit where the killer was waiting for them. He recalled his dreadful sense of helplessness as the rifle shot crashed and echoed against the rocky cliffs and he realized he was too late, the horror of finding his grandfather lying in the track with the ghastly bullet wound which had blown his chest open, and the old Field-Marshal kneeling beside him stricken with grief.

Shasa had chased the killer, using his intimate knowledge of the mountain to cut off his retreat against the top of the cliff. They fought chest to chest, fought for their very lives. White Sword had used his superior strength to break away and escape, but not before Shasa had put a bullet from his 6.5 mm Beretta into his chest. White Sword disappeared and the plot to overthrow Smuts' government collapsed, but the killer had never been brought to justice, and Shasa felt once again the agony of his grandfather's murder. He had loved the old man and named his second son after him.

The telephone rang at last and Shasa snatched it up.

'Louis?' he asked.

'Shasa!' Shasa recognized his voice immediately. 'It's been a long time.'

'It's good to speak to you.'

'Yes, but I wish I was the bearer of better news, I'm sorry.'

'What is it?' Shasa was immediately serious.

'Not on the telephone – can you come down to Caledon Square as soon as possible?'

'Ten minutes,' Shasa said, and hung up.

The headquarters of the CID were only a short walk from the House of Assembly and he stepped it out briskly. The episode with Tara and the chest was put out of his mind as he tried to imagine what bad news Louis Nel had for him.

The sergeant at the front desk had been alerted and he recognized Shasa immediately.

'The colonel is expecting you, Minister. I'll send someone to show you up to his office,' and he beckoned one of the uniformed constables.

Louis Nel was in his shirt-sleeves and he came to the door to welcome Shasa and lead him to one of the easy chairs.

'How about a drink?'

'Still too early for me.' Shasa shook his head, but he accepted the cigarette Louis offered him.

The policeman was lean as ever, but he had lost most of his hair and what remained was ice white. There were dark pouches beneath his eyes and after his welcoming smile his mouth settled back into a thin nervous line. He looked like a man who worried a lot, worked too hard and slept badly at night. He must be past retirement age, Shasa thought.

'How's the family – your wife?' Shasa asked. He had met her only once or twice and could not remember her name or what she looked like.

'We were divorced five years ago.'

'I'm sorry,' Shasa said, and Louis shrugged.

'It was bad at the time.' Then he leaned forward. 'Your family – you have three boys and a girl. That's right?'

'Ah! You have been doing a police number on me,' Shasa smiled, but Louis did not respond. His expression remained serious as he went on.

'Your eldest son – his name is Sean. That's right, isn't it?'

Shasa nodded, he was no longer smiling either, and he was seized by a sudden presentiment.

'You want to speak to me about Sean?' he asked softly.

Louis stood up abruptly and crossed to the window. He was looking down into the street as he answered.

'This is off the record, Shasa. Not the way we usually do things, but there are extraordinary factors here. Our past association, your present rank – ' He turned back from the window. 'In the usual circumstances this would probably not have been brought to my notice at all, at least not at this stage of the investigation.'

The word 'investigation' startled Shasa, and he wanted Louis to give him the bad news and get it over with but he controlled his agitation and impatience and waited quietly.

'For some time now we have been troubled by a series of house-breakings in the better-class suburbs – you have surely read about them. The press are calling the thief the "Cape Raffles".'

'Of course,' Shasa nodded. 'Some of my friends, good friends, have been the victims – the Simpsons, the Westons. Mark Weston lost his collection of gold coins.'

'And Mrs Simpson lost her emeralds,' Louis Nel agreed. 'Some of these emeralds, the earrings, were recovered when we raided a fence in District Six. We were acting on a tip-off and we recovered an enormous quantity of stolen articles. We arrested the fence – he's a coloured chap who was running an electrical business in the front of his premises and receiving stolen goods through the back door. We have had him locked up for two weeks now, and he is beginning to co-operate. He gave us a list of names, and on it was one lovable little rogue named Rufus Constantine, ever heard of him?'

Shasa shook his head. 'How does this link up with my son?'

'I'm coming to that. This Constantine was apparently the one who passed the emeralds and some of the other booty. We picked him up and brought him in for questioning. He is a tough little monkey, but we found a way to open him up and make him sing to us. Unfortunately the tune wasn't very pretty.'

'Sean?' Shasa asked, and Louis nodded.

'I'm afraid so. Looks as though he was the leader of an organized gang.'

'It doesn't make sense. Not Sean.'

'Your son has built up quite a reputation.'

'He was a little wild at one time,' Shasa admitted, 'but he is settling down to his articles now, working hard. And why would he want to get involved in something like that? I mean, he doesn't need the money.'

'Articled clerks are not paid a great fortune.'

'I give him an allowance,' Shasa shook his head again. 'No, I don't believe it. What would he know about house-breaking?'

'Oh, no – he doesn't do it himself. He sets up the job and Rufus and his henchman do the dirty work.'

'Sets it up – what do you mean by that?'

'As a son of yours he is welcome in any home in the city, that is right, isn't it?'

'I suppose so.' Shasa was cautious.

'According to little Rufus, your son studies each prospective victim's home, decides on what valuables there are and pinpoints where they are kept – strong rooms, hidden drawers, wall safes and that sort of thing. Then he begins an affair with one of the family, the mother or a daughter, and uses his opportunities to let his accomplice into the home while he is entertaining the lady of his choice upstairs.'

Shasa stared at him wordlessly.

'By all accounts it works very well, and in more than one case the theft was not even reported to us – the ladies involved were more concerned with their reputations and their husband's wrath than with the loss of their jewellery.'

'Marge Weston?' Shasa asked. 'She was one of the ladies?'

'According to our information – yes, she was.'

Shasa whispered, 'The little bastard.' He was appalled, and totally convinced. It all fitted too neatly not to be true. Marge and Sean, his son and one of his mistresses, it was just not to be tolerated. 'This time he has gone too far.'

'Yes,' Louis agreed. 'Too far by a mile. Even as a first offender, he will probably get five or six years.'

All Shasa's attention snapped back to him. The shock to Shasa's pride and sense of propriety was such that he had not even begun to consider the legal implications, but now his righteous rage was snuffed out at the suggestion of his eldest son standing in the dock and being sentenced to long-term imprisonment.

'Have you prepared a docket yet?' he asked. 'Is there a warrant out?'

'Not yet.' Lousi was speaking as carefully. 'We were only given this information a few hours ago.' He crossed to his desk and picked up the blue interrogation folder.

'What can I do?' Shasa asked quietly. 'Is there anything we can do?'

'I've done all I can,' Louis answered. 'I've done too much already. I could never justify holding up this information, nor could I justify informing you of an investigation in progress. I've already stretched my neck way out, Shasa. We go back a long way, and I'll never forget the work you did on White Sword – that's the only reason I took the chance – ' he paused to take a deep breath, and Shasa, sensing there was more to come, remained silent. 'There is nothing else I can do. Nothing else anyone can do *at this level.*' He placed peculiar emphasis on the last three words, and then he added seemingly incongruously, 'I'm retiring next month, there'll be someone else in this office after that.'

'How long do I have?' Shasa asked, and he did not have to elaborate. They understood each other.

'I can sit on this file for another few hours, until five o'clock today, and then the investigation will have to go ahead.'

Shasa stood up. 'You are a good friend.'

'I'll walk you down,' Louis said, and they were alone in the lift before they spoke again. It had taken Shasa that long to master his perturbation.

'I hadn't thought about White Sword for years,' he changed the subject easily. 'Not until today. All that seems so far away and long ago, even though it was my own grandfather.'

'I've never forgotten it,' Louis Nel said softly. 'The man was a murderer. If he had succeeded, if you hadn't prevented it, all of us in this land would be a lot worse off than we are today.'

'I wonder what happened to White Sword – who he was and where he is now? Perhaps he is long dead, perhaps – '

'I don't think so – there is something that makes me doubt it. A few years ago I wanted to go over the White Sword file – '

The lift stopped at the ground floor and Louis broke off. He remained silent as they crossed the lobby and went out into the sunlight. On the front steps of the headquarters building, they faced each other.

'Yes?' Shasa asked. 'The file, the White Sword file?'

'There is no file,' Louis said softly.

'I don't understand.'

'No file,' Louis repeated. 'Not in police records or the Justice Department or the central records. Officially, White Sword never existed.'

Shasa stared at him. 'There must be a file – I mean, we worked on it, you and I. It was this thick – ' Shasa held his thumb and forefinger apart. 'It can't have disappeared.'

'You can take my word for it. It has.' Louis held out his hand. 'Five o'clock,' he said gently. 'No later, but I will be in my office all day right up to five, if anyone wanted to telephone me there.'

Shasa took his hand. 'I will never forget this.' He glanced at his wristwatch as he turned away. It was a few minutes before noon, and most fortuitously he had a lunch date with Manfred De La Rey. He headed back up Parliament Lane, and the noon-day gun fired just as he went in through the main doors. Everybody in the main lobby, including the ushers, instinctively checked their watches at the distant clap of cannon shot.

Shasa turned towards the members' dining-room, but he was far too early. Except for the white-uniformed waiters, it was deserted. In the members' bar he ordered a pink gin and waited impatiently, glancing every few seconds at his watch, but his appointment with Manfred was for twelve-thirty and it was no good going to search for him. He could be anywhere in the huge rambling building, so Shasa employed the time in cherishing and fanning his anger.

'The bastard!' he thought. 'I've allowed him to fool me all these years. All the signs were there, but I refused to accept them. He's dirty rotten, right to the core – ' and then his indignation went off in a new direction. 'Marge Weston is old enough to be his mother, how many of my other women has he been boffing? Is nothing sacred to the little devil?'

Manfred De La Rey was a few minutes early. He came to the members' bar smiling and nodding and shaking hands, playing the genial politician, so that it took him a few minutes to cross the room. Shasa could barely contain his impatience, but he didn't want anyone to suspect his agitation.

Manfred asked for a beer. Shasa had never seen him take hard spirit, and

only after he had taken his first sip did Shasa tell him quietly, 'I'm in trouble – serious trouble.'

Manfred's easy smile never faltered, he was too shrewd to betray his emotions to a room full of adversaries and potential rivals, but his eyes went cold and pale as those of a basilisk.

'Not here,' he said, and led Shasa through to the men's room. They stood shoulder to shoulder at the urinal and Shasa spoke softly but urgently, and when he finished, Manfred stood staring at the white ceramic trough for only a few seconds before he roused himself.

'What is the number?'

Shasa slipped him a card with Louis Nel's telephone number at CID headquarters.

'I'll have to use the security line from my office. Give me fifteen minutes. I will meet you back at the bar.' Manfred zipped his fly closed and strode out of the lavatory.

He was back in the members' bar within ten minutes, by which time Shasa was entertaining the four other members of the luncheon party, all of them influential back-benchers. When they finished their drinks, Shasa suggested, 'Shall we go through?' As they moved towards the dining-room Manfred took his upper arm in a firm grip, and leaned close to him, smiling as though conveying a pleasantry.

'I've squashed it, but he is to be out of the country within twenty-four hours, and I don't want him back. Is that a bargain?'

'I am grateful,' Shasa nodded, and his anger at his son was compounded by this obligation that had been forced upon him. It was a debt that he would have to repay, with interest.

Sean's Harley was parked down at the sports hall that Shasa had built as a joint Christmas present for all three boys two years previously. It contained a gymnasium and squash court, half Olympic-size indoor swimming-pool and change rooms. As Shasa approached, he heard the explosive echo of the rubber ball from the courts and he went up to the spectators' gallery.

Sean was playing with one of his cronies. He wore white silk shorts but his chest was bare. There was a white sweat band around his forehead, and white tennis shoes on his feet. His body glistened with sweat and was tanned to a golden brown. He was impossibly beautiful, like a romantic painting of himself, and he moved with the unforced grace of a hunting leopard, driving the tiny black ball against the high white wall with such deceptive power that it resounded like a fusillade of rifle fire as it rebounded. He saw Shasa in the gallery and flashed him a dazzle of even white teeth and green eyes, so that despite his anger, Shasa suffered a sudden pang at the idea of having to part from him.

In the change room Shasa dismissed his playing partner curtly: 'I want to speak to Sean – alone,' and as soon as he was gone he turned on his son. 'The police are on to you,' he said. 'They know all about you.' He waited for a reaction, but he was disappointed.

Sean towelled his face and neck. 'Sorry, pater, you've lost me there. What is it they know?' He was cool and debonair, and Shasa exploded.

'Don't play your games with me, young man. What they know can put you behind bars for ten years.'

Sean lowered the towel and stood up from the bench. He was serious at last. 'How did they find out?'

'Rufus Constantine.'

'The little prick. I'll break his neck.' He wasn't going to deny it and Shasa's last hope that he was innocent faded.

'I'll break any necks that have to be broken,' Shasa snapped.

'So what are we going to do?' Sean asked, and Shasa was taken aback by his casual assumption.

'We?' he asked. 'What makes you think that I'm going to save your thieving hide?'

'Family honour,' Sean was matter-of-fact. 'You'll never let me go to court. The family would be on trial with me – you would never allow that.'

'That was part of your calculations?' Shasa asked, and when Sean shrugged, he added, 'You don't understand the words honour or decency.'

'Words,' Sean replied. 'Just words. I prefer actions.'

'God, I wish I could prove you wrong,' Shasa whispered. He was so furious now that he wanted the satisfaction of physical violence. 'I wish I could let you rot in some filthy cell.' His fists were clenched, and before he thought about it, he shifted into balance for the first blow, and instantly Sean was on guard, his hands stiffening into blades crossed before his chest and his eyes were fierce. Shasa had paid hundreds of pounds for his training by the finest instructors in Africa, and all of them had at last admitted that Sean was a natural fighter and that the pupil in each case outstripped the master. Delighted that Sean had at last found something that could hold his interest, Shasa had, before Sean began his articles, sent him to Japan for three months to study under a master of the martial arts.

Now as he confronted his son, Shasa was suddenly aware of every one of his forty-one years, and that Sean was a man in full physical flower, a trained fighter and an athlete in perfect condition. He realized the Sean could toy with him and humiliate him, he could even read in Sean's expression that he was eager to do so. Shasa stepped back and unclenched his fists.

'Pack your bags,' he said quietly. 'You are leaving and you are not coming back.'

They flew north in the Mosquito, landing only to refuel in Johannesburg and then flying on to Messina on the border with Rhodesia. Shasa had a thirty per cent shareholding in the copper mine at Messina, so when he radioed ahead there was a Ford pick-up waiting for him at the airstrip.

Sean tossed his suitcase in the back of the truck and Shasa took the wheel. Shasa could have flown across the border to Salisbury or Lourenço Marques, but he wanted the break to be clean and definite. Sean crossing a border on foot would be symbolic and salutary. As he drove the last few miles through the dry hot bushveld to the bridge over the Limpopo river, Sean slumped down in the seat beside him, hands in his pockets and one foot up on the dashboard.

'I've been thinking,' he spoke in pleasant conversational tones. 'I've been thinking what I should do now, and I have decided to join one of the safari companies in Rhodesia or Kenya or Mozambique. Then when I've finished my apprenticeship, I'll apply for a hunting concession on my own. There is a fortune in it and it must be the best life in the world. Imagine hunting every day!'

Shasa had determined to remain withdrawn and stern, and up until now he had succeeded in speaking barely a word since leaving Cape Town, but at last Sean's total lack of remorse and his cheerfully selfish view of the future forced Shasa to abandon his good intentions.

'From what I hear, you wouldn't last a week without a woman,' he snapped, and Sean smiled.

'Don't worry about me, Pater. There will be bags of jig-jig, that's part of the perks – the clients are old and rich and they bring their daughters or their new young wives with them – '

'My God, Sean, you are completely amoral.'

'May I take that as a compliment, sir?'

'Your plans to apply for your own hunting concession and to run your own safari company – what do you intend using in lieu of money?'

Sean looked puzzled. 'You are one of the richest men in Africa. Just think – free hunting whenever you wanted it, Pater. That would be part of our deal.'

Despite himself, Shasa felt a prickle of temptation. In fact, he had already considered starting a safari operation and his estimates showed that Sean was correct. There was a fortune to be made in marketing the African wilderness and its unique wild life. The only thing that had prevented him doing it before was that he had never found a trustworthy man who understood the special requirements of a safari company to run it for him.

'Damn it – ' he broke off that line of thought, 'I've spawned a devil's pup. He could sell a secondhand car to the judge who was passing the death sentence on him.' He felt his anger softened by reluctant admiration, but he spoke grimly. 'You don't seem to understand, Sean. This is the end of the road for you and me.'

As he said it they topped the rise. Ahead of them lay the Limpopo river, but despite Mister Rudyard Kipling, it was neither grey green nor greasy and there was not a single fever tree on either bank. This was the dry season and though the river was half a mile wide, the flow was reduced to a thin trickle down the centre of the bed. The long low concrete bridge stretched northwards crossing the orange-coloured sand and straggly clumps of reeds.

They drove over the bridge in silence and Shasa stopped the pick-up at the barrier. The border post was a small square building with a corrugated-iron roof. Shasa kept the engine of the Ford running. Sean climbed out and lifted his suitcase out of the back of the truck, then crossed in front of the bonnet and came to Shasa's open window.

'No, Dad.' He leaned into the window. 'You and I will never reach the end of the road. I am part of you, and I love you too deeply for that ever to happen. You are the only person or thing I have ever loved.'

Shasa studied his face for any trace of insincerity, and when he found none, he reached up impulsively and embraced him. He had not meant this to happen, had been determined that it would not, but now he found himself reaching into the inside pocket of his jacket and bringing out the thick sheaf of banknotes and letters that he had carried with him, despite his best intentions to turn Sean loose without a penny.

'Here are a couple of pounds to tide you over,' he said, and his voice was gruff. 'And there are three letters of introduction to people in Salisbury who may be able to help you.'

Carelessly Sean stuffed them into his pocket and picked up his suitcase.

'Thanks, Pater. I don't deserve it.'

'No,' Shasa agreed. 'You don't – but don't worry too much about it. There won't be any more. That's it, Sean, finished. The first and only instalment of your inheritance.'

As always Sean's smile was a little miracle. It made Shasa doubt, despite all the evidence, that his son was thoroughly bad.

'I'll write, Pater. You'll see, one day we'll laugh about this – when we are together again.'

Lugging his suitcase Sean passed through the barrier, and after he disappeared into the customs hut, Shasa was left with an unbearable sense of futility. Was this how it ended after all the care and love over all the years?

* * *

Shasa was amused by the ease with which Isabella was able to overcome her lisp. Within two weeks of enrolling at Rustenberg Girls' Senior School, she was talking, and looking, like a little lady. Apparently the teachers and her fellow pupils had not been impressed by babytalk.

It was only when she was trying to wheedle her father that she still employed the lisp and the pout. She sat on the arm of his chair now and stroked the silver wings of hair above Shasa's ears.

'I have the most beautiful daddy in the world,' she crooned, and indeed the flashes of silver contrasted with the dense darkness of the rest of his hair and the tanned almost unlined skin of his face to enhance Shasa's looks. 'I have the kindest and most loving daddy in the world.'

'And I have the most scheming little vixen in the world for a daughter,' he said, and she laughed with delight, a sound that made his heart contract, and her breath in his face smelled milky and sweet as a newborn kitten, but he shored up his crumbling defences. 'I have a daughter who is only fourteen years old – '

'Fifteen,' she corrected him.

'Fourteen and a half,' he countered.

'Almost fifteen,' she insisted.

'A daughter under fifteen years of age, who is much too precious to allow out of my house after ten o'clock at night.'

'Oh, my big cuddly growly bear,' she whispered in his ear and hugged him hard, and as she rubbed her soft cheek against his, her breasts rubbed against his arm.

Tara's breasts had always been large and shapely, he still found them immensely attractive. Isabella had inherited them from her. Over the last few months Shasa had watched with pride and interest their phenomenal growth, and now they were firm and warm against his arm.

'Are there going to be boys there?' he asked, and she sensed the first crack in his defence.

'Oh, I'm not interested in boys, Papa,' and she shut her eyes tight in case a thunderbolt came crashing down on her for such a fib. These days Isabella could think of little else but boys, they even occupied her dreams, and her interest in their anatomy was so intense that both Michael and Garry had forbidden her to come into their rooms while they were changing. Her candid and fascinated examination was too disconcerting.

'How will you get there and back? You don't expect your mother to wait up until midnight, do you? And I'll be in Jo'burg that night,' Shasa asked and she opened her eyes.

'Stephen can take me and bring me back.'

'Stephen?' Shasa asked sharply.

'Mommy's new chauffeur. He's so nice and awfully trustworthy – Mommy says so.'

Shasa wasn't aware that Tara had taken on a chauffeur. She usually drove herself, but that reprehensible old Packard of hers had finally given up the ghost when she was away at Sundi and he had prevailed on her to accept a new Chevvy station wagon. Presumably the chauffeur went with it. She should have consulted him – but they had drifted further and further apart over the last few years and seldom discussed domestic routine.

'No,' he said firmly. 'I won't have you driving around on your own at night.'

'I'll be with Stephen,' she pleaded, but he ignored the protest. He knew nothing about Stephen, except that he was male and black.

'I'll tell you what. If you can get a written guarantee from one of the other girls' parents – somebody I know – that they will get you there and back before midnight – well, then, all right, you may go.'

'Oh Daddy! Daddy!' She showered soft warm kisses on his face, and then leapt up and did a little victory pirouette around his study. She had long willowy legs under the flaring skirt and a tight little bottom in lace panties.

'She is probably,' he thought, and then corrected himself, 'she is without doubt the most beautiful child in the entire world.'

Isabella stopped suddenly, and assumed a woebegone expression.

'Oh, Papa!' she cried in anguish.

'What is it now?' Shasa leaned back in his swivel chair and hid his smile.

'Both Patty and Leonora are going to have new dresses, and I shall look an awful frump.'

'A frump, forsooth! We cannot have that now, can we?' And she rushed to him.

'Does that mean I may have a new dress, Daddy darling?' She wound both arms around his neck again. The sound of a motor car coming up the drive interrupted their idyll.

'Here comes Mommy!' Isabella sprang from his lap and seizing his hand dragged him to the window. 'We can tell her about the party and the dress now, can't we, darling Daddy.'

The new Chevrolet with the high tailfins and great chromed grille pulled up at the front steps, and the new chauffeur stepped out. He was an imposing man, tall and broad-shouldered in a dove-grey livery and cap with patent-leather peak. He opened the rear door, and Tara slipped out of her seat. As she passed him she tapped the chauffeur on the arm, an over-friendly gesture so typical of Tara's treatment of the servants which irritated Shasa as much as usual.

Tara came up the front stairs and disappeared from Shasa's view, while the chauffeur went back into the driver's seat and pulled away towards the garages. As he drove below the windows of the study, he glanced up. His face was half obscured by the peak of his cap, but there was something vaguely familiar about his jawline and the way his head was set on that corded neck and those powerful shoulders.

Shasa frowned, trying to place him, but the memory was an ancient one, or erroneous, and then behind him Isabella was calling in her special honeyed voice.

'Oh Mommy, Daddy and I have something to tell you,' and Shasa turned

from the window, steeling himself for Tara's familiar accusation of favouritism and indulgence.

* * *

The hidden door to Shasa's parliamentary suite of offices provided the key to the problem that they had been working on over the weeks that Moses Gama had been in Cape Town.

It was simple enough for Moses to enter the parliament building itself, dressed in chauffeur's livery and carrying an armful of shopping – shoe boxes and hat boxes from the most expensive stores. He merely followed Tara as she swept past the doormen at the front entrance. There was virtually no security in operation, no register to sign, no lapel badges were necessary. A stranger might be asked to show a visitor's pass at the entrance, but as the wife of a cabinet minister, Tara merited a respectful salute, and she made a point of getting to know the doormen. Sometimes she paused to ask after a sick child, or the janitor's arthritis, and with her sunny personality and her concerned condescension, she was soon a favourite of the uniformed staff who guarded the entrance.

She did not take Moses in with her on every occasion, only when she was certain that there was no risk of meeting Shasa. She brought him often enough to establish his presence and his right to be there. When they reached Shasa's suite, Tara would order him to place the parcels in the inner office while she paused to chat with Shasa's secretary. Then, when Moses emerged from the office empty-handed, she would dismiss him lightly.

'Thank you, Stephen. You may go down now. I will need the car at eleven. Please bring it around to the front and wait for me.'

Then Moses would walk down the main staircase, standing respectfully aside for parliamentary messengers and members and cabinet members, once he even passed the prime minister on the stairs, and he had to drop his gaze in case Verwoerd recognized the hatred in his eyes. It gave him a weird feeling of unreality to pass only arm's length from the man who was the author of his people's misery, who more than any other represented all the forces of injustice and oppression. The man who had elevated racial discrimination to a quasi-religious philosophy.

Moses found he was trembling as he went on down the stairs, but he passed the doormen without a glance amd the janitor in his cubicle barely lifted his eyes before concentrating once more on his newspaper. It was vital to Moses' plans that he should be able to leave the building unaccompanied, and constant repetition had made that possible. To the doormen he was almost invisible.

However, they had still not solved the problem of access to Shasa's inner office. Moses might go in there long enough to deposit the armful of parcels, but he could not risk remaining longer, and especially he could not be in there behind a closed door, or alone with Tara. Tricia, Shasa's secretary, was alert and observant, and obsessively loyal to Shasa; like all Shasa's female employees she was more than just a little in love with him.

The discovery of the concealed rear door to the suite came as a blessing when they were almost desperately considering leaving the final preparation to Tara alone.

'Heavens, it was so simple, after all our worrying!' Tara laughed with relief,

and the next time Shasa left for his inspection tour of the H'ani Mine, taking Garry with him as usual, she and Moses made one of their visits to parliament to test their arrangement.

After Moses had left her parcels in the inner office and in front of Tricia, Tara sent him away. 'I won't need the car until much later, Stephen, I'm having lunch with my father in the dining-room.'

Then as he left, closing the outer door behind him, Tara turned back to Tricia.

'I have a few letters to write. I'll use my husband's office. Please see that I'm not disturbed.'

Tricia looked dubious, she knew that Shasa was fussy about his desk and the contents of his drawers, but she could not think of any way to prevent Tara making use of it, and while she hesitated, Tara marched into Shasa's office, closed the door and firmly locked it behind her. Another precedent had been set.

On the outside there was a light tap, and it took her a moment to discover the inside lock, disguised as a light switch. She opened the panelled door a crack, Moses slipped through it into the office. She held her breath against the snap of the lock, and then turned eagerly to Moses.

'Both doors are locked,' she whispered, and she embraced him. 'Oh Moses, Moses – it's been so long.'

Even though they spent so much time in each other's company, the moments of total privacy were rare and precious and she clung to him.

'Not now,' he whispered. 'There is work to do.'

Reluctantly she opened her embrace and let him go. He went to the window first, standing to one side as he drew the drapes so that he could not be seen from outside, and then he switched on the desk lamp and removed his uniform jacket, hanging it on the back of Shasa's chair, before crossing to the altar chest. He paused before it, putting Tara in mind of a worshipper, for his head was bowed and his hands clasped before him reverently. Then he roused himself and lifted the heavy bronze Van Wouw sculpture from the top of the chest. He carried it across the room and placed it on Shasa's desk. He went back and carefully opened the lid, wincing as the antique hinges squeaked.

The interior of the chest had been half-filled with the overflow from Shasa's bookshelves. Piles of old copies of *Hansard*, out-of-date white papers and old parliamentary reports. Moses was annoyed at this unexpected obstacle.

'You must help me,' he whispered to Tara, and between them they began to unpack the chest.

'Keep everything in the same order,' Moses warned, as he passed the piles of publications to her. 'We will have to leave it exactly as it was.'

The chest was so deep that at the end Moses found it easier to climb into it and pass the last of the contents out to her. The carpet was covered with stacks of paper now, but the chest was empty.

'Let me have the tools,' Moses ordered. They were in one of the packets that Moses had carried up from the car, and she handed them to him.

'Don't make any noise,' she pleaded.

The chest was large enough to conceal him completely. She went to the door and listened for a moment. Tricia's typewriter was tapping away reassuringly. Then she went back to the chest and peered into it.

Moses was on his knees working on the floor of the chest with a screwdriver. The screws were authentically antique, taken from another old piece of furniture

so that they were not obvious recent additions, and the floor panels of the chest were likewise aged oak and only close examination by an expert would have revealed that they were not original. Once the screws were loose, Moses lifted out the panels to reveal the compartment beneath. This was tightly packed with cotton waste and gently Moses worked it loose, and as he removed the top layer placed it in the package that contained the tools.

Tara watched with awful fascination as the contents of the first secret compartment came into view. They were small rectangular blocks of some dark amorphous material, like sticky toffee or carpenter's putty, each covered with a translucent greaseproof wrapper and with a label marked in Russian Cyrillic script.

There were ten blocks in the top layer, but Tara knew that there must be two layers below that. Thirty blocks in all, each block weighed two pounds, which made a total of sixty pounds of plastic explosive. It looked mundane and harmless as some kitchen commodity, but Moses had warned her of its lethal power.

'A two-pound brick will destroy the span of a steel bridge, ten pounds would knock down the average house, sixty pounds – ' he shrugged. 'It's enough to do the job ten times over.'

Once he had removed the packing and reassured himself of the contents, Moses replaced the panel and screwed it closed. Then he opened the centre panel of the floor. Again it was packed with cotton waste. As he removed it, he explained in a whisper, 'There are four different types of detonators to cover all possible needs. These,' he gingerly lifted a small flat tin the size of a cigarette pack out of its nest of cotton packing, 'these are electrical detonators that can be wired up to a series of batteries or to the mains. These,' he returned the tin to its slot and lifted the loose cotton to reveal a second larger tin, 'these are radio receiver detonators and are set off by a VHF transmission from this miniature transmitter.' It looked to Tara like one of the modern portable radios. Moses lifted it out of its nest. 'It needs only six torch batteries to activate it. Now these are simple acid time-fused detonators, primitive, and the time delay isn't very accurate, but this here is a trembler detonator. Once it is primed, the slightest movement or vibration will set it off. Only an expert will be able to defuse the charge once it is in place.'

Until this moment she had considered only the abstract dialectic of what they were doing, but now she was faced with the actuality. Here before her was the very stuff of violent death and destruction, the innocent appearance no less menacing than the coils of a sleeping mamba, and she found herself wavering.

'Moses,' she whispered. 'Nobody will be hurt. No human life, you said that – didn't you?'

'We have discussed that already.' His expression was cold and scornful, and she felt ashamed.

'Forgive me, please.'

Moses ignored her and unscrewed the third and last panel. This compartment contained an automatic pistol and four clips of ammunition. It took up little space and the rest of the compartment was packed with cotton waste which Moses removed.

'Give me the other packet,' he ordered, and when she passed it to him, he began to pack the contents into the empty recess. Firstly there was a compact tool kit which contained a keyhole saw and hand drill, drill bits and augers, a box of hearing-aid batteries for the detonator and torch batteries for the

transmitter, a Penlite torch, a five-hundred-foot roll of thin electrical wire, diamond glass-cutters, putty, staples and tiny one-ounce tins of touch-up paint. Lastly there was a pack of hard rations, dried biscuits and cans of meat and vegetables.

'I wish you had let me give you something more apetizing.'

'It will be only two days,' Moses said, and she was reminded how little store he set by creature comforts.

Moses replaced the panel, but he did not tighten the retaining screws fully, so that they could be loosened by hand.

'All right, pass the books to me now.' He repacked the chest, replacing the bundles in the same order as he had found them, so that to a casual glance it would not be apparent that the contents of the chest had been disturbed. Carefully Moses closed the chest and replaced the bronze statue on the lid. Then he stood in front of the desk and surveyed the room carefully.

'I need a place to hide.'

'The drapes,' Tara suggested, and he nodded.

'Not very original, but effective.' The curtains were embroidered brocade, cut full, and they reached the floor.

'A key to that door – I'll need one.' He indicated the hidden door in the panelling.

'I will try – ' Tara began and then broke off as there was a knock on the interleading door. For a moment he thought she might panic and he squeezed her arm to calm her.

'Who is it?' Tara called in a level voice.

'It's me, Mrs Courtney,' Tricia called respectfully. 'It's one o'clock and I'm going to take my lunch.'

'Go ahead, Tricia. I'll be a little longer, but I'll lock up when I leave.'

They heard the outer door close, and then Moses released her arm. 'Go out and search her desk. See if she has a key to the back door.'

Tara was back within minutes with a small bunch of keys. She tried them all in the lock and the third one turned the door in the panelling.

'The serial number is on it.' She scribbled a note of the number on Shasa's noteblock and ripped off the top sheet. 'I'll return the keys to Tricia's desk.'

When she came back, Moses was buttoning his uniform jacket, but she locked the door behind her.

'What I need now is a plan of the building. There must be one in the public works department, and you must get me a copy. Tell Tricia to do it.'

'How?' she asked. 'What excuse can I give?'

'Tell her that you want to change the lighting in here,' he gestured at the chandelier in the roof. 'Tell her you must have an electrical plan of this section, showing the circuits and wall-fittings.'

'Yes, I can do that,' she agreed.

'Good. We are finished here for the time being. We can go now.'

'There is no hurry, Moses. Tricia will not be back for another hour.'

He looked down at her, and for a moment she thought she saw a flash of contempt, even disgust, in those dark brooding eyes, but she would not let herself believe that, and she pressed herself to him, hiding her face against his chest. Within seconds she felt the swelling and hardening of his loins through the cloth that separated their lower bodies, and her doubts were dispelled. She was certain that in his own strange African way he loved her still and she reached down to open his clothing and bring him out.

He was so thick that she could barely encompass him within the circle of her thumb and forefinger, and he was hot and hard as a shaft of black ironstone that had lain in the full glare of the sun at midday.

Tara sank down onto the thick silken rug, drawing him down on top of her.

* * *

Every day now increased the danger of discovery and both of them were aware of it.

'Will Shasa recognize you?' Tara asked Moses more than once. 'It is becoming more and more difficult to keep you from meeting him face to face. He asked about my new chauffeur a few days ago.'

Isabella had apparently drawn Shasa's attention to the new employee for her own selfish reasons, and Tara could cheerfully have thrashed her for it. But there had been the danger of establishing the importance of her new driver even more clearly in the child's devious mind, so she had let it pass without comment.

'Will he know you?' she insisted, and Moses considered it carefully.

'It was long ago, before the war. He was a child.' Moses shook his head. 'The circumstances were so different, the place so remote – and yet for a short while we were close. I believe we made a deep impression upon each other – if merely because of the unlikelihood of such a relationship, black man and white boy becoming familiar, developing an intimate friendship.' He sighed. 'It is certain, however, that at the time of the trial he must have read the intelligence reports and known of the warrant for my arrest which, by the way, is still in force. Whether he would connect the wanted revolutionary criminal with his childhood friend, I do not know, but we cannot take that chance. We must do what has to be done as soon as possible.'

'It seems that Shasa has been out of town every weekend for the last five years.' Tara bit her lip with frustration. 'But now that I want him gone, he won't leave Weltevreden for a single day. First it's this damned polo business.' The Argentinian polo team was touring the country, and Shasa was hosting their stay in Cape Town, while the polo fields of Weltevreden would be the venue for the first test match of their visit. 'Then immediately after that it will be the British prime minister, Harold Macmillan's visit. Shasa won't be leaving Cape Town before the end of the month at the very earliest.' She watched his face in the driving-mirror as he pondered it.

'There is risk either way,' he said softly. 'To delay is as dangerous as to act hastily. We must choose the exact moment.'

Neither of them spoke again until they reached the bus stop, and Moses parked the Chev on the opposite side of the road. Then he switched off the engine and asked:

'This polo match. When will it take place?'

'The test match is on Friday afternoon.'

'Your husband will be playing?'

'The South African team will be announced in the middle of the week, but Shasa is almost certain to be on the team. He might even be chosen as captain.'

'Even if he is not, he will be the host. He must be there.'

'Yes,' Tara agreed.

'Friday – that will give me the whole weekend.' He made up his mind. 'We will do it then.' For a few moments Tara felt the suffocating desperation of somebody trapped in quicksand, sinking slowly, and yet there was an inevitability about it that made fear seem superfluous. There was no escape and she felt instead an enervating sense of acceptance.

'Here is the bus,' Moses said, and she heard the faintest tremor of excitement in his voice. It was one of the very few times that she had ever known his personal feelings to betray him.

As the bus drew up at the halt, she saw the woman and child standing on the platform at the rear. They were both peering eagerly at the parked Chev, and when Tara waved the child hopped down and started across the road. The bus pulled away and Miriam Afrika stayed on the platform at the back of the bus, staring back at them until it turned the next corner.

Benjamin came to meet them, his face bright with anticipation. He was growing into a likely lad, and Miriam always dressed him so well – clean white shirt, grey shorts and polished black shoes. His toffee-coloured skin had a scrubbed look and his crisp dark curls were trimmed into a neat cap.

'Isn't he just too gorgeous?' Tara breathed. 'Our son, Moses, our fine son.'

The boy opened the door and jumped in beside Moses. He looked up at him with a beaming smile and Moses embraced him briefly. Then Tara leaned over the seat and kissed him and gave him a brief but fierce hug. In public she had to limit any show of affection, and as he grew older, their relationship became more difficult and obscure.

The child still believed that Miriam Afrika was his mother, but he was almost six years old now, and a bright intelligent and sensitive boy. She knew that he suspected some special relationship between the three of them. These clandestine meetings were too regular, and emotionally charged, for him not to suspect that something had remained to be fully explained to him.

Benjamin had been told merely that they were good friends of the family, but even at his tender age he would be aware of the social taboos that they were flouting, for his very existence must be permeated by the knowledge that white and black were somehow different and set apart from his own light brown, and sometimes he stared at Tara with a kind of wonder as though she were some fabulous creature from a fairy tale.

There was nothing Tara could think of that could fulfil her more than taking him in her arms and telling him, 'You are my baby, my own true baby, and I love you as much as I love your father.' But she could not even let him sit on the seat beside her in case they were seen together.'

They drove out across the Cape Flats towards Somerset West, but before they reached the village, Moses turned off onto a side track, through the dense stands of Port Jackson willow until they came out on to the long deserted curve of beach with the green waters of False Bay before them, and on each side the mountainous ramparts that formed the horns of the wide bay.

Moses parked the Chev and fetched the picnic basket from the boot, and then the three of them followed the footpath along the top of the beach until they reached their favourite spot. From here anyone approaching along the beach would be obvious from half a mile, while inland the exotic growth formed an almost impenetrable jungle. The only persons likely to venture this far along

the lonely beach were surf fishermen casting into the tumbling waves of kob and steenbras, or lovers seeking seclusion. Here they felt safe.

Tara helped Benjamin change into his bathing-costume, and then all three of them went hand in hand to the enclosed rock pool where the child splashed and played like a spaniel puppy. When at last he was chilled through and tired, Tara towelled down his shivering body and dressed him again. Then he helped Moses build a fire amongst the dunes and grill the raw sausages and chops upon the coals.

After they had eaten, Benjamin wanted to swim again, but gently Tara forbade him. 'Not on a full stomach, darling.' So he went to search for shells along the tide-mark of the beach, and Tara and Moses sat on the crest of the dune and watched him. Tara was as happy and contented as she could ever remember being until Moses broke the silence.

'This is what we are working for,' he said. 'Dignity and a chance for happiness for all in this land.'

'Yes, Moses,' she whispered.

'It is worth any price.'

'Oh, yes,' she agreed fervently. 'Oh yes!'

'Part of the price is the execution of the architect of our misery,' he said sharply. 'I have kept this from you until now, but Verwoerd must die and all his henchmen with him. Destiny has appointed me his executioner – and his successor.'

Tara paled at his words, but they came as such a shock that she could not speak. Moses took her hand with a strange and unusual gentleness.

'For you, for me and for the child – that he may live with us in the sunshine of freedom.'

She tried to speak, but her voice faltered, and he waited patiently until she was able to enunciate.

'Moses, you promised!'

'No.' He shook his head. 'You persuaded yourself of that, and it was not the time to disillusion you.'

'Oh God, Moses!' The enormity of it crashed in upon her. 'I thought you were going to blow up the empty building as a symbolic gesture, but all along you planned to – ' she broke off, unable to complete the sentence, and he did not deny it.

'Moses – my husband Shasa, he will be on the bench beside Verwoerd.'

'Is he your husband?' Moses asked. 'Is he not one of them, one of the enemy?' She lowered her eyes to acknowledge the truth of this, and then suddenly she was agitated again.

'My father – he will be in the House.'

'Your father and your husband are part of your old life. You have left that behind you. Now, Tara, I am both your father and your husband, and the struggle is your new life.'

'Moses, isn't there some way they can be spared?' she pleaded.

He did not speak, but she saw the answer in his eyes and she covered her face with both hands and began to weep. She wept silently, but the spasms of grief shook her whole body. Down on the beach the child's happy cries came to her faintly on the wind, and beside her Moses sat unmoving and without expression. After a while, she lifted her head and wiped the tears from her face with the palms of her hands.

'I'm sorry, Moses,' she whispered. 'I was weak, please forgive me. I was

mourning my father, but now I am strong again, and ready to do whatever you require of me.'

* * *

The test match against the visiting Argentinian polo team was the most exciting event that had taken place at Weltevreden in a decade or more.

As mistress of the estate, the planning and organization of the event should have fallen to Tara, but her lack of interest in the sport and her poor organizational skills were too much for Centaine Courtney-Malcomess to abide. She began by giving discreet advice and ended in exasperation by taking all responsibility out of her daughter-in-law' hands. The result was that the occasion was in every respect a towering success. After Centaine had chivvied the coloured greensman, and with Blaine's expert advice, the turf on the field was green and velvety, the going beneath it neither hard enough to jar the legs of the ponies nor soft enough to slow them down. The goalposts were painted in the colours of the teams, the pale blue and white of Argentina, and orange, blue and white of South Africa, and two hundred flags in the same colours flew from the grandstand.

The stand itself was freshly painted, as were the fence pickets and the stables. A fence was erected to keep the general public out of the château's private grounds, but the new facilities designed by Centaine especially for the occasion included an extension to the grandstand, with public toilets below and an open air restaurant that could seat two hundred guests. The extensions of the stables were sufficient for fifty ponies, and there were new quarters for the grooms. The Argentinians had brought their own, and they wore traditional gaucho costume with wide hats and their chaps decorated with silver coins.

Garry tore himself away from his new office at Centaine House which was on the top floor, only three doors down from Shasa, and he spent two days at the stables watching and learning from these masters of horsecraft and the game of polo.

Michael had at last managed to secure an official assignment. He blissfully believed that the *Golden City Mail* in Johannesburg had appointed him their local correspondent on his own merits as a cub-reporter. Centaine, who had made a discreet telephone call to the chairman of Associated Newspapers of South Africa who owned the *Mail*, did nothing to disillusion him. Michael was to be paid five guineas for the day, plus a shilling a word for any copy of his actually printed by the newspaper. He interviewed every member of both teams, including the reserves, all the grooms, the umpire and referees. He drew up a full history and score card of all previous matches played between the two countries going back to the 1936 Olympic Games, and he worked out the pedigrees of all the ponies – but here he showed restraint by limiting the listing to only two generations. Even before the match day he had written enough to make *Gone with the Wind* look like a pamphlet. Then he insisted on telephoning this important copy through to a long-suffering sub at the newspaper offices, and the telephone charges far outstripped his five-guinea salary.

'Anyway, Mickey,' Shasa consoled him, 'if they print everything you have written at a shilling a word, you'll be a millionaire.'

The big disappointment for the family came on the Wednesday when the

South African team was announced. Shasa was chosen to play in his usual position at Number Two but he was passed over for the captaincy. This went to Max Theunissen, a flamboyant, hard-riding millionaire farmer from Natal who was a long-time rival of Shasa's, ever since their first meeting on this same field as juniors many years before.

Shasa hid his disappointment behind a rueful grin. 'It means more to Max than it does to me,' he told Blaine, who was one of the selectors, and Blaine nodded.

'Yes,' he agreed. 'That's why we gave it to him, Shasa. Max values it.'

Isabella fell desperately in love with the Argentinian Number Four, a paragon of masculinity with olive skin, dark flashing eyes, thick wavy hair and dazzling white teeth.

She changed her frock three and four times a day, trying out all the most sophisticated of the clothes with which Shasa had filled her wardrobes. She even applied a very light coat of rouge and lipstick, not enough to catch Shasa's attention but just enough, she hoped, to pique José Jesús Goncalves, De Santos' interest. She exercised all her ingenuity in waylaying him, hanging around the stables endlessly and practising her most languid poses whenever he hove into view.

The object of her adoration was a man in his early thirties who was convinced that the Argentinian male was the world's greatest lover and that he, José Jesús Goncalves De Santos, was the national champion. There were at least a dozen mature and willing ladies vying for his attention at any one time. He did not even notice the antics of this fourteen-year-old child, but Centaine did.

'You are making an exhibition of yourself, Bella,' she told her. 'From now on you are forbidden to go near the stables, and if I see one speck of make-up on your face again, you may be certain your father will learn about it.'

Nobody went against Nana's orders, not even the boldest and most love-lorn, so Isabella was forced to abandon her fantasy of ambushing José in the hayloft above the stables and presenting him with her virginity. Isabella was not entirely certain what this entailed. Lenora had lent her a forbidden book which referred to it as 'a pearl beyond price'. Whatever it was, José Jesús could have her pearl and anything else he wanted.

However, Nana's strictures reduced her to trailing around after him at a discreet distance, and directing burning but long-range looks at him whenever he glanced in her direction.

Garry intercepted one of these passionate looks and was so alarmed by it that he demanded in a loud voice, and within earshot of her beloved, 'Are you sick, Bella? You keep looking like you are going to throw up.' It was the first time in her life that she truly hated her middle brother.

Centaine had planned for two thousand spectators. Polo was an elite sport with a limited following, and at two pounds each, tickets were expensive, but on the day the gate exceeded five thousand. This guaranteed the club a healthy profit but put a considerable strain on Centaine's logistics. All her reserves, which included Tara, were thrown in to deal with the overflow and to organize the additional food and drink required, and only when the teams rode out on to the field could Tara escape her mother-in-law's all-seeing eye and go up into the stand.

For the first chukka Shasa was riding a bay gelding whose hide was burnished until it shone like a mirror in the sunlight. In his green jersey piped with gold, and his snowy white breeches and glossy black boots, Tara had to admit to

herself that Shasa looked magnificent. As he cantered below the stand he looked up and smiled, the black eye-patch gave an intriguing sinister nuance to his otherwise boyish and charming grin, and despite herself Tara responded, waving to him, until she realized that Shasa was not smiling at her but at someone below her in the stand. Feeling a little foolish, she stood on tiptoe and peered down to try and see who it was. The woman was tall with a narrow waist, but her face was obscured by the brim of a garden party hat decorated with roses. However, the arm she lifted to wave at Shasa was slim and tanned with diamond engagement and gold wedding rings on the third finger of her shapely hand.

Tara turned away and removed her hat so that Centaine could not easily pick her out of the crowd, and she worked her way quickly but unobtrusively to the side exit of the stand. As she crossed the carpark and headed around the back of the stables, the first roaring cheer went up from the stand. Nobody would look for her for a couple of hours now, and she began to run. Moses had the Chev parked in the plantation of pines, near the guest cottages and she pulled open the back door and tumbled into the seat.

'Nobody saw me leave,' she panted, and he started the engine and drove sedately down the long driveway and out through the Anreith gateway.

Tara checked her wristwatch; it was a few minutes past three o'clock, but it would take forty minutes to round the mountain and reach the city. They would reach the parliament building at four o'clock when the doormen were thinking about their tea-break. It was a Friday afternoon, and the House was in Committee of Supply, the kind of boring routine business which would leave the members nodding on the benches. In fact, Blaine and Shasa had tactfully arranged this schedule with the whips so that they, and quite a few of their peers, might sneak away to the polo without missing any important debate or division. Many of the other members must have made plans to leave early for the weekend, for the building was quiet and the lobby almost deserted.

Moses parked in the members' carpark and went around to the back of the station wagon to bring out the packages. Then he followed Tara at a respectful distance as she climbed the front staircase. Nobody challenged them, it was all so easy, almost an anti-climax, and they went up to the second floor, past the press gallery entrance, where Tara had a glimpse of three junior reporters slumped dispiritedly on their benches as they listened to the honourable minister of posts and telegraphs droning out his self-congratulations on the exemplary fashion in which he had conducted his department during the previous fiscal year.

Tricia was sitting behind her desk in the outer office painting her fingernails with varnish, and she looked flustered and guilty as Tara walked in.

'Oh, Tricia, that is a pretty colour,' Tara said sweetly, and Tricia tried to look as though her fingers didn't belong to her, but the varnish was wet and she didn't quite know what to do with them.

'I've finished all the letters Mr Courtney left for me,' she tried to excuse herself, 'and it's been so quiet today, and I've got a date tonight – I just thought – ' she petered out lamely.

'I've brought up some samples of curtain material,' Tara told her. 'I thought we'd change them when we installed the new light fittings. I would like it to be a surprise for Shasa, so don't mention it to him, if you can avoid it.'

'Of course not, Mrs Courtney.'

'I will be trying to work out the new colour scheme for the curtains, and I'll

probably be here until long after five o'clock. If you've finished your work, why don't you go off early? I will take any phone calls.'

'Oh, I'd feel bad about that,' Tricia protested half-heartedly.

'Off you go!' Tara ordered firmly. 'I'll hold the fort. You enjoy your date – I hope you have a lovely evening.'

'It's so kind of you, Mrs Courtney. It really is.'

'Stephen, take those samples through and put them on the couch please,' Tara ordered without looking at Moses, and she lingered while Tricia cleared her desk with alacrity and headed for the door.

'Have a super weekend, Mrs Courtney – and thanks a lot.'

Tara locked the door after her and hurried through to the inner office.

'That was a bit of luck,' she whispered.

'We should give her some time to get clear,' Moses told her, and they sat side by side on the sofa.

Tara looked nervous and unhappy, but she kept silent for many minutes before she blurted out, 'Moses, about my father – and Shasa'

'Yes?' he asked, but his voice was bleak, and she hesitated, twisting her fingers together nervously.

'Yes?' he insisted.

'No – you are right,' she sighed. 'It has to be done. I must be strong.'

'Yes, you must be strong,' he agreed. 'But now you must go, and leave me to do my work.'

She stood up. 'Kiss me please, Moses,' she whispered, and then after a moment broke from his embrace. 'Good luck,' she said softly.

She locked the outer door of the office and went down the staircase into the main lobby, and half-way down she was suddenly overwhelmed by a sense of doom. It was so strong that she felt the blood drain from her head and an icy sweat broke out on her forehead and upper lip. For a moment she felt dizzy, and had to clutch the banisters to prevent herself from falling. Then she forced herself to go on down and cross the lobby.

The janitor was staring at her strangely. She kept walking. He was leaving his cubicle and coming to intercept her. She felt panic come at her and she wanted to turn and run back up the stairs, to warn Moses that she had been discovered.

'Mrs Courtney.' The janitor stopped in front of her, blocking her path.

'What is it?' she faltered, trying to think up a plausible reply to his demands.

'I've got a small bet on the polo this afternoon, do you know how it's going?' She stared at him, and for a moment it did not make sense. She almost blurted out, 'Polo, what polo?' and then she caught herself and with an enormous effort of will and concentration chatted with the man for almost a minute before she could escape. In the carpark she could no longer control her panic and she ran to the Chev and flung herself behind the wheel sobbing for breath.

* * *

When he heard the key turn in the lock of the outer door, Moses went back into Shasa's office and drew the drapes over the windows.

Then he went to the bookshelves and studied the titles. He would not unpack the altar chest until the last moment. Tricia might return for something she had

forgotten, there might be a routine check of the offices by the parliamentary staff. Shasa might even come in on the Saturday morning. Although Tara had assured him that Shasa would be fully occupied at Weltevreden with his guests over the whole weekend, Moses would take no chances. He would disturb nothing in the office until it was absoloutely necessary.

He smiled as he saw Macaulay's *History of England* on the shelf. It was an expensive leather-bound edition, and it brought back vivid memories of the time when he and the man he was about to kill had been friends – of that time long ago when there had still been hope.

He passed on down the shelves until he reached a section in which Shasa obviously kept all those works with whose principles he differed, works ranging from *Mein Kampf* to Karl Marx with Socialism in between. Moses chose a volume of the collected works of Lenin and took it across to the desk. He settled down to read, confident that any unwanted visitor must give him sufficient time to reach his hiding-place behind the drapes.

He read until the dusk fell and the light failed in the room, then he took the blanket from the package he had brought up from the Chev and settled down on the sofa.

He woke early on Saturday morning, when the rock pigeons began crooning on the ledge outside the window, and let himself out of the panel door. He used the toilets at the end of the passage in the knowledge that it was going to be a long day, and took a cynical pleasure in defying the 'Whites Only' sign on the door.

Although the House did not sit on a Saturday, the main doors were open and there would still be some activity in the building, cleaners and staff, perhaps ministers using their offices. He could do nothing until the Sunday, when Calvinist principles forbade any work or unnecessary activity outside the body of the church. Again he spent the day reading, and at nightfall he ate from the supplies he had brought with him and disposed of the empty cans and wrappers in the rubbish bin in the toilets.

He slept fitfully and was fully awake before dawn on Sunday morning. He ate a frugal breakfast and changed into workman's overalls and tennis shoes from the package before he began a cautious reconnaissance of the House. The building was utterly silent and deserted. Looking down the stairs he saw that the front doors were barred and all the lights were extinguished. He moved about with more confidence, and tried the door to the press gallery. It was unlocked and he stood at the rail and looked down into the chamber where all the laws that had enmeshed and enslaved his people had been enacted and he felt his rage like a captive animal inside his chest, clamouring to be set free.

He left the gallery and went down the staircase into the entrance lobby and approached the high main doors of the chamber. His footsteps echoed from the marble slabs. As he had expected, the doors were locked, but the locks were massive antiques. He knelt in front of them, and from his pocket took the folding wallet of locksmith's picks. His training in Russia had been exhaustively thorough and the lock resisted him for less than a minute. He opened one leaf of the door a crack and slipped through, closing it behind him.

Now he stood in the very cathedral of *apartheid*, and it seemed to him that the evil of it was a palpable thing that pressed in upon him with a physical weight and shortened his breathing. He moved slowly up the aisle towards the Speaker's throne with the massive coat of arms above it, and then he turned to the left, skirting the table on which the mace and despatch boxes would lie,

until he stood at the head of the government front benches, at the seat of the prime minister, Dr Hendrik Frensch Verwoerd, and Moses' broad nostrils flared open as though he smelled the odour of the great beast.

With an effort he roused himself, setting aside his feelings and his passions and became as objective as a workman. He examined the bench carefully, going down on his stomach to peer beneath it. Of course, he had studied every photograph of the chamber that he had been able to obtain, but these had been pathetically inadequate. Now he ran his hands over the green leather; the padding was indented by the weight of the men who had sat upon it, and at this close range it was scuffed and cracked with wear over the years. The bench frame was of massive mahogany, and when he groped up beneath the seat he found the heavy cross members that strengthened it. There were no surprises here, and he grunted with satisfaction.

He returned to Shasa's office, letting himself in through the panel door, and went immediately to unpack the altar chest. Once again he was careful to lay out the contents so that it could be repacked in exactly the same order. Then he climbed into the chest and lifted the floor panels.

The food he set aside for his evening meal, and he piled the blocks of plastic into the blanket. One of the advantages of this explosive was that it was inert and could endure the roughest handling. Without a detonator, it was completely safe.

He picked up the four corners of the blanket and slung it over his shoulder like a tent bag, and then hurriedly went down to the assembly chamber again. He stowed the blanket and its contents under a bench where it would escape casual discovery and went back to the office to fetch the tool kit. The third time he descended to the chamber, he locked the main doors behind him, so as to be able to work in total security.

He could not risk the noise of using an electric drill. He lay on his back beneath the prime minister's bench and began laboriously setting the staples into the mahogany above his face, boring the holes with the hand drill and then screwing in the threaded staples. He worked meticulously, pausing to measure and mark each hole so it was almost an hour before he was ready to start placing the blocks of plastic. He arranged them in stacks of five, ten pounds of plastic in each stack, and wired them together. Then he wriggled back under the bench and secured each stack of five blocks in place. He threaded each tag of wire through the loop of a separate staple and twisted them up tightly, then he reached for the next stack of bricks and set that in neatly against the last until the entire underside of the bench was lined with explosive.

Then he crawled out and checked his progress. There was a lip of mahogany below the leather cushion which completely hid the layer of blocks. Even when he squatted down as a person might do to retrieve a pen or fallen order paper from under the bench, he could not see a trace of his handiwork.

'That will do,' he murmured, and started to clean up. Meticulously he brushed up every speck, of sawdust from the drilling and the offcuts of wire, then he gathered his tools.

'Now we can test the transmitter,' he told himself and hurried upstairs to Shasa's office.

He inserted the new torch batteries in the transmitter and checked it. The test globe lit up brightly. He switched it off. Next he took the radio detonator from its cardboard box and placed the hearing-aid battery in its compartment. The detonator was the size of a matchbox, made of black bakelite with a small

toggle switch at one end. The switch had three positions: 'off', 'test' and 'receive'. A thin twist of wire prevented the switch accidentally being moved to 'on'. Moses switched it to 'test' and laid it on the sofa, then he went to the transmitter and flipped the 'on' switch. Immediately the tiny globe at the end of the detonator case lit up and there was a loud buzz, like a trapped bee inside the casing. It had received the signal from the transmitter. Moses switched off the transmitter and the buzz ceased and the globe extinguished.

'Now I must check if it will transmit from here to the assembly chamber.'

He left the transmitter on and descended once again to the chamber. Kneeling beside the prime minister's bench, he held the detonator in the palm of his hand and held his breath as he switched it to 'test'.

Nothing happened. He tried it three times more, but it would not receive the signal from the office upstairs. Clearly there was too much brick and reinforced concrete between the two pieces of equipment.

'It was going too easily,' he told himself ruefully. 'There had to be a snag somewhere,' and he sighed as he took the roll of wire from the tool kit. He had wanted to avoid stringing wire from the chamber to the office on the second floor; even though the wire was gossamer thin and the insulating cover was a matt brown, it would infinitely increase the risk of discovery.

'Nothing else for it,' he consoled himself.

He had already studied the electrical wiring plan of the building that Tara had procured from the public works department, but he unrolled it and spread it on the bench beside him to refresh his memory as he worked.

There was a wall plug on the panelling behind the back benches of the government section. From the plan he saw that the conduit was laid behind the panelling and went up the wall into the roof. The diagram also showed the main fuse box in the janitor's office opposite the front door. The office was locked but he picked the lock without difficulty and threw the main switch.

Then he returned to the chamber, located the wall plug and removed the cover, exposing the wiring, and was relieved to find that it was colour-coded. That would make the job a lot easier.

So he left the chamber and went up to the second floor. There was a cleaner's cupboard in the men's toilet that contained a step-ladder. The trap door that gave access to the roof was also in the men's toilet. He found it and set the step-ladder below it. From the top of the ladder he removed the trap door and wriggled up through the square opening.

The space below the roof and the ceiling was dark and smelled of rats. He switched on his Penlite and began to pick his way through the forest of timber joists and roof posts. The dust had been undisturbed for years and rose in a lanquid cloud around his feet. He sneezed and covered his mouth and nose with a handkerchief as he went forward carefully, stepping from beam to beam, counting each pace to keep himself orientated.

Above the exposed section of wall that was certainly the top of the rear side wall of the chamber, he found the electrical conduits. There were fifteen of them laid side by side. Some had been there a long time, while others were obviously new additions.

It took him a while to isolate the conduit that led down to the chamber below, but when he unscrewed the joint in it, he recognized the coded wiring of the wall-socket that it contained. His relief was intense. He had anticipated a number of problems that he might have encountered at this stage, but now it would be a simple matter to get his own wire into the roof.

He uncoiled the long flexible electrician's spring that he had brought from his tools and fed the end of it into the open conduit tubing until he felt it encounter resistance. Then he began the tedious journey back through the roof, down the step-ladder, along the passage, down the staircase and into the chamber.

He found the end of the electrician's spring protruding from the open wall-socket, and he attached the end of the coil of light detonator wire to it and laid out the rest of the wire so that it would feed smoothly into the conduit when he drew the spring in from the other end.

Back in the roof he recovered the spring and the end of the wire came up with it. Gently he drew in the rest of it, working overhand like a fisherman recovering his handline until it came up firmly against the knot that held the far end to the bench in the chamber below. He coiled the wire neatly and left it, while he returned to the chamber. By this time his overalls were filthy with dust and cobwebs.

He untied the loose end of the wire from the bench and laid it out on the floor, leading it to the pack of plastic explosive under the front bench, making certain he had given himself sufficient slack. Then he worked carefully to conceal the exposed wire from casual detection. He threaded it under the green wall-to-wall carpeting and stapled it securely to the underside of the government benches. He filed a notch in the enamelled metal plate that covered the wall-socket and laid the wire into it while he screwed the cover back into place.

Then he went carefully over the floor and carpet to make certain he had left no trace of his work. Apart from the few inches of unobtrusive wire protruding from the wall socket, there was nothing to betray his preparations and he sat on Dr Verwoerd's bench to rest for a few minutes before beginning the final phase. He returned upstairs.

The most difficult and frustrating part of the entire job was placing himself in the roof directly above Shasa's office. Three times he had to climb down the ladder into the toilet and then pace out the angles of the passages and the exact location of the office suite before once more climbing back into the ceiling and attempting to follow the same route through the dust and the roof timbers.

Finally he was sure he was in the correct position and gingerly he bored a small hole through the ceiling between his feet. Light came up through the hole, but even when he knelt and placed his eye to the aperture, it was too small to see what lay below. He enlarged it slightly, but he still could see nothing, and yet again he had to make the journey back to the trap door and along the passage to Shasa's office.

Immediately he let himself into the office he saw that he had misjudged. The hole he had bored through the ceiling was directly above the desk, and in enlarging it he had cracked the plaster and dislodged a few fragments which had fallen on to the desk top. He realized this was a serious mistake. The hole was not large, but the network of hair cracks around it would be apparent to anyone studying the ceiling.

He thought about trying to cover or repair the damage but knew that he would only aggravate it. He brushed the white crumbs of plaster off the desk, but this was all he could do. He would have to take comfort in the unlikelihood that anybody would look at the ceiling, and even if they did, that they would think nothing of the minute blemish. Angrily aware of his mistake, he did what he should have done originally and bored the next hole from below, standing on one of the bookshelves to reach the ceiling. Between the window drapes and

the edge of the bookshelves, the hole was almost invisible to any but the most painstaking inspection. He went up into the roof and paid the end of the wire down through the second hole. When he returned to the office he found it dangling down the wall, the end of it lying in a tangle on the carpet in the corner.

He gathered and coiled the end and tucked it carefully behind the row of *Encyclopaedia Britannica* on the top shelf and then arranged the window drapes to cover the two or three inches that were visible protruding from the puncture in the ceiling. Once again he cleaned up, going over the shelf and floor for the last speck of plaster, and then, still not satisfied, returning to the desk. Another tiny crumb of white plaster had fallen and he wetted his finger with saliva and picked it up. Then he polished the desk top with his sleeve.

He left the office through the panel door, and went back over everything he had done. He closed the trap door in the roof of the toilet and brushed up the dust that he had dislodged. He replaced the cleaner's ladder in the closet and then returned for the last time to the chamber.

At last he was ready to wire up the detonator. He removed the wire safety device and switched the detonator on. He bored a hole in the soft centre block of explosive and placed the detonator into it. He taped it firmly in place, and then scraped the last inch of insulation from the gleaming copper wire and screwed that into the connector in the end of the black cylindrical detonator and crawled out from under the bench.

He gathered up his tools, made one last thorough check for any tell-tale evidence, and then satisfied at last, he left the chamber, locking the main doors behind him and carefully polishing his sweaty fingerprints from the gleaming brass. Then he let himself into the janitor's office and switched on the current at the mains.

He retreated up the stairs for the last time and locked himself in Shasa's office before he checked his wristwatch. It was almost half past four. It had taken him all day, but he had worked with special care and he was well satisfied as he slumped down on the sofa. The strain on his nerves and the unremitting need for total concentration had been more wearying than any physical endeavour.

He rested awhile before repacking the altar chest. He stuffed his dirty overalls into the empty explosives compartment and placed the transmitter on top of them where he could reach it quickly. It would be a few minutes' work to retrieve it, connect it to the loose wire that was concealed behind the row of encyclopaedia, close the circuit and fire the detonator in the chamber below. He had calculated that Shasa's office was far enough from the centre of the blast, and that there were sufficient walls and cast concrete slabs between to cushion the effects of the explosion and ensure his own survival, but the chamber itself would be totally devastated. A good day's work indeed, and as the light in the room faded, he settled down on the sofa and pulled the blanket up over his shoulders.

At dawn he roused himself and made one last check of the office, glancing ruefully up at the insignificant spider-web of cracks in the ceiling. He gathered up his packages, then he let himself out through the panel door and went to the men's toilet.

He washed and shaved in one of the basins. Tara had provided a razor and hand towel in the packet of food. Then he donned his chauffeur's jacket and cap and locked himself in one of the toilets. He could not wait in Shasa's office for Tricia would come in at nine o'clock, nor could he leave until the House

activity was in full swing and he could pass out through through the front doors unremarked.

He sat on the toilet seat and waited. At nine o'clock he heard footsteps passing down the passage. Then somebody came in and used the cubicle next to his, grunting and farting noisily. At intervals over the next hour men came in, singly or in groups, to use the basins and urinals. However, in the middle of the morning there was a lull. Moses stood up, gathered his parcels, braced himself, let himself out of the cubicle, and briskly crossed to the door into the passage.

The passageway was empty and he started towards the head of the staircase, and then halfway there he chilled with horror and checked in mid-stride.

Two men came up the stairs, and into the passageway, directly towards Moses. Walking side by side, they were in earnest conversation and the shorter and elder of the two was gesticulating and grimacing with the vehemence of his explanation. The younger taller man beside him was listening intently, and his single eye gleamed with suppressed amusement.

Moses forced himself to walk on to meet them, and his expression fixed in to that dumb patient mould with which the African conceals all emotion in the presence of his white master. As they approached each other, Moses stepped respectfully aside to let the two of them pass. He did not look directly at Shasa Courtney's face, but let his eyes slide by without making contact.

As they came level, Shasa burst out laughing at what his companion had told him.

'The silly old ass!' he exclaimed, and he glanced sideways at Moses. His laughter checked and a puzzled frown creased his forehead. Moses thought he was going to stop, but his companion seized his sleeve.

'Wait for the best bit – she wouldn't give him his pants until he – ' he led Shasa on towards his own office, and without looking back or quickening his pace, Moses went on down the staircase and out through the front doors.

The Chev was parked in the lot at the top of the lane where he expected it to be. Moses placed his parcels in the back and then went round to the driver's door. As he slid in between the steering-wheel, Tara leaned forward from the back seat and whispered:

'Oh thank God, I was so worried about you.'

* * *

The arrival of Harold Macmillan and his entourage in Cape Town engendered real excitement and anticipation, not only in the mother city but throughout the entire country.

The British prime minister was on the final leg of an extensive journey down the length of Africa where he had visited each of the British colonies and members of the Commonwealth on the continent, of which South Africa was the largest and richest and most prosperous.

His arrival meant different things for different sections of the white population. For the English-speaking community it was an affirmation of the close ties and deep commitment that they felt towards the old country. It reinforced the secure sense of being part of the wider body of the Commonwealth, and the certain knowledge that there still existed between their two countries, who had

stood solidly beside each other for a century and more through terrible wars and economic crises, a bond of blood and suffering that could never be eroded. It gave them an opportunity to reaffirm their loyal devotion to the queen.

For the Nationalist Afrikaners it meant something entirely different. They had fought two wars against the British crown, and though many Afrikaners had volunteered to fight beside Britain in two other wars – Delville Wood and El Alamein were only part of their battle honours – many others, including most members of the Nationalist cabinet, had vehemently opposed the declarations of war against Kaiser Wilhelm and Adolf Hitler. The Nationalist cabinet included members who had actively fought against the Union of South Africa's war efforts under Jan Smuts, and many now high in government, men like Manfred De La Rey, had been members of the *Ossewa Brandwag*. To these men the British prime minister's visit was an acknowledgement of their sovereign rights and their importance as rulers of the most advanced and prosperous nation on the continent of Africa.

During his stay Harold Macmillan was a guest at Groote Schuur the official residence of the South African prime minister, and the climax of his visit was to be an address to both houses of the legislature of the Union of South Africa, the Senate and the House of Assembly, sitting together. On the evening of his arrival in Cape Town, the British prime minister was to be the guest of honour at a private dinner party to meet the ministers of Dr Verwoerd's cabinet, the leaders of the opposition United Party and other dignitaries.

Tara hated these official functions with a passion, but Shasa was insistent. 'Part of our bargain, my dear. The invitation is specifically for Mr and Mrs, and you promised not to make an ass of me in public.'

In the end she even wore her diamonds, something she had not done in years, and Shasa was appreciative and complimentary.

'You really are a corker when you take the trouble to spruce up like that,' he told her, but she was silent and distracted on the drive around the southern slope of Table Mountain to Groote Schuur.

'Something is troubling you,' Shasa said as he steered the Rolls with one hand and lit a cigarette with his gold Ronson lighter.

'No,' she denied quickly. 'Just the prospect of saying the right things to a room full of strangers.'

The true reason for her concern was a long way from that. Three hours previously, while Moses drove her back from a meeting of the executive of the Women's Institute, he had told her quietly. 'The date and the time has been set.' He did not have to elaborate. Since she had picked him up outside the Parliament House just after ten o'clock the previous Monday, Tara had been haunted night and day by her terrible secret knowledge.

'When?' she whispered.

'During the Englishman's speech,' he said simply, and Tara winced. The logic of it was diabolical.

'Both houses sitting together,' Moses went on. 'All of them, all the slave-masters and the Englishman who is their accomplice and their protector. They will die together. It will be an explosion that will be heard in every corner of our world.'

Beside her Shasa snapped the cap of the Ronson and snuffed out the flame. 'It won't be all that unpleasant. I've arranged with protocol that you will be Lord Littleton's dinner partner – you get on rather well with him, don't you?'

'I didn't know he was here,' Tara said vaguely. Their conversation seemed so petty and pointless in the face of the holocaust which she knew was coming.

'Special adviser on trade and finance to the British government.' Shasa slowed the Rolls and lowered his side window as he turned into the main gates of Groote Schuur and joined the line of limousines that were moving slowly down the driveway. He showed his invitation to the captain of the guard and received a respectful salute.

'Good evening, Minister. Please go straight on down to the front entrance.'

Groote schuur was high Dutch for 'The Great Barn'. It had once been the home of Cecil John Rhodes, empire builder and adventurer, who had used it as his residence while he was prime minister of the old Cape Colony before the act of Union in 1910 had united the separate provinces into the present Union of South Africa. Rhodes had left the huge house, restored after it was destroyed by fire, to the nation. It was a massive and graceless building, reflecting Rhodes' confessed taste for the barbaric, a mixture of different styles of architecture all of which Tara found offensive.

Yet the view from the lower slopes of Table Mountain out over the Cape Flats was spectacular, a field of lights spreading out to the dark silhouette of the mountains that rose against the moon-bright sky. Tonight the bustle and excitement seemed to rejuvenate the ponderous edifice.

Every window blazed with light and the uniformed footmen were meeting the guests as they alighted from their limousines and ushering them up the broad front steps to join the reception line in the entrance lobby. Prime Minister Verwoerd and his wife Betsie were at the head of the line, but Tara was more interested in their guest.

She was surprised by Macmillan's height, almost as tall as Verwoerd, and by the close resemblance he bore to all the cartoons she had seen of him. The tufts of hair above his ears, the horsy teeth and the scrubby moustache. His handshake was firm and dry and his voice as he greeted her was soft and plummy, and then she and Shasa had passed on into the main drawing-room where the other dinner guests were assembling.

There was Lord Littleton coming to her, still wearing the genteelly shabby dinner jacket, the watered silk of the lapels tinged with the verdigris of age, but his smile was alight with genuine pleasure.

'Well, my dear, your presence makes the evening an occasion for me!' He kissed Tara's cheek and then turned to Shasa. 'Must tell you of our recent travels across Africa – fascinating,' and the three of them were chatting animatedly.

Tara's forebodiungs were for the moment forgotten, as she exclaimed, 'Now, Milord, you cannot hold up the Congo as being typical of emerging Africa. Left to his own devices, Patrice Lumumba would be an example of what a black leader – '

'Lumumba is a rogue, and a convicted felon. Now Tshombe – ' Shasa interrupted her and Tara rounded on him. 'Tshombe is a stooge and a Quisling, a puppet of Belgian colonialism.'

'At least he isn't eating the opposition like Lumumba's lads are,' Littleton interjected mildly, and Tara turned back to him with the battle light in her eyes.

'That isn't worthy of somebody – ' she broke off with an effort. Her orders were to avoid radical arguments and to maintain her role as a dutiful establishment wife.

'Oh, it's so boring,' she said. 'Let's talk about the London theatre. What is on at the moment?'

'Well, just before I left I saw *The Caretaker*, Pinter's new piece,' Littleton accepted the diversion, and Shasa glanced across the room. Manfred De La Rey was watching him with those pale eyes, and as he caught Shasa's eye he inclined his head sharply.

'Excuse me a moment,' Shasa murmured, but Littleton and Tara were so occupied with each other that they barely noticed him move away and join Manfred and his statuesque German wife.

Manfred always seemed ill at ease in tails, and the starched wing collar of his dress shirt bit into his thick neck and left a vivid red mark on the skin.

'So, my friend,' he teased Shasa. 'The dagoes from South America thrashed you at your horse games, hey?'

Shasa's smile slipped a fraction. 'Eight to six is hardly a massacre,' he protested, but Manfred was not interested in his defence.

He took Shasa's arm and leaned closer to him, still smiling jovially as he said, 'There is some nasty work going on.'

'Ah!' Shasa smiled easily and nodded encouragement.

'Macmillan has refused to show Doctor Henk a copy of the speech he is going to deliver tomorrow.'

'Ah!' This time Shasa had difficulty in maintaining the smile. If this was a fact, then the British prime minister was guilty of a flagrant breach of etiquette. It was common courtesy for him to allow Verwoerd to study his text so as to be able to prepare a reply.

'It's going to be an important speech,' Manfred went on.

'Yes,' Shasa agreed. 'Maud returned to London to consult with him and help him draw it up, they must have been polishing it up since then.' Sir John Maud was the British high commissioner to South Africa. For him to be summoned to London underlined the gravity of the situation.

'You are friendly with Littleton,' Manfred said quietly. 'See if you can get anything out of him, even a hint as to what Macmillan is going to do.'

'I doubt he knows much,' Shasa was still smiling for the benefit of anybody watching them. 'But I'll let you know if I can find out anything.'

The dinner was served on the magnificent East India Company service, but was the usual bland and tepid offering of the civil service chefs whom Shasa was certain had served their apprenticeship on the railways. The white wines were sweet and insipid, but the red was a 1951 Weltevreden Cabernet Sauvignon. Shasa had influenced the choice by making a gift of his own cru for the banquet, and he judged it the equal of all but the very best Bordeaux. It was a pity that the white was so woefully bad. There was no reason for it, they had the climate and the soil. Weltevreden had always concentrated on the red but he made a resolution to improve his own production of whites, even it if meant bringing in another wine-master from Germany or France and buying another vineyard on the Stellenbosch side of the peninsula.

The speeches were mercifully short and inconsequential, a brief welcome from Verwoerd and a short appreciation from Macmillan, and the conversation at Shasa's end of the table never rose above such earth-shaking subjects as their recent defeat by the Argentinians on the polo field, Denis Compton's batting form and Stirling Moss' latest victory in the Mille Miglia. But as soon as the banquet ended Shasa sought out Littleton who was still with Tara, drawing out the pleasure of her company to the last.

'Looking forward to tomorrow,' he told Littleton casually. 'I hear your Super Mac is going to give us some fireworks.'

'Wherever did you hear that?' Littleton asked, but Shasa saw the sudden shift of his gaze and the guarded expression that froze his smile.

'Can we have a word?' Shasa asked quietly, and apologized to Tara. 'Excuse me, my dear.' He took Littleton's elbow and chatting amicably steered him through the glass doors on to the paved stoep under the trellised vines.

'What is going on, Peter?' He lowered his voice. 'Isn't there anything you can tell me?'

Their relationship was intimate and of long standing; such a direct appeal could not be ignored.

'I will be frank with you, Shasa,' Littleton said. 'Mac has something up his sleeve. I don't know what it is, but he is planning on creating a sensation. The press at home have been put on the alert. It's going to be a major policy statement, that is my best guess.'

'Will it alter things between us – preferential trade, for instance?' Shasa demanded.

'Trade?' Littleton chuckled. 'Of course not, nothing alters trade. More than that I can't tell you. We will all have to wait for tomorrow.'

Neither Tara nor Shasa spoke on the drive back to Weltevreden until the Rolls passed beneath the Anreith gateway and then Tara asked, her voice strained and jerky, 'What time is Macmillan making his speech tomorrow?'

'The special session will begin at eleven o'clock,' Shasa replied, but he was still thinking of what Littleton had told him.

'I wanted to be in the visitors' gallery. I asked Tricia to get me a ticket.'

'Oh, the session isn't being held in the chamber – not enough seating. It will be in the dining-room and I don't think they will allow visitors – ' he broke off and stared at her. In the reflected light of the headlamps she had gone deathly pale.

'What is it, Tara?'

'The dining-room,' she breathed. 'Are you sure?'

'Of course I am. Is something wrong, my dear?'

'Yes – no! Nothing is wrong. Just a little heartburn, the dinner – '

'Pretty awful,' he agreed, and returned his attention to the road.

'The dining-room,' she thought, in near panic. 'I have to warn Moses. I have to warn him it cannot be tomorrow – all his arrangements will have been made for the escape. I have to let him know.'

Shasa dropped her at the front doors of the château and took the Rolls down to the garages. When he came back, she was in the blue drawing-room and the servants, who had as usual waited up for their return, were serving hot chocolate and biscuits. Shasa's valet helped him change into a maroon velvet smoking-jacket, and the housemaids hovered anxiously until Shasa dismissed them.

Tara had always opposed this custom. 'I could easily warm up the milk myself and you could put on a jacket without having another grown man to help you,' she complained when the servants had left the room. 'It's feudal and cruel to keep them up until all hours.'

'Nonsense, my dear.' Shasa poured himself a cognac to go with his chocolate. 'It's a tradition they value as much as we do – makes them feel indispensable and part of the family. Besides, chef would have a seizure if you were to mess up his kitchen.'

Then he slumped into his favourite armchair and became unusually serious.

He began to talk to her as he had at the beginning of their marriage when they had still been in accord.

'There is something afoot that I don't like. Here we stand at the opening of a new decade, the 1960s. We have had nearly twelve years of Nationalist rule and none of my direst predictions have come to pass, but I feel a sense of unease. I have the feeling that our tide has been at full flood, but the turn is coming. I think that tomorrow may be the day when the ebb sets in – ' he broke off, and grinned shamefacedly. 'Forgive me. As you know, I don't usually indulge in fantasy,' he said and sipped his chocolate and his cognac in silence.

Tara felt not the least sympathy for him. There was so much she wanted to say, so many recriminations to lay upon him, but she could not trust herself to speak. Once she began, she might lose control and divulge too much. She might not be able to prevent herself gloating on the dreadful retribution that awaited him and all those like him, and she did not want to prolong this *tête-a-tête*, she wanted to be free to go to Moses, to warn him that today was not the day he had planned for. So she rose. 'You know how I feel, we don't have to discuss it. I'm going to bed. Excuse me.'

'Yes, of course.' He stood up courteously. 'I'll be working for the next few hours. I have to go over my notes for my meeting with Littleton and his team tomorrow afternoon, so don't worry about me.'

Tara checked that Isabella was in her room and asleep, before she went to her suite and locked the door. She changed out of her long dress and jewellery into jeans and a dark sweater, then she made a cannabis cigarette and while she smoked it, she waited fifteen minutes by her watch for Shasa to settle down to his work. Then she switched off her lights. She dropped the cigarette butt into the toilet and flushed it away, before she let herself into the passage once again, locking her suite against the unlikely chance that Shasa might come up to look for her. Then she went down the back stairs.

As she crossed the wide stoep, keeping against the wall, staying in the shadows and moving silently, a telephone rang in the library wing and she froze involuntarily, her heart jarring her ribs. Then she realized that the telephone must be Shasa's private line, and she was about to move on, when she heard his voice. Although the curtains were drawn, the windows of his study were open and she could see the shadow of his head against the drapes.

'Kitty!' he said. 'Kitty Godolphin, you little witch. I should have guessed that you'd be here.'

The name startled Tara, and brought back harrowing memories, but she could not resist the temptation to creep closer to the curtained window.

'You always follow the smell of blood, don't you?' Shasa said, and chuckled at her reply.

'Where are you? The Nellie.' The Mount Nelson was simply the best hotel in Cape Town. 'And what are you doing now – I mean right this moment? Yes, I know it's two o'clock in the morning, but any time is a good time – you told me that yourself a long time ago. It will take me half an hour to get there. Whatever else you do, don't start without me.' He hung up and she saw his shadow on the curtain as he stood up from the desk.

She ran to the end of the long stoep and jumped down into the hydrangea bed and crouched in the bushes. Within a few minutes Shasa came out of the side door. He had a dark overcoat over his smoking-jacket. He went down to the garages and drove away in the Jaguar. Even in his haste he drove slowly through the vineyards so as not to blow dust on his precious grapes, and,

watching the headlights disappear, Tara hated him as much as she ever had. She thought that she should have grown accustomed to his philandering, but he was like a tom cat in rut – no woman was safe from him, and his moral outrage against Sean, his own son, for the same behaviour, had been ludicrous.

Kitty Godolphin – she cast her mind back to their first meeting and the television reporter's reaction to the mention of Shasa's name and now the reason for it became clear.

'Oh God, I hate him so. He is totally without conscience or pity. He deserves to die!' She said it aloud, and then clapped her hand over her mouth. 'I shouldn't have said it, but it is true! He deserves to die and I deserve to be free of him – free to go to Moses and my child.'

She rose out of the hydrangea bushes, brushed the clinging soil from her jeans and crossed the lawns quickly. The moon was in its first quarter, but bright enough to throw her shadow in front of her, and she entered the vineyard with relief and hurried down the rows of vines that were heavy with leaf and grape. She skirted the winery and the stables and reached the servants' cottages.

She had placed Moses in the room at the end of the second row of cottages and his window faced out on to the vineyard. She tapped on his window and his response was almost immediate; she knew he slept as lightly as a wild cat.

'It's me,' she whispered.

'Wait,' he said. 'I will open the door.'

He loomed in the doorway, naked except for a pair of white shorts, and his body shone in the moonlight like wet tar.

'You are foolish to come here,' he said, and taking her arm drew her into the single room. 'You are putting everything at risk.'

'Moses, please, listen to me. I had to tell you. It cannot be tomorrow.'

He stared at her contemptuously. 'You were never a true daughter of the revolution.'

'No, no, I am true, and I love you enough to do anything, but they have changed the arrangements. They will not use the chamber where you have set the charge. They will meet in the parliamentary dining-room.'

He stared at her a second longer, then he turned and went to the narrow built-in cupboard at the head of his bed and began to dress in his uniform.

'What are you going to do?' she asked.

'I have to warn the others – they also are in danger.'

'What others?' she asked. 'I did not know there were others.'

'You know only what you have to know,' he told her curtly. 'I must use the Chev – is it safe?'

'Yes, Shasa is not here. He has gone out. Can I come with you?'

'Are you mad?' he asked. 'If the police find a black man and a white woman together at this time of night – ' he did not finish the sentence. 'You must go back to the house and make a phone call. Here is the number. A woman will answer, and you will say only "Cheetah is coming – he will be there in thirty minutes." That is all you will say and then you will hang up.'

Moses threaded the Chev through the maze of narrow streets of District Six, the old Malay quarter. During the day this was a colourful and thriving community of small stores and businesses. General dealers and tailors and tinsmiths and *halaal* butcheries occupied the ground-floor shops of the decrepit Victorian buildings, while from the cast-iron fretwork of the open balconies above hung a festival of drying laundry, and the convoluted streets were

clamorous with the cries of street vendors, the mournful horns of itinerant fishmongers and the laughter of children.

At nightfall the traders shuttered their premises and left the streets to the street gangs and the pimps and the prostitutes. Some of the more daring white revellers came here late at night, to listen to the jazz players in the crowded shebeens or to look for a pretty coloured girl – more for the thrill of danger and discovery than for any physical gratification.

Moses parked the Chev in a dark side street. On the wall were the graffiti that declared this the territory of the Rude Boys, one of the most notorious of the street gangs, and he waited only a few seconds before the first gang member materialized out of the shadows, an urchin with the body of a child and the face of a vicious old man.

'Look after it well,' Moses flipped him a silver shilling. 'If the tyres are slashed when I come back, I'll do the same for your backside.' The child grinned at him evilly.

He climbed the dark and narrow staircase to the Vortex Club. A couple on the landing were copulating furtively but furiously against the wall as Moses squeezed past. The white man turned his face away but he never missed a beat.

At the door to the club somebody studied him briefly through the peephole and then let him enter. The long crowded room was hazy with tobacco smoke and the sweet smell of cannabis. The clientele included the full spectrum from gang members in zoot suits and wide ties to white men in dinner-jackets. Only the women were all coloured.

Dollar Brand and his Quartet were playing a sweet soulful jazz and everybody was still and attentive. Nobody even looked up as Moses slipped down the side wall to the door at the far end, but the man guarding it recognized Moses and stood aside for him to enter.

In the backroom there was only one man sitting at a round gambling table under a green shaded light. There was a cigarette smouldering between his fingers, and his face was pale as putty, his eyes implacable dark pits.

'You are foolhardy to call a meeting now,' said Joe Cicero, 'without good reason. All the preparations have been made. There is nothing more to discuss.'

'I have good reason,' said Moses, and sat down on the empty chair, facing him across the baize-covered table.

Joe Cicero listened without expression, but when Moses finished, he pushed the lank hair off his forehead with the back of his hand. Moses had learned to interpret that gesture as one of agitation.

'We cannot dismantle the escape route and then set it up again later. These things take time to arrange. The aircraft is already in position.'

It was an Aztec chartered from a company in Johannesburg, and the pilot was a lecturer in political philosophy at Witwatersrand University, the holder of a private pilot's licence and a secret member of the South African Communist Party.

'How long can he wait at the rendezvous?' Moses asked, and Cicero thought about it a moment.

'A week at the longest,' he replied.

The rendezvous was an unregistered airstrip on a large drought-stricken ranch in Namaqualand which was lying derelict, abandoned by the discouraged owner. From the airfield it was a four-hour flight to Bechuanaland, the British protectorate that lay against the north-western border of the Union of South

Africa. Sanctuary had been arranged for Moses there, the beginning of the pipeline by which most political fugitives were channelled to the north.

'A week must be enough,' Moses said. 'Every hour increases the danger. At the very first occasion that we can be sure Vorwoerd will take his seat again, I will do it.'

It was four o'clock in the morning before Moses left the Vortex Club and went down to where he had parked the Chev.

* * *

Kitty Godolphin sat in the centre of the bed, naked and cross-legged with all the shameless candour of a child.

In the years Shasa had known her, she had changed very little physically. Her body had matured slightly, her breasts had more weight to them and the tips had darkened. He could no longer make out the rack of her ribs beneath the smooth pale skin, but her buttocks were still lean as a boy's and her limbs coltishly long and slim. Nor had she lost the air of guileless innocence, that aura of eternal youth which so contrasted with the cynical hardness of her gaze. She was telling him about the Congo. She had been there for the last five months and the material she had filmed would surely put her in line for her third Emmy and confirm her position as the most successful television journalist on the American networks. She was speaking in the breathless voice of an *ingénue*.

'They caught these three Simba agents and tried them under the mango trees outside the burnt-out hospital, but by the time they had sentenced them to death, the light was too bad for filming. I gave the commander my Rolex watch, and in return he postponed the executions until the sun was up the next morning so that Hank could film. It was the most incredible footage. The next morning they paraded the condemned men naked through the market-place and the local women bargained for the various parts of their bodies. The Baluba have always been cannibals. When they had sold all three of them, they took them down to the river and shot them, in the head, of course, so as not to damage the meat, and they butchered them there on the river bank and the women queued up to claim their portions.' She was trying to shock him, and it irritated Shasa that she had succeeded.

'Where do you stand, my love?' he asked bitterly. 'One day you are sympathetically interviewing Martin Luther King, and the next you are portraying all the grossest savagery of Africa.'

She laughed, that throaty chuckle that always roused him. 'And the very next day I am recording the British imperialist making bargains with your gang of bully boys while you stand with a foot on the neck of your slaves.'

'Damn it, Kitty. What are you – what are you trying to do?'

'Capture reality,' she told him simply.

'And when reality doesn't conform to your view of it, you bribe somebody with a Rolex watch to alter it.'

'I've made you mad.' She laughed delightedly, and he stood up from the bed and crossed to where he had thrown his clothes over the back of the chair. 'You look like a little boy when you sulk,' she called after him.

'It will be light in an hour. I have to get back home and change,' he said. 'I've got an appointment with my Imperialist slave-masters at eleven.'

'Of course, you've got to be there to hear Supermac tell you how much he wants to buy your gold and diamonds – and he doesn't care whether they are dripping with the sweat and blood – '

'All right, sweetness,' he cut her off. 'That's enough for one night.' He stepped into his trousers, and as he tucked in his shirt, he grinned at her. 'Why do I always pick screaming radical females?'

'You like the stimulation,' she suggested, but he shook his head, and reached for the velvet smoking-jacket.

'I prefer the loving – talking of which, when will I see you again?'

'Why, at eleven o'clock at the houses of parliament, of course. I'll try to get you in the shot, you are so photogenic, darling.'

He went to the bed and stooped over her to kiss that angelic smile on her lips. 'I can never understand what I see in you,' he said.

He was still thinking of her as he went down to the hotel carpark and wiped the dew off the windshield of the Jaguar. It was amazing how she had been able so effortlessly to hold his interest over all these years. No other woman, except Tara, had ever done that. It was silly how good he felt when he had been with her. She could still drive him wild with erotic desire, her tricks still worked on him, and afterwards he felt elated and wonderfully alive – and, yes, he enjoyed arguing with her.

'God, I haven't closed my eyes all night, yet I feel like a Derby winner. I wonder if I am still in love with the little bitch.'

He took the Jaguar down the long palm-lined drive from the Mount Nelson Hotel. Considering the proposition and recalling his proposal of marriage and her outright rejection, he went out through the hotel gates and took the main road that skirted the old Malay quarter of District Six. He resisted the temptation to shoot the red of the traffic lights at the foot of Roeland Street. It was highly unlikely there would be other traffic at this time of the morning, but he braked dutifully and was startled when another vehicle shot out of the narrow cross street and turned in front of his bonnet.

It was a sea-green Chevrolet station wagon, and he didn't have to check the number plate to know that it was Tara's. The headlights of the Jaguar shone into the cab of the Chev and for an instant he had a full view of the driver. It was Tara's new chauffeur. He had seen him twice before, once at Weltevreden and once in the House of Assembly, but this time the driver was bare-headed and Shasa could see the full shape of his head.

As he had on both the previous occasions, Shasa had a strong sense of recognition. He had definitely met or known this man before, but the memory was eroded by time and quickly extinguished by his annoyance. The chauffeur was not permitted to use the Chev for his own private purposes, and yet here he was in the small hours of the morning driving around as though the vehicle belonged to him.

The Chev pulled away swiftly. The chauffeur had obviously recognized Shasa and the speed was proof of his guilt. Shasa's first instinct was to give chase and confront the man, but the traffic light was still red against him and while he waited for it to change, he had time to reflect. He was in too good a mood to spoil it with unpleasantness, besides which any confrontation at four in the morning would be undignified, and would inevitably lead to questions about his own presence at the same hour on the fringes of the city's notorious red-light area. There would be a better time and place to deal with the driver, and Shasa let him go, but he had neither forgiven nor forgotten.

Shasa parked the Jaguar in the garage at Weltevreden, and the green Chev was in its place at the end of the line of cars, between Garry's MG and Shasa's customized Land-Rover. As he passed it, he laid his hand on the bonnet of the Chev and it was till hot, the metal ticking softly as it cooled. He nodded with satisfaction and went on up to the house, amused by the necessity to creep up to his own suite like a burglar.

He still felt light and happy at breakfast and he hummed as he loaded his plate with eggs and bacon from the silver chafing dish on the sideboard. He was the first one down but Garry was only a minute behind him.

'The boss should always be the first man on the job, and the last man off it,' he had taught Garry, and the boy had taken it to heart. 'No, no longer boy.' Shasa corrected himself, as he studied Garry. His son was only an inch shorter than he was, but wider across the shoulders and heavier in the chest. Down the full length of the corridor Shasa had often heard him grunting over his body-building weights. Even though he had just shaved, Garry's jaw was blue with beard that by evening would need the razor again, and despite the Brylcreen his hair was already springing up in unruly spikes.

He sat down beside Shasa, took a mouthful of his omelette and immediately began talking shop. 'He just isn't up to the job any more, Pater. We need a younger man in that position, especially with all the extra responsibility of the Silver River Mine coming on stream.'

'He has been with us twenty years, Garry,' Shasa said mildly.

'I'm not suggesting we shoot him, Dad. Just let him take his retirement. He *is* almost seventy.'

'Retirement will kill him.'

'If he stays it will kill us.'

'All right,' Shasa sighed. Garry was right, of course, the man had outlived his usefulness. 'But I will speak to him personally.'

'Thanks, Dad.' Garry's spectacles gleamed victoriously.

'Talking about the Silver River Mine, I have arranged for you to begin your stint up there just as soon as you have written your sup.'

Garry spent more time at Centaine House than in his lecture rooms at business school. As a consequence, he was carrying one subject for his Bachelor's degree in Commerce. He would write the supplementary examination the following week and Shasa was sending him up to work on the Silver River Mine for a year or two.

'After all, it has taken over from the old H'ani now as the Company flagship. I want you to move more and more into the centre of things.' He saw the glow of anticipation behind Garry's spectacles.

'Oh boy, am I looking forward to really starting work, after bashing the books all these dreary years.'

Michael came bursting breathlessly into the dining-room. 'Thank goodness, Pater, I thought I had missed you.'

'Slow down, Mickey,' Shasa cautioned him. 'You'll burst a blood vessel. Have some breakfast.'

'I'm not hungry this morning.' Michael sat down opposite his father. 'I wanted to talk to you.'

'Well, open fire then,' Shasa invited.

'Not here,' Michael demurred. 'I rather hoped we could talk in the gun room,' and all three of them looked grave. The gun room was only used on the

most portentous occasions, and a request for a meeting in the gun room was not to be taken lightly.

Shasa glanced at his watch. 'Mickey, Harold Macmillan is addressing both houses – '

'I know, Pater, but this won't take long. Please, sir.' The fact that Michael was calling him 'sir' underlined the seriousness of the request, but Shasa resented the deliberate timing.

Whenever Michael wanted to raise a contentious issue, he did so when Shasa's opportunity to respond was severely curtailed. The lad was as devious as his mother, whose child he indubitably was, spiritually as well as physically.

'Ten minutes, then,' Shasa agreed reluctantly. 'Will you, excuse us, please, Garry?' Shasa led the way down the passage and locked the gun-room door behind them.

'Very well.' He took his usual place in front of the fireplace. 'What is it, my boy?'

'I've got a job, Dad.' Michael was breathless again.

'A job. Yes, I know you have a part-time job as a local stringer for the *Mail*. I enjoyed your report on the polo – in fact you read it to me. Very good it was,' Shasa grinned, 'all five lines of it.'

'No, sir, I've got a full-time job. I spoke to the editor of the *Mail* and they have offered me a job as a cub reporter. I start the first of next month.'

Shasa's grin faded into a scowl. 'Damn it, Mickey. You can't be serious – what about your education? You have two more years to go at university.'

'I am serious, sir. I will get my education on the paper.'

'No,' Shasa raised his voice. 'No, I forbid it. I won't have you leaving university before you are capped.'

'I'm sorry, sir. I've made up my mind.' Michael was pale and trembling, yet he had that obstinate set expression that infuriated Shasa even more than the words – but he controlled himself.

'You know the rules,' Shasa said. 'I've made them clear to all of you. If you do things my way, there is no limit to the help I will give you. If you go your own way, then you are on your own – ' he took a breath, and then said it, surprised at how painful it was ' – like Sean.' God, how he still missed his eldest son.

'Yes, sir,' Michael nodded. 'I know the rules.'

'Well?'

'I have to do it, sir. There is nothing else I want to do with my life. I want to learn to write. I don't want to go against you, Pater, but I simply have to do it.'

'This is your mother's doing,' Shasa said coldly. 'She has put you up to this,' he accused, and Michael looked sheepish.

'Mater knows about it,' he admitted, 'but it's my decision alone, sir.'

'You understand that you will be forfeiting my support? You'll not receive another penny from me once you leave this house. You'll have to live on the salary of a cub reporter.'

'I understand, sir,' Michael nodded.

'All right, then, Michael. Off you go,' he said, and Michael looked stunned.

'Is that all, sir?'

'Unless you have some other announcement to make.'

'No, sir.' Michael's shoulders slumped. 'Except that I love you very much, Pater, and I appreciate all that you have done for me.'

'You have,' said Shasa, 'a most peculiar way of demonstrating that appreciation, if you don't mind me saying so.' He went to the door.

He was halfway into the city, racing the Jaguar down the new highway between the university and Groote Schuur, before he recovered from his affront at Michael's disloyalty, for that is how Shasa saw his son's decision. Now suddenly he began to think about newspapers again. Publicly he had always disparaged the strange suicidal impulse that gripped so many successful men in their middle years to own their own newspaper. It was notoriously difficult to milk a reasonable profit from a newspaper, but in secret Shasa had felt the sneaking temptation to indulge in the same rich man's folly.

'Not much profit,' he mused aloud, 'but the power! To be able to influence the minds of people!'

In South Africa the English press was hysterically anti-government, while the Afrikaans press was fawningly and abjectly the slave of the National party. A thinking man could trust neither.

'What about an English-language paper that was aimed at the business community and politically uncommitted,' he wondered, as he had before. 'What if I were to buy one of the smaller weaker papers and build it up? After the Silver River Mine's next dividend is declared, we are going to be sitting on a pile of money.' Then he grinned. 'I must be getting senile, but at least I'll be able to guarantee a job for my drop-out journalist son!' And the idea of Michael as editor of a large influential newspaper had an increasing appeal, the longer he thought about it. 'Still, I wish the little blighter would get himself a decent education first,' he grumbled, but he had almost forgiven him for his treachery by the time he parked the Jaguar in the parking area reserved for cabinet ministers. 'Of course, I'll keep him on a decent allowance,' he decided. 'That threat was just a little bluff.'

A sense of excited expectation gripped the House as Shasa went up the stairs to the front entrance. The lobby was crowded with senators and members of parliament. The knots of dark-suited men formed and dissolved and re-formed, on the intricate play of political cross-currents that fascinated Shasa. As an insider he could read the significance of who was talking to whom and why.

It took him almost twenty minutes to reach the foot of the staircase for as one of the prime actors he was drawn inexorably into the subtle theatre of power and favour. At last he escaped and with only minutes to spare hurried up the stairs and down the passage to his suite.

Tricia was hovering anxiously. 'Oh, Mr Courtney, everybody is looking for you. Lord Littleton telephoned and the prime minister's secretary left a message.' She was reading from her pad as she followed him into the inner office.

'Try to get the PM's secretary first, then Lord Littleton.' Shasa sat at his desk, and frowned as he noticed some chalky white specks on his blotter. He brushed them away irritably, and would have given Tricia an order to speak to the cleaners, but she was still reading from her pad and he had less than an hour to tackle the main items on her list before the joint sitting began.

He dealt with the queries that Verwoerd's secretary had for him. The answers were in his head and he did not have to refer to anybody in his department – and then Littleton was on the line. He wanted to discuss an addition to the agenda for their meeting that afternoon, and once they had agreed that, Shasa asked tactfully, 'Have you found out anything about the speeches this morning?'

'Afraid not, old man. I'm as much in the dark as you are.'

As Shasa reached across the desk to replace the receiver, he noticed another white speck of chalk on his blotter that had not been there a minute before; he was about to brush that away also, when he paused and looked up to see where it had come from. This time he scowled as he saw the small hole in his ceiling and the hair-line cracks around it. He pressed the switch on his intercom.

'Tricia, please come in here a moment.'

When she stood in the doorway, he pointed at the ceiling. 'What do you make of that?'

Tricia looked mystified and came to stand beside his chair. They both peered at the damage.

'Oh, I know,' Tricia looked relieved, 'but I'm not supposed to tell you.'

'Spit it out, woman!' Shasa ordered.

'Your wife, Mrs Courtney, said she was planning some renovations to your office as a surprise. I suppose she had asked Maintenance to do the work for her.'

'Damn!' Shasa didn't like surprises which interfered with the comfortable tenor of his existence. He liked his office the way it was and he didn't want anybody, particularly anyone of Tara's *avant garde* taste, interfering with something that worked extremely well as it was.

'I think she is planning to change the curtains also,' Tricia added innocently. She didn't like Tara Courtney. She considered her shallow, insincere and scheming. She didn't approve of her disrespectful attitude to Shasa, and she wasn't above sowing a few seeds of dissension. If Shasa were free, there was just a chance, a very small and remote chance that he might see her clearly and realize just how much she, Tricia, felt for him, 'And she was talking about altering the light fittings,' she added.

Shasa jumped up from his desk and went to touch his curtains. He and Centaine had studied at least a hundred samples of fabric before choosing this one. Protectively he rearranged the drapes, and then he noticed the second hole in the ceiling and the thin insulated wire that protruded from it. He had difficulty controlling his fury in front of his secretary.

'You get on to Maintenance,' he instructed. 'Talk to Odendaal himself, not one of his workmen, and you tell him I want to know exactly what is going on. Tell him whatever it is, it's damned shoddy workmanship and that there is plaster all over my desk.'

'I'll do that this morning,' Tricia promised, and then, placatingly, 'It's ten minutes to, Mr Courtney – you don't want to be late.'

Manfred De La Rey was just leaving his own office as Shasa came down the passage, and they fell in side by side.

'Have you found out anything?'

'No – have you?'

Manfred shook his head. 'It's too late anyway – nothing we can do now.'

Shasa saw Blaine Malcomess at the door of the dining-room and went to greet him. They filed into the panelled dining-room together.

'How is Mater?'

'Centaine is fine – looking forward to seeing you for dinner tomorrow evening.' Centaine was holding a dinner party in Littleton's honour out at Rhodes Hill. 'I left her giving the chef a nervous breakdown.' They laughed together and then found their seats in the front row of chairs. As minister and deputy leader of the opposition, they both warranted reserved seats.

Shasa swivelled in his seat and looked to the back of the large hall where the

press cameras had been set up. He picked out Kitty Godolphin, looking tiny and girlish beside her camera crew, and she winked at him mischievously. Then the two prime ministers were taking their places at the top table and Shasa leaned across to Manfred De La Rey and murmured, 'I hope this isn't all a hoo-ha over nothing – and that Supermac has really got something of interest to tell us.'

Manfred shrugged. 'Let's hope it isn't too exciting either,' he said. 'Sometimes it's safer to be bored – ' but he broke off as the Speaker of the House called for silence and rose to introduce the prime minister of Great Britain and the packed room, filled with the most powerful men in the land, settled into attentive and expectant silence.

Even when Macmillan, tall and urbane and strangely benign in expression, rose to his feet, Shasa had no sense of being at the anvil while history was being forged and he crossed his arms over his chest and lowered his chin in the attitude of listening and concentration in which he followed all debate and argument.

Macmillan spoke in an unemotional voice, but with weight and lucidity, and his text had all the indications of having been carefully prepared, meticulously polished and rehearsed.

'The most striking of all the impressions I have formed since I left London a month ago,' he said, 'is the strength of this African national consciousness. In different places it may take different forms, but it is happening everywhere. The wind of change is blowing through the continent. Whether we like it or not, this growth of national consciousness is a political fact. We must all accept it as a fact. Our national policies must take account of it.'

Shasa sat up straight and unfolded his arms, and around him there was a similar stirring of incredulity. It was only then that Shasa realized with a clairvoyant flash that the world he knew had altered its shape, that in the fabric of life that had held together their diverse nation for almost three hundred years, the first rent had been torn by a few simple words, a rent that could never be repaired. While he attempted to grasp the full extent of the damage, Macmillan was getting on in those plummy measured tones.

'Of course, you understand this as well as anyone. You are sprung from Europe, the home of nationalism.' Cunningly, Macmillan was including them in this new sweeping view of Africa. 'Indeed, in the history of our times yours will be recorded as the first of the African nationalisms.'

Shasa glanced at the Verwoerd beside the British prime minister and he could see that he was agitated and alarmed. He had been caught unawares by Macmillan's stratagem of withholding his text from him.

'As a fellow member of the Commonwealth, it is our earnest desire to give South Africa our support and encouragement, but I hope you won't mind me saying frankly that there are some aspects of your policies which make it impossible for us to do this without being false to our own deep convictions about the political destinies of free men.'

Macmillan was announcing nothing less than a parting of ways and Shasa was devastated by the idea. He wanted to leap to his feet and shout, 'But I am British also – you cannot do this to us.' He looked around him almost pleadingly and saw his own deep distress echoed on the faces of Blaine and most of the English members of the House.

'

Macmillan's words had devastated them.

Shasa's mood persisted over the remainder of that day and the next. The

atmosphere at the meeting with Littleton and his advisers was one of mourning, and though Littleton himself was apologetic and conciliatory, they all knew that the damage was real and irreparable. The fact was undeniable. Britain was dropping them. She might go on trading with them, but at arm's length. Britain had chosen sides.

Late on the Friday a special session of the House was announced for the following Monday, when Verwoerd would make his accounting to his parliament and his people. They had the weekend to brood over their fate. Macmillan's speech even cast a shadow over Centaine's dinner party on the Friday evening, and Centaine took it as a personal insult.

'The man's timing is atrocious,' she confided to Shasa. 'The day before my party! Perfidious Albion!'

'You French have never trusted the British,' Shasa teased her, his first attempt at humour in forty-eight hours.

'Now I know why,' Centaine retorted. 'Look at the man – typically English. He hides expediency in a cloak of high moral indignation. He does what is best for England and makes himself a saint while he does it.'

It was left for Blaine Malcomess to sum up after the women had left the men to their port and cigars in Rhodes Hill's magnificent dining-room.

'Why are we so incredulous?' he asked. 'Why do we feel it so impossible that Britain would reject us, simply because we fought two wars for her?' He shook his head. 'No, the caravan moves on and so must we. We must ignore the gloating of the London press, we must ignore their delight in this unprecedented rebuke and repudiation of all of us, the Nationalists and those that strenuously oppose them. From now on we will be increasingly alone, and we must learn to stand on our own feet.'

Shasa nodded. 'Macmillan's speech was a huge political gain for Verwoerd. There is only one way for us to go now. The bridge has been chopped down behind us. No retreat is possible. We have to go along with Verwoerd. South Africa will be a republic before the year is out, mark my words, and after that – ' Shasa drew on his cigar while he considered ' – and after that only God and the Devil know for certain.'

* * *

'At times it seems that God and fate take a direct hand in our petty affairs,' Tara said softly. 'But for a tiny detail, the choice of the dining-room rather than the chamber, we might have destroyed the man who had brought us a messenger of hope.'

'For once it does seem that your Christian God favours us.' Moses watched her in the driving-mirror as he drove the Chevrolet through the Monday rush hour traffic. 'Our timing has been perfect. At the moment when the British Government, supported by the British press and the nation, has recognized our rights, the political destinies of free men, as Macmillan put it, we will deliver our first hard blow for the promised freedom.'

'I am afraid, Moses, afraid for you and for all of us.'

'The time for fear has passed,' he told her. 'Now is the time for courage and resolution, for it is not oppression and slavery that breeds revolution. The lesson is clear. Revolution rises out of the promise of better things. For three

hundred years we have borne oppression in weary resignation, but now this Englishman has shown us a glimpse of the future and it is golden with promise. He has given our people hope, and after today, after we have struck down the most evil man in Africa's dark and tormented history, when Verwoerd is dead, the future will at last belong to us.' He had spoken softly, but with that peculiar intensity that made her blood thrill through her veins and pound in her eardrums. She felt the elation, but also the sorrow and the fear.

'Many men will die with him,' she whispered. 'My father. Is there no way he can be spared, Moses?'

He did not reply, but she saw the reflection of his gaze in the mirror and she could not bear the scorn. She dropped her own eyes and murmured.

'I'm sorry – I will be strong. I will not speak of it again.' But her mind was racing. There must be some way to keep her father out of the chamber at the fateful moment, but it would have to be compelling. As deputy leader of the opposition, he must attend such solemn business as Verwoerd's speech. Moses disturbed her thoughts.

'I want you to repeat your duties to me,' he said.

'We have gone over it so often,' she protested weakly.

'There must be no misunderstanding.' His tone was fierce. 'Do as I tell you.'

'Once the House is in session – so that we are certain Shasa will not intercept us – we will go up to his suite in the usual way,' she began, and he nodded confirmation as she went over the arrangements, correcting her when she omitted a detail. 'I will leave the office at exactly ten-thirty and go to the visitors' gallery. We must be certain that Verwoerd is there.'

'Do you have your pass?'

'Yes.' Tara opened her handbag and showed him. 'As soon as Verwoerd rises to begin his address, I will return to the office, using the panel door. By that time you will have – ' her voice faltered.

'Go on,' he ordered harshly.

'You will have connected the detonator. I will confirm that Verwoerd is in his seat, and you will – ' again her voice dried up.

'I will do what has to be done,' he finished for her and then went on, 'After the explosion there will be a period of total panic and confusion – with enormous damage to the ground floor. There will be no control, no organized police or security effort. That period will last sufficiently long for us to go downstairs and leave the building unchallenged, just as most other survivors will be doing.'

'When you leave the country, can I come with you, Moses?' she pleaded.

'No.' He shook his head firmly. 'I must travel swiftly and you would impede us and put us in danger. You will be safer here. It will only be for a short time. After the assassination of the white slave-masters, our people will rise. The young comrades of *Umkhonto we Sizwe* are in position and ready to call the nation to revolution. Millions of our people will spontaneously fill the streets. When they have seized the power, I will return. Then you will have a place of high honour by my side.'

It was amazing how naïvely she accepted his assurances, he thought grimly. Only a besotted woman could doubt that afterwards the security police would take her away, and her interrogation would be brutal. It did not matter. It did not matter if they tried and hanged her. Her husband would be dead with Verwoerd and Tara Courtney's usefulness would be at an end. One day when the people's democratic government of the African National Congress ruled the

land, they would name a street or a square after her, the white woman martyr, but now she was expendable.

'Give me your promise, Moses,' she begged him.

His voice was a deep reassuring rumble. 'You have done well, everything I have required of you. You and your son will have a place at my side just as soon as that is possible. I give you my promise.'

'Oh Moses, I love you,' she whispered. 'I shall always love you.' Then she sat back in her seat and adopted the role of cool white madam, as Moses turned the Chevrolet out of Parliament Lane into the members' carpark and the constable at the gate saw the sticker on the windshield and saluted respectfully.

Moses parked in the reserved bay and switched off the engine. They had fifteen minutes to wait before the House went into session.

* * *

'Ten minutes to, Mr Courtney,' Tricia called Shasa on the intercom. 'You had better start going down, if you don't want to miss the opening of the PM's speech.'

'Thank you, Tricia.' Shasa had been totally absorbed with his own work. Verwoerd had asked him to draw up a full report on the country's ability to respond to an embargo on sales of military equipment to South Africa by her erstwhile western allies. Apparently Macmillan had hinted at this possibility to Verwoerd, a veiled threat in private conversation just before his departure. Verwoerd wanted the report before the month's end, which was typical of the man, and Shasa would have difficulty meeting that deadline.

'Oh, by the way, Mr Courtney,' Tricia stopped him breaking off the connection. 'I spoke to Odendaal.'

'Odendaal?' It took Shasa a moment to make the mental switch.

'Yes, about the work on your ceiling.'

'Oh, I hope you gave him a flea in the ear. What did he say?'

'He says there has been no work done in your office, and no request from your wife or anybody else for rewiring of any kind.'

'That's decidedly odd,' Shasa looked up at the damage, 'because somebody has definitely been fiddling around in here. If it wasn't Odendaal, then have you any idea who it might be, Tricia?'

'No, Mr Courtney.'

'Nobody been in here to your knowledge?' Shasa insisted.

'Nobody, sir, except of course your wife and her driver.'

'All right, thank you, Tricia.' Shasa stood up and fetched his jacket from the dumb valet in the corner. While he shrugged into it, he studied the hole above his desk and the length of wire that had been drawn out of the corner beside the bookcase and the end tucked behind the row of encyclopaedias. Until Tricia mentioned it, he had forgotten his irritation in the face of other more dire considerations, but now he thought about the little mystery with full attention.

He crossed to the mirror and while he reshaped the knot of his tie and adjusted his black eye-patch, he pondered the additional enigma of Tara's new chauffeur. Tricia's remark had reminded him of it. He still hadn't taken the man to task for his unauthorized private use of the chev. 'Damn – where have I seen him before?' he wondered, and with one last glance at the ceiling, he left

the office. He was still thinking about the driver as he went down the corridor. Manfred De La Rey was waiting for him at the head of the stairs. He was smiling and quietly triumphant, and Shasa realized that he had not spoken to him in private since the shock of Macmillan's speech.

'So,' Manfred greeted him, 'Britannia has cut the apron strings, my friend.'

'Do you remember how once you called me *Soutpiel*?' Shasa asked.

'*Ja*.' Manfred chuckled. ' "Salt Prick" – with one foot in Cape Town and the other in London and the best part of you danging in the Atlantic Ocean. *Ja*, I remember.'

'Well, from now on I will have both feet in Cape Town,' Shasa told him. It was not until that moment, when the fact of Britain's rejection had sunk in, that Shasa realized for the first time that above all other things he was first and foremost a South African.

'Good,' Manfred nodded. 'So at last you understand that although we may not always like each other or agree, circumstances have made us brothers in this land. One cannot survive without the other, and in the end we have only each other to turn to.'

They went down into the chamber and took their seats on the green leather benches, side by side.

When the Assembly rose to pray, to ask God's blessing on their deliberations, Shasa looked across the floor at Blaine Malcomess and felt a familiar rush of affection for him. Silver-haired but tanned and handsome with those protruding ears and big strong nose, Blaine had been a tower in his life for as long as he cared to remember. In his new mood of patriotism – and, yes, of defiance of Britain's rejection – he was glad of the knowledge that this would draw them still closer together. It would narrow the political differences between them, just as it had brought Afrikaner and Englishman closer.

As the prayer ended, he sat down and turned his attention to Dr Hendrik Frensch Verwoerd as he rose to make his address. Verwoerd was a strong articulate speaker and a brilliant debater. His address was sure to be long and carefully reasoned. Shasa knew they were in for fine entertainment and he crossed his arms, leaned against the padded back rest with anticipation and closed his eyes.

Then before Verwoerd could say his first word, Shasa opened his eyes and sat up straight on his bench. In that moment when he had cleared his mind of all recent worry, while he was relaxed and receptive, the ancient memory had flashed in upon him – full blown. He remembered where and when he had last seen Tara's new chauffeur.

'Moses Gama,' he said aloud, but his words were lost in the applause that greeted the prime minister.

* * *

Tara gave the doorman at the main entrance to parliament a cheery smile, and was surprised at herself. She felt cocooned in a layer of unreality, as though she watched an actress playing her role.

She heard the muffled applause from the chamber as she swept up the stairs with Moses following her at a respectful distance in his chauffeur's uniform and burdened by an armful of parcels. They had done this so often, and Tara smiled

again as they passed one of the secretaries in the corridor. She tapped on the door to Shasa's suite and without waiting for an answer swept into the outer office. Tricia rose from her desk.

'Oh, good morning, Mrs Courtney. You'll be late for the PM's address. You'd better hurry.'

'Stephen, you can just leave the parcels.' Tara stopped in front of Tricia as Moses closed the outer door.

'Oh, by the way. Somebody has been working on the ceiling of your husband's office,' Tricia came around the desk, as though to lead the way to Shasa's office. 'We wondered if you knew anything – '

Moses placed the armful of parcels on a chair, and with his hands free turned to Tricia as she came level with him. He whipped one arm around her neck and with his other hand covered her mouth. Tricia was powerless in his grip, but her eyes flew wide with shock.

'There are ropes and a gag in the top packet,' Moses spoke softly to Tara. 'Get them out.'

Tara stood paralysed. 'You said nothing about this,' she blurted.

'Get them.' His voice was still low, but it crackled with impatience and Tara sprang to obey.

'Tie her hands behind her,' Moses ordered, and while Tara fumbled at the knots, he stuffed a clean, white, folded cloth into the terrified girl's mouth and taped it in place.

'Stay in here,' he ordered Tara, 'in case somebody comes in,' and he bundled Tricia through into the inner office and forced her down on her stomach behind the desk. Swiftly he checked Tara's knots. They were loose and sloppy. He retied them and then bound Tricia's ankles as securely.

'Come in here,' he called, and Tara was flustered and stammering as she rushed in.

'Moses, you haven't hurt her?'

'Stop that!' he told her. 'You have important work to do and you are behaving like a hysterical child.'

She closed her eyes, clenched her fists and took a deep breath. 'I'm sorry.' She opened her eyes. 'I realized that it was necessary. I didn't think. I am all right now.'

Moses had already crossed to the corner of the bookshelf and he reached up and brought down the roll of wire from behind the encyclopaedias. He paid it out across the carpet as he moved back to the desk.

'Good,' he said. 'Now go to your seat in the gallery. Wait five minutes after Verwoerd begins to speak and then come back here. Do not run, do not even hurry. Do everything calmly and deliberately.'

'I understand.' Tara crossed to the mirror and opened her handbag. Quickly she ran a comb through her hair and retouched her lipstick.

Moses had gone to the altar chest and lifted the heavy bronze Bushman statue. He placed it on the carpet and lifted the lid of the chest. Tara hesitated, watching him anxiously.

'Why are you waiting?' he asked. 'Go, woman, and do your duty.'

'Yes, Moses.' She hurried to the door of the outer office.

'Lock both doors behind you,' he ordered.

'Yes, Moses,' she whispered.

As Tara went down the corridor, she was searching in her handbag again, and she found her leather-bound notepad with the miniature gold-plated pencil

in the spine loops. At the head of the stairs she paused, and used the banisters to steady the notepad while she scribbled hastily on a blank page.

Daddy,
Centaine has been seriously injured in a motorcar accident. She is asking for you. Please come quickly.
Tara

She tore the page out of the notebook and folded it. It was the one appeal to which she knew her father would respond and she wrote his name on the folded note.

Instead of going directly to the visitors' gallery, she hurried down the wide staircase into the lobby and ran to one of the uniformed parliamentary messengers who was standing outside the main doors to the chamber.

'You have got to get this message to Colonel Malcomess,' she told him.

'I don't like to go in now, Dr Verwoerd is speaking,' the messenger demurred, but she thrust the note into his hand.

'It's terribly urgent,' she pleaded and her distress was evident. 'His wife is dying. Please – please.'

'I'll do what I can.' The messenger accepted the note, and Tara ran back up the stairs. She showed her pass to the doorman at the entrance to the visitors' gallery and squeezed past him.

The gallery was crowded. Somebody had taken Tara's seat, but she edged forward and craned to look down into the chamber. Dr Verwoerd was on his feet, talking in Afrikaans. His silvery curls were neatly cropped and his eyes slitted with concentration as he used both hands to emphasize his words.

'The question that this person from Britain put to us was not addressed to the South African monarchists, nor was it addressed to the South African republicans. It was to all of us that he spoke.' Verwoerd paused. 'The question he asked was simply this. Does the white man survive in Africa or does he perish?'

He had electrified the chamber. There was not a movement nor a shift of eyes from his face – until the uniformed parliamentary messenger slipped unobtrusively down the front row of opposition benches and stopped beside Blaine.

Even then he had to touch Blaine's shoulder to draw his attention, and Blaine accepted the note without seeming to realize what he was doing. He nodded at the messenger, and, with the folded scrap of paper unread in his fingers, once more focused all his attention on Verwoerd where he stood below the Speaker's throne.

'Read it, Daddy!' Tara whispered aloud. 'Please read it.'

* * *

In all that multitude Shasa was the only one who was not mesmeried by Verwoerd's oratory. His thoughts were a jumbled torrent, one racing after another, overtaking and mingling as they followed without logical sequence.

'*Moses Gama!*' It was scarcely believable that the memory had taken so long to return to him, even over the years and in spite of changes that time had wrought in both of them. They had once been good friends, and the man had made a deep impression on Shasa at a formative period of his life.

Then again, Shasa had heard the name much more recently, it had been on the list of wanted revolutionaries during the 1952 troubles. While the others, Mandela and Sobukwe and the rest, had stood trial, Moses Gama had disappeared, and the warrant for his arrest was outstanding. Moses Gama was still a criminal at large, and a dangerous revolutionary.

'*Tara!*' His mind darted aside. She had selected Gama as her chauffeur and, given her political leanings, it was impossible that she didn't know who he was. Suddenly Shasa knew that Tara's meek repudiation of her previous left-wing companions and her new conciliatory behaviour had all been a sham. She had not changed at all. This man Moses Gama was more dangerous than all and any of her previous effete companions. Shasa had been hoodwinked. In fact she must have moved even further to the left, crossing the delicate line between the legitimate political opposition and criminal involvement. Shasa almost rose to his feet, and then remembered where he was. Verwoerd was speaking already.

'The need to do justice to all, does not mean only that the black men must be nurtured and protected. It means justice and protection for the white men in Africa also – '

Shasa glanced up at the visitors' gallery, and there was a stranger sitting in Tara's seat. Where was Tara? She must be in his office – and the association of ideas led him on.

Moses Gama had been in his office. Shasa had seen him in the corridor and Tricia had told him, 'Only Mrs Courtney and her driver.' Moses Gama had been in his office and somebody had drilled the ceiling and laid electrical wires. It had not been Odendaal or Maintenance. It hadn't been anyone who had authority to do so.

'We are not newcomers to Africa. Our forefathers were here before the first black man,' Verwoerd was saying. 'Three hundred years ago when our ancestors set out into the interior of this land, it was an empty wilderness. The black tribes were still far to the north, making their way slowly southwards. The land was empty and our forefathers claimed it and worked it. Later they built the cities and laid the railways and sank the mine-shafts. Alone, the black man was incapable of doing any of these things. Even more than the black tribes we are men of Africa and our right to be here is as God-given and inalienable as is theirs.'

Shasa heard the words but made no sense of them – Moses Gama, probably with the help and connivance of Tara, had laid electrical wires in his office and – suddenly, he gasped aloud. The altar chest. Tara had placed the chest in his office, like the Trojan horse.

Wild with anxiety now, he swivelled his whole body towards the visitors' gallery, and this time he saw Tara. She was squeezed against one wall and even at this distance Shasa could see that she was pale and distraught. She was watching someone or something on the opposition side of the chamber, and Shasa followed her gaze.

Blaine Malcomess was oblivious to all else as he followed the prime minister's speech. Shasa saw the messenger reach him and hand him the note.

Shasa looked back at the gallery and Tara was still concentrated on her father. After all the years Shasa could read her expression, and he had never seen her so worried and concerned, even when one of the children was gravely ill.

Then her face cleared with patent relief and Shasa glanced back at Blaine. He had unfolded the note and was reading it. Suddenly Blaine leapt to his feet and hurried towards the main doors.

Tara had summoned her father – that much was obvious. Shasa stared at her, trying to divine her purpose. Almost as though she sensed his gaze, Tara looked directly at him, and her relief crumbled into horror and wild guilt. She turned and fled from the visitors' gallery, pushing aside those who stood in her way.

A second longer Shasa stared after her. Tara had enticed her father out of the chamber, and her concern could only have been so intense had she belived he was in some kind of dire danger. This was followed by guilt and horror as she realized that Shasa was watching her. It was clear to Shasa then that something terrible was about to happen. Moses Gama and Tara – there was danger, mortal danger – and Tara was trying to save her father. The danger was pressing and imminent – the wires in his office, the chest, Blaine and Tara and Moses Gama. He knew they were all interwoven and that he had little time in which to act.

Shasa jumped to his feet and strode down the aisle. Verwoerd frowned and checked his speech, watching him, while all around the chamber heads turned. Shasa quickened his stride. Manfred De La Rey reached out to touch him as he passed his bench, but without a glance at him Shasa brushed past his outstretched hand and went on.

As he hurried out into the lobby Shasa saw Blaine Malcomess near the front door talking agitatedly to the janitor. As soon as he saw Shasa he said, 'Thank God!' and came towards him across the chequered marble floor.

Shasa turned away from him and looked up the staircase. From the top Tara stared down at him, white-faced and terrified, held by some unnatural passion.

'Tara!' Shasa called and started towards the foot of the staircase, but she whirled and disappeared around the angle of the corridor.

Shasa flew at the stairs, taking them three at a time.

'What's happening, Shasa?' Blaine called after him, but Shasa did not answer.

He came out of the staircase still at a run, and as he rounded the corner Tara was halfway down the corridor ahead of him. He did not waste time by shouting at her, and instead flung himself forward, and sprinted after her. As he ran, Tara glanced over her shoulder and saw him swiftly overtaking her.

'Moses!' she screamed. 'Look out, Moses!'

It was futile, the panelled walls of Shasa's office were too thick and soundproof for her warning to reach him, and her cry confirmed all Shasa's worst suspicions.

Instead of running straight on towards the front door of his suite as Shasa expected, Tara jinked suddenly into the side passage, ducking under Shasa's outstretched arm and he tried to turn with her but he was off balance as she disappeared into his blind spot.

Shasa ran into the corner of the wall, crashing into it head-first, taking it on the brow above his blind eye. The silk patch cushioned the impact slightly, but still the skin split and blood poured down his cheek. Although he was stunned, Shasa managed to keep his feet. He staggered in a full circle, still dazed. Blaine was following him, his face flushed with effort and concern as he ran down the corridor.

'What the hell is going on, Shasa?' he roared.

Shasa turned from him, and saw Tara at the door to the back entrance of his office. She had a key, but she was in such a state that her hands were shaking too wildly to insert it in the lock.

Shasa gathered himself, shaking the darkness out of his head, and the droplets of his blood splattered the wall beside him. Then he launched himself after

Tara. She saw him coming and dropped the key, it tinkled at her feet, and she clenched her fists and beat with them on the closed door.

'Moses!' she screamed. 'Moses!'

As Shasa reached her the door was jerked open from the inside, and Moses Gama stood on the threshold. The two men confronted each other over Tara's head until Tara ran forward.

'Moses, I tried to warn you,' she screamed and threw both arms around him.

In that instant Shasa looked beyond the pair and saw that the altar chest stood open, its contents piled on the carpet. The coil of wire that he had found behind the encyclopaedias had been laid across the floor to his desk and connected to some kind of compact electrical apparatus. Shasa had never seen one before, but he knew instinctively that it was a detonation device and that it was ready to fire. On the desk top beside it lay an automatic pistol. As a firearms enthusiast and collector, he recognized it as a Tokarev 7.62 mm, the standard Russian military issue. On the floor behind his desk Tricia lay on her side. She was gagged and bound at wrists and ankles, but she was wriggling desperately and giving little muffled cries.

Shasa lunged forward to tackle Moses Gama, but the black man gathered Tara in his arms and hurled her into Shasa's chest. The two of them reeled backwards against the jamb of the door. Moses spun around and leapt to the desk, as Shasa tried to get free of Tara. She was clinging to him and moaning.

'No! No! He must do it.'

Shasa broke her grip and flung her aside, but across the room Moses was standing over the electrical transmitter. He pressed the switch and a bulb on the panel of the casing glared redly.

Shasa knew that he could not reach Moses across the floor before he fired the device, but his mind was racing ahead of his limbs and body. He saw the wire strung out across the carpet, almost at his feet, and he stooped and took a twist of it around his right hand and heaved back against it with all his strength.

The end of the wire was firmly attached to the transmitter, and as Shasa hauled on it the device was jerked out of Moses' hands and flew off the desk top to clatter across the floor, midway between the two of them.

They both leapt for it at the same instant, but Moses was by a fraction of a second the quickest, and his hands scrabbled on the transmitter. Shasa was in full stride, and he did not check. He leaned forward, and transferred all the weight and power of his body into his hips, swinging his right leg into the kick he aimed at Moses' head.

The kick caught Moses in the side of the temple, and snapped his head over. The transmitter tumbled from his grip and he was flung over backwards, rolling until he crashed into the desk.

Shasa followed him and aimed another flying kick at his head, but Moses caught his foot on his raised forearm and seized his ankle. He twisted violently, lifting the ankle and Shasa was caught on one foot with his weight backwards until he fell heavily.

Moses pulled himself up the side of the desk and reached out for the Tokarev pistol, and Shasa scrambled after him on hands and knees. As Moses swung the pistol around, Shasa lunged at him again and grabbed his wrist with both hands. They wrestled over the floor, rolling and kicking and grunting, fighting for the Tokarev.

Tara had recovered and now she ran into the room and picked up the fallen transmitter. She stood helplessly with it in her hands.

'Moses, what must I do?' she cried.

Moses grunted with a supreme effort as he rolled on top of Shasa. 'The yellow button. Push the yellow button!'

At that instant Blaine Malcomess ran in through the open door. 'Stop her, Blaine!' Shasa yelled. 'They are going to blow – ' Moses' elbow hit him in the mouth and cut off the words.

While the two of them still struggled on the floor, Blaine held out both hands to his daughter.

'Here, give that to me, Tara.'

'Don't touch me, Daddy.' She backed away from him, but she was trying to locate the yellow button, groping for it while she stared at her father. 'Don't try and stop me, Daddy.'

'Blaine,' Shasa gasped, but broke off as Moses attempted once more to wrench his pistol arm out of Shasa's grip. The corded black muscles in Moses' arm bulged and writhed with the effort and Shasa made a choking sound in his throat as he tried to hold him.

The muzzle blast of the pistol lit the room like a flash bulb and there was the immediate sharp stink of burnt powder.

Blaine Malcomess, his arms outstretched towards Tara, spun around as the bullet hit him and he went reeling into the bookcase. He stood there for a moment with the blood starting to spread in a dark tide down the front of his white shirt and then he sagged slowly on to his knees.

'Daddy!' Tara dropped the transmitter and ran to him. She fell on her knees beside him.

Shock had weakened Shasa's grip for an instant and Moses twisted free and jumped to his feet, but as he lunged for the transmitter, Shasa was after him. He caught Moses from behind as he stooped over the transmitter and with one arm around his throat pulled him away from it. In his effort to break the throttling grip, Moses dropped the pistol and clawed at Shasa's arm with both hands. They grappled wildly, twisting and grunting, and the transmitter lay at their feet.

Shasa shifted his weight, lifted one foot and drove his heel into the panel of the transmitter, the panel crackled as it was stove in, but the red bulb still burned.

Moses was galvanized to fresh effort by the damage to the transmitter, and he almost tore himself free of Shasa's grip, twisting to face him, but Shasa put out all his strength and they stood chest to chest, gasping and heaving, spittle and sweat and droplets of blood from Shasa's head wound smearing both their faces.

Again Shasa had him off balance for a moment, but he aimed another kick at the transmitter. He landed solidly and it went skidding across the floor and crashed into the wall beyond the desk. The plastic case split open at the impact, the wire tore loose from the terminal and the red bulb flickered and then extinguished.

Moses gave a wild despairing cry and sent Shasa flying backwards over the desk. As he lay sprawled across the desk top, Moses scooped up the pistol from the carpet and staggered to the open doorway. There he turned and raised the Tokarev and aimed at Shasa.

'You!' he gasped. 'You!' but his hands were shaking and the pistol wavered. He fired and the bullet thudded into the desk top beside Shasa's head, tearing up a blur of splinters.

Before Moses could fire again, Manfred De La Rey bulked in the doorway

behind him. He had seen Shasa's agitation and followed him up from the chamber.

He took in the situation at first glance, and he reacted instantly. He swung the big hard fist that had won him an Olympic gold medal, and it crashed into the side of Moses Gama's neck below the ear.

The pistol fell from Moses' hand and he toppled forward unconscious on top of it.

Shasa dragged himself off the desk and tottered across to Blaine.

'Here,' he whispered, as he dropped to his knees beside him. 'Let me have a look.'

Tara was blubbering incoherently. 'Daddy, I'm sorry. I didn't mean this to happen. I only did what I thought was right.'

Shasa tried to pull her away, but she clung to Blaine, blood on her hands and down the front of her dress.

'Let him alone,' Shasa said, but she was hysterical now, and tugged at her father so that his head jerked from side to side loosely. 'Daddy, speak to me, Daddy.'

Shasa leaned back and slapped her hard, knocking her head across.

'Leave him, you murderous bitch,' he hissed at her, and she crawled away from him, her face beginning to redden and swell from the blow. Shasa ignored her and gently opened the jacket of Blaine's dark suit.

Shasa was a hunter, and he recognized the bright clear colour of arterial blood seething wtih tiny bubbles from the torn lungs.

'No,' he whispered. 'Please, no!'

Only then he realized Blaine was watching his face, reading in it his own death.

'Your mother – ' he said, and the wind of his lungs puffed through the bullet hole in his chest. 'Tell Centaine – ' he could not go on.

'Don't talk,' Shasa said. 'We will get a doctor.' He shouted over his shoulder at Manfred who was already on the telephone, 'Hurry, man. Hurry!'

But Blaine gripped his sleeve, tugging it urgently. 'Love – ' he choked on his own blood. 'Tell her – love – tell her I love her.' He got it out at last, and panted as the blood gurgled in his chest – and then he gathered himself for his last great effort.

'Shasa,' he said, 'Shasa, my son – my only son.'

The noble silver head fell forward, and Shasa held it to his chest, hugging him as he had never been able to before.

Then still holding him, Shasa wept for the man who had been his friend and father. The tears squeezed out of his empty eyesocket and trickled from under the silk eye-patch down his face to mingle with his own blood and drip from his chin.

When Tara crawled forward on her knees, and reached out to touch her father's corpse, Shasa lifted his head and looked at her.

'Don't touch him,' he said softly. 'Don't you dare soil him with your touch.' There was such a look in his single eye, such contempt and hatred in his face, that she recoiled from him and covered her face with both hands. Still on her knees, she began to sob hysterically. The sound of it rallied Shasa. Gently he laid Blaine on his back and closed his eyes with his fingertips.

In the doorway Moses groaned and shuddered, and Manfred slammed the telephone back on its cradle and crossed to him. He stood over him, with those huge fists clenched and asked, 'Who is he?'

'Moses Gama.' Shasa stood up, and Manfred grunted.

'So, we have been looking for him for years. What was he doing?'

'I'm not sure.' Shasa went to where Tricia lay and stooped over her. 'But I think he has laid explosives somewhere in the House. That is the transmitter. We'd better clear the place and have the army bomb disposal – ' He didn't have to finish, for at that moment there was the sound of running men in the corridor and three of the security guards burst into the suite.

Manfred took over immediately, snapping orders at them. 'Get the handcuffs on that black bastard.' He pointed at Moses. 'And then I want the building cleared.'

Shasa freed Tricia, leaving the gag until last, but the instant her mouth was clear Tricia pointed at Tara where she still knelt sobbing beside Blaine's corpse.

'She – ' Shasa did not let her finish. He seized her wrist and jerked Tricia to her feet.

'Quiet!' he snarled at her, and his fury silenced the girl for a moment. He dragged her through into the outer office and closed the door.

'Listen to me, Tricia.' He faced her, still holding both her wrists.

'But she was with him.' Tricia was trembling. 'It was her – '

'Listen to me.' Shasa shook her into silence. 'I know. I know all about it. But I want you to do something for me. Something for which I will always be grateful. Will you do it?'

Tricia sobered and stared at him. She saw the blood and the tears on his face and thought her heart might break for him. Shasa took the handkerchief from his top pocket and wiped his face.

'For me, Tricia. Please,' he repeated and she gulped noisily and nodded.

'If I can,' she agreed.

'Don't say anything about my wife's part in this until the police take a formal statement from you. That won't be until much later. Then you can tell them everything.'

'Why?'

'For me and for my children. Please Tricia.'

Again she nodded and he kissed her forehead. 'You are a good brave girl,' he said and left her.

He went back into the inner office. The security police were grouped around Moses Gama. He was manacled but he lifted his head and stared at Shasa for a moment. It was a smouldering gaze, dark and filled with outrage. Then they led him away.

The office was crowded and noisy. White-uniformed ambulance attendants were bringing a stretcher through the doorway. A doctor, a member of parliament summoned from the chamber, was working over Blaine as he lay on his back, but now he stood up, shook his head and gestured at the stretcher bearers to take Blaine's body. The uniformed guards, supervised by Manfred De La Rey, were already gathering up the pieces of the smashed transmitter and beginning to trace the wire to its source.

Tara was sitting in the chair behind his desk, weeping silently into her hands. Shasa went past her to the wall safe hidden behind one of the paintings.

He tumbled the combination and swung open the steel door, screening it with his own body. Shasa always kept two or three thousand pounds in banknotes against an emergency. He stuffed the wads into his pockets, and then quickly he sorted through the stack of family passports until he found Tara's. He relocked the safe, went to where she sat and pulled her to her feet.

'Shasa, I didn't – '

'Keep quiet,' he hissed at her, and Manfred De La Rey glanced at him across the office.

'She's had a terrible shock,' Shasa said. 'I'm taking her home.'

'Come back here as soon as you can,' Manfred nodded. 'We'll need a statement.'

Still gripping her arm, Shasa marched her out of the office and down the corridor. The fire alarm bells were ringing throughout the building and members and visitors and staff were streaming out through the front doors. Shasa joined them, and as soon as they were out in the sunlight he led Tara to the Jaguar.

'Where are we going?' Tara asked, as they drove away. She sat very small and subdued in her corner of the bucket seat.

'If you talk to me again, I may lose control,' he warned her tightly. 'I may not be able to stop myself strangling you.'

She did not speak again until they reached Youngsfield Airport, and Shasa pushed her up into the cockpit of the silver and blue Mosquito.

'Where are we going?' she repeated, but he ignored her as he went through the start-up procedures and taxied out to the end of the runway. He did not speak until they had climbed to cruise altitude and were flying straight and level.

'The evening flight for London leaves Johannesburg at seven o'clock. As soon as we are in radio contact, I will reserve your seat,' he told her. 'We will get there with an hour or so to spare.'

'I don't understand,' she whispered into her oxygen mask. 'Are you helping me to escape? I don't understand why.'

'For my mother, firstly. I don't want her to know that you murdered her husband – it would destroy her.'

'Shasa, I didn't – ' she was weeping again, but he felt no twinge of compassion.

'Shut up,' he said. 'I don't want to listen to your blubbering. You will never know the depths of my feelings for you. Hatred and contempt are gentle words that do not describe them.' He drew a breath. Then he went on, 'After my mother, I am doing it for my children. I don't want them to live their lives with the knowledge of what their mother truly was. That is too much for a young man or woman to be burdened with.'

Then they were silent, and Shasa allowed the terrible grief of Blaine's death, which up until then he had suppressed, to rise up and engulf him. In the seat beside him Tara was mourning her father also, spasms of weeping shook her shoulders. Her face above the mask was chalky and her eyes were like wounds.

As strong as his grief was Shasa's hatred. After an hour's flying, he spoke again.

'If you ever return to this country again, I will see you hanged. That is my solemn promise. I will be divorcing you for desertion as soon as possible. There will be no question of alimony or maintenance or child custody. You will have no rights nor privileges of any kind. As far as we are concerned, it will be as though you have never existed. I expect you will be able to claim political asylum somewhere, even if it is in Mother Russia.'

Again he was silent, gathering himself, regaining full control.

'You will not even be at your father's funeral, but every minute of every day his memory will stalk you. That is the only punishment I am able to inflict

upon you – God grant it is enough. If He is just, your guilt will slowly drive you mad. I pray for that.'

She did not reply, but turned her face away. Later, when they were on approach to Johannesburg, descending through ten thousand feet, with the skyscrapers and the white mine dumps glowing in the late sunlight ahead of them, Shasa asked:

'You were sleeping with him, weren't you?'

Instinctively, she knew it was the last chance she would ever have to inflict pain upon him, and she turned in the seat to watch his face as she replied.

'Yes, I love him – and we are lovers.' She saw him wince, but she wanted to hurt him more and she went on. 'Apart from my father's death, there is nothing I regret. Nothing I have done of which I am ashamed. On the contrary, I am proud to have known and loved a man like Moses Gama – proud of what I have done for him and for my country.'

'Think of him kicking and choking on the rope, and be proud of that also,' Shasa said quietly, and landed. He taxied the Mosquito to the terminal buildings and they climbed down on to the tarmac and faced each other. There was a bruise on her face where he had struck her, and the icy highveld wind pulled at their clothing and ruffled their hair. He handed her the little bundle of bank notes and her passport.

'Your seat on the London flight is reserved. There is enough here to pay for it and to take you where you want to go.' His voice broke as his rage and his sorrow took control of him again. 'To hell or the gallows, if my wish for you comes true. I hope never to see or hear of you again.'

He turned away from her, but she called after him.

'We were always enemies, Shasa Courtney, even in the best times. And we will be enemies to the very end. Despite your wish, you will hear of me again. I promise you that much.'

He climbed into the Mosquito and it was minutes before he had himself sufficiently in hand to start the engines. When he looked out through the windshield again, she was gone.

* * *

Centaine would not let them bury Blaine. She could not bear the thought of him lying in the earth, swelling and putrefying.

Mathilda Janine, Blaine's younger daughter, came down from Johannesburg with David Abrahams, her husband, in the company Dove, and they sat with the family in the front row of the memorial chapel at the crematorium. Over a thousand mourners attended the service and both Dr Verwoerd and Sir De Villiers Graaff, the leader of the opposition, were amongst them.

Centaine kept the little urn of Blaine's ashes on the table beside her bed for almost a month, before she could get up her courage. Then she summoned Shasa, and the two of them climbed the hill to her favourite rock.

'Blaine and I used to come here so often,' she whispered. 'This will be the place where I shall come when I need to know that he is still close to me.'

She was nearly sixty years old, and when Shasa studied her with compassion, he saw that for the first time she truly looked that old. She was letting the grey grow out in the thick bush of her hair and he saw that soon there would be

more of it than the black. Grief had dulled her gaze and weighed down the corners of her mouth, and that clear youthful skin which she so carefully cherished, seemed overnight to have seamed and puckered.

'Do it for me, please Shasa,' she said, and handed him the urn.

Shasa opened it and stepped out of the lee of the rock, into the full force of the south-easter. The wind fluttered his shirt like a trapped bird, and he turned to look back at her.

Centaine nodded encouragement, and he held the urn high and upended it. The ashes streamed away like dust in the wind, and when the urn was empty, Shasa turned to her once more.

'Break it!' she commanded, and he hurled the vessel against the rock face. It shattered, and she gasped and swayed on her feet.

Shasa ran to her and held her in his arms.

'Death is the only adversary I know I shall never overcome. Perhaps that is why I hate it so,' she whispered.

He led her to her seat on the rock and they were silent for a long while, staring out over the wind-speckled Atlantic and then Centaine said, 'I know you have been protecting me. Now tell me about Tara. What was her part in this?'

So he told her, and when he finished Centaine said, 'You have made yourself an accessory to murder. Waw it worth it?'

'Yes. I think so,' he answered without hesitation. 'Could any of us have survived her trial if I had allowed her to be arrested and charged?'

'Will there be consequences?'

Shasa shook his head. 'Manfred – he will protect us again. Just as he did with Sean.'

Shasa saw her pain at the mention of Sean's name. Like him she had never recovered from it, but now she said quietly. 'Sean was one thing, but this murder and treason and attempting to assassinate a head of state. It is fostering bloody revolution and attempting by force to overthrow a government. Can Manfred protect us from that? And if he can, why should he?'

'I don't know the answers to that, Mater.' Shasa looked at her searchingly. 'I thought that perhaps you did.'

'What do you mean?' she asked, and he thought that he might have taken her unawares, for there was fear and confusion in her eyes for an instant. Blaine's death had slowed her and weakened her. Before that, she would never have betrayed herself so readily.

'In protecting us, me in particular, Manfred is protecting himself and his political ambitions,' Shasa reasoned it out carefully. 'For if I am destroyed, then – I am his *protégé* – his own career would be blighted. But there is more than that. More than I can fathom.'

Centaine did not reply, but she turned her head away and looked out to sea.

'It's as though Manfred De La Rey feels some strange loyalty to us, or a debt that he must repay – or even a sense of deep guilt towards our family. Is that possible, Mater? Is there something that I do not know of that would put him under an obligation to us? Have you withheld something from me all these years?'

He watched her struggle with herself, and at one moment it seemed she might burst out with some long-hidden truth, or with a terrible secret that she had carried too long alone. Then he saw her expression firm and it was almost possible to watch the strength and force which had been drained from her since Blaine's death flow back into her.

It was a little miracle. Age seemed to fall away from her. Her eyes brightened and her carriage of head and shoulders was once more erect and perky. Even the lines and creases around her eyes and mouth seemed to smooth away.

'What ever gave you that idea?' she asked crisply, and stood up. 'I've been moping and pining far too long. Blaine would never have approved of that.' She took Shasa's arm. 'Come along. I've still got a life to live and work to do.'

Half-way down the hill, she asked suddenly, 'When does the trial of Moses Gama begin?'

'The tenth of next month.'

'Do you know he once worked for us, this Moses Gama?'

'Yes, Mater. I remembered him. That was how I was able to stop him.'

'He was a terrible troublemaker even in those days. We must do all we can to ensure that he pays the extreme penalty. That is the least we can do for Blaine's memory.'

* * *

'I don't understand why you are saddling me with this little scrubber,' Desmond Blake protested acidly. He had been twenty-two years on the newspaper and before the gin bottle had taken over, he had been the best courtroom and political journalist on the staff of the *Golden City Mail*. The quantities of gin which he absorbed had not only placed a ceiling on his career but had greyed and prematurely lined his face, ruined his liver and soured his disposition without, however, clouding his insight into the crimninal mind nor spoiling his political acumen.

'Well, he is a bright lad,' his editor explained reasonably.

'This is the biggest, most sensational trial of our century,' Desmond Blake said, 'and you want me to drag a cub reporter with me, a puking infant who couldn't even cover a local flower show or a mayoral tea party.'

'I think he has a lot of potential – I just want you to take him in hand and show him the ropes.'

'Bullshit!' said Desmond Blake. 'Now tell me the real reason.'

'All right.' The editor showed his exasperation. 'The real reason is that his grandmother is Centaine Courtney and his father is Shasa Courtney, and Courtney Mining and Finance have acquired thirty-five per cent of the shareholding of our parent company over the past months, and if you know nothing else you should know that nobody bucks Centaine Courtney, not if they want to remain in business. Now take the kid with you and stop bitching. I haven't got time to argue any more – I've got a paper to get out.'

Desmond Blake threw up both hands in despair, and as he rose to leave the office his editor added one last unsubtle threat.

'Just look at it this way, Des. It will be good job insurance, especially for an aging newshound who needs the price of a bottle of gin a day. Just think of the kid as the boss's son.'

Desmond wandered lugubriously down the length of the city room. He knew the boy by sight. Somebody had pointed him out as a sprig of the Courtney empire and wondered aloud what the hell he was doing here instead of on the polo field.

Desmond stopped beside the corner desk which Michael was sharing with two other juniors.

'Your name is Michael Courtney?' he asked, and the boy leapt to his feet.

'Yes, sir.' Michael was overcome at being directly addressed by somebody who had his own column and by-line.

'Shit!' said Desmond bitterly. 'Nothing is more depressing than the shining face of youth and enthusiasm. Come along, boy.'

'Where are we going?' Michael snatched up his jacket eagerly.

'To the George, boy. I need a double to give me the strength to go through with this little lark.'

At the bar of the George, he studied Michael over the rim of his glass.

'Your first lesson, boy – ' he took a swallow of gin and tonic. 'Nothing is ever what it seems to be. Nobody is ever what he says he is. Engrave that on your heart. Your second lesson. Stick to your orange juice. They don't call this stuff mother's ruin for nothing. Your third lesson. Always pay for the drinks with a smile.' He took another swig. 'So you are from Cape Town, are you? Well that's just fine, because that is where we are going, you and me. We are going to see a man condemned to die.'

* * *

Vicky Gama took the bus from Baragwanath Hospital to Drake's Farm. It went only as far as the administration building and the new government school. She had to walk the last mile through the narrow dusty lanes between the rows of raw brick cottages. She walked slowly, for although her pregnancy was only four months advanced, she was beginning to tire easily.

Hendrick Tabaka was in the crowded general dealer's shop, watching the tills, but he came to Vicky immediately and she greeted him with the respect due to her husband's eldest brother. He led her through to his office, and called for one of his sons to bring her a comfortable chair.

Vicky recognized Raleigh Tabaka, and smiled at him as he placed her chair. 'You have grown into a fine young man, Raleigh. Have you finished your schooling now?'

'*Yebo, sissie.*' Raleigh returned her greeting with polite reserve, for even though she was the wife of his uncle, she was a Zulu. His father had taught him to distrust all Zulus. 'I help my father now, *sissie*. I learn the business from him and soon I will manage one of the shops on my own.'

Hendrick Tabaka smiled proudly at his favourite son. 'He learns fast, and I have great faith in the boy.' He endorsed what Raleigh had said. 'I am sending him soon to our shop at Sharpeville near Vereeniging to learn the bakery business.'

'Where is your twin brother, Wellington?' Vicky asked, and immediately Hendrick Tabaka frowned heavily and waved at Raleigh to leave the office. As soon as they were alone, he answered her question angrily. 'The white priests have captured Wellington's heart. They have seduced him from the gods of his tribe and his ancestors and taken him to the service of the white man's God. This strange Jesus God with three heads. It grieves me deeply, for I had hoped that Wellington, like Raleigh, would be the son of my old age. Now he studies to be a priest, and I have lost him.'

He sat down at the tiny cluttered table that served him as a desk and studied

his own hands for a moment. Then he raised that bald cannonball head, the scalp criss-crossed with ridged scars from old battles.

'So, wife of my brother, we live in a time of great sorrow. Moses Gama has been taken by the white men's police, and we cannot doubt what they will do with him. Even in my sorrow, I must recall that I warned him that this would happen. A wise man does not throw stones at the sleeping lion.'

'Moses Gama did what he knew was his duty. He lived out the deed for which he was born,' Vicky said quietly. 'He struck a blow for all of us – you and me and our children.' She touched her belly where beneath the white nurse's uniform the first bulge of her pregnancy showed. 'And now he needs our help.'

'Tell me how I can help.' Hendrick inclined his head. 'For he was not only my brother, but my chief as well.'

'We need money to hire a lawyer to defend him in the white man's court. I have been to see Marcus Archer and the others of the ANC at the house in Rivonia. They will not help us. They say that Moses acted without their agreement or approval. They say that it was agreed not to endanger human life. They say that if they give us money to help in the defence, the police will trace it to them. They say many other things – everything but the truth.'

'What is the truth, my sister?' Hendrick asked.

And suddenly Vicky's voice was quivering with fury. 'The truth is that they hate him. The truth is that they are afraid of him. The truth is that they are jealous of him. Moses has done what none of them would have dared. He has aimed a spear at the heart of the white tyrant, and though the blow failed, now all the world knows that it was struck. Not only in this land, but beyond the sea, all the world knows now who is the leader of our people.'

'That is true,' Hendrick nodded. 'His name is on every man's lips.'

'We must save him, Hendrick my brother. We must do everything we can to save him.'

Hendrick rose and went to the small cupboard in the corner. He dragged it aside to reveal the door of an ancient Chatwood safe built into the wall behind it.

When he opened the green steel door, the safe was packed with wads of banknotes.

'This belongs to Moses. It is his share. Take what you need,' said Hendrick Tabaka.

* * *

The Supreme Court of the Cape Province of South Africa stands on one side of the gardens that Jan van Riebeeck, the first governor of the Cape, laid out in the 1650s to provision the ships of the Dutch East India Company. On the opposite side of the beautiful gardens stand the houses of parliament that Moses Gama had attempted to destroy. So he was to be tried within a quarter of a mile of the scene of the crime of which he stood accused.

The case aroused the most intense international interest and the film crews and journalists began flying into Cape Town a week before it was set down to commence.

Vicky Gama arrived by train after the thousand-mile journey down the

continent from the Witwatersrand. She travelled with the white lawyer who would defend Moses and more than fifty of the more radical members of the African National Congress, most of them, like herself, under thirty years of age, and many of them secret members of Moses Gama's *Umkhonto we Sizwe* military wing of the party. Amongst these was Vicky's half brother, Joseph Dinizulu, now a young man of almost twenty-one studying to be a lawyer at the black university of Fort Hare. The money given to Vicky by Hendrick Tabaka paid for all of them.

Molly Broadhurst met them at the Cape Town station. Vicky, Joseph and the defence lawyer would be staying at her home in Pinelands during the trial, and she had arranged accommodation for all the others in the black townships of Langa and Guguletu.

Desmond Blake and Michael Courtney flew down together from Johannesburg on the commercial flight, and while Desmond put a severe strain on the bar service, Michael pored over the notebook in which he was roughing out a schedule of all the research into the history of the ANC and the background of Moses Gama and his tribe that he felt they would need.

Centaine Courtney-Malcomess was at the airport to meet the flight. Much to Michael's embarrassment, she had two servants to carry Michael's single valise out to the daffodil-yellow Daimler that, as usual, she was driving herself. Since Tara had left, Centaine had once more taken over the running of Weltevreden.

'The paper has booked rooms for us at the Atlantic Hotel, Nana.' Michael protested, after he had dutifully embraced his grandmother. 'It's very convenient for the law courts and the national library.'

'Nonsense,' said Centaine firmly. 'The Atlantic is a bug-run and Weltevreden is your home.'

'Father said I wouldn't be welcome back.'

'Your father has missed you even more than I have.'

Shasa sat Michael beside him at dinner, and even Isabella was almost totally excluded from their conversation. Shasa was so impressed by his youngest son's sudden new maturity that the following morning he instructed his broker to purchase another hundred thousand shares in the holding company that owned the *Golden City Mail*.

Manfred and Heidi dined at Weltevreden the evening before the trial began and while they drank pre-prandial cocktails Manfred expressed the concern that Shasa and Centaine shared.

'What the prosecution and the court must avoid is allowing the proceedings to deteriorate into a trial not of a murderer and a terrorist, but of our social system and our way of life. The vultures of the international press are already assembled, eager to show us in the worst possible light, and as usual to distort and misrepresent our policy of *apartheid*. I only wish we had some control over the courts and the press.'

'You know I can't agree with you on that one.' Shasa shifted in his chair. 'The complete independence of our press and the impartialilty of our judicial system gives us credibility in the eyes of the rest of the world.'

'Don't lecture me. I am a lawyer,' Manfred pointed out stiffly.

It was strange how despite their enforced and mutually beneficial relationship, they were never truly friends and antagonism was always ready to surface between them. Now it took some little time for the tension to ease, and for them to adopt once more an outward show of cordiality. Only then could Manfred tell Shasa, 'We have finally agreed with the prosecution not to raise in court the

matter of your wife's involvement with the accused. Apart from the difficulty of beginning extradition proceedings with Britain – she would almost certainly ask for political asylum – there is the consideration of her relationship with Gama. Black man and white woman – ' Manfred's expression was one of deep disgust. 'It is repugnant to all decent principles. Raising the subject would not further the prosecution, but would simply give the yellow press something more to drool over. No, it will do none of us any good at all.' Manfred put special emphasis on this last sentence. It was all that needed to be said, but Shasa did not let it pass.

'I owe you a gread deal – for my son, Sean, and now my wife.'

'*Ja*, you owe me a great deal,' Manfred nodded. 'Perhaps I will ask you for something in return one day.'

'I hope so,' said Shasa. 'I do not like having outstanding debts.'

* * *

Outside the Supreme Court both pavements were filled with people. They were standing shoulder to shoulder and overflowing into the street, complicating the efforts of the traffic wardens and impeding the flow of traffic until it was reduced to a crawl.

A newspaper poster, 'GUY FAWKES KILLER TRIAL BEGINS TODAY', hung drunkenly from one of the lampposts until it was knocked down by the push of the crowd and trodden underfoot.

The throng was thickest at the colonnaded entrance to the Supreme Court and each time one of the players in the drama arrived, the journalists and photographers surged forward. The state prosecutor smiled and waved to them like a film star, but most of the others, intimidated by the crowds and the exploding flash bulbs and shouted questions, scurried for the entrance and the protection of the police guards.

Only minutes before the court was due to go into session, a chartered bus turned into the slow-moving stream of traffic and came down towards the entrance. The sound of singing grew louder as it approached, the lovely haunting chorus of African voices rising and sinking and weaving the intricate tapestry of sound that thrilled the ears and raised the gooseflesh on the skins of the listeners.

When the bus finally halted in front of the Supreme Court, a young Zulu woman stepped down into the street. She wore a flowing caftan of green and yellow and black, the colours of the African National Congress, and her head was bound in a turban of the same colours.

Her pregnancy had given Vicky a fullness of body that enhanced her natural fine looks. There was no trace left of the shy little country girl. She carried her head high, and moved with all the confidence and style of an African Evita.

The press cameramen recognized instantly that they were being presented with an unusual opportunity and they rushed forward with their equipment to capture her dark beauty, and the sound of her voice as she sang the thrilling hymn to freedom.

'*Nkosi Sikelel' iAfrika* – God Save Africa.'

Behind her, holding hands, and singing, came all the others, some of them white like Molly Broadhurst and some of them Indians and coloured like

Miriam and Ben Afrika, but most of them pure African. They streamed up the steps into the court house to fill the section of the gallery of the courtroom reserved for non-whites and to overflow into the corridors outside.

The rest of the court was packed with the press and the curious, while a separate section had been set aside for observers from the diplomatic corps. Every one of the embassies was represented.

At every entrance to the court were police guards wearing sidearms, and four policemen of warrant officer rank were drawn up around the dock. The prisoner was a killer and a dangerous revolutionary. They were taking no chances.

Yet when he stepped up into the dock, Moses Gama seemed none of these things. He had lost weight during his imprisonment, but this merely enhanced his great height and the wide angularity of his shoulders. His cheeks were hollow, and the bones of his face and forehead were more prominent, but he stood proudly as ever with his chin up and that dark messianic glow in his eyes.

His presence was so overpowering that he seemed to take possession of the room; the gasp and hum of curiosity as he stood before them was subdued by an almost tangible sense of awe. In the back of the gallery Vicky Dinizulu sprang to her feet and began to sing, and those around her came in with the chorus. As he listened to her beautiful ringing voice, Moses Gama inclined his head slightly, but he did not smile or give any other sign of recognition.

Vicky's freedom song was interrupted by a cry of '*Stilte in die hof! Opstaan!* Silence in the court! Stand up!'

The judge-president of the Cape, wearing the scarlet robes which indicated that this was a criminal trial, took his seat on the bench beneath the carved canopy.

Justice André Villiers was a big man with a flamboyant courtroom style. He had a reputation for being a connoisseur of food, good wine and pretty girls. He was also noted for handing down savage sentences for crimes of violence.

Now he slumped massively on the bench and glowered around his court as the charge sheet was read, but his gaze checked momentarily as it reached each female, the length of the pause proportional to the prettiness of the recipient. On Kitty Godolphin he spent at least two seconds and when she smiled her angelic little-girl smile at him, he hooded his eyes slightly before passing on.

There were four main charges on the sheet againt Moses Gama, two of attempted murder, and one each of high treason and murder. Every one of these was a capital offence but Moses Gama showed no emotion as he listened to them read out.

Judge Villiers broke the expectant silence that followed the reading. 'How do you plead to these charges?'

Moses leaned forward, both clenched fists on the rail of the dock and his voice was low and full of scorn, but it carried to every corner of the crowded court.

'Verwoerd and his brutal government should be in this dock,' he said. 'I plead not guilty.'

Moses sat down and did not raise his eyes while the judge enquired who appeared for the crown, and the prosecutor introduced himself to the court, but when Mr Justice Villiers asked:

'Who appears for the defence?' before the advocate whom Vicky and Hendrick Tabaka had retained could reply, Moses sprang to his feet again.

'I do,' he cried. 'I am on trial here for the aspirations of the African people.

No other can speak for me. I am the leader of my people, I will answer for myself and for them.'

There was such consternation in the court now, such uproar that for a few moments the judge pounded his gavel in vain, demanding silence, and when it was at last obtained, he threatened them.

'If there is another such demonstration of contempt for this court, I will not hesitate to have it cleared.'

He turned back to Moses Gama to reason with him and try to persuade him to accept legal representation, but Moses forestalled him.

'I wish to move immediately that you, Judge Villiers, recuse yourself from this case,' he challenged, and the scarlet-robed judge blinked and was for a moment stunned into silence.

Then he smiled grimly at the prisoner's effrontery and asked, 'On what grounds do you make this application?'

'On the grounds that you, as a white judge, are incapable of being impartial and fair to me, a black man, forced to submit to the immoral laws of a parliament in which I have no representation.'

The judge shook his head, half in exasperation and half in admiration. 'I am going to deny your application for recusal,' he said. 'And I am going to urge you to accept the very able services of the counsel who has been appointed to represent you.'

'I accept neither his services, not the competence of this court to condemn me. For all the world knows that is what you propose. I accept only the verdict of my poor enslaved people and of the free nations out there. Let them and history decide my innocence or guilt.'

The press were electrified, some of them so enchanted that they made no effort to write down his words. None of them would ever forget them. For Michael Courtney sitting in the back row of the press section, it was a revelation. He had lived with Africans all his life, his family employed them by the tens of thousands, but until this moment he had never met a black man of such dignity and awe-inspiring presence.

Judge Villiers sagged down in his seat. He always maintained his place firmly in the centre-stage of his court, overshadowing everybody in it with the ruthless authority of a born actor. Here he sensed he had met an equal. The entire attention of everybody in the court was captivated by Moses Gama.

'Very well,' Judge Villiers said at last. 'Mr Prosecutor, you may proceed to present the case for the crown.'

The prosecutor was a master of his profession and he had an infallible case. He worked it up with meticulous attention to detail, with logic and with skill.

One at a time he submitted his exhibits to the court. The wiring and the electrical detonator, the Tokarev pistol and spare magazines. Although it was considered too dangerous to allow the blocks of plastic explosives and the detonators into the courtroom, photographs were submitted and accepted. The altar chest was too large to bring into court, and again photographs were accepted by Judge Villiers. Then there were the gruesome photographs of Shasa's office, with Blaine's covered body against the bookcases and his blood splashed over the carpet, and the wreckage of broken furniture and scattered papers. Centaine turned her face away as the photographs were handed in and Shasa squeezed her arm and tried to shield her from the curious glances.

After all the exhibits had been tabled, the prosecutor called his first witness. 'I call the honourable Minister of Mines and Industry, Mr Shasa Courtney.'

Shasa was on the witness stand for the rest of that day and all of the following morning, describing in detail how he had discovered and thwarted the bombing.

The prosecutor took him back to his first childhood meeting with Moses Gama, and as Shasa described their relationship, Moses raised his head and for the first time since he had taken the stand looked directly into Shasa's face. In vain Shasa searched for the slightest trace of that sympathy they had once shared, but there was none. Moses Gama's stare was baleful and unwavering.

When at last the prosecutor had finished with Shasa, he turned to the accused. 'Your witness,' he said, and Justice Villiers roused himself.

'Do you wish to cross-examine the witness?'

Moses shook his head and looked away, but the judge insisted. 'This will be your last opportunity to query or refute the witness's evidence. I urge you to make full use of it.'

Moses crossed his arms over his chest, and closed his eyes as though in sleep, and from the non-white section of the court there were hoots of laughter and the stamping of feet.

Justice Villiers raised his voice, 'I will not warn you again,' and there was silence in the face of his anger.

Over the next four days the prosecutor placed his witnesses on the stand.

Tricia, Shasa's secretary, explained how Moses had gained entrance to the office suite in the guise of a chauffeur and how on the day of the murder Moses had seized and bound her. How she had watched him fire the fatal shot that killed Colonel Malcomess.

'Do you wish to cross-examine the witness?' Judge Villiers asked, and once again Moses shook his head.

Manfred De La Rey gave his evidence and described how he had found Moses Gama with the pistol in his hand and Blaine Malcomess lying on the floor dying. How he had heard him cry, 'You! You!' and saw him deliberately fire the pistol at Shasa Courtney.

'Do you wish to cross-examine the witness?' the judge asked, and this time Moses did not even look up.

An electrical engineer described the captured equipment and indentified the transmitter as being of Russian origin. An explosives expert told the court of the destructive power of the plastic explosives placed beneath the government benches.

'In my opinion it would have been sufficient to destroy totally the entire chamber and the adjoining rooms. It would certainly have killed every person in the main chamber, and most of those in the lobby and the surrounding offices.'

After each witness had finished his evidence Moses again refused to cross-examine. At the end of the fourth day the crown had presented its case, and Judge Villiers adjourned the court with one last appeal to the prisoner.

'When the court reconvenes on Monday, you will be required to answer the charges against you. I must once more impress upon you the grave nature of the accusations, and point out to you that your very life is at stake. Yet again I urge you to accept the services of legal counsel.'

Moses Gama smiled at him with contempt.

* * *

Dinner at Weltevreden that evening was a sombre affair. The only one who was unaffected by the day's events was Garry, who had flown down in the Mosquito from the Silver River Mine for the weekend.

While the rest of the family sat in silence, each of them brooding on the events of these last days and their own particular part in them, Garry was enthusiastically selling to Centaine and Shasa his latest plan for reducing costs at the mine.

'Accidents cost us money in lost production. I'll admit that in the last two years our safety record has been about average for the industry as a whole, but if we could cut down our fatalities to one per hundred thousand shifts or better, we could reduce our overall production costs by over twelve per cent. That is twenty million pounds a year. On top of that we would get the added bonus of worker satisfaction and co-operation. I have put all the figures through the computer.' Garry's eyes behind his spectacles glittered as he mentioned that piece of equipment. Shasa had reports from Dave Abrahams and the general manager of the Silver River that Garry sometimes sat all night at one of the terminals of the new IBM computer that the company had at last installed.

'The lad knows his way around the machine as well, if not better, than any of our full-time operators. He can almost make it sit up and whistle "God Save the Queen".' David Abrahams had not attempted to conceal his admiration and Shasa had remarked deprecatingly, to conceal his paternal pride, 'That will be a redundant accomplishment by next year, when we become a republic.'

'Oh, Garry, you are being an utter bore,' Isabella interrupted him at last. 'All that business about tonnages and penny weights – at the dinner table, what's more. No wonder you can't find a girlfriend.'

'For once I think Bella is right,' Centaine said quietly from the end of the table. 'That's enough for one night, Garry. I just cannot concentrate at the moment. I think this has been one of the worst weeks of my entire life, having to watch that monster, with Blaine's blood on his hands, sitting there defying us and making a mockery of our system of justice. He threatens to tear down the whole structure of government, to plunge us all into anarchy and the same savagery of Africa which rent the land before we whites arrived. Then he smirks at us from the dock. I hate him. I have never hated anything or anybody as much as I hate him. I pray each night that they hang him.'

Unexpectedly it was Michael who replied. 'Yes, we hate him, Nana. We hate him because we are afraid of him, and we are afraid of him because we do not understand him or his people.'

They all stared at him in astonishment.

'Of course we understand him,' Centaine said. 'We have lived in Africa all our lives. We understand them as nobody else does.'

'I don't think so, Nana. I think if we had truly understood and listened to what this man had to say, Blaine would be alive today. I think he could have been an ally and not our deadly enemy. I think Moses Gama could have been a useful and highly respected citizen, and not a prisoner on trial for his life.'

'What strange ideas you have picked up on that newspaper of yours! He murdered your grandfather,' Centaine said, and shot a glance down the table at Shasa. Shasa interpreted it fluently and it meant, 'We have another problem on our hands here,' But Michael was going on obliviously.

'Moses Gama will die on the gallows – I think we all know that. But his words and his ideas will live on. I know now why I had to be a journalist. I know what I have to do. I have to explain those ideas to the people of this land,

to show them that they are just and fair, and not dangerous at all. In those ideas are the hopes for our survival as a nation.'

'It is a good thing I sent the servants out,' Centaine interrupted him. 'I never thought to hear words like those spoken in the dining-room of Weltevreden.

* * *

Vicky Gama waited for over an hour in the visitors' room at Roeland Street prison while the warders examined the contents of the package she had brought for Moses and made up their minds whether or not to allow her to hand it to the prisoner.

'It is only clothing,' Vicky pointed out reasonably.

'These aren't ordinary clothes,' the senior warden protested.

'They are the traditional robes of my husband's tribe. He is entitled to wear them.'

In the end the prison governor was called in to arbitrate and when he finally gave his permission, Vicky complained, 'Your men have been deliberately rude and obstructive to me.'

He smiled at her sarcastically. 'I wonder how you will treat us, madam, if you and your brothers in the ANC ever seize power. I wonder if you will allow us even the courtesy of a trial or whether you will slaughter us in the streets, as your husband tried to do.'

When Vicky was at last allowed to hand the parcel to Moses under the watchful eye of four warders, he asked her, 'Whose idea was this?'

'It was mine but Hendrick paid for the skins and his wives sewed them.'

'You are a clever woman,' Moses commended her, 'and a dutiful wife.'

'You, my lord, are a great chief, and it is fitting that you should wear the robes of your office.'

Moses held up the full length cloak of leopard skins, heavy and glossy golden, studded with the sable rosettes.

'You have understood,' he nodded. 'You have seen the necessity of using the white man's courtroom as a stage from which to shout our craving for freedom to the world.'

Vicky lowered her eyes and her voice. 'My lord, you must not die. If you die, then the great part of our dream of freedom dies with you. Will you not defend yourself, for my sake and for the sake of our people?'

'No, I will not die,' he assured her. 'The great nations of the world will not let that happen. Britain has already made her position clear and America cannot afford to let them execute me. Her own nation is wracked by the struggle of the American coloured people – she cannot afford to let me go to my death.'

'I do not trust the altruism of great nations,' Vicky said softly.

'Then trust in their own self-interest,' Moses Gama told her. 'And trust in me.'

* * *

When Moses Gama rose before the court in the golden and black robes of leopard skin, he seemed a reincarnatin of one of the ancient black kings. He riveted them.

'I call no witnesses,' Gama told them gravely. 'All I will do is to make a statement from the dock. That is as far as I am prepared to co-operate in this mockery of justice.'

'My lord,' the prosecutor was on his feet immediately. 'I must point out to the court – '

'Thank you!' Judge Villiers interrupted him in frigid tones. 'I do not need to be told how to conduct this trial,' and the prosecutor sank back into his seat, still making inarticulate sounds of protest.

Heavily the scarlet-robed justice turned his attention back to Moses Gama.

'What counsel for the prosecution is trying to tell me is that I should make it clear to you that if you do not enter the witness stand and take the oath, if you do not submit to cross-examination, then what you have to say will have little relevance to the proceedings.'

'An oath to your white man's God, in this courtroom with a white judge and a white prosecutor, with white prosecution witnesses and white policemen at the doors. I do not deign to submit to that kind of justice.'

Judge Villiers shook his head with a woeful expression and turned both his hands palms up. 'Very well, you have been warned of the consequences. Proceed with your statement.'

Moses Gama was silent for a long time, and then he began softly.

'There was once a small boy who wandered with joy through a beautiful land, who drank from the sweet clear rivers, who listened with pleasure to the song of the bird and studied the antics of the springbok and pangolin and all the marvellous wild things, a small boy who tended his father's herds, and sat at night by the fire and listened to the tales of the great heroes of his people, of Bambata and Sekhukhuni and mighty Chaka.

'This boy believed himself to be one of a peaceful people who owned the land on which they lived and were free to move wherever they wished in confidence and joy. Then one day when the boy was nine years of age a curious being came to the kraal at which the boy lived, a creature with a red face and a lordly manner, and the boy saw that the people were afraid, even his father and his grandfather who were chieftains of the tribe, were afraid as the boy had never seen them afraid before.'

There was no sound nor movement in the crowded courtroom as Moses Gama described his loss of innocence and how he had learned the bitter truths of his existence. He described his bewilderment as the universe he knew was proved an illusion. He told them of his first journey into the outside world, where he learned that as a man with a black skin there were places where his existence was circumscribed and limited.

When he went to the white man's towns, he found that he could not walk the streets after curfew without a pass, that he could not live outside the areas that had been set aside for his people on the outskirts of that town, but most important to him he found that he could not attend the white man's schools.He learned that in nearly every public building there was a separate entrance for him to use, that there were skills he was not allowed to acquire, and that in almost every way he was considered different and inferior, condemned by the pigmentation of his skin, always to remain on the bottom rung of existence.

Yet he knew that he was a man like other men, with the same hopes and

desires. He knew that his heart beat as fiercely and that his body was as strong, and his brain was as bright and quick as any other. He decided that the way to rise above the station in life that had been allotted him was to use that brain rather than employ his body like a beast of burden as most of his people were forced to do.

He turned to the white man's books and was astonished to find that the heroes of his people were described as savages and cattle-thieves and treacherous rebels. That even the most sympathetic and charitable of the authors he read referred to his people as children, unable to reason or think for themselves, children who must be sternly protected but prevented from taking part in the decisions which governed their lives.

He described to them how at last he had realized that is was all some monstrous lie. That he was not different, that because his skin was black he was not unclean or contaminated or childlike. He knew then for what purpose he had been put upon this earth.

'I came to know that the struggle against injustice was my life,' he said simply. 'I knew that I had to make the white men who ruled me and my people understand.'

He explained how each of his attempts to get the white men to listen had failed. How all his people's efforts had resulted only in more savage and draconian laws, in fiercer oppressions.

'In the end I had to accept that there was only one course left to me. That was to take up arms and to strike at the head of the serpent whose venom was poisoning and destroying my people.'

He was silent and his audience who had listened in complete and rigid silence for most of the morning, sighed and stirred, but as soon as Moses Gama spread his arms they were completely attentive once more.

'Every man has a right and a sacred duty to protect his family and his nation from the tyrant, to fight against injustice and slavery. When he does so he becomes a warrior and not a criminal. I challenge this judge and this white man's court to treat me as a soldier and a prisoner of war. For that is what I am.'

Moses Gama drew his leopard skins about him and sat down, leaving them all shaken and silenced.

Judge Villiers had sat through the entire address with his chin couched in his hand, his eyes hooded with concentration, but now he let his hand drop and he leaned forward to glower at the prisoner.

'You claim to be the leader of your people.'

'I do,' Moses replied.

'A leader is chosen or elected. How were you chosen?'

'When an oppressed people has no voice, then their leaders come forward of their own accord to speak for them,' Moses told them.

'So you are a self-proclaimed leader,' the judge said quietly. 'And your decision to declare war on our society was taken alone. Is that correct?'

'We are involved in a colonial war of liberation,' Moses Gama replied. 'Like our brothers in Algeria and Kenya.'

'You approved of the methods of the Mau Mau then?' Judge Villiers asked.

'Their cause was just – their methods, whatever they might have been, were therefore just.'

'The end justified the means – any means?'

'The struggle for liberation is all, in the name of liberty any deed is sanctified.'

'The slaughter and mutilation of innocents, of women and children. These are also justified?'

'If one innocent should die that a thousand might go free, then it is justified.'

'Tell me, Moses Gama, do you believe in democracy – in the concept of "One man, one vote"?'

'I believe that every man should have one vote to elect the leaders of the nation.'

'And after the leaders are chosen, what should happen?'

'I believe that the people should submit to the wisdom of their chosen leaders.'

'A one-party state – with a president for life?'

'That is the African way,' Moses Gama agreed.

'It is also the way of the Marxists,' Judge Villiers observed drily. 'Tell me, Moses Gama, what makes a black totalitarian government superior to a white totalitarian government?'

'The wishes of the majority of the people.'

'And the sanction of your people, of which only you are aware, makes you a holy crusader – above the laws of civilized man?'

'In this land there are no such laws, for the men who make the laws are barbarians,' said Moses Gama softly, and Judge Villiers had no more questions to put to him.

* * *

Twenty-four hours later Mr Justice André Villiers delivered his judgement to a hushed and expectant court.

'The basis of the case brought by the crown against the accused rests upon the consideration of how an individual reacts to what he perceives as an injustice. It raises the question of the individual's right or duty to resist those laws which he considers unjust or evil. I have had to consider what loyalty a person owes to a government, which was elected by a process from which he was totally excluded, a government which has furthermore embarked upon a programme of legislation that will deliberately alienate that person from most of the major rights, privileges and benefits of the society of which he is a member – ' For almost an hour Judge Villiers enlarged on and examined this proposition, then he summed up. 'I have therefore reached the conclusion that no duty of loyalty exists towards a state in which the individual is denied the basic democratic right of representation. Accordingly, on the charge of high treason I find the accused not guilty.'

There was a throaty roar from the body of the court and in the non-white section of the gallery they were dancing and singing. For almost a full minute Judge Villiers watched them, and those members of the court who knew him well were amazed by his forbearance. But the judge's features were crumpled with an unusual compassion and terrible sadness as he took up his gavel to quieten them.

In the silence he spoke again. 'I come now to the other charges against the accused. Those of murder and attempted murder. The crown has, with the help of the most eminent and trustworthy witnesses, made out a case which the accused has not attempted to challenge. I accept that the accused placed a large

body of explosive in the assembly chamber of the South African parliament with the intention of detonating that charge during a speech by the prime minister and thereby inflicting the greatest possible damage and death. I accept also that when his plot was discovered, he slew Colonel Blaine Malcomess and immediately thereafter attempted to murder Minister Courtney.' The judge paused and turned his head towards Moses Gama who sat impassively in the dock, still wearing his leopard-skin robes of chieftainship.

'The accused has offered the defence that he is a soldier in a war of liberation and is therefore not subject to the civil law. While I have already expressed my sympathy for and understanding of the accused's aspirations and those of the black people whom he claims to represent, I cannot entertain his demand that he be treated as a prisoner of war. He is a private individual who, while fully aware of the consequences of his actions, set out on the dark road of violence, determined to inflict the greatest possible destruction in the most indiscriminate fashion. It is therefore without any hesitation whatsoever that I find the accused guilty of murder and two charges of attempted murder.'

There was no sound in the courtroom as Judge Villiers went on softly. 'The prisoner will rise for sentence.'

Slowly Moses Gama came to his full height and he regarded Judge Villiers with an imperial stare.

'Is there anything you wish to say before sentence is passed upon you?' the judge asked.

'This is not justice. We both know that – and history will record it so.'

'Is there anything further you wish to say?'

When Moses shook his head, Judge Villiers intoned, 'Having found you guilty on the three main charges, I have carefully considered whether any extenuating circumstances exist in your case – and at last having determined that there are none, I have no alternative but to impose upon you the maximum penalty which the law decrees. On all the remaining charges, taken jointly and severally, I sentence you, Moses Gama, to death by hanging.'

The silence persisted for a moment longer and then from the rear of the court a woman's voice rose in keening ululation, the harrowing wail of African mourning. It was taken up immediately by all the other black women in the courtroom and Judge Villiers made no attempt to silence it.

In the dock Moses Gama raised a clenched fist above his head.

'*Amandla!*' he roared, and his people answered him with a single voice: '*Ngawethu! Mayibuye! Afrika!*'

* * *

Manfred De La Rey sat high in the grandstand, in one of the special boxes reserved for the most important spectators. Every single seat in the stand had been sold weeks before and the standing areas around the field were crammed to capacity. This great concourse of humanity had assembled to watch one of the major events of the sporting calendar, the clash betweem the Western Province and Northern Transvaal rugby football teams. At stake was the Currie Cup, a trophy for which every province of South Africa competed annually in a knock-out tournament. The fanatical partisanship which this contest evoked went far beyond that of mere sporting competition.

Manfred smiled sardonically as he looked around him. The Englishman Macmillan had said that theirs was the first of the African nationalisms. If that was correct, then this was one of their most important tribal rituals, one that united and reaffirmed the Afrikaners as a cohesive entity. No outsider could grasp the significance of the game of rugby football in their culture. True it had been developed at a British public school almost one hundred and fifty years ago, but then, Manfred thought wryly, it was too good for the *rooinekke* and it took an Afrikaner to understand the game and play it to its full potential.

Then again to call it a game was the same as calling politics or war, a game. It was more, a thousand times more. To sit here amongst his own, to be part of this immense spirit of Afrikanerdom, gave him the same sort of religious awe that he felt when he stood within the congregation of the Dutch Reformed Church, or when he was part of the throng that gathered before the massive Voortrekker Monument that stood on the hills above the city of Pretoria. On the day of the Covenant with God, his people gathered there each year to celebrate the victory that the Almighty had given them over the Zulu King Dingaan at the battle of Blood River.

As was fitting on such an occasion as this, Manfred wore his green blazer piped in gold with the flying Springbok emblem on the pocket and the legend 'Boxing 1936' below it. No matter that the buttons could no longer fasten across his dignified girth, he wore it with pride.

His pride was infinitely magnified when he looked down on the field. The turf was seared by the frosts of early winter but the highveld sunlight gave everything a lucid quality so that Manfred could make out every detail of his son's beloved features as he stood out near the centre of the field.

Lothar De La Rey's magnificent torso was not obscured by the blue woollen jersey that he wore, rather it was emphasized by the thin stuff, so that the lean hard muscle in his belly and chest stood proud. His bare legs were sturdy, but at the same time long and shapely, and the cap of close-cropped hair, coppery blond, burned like fire in the bright highveld sunshine.

Slowly Lothar bowed his head, as though to pray, and a hush fell over the packed grandstand. There was no breath of sound from even one of the forty thousand throats, and Lothar's dark brows clenched in complete concentration.

Slowly he lifted his arms, spreading them like the wings of a falcon on the edge of flight, until they were at the level of his shoulders, a strangely graceful gesture, and he raised his body on tiptoe so that the great muscles of his thighs tightened and changed shape – and then he began to run.

He ran with the bounding motion of that hunting cat, the cheetah, lifting his knees high and driving his whole body forward. Behind him the turf was scarred by the power of his studded boots, and in the immense silence of the arena his grunting breaths, timed to the long elastic strides, carried to where Manfred sat.

The leather ball, shiny brown and ovate, was balanced on one point, and as Lothar bore down on where it stood on the green turf, his pace quickened yet his body remained in perfect balance. The kick was a continuation of that long driving stride, his right leg whipped straight at the exact instant that his toe struck the ball and his weight was so far forward that his leg swung on up in an arcing parabola until his foot, with his toe extended like that of a ballet dancer, was high above his head, while both his arms were flung forward to maintain that graceful balance. The ball was grossly deformed by the brutal impact of the kick, but in flight it snapped back into shape, and rose in a flat hard trajectory

towards the two tall white goalposts at the end of the field. It neither tumbled nor wobbled, but flew with a stable motion, as steady in the air as a flighted arrow.

However, a hoarse and anxious sigh went up from the watchers, as they realized that it was aimed too far to the right. Although the power of that mighty right leg had driven it high above the level of the cross bar, it was going to miss the goalposts on the right and Manfred came to his feet with forty thousand others and groaned in helpless agony.

A miss would mean ignominious defeat, but if the ball passed between the white uprights, it would be victory, sweet and famous, by a single point.

The ball rose higher still, up out of the sheltered arena, and it caught the wind. Lothar had studied the flags on the roof of the grandstand before he began his run, and now the wind swung the ball in gently, but not enough, oh, sweet God, not nearly enough. Then gradually the ball lost impetus and power as it reached the zenith of its trajectory, and as it slowed, so the wind took charge, curving it ever more sharply to the left, and Manfred's groan turned to a roar of delight as it fell through the very centre of the goalposts, grazing the white cross bar, and the referee's shrill long-drawn-out whistle signalled the end of the match.

Beside Manfred, his boyhood friend, Roelf Stander, was pounding his back in congratulation.

'Man, I tell you, he is going to be a Springbok for sure, just like his Pa.'

On the field Lothar was surrounded by his team mates who were fighting for a chance to embrace him, while from the stands a wave of spectators was sweeping across the field to lionize him.

'Come, let's go down to the dressing-room.' Manfred took his companion's arm, but it was not that easy. They were stopped every few paces by the well-wishers and Manfred smiled and shook their hands and accepted their congratulations. Although this was part of his life, and his very soul fed on the adulation and enormous respect which every one of them, even the richest and most famous of them, showed towards him, yet today it irked Manfred to be kept from his son.

When at last they reached the dressing-room, the crowd that filled the corridor outside opened miraculously before them, and where others were turned away, they were respectfully ushered through into the steamy noisy room that stank of sweaty clothing and stale urine and hot masculine bodies.

Lothar was in the centre of the crowd of naked young men, singing and wrestling in rough camaraderie, but when he saw his father he broke away and came to him immediately, dressed only in a pair of grass-stained shorts with his magnificent young body glossy with sweat and a brown beer bottle clutched in one hand. His face was rapturous with pride and the sense of his own achievement.

'My son – ' Manfred held out his right hand and Lothar seized it joyously.

'My son – ' Manfred repeated, but his voice failed him and his vision misted over with pride. He jerked his son's hand, pulling him against his own chest, and held him hard, hugging him unashamedly, even while Lothar's sweat stained his shirt and his team mates howled with delight.

The three of them, Manfred, Roelf Stander and Lothar, drove home in the new ministerial Cadillac. They were happy as schoolboys, grinning and joshing each other and singing the bawdy old rugby songs. When they stopped at the traffic lights before entering the main traffic stream at Jan Smuts Drive that

would take them the thirty miles across the grassy undulating highveld to Pretoria, there were two small black urchins darting and dodging perilously amongst the vehicles, and one of them peered through the side window of the Cadillac at Manfred, grinning cockily and holding up a copy of the *Mail* from the bundle of newspapers he carried under his arm.

Manfred was about to dismiss him with an impatient gesture, for the *Mail* was an English rag. Then he saw the headlines: 'Appeal Fails: Guy Fawkes Killer to Hang' and he rolled down his side window and flipped the child a coin.

He passed the paper to Roelf Stander with the terse command, 'Read it to me!' and drove on.

This morning the appeal of Moses Gama against his conviction for murder and attempted murder by the Cape division of the Supreme Court was dismissed by a full bench of the Appellate Division in Bloemfontein and the date set for the execution by hanging was confirmed.

'*Ja, goed.*' Although Manfred scowled with concentration as he listened, his relief was intense. Over the months the media and the public had come to accept the Gama case as something intimately linked to Manfred De La Rey. The fact that he had personally made the arrest and that he was minister of police had combined so that the prosecution of the case had become in the public imagination, a measure of the strength and efficiency of the police force and of Manfred's *kragdadigheid*, his own personal power.

More than any other quality the Afrikaner *Volk* demanded strength and determination in its leaders. This case, with its terrifying message of black peril and bloody revolution, had invoked the most intense feelings of insecurity throughout the land. People wanted to be reassured that their safety and the security of the state were in strong hands. Manfred, with his sure political instincts, had realized that the dice of his future were being cast.

Unfortunately, there had been a complication in what should have been a straightforward matter of justice and swift retribution. The fact that the judge of the Supreme court had dismissed the charge of high treason and had made some controversial and ill-considered remarks about the individual's duty of loyalty to a state in which he was denied direct representation had been taken up by the foreign press and the case had captured the attention of left-wing liberals and Bolsheviks around the western world. In America the bearded hippies and commie university students had formed 'Save Moses Gama' committees and had picketed the White House and the South African embassy in Washington, while even in England there had been demonstrations in Trafalgar Square outside South Africa House by communist-inspired and -financed gangs of black expatriates and some white riff-raff. The British prime minister had summoned the South African high commissioner for consultations and President Eisenhower had instructed his ambassador in Pretoria to call upon Hendrik Verwoerd and appeal for mercy for the condemned man.

The South African government had stood firm in its rejection of these appeals. Their position was that the matter was one for the judiciary and that they would not interfere with the course of justice. However, their lordships of the Appellate Division were occasionally known to indulge in unwise demonstrations of compassion or obscure legal dialectic, in fits of independent thinking which accorded ill with the hard task of the police and the aspirations of the Afrikaner *Volk*.

This time, mercifully, they had been spared one of their lordships' quirky decisions and in that little green-painted room in Pretoria Central Prison the noose now waited for Moses Gama, and he would crash through the trap to the eternity into which he had planned to send the leaders of the nation.

'*Ja, goed!* Now read the editorial!' Manfred ordered Roelf Stander. The *Golden City Mail* was one of the English language newspapers, and even for that section of the press the views it held were liberal. Manfred would never have bought it for preference, but having done so he was now prepared to dilute his grim satisfaction at the appeal court's verdict, with the irritation of listening to the left-wing erudition of the *Mail*'s editorial staff.

Roelf Stander rustled the news sheet and cleared his throat.

'A Martyr is Born,' he read, and Manfred gave a growl of anger.

When Moses Gama dies at the end of the hangman's rope, he will become the most significant martyr in the history of the black African struggle for liberation.

Moses Gama's elevation will not be on account of his moving eloquence nor from the awe-inspiring power of his presence. Rather it will be for the simple reason that he has posed a question so grave and so fateful that by its very nature the answer to it can never be given by a single national court of law. The answer rests instead in the heart of mankind itself. For that question is aimed at the very foundation of man's existence upon this earth. Simply stated, it is this: is a man who is deprived of any peaceful or lawful means of asserting his basic human rights justified in turning, in the last resort, to violence?

Manfred snorted. 'Enough of that. I should not have bothered to have you read it out. It is so predictable. If the black savages cut the throats of our children and eat their raw livers, there would still be those *rooinekke* who would chastize us for not having provided salt for the feast! We will not listen to any more of that. Turn to the sports page. Let us hear what they have to say about Lothie and his *manne*, though I doubt that those *souties* can tell the difference between a stick of biltong and a rugby ball.'

When the Cadillac pulled up the long drive to Manfred's official residence in the elite suburb of Waterkloof, there was a large gathering of family and friends at the swimming-pool at the far end of the wide green lawns and the younger ones came running to meet them and to embrace Lothar as soon as he stepped out of the Cadillac.

'We listened on the radio,' they cried, as they clamoured for a turn to hug and kiss him. 'Oh Lothie, you were wonderful.' Each of his sisters took one of his arms, while their friends and the Stander girls crowded as close as they could to him as they escorted him down to the pool where the older women waited to congratulate him.

Lothar went to his mother first, and while they embraced Manfred watched them with an indulgent smile of pride. What a fine-looking family he had. Heidi was still a magnificent woman and no man could ask for a more dutiful wife. Not once in all the years had he ever regretted his choice.

'My friends, my family, all my loved ones,' Manfred raised his voice, and they turned to him and fell into silent expectation. Manfred was a compelling speaker, and as a nation they were susceptible to oratory and fine words for they were constantly exposed to them, from pulpit and political platform, from the cradle to the grave.

'When I look at this young man who is my son, at this fine young South African, and those of our young people like him, then I know that I need not worry for the future of our *Volk*,' Manfred proclaimed in the sonorous tones to

which his listeners responded instinctively, and they applauded and cried '*Hoor, hoor!*' each time he paused.

Amongst the listeners there was one at least who was not entirely captivated by his artistry. Although Sarah Stander smiled and nodded, she could feel her stomach churn and her throat burn with the acid of her rejected love.

Sitting in this lovely garden, watching the man she had loved beyond life itself, the man to whom she would have dedicated every moment of her existence, the man to whom she had given her girlish body and the tender blossom of her virginity, the man whose seed she had taken joyously into her womb, that ancient, now rancid passion changed its shape and texture to become hard and bitter hatred. She listened to Manfred extolling his wife, and she knew that she should have been that woman, those praises should have been for her alone. She should have been at his side to share his triumphs and his achievements.

She watched Manfred embrace Lothar and with his arm around his shoulders, commend his firstborn to them all, smiling with pride as he recited his virtues, and Sarah Stander hated them both, father and son, for Lothar De La Rey was not his firstborn.

She turned her head and saw Jakobus standing on the periphery, shy and self-effacing, but every bit as handsome as the big golden-headed athlete. Jakobus, her own son, had the dark brows and pale topaz-coloured eyes of the De La Reys. If Manfred were not blind, he would see that. Jakobus was as tall as Lothar, but was not possessed of his half-brother's raw-boned frame and layers of rippling muscle. He had an appealing fragility of body, and his features were not so dashingly masculine. Instead, he had the face of a poet, sensitive and gentle.

Sarah's own expression went dreamy and soft as she remembered his conception. She had been little more than a child, but her love had been that of a mature woman, as she crept through the silent old house to the room in which Manfred slept. She had loved him all her life, but in the morning he was leaving, sailing away to a far-off land, to Germany as a member of the Olympic team, and she had been troubled for weeks with a deep premonition of losing him for ever. She had wanted in some way to ensure against that insupportable loss, to try to make certain of his return, so she had given him everything that she had, her heart and her soul and her barely matured body, trusting him to return them to her.

Instead he had met the German woman and had married her. Sarah could still vividly recall the cablegram from Germany that had announced his dreadful betrayal, and her own devastation when she read the fateful words. Part of her had shrivelled and died on that day, part of her soul had been missing ever since.

Manfred De La Rey was still speaking, and he had them laughing now with some silly joke, but he looked towards her and saw that she was serious. Perhaps he read something of her thoughts in her eyes for his own gaze flicked across to where Jakobus stood and then back to her and for an instant she sensed an unusual emotion – regret or guilt – within him.

She wondered not for the first time if he knew about Jakobus. Surely he must at least have suspected it. Her marriage to Roelf had been so hasty, so unheralded, and the birth of Kobus had followed so swiftly. Then the physical resemblance of son to father was so strong, surely Manfred knew it.

Roelf knew, of course. He had loved her without hope until Manfred rejected

her, and he had used her pregnancy to gain her consent. Since then he had been a good and dutiful husband and his love and concern for her had never faltered – but he was not Manfred De La Rey. He was not, nor could he ever be, a man as Manfred De La Rey was a man. He had never had Manfred's force and power, his drive and personality and ruthlessness, and she could never love him as she loved Manfred.

Yes, she admitted to herself, I have always loved Manfred, and I will love him to the end of my life, but my hatred of him is as strong as my love and with time it will grow stronger still. It is all that I have to sustain me.

Manfred was ending his speech now, talking about Lothar's promotion. Of course, Sarah thought bitterly, his promotion would not have been so rapid if his father had not been the minister of police and he had not had such skill with a rugby ball. Her own Kobus could expect no such preferment. Everything he achieved would be with his own talent and by his own efforts. She and Roelf could do little for him. Roelf's influence was minimal, and even the university fees for Jakobus' education were a serious drain on their family finances. She had been forced to face the fact that Roelf would never go much further than he was now. His entry into legal practice had been a mistake and a failure. By the time he had accepted that fact and returned to the academic life as a lecturer in law, he had lost so much seniority that it would be many years, if ever, before he was given the chair of law. No there was not much they could do to help Kobus – but then, of course, none of the family, not even Kobus himself, knew what he wanted from life. He was a brilliant student, but he totally lacked direction or purpose, and he had always been a secretive lad. It was so difficult to draw him out. Once or twice Sarah had succeeded in doing so, but she had been frightened by the strange and radical views he expressed. Perhaps it was best not to explore her son's mind too deeply, she thought, and smiled across at him just as, at last, Manfred stopped singing his own son's praises.

Jakobus came to her side now. 'Can I get you another orange juice, Mama? Your glass is empty.'

'No thank you, Kobus, Stay with me for a while. I see so little of you these days.'

The men had charged their beer tankards and led by Manfred trooped towards the barbecue fires on the far side of the pool. Amid laughter and raillery Manfred and Lothar were tying candy-striped aprons around their waists and arming themselves with long-handled forks.

On a side table there was a huge array of platters piled with raw meat, lamb chops and *sosaties* on long skewers, German sausages and great thick steaks, enough to feed an army of starving giants and, Sarah calculated sourly, costing almost her husband's monthly salary.

Since Manfred and his one-armed demented father had mysteriously acquired shares in that fishing company in South West Africa, he had become not only famous and powerful, but enormously rich as well. Heidi had a mink coat now and Manfred had purchased a large farm in the rich maize-producing belt of the Orange Free State. It was every Afrikaner's dream to own a farm, and Sarah felt her envy flare as she thought about it. All that should have been hers. She had been deprived of what was rightly hers by that German whore. The word shocked her, but she repeated it silently – whore!

He was mine, whore, and you stole him from me.

Jakobus was talking to her, but she found it difficult to follow what he was saying. Her attention kept stealing back to Manfred De La Rey. Every time his

great laugh boomed out she felt her heart contract and she watched him from the corners of her eyes.

Manfred was holding court; even dressed in that silly apron and with a cooking fork in his hand, he was still the focus of all attention and respect. Every few minutes more guests arrived to join the gathering, most of them important and powerful men, but all of them gathered slavishly around Manfred and deferred to him.

'We should understand why he did it,' Jakobus was saying, and Sarah forced herself to concentrate on her son.

'Who did it, dear?' she asked vaguely.

'Mama, you haven't been listening to a word,' Jakobus smiled gently. 'You really are a little scatterbrain sometimes.' Sarah always felt vaguely uncomfortable when he spoke to her in such a familiar fashion, none of her friends' children would show such disrespect, even in fun.

'I was talking about Moses Gama,' Jakobus went on, and at the mention of that name everybody within earshot turned towards the two of them.

'They are going to hang that black thunder, at last,' somebody said, and everybody agreed immediately.

'*Ja*, about time.'

'We have to teach them a lesson – you show mercy to a kaffir and he takes it as weakness.'

'Only one thing they understand – '

'I think it will be a mistake to hang him,' Jakobus said clearly, and there was a stunned silence.

'Kobie! Kobie!' Sarah tugged at her son's arm, 'Not now, darling. People don't like that sort of talk.'

'That is because they never hear it – and they don't understand it,' Jakobus explained reasonably, but some of them turned away deliberately while a middle-aged cousin of Manfred's said truculently,

'Come on, Sarie, can't you stop your brat talking like a commie.'

'Please, Kobie,' she used the diminutive as a special appeal, 'for my sake.'

Manfred De La Rey had become aware of the disturbance and the flare of hostility amongst his guests, and now he looked across the fires on which the steaks were sizzling and he frowned.

'Don't you see, Mama, we have to talk about it. If we don't, people will never hear any other point of view. None of them even read the English newspapers – '

'Kobie, you will anger your uncle Manie,' Sarah pleaded. 'Please stop it now.'

'We Afrikaners are cut off in this little make-believe world of ours. We think that if we make enough laws the black people will cease to exist, except as our servants – '

Manfred had come across from the fires now, and his face was dark with anger.

'Jakobus Stander,' he rumbled softly. 'Your father and your mother are my oldest and dearest friends, but do not trespass on the hospitality of this house. I will not have wild and treasonable ideas bandied about in front of my family and friends. Behave yourself, or leave immediately.'

For a moment it seemed the boy might defy him. Then he dropped his gaze and mumbled, 'I'm sorry, *Oom* Manie.' But when Manfred turned and strode back to the barbecue fire, he said just loud enough for Sarah to hear, 'You see,

they won't listen. They don't want to hear. They are afraid of the truth. How can you make a blind man see?'

Manfred De La Rey was still inwardly seething with anger at the youth's ill-manners, but outwardly he was his usual bluff self as he resumed his self-imposed duties over the cooking fires, and led the jovial banter of his male guests. Gradually his irritation subsided, and he had almost put aside Moses Gama and the long shadow that he had thrown over them all, when his youngest daughter came running down from the long low ranch-type house.

'Papa, Papa, there is a telephone call for you.'

'I can't come now, *skatjie*,' Manfred called. 'We don't want our guests to starve. Take a message.'

'It's *Oom* Danie,' his daughter insisted, 'and he says he must talk to you now. It's very important.'

Manfred sighed and grumbled good-naturedly as he untied his apron, and handed his fork to Roelf Stander. 'Don't let them burn!' and he strode up to the house.

'*Ja!*' he barked into the telephone.

'I don't like to disturb you, Manie.'

'Then why do you do it?' Manfred demanded. Danie Leroux was a senior police general, and one of his most able officers.

'It's this man Gama.'

'Let the black bastard hang. That is what he wants.'

'No! He wants to do a deal.'

'Send someone else to speak to him, I do not want to waste my time.'

'He will only talk to you, and we believe he has something important he will be able to tell you.'

Manfred thought for a moment. His instinct was to dismiss the request out of hand, but he let reason dictate to him.

'All right,' he agreed heavily. 'I will meet him.' There would also be a perverse pleasure in confronting a vanquished foe. 'But he is going to hang – nothing will stop that,' he warned quietly.

* * *

The prison authority had confiscated the leopard-skin robes of chieftainship, and Moses Gama wore the prison-issue suiting of coarse unbleached calico.

The long unremitting strain of awaiting the outcome of his appeal had told heavily. For the first time Vicky noticed the frosting of white in his cap of dark crinkling hair, and his features were gaunt, his eyes sunken in dark bruised-looking hollows. Her compassion for him threatened to overwhelm her, and she wished that she could reach out and touch him, but the steel mesh screen separated them.

'This is the last time I am allowed to visit you,' she whispered, 'and they will only let me stay for fifteen minutes.'

'That will be long enough, for there is not much to say, now that the sentence has been confirmed.'

'Oh, Moses, we were wrong to believe that the British and the Americans would save you.'

'They tried,' he said quietly.

'But they did not try very hard, and now what will I do without you. What will the child I am carrying do without a father?'

'You are a daughter of Zulu, you will be strong.'

'I will try, Moses my husband,' she whispered. 'But what of your people? They are also children without a father. What will become of them?'

She saw the old fierce fire burn in his eyes. She had feared it had been for ever extinguished, and she felt a brief and bitter joy to know it was still alight.

'The others will seek to take your place now. Those of the Congress who hate and envy you. When you die they will use your sacrifice to serve their own ambitions.'

She saw that she had reached him again, and that he was angry. She sought to inflame his anger to give him reason and strength to go on living.

'If you die, your enemies will use your dead body as a stepping-stone to climb to the place you have left empty.'

'Why do you torment me, woman?' he asked.

'Because I do not want you to die, because I want you to live – for me, for our child, and for your people.'

'That cannot be,' he said. 'The hard Boers will not yield, not even to the demands of the great powers. Unless you can find wings for me to fly over these walls, then I must go to my fate. There is no other way.'

'There is a way,' Vicky told him. 'There is a way for you to survive – and for you to put down the enemy who seek to usurp your place as the leader of the black nations.'

He stared at her as she went on.

'When the day comes that we sweep the Boers into the sea, and open the doors of the prisons, you will emerge to take your rightful place at the head of the revolution.'

'What is this way, woman? What is this hope that you hold out to me?'

He listened without expression as she propounded it to him, and when she had finished, he said gravely, 'It is true that the lioness is fiercer and crueller than the lion.'

'Will you do it, my lord – not for your own sake, but for all us weak ones who need you so?'

'I will think on it,' he conceded.

'There is so little time,' she warned.

* * *

The black ministerial Cadillac was delayed only briefly at the gates to the prison for they were expecting Manfred De La Rey. As the steel gates swung open, the driver accelerated through into the main courtyard and turned into the parking slot that had been kept free. The prison commissioner and two of his senior staff were waiting, and they hurried forward as soon as Manfred climbed out of the rear door.

Briefly Manfred shook hands with the commissioner and said, 'I wish to see the prisoner immediately.'

'Of course, Minister, it has been arranged. He is waiting for you.'

'Lead the way.'

Manfred's heavy footfalls echoed along the dreary green-painted corridors,

while the senior warders scurried ahead to unlock the interleading doors of each section and relock them as Manfred and the prison commissioner passed through. It was a long walk, but they came at last to the condemned block.

'How many awaiting execution?' Manfred demanded.

'Eleven,' the commissioner replied. The figure was not unusually high, Manfred reflected. Africa is a violent land and the gallows play a central role in the administration of justice.

'I do not want to be overheard, even by those soon to die.'

'It has been arranged,' the commissioner assured him. 'Gama is being kept separate from the others.'

The warders opened one last steel door and at the end of a short passage was a barred cell. Manfred went through but when the commissioner would have followed, Manfred stopped him.

'Wait here!' he ordered. 'Lock the door after me and open it again only when I ring.'

As the door clanged shut Manfred walked on to the end of the passage.

The cell was small, seven foot by seven, and almost bare. There was a toilet bowl against the side wall and a single iron bunk fixed to the opposite wall. Moses Gama sat on the edge of the bunk and he looked up at Manfred. Then slowly he came to his feet and crossed the cell to face him through the green-painted bars.

Neither man spoke. They stared at each other. Though only the bars separated them, they were a universe and an eternity apart. Though their gazes locked, there was no contact between their minds, and the hostility was a barrier between them more obdurate and irreconcilable than the steel bars.

'Yes?' Manfred asked at last. The temptation to gloat over a vanquished adversary was strong, but he withstood it. 'You asked to see me?'

'I have a proposal to put to you,' Moses Gama said.

'You wish to bargain for your life?' Manfred corrected him, and when Moses was silent, he smiled. 'So it seems that you are no different from other men, Moses Gama. You are neither a saint nor even the noble martyr that some say you are. You are no better than other men, no better than any of us. In the end your loyalty is to yourself alone. You are weak as other men are weak, and like them, you are afraid.'

'Do you wish to listen to my proposal?' Moses asked, without a sign of having heard the taunts.

'I will hear what you have to say,' Manfred agreed. 'That is why I came here.'

'I will deliver them to you,' Moses said, and Manfred understood immediately.

'By "them" you mean those who also claim to be the leaders of your people? The ones who compete with your own claim to that position?'

Moses nodded and Manfred chuckled and shook his head with admiration.

'I will give you the names and the evidence. I will give you the times and the places.' Moses was still expressionless. 'You have underestimated the threat that they are to you, you have underestimated the support they can muster, here and abroad. I will give you that knowledge.'

'And in return?' Manfred asked.

'My freedom,' said Moses simply.

'*Magtig!*' The blasphemy was a measure of Manfred's astonishment. 'You

have the effrontery of a white man.' He turned away so that Moses could not see his face while he considered the magnitude of the offer.

Moses Gama was wrong. Manfred was fully aware of the threat, and he had a broad knowledge of the extent and the ramifications of the conspiracy. He understood that the world he knew was under terrible siege. The Englishman had spoken of the winds of change – they were blowing not only upon the African continent, but across the world. Everything he held dear, from the existence of his family to that of his *Volk* and the safety of the land that God had delivered unto them, was under attack by the forces of darkness.

Here he was being offered the opportunity to deal those forces a telling blow. He knew then what his duty was.

'I cannot give you your freedom,' he said quietly. 'That is too much – but you knew that when you demanded it, didn't you?' Moses did not answer him, and Manfred went on, 'This is the bargain I will offer you. I will give you your life. A reprieve, but you will never leave prison again. That is the best I can do.'

The silence went on so long that Manfred thought he had refused and he began to turn away when Moses spoke again.

'I accept.'

Manfred turned back to him, not allowing his triumph to show.

'I will want all the names, all the evidence,' he insisted.

'You will have it all,' Moses assured him. 'When I have my reprieve.'

'No,' Manfred said quietly. 'I set the terms. You will have your reprieve when you have earned it. Until then you will get only a stay of execution. Even for that I will need you to name a name so that I can convince my compatriots of the wisdom of our bargain.'

Moses was silent, glowering at him through the bars.

'Give me a name,' Manfred insisted. 'Give me something to take to the prime minister.'

'I will do better than that,' Moses agreed. 'I will give you two names. Heed them well. They are – Mandela and Rivonia.'

* * *

Michael Courtney was in the city room of the *Mail* when the news that the Appellate Division had denied Moses Gama's appeal and confirmed the date of his execution, came clattering out on the tape. He let the paper strip run through his fingers, reading it with total concentration, and when the message ended, he went to his desk and sat in front of his typewriter.

He lit a cigarette and sat quietly, staring out of the window over the tops of the scraggly trees in Joubert Park. He had a pile of work in his basket and a dozen reference books on his desk. Desmond Blake had slipped out of the office to go down to the George to top up his gin tank and left Michael to finish the article on the American elections. Eisenhower was nearing the end of his final term and the editor wanted a pen portrait of the presidential candidates. Michael was working on his biographical notes of John Kennedy, but having difficulty choosing the salient facts from the vast amount that had been written about the young Democratic candidate, apart from those that everybody knew, that he was a Catholic and a New Dealer and that he had been born in 1917.

America seemed very far away that morning, and the election of an American president inconsequential in comparison with what he had just read on the tape.

As part of his self-education and training, Michael made a practice each day of selecting an item of important news and writing a two-thousand-word mock editorial upon it. These exercises were for his own sake, the results private and jealously guarded. He showed them to no one, especially not Desmond Blake whose biting sarcasm and whose willingness to plagiarize Michael had learned to fear. He kept these articles in a folder in the locked bottom drawer of his desk.

Usually Michael worked on these exercises in his own time, staying on for an hour or so in the evening or sitting up late at night in the little bed-sitter he rented in Hillbrow, pecking them out on his rickety old secondhand Remington.

However, this morning he had been so moved by the failure of Gama's appeal that he could not concentrate on the Kennedy story. The image of the imperial-looking black man in his leopard-skin robes kept recurring before Michael's eyes, and his words kept echoing in Michael's ears.

Suddenly he reached forward and ripped the half-completed page out of his machine. Then he swiftly rolled a clean sheet into it. He didn't have to think, his fingers flew across the keys, and the words sprang up before his eyes: 'A Martyr is Born.'

He rolled the cigarette to the side of his mouth and squinted against the spiral of blue smoke, and the words came in short staccato bursts. He did not have to search for facts or dates or figures. They were all there, crisp and bright in his head. He never paused. He never had to weigh one word against another. The precise word was there on the page almost of its own volition.

When he finished it half an hour later, he knew that it was the best thing he had ever written. He read it through once, shaken by the power of his own words, and then he stood up. He felt restless and nervous. The effort of creation rather than calming or exhausting him had excited him. He had to get outside.

He left the sheet in the typewriter and took his jacket off the back of his chair. The sub glanced up at him enquiringly.

'Going to find Des,' he called. In the newsroom there was a conspiracy to protect Desmond Blake from himself and the gin bottle and the sub nodded agreement and returned to his work.

Once he was out of the building, Michael walked fast, pushing his way through the crowds on the sidewalks, stepping out hard with both hands thrust into his pockets. He didn't look where he was going, but it didn't surprise him when he found himself in the main concourse of the Johannesburg railway station.

He fetched a paper cup of coffee from the kiosk near the ticket office and took it to his usual seat on one of the benches. He lit a cigarette and raised his eyes towards the domed glass ceiling. The Pierneef murals were placed so high that very few of the thousands of commuters who passed through the concourse each day ever noticed them.

For Michael they were the essence of the continent, a distillation of all of Africa's immensity and infinite beauty. Like a celestial choir, they sang aloud all that he was trying to convey in clumsy stumbling sentences. He felt at peace when at last he left the massive stone building.

He found Des Blake on his usual stool at the end of the bar counter at the George.

'Are you your brother's keeper?' Des Blake enquired loftily, but his words were slurred. It took a great deal of gin to make Des Blake slur.

'The sub is asking for you,' Michael lied.

He wondered why he felt any concern for the man, or why any of them bothered to protect him – but then one of the other senior journalists had given him the answer to that. 'He was once a great newspaperman, and we have to look after our own.'

Des was having difficulty fitting a cigarette into his ivory holder. Michael did it for him, and as he held a match he said, 'Come on, Mr Blake. They are waiting for you.'

'Courtney, I think I should warn you now. You haven't got what it takes, I'm afraid. You'll never cut the mustard, boy. You are just a poor little rich man's son. You'll never be a newspaperman's anus.'

'Come along, Mr Blake,' said Michael wearily, and took his arm to help him down off the stool.

The first thing Michael noticed when he reached his desk again was that the sheet of paper was missing from his typewriter. It was only in the last few months, since he had been assigned to work with Des Blake, that he had been given his own desk and machine, and he was fiercely jealous and protective of them.

The idea of anyone fiddling with his typewriter, let alone taking work out of it, infuriated him. He looked around him furiously, seeking a target for his anger, but every single person in the long, crowded noisy room was senior to him. The effort it cost him to contain his outrage left him shaking. He lit another cigarette, the last one in his pack, and even in his agitation he realized that that made it twenty since breakfast.

'Courtney!' The sub called across to him, raising his voice above the rattle of typewriters. 'You took your time. Mr Herbstein wants you in his office right away.'

Michael's rage subsided miraculously. He had never been in the editor's office before, Mr Herbstein had once said good morning to him in the lift but that was all.

The walk down the newsroom seemed the longest of his life, and though nobody even glanced up as he passed, Michael was certain that they were secretly sniggering at him and gloating on his dilemma. He knocked on the frosted-glass panel of the editor's door and there was a bellow from inside.

Timidly Michael pushed the door open and peered round it. Leon Herbstein was on the telephone, a burly man in a sloppy hand-knitted cardigan with thick horn-rimmed spectacles and a shock of thick curly hair shot through with strands of grey. Impatiently he waved Michael into the room and then ignored him while he finished his conversation on the telephone.

At last he slammed down the receiver and swivelled his chair to regard the young man who was standing uneasily in front of his desk.

Ten days before, Leon Herbstein had received a quite unexpected invitation to a luncheon in the executive dining-room of the Courtney Mining and Finance Company's new head office building. There had been ten other guests present, all of them leaders of commerce and industry, but Herbstein had found himself in the righthand seat beside his host.

Leon Herbstein had never had any great admiration for Shasa Courtney. He was suspicious of vast wealth, and the two Courtneys – mother and son – had a formidable reputation for shrewd and ruthless business practices. Then again,

Shasa Courtney had forsaken the United Party of which Leon Herbstein was an ardent supporter, and had gone across to the Nationalists. Leon Herbstein had never forgotten the violent anti-semitism which had attended the birth of the National Party, and he considered the policy of *apartheid* as simply another manifestation of the same grotesque racial bigotry.

As far as he was concerned, Shasa Courtney was one of the enemy. However, he sat down at his luncheon table quite unprepared for the man's easy and insidious charm and his quick and subtle mind. Shasa devoted most of his attention to Leon Herbstein, and by the end of the meal the editor had considerably moderated his feelings towards the Courtneys. At least he was convinced that Shasa Courtney truly had the best interests of all the people at heart, that he was especially concerned with improving the lot of the black and underprivileged sections, and that he was wielding an important moderating influence in the high councils of the National Party.

In addition, he left the Courtney building with a heightened respect for Shasa Courtney's subtlety. Not once had Shasa mentioned the fact that he and his companies now owned 42 per cent of the stock of Associated Newspapers of South Africa or that his son was employed as a junior journalist on the *Mail*. It hadn't been necessary, both men had been acutely aware of these facts while they talked.

Up to that time Leon Herbstein had felt a natural antagonism towards Michael Courtney. Placing him in the care of Des Blake had been all the preference he had shown to the lad. However, after that luncheon he had begun to study him with more attention. It didn't take an old dog long to attribute the improvement in much of the copy that Des Blake had been turning out recently to the groundwork that Michael Courtney was doing for him. From then onwards whenever he passed Michael's desk, Herbstein made a point of quickly and surreptitiously checking what work was in his machine or in the copy basket.

Herbstein had the journalist's trick of being able to assimilate a full typed sheet at a single glance, and he was grimly amused to notice how often Des Blake's column was based on the draft by his young assistant, and how often the original was better than the final copy.

Now he studied Michael closely as he stood awkwardly before his desk. Despite the fact that he had cropped his hair in one of those appalling brush cuts that the youth were affecting these days and wore a vividly patterned bow tie, he was a likable-looking lad, with a strong determined jawline and clear intelligent eyes. Perhaps he was too thin for his height, and a little gawky, but he had quite noticeably matured and gained in self-assurance during the short period he had been at the *Mail*.

Suddenly Leon realized that he was being cruel, and that his scrutiny was subjecting the lad to unnecessary agony. He picked up the sheet of typescript that lay in front of him, and slid it across his untidy desk.

'Did you write that?' he demanded gruffly, and Michael snatched up the sheet protectively.

'I didn't mean anybody to read it,' he whispered, and then remembered who he was talking to and threw in a lame, 'sir.'

'Strange,' Leon Herbstein shook his head. 'I always believed we were in the business of writing so that others could read.'

'I was just practising.' Michael held the sheet behind his back.

'I made some corrections,' Herbstein told him, and Michael jerked the page out from behind him and scanned it anxiously.

'Your third paragraph is redundant, and "scar" is a better word than "cicatrice" – otherwise we'll run it as you wrote it.'

'I don't understand, sir,' Michael blurted.

'You've saved me the trouble of writing tomorrow's editorial.' Herbstein reached across and took the page from Michael's limp fingers, tossed it into his out basket and then concentrated all his attention on his own work.

Michael stood gaping at the top of his head. It took him ten seconds to realize that he had been dismissed and he backed towards the door and closed it carefully behind him. His legs just carried him to his desk, and then collapsed under him. He sat down heavily in his swivel chair and reached for his cigarette packet. It was empty and he crumpled it and dropped it into his wastepaper basket.

Only then did the full significance of what had happened hit him and he felt cold and slightly nauseated.

'The editorial,' he whispered, and his hands began to tremble.

Across the desk Desmond Blake belched softly and demanded, 'Where are the notes on that American what's-'is-name fellow?'

'I haven't finished it yet, Mr Blake.'

'Listen, kid. I warned you. You'll have to extract your digit from your fundamental orifice if you want to get anywhere around here.'

Michael set his alarm clock for five o'clock the next morning and went downstairs with his raincoat over his pyjamas. He was waiting on the street corner with the newspaper urchins when the bundles of newsprint were tossed on to the pavement from the back of the *Mail*'s delivery van.

He ran back up the stairs clutching a copy of the paper and locked the door to his bed-sitter. It took all his courage to open it at the editorial page. He was actually shaking with terror that Mr Herbstein might have changed his mind, or that it was all some monstrous practical joke.

There under the *Mail*'s crest at the very top of the editorial page was his headline: 'A MARTYR IS BORN.'

He read it through quickly, and then started again and read it aloud, mouthing each word, rolling it over his tongue like a noble and precious wine. He propped the paper, open at the editorial, beside the mirror while he shaved, and then carried it down to the Greek fast-food café where he had his breakfast each morning and showed it to Mr Costa, who called his wife out of the kitchen.

'Hey, Michael, you a big shot now.' Mrs Costa embraced him, smelling of fried bacon and garlic. 'You a big shot newspaperman now.'

She let him use the telephone in the back room and he gave the operator the number at Weltevreden. Centaine answered on the second ring.

'Mickey!' she cried delightedly. 'Where are you? Are you in Cape Town?'

He calmed her down and then read it to her. There was a long silence. 'The editorial, Mickey. You aren't making this up, are you? I'll never forgive you if you are.'

Once he had reassured her, Centaine told him, 'I can't remember ever being so excited about anything in years. I'm going to call your father, you must tell him yourself.'

Shasa came on the line, and Michael read it to him. 'You wrote that?' Shasa asked. 'Pretty hot stuff, Mickey. Of course I don't agree with your conclusions – Gama must hang. However, you almost convinced me otherwise, but we can

debate that when next we are together. In the meantime, congratulations, my boy. Perhaps you did make the right decision after all.'

Michael found that he was a minor celebrity in the newsroom, even the sub stopped by his desk to congratulate him and discuss the article for a few moments, and the pretty little blonde on the reception desk who had never before been aware of his existence, smiled and greeted him by name.

'Listen, kid,' said Desmond Blake. 'One little fart doesn't make a whole sewage farm. In future I don't want you pushing copy over my head. Every bit of shit you write comes across my desk, get it?'

'I'm sorry, Mr Blake. I didn't – '

'Yeah! Yeah! I know, you didn't mean it. Just don't go getting a big head. Remember whose assistant you are.'

The news of Moses Gama's reprieve threw the newsroom into a state of pandemonium that didn't subside for almost a week. Michael was drawn in and some of his days ended at midnight when the presses began their run, and began when the first papers hit the streets the next morning.

However, he found that the excitement seemed to release limitless reserves of energy in him and he never felt tired. He learned to work quickly and accurately and his way with words gradually assumed a deftness and polish that was apparent even to himself.

Two weeks after the reprieve the editor called him into his office. He had learned not to knock, any waste of time irritated Leon Herbstein and made him bellow aggressively. Michael went straight on in, but he had not yet entirely mastered the pose of world-weary cynicism which he knew was the hallmark of the veteran journalist, and he was all radiant eagerness as he asked, 'Yes, Mr Herbstein?'

'Okay, Mickey, I've got something for you.' Every time Mr Herbstein used his Christian name, Michael still thrilled with delicious shock.

'We are getting a lot of requests from readers and overseas correspondence. With all the interest in the Gama case, people want to know more about the black political movements. They want to know the difference between the Pan Africanist Congress and the African National Congress, they want to know who's who – who the hell are Tambo and Sisulu, Mandela and Moses Gama and what do they stand for? All that stuff. You seem to be interested in black politics and enjoy digging around in the archives – besides I can't spare one of my top men on this sort of background stuff. So get on with it.' Herbstein switched his attention back to the work on his desk, but Michael by now had sufficient confidence to stand his ground.

'Am I still working under Mr Blake?' he asked. He had learned by this time if you called him 'sir' it just made Leon Herbstein mad.

Herbstein shook his head but did not even look up. 'You are on your own. Send everything to me. No hurry, any time in the next five minutes will do nicely.'

Michael soon discovered that the *Mail*'s archives were inadequate, and served merely to initiate him into the complexity and daunting size of the project he had been set. However, from them he was at least able to draw up a list of the various black political groups and related associations such as the officially unrecognized black trade unions, and from there to compile a list of their own leaders and officials.

He cleared one wall of his bed-sitting room and put up a board on which he pinned all this information, using different-coloured cards for each grouping

and press photographs of the principal black leaders. All this achieved was to convince him of how little was known about the black movements by even the most well-informed of the white section of the nation.

The public library added very little to his understanding. Most of the books on the subject had been written ten or more years before and simply traced the African National Congress from those distant days of its inception in 1912 and the names mentioned were all of men now dead or in their dotage.

Then he had his first inspiration. One of the *Mail*'s sister publications under the banner of Associated Newspapers of South Africa was a weekly magazine called *Assegai* after the broad-bladed war spear that the impis of Chaka the Zulu conqueror had wielded. The magazine was aimed at the educated and more affluent section of the black community. Its editorial policy was dictated by the white directors of Associated Newspapers but amongst the articles and photographs of African football stars and torch singers, of black American athletes and film actors, an occasional article slipped through of a fiercely radical slant.

Michael borrowed a company car and went out to see the editor of *Assegai* in the vast black location of Drake's Farm. The editor was a graduate of the black university of Fort Hare, a Xhosa named Solomon Nduli. He was polite but cool, and they had chatted for half an hour before a barbed remark let Michael know that he had been recognized as a spy for the security police, and that he would learn nothing of value.

A week later the *Mail* published the first of Michael's articles in its Saturday magazine edition. It was a comparison of the two leading African political organizations: the Pan Africanist Congress which was a jealously exclusive body to which only pure-blooded African blacks were admitted and whose views were extremely radical, and the much larger African National Congress which, although predominantly black, also included whites and Asians and mixed blood members such as the Cape coloureds, and whose objectives were essentially conciliatory.

The article was accurate, obviously carefully researched, but, most important, the tone was sympathetic, and carried the by-line 'by Michael Courtney.'

The following day Solomon Nduli called Michael at the offices of the *Mail*, and suggested another meeting. His first words when they shook hands were, 'I'm sorry. I think I misjudged you. What do you want to know?'

Solomon took Michael into a strange world that he had never realized existed – the world of the black townships. He arranged for him to meet Robert Sobukwe, and Michael was appalled by the depth of the resentment the black leader of the Pan Africanist Congress expressed, particularly for the pass laws, by his enormous impatience to effect an upheaval of the entire society, and by the thinly veiled violence in the man.

'I will try to arrange for you to meet Mandela,' Solomon promised, 'although, as you know, he is underground now, and wanted by the police. But there are others you must talk to.'

He took Michael to Baragwanath Hospital and introduced him to the wife of Moses Gama, the lovely young Zulu woman he had seen at the trial in Cape Town. Victoria was heavily pregnant, but with a calm dignity that impressed Michael deeply until he sensed the same terrible resentment and latent violence in her that he had found in Robert Sobukwe.

The next day Solomon took him back to Drake's Farm to meet a man named Hendrick Tabaka, a man who seemed to own most of the small businesses in

the location and looked like a heavyweight wrestler with a head like a cannonball crisscrossed with scars.

He appeared to Michael to represent the opposite end of the black protest consciousness. 'I have my family and my business,' he told Michael, 'and I will protect them from anybody, black or white.' And Michael was reminded of a view that his father had often expressed, but to which Michael had not given much consideration before this. 'We must give the black people a piece of the pie,' Shasa Courtney had said. 'Give them something of their own. The truly dangerous man is one with nothing to lose.'

Michael gave the second article in the series the title 'Rage' and in it he tried to describe the deep and bitter resentment that he had encountered on his journeys into the half-world of the townships. He ended the article with the words:

> Despite this deep sense of outrage, I never found the least indication of hatred towards the white person as an individual by any of the black leaders with whom I was able to speak. Their resentment seemed to me to be directed only at the Nationalist government's policy of *apartheid* while the vast treasure of mutual goodwill built up over three hundred years between the races seems to be entirely undiminished by it.

He delivered the article to Leon Herbstein on the Thursday and found himself immediately embroiled in an editorial review of it that lasted until almost eight o'clock that evening. Leon Herbstein called in his assistant and his deputy editor, and their views were divided between publishing with only minor alterations and not publishing at all, for fear of bringing down the wrath of the publications control board, the government censors who had the power to ban the *Mail* and put it out of business.

'But it's all true,' Michael protested. 'I have substantiated every single fact I have quoted. It's true and it's important – that is all that really matters.' And the three older journalists looked at him pityingly.

'All right, Mickey,' Leon Herbstein dismissed him at last. 'You can go on home. I will let you know the final decision in due course.'

As Michael moved dispiritedly towards the door, the deputy editor nodded at him. 'Publish or not, Mickey, it's a damned good effort. You can be proud of it.'

When Michael got back to his apartment he found somebody sitting on a canvas holdall outside his front door. Only when the person stood up did he recognize the massively developed shoulders, the glinting steel-rimmed spectacles and spiky hairstyle.

'Garry,' he shouted joyously, and rushed to embrace his elder brother.

They sat side by side on the bed and talked excitedly, interrupting each other and laughing and exclaiming at each other's news.

'What are you doing in Jo'burg?' Michael demanded at last.

'I've come up from Silver River just for the weekend. I want to get at the new computer main frame in head office, and there are a few things I want to check at the land surveyor's office. So I thought, what the hell – why spend money on a hotel when Mickey has a flat? So I brought my sleeping-bag. Can I doss on your floor?'

'The bed pulls out into a double,' Mickey told him happily. 'You don't have to sleep on the floor.'

They went down to Costa's restaurant and Garry bought a pack of chicken curry and half a dozen Cokes. They ate the food out of the pack, sharing a

spoon to save washing up, and they talked until long after midnight. They had always been very close to each other. Even though he was younger, Michael had been a staunch ally during those dreadful childhood years of Garry's bed-wetting and stuttering and Sean's casually savage bullying. Then again Michael had not truly realized how lonely he had been in this strange city until this moment, and now there were so many nostalgic memories and so much unrequited need for affection to assuage, so many subjects of earth-shattering importance to discuss. They sat up into the small hours dealing with money and work and sex and the rest of it.

Garry was stunned to learn that Michael earned thirty-seven pounds ten shillings a month.

'How much does this kennel cost you a month?' he demanded.

'Twenty pounds,' Michael told him.

'That leaves you seventeen pounds ten a month to eat and exist. They should be arrested for slave labour.'

'It's not as bad as that – Pater gives me an allowance to make do. How much do you earn, Garry?' Michael demanded, and Garry looked guilty.

'I get my board and lodging and all my meals at the mine, single quarters, and I am paid a hundred a month as an executive trainee.'

'Son of a gun!' Michael was deeply impressed. 'What do you do with all that?'

It was Garry's turn to look amazed. 'Save it, of course. I've got over two thousand in the bank already.'

'But what are you going to do with all that?' Michael insisted. 'What are you going to spend it on?'

'Money isn't for spending,' Garry explained. 'Money is for saving – that is, if you want to be rich.'

'And you want to be rich?' Michael asked.

'What else is there?' Garry was genuinely puzzled by the question.

'What about doing an important job the best way you can? Isn't that something to strive for, even better than getting rich.'

'Oh sure!' said Garry with vast relief. 'But then, of course, you won't get rich unless you do just that.'

It was almost two in the morning when Michael at last switched off the bedside lamp and they settled down nose to toes, until Garry asked in the darkness the question he had not been able to ask until then.

'Mickey, have you heard from Mater at all?'

Michael was silent for so long that he went on impetuously. 'I have tried to speak to Dad about her, but he just clams up and won't say a word. Same with Nana, except she went a little further. She said "Don't mention that woman's name in Weltevreden again. She was responsible for Blaine's murder." I thought you might know where she is.'

'She's in London,' Michael said softly. 'She writes to me every week.'

'When is she coming back, Mickey?'

'Never,' Michael said. 'She and Pater are getting a divorce.'

'Why, Mickey, what happened that she had to leave like that, without even saying goodbye?'

'I don't know. She won't say. I wrote and asked her, but she wouldn't tell me.'

Garry thought he had gone to sleep, but after a long silence Michael said so

softly that he barely caught the words, 'I miss her, Garry. Oh God, how much I miss her.'

'Me too,' said Garry dutifully, but each week that passed was so filled with excitement and new experience that for Garry her memory had already faded and blurred.

The next morning Leon Herbstein called Mickey into his office.

'Okay, Mickey,' he said. 'We are going to run the "Rage" article as you wrote it.' Only then did Michael realize how important that decision had been to him. For the rest of that day his jubilation was tempered by that reflection. Why was his feeling of relief so powerful? Was it the personal achievement, the thought of seeing his name in print again? It was part of that, he was honest with himself, but there was something else even deeper and more substantial. The truth. He had written the truth and the truth had prevailed. He had been exonerated.

Michael went down early the next morning and brought a copy of the *Mail* up to the bed-sitter. He woke Garry up and read the 'Rage' feature to him. Garry had only come in a few hours before dawn. He had spent most of the night in the computer room at the new Courtney Mining building in Diagonal Street. David Abrahams, on Shasa's discreet suggestion, had arranged for him to have a free hand with the equipment when it was not being used on company business. This morning Garry was red-eyed with exhaustion and his jowls were covered with a dense dark pelt of new beard. However, he sat up in his pyjamas and listened with attention while Michael read to him, and when he had finished Garry put on his spectacles and sat solemnly reading it through for himself while Michael brewed coffee on the gas-ring in the corner.

'It's funny isn't it,' Garry said at last. 'How we just take them for granted. They are there, working the shifts at the Silver River or harvesting the grapes at Weltevreden, or waiting on table. But you never think of them as actually having feelings and desires and thoughts the same as we do – not until you read something like this.'

'Thank you, Garry,' Michael said softly.

'What for?'

'That's the greatest compliment anybody has ever paid me,' Michael said.

He saw very little more of Garry that weekend. Garry spent the Saturday morning at the deeds registry until that office closed at noon and then went on up to the Courtney building to take over the computer as soon as the company programmers went off for their weekend.

He let himself back into the flat at three the next morning and climbed into the bottom end of Michael's bed. When they awoke late on the Sunday morning, Michael suggested, 'Let's go out to Zoo Lake. It's a hot day and the girls will be out in their sundresses.' He offered the bait deliberately for he was desperate for Garry's company, lonely and suffering from a sense of anti-climax after all the worry and uncertainty previous to the printing of the 'Rage' article and the subsequent apparent lack of any reaction to it.

'Hey, Mickey, I'd love to come with you – but I want to do something on the computer. It's Sunday, I'll have it to myself all day.' Garry looked mysterious and self-satisfied. 'You see, I'm on to something, Mickey. Something incredible, and I can't stop now.'

Alone Michael caught the bus out to Zoo Lake. He spent the day sitting on the lawns reading and watching the girls. It only made him feel even more lonely and insignificant. When he got back to his dreary little flatlet, Garry's

bag was gone and there was a message written with soap on his shaving mirror: 'Going back to Silver River. Might see you next weekend. G.'

When Michael walked into the *Mail*'s offices on the Monday morning he found that those members of the newspaper's staff who had arived ahead of him were gathered in a silent nervous cluster in the middle of the newsroom while half a dozen strangers were going through the filing cabinets and rifling the papers and books on the desks. They had already assembled a dozen large cardboard cartons of various papers, and these were stacked in the aisle between the desks.

'What is happening?' Michael asked innocently, and his sub gave him a warning glance as he explained.

'These are police officers of the security branch.'

'Who are you?' The plain-clothes officer who was in charge of the detail came across to Michael, and when he gave his name the officer checked his list.

'Ah yes – you are the one we want. Come with me.' He led Michael down to Leon Herbstein's office and went in without knocking.

There was another stranger with Herbstein. 'Yes, what is it?' he snapped, and the security policeman answered diffidently.

'This is the one, Captain.'

The stranger frowned at Michael, but before he could speak Leon Herbstein interrupted quickly.

'It's all right, Michael. The police have come to serve a banning order on the Saturday edition with the "Rage" article in it, and they have a warrant to search the offices. They also want to talk to you, but it's nothing to worry about.'

'Don't be too sure of that,' said the police captain heavily. 'Are you the one who wrote that piece of commie propaganda?'

'I wrote the "Rage" article,' Michael said clearly, but Leon Herbstein cut in.

'However, as the editor of the *Golden City Mail* it was my decision to print it, and I accept full responsibility for the article.'

The captain ignored him and studied Michael for a moment before going on. 'Man, you are just a kid. What do you know, anyway?'

'I object to that, Captain,' Herbstein told him angrily. 'Mr Courtney is an accredited journalist – '

'*Ja*,' the captain nodded, 'I expect that he is.' But he went on addressing Michael, 'What about you? Do you object to coming down to Marshall Square police headquarters to help us with our investigations?'

Michael glanced at Herbstein and he said immediately, 'You don't have to go, Michael. They don't have a warrant for your arrest.'

'What do you want from me, Captain?' Michael hedged.

'We want to know who told you all that treasonable stuff you wrote about.'

'I can't disclose my sources,' Michael said quietly.

'I can always get a warrant if you refuse to co-operate,' the captain warned him ominously.

'I'll come with you,' Michael agreed. 'But I won't disclose my sources. That's not ethical.'

'I'll be down there with a lawyer right away, Michael,' Herbstein promised. 'You don't have to worry, the *Mail* will back you all the way.'

'All right. Let's go,' said the police captain.

Leon Herbstein accompanied Michael down the newsroom and as they passed the cartons of impounded literature the captain observed gloatingly, 'Man,

you've got a pile of banned stuff there, Karl Marx and Trotsky even – that's really poisonous rubbish.'

'It's research material,' said Leon Herbstein.

'*Ja*, try telling that to the magistrate,' the captain chortled.

As soon as the doors of the elevator closed on the captain and Michael, Herbstein trotted heavily back to his office and snatched up the telephone.

'I want an urgent call to Mr Shasa Courtney in Cape Town. Try his home at Weltevreden, his office in Centaine House and his ministerial office at the houses of parliament.'

He got through to Shasa in his parliamentary suite and Shasa listened in silence while Herbstein explained to him what had happened.

'All right,' Shasa said crisply at the end of it. 'You get the Associated Newspapers lawyers down to Marshall Square immediately, then ring David Abrahams at Courtney Mining and tell him what has happened. Tell him I want a massive reaction, everything we have got. Tell him also that I will be flying up immediately in the company jet. I want a limousine at the airport to meet me, and I will go to see the minister of police at the Union Buildings in Pretoria the minute I arrive.'

Even Leon Herbstein, who had seen it all before, was impressed by the mobilization of the vast resources of the Courtney empire.

At ten o'clock that evening Michael Courtney was released from interrogation on the direct orders of the minister of police and when he walked out the front entrance of Marshall Square headquarters he was flanked by half a dozen lawyers of formidable reputation who had been retained by Courtney Mining and Associated Newspapers.

At the pavement Shasa Courtney was waiting in the back seat of the black Cadillac limousine. As Michael climbed in beside him, he said grimly, 'It is possible, Mickey, to be a bit too bloody clever for your own good. Just what the hell are you trying to do? Burn down everything we have worked for all our lives?'

'What I wrote was the truth. I thought you, of all people, would understand, Pater.'

'What you wrote, my boy, is incitement. Taken by the wrong people and used on simple ignorant black folk, your words could help to open a Pandora's box of horrors. I want no more of that sort of thing from you, do you hear me, Michael?'

'I hear you, Pater,' Michael said softly. 'But I can't promise to obey you. I'm sorry, but I have to live with my own conscience.'

'You are as bad as your bloody mother,' said Shasa. He had sworn twice in as many minutes, the first time in his life that Michael had ever heard his father use coarse language. That and the mention of his mother, also the first time Shasa had done so since she left, silenced Michael completely. They drove without speaking to the Carlton Hotel. Shasa only spoke again when they were in his permanent suite.

'All right, Mickey,' he said with resignation. 'I take that back. I can't demand that you live your life on my terms. Follow your conscience, if you must, but don't expect me to come rushing in to save you from the consequences of your actions every time.'

'I have never expected that, sir,' Michael said carefully. 'And I won't in future either.' He paused and swallowed hard. 'But all the same, sir, I want to thank you for what you did. You have always been so good to me.'

'Oh Mickey, Mickey!' Shasa cried, shaking his head sorrowfully. 'If only I could give you the experience I earned with so much pain. If only you didn't have to make exactly the same mistakes I made at your age.'

'I am always grateful for your advice, Pater,' Michael tried to placate him.

'All right then, here's a piece for nothing,' Shasa told him. 'When you meet an invincible enemy you don't rush headlong at him, swinging with both fists. That way you merely get your head broken. What you do is you sneak around behind him and kick him in the backside, then run like hell.'

'I'll remember that, sir,' Michael grinned, and Shasa put his arm around his shoulders. 'I know you smoke like a bush fire, but can I offer you a drink, my boy?'

'I'll have a beer, sir.'

The next day Michael drove out to visit Solomon Nduli at Drake's Farm. He wanted to have his views on the 'Rage' article, and tell him of the consequences he had suffered at Marshall Square.

That was not necessary. Solomon Nduli somehow knew every detail of his detention and interrogation and Michael found he was a celebrity in the offices of *Assegai* magazine. Nearly every one of the black journalists and magazine staff wanted to shake his hand and congratulate him on the article.

As soon as they were alone in his office, Solomon told him excitedly, 'Nelson Mandela has read your piece and he wants to meet you.'

'But he is wanted by the police – he's on the run.'

'After what you wrote, he trusts you,' Solomon said, 'and so does Robert Sobukwe. He also wants to see you again.' Then he noticed Michael's expression, and the excitement went out of him as he asked quietly, 'Unless you think it's too dangerous for you.'

Michael hesitated only a moment. 'No, of course not. I want to meet them both. Very much.'

Solomon Nduli said nothing. He simply reached across the desk and clasped Michael's shoulder. It was strange what a pleasurable sensation that grip gave Michael, the first comradely gesture he had ever received from a black man.

* * *

Shasa banked the HS 125 twin-engined jet to give himself a better view of the Silver River Mine a thousand feet below.

The headgear was of modern design, not the traditional scaffolding of steel girders with the great steel wheels of the haulage exposed. It was instead a graceful unbroken tower of concrete, tall as a ten-storey building, and around it the other buildings of the mine complex, the crushing works and the uranium extraction plant and the gold refinery, had been laid out with equal aesthetic consideration. The administration block was surrounded by green lawns and flowering gardens, and beyond that there were an eighteen-hole golf course, a cricket pitch and a rugby field for the white miners. An Olympic-size swimming-pool adjoined the mine club and single quarters. On the opposite side of the property stood the compound for the black mineworkers. Here again Shasa had ordered that the traditional rows of barracks be replaced by neat cottages for the senior black staff and the bachelor quarters were spacious and pleasant, more like motels than institutions to house and feed the five thousand tribesmen

who had been recruited from as far afield as Nyasaland in the north and Portuguese Mozambique in the east. There were also soccer fields and cinemas and a shopping complex for the black employees, and between the buildings were green lawns and trees.

The Silver River was a wet mine and each day millions of gallons of water were pumped out of the deep workings and these were used to beautify the property. Shasa had reason to be proud.

Although the main shaft had intersected the gold-bearing reef at great depth – more than a mile below the surface – still the ore was so rich that it could be brought to the surface for enormous profit. What's more, the price could not be pegged at $35 per ounce for much longer. Shasa was convinced that it would double and even treble.

'Our guardian angel,' Shasa smiled to himself as he levelled the wings of the HS 125, and began his preparations for landing.

'Of all the blessings that have been heaped upon this land, gold is the greatest. It has stood us through the bad times, and made the good times glorious. It is our treasure and more, for when all else fails, when our enemies and the fates conspire to bring us down, gold glows with its bright particular lustre to protect us. A guardian angel indeed.'

Although the company pilot in the right-hand seat watched critically, for Shasa had only converted to jets within the last twelve months, Shasa brought the swift machine in to the long blue tarmac strip with casual ease. The HS 125 was painted in silver and blue with the stylized diamond logo on the fuselage, just as the old Mosquito had been. It was a magnificent machine. With its seating for eight passengers and its blazing speed, it was infinitely more practical than the Mosquito, but Shasa still occasionally mourned her loss. He had flown over five thousand hours in the old Mosquito before at last donating her to the airforce museum, where, restored to her combat camouflage and armaments, she was one of the prime exhibits.

Shasa rolled the glistening new jet down to the hangar at the far end of the strip, and reception committee was out to meet him headed by the general manager of the Silver River, all of them holding their ears against the shrill wail of the engines.

The general manager shook Shasa's hand and said immediately, 'Your son asked me to apologize that he wasn't able to meet you, Mr Courtney. He is underground at the moment, but asked me to tell you he will come up to the guest house as soon as he gets off shift.' The general manager, emboldened by Shasa's smile of paternal approval, risked a pleasantry. 'It must run in the family, but it's difficult to get the little blighter to stop working, we almost have to tie him down.'

There were two guest houses, one for other important visitors to the mine, and this one set aside exclusively for Shasa and Centaine. It was so sybaritic and had cost so much that embarrassing questions had been put to Shasa at the annual general meeting of the company by a group of dissident shareholders. Shasa was totally unrepentant. 'How can I work properly if I'm not allowed at least some basic comforts? A roof over my head – is that too much to ask?'

The guest house had its own squash court and heated indoor pool, cinema, conference room, kitchens and wine cellar. The design was by one of Frank Lloyd Wright's most brilliant pupils and Hicks had come out from London to do the interior. It housed the overflow of Shasa's art collection and Persian carpets from Weltevreden, and the mature trees in the landscaped garden had

been selected from all over the country to be replanted here. Shasa felt very much at home in this little *pied-à-terre*.

The underground engineer and the chief electrical engineer were already waiting in the conference room and Shasa went straight in and was at work within ten minutes of landing the jet. By eight o'clock that evening he had exhausted his engineers and he let them go.

Garry was waiting next door in Shasa's private study, filling in the time playing with the computer terminal, but he leapt up as Shasa walked in.

'Dad, I'm so glad I've found you. I've been trying to catch up with you for days – I'm running out of time.' He was stuttering again. These days he only did that when he was wildly over-excited.

'Slow down, Garry. Take a deep breath,' Shasa advised him, but the words kept tumbling out, and Garry seized his father's hand and led him to the computer to illustrate what he was trying to put across.

'You know what Nana has always said, and what you are always telling me about land being the only lasting asset, well – ' Garry's powerful spatulate fingers rippled over the computer keys. Shasa watched with curiosity as Garry presented his case, but when he realized what the boy was driving at, he quickly lost interest and concentration.

However, he listened to it all before he asked quietly, 'So you have paid for the option with your own money?'

'I have it signed, here!' Garry brandished the document. 'It cost me all my savings, over two thousand pounds just for a one-week option.'

'Let me recap, then,' Shasa suggested. 'You have spent two thousand pounds to acquire a one-week option on a section of agricultural ground on the northern outskirts of Johannesburg which you intend to develop as a residential township, complete with a shopping complex, theatres, cinemas and all the trimmings – '

'There is at least twenty million pounds of profit in the development – at the very least.' Garry manipulated the computer keyboard and pointed to the rippling green figures. 'Just look at that, Dad!'

'Garry! Garry!' Shasa sighed. 'I think you have just lost your two thousand pounds, but the experience will be worth it in the long run. Of course, there is twenty million profit in it. Everybody knows that, and everybody wants a piece of that action. It's just for that reason that there is such strict control on township development. It takes at least five years to get government approval for a new township, and there are hundreds of pitfalls along the way. It's a highly complex and specialized field of investment, and the outlay is enormous – millions of pounds at risk. Don't you see, Garry? Your piece of land is probably not the best available, there will be a dozen other projects ahead of yours and township development just isn't one of the areas which we deal in – ' Shasa broke off and stared at his son. Garry was flapping his hands and stuttering so badly that Shasa had to warn him again, 'Big breath.'

Garry gasped and his barrel chest expanded until his shirt buttons strained. It came out quite clearly.

'I already have approval,' he said.

'That takes years – I've explained.' Shasa was brusque. He began to rise. 'We should change for dinner. Come on.'

'Dad you don't understand,' Garry insisted. 'Approval has already been granted.'

Shasa sat down slowly. 'What did you say?' he asked quietly.

'Township approval was granted in 1891 by the *Volksraad* of the old Transvaal republic. It was signed by President Kruger himelf, but it is still perfectly legal and binding. It was just forgotten, that is all.'

'I don't believe it,' Shasa shook his head. 'How on earth did you get on to this, Garry?'

'I was reading a couple of old books about the early days of the Witwatersrand and the gold-mines. I thought that if I was going to learn mining, the very least I could do was bone up on the history of the industry.' Garry explained, 'And in one of the books there was a mention of one of the old Rand lords and his grandiose idea of building a paradise city for the very rich away from the coarse and rowdy centre of Johannesburg. The author mentioned that he had actually bought a six-thousand-acre farm and had it surveyed and that approval had been granted by the *Volksraad*, and then the whole idea had been abandoned.'

'What did you do then?'

'I went to the archives and looked up the proceedings of the *Volksraad* for the years 1889 to 1891 and there it was – the approval. Then I researched the title deeds of the property at the deeds registry and went out to the farm itself. It's called Baviaansfontein and it's owned by two brothers, both in their seventies. Nice old fellows, we got on well and they showed me their horses and cattle, and invited me to lunch. They thought the option was a big joke, but when I showed them my two thousand pounds, they had never seen so much money in one pile in their lives.' Garry grinned. 'Here are the copies of the title deeds and the original township approval.' Garry handed them to his father and Shasa read through slowly, even moving his lips like a semi-literate so as to savour every word of the ancient documents.

'When does your option expire?' he asked at last, without looking up.

'Noon on Thursday. We will have to act fast.'

'Did you take out the option in the name of Courtney Mining?' Shasa asked.

'No. In my own name, but of course, I did it for you and the company.'

'You thought this out alone,' Shasa said carefully. 'You researched it yourself, dug up the original approval, negotiated the option with the owners, paid for it with two thousand of your own hard-earned cash. You did all the work and took all the risks and now you want to hand it over to someone else. That isn't very bright, is it?'

'I don't want to hand it over to just anybody – to you, Dad. Everything I do is for you, you know that.'

'Well, that changes as of now,' said Shasa briskly. 'I will personally lend you the two hundred thousand purchase price and we will fly up to Johannesburg first thing tomorrow to clinch the deal. Once you own the land, Courtney Mining will begin negotiating with you the terms of a joint venture to develop it.'

The negotiations started tough, and then as Garry got his first taste of blood, they grew tougher.

'My God, I've sired a monster,' Shasa complained, to hide his pride in his offspring's bargaining technique. 'Come on, son, leave something in it for us.'

To mollify his father a little Garry announced a change in the name of the property. In future it would be known as Shasaville. When they at last signed the final agreement, Shasa opened a bottle of champagne and said, 'Congratulations, my boy.'

That approbation was worth more to Garry than all the townships and every grain of gold on the Witwatersrand.

* * *

Lothar De La Rey was one of the youngest police captains on the force, and this was not entirely on account of his father's position and influence. From the time he had been awarded the sword of honour at police college, he had distinguished himself in every field that was considered important by the higher command. He had studied for and passed all his promotion examinations with distinction. A great emphasis was placed on athletic endeavour and rugby football was the major sport in the police curriculum. It was now almost certain that Lothar would be chosen as an international during the forthcoming tour by the New Zealand All Blacks. He was well liked both by his senior officers and his peers, and his service record was embellished by an unbroken string of excellent ratings. Added to this he had shown an unusual aptitude for police work. Neither the plodding monotony of investigatiin nor the routine of patrol wearied him, and in those sudden eruptions of dangerous and violent action, Lothar had displayed resourcefulness and courage.

He had four citations on his service record, all of them for successful confrontation with dangerous criminals. He was also the holder of the police medal for gallantry, which he had been awarded after he had shot and killed two notorious drug dealers during a foot-chase through the black township at night, and a single-handed shoot-out from which he had emerged unscathed.

Added to all this was the assessment by his superiors that while himself amenable to discipline, he had the qualities of command and leadership highly developed. Both these were very much Afrikaner characteristics. During the North African campaign against Rommel, General Montgomery, when told that there was a shortage of officer material, had replied, 'Nonsense, we've got thousands of South Africans. Each of them is a natural leader – from childhood they are accustomed to giving orders to the natives.'

Lothar had been stationed at the Sharpeville police station since graduating from police college and had come to know the area intimately. Gradually he had built up his own network of informers, the basis of all good police work, and through these prostitutes and sheveen owners and petty criminals, he was able to anticipate much of the serious crime and to identify the organizers and perpetrators even before the offence was committed.

The higher command of the police force was well aware that the young police captain with illustrious family connections was in a large measure responsible for the fact that the police in the Sharpeville location had over the past few years built up a reputation of being one of the most vigorous and active units in the heavily populated industrial triangle that lies between Johannesburg, Pretoria and Vereeniging.

In comparison to greater Soweto, Alexandra or even Drake's Farm, Sharpeville was a small black township. It housed a mere forty thousand or so of all ages, and yet the police raids for illicit liquor and pass offenders were almost daily routine, and the lists of arrests and convictions by which the efficiency of any station is judged were out of all proportion to its size. Much of this industry

and dedication to duty was quite correctly attributed to the energy of the young second-in-command.

Sharpeville is an adjunct to the town of Vereeniging where in 1902 the British Commander Lord Kitchener and the leaders of the Boer commandos negotiated the peace treaty which brought to an end the long-drawn-out and tragic South African war. Vereeniging is situated on the Vaal river fifty miles south of Johannesburg and its reasons for existing are the coal and iron deposits which are exploited by Iscor, the giant state-owned Iron and Steel Corporation.

At the turn of the century the black workers in the steel industry were originally housed in the Top Location, but as conditions there became totally inadequate and outmoded, a new location was set aside for them in the early 1940s and named after John Sharpe, the mayor for the time being of the town of Vereeniging. As the new dwellings in Sharpeville became available, the population was moved down from Top Location, and although the rents were as high as £2 7*s* 6*d* per month, the translocations were effected gradually and peaceably.

Sharpeville was, in fact, a model township, and though the cottages were the usual box shape, they were all serviced with water-borne sewerage and electricity, and there were all the other amenities including a cinema, shopping areas and sports facilities, together with their very own police station.

In the midst of one of the most comprehensive pieces of social engineering of the twentieth century – which was the policy of *apartheid* in practice – Sharpeville was a remarkable area of calm. All around, hundreds of thousands of people were being moved and regimented and reclassified in accordance with those monumental slabs of legislation, the Group Areas Act and the Population Registration Act. All around the fledgeling leaders of black consciousness and liberation were preaching and exhorting and organizing, but Sharpeville seemed untouched by it all. The white city fathers of Vereeniging pointed out with quite justifiable satisfaction that the communist agitators had been given short shrift in the Sharpeville location and that their black people were law-abiding and peaceful. The figures for serious crime were amongst the lowest in the industrialized section of the Transvaal, and offenders were taken care of with commendable expedition. Even the rent-defaulters were evicted from the location in summary fashion, and the local police force was always co-operative and conscientious.

When the law was extended to make it obligatory for black women to carry passes, as well as their menfolk, and when throughout most of the country this innovation was strenuously resisted, the ladies of Sharpeville presented themselves at the police station in such numbers and in such co-operative spirit that most of them had to be turned away with the injunction to 'come back later'.

In early March of 1960 Lothar De La Rey drove his official Land-Rover through this stable and law-abiding community, following the wide road across the open space in front of the police station. The cluster of police buildings, in the same austere and utilitarian design as the others in the location, were surrounded by a wire mesh fence about eight feet high, but the main gates were standing open and unguarded.

Lothar drove through and parked the Land-Rover below the flagpole on which the orange, blue and white national flag floated on a breeze that carried the faint chemical stink of the blast furnaces at the ISCOR plant. In the charge office he was immediately the centre of attention as his men came to congratulate him on the kick that had won the Currie Cup.

'Green and gold next,' the duty sergeant predicted as he shook Lothar's hand, referring to the colours of the national rugby team jersey.

Lothar accepted their admiration with just the right degree of modesty, and then put an end to this breach of discipline and routine.

'All right, back to work everybody,' he ordered, and went to check the charge book. Where a charge office in Soweto might expect to have three or four murders and a dozen or so rape cases, there had not been a single 'schedule one' crime committed in Sharpeville during the previous twenty-four hours and Lothar nodded with satisfaction and went through to report to his station commander.

In the doorway he came to attention and saluted, and the older man nodded and indicated the chair opposite him.

'Come in, Lothie. Sit down!'

He rocked his chair on to its back legs and watched Lothar as he removed his uniform cap and gloves.

'*Bakgat* game on Friday,' he congratulated him. 'Thank you for the tickets. Hell, man, that last kick of yours!'

He felt a stab of envy as he examined his number two. *Liewe land!* Beloved Land, but he looked like a soldier, so tall and straight! The commander glanced down at his own slack guts, and then back at the way the lad wore his uniform on those wide shoulders. You had only to look at him to see his class. It had taken the commander until the age of forty to gain the rank of captain, and he was resigned to the fact that he would go on pension at the same rank – but this one. No what! He would probably be a general before he was forty.

'Well, Lothie,' he said heavily. 'I'm going to miss you.' He smiled at the gleam in those alert but strangely pale yellow eyes. '*Ja*, my young friend,' he nodded, 'your transfer – you leave us at the end of May.'

Lothar leaned back in his chair and smiled. He suspected that his own father had been instrumental in keeping him so long on this station, but although it had been increasingly irksome to waste time in this little backwater, his father knew best and Lothar was grateful for the experience he had gained here. He knew that a policeman only really learns his job on the beat, and he had put in his time. He knew he was a good policeman, and he had proved it to them all. Anybody who might be tempted to attribute his future promotions to his father's influence had only to look at his service record. It was all there. He had paid his dues in full, but now it was time to move on.

'Where are they sending me, sir?'

'You lucky young dog.' The commander shook his head with mock envy. 'You are going to CID headquarters at Marshall Square.'

It was the plum. The most sought-after, the most prestigious posting that any young officer could hope for. CID headquarters was right at the very nerve centre and heart of the entire force. Lothar knew that from there it would be swift and sure. He would have his general's stars while he was still a young man, and with them the maturity and reputation to make his entry into politics smooth and certain. He could retire from the force on the pension of a general, and devote the rest of his life to his country and his *Volk*. He had it all planned. Each step was clear to Lothar. When Dr Verwoerd went, he knew that his father would be a strong contender to take over the premiership. Perhaps one day there would be a second minister of police with the name of De La Rey, and after that another De La Rey at the head of the nation. He knew what he

wanted, what road he had to follow, and he knew also that his feet were securely upon that road.

'You are being given your chance, Lothie,' the commander echoed his own thoughts. 'If you take it, you will go far – very far.'

'However far it is, sir, I will always remember the help and encouragement you have given me here at Sharpeville.'

'Enough of that. You have a couple of months before you go.' The Commander was suddenly embarrassed. Neither of them were men who readily displayed their emotions. 'Let's get down to work. What about the raid tonight? How many men are you going to use?'

Lothar had the headlights of the Land-Rover switched off, and he drove slowly for the four-cylinder petrol engine had a distinctive beat that his quarry would pick up at a distance if the vehicle was driven hard.

There was a sergeant beside him, and five constables in the rear of the Land-Rover, all of them armed with riot batons. In addition, the sergeant had an automatic twelve-gauge Greener shotgun and Lothar wore his sidearm on his Sam Browne belt. They were lightly armed, for this was merely a liquor raid.

Sale of alcohol to blacks was strictly controlled, and was restricted to the brewing of the traditional cereal-based beer by state-controlled beer-halls. The consumption of spirits and wines by blacks was forbidden, but this prohibition caused illicit shebeens to flourish. The profits were too high to be passed by. The liquor was either stolen or purchased from white bottle stores or manufactured by the shebeen owners themselves. These home brews were powerful concoctions known generally as *skokiaan*, and according to the recipe of the individual distiller, could contain anything from methylated spirits to the corpses of poisonous snakes and aborted infants. It was not uncommon for the customers of the shebeens to end up permanently blinded, or demented, or occasionally dead.

Tonight Lothar's team was setting out to raid a newly established shebeen which had been in business for only a few weeks. Lothar's information was that it was controlled by a black gang called 'The Buffaloes'.

Of course, Lothar was fully aware of the size and scope of the Buffaloes' operations. They were without doubt the largest and most powerful underworld association on the Witwatersrand. It was not known who headed the gang but there had been hints that it was connected to the African Mineworkers' Union and to one of the black political organizations. Certainly it was most active on the gold-mining properties closer to Johannesburg, and in the large black townships such as Soweto and Drake's Farm.

Until now they had not been bothered by the Buffaloes here in Sharpeville, and for this reason the setting up of a controlled shebeen was alarming. It might herald a determined infiltration of the area which would almost certainly be followed by a campaign to politicize the local black population, with the resulting protest rallies and boycotts of the bus line and white-owned businesses, and all the other trouble whipped up by the agitators of the African National Congress and the newly formed Pan Africanist Congress.

Lothar was determined to crush it before it spread like a bush fire through his whole area. Above the soft burble of the engine, out there in the darkness he heard a sharp double fluted whistle and almost immediately it was repeated at a distance, down near the end of the avenue of quiet cottages.

'*Magtig!*' Lothar swore softly but bitterly. 'They've spotted us!' The whistles were the warnings of the shebeen lookouts.

He switched on the headlights and gunned the Land-Rover. They went hurtling down the narrow street.

The shebeen was at the end of the block, in the last cottage hard up against the boundary fence with a stretch of open veld beyond. As the headlights swept across the front of the cottage, he saw half a dozen dark figures pelting away from it, and others were fighting each other to get out of the front door and leaping from the windows.

Lothar swung the Land-Rover up over the pavement, through the tiny garden, and braked it into a deliberate and skilfully executed broadside, blocking the front door.

'Let's go!' he yelled, and his men flung the doors open and sprang out.

They grabbed the bewildered shebeen drinkers who were trapped between the Land-Rover and the cottage wall. As one of them began to resist, he dropped to a practised swing of a riot baton and the limp body was bundled into the back of the vehicle.

Lothar sprinted around the side of the cottage, and caught a woman in his arms as she jumped through the window. He turned her upside down in the air and held onto one ankle as he reached out and seized the arm of the next man through the window. In a single swift motion he handcuffed the two of them together, wrist to ankle, and left them floundering and falling over each other like a pair of trussed hens.

Lothar reached the back door of the cottage, and made his first mistake. He seized the handle and jerked the door open. The man had been waiting on the inside, poised and ready, and as the door began to open he hurled his full weight upon it and the edge of it crashed into Lothar's chest. The wind was driven from his lungs, and hissed up his throat as he went over backwards down the steps, sprawling on the hard sun-baked earth, and the man leaped clean over him.

Lothar caught a glimpse of him against the light, and saw that he was young and well built, lithe and quick as a black cat. Then he was racing away into the darkness, heading for the boundary fence that backed up to the cottage.

Lothar rolled over on to his knees and came to his feet. Even with the start the fugitive had, there was nobody who could outrun Lothar in a fair match. He was at the peak of fitness, after months of rigorous training for the Currie Cup match and the national trials, but as he started forward the agony of his empty lungs made him double over and wheeze for breath.

Ahead of him the fleeing figure ducked through a hole in the mesh of the fence, and Lothar fell to his knees and snapped open the holster at his side. Three months before, he had been runner-up in the police pistol championships at Bloemfontein, but now his aim was unsteady with agony and the dark figure was merging with the night, quartering away from him. Lothar fired twice but after each long bright muzzle flash there was no thumping impact of bullet into flesh and the runner was swallowed up by darkness. Lothar slid the weapon back into his holster, and fought to fill his lungs – his humiliation was more painful than his injury. Lothar was unaccustomed to failure.

He forced himself to get to his feet. None of his men should see him grovelling, and after only a minute, and even though his lungs were still on fire, he went back and dragged his two captives to their feet with unnecessary violence. The woman was stark naked. Obviously she had been entertaining a client in the back bedroom, but now she was wailing tragically.

'Shut your mouth, you black cow,' he told her, and shoved her through the back door of the cottage.

The kitchen had been used as the bar. There were cases of liquor stacked to the ceiling, and the table was piled with a high pyramid of empty tumblers.

In the front room the floor was covered with broken glass and spilled liquor, evidence of the haste with which it had been vacated, and Lothar wondered how so many customers had fitted into a room that size. He had seen at least twenty escape into the night.

He shoved the naked prostitute towards one of his black constables. 'Take care of her,' he ordered, and the man grinned lasciviously and tweaked one of her tawny melon-round breasts.

'None of that,' Lothar warned him. He was still angry at the one who had got away, and the constable saw his face and sobered. He led the woman through into the bedroom to find her clothing.

Lothar's other men were coming in, each of them leading two or three sorry-looking captives.

'Check their passes,' Lothar ordered, and turned to his sergeant. 'All right, Cronje, let's get rid of this stuff.'

Lothar watched as the cases of liquor were carried out and stacked in front of the cottage. Two of his constables opened them and smashed the bottles against the edge of the kerb. The sweet fruity smell of cheap brandy filled the night and the gutter ran with the amber-brown liquid.

When the last bottle had been destroyed, Lothar nodded at his sergeant 'Right, Cronje, take them up to the station.' And while the prisoners were loaded into the two police trucks that had followed his Land-Rover, Lothar went back into the cottage to check that his men had not overlooked anything of importance.

In the back room with its tumbled bed and stained sheets, he opened the single cupboard and distastfully used the point of his riot baton to rummage through it.

Beneath the pile of clothing at the bottom of the cupboard was a small cardboard carton. Lothar pulled it out and tore open the lid. It was filled with a neat stack of single-leaf pamphlets, and idly he glanced at the top one until its impact struck him. He snatched up the sheet and turned it to the light from the bare bulb in the ceiling.

'This is the *Poqo* of which it is said, "Take up your spear in your right hand, my beloved people, for the foreigners are looting your land"'

Poqo was the military branch of the Pan Africanist Congress. The word *Poqo* meant pure and untainted, for none other than pure-blooded African Bantu could become members, and Lothar knew it for an organization of young fanatics already responsible for a number of vicious and brutal murders. In the little town of Paarl in the Cape, *Poqo* had marched hundreds strong upon the police station and when driven back had vented their fury upon the civilian population, massacring two white women, one a girl of seventeen years. In the Transkei they had attacked a road-party encampment and murdered the white supervisor and his family in the most atrocious manner. Lothar had seen the police photographs and his skin crawled at the memory. *Poqo* was a name to fear and Lothar read the rest of the pamphlet with full attention.

On Monday we are going to face the police. All the people of Sharpeville will be as one on that day. No man or woman will go to his place of work. No man or woman will leave the township by bus or train or taxi. All the people will gather as one and march to the police station. We are going to protest at the pass law which is a terrible burden, too heavy for us to carry. We will make the white police fear us.

Any man or woman who does not march with us on Monday will be hunted down. On that day all the people will be as one.

Poqo has said this thing. Hear it and obey it.

Lothar read the crudely printed pamphlet through again, and then he murmured, 'So it has come at last.' He picked out the sentence which had offended him most, 'We will make the white police fear us,' and he read it aloud.

'So! We will see about that!' And he shouted for his sergeant to take the carton of subversive leaflets out to the truck.

* * *

There was an inevitability in Raleigh Tabaka's life. The great river of his existence carried him along with it so that he was powerless to break free of it or even swim against the current.

His mother, as one of the most adept of the tribal *sangomas* of Xhosa had first instilled in him the deep awareness of his African self. She had showed him the mysteries and secrets, and read the future for him in the casting of the bones.

'One day you will lead your people, Raleigh Tabaka,' she prophesied. 'You will become one of the great chiefs of Xhosa and your name will be spoken with those of Makana and Ndlame – all these things I see in the bones.'

When his father, Hendrick Tabaka, sent him and his twin brother Wellington across the border to the multi-racial school in Swaziland, his Africanism had been confirmed and underscored, for his fellow pupils had been the sons of chiefs and black leaders from countries like Basutoland and Bechuanaland. These were countries where black tribes ruled themselves, free of the white man's heavy paternal fluences, and he listened with awe as they spoke of how their families lived on equal terms with the whites around them.

This came as a total revelation to Raleigh. In his existence the whites were a breed apart, to be feared and avoided, for they wielded an unchallenged power over him and all his people.

At Waterford he learned that this was not the law of the universe. There were white pupils, and although it was at first strange, he ate at the same table as they did, from the same plates and with the same utensils, and slept in a bed alongside them in the school dormitory, and sat on the toilet seat still warm from a white boy's bottom and vacated it to another little white boy waiting impatiently outside the door for him to finish. In his own country none of these things were allowed, and when he went home for the holidays he read the notices with his eyes wide open – the notices that said 'Whites Only – *Blankes Alleenlik*'. From the windows of the train he saw the beautiful farms and the fat cattle that the white men owned, and the bare eroded earth of the tribal reservations, and when he reached home at Drake's Farm he saw that his father's house, which he remembered as a palace, was in reality a hovel – and the resentment began to gnaw at his soul and the wounds it left festered.

Before Raleigh left to go to school, his Uncle Moses Gama used to visit his father. From infancy he had been in awe of his uncle, for power burned from him like one of those great veld fires which consumed the land and towered into the heavens in a column of dense smoke and ash and sparks.

Even though Moses Gama had been absent from Drake's Farm for so many years, his memory had never been allowed to grow dim, and Hendrick had read aloud to the family the letters that he had received from him in distant lands.

So when at last Raleigh matriculated and left Waterford to return to Drake's Farm and begin work in his father's businesses, he announced that he wanted to take his place in the ranks of the young warriors.

'After you have been to initiation camp,' his father promised him, 'I will introduce you to *Umkhonto we Sizwe*.'

Raleigh's initiation set the final stamp on his special sense of Africanism. With his brother Wellington and six other young men of his initiation class, he left Drake's Farm and travelled by train in the bare third-class carriage to the little magisterial town of Queenstown which was the centre of the Xhosa tribal territories.

It had all been arranged by his mother, and the elders of the tribe met them at Queenstown station. In a rickety old truck they were driven out to a kraal on the banks of the great Fish river and delivered into the care of the tribal custodian, an old man whose duty it was to preserve and safeguard the history and customs of the tribe.

Ndlame, the old man, ordered them to strip off their clothing and to hand over all the possessions they had brought with them. These were thrown on a bonfire on the river bank, as a symbol of childhood left behind them. He took them naked into the river to bathe, and, then still glistening wet, he led them up the far bank to the circumcision hut where the tribal witchdoctors waited.

When the other initiates hung back fearfully, Raleigh went boldly to the head of the column and was the first to stoop through the low entrance to the hut. The interior was thick with smoke from the dung fire and the witchdoctors, in their skins and feathers and fantastic headdresses, were weird and terrifying figures.

Raleigh was smitten with terror, for the pain which he had dreaded all his childhood and for the forces of the supernatural which lurked in the gloomy recesses of the hut, yet he forced himself to run forward and leap over the smouldering fire.

As he landed on the far side the witchdoctors sprang upon him and forced him into a kneeling position, holding his head so he was forced to watch as one of them seized his penis and drew out the rubbery collar of his foreskin to its full length. In ancient times the circumciser would have used a hand-forged blade, but now it was a Gillette razor blade.

As they intoned the invocation to the tribal gods, Raleigh's foreskin was cut away, leaving his glans soft and pink and vulnerable. His blood spattered on to the dung floor between his knees, but he uttered not a sound.

Ndlame helped him rise, and he staggered out into the sunlight and fell upon the river bank, riding the terrible burning pain, but the shrieks of the other boys and the sounds of their wild struggles carried clearly to where he lay. He recognized his brother Wellington's cries of pain as the shrillest and loudest of them all.

Raleigh knew that their foreskins would be gathered up by the witchdoctors, salted and dried and added to the tribal totem. A part of them would remain for

ever with the custodians and no matter how far they wandered, the witchdoctors could call them back with the foreskin curse.

When all the other initiates had suffered the circumciser's knife, Ndlame led them down to the water's edge and showed them how to wash and bind their wounds with medicinal leaves and herbs, and to strap their penis against their stomachs. 'For if the Mamba looks down, he will bleed again,' he warned them.

They smeared their bodies with a mixture of clay and ash. Even the hair on their heads was crusted with the dead white ritual paint, so that they looked like albino ghosts. Their only clothing was skirts of grass and they built their huts in the deepest and most secret parts of the forest, for no woman might look upon them. They prepared their own food, plain maize cakes without any relish, and meat was forbidden to them during the three moons of the initiation. Their only possession was their food bowl of clay.

One of the boys developed an infection in his circumcision wound, the stinking green pus ran from it like milk from a cow's teat, and the fever consumed him so his skin was almost painfully hot to the touch. The herbs and potions that Ndlame applied were of no avail. He died on the fourth day and they buried him in the forest and Ndlame took his food bowl away. It would be thrown through the front door of his mother's hut by one of the witchdoctors, without a word being spoken, and she would know that her son had not been acceptable to the tribal gods.

Each day from before dawn's light until after sunset, Ndlame gave them instruction and taught them their duties as members of the tribe, as husbands and as fathers. They learned to endure pain and hardship with stoicism. They learned discipline and duty to their tribe, the ways of the wild animals and plants, how to survive in the wilderness, and how to please their wives and raise their children.

When the wounds of the circumcision blade had healed, Ndlame bound up their members each night in the special knot called the Red Dog, to prevent them spilling their seed in the sacred initiation huts. Each morning Ndlame inspected the knots carefully to ensure that they had not been loosened to enjoy the forbidden pleasure of masturbation.

When the three moons had passed, Ndlame led them back to the river and they washed away the white initiation clay and anointed their bodies with a mixture of fat and red ochre, and Ndlame gave them each a red blanket, symbol of manhood, with which they covered themselves. In procession, singing the manhood songs which they had practised, they went to where the tribe waited at the edge of the forest.

Their parents had gifts for them, clothing and new shoes and money, and the girls giggled and ogled them boldly, for they were men now and able at last to take a wife, as many wives as they could afford, for the *lobola*, the marriage fee, was heavy.

The two brothers, accompanied by their mother, journeyed back to Drake's Farm, Wellington to take leave of their father, for he was going on to take holy orders, and Raleigh to remain at his father's side, to learn the multifarious facets of Hendrick Tabaka's business activities and eventually to take the helm and become the comfort and mainstay of Hendrick's old age.

These were fascinating and disturbing months and years for Raleigh. Until this time he had never guessed at his father's wealth and power, but gradually it was revealed to him. The pages in the ledger turned for him one at a time. He learned of his father's general dealer stores, and the butcheries and bakeries

in all the black townships spread throughout the great industrial triangle of the Transvaal that was based on the gold-mines and the iron-deposits and the coalfields. Then he went on to learn about the cattle herds and rural general dealer's stores in the tribal reservations owned by his father and cared for by his myriad brothers, about the shebeens and the whores that operated behind the front of legitimate business, and finally he learned about the Buffaloes, that ubiquitous and shadowy association of many men from all the various tribes, whose chief was his own father.

He realized at last just how rich and powerful his father was, and yet how because he was a black man, he could not display his importance and could wield his power only covertly and clandestinely. Raleigh felt his anger stir, as it did whenever he saw those signs 'Whites Only – *Blankes Alleenlik*' and saw the white men pass in their shiny automobiles, or when he stood outside the universities and hospitals which were closed to him.

He spoke to his father about these things that troubled him and Hendrick Tabaka chuckled and shook his head. 'Rage makes a man sick, my son. It spoils his appetite for life and keeps him from sleep at night. We cannot change our world, so we must look for the good things in life and enjoy those to the full. The white man is strong, you cannot imagine how strong, you have not seen even the strength of his little finger. If you take up the spear against him, he will destroy you and all the good things we have – and if the gods and the lightnings intervened and by chance you destroyed the white man, think what would follow him. There would come a darkness and a time without law and protection that would be a hundred times worse than the white man's oppressions. We would be consumed by the rage of our own people, and we would not have even the consolation of these few sweet things. If you open your ears and your eyes, my son, you will hear how the young people call us collaborators and how they talk of a redistribution of wealth, and you will see the envy in their eyes. The dream you have, my son, is a dangerous dream.'

'And yet I must dream it, my father,' said Raleigh, and then, one unforgettable day, his uncle, Moses Gama, returned from foreign lands and took him to meet other young men who shared the same dream.

So during the day Raleigh worked at his father's business and in the evenings he met with the other young comrades of *Umkhonto we Sizwe*. At first they only talked, but the words were sweeter and headier than the smoke of the *dagga* pipes of the old men.

Then Raleigh joined the comrades who were enforcing the decrees of the African National Congress, the boycotts and the strikes and the work stoppages. He went to Evaton location with a small task force to enforce the bus boycott and they attacked the black workers in the bus queues who were trying to get to their places of employment or who were going to shop with their families, and they beat them with *sjamboks*, the long leather quirts, and with their fighting-sticks.

On the first day of the attacks, Raleigh was determined to demonstrate his zeal to his comrades and he used his fighting-stick with all the skill which he had learned as a child in faction fights with the boys of the other tribes.

There was a woman in the queue for the bus who defied Raleigh's order to go home, and she spat at him and his comrades and called them *tsotsies* and *skelms*, gangsters and rogues. She was a woman in middle age, large and matronly, with cheeks so plump and shiny that they looked as though they had been rubbed up with black shoe polish, and with such a queenly manner that at

first the young comrades of *Umkhonto we Sizwe* were abashed by her scorn and might have withdrawn.

Then Raleigh saw that this was his opportunity to prove his ardour and he leaped forward and confronted the women. 'Go home, old woman,' he warned her. 'We are no longer dogs to eat the white man's shit.'

'You are a little uncircumcised boy with filth on your tongue,' she began, but Raleigh would not let her continue. He swung the long supple fighting-stick, and it split her shiny black cheek as cleanly as the cut of an axe, so for an instant Raleigh saw the bone gleam in the depths of the wound before the swift crimson flood obscured it. The big woman screamed and fell to her knees, and Raleigh felt a strange sensation of power and purpose, a euphoria of patriotic duty. For a moment the woman kneeling before him became the focus of all his frustration and his rage.

The woman saw it in his eyes and held up both arms over her head to ward off the next blow. Raleigh struck again, with all his strength and skill, using his wrist so that the fighting-stick whined in the air and the blow landed on the woman's elbow. Her arms were wreathed in layers of deep fat. It hung in dewlaps from her upper arms and in bracelets about her wrists, but it could not cushion the power behind that whistling stick. The joint of her elbow shattered, and her forearm dropped and twisted at an impossible angle as it hung helplessly at her side.

The woman screamed again, this time the sound was so filled with outrage and agony that it goaded the other young warriors and they fell upon the bus passengers with such fury that the terminus was strewn with the wailing and sobbing injured and the concrete floor was washed sticky red.

When the ambulances came with sirens wailing to collect the casualties, the comrades of *Umkhonto we Sizwe* pelted them with stones and half bricks and Raleigh led a small group of the bolder ones who ran out into the street and turned one of the stranded ambulances on its side, and when the petrol poured from the tank, Raleigh lit a match and tossed it on to the spread pool.

The explosive ignition singed his eyelashes and burned away the front of his hair, but that evening when they got back to Drake's Farm, Raleigh was the hero of the band of warriors, and they gave him the praise-name of *Cheza* which means 'the burner'.

As Raleigh was accepted into the middle ranks of the Youth League of the ANC and *Umkhonto we Sizwe*, so he gradually understood the cross-currents of power within them and the internal politics of the rival groups of moderates and radicals – those who thought that freedom could be negotiated and those who believed that it must be won with the blade of the spear, those who thought that the treasures so patiently built up over the years – the mines and the factories and the railways – should be preserved and those who believed that it should all be destroyed and rebuilt again in the name of freedom by the pure ones.

Raleigh found himself inclining more and more towards the purists, the hard fighting men, the exclusive Bantu elite, and when he heard the name *Poqo* for the first time, he thrilled to the sound and sense of it. It described exactly his own feelings and desires – the pure, the only ones.

He was present in the house in Drake's Farm when Moses Gama spoke to them and promised them that the long wait was almost at an end.

'I will take this land by its heels and set it upon its head,' Moses Gama told the group of intense loyal young warriors. 'I will give you a deed, a sign that every man and woman will understand instantly. It will bring the tribes into the

streets in their millions and their rage will be a beautiful thing, so pure and strong that nobody, not even the hard Boers, will be able to resist.'

Soon Raleigh came to sense in Moses Gama a divinity that set him above all other humans, and he was filled with a religious love for him and a deep and utter commitment. When the news reached Raleigh that Moses Gama had been caught by the white police as he was on the point of blowing up the houses of parliament and destroying all the evil contained in that iniquitous institution, Raleigh was almost prostrated by his grief, and yet set on fire by Moses Gama's courage and example.

Over the weeks and months that followed, Raleigh was exasperated and angered by the calls for moderation from the high councils of the ANC, and by the dispirited and meek acceptance of Moses Gama's imprisonment and trial. He wanted to vent his wrath upon the world, and when the Pan Africanist Congress broke away from the ANC Raleigh followed where his heart led.

Robert Sobukwe, the leader of the Pan Africanist Congress, sent for him. 'I have heard good words of you,' he told Raleigh. 'And I know the man who is your uncle, the father of us all who languishes in the white man's prison. It is our duty – for we are the pure ones – to bring our message to every black man in the land. There is much work to do, and this is the task I have set for you alone, Raleigh Tabaka.' He led Raleigh to a large-scale map of the Transvaal. 'This area has been left untouched by the ANC.' He placed his hand over the sweep of townships and coalfields and industry around the town of Vereeniging. 'This is where I want you to begin work.'

Within a week Raleigh had conditioned his father to the idea that he should move to the Vereeniging area to take charge of the family interests there, the three stores in Evaton and the butchery and bakery in Sharpeville, and his father liked the idea the more he thought about it, and he agreed.

'I will give you the names of the men who command the Buffaloes down there. We can begin moving the shebeens into the Sharpeville area. So far we have not put our cattle to graze on those pastures, and the grass there is tall and green.'

Raleigh moved slowly at first. He was a stranger in Sharpeville and he had to consolidate his position. However, he was a strong and comely young man, and he spoke fluently all the major languages of the townships. This was not an unusual achievement, there were many who spoke all the four related languages of the Nguni group of peoples, the Zulus, the Xhosas, the Swazi and the Ndebele, which make up almost seventy per cent of the black tribes of South Africa and whose speech is characterized by elaborate clicking and clucking sounds.

Many others, like Raleigh, were also conversant with the other two languages which are spoken by almost the entire remainder of the black population, the Sotho and the Tswana.

Language was no barrier, and Raleigh had the additional advantage of being placed in charge of his father's business interest in the area, and therefore was accorded almost immediate recognition and respect. Sooner or later every single resident of Sharpeville would come to either Tabaka's bakery or butcher shop and be impressed by the articulate and sympathetic young man who listened to their worries and troubles and extended them credit to buy the white bread and fizzy drinks and tobacco; these were the staple diet of the townships where much of the old way of life was abandoned and forgotten, where the soured milk and maize meal were difficult to procure and where rickets made the

children lethargic, bent their bones and turned their hair fine and wispy and dyed a peculiar bronze colour.

They told Raleigh their little troubles, like the cost of renting the township houses and the hardship of commuting such distances to their place of work that it was necessary to rise long before the sun. And then they told Raleigh their greater worries, of being evicted from their homes and of the harassment by the police who were always raiding for liquor and pass offences and prostitution and to enforce the influx control laws. But always it came down to the passes, the little booklets that ruled their lives. The police always were there to ask 'Where is your pass? Show me your pass book.' The *dompas*, they called them, 'the damned pass', in which were stamped all their details of birth and residence and right to reside; no black person could get a job unless he or she produced the damned pass book.

From all the people who came to the shops, Raleigh chose the young vital ones, the brave ones with rage in their hearts, and they met discreetly at first in the storeroom at the back of the bakery, sitting on the bread baskets and the piles of flour bags, talking the night through.

Then they moved more openly, speaking to the older people and the children in the schools, going about as disciples to teach and explain. Raleigh used the funds of the butchery to buy a secondhand duplicator, and he typed the pamphlets on the pink wax sheets and ran them off on the machine.

They were crude little pamphlets, with botchy typing errors and obvious corrections and each one began with the salutation, 'This is *Poqo* of which it is said – ' and ended with the stern injunction, '*Poqo* has said this thing. Hear it and obey.' The young men whom Raleigh had recruited distributed these and read them to those who could not read for themselves.

At first Raleigh allowed only men to come to the meetings in the back room of the bakery store, for they were purists and it was the traditional role of the men to herd the cattle and hunt the game and defend the tribe, while the women thatched the huts and tilled the earth for maize and sorghum and carried the children on their backs.

Then the word was passed down from the high command of *Poqo* and PAC that the women were also part of the struggle. So Raleigh spoke with his young men and one evening a girl came to their Friday-night meeting in the bakery storeroom.

She was a Xhosa and she was tall and strong with beautiful swelling buttocks and the round sweet face like one of the wild veld flowers. While Raleigh spoke she listened silently. She did not move or fidget or interrupt and her huge dark eyes never left Raleigh's face.

Raleigh felt that he was inspired that night, and though he never looked directly at the girl and seemed to address himself to the young warriors, it was to her he spoke and his voice was deep and sure and his own words reverberated in his skull and he listened to them with the same wonder as the others did.

When he finished speaking at last, they all sat in silence for a long time and then one of the young men turned to the girl and said, 'Amelia – ' that was the first time ever that Raleigh heard her name, 'Amelia, will you sing for us?'

She did not simper or hang her head or make modest protestations. She simply opened her mouth, and sound poured out of her, glorious sound that made the skin on Raleigh's forearms and at the back of his neck tingle.

He watched her mouth while she sang. Her lips were soft and broad, shaped like two leaves of the wild peach tree, with a dark iridescence that shaded to

soft pink on the inside of her mouth, and when she reached for an impossibly sweet high note, he saw that her teeth were perfect white as bone that had lain for a season in the veld, polished by the wind and bleached by the African sun.

The words of the song were strange to him, but like the voice that sang them, they thrilled Raleigh:

'When the roll of heroes is called,
Will my name be on it?
I dream of that day when I will
Sit with Moses Gama,
And we will talk of the passing of the Boers.'

She went away with the young men who had brought her, and that night Raleigh dreamed of her. She stood beside the pool in the great Fish river in which he had washed away the white clay paint of his childhood and she wore the short beaded kilt and her breasts and her legs were bare. Her legs were long and her breasts were round and hard as black marble and she smiled at him with those even white teeth, and when Raleigh awoke his seed was splashed upon the blanket which covered him.

Three days later she came to the bakery to buy bread and Raleigh saw her through the peephole above his desk through which he could watch all that was happening in the front of the store and he went through to the counter and greeted her gravely.

'I see you, Amelia.'

She smiled at him and replied, 'I see you also, Raleigh Tabaka,' and it seemed that she sang his name, for she gave it a music that he had never heard in it before.

She purchased two loaves of white bread, but Raleigh lingered over the sale, wrapping each loaf carefully and counting the pennies of her change as though they were gold sovereigns.

'What is your full name?' he asked her.

'I am called Amelia Sigela.'

'Where is your father's kraal, Amelia Sigela?'

'My father is dead, and I live with my father's sister.'

She was a teacher at the Sharpeville primary school and she was twenty years old. When she left with her bread wrapped in newspaper and her buttocks swinging and jostling each other beneath the yellow European-style skirt, Raleigh returned to his desk in the cubicle of his office and sat for a long time staring at the wall.

On Friday Amelia Sigela came again to the meeting in the back room of the bakery and at the end she sang for them once more. This time Raleigh knew the words and he sang with her. He had a good deep baritone but she gilded it and wreathed it in the glory of her startling soprano and when the meeting broke up, Raleigh walked back with her through the dark streets to her aunt's house in the avenue beyond the school.

They lingered at the door and he touched her arm. It was warm and silky beneath his fingers. On the Sunday when he took the train back to Drake's Farm to make his weekly report to his father, he told his mother about Amelia Sigela and the two of them went through to the sacred room where his mother kept the family gods.

His mother sacrificed a black chicken and spoke to the carved idols, particularly to the totem of Raleigh's maternal great-grandfather, and he replied

in a voice that only Raleigh's mother could hear. She listened gravely, nodding at what he said, and later while they ate the sacrificial chicken with rice and herbs, she promised, 'I will speak to your father on your behalf.'

The following Friday after the meeting, Raleigh walked home with Amelia again, but this time as they passed the school where she taught, he drew her into the shadow of the buildings and they stood against the wall very close together. She made no attempt to pull away when he stroked her cheek, so he told her:

'My father is sending an emissary to your aunt to agree a marriage price.' Amelia was silent and he went on, 'However, I will ask him not to do so, if you do not wish it.'

'I wish it very much,' she whispered, and slowly and voluptuously she rubbed herself against him like a cat.

The *lobola*, the marriage price, was twenty head of cattle, worth a great deal of money, and Hendrick Tabaka told his son, 'You must work for it, just like other young men are forced to do.'

It would take Raleigh three years to accumulate enough to buy the cattle, but when he told Amelia, she smiled and told him, 'Each day will make me want you more. Think then how great will be my want after three years, and think how sweet will be that moment when the wanting is assuaged.'

Every afternoon, when school was out, Amelia came to the bakery and quite naturally she took to working behind the counter selling the bread and the round brown buns. Then when Raleigh closed the shop, she would cook his evening meal for him and when he had eaten, they walked back to her aunt's house together.

Amelia slept in a tiny room hardly bigger than a closet, across the passage from her aunt. They left the interleading doors open and Raleigh lay on Amelia's bed with her and under the blanket they played sweet games that custom and tribal law sanctioned all engaged couples to play. Raleigh was allowed to explore delicately and with his fingertips hunt for the little pink bud of flesh hidden between soft furry lips that old Ndlame had told him about at initiation camp. The Xhosa girls are not circumcised like the women of some of the other tribes, but they are taught the arts of pleasing men, and when he could stand it no longer, she took him and held him between her crossed thighs, avoiding only the final penetration that was reserved by tribal lore for their wedding night, and skilfully she milked him of his seed. Strangely, it seemed that every time she did this, rather than depleting him, she replenished the well of his love for her until it was overflowing.

Then the time came when Raleigh judged it expedient to begin infiltrating the Buffaloes into the township. With Hendrick Tabaka's blessing and under Raleigh's supervision, they opened their first shebeen in a cottage at the far end of the township, hard up against the boundary fence.

The shebeen was run by two of the Buffaloes from Drake's Farm who had done this type of work for Hendrick Tabaka before. They knew all the little tricks like adulterating the liquor to make it go further and having one or two girls in the back room for the men that liquor had made amorous.

However, Raleigh warned them about the local police force who had an ugly reputation, and about one of the white officers in particular, a man with pale predatory eyes that had given him his nickname 'Ngwi' the leopard. He was a hard cruel man who had shot to death four men in the time he had been in

Sharpeville, two of them members of the Buffaloes who had been supplying the township with *dagga*.

At first they were cautious and wary, vetting their customers carefully and placing lookouts on all approaches to the shebeen, but then as the weeks passed, with business improving each night, they relaxed a little. There was very little competition. Other shebeens had been closed down swiftly, and the customers were so thirsty that the Buffaloes could charge three and four times the usual rate.

Raleigh brought the liquor stocks into the township in his little blue Ford pick-up, the crates hidden beneath sacks of flour and sheep carcasses. He spent as little time as possible at the shebeen, for every minute was dangerous. He would drop off the supplies, collect the empty bottles and the cash and be gone within half an hour. He never drove the pick-up directly to the front door of the cottage, but parked it in the dark veld beyond the boundary fence and the two Buffaloes would come through the hole in the wire mesh and help him carry the crates of cheap brandy.

After a while Raleigh realized that the shebeen offered another good distribution point for the *Poqo* pamphlets that he printed on the duplicator. He usually kept a stock of these in the cottage and the two Buffaloes who ran the shebeen and the girls who worked in the back room had orders to give one to each of their customers.

In early March, not long after the glad tidings of Moses Gama's reprieve and the mitigation of his death sentence to life imprisonment, Sobukwe sent for Raleigh. The rendezvous was in a house in the vast black township of Soweto. It was not one of the boxlike flat-roofed cottages, but was rather a large modern bungalow situated in the elite section of the township known as 'Beverly Hills'. It had a tiled roof, its own swimming-pool, garaging for two vehicles and large plate-glass windows overloooking the pool.

When Raleigh arrived in the blue pick-up, he found that he was not the only invited guest and there were a dozen or so other vehicles parked along the kerb. Sobukwe had invited all his middle-ranking field officers to this briefing and over forty of them crowded into the sitting-room of the bungalow.

'Comrades,' Sobukwe addressed them. 'We are ready to flex our muscles. You have worked hard and it is time to gather in some of the fruits of your labours. In all the places where the Pan Africanist Congress is strong – not only here on the Witwatersrand but across the country – we are going to make the white police fear our power. We are going to hold a mass protest demonstration against the pass laws – '

Listening to Sobukwe speak, Raleigh was reminded of the power and personality of his own imprisoned uncle, Moses Gama, and he was proud to be part of this magnificent company. As Sobukwe unfolded his plans Raleigh made a silent but fervent resolution that at Sharpeville, the area for which he was responsible, the demonstration would be impressive and solid.

He related every detail of the meeting, and every word that Sobukwe had spoken, to Amelia. Her lovely round face seemed to glow with excitement as she listened and she helped him print the sheets announcing the demonstration and to pack them into the old liquor cartons in lots of five hundred.

On the Friday before the planned demonstration, Raleigh ran a shipment of liquor down to the Buffaloes' shebeen, and he took a carton of pamphlets with him. The Buffaloes were waiting for him in the darkness beside the track, and

one of them flashed a torch to guide the pick-up into the scraggy patch of black wattle, and they unloaded the liquor and trudged across to the township fence.

In the cottage Raleigh counted the empty bottles and the full ones and checked these figures against the cash in the canvas bank bag. It tallied and he gave a brief word of commendation to the two Buffaloes, and looked into the front room which was packed with cheerful noisy drinkers.

Then when the door to the nearest bedroom opened and a big Basuto iron-worker came out, grinning and buttoning the front of his blue overalls, Raleigh squeezed past him into the back room. The girl was straightening the sheets on the bed. She was bending over with her back to Raleigh and she was naked, but she looked over her shoulder and smiled when she recognized him. Raleigh was popular with all the girls. She had the money ready for him, and Raleigh counted it in front of her. There was no means of checking her, but over the years Hendrick Tabaka had developed an instinct for a cheating girl, and when Raleigh delivered the money to him he would know if she were holding out.

Raleigh gave her a box of pamphlets and she sat beside him on the bed while he read one of them to her.

'I will be there on Monday,' she promised. 'And I will tell all my men these things and give them each a paper.' She placed the box in the bottom of the cupboard and then came back to Raleigh and took his hand.

'Stay a little while,' she invited him. 'I will straighten your back for you.'

She was a pretty plump little thing and Raleigh was tempted. Amelia was a traditional Nguni maiden, and she did not suffer the curse of western-style jealousy. In fact she had urged him to accept the offers of the other girls. 'If I am not allowed to sharpen your spear, let the joy-girls keep it bright for the time when I am at last allowed to feel its kiss.'

'Come,' the girl urged Raleigh now, and stroked him through the cloth of his trousers. 'See how the cobra awakes,' she laughed. 'Let me wring his neck!'

Raleigh took one step back towards the bed, laughing with her – then suddenly he froze and the laugh was cut off abruptly. Out in the darkness he had heard the whistle of the lookouts.

'Police,' he snapped. 'The leopard – ' and there was the sudden distinctive rumble of a Land-Rover being driven hard and headlights flashed across the cheap curtaining that covered the window.

Raleigh sprang to the door. In the front room the drinkers were fighting to escape through the door and windows, and the table, covered with glasses and empty bottles, was overturned and glass shattered. Raleigh shouldered panic-stricken bodies out of his way and reached the kitchen door. It was locked but he opened it with his own key and slipped through, locking it again behind him.

He switched off the lights and stole across to the back door and placed his hand on the door knob. He would not make the mistake of running out into the yard. The leopard was notoriously quick with his pistol. Raleigh waited in the darkness, and he heard the screams and the scuffling, the crack of the riot batons on flesh and bone and the grunting of the men who swung them and he steeled himself.

Just beyond the door, he heard light running footsteps and suddenly the door handle was seized from the far side and violently twisted. As the man on the outside tried to pull the door open, Raleigh held it, and the other man heaved and swore, leaning back on it with all his weight.

Raleigh let the handle go, and reversed his resistance, throwing his body

against the cheap pine door so that it burst open. He felt it crash into human flesh and he had a glimpse of the brown-uniformed figure hurtling backwards down the stairs. Then he used his own momentum to leap up and outwards, clearing the police officer like a steeplechaser, and he went bounding away towards the hole in the mesh fence.

As he ducked through it he glanced back and saw the police officer on his knees. Though his features were contracted and swollen with pain and anger, Raleigh recognized him. It was Ngwi, the killer of men, and the blue service revolver glinted in his hand as it cleared the holster at his side.

Fear sped Raleigh's feet as he darted away into the darkness, but he jinked and twisted as he ran. Something passed close to his head with a snapping report that hurt his eardrums and made him flinch his head wildly and he jinked again. Behind him was another thudding report but he did not hear the second bullet and he saw the dark shape of the Ford ahead of him.

He tumbled into the front seat and started the engine. Without switching on the headlights he bumped over the verge on to the track and accelerated away into the darkness.

He found that he still had the canvas bag of money clutched in his left hand, and his relief was intense. His father would be incensed at the loss of the liquor stocks, but his anger would have been multiplied many times if Raleigh had lost the money as well.

* * *

Solomon Nduli telephoned Michael Courtney at his desk in the newsroom. 'I have something for you,' he told Michael. 'Can you come out to the *Assegai* offices right away.'

'It's after five already,' Michael protested, 'and it's Friday night. I won't be able to get a pass to enter the township.'

'Come,' Solomon insisted. 'I will wait for you at the main gate.'

He was as good as his promise, a tall gangly figure in steel-rimmed glasses, waiting under the street lamp near the main gates, and as soon as he slipped into the front seat of the company car, Michael passed him his cigarette packet.

'Light one for me, as well,' he told Solomon. 'I brought some sardine and onion sandwiches and a couple of bottles of beer. They are on the back seat.' There was no public place in Johannesburg, or in the entire land for that matter, where two men of different colour could sit and drink or eat together. Michael drove slowly and aimlessly through the streets while they ate and talked.

'The PAC are planning their first big act since they broke away from the ANC,' Solomon told Michael through a mouthful of sardine and onion. 'In some areas they have built up strong support. In the Cape and the rural tribal areas, even in some parts of the Transvaal. They have pulled in all the young militants who are unhappy with the pacifism of the old men. They want to follow Moses Gama's example, and take on the Nationalists in a head-on fight.'

'That's crazy,' Michael said. 'You can't fight sten guns and Saracen armoured cars with half bricks.'

'Yes, it's crazy, but then some of the young people would prefer to die on their feet than live on their knees.'

They were together for an hour, talking all that time, and then at last Michael drove him back to the main gates of Drake's Farm.

'So that's it then, my friend.' Solomon opened the car door. 'If you want the best story on Monday, I would suggest you go down to the Vereeniging area. The PAC and *Poqo* have made that their stronghold on the Witwatersrand.'

'Evaton?' Michael asked.

'Yes, Evaton will be one of the places to watch,' Solomon Nduli agreed. 'But the PAC have a new man in Sharpeville.'

'Sharpeville?' Michael asked. 'Where is that? I've never heard of it.'

'Only twelve miles from Evaton.'

'I'll find it on my road map.'

'You might think it worth the trouble to go there,' Solomon encouraged Michael. 'This PAC organizer in Sharpeville is one of the party's young lions. He will put on a good show, you can count on that.'

* * *

Manfred De La Rey asked quietly. 'So, how many reinforcements can we spare for the stations in the Vaal area?'

General Danie Leroux shook his head and smoothed back the wings of silver hair at his temples with both hands. 'We have only three days to move in reinforcements from the outlying areas and most of those will be needed in the Cape. It will mean stripping the outlying stations and leaving them very vulnerable.'

'How many?' Manfred insisted.

'Five or six hundred men for the Vaal,' Danie Leroux said with obvious reluctance.

'That will be enough,' Manfred growled. 'So we will reinforce all stations lightly, but hold most of our forces in mobile reserve and react swiftly to the first hint of trouble.' He turned his full attention to the map that covered the operations table in the control room of police headquarters in Marshall Square. 'Which are the main danger centres on the Vaal?'

'Evaton,' Danie Leroux replied without hesitation. 'It's always one of the trouble spots, and then Van Der Bijl Park.'

'What about Sharpeville?' Manfred asked, and held up the crudely printed pamphlet that he had tightly rolled into his right hand. 'What about this?'

The general did not reply immediately, but he pretended to study the operations map as he composed his reply. He was well aware that the subversive pamphlets had been discovered by Captain Lothar De La Rey, and he knew how the minister felt about his son. Indeed Danie Leroux shared the general high opinion of Lothar, so he did not want to belittle him in any way or to offend his minister.

'There may well be disturbances in the Sharpeville area,' he conceded. 'But it is a small township and has always been very peaceful. We can expect our men there to behave well and I do not see any immediate danger. I suggest we send twenty or thirty men to reinforce Sharpeville, and concentrate our main efforts on the larger townships with violent histories of boycotts and strikes.'

'Very well,' Manfred agreed at last. 'But I want you to maintain at least forty

per cent of our reinforcements in reserve, so that they can be moved quickly to any area that flares up unexpectedly.'

'What about arms?' Danie Leroux asked. 'I am about to authorize the issue of automatic weapons to all units.' He turned the statement into a query and Manfred nodded.

'*Ja*, we must be ready for the worst. There is a feeling amongst our enemies that we are on the verge of capitulation. Even our own people are becoming frightened and confused.' His voice dropped, but his tone was fiercer and more determined. 'We have to change that. We have to crush these people who wish to tear down and destroy all we stand for and give this land over to bloodshed and anarchy.'

* * *

The centres of support for the PAC were widely scattered across the land, from the eastern tribal areas of the Ciskei and the Transkei to the southern part of the great industrial triangle along the Vaal river, and a thousand miles south of that in the black township of Langa and Nyanga that housed the greater part of the migrant worker force that serviced the mother city of Cape Town.

In all these areas Sunday 20 March 1960 was a day of feverish effort and planning, and of a peculiar expectancy. It was as though everybody at last believed that this new decade would be one of immense change.

The radicals were filled with a feeling of infinite hope, however irrational, and with a certainty that the Nationalist government was on the verge of collapse. They felt that the world was with them, that the age of colonialism had blown away on the winds of change, and that after a decade of massive political mobilization by the black leaders, the time of liberation was at last at hand. All it needed now was one last shove, and the walls of *apartheid* would crash to earth, crushing under them the evil architect Verwoerd and his builders who had raised them up.

Raleigh Tabaka felt that marvellous euphoria as he and his men moved through the township, going from cottage to cottage with the same message: 'Tomorrow we will be as one people. No one will go to work. There will be no buses and those who try to walk to the town will be met by the *Poqo* on the road. The names of all who defy the PAC will be taken and they will be punished. Tomorrow we are going to make the white police fear us.'

They worked all that day, and by evening every person, man and woman, in the township had been warned to stay away from work and to assemble in the open space near the new police station early on the Monday morning.

'We are going to make the white police fear us. We want everybody to be there. If you do not come, we will find you.'

Amelia had worked as hard and unremittingly as Raleigh had done, but like him she was still fresh, unwearied and excited as they ate a quick and simple meal in the back room of the bakery.

'Tomorrow we will see the sun of freedom rise,' Raleigh told her as he wiped his bowl with a crust of bread. 'But we cannot afford to sleep. There is still much work to do this night.' Then he took her hand and told her, 'Our children will be born free, and we will live our life together like men, not like animals.'

And he led her out into the darkening township to continue the preparations for the great day that lay ahead.

They met in groups on the street corners, all the eager young ones, and Raleigh and Amelia moved amongst them delegating their duties for the morrow, selecting those who would picket the road leading from Sharpeville to Vereeniging.

'You will let no one pass. Nobody must leave the township,' Raleigh told them. 'All the people must be as one when we march on the police station tomorrow morning.'

'You must tell the people not to fear,' Raleigh urged them. 'Tell them that the white police cannot touch them and that there will be a most important speech from the white government concerning the abolition of the pass laws. Tell the people they must be joyful and unafraid and that they must sing the freedom songs that PAC has taught them.'

After midnight Raleigh assembled his most loyal and reliable men, including two Buffaloes from the shebeen, and they went to the homes of all the black bus drivers and taxi drivers in the township and pulled them from their beds.

'Nobody will leave Sharpeville tomorrow,' they told them. 'But we do not trust you not to obey your white bosses. We will guard you until the march begins. Instead of driving your buses and taxis tomorrow and taking our people away, you will march with them to the police station. We will see to it that you do. Come with us now.'

As the false dawn flushed the eastern sky, Raleigh himself scaled a telephone pole at the boundary fence and cut the wires. When he slid down again he laughed, as he told Amelia, 'Now our friend the leopard will not find it so easy to call in other police to help him.'

* * *

Captain Lothar De La Rey parked his Land-Rover and left it in a sanitary lane in a patch of shadow out of the street lights and he moved quietly to the corner and stood alone.

He listened to the night. In the years he had served at Sharpeville he had learned to judge the pulse and the mood of the township. He let his feelings and his instincts take over from reason, and almost immediately he was aware of the feral excitement and sense of expectation which had the township in its grip. It was quiet until you listened, as Lothar was listening now. He heard the dogs. They were restless, some close, others at a distance, yapping and barking, and there was an urgency in them. They were seeing and scenting groups and single figures in the shadows. Men hurrying on secret errands.

Then he heard the other sounds, soft as insect sounds in the night. The whistle of lookouts on the watch for his patrols and the recognition signals of the street gangs. In one of the dark cottages nearby a man coughed nervously, unable to sleep, and in another a child whimpered fretfully and was instantly hushed by a woman's soft voice.

Lothar moved quietly through the shadows, listening and watching. Even without the warning of the pamphlets, he would have known that tonight the township was awake and strung up.

Lothar was not an imaginative or romantic young man, but as he scouted the

dark streets he suddenly had a clear mental picture of his ancestors performing this same dire task. He saw them bearded and dressed in drab homespun, armed with the long muzzle-loaders, leaving the security of the laagered wagons, going out alone into the African night to scout for the enemy, the *swartgevaar*, the black danger. Spying out the bivouac where the black impis lay upon their war shields, waiting for the dawn to rush in upon the wagons. His nerves crawled at those atavistic memories, and he seemed to hear the battle chant of the tribes in the night and the drumming of assegai on rawhide shield, the stamp of bare feet and the crash of war rattles on wrist and ankle as they came in upon the wagons for the dawn attack.

In his imagination the cry of the restless infant in the nearby cottage became the death screams of the little Boer children at Weenen, where the black impis had come sweeping down from the hills to massacre all in the Boer encampment.

He shivered in the night as he realized that though so much had changed, as much had remained the same. The black danger was still there, growing each day stronger and more ominous. He had seen the confident challenging look of the young bucks as they swaggered through the streets and heard the warlike names they had adopted, the Spear of the Nation and the Pure Ones. Tonight, more than ever, he was aware of the danger and he knew where his duty lay.

He went back to the Land-Rover and drove slowly through the streets. Time and again he glimpsed small groups of dark figures, but when he turned the spotlight on them, they melted away into the night. Everywhere he went he heard the warning whistles out there in the darkness, and his nerves tightened and tingled. When he met his own foot-patrolling constables, they also were nervous and ill-at-ease.

When the dawn turned the eastern sky pale yellow and dimmed out the street lamps, he drove back through the streets. At this time in the morning they should have been filled with hurrying commuters, but now they were empty and silent.

Lothar reached the bus terminus, and it too was almost deserted. Only a few young men in small groups lounged at the railings. There were no buses, and the pickets stared at the police Land-Rover openly and insolently as Lothar drove slowly past.

As he skirted the boundary fence, passing close to the main gates, he exclaimed suddenly and braked the Land-Rover. From one of the telephone poles the cables trailed limply to the earth. Lothar left the vehicle and went to examine the damage. He lifted the loose end of the dangling copper wire, and saw immediately that it had been cut cleanly. He let it drop and walked slowly back to the Land-Rover.

Before he climbed into the driver's seat, he glanced at his wrist-watch. It was ten minutes past five o'clock. Officially he would be off duty at six, but he would not leave his post today. He knew his duty. He knew it would be a long and dangerous day and he steeled himself to meet it.

* * *

That Monday morning, 21 March 1960, a thousand miles away in the Cape townships of Langa and Nyanga the crowds began assembling. It was raining. That cold drizzling Cape north-wester blew from the sea, dampening the ardour

of the majority, but by 6 a.m. there was a crowd of almost ten thousand gathered outside the Langa bachelor quarters, ready to begin the march on the police station.

The police anticipated them. During the weekend they had been heavily reinforced and all officers and senior warrant officers issued with sten guns. Now a Saracen armoured car in drab green battle paint entered the head of the wide road in which the crowd had assembled, and a police officer addressed them over the loudspeaker system. He told them that all public meetings had been banned and that a march on the police station would be treated as an attack.

The black leaders came forward and negotiated with the police, and at last agreed to disperse the crowd, but warned that nobody would go to work that day and there would be another mass meeting at 6 p.m. that evening. When the evening meeting began to assemble, the police arrived in Saracen armoured cars, and ordered the crowd to disperse. When they stood their ground, the police baton-charged them. The crowd retaliated by stoning the police and in a mass rushed forward to attack them. The police commander gave the command to fire and the sten guns buzzed in automatic fire and the crowd fled, leaving two of their number dead upon the field.

From then on weeks of rioting and stoning and marches racked the Cape peninsula, culminating in a massed march of tens of thousands of blacks. This time they reached the police headquarters at Caledon Square, but dispersed quietly after their leaders had been promised an interview with the minister of justice. When the leaders arrived for this interview, they were arrested on orders of Manfred De La Rey, the minister of police, and because police reserves had by this time been stretched almost to breaking point, soldiers and sailors of the defence force were rushed in to supplement the local police units and within three days the black townships were cordoned off securely.

In the Cape the struggle was over.

* * *

In Van Der Bijl Park ten miles from Vereeniging and in Evaton, both notorious centres of radical and violent black political resistance, the crowds began to gather at first light on Monday 21 March.

By nine o'clock the marchers, thousands strong, set out in procession for their local police stations. However, they did not get very far. Here, as in the Cape, the police had been reinforced and the Saracen armoured cars met them on the road and the loud-hailers boomed out the orders to disperse. The orderly columns of marchers bogged down in the quicksands of uncertainty and ineffectual leadership and the police vehicles moved down on them ponderously, forcing them back, and finally broke up their formations with baton charges.

Then abruptly the sky was filled with a terrible rushing sound and every black face was turned upwards. A flight of Sabre jet fighter aircraft of the South African airforce flashed overhead, only a hundred feet above the heads of the crowd. They had never seen modern jet fighters in such low-level flight and the sight and the sound of the mighty engines was unnerving. The crowds began to

break up, and their leaders lost heart. The demonstrations were over almost before they had begun.

* * *

Robert Sobukwe himself marched to Orlando police station in great Soweto. It was five miles from his house in Mofolo, and although small groups of men joined him along the way, they were less than a hundred strong when they reached the police station and offered themselves for arrest under the pass laws.

In most other centres there were no marches, and no arrests. At Hercules police station in Pretoria six men arrived passless and demanded to be arrested. A jocular police officer obligingly took their names and then sent them home.

In most of the Transvaal it was undramatic and anti-climactic – but then there was Sharpeville.

* * *

Raleigh Tabaka had not slept all night, he had not even lain down to rest but had been on his feet exhorting and encouraging and organizing.

Now at six o'clock in the morning he was at the bus depot. The gates were still locked, and in the yard the long ungainly vehicles stood in silent rows while a group of three anxious-looking supervisors waited inside the gates for the drivers to arrive. The buses should have commenced their first run at 4.30 a.m. and by now there was no possibility that they could honour their schedules.

From the direction of the township a single figure jogged down the deserted road and behind the depot gate the bus company supervisors brightened and moved forward to open the gate for him. The man hurrying towards them wore the brown peaked driver's cap, with the brass insignia of the bus company on the headband.

'Ha,' Raleigh said grimly, 'We have missed one of them,' and he signalled his men to intercept the black-leg driver.

The driver saw the young men ahead of him and he stopped abruptly.

Raleigh sauntered up to him smiling and asked, 'Where are you going, my uncle?'

The man did not reply but glanced around him nervously.

'You were not going to drive your bus, were you?' Raleigh insisted. 'You have heard the words of PAC of which all men have taken heed, have you not?'

'I have children to feed,' the man muttered sullenly. 'And I have worked twenty-five years without missing a day.'

Raleigh shook his head sorrowfully. 'You are a fool, old man. I forgive you for that – you cannot be blamed for the worm in your skull that has devoured your brains. But you are also a traitor to your people. For this I cannot forgive you.' And he nodded to his young men. They seized the driver and dragged him into the bushes beside the road.

The driver fought back, but they were young and strong and many in number and he went down screaming under the blows and after a while, when he was quiet, they left him lying in the dusty dry grass. Raleigh felt no pity or remorse

as he walked away. The man was a traitor, and he should count himself fortunate if he survived his punishment to tell his children of his treachery.

At the bus terminus Raleigh's pickets assured him that only a few commuters had attempted to defy the boycott, but they had scurried away as soon as they had seen the waiting pickets.

'Besides,' one of them told Raleigh, 'not a single bus has arrived.'

'You have all begun this day well. Now let us move on to greet the sun of our freedom as it dawns.'

They gathered in the other pickets as they marched, and Amelia was waiting with her children and the other school staff at the corner of the school yard. She saw Raleigh and ran laughing to join him. The children giggled and shrieked with excitement, delighted with this unexpected release from the drudgery of the schoolroom, and they skipped behind Raleigh and his young pickets as they went on.

From each cottage they passed the people swarmed out and when they saw the laughing children, they were infected by the gaiety and excitement. Amongst them by now there were grey heads, and young mothers with their infants strapped to their backs, older women in aprons leading a child on each hand, and men in the overalls of the steel company or the more formal attire of clerks and messengers and shop assistants, and the black petty civil servants who assisted in the administration of the *apartheid* laws. Soon the road behind Raleigh and his comrades was a river of humanity.

As they approached the open common ground they saw that there was already a huge concourse of people gathered there, and from every road leading on to the common more came swarming each minute.

'Five thousand?' Raleigh asked Amelia, and she squeezed his hand and danced with excitement.

'More,' she said. 'There must be more, ten thousand – even fifteen thousand. Oh, Raleigh, I am so proud and happy. Look at our people – isn't it a fine sight to see them all here?' She turned and looked up at him adoringly. 'And I am so proud of you, Raleigh. Without you these poor people would never realize their misery, would never have the will to do anything to change their lot, but look at them now.'

As Raleigh moved forward the people recognized him and made way for him, and they shouted his name and called him 'brother' and 'comrade'.

At the end of the open common was a pile of old bricks and builders' rubble and Raleigh made his way towards it, and when he reached it he climbed up on top of it and raised his arms for silence.

'My people, I bring you the word of Robert Sobukwe who is the father of PAC, and he charges you thus – Remember, Moses Gama! Remember all the pain and hardships of your empty lives! Remember the poverty and the oppression!.'

A roar went up from them and they raised their clenched fists or gave the thumbs-up sign and they shouted '*Amandla*' and 'Gama'. It was some time before Raleigh could speak again, but he told them, 'We are going to burn our passes.' He brandished his own booklet as he went on. 'We are going to make fires and burn the *dompas*. Then we are going to march as one people to the police station and ask them to arrest us. Then Robert Sobukwe will come and speak for us – ' this was a momentary inspiration of Raleigh's, and he went on happily, 'then the police will see that we are men, and they will fear us. Never again will they force us to show the *dompas*, and we will be free men as our

ancestors were free men before the white man came to this land.' He almost believed it as he said it. It all seemed so logical and simple.

So they lit the fires, dozens of them across the common, starting them with dry grass and crumpled sheets of newspaper, and then they clustered around them and threw their pass books into the flames. The women began swaying their hips and shuffling their feet, and the men danced with them and the children scampered around between their legs and they all sang the freedom songs.

It was past eight o'clock before the marshals could get them moving, and then the mass of humanity began to uncoil like a huge serpent and crawl away towards the police station.

* * *

Michael Courtney had watched the Evaton demonstration fizzle out ignominiously, and from a public telephone booth he phoned the Van Der Bijl Park police station to learn that after a police baton-charge on the marchers, all was now quiet there also. When he tried to telephone the Sharpeville police he could not get through, although he wasted almost ten shillings in the coin slot and spent forty frustrating minutes in the telephone booth. In the end he gave up in disgust and went back to the small Morris station wagon which Nana had given him for his last birthday present.

He set off back towards Johannesburg, steeling himself for Leon Herbstein's sarcasm. 'So you got a fine story of the riot that didn't take place. Congratulations, Mickey, I knew I could rely on you.'

Michael grimaced and lit another cigarette to console himself, but as he reached the junction with the main road he saw the sign 'Vereeniging 10 miles' and a smaller sign below it 'Sharpeville Township', and instead of turning towards Johannesburg, he turned south and the Morris buzzed merrily down the strange open and uncrowded roadway.

* * *

Lothar De La Rey kept a toilet kit in his desk, complete with razor and toothbrush. When he got back to the station he washed and shaved in the hand basin in the men's toilet and he felt refreshed, although the sense of ominous disquiet that he had experienced during his night patrol still remained with him.

The sergeant at the charge office saluted him as he entered.

'Good morning, sir, are you signing off duty?' but Lothar shook his head.

'Has the *kommandant* come on duty yet?'

'He came in ten minutes ago.'

'Have you had any telephone calls since midnight, sergeant?'

'Now you come to mention it, sir, no, we haven't. That's funny, isn't it?'

'Not so funny – the lines have been cut. You should have seen that in the station log,' Lothar snapped at him and went through to the station commander's office.

He listened gravely to Lothar's report. '*Ja*, Lothie. You did good work. I'm not happy about this business. I've had a bad feeling ever since you found those damned pamphlets. They should have given us more men here, not just twenty raw recruits. They should have given us experienced men, instead of sending them to Evaton and the other stations.'

'I have called in the foot patrols,' Lothar told him crisply. He did not want to listen to complaints about the decisions of his superiors. He knew there were good reasons for everything. 'I suggest we hold all our men here at the station. Concentrate our forces.'

'*Ja*, I agree,' said the commander.

'What about weapons? Should I open the armoury?'

'*Ja*, Lothie. I think you can go ahead.'

'And I'd like to talk to the men before I go out on patrol again.'

'All right Lothie. You tell them we have everything in hand. They must just obey orders and it will be all right.'

Lothar saluted and strode back into the charge office.

'Sergeant, I want an issue of arms to all white members.'

'Sten guns?' The man looked surprised.

'And four spare magazines per man,' Lothar nodded. 'I will sign the order into the station log.'

The sergeant handed him the keys and together they went through to the strong room, unlocked and swung open the heavy steel Chubb door. The sten guns stood in their racks against the side wall. Cheap little weapons of pressed steel manufacture, they looked like toys, but the 9 mm parabellum cartridges they fired would kill a man as efficiently as the finest crafted Purdey or square-bridged Mauser.

The reinforcements were almost entirely from the police college, fresh-faced and crew-cut, eager boys who looked up at the decorated captain with awe as he told them, 'We are expecting trouble. That's why you are here. You have been issued stens – that alone is a responsibility that each of you must take seriously. Wait for orders, do not act without them. But once you have them, respond swiftly.'

He took one of his constables with him, and drove down to the main township gates with his sten gun on the seat beside him. It was well after six o'clock by then, but the streets were still quiet. He passed fewer than fifty people, all of them hurrying in the same direction. The post office repair truck was waiting at the gate, and Lothar escorted it down to where the telephone wires had been severed. He waited while a linesman scaled the pole and spliced the wires, and then he escorted the truck back to the gates. Before he reached the broad avenue that led up to the station gates, Lothar pulled to the side of the road and switched off the engine.

The constable in the back seat shifted in his seat and began to say something, but Lothar snapped at him, 'Quiet!' and the man froze. They sat in silence for several seconds, before Lothar frowned.

There was a sound like the sea heard from afar, a gentle susurration and he opened the door of the Land-Rover and stepped out. The whisper was like the wind in tall grass, and there was a faint vibration that he seemed to feel in the soles of his feet.

Lothar jumped back into the Land-Rover and drove swiftly to the next road junction, and turned down it towards the open commonage and the school. The sound grew until he could hear it above the beat of the engine. He turned the

next corner and tramped so hard on the brakes that the Land-Rover shuddered and skidded to a halt.

Ahead of him from side to side the road was blocked solid with humanity. They were shoulder to shoulder, rank upon rank, thousand upon thousands, and when they saw the police vehicle ahead of them a great shout of '*Amandla*' went up, and they surged forward.

For a moment Lothar was paralysed by shock. He was not one of those unusual creatures who never felt fear. He had known fear intimately, on the clamorous field when standing to meet the concerted rush of muscled bodies across the turf as well as in the silent streets of the township as he hunted dangerous unscrupulous men in the night. He had conquered those fears and found a strange exhilaration in the feat. But this was a new thing.

This was not human, this was a monster he faced now. A creature with ten thousand throats and twenty thousand legs, a sprawling insensate monster that roared a meaningless word and had no ears to hear nor mind to reason. It was the mob and Lothar was afraid. His instinct was to swing the Land-Rover around and race back to the security of the station. In fact, he had already slammed the gear lever into reverse before he had control of himself.

He left the engine running and opened the side door, and the constable in the back seat blasphemed and his voice was thick with terror. 'Sodding Christ, let's get out of here.'

It served to steel Lothar, and he felt contempt for his own weakness. As he had done so many times before, he strangled his fear and climbed onto the bonnet of the Land-Rover.

Deliberately he had left the sten gun on the front seat and he did not even unbutton the holster on his belt. A single firearm was useless against this sprawling monster.

He held up his arms and shouted, 'Stop! You people must go back. That is a police order.' But his words were drowned in the multitudinous voice of the monster, and it came on apace. The men in the front rank started to run towards him and those behind shouted and pressed forward faster.

'Go back,' Lothar roared, but there was not the slightest check in the ranks and they were close now. He could see the expressions on the faces of the men in front, they were grinning, but Lothar knew how swiftly the African mood can change, how close below the smiles lies the violence of the African heart. He knew he could not stop them, they were too close, too excited, and he was aware that his presence had inflamed them, the mere sight of his uniform was enough.

He jumped down and into the cab, reversed the Land-Rover and then accelerated forward, swinging the wheel into a full lock, and he pulled away as the leaders were within arm's reach.

He pushed the accelerator flat against the floorboards. It was almost two miles back to the station. As he made a quick calculation on how long it would take the march to reach it, he was already rehearsing the orders he would give and working out additional precautions to secure the station.

Suddenly there was another vehicle in the road ahead of him. He had not expected that, and as he swerved to avoid it he saw it was a Morris with lacquered wooden struts supporting the station wagon body. The driver was a young white man.

Lothar slowed and pulled his side window open. 'Where in hell do you think

you're going?' he shouted, and the driver leaned out of the window and smiled politely.

'Good morning, Captain.'

'Have you got a permit to be here?'

'Yes, do you want to see it?'

'No, hell,' Lothar told him. 'The permit is cancelled. You are ordered to leave the township immediately, do you here?

'Yes, Captain, I hear.'

'There might be trouble,' Lothar insisted. 'You are in danger. I order you to leave immediately for your own safety.'

'Right away,' Michael Courtney agreed, and Lothar accelerated away swiftly.

Michael watched him in the rear-view mirror until he was out of sight, and then he lit a cigarette and drove sedately on in the direction from which the police vehicle had come in such desperate haste. The police captain's agitation had confirmed that he was heading in the right direction and Michael smiled with satisfaction as he heard the distant sounds of many voices.

At the end of the avenue he turned towards the sound, and then pulled in to the side of the road and switched off the engine. He sat behind the wheel and stared ahead at the huge crowd that poured down the street towards him. He was unafraid, detached – an observer not a participant – and as the crowd came on he was studying it avidly, anxious not to miss a single detail, already forming the sentences to describe it and scribbling them in his notebook.

'Young people in the vanguard, many children amongst them, all of them smiling and laughing and singing – '

They saw Michael in the parked Morris and they called to him and gave him the thumbs-up signal.

'The good will of these people always amazes me,' he wrote. 'Their cheerfulness and the lack of personal antipathy towards us ruling whites – '

There was a handsome young man in the van of the march, he walked a few paces ahead of the rest. He had a long confident stride so the girl beside him had to skip to keep up with him. She held his hand and her teeth were even and very white in her lovely dark moon face. She smiled at Michael and waved as she passed him.

The crowd split and flowed past on each side of the parked Morris. Some of the children paused to press their faces against the windows, peering in at Michael, and when he grinned and pulled a face at them they shrieked with laughter and scampered on. One or two of the marchers slapped the roof of the Morris with open palms, but it was rather a cheerful greeting than a hostile act and they scarcely paused but marched on after the young leaders.

For many minutes the crowd flowed past and then only the stragglers, the latecomers, cripples and the elderly with stiff hampered gait were going by, and Michael started the engine of the Morris and U-turned across the street.

In low gear he followed the crowd at a walking pace, driving with one hand while he scribbled notes in the open pad on his lap.

'Estimate between six and seven thousand at this stage, but others joining all the time. Old man on crutches with his wife supporting him, a toddler dressed only in a short vest showing his little bum. A woman with a portable radio balanced on her head playing rock 'n' roll music as she dances along. Many peasant types, probably illegals, still wearing blankets and barefooted. The singing is beautifully harmonized. Also many well-dressed and obviously educated types, some wearing government uniforms, postmen and bus drivers,

and workers in overalls of the steel and coal companies. For once, a call has gone out that has reached all of them, not just the politicized minority. A sense of excited and naïve expectation that is palpable. Now the song changes – beginning at the head of the march, but the others pick it up swiftly. They are all singing, doleful and tragic, not necessary to understand the words. This is a lament – '

At the head of the march Amelia sang with such fervour that the tears burst spontaneously from her huge dark eyes and glistened down her cheeks:

The road is long
Our burden is heavy
How long must we go on –

The mood of gaiety changed, and the music of many thousand voices soared in a great anguished cry.

How long must we suffer?
How long? How long?

Amelia held hard to Raleigh's hand and sang with all her being and her very soul, and they turned the last corner. Ahead of them at the end of the long avenue was the diamond-meshed fence that surrounded the police station.

Then in the hard china blue of the highveld sky above the corrugated-iron roof of the police station, a cluster of tiny dark specks appeared. At first they seemed to be a flock of birds, but they swelled in size with miraculous speed as they approached, shining in the early rays of the morning sun with a silent menace.

The head of the march stopped and those behind pressed up behind and then halted also. All their faces turned up towards the menacing machines that bore down upon them, with gaping shark mouths and outstretched pinions, so swiftly that they outran their own engine noise.

The leading Sabre jet dropped lower still, skimming the roof of the police station and the rest of the formation followed it down. The singing faltered into silence, and was followed by the first wails of terror and uncertainty. One after another the great airborne machines hurtled over their heads. It seemed they were low enough to reach up and touch, and the ear-splitting whine of their engines was a physical assault that drove the people to their knees. Some of them crouched in the dusty roadway, others threw themselves flat and covered their heads, while still others turned and tried to run back, but they were blocked by the ranks behind them and the march disintegrated into a confused struggling mass. The men were shouting and the women wailed and some of the children were shrieking and weeping with terror.

The silver jets climbed out and banked steeply, coming around in formation for the next pass; their engines screamed and the shock waves of their passing rumbled across the sky.

Raleigh and Amelia were amongst the few who had stood their ground, and now Raleigh shouted, 'Do not be afraid, my friends. They cannot harm you.'

Amelia took her lead from him and she called to her children, 'They will not hurt you, my little ones. They are pretty as birds. Just look how they shine in the sun!' And the children stifled their terror and a few of them giggled uncertainly.

'Here they come again!' Raleigh shouted. 'Wave to them like this.' And he cavorted and laughed, and the other young people quickly imitated him and the people began to laugh with them. This time as the machines thundered over their heads, only a few of the old women fell over and grovelled in the road, but most of them merelly cringed and flinched and then laughed uproariously with relief when the machines were past.

Under the urging of Raleigh and his marshals, the march began slowly to disentangle itself and move forward again, and when the jet fighters made their third pass, they looked up and waved at the helmeted heads under the transparent canopies. This time the aircraft did not bank and come around. Instead they winged away into the blue and the terrible sound of their engines dwindled and the people began to sing again and to embrace each other as they marched, celebrating their courage and their victory.

'Today you will all be free,' Raleigh shouted, and those close enough to hear him believed him, and turned to shout to those farther back.

'Today we will all be free!'

Ahead of them the gates of the police station yard were closed and locked, but they saw the ranks of men drawn up beyond the wire. The uniforms were dark khaki and the morning sun sparkled on the badges and on the ugly stubby blue weapons that the white police carried.

* * *

Lothar De La Rey stood on the front steps leading up to the charge office, under the lamp with the words 'Police – *Polisie*' engraved upon the blue glass and steeled himself not to duck as the formation of jet fighters flashed low over the station roof.

He watched the distant mob pulse and contract like some giant black amoeba as the aircraft harassed them, and then regain its shape and come on steadily. He heard the singing swell up in chorus and he could make out the features of those in the front ranks.

The sergeant beside him swore softly. 'My God, just look at those black bastards, there must be thousands of them,' and Lothar recognized in the man's tone his own horror and trepidation.

What they were looking upon was the nightmare of the Afrikaner people that had recurred for almost two centuries, ever since their ancestors moving up slowly from the south through a lovely land populated only by wild game had met suddenly upon the banks of the great Fish river the cohorts of this dark multitude.

He felt his nerves crawl like poisonous insects upon his skin as the tribal memories of his people assaulted him. Here they were once more, the tiny handful of white men at the barricades, and there before them was the black barbaric host. It was as it had always been, but the horror of his situation was not in the least diluted by the knowledge that it had all happened before. Rather it was made more poignant, and the natural reaction of defence more compelling.

However, the fear and loathing in the sergeant's voice braced Lothar against his own weakness, and he tore his gaze from the approaching horde and looked to his own men. He saw how pale they were, how deathly still they stood and

how very young so many of them were – but then it was the Afrikaner tradition that the boys had always taken their places at the laager barricades even before they were as tall as the long muzzle-loading weapons they carried.

Lothar forced himself to move, to walk slowly down the line in front of his men, making certain that no trace of his own fear was evident in expression or gesture.

'They don't mean trouble,' he said, 'they have their women and children with them. The Bantu always hide the women if they mean to fight.' His voice was level and without emotion. 'The reinforcements are on their way,' he told them. 'We will have three hundred men here within the hour. Just stay calm and obey orders.' He smiled encouragement at a cadet whose eyes were too big for his pale face, whose ears stuck out from under his cap, and who chewed his lower lip nervously as he stared out through the wire. 'You haven't been given orders to load, *Jong*. Get that magazine off your weapon,' he ordered quietly and the boy unclipped the long straight magazine from the side of his sten gun without once taking his eyes from the singing, dancing horde in front of them.

Lothar walked back down the line with a deliberate tread, not once glancing at the oncoming mob, nodding encouragement at each of his men as he came level or distracting them with a quiet word. But once he reached his post on the station steps again he could no longer contain himself and he turned to face the gate and only with difficulty prevented himself exclaiming out loud.

They filled the entire roadway from side to side and end to end and still they came on, more and more of them pouring out of the side road like a Karoo river in flash flood.

'Stay at your posts, men,' he called. 'Do nothing without orders!' And they stood stolidly in the bright morning sunlight while the leaders of the march reached the locked gates and pressed against them, gripping the wire and peering through the mesh, chanting and grinning as behind them the rest of the huge unwieldy column spread out along the perimeter. Like water contained by a dam wall, compressed by their own multitudes, they were building up rank upon rank until they completely surrounded the station yard, hemming in the small party of uniformed men. And still they came on, those at the back joining the dense throng at the main gates until the station was a tiny rectangular island in a noisy restless black sea.

Then the men at the gates called for silence and gradually the chanting and laughter and general uproar died away.

'We want to speak with your officers,' called a young black man in the front rank at the closed gates. He had his fingers hooked through the mesh and the crowd behind him pushed him so hard against the wire that the high gates shook and trembled.

The station commander came out of the charge office, and as he went down the steps Lothar fell in a pace behind him. Together they crossed the yard and halted in front of the gate.

'This is an illegal gathering,' the commander addressed the young man who had called out to them. 'You must disperse immediately.' He was speaking in Afrikaans.

'It is much worse than that, officer,' the young man smiled at him happily. He was replying in English, a calculated provocation. 'You see, none of us are carrying our pass books. We have burned them.'

'What is your name, you?' the commander demanded in Afrikaans.

'My name is Raleigh Tabaka and I am the branch secretary of the Pan

Africanist Congress, and I demand that you arrest me and all these others,' Raleigh told him in fluent English. 'Open the gates, policeman, and take us into your prison cells.'

'I am going to give you five minutes to disperse,' the commander told him menacingly.

'Or what?' Raleigh Tabaka asked. 'What will you do if we do not obey you?' and behind him the crowd began to chant.

'Arrest us! We have burned the *dompas*. Arrest us!'

There was an interruption and a burst of ironic cheers and hooted laughter from the rear of the crowd, and Lothar jumped up on the bonnet of the nearest police Land-Rover to see over their heads.

A small convoy of three troop carriers filled with uniformed constables had driven out of the side road and was now slowly forcing its way through the crowd. The densely packed ranks gave way only reluctantly before the tall covered trucks, but Lothar felt a rush of relief.

He jumped down from the Land-Rover and ordered a squad of his men to the gates. As the convoy came on the people beat upon the steel sides of the trucks with their bare fists and jeered and hooted and gave the ANC salute. A fine mist of dust rose around the trucks and the thousands of milling shuffling feet of the crowd.

Lothar's men forced the gates open against the pressure of black bodies and as the trucks drove through, they swung them shut, and hurriedly locked them again as the crowd surged forward against them.

Lothar left the commander to haggle and bluster with the leaders of the crowd and he went to deploy the reinforcements along the perimeter of the yard. The new men were all armed and Lothar posted the older more steady-looking of them on top of trucks from where they had a sweeping field of fire over all four sides of the fence.

'Stay calm,' he kept repeating. 'Everything is under control. Just obey your orders.'

He hurried back to the gateway as soon as he had placed the reinforcements, and the commander was still arguing with the black leaders through the wire.

'We will not leave here until either you arrest us, or the pass laws are abolished.'

'Don't be stupid, man,' the commander snapped. 'You know neither of those things is possible.'

'Then we will stay,' Raleigh Tabaka told him and the crowd behind him chanted:

'Arrest us! Arrest us! Now!'

'I have placed the new men in position,' Lothar reported in a low voice. 'We have nearly two hundred now.'

'God grant it will be enough if they turn nasty,' the commander muttered and glanced uneasily along the line of uniformed men. It seemed puny and insignificant against the mass that confronted them through the wire.

'I have argued with you long enough.' He turned back to the men behind the gate. 'You must take these people away now. That is a police order.'

'We stay,' Raleigh Tabaka told him pleasantly.

As the morning wore on, so the heat increased and Lothar could feel the tension and the fear in his men rising with the heat and the thirst and the dust and the chanting. Every few minutes a disturbance in the crowd made it eddy and push like a whirlpool in the flow of a river, and each time the fence shook

and swayed and the white men fingered their guns and fidgeted in the baking sun. Twice more during the morning reinforcements arrived and the crowd let them through until there were almost three hundred armed police in the compound. But instead of dispersing, the crowd continued to grow as every last person who had hidden away in the township cottages, expecting trouble, finally succumbed to curiosity and crept out to join the multitude.

After each new arrival of trucks there was another round of argument and futile orders to disperse, and in the heat and the impatience of waiting, the mood of the crowd gradually changed. There were no more smiles and the singing had a different tone to it as they began to hum the fierce fighting songs. Rumours flashed through the throng – Robert Sobukwe was coming to speak to them, Verwoerd had ordered the passes to be abolished and Moses Gama to be released from jail, and they cheered and sang and then growled and surged back and forth as each rumour was denied.

The sun made its noon, blazing down upon them, and the smell of the crowd was the musky African odour, alien and yet dreadfully familiar.

The white men who had stood to arms all that morning were reaching the point of nervous exhaustion and each time the crowd surged against the frail wire fence they made little jumpy movements and one or two of them without orders loaded their sten guns and lifted them into the high port position. Lothar noticed this and went down the line, ordering them to unload and uncock their weapons.

'We have to do something soon, sir,' he told his commander. 'We can't go on like this – someone or something is going to snap.' It was in the air, strong as the odour of hot African bodies, and Lothar felt it in himself. He had not slept that night, and he was haggard and he felt brittle and jagged as a blade of obsidian.

'What do you suggest, De La Rey?' the commander barked irritably, just as edgy and tense. 'We must do something, you say. *Ja*, I agree – but what?'

'We should take the ringleaders out of the mob.' Lothar pointed at Raleigh Tabaka who was still at the gate. It was almost five hours since he had taken up his station there. 'That black swine there is holding them together. If we pick him and the other ringleaders out, the rest of them will soon lose interest.'

'What is the time?' the commander asked, and although it seemed irrelevant, Lothar glanced at his watch.

'Almost one o'clock.'

'There must be more reinforcements on the way,' the commander said. 'We will wait another fifteen minutes and then we will do as you suggest.'

'Look there,' Lothar snapped and pointed to the left.

Some of the younger men in the crowd had armed themselves with stones and bricks, and from the rear other missiles, chunks of paving slab and rocks, were being passed over the heads of the crowd to those in the front ranks.

'*Ja*, we have to break this up now,' the commander agreed, 'or else there will be serious trouble.'

Lothar turned and called a curt order to the constables nearest him. 'You men, load your weapons and move up to the gate with me.'

He saw that some of the other men further down the line had taken his words as a general order to load, and there was the snicker of metal on metal as the magazines were clamped on to the sten guns and the cocking handles jerked back. Lothar debated with himself for a moment whether he should countermand, but time was vital. He knew he had to get the leaders out of the crowd,

for violence was only seconds away. Some of the black youths in front of the crowd were already shaking the mesh and heaving against it.

With his men behind him he marched to the gate and pointed at Raleigh Tabaka. 'You,' he shouted. 'I want to speak to you.' He reached through the square opening beside the gate lock and seized the front of Raleigh's shirt.

'I want you out of there,' he snarled, and Raleigh pulled back against his grip, jostling the men behind him.

Amelia screamed and clawed at Lothar's wrist. 'Leave him! You must not hurt him.'

The young men around them saw what was happening and hurled themselves against the wire.

'Jee!' they cried, that long, deep, drawn-out war cry that no Nguni warrior can resist. It made their blood smoke with the fighting madness, and it was taken up as others echoed them.

'Jee!'

The section of the crowd behind where Raleigh struggled with Lothar De La Rey heaved forward, throwing themselves upon the fence, humming the war cry, and the fence buckled and began to topple.

'Get back!' Lothar shouted at his men, but the back ranks of the crowd surged forward to see what was happening in the front – and the fence went.

It came crashing over, and though Lothar jumped back, one of the metal posts hit him a glancing blow and he was knocked to his knees. The crowd was no longer contained, and the ranks behind pushed those in front so they came bursting into the yard, trampling over Lothar as he struggled to get to his feet.

From one side a brick came sailing out of the crowd in a high parabola. It struck the windscreen of one of the parked trucks, and shattered it in a shower of diamond-bright chips.

The women were screaming, and falling under the feet of those who were borne forward by the pressure from behind, and men were fighting to get back behind the wire as others thrust them forward uttering that murderous war cry *'Jee!'* that brought on the madness.

Lothar was sprawled under the rushing tide, struggling to regain his feet, while a hail of stones and bricks came over the wire. Lothar rolled to his feet, and only because he was a superb athlete he kept his balance as the rush of frenzied bodies carried him backwards.

There was a loud and jarring sound close behind him that Lothar did not at first recognize. It sounded as though a steel rod had been drawn rapidly across a sheet of corrugated iron. Then he heard the other terrible sounds, the multiple impact of bullets into living flesh, like ripe melons bursting open from blows with a heavy club, and he shouted, 'No! Oh good Christ, no!' But the sten guns rushed and tore the air with a sound like sheets of silk being ripped through, drowning out his despairing protest, and he wanted to shout again, 'Cease fire!' but his throat had closed and he was suffocating with horror and terror.

He made another strenuous effort to give the order, and his throat strained to enunciate the words, but no sound came and his hands moved without his conscious volition, lifting the sten gun from his side, jerking back the cocking handle to feed a round into the breech. In front of him the crowd was breaking and turning, the pressure of human bodies against him was relieved, so he could mount the machine pistol to waist height.

He tried to stop himself, but it was all a nightmare over which he had no control, the weapon in his hands shuddered and buzzed like a chain saw. In a

few fleeting seconds the magazine of thirty rounds was empty, but Lothar had traversed the sten gun like a reaper swinging a scythe, and now the bloody harvest lay before him in the dust twitching and kicking and moaning.

Only then did he realize fully what he had done, and his voice returned.

'Cease fire!' he screamed and struck out at the men around him to reinforce the order. 'Cease fire! Stop it! Stop it!'

Some of the younger recruits were reloading to fire again, and he ran amongst them striking out with the empty sten to prevent them. A man on the roof of one of the troop carriers lifted his weapon and fired another burst and Lothar leapt on to the cab and knocked up the barrel so that the last spray of bullets went high into the dusty air.

From his vantage point on the cab of the truck, Lothar looked out over the sagging fence across the open ground where the dead and the wounded lay, and his spirit quailed.

'Oh, God forgive me. What have we done?' he choked. 'Oh, what have we done?'

* * *

In the middle of the morning Michael Courtney took a chance, for there seemed to be a lull in the activity around the police station. It was, of course, difficult to make out exactly what was happening. He could see only the backs of the rear ranks of the crowd, and over their heads the top of the wire fence and the iron roof of the station. However, the situation seemed for the moment to be quiet and apart form a little desultory singing the crowd was passive and patient.

He jumped into the Morris and drove back down the avenue to the primary school. The buildings were deserted, and without any qualms he tried the door which was marked 'Headmaster' and it was unlocked. There was a telephone on the cheap deal desk. He got through to the *Mail* offices on the first try, and Leon Herbstein was in his office.

'I've got a story,' Michael said, and read out his copy. When he finished he told Leon, 'If I were you, I'd send a staff photographer down here. There is a good chance of some dramatic pictures.'

'Give me the directions how to find you.' Leon acquiesced immediately, and Michael drove back to the police station just as another convoy of police reinforcements pushed through the crowd and entered the station gates.

The morning wore on and Michael ran out of cigarettes, a minor tragedy. He was also hot and thirsty and wondered what it was like standing in that mob out there, hour after hour.

He could sense the mood of the crowd changing. They were no longer cheerful and expectant. There was a sense of frustration, of having been cheated and duped for Sobukwe had not arrived, nor had the white police made the promised announcement to abolish the *dompas*.

The singing started again, but in a harsh and aggressive tone. There were scuffles and disturbances in the crowd, and over their heads Michael saw the armed police take up positions on the cabs of the trucks parked beyond the wire.

The staff photographer from the *Mail* arrived, a young black journalist who

was able to enter the township without a permit. He parked his small brown Humber beside the Morris and Michael cadged a cigarette from him and then quickly briefed him on what was happening, and sent him forward to mingle with the back rows of the crowd and get to work.

A little after noon, some of the youths broke away from the crowd and began to search the verges of the road and the nearest gardens for missiles. They pulled up the bricks that bordered the flower-beds and broke chunks off the concrete paving slabs, then hurried back to join the crowd, carrying those crude weapons. This was an ominous development, and Michael climbed up on the bonnet of his beloved Morris, careless of the paintwork which he usually cherished and polished every morning.

Although he was over a hundred and fifty yards from the station gate, he now had a better view over the heads of the crowd, and he watched the growing agitation and restlessness until the police on the vehicle cabs, the only ones he could see, raised and began loading and cocking their weapons. They were obviously responding to an order and Michael felt a peculiar little chill of anxiety.

Suddenly there was a violent disturbance in the densest part of the crowd directly in front of the main gates. The mass of people surged and heaved and there was an uproar of protesting shouts and cries. Those in the rear of the crowd, closest to where Michael stood, pushed forward to see what was going on, and suddenly there was a metallic rending sound.

Michael saw the tops of the gates begin to move, toppling and bending under the strain, and as they went over, there was a scattered volley of thrown rocks and bricks, and then like the waters of a broken dam, the crowd rushed forward.

Michael had never heard the sound of submachine-gun fire before. So he did not recognize it, but he had heard a bullet striking flesh during that childhood safari on which his father had taken the brothers.

The sound was unmistakable, a meaty thumping, almost like a housewife beating a dusty carpet. However, he couldn't believe it, not until he saw the policemen on the cabs of the vehicles. Even in his horror he noticed how the weapons they held jumped and spurted tiny petals of fire an instant before the sound reached him.

The crowd broke and ran at the first buzzing bursts of fire. They spread out like ripples across a pond, streaming back past where Michael stood, and incredibly some of them were laughing, as though they had not realized what was happening, as though it were all some silly game.

In front of the broken gates the bodies were strewn most thickly, nearly all of them face down and with their heads pointing outwards, in the direction they were running as they were struck down, but there were others farther out and the guns were still clamouring and people were still falling right beside where Michael stood, and the area around the police station was clear, so that through the dust he could see the figures of the uniformed police beyond the sagging wire. Some of them were reloading and others were still firing.

Michael heard the flitting sound of bullets passing close beside his head, but he was too mesmerized and shocked to duck or even to flinch.

Twenty paces away a young couple ran back past him. He recognized them as the pair who had headed the procession earlier, the tall good-looking lad and the pretty moon-faced girl. They were still holding hands, the boy dragging the

girl along with him, but as they passed Michael the girl broke free and doubled back to where a child was standing bewildered and lost amongst the carnage.

As the girl stooped to pick up the child, the bullets hit her. She was thrown back abruptly as though she had reached the end of an invisible leash, but she stayed on her feet for a few seconds longer, and Michael saw the bullets come out through her back at the level of her lowest ribs. For a brief moment they raised little tented peaks in the cloth of her blouse, and then erupted in pink smoky puffs of blood and tissue.

The girl pirouetted and began to sag. As she turned, Michael saw the two entry wounds in her chest, dark studs on the white cloth, and she collapsed on to her knees.

Her companion ran back to try and support her, but she slipped through his hands and fell forward on her face. The boy dropped down beside her and lifted her in his arms, and Michael saw his expression. He had never before seen such desolation and human suffering in another being.

* * *

Raleigh held Amelia in his arms. Her head dropped against his shoulder like that of a sleepy child and he could feel her blood soaking into his clothing. It was hot as spilled coffee and it smelled sickly sweet in the heat.

Raleigh groped in his pocket and found his handkerchief. Gently he wiped the dust from her cheeks and from the corners of her mouth, for she had fallen with her face against the earth.

He was crooning to her softly, 'Wake up, my little moon. Let me hear your sweet voice – '

Her eyes were open and he turned her head slightly to look into them. 'It is me, Amelia, it is Raleigh – don't you see me?' But even as he stared into her widely distended pupils a milky sheen spread over them, dulling out their dark beauty.

He hugged her harder, pressing her unresisting head against his chest and he began to rock her, humming softly to her as though she were an infant, and he looked out across the field.

The bodies were strewn about like overripe fruit fallen from the bough. Some of them were moving, an arm straightened or a hand unclenched, an old man began to crawl past where Raleigh knelt, dragging a shattered leg behind him.

Then the police officers were coming out through the sagging gates. They wandered about the field in a dazed uncertain manner, still carrying their empty weapons dangling from limp hands, stopping to kneel briefly beside one of the bodies, and then standing again and walking on.

One of them approached. As he came closer Raleigh recognized the blond captain who had seized him at the gate. He had lost his cap and the top button was missing from his tunic. His crew-cut hair was darkened with sweat, and droplets of sweat stood on his waxen pale forehead. He stopped a few paces off and looked at Raleigh. Although his hair was blond, his eyebrows were dark and thick and his eyes were yellow as those of a leopard. Raleigh knew then how he had earned his nickname. Those pale eyes were underscored with smudges of fatigue and horror, dark as old bruises, and his lips were dry and cracked.

They stared at each other – the black man kneeling in the dust with the dead woman in his arms and the uniformed white man with the empty sten gun in his hands.

'I didn't mean it to happen – ' said Lothar De La Rey and his voice croaked, 'I'm sorry.'

Raleigh did not answer, gave no sign of having heard or understood and Lothar turned away and walked back, picking his way amongst the dead and the maimed, back into the laager of wire mesh.

The blood on Raleigh's clothing began to cool, and when he touched Amelia's cheek again he felt the warmth going out of it also. Gently he closed her eyelids, and then he unbuttoned the front of her blouse. There was very little bleeding from the two entry wounds. They were just below her pointed virgin breasts, small dark mouths in her smooth amber-coloured skin, set only inches apart. Raleigh ran two fingers of his right hand into those bloody mouths, and there was residual warmth in her torn flesh.

'With my fingers in your dead body,' he whispered. 'With the fingers of my right hand in your wounds, I swear an oath, my love. You will be avenged. I swear it on our love, upon my life and upon your death. You will be avenged.'

* * *

In the days of anxiety and turmoil following the massacre of Sharpeville, Verwoerd and his minister of police acted with resolution and strength.

A state of emergency was declared in almost half of South Africa's magisterial districts. Both the PAC and ANC were banned and those of their supporters suspected of incitement and intimidation were arrested and detained under the emergency regulations. Some estimates put the figure of detainees as high as eighteen thousand.

In early April at the meeting of the full cabinet to discuss the emergency, Shasa Courtney risked his political future by rising to address a plea to Dr Verwoerd for the abolition of the pass book system. He had prepared his speech with care, and the genuine concern he felt for the importance of the subject made him even more than usually eloquent. As he spoke he became gradually aware that he was winning the support of some of the other senior members of the cabinet.

'In a single stroke we will be removing the main cause of black dissatisfaction, and depriving the revolutionary agitators of their most valuable weapon,' he pointed out.

Three other ministers followed Shasa, each voicing their support for the abolition of the *dompas*, but from the top of the long table Verwoerd glowered at them, becoming every minute more angry until at last he jumped to his feet.

'The idea is completely out of the question. The reference books are there for an essential purpose: to control the influx of blacks into the urban areas.'

Within a few minutes he had brutally bludgeoned the proposal to death, and made it clear that to try to resurrect it would be political suicide for any member of the cabinet, no matter how senior.

Within days Dr Hendrik Verwoerd was himself on the brink of the chasm. He visited Johannesburg to open the Rand Easter Show. He made a reassuring speech to the huge audience that filled the arena of the country's largest

agricultural and industrial show, and as he sat down to thunderous applause, a white man of insignificant appearance made his way between the tiers of seats and in full view of everybody drew a pistol and holding it to Dr Verwoerd's head fired two shots.

With blood pouring down his face Verwoerd collapsed, and security guards overpowered his assailant. Both bullets, fired at point-blank range, had penetrated the prime minister's skull, and yet his most remarkable tenacity and will to survive combined with the expert medical attention he received, saved him.

In little more than a month he had left hospital and had once more taken up his duties as the head of state. The assassination attempt seemed to have been without motive or reason, and the assailant was judged insane and placed in an asylum. By the time Dr Verwoerd had fully recovered from the attempt on his life calm had been restored to the country as a whole, and Manfred De La Rey's police were in total control once more.

Naturally the reaction of the international community towards the slaughter and the subsequent measures to regain control was heavily critical. America led the rest in her condemnations, and within months had instituted an embargo on the sale of arms to South Africa. More damaging than the reaction of foreign governments was the crash on the Johannesburg stock exchange, the collapse of property values and the attempted flight of capital out of the country. Strict exchange-control regulations were swiftly imposed to forestall this.

Manfred De La Rey had come out of it all with his power and position greatly enhanced. He had acted the way his people expected him to, with strength and forthright determination. There was no doubt at all now that he was one of the senior members of the cabinet and in the direct line of succession to Hendrik Verwoerd. He had smashed the Pan Africanist Congress and the ANC. Their leaders were in total disarray and all of them were in hiding or had fled the country.

With the safety of the state secured, Dr Verwoerd could at last turn his full attention to the momentous business of realizing the golden dream of Afrikanerdom – the Republic.

The referendum was held in October 1960, and so great were the feelings, for and against, engendered by the prospect of breaking with the British crown that there was a ninety per cent poll. Cunningly, Verwoerd had decreed that a simple majority, and not the usual two-thirds majority, would suffice, and on the day he got his majority: 850,000 to 775,000. The Afrikaner response was an hysteria of joy, of speeches and wild rejoicing.

In March of the following year Verwoerd and his entourage went to London to attend the conference of the Commonwealth prime ministers. He came out of the meeting to tell the world, 'In the light of opinions expressed by other member governments of the Commonwealth regarding South Africa's race policies, and in the light of future plans regarding the race policies of the South African government, I told the other prime ministers that I was withdrawing my country's application for continued membership of the Commonwealth after attaining the status of a republic.'

From Pretoria Manfred De La Rey cabled Verwoerd, 'You have preserved the dignity and pride of your country, and the nation owes you eternal gratitude.'

Verwoerd returned home to the adulation and hero worship of his people. In the heady euphoria, very few, even amongst the English-speaking opposition, realized just how many doors Verwoerd had locked and barred behind him and

just how cold and bleak the winds that Macmillan had predicted would blow across the southern tip of Africa in the coming years.

* * *

With the Republic safely launched Verwoerd could at last select his praetorian guard to protect it and hold it strong. Erasmus, the erstwhile minister of justice who had acted neither as ruthlessly nor as resolutely as was expected during the emergency, was packed off as the ambassador of the new Republic to Rome, and Verwoerd presented two new ministers to his cabinet.

The new minister of defence was the member for the constituency of George in the Cape, P. W. Botha, while Erasmus's replacement as minister of justice was Balthazar Johannes Vorster. Shasa Courtney knew Vorster well, and as he listened to him make his first address to the cabinet, he reflected how much like Manfred De La Rey the man was.

They were almost the same age and, like Manfred, Vorster had been a member of the extreme right-wing anti-Smuts pro-Nazi *Ossewa Brandwag* during the war. Whereas it was generally accepted that Manfred had remained in Germany during the war years – although he was very mysterious and secretive about that period of his life – John Vorster had been interned in Smuts' Koffiefontein concentration camp for the duration.

Both Vorster and De La Rey had been educated at Stellenbosch University, the citadel of Afrikanerdom, and their political careers had run closely parallel courses. Although Manfred had won his seat in parliament in the historic 1948 elections, John Vorster in the same elections had gained the distinction of being the only candidate in South African history to lose by a mere two votes. Later, in 1953, he vindicated himself by winning the same Brakpan seat with a majority of seven hundred.

Now that the two of them were seated at the long table in the cabinet room, their physical resemblance was striking. They were both heavy rugged-looking men, with bulldog features, both obdurate, unflinching and tough, the epitome of the hard Boer.

Vorster confirmed this for Shasa as he began to speak, leaning forward aggressively, confident and articulate. 'I believe we are in a fight to the death with the forces of communism, and that we cannot defeat subversion or thwart revolution by closely observing the Queensberry rules. We have to put aside the old precepts of *habeas corpus* and arm ourselves with new legislation that will enable us to preempt the enemy, to pick out their leaders and put them away where they can do little harm. This is not a new concept, gentlemen.'

Vorster smiled down the table and Shasa was struck by the way in which his dour features lit up with that impish smile.

'You all know where I spent the war years, without the benefit of trial. Let me tell you right now – it worked. It kept me out of mischief and that's what I intend to do with those who would destroy this land – keep them out of mischief. I want power to detain any person whom I know to be an enemy of the state, without trial, for a period of up to ninety days.'

It was a masterly performance and Shasa felt some trepidation in having to follow it, especially when he could not be so sanguine in his own view of the future.

'At the moment I have two major concerns,' he told his colleagues seriously. 'The first is the arms embargo placed upon us by the Americans. I believe that other countries are soon going to bow to American pressure and extend the embargo. One day we might even have the ridiculous situation where Great Britain will refuse to sell us the arms we need for our defence.' Some of the others at the table fidgeted and looked incredulous. Shasa assured them: 'We cannot afford to underestimate this hysteria of America for what they call civil rights. Remember that they sent troops to help force blacks into white schools.' The memory of that appalled them all and there were no further signs of disbelief as Shasa went on. 'A nation who can do that will do anything. My aim is to make this country totally self-sufficient in conventional armaments within five years.'

'Is that possible?' Verwoerd asked sharply.

'I believe so.' Shasa nodded. 'Fortunately, this eventuality has been anticipated. You yourself warned me of the possibility of an arms embargo when you appointed me, Prime Minister.'

Verwoerd nodded and Shasa repeated, 'This is my aim; self-sufficient in conventional weapons in five years – ' Shasa paused dramatically. 'And nuclear capable in ten years.'

This was stretching their credulity and there were interjections and sharp questions, so that Shasa held up his hands and spoke firmly.

'I am deadly serious, gentlemen. We can do it! Given certain circumstances.'

'Money,' said Hendrik Verwoerd, and Shasa nodded.

'Yes, Prime Minister, money. Which brings me to my second major consideration.' Shasa drew a deep breath, and steeled himself to broach an unpalatable truth. 'Since the Sharpeville shootings, we have had a crippling flight of capital from the country. Cecil Rhodes was wont to say that the Jews were his birds of good omen. When the Jews came, an enterprise or a country was assured of success, and when the Jews left you could expect the worst. Well the sad truth, gentlemen, is that our Jews are leaving. We have to entice them to stay and bring back those who have already left.'

Again there was restlessness around the table. The National Party had been conceived on that wave of anti-semitism between the world wars, and although it had abated since then, traces of it still existed.

'These are the facts, gentlemen.'Shasa ignored their discomfort. 'Since Sharpeville, the value of property has collapsed to half what it was before the shooting, and the stock market is at its lowest since the dark days of Dunkirk. The businessmen and investors of the world are convinced that this government is tottering and on the point of capitulating to the forces of communism and darkness. They see us as being engulfed in despondency and anarchy, with black mobs burning and looting and white civilization about to go up in flames.' They laughed derisively and John Vorster made a bitter interjection.

'I have just explained what steps we will take.'

'Yes.' Shasa cut him off quickly. 'We know that the foreign view is distorted. We know that we still have a strong and stable government, that the country is prosperous and productive and that the vast majority of our people, both black and white, are law-abiding and content. We know that we have our guardian angel, gold, to protect us. But we have to convince the rest of the world.'

'Do you think that's possible, man?' Manfred asked quickly.

'Yes, with a full-scale and concerted campaign to give the truth of the situation to the businessmen of the world,' Shasa said. 'I have recruited most of

our own leaders in industry and commerce to assist. We will go out at our own expense to explain the truth. We will invite them here – journalists, businessmen and friends – to see for themselves how tranquil and how under control the country truly is, and just how rich are the opportunities.'

Shasa spoke for another thirty minutes and when he ended, his own fervour and sincerity had exhausted him; but then he saw how he had finally convinced his colleagues and he knew the results were worth the effort. He was convinced that from the horror of Sharpeville he could mount a fresh endeavour that would carry them to greater heights of prosperity and strength.

Shasa had always been resilient, with extraordinary recuperative powers. Even in his airforce days, when he brought the squadron in from a sortie over the Italian lines and the others had sat around the mess, stunned and shattered by the experience, he had been the first to recover and to start the repartee and boisterous horse-play. Shasa left the cabinet room drained and exhausted but by the time he had driven the vintage SS Jaguar around the mountain and through the Anreith gate of Weltevreden, he was sitting up straight in the bucket seat, feeling confident and jaunty again.

The harvest was long past and the labourers were in the vineyards pruning the vines. Shasa parked the Jaguar and went down between the rows of bare leafless plants to talk to them and give them encouragement. Many of these men and women had been on Weltevreden since Shasa had been a child, and the younger ones had been born here. Shasa looked upon them as an extension of his family and they in turn regarded him as their patriarch. He spent half an hour with them listening to their small problems and worries, and settling most with a few words of assurance, then he broke off and left them abruptly as a figure on horseback came down the far side of the vineyard at full gallop.

From the corner of the stone wall Shasa watched Isabella gather her mount, and he stiffened as he realized what she was going to do. The mare was not yet fully schooled and Shasa had never trusted her temperament. The wall was of yellow Table Mountain sandstone, five foot high.

'No, Bella!' he whispered. 'No, baby!'

But she turned the mare and drove her at the wall, and the horse reacted gamely. Her quarters bunched and the great muscles rippled below the glossy hide. Isabella lifted her and they went up.

Shasa held his breath, but even in his suspense he could appreciate what a magnificent sight they made, horse and rider, thoroughbreds both – the mare with her forelegs folded up under her chest and her ears pricked forward, soaring away from the earth, and Isabella leaning back in the saddle, her back arched and her young body supple and lovely, long legs and fine thrusting breasts, red mouth laughing and her hair flying free, sparkling with ruby lights in the late yellow sunlight.

They they were over and Shasa exhaled sharply. Isabella swung the mare down to where he stood at the corner.

'You promised to ride with me, Pater,' she scolded him. Shasa's instinct was to reprimand her for that jump, but he prevented himself. He knew she would probably respond by pulling the mare's head around and taking the jump from this side. He wondered just when he had lost control of her, and then grinned ruefully as he answered himself.

'About ten minutes after she was born.'

The mare was dancing in a circle and Isabella flung her hair back with a toss of her head.

'I waited almost an hour for you,' she said.

'Affairs of state – ' Shasa began.

'That's no excuse, Pater. A promise is a promise.'

'It's still not too late,' he pointed out, and she laughed as she challenged him.

'I'll race that old banger of yours down to the stables!' And she booted the mare into a gallop.

'Not fair,' he called after her. 'You have too much start,' but she turned in the saddle and stuck her tongue out at him. He ran to the Jag, but she cut across north field and was dismounted by the time he drove into the stableyard.

She tossed her reins to a groom and ran to embrace him. Isabella had a variety of kisses, but this type, lingering and loving, with a little bit of ear-nuzzling at the end, was reserved for when she badly wanted something from him, something that she knew he was going to try to refuse.

While he pulled on his riding boots she sat close beside him on the bench and told him a funny story about her sociology professor at varsity.

'This huge shaggy St Bernard wandered into the lecture theatre and Prof. Jacobs was quick as a flash. Better that the dogs should come to learning, he said, than learning should go to the dogs.' She was a natural mimic. As they left the saddle room, she hugged his arm.

'Oh, Daddy, if only I could find a boy like you, but they're all so utterly dreary.'

'Long may they remain that way,' he wished fervently.

He made a cup with his hands for her to mount, but she laughed at him and sprang to the saddle easily on those long lovely legs.

'Come on, slowcoach. It'll be dark soon.'

Shasa enjoyed being alone with her. She enchanted him with her mercurial changes of mood and subject. She had a quick mind and quirky sense of humour, to go with her extraordinary face and body, but she alarmed him when she showed flashes of that restless refusal to concentrate for long on a single topic. Sean had been like that, needing constant stimulation to hold his interest, easily bored by anything that could not keep the same breathless pace that he set. Shasa was amazed that Isabella had lasted out a year of university studies, but he was resigned to the fact that she wasn't going to graduate. Every time they discussed it, she was more disparaging of the academic life. Make-believe, she called it. Kid's stuff. And when he replied, 'Well, Bella, you are still a kid,' she bridled at him.

'Oh, Daddy, you don't understand!'

'Don't I? Don't you think I was your age once?'

'I suppose so – but that was in biblical times, for God's sake.'

'Ladies don't swear,' he remonstrated automatically.

She attracted admirers in slavish droves, and treated them with callous indifference for a while and then dropped them with almost feline cruelty, and all the time the restlessness in her was more apparent.

'I should have been stricter with her right from the beginning,' he decided grimly, and then grinned. 'What the hell, she's my only indulgence – and she'll be gone soon enough.'

'Do you know that when you smile like that you are the sexiest man in the world?' she interrupted his thoughts.

'What do you know about sexiness, young lady?' he demanded gruffly to cover his gratification, and she tossed her head at him.

'Wouldn't you like to know?'

'No thank you,' he refused hastily. 'I'd probably have a hernia on the spot.'

'My poor old Daddy.' She edged the mare over until their knees touched and she leaned across to hug him.

'All right, Bella,' he smiled. 'You'd better tell me what you want. Your heavy artillery has demolished my defences entirely.'

'Oh, Daddy, you make me seem so scheming. I'll race you down to the polo grounds.'

He let her lead, holding his stallion's nose just behind her stirrup all the way down the hill. Nonetheless, she was flushed with triumph as she pulled in the mare and turned back to him.

'I had a letter from Mater,' she said.

For a moment Shasa didn't realize what she had said, then his smile iced over and he glanced at his gold Rolex wristwatch.

'We'd better be getting back.'

'I want to talk about my mother. We haven't talked about her since the divorce.'

'There isn't anything to discuss. She's out of our lives.'

'No.' Isabella shook her head. 'She wants to see me – me and Mickey. She wants us to go to London and visit her.'

'No,' he said fiercely.

'She's my mother.'

'She signed away all claim to that title.'

'I want to see her – she wants to see me.'

'We'll talk about it some other time.'

'I want to talk about it now. Why won't you let me go?'

'Your mother did things which put her beyond the pale. She would exert an influence of evil upon you.'

'Nobody influences me – unless I want them to,' she said. 'And what did mother do anyway? Nobody has ever explained that.'

'She committed an act of calculated treachery. She betrayed us all – her husband, her father, her family, her children and her country.'

'I don't believe it.' Isabella shook her head. 'Mater was always so concerned for everybody.'

'I cannot, and will not, give you all the details, Bella. Just believe me when I tell you that if I had not spirited her out of the country, she would have stood trial as an accessory to the murder of her own father and for the crime of high treason.'

They rode up to the stables in silence, but as they entered the yard and dismounted, Isabella said quietly, 'She should have a chance to explain it to me herself.'

'I can forbid you to go, Bella, you are still a minor. But you know I won't do that. I'll simply ask you not to go to London to see that woman.'

'I'm sorry, Daddy. Mickey is going, and I am going with him.' She saw his expression and went to him quickly, 'Please try to understand. I love you, but I love her too. I have to go.'

They drove up to the house in the Jaguar without speaking again, but as he parked the car and switched off the ignition, Shasa asked, 'When?'

'We haven't decided yet.'

'I tell you what. We'll go together some time and perhaps we could go on to Switzerland for a week's skiing or Italy to do some sight-seeing. We might even stop in Paris to get you a new frock. Lord knows, you are short of clothes.'

'My dear father, you are a crafty old dog, aren't you?'

They were still laughing as they went arm in arm up the front steps of Weltevreden. Centaine came out of her study door across the lobby. When she saw them she snatched the gold-rimmed reading glasses off her nose – she hated even the family to see her wearing them – and she demanded, 'What are you two so merry about? Bella is wearing her triumphant expression. What has she talked you into this time?'

Centaine didn't wait for an answer, but pointed to the huge banana-shaped package almost ten foot long, wrapped in thick layers of brown hessian, that lay in the middle of the chequered marble floor.

'Shasa, this arrived for you this morning and it has been cluttering up the house all day. Please get rid of it, whatever it is.'

Centaine had lived on alone at Rhodes Hill for almost a year after Blaine's death before Shasa had been able to persuade her to close the house up and return to Weltevreden. Now she ran a strict routine to which they were all expected to conform.

'Now what on earth is this?' Shasa tentatively attempted to lift one end of the long package, and then grunted, 'It's made of lead, whatever it is.'

'Hold on, Pater,' Garry called from the top of the staircase. 'You'll bust something.' He came bounding down the stairs, three at a time. 'I'll do that for you – where do you want it?'

'The gun room will do. Thanks, Garry.'

Garry enjoyed showing off his strength and he lifted the heavy package easily, and manoeuvred it down the passageway, then through the gun-room door and laid it on the lion skin in front of the fireplace.

'Do you want me to open it?' he asked, and without waiting for an answer went to work on it.

Isabella perched on the desk, determined not to miss anything, and none of them spoke until Garry had stripped away the last sheet of hessian and stood back.

'It's magnificent,' Shasa breathed. 'I have never seen anything quite like that in my life before.' It was a single tusk of curved ivory, almost ten foot long, as thick as a pretty girl's waist at one end and tapering to a blunt point at the other.

'It must weigh almost a hundred and fifty pounds,' Garry said. 'But just look at the workmanship.'

Shasa knew that the ivory workers of Zanzibar were the only ones who could do something like this. The entire length of the tusk had been carved with hunting scenes of exquisite detail and the finest execution.

'It's beautiful.' Even Isabella was impressed. 'Who sent it to you?'

'There is an envelope – ' Shasa pointed to the litter of discarded wrappings, and Garry picked it out and passed it to him.

The envelope contained a single sheet of notepaper.

In camp on the Tana river
Kenya.

Dear Dad,
Happy birthday – I'll be thinking of you on the day. This is my best jumbo to date – 146 lbs. before the carving.
Why don't you come hunting with me?

Love,
Sean.

With the note in one hand, Shasa squatted beside the tusk and stroked the creamy smooth surface. The carvings depicted a herd of elephant, hundreds of them in a single herd. From old bulls and breeding cows to tiny calves, they fled in a long spiral frieze around the ivory shaft, diminishing in elegant perspective towards the point. The herd was harassed and attacked by hunters along its length, beginning with men in lionskins armed with bows and poisoned arrows, or with broad-bladed elephant spears; towards the end of this primeval cavalcade the hunters were on horseback and wielding modern firearms. The path of the herd was strewn with great fallen carcasses, and it was beautiful and real and tragic.

However, it was neither the beauty nor the tragedy that thickened Shasa's voice as he said, 'Will you two leave me alone, please.' He did not look around at them, he did not want them to see his face.

For once Isabella did not argue, but took Garry's hand and led him from the room.

'He hasn't forgotten my birthday,' Shasa murmured, as he stroked the ivory. 'Not once since he left.' He coughed and stood up abruptly, jerked the handkerchief from his breast pocket and blew his nose loudly and then wiped his eyes.

'And I haven't even written to him, I haven't even replied to one of his letters.' He stuffed the handkerchief back into his pocket and went to stand at the window, staring out over the lawns where the peacocks strutted. 'The stupid cruel thing is that he has always been my favourite of the three of them. Oh God, I'd give anything to see him again.'

* * *

The rain was icy grey, drifting like smoke over the thick forests of bamboo that cloaked the crests of the Aberdare Mountains.

The four of them moved in single file with the Ndorobo tracker on the point, following the spoor in the forest earth that beneath the litter of fallen bamboo leaves was the colour and consistency of molten chocolate.

Sean Courtney took the second position, covering the tracker and poised to make any quick decision. He was the youngest of the three white men but command had quite naturally devolved upon him. Nobody had contested it.

The third man in the line, Alistair Sparks, was the youngest son of a Kenyan settler family. Although he possessed enormous powers of endurance, was a fine natural shot and a consummate bushman, he was lazy and evasive and needed to be pushed to exercise all his skills to the full.

Raymond Harris was on the drag at number four. He was almost fifty years old, full of malaria and gin, but in his time had been one of the legendary white hunters of East Africa. He had taught Sean everything he knew, until the pupil had excelled the master. Now Raymond was content to bring up the rear and let Sean and Matatu, the tracker, get them into position for the kill.

Matatu was naked except for his filthy tattered loincloth and the rain made tiny rivulets down his glossy black hide. He worked the spoor with the same instinct and superhuman sense of sight, smell and hearing, as one of the wild animals of the forest. They had been following these tracks for two days already,

stopping only when the light failed completely each night, and taking up the chase again with the first flush of dawn.

The spoor was running sweet and hot. Sean was probably as good a tracker as a white man could be and he judged that they were only four or five hours behind and gaining swiftly. The quarry had angled up the steep slope of this nameless peak, heading to cross the ridge just below the main crest. Sean caught glimpses of the top through the dense vault of bamboo over their heads and the blown streamers of misty rain.

Suddenly Matatu stopped dead, and Sean popped his tongue to warn the others and froze with his thumb on the safety-catch of the big double-barrelled Gibbs.

After a moment Matatu turned abruptly aside, dropping the spoor, and went sliding as swiftly and silently as a dark serpent down the slope, away from the line and direction of the quarry.

Five years before, when Sean had first taken Matatu into his service, he might have protested and tried to force him to stay with the run of the spoor, but now he followed without argument, and although he was going at his best hunting speed, he just managed to hold the tracker in sight.

Sean was dressed in a cloak of colobus monkey skins and he wore Somali sandals of elephant hide on his feet and a shaggy cap of monkey skin covered his obviously Caucasian hair. His arms, legs and face were blackened with a mixture of rancid hippo fat and soot, and he had not bathed in two weeks. He looked and smelled like the men he was hunting.

There were five Mau Mau in the band that they were pursuing, all of them members of the notorious gang run by the self-styled General Kimathi. Five days previously they had attacked one of the coffee shambas near Nyeri in the foothills of the mountain range. They had disembowelled the white overseer and stuffed his severed genitals into his mouth, and they had chopped off his wife's limbs with the heavy-bladed pangas, beginning at wrist and ankle and working gradually towards the trunk of her body, until they hacked through the great joints in her shoulders and groin.

Sean and his group of scouts had reached the shamba almost twelve hours after the gang had fled. They had left the Land-Rover and taken the spoor on foot.

Matatu took them directly down the slope. The narrow river at the bottom was a tumultuous silver torrent. Sean stripped off his furs and sandals and went into it naked. The cold chilled his bones until they ached and the roaring waters swirled over his head but he carried the line across and then brought the others safely over.

Matatu was the last across, carrying Sean's clothing and his rifle, and he was immediately off again, like a wraith of the forest. Sean followed him with the agony of cold shuddering through his body and the sodden furs a heavy burden to add to the rifle and his pack.

A herd of buffalo crashed away through the forest ahead of them, and the bovine stink lingered in their nostrils long after they were gone. Once Sean had a glimpse of a huge antelope, ginger red with vertical white stripes down its heavy body and a head of magnificent spiral horns. It was a bongo. He would have charged one of his rich American clients $1000 for a shot at that rarest and most elusive of all antelopes, but it ghosted away into the bamboo and Matatu led them on without apparent purpose or direction, the spoor three hours cold behind them.

Then Matatu skirted one of the rare forest clearings and stopped again. He glanced back over his naked shoulder and grinned at Sean with the patent adoration of a hunting dog who acknowledges the most important being in its universe.

Sean stepped up beside him and looked down at the spoor. He would never know how Matatu did it. He had tried to make him explain, but the wizened little gnome had merely laughed with embarrassment and hung his head. It was a kind of magic that went beyond the mere art of observation and deduction. What Matatu had just done was to drop the spoor when it was sweet and hot, and go off at an improbable tangent, running blind through trackless bamboo and over wild peaks, to meet the spoor again with the unerring instinct of a migrating swallow, having cut the corner and gained three hours on the quarry.

Sean squeezed his shoulder and little Ndorobo wriggled his whole body with pleasure.

They were less than an hour behind the gang now, but the rain and the mist were bringing on the night prematurely. Sean signalled Matatu on. Not one of them had spoken a single word all that day.

The men they were chasing were becoming careless. In the beginning they had anti-tracked and covered spoor, doubled and jinked so cunningly that even Matatu had puzzled to unravel the sign and get away on the run of it – but now they were feeling confident and secure. They had broken off the succulent bamboo shoots to chew as they marched, leaving glaring wounds on the plants, and they had trodden deeply, heeling with fatigue, leaving sign that Matatu could follow like a tarmac road. One of the fugitives had even defecated on the track, not bothering to cover his faeces, and they were still steaming with his body warmth. Matatu grinned at Sean over his shoulder and made the fluttery hand signal which said 'Very close.'

Sean eased open the action of the double-barrelled Gibbs, without allowing the sidelock to click. He slid the brass-cased cartridges out of the breeches, and replaced them with two others from the leather ammunition pouch beneath his monkey-skin cape. The .577 cartridges were thicker than a man's thumb and the clumsy, blunt-nosed bullet heads were jacketed in copper and capped with soft blue lead so they could mushroom through living tissue, tearing open a wide channel and inflicting terrible damage. This little ritual of changing his cartridges was one of Sean's superstitions – he always did it just before he closed with dangerous game. He closed the rifle as gently and silently as he had opened it and glanced back at the two men behind him.

The whites of Alistair's eyes gleamed in his blackened face. He carried the Bren gun. Sean had not been able to wean him from it. Despite its unwieldy long barrel and great weight, Alistair loved the automatic weapon. 'When I'm after Mickey Mouse I like to be able to turn the air blue with lead,' he explained with that lazy grin. 'Nobody is going to get a chance to stuff my knackers down my throat, matey!'

At the rear Ray Harris gave Sean the thumbs-up signal, but the sweat and rain had cut pale runnels through the soot and fat on his face, and even through the camouflage Sean could see how haggard he was with fear and fatigue. 'The old man is getting past it,' Sean thought dispassionately. 'Have to put him out to grass soon.'

Ray carried the Stirling sub-machine-gun. Sean suspected it was because he could no longer manage the weight of a more substantial weapon. 'In the bamboo it's point blank.' Ray excused his choice, and Sean had not bothered to

argue or to point out that the tiny 9 mm bullets would be deflected by the frailest twig, and smothered in the dense vegetation of the Aberdares – while the big .600 grain slug from his own Gibbs would plough straight through branch and stem and still blow the guts out of the Mickey Mouse on the other side, while the stubby 20-inch barrels were perfect for close work in the bamboo, and he could swing them without risking hooking up in the brush.

Sean clicked his tongue softly and Matatu went away on the spoor in that soft-footed, ungainly lope which he could keep up day and night without tiring. They crossed another heavily bambooed ridge and in the valley beyond Matatu stopped again. It was so dark by now that Sean had to move up beside him, and go down on one knee to examine the sign. It took him almost a minute to make sense of it, even after Matatu had pointed out the other set of tracks coming in from the right.

Sean gestured Ray to move up and laid his lips to his ear. 'They have joined another party of Mickey Mice – probably from the base camp. Eight of them, three women, so we have thirteen in a bunch now. A lovely lucky number.'

But as he spoke the light was going, and the rain started again, spilling softly out of the purple-black sky. Within five hundred yards Matatu stopped for the last time and Sean could just make out the pale palm of his right hand as he made the wash-out signal. Night had blanketed the spoor.

The white men each found a treetrunk to prop themselves against, spreading out in a defensive circle facing outwards. Sean took Matatu under the monkey-skin cloak with him as though he were a tired gun dog. The little man's skinny body was as cold and wet as a trout taken from a mountain stream and he smelled of herbs and leaf mould and wild things. They ate the hard salted dry buffalo meat and cold maize cakes from their belt pouches and slept fitfully in each other's warmth while the raindrops pattered down on the fur over their heads.

Matatu touched Sean's cheek and he was instantly awake in the utter darkness, slipping the safety-catch of the Gibbs that lay across his lap. He sat rigid, listening and alert.

Beside him Matatu snuffled the air and after a moment Sean did the same. 'Woodsmoke?' he whispered, and both of them came to their feet. In the darkness, Sean moved to where Alistair and Ray were lying and got them up. They went forward in the night, holding the belt of the man ahead to keep in contact. The whiffs of smoke were intermittent but stronger.

It took almost two hours for Matatu to locate the Mau Mau encampment precisely, using his sense of smell and hearing, and at the end the faint glow of a patch of camp-fire coals. Although the bamboo dripped all around, they could hear them – a soft cough, a strangled snore, the gabble of a woman in a nightmare – and Sean and Matatu moved them into position.

It took another hour; but in the utter darkness before the true dawn, Alistair was lying up the slope, forty feet from the dying camp fire. Raymond was amongst the rocks on the bank of the stream on the far side, and Sean lay with Matatu in the dense scrub beside the path that led into the camp.

Sean had the barrel of the Gibbs across his left forearm and his right hand on the pistol grip with the safety-catch under his thumb. He had spread the fur cloak over both himself and Matatu, but neither of them even drowsed. They were keyed up to the finest pitch. Sean could feel the little Ndorobo trembling with eagerness where their bodies touched. He was like a bird dog with the scent of the grouse in his nostrils.

The dawn came stealthily. First Sean realized that he could see his own hand on the rifle in front of his face, and then the short thick barrels appeared before his eyes. He looked beyond them and made out a tendril of smoke from the fire rising out of the Stygian forest towards the lighter pitch of darkness that was the sky through the canopy of bamboo.

The light came on more swiftly, and he saw that there were two crude shelters, one on each side of the fire, low lean-tos not more than waist high, and he thought he saw a movement in one of them, perhaps a recumbent figure rolling over and pulling up a skin blanket over his head.

Again somebody coughed, a thick phlegmy sound. The camp was waking. Sean glanced up the slope and then down into the stream bed. He could see the soft sheen of the water-polished boulders – but nothing of the other two hunters.

The light hardened. Sean closed his eyes for a moment and then opened them again. He could see sharply the support of the roof of the nearest shelter, and dimly beyond it a human shape wrapped in a fur blanket.

'Shooting light in two minutes,' he thought. The others would know it also. All three of them had waited like this in countless dawns beside the rotting carcass of pit or antelope for the leopard to come to the bait. They could judge that magical moment when the sights were crisp enough to make the sure killing shot. This dawn they would wait for Sean before they came in with the Bren and the Stirling.

Again Sean closed his eyes and when he opened them again the figure in the nearest shelter was sitting up and looking towards him. For a gut-swooping instant he thought he had been spotted and he almost fired. Then he checked himself as the head turned away from him.

Abruptly the figure threw the fur blanket aside and stood up, crouching under the low roof of the shelter.

Sean saw it was a woman, one of the Mau Mau camp followers, but for Sean just as cruel and depraved as any of her menfolk. She stepped out into the open beside the dead fire wearing only a short kilt of some pale material. Her breasts were high and pointed and her skin smooth and glossy as newly mined anthracite in the soft dawn light.

She came directly towards where Sean lay, and though her gait was still clumsy and unsteady with sleep, he saw that she was young and comely. A few more paces and she would stumble over him, but then she stopped and yawned and her teeth were very white, gleaming in the soft grey light.

She lifted her kilt around her waist and squatted facing Sean, spreading her knees and bowing her head slightly to watch herself as she began to urinate. Her water splashed noisily and the sharp ammoniacal tang of it made Sean's nostrils flare.

She was so close that he did not have to lift the Gibbs to his shoulder. He shot her in the stomach. The heavy rifle bounded in his grip and the bullet picked the girl up and while she was in the air it broke her in half, blowing a hole through her spine into which her own head would have fitted, and she folded up, loose and floppy as a suit of discarded clothing as she fell back onto the muddy forest floor.

Sean fired the second barrel as one of the other Mau Mau bolted out of the nearest shelter. The Gibbs made a sound like the slamming of a great steel door, and the man was hurled back into the shelter with half his chest torn away.

Sean had two more cartridges held between the fingers of his left hand, and

as he opened the breech of the Gibbs the spent brass cases pinged away over his shoulder and he slid the fresh cartridges into the empty breeches and closed the rifle again in the same movement.

The Bren and the Stirling were firing now. Their muzzle flashes were bright and pretty as fairy lights in the gloom, twinkling and sparkling, and the bullets went *frip! frip! frip!* amongst the leaves and sang shrilly as they ricocheted into the forest.

Sean shot again and the Gibbs cannoned down another naked figure, knocking him flat against the soft earth as though he had been run down by a locomotive. And again he shot, but this one was a snap shot and the Mau Mau jinked just as the Gibbs thundered. The bullet hit him in the shoulder joint and blew his right arm off so it hung by a tatter of torn flesh and flapped against his side as he spun around. Raymond's Stirling buzzed and cut him down.

Sean reloaded and shot left and right, clean kills with each barrel and by the time he had reloaded again the camp was silent, and the Bren and the Stirling had ceased firing.

Nothing moved. All three men were deadly natural shots, and the range was point blank. Sean waited a full five minutes. Only a fool walked directly up to dangerous game no matter how dead it appeared to be. Then he rose cautiously to his knees with the rifle at high port across his chest.

The last Mau Mau broke. He had been feigning dead in the far shelter, and he had judged his moment finely, waiting until the attackers relaxed and began to move. He flushed like a jack rabbit and shot into the bamboo on the far side of the clearing. Alistair's Bren was blanketed by the wall of the nearest shelter but he fired nevertheless and the bullets futilely thrashed the hut. From the river bank Ray had a clearer shot, but he was a fraction of a second slow, the cold had brought out the malaria in his blood and his hand shook. The bamboo absorbed the light 9 mm bullets as though he had fired into a haystack.

For the first ten paces the running Mau Mau was screened from Sean's view by the wall of the nearest hut, and then Sean caught only a flickering glimpse of him as he dived into the bamboo, but already Sean was on him, swinging the stubby double barrels as though he were taking a right-hand passing shot on a driven francolin. Although he could no longer see his quarry in the dense bamboo, he continued his swing on the line of the man's run, instinctively leading him. The Gibbs gave its angry bellow and red flame blazed from the muzzle.

The huge bullet smashed into the wall of bamboo, and at Sean's side Matatu shouted gleefully, '*Piga!* Hit!' as he heard the bullet tell distinctly on living flesh.

'Take the blood spoor!' Sean commanded and the little Ndorobo loped across the clearing. But it was not necessary: the Mau Mau lay where he had dropped. The bullet had ploughed through bamboo, leaf and stem, without being deflected an inch from its track.

Ray and Alistair came into the camp, weapons ready, and picked over the bodies. One of the other Mau Mau women was still breathing, though bloody bubbles seethed on her lips, and Ray shot her in the temple with the Sten.

'Make sure none of them got away,' Sean ordered Matatu in Swahili.

The little Ndorobo made a quick circuit of the encampment to check for outgoing spoor, and then came back grinning. 'All here.' He gloated. 'All dead'. Sean tossed the Gibbs to him and drew the ivory-handled hunting-knife from the sheath on his belt.

'Damn it, laddie,' Ray Harris protested as Sean walked back to where the body of the first girl lay. 'You are the bloody end, man.' He had seen Sean do this before and although Ray Harris was a hard, callous man who for thirty years had made his living out of blood and gunfire, still he gagged as Sean squatted over the corpse and stropped the blade on the palm of his hand.

'You are getting soft, old man.' Sean grinned at him. 'You know they make beautiful tobacco pouches,' he said, and took the dead girl's breast in his hand, pulling the skin taut for the stroke of the knife blade.

* * *

Shasa found Garry in the boardroom. He was always there twenty minutes before any of the other directors arrived, arranging his piles of computer print-out sheets and other notes around hm and going over his facts and figures for one last time before the meeting began. Shasa and Centaine had argued before appointing Garry to the board of Courtney Mining.

'You can ruin a pony by pushing him too hard too soon.'

'We aren't talking about a polo pony,' Centaine had replied tartly. 'And it's not a case of pushing. He's got the bit between his teeth, to continue your chosen metaphor, Shasa, and if we try and hold him back we will either discourage him or drive him out on his own. Now is the time to give him a bit of slack rein.'

'But you made me wait much longer.'

'You were a late-blooming rose, and the war and all that business held you up. At Garry's age you were still flying Hurricanes and chasing around Abyssinia.'

So Garry had gone on the board, and like everything else in his life he had taken it very seriously indeed. Now he looked up as his father confronted him down the length of the boardroom.

'I heard you have been borrowing money on your own bat,' Shasa accused.

Garry removed his spectacles, polished them diligently, held them up to the light and then replaced them on his large Courtney nose, all to gain time in which to compose his reply.

'Only one person knows about that. The manager of the Adderly Street branch of Standard Bank. He could lose his job if he blabbed about my personal business.'

'You forget that both Nana and I are on the board of the Standard Bank. All loans of over a million pounds come up before us for approval.'

'Rand,' Garry corrected his father pedantically. 'Two million rand – the pound is history.'

'Thanks,' Shasa said grimly. 'I'll try to move with the times. Now how about this two million rand you have borrowed?'

'A straightforward transaction, Dad. I put up my shares in the Shasaville township as collateral, and the bank lent me two million rand.'

'What are you going to do with it? That's a small fortune.' Shasa was one of the few men in the country who would qualify that amount with that particular adjective, and Garry looked mildly relieved.

'As a matter of fact, I have used half a million to buy up fifty-one per cent of

the issued shareholding of Alpha Centauri Estates, and loaned the company another half million to get it out of trouble.'

'Alpha Centauri?' Shasa looked mystified.

'The company owns some of the prime property on the Witwatersrand and here in the Cape Peninsula. It was worth almost twenty-six million before the crash at Sharpeville.'

'And now it's worth zero,' Shasa suggested, and before Garry could protest. 'What have you done with the other million?'

'Gold shares – Anglos and Vaal Reefs. At the fire sale prices I paid for them they are returning almost twenty-six per cent. The dividends will pay the interest on the entire bank loan.'

Shasa sat down in his seat at the head of the boardroom table and studied his son carefully. He should have been conditioned by now, but Garry still managed to surprise Shasa. It was an imaginative but neatly logical coup, and if it had not been his own son, Shasa would have been impressed. As it was, he felt duty bound to find flaws in it.

'What about your Shasaville shares – you are taking an awful chance.'

Garry looked puzzled. 'I don't have to explain it to you, Pater. You taught me. Shasaville is tied up. We can't sell or develop aggressively until land values recover, so I've used my shares to take full advantage of the crash.'

'What if land values never recover?' Shasa demanded relentlessly.

'If they don't, it will mean the country is finished anyway. I will lose my share of nothing which is nothing. If they do recover, I will be in profit twenty or thirty million.'

Shasa picked at that for a while and then changed his angle of attack. 'Why didn't you come to me to borrow the money, instead of going behind my back?'

Garry grinned at him and tried to smooth down the crest of wiry black hair that stuck up on his crown. 'Because you would have given me a list of five hundred reasons why not, just as you are doing now. Besides, I wanted to do this one on my own. I wanted to prove to you that I'm not a kid any more.'

Shasa twiddled the gold pen on the pad in front of him and when he could think of no other criticism, he grumbled, 'You don't want to get too damned clever for your own good. There is a line between good business sense and outright gambling.'

'How do you tell the difference?' Garry asked. For a moment Shasa thought he was being facetious and then he realized that as usual Garry was deadly serious. He was leaning forward eagerly waiting for his father to explain, and he really wanted to know.

Shasa was saved by the entry of the other senior directors: Centaine on the arm of Dr Twentyman-Jones and David Abrahams arguing amiably but respectfully with his father, and thankfully he let the subject drop. Once or twice during the meeting he glanced down the table at Garry, who was following all the discussion with a rapt expression, the light from the picture window reflecting a miniature image of the crest of Table Mountain in the lenses of his spectacles. When all the business on the agenda had been completed and Centaine had started to rise to lead them through to the executive dining-room, Shasa arrested them.

'Madame Courtney and gentlemen, one additional piece of business. Mr Garry Courtney and I have been discussing the general state of the property market. We both feel that property and equities are very much undervalued at the moment and that the company should take advantage of this fact, but I'd

like him to tell you in his own words and to put forward certain proposals. Would you oblige us please, Mr Courtney?'

It was Shasa's own way of giving the lad a jolt and cutting him back a little. In the six months since his elevation, Garry had never been called upon to address the full board and now Shasa dropped it on him without warning and sat back with vindictive relish in his wing-backed leather chairman's throne and folded his arms.

At the bottom of the table Garry blushed furiously, and glanced longingly at the stinkwood door, his only escape, before giving the traditional salutation to his fellow directors.

'Ma-Ma-dame Courtney and ge-ge-gentlemen.' He stopped and threw his father a pitiful look of appeal, but when he received a stern uncompromising frown in return, he took a deep breath and launched into it. He stumbled once or twice, but when first Abe Abrahams and then Centaine shot cutting questions at him, he forgot about his stutter and talked for forty-five minutes.

At the end they were silent for a while, and then David Abrahams said, 'I should like to propose that we appoint Mr Garrick Courtney to prepare a list of specific proposals to follow up the presentation that he has just made to this meeting, and to report back to us at an extraordinary meeting early next week, at a time convenient to all members of the board.'

Centaine seconded, and it was adopted unanimously, and then David Abrahams ended, 'I should like the minutes to record the board's gratitude to Mr Courtney for his lucid address and to thank him for bringing these considerations to the board's attention.'

The glow of achievement and recognition lasted Garry all the way down in the elevator to the basement garage where his MG stood in his private parking bay beside Shasa's Jaguar. It stayed with him all the way down Adderley Street to the lonely skyscraper of the Sanlam building which stood on the open ground of the foreshore that had been reclaimed from the sea. Even going up in the lift to the twentieth floor of the Sanlam building he still felt tall and important and decisive. Only when he entered the reception area of Gantry, Carmichael and Associates did the vital glow begin to fade, and his stiff van Heusen collar bit painfully into the corded muscles of his bull neck.

The two pretty young girls at the desk showed him the full amount of deference due to one of the partnership's important clients, but by this time Garry was too nervous to take advantage of the chair he was offered and he wandered around the lobby pretending to admire the tall vases of proteas while surreptitiously checking his image in the floor-to-ceiling mirrors behind the floral display.

He had paid forty guineas off the peg for the double-breasted suit in his favourite Prince of Wales check, but the swell of his chest muscles made the lapels flare unevenly and the material rucked up around his biceps. He yanked at the cuffs in an attempt to smooth the sleeves, and then abandoned that effort and instead concentrated on trying to press his hair flat with the heel of his palm. He started guiltily as he saw in the mirror the door to the partners' sanctum open and Holly Carmichael come striding into the reception lobby.

As Garry turned to face her, all his recent bravado and confidence collapsed around him and he gawked at her. It was impossible but she was even more poised and chic than the vivid image of her he had carried with him since their last meeting.

Today she was wearing a blue and white striped Chanel suit with a pleated

skirt that swirled around her calves, allowing just a flash of her perfect rounded knees as she came towards him. Her lightly tanned legs in sheer nylon had the patina of polished ivory, and her ankles and her wrists in the cuffs of the Chanel suit were elegantly turned, her feet and hands narrow and yet perfectly proportioned to her long willowy limbs.

She was smiling and Garry felt the same sensuous vertigo that he sometimes experienced after bench pressing five times his own body-weight of iron. Her teeth were opalescent, and as her mouth formed his name and smiled, he watched it with breathless fascination.

She was as tall as he was, but he knew he could lift her with one hand and he quivered at the almost sacrilegious thought of taking this divine creature in his hands.

'Mr Courtney, I hope we haven't kept you waiting.' She took his arm, and led him towards her office. He felt like a performing bear on a chain beside her grace and lightness. The light touch of her fingers on his arm burned like a branding iron.

Her hair was streaked with a shading of all the colours of blond from platinum to dark burnt honey, and it fell in a lustrous cascade to just above the padded shoulders of the Chanel suit, and every time she moved her head he caught the perfume of those shining tresses and his stomach muscles contracted.

Her fingers were still on his biceps and she was talking directly into his face, still smiling. Her breath smelled like a flower and her mouth was so beautiful and soft and red that he felt guilty looking at it, as though he were spying on some secret and intimate part of her body. He tore his eyes from her mouth and raised them to her eyes. His heart jumped against his ribs like a maniac in a padded cell for one eye was sky blue and the other violet flecked with gold. It gave her face a striking asymmetry, not exactly a squint but a disconcerting myopic imbalance and Garry's legs felt as weak as if he had run ten miles.

'I have something for you at last,' Holly Carmichael said, and led him into her office.

The long room reflected her own extraordinary style, which had attracted Garry to her work long before he had met her. He had first seen an example of it in the *Institute of Architects Year-book*. Holly Carmichael had won the 1961 award of the Institute for a beach house on the dunes overlooking Plettenburg Bay that she had designed as a holiday home for one of the Witwatersrand insurance magnates. She used wood and stone and material in a blend that was at the same time modern and classical, that married space and shape in a natural harmony that excited the eye and yet gave solace to the soul.

Her office was decorated in soft mulberry and ethereal blue, functional and yet both restful and unmistakably feminine. The delicate pastel drawings on all four walls were her own work.

In the centre of the floor on a low table stood a miniature-scale reproduction of the Shasaville estate, as she visualized it after development was complete. Holly led Garry to it and stood back while he circled it slowly, studying it from every angle.

She watched the change come over him.

All the gawkiness was gone. Even the shape of his body seemed to change. It was imbued with the same kind of massive grace as that of the bull in the arena tensing for the charge.

Holly researched the background of all her clients, in order to better anticipate their requirements. With this one she had taken special care. The

word in the marketplace was that, despite appearances, Garrick Courtney was a formidable presence and had already demonstrated his acumen and courage by procuring the Shasaville title and a controlling interest in Alpha Centauri Estates.

Her accountant had drawn up an approximate list of his assets which included, along with his property interests, considerable equity in blue chip gold companies and the Courtney mining shares which he had acquired from his family when he was appointed to the board of that company.

More significant was the prevailing view that both Centaine and Shasa Courtney had given up on his brothers, and decided that Garrick Courtney was their hope for the future. He was the heir apparent to the Courtney millions and nobody knew the sum total of those – two hundred million, five hundred million – not inconceivably a billion rand. Holly Carmichael shivered slightly at the thought.

As she watched him now she saw not a large bumbling young man in steel-rimmed spectacles, who made an expensive suit of fine wool look like a bag of laundry, and whose hair stood up in a startled tuft at the crown. She saw power.

Power fascinated Holly Carmichael, power in all its forms – wealth, reputation, influence and physical power. She shivered slightly as she recalled the feel of the muscle under his sleeve.

Holly was thirty-two years of age, almost ten years senior to him, and her divorce would count heavily against her. Both Centaine and Shasa Courtney were conservative and old-fashioned.

'They'll have to be good to stop me,' she told herself. 'I get what I want – and this is what I want, but it's not going to be a push-over.'

Then she considered the effect she had on Garry Courtney. She knew he was besotted with her. The first part would be easy. Without any effort at all she had already enmeshed him, she could enslave him as readily. After that would come the difficult part. She thought of Centaine Courtney and all she had heard about her, and she shivered again, this time with neither pleasure nor excitement.

Garry stopped in front of her. Although their eyes were on a level, he now seemed to tower over her as he glowered at her. A moment before she had felt herself perfectly in control, now suddenly she was uncertain.

'I've seen what you can do when you really try,' he said. 'I want you to try for me. I don't want second best. I don't want this.'

Holly stared at him in amazement. She had not even contemplated his rejection, certainly not in such brutal terms. Her shock persisted a moment longer and then was replaced with anger.

'If that is your estimate of my work, Mr Courtney, I suggest you find yourself another architect,' she told him in a cold fury and he didn't even flinch.

'Come here,' he ordered. 'Look at it from this angle. You've stuck that roof on the shopping centre without any regard to the view from the houses on this slope of the hill. And look here. You could have used the fairways of the golf course to enhance the aspect of these flagship properties instead of shutting them off the way you have.'

He had taken hold of her arm, and though she knew he was not extending even a small part of his strength, still the potential she could feel in his fingers frightened her a little. She no longer felt confident and patronizing as he pointed out the flaws in her design. While he spoke she knew that he was right. Instinctively she had been aware of the defects he was now exposing, but she

had not taken the trouble to find solutions to them. She had not expected somebody so young and inexperienced to be so discriminating – she had treated him like a doting boy who would accept anything she offered. Her anger was directed at herself as much as at him.

He finished his criticism at last and she said softly, 'I'll return your deposit and we can tear up the contract.'

'You signed the contract and accepted the deposit, Mrs Carmichael. Now I want you to deliver. I want something beautiful and startling and right. I want something that only you can give me.'

She had no answer, and his manner changed, he became peculiarly gentle and solicitous.

'I didn't mean to insult you. I think at the least you are the very best, and I want you to prove me right – please.'

She turned away from him and went to her drawing-board at the end of the room, slipped out of her jacket and tossed it over the desk and picked up one of her pencils.

With the pencil poised over the blank sheet, she said, 'It seems that I've got a lot of lost ground to make up. Here we go – ' and she drew the first bold decisive line across the sheet. 'At least we know now what we don't want. Let's find out what we do want. Let's start with the shopping centre.'

He came to stand behind her and watched in silence for almost twenty minutes before she glanced back at him with the violet eye glinting through the veil of shining blond hair. She didn't have to ask the question.

'Yes,' he nodded.

'Don't go away,' she said. 'When you are near I can feel your mood and judge your response.'

He took off his jacket and threw it beside hers over the desk top, and he stood beside her in his shirtsleeves with his hands thrust into his trouser pockets and his shoulders hunched. He remained absolutely still, his concentration monumental, and yet his presence seemed to inspire her to tap the mystical springs of her talent. At last she saw in her mind how it should have been and she began to rough it out, her pencil flying and flicking over the sheet.

When the day faded, he went to close the curtains and switch on the overhead lights. It was after eight when she at last threw down her pencil and turned to him. 'That's the feeling I want to give it. You were right – the first attempt wasn't worthy.'

'Yes, I was right in one other respect. You are the very best.' He picked up his jacket and shrugged it over his massive shoulders, and she felt a tingle of dismay. She didn't want him to go yet, she knew when he did she would feel exhausted and spent. The effort of creation had drained her resources.

'You can't send me home to begin cooking at this hour,' she said. 'That would be the sadistic act of a truly cruel taskmaster.'

Suddenly all his confidence evaporated, and he blushed and mumbled something inaudible. She knew she would have to take charge from here.

'The least you can do is feed the slave. How about offering me dinner, Mr Courtney?'

She created her usual stir of masculine interest as she preceded Garry into the restaurant, and she was glad he had noticed. She was surprised by the aplomb with which he discussed the wine list with the *maître* until she remembered that Weltevreden was one of the leading wineries of the Cape of Good Hope.

During dinner their conversation was serious, and she was relieved not to

have to endure the usual banalities of a first date. They discussed the Sharpeville crisis and its implications, social and economic, and she was amazed at the depth of his political insight until she remembered that his father was a minister in Verwoerd's cabinet. He had a ringside seat.

'If it wasn't for that Prince of Wales check suit and those ghastly steel-framed spectacles,' she thought, 'and the crest of hair that makes him look like Woody Woodpecker – '

When he asked her to dance she had misgivings. They were the only couple on the tiny circular floor, and there were a dozen people in the room she knew. However, the moment he put his arm around her waist she relaxed. Despite his bulk he was agile and light on his feet with an excellent sense of timing, and she began to enjoy herself, until abruptly his dancing style changed and he held her differently. For a while she was puzzled. She attempted to maintain the close contact of hips which had enabled her to anticipate his moves, and only then she became aware of his arousal. She was at first amused and then despite herself intrigued. Like the rest of him it was massive and hard. She played a little game of brushing lightly against him and withdrawing, all the while chatting casually and feigning total ignorance of his predicament. Afterwards he drove her in the MG to where her own car was parked. She hadn't ridden in an open sports car since her varsity days and the wind in her hair gave her a nostalgic thrill.

He insisted on following her Mercedes back to Bantry Bay to see her safely home and they said goodnight on the pavement outside her apartment block. She considered inviting him up for coffee, but her sure instinct warned her to protect the shining image of her that he so obviously had conceived.

Instead she told him, 'I'll have some more drawings for you to look at by the end of next week.'

This time she put everything of her talent into the preliminary sketches, and she knew they were good. He came to her office again and they worked over them until late and then dined together. It was Thursday night and the restaurant was half empty. They had the dance floor to themselves and this time she worked her hips lightly and cunningly against him as they moved.

When she said goodnight outside her apartment block, she asked, 'I suppose you will be at the Met on Saturday?'

The Metropolitan Handicap was the premier race on the Cape turf calendar.

'I don't race,' Garry replied reluctantly. 'We are polo people, and Nana, my grandmother, doesn't approve of me – ' he stopped himself as he realized how callow that sounded and he ended, ' – well, somehow I've just never got around to racing.'

'Well, it's about time you did,' she said firmly. 'And I need a partner for Saturday – that's if you don't object.'

Garry sang all the way home to Weltevreden, bellowing happily into the rushing night air as he drove the MG through the curves and dips of the mountain road.

It took Garry a while to understand that the actual racing was not the main attraction of the meeting. It was secondary to the fashion show and the conplicated social interaction of the racegoers.

Amongst the bizarre and outrageous creations that some of the women wore, Holly's floating blue silk and the wide brimmed hat with a single real pink rose on the brim were elegant and understated, but drew envious glances from the other women. Garry discovered that he knew nearly everybody in the members'

enclosure; many of them were friends of his family, and Holly introduced him to those he did not know. They all reacted to the Courtney name, and Holly was subtly attentive, drawing him into conversation with these strangers until he felt at ease.

They made a remarkable couple, 'Beauty and the Beast', as one of the unkind wags suggested, and a buzz of gossip followed them around the ring: 'Holly has been out cradle-snatching', and 'Centaine will have her burned at the stake'.

Garry was totally oblivious to the stir they were creating, and once the horses were brought into the ring for the first race, he was in his element. Horses were part of the life at Weltevreden. Shasa had carried him on the saddle before he could walk, and he had a natural eye for horseflesh.

The first race was a maiden handicap, and the betting was wide open as none of these two-year-olds had raced before. Garry singled out a black colt in the parade. 'I like his chest and legs,' he told Holly and she checked his number on the card.

'Rhapsody,' she said. 'There has never been a good horse with an ugly name – and he's trained by Miller and ridden by Tiger Wright.'

'I don't know about that, but I do know that he is in peak condition and he wants to work,' Garry told her. 'Just look at him sweating already.'

'Let's have a bet on him,' Holly suggested, and Garry looked dubious. The family strictures against gambling echoed in his ears, but he didn't want to offend Holly or appear childish in her eyes.

'What do I do?' he asked.'

'You see those gangsters standing up there?' She pointed at the line of bookmakers. 'You pick any one of them, give him your money and say, "Rhapsody to win."' She handed Gerry a ten-rand note. 'Let's dib ten each.'

Garry was appalled. Ten rand was a great deal of money. It was one thing to borrow two million on a legitimate business scheme, but quite another thing to hand ten to a stranger in a loud suit with a cigar. Reluctantly he produced his wallet.

Rhapsody was in the ruck at the turn, but as they came clear of the bend, Tiger Wright steered him wide and then asked him to run. The colt jumped away and caught the leaders in front of the stand where Holly was hopping up and down and holding her hat on with one hand.He was two lengths clear at the post and Holly threw both arms around Garry's neck and kissed him in front of ten thousand beady eyes.

As Garry handed over her share of their winnings, she said, 'Oh, wouldn't it be fun to own one's very own racehorse.'

He phoned her apartment at six o'clock the following morning.

'Garry?' she mumbled. 'It's Sunday. You can't do this to me – not at six o'clock.'

'This time I've got something to show you,' he said, and his enthusiasm was so infectious that she agreed weakly.

'Give me an hour to wake up properly.'

He drove her down to the curving beach of False Bay beyond Muizenberg and parked at the top of the dunes. Forty horses with their apprentice jockeys and grooms were cantering along the edge of soft white sand or wading bareback in the curling green surf. Garry led her down to the group of four men who were supervising the training and introduced her.

'This is Mr Miller.' The trainer and his assistants looked at Holly approvingly. She wore a pink scarf around her forehead but her thick blond hair fell

freely down the back of her neck and the short marine peajacket emphasized the length and shape of her legs in the ski pants and calf boots.

The trainer whistled to one of his apprentices and only when he turned the colt out of the circle of horses did Holly recognize it.

'Rhapsody,' she cried.

'Congratulations, Mrs Carmichael,' the trainer said. 'He's going to do us all proud.'

'I don't understand.' She was bewildered.

'Well,' Garry explained, 'you said it would be fun to own your own horse, and it is your birthday on the twelfth of next month. Happy birthday.'

She stared at him in confusion, wondering how he knew that date and how she was going to tell him that she couldn't possibly accept such an extravagant gift. But Garry was so rosy with self-satisfaction, waiting to be thanked and applauded, that she thought, 'And why not – just this once! The hell with conventions!'

She kissed him for the second time, while the others stood around and grinned knowingly.

In the MG on the way home she told him. 'Garry, I cannot possibly accept Rhapsody. It's much too generous of you.' His disappointment was transparent and pathetic. 'But,' she went on, 'I could accept half of him. You keep the other half and we will race him together, as partners. We could even register our own racing colours.' She was amazed at her own genius. A living creature owned jointly would cement the bond between them. 'Let all the Courtneys rant and rave. This one is mine,' she promised herself.

When they reached her apartment, she told him, 'Park there, next to the Mercedes.' And she took his arm and led him to the elevator.

Like her office her apartment was an expression of her artistry and sense of form and colour. The balcony was high above the rocks, and the surf crashed and sucked back and forth below them so that it seemed they stood on the prow of an ocean liner.

Holly brought a bottle of champagne and two tulip glasses from the kitchen, 'Open it!' she ordered and held the glasses while he spilled the creaming wine into them.

'Here's to Rhapsody,' she gave him the toast.

While she made a huge bowl of salad for their brunch, she instructed him in the art of mixing a dressing for it.

They drank the rest of the champagne with the salad and then sprawled on the thick carpet of her living-room floor, surrounded by books of silk samples as they discussed their racing colours, and they finally decided on a vivid fuchsia pink.

'It will look beautiful against Rhapsody's glossy black skin.' She looked up at him. He was kneeling beside her, and her instinct told her that this was the precise moment.

She rolled slowly on to her back and hooded those bi-coloured eyes invitingly, but still he hesitated and she had to reach up with one hand and draw his head down to hers, and then his strength shocked her.

She felt helpless as an infant in his embrace, but after a while when she was certain that he would not hurt her, she began to enjoy the sensation of physical helplessness in the storm of his kisses and let him take control for a while until she sensed that he needed guidance once again.

She bit him on the cheek and when he released her and started back in

surprise and consternation, she broke from his grip and darted to the bedroom door. As she looked back he was still kneeling in the centre of the floor, staring after her in confusion, and she laughed and left the door open.

He came in like a bull at the cape, but she stopped him dead with another kiss and, holding his mouth with hers, unbuttoned his shirt and slipped her hand into the opening. She was unprepared for the thick pelt of springing dark hair that covered his chest, and her own reaction to it. All her other men had been smooth and soft. She believed that was her preference, but now her sexual arousal was instantaneous and her loins swam with excitement.

She dominated him with her lips and fingertips, not allowing him to move while she undressed him and then, as the last of his clothing fell around his ankles, she exclaimed aloud, 'Oh dear God!' and then caught his wrist to prevent him covering himself with his hands.

None of her other men had been like this, and for a moment she felt uncertain of her ability to cope with him. Then her wanting overwhelmed any doubts and she led him to the bed. She made him lie there while she undressed in front of him, and every time he tried to cover himself she ordered him. 'No! I like to look at you.'

He was so different, all muscle and hair: his concave belly was rippled with muscle like the sand on a wind-swept beach and his limbs were clad in muscle. She wanted to begin, but she wanted even more to ensure that this would be something that he would never forget, that would make him hers for all his life.

'Don't move,' she whispered, and naked she stooped over him. She let her breasts swing forward and her nipples just brush the curls on his chest, and she touched the tip of her tongue to the corner of his eye and then ran it down slowly to his mouth.

'I have never done this before,' he whispered hoarsely. 'I don't know how.'

'Shh, my darling, don't talk,' she whispered into his mouth, but the idea of his virginity elated her.

'He's mine,' she told herself triumphantly. 'After today he will be mine for ever!' And she ran her tongue down across his chin, down over his throat, until she felt him thrust up hard and thick between her dangling breasts and then she reached down and took him in both hands.

It was darkening in the room when at last they lay exhausted. Outside the sun had sunk into the Atlantic and left the evening sky infuriated by its going. Garry lay with his cheek cushioned on her breasts. Like an unweaned child he could not get enough of them. Holly was proud of her bosom and his fascination with it amused and flattered her. She smiled contentedly as he nuzzled against her.

His spectacles lay on the bedside table and she studied his face in the half light. She liked the big virile nose and the determined line of his jaw, but the steel-framed spectacles had to go, she decided, those and the Prince of Wales checks which emphasized the squatness of his body. On Monday her first concern would be to find out from Ian Gantry, her partner, the name of his personal tailor. She had already chosen the pattern – crisp grey or distinguished blue, with a vertical chalk stripe that would make him taller and slimmer. His reconstruction would be one of her most challenging and rewarding projects and she looked forward to it.

'You are wonderful,' Garry murmured. 'I've never met anybody like you in my life.' Holly smiled again and stroked his thick dark hair. It sprang up under her fingers.

'You've got a double crown,' she told him softly. 'That means you are lucky and brave.'

'I didn't know that,' he said, which was not surprising, as Holly had invented it as she said it.

'Oh yes,' she assured him. 'But it also means that we have to grow our hair a little fuller over the crown, otherwise it will stand up in a tuft like this.'

'I didn't know that either.' Garry reached up and felt his tuft. 'I'll try that, but you'll have to tell me how long to let it grow – I don't want to look like a hippy.'

'Of course.'

'You are wonderful,' he repeated. 'I mean, totally wonderful.'

* * *

'The woman is obviously a gold-digger,' Centaine said firmly.

'We can't be sure of that, Mater,' Shasa demurred. 'I have heard that she is a damned good architect.'

'That has absolutely nothing to do with it. She is old enough to be his mother. She is after one thing, and one thing only. We'll have to put a stop to this immediately. Otherwise it could get out of hand. It's the talk of the town, all my friends are gloating. They were at Kelvin Grove on Saturday, smooching all over the dance floor.'

'Oh, I think it will blow over,' Shasa suggested. 'Just so long as we take no notice.'

'Garry hasn't slept at Weltevreden for a week. The woman is as blatant and shameless – ' Centaine broke off and shook her head. 'You'll have to speak to her.'

'Me?' Shasa raised an eyebrow.

'You are good with females. I'd be sure to lose my temper with the hussy.'

Shasa sighed, although secretly he welcomed the excuse to have a look at this Holly Carmichael. He couldn't imagine what Garry's taste in women would be. The lad had never given any indications before. Shasa imagined sensible shoes and horn-rimmed glasses, fat and fortyish, serious and erudite – and he shuddered. 'All right, Mater, I'll warn her off, and if that doesn't work we can always send Garry down to the vet to be fixed.'

'I wish you wouldn't joke about something as worrying as this,' said Centaine severely.

Although Holly had been expecting it for almost a month, when the call finally came the shock was unmitigated. Shasa Courtney had addressed the Businesswomen's Club the previous year, so she recognized his voice instantly, and was glad that it was he rather than Centaine Courtney she had to contend with.

'Mrs Carmichael, my son Garry has shown me some of your preliminary sketches for the Shasaville township. As you know, Courtney Mining and Finance are considerable shareholders in the project. Although Garry is responsible for the development, I hoped we could meet to exchange a few ideas.'

She had suggested her own office, but Shasa neatly thwarted her attempt to choose the field of battle and sent a chauffeur to bring her out to Weltevreden

in the Rolls. She realized that she was being deliberately placed in surroundings which were intended to overpower her, and show her up in the splendour of a world in which there was no place for her. So she went to endless pains with her dress and appearance, and as she was ushered into Shasa Courtney's study she saw him start and knew that first blood was hers. She made the room with all its treasures seem as though it had been designed around her, and Shasa Courtney's cool supercilious smile faded as he came to take her hand.

'What a magnificent Turner,' she said. 'I always think he must have been an early riser. The sunlight only has that golden lustre in the early morning.' His expression changed again as he realized there was depth below her striking exterior.

They circled the room, ostensibly admiring the other paintings, fencing elegantly, testing each other for weakness and finding none, until Shasa deliberately broke the pattern with a direct personal compliment to fluster her.

'You have the most remarkable eyes,' he said, and watched her keenly to see how she would react. She counter-attacked instantly.

'Garry calls them amethyst and sapphire.' She had wrongfooted him neatly. He had expected her to avoid that name until he raised it.

'Yes, I understand the two of you have been working closely.'

He went to the ivory-inlaid table on which glasses and decanters had been set out.

'May I offer you one of our sherries? We are very proud of them.'

He brought her the glass and looked into those extraordinary eyes. 'The little devil,' he thought ruefully. 'He has done it again. Who would have expected Garry to come up with something like this!'

She sipped the wine. 'I like it,' she said. 'It's dry as flint without any astringency.'

He inclined his head slightly to acknowledge the accuracy of her judgment.

'I can see that it would be fruitless to attempt to obfuscate. I didn't ask you here to discuss the Shasaville project.'

'That's good,' she said. 'Because I didn't even bother to bring the latest drawings.'

He laughed delightedly. 'Let's sit down and get comfortable.'

She chose the Louis Quatorze chair with Aubusson embroidered upholstery because she had seen the twin to it in the Victoria and Albert Museum, and she crossed one ankle over the other and watched him struggle to get his eyes back up again.

'I had fully intended to buy you off,' he said. 'I realize, after having met you, that would have been a mistake.'

She said nothing, but watched him over the rim of the glass, and her foot swung like a metronome, with the same ominous rhythm.

'I wondered what price to set,' he went on. 'And the figure of one hundred thousand came to mind.'

The foot kept swinging and despite himself Shasa glanced down at her calf and exquisitely turned ankle.

'Of course, that was ludicrous,' he went on, still watching her foot in the Italian leather court shoe. 'I realize now that I should have considered at least half a million.'

He was trying to find her price, and he looked back at her face, searching for the first glint of avarice, but it was hard to concentrate. Sapphire and amethyst,

forsooth, Garry's hormones must be boiling out of his ears – and Shasa felt a stab of envy.

'Naturally, I was thinking in pounds sterling. I haven't adjusted to this rand business yet.'

'How fortunate, Mr Courtney,' she said, 'that you decided not to insult us both. This way we can be friends. I'd prefer that.'

All right, that didn't work out the way he had planned. He set down his sherry glass. 'Garry is still a child,' he changed tack.

She shook her head. 'He's a man. It just needed somebody to convince him of that. It wasn't difficult to do.'

'He doesn't know his own mind.'

'He is one of the most definite and determined men I have ever met. He knows exactly what he wants and he will do anything to get it.' She waited a moment to let the challenge contained in those words become clearer, then she repeated softly, 'Anything.'

'Yes,' he agreed softly. 'That's a Courtney family trait. We will do anything to get what we want – or to destroy anything that stands in our way.' He paused, just as she had done and then repeated quietly, 'Anything.'

'You had three sons, Shasa Courtney. You have one left. Are you willing to take that chance?'

He reared back in his chair and stared at her. She was unprepared for the agony that she saw in his expression and for a moment she thought she had gone too far. Then he subsided slowly.

'You fight hard and dirty,' he acknowledged sadly.

'When it is worthwhile.' She knew it was dangerous with an opponent of this calibre, but she felt sorry for him. 'And for me this is worthwhile.'

'For you, yes, I can see that – but for Garry?'

'I think I owe you complete honesty. At the beginning it was a little bit of daring. I was intrigued by his youth – that in itself can be devastatingly appealing. And by the other obvious attractions which you have hinted at.'

'The Courtney empire and his place in it.'

'Yes. I would have been less than human if that hadn't interested me. That's the way it started, but almost immediately it began to change.'

'In what way?'

'I began to understand his enormous potential, and my own influence in developing it fully. Haven't you noticed any change in him in the three months since we have been together? Can you truly tell me my influence on him has been detrimental?'

Despite himself Shasa smiled. 'The pinstripe suits and the horn-rimmed glasses. They are a vast improvement, I'll admit.'

'Those are only the unimportant outward signs of the important inward changes. In three months Garry has become a mature and confident man, he has discovered many of his own strengths and talents and virtues, not the least of which is a warm and loving disposition. With my help he will discover all the others.'

'So you see yourself in the role of architect still, building a marble palace out of clay bricks.'

'Don't mock him.' She was angry, protective and defensive as a lioness. 'He is probably the best of all the Courtneys and I am probably the best thing that will ever happen to him in his life.'

He stared at her, and exclaimed with wonder as it dawned upon him. 'You love him – you really love him.'

'So you understand at last.'

She stood up and turned towards the door.

'Holly,' he said, and the unexpected use of her first name arrested her. She wavered, still pale with anger, and he went on softly, 'I didn't understand, forgive me. I think Garry is a fortunate young man to have found you.' He held out his hand. 'You said we might be friends – is that still possible?'

* * *

Table Bay is wide open to the north-westerly gales that bore in off the wintry grey Atlantic. The ferry took the short steep seas on her bows and lurched over the crests, throwing the spray as high as the stubby masthead.

It was the first time Vicky had ever been at sea and the motion terrified her as nothing on earth had ever done. She clutched the child to her, and stared ahead, but it was difficult to maintain her balance on the hard wooden bench, and thick spray dashed against the porthole and poured over the glass in a wavering mirage that distorted her view. The island looked like some dreadful creature swimming to meet them, and she recalled all the legends of her tribe of the monsters that came out of the sea and devoured any human being found upon the shore.

She was glad that Joseph was with her. Her half-brother had grown into a fine young man. He reminded her of the faded photograph of her grandfather, Mbejane Dinizulu, that her mother kept on the wall of her hut. Joseph had the same broad forehead and wide-spread eyes, and although his nose was not flattened but high-bridged, his clean-shaven chin was rounded and full.

He had just completed his law degree at the black University of Fort Hare, but before he underwent his consecration into the hereditary role of Zulu chieftainship, Vicky had prevailed upon him to accompany her upon the long journey down the length of the sub-continent. As soon as he returned to the district of Ladyburg in Zululand, he would begin his training for the chieftainship. This was not the initiation to which the young men of the Xhosa and the other tribes were forced to submit. Joseph would not suffer the brutal mutilation of ritual circumcision. King Chaka had abolished that custom. He had not tolerated the time that his young warriors wasted in recuperation, which could better be spent in military training.

Joseph stood beside Vicky, balancing easily to the ferry's agitated plunges, and he placed his hand upon her shoulder to reassure her. 'Not much longer,' he murmured. 'We will soon be there.'

Vicky shook her head vehemently, and clutched her son more securely to her bosom. The cold sweat broke out upon her forehead, and waves of nausea assailed her, but she fought them back.

'I am the daughter of a chief,' she told herself. 'And the wife of a king. I will not surrender to womanly weakness.'

The ferry ran out of the gale into the calm waters in the lee of the island, and Vicky drew a long ragged breath and stood up. Her legs were unsteady, and Joseph helped her to the rail.

They stood side by side and stared at the bleak and infamous silhouette of

Robben Island. The name derived from the Dutch word for seal, and the colonies of these animals that the first explorers had discovered upon its barren rocks.

When the fishing and sealing industries based upon the island failed, it was used as a leper colony and a place of banishment for political prisoners, most of them black. Even Makana, the prophet and warrior, who had led the first Xhosa onslaughts against the white settlers cross the great Fish river had been sent here after his capture, and here he had died in 1820, drowned in the roaring seas that beat upon the island as he tried to escape. For fifty years his people had refused to believe he was dead, and to this day his name was a rallying cry for the tribe.

One hundred and forty-three years later, there was another prophet and warrior imprisoned upon the island, and Vicky stared out across the narrowing strip of water at the low square unlovely structure, the new high-security prison for dangerous political prisoners where Moses Gama was now incarcerated. After his stay of execution, Moses had remained on death row at Pretoria Central Prison for almost two years, until finally mitigation of the death sentence to life imprisonment at hard labour had been officially granted by the state president and he had been transferred to the island. Moses was allowed one visit every six months, and Vicky was bringing his son to see him.

The journey had not been easy, for Vicky herself was the subject of a banning order. She had shown herself an enemy of the state by her appearances at Moses' trial, dressed in the colours of the African National Congress, and her inflammatory utterances which were widely reported by the news media.

Even to leave the township of Drake's Farm to which the banning order confined her, she had to obtain a travel permit from the local magistrate. This document set out precisely the terms upon which she was allowed to travel, the exact time which she was required to leave her cottage, the route and the means of transport she must take, the duration of her visit to her husband and the route she must take upon her return journey.

The ferry manoeuvred in towards the jetty and there were uniformed warders to seize the mooring ropes as they were thrown across. Joseph took the boy's hand from her and with his free hand helped Vicky across the narrow gap. They stood together on the wooden boards of the jetty and looked around uncertainly. The warders ignored them as they went on with the business of docking and unloading the ferry.

It was ten minutes before one of them called across to them, 'All right, come this way,' and they followed him up the paved road towards the security block.

The first glimpse that Vicky had of her husband after six months appalled her.

'You are so thin,' she cried.

'I have not been eating very well.' He sat down on the stool facing her through the mesh of the screen. They had developed a cryptic code during the four visits she had been allowed at Pretoria Central, and not eating well meant that he was on another hunger strike.

He smiled at her and his face was skull-like so that his lips had retracted and his teeth were too big for his face. When he placed his hands on the shelf in front of him his wrists protruded from the cuffs of his khaki prison uniform and they were bone covered with a thin layer of skin.

'Let me see my son,' he said, and she drew Matthew to her.

'Greet your father,' she told the boy, and he stared solemnly at Moses through

the grille. The gaunt stranger on the other side of the wire had never picked him up or held him on his lap, had never kissed or fondled him, had never even touched him. The mesh was always between them.

A warder sat beside Moses to see that the visiting rules were strictly observed. The time allowed was one hour, sixty minutes exactly, and only family matters could be discussed – no news of the day, no discussion of prison conditions and especially nothing with a political flavour to it.

One hour of family matters, but they used their code. 'I am sure that my appetite will return once I have news of the family,' Moses told her, 'on paper.' So she knew that he was hunger-striking to be allowed to read the newspapers. Therefore he would not have heard the news about Nelson Mandela.

'The elders have asked *Gundwane* to visit them,' she told him. *Gundwane* was their code name for Mandela. It meant 'cane rat' and the elders were the authorities. He nodded to show that he understood that Mandela had at last been arrested, and he smiled tautly. The information he had given to Manfred De La Rey had been used effectively.

'How are the family members on the farm?' he asked.

'All is well, and they are planting their crops,' Vicky told him, and he understood that the *Umkhonto we Sizwe* teams working out of Puck's Hill had begun their campaign of terror bombings. 'Perhaps you will all be reunited sooner that we think,' she suggested.

'Let's hope so,' Moses agreed. A reunion would mean that the Puck's Hill team would join him here on the island, or take the shorter road to the gallows.

The hour passed too swiftly, and the warder was standing up. 'Time up. Say your goodbyes.'

'I leave my heart with you, my husband,' Vicky told him, and watched the warder lead him away. He did not look back at her, and his gait dragged like that of an exhausted old man.

'It is only the starvation,' she told Joseph as they walked back to the ferry. 'He is still courageous as a lion, but weak from lack of food.'

'He is finished,' Joseph contradicted her quietly. 'The Boers have beaten him. He will never breathe the air of freedom again. He will never see the outside of his prison again.'

'For all of us, born black, this whole country is a prison,' Vicky said fiercely, and Joseph did not reply until they were once more aboard the ferry and running back before the gale, towards the flat-topped mountain whose lower slopes were flecked with white walls and shining glass.

'Moses Gama chose the wrong road,' Joseph said. 'He tried to assault the walls of the white fortress. He tried to burn it down, not realizing that even if he had succeeeded all he would have inherited would have been ashes.'

'And you, Joseph Dinizulu,' Vicky flashed at him scornfully, 'you are wiser?'

'Perhaps not, but at least I will learn from the mistakes of Moses Gama and Nelson Mandela. I will not spend my life rotting in a white man's prison.'

'How will you assault the white man's fortress, my clever little brother?'

'I will cross the lowered drawbridge,' he said. 'I will go in through the open gates, and one day the castle and its treasures will be mine, even if I have to share a little of them with the white man. No, my angry little sister, I will not destroy those treasures with bombs and flames. I will inherit them.'

'You are mad, Joseph Dinizulu.' She stared at him, and he smiled complacently at her.

'We shall see who is mad and who is sane,' he said. 'But remember this, little

sister, that without the white man we would still be living in grass huts. Look to the north and see the misery of those countries which have driven out the whites. No, my sister, I will keep the white man here – but one day he will work for me, not I for him.'

* * *

'Forget your anger, my son.' Hendrick Tabaka leaned forward and placed his right hand on Raleigh's shoulder. 'Your anger will destroy you. Your enemy is too strong. See what happened to Moses Gama, my own brother. See what is the fate of Nelson Mandela. They went out to fight the lion with bare hands.'

'Others are still fighting,' Raleigh pointed out. 'The warriors of *Umkhonto we Sizwe* are still fighting. Every day we hear of their brave deeds. Every day their bombs explode.'

'They are throwing pebbles at a mountain,' Hendrick said sadly. 'Every time they explode a little bomb against the pylon of a power line, Vorster and De La Rey arm another thousand police and write another hundred banning orders.' Hendrick shook his head. 'Forget your anger, my son, there is a fine life for you at my side. If you follow Moses Gama and Mandela, you will end the way they have ended – but I can offer you wealth and power. Take a wife, Raleigh, a good fat wife and give her many sons, forget the madness and take your place at my side.'

'I had a wife, my father, and I left her at Sharpeville,' Raleigh said. 'But before I left her, I made a vow. With my fingers deep in her bloody wounds, I made a vow.'

'Vows are easy to make,' Hendrick whispered, and Raleigh saw how age had played like a blowtorch across his features, withering and searing and melting the bold lines of his cheekbones and jaw. 'But vows are difficult to live with. Your brother Wellington has also made a vow to the white man's god. He will live like a eunuch for the rest of his life, without ever knowing the comfort of a woman's body. I fear for you, Raleigh, fruit of my loins. I fear that your own vow will be a heavy burden for all of your life.' He sighed again. 'But since I cannot persuade you, what can I do to ease the rocky pathway for you?'

'You know that many of the young people are leaving this country?' Raleigh asked.

'Not only the young ones,' Hendrick nodded. 'Some of the high command have also gone. Oliver Tambo has fled and Mbeki and Joe Modise with many others.'

'They have gone to set the first phase of the revolution afoot.' Raleigh's eyes began to shine with excitement. 'Lenin himself taught us that we cannot move immediately to the communist revolution. We must achieve the phase of national liberation first. We have to create a broad front of liberals and churchmen and students and workers under the leadership of the vanguard party. Oliver Tambo has gone to create that vanguard party – the anti-*apartheid* movement in exile – and I want to be part of that spearhead of the revolution.

'You wish to leave the country of your birth?' Hendrick stared at him in bewilderment. 'You wish to leave me and your family?'

'It is my duty, Father. If the evils of this system are ever to be destroyed, we will need the help of that world out there, of all the united nations of the world.'

'You are dreaming, my son,' Hendrick told him. 'Already that world, in which you place so much trust and hope, has forgotten Sharpeville. Once again money from the foreign nations, from America and Britain and France, is pouring into this country. Every day the country prospers – '

'America has refused to supply arms.'

'Yes,' Hendrick chuckled ruefully. 'And the Boers are making their own. You cannot win, my son, so stay with me.'

'I must go, my Father. Forgive me, but I have no choice. I must go, but I need your help.'

'What do you want me to do?'

'There is a man, a white man, who is helping the young ones to escape.'

Hendrick nodded. 'Joe Cicero.'

'I want to meet him, Father.'

'It will take a little time, for he is a secret man, this Joe Cicero.'

It took almost two weeks. They met on a municipal bus that Raleigh boarded at the central depot in Vereeniging. He wore a blue beret, as he had been instructed, and sat in the second row of seats from the back.

The man who took the seat directly behind him lit a cigarette and as the bus pulled away, said softly, 'Raleigh Tabaka.'

Raleigh turned to look into a pair of eyes like puddles of spilled engine oil.

'Do not look at me,' Joe Cicero said. 'But listen carefully to what I tell you – '

Three weeks later Raleigh Tabaka, carrying a duffel bag and authentic seaman's papers, went up the gangplank of a Dutch freighter that was carrying a cargo of wool to the port of Liverpool. He never saw the continent disappear below the watery horizon for he was already below decks at work in the ship's engine room.

* * *

Sean did the deal at breakfast on the last day of the safari. The client owned seventeen large leather tanneries in as many different states and half the real estate in Tucson, Arizona. His name was Ed Liner and he was seventy-two years of age.

'Son, I don't know why I want to buy myself a safari company. I'm getting a little long in the tooth for this big game stuff,' he grumbled.

'That's bullshit, Ed,' Sean told him. 'You nearly walked me off my feet after that big jumbo, and the trackers all call you *Bwana* One-Shot.'

Ed Liner looked pleased with himself. He was a wiry little man with a ruff of snowy hair around his brown-freckled pate.

'Give me the facts again,' he invited. 'One last time.'

Sean had been working on him for three weeks, since the first day of the safari, and he knew Ed had the figures by heart, but he repeated them now.

'The concession is five hundred square miles, with a forty-mile frontage on the south bank of Lake Kariba – ' As he listened, Ed Liner stroked his wife as though he were caressing a pet kitten.

She was his third wife and she was just two years younger than Sean, but fifty years younger than her husband. She had been a dancer at the Golden Egg in

Vegas, and she had a dancer's legs and carriage with big innocent blue eyes and a curling cloud of blond hair.

She watched Sean with a vicious little curl to her cupid-bow lips as he made his pitch. Sean had been working on her just as assiduously as he had on her husband, thus far with as little success.

'All you've got, honey,' she had told Sean, 'is a pretty face and a hungry dick. The woods are full of those. Daddy Eddie has got fifty million bucks. It's no contest, sonny boy.'

The camp table was set under a magnificent wild fig tree on the banks of the Mara river. It was a bright African morning. The plain beyond the river was golden with winter grass, and studded with flat-topped acacia trees. The herds of wildebeest were dark shadows on the gold and a giraffe was feeding from the upper branches of the nearest acacia, his long graceful neck swaying against the brittle blue of the sky, his hide paved with bold rectangles of red brown. From up-river there came the bellowing sardonic laughter of a bull hippo, while from the branches of the fig tree above them the golden weaver birds dangled upside down from their woven basket nests, fluttering and shrilling to entice the drab brown females to move in and take up residence. Legend had it that both Hemingway and Ruark had camped at this very spot and breakfasted beneath this same wild fig.

'What do you think, Sugar Sticks?' Ed Liner ran his bony brown fingers down the inside of his wife's thigh. She wore wide-legged khaki culottes and from where Sean sat he could see a little red blond pubic curl peeking out from under the elastic of her panties. 'Do you think we should give old Sean here a half million bucks to set up our very own safari outfit down in the Zambezi valley of Rhodesia?'

'You know best, Daddy Eddie,' she affected a cute little-girl voice, and she batted her long eyelashes at him and turned so that her bosom strained the buttons of her khaki shirt.

'Just think of it,' Sean invited. 'Your very own hunting concession, to do with as you want.' He watched her carefully as he went on. 'You could shoot the full quota all yourself if you wanted, as many animals as you wanted.' Despite her curls and pouting lips, Lana Liner had as vicious a sadistic streak as any man Sean had ever hunted with. While Ed had chosen only to take the lion and elephant that he had paid for, Lana had killed every single animal she was entitled to, and then had killed those her husband had refused.

She was a passable shot, and derived as much pleasure from cutting down one of the dainty little Thompson's gazelle with her .300 Weatherby magnum as she had when she dropped her black-maned Masai lion with a perfect heart shot. He had seen the sexual radiance in her immediately after each kill, heard her rapid breathing and seen the pulse beat in her throat with excitement, and his philanderer's instinct had assured him that Lana Liner was vulnerable to him only in those few minutes after she had seen the bullet strike and the blood flash.

'As much hunting as you want, whenever you want it.' Sean tempted her, and saw the excitement in her baby blue eyes.

She ran the tip of her tongue over her scarlet lips and said in her breathless little-girl voice, 'Why don't you buy it for my birthday, Daddy Eddie.'

'Goddamm!' Ed laughed. 'Why not! Okay, son, you've got yourself a deal. We'll call it Lana Safaris. I'll get my lawyers to draw up the papers soon as we get home to Tucson.'

Sean clapped his hands and shouted at the kitchen tent. 'Maramba! *Lete* champagne *hapa*. *Pesi*! *Pesi*!' and the camp waiter in his long white kanza and red pill-box fez brought the green bottle on its silver tray, dewed with cold from the refrigerator.

They drank the wine and laughed in the morning sunlight, and shook hands and discussed the new venture until the gunbearer brought the hunting car around with the rifles in the racks and Matatu, the Ndorobo tracker, perched up on the back and grinning like a monkey.

'I've had enough,' Ed said. 'Guess I'll get packed up and ready to meet the charter plane when it comes in this afternoon.' Then he saw the pout of disappointment on Lana's red lips. 'You go off with Sean, Sugar Sticks,' he told her. 'Have a good hunt, but don't be late back. The charter flight is due to arrive at three, and we must get back to Nairobi before dark.'

Sean drove with Lana in the seat beside him. He had cut the sleeves out of his shirt to leave his upper arms bare, and they were sleek and glossy with muscle. Dark chest hair curled out of the vee neck of the shirt, and he wore his shining dark hair in a page boy almost to his shoulders, but bound up around the forehead with a patterned silk bandana to keep it out of his eyes.

When he grinned at her, he was almost impossibly handsome, but there was a vindictive twist to his smile as he said, 'Ready for a bit of sport, sport?' And she said, 'Just as long as I get to do the shooting, sonny boy.'

They followed the track along the river bank, heading back towards the hills. The Land-Rover was stripped and the windshield removed, and Matatu and the gunbearer in the raised back seat scanned the edges of the riverine bush and searched the track for sign of passage during the night.

Alarmed by the engine beat, a bushbuck family came dancing up the bank from the river, heading for the dense cover with the ewe and the lamb leading, and the ram, striped and spotted with cream on a dark chocolate ground, his corkscrew horns held high.

'I want him,' Lana cried and reached over her shoulder for the Weatherby.

'Leave him,' Sean snapped. 'He won't go fifteen inches and you've got a better trophy already.'

She pouted at him sulkily, and he ignored her as the bushbuck scampered into the bush. Sean hit four-wheel drive and angled the Land-Rover down the bank of one of the Mara's tributaries, splashed and jolted through water as deep as the hubs and then roared up the far bank.

A small herd of Burchell's zebra cantered away ahead of them, stiff black manes erect, their vivid stripes shaded to nondescript grey at a distance, uttering their abrupt honking bark. Lana eyed them hungrily, but she had already shot the twenty zebra allowed on both her and Ed's licences.

The track swung back towards the river and through trees they had a view across the wide plains. The Masai Mara, which meant the great spotted place of the Masai, and the grassland were blotched with herds of game and clumps of acacia.

'*Bwana*,' Matatu cried, and at the same instant Sean saw the sign.He braked the Land-Rover and with Matatu beside him went to examine the splashes of khaki-green dung and the huge round bovine prints in the soft earth of the track. The dung was loose and wet, and Matatu thrust his forefinger into one of the pats to test for body heat.

'They drank at the river an hour before dawn,' he said.

Sean walked back to the Land-Rover and stood close to Lana, almost touching

her as he said, 'Three old bulls. They crossed three hours ago, but they are feeding and we could catch them within an hour. I think they are the same three we saw the day before yesterday.' They had spotted the dark shapes in the dusk, from the opposite bank of the wide Mara river, but with insufficient daylight left for them to circle upstream to the ford and take up the chase. 'If they are the same old mud bulls, one of them is a fifty-incher, and there aren't many of them that size around any more. Do you want to have a go?'

She jumped down from the Land-Rover, and reached for the Weatherby in the gun rack.

'Not that popgun, Sugar Sticks,' Sean warned her. 'Those are big mean old buff out there. Take Ed's Winchester.' The .458 threw a bullet more than twice as heavy as the 200-grain Nosler that the Weatherby fired.

'I shoot better with my own piece than with Ed's cannon,' Lana said. 'And only Ed is allowed to call me Sugar Sticks.'

'Ed is paying me a thousand dollars a day for the best advice on Harley Street. Take the .458, and is it all right if I call you Treacle Pins then?'

'You can go screw, sonny boy,' Lana said and her baby voice gave the obscenity a strangely lascivious twist.

'That's exactly what I had in mind, Treacle Pins, but let's go kill a buff first.'

She tossed the Weatherby to her gunbearer, and strode away from him with her hard round buttocks oscillating in the khaki culottes. 'Just like the cheeks of a squirrel chewing a nut,' Sean thought happily, and took the big double-barrelled Gibbs down from the rack.

The spoor was gross, three big bull buffalo weighing over a ton each and scarring the earth with brazen hooves and grazing as they went. Matatu wanted to run away with it, but Sean checked him. He didn't want to bring Lana up to the chase shaking and panting with fatigue, so they went out on it at an extended walk, going hard but keeping within the girl's capabilities.

In the open acacia forest they reached the spot where the bulls had ceased feeding and bunched up, then struck determinedly towards the blue silhouette of distant hills, and Sean explained to Lana in a whisper, 'This is where they were when the sun rose. As soon as it was light, they headed for the thick stuff. I know where they will lie up, we'll catch them with another half hour.'

Around them the forest closed in, and acacia gave way to the dense claustrophobic thorn and green jess. Visibility ahead dropped to a hundred and then fifty feet, and they had to crouch beneath the interlacing branches. The heat built up, and the dappled light was deceptive, filling the forest with strange shapes and menacing shadow. The stink of the buffalo seemed to steam around them in the heat, a rank gamy smell, and they found the flattened beds and smeared yellow dung where the bulls had lain down for the first time, and then stood up and moved on.

Ahead of them Matatu made the open-handed sign for 'Very close', and Sean opened the breech of the Gibbs and changed the big brass .577 Kynoch cartridges for two others from his bullet pouch. He kept the original pair between the fingers of his left hand ready for an instant reload. He could fire those four cartridges in half the time it would take even the most skilled rifleman to fire four from a magazine rifle. It was so silent and still in the jess that they could hear each other breathe, and the blood pounding in their own ears.

Suddenly there was a clatter, and they all froze. Sean recognized the sound. Somewhere just ahead of them a buffalo had shaken his great black head to drive away the plaguing flies, and one of his curved horns had struck a branch.

Sean sank on to his knees signalling Lana to come up beside him, and together they crawled forward.

Suddenly and unexpectedly they came to a hole in the jess, a tiny clearing twenty paces across, and the earth was trodden like a cattle kraal and littered with pancakes of old black dung.

They lay on the edge of the clearing and peered across into the tangled vegetation on the far side. The sunlight into the clearing dazzled them, and the shadow beyond it was confused and obscure.

Then the bull shook his head again, and Sean saw them. They were lying in a bunch, a mountainous mass of blackness in the shadows, and their heads overlapped so that the heavy bosses and curls of horn formed an inextricable puzzle. Though they were less than thirty paces away, it was impossible to separate one animal from the others, or one set of horns from the bunch.

Slowly Sean turned his head and laid his lips against Lana's ear. 'I am going to get them up,' he whispered. 'Be ready to take the shot as I call it.'

She was sweating and trembling. He could smell her fear and excitement, and it excited him also. He felt his loins thicken and stiffen, and for a moment he savoured the sensation, pressing his hips against the earth as though he had her body under him. Then deliberately he knocked the brass cartridges in his left hand against the steel barrels of the Gibbs. The sharp metallic sound was shocking in the silence.

Across the clearing the three bulls lumbered to their feet, and faced the sound. Their heads were lifted, drooling wet muzzles held high and the bosses of rough horn, black as ironstone, joined above their vicious piggy little eyes, the tips curving down and up again to the wide points, and their ears flared like trumpets.

'The middle one,' Sean said softly. 'Rake him through the chest.'

He stiffened in anticipation of her shot, and then glanced sideways. The barrel of the Weatherby was describing small erratic circles as Lana tried to hold her aim, and it flashed upon Sean that she had forgotten to change the power of her variable telescopic sight. She was looking at a bull buffalo from thirty paces through a lens of ten multiplications. It was like looking at a battle ship through a microscope: all she was seeing was a black shapeless mass.

'Don't shoot!' he whispered urgently but the Weatherby erupted in a long blazing muzzle-flash across the clearing, and the big bull lurched and tossed his head, grunting to the strike of shot. Sean saw the dried mud puff from his scabby black skin, low down in the joint of his right shoulder, and as the bull spun away into the jess, Sean swung the Gibbs on him to take the back-up shot. But one of the other buffalo turned across the wounded animal, screening him for the instant that it took for him to crash away into the jess, and Sean lifted the Gibbs without firing.

They lay side by side and listened to the thunderous rush of bodies dwindle into the jess.

'I couldn't see clearly,' Lana said in her childish piping treble.

'You had the scope on full power, you dilly bitch.'

'But I hit him!'

'Yes, Treacle Breeches, you hit him – more's the pity. You broke his right front leg.' Sean stood up and whistled for Matatu. In a few quick words of Swahili he explained the predicament, and the little Ndorobo looked at Lana reproachfully.

'Stay here with your gunbearer,' Sean ordered Lana. 'We'll go and finish the business.'

'I'm going with you.' Lana shook her head.

'This is what I'm paid for,' Sean told her. 'Cleaning up the mess. Stay here and let me do my job.'

'No,' she said. 'It's my buff. I'll finish it.'

'I haven't got time to argue,' Sean said bitterly. 'Come on then, but do as you are told.' And he waved Matatu forward to pick up the blood spoor.

There were bone splinters and hair where the bull had stood.

'You smashed the big bone,' Sean told her. 'It's a racing certainty that the bullet broke up. At that range it was probably still going 3500 foot per second when it hit – even a Nosler bullet can't stand that.'

The bull was bleeding profusely. Bright blood had sprayed the jess as he blundered through, and blood had formed a dark gelatinous puddle where he stood for the first time to listen for his pursuers. The other two bulls had deserted him and Sean grunted with satisfaction. That would prevent confusion, shooting at the wrong animal in the mix-up.

Lana kept close beside him. She had removed the scope from the Weatherby and left it with the gunbearer, and now she carried the rifle at high port across her chest.

Abruptly they stepped into another narrow clearing, and Matatu squeaked and bolted back between Sean and the girl as the bull broke from the far side of the clearing and came down on them in a bizarre crabbing sideways gait. His nose was up, and the long mournful droop of his horns gave him a funereal menace. His broken leg flapped loosely, hampering his gait, so he rocked and plunged, and bright blood was forced in a spurting stream from the wound by the movement.

'Shoot!' said Sean. 'Aim at his nose!' But without looking at her he sensed her terror, and her first movement as she turned to run.

'Come on, you yellow bitch. Stand and shoot it out,' he snarled at her. 'This is what you wanted – now do it.'

The Weatherby whiplashed, and flame and thunder tore across the clearing. The buffalo flinched to the shot, and black flinty chips flew from the boss of his horns.

'High!' Sean called. 'Shoot him on the nose.' And she shot again, and hit the horn a second time and the bull kept coming.

'Shoot!' Sean called, watching the great armoured head over the express sights of the Gibbs. 'Come on, bitch, kill him!'

'I can't' she screamed. 'He's too close!' The bull filled all their existence, a mountain of black hide and muscle and lethal horn, so close that at last he dropped his head to toss and gore them, to rip and trample and crush them under the anvil of his crenellated boss.

As the massive horns went down, Sean shot him through the brain and the bull rolled forward over his own head. Sean pulled Lana out from under the flying hooves as the bull somersaulted. She had dropped the rifle and now she clung to him helplessly, shaking, her red mouth slack and smeared with terror.

'Matatu!' Sean called quietly, holding her to his chest, and the little Ndorobo reappeared at his side like a genie. 'Take the gunbearer with you,' Sean ordered. 'Go back to the Land-Rover and bring it back here, but do not hurry.'

Matatu grinned lewdly and ducked his head. He had an enormous respect for his *Bwana*'s virility and he knew what Sean was going to do. He only wondered

that it had taken so long for the *Bwana* to straighten this pale albino creature's back for her. He disappeared into the jess like a black shadow and Sean turned the girl's face up to his own and thrust his tongue deeply into the wet red wound of her mouth.

She moaned and clung to him, and with his free hand he unbuckled her belt and jerked down the culottes. They fell in a tangle around her ankles and she kicked them away. He hooked his thumbs into the waistband of her panties and tore them off her, then he pushed her down on top of the hot and bleeding carcass of the buffalo. She fell with her legs sprawled open and the muscles of the dead animal were still twitching and contracting from the brain shot, and the sweet coppery smell of blood mingled with the rank wild stink of game and dust.

Sean stood over her and tore open the front of his breeches and she looked up at him with the terror still clouding her eyes.

'Oh you bastard,' she sobbed. 'You filthy rotten bastard.'

Sean dropped on his knees between her long loose limbs and cupped his hands under her hard little buttocks. As he lifted her lower body he saw that her fluffy blond mount was already as sodden as the fur of a drowned kitten.

They drove back to camp with the body of the dead bull crammed into the back of the Land-Rover, the great horned head dangling over the side, and Matatu and the gunbearer perched upon it, singing the hunter's song.

Lana never said a word all the way back. Ed Liner was waiting for them under the dining tent, but his welcoming grin faded as Lana threw her torn panties on the table in front of him and piped in her little-girl voice, 'You know what naughty old Sean did, Daddy Eddie? He raped your little girl, that's what he did – he held her down and stuck his big dirty thing into her.'

Sean saw the fury and the hatred in the old man's faded eyes, and he groaned inwardly, 'The bitch,' he thought. 'The sneaky little bitch. You loved it. You screamed for more.'

Half an hour later Lana and Ed were in the red and silver Beechcraft Baron when it took off from the narrow bush strip. As it banked away on course for Nairobi, Sean glanced down at his own trouser front.

Well okay, King Kong,' he murmured. 'I hope you are satisfied, that just cost us fifty thousand dollars an inch.' He turned back to the Land-Rover still shaking his head sadly as he picked up the bundle of mail that the pilot of the Beechcraft had brought down from the office in Nairobi. There was a yellow cable envelope on top of the pile and he opened it first.

'I am marrying Holly Carmichael on 5th August. Please be my best man. Love. Garry.'

Sean read it through twice, and Lana and Ed Liner were forgotten.

'I'd love to see what kind of bag would marry Garry,' he chuckled. 'Pity I can't go home – ' he broke off and thought about it. 'But why not! Why the hell not! Living dangerously is half the fun.'

* * *

Shasa Courtney sat at his desk in the study at Weltevreden, studying the Turner on the opposite wall as he composed the next paragraph in his mind.

He was drafting his Chairman's Report for the cabinet select committee of

Armscor. The armaments company had been set up by special act of parliament, and the strict secrecy of its operations was ensured by that act.

When President Eisenhower had initiated the arms embargo against South Africa as a punitive reaction to the Sharpeville massacre and the racial policies of the Verwoerd government, the country's annual expenditure on weapons manufacture had been a mere £300,000. Four years later they had an annual budget of half a billion.

'Dear old Ike did us a big favour,' Shasa smiled now. 'The law of unforeseen consequences in action again, sanctions always backfire. Now our biggest worry is to find a testing ground for our own atomic bomb.'

He addressed himself once more to that section of his report, and wrote:

> Taking into consideration the foregoing, I am of the opinion that we should adopt the third option, i.e. underground testing. With this in view, the corporation has already conducted investigations to determine the most suitable geological areas. (See attached geological survey reports.)
>
> The shot holes will be drilled by a commercial diamond drilling company to a depth of four thousand feet to obviate contamination of the underground water supplies.

There was a knock on the door and Shasa looked up in angry disbelief. The entire household knew that he was not to be disturbed, and there was no reason nor excuse for this intrusion.

'Who is it?' he barked, and the door was opened without his permission.

For a moment he did not recognize the person who stepped into the study. The long hair and deep tan, the flamboyant costume – the gilet of kudu skin, and the bright silk scarf knotted at the throat, the mosquito boots and cartridge belt were all unfamiliar. Shasa stood up uncertainly.

'Sean?' he asked. 'No, I don't believe this is happening.' He wanted to be angry and outraged. 'Damn it, Sean, I warned you never – ' but he could not go on, his joy was too intense and his voice petered out.

'Hello, Dad.' Sean came striding towards him, and he was taller and more handsome and self-assured than Shasa remembered. Shasa abhorred all manner of theatrics and affectation of dress, but Sean wore his costume with such panache that it appeared natural and correct.

'What the hell are you doing here?' Shasa found his voice at last, but there was no rancour in his question.

'I came as soon as I got Garry's cable.'

'Garry cabled you?'

'Best man – he wanted me to be his best man, and I didn't even have a chance to change.' He stopped in front of Shasa, and for a moment they studied each other.

'You are looking good, Pater,' Sean smiled, and his teeth were white as bone against the tan.

'Sean, my boy.' Shasa lifted his hands, and Sean seized him in a bear hug.

'I thought about you every single day – ' Sean's voice was tight and his cheek was pressed to Shasa's cheek. 'God, how I missed you, Dad.'

Shasa knew instinctively that it was a lie, but he was delighted that Sean had bothered to tell the lie.

'I've missed you, too, my boy,' he whispered. 'Not every day, but often enough to hurt like hell. Welcome back to Weltevreden.' And Sean kissed him. They had not kissed since Sean was a child, that sort of sentimental display was not Shasa's usual style, but now the pleasure of it was almost unbearable.

Sean sat at Centaine's right hand at dinner that evening. His dinner jacket was a little tight around the chest and smelled of moth balls, but the servants, overjoyed to have him home, had pressed razor edges into the crease of his trousers and steamed out the silk lapels. He had shampooed his hair, and oddly the thick glossy locks seemed to enhance rather than detract from his overpowering masculinity.

Isabella, taken by surprise like everybody else, had come drifting downstairs, dressed for dinner with her shoulders and back bare, but her cool and distant poise had evaporated as she saw Sean. She squealed and rushed at him.

'It's been so boring since you went away!'

She wouldn't let go of his arm until they went in to dinner, and even now she leaned forward to watch his lips as he talked, her forgotten soup cooling, avid to take in every word. When Shasa at the end of the table made a remark about Kenyan barbers and Sean's hair style, she rushed to her eldest brother's defence.

'I love his hair like that. You are so antediluvian sometimes, Papa. He's beautiful. I swear if Sean ever cuts a single hair on his beautiful head, I will take vows of silence and chastity on the spot.'

'A consummation devoutly to be prayed for,' murmured her father.

Centaine, although less effusive, was as delighted as any of them to have Sean home again. Of course, she knew every detail of the circumstances in which he had left. She and Shasa were the only ones in the family who did, but that had been almost six years ago, and things could change in that time. It was difficult to believe that anybody who looked like that, even more beautiful than her own beloved Shasa, and who possessed such charm and natural grace, could be entirely bad. She consoled herself that although he had made a few mistakes when he was a child, he was now a man. Centaine had seldom seen more of a man, and she listened as attentively as the rest of them to his stories and laughed as merrily at his sallies.

Garry kept repeating, 'I didn't really believe you'd come. I sent that cable on an impulse. I wasn't even sure of your address.' And then to Holly who was sitting beside Sean at the long table, 'Isn't he wonderful, Holly – isn't he everything I told you?'

Holly smiled and murmured polite agreement, and twisted slightly in her chair to prevent Sean pointing up the story he was telling by placing his hand on her thigh again. She glanced around the table, and caught Michael's eye. He was the only one who was not following Sean's tale with total concentration. Holly had only met Michael for the first time the previous day, when he arrived from Johannesburg for the wedding, but the two of them had found an immediate *rapport*, which had swiftly deepened as Holly had discovered Michael's protective concern and affection for Garry.

Now Michael raised an eyebrow at Holly, and smiled an apology at her. He had seen his elder brother looking at her, he had seen through Sean's devices to attract her attention, and had even seen her start and pale as Sean touched her beneath the table. He would talk to Sean after dinner, and quietly warn him off, for Garry himself would never see what was happening. He was too besotted by his elder brother's return. It was up to Michael – it had always been his duty to protect Garry from Sean. In the meantime he smiled reassurance at Holly, and Sean intercepted the look and interpreted it accurately. He showed no reaction.His expression was frank and open and his voice sparkling and full of

humour as he finished the story and the others all laughed, all except Michael and Holly.

'You are so funny,' Isabella sang. 'I just hate you for being my brother. If only I could find another boy who looked like you.'

'There's not one of them good enough for you, Bella,' Sean said, but he was watching Michael, and as the laughter subsided, he asked lightly, 'And so, Mickey, how is life on that commie newspaper of yours? Is it true that you are going to change its name to the *ANC Times*, or is it the *Mandela Mail* or the *Moses Gama Gazette*?'

Michael laid down his knife and fork and met Sean's gaze squarely.

'The policy of the *Golden City Mail* is to defend the helpless, to attempt to secure a decent dignified existence for all, and to tell the truth as we see it – at any cost.'

'I don't know about that, Mickey,' Sean grinned at him. 'But a couple of times out there in the bush I've wished that I had a copy of the *Golden City Mail* with me – yes, sir, every time I run out of toilet paper, I wish I had your column right there.'

'Sean!' Shasa said sharply, and his indulgent expression faded for the first time since Sean's arrival. 'There are ladies present.'

'Nana.' Sean turned to Centaine. 'You have read Mickey's column, haven't you? Don't tell me you agree with those bright pink sentiments of his?'

'That's enough,' Shasa said sternly. 'This is a reunion and a celebration.'

'I'm sorry, Pater.' Sean was mock contrite. 'You are right. Let's talk about fun things. Let me tell Mickey about the Mau Mau in Kenya, and what they did to the white kids. Then he can tell me about his commie ANC friends here, and what he wants them to do to our kids.'

'Sean, that's not fair,' Michael said softly. 'I am not a communist, and I have never advocated communism or the use of force – '

'That's not what you wrote in yesterday's edition. I had the great and glorious privilege of reading your column on the plane down from Jo'burg.'

'What I actually wrote, Sean, was that Vorster and De La Rey between them are making the mistake of labelling as communist everything that our black population sees as desirable – civil rights, universal franchise, trade unions and black political organizations such as the ANC. By naming these as communist-inspired they are making the idea of communism highly attractive to our blacks.'

'We've just got a black government in Kenya, with a convicted terrorist and murderer as the new head of state. That's why I'm getting out and moving to Rhodesia. And here is my own beloved brother paving the way for another black Marxist government of rabble-rousers and bomb-throwers right here in the good old Republic. Tell me, which of the terrorists do you fancy for president, Mickey, Mandela or Moses Gama?'

'I won't warn either of you again,' Shasa told them ominously. 'I will not abide politics at the dinner table.'

'Daddy is right,' Isabella joined in. 'You are both being so utterly dreary – and just when I was beginning to really enjoy myself.'

'And that's enough from the peanut gallery also,' Centaine picked out Isabella. 'Eat your food please, Mademoiselle, you are all skin and bones as it is.' But she was studying Sean.

'He has been home six hours and already we are all at each other's throats,'

she thought. 'He still has a talent for controversy. We must be wary of him – I wonder why he really came home.'

She found out very soon after dinner, when Sean asked to see her and Shasa in the gun room.

After Shasa had poured a tiny glass of Chartreuse for her, and balloon snifters of Hennessy for Sean and himself, they all settled down in the leather chairs. The men went through the ritual of preparing their cigars, cutting the tips and warming and finally lighting them with the cedarwood tapers.

'All right, Sean,' Shasa said. 'What did you want to talk to us about?'

'You know how we discussed the safari business, Pater, just before I left?' Shasa noticed how he showed no contrition as he mentioned his enforced departure. 'Well, I have had six years of experience now, and I won't offend you with false modesty. I'm one of the top hunters in the business. I've a list of over fifty clients who want to hunt with me again. I have their telephone numbers, you can ring them and ask them.'

'All right, I will,' Shasa said. 'But go on.'

'Ian Smith's government in Rhodesia is developing the safari business there. One of the concessions they are putting up for auction in two months' time is a plum.' Shasa and Centaine listened in attentive silence, and when Sean finished almost an hour later, they exchanged a significant glance. They understood each other perfectly after thirty years of working so closely, and they did not have to speak to agree that Sean had made a virtuoso performance. He was a good salesman, and his figures added up to the promise of rich profits, but Shasa saw the little shadow at the back of his mother's dark eyes.

'Just one thing perturbs me a little, Sean. After all these years you come breezing in again – and the first thing you do is ask for half a million dollars.'

Sean stood up and strolled across the gun room. The carved tusk hung above the stone fireplace, the central position in the room, pride of place amongst all Shasa's own hunting trophies.

Sean studied it for a moment, and then turned back slowly to face them.

'You never wrote to me once in all those years, Pater. That's all right, I understand why. But don't accuse me of not caring. I thought about you and Nana every day I was away.' It was cleverly done. He did not mention the tusk on the wall, and Centaine could have sworn there were genuine tears just at the back of his marvellously green clear eyes. She felt her doubts soften and begin to dissolve.

'My God, how can any woman resist him,' she thought. 'Even his own grandmother!'She looked across at Shasa and was amazed to see that Sean had shamed him. Neatly and adroitly he had shifted guilt and Shasa had to cough and clear his throat before he could speak.

'I must admit it sounds interesting,' he said gruffly. 'But you'll have to speak to Garry.'

'Garry?' Sean asked in surprise.

'Garry is the director in charge of new projects and investments,' Shasa told him and Sean smiled.

He had just knocked together two of the toughest, shrewdest heads in the business. Garry would be a piece of cake.

* * *

Holly Carmichael's father was the Presbyterian minister of a small parish in Scotland, and he and his wife flew out to Africa quite determined to see their daughter decently married, and to pay for the privilege.

Centaine took him for a ride around the estate and explained kindly that only by being very selective could she restrict her guest list to under a thousand. 'Those are just family friends, and our most important business and political associates. Of course it does not include the workers here on Weltevreden or the employees of Courtney Mining and Finance who will be accorded their own separate festivities.'

The Reverend Carmichael looked stricken.

'Madam, I love my daughter – but a clergyman's stipend – '

'I don't really like to mention it,' Centaine went on smoothly, 'but it is Holly's second marriage – and you have already done your duty with the first. I would be grateful if you would consent to perform the ceremony, and let me take care of the other small details.' With one deft stroke Centaine had procured a clergyman to marry her grandson, for despite veiled offers to install stained-glass windows and restore church roofs, both the local Church of England and Anglican priests had refused to perform the offices. At the same time she had achieved a free hand with the wedding arrangements.

'It will be,' she promised herself, 'the wedding of the decade.'

The old slave church on the estate had been rethatched and restored for the occasion, and the bougainvillaea blossom of exactly the shade that Holly had chosed for her dress was flown down from the eastern Transvaal in the company aircraft to decorate it. The rest of the ceremony and the following celebrations were arranged on the same scale and with similar attention to detail with all the resources of Weltevreden and the Courtney group of companies to carry them through.

The church could seat only 150, and twenty of those were the coloured family retainers from the estate who had known and cared for Garry since the day of his birth. The other thousand guests waited in the marquee on the polo field and the ceremony was relayed to them over the public address system.

The road down the hill from the church to the polo field was lined with the other estate workers whose seniority and length of service were insufficient to procure them a seat in the church. They had stripped Centaine's rose garden of blooms and they showered Garry and his new bride with rose petals as they led the procession down the hill in the open carriage, and the women danced and sang and tried to touch Holly for luck as she went by.

In his grey topper Garry stood taller than Holly and his bulk of shoulder and chest made her seem light as a cloud of pink mist beside him, so lovely that the guests gasped and hummed with admiration as he brought her into the marquee on his arm.

The best man's speech was one of the highlights of the afternoon. Sean had them roaring and squealing with laughter and clapping his most amusing sallies, although Holly frowned and reached for Garry's hand under the table when Sean made oblique references to Garry's stutter and his Charles Atlas course.

Sean was the first to dance with Holly after she and Garry had circled the floor in the wedding waltz. He held her close as they turned together and murmured, 'Silly girl, you could have had the pick of the litter, but, never fear, it's still not too late.'

'I did and it is,' she replied, and her smile was cold and thorny. 'Now why

don't you go off and give my bridesmaids the benefit of your charms. The poor things are panting like puppy dogs.'

Sean turned the rebuff with a light laugh and handed her over to Michael for the rest of the dance. While he snapped his fingers at one of the waiters to bring him another glass of champagne, he surveyed the tent from the vantage point of the raised dais, picking out the interesting females, making his selections not only on the basis of their looks but on their apparent availability. Those who sensed his scrutiny and blushed or simpered or boldly returned his regard went immediately to the head of his list.

In passing he noticed that Isabella had finally got around Nana, and was wearing one of those mini-skirts that were all the rage. The hem finished just below the creases of her cheeky little buttocks, and with the impartial eye of the connoisseur he saw that her legs were quite extraordinary, and that every man, no matter what his age, glanced down at them as she circled the dance floor.

Thinking of Nana, he looked around for her quickly. Her seat at the high table was empty. Then he found her. She was near the back of the tent, sitting at a table with a big burly man who had his back turned to Sean. They were in earnest conversation, and his grandmother's intensity interested him. He knew that Centaine never wasted effort on the trivialities. The man must be important. As he thought that, the man turned slightly and Sean recognized him. His heart skipped guiltily. It was the miniter of police, Manfred De La Rey. He was the one who had quashed the charges against Sean, in return for his guarantee to leave the country and never return.

Sean's instinct was to slip away without drawing De La Rey's attention to himself and then he grinned at his own stupidity. He had just stood up and made a dashing speech in front of them all. 'How's that for drawing attention?' he thought, and then grinned again at his own daring. 'Living dangerously is half the fun,' he reminded himself, and jumped down off the dais without spilling a drop of champagne and deliberately sauntered across the tent towards his grandmother and her companion.

Centaine saw him coming and placed her hand on Manfred's sleeve. 'Careful, here he comes now.' It had just taken all her influence, a recital of all the debts and secrets between them, to protect Sean, and now here was the impudent young devil flaunting himself in front of Manfred.

She tried to warn him off with a frown, but Sean stooped and kissed her cheek. 'You are a genius, Nana, there has never been a party like this. The planning and the eye to detail – we are all proud of you!'

He hugged her and though she pushed him off haughtily saying, 'Now don't be a big booby,' her frown was displaced by the ghost of a smile. 'Damn it, he's got the cheek of all the Courtneys' she thought proudly, and then turned to Manfred.

'You don't know my grandson. Sean, this is Minister De La Rey.'

'I've heard of you,' Manfred growled without offering to shake hands. 'I've heard a great deal about you.' And with relief Centaine turned to the couple who were returning to the table from the dance floor. 'And this is Mrs De La Rey and her son Lothar – all old friends of the family. Heidi, may I present my grandson Sean.'

Sean bowed over her hand, and Heidi considered him thoughtfully and said in her lisping German accent, 'He is the only one of your grandchildren I have not met, Centaine. A fine boy.'

Sean turned to Lothar and held out his hand. 'Hello. I'm Sean – and if I

didn't know who you were, I'd be the only one in the country. Your play against the Lions on the last tour was magical, that boot of yours is worth a million rand.'

The two young men sat down on a pair of empty chairs and were immediately engrossed in a discussion of rugby football and the recent visit of the British team. Although she continued her conversation with Manfred, Centaine watched her two grandsons covertly. Apart from their youth and self-assurance, they were so different in appearance, one blond and Germanic, the other dark and romantic, yet she sensed that they were in other ways very similar. Strong men, untroubled by unnecessary scruples, men who knew what they wanted and how to go about getting it. Perhaps they inherited that from her, she smiled to herself, and perhaps like her they were hard and unrelenting adversaries, prepared to destroy anything that stood in their way.

Centaine had the trick of listening to two conversations at once and she heard Lothar De La Rey say, 'Mind you, I've heard about you also and what you did in Kenya. Didn't you get a citation for the George Cross for cleaning up the last of the Mau Mau gangs?'

Sean laughed. 'My timing was wrong. The Brits couldn't give me a gong for shooting Mickey Mice at the same time as they were handing the country over to Kenyatta. Not really cricket, you know, old boy. But how did you find out about that?'

'It's my job to know these things,' Lothar told him, and Sean nodded.

'Yes, of course, you are in the police. Aren't you a major or something?'

'As of last week, a colonel in the bureau for state security.'

'Congratulations.'

'You know, anything you could tell us about Mau Mau will be useful. I mean the real first-hand stuff about anti-terrorist work. You see, I think we might have the same problem here one of these days.'

'Well, the worst was over by the time I got there, but yes, of course – anything I can do. I'm going back up north in a few weeks, to Rhodesia. But if I can help – '

'Rhodesia.' Lothar dropped his voice so that Centaine could no longer hear. 'That's interesting. We'd like to know what's going on there also. Yes, I think it is vital that we get together before you leave. A man like you in place could be of really crucial help to us – ' Lothar broke off. His expression changed and he stood up hurriedly, looking over Sean's shoulders.

Following his gaze Sean looked around and Isabella stood close behind him. She draped one hand languidly over Sean's shoulder, and leaned one hip against him, but she was watching Lothar.

'This is Bella, my baby sister,' Sean told Lothar, and Isabella murmured, 'Not such a baby any more, big brother.' She had not taken her eyes off Lothar's face.

She had first noticed him in the church during the ceremony and recognized him immediately. He was one of the most famous athletes in the country, a national heart-throb. Sean's conversation with him had given her the opportunity she had been waiting for.

Despite the fact that her voice was cool and her manner aloof and distant, Sean felt her tremble against him and he grinned inwardly, 'Your ovaries are going off like fire crackers, little sister.' But he said, 'Why don't you sit down and bring a little sunlight into our drab existence, Bella?'

She ignored him and spoke directly to Lothar. 'Do you spend all your time

dressed up in a rugby jersey, pushing people around in scrums and kicking little balls? Or somewhere along the line did you learn to dance, Lothar De La Rey?'

'Ouch!' Sean murmured. Even for a Courtney, that was pretty direct. And Lothar inclined his head and asked gravely,

'May I have the pleasure of this dance, Isabella Courtney?'

They made one circuit of the floor without speaking and then Lothar said, 'If you were my woman, I would not allow you to wear a skirt like that.'

'Why? Don't you like my legs?' she asked.

'I like your legs very much indeed,' he replied. 'But if you were my woman, I would not like other men to look at them the way they are doing now.'

'You are a prude, Lothar De La Rey.'

'Perhaps, Isabella Courtney, but I believe there is a time and a place for everything.'

She pushed a little closer to him and thought happily to herself, 'So let's find that time and place, you big gorgeous hunk of brawn.'

* * *

Morosely Manfred watched his son on the dance floor and his wife leaned across and echoed his thoughts.

'That hussy is throwing herself at Lothie. Just look at her, showing everything she has. I wish I could go and pull her away from him.'

'I wouldn't do that, *skat*,' Manfred advised soberly. 'Nothing could make her more attractive to him than our disapproval. But don't worry, Heidi. We have brought him up the right way. He might have a little man's sport with her, but that's not the kind of girl he will bring home.' He stood up heavily. 'Trust our boy, Heidi. But now you must forgive me. I must talk to Shasa Courtney – it's very important.'

Shasa in full morning dress, a white carnation in his buttonhole, the black patch over one eye and a long black cheroot between his teeth was in deep conversation with the groom, but when he saw Manfred approaching and recognized the seriousness of his mien, he slapped Garry's shoulder lightly and said, 'I think it's a good bet, but you listen to what Sean has to say. Make up your own mind, then come and discuss it with me,' and then he left Garry and came to meet Manfred.

'We must talk – privately,' Manfred greeted him.

'Now?' Shasa looked incredulous, but Manfred insisted.

'It will not take long.'

'Let's go up to the house.' Shasa took his arm, and chatting amiably led him to the exit, as though they were going off to the men's room together. As soon as they were outside the marquee, they headed for the carpark behind the grandstand.

Manfred prowled around Shasa's gun room, restlessly peering at the framed photographs of hunting safaris, at the mounted animal heads and the racks of sporting rifles and shotguns in their glass-fronted cabinet, while Shasa slouched in one of the armchairs and watched him patiently, letting him take his time, puffing on the black cheroot.

'Is this room secure? We cannot be overheard?' Manfred asked. And Shasa nodded.

'Perfectly secure. I do much of my private business here – besides which, the house is deserted. Every last servant is down at the polo field.'

'Ja, nee, goed!' Manfred came to take the armchair facing Shasa.

'You cannot go off to England as you planned,' he said, and Shasa laughed.

'Why on earth not?'

'I will tell you why.' Manfred assured him, but made no attempt to do so. Instead he asked, 'Did you ever see a film called *The Manchurian Candidate*?' He pronounced it in the Afrikaans fashion 'fi-lim'.

For a moment Shasa was surprised by the irrelevance of the question. Then he replied, 'No, I didn't get around to the movie, but I did read the book by Richard Condon. Rather enjoyed it, to tell the truth.'

'Do you remember the story-line?'

'Yes. It was about a plot to assassinate one of the American presidential canditates.'

'That's right,' Manfred nodded. 'The assassin was hypnotized and programmed to respond to the sight of a playing card, one of the aces, I think.'

'Ace of spades,' Shasa agreed. 'The death card. He would respond like an automaton to any command he received after he had seen the ace. In a hypnotic trance he was ordered to carry out the assassination.'

'Do you think the idea was credible? Do you think a man could be completely subjected to the hypnotic suggestion of another?'

'I don't know,' Shasa admitted. 'The Koreans and the Russians are supposed to have perfected the technique of brainwashing. Perhaps it is possible, in special circumstances, with a particularly susceptible subject – I don't know.'

Manfred sat in silence for so long that Shasa began to fidget. Then he spoke curtly, 'Our jobs are in danger,' he said, and Shasa went very still. *'Ja.'* Manfred nodded heavily. 'Verwoerd is thinking of reshuffling the cabinet. You and I will be sacked.'

'You have done a difficult job,' Shasa said softly. 'And you have done it as well as was humanly possible. The storm is over, the country is calm and stable.'

Manfred sighed. *'Ja*, you also. In a few short years since Sharpeville, you have helped rally the economy. Foreign investment is pouring in, thanks to your efforts. The value of property is higher than it was before the crisis. You have done an excellent job building up the armaments industry. Very soon our own atomic bomb – but we are going to be sacked. My information is always reliable.'

'Why?' Shasa asked, and Manfred shrugged.

'Verwoerd took two bullets in the head. Who knows what damage that caused.'

'He showed no signs of any permanent damage. He is just as logical, rational and decisive after the operation to remove the bullets.'

'Do you think so?' Manfred asked. 'Do you think his obsession with race is logical and rational?'

'Verwoerd was always obsessed with racial matters.'

'No, my friend, that is not so,' Manfred contradicted him. 'He didn't want the ministry of Bantu affairs when Malan first offered it to him. Race meant nothing to him. He was concerned only with the growth and survival of Afrikaner nationalism.'

'He certainly threw himself into it body and soul, when he did take the job,' Shasa smiled.

'*Ja*, that's true, but then he saw *apartheid* as uplifting to the blacks, a chance to conduct their own affairs and become masters of their own destiny. He saw it as exactly similar to the partition of India and Pakistan. He was concerned with racial differences, but he was not a racist. Not in the beginning.'

'Perhaps.' Shasa was dubious.

'Since those bullets in the head he has changed,' Manfred said. 'Before that he was strong-willed and certain of his own infallibility, but since then he will brook not the slightest criticism or even a hint that anything he says or does might be wrong. Race has become an obsession, to the point of lunacy – this business with the coloured English cricketer, what is his name again?'

'Basil D'Oliveira – and he is South African. He plays for England because he can't play for South Africa.'

'*Ja*, it's madness. Now Verwoerd even refuses to have a black servant to tend him. He would not attend the film version of *Othello* because Laurence Olivier had painted his face black. He has lost all sense of proportion. He is gong to undo all the hard painstaking work we have done to restore calm and prosperity. He is going to destroy this country – and he is going to destroy us personally, you and me, because we have stood up to some of his wilder excesses in cabinet. You even suggested he permanently abolish the pass laws – he has never forgiven you for that. He calls you a liberal.'

'All right, but I can't believe he would take the ministry of police away from you.'

'That is what he plans. He wants to give it all to John Vorster – combine justice and police into a single portfolio and call it "Law and Order", or some such other title.'

Shasa stood up and went to the cabinet at the end of the room. He poured two large cognacs and Manfred did not protest when he placed one of them on the table at his elbow.

'You know, Shasa, for a long time now I have had a dream. I've never told anybody about it, not even Heidi, but I will tell you. I dreamed that one day I would be the prime minister, and that you, Shasa Courtney, would be the state president of this country of ours. The two of us, Englishman and Afrikaner, side by side as South Africans.'

They sat quietly and thought about it, and Shasa found himself becoming angry at being cheated of that honour. Then Manfred went off at another tangent.

'Do you know that even though the Americans are refusing to sell us arms, we still co-operate very closely with their CIA on all matters of intelligence that affect our mutual interests in southern Africa?' Manfred asked, and although Shasa could not fathom this new change of direction, he nodded.

'Yes, of course, I know that.'

'The Americans have just interrogated a Russian defector in west Berlin. They passed on some of the intelligence to us. There is a Manchurian Candidate in place, and his target is Verwoerd.'

Shasa gaped at him. 'Who is the assassin?'

'No.' Manfred held up his hands. 'They don't know. Even though the Russian was highly placed, he did not know. All he could tell the Americans was that the assassin has access to the prime minister, and he will be used soon, very soon.' He picked up the cognac glass, and swirled the oily brown liquid

around the crystal bowl. 'There was one other small clue. The assassin has a history of mental illness, and he is a foreigner, not born in this country.'

'With that information it should be possible to identify him,' Shasa mused. 'You could check every single person who has access to the PM.'

'Perhaps,' Manfred agreed. 'But what we must decide – here in secret, just the two of us – is do we really want to find the Manchurian Candidate and stop him. Would it be in the best interest of our country to prevent the assassination?'

Shasa spilled the cognac down the lapels of his morning jacket, but he did not seem to notice. Aghast, he was staring at Manfred. After a long pause, he set down his glass, drew a silk handkerchief from his inner pocket and began to mop the spilled liquor.

'Who else knows about this?' he asked, concentrating on his cleaning, not looking up.

'One of my senior officers. He is the liaison with the military attaché at the American embassy, who is the CIA man here.'

'No one else?'

'Only me – and now you.'

'Your officer is trustworthy?'

'Completely.'

At last Shasa looked up. 'Yes, now I see why I should cancel my trip to London. If something happened to Verwoerd, it would be essential for me to be here when his successor is chosen.'

He lifted his glass in a salute, and after a moment Manfred returned the gesture. They drank the silent toast, watching each other's eyes over the rims of the crystal glasses.

* * *

There were only two couples left on the dance floor, and except for the band and the servants who were cleaning up and stacking the chairs, the marquee was empty.

At last the coloured band-master descended from the stand and approached Sean diffidently. 'Master, it's after two o'clock already.' Sean glared at him over the head of the girl he was dancing with, and the man quailed. 'Please, Master, we've been playing since lunchtime, nearly fourteen hours.'

Sean's thunderous expression changed dramatically into that radiant boyish smile of his. 'Off you go then! You have been just great – and this is for you and your boys.' He tucked a crumpled wad of banknotes into the band-leader's top pocket, and called to the other couple.

'Come on, gang. We are off to Navvies.'

Isabella had her face pressed to Lothar's shirt front, but she looked up brightly.

'Oh goody!' she cried. 'I've never been there. Nana says it's sordid and disreputable. Let's go!'

Sean had borrowed Garry's MG and Isabella raced him in her new Alfa Romeo, and managed to keep up with him through the curves of the mountain drive. They were neck and neck as they tore down Buitenkant Street to the notorious Navigator's Den in the Bo-kaap area near the docks.

Sean had purloined two bottles of whisky from the bar in the marquee, and his partner was draped around his neck.

'Let's carouse,' he suggested, and pushed his way through the cluster of seamen and prostitutes who crowded the entrance to the nightclub.

The interior was so dark that they could only barely make out the band, and the music was so loud that they had to sit close and yell at each other.

'You are a marvellous brother,' Isabella shouted and leaned across to kiss Sean. 'You don't preach to me.'

'It's your life, Bella baby, you enjoy it – and call me if anybody tries to stop you.'

She perched on Lothar's knee and nuzzled his neck. Sean's partner had collapsed, and he laid her out full length on the padded bench, with her head in his lap, while he and Lothar sat with their shoulders touching and talked seriously. The music blanketed their voices, so that from farther than a few feet nobody could overhear them.

'Do you know that you still have a rather prominent billing in the police files?' Lothar asked.

'It does not come as any great surprise,' Sean admitted.

'You don't mind taking a chance, do you?' Lothar smiled. 'I like your nerve.'

'From what I know and see, I'd say that you are a fairly nerveless customer yourself,' Sean grinned back at him.

'I could make sure that your file disappeared,' Lothar offered.

'In exchange for a little something or other, no doubt?'

'Naturally,' Lothar agreed. 'You get nothing for nothing.'

'And all you get for a pinch of dung is a cloud of flies,' Sean laughed, and refilled the whisky glasses. 'What do you want from me?'

'If you were to act as an intelligence agent for the bureau of state security – our man in Rhodesia – we might forget about your little indiscretions.'

'Why not?' Sean agreed instantly, 'Anything for a laugh and living dangerously is half the fun.'

'Do stop being so boring you two,' Isabella cried, stroking Lothar's cheek. 'Come and dance with me.'

Sean's partner sat up groggily and blurted, 'I'm going to be sick.'

'Emergency,' said Sean. He hauled her to her feet and hustled her through to the tiny women's room.

There were two other females fussing over the single wash hand basin, and they squealed demurely.

'Don't worry about us, ladies.' Sean pushed his partner into the cubicle and aimed her at the toilet bowl. Noisily she got shot of what was troubling her and then straightened up and grinned at him shakily. Tenderly he wiped her mouth with a wad of toilet paper.

'How are you feeling?'

'I feel better now.'

'Good, let's go somewhere and ball.'

'Okay,' she said, perking up miraculously. 'That's what I've been waiting for the whole evening.'

Sean stopped beside Lothar and Isabella on the crowded floor.

'We are cutting out of here – something just came up, if you will pardon the expression.'

'I'll call you at Weltevreden some time tomorrow,' Lothar said. 'Just to arrange the details.'

'Don't make it too early,' Sean advised and grinned at his sister. 'See you later, Bella Bunny.'

'For God's sake, don't say "Be good!"' Isabella pleaded.

'Perish the thought.' Sean picked up his partner and carried her down the stairs.

Isabella made one more circuit of the floor, just to let Sean get clear, then she murmured, 'That's enough dancing for one night – let's go.'

Lothar had never seen a woman drive with Isabella's skill and flair. He relaxed in the passenger seat and watched her. Despite the long day and its excesses, she was still dewy fresh as a rosepetal and her eyes were clear and sparkling.

She was the first English girl he had ever been with, and her free and forthright manner at once appalled and intrigued him. With their strict Calvinist upbringing Afrikaner girls would never make themselves so available or behave with such abandon. Yet although she shocked him more than a little, she was without any doubt the most strikingly lovely girl he had ever met.

Isabella drove straight through the intersection of Paradise Road and Rhodes Drive.

'You've missed the turn to Weltevreden,' he pointed out, and she gave him a brief impish grin.

'That's not where we are going. From here you are in my hands, Lothar De La Rey.'

They followed the coastal road from Muizenberg around the bay, through the deserted streets of Simonstown, the British naval base, and then on towards the tip of the continent.

Where the road skirted a high cliff above the sea, Isabella pulled the Alfa off the road and cut the engine.

'Come on,' she ordered, took his hand and led him to the edge of the cliff. The dawn was turning the eastern sky to lemon and orange, and far beneath them the cliffs were folded upon themselves to form a sheltered bay. 'It's so beautiful here,' Isabella whispered. 'One of my favourite places.'

'Where are we?' Lothar asked.

'It's called Smitswinkel Bay,' she told him, and led him by the hand to the start of the steep pathway that descended the cliff.

At the bottom a narrow horse-shoe of silver sand surrounded the bay, and above the beach a few locked and shuttered shacks were crammed against the foot of the cliff. The dawn light filtered down, soft and pearly, and the waters of the bay glowed with the misty sheen of moonstones.

Isabella kicked off her shoes and walked down to the water's edge, and then without looking round at him she slipped her dress off her shoulders and let it drop to the sand. Beneath it she wore only a pair of silk and lace panties. For a long moment she stood staring out across the bay and her back was long and shaped like the neck of a lovely vase, the beads of her spine just showed beneath skin that was pale and lustrous as mother-of-pearl. Then she stooped to pull the panties down to her ankles, and stepped out of them.

She was naked and Lothar's breathing caught in his throat as he watched her walk slowly down to the water's edge, her hips rolling in time to the lazy pulse of the ocean. She walked out until she was waist-deep and she lowered herself until only her head was above the surface. Then she turned and looked back at him. The challenge and the invitation were as clear as if she had called them aloud.

Lothar undressed as unhurriedly as she had done. Naked, he walked into the bay and she rose to meet him, the waters streaming from her bare shoulders down her breasts, and she lifted her arms and placed them around his neck.

She teased him with her tongue, letting him explore the warmth and softness of her mouth, and she gave a little purring chuckle as she felt how much he wanted her.

The sound goaded him and he lifted her in his arms and carried her out beyond her depth. She was forced to cling to him, and her body was weightless. He handled her like a doll and she offered no resistance. His strength seemed limitless – it made her feel helpless and vulnerable, but she was grateful for his patience. To hurry now would spoil it all. She wanted this to be something far beyond the frenzied groping and often painful thrusting that was all she had been offered by the three or four college lads she had allowed this far.

She learned quickly that he could tease as well as she could, and he let her float around him, light as the buoyant kelp in the gentle swell of the ocean while he stood foursquare and refused to make the final assault. In the end it was she who succumbed to impatience.

In contrast to the cool water that eddied around her, he was like a flaming brand buried deep in her body. She could not believe the hardness and the heat, and she cried aloud with incredible delight. None of the others had been anything like this. From now on this was all that counted, this was what she had been searching for all along.

Still clinging together they waded ashore, and by now it was full morning. They bundled up their clothes and still naked she led him to the last shack in the row. While she searched for the key in her purse, he asked, 'Who does this belong to?'

'It's one of Daddy's hiding places. I only discovered it quite by chance and he doesn't know that I have a key.'

She got the door open and led him into the single room.

'Towels,' she said, and opened one of the cupboards. They made a game out of drying each other, but the light-hearted mood changed quickly to serious intent, and she dragged him to the bunk against the wall.

'Where I come from the man does the asking,' he chuckled.

'You are an old-fashioned chauvinist prude,' she told him.

As she clambered up onto the bunk he saw that her bottom was still bright pink from the cold waters of the bay; he found that peculiarly endearing and he was suddenly overwhelmed by a sense of tenderness towards her.

'You are so gentle,' she whispered. 'So strong and yet so gentle.'

It was mid-morning before they felt hungry, and dressed only in one of her father's old fishing jerseys, Isabella raided the larder for their breakfast.

'How do you fancy smoked oysters and asparagus with your baked beans?'

'Won't your father miss you?' he asked as he opened the cans.

'Oh, Daddy is a push-over. He will believe anything I tell him. It's my grandmother we have to watch out for, but I've arranged with one of my girlfriends to cover for us.'

'Ah, so you knew where we were going to end up?' he asked.

'Of course.' She rolled her eyes at him. 'Didn't you?'

They sat cross-legged on the bunk with the plates on their laps and Isabella tasted the mixture. 'It's ghastly,' she gave her opinion, 'if I wasn't starving I wouldn't touch it.'

'Of course, you will see your mother while you are in London?' he asked, and the loaded spoon stopped half-way to Isabella's mouth.

'How did you know I was going to London – and how did you know my mother was there?'

'I probably know more about your mother than you do,' Lothar told her, and she replaced the spoon on her plate and stared at him.

'For instance?' she challenged.

'Well, for instance, your mother is a rabid enemy of this country. She is a member of the banned ANC and of the anti-*apartheid* group. She associates regularly with members of the South African Communist Party. In London she runs a safe house for political refugees and escaped terrorists.'

'My mother?' Isabella shook her head.

'Your mother was deeply implicated in the plot to blow up the houses of parliament and assassinate most of the members of the House, including the prime minister – and your father and my father.'

Isabella was still shaking her head, but he went on expressionlessly, watching her with those golden leopard eyes.

'She was directly responsible for the death of her own father, your grandfather, Colonel Blaine Malcomess. She was an accomplice of Moses Gama who is now serving a life sentence for terrorism and murder, and if she had not escaped she would probably be in jail with him.'

'No,' said Isabella softly. 'I don't believe it.'

She was amazed and distressed by the change in him. Minutes before he had been so gentle, now he was hard and cruel, wounding her with words as he went on, 'For instance, did you know that your mother was Moses Gama's lover, and that she bore him a son? Your half-brother is an attractive coffee colour.'

'No!' Isabella recoiled, shaking her head in disbelief. 'How do you know all this?'

'From the signed confession of Moses Gama, the man himself. I can arrange for you to see a copy, but that is not really necessary. You will almost certainly meet your bastard half-brother in London. He is living there with your mother. His name is Benjamin Afrika.'

Isabella jumped up and carried her plate to the kitchenette. She dumped the food into the garbage bin and without looking around, she asked, 'Why are you telling me all this?'

'So that you will know your duty.'

'I don't understand.' She still would not look at him.

'We believe your mother and her associates are planning some sort of violent action against this country. We are not sure what it is. Any information on their activities would be invaluable.'

Isabella turned slowly and stared at him. Her face was pale and stricken.

'You want me to spy on my own mother?'

'We simply would like to know the names of the people you meet in her company while you are in London.'

She was not listening. She cut in on what he was saying.

'You planned this. You picked me out, not because you thought I was attractive or sweet or desirable. You deliberately set out to seduce me, just for this.'

'You are beautiful, not attractive. You are magnificent, not sweet' he said.

'And you are a bastard, a ruthless heartless bastard.'

He stood up and went to where his clothes hung behind the door.
'What are you going to do?' she demanded.
'Get dressed and go,' he told her.
'Why?'
'You called me a bastard.'
'You are.' Her eyes were glutted with tears. 'An irresistible bastard. Don't go, Lothar, please don't go.'

* * *

Isabella was relieved when her father told her that he was unable to fly to London with her and Michael. Meeting her mother again after all these years, and after what Lothar had told her, would be difficult enough, without her father there to complicate matters and confuse her feelings. She had, indeed, tried to beg off going to London herself. She wanted to be close to Lothar, but he had been the one who insisted she make the trip.

'I will be back in Johannesburg and we wouldn't see much of each other anyway,' he told her. 'And besides that you have your duty and you have given me your word.'

'I know Daddy would give me a PR job with the company in Jo'burg. I could get a flat and we could see lots of each other, I mean lots and lots!'

'When you come back from London,' he promised.

* * *

There were representatives from South Africa House and the London office of Courtney Mining to meet Isabella and Michael at Heathrow and a company limousine to take them to the Dorchester.

'Pater always overdoes it by a mile,' Michael remarked, embarrassed by the reception. 'We could have taken a taxi.'

'No point in being a Courtney, unless you get to enjoy it,' Isabella disagreed.

When Isabella was shown up to her suite which looked out over Hyde Park, there was an enormous bouquet of flowers waiting for her with a note:

Sorry I can't be with you, darling. Next time we will paint the town bright scarlet together.
Your old Dad.

Even before the porter had brought her bags up, Isabella dialled the number that Tara had given her and she was answered on the third ring.

'This is the Lord Kitchener Hotel, may I help you?'

It was strangely nostalgic to be greeted by an African accent in a strange city.

'May I speak to Mrs Malcomess, please?'

In her letter Tara had warned her that she had reverted to her maiden name after the divorce.

'Hello, Mater.' Isabella tried to sound natural when Tara came on the line, but Tara's delight was unrestrained.

'Oh Bella darling, where are you? Is Mickey with you? How soon can you get here? You have got the address, haven't you? It's so easy to find.'

Isabella tried to match Michael's enthusiasm and excitement as they drove through the streets of London and the taxi-driver pointed out the landmarks they passed, but she was in a funk at the prospect of seeing her mother again.

It was one of those rather seedy little tourist hotels in a side street off the Cromwell Road. Only part of the neon sign was lit. 'The Ord Kitch', it flashed in electric blue, and on the glass of the front door were plastered the emblems of the AA and *Routiers* and a blaze of credit card stickers.

Tara rushed out through the glass doors while they were still paying off the taxi. She embraced Michael first, which gave Isabella a few moments to study her mother.

She had put on weight, her backside in the faded blue jeans was huge, and her bosom hung shapelessly in the baggy man's sweater.

'She's an old bag.' Isabella was appalled. Even though Tara had never gone to any pains with her appearance, she had always had an air of freshness and neatness. But now her hair had turned grey, and she had obviously made a half-hearted attempt to henna it back to its original colour, and then given up. The grey was streaked brassy ginger and violent mulberry red, and it was twisted up into a careless bun at the nape of her neck from which parti-coloured wisps had escaped.

Her features had sagged almost to obscure the bone structure which had been one of her most striking assets, and though her eyes were still large and bright the skin around them had creased and bagged.

At last she released Michael, and turned to Isabella.

'My darling little girl, I would hardly have recognized you. What a lovely young woman you have become.'

They embraced. Isabella recalled how her mother had smelled, it was one of her pleasant childhood memories, but this woman smelled of some cheap and flowery perfume, of cigarette smoke and boiled cabbage, and – Isabella could barely credit her own senses – of underclothing that had been worn too long without changing.

She broke off the embrace, but Tara kept hold of her arm, and with Michael on the other side of her led them into the Lord Kitchener Hotel. The receptionist was a black lad, and Isabella recognized his voice as the one who had answered her phone call.

'Phineas is from Cape Town also,' Tara introduced them. 'He is one of our other runaways. He left after the troubles in sixty-one and, like the rest of us, he won't be going home yet. Now let me show you around the Lordy – ' she laughed. 'That's what my permanent guests call it, the Lordy. I thought of changing the name, it's so colonial and Empire – '

Tara chattered on happily, as she led them around the hotel. The carpets in the passages were threadbare, and the rooms had washbasins, but shared the toilet and bathroom at the end of each passage.

Tara introduced them to any of her guests they met in the corridors or public rooms. 'These are my son and daughter from Cape Town,' and they shook hands with German and French tourists who spoke no English, Pakistanis and Chinese, black Kenyans and coloured South Africans.

'Where are you staying?' Tara wanted to know.

'At the Dorchester.'

'Of course.' Tara rolled her eyes. 'Fifty guineas a day, paid for by the sweat

of the workers in the Courtney mines. That is what your father would have chosen. Why don't you and Mickey move in here? I have two nice rooms on the top floor free at the moment. You would meet so many interesting people, and we'd see so much more of each other.'

Isabella shuddered at the thought of sharing the toilet at the end of the passage and jumped in before Michael could agree.

'Daddy would be furious, he has prepaid for us – and now we know our way, it's only a short taxi ride.'

'Taxis,' Tara sniffed. 'Why not take the bus or the underground like any ordinary person?'

Isabella stared at her speechlessly. Didn't she understand that they weren't ordinary people? They were Courtneys. She was about to say so, when Michael sensed her intention and intervened smoothly.

'Of course you are quite right. You'll have to tell us what number bus to take and where to get off, Mater.'

'Mickey darling, please don't call me Mater any longer. It's so terribly *bourgeois*. Call me Mummy or Tara, but not that.'

'All right. It will be a little bit strange at first, but okay. I'll call you Tara.'

'It's almost lunch time,' Tara announced blithely. 'I asked cook to make a bread and butter pudding, I know it's one of your favourites, Mickey.'

'I'm not awfully hungry, Mater – Tara,' Isabella announced. 'And it must be jet-lag or something, but – '

Michael pinched her sharply. 'That's lovely, Tara. We'd love to stay for lunch.'

'I just have to look into the kitchen – make sure it's all under control – come along.'

As they entered the kitchen a child came running to Tara. He must have been helping the Irish cook, for his hands were white with flour to the elbows. Tara hugged him, happily heedless of the flour that rubbed off on her sweater.

A mat of short woolly curls covered his pate, and his skin was a clear light toffee colour. His eyes were huge and dark, and he had appealing gamine features. He reminded Isabella of any one of the dozens of children of the estate workers on Weltevreden. She smiled at him, and he gave back a cocky but friendly grin.

'This is Benjamin,' Tara said. 'And these, Benjamin, are your brother and sister – Mickey and Isabella.'

Isabella stared at the child. She had tried to discount and forget all that Lothar had told her, and in some measure she had succeeded. But now it all came rushing back, the words roaring in her ears like flood waters.

'Your half brother is an attractive coffee colour,' Lothar had told her and she wanted to scream, 'How could you, Mater, how could you do this to us?' But Michael had recovered from his obvious surprise, and now he held out his hand towards the child and said,

'Hi there, Ben. It's fine that we are brothers – but how about you and me being friends also?'

'Hey, man – I like that,' Benjamin agreed instantly. To add to Isabella's dismay and confusion, he spoke in a broad south London accent.

Isabella spoke barely a dozen words during lunch. The pea soup was thickened with flour that had not cooked through and it stuck to the roof of her mouth. The boiled silverside lay limply in its own watery gravy, and the cabbage was cooked pink.

They sat at the table with Phineas, the receptionist, and five other of Tara's guests, all black South African expatriates, and the boisterous conversation was almost entirely conducted in left-wing jargon. The government of which Isabella's beloved father was a minister was always referred to as the 'racist regime' and Michael joined cheerfully in the discussion about the redistribution of wealth and the return of the land to those who worked it after the revolution had succeeded and the People's Democratic Rupublic of Azania had been established. Isabella wanted to scream at him, 'Damn you, Mickey, they are talking about Weltevreden and the Silver River Mine. These are terrorists and revolutionaries – and their sole purpose is to destroy us and our world.'

When the bread-and-butter pudding was served, she could take it no longer.

'I'm sorry, Tara,' she whispered. 'I have a splitting headache, and I simply have to get back to the Dorchester and lie down.' She was so pale and discomforted that Tara made only a token protest and genuine noises of concern. Isabella refused to let Michael escort her. 'I won't spoil your fun. You haven't seen Mater – Tara – in ages. I'll just grab a taxi.'

Perhaps it really was fatigue that had weakened her, but in the cab she found herself weeping with chagrin and shame and fury.

'Damn her! Damn her to hell,' she whispered. 'She has disgraced and dishonoured all of us, Daddy and Nana and me and all the family.'

As soon as she reached her room she locked her door, threw herself on the bed and reached for the telephone.

'Exchange, I want to put a call through to Johannesburg in South Africa – ' She read the number out of her address book.

The delay was less than half an hour and then a marvellously homey Afrikaans accent said, 'This is police headquarters, bureau for state security.'

'I want to speak to Colonel Lothar De La Rey.'

'De La Rey.'

Despite the thousands of miles that separated them, his voice was crisp and clear, and in her imagination she saw him again naked on the beach in the dawn, like a statue of a Greek athlete but with those glowing golden eyes, and she whispered, 'Oh God Lothie, I've missed you. I want to come home. I hate it here.'

He spoke quietly, reassuring and consoling her, and when she had calmed he ordered her. 'Tell me about it.'

'You were right. Everything you said was true – even to her little brown bastard, and the people are all revolutionaries and terrorists. What do you want me to do, Lothie? I'll do anything you tell me.'

'I want you to stay there, and stick it out for the full two weeks. You can telephone me every day, but you must stay on. Promise me, Bella.'

'All right – but, God, I miss you and home.'

'Listen, Bella. I want you to go to South Africa House the first opportunity you have. Don't let anybody know, not even your brother Michael. Ask for Colonel Van Vuuren, the military attaché. He will show you photographs and ask you to identify the people you meet.'

'All right, Lothie – but I've told you twice already how much I miss you, while you, you swine, haven't said a word.'

'I have thought about you every day since you left,' Lothar said. 'You're beautiful and funny and you make me laugh.'

'Don't stop,' Isabella pleaded. 'Just keep talking like that.'

Adrian Van Vuuren was a burly avuncular man, who looked more like a

friendly Free State farmer than a secret service man. He took her up to the ambassador's office and introduced her to His Excellency who knew Shasa well and they chatted for a few minutes. His Excellency invited Isabella to the races at Ascot the coming Saturday but Colonel Van Vuuren intervened apologetically.

'Miss Courtney is doing a little job for us at present, Your Excellency. It might not be wise to make too much public display of her connections to the embassy.'

'Very well,' the ambassador agreed reluctantly, 'But you will come to lunch with us, Miss Courtney – not often we have such a pretty girl at our gatherings.'

Van Vuuren gave her the short tour of the embassy and its art treasures, which ended in his office on the third floor.

'Now, my dear, we have some work for you.'

A pile of albums was stacked on his desk, each full of head-and-shoulder photographs of men and women. They sat side by side and Van Vuuren flicked through the pages, picking out the mug shots of the people she had met at the Lord Kitchener Hotel.

'You make it easier for us by knowing their names,' Van Vuuren remarked, and turned to a photograph of Phineas, the hotel receptionist.

'Yes, that's him,' Isabella confirmed, and Van Vuuren looked up his details in a separate ledger. 'Phineas Mophoso. Born 1941. Member of PAC. Convicted of public violence 16 May 1961. Violated bail conditions. Illegal emigration late 1961. Present location believed UK.'

'Small fry,' Van Vuuren grunted, 'but small fry often shoal with big fish.' He offered to provide an embassy car to drive Isabella back to the Dorchester.

'Thank you, but I'll walk.'

She had tea alone at Fortnum & Masons and when she got back to the hotel Michael was frantic with worry.

'For heaven's sake, Mickey. I'm not a baby. I can look after myself. I just felt like exploring on my own.'

'Mater is giving a party for us at the Lord Kitchener this evening. She wants us there before six.'

'You mean Tara, not Mater – and the Lordy, not the Lord Kitchener. Don't be so *bourgeois* and colonial, Mickey darling.'

At least fifty people crowded into the residents' lounge of the Lordy for Tara's party, and she provided unlimited quantities of draught bitter and Spanish red wine to wash down the Irish cook's unforgettable snacks. Michael entered into the spirit of the occasion. He was at all times the centre of an arguing gesticulating group. Isabella backed herself into a corner of the lounge and with a remote and icy *hauteur* discouraged any familiar approach from the other guests, while at the same time memorizing their names and faces as Tara introduced them.

After the first hour the smoky claustrophobic atmosphere, and the volume of conversation lubricated by Tara's Spanish plonk, became oppressive and Isabella's eyes felt gritty and a dull ache started in her temples. Tara had disappeared and Michael was still enjoying himself.

'That's my patriotic duty for tonight,' she decided, and sidled towards the door taking care not to alert Michael to her departure.

As she passed the deserted reception desk, she heard voices from behind the frosted glass door of Tara's tiny office, and she had an attack of conscience.

'I can't just go off without thanking Mater,' she decided. 'It was an awful party, but she went to a lot of trouble and I am one of the guests of honour.'

She slipped behind the desk, and was about to tap on the panel of the door when she heard her mother say, 'But, comrade, I didn't expect you to arrive tonight.' The words were commonplace, but the tone in which Tara said them was not. She was more than agitated – she was afraid, deadly afraid.

A man's voice replied, but it was so low and hoarse that Isabella could not catch the words, and then Tara said, 'But they are my own children. It's perfectly safe.'

This time the man's reply was sharper. 'Nothing is ever safe,' he said. 'They are also your husband's children, and your husband is a member of the fascist racist regime. We will leave now and return later after they have gone.'

Isabella acted instinctively. She darted back into the lobby and out through the glass front doors of the hotel. The narrow street was lined with parked vehicles, one of them a dark delivery van tall enough to screen her. She hid behind it.

After a few minutes, two men followed her out of the front entrance of the hotel. They both wore dark raincoats but their heads were bare. They set off briskly, walking side by side towards the Cromwell Road and as they came level with where she leaned against the side of the van, the street light lit their faces.

The man nearest to her was black, with a strong, resolute face, broad nose and thick African lips. His companion was white and much older. His flesh was pale as putty and had the same soft amorphous look. His hair was black and lank and lifeless. It hung on to his forehead, and his eyes were dark and fathomless as pools of coal tar – and Isabella understood why her mother had been afraid. This was a man who inspired fear.

Colonel Van Vuuren sat beside her at his desk with the pile of albums in front of them. 'He is a white man. That makes life a lot easier for all of us,' he said as he selected one of the albums.

'These are all white,' he explained. 'We have got them all in here. Even the ones safely behind bars, like Bram Fischer.'

She found his photograph on the third page.

'That's the one.'

'Are you sure?' Van Vuuren asked. 'It's not a very good photo.'

It must have been taken as he was climbing into a vehicle, for the background was a city street. He was glancing back, most of his body obscured by the open door of the vehicle, and movement had blurred his features slightly.

'Yes. That's him all right,' Isabella repeated. 'I could never mistake those eyes.'

Van Vuuren referred to the separate ledger. 'The photograph was taken in East Berlin by the American CIA two years ago. He is a wily bird, that's the only picture we have. His name is Joe Cicero. He is the secretary general of the South Africa Communist Party and a colonel in the Russian KGB. He is a chief of staff of the military wing of the banned ANC, the *Umkhonto we Sizwe*.' Van Vuuren smiled. 'And so, my dear, the big fish has arrived. Now we must try and identify his companion. That will not be so easy.'

It took almost two hours. Isabella paged through the albums slowly. When she finished one pile, Van Vuuren's assistant brought in another armful of albums and she began again. Van Vuuren sat patiently beside her, sending out for coffee and encouraging her with a smile and a word when she flagged.

'Yes.' Isabella straightened up at last. 'This is the one.'

'You have been wonderful. Thank you.' Van Vuuren reached for the ledger and turned to the *curriculum vitae* of the man in the photograph.

'Raleigh Tabaka,' he read out. 'Secretary of the Vaal branch of PAC and member of *Poqo*. Organizer of the attack on the Sharpeville police station. Disappeared three years ago, before he could be detained. Since then there have been rumours that he was seen in training camps in Morocco and East Germany. He is rated as a trained and dangerous terrorist. Two big fish together. Now, if we could just find what they are up to!'

* * *

Tara Courtney waited up long after her party had broken up. The last guests had staggered through the glass doors, and Michael had kissed her goodnight and gone off to try and pick up a late cruising taxi in the Cromwell Road.

Since first she had met him, Joe Cicero had been associated with danger and suffering and loss. There was always an aura of mystery and a passionless evil surrounding him. He terrified her. The man with him she had met for the first time that night. Joe Cicero had introduced him only as Raleigh, but Tara's heart had gone out to him immediately. Although he was much younger, he reminded her so strongly of her own Moses. He had the same smouldering intensity and compelling presence, the same dark majesty of bearing and command.

They came back a little after two in the morning, and Tara let them in and led them through to her own bedroom in the back area of the hotel.

'Raleigh will stay with you for the next two or three weeks. Then he will return to South Africa. You will provide everything he asks for, particularly the information.'

'Yes, comrade,' Tara whispered. Although she was the registered owner and licensed proprietress of the hotel, the money for the purchase had been provided by Joe Cicero and she took her orders directly from him.

'Raleigh is the nephew of Moses Gama,' Joe said, watching her carefully with those expressionless black eyes as she turned to the younger man.

'Oh, Raleigh, I didn't realize. It is almost as though we are one family. Moses is the father of my son, Benjamin.'

'Yes,' Raleigh answered. 'I know that. This is the reason that I am able to give you the object of my mission to South Africa. Your dedication is proven and unquestioned. I am going back to Africa to free your husband and my uncle, Moses Gama, from the prison of the fascist racist Verwoerd regime to lead the democratic revolution of our people.'

Her joy dawned slowly with her understanding. Then she went to Raleigh Tabaka and as she embraced him she was weeping with happiness.

'I will give anything to help you succeed,' she whispered through her tears. 'Even my life.'

* * *

Jakobus Stander had only two classes on a Friday morning, and the last one ended at 11.30. He left the grounds of the University of the Witwatersrand immediately afterwards and caught the bus down to Hillbrow. It was a ride of only fifteen minutes and he reached his flat a little after midday.

The suitcase was still on the low coffee table where he had placed it the night before, after he had finished working on it. It was a cheap brown case made of imitation leather with a pressed metal lock.

He stood staring at it with pale topaz-coloured eyes. Except for the eyes, he was an unremarkable young man. Although he was tall, he was too thin and the grey flannel trousers hung loosely around his waist. His hair was long, flecked with dandruff, hanging over the back of his collar, and the elbows of his baggy brown corduroy jacket were patched with leather. Rather than a tie he wore a turtle-neck jersey with the collar rolled over. It was the self-consciously shabby uniform of the left-wing intellectual, adopted by even the Professor of the Department of Sociology in which Jakobus was a senior lecturer.

Without removing the jacket, he sat down on the narrow bed and stared at the suitcase.

'I am one of the only ones left,' he thought. 'It's all up to me now. They have taken Baruch and Randy and Berny – I am all alone.'

There had been less than fifty of them even in the best times. A small band of true patriots, champions of the proletariat, almost all of them white and young, members of the young liberals or students and faculty members involved in radical student politics at the English-speaking universities of Cape Town and the Witwatersrand. Kobus had been the only Afrikaner in their ranks.

At first they had called themselves the National Committee of Liberation, and their methods had been more sophisticated than *Umkhonto we Sizwe* and the Rivonia group. They had used dynamite and electrical timing devices, and their successes had been many and heartening. They had destroyed power substations and railway switching systems, even a reservoir dam, and in the triumphant mood of those early days they had restyled themselves the African Resistance Movement.

In the end they had been destroyed in exactly the same manner as Mandela and his Rivonia group, by the inefficiency of their own security and the inability of the members who were captured by security police to withstand interrogation.

He was one of the only ones left, but he knew that his hours of freedom were numbered. The security police had taken Berny two days ago and by now he would have talked. Berny was not made of heroic stuff, a small pale and nervous creature, too soft-hearted for the cause. Jakobus had argued against his recruitment, but that was too late now. The bureau for state security had Berny, and Berny knew his name. There was very little time left, but still he procrastinated. He looked at his wristwatch. It was almost one o'clock. His mother would be home by now, preparing his father's lunch. He lifted the telephone.

Sarah Stander stood over the kitchen stove. She felt tired and dispirited, but she seemed always to be tired these days. The telephone rang and she turned down the hot plate of the stove, and wiped her hands on her apron as she went through to her husband's study.

The room was lined with shelves of dusty law books that had once been a promise of hope to her, a symbol of success and advancement, but now seemed rather to be the fetters that bound Roelf and her in penury and mediocrity.

She lifted the phone. 'Hello. This is Mevrou Stander.'

'Mama,' Jakobus replied, and she gave a little coo of joy.

'My boy – where are you?' But at his reply her spirits plunged again.

'In the flat in Johannesburg, Mama.' That was a thousand miles away, and her longing to see him devastated her.

'I hoped you were – '

'Mama,' he cut her off. 'I had to speak to you. I had to explain. Something terrible is going to happen. I wanted to tell you – I don't want you to be angry with me, I don't want you to hate me.'

'Never!' she cried. 'I love you too much, my boy – '

'I don't want Papa and you to feel bad. What I do is not your fault. Please understand and forgive me.'

'Kobus, my son, what is it? I don't understand what you are saying.'

'I can't tell you, Mama. Soon you will understand. I love you and Papa – please remember that.'

'Kobus,' she cried. 'Kobus!' but the earpiece clicked and then there was only the hum of a broken connection.

Frantically she rang the exchange and asked to be reconnected but it took fifteen minutes before the operator called her back.

'There is no reply from your Johannesburg number.'

Sarah was distraught. She roamed around her kitchen, the midday meal forgotten, twisting her apron in her fingers, trying desperately to think of some way of reaching her son. When her husband came in through the front door she rushed down the passageway and threw her arms around his neck, and she gabbled out her fears.

'Manie!' Roelf said. 'I will telephone him. He can send one of his men around to Kobus's flat.'

'Why didn't I think of that?' Sarah sobbed.

The secretary in Manfred's ministry told them he was not available and would not be in again until Monday morning.

'What will we do now?' Roelf was as worried as she was.

'Lothie,' Sarah brightened. 'He is in the police in Johannesburg. Ring Lothie, he will know what to do.'

* * *

Jakobus Stander broke the connection to his mother, and jumped to his feet. He knew he must act quickly and decisively now. Already he had wasted too much time, they would be coming for him soon.

He picked up the suitcase and left the flat, locking the door behind him. He rode down in the lift, still holding the heavy suitcase, even though the handle cut into his fingers. There were two girls in the lift with him. They ignored him and chattered to each other all the way down. He watched them surreptitiously. 'It may be you,' he thought. 'It could be anybody.'

The girls barged out of the lift ahead of him, and he followed slowly, walking lopsidedly because of the weight of the brown suitcase.

He caught the bus at the corner and took the seat nearest the door, placing the suitcase on the seat beside him, but retaining his grip on the handle all the way.

The bus stopped outside the side entrance of the Johannesburg railway

station, and Jakobus was the first passenger to alight. Lugging his suitcase, he started towards the station entrance, and then his steps began to drag and his mouth went dry with terror. There was a constable of the railway police at the entrance, and as Jakobus hesitated he looked directly at him. Jakobus wanted to drop the suitcase and run back to the bus which was pulling away behind him, but the press of other passengers bore him forward like a dead leaf in a stream.

He did not want to catch the constable's eye. He trudged forward head bowed, concentrating on the heels of the fat woman in white shoes just ahead of him. He looked up as he came level with the station portals, and the constable was walking away from him, his hands clasped lightly behind his back. Jakobus's legs felt rubbery and his relief was so intense that he thought he was going to be ill. He fought down his nausea and kept on going with the stream of commuters.

At the centre of the concourse under the high arched skylight of glass there was a goldfish pond surrounded by wooden benches. Although most of the benches were crowded with travellers snatching a few minutes' rest between trains or awaiting the arrival of friends, there was room for Jakobus at the end of one of them.

He sat down and placed the suitcase between his feet. He was sweating heavily and he had difficulty in breathing. Waves of nausea kept welling up from the pit of his guts and there was a bitter sick taste at the back of his throat.

He wiped his face with his handkerchief and kept swallowing hard until gradually he had control of himself again. Then he looked around him. The other benches were still crowded. In the centre of the one facing him there was a mother with two daughters. The youngest one was still in napkins, she sat on her mother's lap with a dummy in her mouth. The elder girl had skinny sun-browned legs and arms and frilly petticoats under her short skirt. She leaned against her mother's side and sucked a lollipop on a stick. Her mouth was dyed bright red by the sticky candy.

All around Jakobus passed a continual stream of humanity, coming and going down the broad staircase that led up to the street. Like columns of ants, they spread out to reach the separate platforms, and the loudspeakers boomed out information on arriving and departing trains, and the hiss and huff of escaping steam from the locomotives echoed against the high arches of glass above where Jakobus sat.

He looked down at the suitcase between his feet. He had drilled a needle hole through the imitation leather. A strand of piano wire emerged from the aperture, and he had fixed a brass curtain ring to the end of it, and taped the ring to the brown leather beside the handle.

Now he picked at the tape with his fingernail and peeled it away. He stuck his forefinger through the brass ring and gently pulled the wire taut. There was a muted click from the interior of the suitcase and he started guiltily and looked around him again. The little girl with the lollipop stuck in her cheek had been watching him. She gave him a sticky smile and shyly cuddled closer to her mother's side.

Using his heels and the back of his legs, Jakobus pushed the suitcase slowly under the bench on which he was seated. Then he stood up and walked briskly across to the men's toilets on the far side of the concourse. He stood in front of one of the porcelain urinals and checked his wristwatch. It was ten minutes after two. He zipped up his fly and walked out of the men's room.

The mother and the two little girls were still sitting where he had left them, and the brown suitcase lay under the bench opposite. As he passed the child recognized him and smiled again. He did not return the smile but went up the staircase into the street. He walked down to the Langham Hotel at the corner and went into the men's bar. He ordered a cold Castle beer and drank it slowly, standing at the bar, checking his wristwatch every few minutes. He wondered if the mother and the two little girls had left, or if they were still sitting on the bench.

The ferocity of the explosion shocked him. He was almost a block away but it knocked over his glass and the dregs of the beer ran across the bar top. There was consternation throughout the bar room. Men were swearing with surprise and astonishment and rushing to the door.

Jakobus followed them out into the street. The traffic had stopped, and people were swarming out of the buildings to block the pavements. From the station entrance a cloud of dust and smoke billowed and through it staggered vague shadowy figures, powdered with dust, their clothing hanging off them in rags. Somewhere a woman began to scream, and all around him there were shouted questions.

'What is it? What happened?'

Jakobus turned and walked away. He heard the sirens of the police cars and the fire engines coming closer, but he did not look back.

* * *

'No, *Tannie* Sarie. I haven't seen Kobus since we last met at Waterkloof.' Lothar De La Rey tried to be patient. The Standers were old friends of his parents, and he had spent many happy childhood holidays at the cottage on the Stander farm at the seaside. That was before *Oom* Roelf Stander had been forced to sell the farm. 'Yes, yes *Tannie*. I know, but Kobus and I live in different worlds now – I know how worried you must be. Yes, of course.'

Lothar was taking the call in his private office in the headquarters complex of Marshall Square, and he glanced at his wristwatch as he listened to Sarah Stander's plaintive voice. It was just before two o'clock.

'What time was it when he telephoned you?' Lothar asked, and listened to her reply. 'That was an hour ago. Where did he say he was speaking from? All right, *Tannie*, what is his address in Hillbrow?' He scribbled it on the pad in front of him. 'Now tell me, *Tannie*, what was it exactly he said. Something terrible and you must forgive him? Yes, that doesn't sound very good, I agree. Suicide? No, *Tannie* Sarie, I'm sure he didn't mean that, but I will send one of my men to check his flat, why don't you ring the university in the meantime?'

One of the other telephones on his desk squealed and he ignored it. 'What did they say at the university?' he asked. 'All right, *Tannie*, I will telephone you and *Oom* Roelf just as soon as I have any news.' By now all three of his telephones were shrilling, and Captain Lourens, his assistant, was signalling him frantically from the door of his office.

'Yes, I understand, *Tannie* Sarie. Yes, I promise I will telephone you. But I must ring off now. ' Lothar replaced the receiver and looked up at Lourens.

'*Ja*, what is it, man?'

'An explosion at the main railway station. It looks like another bomb.'

Lothar jumped to his feet and snatched up his jacket. 'Casualties?' he demanded.

'There are bodies and blood all over the place.'

'The bloody swines,' Lothar said bitterly.

The street was cordoned off. They left the police car at the barrier and Lothar, who was in plain clothes, showed his identification and the sergeant saluted him. There were five ambulances parked outside the station entrance with their lights flashing.

At the head of the staircase leading into the main concourse Lothar paused. The damage was terrible. The glass in the arched skylights had been blown out and it coated the marble floors, glittering like a field of ice crystals.

The restaurant had been turned into a first-aid station and the white-jacketed doctors and ambulance crews were at work. The stretcher-bearers were carrying their grisly loads up the staircase to the waiting vehicles.

The officer in charge of the investigation was a major from Marshall Square. He had his men searching the wreckage already, working methodically in an extended line across the concourse. He recognized Lothar and beckoned to him. The glass crunched under Lothar's feet as he crossed to join him.

'How many dead?' he asked without any preamble.

'We have been incredibly lucky, Colonel. About forty injured, mostly by flying glass, but only one dead.'

He reached down and pulled back the plastic sheet that was spread at his feet.

Under it lay a little girl in a short dress with a frilly lace petticoat. Both her legs and one arm had been blown away, and the dress was soaked with her blood.

'Her mother lost both eyes, and her little sister will lose one arm,' the major said, and Lothar saw that the child's face was miraculously unscathed. She seemed to be sleeping. Her mouth was bright red with sticky sugar and in her remaining hand she still clutched the stick of a half-eaten lollipop.

'Lourens,' Lothar said quietly to his assistant. 'Ring Records. Use the telephone in the restaurant. Tell them I want a computer run on my desk when I get back to the square. I want the name of every known white radical on the list. It had to be a white man in this section of the station.'

He watched Lourens cross the concourse and then he looked down at the tiny body under the plastic sheet.

'I'm going to get the bastard who did this,' he whispered. 'This one isn't going to get away.'

His staff were waiting for him when he got back to the office forty minutes later. They had already vetted the computerized list and checked the names of those in detention, in exile or those whose whereabouts could be assumed to be outside the Witwatersrand area.

There remained 396 suspects unaccounted for. They were listed in alphabetical order and it was almost four o'clock before they had worked down to the 'S' section. As Lothar folded over the last sheet of the print-out the name seemed to leap from the page at him:

STANDER, JAKOBUS PETRUS

In the same moment Sarah Stander's plaintive voice echoed in his ears.

'Stander,' he said crisply. 'This one is a new addition.' He had last checked

the list twenty-four hours before. It was one of the most important tools of his trade, the names upon it so familiar that he could conjure up each face clearly in his mind's eye. Kobus' name had not been there on his last reading.

Captain Lourens picked up the internal telephone to Records, and spoke to the files clerk on the section, then he turned back to Lothar as he hung up the receiver.

'Stander's name comes from the interrogation of a member of the African Resistance Movement. Bernard Fisher. He was arrested on the fifth, two days ago. Stander is a lecturer at Wits University.'

'I know who he is.' Lothar strode out of the operations room into his private office and ripped the top sheet off his notepad. 'And I know where he is.' He drew the .38 police special from his shoulder holster and checked the load as he gave his orders. 'I want four units of the flying squad and a break-in team with flak jackets and shotguns – and I want photographs of the bomb victims, the girl – '

The flat was on the fifth floor at the end of a long open gallery. Lothar placed men on every stairwell and both fire escapes, at the lift station and in the main lobby. He and Lourens went up with the break-in team, and they all moved stealthily into position.

With the police special cocked in his right hand, his back against the wall clear of the door, he reached out and rang the bell.

There was no reply. He rang again, and they waited tensely. The silence drew out. Lothar reached out to ring a third time, when there were light hesitant footsteps beyond the glass panel door.

'Who is it?' a breathless voice called.

'Kobus – it's me, Lothie.'

'*Liewe Here!* Sweet God!' and the sound of running footsteps receded into the flat.

'Go!' said Lothar and the hammer man from the break-in team stepped up to the door with the ten-pound sledgehammer. The lock burst open at the first stroke and the door crashed back against its hinges.

Lothar was the first one in. The lounge was deserted and he ran straight through into the bedroom.

Behind him Lourens shouted, '*Pasop!* Look out! He might be armed,' But Lothar wanted to stop him reaching a window and jumping.

The bathroom door was locked and he heard running water beyond it. He took the door with his shoulder, and the panel splintered. His own momentum carried him on into the bathroom.

Jakobus was leaning over the wash basin, shaking tablets form a bottle into the palm of his hand and cramming them into his mouth. His cheeks bulged, and he was gagging and swallowing.

Lothar brought the barrel of the revolver down on the wrist that held the bottle, and the bottle shattered into the basin. He caught Jakobus by his long hair and forced him to his knees. He wedged open his jaws with thumb and forefinger and with the fingers of his other hand hooked the crushed damp porridge of tablets out of his mouth.

'I want an ambulance team with a stomach pump up here,' he yelled at Lourens. 'And get an analysis of that bottle – its label and contents.'

Jakobus was struggling and Lothar hit him open-handed, back and across the face. Jakobus whimpered and subsided, and Lothar thrust his forefinger deeply down his throat.

Gasping and choking and retching, Jakobus started struggling again, but Lothar held him easily. He worked his forefinger around in his throat, keeping on even when hot vomit spurted up over his hand. Satisfied at last he let Jakobus lie in a puddle of his own vomit while he rinsed his hands in the basin.

He dried his hands and seized Jakobus by the back of the shirt. He hauled him to his feet, dragged him through into the lounge and flung him into one of the armchairs.

Lourens and the forensic team were already working over the apartment.

'Did you get the photographs?' Lothar asked, and Lourens handed him a buff envelope.

Jakobus sat huddled in the chair. His shirt was fouled with vomit, and his nose and eyes were red and running. The corner of his mouth was torn where Lothar had forced it open, and he was trembling violently.

Lothar sorted through the contents of the envelope and then he laid a glossy black and white print on the coffee table in front of Jakobus.

Jakobus stared at it. It was a photograph of the truncated body of the child, nestled in a pool of her own blood with the lollipop in her hand. He began to weep. He sobbed and choked and turned his head away. Lothar moved around behind his chair and caught the back of his neck, forced his head back.

'Look at it!' he ordered.

'I didn't mean it,' Jakobus whispered brokenly. 'I didn't mean it to happen.'

The cold white fury faded from Lothar's brain, and he released Jakobus's head and stepped back from him uncertainly. Those were the words he had used. 'I didn't mean it to happen.' The exact words he had used as he had stood over the black boy with the dead girl's head cradled in his lap and the raw wounds running red into the dust of Sharpeville.

Suddenly Lothar felt weary and sickened. He wanted to go away by himself. Lourens could take over from here, but he braced himself to fight off the despair.

He laid his hand on Jakobus's shoulder, and the touch was strangely gentle and compassionate.

'*Ja*, Kobus, we never mean it to happen – but they still die. Now it is your turn, Kobus, your turn to die. Come, let's go.'

* * *

The arrest was made six hours after the bomb blast, and even the English press was fulsome in its praise of the efficiency of the police investigation. Every front page across the nation carried photographs of Colonel Lothar De La Rey.

Six weeks later in the Johannesburg Supreme Court, Jakobus Stander pleaded guilty to the charge of murder and was sentenced to death. Two weeks later his appeal was denied by the Appellate Division in Bloemfontein and sentence of death was confirmed. Lothar De La Rey's promotion to brigadier was announced within days of the Appellate Division's decision.

* * *

Raleigh Tabaka arrived in Cape Town while the Stander trial was still in progress. He came back the way he had left, as a crewman on a Liberian-registered tramp steamer.

His papers, although issued in the name of Goodwill Mhlazini, were genuine and he passed quickly through customs and immigration and with his bag over his shoulder walked up the foreshore to the main Cape Town railway station.

When he reached the Witwatersrand the following evening, he caught the bus out to Drake's Farm and went to the cottage where Victoria Gama was staying. Vicky opened the door and she had the child by the hand. There was the smell of cooking from the little kitchenette in the back.

She started violently as she saw him. 'Raleigh, come in quickly.' She drew him into the cottage and bolted the door.

'You shouldn't have come here. You know that I am banned. They watch this place,' she told him as she went quickly to the windows and drew the curtains. Then she came back to where he stood in the centre of the room and studied him.

'You have changed,' she said softly. 'You are a man now.' The training and the discipline of the camps had left their mark. He stood straight and alert, and he seemed to exude an intensity and a force that reminded her of Moses Gama.

'He has become one of the lions,' she thought, and she asked, 'Why have you come here, Raleigh, and how can I help you?'

'I have come to free Moses Gama from the prison of the Boers – and I will tell you how you can help me.'

Victoria gave a little cry of joy, and clutched the child closer to her. 'Tell me what to do,' she pleaded.

He would not stay to eat the evening meal with Victoria, would not even sit down on one of the cheap deal chairs.

'When is your next visit to Moses?' he asked in a low but powerful voice.

'In eight days' time,' Victoria told him, and he nodded.

'Yes, I knew it was soon. That was part of our planning. Now, here is what you must do – '

When the prison launch ran out from Cape Town harbour, carrying Victoria and the child to exercise their six-monthly visiting rights, Raleigh Tabaka was on the deck of one of the crayfish trawlers that was moored alongside the repair wharf in the outer harbour. Raleigh was dressed like one of the trawlermen in a blue jersey, yellow plastic overalls and sea boots. He pretended to be working on the pile of crayfish pots on the foredeck, but he studied the ferry as it passed close alongside before it made the turn out through the entrance to the breakwater. He made out Victoria's regal figure in the stern. She was wearing her caftan in yellow, green and black, the colours of the ANC which always infuriated the jailers.

When the ferry had cleared the harbour and was set on course towards the low whale-backed profile of Robben Island far out in the bay, Raleigh walked back along the deck of the eighty-foot trawler to the wheelhouse.

The skipper of the trawler was a burly coloured man, dressed like Raleigh in jersey and waterproofs. Raleigh had met his son at the Lord Kitchener Hotel in London, an activist who had taken part in the Langa uprising and had fled the country immediately aferwards.

'Thank you, comrade,' Raleigh said, and the skipper came to the door of the wheelhouse and took the black pipe from between his even white teeth.

'Did you find out what you wanted?'

'Yes, comrade.'

'When will you need me for the next part?'

'Within ten days.' Raleigh replied.

'You must give me at least twenty-fours' warning. I have to get a permit from the fisheries department to work in the bay.'

Raleigh nodded. 'I have planned for that.' He turned his head to look forward towards the trawler's bows. 'Is your boat strong enough?' he asked.

'You let me worry about that,' the skipper chuckled. 'A boat that can live in the South Atlantic winter gales is strong enough for anything.' He handed Raleigh the small canvas airline bag that contained his street clothes. 'We will meet again soon then, my friend?'

'You can be sure of that, comrade,' Raleigh said quietly and went up the gangplank on to the wharf.

Raleigh changed out of his trawlerman's gear in the public toilet near the harbour gates, and then went across to the carpark behind the customs house. Ramsami's old Toyota was parked up against the fence, and Raleigh climbed into the back seat.

Sammy Ramsami looked up from the copy of *The Cape Times* he was reading. He was a good-looking young Hindu lawyer who specialized in political cases. For the previous four years he had represented Vicky Gama in her never-ending legal battle with authority, and he had accompanied her from the Transvaal on this visit to her husband.

'Did you get what you wanted?' he asked, and Raleigh grunted noncommittally.

'I don't want to know what this is all about,' Sammy Ramsami said, and Raleigh smiled coldly.

'Don't worry, comrade, you will not be burdened with that knowledge.'

They did not speak again, not for the next four hours while they waited for Vicky to return from the island. She came at last, tall and stately in her brilliant caftan and turban, the child beside her, and the coloured stevedores working on the dock recognized her and cheered her as she passed.

She came to the Toyota and climbed into the front seat with the child on her lap.

'He is on another hunger strike,' she said, 'He has lost so much weight he looks like a skeleton.'

'That will make our work a lot easier,' said Sammy Ramsami and started the Toyota.

At nine o'clock the next morning Ramsami presented an urgent application to the Supreme Court for an order that a private physician be allowed access to the prisoner Moses Gama, and as grounds to support his application he presented the sworn affidavits of Victoria Dinizulu Gama and the local representative of the International Red Cross as to the deterioration in the prisoner's physical and mental condition.

The judge in chambers issued an order calling on the minister of justice to show cause within twenty-four hours why the access order should not be granted. The state attorney general opposed the application strenuously, but after listening to Mr Samuel Ramsami's submission, the judge granted the order.

The physician named in the order was Dr Chetty Abrahamji, the same man who had delivered Tara Courtney's son. He was a consulting physician at Groote Schuur Hospital. In company with the government district physician,

Dr Abrahamji made the ferry trip out to Robben Island where for three hours he examined the prisoner in the prison clinic.

At the end of the examination he told the State doctor, 'I don't like this at all. The patient is very much under weight, complaining of indigestion and chronic constipation. I don't have to spell out what those presentations suggest.'

'Those symptoms have been caused by the fact that the prisoner has been on hunger strike. In fact I have been considering attempting to force-feed.'

'No, Doctor,' Abrahamji interrupted him. 'I see the symptoms as much more significant. I am ordering a Cat Scan.'

'There are no facilities available for a Cat Scan on the island.'

'Then he will have to be moved to Groote Schuur for the examination.'

Once again the state attorney general opposed the order for the prisoner to be removed from Robben Island to Groote Schuur Hospital, but the judge was influenced by Dr Abrahamji's written report and impressed by his verbal evidence and once again granted the order.

Moses Gama was brought to the mainland amid the strictest conditions of secrecy and security. No previous warning of the move was given to any person outside those directly involved, to prevent the organization of any form of demonstration by liberal political bodies, and to frustrate the intense desire of the press to obtain a photograph of this patriarch of black aspirations.

It was necessary, however, to give Dr Abrahamji twenty-four hours' advance notice to enable him to reserve the use of the test equipment at the hospital, and the police moved into the area of the hospital the evening before the transfer. They cleared the corridors and rooms through which the prisoner would move of all but essential hospital staff, and searched them for explosives or any indication of illegal preparations.

From the public telephone booth in the main hospital administration block Dr Abrahamji rang Raleigh Tabaka at Molly Broadhurst's house in Pinelands.

'I am expecting company at two o'clock tomorrow afternoon,' he said simply.

'Your guest must not leave you until after nightfall,' Raleigh replied.

'That can be arranged,' Abrahamji agreed, and hung up.

The prison ferry came in through the harbour entrance at one o'clock in the afternoon. The deadlights of the cabin portholes were closed, and there were armed prison warders on deck, fore and aft, and their vigilance was apparent, even from where Raleigh was working on the foredeck of the trawler.

The ferry sailed across the harbour to 'A' berth, its usual mooring. There was an armoured prison van waiting on the dock, with four motor-cycle police in uniform and a grey police Land-Rover. Through the riot screens on the cab of the Land-Rover Raleigh could make out the shape of helmets and the short thick barrels of automatic shotguns held at port arms.

As the ferry touched the wharf, the prison van reversed up and the rear doors swung open. The armed warders seated on the padded benches in the body of the truck jumped down to meet the prisoner. Raleigh had just a glimpse of a tall gaunt figure in plain prison khaki uniform as he was hustled up the gangplank and into the waiting van, but even across the width of the harbour basin he could see that Moses Gama's hair was now pure silvery white, and that he was manacled at the wrists and that heavy leg-irons hampered his gait.

The doors of the van slammed shut. The motor-cycle escort closed in formation around it and the Land-Rover followed closely behind it as it sped away towards the main dock gates.

Raleigh left the trawler and Molly Broadhurst was waiting for him beyond

the main gates. They drove up the lower slopes of Table Mountain to where the hospital stood, a massive complex of white walls and red clay tiles below the stone pines and open meadows of Rhodes Estate and the tall grey rock buttresses of the mountain itself. Raleigh made a careful note of the time required for the journey from the docks to the hospital.

They drove slowly up the busy road to the main entrance of the hospital. The police Land–Rover , motor-cycles and armoured van were lined up in the public carpark beyond the entrance to the out-patients section. The warders had doffed their riot helmets and were standing around the vehicles in relaxed attitudes.

'How will Abrahamji keep him there until dark?' Molly wanted to know.

'I did not ask,' Raleigh replied. 'I expect he will keep on demanding further tests, or will deliberately sabotage the machinery – I don't know.'

Raleigh turned the car in a circle in front of the main entrance and they drove back down the hill.

'You are sure there is no other way to leave the hospital grounds?' Raleigh asked.

'Quite sure,' Molly replied. 'The van must pass here. Drop me at the bus stop. It will be a long wait and at least I will have a bench to sit on.'

Raleigh pulled into the kerb. 'You have the number of the telephone on the dock, and coins?' She nodded.

'Where is your nearest telephone from here?' he insisted.

'I have checked it all carefully. There is a public phone booth at the corner.' She pointed. 'It will take two minutes for me to reach it, and if it is out of order or occupied, there is another telephone in the café across the street. I have already made friends with the proprietor.'

Raleigh left her at the bus stop and drove back to the centre of town. He left Molly's car in the side street they had agreed upon so that it would not be found at the docks or anywhere in the vicinity and he walked back down the Heerengracht showing his seaman's papers at the gate.

The skipper of the trawler was in the wheelhouse and he handed Raleigh a mug of heavily sweetened coffee which he sipped as they went over the final arrangements.

'Are my men ready?' Raleigh asked as he stood up, and the skipper shrugged. 'That is your business, not mine.'

They were in the bottom of the trawler's deep hold where the heat in the unventilated space was oppressive. Robert and Changi were stripped to vests and jogging shorts. They jumped up as Raleigh came down the ladder.

'So far it goes well,' Raleigh assured them. They were old companions from the PAC *Poqo* days, and Changi had been at Sharpeville on the terrible day that Amelia died.

'Are you ready?' Raleigh asked him.

'We can check,' Changi suggested. 'Once more will not hurt us.'

The inflatable Zodiac boat that stood on the floor of the hold was the 17-foot 6-inch model that could carry ten adults with ease. The fifty-horsepower Evinrude outboard motor could push it at thirty knots. The cover of the engine had been painted matt black.

The rig had been stolen by Robert and Changi working together from the yard of a boat dealer two days before, and could not be traced back to any of them.

'The engine?' Raleigh demanded

'Robert has checked and serviced it.'

'I even changed the gear-box oil,' Robert agreed. 'She runs beautifully.'

'Tanks?'

'Both full,' Robert said. 'We have a range of a hundred miles or better.'

'Wet suits?'

'Check,' Changi said. 'And thermal blankets for the leader.'

'Tools?' Raleigh asked, and Changi opened the padded flotation bag and laid out the tools on the deck, checking each as Raleigh called them from his list.

'Good,' Raleigh agreed at last. 'You can rest now. Nothing more to do.'

Raleigh climbed up out of the hold. It was still too early. He glanced at his wristwatch. Not yet four o'clock, but he left the trawler and went down the dock to the public telephone booth at the end.

He telephoned directory enquiries and asked for a fictitious number in Johannesburg, just to make certain the line was in order. Then he sat on the edge of the wharf with his legs dangling and watched the seagulls squabbling over the offal and refuse that floated on the harbour waters.

It was fully dark by seven-forty but it was another twenty minutes before the telephone in the booth rang and Raleigh jumped up.

'They are on their way,' Molly's voice was soft and muffled.

'Thank you, comrade,' Raleigh said. 'Go home now.'

He hurried back down the wharf and the trawler skipper had seen him coming. As Raleigh jumped down on to the dock the two deckhands threw off the lines. The big caterpillar motor blustered and the trawler surged away from the dock and headed out through the entrance.

Raleigh swarmed down into the hold where Robert and Changi were already in their wet suits. They had Raleigh's suit laid out for him and they helped him into it.

'Ready?' one of the deckhands called down from above.

'Send it down,' Raleigh shouted back, and they watched the arm of the derrick swing out over the hold, silhouetted against the stars, and the line came down from the boom.

The three of them worked swiftly, hooking the Zodiac on, but before they had finished, the beat of the trawler's engine died away and the motion of the hull in the water changed as the vessel's way died and she began to drift.

Raleigh led them up the ladder on to the deck. The night was moonless, but the stars were bright and clear. The light breeze was from the south-east, so there was unlikely to be a change in this fair weather. All the trawler's navigational lights and the lights in the wheelhouse were extinguished.

Cape Town was ablaze with lights. The mountain was floodlit, a great ghostly silver hulk under the stars, while behind them the lights on Robben Island twinkled low on the black sea. Raleigh judged that they were about half-way between the city and the island.

The skipper was waiting for him on deck.

'We must move fast now,' he said.

Robert and Changi climbed into the Zodiac. Their wet suits were black, the rubber sides of the boat were black and the engine cover of the Evinrude was black. They would be almost invisible on the black waters.

'Thank you, comrade,' Raleigh said and offered the skipper his hand.

'*Amandla!*' said the skipper as he gripped it. 'Power!' and Raleigh took his place at the bows of the Zodiac.

The winch clattered and the Zodiac rose swaying, swung out over the side, and then fell swiftly to the surface of the water.

'Start up,' Raleigh instructed, and Robert whipped the starter cord and the engine fired and caught with the first pull.

'Cast off,' Raleigh ordered, and Changi unhooked the line from the boom, while Robert manoeuvred the Zodiac alongside the trawler and tied on to the light line from the rail. He let the engine idle for five minutes to warm it thoroughly and then cut it.

The two vessels lay silently linked together and the minutes passed torturously.

Suddenly the skipper called down. 'I have them in sight.'

'Are you certain?' Raleigh cupped his hands around his mouth to reply.

'I've seen that ferry every day of my life.' The skipper was leaning over the rail. 'Start your motor and cast off.'

The Evinrude roared into life and the Zodiac dropped back astern of the trawler. Now Raleigh could make out the ferry. It was coming almost directly towards them, both the green and red navigational lights showed.

The trawler moved forward, a wash of white water churning out from under her stern. She was still completely blacked out, and her speed built up rapidly. The skipper had assured Raleigh that she was capable of fourteen knots. She turned in a wide arc across the black surface and headed straight for the approaching ferry at speed.

Robert ran the Zodiac out to one side, and dropped back slightly, shearing off two hundred feet from the larger vessel.

The ferry held its course. Clearly it hadn't spotted the darkened ship bearing down out of the night. Raleigh stood up in the bows of the Zodiac steadying himself with two turns of the painter around his wrist and he watched the two vessels come together. The ferry was half the length of the steel-hulled trawler and it lay much lower in the water.

At the very last moment somebody on board the ferry shouted and then the bows of the trawler crashed into her, taking her just forward of the beam. Raleigh had warned the skipper not to damage the cabin and risk harming the occupants.

The trawler checked and the bows rose high as she trod the smaller vessel down, and then the ferry rolled over in a flurry of foam and breaking water. The trawler drove over her, broke free of her swamped hull, and went dashing away into the darkness. Within a hundred yards she had disappeared.

'The chains will pull him under,' Raleigh shouted. 'Work quickly!' He fitted his face plate over his mouth and nose.

Robert sent the Zodiac roaring alongside the sinking ferry. She had turned turtle and her bottom was painted with orange anti-fouling. Her lights were still burning beneath the water and there were three or four swimming warders thrashing around, trying to get a grip on the sides.

Raleigh and Changi, each carrying a short jemmy bar, slid over the side and dived under the trawler's submerged transom.

Raleigh jammed the point of the jemmy into the lock of the cabin door and with a single heave tore it away. The door slid back and a burst of trapped air exploded in silver bubbles around his head.

The cabin was flooded, but the lights were still burning, lighting the interior like a goldfish bowl, and a confusion of bodies, clad in the serge uniform of the prison service, were struggling and kicking and swirling around the cabin. Amongst them Raleigh picked out the khaki cotton drill tunic of a prisoner. He seized a handful of it and pulled Moses Gama clear.

Changi took Moses Gama's other arm and they swam him between them out from under the heaving transom and up to the surface. It had taken less than sixty seconds since the trawler had rammed, and Robert gunned the Zodiac up to them the moment they surfaced. He reached down and caught hold of Moses Gama's arm, the two men in the water heaved from under him and he rolled over the side of the Zodiac on to the floor boards.

Raleigh and Changi seized the loops of rope on the Zodiac's side to pull themselves up and the moment they were on board Robert gunned the Evinrude and they shot away from the foundering vessel. The splashing and cries of distress faded behind them as Robert turned the Zodiac back towards the shore. The long deserted stretch of Woodstock beach showed as a pale line of sand and surf in the starlight ahead.

Raleigh stripped off his face plate and leaned solicitously over the figure on the deck. He lifted him into a sitting position, and Moses Gama coughed painfully.

'I see you, my uncle,' Raleigh said softly.

'Raleigh?' Moses' voice was rough with the salt water he had swallowed. 'Is it you, Raleigh?'

'We will be ashore in ten minutes, my uncle.' Raleigh tucked one of the thermal blankets around Moses' shoulders. 'All the plans for your escape have been carefully laid. Everything's ready for you, my uncle. Soon now you will be where nobody can touch you.'

Robert ran the rubber inflatable in through the surf at full throttle and they shot up the sand, clear of the water. As they came to a standstill, they lifted Moses Gama out of the Zodiac and ran with him up the beach, carrying him between them so his chained feet barely touched the sand.

There was a small closed van parked amongst the dunes and Raleigh jerked the rear doors open and they lifted Moses into the back and laid him on the mattress that covered the floorboards. Changi jumped in beside him and Raleigh slammed the rear doors closed. Robert would take the Zodiac out and sink it.

Raleigh stripped off the jacket of his wet suit. The key to the van was on a loop of nylon line around his neck. He opened the driver's door and slid behind the wheel. The van was facing back along the track. The track joined the road that skirted the industrial area of Paarden Eiland and Raleigh drove sedately along it, towards the black township of Langa.

* * *

The official Cape Town residence of the minister of police was one of those clustered around the prime minister's residence at Groote Schuur. The cumbersome physical division of the legislative and executive arms of government between the cities of Cape Town and Pretoria made for costly duplications. During the annual session of parliament in Cape Town all the ministers and the entire diplomatic corps were forced to move down from Pretoria a thousand miles to the north, and official residences had to be maintained in both cities at enormous expense.

Manfred De La Rey's ministerial residence was an elegant Edwardian mansion set in acres of its own private lawns and gardens. As Roelf Stander

parked his shabby little secondhand Morris in front of this imposing building, it seemed oddly out of place.

Sarah Stander had been desperately trying to arrange a private meeting with Manfred ever since her son had been convicted and sentenced to death. However, Manfred had been in Pretoria, or at his ranch in the Free State or opening a memorial to the women who had died in the British concentration camps during the Boer war, or addressing the National Party caucus, and therefore unable to see her.

Sarah had persisted, telephoning his office at parliament every day, telephoning Heidi at home and pleading with her, until at last Manfred had agreed to see her at seven o'clock in the morning before he left for parliament.

Sarah and Roelf had driven in the Morris from Stellenbosch, leaving before sun-up so as not to be late for the appointment. When the coloured butler showed them through to the dining-room, Manfred and Heidi were seated at the breakfast table.

Heidi sprang up and came to kiss Sarah's cheek.

'I am sorry we have not seen you for so long, Sarie.'

'Yes,' Sarah agreed bitterly. 'I also am sorry – but as you explained to me, Manie has been too busy for us.'

Manfred stood up from the head of the table. He was in his shirt-sleeves and the linen table napkin was tucked into the top of his dark suit trousers.

'Roelf,' he smiled, and they shook hands like old friends.

'Thank you for agreeing to see us, Manie,' Roelf said humbly. 'I know how busy you are these days.' The years had not been kind to Roelf Stander, he had greyed and shrunk and Manfred felt a secret satisfaction as he studied him.

'Sit down, Roelf.' Manfred led him to a place at the breakfast table. 'Heidi has ordered breakfast for you – will you start with porridge?'

He seated Roelf and then reluctantly turned back to Sarah. She was still standing beside Heidi.

'Hello Sarie,' he said. She had been such a pretty little thing. They had grown from childhood together. There were still the remains of that girlhood beauty in her eyes and the shape of her face. The memory of the love they had once shared rushed back to him, and he felt the sweet nostalgic yearning for his youth. He had a vivid image of her lying naked on a bed of pine needles in the forest high up on the slopes of the Hottentots Holland mountains on the day that they had become lovers.

He searched in his heart for a vestige of what he had felt for her then, but he found none. Any love that once had flowered between them had been smothered by the knowledge of her treachery. For more than two decades he had delayed his revenge, contenting himself with slowly undermining and reducing this woman to her present state, waiting for exactly the right moment to extract the final retribution. It had come – and he savoured the moment.

'Hello, Manie,' she whispered, and she thought, 'He has been so cruel. He has filled my life with pain that has been difficult to bear. Now all I ask from him is my son's life – surely he will not deny me that also.'

'So, why have you come to see me?' Manie asked, and Heidi led Sarah to a seat at the table. She took the silver tea-pot from the coloured servant and told him, 'Thank you, Gamat, you can leave us now. Please close the door.' And she poured steaming coffee into Sarah's cup.

'Yes, Sarie,' she agreed. 'Tell us why you have come to see us.'

'You know why I have come to you,' Sarah said. 'It is Kobus.'

A deathly stillness held them all over the slow passage of the seconds, and then Manfred sighed.

'*Ja*,' he said. 'Kobus. Why do you come to me about Kobus?'

'I want you to help him, Manie.'

'Kobus has been tried and convicted of a sickening act of senseless brutality,' Manfred said slowly. 'The highest court in the land has decreed that he must die on the gallows. How can I help Kobus?'

'The same way you helped that black terrorist, Moses Gama.' Sarah was pale and the coffee cup clattered as she tried to set it down on the saucer. 'You saved his life – now save the life of my son.'

'The state president exercised leniency in Gama's case – '

'No, Manie,' Sarah interrupted. 'It was you that changed it. I know – you have the power to save Kobus.'

'No.' He shook his head. 'I haven't got that sort of power. Kobus is a murderer. The worst kind of killer – one without compassion or remorse. I cannot help him.'

'You can. I know you can, Manie. Please, I beg of you, save my son.'

'I cannot.' Manfred's expression set. His mouth hardened into a straight unrelenting line. 'I will not.'

'You must, Manie. You have no choice – you must save him.'

'Why do you say that?' He was becoming angry. 'There is nothing I *must* do.'

'You must save him, Manie, because he is your son also. He is the child of our love, Manie, you have no choice. You must save him.'

Manfred sprang to his feet and placed his hand protectively on Heidi's shoulder. 'You come into my house and insult me and my wife.' His voice shook with the force of his anger. 'You come here with wild stories and accusations.'

Roelf Stander had sat quietly through it all, but now he lifted his head and spoke softly. 'It is true, Manie. Every word she tells you is true. I knew she was carrying your child when I married her. She told me frankly. You had deserted her – you had married Heidi and I loved her.'

'You know it is true,' Sarah whispered. 'You have always known, Manie. You cannot have looked into Kobus's eyes without knowing. Both your sons have your yellow eyes, Manie, Lothar and Kobus – both of them. You know he is your son.'

Manfred sank back on to his chair. In the silence Heidi reached across and deliberately took his hand. That reassuring touch seemed to rally him.

'Even if that were true, there is nothing I would do. No matter whose son he is, justice must run its course. A life for a life. He must pay the penalty for his deed.'

'Manie, please. You must help us – ' Sarah was weeping now, and the tears at last spilled down her pale cheeks. She tried to throw herself at Manfred's feet, but Roelf caught her and held her. She struggled weakly in his arms, but he held her and looked at Manfred.

'In the name of our friendship, Manie, everything we have done and shared – won't you help us?' he pleaded.

'I am sorry for you, Roelf.' Manfred stood up again. 'You must take your wife home now.'

Roelf drew Sarah gently towards the door, but before they reached it Sarah pulled out of his hands and faced Manfred again.

'Why?' she cried in anguish. 'I know you can – why will you not help us?'

'Because of you White Sword failed,' he said softly. 'That is why I will not help you.'

She was struck dumb by the words, and Manfred turned to Roelf. 'Take her away now,' he ordered. 'I have finished with her at last.'

During the long journey back to Stellenbosch Sarah huddled in the passenger seat and sobbed brokenly. Only when Roelf parked the Morris outside their cottage did she straighten up, and her voice and her face were ruined with grief.

'I hate him,' she repeated. 'Oh God, how I hate him.'

* * *

'I spoke to David Abrahams this morning,' Isabella said, leaning forward in the saddle to pat the mare's neck so that her father couldn't see her face. 'He offered me a job at the Johannesburg office.'

'Correction,' said Shasa. 'You telephoned David and told him that Johannesburg needed a PRO at a salary of two thousand a month plus dress allowance plus five-day week and a company car – and I believe you even stipulated the make, Porsche 911, wasn't it? David called me the minute you hung up.'

'Oh, Daddy, don't be so technical.' Isabella tossed her head defiantly. 'You wouldn't want me to dress in rags and starve up there would you?'

'What I would want is for you to stay here where I can keep an eye on you.' Shasa felt the leaden weight of impending loss in his chest as he looked at her. She was the spice of his life, and she had only been back from London a month or so. Now she wanted to be off again. His instinct was to fight to keep her, but Centaine had advised, 'Let them go gently, and there is a chance they will come back to you.'

'It isn't Siberia or the Outer Hebrides, Daddy. Do be practical. It's just up the road.'

'A thousand miles up the road,' Shasa agreed. 'And much closer to the rugby stadium at Loftus Versveld.'

'I don't know what you mean.' It was very seldom Shasa could catch her off-balance, and vindictively he relished her agitation.

'Rugby football,' he explained. 'Great sweaty oafs beating their bony heads together.'

She recovered splendidly. 'Pater, if this has anything to do with Lothar De La Rey, I would just like to point out that he is one of the greatest athletes of our time and the youngest brigadier in the history of the police force – and that he means absolutely nothing to me at all.'

'Your indifference is monumental. I am greatly relieved.'

'Does that mean I can accept David's job offer?'

Shasa sighed and the loneliness descended upon him like a winter's evening. 'How can I stop you, Bella?'

She let out a triumphant squeal and leaned out of the saddle to wrap those long tanned arms around his neck, and Shasa's stallion danced under him with aristocratic affront.

Isabella chattered merrily all the way back to the château.

'One thing I forgot to mention to David was a housing allowance. Flats are so awfully expensive in Joey's. I couldn't find anything suitable on the pittance he is paying me.' Shasa shook his head with admiration.

The grooms were waiting in the kitchen yard to take the horses, and still in their jodhpurs and riding boots they went through to the breakfast room with Isabella hanging lovingly on her father's arm.

Centaine was at the sideboard, helping herself to scrambled eggs from the chafing dish. She was still in her gardening clothes and had been amongst her roses since dawn. Now she looked at Isabella inquiringly – and Isabella gave her a happy wink.

'Damn it,' Shasa intercepted the exchange. 'I've been set up. It's a conspiracy.'

'Of course, I told Nana first.' Isabella hugged his arm. 'I always start at the top.'

'When she was little I always threatened to hand her over to a policeman if she was naughty,' Centaine said complacently as she carried her plate to the breakfast table. 'I hope this policeman can cope with her.'

'He's not a policeman,' Isabella protested. 'He's a brigadier.'

Shasa ladled eggs and fried tomato on to his plate and went to his place at the head of the table. The morning paper was folded neatly on his side plate, and he shook it open at the front page as he sat down. The main news was the proposed meeting between the British prime minister, Harold Wilson, and Ian Smith to settle the Rhodesian issue. Now he saw that the suggested venue was a British warship at sea. Israel and Jordan were still disputing the Hebron Valley, and closer to home the Robben Island ferry had capsized during the night with the certain loss of at least two lives, while eight others were missing.

The telephone on the sideboard rang and Centaine looked up from buttering her toast. 'That will be Garry,' she said. 'He rang twice while you were out riding.'

'It's only eight o'clock in the morning,' Shasa protested, but he went to answer the telephone. 'Hello Garry, where are you?'

Garry sounded surprised. 'At the office, of course.'

'What's the problem?'

'Swimming-pools,' Garry answered. 'I have a chance to get the franchise for a new process of making cheap swimming-pools. It's called Gunite. Holly and I saw it when we were on honeymoon in the States.'

'Good Lord, only the very rich can afford private swimming-pools,' Shasa protested.

'Everybody will buy my swimming-pools – every home in the country will have one by the time I'm finished.'

Garry's enthusiasm was infectious.

'It works, Pater. I've seen it, and the figures add up perfectly. Only trouble is I have to give an answer by noon today. Someone else is interested.'

'How much?' Shasa asked.

'Four million initially – that's for the franchise and plant. Another four million over two years for running costs, then we will be into profit.'

'All right,' Shasa said. 'Go ahead.'

'Thanks, Pater. Thanks for trusting me.'

'Well you haven't let me down yet. How is Holly?'

'She's fine. She's right here with me.'

'At the office at eight in the morning?' Shasa laughed.

'Of course.' Again Garry sounded surprised. 'We are a team. The swimming-pools were her idea.'

'Give her my love,' Shasa said and hung up.

As he went back to his seat, Centaine said, 'It's the prime minister's budget vote this afternoon. I thought I'd drop in.'

'It should be interesting,' Shasa agreed. 'I think Verwoerd is going to make a major policy speech about the country's international position. I have a committee meeting on armaments this morning, but why don't you meeet me for lunch and you can listen to Doctor Henk's speech from the public gallery afterwards. I'll ask Tricia to get you a ticket.'

Tricia was waiting for him anxiously when an hour later Shasa walked into his parliamentary suite.

'The minister of police wants to see you most urgently, Mr Courtney. He asked me to let him know the moment you arrived. He said he'd come to your office.'

'Very well.' Shasa glanced at his appointment book on her desk. 'Let him know I'm here and then get a ticket for my mother for the public gallery this afternoon. Is there anything else?'

'Nothing important,' Tricia picked up the in-house telephone to ring the minister of police's office and then paused. 'There has been a strange woman ringing you this morning. She called three times. She wouldn't give her name and she asked for Squadron Leader Courtney. Funny, isn't it?'

'All right, let me know if she calls again.' Shasa was frowning as he went through to his own office. The use of his old airforce rank was strangely disquieting. He went to his desk and began work on the mail and the memoranda that Tricia had placed on his blotter, but almost immmediately the buzzer rang on his intercom.

'Minister De La Rey is here, sir.'

'Ask him to come right in, Tricia.'

Shasa rose and went to meet Manfred, but as they shook hands he could see that Manfred was a worried man.

'Did you read the news report about the sinking of the ferry?' Manfred did not even return his greeting but came immediately to business.

'I noticed it, but didn't read it all.'

'Moses Gama was on the boat when it sank,' Manfred said.

'Good Lord.' Shasa glanced involutarily at the ivory and goldleaf altar chest which still stood against the wall of his office. 'Is he safe?'

'He is missing,' Manfred said. 'He may have drowned, or he may be alive. Either way we are in a very serious predicament.'

'Escaped?' Shasa asked.

'One of the survivors, a prison officer, says that there were two vessels at the accident scene, a large ship without lights that collided with the ferry and another smaller craft that arrived seconds after the ferry capsized. In the darkness it was impossible to see any details. It is a distinct possibility that Gama was spirited away.'

'If he drowned, we will be accused of murdering him,' Shasa said softly, 'with disastrous international repurcussions.'

'And if he is at large, we will face the possibility of a popular uprising of the blacks similar to Langa and Sharpeville.'

'What are you doing about it?' Shasa asked.

'The entire police force is on full alert. One of our best men, my own son Lothar, is flying down from the Witwatersrand in an airforce jet to take charge of the investigation. He will land within the next few minutes. Navy divers are already attempting to salvage the wreckage of the ferry.'

For another ten minutes they discussed all the implications of the wreck, and then Manfred moved to the door.

'I will keep you informed as we get further news.'

Shasa followed him into the outer office, and as they passed Tricia's desk she stood up.

'Oh, Mr Courtney, that woman called again while you were with Minister De La Rey.' Manfred and Shasa both paused, and Tricia went on, 'She asked for Squadron Leader Courtney again, sir, and when I told her you were in conference, she said she had news for you about White Sword. She said you'd understand.'

'White Sword!' Shasa froze and stared at her. 'Did she leave a number?'

'No sir, but she said that you must meet her at the Cape Town railway station at five-thirty this afternoon. Platform four.'

'How will I know who she is?'

'She says she knows you by sight. You are merely to wait on the platform, she will come to you.'

Shasa was so preoccupied with the message that he did not notice Manfred De La Rey's reaction to the code name, 'White Sword'. All colour had drained from Manfred's craggy features, and his upper lip and jowls were covered by a sheen of perspiration. Without another word he turned and strode out into the corridor.

The name 'White Sword' kept plaguing Shasa all through the Armscor meeting. They were discussing the new air-to-ground missiles for the airforce but Shasa found it difficult to concentrate. He was plagued by the memory of his grandfather, that good and gentle man whom Shasa had loved and who had been murdered by White Sword. His death had been one of the fiercest tragedies of his young life, and the rage that he had felt at the brutal killing came back to him afresh.

'White Sword,' he thought. 'If I can find out who you are, even after all these years, you will pay, and the interest will be more onerous for the time the debt has stood.'

* * *

Manfred De La Rey went directly to his office at the end of the corridor after he had left Shasa. His secretary spoke to him as he passed her desk but he did not seem to hear her.

He locked the door to his own office, but did not sit at the massive mahogany desk. He prowled the floor restlessly, his eyes unseeing and his heavy jaws chewing like a bulldog with a bone. He took the handkerchief from his jacket pocket and wiped his chin and then paused to examine his face in the wall mirror behind his desk. He was so pale that his cheeks had a bluish sheen, and his eyes were savage as those of a wounded leopard caught in a trap.

'White Sword,' he whispered aloud. It was twenty-five years since he had used that code name, but he remembered standing on the bridge of the German U-boat, coming in towards the land in darkness, with his hair and great bushy beard dyed black, staring out at the signal fires on the beach where Roelf Stander waited for him.

Roelf Stander had been with him through all the dangerous days and the wild

endeavours. They had planned many of their operations in the kitchen of the Stander cottage in the little village of Stellenbosch. It was there in that kitchen that he had given them the details of the action that would be the signal for the glorious uprising of Afrikaner patriots. And at all those meetings Sarah Stander had been present, a quiet unobtrusive presence, serving coffee and food, never speaking – but listening. It was only many years later that Manfred had been able to guess at how well she had listened.

In 1948, when the Afrikaners had at last won at the ballot box the power which they had failed to seize at the point of the sword, Manfred's hard and loyal work had been rewarded with a deputy minister's post in the department of justice.

One of his first acts had been to send for the files of the unsolved attempt on the life of Jan Smuts, and the murder of Sir Garrick Courtney. Before he destroyed the files he read them through carefully, and he learned that they had been betrayed. There had been a traitor in their gallant band of patriots – a woman who had telephoned the Smuts police officers to warn them of the assassination.

He had guessed at the woman's identity, but had never extracted his full retribution, waiting for the moment to ripen, savouring the thought of revenge over the decades, watching the traitor's misery, watching her growing old and bitter, while frustrating her husband's efforts to succeed in law and politics, in the guise of mentor and adviser, steering him into folly and disaster until Roelf Stander had lost all his sustenance, his property and his will to carry on. All that time Manfred had waited for the perfect moment for the final revenge stroke – and at last it had arrived. Sarah Stander had come to him to plead for the life of the bastard he had placed in her womb – and he had denied her. The pleasure of it had been exquisite, made more poignant by the years he had waited for it.

Now the woman had turned vindictive. He had not anticipated that. He had expected the blow to break and destroy her. Only the greatest good fortune had given him forewarning of this new betrayal she planned.

He turned from the mirror and sat down at his desk. He reached determinedly for the telephone and told his secretary, 'I want Colonel Bester in the bureau for state security.'

Bester was one of his most trusted officers.

'Bester,' he barked. 'I want a detention order drawn up urgently. I will sign it myself, and I want it executed immediately.'

'Yes, Minister. Can you give me the name of the detainee?'

'Sarah Stander,' Manfred said. 'Her address is 16 Eike Laan, Stellenbosch. If the arresting officers cannot find her there, she should be on platform four of the Cape Town railway station at five-thirty p.m. this afternoon. The woman must speak to no one before she is arrested – your men must make certain of that.'

As Manfred hung up he smiled grimly. Under the law he had the power to arrest and detain any persons for ninety days, and to hold that person completely *incommunicado*. A great deal could happen in ninety days. Things could change, a person might even die. It was all taken care of. The woman could cause no further trouble.

The telephone on his desk rang, and Manfred snatched it up, expecting it to be Bester again.

'Yes, what is it?'

'Pa, it's me – Lothie.'

'Yes, Lothie. Where are you?'

'Caledon Square. I landed twenty minutes ago, and I have taken over the investigation. There is news, Pa. The divers have found the ferry. There is no sign of the prisoner's body but the cabin door has been forced open. We must assume that he escaped. Worse than that, somebody engineered his escape.'

'Find him,' Manfred said softly. 'You must find Moses Gama. If we don't, the consequences could be disastrous.'

'I know,' Lothar said. 'We will find him. We have to find him.'

* * *

Centaine refused to eat the food in the parliamentary dining-room. 'It's not that I am fussy, *chéri*, in the desert I ate live locusts and meat that had lain four days in the sun, but – ' She and Shasa walked down through the gardens, across the top end of town to the Café Royal on Greenmarket Square, where the first oysters of the season had arrived from Knysna lagoon.

Centaine sprinkled lemon juice and tabasco sauce, scooped a gently pulsating mouthful from the half shell and sighed with pleasure.

'And now, *chéri*,' she dabbed the juice from her lips, 'tell me why you are so far away that you do not laugh at even my best efforts.'

'I'm sorry Mater.' Shasa signalled to the waiter to top up his champagne glass. 'I had a strange phone call this morning – and I haven't been able to concentrate on anything else. Do you remember White Sword?'

'How can you ask?' Centaine laid down her fork. 'Sir Garry was more dear to me than my own father. Tell me all about it.'

They spoke of nothing else for the rest of the lunch, exploring together ancient memories of that terrible day on which a noble and generous man had died, a man who had been precious to them both.

At last Shasa called for the bill. 'It's half past one already. We will have to hurry to reach the House before it begins. I don't want to miss any part of Verwoerd's speech.'

At sixty-six years of age Centaine was still active and agile, and Shasa was not forced to moderate his stride for her. They were still talking animatedly as they passed St George's Cathedral and turned into the gardens.

Ahead of them two men sat on one of the park benches, and there was something about them that caught Shasa's attention even at a distance of a hundred yards. The taller of the pair was a swarthy-complexioned man who wore the uniform of a parliamentary messenger. He sat very stiffly upright and stared straight ahead of him with a fixed expression.

The man beside him was also dark-haired but his face was colourless as putty, the dead black hair fell forward on to his forehead. He was leaning close to the parliamentary messenger, speaking into his ear as though imparting a secret, but the messenger's face was expressionless and he showed not the least reaction to the other man's words.

As they came level with the bench, Shasa leaned forward to see past Centaine, and at less than five paces looked directly into the pale face of the smaller of the men. His eyes were black and implacable as pools of liquid tar, but as Shasa studied him, the man deliberately turned his face away. Yet his lips kept

moving, talking so softly to the man in the parliamentary uniform that Shasa could not catch even a murmur of his voice.

Centaine tugged at his sleeve. '*Chéri*, you are not listening to me.'

'I'm sorry, Mater,' Shasa apologized absentmindedly.

'I wonder why this woman chose the railway station,' Centaine repeated.

'I suppose she feels safer in a public place,' Shasa hazarded, and glanced back over his shoulder. The two men were still on the bench, but even in his preoccupation with other things, the passionless malevolence that Shasa had seen in that tar-black gaze made him shiver as though an icy wind had blown upon the back of his neck.

As they turned into the lane that led to the massive edifice of parliament, Shasa felt suddenly confused and uncertain. There was too much happening all around him over which he had no control It was a sensation to which he was not accustomed.

* * *

Joe Cicero whispered the formula softly, 'You can feel the worm in your belly.'

'Yes,' the man beside him replied, staring straight ahead. Only his lips moved as he made the reply, 'I can feel the worm.'

'The worm asks if you have the knife.'

'Yes, I have the knife,' said the man. His father had been a Greek and he had been born illegitimate in Portuguese Mozambique of a Mulatto woman. His mixed blood was not apparent. It seemed merely as though he was of Mediterranean extraction. Only Europeans were employed as messengers in the South African parliament.

'You can feel the worm in your belly,' Joe Cicero reinforced the man's conditioning.

'Yes, I can feel the worm.'

Eight times in the past few years he had been in mental institutions. It was while he was in the last of these that he had been selected and the conditioning of his mind accomplished.

'The worm asks if you know where to find the devil,' Joe Cicero told him. The man's name was Demetrio Tsafendas and he had been introduced into South Africa the previous year, once his conditioning was completed.

'Yes,' said Tsafendas. 'I know where to find the devil.'

'The worm in your belly orders you to go straight to where the devil is,' Joe Cicero said softly. 'The worm in your belly orders you to kill the devil.' Tsafendas stood up. He moved like an automaton. 'The worm orders you to go now!'

Tsafendas started towards the parliament building with an even unhurried tread.

Joe Cicero watched him go. It was done. All the pieces had been placed with great care. At last the first boulder had started to roll down the hillside. It would gather others as it built up speed and momentum. Soon it would be a mighty avalanche and the shape of the mountain would be changed for ever.

Joe Cicero stood up and walked away.

* * *

The first person Shasa saw as he and Centaine walked up the front steps to the parliament entrance was Kitty Godolphin and his heart surged with excitement and unexpected pleasure. He hadn't seen her since that illicit interlude in the south of France eighteen months before. Shasa had chartered a luxury yacht and they had cruised as far as Capri. When they parted, she had promised to write – but she never kept her promises, and here she was again with no warning, smiling that sweet girlish smile with the devilment in her eyes, coming to greet him as innocently and naturally as though their last kiss had been hours before.

'What are you doing here?' he demanded without any preliminaries, and Kitty said to Centaine,

'Hello, Mrs Courtney. How did such a nice cultured lady ever end up with such an ill-mannered son?'

Centaine laughed, she liked Kitty. Shasa thought that it was a case of kindred spirits. Kitty explained, 'I was in Rhodesia to get a profile on Ian Smithy before he meets Harold Wilson, and I made a side trip for the speech that Verwoerd is giving today, and of course to visit with you.'

They chatted for a few minutes, then Centaine excused herself. 'I must get a good seat in the gallery.'

As she moved away Shasa asked Kitty softly, 'When can I see you?'

'This evening?' Kitty suggested.

'Yes – oh no, damn it.' He remembered his rendezvous with the White Sword informer. 'Where are you staying?'

'The Nellie as usual.'

'Can I call you there later?'

'Sure,' she smiled. 'Unless I get any better offers.'

'You little bitch! Why don't you marry me?'

'I'm too good for you, buster,' It had become one of their stock jokes. 'But I don't mind an order of small beer and chips on the side. See you later.'

Shasa watched her climb the staircase towards the press gallery. Over all the years he had known her, she seemed not to have aged a day. She still had the body of a girl, and the light spring of youth in her step. He pushed back the sudden cold gloom of loneliness that threatened to engulf him and walked into the chamber.

The benches were filling. Shasa saw that the prime minister was in his seat at the head of the government benches. He was talking to Frank Waring, the minister of sport, and the only other Englishman in the cabinet.

Verwoerd looked fit and vigorous. It seemed impossible that he had taken two revolver bullets through his skull and had come back with such power to dominate his own party and the entire chamber this way. He seemed to have an infinite capacity for survival and, of course, Shasa grinned cynically, the luck of the devil himself.

Shasa started towards his own seat, and Manfred De La Rey jumped up and came to intercept him.

He seized Shasa's arm and leaned close to him. 'The divers have raised the ferry. Gama's body is not in it and the door of the cabin has been forced. It looks as though the bastard has got clean away. But we have every exit from the country guarded and my men will get him. He cannot get away. I think the prime minister is going to make the announcement of his disappearance during his speech this afternoon.'

Shasa and Manfred began walking towards their seats on the front bench,

when somebody bumped so roughly against Shasa that he exclaimed and glanced round. It was the uniformed messenger that Shasa had noticed on the park bench.

'Be careful, fellow,' Shasa snapped at him as he recovered his balance, but the man did not seem to hear.

Although his expression was vacant and his eyes staring and unseeing, the messenger walked with a quick determined step, brushing past Manfred and heading towards the opposition benches on the left side of the Speaker's throne.

'Damned rude,' Shasa said, pausing to watch him.

Suddenly the messenger seemed to change his mind, he veered across the chamber and hurried towards where Dr Verwoerd was sitting. The prime minister saw him coming and looked up expectantly, supposing that the man had a message for him. Nobody else in the chamber seemed to be taking any notice of the messenger's erratic behaviour, but Shasa was watching with puzzlement.

As the messenger stood over Dr Verwoerd, he swept his dark uniform jacket open and Shasa saw the silver flash of steel.

'Good Christ!' he exclaimed. 'He's got a knife.'

The messenger lifted the blade and struck once, and strangely the prime minister was smiling, as though he did not realize what was happening. The blade came free and the silver was misted pink with blood.

Shasa started forward, but Manfred still had hold of his arm. 'The Manchurian Candidate,' he hissed and Shasa froze.

Standing over the prime minister, the assassin struck again and then again. With each blow the blood spurted down his white shirt front and Dr Verwoerd lifted his hands in a pathetic gesture of appeal.

At last the men closest to him realized what was happening and they leapt upon the assailant. A knot of struggling men swarmed over him but the man was fighting back with a kind of demonic strength.

'Where is the Devil?' he shouted wildly. 'I'll get the Devil.'

They bore him to the green carpet and pinned him there.

Dr Verwoerd still sat in his seat staring down at his own chest from which the bright flood poured. Then he pulled the lapels of his jacket closed as though to hide the terrible sight of his own blood, and with a sigh slid forward and crumpled on to the carpeted floor of the chamber.

Shasa and Manfred De La Rey were in Shasa's parliamentary office when Tricia brought the news through.

'Gentlemen, the party whip has just telephoned. Dr Verwoerd has been declared dead on arrival at the Volks Hospital.'

Shasa went to the liquor cabinet behind his desk and poured two glasses of cognac.

They watched each other's eyes as they drank silently, and then Shasa lowered his glass and said, 'We must start at once to draw up a list of those we can rely on to support you. I think John Vorster is the man you will have to beat for the premiership, and his people will already be busy.'

They worked together through the afternoon preparing their lists, placing ticks and crosses and queries against the names. Telephoning, wheedling and extorting, arranging meetings, making promises and commitments, trading and compromising, and as the afternoon wore on a stream of important visitors, allies and potential allies, passed through Shasa's suite.

While they worked, Shasa watched Manfred, and wondered again how fate

had chosen such strange travelling companions as they were. It seemed that they had nothing in common except that one most vital trait – burning unrelenting ambition and hunger for power.

Well, it was at their fingertips now, almost within their grasp, and Manfred was a man possessed. The effect of his enormous force of character was apparent on the men who came up to Shasa's office suite. One by one they were swept along by it, and one by one they swore their allegiance to him.

Slowly it dawned upon Shasa that it was no longer a possibility – or even a probability. They were going to win. He knew in his guts and his heart. It was theirs – the premiership and the presidency between them. They were going to win.

In the heady excitement of it all the afternoon passed swiftly, the grandfather clock in the corner of Shasa's office chimed the hours softly, such a familiar sound that he hardly noticed it until it struck five and he started and jumped to his feet, confirming the time with his wristwatch.

'It's five o'clock.' He started towards the door.

'Where are you going? I need you here,' Manfred called after him. 'Come back, Shasa.'

'I'll be back,' Shasa answered, and ran into the outer office.

There were men waiting there, important men. They stood up to greet him, and Tricia called, 'Mr Courtney – '

'Not now,' Shasa ran past them. 'I'll be back soon.'

It would be quicker on foot than trying to take the Jaguar through the five o'clock rush-hour traffic, and Shasa began to run.

He realized that the woman informer was so nervous and afraid that she would probably not linger at the rendezvous. He had to get there before the appointed time. As he ran he reviled himself for having forgotten such an important appointment, but it was all confusion and uncertainty.

He raced down the sidewalk, crowded with office workers relieved of the tedium of their day who poured out of the buildings. Shasa pushed and shoved, and weaved and ducked. Some of those he barged into shouted angrily after him.

He sprinted through the columns of slowly moving vehicles, and ran into the Adderley street entrance of the railway station. The clock above the main concourse stood at five thirty-seven. He was already late, and platform four was at the far end of the building.

Wildly he raced down the concourse, and barged on to the quay. He slowed to a hurried walk, and made his way down the platform, examining the faces of the commuters waiting there. They stared back at him incuriously, and he glanced up at the platform clock: five-forty. Ten minutes late. She had come and gone. He had missed her.

He stood in the centre of the platform and looked despairingly around him, not certain what to do next. Overhead the public address system squawked, 'Train from Stellenbosch and the Cape Flats arriving Platform Four.'

That was it, of course. Shasa felt a vast relief. The train was late. She must be on the train, that was why she had chosen this place and time.

Shasa craned his head anxiously as the carriages rumbled slowly into the platform and, with a squeal and hiss of vacuum brakes, came to a halt. The doors were thrown open and passengers spewed out of them, beginning to move in a solid column towards the platform exit.

Shasa jumped up on the nearest bench, the better to see and to be seen.

'Mr Courtney.' A woman's voice. Her voice – he recognized it, even after all the years. 'Mr Courtney.'

He stood on tiptoe, trying to see over the heads of the passengers.

'Mr Courtney!' There she was, caught up in the crowd, trying to push her way through to him, and waving frantically to attract his attention.

He recognized her instantly. The shock immobilized him for a few seconds as he stared at her. It was the Stander woman, the one he had met briefly at Manfred's holiday cottage when he had flown there to make the cannery deal with him. That was years ago, but he remembered that she had called him Squadron Leader. He should have pieced it together at that time. How foolish and unperceptive he had been. Shasa was still standing on the bench staring at her, when suddenly something else caught his attention.

Two men were roughly pushing their way through the crowds of passengers. Two big men in dark ill-fitting suits and the fedora hats that were somehow the mark of the plain-clothes security police. Clearly they were making for the Stander woman.

At the same moment as Shasa, she saw the two detectives and her face went white with terror.

'Mr Courtney!' she screamed. 'Quickly – they are after me.' She broke out of the crowd and began to run towards Shasa. 'Hurry, please hurry.'

Shasa jumped down from the bench and ran to meet her, but there was an old woman carrying an armful of parcels in his way. He almost knocked her down, and in the moments it took to untangle himself, the two detectives had caught up with Sarah Stander, and seized her from either side.

'Please!' She gave a despairing scream, then with wild, improbable strength broke free of her captors, and ran the last few paces to Shasa.

'Here!' She thrust an envelope into Shasa's hand. 'Here it is.'

The two security officers had recovered swiftly and bounded after her. One of them seized both her arms from behind and dragged her away. The other came to confront Shasa.

'We are police officers. We have a warrant for the arrest of the woman.' He was panting with his efforts. 'She gave something to you. I saw it. You must hand it over to me.'

'My good man!' Shasa drew himself up and gave the detective his most haughty stare. 'Do you have any idea just who you are speaking to?'

'Minister Courtney!' The man recognized him then, and his confusion was comic. 'I'm sorry, sir. I didn't know – '

'What is your name, rank and serial number?' Shasa snapped.

'Lieutenant Van Outshoorn No. 138643.' Instinctively the man stood to attention.

'You can be sure you will hear more of this, Lieutenant,' Shasa warned him frostily. 'Now carry on with your other duties.' Shasa turned on his heel and strode away down the platform, tucking the envelope into his inner pocket, leaving the detective staring after him in dismay.

He did not open the envelope until he reached his office again. Tricia was still waiting for him.

'I was so worried when you ran out like that,' she cried. Good, loyal Tricia.

'It's all right,' he reassured her. 'It all worked out fine. Where is Minister De La Rey?'

'He left soon after you, sir. He said he would be at home at Groote Schuur. You could reach him there if you needed him.'

'Thank you Tricia. You may go home now.'

Shasa went through to his own office and locked the door. He went to his desk and sat down in his studded leather chair. He took the envelope from his inner pocket and laid it in front of him on the desk blotter, and he studied it.

It was of cheap coarse paper, and his name was written in a round girlish hand. The ink had smeared and run.

'Meneer Courtney.'

Shasa was suddenly reluctant to touch it again. He had a premonition of some terrible revelation which would turn the even tenor of his existence into strife and turmoil.

He picked up the Georgian silver paper knife from his desk and tested the point with his thumb. He turned the envelope over and slid the point of the knife under the flap. The envelope contained a sheet of ruled notepaper with a single line of writing in the same girlish script.

Shasa stared at it. There was no sense of shock. Deep in his subconscious he must have known the truth all along. It was the eyes, of course, the yellow topaz eyes of White Sword that had stared into his own on the day his grandfather died.

There was not even a moment of doubt, no twinge of incredulity.He had even seen the scar, the ancient gun-shot wound in Manfred's body, the mark of the bullet he had fired at White Sword and every other detail fitted perfectly.

'Manfred De La Rey is White Sword.'

From the moment they had first met that childhood day upon the fishing jetty at Walvis Bay, the fates had stalked them, driving them inexorably towards their destiny.

'We were born to destroy each other,' Shasa said softly, and reached for the telephone.

It rang three times before it was answered.

'De La Rey.'

'It's me.' Shasa said.

'*Ja*. I have been waiting.' Manfred's voice was weary and resigned, in bitter contrast to the powerful tones in which he had exhorted and rallied his supporters just a short while before. 'The woman reached you. My men have informed me.'

'The woman must be set free,' Shasa told him.

'It has been done already. On my orders.'

'We must meet.'

'*Ja*. It is necessary.'

'Where?' Shasa asked. 'When?'

'I will come to Weltevreden,' Manfred said, and Shasa was taken too much by surprise to respond. 'But there is one condition.'

'What is your condition?' Shasa asked warily.

'Your mother must be there when we meet.'

'My mother?' This time Shasa could not contain his amazement.

'Yes your mother – Centaine Courtney.'

'I don't understand – what has my mother got to do with this business?'

'Everything,' said Manfred heavily. 'She has everything to do with it.'

* * *

When Kitty Godolphin got back to her suite that evening, she was in a mood of jubilation. Under her direction, Hank's camera had captured the dramatic moments as the blood-stained body of Dr Verwoerd was carried from the chamber to the waiting ambulance, and she had recorded the panic and confusion, the spontaneous unrehearsed words and expressions of his friends and his bitter enemies.

The moment she entered the suite, she booked a call through to her news editor at NABS in New York to warn him of the priceless footage she had obtained. Then she poured herself a gin and tonic and sat impatiently beside the telephone waiting for her call to come through.

She lifted it as it rang.

'Kitty Godolphin.' she said.

'Miss Godolphin,' A strange voice, speaking with a deep melodious African accent, greeted her. 'Moses Gama sends you his greetings.'

'Moses Gama is serving a life sentence in a high security prison,' Kitty replied brusquely. 'Don't waste my time, please.'

'Last night Moses Gama was rescued by warriors of the *Umkhonto we Sizwe* from the Robben Island prison ferry,' said the voice, and Kitty felt the flesh of her cheeks and lips go numb with the shock of it. She had read the reports of the ferry sinking. 'Moses Gama is in a safe place. He wishes to speak to the world through you. If you agree to meet him, you will be allowed to use your camera to record his message.'

For a full three seconds she could not answer. Her voice had failed her but her mind was racing. 'This is the big one,' she thought. 'This is the one that comes only once in a lifetime of work and striving.' She cleared her throat and said, 'I will come.'

'A dark blue van will arrive at the ballroom entrance to the hotel in ten minutes from now. The driver will flick his lights twice. You are to enter the rear doors of the van immediately, without speaking to any person.'

The vehicle was a small Toyota delivery van, and Kitty and Hank with the sound and camera equipment were cramped in the interior so that it was difficult to move, but Kitty crawled forward until she could speak to the driver.

'Where are we going?'

The driver glanced at her in the rear-view mirror. He was a young black man of striking appearance, not handsome but with a powerful African face.

'We are going into the townships. There will be police patrols and road-blocks. The police are everywhere searching for Moses Gama. It will be dangerous, so you must do exactly as I tell you.'

For almost an hour they were in the van, driving through darkened back streets, sometimes stopping and waiting in silence until a shadowy figure came out of the night to whisper a few words to the driver of the van, then going on again until at last they parked for the last time.

'From here we walk,' their guide told them, and led them down the alleys and secret routes of the gangs and comrades, slipping past the rows of township cottages, twice hiding while police Land-Rovers cruised past, and finally entering the back door of one of the thousands of identical undistinguished cottages.

Moses Gama sat at a table in the tiny back kitchen,. Kitty recognized him instantly although his hair was now almost completely silver and his great frame was skeletally wasted. He wore a white open-neck shirt and dark blue slacks,

and as he rose to greet her, she saw that though he had aged and his body was ravaged, the commanding presence and his messianic dark gaze were as powerful as when she had first met him.

'I am grateful that you have come,' he told her gravely. 'But we have very little time. The fascist police follow closely as a pack of wolves. I have to leave here within a short while.'

Hank was already at work, setting up his camera and lights, and he nodded to Kitty. She saw that the gritty reality of the surroundings, the bare walls and plain unadorned wooden furniture would add drama to the setting, and Moses' silver hair and enfeebled condition would touch the hearts of her audience.

She had prepared a few questions in her mind, but they were unnecessary. Moses Gama looked at the camera and spoke with a sincerity and depth that was devastating.

'There are no prison walls thick enough to hold the longing of my people for freedom,' he said. 'There is no grave deep enough to keep the truth from you.'

He spoke for ten minutes and Kitty Godolphin who was old in experience and hardened in the ways of a naughty world was weeping unashamedly as he ended, 'The struggle is my life. The battle belongs to us. We will prevail, my people. *Amandla! Ngawethu!*'

Kitty went to him and embraced him. 'You make me feel very humble,' she said.

'You are a friend,' he replied. 'Go in peace my daughter.'

'Come.' Raleigh Tabaka took Kitty's arm and led her away. 'You have stayed too long already. You must leave now. This man's name is Robert. He will lead you.'

Robert was waiting at the kitchen door of the cottage.

'Follow me,' he ordered, and led them across the bare dusty backyard, through the shadows to the corner of the road. There he stopped unexpectedly.

'What happens now?' Kitty asked in a whisper. 'Why are we waiting here?'

'Be patient,' Robert said. 'You will learn the reason soon.'

Suddenly Kitty was aware that they were not alone. There were others waiting like them in the shadows. She could hear them now, the murmur of voices, quiet but expectant. She could see them as her eyes adjusted to the night, many figures, in small groups, huddled beside the hedges or in the shelter of the buildings.

Dozens, no hundreds of people, men and women, and every moment their numbers increased as more came out of the night shadows, gathering round the cottage that contained Moses Gama, as though his presence was a beacon, a flame that, like moths, they could not resist.

'What is happening?' Kitty asked softly.

'You will see,' Robert replied. 'Have your camera ready.'

The people were beginning to leave the shadows, creeping closer to the cottage, and a voice called out

'*Baba!* Your children are here. Speak to us, Father.'

And another cried. 'Moses Gama we are ready. Lead us!'

And then they began to sing, softly at first, '*Nkosi Sikelel' iAfrika* – God save Africa!' and the voices joined and began to harmonize, those beautiful African voices, thrilling and wonderful.

Then there was another sound, distant at first, but swiftly growing closer, the sobbing undulating wail of police sirens.

'Have your camera ready,' said Robert again.

* * *

As soon as the American woman and her cameraman had left the cottage, Moses Gama began to rise from the table.

'It is done,' he said. 'Now we can leave.'

'Not yet, my uncle,' Raleigh Tabaka stopped him. 'There is something else that we must do first.'

'It is dangerous to delay,' Moses insisted. 'We have been in this place too long. The police have informers everywhere.'

'Yes, my uncle. The police informers are everywhere.' Raleigh put a peculiar emphasis on his agreement. 'But before you go on to the place where the police cannot touch you, we must talk.'

Raleigh came to stand at the front of the table facing his uncle.

'This was planned with geat care. This afternoon the white monster Verwoerd was assassinated in the racist parliament.'

Moses started. 'You did not tell me this,' he protested, but Raleigh went on quietly.

'The plan was that in the confusion after Verwoerd's assassination you would emerge to lead a spontaneous rising of our people.'

'Why was I not told of this?' Moses asked fiercely.

'Patience, my uncle. Hear me out. The men who planned this are from a cold bleak land in the north, they do not understand the African soul. They do not understand that our people will not rise until their mood is ready, until their rage is ripe. That time is not yet. It will take many more years of patient work to bring their rage to full fruit. Only then can we gather the harvest. The white police are still too strong. They would crush us by raising their little finger and the world would stand by and watch us die as they watched the rebellion in Hungary die.'

'I do not understand,' Moses said. 'Why have you gone this far if you did not intend to travel to the end of the road?'

'The revolution needs martyrs as well as leaders. The mood and temper of the world must be roused, for without them we can never succeed. Martyrs and leaders, my uncle.'

'I am the chosen leader of our people,' Moses Gama said simply.

'No, my uncle.' Raleigh shook his head. 'You have proved unworthy. You have sold out your people. In exchange for your life, you delivered the revolution into the hands of the enemy. You gave Nelson Mandela and the heroes of Rivonia to the foe. Once I believed you were a god, but now I know that you are a traitor.'

Moses Gama stared at him silently.

'I am glad you do not deny this, my uncle. Your guilt is proven beyond any doubt. By your action you have forfeited any claim to the leadership. Nelson Mandela alone has the greatness for that role. However, my uncle, the revolution needs martyrs.'

From the pocket of his jacket Raleigh Tabaka took something wrapped in a

clean white cloth. He laid it on the table. Slowly he opened the bundle, taking care not to touch what it contained.

They both stared at the revolver.

'This pistol is police issue. Only hours ago it was stolen from a local police arsenal. The serial number is still on the police register. It is loaded with police-issue ammunition.'

Raleigh folded the cloth around the grip of the pistol. 'It still has the fingerprints of the police officers upon it,' he said.

Carrying the pistol he went round the table to stand behind Moses Gama's chair and placed the muzzle of the pistol at the back of his neck.

From outside the cottage they heard the singing begin.

'God save Africa.' Raleigh repeated the words. 'You are fortunate, my uncle. You have a chance to redeem yourself. You are going to a place where nobody can ever touch you again, and your name will live for ever, pure and unsullied. "The great martyr of Africa who died for his people."'

Moses Gama did not move or speak, and Raleigh went on softly, 'The people have been told you are here. They are gathered outside in their hundreds. They will bear witness to your greateness. You name will live for ever.'

Then above the singing they heard the police sirens coming closer, wailing and sobbing.

'The brutal fascist police have also been told that you are here,' Raleigh said softly.

The sound of the sirens built up and then there were the roar of engines, the squeal of brakes, the slamming of Land-Rover doors, the shouted commands, the pounding footsteps, and the crash of the front door being smashed in with sledgehammers.

As Brigadier Lothar De La Rey led his men in through the front door of the cottage, Raleigh Tabaka said softly, 'Go in peace, my uncle,' and he shot Moses Gama in the back of the head.

The heavy bullet threw Moses forward, his shattered head slammed face down upon the table, the contents of his skull and chips of white bone splattered against the wall and over the kitchen floor.

Raleigh dropped the police pistol onto the table and slipped out into the dark yard. He joined the watching throng in the street ouside, mingling with them, waiting with them until the covered body was carried out of the front door of the cottage on a stretcher. Then he shouted in a strong clear voice, 'The police have murdered our leader. They have killed Moses Gama.'

As the cry was taken up by a hundred other voices, and the women began the haunting ululation of mourning, Raleigh Tabaka turned and walked away into the darkness.

* * *

A servant opened the front door of Weltevreden to Manfred De La Rey.

'The master is expecting you,' he said respectfully. 'Please come with me.'

He led Manfred to the gun room and closed the double manogany doors behind him.

Manfred stood on the threshold. There was a log fire burning in the hearth of the stone fireplace and Shasa Courtney stood before it. He was wearing a

dinner-jacket and black tie and a new black silk patch over his eye. He was tall and debonair with silver wings of hair at his temples, but his expression was merciless.

Centaine Courtney sat at the desk below the gun racks. She also wore evening dress, a brocaded Chinese silk in her favourite shade of yellow with a necklace of magnificent yellow diamonds from the H'ani Mine. Her arms and shoulders were bare and in the muted light her skin seemed flawless and smooth as a young girl's.

'White Sword,' Shasa greeted him softly.

'*Ja*,' Manfred nodded. 'But that was long ago – in another war.'

'You killed an innocent man. A noble old man.'

'The bullet was intended for another – for a traitor, an Afrikaner who had delivered his people to the British yoke.'

'You were a terrorist then, as Gama and Mandela are terrorists now. Why should your punishment be any different from theirs?'

'Our cause was just – and God was on our side,' Manfred replied.

'How many innocents have died for what other men call "Just causes"? How many atrocities have been committed in God's name?'

'You cannot provoke me,' Manfred shook his head. 'What I attempted was right and proper.'

'We shall see whether or not the courts of this land agree with you,' Shasa said, and looked across the room to Centaine. 'Please ring the number on the pad in front of you, Mater. Ask for Colonel Bothma of CID. I have already asked him to be available to come here.'

Centaine made no move, and her expression, as she studied Manfred De La Rey, was tragic.

'Please do it, Mater,' Shasa insisted.

'No,' Manfred intervened. 'She cannot do it – and nor can you.'

'Why do you believe that?'

'Tell him, Mother,' said Manfred.

Shasa frowned quickly and angrily, but Centaine held up her hand to stop him speaking.

'It is true,' she whispered. 'Manfred is as much my son as you are, Shasa. I gave birth to him in the desert. Although his father took him still wet and blind from my child bed, although I did not see him again for almost thirteen years, he is still my son.'

In the silence one of the logs in the fireplace fell in a soft shower of ash and it sounded like an avalanche.

'Your grandfather has been dead for twenty years and more, Shasa. Do you want to break my heart by sending your brother to the gallows?'

'My duty – my honour,' Shasa faltered.

'Manfred was as merciful once. He had it in his power to destroy your political career before it began. At my request and in the knowledge that you were brothers, he spared you.' Centaine was speaking softly, but remorselessly. 'Can you do less?'

'But – he is only your bastard,' Shasa blurted.

'You are my bastard also, Shasa. Your father was killed on our wedding day, before the ceremony. That was the fact that Manfred could have used to destroy you. He had you in his power – as he is now in your power. What will you do, Shasa?'

Shasa turned away from her, and stood with his head bowed staring into the fireplace. When he spoke at last, his voice was racked with pain.

'The friendship – the brotherhood even – all of it is an illusion,' he said. 'It is you, Mater, whom I must honour.'

No one replied to him, and he turned back to Manfred.

'You will inform the caucus of the National Party that you are not available for the premiership and you will retire from public life,' he said quietly, and saw Manfred flinch and the ruination of his dreams in the agony of his expression. 'That is the only punishment I can inflict upon you, but perhaps it is more painful and lingering than the gallows. Do you accept it?'

'You are destroying yourself at the same time,' Manfred told him. 'Without me the presidency is beyond your grasp.'

'That is my punishment,' Shasa agreed. 'I accept it. Do you accept yours?'

'I accept,' said Manfred De La Rey. He turned to the double mahogany doors, flung them open and strode from the room.

Shasa stared after him. Only when they heard his car pull away down the long driveway did he turn back to Centaine. She was weeping as she had wept on the day that he brought her the news of Blaine Malcomess' death.

'My son,' she whispered. 'My sons.' And he went to comfort her.

* * *

A week after the death of Dr Hendrik Verwoerd, the caucus of the National Party elected Balthazar Johannes Vorster to the premiership of South Africa.

He owed his elevation to the awe-inspiring reputation that he had built for himself while he was minister of justice. He was a strong man in the mould of his predecessor and in his acceptance speech he stated boldly, 'My role is to walk fearlessly along the road already pointed out by Hendrik Verwoerd.'

Three days after his election he sent for Shasa Courtney.

'I wanted personally to thank you for your hard work and loyalty over the years, but now I think it is time for you to take a well-earned rest. I would like you to go as the South African ambassador to the Court of St James in London. I know that with you there South Africa House will be in good hands.'

It was the classic dismissal, but Shasa knew that the golden rule for politicians is never to refuse office.

'Thank you, Prime Minister,' he replied.

* * *

Thirty thousand mourners attended the funeral of Moses Gama in Drake's Farm township.

Raleigh Tabaka organized the funeral and was the captain of the honour guard of *Umkhonto we Sizwe* that stood at the graveside and gave the ANC salute as the coffin was lowered into the earth.

Vicky Dinizulu Gama dressed in her flowing caftan of yellow and green and black, defied her banning order to make a speech to the mourners.

Fierce and strikingly beautiful, she told them, 'We must devise a death for the collaborators and sell-outs, that is so grotesquely horrible that not one of our people will ever dare to turn traitor upon us.'

The sorrow of the multitudes was so terrible that when a young woman amongst them was pointed out as a police informer, they stripped her naked and whipped and beat her until she fell unconscious. Then they doused her in petrol and set her alight and kicked her while she burned. Afterwards the children urinated on her charred corpse. The police dispersed the mourners with tear gas and baton-charges.

Kitty Godolphin filmed it all, and when the footage was cut in with the Moses Gama interview and the graphic footage from the scene of his brutal slaying by the police, it was amongst the most gripping and horrifying ever shown on American television.

When Kitty Godolphin was promoted to head of NABS news, she became the highest paid female editor in American television.

* * *

Before taking up his post as ambassador in London, Shasa went on a four-week safari in the Zambezi valley with his eldest son. The Courtney Safaris hunting concession covered five hundred square miles of wonderful game-rich wilderness, and Matatu led Shasa to lion and buffalo and a magnificent old bull elephant.

The Rhodesian bush war was becoming deadly earnest. Sean had been awarded the Silver Cross of Rhodesia for gallantry and around the camp fire he described how he had won it.

'Matatu and I were following a big bull jumbo when we cut the spoor of twelve ZANU gooks. We dropped the jumbo and tracked the terrs. It was pissing with rain and the cloud was on the treetops so the fire force couldn't get in to back us up. The terrs were getting close to the Zambezi so we pushed up on them. The first warning we had that they had set an ambush for us was when we saw the fairy lights in the grass just ahead of us.

'Matatu was leading and he took the first burst in the belly. That made me fairly bitter and I went after the gooks with the old .577. It was five miles to the river and they ran like the clappers of hell, but I polished off the last two in the water before they could reach the Zambian side. When I turned around, there was Matatu standing right behind me. The little bugger had backed me up for five miles with his tripes hanging out of the hole in his guts.'

Across the camp fire the little Ndorobo's face had brightened as he heard his name mentioned, and Sean told him in Swahili, 'Show the *Bwana Makuba* your new belly button.'

Obligingly Matatu hoisted his tattered shirt tails and displayed for Shasa the fearsome scars the AK 47 bullets had left on his stomach.

'You are a stupid little bugger,' Sean told him severely, 'running around with a hole in your guts, instead of lying down and dying like you should have. You are bloody stupid, Matatu.'

Matutu's whole body wriggled with pleasure. 'Bleddy stupid bugger,' he

agreed proudly. He knew that this was the highest accolade to which he could possibly aspire, uttered as it was by the godhead of his entire firmament.

* * *

While Shasa was still packing his books and paintings for the journey to London, Garry and Holly moved into Weltevreden.

'I'll be over there for at least three years,' Shasa said. 'And when I come back we can talk again, but I shall probably get myself a flat in town. On my own the old place is just too big for me.'

Holly was pregnant, and prevailed on Centaine to stay on to help her 'just until the baby is born'.

'Holly is the only woman that Mater can stand within half a mile of her on a permanent basis,' Shasa remarked to Garry as the two ladies of Weltevreden began planning the redecoration of the nursery wing together.

* * *

Isabella's love affair with Lothar De La Rey survived in stormy seas and wild winds during the months of the enquiry into the death of Moses Gama.

The commission of enquiry exonerated Brigadier Lothar De La Rey with a verdict of 'No Guilt'. The local English-language as well as the international press jeered cynically at this verdict and an emergency meeting of the General Assembly of the United Nations passed a resolution calling for comprehensive mandatory sanctions on South Africa, which was predictably vetoed in the Security Council. However, amongst his own people, Lothar's reputation was greatly enhanced and the Afrikaans press lauded him as its chosen hero.

Not a week after the commission made its findings public, Isabella woke in the bedroom of her luxurious Sandton flat to find Lothar already fully dressed, standing over the bed and watching her with an expression of such deep regret that she sat up quickly, fully awake, and let the pink satin sheets fall to her waist.

'What is it, Lothie?' she cried. 'Why are you leaving so early? Why are you looking at me like that?'

'There will be a by-election in the Doornberg constituency. It's one of our safe seats. The party organizers have offered it to me, and I have accepted. I'm resigning my police commission and going into politics.'

'Oh, that's wonderful,' Isabella cried, and reached out to him with both arms. 'I was reared on politics. We will make a great team, Lothie. I'll be an amazing help to you – you'll see.'

Lothar lifted his eyes from her naked breasts, but made no move to touch her, and she let her arms drop.

'What is it?' Her expression changed.

'I'm going back to my own people, Bella,' he said quietly. 'Back to my *Volk* and my God. I know what I want. I want one day to succeed where my father failed. I want the position he almost achieved, but I need a wife who is one of my own people. A good Afrikaner girl. I have already chosen her. I am going

to her now. So we must say goodbye, Bella. Thank you. I will never forget you, but it is over now.'

'Get out,' she said. 'Get out – and don't come back.'

He hesitated and her voice rose to a scream. 'Get out, you bastard. Get out!'

He went to the bedroom door and closed it softly behind him, and Isabella snatched the water jug from the bedside table and hurled it at the door. It shattered and she threw herself face down on the bed and began to weep.

She cried all that day, and at nightfall went into the bathroom and filled the bath with hot water. Lothar had left a packet of razor blades on the shelf next to her douche bag, and she unwrapped one of them slowly and held it up in front of her eyes. It looked terrifyingly evil, and the light glinted on the edge, but she lowered it until it touched the skin of her wrist. It stung like a scorpion and she jerked her wrist away.

'No, Lothar De La Rey, I won't give you the satisfaction,' she said angrily, and dropped the blade into the toilet bowl and went back into the bedroom. She picked up the phone.

When she heard her father's voice, Isabelly trembled with the shock of what she had almost done.'

'I want to come home, Daddy,' she whispered.

'I'll send the jet for you,' Shasa said without hesitation. 'No, hell, I'll fly up to fetch you myself.'

She was waiting on the tarmac and she ran into his arms. Halfway back to Cape Town he touched her cheek and said, 'I'll need an official hostess at "Highveld".' That was the ambassador's residence in London. 'I'm even prepared to renegotiate your salary.'

'Oh, Daddy,' she said. 'Why aren't all the men in the world like you!'

* * *

Jakobus Stander was hanged in the Pretoria Central prison. Sarah Stander and her husband were waiting outside when the death notice was posted on the main gates of the prison.

The night that they returned to the cottage in Stellenbosch Sarah rose once Roelf was asleep and in the bathroom she took a massive overdose of barbiturates.

She was dead in the bed beside him when Roelf Stander woke the following morning.

* * *

Manfred and Heidi went to live on their farm in the Free State where Manfred raised pedigree merino sheep.

At the agricultural show in Bloemfontein Manfred won a blue ribbon for the champion ram on show three years in succession.

Always fleshy, Manfred put on a great deal of weight, eating out of boredom more than appetite. Only Heidi knew how he chaffed at inactivity, how much

he longed to walk once again the corridors of power, and how pointless and frustrating he felt his existence had become.

He suffered his heart attack while wandering alone in the veld and shepherds found his body the next morning lying where he had fallen. Centaine flew up in the company jet for his funeral. She was the only member of the Courtney family present when Manfred was buried with full honours in Heroes Acre, surrounded by the graves of many other outstanding Afrikaners, including Dr Hendrik Verwoerd.

* * *

When Shasa Courtney was driven back from Buckingham Palace in the ambassadorial limousine after presenting his credentials to Her Majesty Queen Elizabeth II, the streets were wet with the grey London drizzle.

Despite the weather, the demonstrators were waiting for him in Trafalgar Square with their placards: 'The spirit of Moses Gama lives on' and '*Apartheid* is a crime against humanity.'

As Shasa alighted from the limousine in front of the embassy, the demonstrators tried to push forward, but a line of blue-uniformed London bobbies linked arms to hold them back.

'Shasa Courtney!' Half-way across the side-walk Shasa stopped dead in his tracks at the familiar voice, and he looked around.

He did not recognize her at first, then he saw her in the front rank of the demonstration and he turned back. He struck a tall elegant figure in his court dress and top hat. He stopped in front of her and spoke to one of the constables.

'Thank you, officer, but I know this lady, you may let her through.' Then, as she ducked under the constable's outstretched arm, he greeted her, 'Hello, Tara.'

He found it difficult to believe how she had changed. She was a blowsy middle-aged drab, only her eyes were still beautiful as they blazed at him.

'Moses Gama lives on. The monsters of *apartheid* can murder our heroes, but the battle is ours. In the end we will inherit the earth.' Her voice was a screech.

'Yes, Tara,' he replied. 'There are heroes and there are monsters, but most of us are ordinary mortals caught up in events too turbulent for any of us. Perhaps when the battle is over, all we will inherit will be the ashes of a once beautiful land.'

He turned away from her and walked into the entrance of the embassy without looking back.

Author's Note

Once again I have taken some small liberties with the timetables of history, in particular the dates on which the *Umkhonto we Sizwe* and *Poqo* movements began, Nelson Mandela was acquitted in his first treason trial, and Harold Macmillan made his 'Winds of Change' speech.

I hope that you, the reader, will forgive me for the sake of the narrative.

Wilbur Smith

The Courtneys:

WHEN THE LION FEEDS

'Mr Smith is a natural story-teller . . .'
(*The Scotsman*)

THE SOUND OF THUNDER

'A violent sage-type story set in Boer War Africa and told with vigour and enthusiasm.'
(*The London Standard*)

A SPARROW FALLS

'He packs humanity into a bag already overflowing with adventure, excitement, and realism.'
(*Yorkshire Post*)

The Courtneys of Africa:

THE BURNING SHORE

'. . . Courage, drama, love and revenge on land, sea and in the air towards the end of the first world war and blended in fine style. Mr Smith's research into events and places is spot-on, as usual.'
(*Bolton Evening News*)

POWER OF THE SWORD

'. . . A stupendous story, written in the grand old manner, from the master of thoroughgoing adventure.'
(David Hughes, *The Mail on Sunday*)

RAGE

'. . . The prose is as lean and muscular as ever, the pace would do credit to a Porsche, and the invention is as bright and explosive as a firework display.'
(Ted Willis, *Sunday Telegraph*)

The Ballantyne Novels:

A FALCON FLIES

'There is throughout *A Falcon Flies* a genuine sense of excitement and wonder.' (*Sunday Telegraph*)

MEN OF MEN

'A splendid read.' (*Financial Times*)

THE ANGELS WEEP

'. . . action, adventure and romance . . .' (*Yorkshire Post*)

THE LEOPARD HUNTS IN DARKNESS

'. . . big, bold and bloody' (*The Scotsman*)

Also by Wilbur Smith:

THE DARK OF THE SUN

'If the phrase "a man's book" has any meaning, it describes this powerful savage story.'
(*Books & Bookmen*)

SHOUT AT THE DEVIL

'A fast and thrilling adventure.' (*Northern Echo*)

GOLD MINE

'. . . violent action and informed technical detail . . . Mr Smith is at his liveliest and best.'
(*The London Standard*)

THE DIAMOND HUNTERS

'A gem of a suspense/adventure novel.' (*Mirror*)

THE SUNBIRD

'A splendid panoramic piece of writing, with colourful characters woven into an enthralling plot.'
(*Oxford Times*)

EAGLE IN THE SKY

'Wilbur Smith . . . rarely misses a trick . . . Terribly competent.' (*Sunday Times*)

THE EYE OF THE TIGER

'. . . Supreme professionalism, vividness, and attention to detail.'

(*Sunday Express*)

CRY WOLF

'A rattling good adventure yarn . . .'

(*The London Standard*)

HUNGRY AS THE SEA

'Hardly time to draw a breath. You can see at once why this is a bestseller.'

(*The London Standard*)

WILD JUSTICE

'. . . a gold-plated guarantee of pace, tension, and a thoroughly satisfying plot.'

(*Morning Telegraph*)

BOOKS BY

WILBUR SMITH

The Courtneys:
When the Lion Feeds
The Sound of Thunder
A Sparrow Falls

The Courtneys of Africa:
The Burning Shore
Power of the Sword
Rage

The Ballantyne novels:
A Falcon flies
Men of Men
The Angels Weep
The Leopard Hunts in Darkness

Also:
The Dark of the Sun
Shout at the Devil
Gold Mine
The Diamond Hunters
The Sunbird
Eagle in the Sky
The Eye of the Tiger
Cry Wolf
Hungry as the Sea
Wild Justice

THE COURTNEYS OF AFRICA